FOR REAL

SERGIO AGÜERO
WEARS evoSPEED

PUMA
puma.com

STUD CONFIGURATION

The bladded stud configuration in the heel ensures a smooth ground penetration.

The combination of bladed and conical studs in the forefoot provide optimal traction maneuverability and stability.

The tapered stud base helps to avoid stud pressure.

MIDFOOT STABILITY BARS

The midfoot area of the outsole is reinforced with two stability bars which secure stability and help to avoid the midfoot from bending.

EXTERNAL HEEL COUNTER

The minimalistic external heel counter provides optimal heel fit, stability and support.

SOFT HEEL INSERT

The super soft heel insert takes away pressure from the achilles tendon and thus reduces the risk of injuries.

CENTRAL LACING WITH SPEEDLACES

The central lacing makes the instep easy and the evoSPEED 1 suitable for various footshapes.

The evoSPEED 1 features special speedlaces that go from thin at the bottom of the eyestay to thicker for better handling.

GRIPTEX PRINT

Super thin griptex film on the vamp which improves the grip to the ball especially in wet conditions.

ONE-PIECE OUTSOLE

Super thin and lightweight one-piece pebax outsole with excellent pressure distribution properties and duoflex technology in the forefoot for optimal flexibility.

MONOLAYER MICROFIBER UPPER MATERIAL

Soft yet highly abrasion resistant premium monolayer microfiber upper material which offers a glove like fit and a superb touch with the ball.

The eyestay is welded with a thin film of TPU.

EVERFIT CAGE

The monolayer microfiber material is reinforced on the inside with the strategically placed internal everfit cage that wraps the foot inside the shoe and provides excellent midfoot stability.

ANATOMICALLY SHAPED SOCKLINER

The anatomically shaped removable sockliner with a memory foam insert provides cushioning and enhances comfort.

The sockliner is covered by a layer of synthetic suede material which prevents the foot from slipping inside the shoe.

ANATOMICALLY SHAPED EVOAPTOLAST

The new puma evoAptoLast is an evolution of puma's revolutionary anatomically shaped aptolast.

The new puma evoAptoLast is less pointed and offers more volume in the forefoot. It follows the foot's natural contours, provides a glove like fit and allows the upper to mold perfectly to the players foot.

PUMA®
puma.com

BLADED STUD CONFIGURATION

The bladed stud configuration ensures smooth ground penetration and pressure distribution, while providing maximum traction and maneuverability.

PUMA POWERLAST

The new anatomically shaped PUMA PowerLast provides more volume in the forefoot and instep. It follows the foot's antural contours, provides a glove like fit, and allows the upper to mold to the player's foot.

EXTERNAL TPU HEELCOUNTER

Asymmetrical external TPU-injected heel counter. Provides optimal support, stability, and protection.

LACING SYSTEM

Off-centered lacing system for better fit & comfort.

DOUBLE-DENSITY 3D PUMA PST DUO

Increases kicking power. Does not absorb energy upon ball impact. Responsive middle bars. Improves grip to the ball.

PowerCat 1.12

K-LEATHER

The premium K-Leather provides long lasting high quality, and the soft kicking area enhances fit and comfort.

REMOVABLE SOCKLINER

Lightweight anatomically-shaped sockliner provides excellent cushioning properties and comfort.

HEEL LINING

Inserted memory foam provides softness and comfort.

MICROFIBER MATERIAL

Supports midfoot. Keeps weight down. Creates innovative look.

PUMA
puma.com

CESC FÀBREGAS WEARS POWERCAT FOR REAL

♡ = ⬡ PUMA
puma.com

NON-LEAGUE CLUB DIRECTORY 2013

(35th Edition)

EDITORS
MIKE WILLIAMS & TONY WILLIAMS

ASSISTANT EDITOR
CRAIG POTTAGE

NON-LEAGUE CLUB DIRECTORY 2013
ISBN 978-1-869833-77-0

Editors
Mike Williams
(Tel: 01548 531 339)
tw.publications@btinternet.com)
Tony Williams
(Tel: 01823 490 684)
Email: t.williams320@btinternet.com

Published by Tony Williams Publications Ltd
(Tel: 01548 531 339)
Email: tw.publications@btinternet.com

Printed by Polestar Wheatons (Exeter, Devon)

Sales & Distribution
T.W. Publications (01548 531 339)

Front Cover: (Main Picture) Dwayne Robinson of Continental Star is tackled by a Pershore
Town player during their 2-1 home win. They clinched the Midland
Combination Premier League title a few days later. Photo: Jonathan Holloway
Inset Pictures (L-R): St Margaretsbury F.C. (Spartan South Midlands). Photo: Alan Coomes.
Ash United v Camberley Town action (Combined Counties League). Photo: Eric Marsh.
Tudor Sports (Haart of Kent County League) Photo: Alan Coomes.

foreword....

I am delighted to welcome you to the 35th edition of the non-league club directory. Many of you , like me, will already know the exceptional quality of each year's offering , a wonderful testimony to the Herculean work of Mike and Tony Williams.

If you are a first-time browser make sure you have time on your side. At such a size the directory isn't easy to pick up . Believe you me it is much, much harder to put down.

My passion , indeed obsession, with the game started in non-League as a Woking fan in the 1950's and I am delighted that this edition records the details of a title-winning season at Kingfield which thanks to the excellent management of Garry Hill and Steve Thompson has taken "The Cards " back into the Blue Square Premier.

I wish I could say that it had been a similar success story at Kingstonian. When I am not needed by Sky Sports I have been helping Alan Dowson and Mark Hams on the coaching side since we three went to the club in January 2007. Mid-table in the Ryman Premier was most disappointing for us. It was left to another member of the Tyler family , my son Adam, to give the K's fans more of a feel-good factor when his film "Kingsmeadow" was aired on both Channel 4 and ESPN.

It featured Kingstonian but Adam's purpose was to show that wherever you live there is a non-league club round the corner at which you can find camaraderie , community spirit and entertaining football. You will find the actual addresses of your local clubs in these pages!

In the year of the Olympic flame in our country the non-League flame still burns brightly.
This wonderful tome is testimony to that.

Martin Tyler.

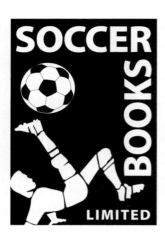

SOCCER BOOKS LIMITED

72 ST. PETERS AVENUE (Dept. NLD)
CLEETHORPES
N.E. LINCOLNSHIRE
DN35 8HU
ENGLAND

Tel. 01472 696226   Fax 01472 698546

Web site   www.soccer-books.co.uk
e-mail   info@soccer-books.co.uk

Established in 1982, Soccer Books Limited has one of the largest ranges of English-Language soccer books available. We continue to expand our stocks even further to include many more titles including German, French, Spanish and Italian-language books.

With well over 200,000 satisfied customers over the past 30 years, we supply books to virtually every country in the world but have maintained the friendliness and accessibility associated with a small family-run business. The range of titles we sell includes:

YEARBOOKS – All major yearbooks including many editions of the Sky Sports Football Yearbook (previously Rothmans), Supporters' Guides, Playfair Annuals, South and North & Central American Yearbooks, Non-League Club Directories, Almanack of World Football.

CLUB HISTORIES – Complete Statistical Records, Official Histories, Definitive Histories plus many more including photographic books.

WORLD FOOTBALL – World Cup books, European Championships History, Statistical histories for the World Cup, European Championships, South American and European Club Cup competitions and foreign-language Season Preview Magazines for dozens of countries.

BIOGRAPHIES & WHO'S WHOS – of Managers and Players plus Who's Whos etc.

ENCYCLOPEDIAS & GENERAL TITLES – Books on Stadia, Hooligan and Sociological studies, Histories and hundreds of others, including the weird and wonderful!

DVDs – Season reviews for British clubs, histories, European Cup competition finals, World Cup matches and series reviews, player profiles and a selection of almost 60 F.A. Cup Finals with many more titles becoming available all the time.

For a printed listing showing a selection of our titles, contact us using the information at the top of this page. Alternatively, our web site offers a secure ordering system for credit and debit card holders and Paypal users and lists our full range of 2,000 new books and 400 DVDs.

CONTENTS

THE DIRECTORY'S 'TEAM SHEET'

TONY WILLIAMS
Editor

Educated at Malvern College, one of the country's best football schools in the late sixties, he represented England Under 18 against Scotland at Celtic Park before serving as an administrative officer in the Royal Air Force for five years.

He was on Reading's books from the age of 16 to 22, but also represented F.A. Amateur XI's and the R.A.F. while playing mainly in the old Isthmian League for Corinthian Casuals, Dulwich Hamlet and Kingstonian and joining Hereford United and Grantham during R.A.F. postings.

After taking an F.A. Coaching badge he coached at Harrow Borough, Epsom & Ewell and Hungerford Town and was asked to edit Jimmy Hill's Football Weekly after initial experience with the Amateur Footballer. Monthly Soccer and Sportsweek followed before he had the idea for a football Wisden and was helped by The Bagnall Harvey Agency to find a suitable generous sponsor in Rothmans.

After launching the Rothmans Football Yearbook in 1970 as its founder and co-compiler with Roy Peskett, he was asked to join Rothmans (although a non-smoker!) in the company's public relations department and was soon able to persuade the Marketing Director that Rothmans should become the first ever sponsor of a football league.

After a season's trial sponsoring the Hellenic and Isthmian Leagues, it was decided to go national with the Northern and Western Leagues and for four years he looked after the football department at Rothmans, with Jimmy Hill and Doug Insole presenting a brilliant sponsorship package which amongst many other innovations included three points for a win and goal difference.

So Non-League football led the way with league sponsorship and two, now well accepted, innovations.

Sportsmanship and goals were also rewarded in a sponsorship that proved a great success for football and for Rothmans. Indeed the sportsmanship incentives could be of great value to-day in the Football Association's bid to improve the game's image by ridding the game of dissent and cheating.

After the cigarette company pulled out of their sports sponsorship Tony produced the first Non-League Annual and later The Football League Club Directory, launching 'Non-League Football' magazine with "The Mail on Sunday" and then "Team Talk."

After his ten years with Hungerford Town, he moved West and served Yeovil Town as a Director for seven years but was thrilled when David Emery's plans for the exciting Non-League Media emerged and came into reality, thus giving the grass roots of the game the publicity and promotion that he and his team had been attempting to set up since the Annual (now Directory) was launched in 1978.

The aim of the company has always been to promote the non-league 'family,' its spirit and its general development. So a plaque from The Football Association inscribed 'To Tony Williams for his continued promotion of all that's good in football' was greatly appreciated as was the trophy to commemorate the thirtieth edition of the Directory and the recent GLS "Lifetime Award' for promoting non-league football.

MIKE WILLIAMS
Editorial Manager

What started out as a holiday job in 1988 helping put together (literally in those days) the Non-League Club Directory and League Club Directory, in the end forged a career which saw him work for Coventry City Football Club, e-comsport in London and finally return to TW Publications in 2003.

During his eight year spell with TW Publications he learned the ropes of all aspects of publishing culminating in the roll of production manager for the Non-League Club Directory, Team Talk Magazine, the League Club Directory and many more publications published by the company.

1995 saw the opportunity to take up the post of Publications Manager at Coventry City Football Club, and the transfer was made in the April of that year. Sky Blue Publications was formed and the League Club Directory became their leading title. Re-branded as the Ultimate Football Guide he was to deal with all aspects of the book, from design to sales and was also put on a steep learning curve into the world of Premiership programme production. The three years spent at the Midland's club gave him a great insight into all departments of a Premiership club, having produced publications for them all.

Leaving Coventry F.C. in 1998, and after a spell working on a world wide football player database for e-comsport in London, he returned to the West Country in 2001 to set up his own design/publishing company, which incorporated working on the Directory again. 2009 saw the full time switch to TW Publications and the responsibilities of publishing the Directory.

Having gone to a rugby school his football playing career was delayed. However, becoming the youngest player to have played for the First XV and representing Torbay Athletics club at 100 and 200m proved his sporting background. At the age of 20 he begun his football career which, at it's height, saw him playing for Chard Town in the Western League Premier Division.

Now enjoying his time helping run local side Loddiswell Athletic in the South Devon League, with the odd appearance here and there for their Reserve team when needed, he relishes the challenge of maintaining the club's status as the top club in the South Hams area.

CRAIG POTTAGE
Assistant Editor

Has been a football aficionado since an early age and has always had an interest in players careers. Craig has kept detailed records of non league players for the last few years and this is his seventh year involved in this publication.

Started work in Golf Course Design and Project Management for John Jacobs Golf Associates, doing design work on projects in the UK, France, China and Tenerife plus Project Management work in the UK and Tenerife. Moved onto a career in Business Development and Project Management for an IT Facilitation Company in Stevenage which lasted fourteen years until redundancy struck late last year. He is now a Warehouse Manager for a large Organisation in Milton Keynes. Craig lives in Stevenage with his wife and daughter.

Unfortunately due to work commitments he will be unable to help out on next year's book.

Used to help run a Sunday League Side a few years ago but has put his management career on hold for now. He has been an Arsenal season ticket holder for over twenty years and also goes to watch Stevenage Borough when time allows.

ACKNOWLEDGMENTS

To many, the close season is the busiest time of year when running a football association, league or club and the same is very much true for me too. This year has been made slightly more hectic with the launch of our very own website (www.non-leagueclubdirectory.co.uk), which aims to bring back some memories from the past 35 years of non-League football. However, despite this hectic period in football I am always greatly heartened by the time given by the Football Association, league officials, club secretaries, programme editors and contributors in supporting our publication. Along with our photographers their support has helped maintain our publication for the last 35 years.

I haven't got room to personally thank everyone
who has helped along the way but in particular I'd like to mention:

'OUR TEAM' OF PHOTOGRAPHERS
Peter Barnes, Graham Brown, Keith Clayton, Alan Coomes, Jonathan Holloway,
'Uncle Eric' Marsh, Roger Turner, Bill Wheatcroft and Gordon Whittington.

FA COMPETITIONS DEPARTMENT
Steve Clark, Chris Darnell and Scott Bolton

CONTRIBUTORS
Louise Edwards (Football Conference)
Alan Allcock (Northern Premier League). Kellie Disapline (Isthmian League).
Arthur Evans (Photographer & reports).
Craig Pottage (Conference Players) - *A special mention to Craig who, due to work commitments, will not be able to carry on his fantastic coverage of the Conference players next season, your time and efforts have been very much appreciated, thank you.*
Dr. Andrew Sarnecki (Pecking Order). Mike Simmonds (Schools).
James Wright. Richard Rundle (Football Club History Database).
And not forgetting Dad!

Thank you

Mike Williams

AND A SPECIAL THANK YOU TO OUR MAIN SPONSOR
Who continue to show their support towards grass roots football.

Why not show your appreciation to Puma by checking out their website: www.**genesis**sports.co.uk

and see for yourself the great football kits, training gear and footballs on offer.

'THE PURE JOY OF SPORT'

This was John Inverdale's wonderful description after watching Jonathan Marray and Frederick Nielson win the Wimbledon Mens Doubles Championship on 7th July.

It made me think of the multitude of football memories that had given me the same thrill, including The World Cup 1966 and finishing with the superb sporting spectacle provided by Spain and Italy in the 'Euro 2012' Final.

It was also uplifting to have seen our domestic season finish in such an exciting manner. The last day of thrilling Premier League Fixtures, The FA Cup Final and The European Nations Tournament gave us all outstanding memories of our wonderful game.

It was particularly uplifting as in the rest of our season we had seen a depressing increase in cheating and deliberate acting to encourage the referees to show yellow and red cards to the opposition. With referees also tending to issue regular unwarranted dismissals for innocent tackles, many important games had been ruined as spectacles and honest sporting contests.

A few of the retired players were very scathing with their comments on television but many of the media regulars brushed the incidents aside and accepted it as part of the modern game where supporters, players and management don't mind how they get results as long as they win and achieve their financial rewards. I wonder whether all these 'win at all costs' characters teach their children to cheat in the same way - 'if you don't get caught love, cheat as much you like, it doesn't matter as long as you are successful"!

Watching non-league football, one sees the feigned trip, the scream and the clutching of the knee (when, if anything has been touched, its the foot!) and the persistent holding of attacking players by defenders (often with their backs to the ball) at free-kicks and corners. Because there is rarely enough noise to drown swearing at non-league matches, players often hear their management on the bench abusing the officials, so they, and sometimes supporters, join in as well, as they have also seen it all regularly on television.

The Chief Sports writer of The Daily Telegraph recently wrote:

'Only football among our sports keeps up this flow of spite and stupidity on and off the pitch'.

This sort of publicity really hurts all true lovers of our game, so it would be greatly appreciated if our 'leaders' at The Football Association, were seen to be standing up for our national sport and doing something about its national image. We want to be inspired by our sport not ashamed.

Those of us who have been involved in the game for at least forty years, have seen referees booking and dismissing more and more players for mistimed tackles without an ounce of deliberate malice involved. Two players cannot always arrive at the ball in a tackle at exactly the same time, any more than a player can always shoot on target or pass accurately to a colleague - but they don't deliberately make mistakes.

The first game of 'Euro 2012' filled us all with dread as the referee, appearing to be determined to make a name for himself, sent off a player for two 'bookable' offenses. Not one TV pundit, football writer in the national press, or anyone I knew who watched the game, considered that the first incident was even a foul and the second one, at worst, was clumsy but not a deliberate physical foul challenge. Referees have a tough time, as the actors are very good and many match officials give the excuse that if they dismissed all the deliberate cheats, abusers or punished fouling in the penalty areas at set pieces, there would be too many players regularly sent off.

Well, the general opinion of the suffering spectators is - start sending them all off, and the offenses will disappear well within a month!

Thanks to the wonderful television coverage, where we see incidents from all angles over and over again, we know who are cheating and so do the Football Association. Nothing makes a true football lover more annoyed than seeing the cheats get away with conning the referees and getting fellow members of the professional footballers union sent off and probably banned. The game is once again brought into disrepute and surely it needs support and leadership.

I have been involved with the English game for a long time and I have seen at first hand leadership from The Football Association, who after all, should be looking after our national sport. Sir Stanley Rous, Dennis Follows, Ted Croker and Graham Kelly were all 'real football people' who loved the game and were leaders working with a staff, who felt it was an honour to work for The Football Association, most of whom went to watch a game every Saturday of the season and probably discussed it with colleagues most of Monday back at the office.

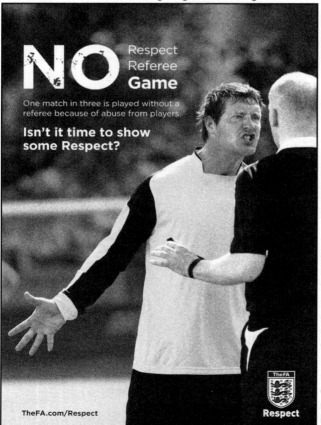

NO Respect Referee **Game**

One match in three is played without a referee because of abuse from players.

Isn't it time to show some Respect?

TheFA.com/Respect

Respect

They cared about the image of the game and were so proud to be part of football's parent body. They didn't change jobs every few years but proudly served the game through the Association for most of their lives. So it was good to see David Bernstein taking responsibility for making sure the media got their wires straight concerning England's new manager, the Rio Ferdinand information and the general preparation for Euro 2012.

One suspects that referees at the European tournament were given a sharp reminder of the standards expected and after their first game disgrace, it worked brilliantly. The competing nations also appeared to be concentrating on their football rather than cheating and in the rare case it reared its ugly head, the referees either ignored the diving or warned the players involved. It was a great success and good to watch.

When watching Rugby League, a game played where the toughest of physical contact is taken for granted, it makes a loyal football lover embarrassed to think of the fuss and histrionics we often see after the slightest nudge in our game - how many times do we hear a commentator say ' well he did touch him' !

So surely, strong leadership from people who really care at our parent body, The Football Association, would be welcomed and appreciated by everyone in the game. What a difference it would make if we all knew that:-

1 - Referees were being strongly encouraged to clamp down completely on:
   a) Blatant abuse to officials
   b) Deliberate fouling at all set pieces. (Especially standing with their backs to the ball and deliberately holding or blocking attacking players)

2 - For obvious cheating and deliberate abuse of the rules that the referee fails to see on the day, regional panels (perhaps made up of three respected ex referees or players) could decide which incidents were deliberate fouling or cheating, as all matches are filmed these days. Heavy punishments handed out to those found guilty. i.e Their cheating may have won three points, but for missing six games was it worth it?

Players would accept the fact that they would be watched all the time and would soon realize it would be better to concentrate on their football, so surely, management, players, fans and media would benefit and everyone would enjoy football skills, tactics and honest excitement with pride.

An example of this wonderful sporting satisfaction was displayed perfectly when tennis player Jonathan Marray, playing in the most important game of his life, broke a rule (when his racket hit the net) unseen by the umpire and owned up, thus losing a vital point. No wonder the nation celebrated when he and his partner became Wimbledon Champions!

That certainly was an illustration of 'The Pure Joy of Sport !

Tony Williams

PS The sportsmanship and general spirit shown throughout the Olympic games has been uplifting to everyone involved in sport, so let's hope that in the new football season those standards are upheld on and off the field.

A click away from memory lane!

Over 35 years of publishing the Non-League Club Directory has filled a room full of information and photographs covering the game we know and love.

What we intend, over time, is to create a website that shares with you everything we have accumulated, which we hope will bring back some fond memories of season's gone by.

Log on to **www.non-leagueclubdirectory.co.uk** today and see how many faces from teams gone by you recognise

The Real Football Person of the Year.

Many publications nominate football players and managers for awards so we thought we would be a little different this year.

The fact that money is so important to the game cannot be denied and as money is attracted by success, football players, officials, administrators and even their supporters have become more desperate to succeed.

Massive money is involved within the Premier League, who give the impression of being the strongest influence in the rest of the English game and although The Football Association was once the parent body of the game, it is difficult to see what influence they now have over the Premier League or the nation's match officials.

Steve Clark (left) presents a Non-League Directory's 'North West Team of the Year' award to Stalybridge Celtic in 1992.

The game has changed on and off the field, so its not surprising that The Football Association's influence has also changed in the last thirty years. When the F.A. were based at Lancaster Gate a staff of about ninety football enthusiasts considered working at football's headquarters to be a privilege, they nearly all watched a match at least once a week and on Mondays the headquarters would be full of enthusiasts discussing the games they had watched at the weekend.

Today, it's not quite the same, but luckily there are still some real football people proud to be working at Wembley with a real love of the game and all that it means to so many enthusiasts throughout the country. Steve Clark is one of those special people and he has worked at The Football Association's Headquarters since May 1969.

Steve is officially known as 'The F.A. Competitions Manager' and has responsibilities for the entries, rules, round by round draws and of course the special Final arrangements of all FA competitions. His department's responsibilities are massive, but Steve is known and respected by club officials throughout the country.

Steve also tours the country watching football at all levels and has always been available when we have needed information and help for our football publications over the years. He is one of a small band of real football people, who was originally proud to be invited to work at English Football's Headquarters and has managed to uphold the game's special, but possibly old fashioned standards ever since.

Thank you Steve Clark.

Follow us on Twitter or Facebook

For news about the Directory.

Updates from around the Non-League world.

Latest news from all FA Competitions.

Plus have your say on anything Football related.

LOG ON TO: www.non-leagueclubdirectory.co.uk and join in today!

PECKING ORDER 2011-2012 — by A J Sarnecki

08-09	09-10	10-11	11-12	Step	League	FA Cup ent 1	FA Cup xmt	FA Cup won 1	FA Trophy ent 3	FA Trophy xmt 2/8	FA Trophy won 1	FA Vase ent 1	FA Vase xmt 4/6	FA Vase won	C pts	T pts	V pts	Total pts
1	1	1	1	1	FOOTBALL CONFERENCE Premier	24	240	36	24	192	36				287	300	0	587
2	2	2	2	2	FOOTBALL CONFERENCE South	22	132	37	22	132	18				191	216	0	407
3	3	3	3	2	FOOTBALL CONFERENCE North	22	132	26	22	132	18				180	216	0	396
6	4	4	4	3	ISTHMIAN Premier	22	88	25	22	44	32				135	142	0	277
5	5	5	5	3	NORTHERN PREMIER Premier	21	84	28	22	44	29				135	139	0	274
4	6	6	6	3	SOUTHERN Premier	22	88	29	22	44	24				139	134	0	273
7	8	11	7	4	SOUTHERN First Central	22	44	27	22	0	24				93	90	0	183
11	12	7	8=	4	ISTHMIAN First North	22	44	27	22	0	21				92	87	0	179
8	10	12	8=	4	ISTHMIAN First South	21	44	25	22	0	20				93	86	0	179
9	7	8	10=	4	NORTHERN PREMIER First North	21	42	20	22	0	22				88	88	0	176
10	9	10	10=	4	SOUTHERN First South & West	21	44	28	22	0	24				86	90	0	176
12	11	9	12	4	NORTHERN PREMIER First South	22	42	22	22	0	21				83	87	0	170
13	13	13	13	5	NORTHERN First	22		28				22	44	51	50	0	117	167
15	15	20=	14	5	UNITED COUNTIES Premier	23		21				23	26	42	41	0	89	130
14	14	14	15	5	MIDLAND ALLIANCE	20		26				20	36	36	49	0	77	126
21	23=	20=	16	5	NORTHERN COUNTIES EAST Premier	23		23				21	20	33	40	0	73	113
18	18	16	17=	5	SPARTAN SOUTH MIDLANDS Premier	21		19				22	20	22	47	0	63	110
23	23=	18	17=	5	HELLENIC Premier	19		17				21	16	40	32	0	78	110
17	16	20=	19	5	NORTH WEST COUNTIES Premier	21		18				19	18	30	40	0	69	109
19	21	15	20	5	WESSEX Premier	20		17				22	14	34	37	0	69	106
20	19	18	21	5	COMBINED COUNTIES Premier	19		13				18	20	26	37	0	66	103
22	22	23	22=	5	ESSEX SENIOR	21		17				21	14	27	40	0	62	102
25	25	26	22=	5	EASTERN COUNTIES Premier	19		10				19	18	26	30	0	72	102
15	17	17	24	5	SUSSEX COUNTY First	17		10				17	24	29	36	0	62	98
24	20	25	25	5	KENT Premier	17		19				14	14	20	36	0	53	89
26	26	24	26	6	EAST MIDLAND COUNTIES	14		10				18	6	27	33	0	55	88
27=	27	27	27	6	SOUTH WEST PENINSULA Premier	10		9				13	12	22	20	0	44	64
32	32	30=	28	6	NORTHERN COUNTIES EAST First	13		5				20	0	22	16	0	47	63
34	34	29	29	6	NORTHERN Second	12		5				12	0	26	18	0	44	62
27=	27=	30=	30=	6	WESTERN First	12		7				16	6	17	19	0	37	56
33	33	34	31	6	MIDLAND COMBINATION Premier	9		2				16	6	16	17	0	39	56
29=	31	28	32	6	WEST MIDLAND REGIONAL Premier	11		6				17	0	20	11	0	42	53
29=	35=	32	33=	6	NORTH WEST COUNTIES First	10		6				16	18	15	17	0	34	51
30	30	35	33=	6	EASTERN COUNTIES First	9		4				15	0	18	16	0	35	51
37	37	36	35	6	WESSEX First	9		1				12	0	14	14	0	36	50
35=	35=	37	36	6	SPARTAN SOUTH MIDLANDS First	6		5				10	0	14	15	0	26	41
39	39	40	37	6	UNITED COUNTIES First	7		7				7	0	11	10	0	25	35
40	40	38	38	6	COMBINED COUNTIES First	4		0				6	0	11	10	0	24	34
41	43	41	39	6	HELLENIC First West	0		0				5	0	6	14	0	16	30
36	38	39	40	6	SUSSEX COUNTY Second	0		0				3	0	14	14	0	11	25
44=	new	42	41	6	CENTRAL MIDLANDS South	2		0				3	0	8	8	0	11	19
43	41	44=	42	6	LEICESTERSHIRE SENIOR Premier	0		0				2	0	6	4	0	8	12
49=	47=	44=	43	6	HELLENIC First East	0		0				3	0	5	0	0	10	10
44=	44=	44=	44	7	WEARSIDE	0		0				2	0	2	3	0	4	7
44=	46=	46=	45=	7	SOUTH WEST PENINSULA First West	0		0				2	0	1	0	0	4	4
46	50=	50=	45=	7	SUSSEX COUNTY Third	0		0				2	0	3	0	0	4	4
52=			45=	7	WEST CHESHIRE First	0		0				2	0	2	3	0	1	4
	new		45=	7	CENTRAL MIDLANDS North	0		0				1	0	1	2	0	2	4
52=	49	55=	45=	7	SOMERSET SENIOR Premier	0		0				1	0	1	1	0	3	4
49=	55=	new	45=	7	SOUTH WEST PENINSULA First East	0		0				2	0	1	3	0	1	4
		51=	45=	6	SPARTAN SOUTH MIDLANDS Second	0		0				1	0	1	2	0	2	4
49=	47=	46=	51=	7	KENT INVICTA	0		0				1	0	0	1	0	2	3
46=	46=	50=	51=	7	HERTS SENIOR COUNTY Premier	0		0				1	0	0	1	0	2	3
	50=		54=	7	SUFFOLK & IPSWICH Premier	0		0				1	0	1	1	0	2	3
			54=	7	MANCHESTER Premier	0		0				1	0	0	1	0	1	2
47=	50=	50=	54=	7	WEST MIDLAND REGIONAL First	0		0				1	0	2	0	0	2	2
46=	50=	50=	57=	7	ESSEX OLYMPIAN Premier	0		0				1	0	1	0	0	1	1
52=	50=	55=	57=	7	NORTH BERKSHIRE First	0		0				0	0	0	0	0	1	1
52=			57=	7	DORSET PREMIER	0		0				1	1	1	1	0	0	1
					no league	0		0				0	0	1	0	0	2	2

Points are given for status (acceptance into each of the three competitions), for prestige (exemption from early rounds) and performance (number of wins, however achieved, even by walkover). Entry to the Vase is valued at one point, that to the Trophy at 3. Cup entry gives a further bonus of one point. The number of entries from each league is shown in the appropriate column. Points for exemptions are valued at two for each round missed. The entry in the table is of the total points so gained by the given league, not the number of teams given exemptions. Finally, all wins are valued at one point, regardless of opposition: giving extra points for defeating 'stronger' opponents would be too arbitrary. After all, if they lost then they were not stronger on the day!

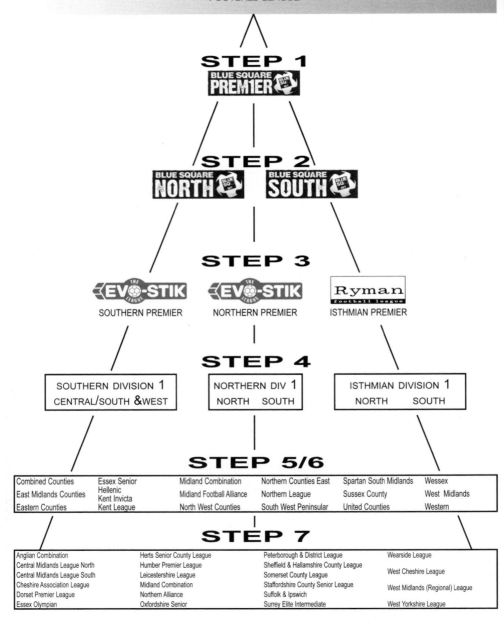

FOOTBALL LEAGUE

STEP 1
BLUE SQUARE PREMIER

STEP 2
BLUE SQUARE NORTH   **BLUE SQUARE SOUTH**

STEP 3
EVO-STIK SOUTHERN PREMIER   **EVO-STIK** NORTHERN PREMIER   **Ryman** football league ISTHMIAN PREMIER

STEP 4

| SOUTHERN DIVISION 1 CENTRAL/SOUTH &WEST | NORTHERN DIV 1 NORTH   SOUTH | ISTHMIAN DIVISION 1 NORTH   SOUTH |

STEP 5/6

Combined Counties	Essex Senior	Midland Combination	Northern Counties East	Spartan South Midlands	Wessex
East Midlands Counties	Hellenic	Midland Football Alliance	Northern League	Sussex County	West Midlands
Eastern Counties	Kent Invicta Kent League	North West Counties	South West Peninsular	United Counties	Western

STEP 7

Anglian Combination	Herts Senior County League	Peterborough & District League	Wearside League
Central Midlands League North	Humber Premier League	Sheffield & Hallamshire County League	
Central Midlands League South	Leicestershire League	Somerset County League	West Cheshire League
Cheshire Association League	Midland Combination	Staffordshire County Senior League	West Midlands (Regional) League
Dorset Premier League	Northern Alliance	Suffolk & Ipswich	
Essex Olympian	Oxfordshire Senior	Surrey Elite Intermediate	West Yorkshire League

		P	W	D	L	F	A	GD	Pts
1	Fleetwood Town	46	31	10	5	102	48	54	103
2	Wrexham	46	30	8	8	85	33	52	98
3	Mansfield Town	46	25	14	7	87	48	39	89
4	(P) York City	46	23	14	9	81	45	36	83
5	Luton Town	46	22	15	9	78	42	36	81
6	Kidderminster Harriers	46	22	10	14	82	63	19	76
7	Southport	46	21	13	12	72	69	3	76
8	Gateshead	46	21	11	14	69	62	7	74
9	Cambridge United	46	19	14	13	57	41	16	71
10	Forest Green Rovers	46	19	13	14	66	45	21	70
11	Grimsby Town	46	19	13	14	79	60	19	70
12	Braintree Town	46	17	11	18	76	80	-4	62
13	Barrow	46	17	9	20	62	76	-14	60
14	Ebbsfleet United	46	14	12	20	69	84	-15	54
15	Alfreton Town	46	15	9	22	62	86	-24	54
16	Stockport County	46	12	15	19	58	74	-16	51
17	Lincoln City	46	13	10	23	56	66	-10	49
18	Tamworth	46	11	15	20	47	70	-23	48
19	Newport County	46	11	14	21	53	65	-12	47
20	AFC Telford United	46	10	16	20	45	65	-20	46
21	(R) Hayes & Yeading	46	11	8	27	58	90	-32	41
22	(R) Darlington (-10pts)	46	11	13	22	47	73	-26	36
23	(R) Bath City	46	7	10	29	43	89	-46	31
24	(R) Kettering Town (-3pts)	46	8	9	29	40	100	-60	30

PLAY-OFFS
Semi-Finals
York City 1-1 Mansfield Town / Mansfield Town 0-1 York City
Luton Town 2-0 Wrexham / Wrexham 0-1 Luton Town

Final (@ Wembley, 20/5/12)
Luton Town 1-2 York City

		1	2	3	4	5	6	7	8	9	10	11	12	13	14	15	16	17	18	19	20	21	22	23	24
1	AFC Telford United		1-0	1-0	2-1	1-0	1-2	3-3	0-2	1-4	2-0	1-2	0-0	1-1	3-1	2-1	1-2	0-2	0-0	2-1	0-1	1-1	1-0	0-2	0-0
2	Alfreton Town	0-0		2-1	2-1	0-1	2-1	3-1	2-2	1-4	1-6	1-1	2-5	3-2	1-1	0-2	1-3	0-0	3-6	3-2	0-0	6-1	5-2	1-4	0-2
3	Barrow	2-1	1-0		0-1	0-4	1-3	3-0	1-1	4-0	1-1	2-2	2-3	3-0	3-1	1-0	1-2	2-3	3-1	2-2	1-0	1-1	3-1	0-0	
4	Bath City	3-1	0-3	0-1		1-1	3-4	2-0	2-3	1-4	0-2	4-2	2-1	0-1	1-2	2-1	1-1	1-1	3-2	1-2	0-2	0-2	0-2	0-1	
5	Braintree Town	2-1	1-2	1-0	3-3		3-2	3-1	1-2	1-5	3-1	5-0	0-3	2-1	1-4	1-0	3-1	1-1	1-0	0-0	2-2	3-1	0-0	0-1	
6	Cambridge United	1-0	3-0	1-0	1-1	2-0		2-0	2-0	2-0	1-1	0-1	0-1	2-1	2-0	1-2	2-0	1-1	1-2	1-1	3-0	2-2	0-1	1-1	0-1
7	Darlington	1-0	1-1	0-1	2-2	1-0	2-0		0-2	0-1	0-0	0-1	0-0	1-1	3-1	1-0	3-1	1-1	0-2	2-0	0-3	0-1	2-0	2-4	2-2
8	Ebbsfleet United	3-2	1-2	1-2	3-0	1-1	0-0	1-3		1-3	1-1	0-1	3-1	1-1	1-0	3-3	2-3	2-2	0-3	1-1	1-2	3-0	0-5	1-2	
9	Fleetwood Town	2-2	4-0	4-1	4-1	3-1	1-0	0-0	6-2		0-0	3-1	2-1	1-0	3-0	5-2	2-2	0-2	2-0	1-4	2-2	2-1	2-2	1-1	0-0
10	Forest Green Rovers	2-1	4-1	3-0	3-0	0-2	2-1	2-0	3-1	1-2		2-1	0-1	1-3	0-1	1-1	0-2	3-0	1-1	1-1	2-3	1-1	3-1	1-0	1-1
11	Gateshead	3-0	2-0	2-0	1-0	2-2	1-1	1-1	2-3	1-1	1-0		1-0	2-0	1-1	2-3	3-0	2-3	2-3	2-0	1-1	1-1	1-4	3-2	
12	Grimsby Town	2-0	5-2	5-2	6-0	1-1	2-1	1-2	4-3	0-2	2-1	2-0		3-0	2-1	1-2	3-1	1-0	0-0	2-2	0-1	7-0	0-0	1-3	2-3
13	Hayes & Yeading U.	0-0	3-1	1-1	1-1	1-2	0-0	3-2	1-2	1-3	2-0	2-3	1-2		1-0	1-3	1-2	2-2	1-3	0-4	0-2	1-2	1-0	0-2	2-4
14	Kettering Town	2-1	0-2	1-1	1-1	2-1	0-0	0-0	2-2	2-3	1-3	2-1	1-2	3-5		0-1	1-0	0-5	0-3	3-2	2-3	1-3	0-2	0-1	1-5
15	Kidderminster H.	2-2	3-1	1-2	4-1	5-4	0-0	3-1	2-2	0-2	1-0	2-3	1-1	3-1	6-1		1-1	1-2	0-3	3-2	2-0	1-1	2-0	0-1	1-1
16	Lincoln City	1-1	0-0	1-2	2-0	3-3	0-1	5-0	3-0	1-3	1-1	1-0	1-2	0-1	0-2	0-1		1-1	1-1	2-0	1-0	4-0	1-1	1-2	0-2
17	Luton Town	1-1	1-0	5-1	2-0	3-1	0-1	2-0	3-0	1-2	1-1	5-1	1-1	4-2	5-0	1-0	1-0		0-0	2-0	5-1	1-0	3-0	0-1	1-2
18	Mansfield Town	1-1	3-2	7-0	1-1	4-1	1-2	5-2	1-0	1-1	1-1	1-1	2-1	3-2	3-0	0-3	2-1	1-1		5-0	1-3	2-1	2-1	2-0	1-1
19	Newport County	0-0	1-0	2-2	1-0	3-4	0-1	0-0	0-1	0-1	0-0	0-0	4-0	3-1	1-3	1-1	1-0		0-3		1-1	1-2	0-1	2-1	
20	Southport	3-2	2-1	2-1	2-1	0-4	1-0	1-0	0-3	0-6	1-3	1-3	1-2	1-2	0-0	1-2	2-2	3-3	3-1	1-1		5-0	1-1	0-0	1-1
21	Stockport County	2-2	0-0	3-2	4-0	1-1	0-1	3-4	1-1	2-4	0-1	0-1	2-0	3-3	1-0	2-1	4-0	1-1	0-1	2-2	0-1		2-0	1-0	1-2
22	Tamworth	2-2	2-2	2-3	0-1	1-0	2-1	1-0	1-0	0-3	0-1	1-1	1-1	2-1	2-2	0-0	4-0	1-3	0-1	2-1	2-2	1-1		1-2	2-1
23	Wrexham	4-0	0-1	2-0	2-0	5-1	1-1	2-1	1-0	2-0	1-0	1-2	2-1	2-2	4-1	4-1	2-0	2-0	1-3	0-0	2-0	4-0	3-0		0-3
24	York City	0-1	0-1	3-1	1-0	6-2	2-2	2-2	3-2	0-1	1-0	1-2	2-1	2-0	7-0	2-3	2-0	0-2	1-1	2-1	0-0	1-1	0-0	0-0	

		P	W	D	L	F	A	GD	Pts
1	Hyde FC	42	27	9	6	90	36	54	90
2	Guiseley	42	25	10	7	87	50	37	85
3	FC Halifax	42	21	11	10	80	59	21	74
4	Gainsborough Trinity	42	23	5	14	74	61	13	74
5	(P) Nuneaton (-6pts)	42	22	12	8	74	41	33	72
6	Stalybridge	42	20	11	11	83	64	19	71
7	Worcester City	42	18	11	13	63	58	5	65
8	Altrincham	42	17	10	15	90	71	19	61
9	Droylsden	42	16	11	15	83	86	-3	59
10	Bishops Stortford	42	17	7	18	70	75	-5	58
11	Boston United	42	15	9	18	60	67	-7	54
12	Colwyn Bay	42	15	8	19	55	70	-15	53
13	Workington	42	14	10	18	56	61	-5	52
14	Gloucester	42	15	7	20	53	60	-7	52
15	Harrogate Town	42	14	10	18	59	69	-10	52
16	Histon	42	12	15	15	67	72	-5	51
17	Corby	42	14	8	20	65	71	-6	50
18	Vauxhall Motors	42	14	8	20	63	78	-15	50
19	Solihull Moors	42	13	10	19	44	54	-10	49
20	Hinckley	42	13	9	20	75	90	-15	48
21	(R) Blyth Spartans	42	7	13	22	51	81	-30	34
22	(R) Eastwood Town	42	4	8	30	37	105	-68	20

PLAY-OFFS

Semi-Finals

Gainsborough Trinity 2-2 FC Halifax Town / FC Halifax Town 0-1 Gainsborough Trinity
Nuneaton Town 1-1 Guiseley / Guiseley 0-1 Nuneaton Town

Final (@ Gainsborough Trinity, 13/5/12)
Gainsborough Trinity 0-1 Nuneaton Town

		1	2	3	4	5	6	7	8	9	10	11	12	13	14	15	16	17	18	19	20	21	22
1	Altrincham		0-2	2-1	6-1	3-4	1-1	5-1	2-0	1-1	2-3	1-2	2-2	5-2	2-2	3-0	1-3	2-0	1-1	2-1	3-2	4-1	1-1
2	Bishops Stortford	1-0		3-3	0-1	0-2	0-2	5-0	4-0	1-3	1-1	3-2	4-1	3-4	5-0	0-2	0-1	0-3	1-0	0-3	2-0	1-1	1-1
3	Blyth Spartans	1-1	3-1		1-0	2-2	1-2	1-3	1-0	2-3	2-3	0-1	1-2	3-3	3-3	2-1	0-1	2-3	2-1	1-1	1-2	1-2	0-3
4	Boston United	1-1	0-2	1-1		2-2	1-1	2-1	4-2	0-0	1-2	2-0	3-3	0-2	2-0	1-1	0-2	0-0	0-1	3-2	1-2	2-3	2-1
5	Colwyn Bay	1-6	4-1	0-2	3-2		0-2	6-3	2-0	0-1	2-1	4-2	1-2	2-2	0-5	2-1	0-1	1-6	0-0	2-0	0-0	0-2	1-0
6	Corby Town	1-3	6-1	4-0	1-2	1-0		5-2	5-0	2-4	1-3	0-1	0-1	0-5	0-2	0-4	0-2	0-3	1-2	1-0	2-3	3-3
7	Droylsden	3-1	2-2	3-0	2-1	2-1	2-1		3-3	2-1	1-2	1-2	2-3	2-3	2-3	2-1	1-0	3-3	5-2	4-1	1-1
8	Eastwood Town	1-6	3-4	0-0	2-2	0-1	1-4	2-2		2-2	1-6	2-1	2-2	0-3	1-2	2-2	0-5	1-1	0-1	2-4	0-1	0-3
9	FC Halifax Town	2-4	0-1	3-0	3-2	1-1	1-3	2-1	2-1		2-2	0-0	1-2	3-1	6-1	4-0	3-2	0-0	2-2	1-5	2-1	3-1
10	Gainsborough Trinity	2-0	4-2	2-0	1-3	2-0	1-0	1-2	2-0	0-1		1-4	1-0	0-1	2-1	3-2	2-0	3-1	3-1	1-1	2-2	2-0
11	Gloucester City	1-1	0-2	4-0	1-3	0-1	0-0	1-3	2-0	1-3	0-2		2-1	1-0	2-2	0-1	1-2	1-0	1-2	2-1	3-1	2-0
12	Guiseley	3-2	0-1	5-0	2-1	2-0	3-0	4-3	1-2	3-4	2-0	3-2		2-1	3-0	2-2	2-0	1-1	3-1	1-1	4-1	4-1	2-1
13	Harrogate Town	3-2	1-1	0-0	0-2	4-0	6-2	0-0	2-1	0-0	2-1	2-0	0-4		2-1	0-0	0-3	0-2	1-1	1-1	1-2	0-2	0-0
14	Hinckley United	1-4	1-3	1-3	1-2	3-1	0-3	1-1	4-0	3-2	3-0	2-3	0-1	1-2		0-3	0-0	1-1	1-2	5-5	2-2	2-3	4-2
15	Histon	2-3	2-3	2-2	1-3	0-0	1-1	5-5	3-0	1-4	1-1	4-3	2-2	4-0	2-3		1-1	1-1	3-0	0-1	3-3	1-5	2-0
16	Hyde	2-1	5-0	1-0	4-1	3-2	2-2	4-0	4-1	1-1	3-1	0-0	0-1	3-2	4-0	4-0		1-1	3-0	1-1	4-2	2-1	4-0
17	Nuneaton Town	2-1	2-0	2-2	2-0	1-1	2-0	2-1	4-0	1-0	0-1	0-1	2-0	2-5	3-2	2-0		0-1	1-2	2-1	3-0	2-1
18	Solihull Moors	2-0	3-1	2-2	1-0	1-0	1-2	0-2	0-2	1-2	5-3	1-0	0-1	5-1	1-2	0-2	1-0	0-0		1-1	2-3	0-0	2-1
19	Stalybridge Celtic	5-1	2-3	2-0	3-0	0-4	2-2	1-3	2-1	2-1	4-0	2-2	0-3	3-2	4-2	2-0	1-3	4-1	2-0		4-2	2-0	1-3
20	Vauxhall Motors	2-2	4-3	2-1	0-4	1-0	2-1	1-1	1-2	1-3	3-1	1-1	0-2	1-1	0-1	1-2	1-1	0-2	1-2	2-1	1-0		3-2	0-1
21	Worcester City	3-0	2-1	2-1	3-0	0-1	0-2	0-2	1-0	1-1	2-1	2-1	2-2	3-2	1-1	1-1	2-2	1-1	3-0	0-0	2-0		0-1
22	Workington	1-2	1-1	2-0	1-2	1-1	3-1	3-1	3-0	1-2	0-2	3-0	1-3	2-1	3-1	0-0	1-2	1-1	1-1	1-1	2-5	2-1	0-0

		P	W	D	L	F	A	GD	Pts
1	Woking	42	30	7	5	92	41	51	97
2	(P) Dartford	42	26	10	6	89	40	49	88
3	Welling United	42	24	9	9	79	47	32	81
4	Sutton United	42	20	14	8	68	53	15	74
5	Basingstoke Town	42	20	11	11	65	50	15	71
6	Chelmsford City	42	18	13	11	67	44	23	67
7	Dover Athletic	42	17	15	10	62	49	13	66
8	Boreham Wood	42	17	10	15	66	58	8	61
9	Tonbridge Angels	42	15	12	15	70	67	3	57
10	Salisbury City	42	15	12	15	55	54	1	57
11	Dorchester Town	42	16	8	18	58	65	-7	56
12	Eastleigh	42	15	9	18	57	63	-6	54
13	Weston-S-Mare	42	14	9	19	58	71	-13	51
14	Truro City	42	13	9	20	65	80	-15	48
15	Staines Town	42	12	10	20	53	63	-10	46
16	Farnborough (-5pts)	42	15	6	21	52	79	-27	46
17	Bromley	42	10	15	17	52	66	-14	45
18	Eastbourne Borough	42	12	9	21	54	69	-15	45
19	Havant and Waterlooville	42	11	11	20	64	75	-11	44
20	Maidenhead United	42	11	10	21	49	74	-25	43
21	(R) Hampton & Richmond	42	10	12	20	53	69	-16	42
22	(R) Thurrock	42	5	11	26	33	84	-51	26

PLAY-OFFS
Semi-Finals
Basingstoke Town 0-1 Dartford / Dartford 2-1 Basingstoke Town
Sutton United 1-2 Welling United / Welling United 0-0 Sutton United

Final (@ Dartford, 13/5/12)
Dartford 1-0 Welling United

		1	2	3	4	5	6	7	8	9	10	11	12	13	14	15	16	17	18	19	20	21	22
1	Basingstoke Town		1-1	1-0	1-1	3-2	1-0	1-1	3-0	1-0	4-3	2-2	3-2	2-3	2-2	1-1	1-2	3-1	0-2	2-1	0-1	4-1	0-3
2	Boreham Wood	1-1		2-1	1-3	3-1	2-2	4-2	1-1	6-1	4-0	2-1	0-1	1-0	1-1	1-2	1-1	2-1	4-2	1-2	2-1	3-0	1-2
3	Bromley	1-3	4-0		1-0	1-2	0-0	0-1	1-3	0-0	1-1	1-2	0-0	0-1	2-2	1-1	3-0	0-0	2-2	1-1	1-1	1-0	2-4
4	Chelmsford City	0-1	0-0	6-1		0-0	0-0	2-3	1-0	3-0	2-2	1-0	3-1	2-0	2-3	0-1	2-3	1-0	2-2	0-1	1-2	3-2	2-3
5	Dartford	4-1	2-2	3-1	0-0		1-1	3-1	2-1	3-0	3-0	2-1	3-1	2-1	2-0	2-1	6-1	6-0	3-1	1-2	1-0	1-1	2-3
6	Dorchester Town	2-1	0-1	1-2	1-0	1-0		1-1	0-3	1-3	3-3	1-0	3-6	4-0	0-3	0-3	0-0	3-0	3-1	2-3	3-2	1-3	0-0
7	Dover Athletic	0-0	0-2	4-1	2-1	2-2	4-0		1-1	2-0	0-0	0-1	1-1	2-2	1-1	0-4	0-2	3-1	0-0	3-1	0-1	1-0	0-3
8	Eastbourne Borough	0-2	3-2	5-0	1-3	0-1	1-4	2-2		3-0	1-1	2-0	2-1	0-2	1-3	0-1	0-0	2-1	1-2	2-2	0-3	1-2	2-1
9	Eastleigh	0-2	2-0	0-2	1-1	2-2	0-1	2-3	2-1		0-1	1-1	3-2	4-1	1-1	2-1	4-0	3-2	1-2	3-1	3-0	2-1	0-0
10	Farnborough	1-0	4-0	2-1	1-3	1-2	1-2	0-2	1-0	1-3		0-2	1-0	0-3	1-0	1-0	0-3	0-2	3-2	2-1	1-4	0-1	0-1
11	Hampton & Richmond Borough	0-2	1-1	1-2	0-4	1-3	0-2	2-2	3-1	0-4	1-0		3-3	0-1	1-2	1-0	0-2	1-1	4-3	0-2	3-1	1-1	
12	Havant & Waterlooville	0-1	2-4	1-2	2-3	0-4	4-2	0-1	0-0	0-0	5-0	2-2		2-1	2-1	3-2	2-2	3-0	1-1	4-1	1-2	1-1	3-4
13	Maidenhead United	1-1	0-3	3-3	1-1	1-1	0-1	1-4	1-0	4-3	3-4	0-2	2-0		0-1	1-1	1-1	4-0	0-4	1-3	0-4	1-3	0-1
14	Salisbury City	1-1	0-2	0-2	0-1	1-2	0-1	0-1	3-0	2-0	1-3	4-2	4-1	0-2		1-0	3-1	1-1	2-0	2-1	0-0	0-0	2-0
15	Staines Town	0-2	2-1	1-1	1-4	1-2	0-2	0-3	1-2	2-2	1-1	1-0	0-0	1-1	1-4		2-3	1-1	1-1	4-2	2-1	0-1	1-1
16	Sutton United	1-0	2-1	1-1	3-2	1-1	3-1	0-0	1-1	2-0	2-0	2-2	2-0	4-1	5-0	1-0		1-1	0-1	2-2	4-3	3-2	0-5
17	Thurrock	1-2	1-0	1-1	0-2	0-3	2-0	0-4	1-4	1-3	0-1	0-2	0-0	1-1	1-1	1-2	0-1		0-0	1-1	1-4	0-3	1-1
18	Tonbridge Angels	2-3	1-1	1-1	0-0	0-1	2-1	2-3	5-1	4-0	1-5	1-0	1-2	1-0	3-1	3-2	1-4	3-2		3-0	1-1	3-0	3-6
19	Truro City	2-5	2-1	1-2	0-2	1-1	0-1	1-0	0-2	2-1	8-2	3-3	0-1	1-2	2-2	2-1	0-3	3-0	2-0		2-3	0-1	1-4
20	Welling United	1-1	2-0	2-1	1-1	1-3	2-0	3-0	0-1	1-0	2-1	3-1	4-0	4-3	1-1	0-0	1-0	3-2	5-1		2-0	3-2	
21	Weston-super-Mare	2-1	4-1	0-3	1-2	0-4	0-4	1-1	3-3	0-0	5-2	1-2	3-1	4-2	2-0	2-1	0-0	2-2	2-2	0-1	2-0		0-3
22	Woking	1-0	0-0	3-2	1-1	1-0	4-1	3-1	3-1	1-0	1-0	2-1	3-0	0-2	0-0	0-1	4-1	5-1	2-1	3-3	2-1	4-1	

CONFERENCE ATTENDANCES

BLUE SQUARE PREMIER	Largest Home Attendance	Aggregate	Average
Luton Town	7,270 v Wrexham	80,187	6,160
Wrexhan	5,812 v AFC Telford United	53,072	3,790
Fleetwood Town	3,029 v Southport	47,714	3,412
Grimsby Town	6,672 v Lincoln City	44,217	3,158
Stockport County	4,540 v Southport	44,417	3,150
York City	4,295 v Wrexham	44,117	3,149
Mansfield Town	3,997 v Bath City	35,245	2,517
Lincoln City	5,506 v Grimsby Town	35,067	2,505
Cambridge United	4,796 v Luton Town	31,333	2,410
AFC Telford United	4,591 v Wrexham	32,122	2,294
Kidderminster Harriers	3,332 v Luton Town	26,854	1,918
Darlington	2,647 v Mansfield Town	26,382	1,885
Kettering Town	3,247 v Luton Town	21,732	1,523
Barrow	2,190 v York City	19,888	1,420
Newport County	1,675 v Grimsby Town	18,240	1,403
Southport	2,589 v Fleetwood Town	16,688	1,283
Bath City	1,158 v Luton Town	12,583	1,158
Tamworth	1,467 v Luton Town	13,011	1,084
Ebbsfleet United	1,651 v Luton Town	14,994	1,070
Forest Green Rovers	1,848 v Stockport County	13,703	978
Gateshead	1,604 v York City	12,593	969
Braintree Town	2,029 v Cambridge United	12,895	921
Alfreton Town	1,924 v Grimsby Town	12,107	865
Hayes & Yeading	1,015 v Luton Town	4,795	369
Total		**673,956**	

BLUE SQUARE NORTH	Largest Home Attendance	Aggregate	Average
F.C.HalifaxTown	1,738 v Corby Town	14,169	1,288
Boston United	1,081 v FC Halifax Town	13,090	1,081
Worcester City	1,501 v Gloucester City	10,090	833
Altrincham	846 v Droylsden	9,110	751
Nuneaton Town	1,373 v Hinckley United	8,081	735
Stalybridge Celtic	1,806 v Hyde United	8,134	688
Corby Town	827 v Bishop's Stortford	7,882	666
Hyde United	1,868 v Stalybridge Celtic	7,101	591
Gainsborough Trinity	1,201 v FC Halifax Town	7,097	589
Guiseley	897 v FC Halifax Town	5,868	533
Hinckley United	1,337 v Nuneaton Town	5,613	510
Blyth Spartans	736 v FC Halifax Town	5,777	481
HarrogateTown	456 v FC Halifax Town	5,937	456
Workington	413 v Blyth Spartans	4,957	413
Droylsden	683 v FC Halifax Town	4,529	411
Bishop's Stortford	394 v Boston United	4,752	394
Histon	649 v Bishop's Stortford	4,617	383
Colwyn Bay	444 v Altrincham	4,028	366
Gloucester City	802 v Worcester City	4,699	360
Eastwood Town	596 v Boston United	3,757	314
Solihull Moors	450 v Stalybridge Celtic	3,546	279
Vauxhall Motors	382 v Altrincham	2,924	225
Total		**145,758**	

BLUE SQUARE SOUTH	Largest Home Attendance	Aggregate	Average
Woking	3,014 v Farnborough	18,146	1,395
Chelmsford City	1,068 v Sutton United	11,290	941
Dover Athletic	1,455 v Dartford	10,758	895
Salisbury City	1,003 v Dorchester Town	8,450	768
Dartford	2,559 v Welling United	8,751	729
Sutton United	1,332 v Maidenhead United	7,919	719
Havant & Waterlooville	938 v Eastleigh	8,402	700
Farnborough	2,017 v Woking	7,485	680
Welling United	1,815 v Dartford	8,137	676
Eastbourne Borough	925 v Tonbridge Angels	5,439	629
Tonbridge Angels	905 v Bromley	7,424	618
Truro City	1,017 v Dover Athletic	6,712	610
Dorchester Town	981 v Salisbury City	8,751	501
Eastleigh	665 v Woking	5,439	494
Bromley	771 v Tonbridge Angels	5,328	484
Hampton & Richmond	629 v Staines Town	5,159	469
Staines Town	1,019 v Woking	4,974	452
Weston-s-Mare	620 v Truro City	4,927	410
Basingstoke Town	614 v Farnborough	4,434	403
Thurrock	729 v Chelmsford City	4,007	364
Maidenhead United	405 v Bromley	4,164	320
Boreham Wood	441 v Dartford	3,095	277
Total		**159,191**	

A.F.C. TELFORD UNITED

Chairman: Lee Carter
Secretary: Mrs Sharon Bowyer **(T)** 01952 640064 **(E)** office@telfordutd.co.uk
Additional Committee Members:
Ian Tyrer, David Topping, Ian Dosser, Stuart Massey

Manager: Andy Sinton
Programme Editor: James Baylis **(E)** james.baylis@ppmedia.co.uk

Back row left to right: Darryl Smith, Will Salmon, Jake Reid, Phil Trainer, Michael Briscoe, Kieron St Aime, Chris Blackburn, Kris Taylor and Mike Pugh.
Middle row left to right: Derek Wellings, Jon Brown, Steve Leslie, Dan Preston, Jack Cudworth, Chris Sharp, Ryan Young, Richard Davies, James Spray, Ryan Valentine and Steve Clark.
Front row left to right: Luke Hubbins, Tom Roberts, Steve Jones, Mike Davies, Andy Sinton, John Psaras, Nathan Rooney, Jay Smith and Joe Yoffe.

Club Factfile

Founded: 2004 **Nickname:** The Bucks
Previous Names: AFC Telford United was formed when Telford United folded in May 2004
Previous Leagues: As AFC Telford United: Northern Premier 2004-06
As Telford United: Southern 1969-79. Alliance/Conference 1979-2004

Club Colours (change): White/black/black (Purple & white/purple/purple)

Ground: New Bucks Head Stadium, Watling Street, Wellington, Telford TF1 2TU **(T)** 01952 640 064
Capacity: 6,380 **Seats:** 2,004 **Covered:** 5,000 **Clubhouse:** Yes **Shop:** Yes

Directions: (Sat Nav follow TF1 2NW into Haybridge Road) From M54 Junction 6, A5223 towards Wellington, straight over first roundabout (retail park). Straight over second roundabout (B5067). Left at third roundabout (Furrows garage). Continue over railway bridge and follow road round to the right, then turn left into AFC Telford United Car Park.

Previous Grounds:

Record Attendance: 4,215 v Kendal Town - Northern Premier League play-off final
Record Victory: 7-0 v Runcorn (A) - Northern Premier League Division One 2005-06
Record Defeat: 3-6 v Bradford P.A. (H) - Northern Premier League Division One 2005-06
Record Goalscorer: Kyle Perry - 32 (2004-06)
Record Appearances: Stuart Brock - 132 (2004-09)
Additional Records: Paid £5,000 to Tamworth for Lee Moore 08/12/06
Received £33,000 from Burnley for Duane Courtney 31/08/05
Senior Honours:
Northern Premier League Division 1 Play-off 2004-05, Premier Division Play-off 2006-07. Conference League Cup 2008-09.

10 YEAR RECORD

02-03		03-04		04-05		05-06		06-07		07-08		08-09		09-10		10-11		11-12	
Conf	15	Conf	12	NP 1	3	NP P	10	NP P	3	Conf N	2	Conf N	4	Conf N	11	Conf N	2	Conf	20

AFC TELFORD

No.	Date	Comp	H/A	Opponents	Att:	Result	Goalscorers	Pos
	AFC Telford							
1	Tue-16-Aug	BSP	A	Cambridge United	2482	L 0-1		22
2	Sat-20-Aug	BSP	A	York City	2723	W 1-0	Farrell 86	16
3	Tue-23-Aug	BSP	H	Lincoln City	2323	L 1-2	Mills 90	19
4	Sat-27-Aug	BSP	H	Newport County	2147	W 2-1	Davies 17, Newton pen 57	15
5	Mon-29-Aug	BSP	A	Tamworth	1316	D 2-2	Rooney 70, Meechan 79	14
6	Sat-03-Sep	BSP	A	Southport	1123	L 2-3	Mills 33, A Brown 35	16
7	Sat-10-Sep	BSP	H	Stockport County	2375	D 1-1	Newton pen 49	17
8	Tue-13-Sep	BSP	H	Luton Town	2640	L 0-2		17
9	Sat-17-Sep	BSP	H	Bath City	2093	W 2-1	Sharp 3, A Brown 46	15
10	Tue-20-Sep	BSP	A	Mansfield Town	2481	D 1-1	Sharp 86	17
11	Sat-24-Sep	BSP	A	Fleetwood Town	1686	D 2-2	Killock 43, Newton 58	15
12	Tue-27-Sep	BSP	H	Alfreton Town	1781	W 1-0	Sharp 68	13
13	Sat-01-Oct	BSP	H	Hayes & Yeading United	1941	D 1-1	Davies 38	13
14	Sat-08-Oct	BSP	A	Barrow	1109	L 1-2	Farrell 58	14
15	Tue-11-Oct	BSP	A	Kidderminster Harriers	2440	D 2-2	Adams 8, Sharp 75	15
16	Sat-15-Oct	BSP	H	Ebbsfleet United	2004	L 0-2		15
17	Tue-18-Oct	BSP	A	Forest Green Rovers	632	L 1-2	Proudlock 77	18
18	Sat-22-Oct	BSP	H	Gateshead	2484	L 1-2	Preston 65	19
19	Sat-05-Nov	BSP	A	Darlington	1680	L 0-1		20
20	Sat-19-Nov	BSP	H	Mansfield Town	2203	D 0-0		19
21	Sat-26-Nov	BSP	H	Barrow	1814	W 1-0	Jones 77	17
22	Tue-29-Nov	BSP	A	Luton Town	5399	D 1-1	Newton 55	17
23	Sat-03-Dec	BSP	A	Bath City	761	L 1-3	Jones 45	17
24	Tue-06-Dec	BSP	H	York City	1601	D 0-0		17
25	Sat-17-Dec	BSP	A	Braintree Town	605	L 1-2	Smith 7	18
26	Mon-26-Dec	BSP	H	Wrexham	4591	L 0-2		18
27	Sun-01-Jan	BSP	A	Wrexham	5812	L 0-4		18
28	Sat-07-Jan	BSP	H	Kettering Town	2035	W 3-1	Sharp 43, Trainer 46, Jackson 86	17
29	Sat-21-Jan	BSP	H	Cambridge United	1903	L 1-2	Sharp 53	17
30	Tue-24-Jan	BSP	A	Stockport County	2831	D 2-2	Sharp 16, Jones 34	17
31	Sat-28-Jan	BSP	A	Grimsby Town	3704	L 0-2		18
32	Sat-18-Feb	BSP	H	Braintree Town	1776	W 1-0	Brooke 75	18
33	Sat-25-Feb	BSP	A	Lincoln City	2438	D 1-1	Perry 24	18
34	Sat-03-Mar	BSP	A	Alfreton Town	940	D 0-0		19
35	Sat-10-Mar	BSP	H	Southport	2025	L 0-1		20
36	Tue-13-Mar	BSP	H	Kidderminster Harriers	2192	W 2-1	Trainer 3, Blackburn 66	16
37	Sat-17-Mar	BSP	H	Fleetwood Town	2313	L 1-4	J Brown 74	17
38	Tue-20-Mar	BSP	A	Kettering Town	939	L 1-2	Sharp 85	17
39	Sat-24-Mar	BSP	A	Hayes & Yeading United	307	D 0-0		18
40	Tue-27-Mar	BSP	H	Forest Green Rovers	1674	W 2-0	Sharp 2 (8, 38)	17
41	Sat-31-Mar	BSP	H	Darlington	1908	D 3-3	Sharp 9, Davies 52, Trainer 60	18
42	Fri-06-Apr	BSP	A	Newport County	1540	D 0-0		20
43	Sat-14-Apr	BSP	A	Ebbsfleet United	875	L 2-3	Proudlock 66, Brooke 74	20
44	Tue-17-Apr	BSP	H	Tamworth	3477	W 1-0	Trainer 77	18
45	Sat-21-Apr	BSP	H	Grimsby Town	2676	D 0-0		20
46	Sat-28-Apr	BSP	A	Gateshead	606	L 0-3		20

CUPS

No.	Date	Comp	H/A	Opponents	Att:	Result	Goalscorers	
1	Sat-29-Oct	FAC 4Q	H	Gainsborough Trinity	1075	W 5-0	Pitt 2 (9, 64), Killock 42, Sharp 2 (52, 71)	
2	Sat-12-Nov	FAC 1	A	Chelmsford City	1430	L 0-4		
3	Sun-11-Dec	FAT 1	A	Nuneaton Town	945	W 2-0	Brown 25, Sharp 90	
4	Sat-14-Jan	FAT 2	A	Cambridge United	1259	L 1-4	Sharp 53	

League
Starts
Substitute
Unused Sub

Cups
Starts
Substitute
Unused Sub

Goals (Lg)
Goals (Cup)

	YOUNG	NEWTON	VALENTINE	KILLOCK	PRESTON	ADAMS	TRAINER	REID	DAVIES	A BROWN	MEECHAN	FARRELL	SAMUELS	ROONEY	SALMON	EVANS	KING	MILLS	WHITEHEAD	R WILLIAMS	SHARP	ROBINSON	RODGERS	PROUDLOCK	PLATT	WEIR-DALEY	PITT	SMITH	CAIN	JONES	CHAMBERLAIN	BLACKBURN	JACKSON	PERRY	FUTCHER	J BROWN	BROOKE	CLOUGH	KINNIBURGH
No.	1	3	23	6	16	11	8	7	20	10	9	19	12	15	2	13	17	24	5	14	25	32	4	31	26	30	22	27	28	29	26	18	9	17	5	22	21	17	13
	X	X	X	X	X	X	X	X	X	X	X	X	S	S	S	U	U																						
	X	X	X	X	X	U	X	X	X	X	X	S	S	S		X	U	X																					
	X	X	X	X	X	U	X	X	X	X	X	S				X	U	S	S																				
	X	X	X		X		X		X	X	S	X	U	X	U		X	X	U																				
	X	X	X			X		X		X	S	S	X	S	X	S	X	U		X	X	U																	
	X	X	X	U	X		X		X	X	S			S	S	X		X	X		X	U																	
	X	X	U	X			X	X		X				S	X	X		X	X		S	U	X																
	X	X	U	X			S	X		X		S	X	X		X		X	X		X	U	X			S													
	X	X	S	X		X	X			X		U	X	X	X			X	X		X	U	X			S													
	X	X	X	X	X	X	X			X		U	S		X			X	X		X	U	U	S															
	X	X	X	X	X	X	X			X				X				X	X		X	U	U	S															
	X	X	X	X	X	X	X		X					X				S	U		X	U	U	U	S														
	X	X	X	X	X	X	X		X					U				S	U		X	U		X	X	S													
	X	X	X	X	X	X	X		X			X		U				S			X	U		S	X														
	X	X	U	X	X	X	X			X				X				S	U	X	S						X												
	X	X	U	X	X	X	X		S				X					X	U		S	S				X													
	X	X	S	X		X	X		X	S		X						S	X		U	X	U				X												
	X	X	U	X	X	X	S		X				X					X	X	X	U						X												
	X	X		X	X	X	S	S	X			S						X	U		X						X												
	X	X	X	X	X	U	S		X			X						X	U		X	X	S					X	X	S									
	X	X	X	X	X	U	S		X			S						X	U		X	X	S	X				X	X	S	X								
	X	X	X	X	S	S			X	S		X						X			X	X						X	X	X	U								
	X	X	X		X	U	S		X	S		X			X			X			X							X	X	X									
	X	X	X		X	U	X		X	U		X		U				X			S	X	U	U				X	X	X									
	X	X	X		X	U	X		X			X		U				X	X		S	X						X	X	X									
	X	X	X		X	X	X		X			X		U				S	U		S	X						X	X	X									
	X		X	X	S		X			X				S				X	U	U								X	X	S	X	X	X						
	X		X	U			X			X				S				X	U									X	X	S	X		X	X					
	X		X	S			X			X				S	U			X	U	S								X	X	S	X		X	X					X
	X	X	X	U	X		X			S								X	S									U			X	X	X	S		X	X		
	X		X	S	X		X			X								S	U	X	S							U			X	X	X			X		U	
	X		X	X	X		X			X								X	U		S							U	S		X	X	X			X			
	X		X	U	X		X			X								X	U	S	S							U	S		X	X	X			X			
	X		X	U	X		X			X								X	U		X							S	X		X		X			X	X		
	X		X	U	X		X			X								X	U			X						X	U	S		X		S		X	X		
	X		X	S	X		X			X					S	X			X	U	X	X						U			X	S			X	X			
	X		X		X		X			X					S	X			X		X	X						S		X		S			X	X			
	X	X	U	X	X	X	U		S	X	S			X	S	X			U			X	U			X			X			X							
	X	X	U	X	X	X	X			X	X			S		S	X		X	U		X	U					S	U										
	X	X	X	X	X	U	X				X			X	U		X	X			U			X				S	U		X	X							
	X	X		X	X		X			X					S		X				U			X	U	U			X	S				X	X				
Apps	46	33	35	32	25	14	34	4	29	15	2	7	6	7	39	0	2	7	13	0	32	0	8	6	2	0	4	15	15	9	1	19	8	13	3	14	6	0	1
Sub	0	0	2	3	3	6	2	1	5	6	3	9	10	9	0	0	2	9	1	0	5	0	3	12	1	2	0	2	8	6	1	0	0	6	0	0	5	0	0
Un	0	1	5	5	11	3	1	0	0	0	1	2	0	4	3	6	1	0	7	1	0	39	3	0	1	0	0	5	2	0	1	0	0	0	0	0	0	3	0
	4	4	1	4	4	2	3	0	3	2	0	0	1	1	4	0	0	1	0	0	3	0	0	1	0	0	1	1	2	0	0	0	1	1	0	0	0	0	0
	0	0	0	0	0	0	0	1	0	1	0	1	1	2	0	0	0	0	0	0	1	0	0	0	0	0	1	0	0	0	1	0	0	0	0	0	0	0	0
	0	0	2	0	0	1	1	0	0	0	1	0	0	0	0	2	2	0	4	1	0	0	1	0	0	0	1	0	0	0	0	0	0	0	0	0	0	0	0
	0	4	0	1	1	4	0	3	2	1	2	0	1	0	0	2	0	0	11	0	0	2	0	0	1	0	3	0	1	1	1	1	0	1	2	0	0		
	0	0	0	1	0	0	0	0	0	0	0	0	0	0	0	0	0	4	0	0	0	0	2	0	0	0	0	1	0	0	0	0	0	0	0	0	0		

PLAYING SQUAD

Existing Players		SN	HT	WT	DOB	AGE	POB	Career	Apps	Goals
GOALKEEPERS										
Jack	Cudworth	20	5'11"	11 04	11/09/1990	21	Preston	Preston (Scholar) Rel c/s 09, Welshpool c/s 09, Rhyl 1/10, Macclesfield 7/10 Rel c/s 12, Colwyn Bay (L) 12/11, Barrow (SL) 3/12, AFC Telford 8/12		
Ryan	Young	1			25/12/1979	32	Birmingham	Plymouth (Trainee), Chasetown, Nuneaton, Halesowen T (L) 10/01, Hucknall T 2/02, Hednesford 5/03, Redditch 6/05, AFC Telford 9/05, Kettering 2/06, Willenhall 3/06, Hednesford 6/06, AFC Telford 5/07	46	0
DEFENDERS										
Chris	Blackburn	4	5'07"	10 06	02/08/1982	30	Crewe	Chester Rel c/s 03, Northwich 8/03, Morecambe 2/04, Swindon 7/07 Rel 5/08, Weymouth (SL) 3/08, Aldershot 5/08, Wrexham 5/10 Rel 8/11, Stockport 8/11, AFC Telford 1/12	19	1
Michael	Briscoe	14	5'11"	12 00	04/07/1983	29	Northampton	Harpole, Coventry 4/03 Rel c/s 04, Macclesfield 7/04 Rel 5/06, Burton (SL) 3/05, Kettering (Trial) c/s 06, Hucknall 9/06, Tamworth (L) 2/07, Tamworth 5/07, Halesowen T 8/08, Redditch 2/09, Tamworth 6/09, Kidderminster 7/10, AFC Telford 6/12		
Dan	Preston	5	5'11"	12 04	26/09/1991	20	Birmingham	Birmingham Rel c/s 11, Hereford (L) 2/10, Hereford (3ML) 1/11, AFC Telford 7/11	28	1
Tom	Roberts				23/09/1991	20		Man Utd (Yth), Aston Villa (Scholar) Rel c/s 11, The New Saints 8/11 Rel c/s 12, AFC Telford 8/12		
Will	Salmon	2			25/11/1986	25	Basingstoke	Aldershot Rel c/s 07, Fleet T (SL) c/s 05, Fleet T (SL) 8/06, AFC Wimbledon 6/07 Rel 5/08, Fleet T (L) 2/08, Fleet T c/s 08, Ebbsfleet 8/09, AFC Telford 8/10	39	0
Ryan	Valentine	3	5'11"	11 11	19/08/1982	30	Wrexham	Everton Rel c/s 02, Oxford U (Trial) 4/02, Darlington 8/02 Rel c/s 06, Wrexham 8/06, Darlington 1/08, Hereford 5/09 Rel c/s 11, AFC Telford 6/11	37	0
MIDFIELDERS										
Richard	Davies	6	5'11"	11 05	15/05/1990	22	Willenhall	Walsall Rel c/s 10, Solihull Moors (L) 12/09, AFC Telford 8/10, Chasetown (3ML) 11/10, Chasetown (Dual) 2/11	34	3
Luke	Hubbins	11	5'09"	10 07	11/09/1991	20	Birmingham	Birmingham Rel c/s 12, Notts County (5ML) 8/12, Tamworth (L) 1/12, AFC Telford 5/12		
Steven	Leslie	18	5'10"	11 02	05/11/1987	24	Glasgow	Shrewsbury Rel 1/12, Hereford (SL) 3/11, Hereford (3ML) 10/11, Wrexham 1/12 Rel c/s 12, AFC Telford 8/12		
Nathan	Rooney	7	6'00"	11 11	02/10/1992	19	Telford	Wolves Rel 3/11, Shrewsbury (Trial) 3/11, AFC Telford 7/11	16	1
Jay	Smith	12	5'07"	12 00	24/09/1981	30	Lambeth	Aston Villa, Southend (3ML) 8/02, Southend 11/02 Rel 1/07, Oxford U (SL) 3/06, Notts County (3ML) 11/06 Perm 1/07 Rel 1/09, Wigan (Trial), Eastwood T 12/09, Tamworth 1/10, AFC Telford (6WL) 11/11 Perm 1/12	17	1
Kris	Taylor	19	5'09"	13 05	12/01/1984	28	Stafford	Wolves (Yth), Man Utd, Walsall 2/03 Rel c/s 07, Burton (L) 12/04, Burton (3ML) 1/06, Hereford 8/07 Rel c/s 09, Port Vale 8/09 Rel c/s 11, Darlington 6/11, AFC Telford 8/12		
Phil	Trainer	8	6'00"	12 00	03/07/1981	31	Wolverhampton	Crewe Rel c/s 02, Hyde (3ML) 12/00, Hednesford (3ML) 11/01, Stalybridge (L) 3/02, Northwich 8/02, Kidsgrove 9/02, Halesowen 12/02, Tamworth 8/03, Stourport S (L) 9/03, Moor Green/Solihull Moors (L) 10/03 Perm 11/03, Oxford U 7/07 Rel 4/09, AFC Telford (SL) 1/09, AFC Telford 5/09	36	4
FORWARDS										
Jonathan	Brown	21	5'11"	11 04	17/04/1990	22	Bridgend	Cardiff Rel c/s 09, Wrexham (SL) 11/08, L.Orient (Trial), Bryntirion Ath 8/09 Rel 11/09, Central Coast Mariners (Aust) 12/09 Rel c/s 10, Bath C 1/11, Southport 7/11 Rel c/s 12, AFC Telford (SL) 1/12, AFC Telford 7/12	14	1
Steve	Jones	10	5'10"	10 05	25/10/1976	35	Derry, NI	Chadderton (Yth), Blackpool Rel c/s 96, Bury 7/96 Rel c/s 97, Sligo R 8/97, Bray W (L), Chorley, Leigh RMI c/s 99, Tranmere (Trial) 7/01, Crewe £75,000 7/01, Rochdale (2ML) 2/02, Burnley 6/06, Crewe (SL) 3/08, Huddersfield (5WL) 10/08, Bradford C (SL) 11/08, Walsall 7/09 Rel c/s 11, Motherwell (SL) 1/11, Droylsden 8/11, AFC Telford 11/11	15	3
Jake	Reid	15			22/06/1987	25	London	Yeovil (Yth), Team Bath, Paulton (L) 1/07, Yate T (L) 3/07, Chippenham 6/07, Mangotsfield (L) 1/08, Yate L 3/08, Weymouth 8/09, Grays 12/09, Weymouth 1/10 Rel 3/10, Salisbury 3/10, Bath C 7/10 Rel 9/10, Salisbury 9/10 Rel 1/12, Newport C 1/12 Rel c/s 12, AFC Telford 7/12		

		SN	HT	WT	DOB	AGE	POB	From - To	APPS	GOA
Chris	Sharp	9	5'11"	10 09	19/06/1986	26	Liverpool	Vauxhall Motors (Yth), Capenhurst Villa, Rhyl 7/05 Rel c/s 08, Bangor C c/s 08, Wrexham (Trial) 5/09, Notts County (Trial) 7/09, The New Saints 1/10, AFC Telford Undisc 8/11	37	11
James	Spray	17	6'00"	12 01	02/12/1992	19	Halesowen	Wolves Rel c/s 12, Accrington (L) 10/11, AFC Telford 8/12		
Kieron	St Aimie	16	6'01"	13 00	04/05/1989	23	Brent	QPR Rel 1/08, Oxford U (L) 10/07, Barnet 1/08 Rel 2/09, Grays (L) 9/08, Stevenage (L) 11/08, Lewes (L) 1/09, St Albans (Trial), Thurrock 3/09, Hitchin 3/09, Maidenhead 8/09 Rel 3/11, Lewes 3/11, AFC Hornchurch 3/11, Kettering 3/11, Tamworth 6/11, AFC Telford 8/12		
Joe	Yoffe				26/05/1987	25		FCUM Rel c/s 10, Ottawa Fury (Can), Crevillente Deportivo (Spa), Galway U 3/11, AFC Telford 8/12		

Loanees		SN	HT	WT	DOB	AGE	POB	From - To	APPS	GOA
(F)Conal	Platt		5'09"	10 10	14/10/1986	25	Preston	Cambridge U 9/11 - Lincoln C (2ML) 11/11 Perm 1/12	3	0
(M)Elliott	Chamberlain				29/04/1992	20	Paget, Ber	Leicester 11/11 -	2	0
(F)Kyle	Perry		6'04"	14 05	05/03/1986	26	Birmingham	Lincoln C (SL) 1/12 - Rel c/s 12, Nuneaton 7/12	19	1
(F)Marlon	Jackson		5'11"	11 12	06/12/1990	21	Bristol	Bristol C 1/12, 3/12 - Rel c/s 12, Hereford 7/12	8	1
(D)Ben	Futcher		6'07"	12 05	20/02/1981	31	Manchester	Bury 1/12 - Macclesfield (3ML) 2/12, FC Halifax (SL) 7/12	0	3
(F)Ryan	Brooke		6'01"	11 07	04/10/1990	21	Congleton	Oldham (SL) 1/12 - Rel c/s 12, Altrincham 5/12	11	2
(D)Charlie	Clough		6'02"	12 08	04/09/1990	21	Taunton	Bristol R 3/12 -	0	0

Departures		SN	HT	WT	DOB	AGE	POB	From - To	APPS	GOA
(F)James	Lawrie		6'00"	12 05	18/12/1990	21	Belfast	Port Vale 8/10 - Rel 12/11, Altrincham (3ML) 8/11, Altrincham 12/11		
(M)Jordan	Johnson							Newcastle T 7/11 - Chasetown (L) 9/11, Northwich (L) 10/11, Northwich Undisc 12/11, Airbus UK 5/12		
(F)Alex	Meechan		5'08"	10 10	29/01/1980	32	Plymouth	Droylsden 7/10 - Rel 12/11, Harrogate T (10WL) 10/11, Harrogate T 1/12	5	1
(M)Levi	Reid		5'05"	11 04	19/01/1983	28	Stafford	Stafford R 3/11 - Chasetown (L) 9/11, Gainsborough 1/12		
(F)Craig	King		5'11"	11 12	06/10/1990	21	Chesterfield	Leicester 7/11 - Rel 1/12, Worksop 1/12	4	0
(G)Lee	Evans				24/05/1983	29	Sutton Coldfield	Stafford R 8/11 - Rel 1/12, Leamington (Dual) 10/11, Walsall Wood (Dual) 2/12, Romulus 2/12, Chasetown 3/12	0	0
(M)Curtley	Williams							Chelmsford 8/11 - Rel 1/12, Buxton (Dual) 9/11		
(M)Philip	John				18/08/1985	27		Fleet T 8/10 - Hayes & Yeading (Trial) 8/11, Didcot T (L) 8/11, Reading T (L) 9/11, Redditch 10/11, Reading T (L)		
(F)Spencer	Weir-Daley		5'09"	10 11	05/09/1985	26	Leicester	Boston U 8/11 - Buxton (Dual) 9/11, Boston U 1/12	2	0
(D)Stuart	Whitehead		6'00"	12 02	17/07/1976	36	Bromsgrove	Kidderminster 1/08 - Rel 1/12, Worcester 1/12	14	0
(M)Greg	Mills		6'02"	13 01	18/09/1990	21	Derby	Derby 8/11 - Rel 1/12, Worcester 1/12	16	2
(M)James	Reid		5'10"	11 04	28/02/1990	22	Nottingham	Hinckley U 4/11 - Rel 1/12, Ilkeston FC (3ML) 11/11, Ilkeston FC 1/12	5	0
(F)Craig	Farrell		6'00"	12 11	05/12/1982	29	Middlesbrough	Rushden & D 6/11 - Hinckley U (L) 1/12 Perm 2/12, Blyth 6/12	16	2
(M)Courtney	Pitt		5'07"	10 08	17/12/1981	30	Paddington	Weymouth 11/10 - Chasetown 2/12	4	0
(D)Dwayne	Samuels		5'08"	11 00	11/10/1990	21	Wolverhampton	Grimsby 7/11 - Worcester 3/12, Harrogate T 5/12	16	0
(F)Andy	Brown				03/03/1986	26	Lincoln	Nuneaton 6/08 - Nuneaton T (3ML) 1/12 Perm 3/12	21	2
(D)Robbie	Williams		6'05"		06/07/1987	25	Blackpool	Altrincham 6/11 - Rel c/s 12, Altrincham (3ML) 9/11, Lincoln C (SL) 1/12, Hyde U 8/12	0	0
(G)Ryan	Robinson		6'02"	13 02	13/10/1982	29	Tebay	Bath C 8/11 - Rel c/s 12, Northwich 6/12	0	0
(D)Shane	Killock		6'00"	12 04	12/03/1989	23	Huddersfield	Oxford U (2ML) 8/09 Perm 10/09 - Rel c/s 12, Harrogate T 5/12	35	1
(M)Jon	Adams				08/01/1985	27		Leamington c/s 07 - Rel c/s 12, Leamington (L) 1/12, Nuneaton 5/12	20	1
(D)Sean	Newton		6'02"	13 00	23/09/1988	23	Liverpool	Barrow (2ML) 8/09 Perm 10/09 Stockport (SL) 3/12 Nominal 5/12	33	4
(M)Ashley	Cain		6'02"	12 06	27/09/1990	21	Nuneaton	Tamworth (6WL) 11/11 Perm 1/12 - Rel c/s 12	23	0
(M)Carl	Rodgers				26/03/1983	29	Chester	Colwyn Bay 5/06 - Rel c/s 12, Altrincham 5/12	11	0
(F)Adam	Proudlock		6'00"	13 07	09/05/1981	31	Wellington	Grimsby 9/10 - Chester FC 6/12	18	2
(D)Steve	Kinniburgh		6'00"	11 02	13/06/1989	23	Glasgow	Oxford U 3/12 - Rel c/s 12	1	0
(M)David	McDermott		5'05"	10 00	06/02/1988	24	Stourbridge	York C 2/12 -	0	0

Conference Action...

Alfreton's Jordan Hall shields the ball from the incoming Wrexham player.

Photo: Bill Wheatcroft.

ALFRETON TOWN

Chairman: Wayne Bradley
Secretary: Bryan Rudkin   **(T)** 07710 444 195   **(E)** bryanrudkin@hotmail.com
Additional Committee Members:
Sean Egan, Dave Gregory, John Glasby, Roger Webster

Manager: Nicky Law
Programme Editor: Chris Tacey   **(E)** ctacey5087@aol.com

Alfreton celebrate a last minute winner against Barrow last season. Photo: Bill Wheatcroft.

Club Factfile

Founded: 1959   **Nickname:** The Reds
Previous Names: None
Previous Leagues: Central Alliance (pre reformation 1921-25) 59-61. Midland Combination 1925-27, 61-82. Northern Counties East 1982-87. Northern Premier 1987-99.

Club Colours (change): All red (All blue)

Ground: Impact Arena, North Street, Alfreton, Derbyshire DE55 7FZ   **(T)** 01773 830 277
Capacity: 3,600   **Seats:** 1,500   **Covered:** 2,600   **Clubhouse:** Yes   **Shop:** Yes

Directions
From M1 Junction 28 Take A38 towards Derby for 2 miles.
Then take slip road onto B600 Turn right at Tjunction towards town centre.
At pedestrian crossing turn left into North Street and the ground is on the right hand side.

Previous Grounds:

Record Attendance: 5,023 v Matlock Town - Central Alliance 1960
Record Victory: 15-0 v Loughbrough Midland League 1969-70
Record Defeat: 1-9 v Solihull - FAT 1997. 0-8 v Bridlington - 1992
Record Goalscorer: J Harrison - 303
Record Appearances: J Harrison - 560+
Additional Records: Paid £2,000 to Worksop Town for Mick Goddard
          Received £7,000 from Ilkeston Town for Paul Eshelby
Senior Honours:
Northern Counties East 1984-85, 2001-02. Northern Premier League Division 1 2002-03.
Conference North 2010-11.
Derbyshire Senior Cup x7

10 YEAR RECORD

02-03		03-04		04-05		05-06		06-07		07-08		08-09		09-10		10-11		11-12	
NP 1	1	NP P	4	Conf N	14	Conf N	17	Conf N	14	Conf N	16	Conf N	3	Conf N	3	Conf N	1	Conf	15

ALFRETON TOWN

No.	Date	Comp	H/A	Opponents	Att:	Result	Goalscorers	Pos
1	Sat-13-Aug	BSP	A	Hayes & Yeading United	262	L 1-3	Mullan 70	23
2	Tue-16-Aug	BSP	H	Southport	777	D 0-0		19
3	Sat-20-Aug	BSP	H	Forest Green Rovers	686	L 1-6	Streete 13	23
4	Tue-23-Aug	BSP	A	Darlington	1965	D 1-1	Jarman pen 83	24
5	Sat-27-Aug	BSP	H	Wrexham	1165	L 1-4	Jarman pen 21	24
6	Mon-29-Aug	BSP	A	York City	3166	W 1-0	Mackin pen 43	21
7	Sat-03-Sep	BSP	A	Gateshead	991	L 0-2		23
8	Sat-10-Sep	BSP	H	Braintree Town	656	L 0-1		23
9	Sat-17-Sep	BSP	A	Kidderminster Harriers	1939	L 1-3	Broughton pen 31	23
10	Tue-20-Sep	BSP	H	Barrow	678	W 2-1	Mullan 73, Ellison 90	21
11	Sat-24-Sep	BSP	H	Ebbsfleet United	661	D 2-2	Brown 49, Jarman 64	21
12	Tue-27-Sep	BSP	A	AFC Telford	1781	L 0-1		22
13	Sat-01-Oct	BSP	A	Grimsby Town	2941	L 2-5	Clayton 18, Jarman pen 90	22
14	Sat-08-Oct	BSP	H	Kettering Town	851	D 1-1	Brown 24	22
15	Tue-11-Oct	BSP	H	Lincoln City	1232	L 1-3	Clayton 18	23
16	Sat-15-Oct	BSP	A	Cambridge United	2741	L 0-3		23
17	Tue-18-Oct	BSP	H	Fleetwood Town	625	L 1-4	Clayton 70	23
18	Sat-22-Oct	BSP	A	Mansfield Town	2982	L 2-3	Brown 13, Clayton 21	23
19	Sat-05-Nov	BSP	A	Forest Green Rovers	764	L 1-4	A Wilson 62	23
20	Sat-19-Nov	BSP	H	Gateshead	651	D 1-1	Clayton 37	23
21	Sat-26-Nov	BSP	H	Hayes & Yeading United	600	W 3-2	Arnold 64, Jarman 90+4, J Moult 90+6	23
22	Tue-29-Nov	BSP	A	Barrow	963	L 0-1		23
23	Sat-03-Dec	BSP	A	Southport	1061	L 1-2	Quinn 63	23
24	Tue-06-Dec	BSP	H	Newport County	579	W 3-2	Church 28, J Moult 38, Jarman 89	23
25	Sat-17-Dec	BSP	A	Stockport County	2802	D 0-0		23
26	Mon-26-Dec	BSP	H	Tamworth	1012	W 5-2	Brown 1, Arnold 3, J Moult 36, A Wilson 55, Jarman 67	22
27	Sun-01-Jan	BSP	A	Tamworth	1241	D 2-2	Streete 43, Brown 62	21
28	Sat-07-Jan	BSP	H	Grimsby Town	1924	L 2-5	Arnold 33, M Wilson 73	21
29	Sat-21-Jan	BSP	H	Kidderminster Harriers	990	L 0-1		21
30	Tue-24-Jan	BSP	A	Bath City	739	W 3-0	Og (Connolly) 17, Jarman pen 88, Clay 90	20
31	Sat-28-Jan	BSP	A	Luton Town	5658	L 0-1		22
32	Sat-18-Feb	BSP	H	Darlington	950	W 3-1	Arnold 2 (33, 69), Clayton 58	21
33	Sat-25-Feb	BSP	A	Fleetwood Town	1929	L 0-4		21
34	Sat-03-Mar	BSP	H	AFC Telford	940	D 0-0		20
35	Tue-06-Mar	BSP	H	Stockport County	1115	W 6-1	Jarman 3 (1, pen 37, pen 86), A Wilson 25, Clayton 68, Arnold 77	20
36	Sat-10-Mar	BSP	A	Lincoln City	2253	W 1-0	J Moult 45	17
37	Sat-17-Mar	BSP	A	Kettering Town	1093	W 2-0	Kempson 4, J Moult 10	16
38	Tue-20-Mar	BSP	H	Mansfield Town	3354	L 3-6	J Moult 6, Jarman 21, Brown 45	16
39	Sat-24-Mar	BSP	H	Cambridge United	965	W 2-1	Og (Thorpe) 1, A Wilson 54	16
40	Tue-27-Mar	BSP	A	Ebbsfleet United	687	W 2-1	Cunnington 35, Law 48	16
41	Sat-31-Mar	BSP	A	Braintree Town	620	W 2-1	Cunnington 23, Brown 63	15
42	Fri-06-Apr	BSP	A	Wrexham	4673	W 1-0	A Wilson 43	14
43	Mon-09-Apr	BSP	H	York City	1603	L 0-2		15
44	Sat-14-Apr	BSP	H	Luton Town	1654	D 0-0		15
45	Sat-21-Apr	BSP	A	Newport County	1239	L 0-1		15
46	Sat-28-Apr	BSP	H	Bath City	786	W 2-1	Meadows 17, A Wilson 20	15

CUPS

No.	Date	Comp	H/A	Opponents	Att:	Result	Goalscorers	
1	Sat-29-Oct	FAC 4Q	H	Lincoln City	1000	D 1-1	Jarman pen 41	
2	Tue-01-Nov	FAC 4QR	A	Lincoln City	1728	W 2-1	Brown 27, Jarman pen 60	
3	Sat-12-Nov	FAC 1	A	Carlisle United	1488	L 0-4		
4	Sat-10-Dec	FAT 1	H	Southport	394	W 4-0	Brown 38, A Wilson 45, Jarman 47, Clayton 80	
5	Sat-14-Jan	FAT 2	A	Weymouth	739	W 6-0	Jarman 2 (4, 38), Arnold 2 (12, 25), L Moult 44, Clayton 77	
6	Tue-14-Feb	FAT 3	A	Gateshead	347	L 1-2	Og (Odhiambo) 6	

League
Starts
Substitute
Unused Sub

Cups
Starts
Substitute
Unused Sub

Goals (Lg)
Goals (Cup)

Appearances / team-sheet grid:

	LOWSON	LAW	YOUNG	M WILSON	FRANKLIN	JARMAN	STREETE	BROWN	ARNOLD	CLAYTON	SENIOR	MULLAN	J MOULT	HALL	MACKIN	HAWES	A WILSON	FRANKS	ELLISON	BROGAN	HOLDSWORTH	BROUGHTON	TURNER	DAY	STEVENSON	POTTER	CHURCH	QUINN	EAGLE	L MOULT	CLAY	KEMPSON	STEWART	DEVERDICS	CONNEELY	CUNNINGTON	MEADOWS
No.	1	2	5	6	3	16	4	7	11	9	10	19	8	14	17	20	15	12	22	25	23	26	18	21	23	25	22	25	23	17	22	26	27	17	29	28	22
	X	X	X	X	X	X	X	X	X	X	X	X	S	S	S	U	U																				
	X	X	X	X	X	U	X	X	X	X	X	U	X	X	S	U		S																			
	X	X	X	X	X	S	X	X	X	X	X	S	X	X	U	U		S																			
	X	X		X	X	S	X	X	X	X	X	U	U	S	X	U		X																			
	X		U	X	X	X	X	X		X	S	S	U	X	X	X		X	S																		
	X		X	X	X	X	X	X		X	X	X	U	U	X	U		X	S																		
	X		X	X	X	X	X	X		X	X	U	U	X		X	S	S	S																		
	X	X	X	U	U	S	X	X		X	X	X		X		X	S	S	S	X																	
	X	X	X	X	S	X	X	X		X	S		X	S	U	U		X		X																	
	X	X	X	X	X	X	X	X		X	S	S	X		X			S	U	U																	
	X	X	X	X	X	X	X	X		X	U	S	X		X	U		X	S		S																
	X	X	X		X		X			U	X	S	X	S		S		X	X		X		U														
	X		X		X		X			X	S	X	S	X	X		X		X	S		X	U														
		X	U	X	X	X	X			X	S	X	X	U	X		S	S							X												
		X		X	S	X	X			X	S	X	S	U	X	U	X	X							X	X											
	X	X		X	U	X	X			X	S	S		S	X	U	X	X							X	X											
	X	S		X	U	X	X			X	S	X	S	X	X	X		U	X							X	X										
	X	X			S		X			X	S	X	S	X	X	X	U	S	X	X	U					X		X									
	X	X				X	X			S	X	X	X	S		X	X		U	U						X	U	X									
		X		X	S	X	S	X	X	X	X		S	X	X		U	U			X					X			X								
	U	X		X	S	X	U	X	X	U	X	X					X								X				X	X	S						
	S	X		X	S	X	U	X	X	S							X	U							X				X	X	X						
	S	X	U	X	S	X	X	X	X				X				X	U							X				X	X	X						
	X	X	U	X	S	X	X	X	X				X				S	U							X				X	X	U						
	X	U		X	X	X	X	X	S		U	X		U			X								X				X	X	U						
	X	X	S	X	X	X	X	X	S		S	X	U	U			X								X				X								
	X	X	S	X	X	X	X	X	S		S	X	U				X	U							X				U	X							
	X	X	S	X	X	X	X	X	S		S	X	U				X	U							X				X								
	X	X	X	U	X	X	X		X	S			X	X			S	U								X				X	X	U					
	X	S	X	U	U	X	X		X	S			X	X			X	X								X				S							
	X	S	X	U	S	X	X		X		X	X			X	S		U	X										X	X							
	X	S	X		U	X	X		X	X			X	X	S		S	X								X				S	X						
	X	S	X	X	U	X	X				U	X		S	X		S	X								X				X	X						
		S		X	X	X	X	X	X		S	U					X	X								X				U	X	X	U				
	U	X		X	X	X	X	X	X		S	X					X													X	X	X	S				
	U	X		X	X	X	X	X		X	X						U	X												X	X	X	X	S	S		
	U	X		X	X	S	X	X		X	X						S	X												X	X	X	X	X	S		
		X	S	X	X	X	X	X	X		S	X					X	U												X	X	U		S			
	U			X	X	X	X	X	S		X						X	U												X	X	S	X	X	U		
		X	U	X		X	X	X			S	X					X	S							X					X	U	X	X	U		
	U	X	U		X		X	X		S		X					X								X					X	U	X	X	U		
		X			X		X		S	X	X	U					X								X					X	X	S	X	X	U		
		X		X	S	X	X	U	U		X	X					X													X	X	S	X	X	S		
		X		X	X	S	X	X	S		U						S	X												X	X	X	U	X	X		
	X	S		S	S	X	U	X			U	X					X	X														X	X	X	X		
	X	X			X	X	U	X	X	U			S	S			X	X											X				X	S	X		
	X					X	X			X	X	X	X	X			X	S			U			X				U		X							
	X	S	X				X	X	X	U	X	U	X	X	S		X	X	S						U												
	U	X	X		U	S	X	X	X	X	S	S		X	U		X	X						X			X		X								
		X	X	U	X	X	X	X	X	X	S		S	X	S		X	U						X				X									
	X	X	X	S	X	X	X	X	S		X	X					S	U					U							X							
	X	X	X	X	X	X	X	X	X	S	X		S	S	U		X															U	X				

Apps	20	30	28	12	37	25	40	38	27	30	7	16	33	5	11	2	26	21	1	0	2	2	0	15	3	2	6	17	2	1	2	13	11	3	8	7	3
	0	8	2	3	2	14	3	2	1	10	12	19	4	7	0	2	7	2	7	2	2	0	0	0	0	0	0	0	0	1	0	2	0	0	3	1	4
	4	2	4	7	4	3	1	2	3	4	3	6	5	9	9	7	2	7	2	1	1	0	2	0	1	0	1	0	2	0	2	0	0	5	1	0	4
Goals	4	4	5	1	3	5	6	5	3	4	2	2	4	3	1	0	4	3	0	0	0	0	0	2	0	1	1	1	0	1	0	1	0	0	0	0	0
	0	1	0	1	0	1	0	0	0	1	2	1	3	1	1	1	1	0	1	0	2	0	0	0	0	0	0	0	0	0	0	0	0	0	0	0	0
	1	0	0	1	1	0	0	1	0	0	1	0	0	1	0	1	1	0	0	2	0	0	0	0	0	3	0	0	0	0	0	1	0	0	0	0	0
	0	1	0	1	0	12	2	7	6	7	0	2	6	0	1	0	6	0	1	0	0	1	0	0	1	0	0	0	0	1	1	0	0	1	1	0	0
	0	0	0	0	0	5	0	2	2	2	0	0	0	0	0	0	1	0	0	0	0	0	0	0	0	0	0	0	0	1	0	0	0	0	0	0	0

PLAYING SQUAD

Existing Players		SN	HT	WT	DOB	AGE	POB	Career	Apps	Goals
GOALKEEPERS										
Phil	Barnes	1	6'01"	11 01	02/03/1979	33	Sheffield	Rotherham, Blackpool £100,000 7/97 Rel c/s 04, Sheff Utd 7/04, Torquay (L) 2/05, QPR (L) 2/06, Grimsby Undisc 6/06 Rel 3/09, Gainsborough 4/09, Alfreton 7/12		
DEFENDERS										
Anton	Brown	7	6'01"		03/07/1987	25		Mansfield (Scholar), Greenwood Meadows, Alfreton 7/06	40	7
Connor	Franklin	3	5'09"		01/09/1987	24	Leicester	Leicester (Trainee), Nuneaton 11/06, Hinckley U 6/08, Lincoln C (Trial) 2/10, Coventry (Trial) 3/10, Burton (Trial) 7/10, Kidderminster (Trial) 8/10, Alfreton 8/10	39	0
Leigh	Franks	12	5'11"	12 00	07/03/1991	21	Scarborough	Scarborough (Yth), Bridlington T (Yth), Huddersfield (Scholar) 7/07 Pro 7/09 Rel c/s 11, Fleetwood (L) 1/10, Oxford U (6ML) 7/10, Alfreton 6/11	23	0
Darran	Kempson	6	6'02"	12 13	06/12/1984	27	Blackpool	Preston (Sch), Accrington (L) 2/04, Morecambe (3ML) 12/04 Perm 3/05, Crewe 7/06 Rel 5/07, Bury (SL) 2/07, Shrewsbury 7/07, Accrington (L) 2/08, Wrexham 7/08, Forest Green (2ML) 11/08, Accrington 7/09, Grimsby 6/10 Rel 12/11, Alfreton 1/12 13		1
Adam	Quinn	5	6'02"	13 00	02/06/1983	29	Sheffield	Sheff Wed, Carlisle (Trial) 3/02, Halifax 8/02, Crawley 8/08, Forest Green (2ML) 11/10, Darlington £25,000 1/11, Barrow (3ML) 8/11, Alfreton (5WL) 11/11 Perm 1/12	17	1
Theo	Streete	17	6'01"	12 06	23/11/1987	24	Birmingham	Walsall NC, Solihull College, Derby 7/06, Doncaster (4ML) 9/06, Bristol R (Trial) 1/07, Grimsby (Trial) 1/07, Rotherham 1/07, Solihull Moors 6/07, Alfreton Undisc 2/11	43	2
MIDFIELDERS										
Nathan	Arnold	11	5'08"	10 07	26/07/1987	25	Mansfield	Mansfield Rel c/s 09, Grimsby (Trial) c/s 09, Hyde U 8/09, Alfreton 6/10	28	6
Daniel	Bradley	10	6'00"		13/05/1991	21	Stafford	Aston Villa (Scholar) Rel c/s 10, Atherstone T (L) 2/10, Tamworth 8/10 Rel 12/11, Rushall O 12/11, Kidderminster 1/12, Alfreton 7/12		
Josh	Law	2	5'11"	11 06	19/08/1989	23	Nottingham	Chesterfield Rel c/s 08, Alfreton (SL) 10/07, Alfreton 5/08	38	1
Daniel	Meadows	14			26/09/1992	19	Newark	Notts Forest Rel c/s 12, Alfreton (L) 3/12, Alfreton 5/12	4	1
Jake	Moult	16	5'10"	10 05	10/02/1989	23	Stoke	Port Vale (Scholar), Plymouth 7/07 Rel c/s 08, Kidderminster (SL) 3/08, Leek T 8/08, Stafford R 10/08, Alfreton 1/10, Hednesford (L) 11/10	37	6
Simon	Russell	19	5'07"	10 06	19/03/1985	26	Hull	Hull C, Kidderminster 7/04, York C 8/08 Rel 5/10, Tamworth (3ML) 9/09, Cambridge U (SL) 1/10, Cambridge U 5/10, Lincoln C 7/11 Rel c/s 12, Alfreton 7/12		
Alistair	Taylor	4	6'01"	10 06	13/09/1991	20	Sheffield	Barnsley Rel c/s 12, Alfreton 8/12		
Matt	Wilson	18	6'02"		10/03/1987	25		Darlington (Yth), Mackinlay Park, Sheffield Hallam Univ, Diddington T, Grantham 3/07, Alfreton 8/07, Worksop (3ML) 8/08, Guiseley (SL) 3/12, Boston U (3ML) 8/12	15	1
FORWARDS										
Iyseden	Christie	20	5'10"	12 02	14/11/1976	35	Coventry	Coventry Rel c/s 97, Bournemouth (L) 11/96, Mansfield (2ML) 2/97, Mansfield 6/97, L.Orient £40,000 7/99 Rel c/s 02, Rushden & D (Trial) 7/02, Mansfield 8/02 Rel c/s 04, Kidderminster 8/04, Rochdale £17,500 1/06, Kidderminster (4ML) 8/06 Perm 1/07, Stevenage 7/08 Rel 1/09, Kettering (4ML) 9/08, Torquay 2/09 Rel 5/09, Hibernians (Mal) (Trial) c/s 09, Kings Lynn 8/09, AFC Telford 9/09 Rel 10/09, Farnborough 10/09, Tamworth 11/09, Kettering 5/10 Rel 5/11, Nuneaton T (SL) 3/11, Tamworth 8/11, Alfreton 8/12		
Paul	Clayton	9	5'10"		31/08/1984	28		Barnsley (Scholar), Parkgate, Gainsborough 7/07, Alfreton 12/07	40	7
Tom	Denton	8	6'06"	14 00	24/07/1989	23	Huddersfield	Wakefield, Huddersfield Undisc 8/08, Woking (2ML) 11/08, Wakefield (SL) 3/09, Cheltenham (6ML) 7/09, Wakefield (L) 2/10, Wakefield Undisc 6/10, Mossley 12/11, Alfreton 8/12		
Ben	Tomlinson	21	5'11"	11 11	31/10/1989	22	Dinnington	Worksop, Macclesfield 5 fig 6/11, Alfreton Undisc 8/12		
Anthony	Wilson	15			25/08/1987	25		Hallam, Belper 8/07, Alfreton 5/10, Matlock (L) 1/11	33	6

Loanees		SN	HT	WT	DOB	AGE	POB	From - To	APPS	GOA
(F)James	Ellison		5'10"	12 08	25/10/1991	20	Liverpool	Burton (3ML) 8/11 - Chester FC (L) 11/11, Rel 12/11,		
								Hyde FC 12/11, Southport 1/12, Skelmersdale (L) 3/12	8	1
(G)Joe	Day				13/08/1990	22	Brighton	Peterborough (SL) 10/11 -	15	0
(M)Lee	Stevenson		5'10"		01/06/1984	28	Sheffield	Mansfield 10/11 -	3	0
(D)Luke	Potter		6'04"	14 08	17/07/1989	23	Barnsley	Barnsley 10/11 -	2	0
(M)Anthony Church					29/03/1987	25	Newham	Grimsby (2ML) 11/11 - Rel c/s 12	6	1
(M)Robert	Eagle		5'08"	11 08	23/02/1987	25	Leiston	Grimsby (2ML) 11/11 - Rel 1/12, Lowestoft T 1/12	3	0
(F)Louis	Moult		6'00"	13 05	14/05/1992	20	Stoke	Stoke 1/12 -	1	0
(M)Craig	Clay		5'11"	11 07	05/05/1992	20	Nottingham	Chesterfield (6WL) 1/12 -	4	1
(G)Jon	Stewart		6'02"	13 01	13/03/1989	23	Hayes	Burnley (SL) 3/12 -	11	0
(F)Adam	Cunnington				07/10/1987	24	Leighton Buzzard	Dag & Red (SL) 3/12 - Tamworth 7/12	11	2
(D)Seamus Conneely					09/07/1988	24	Galway	Sheff Utd (SL) 3/12 - Rel c/s 12	9	0

Departures		SN	HT	WT	DOB	AGE	POB	From - To	APPS	GOA
(M)Steve	Brogan		5'07"	10 04	12/04/1988	24	Rotherham	Rotherham 8/11 - Stalybridge 9/11	2	0
(M)Andy	Holdsworth		5'09"	11 02	29/01/1984	28	Pontefract	Morecambe 8/11 - Guiseley 10/11	4	0
(F)Drewe	Broughton		6'03"	12 01	25/10/1978	33	Hitchin	Lincoln C 9/11 - Rel 10/11, Thurrock 10/11, Arlesey 1/12,		
								Darlington 3/12	2	1
(M)Levi	Mackin		6'01"	12 00	04/04/1986	26	Chester	York C 7/11 - Rel 1/12, Chester FC 1/12	11	1
(M)Jordan	Hall		5'08"	11 13	07/05/1984	28	Chesterfield	Buxton 3/08 - Rel 3/12, Buxton NC 5/12	12	0
(G)Dan	Lowson		6'01"		04/02/1988	24	Whitley Bay	Blyth 6/11 - Rel c/s 12, Ilkeston FC (L) 12/11	20	0
(M)Jamie	Mullan		5'06"	11 13	10/02/1988	24	Nottingham	Fleetwood 7/11 - Rel c/s 12, Stalybridge 6/12	35	2
(M)Nicky	Deverdics		5'11"	12 03	24/11/1987	24	Gateshead	Team Northumbria 2/12 - Rel c/s 12	6	0
(F)Nathan	Jarman		5'11"	11 03	19/09/1986	25	Scunthorpe	Corby T Undisc 3/11 - Chester FC 5/12	39	12
(D)Greg	Young		6'02"	12 03	24/04/1983	29	Doncaster	York C 6/11 - Gainsborough 6/12	30	0
(D)Adrian	Hawes		6'03"		23/11/1987	24		Eastwood T Undisc 7/11 - Altrincham (2ML) 12/11,		
								Buxton (SL) 2/12, Worksop 6/12	4	0
(F)Chris	Senior		5'06"	9 01	18/11/1981	30	Huddersfield	Darlington 6/11 - Guiseley (SL) 12/11, Retired c/s 12,		
								Huddersfield Masseur 7/12	19	0
(G)Paddy	Gamble		5'10"	10 12	01/09/1988	23	Bulwell	Notts Forest 8/09 -		
(G)Ross	Turner		5'11"	12 00	17/06/1979	33	Sheffield	Retford U 3/10 -	0	0
(D)Nikolaus Kudiersky					15/02/1991	21	Glossop	New Mills (Dual) 8/11 -		
(M)Kingsley Williams								Bacup B 3/12 -		

Conference Action...

Barrow's Pearson gets above Witton Albion's Titchiner to head clear during the Conference side's 4-1 win in the Fourth Qualifying Round of the FA Cup.

Photo: Keith Clayton.

BARROW

Chairman: Brian Keen
Secretary: Russell Dodd   **(T)** 07789 757 639   **(E)** secbafc@aol.com
Additional Committee Members:
Steve Patton, Keith Allen, Russell Dodd, Brian Keen, Tony Keen, John Mackay, Dave Ryder, Martin Lewis.
Manager: Dave Bayliss
Programme Editor: Bob Herbert   **(E)** robertbobherb@aol.com

Club Factfile

Founded: 1901   **Nickname:** Bluebirds
Previous Names: None
Previous Leagues: Lancashire Combination 1901-21. Football League 1921-72. Northern Premier 1972-79, 83-84, 86-89, 92-98, 99-04. Conference 1979-83, 84-86, 89-92, 98-99.

Club Colours (change): White with royal blue trim/royal blue/white (Sky blue/sky blue/black)

Ground: Holker Street Stadium, Wilkie Road, Barrow-in-Furness LA14 5UW   **(T)** 01299 823 061
Capacity: 4,500   **Seats:** 1,000   **Covered:** 2,200   **Clubhouse:** Yes   **Shop:** Yes
Directions: M6 Junction 36, onto A590 signposted Barrow. Follow A590 all the way to the outskirts of Barrow (approx. 27 miles) entering via Industrial route. In a further 2 miles you pass the Fire Station on the right hand side, take next left into Wilkie Road, the ground is on the right.

Previous Grounds: Strawberry & Little Park, Roose.

Record Attendance: 16,854 v Swansea Town - FA Cup 3rd Round 1954
Record Victory: 12-0 v Cleator - FA Cup 1920
Record Defeat: 1-10 v Hartlepool United - Football League Division 4 1959
Record Goalscorer: Colin Cowperthwaite - 282 (December 1977 - December 1992)
Record Appearances: Colin Cowperthwaite - 704
Additional Records: Paid £9,000 to Ashton United for Andy Whittaker (07/94)
Senior Honours: Received £40,000 from Barnet for Kenny Lowe (01/91)
Lancashire Senior Cup 1954-55. Lancashire Challenge Trophy 1980-81. Northern Premier League 1983-84, 88-89, 97-98. FA Trophy 1989-90, 2009-10.

10 YEAR RECORD

02-03		03-04		04-05		05-06		06-07		07-08		08-09		09-10		10-11		11-12	
NP P	2	NP P	3	Conf N	16	Conf N	14	Conf N	16	Conf N	5	Conf	20	Conf	15	Conf	18	Conf	13

BARROW

No.	Date	Comp	H/A	Opponents	Att:	Result	Goalscorers	Pos
	Barrow							
1	Sat-13-Aug	BSP	H	Tamworth	1371	D 1-1	Boyes 69	9
2	Tue-16-Aug	BSP	A	York City	3075	L 1-3	Boyes 81	18
3	Sat-20-Aug	BSP	A	Bath City	781	W 1-0	Boyes 66	15
4	Tue-23-Aug	BSP	H	Fleetwood Town	1482	W 4-0	Cook 3 (11, 38, 81), Og (Edwards) 37	5
5	Sat-27-Aug	BSP	H	Gateshead	1291	L 1-2	Boyes 33	10
6	Mon-29-Aug	BSP	A	Southport	1204	L 1-2	Rutherford 45	13
7	Sat-03-Sep	BSP	A	Ebbsfleet United	983	W 2-1	Boyes 17, Smith 79	12
8	Sat-10-Sep	BSP	H	Wrexham	1463	W 3-1	Bolland 53, Boyes 2 (63, 85)	9
9	Sat-17-Sep	BSP	H	Mansfield Town	1244	L 2-3	Almond 26, Boyes 56	11
10	Tue-20-Sep	BSP	A	Alfreton Town	678	L 1-2	Hollis 41	13
11	Sat-24-Sep	BSP	A	Newport County	1315	D 2-2	Boyes 5, Baker pen 90	13
12	Tue-27-Sep	BSP	H	Lincoln City	1181	W 1-0	Baker pen 45	12
13	Sat-01-Oct	BSP	A	Luton Town	5613	L 1-5	Mackreth 2	12
14	Sat-08-Oct	BSP	H	AFC Telford	1109	W 2-1	Boyes pen 21, Baker 83	12
15	Tue-11-Oct	BSP	A	Grimsby Town	2675	L 2-5	Smith 19, Mackreth 54	13
16	Sat-15-Oct	BSP	H	Hayes & Yeading United	1074	W 3-1	Cook 3 (1, 32, 48)	12
17	Tue-18-Oct	BSP	A	Darlington	1786	W 1-0	Boyes 23	12
18	Sat-22-Oct	BSP	H	Kidderminster Harriers	1246	W 3-1	Boyes 18, Cook 21, Rowe 23	11
19	Sat-05-Nov	BSP	A	Lincoln City	2090	L 1-2	M Pearson 90	12
20	Sat-19-Nov	BSP	H	York City	2190	D 0-0		12
21	Sat-26-Nov	BSP	A	AFC Telford	1814	L 0-1		14
22	Tue-29-Nov	BSP	H	Alfreton Town	963	W 1-0	Cook 10	12
23	Sat-03-Dec	BSP	H	Ebbsfleet United	1047	D 1-1	Cook 6	11
24	Sat-17-Dec	BSP	A	Hayes & Yeading United	313	L 1-2	Mackreth 23	12
25	Mon-26-Dec	BSP	H	Stockport County	2103	W 1-0	Bolland 42	10
26	Sun-01-Jan	BSP	A	Stockport County	3301	L 2-3	Baker 2 (57, pen 67)	12
27	Sat-07-Jan	BSP	H	Darlington	2144	W 3-0	Boyes 15, Cook 2 (32, 63)	11
28	Tue-10-Jan	BSP	A	Fleetwood Town	2091	L 1-4	Jackson 70	11
29	Sat-21-Jan	BSP	A	Tamworth	1222	W 3-2	Smith 11, Cook 2 (79, 84)	11
30	Tue-24-Jan	BSP	H	Grimsby Town	1081	D 2-2	Boyes 21, Jackson 90	11
31	Sat-28-Jan	BSP	H	Braintree Town	685	L 0-1		11
32	Sat-18-Feb	BSP	H	Kettering Town	1090	W 3-0	Baker pen 20, Cook 2 (78, 83)	11
33	Tue-21-Feb	BSP	H	Luton Town	925	W 1-0	Harvey 73	9
34	Sat-25-Feb	BSP	H	Forest Green Rovers	1194	D 1-1	Cook 64	10
35	Sat-03-Mar	BSP	A	Kidderminster Harriers	2135	W 2-1	Mackreth 20, Baker pen 25	9
36	Tue-06-Mar	BSP	H	Bath City	1190	L 0-1		10
37	Sat-10-Mar	BSP	A	Wrexham	3432	L 0-2		10
38	Tue-13-Mar	BSP	A	Cambridge United	1651	L 0-1		11
39	Sat-17-Mar	BSP	A	Mansfield Town	2510	L 0-7		11
40	Sat-24-Mar	BSP	H	Braintree Town	939	L 0-4		13
41	Sat-31-Mar	BSP	A	Forest Green Rovers	1070	L 0-3		13
42	Sat-07-Apr	BSP	A	Gateshead	701	L 0-2		13
43	Mon-09-Apr	BSP	H	Southport	918	D 2-2	Jackson 7, Baker 71	13
44	Sat-14-Apr	BSP	H	Cambridge United	870	L 1-3	Mackreth 20	13
45	Sat-21-Apr	BSP	A	Kettering Town	896	D 1-1	Boyes 81	13
46	Sat-28-Apr	BSP	H	Newport County	900	W 3-1	Cook 7, Baker 51, Boyes 69	13

CUPS

No.	Date	Comp	H/A	Opponents	Att:	Result	Goalscorers	
1	Sat-29-Oct	FAC 4Q	A	Witton Albion	860	W 4-1	Boyes 4 (66, 77, 88, 90)	
2	Sat-12-Nov	FAC 1	H	Rotherham United	3030	L 1-2	Rutherford 16	
3	Sat-10-Dec	FAT 1	H	Harrogate Town	868	W 3-2	Hone 10, Boyes 2 (47, 60)	
4	Sat-14-Jan	FAT 2	A	Wealdstone	722	L 1-2	Baker 42	

	League
	Starts
	Substitute
	Unused Sub
	Cups
	Starts
	Substitute
	Unused Sub
	Goals (Lg)
	Goals (Cup)

Player appearances and goals grid:

	HURST	LOMAX	BOLLAND	QUINN	SKELTON	BAKER	HULBERT	FERRELL	RUTHERFORD	BOYES	ALMOND	SHERIDAN	COOK	MACKRETH	M PEARSON	S PEARSON	SMITH	OWEN	BROOKE	MOYO	JONES	HOLLIS	NICHOLAS	ROWE	CLANCY	HONE	HARVEY	JACKSON	TURNER	CAIRNS	DIXON	EDWARDS	CUDWORTH
	1	19	5	17	3	8	6	10	7	11	18	14	9	16	2	21	15	12	22	20	31	23	4	24	31	22	24	17	25	27	27	14	31
1	X	X	X	X	X	X	X	X	X	X	X	X	S	S	S	U	U	U															
	X	X	X	X	X			X	X	X	X	X	S	S	S	U		X															
	X		U	X	X		S	X	X	X	X	X		X	X	X	U	X	U														
	X	S	U	X	X	S		X	X	X	X	S		X	X	X	U	X															
	X	U	X	X	X	S		X	X	X	X	S		X	X	X	U	X															
	X	S	U	X	X	S		X	X	X	X	S		X	X	X	U	X															
	X	X	S	X	X	U			U	X	X	S		X	X	X	U	X															
	X	X	X	X	X	S				X	X	X			X		U	X	X	S													
	X	X		X	X	U	U	U	X	X	X			X			X	X	S	X	U												
	X	X		X	U	X	U	X	X	X			X			S	X	U		U	X												
	X	X		X		X	X	X	X	X	X		S	S		X	U	S	U			X											
	X	X		X		X	X	U		X	X			X		X	S	S	S			X											
	X	X		X		X		S		X	X			X	X	X			X	S	U												
	X	X		X	X	S			S		X	X		X	X	S		U	X	X	U												
	X	X		X	X		U	S	X		X		U	S	X	X	U		S	X	X	U											
	X			X	X	X	U		X	S		X	X	X	X		U	U	X	U													
	X			X	X	X	U	S	X	U		X	X	X	X		X	S	X	U													
	X	U	X	X	X		U	X	X	S		X	X	X	X	U	X	X			S												
	X	U	X		X	X		U	X	X	S		X	X		X	X				S		X										
	X	U	X		X	X		X	X	X	S		X	X		X	X	U			S	S		X									
		U	X		X	X		X	X	X	U			X	S		X	X	X	U		S		X			X						
		X	X		X	X		X	X	X	X	S		X	X		X		S			U		U	U	X							
	U	X	X		X	S		X	X	X	X			X	X		X	U	X			U			X								
	X	X	X		X	X		U	X	X	S			X	X		U	S	X					X									
	X	X	X		X	X		U	X	X	S			X	X		U	S	X	U			S		X								
	X	S	X		X	X			X	X		U		X	X		U	X	X	S			S		X								
	X	U	X		X	X			U	X	X			X	X		U	X			U				X	X	S						
		X	X		X	X			U	X	X		U	S	X	X		S			S			X	X	X							
		X	X		X	X			U		X	X		X	X		S			X	U	S											
		X	X		X	X		U			X	X		X	X	X		U			X	U	S										
		X	X		X			S	S				X	X	X	X		U	S		X	X		X	U								
		X	X		X			U	S			X	U	X	X	X		U	U		X	X		X	U								
	U	X	X		X				S			X		X	X	X	X	X			U	X		X	X		U						
		X	X		X			S	S			X		X	X	X	X	X			S			X	X	U	X		U				
	U	X	X		X				X	X			X	X	X	X	X				S			X	S		U		U				
	S	X	X		X			S	S			X		X	X	X	X				U			X	X		X		U				
	X	X	X						X	X			X	S	X	X	X				S			X	U		U	X					
	X	X		X	U				X	X			X	S	X	X	X				X			X	S	U		S	X				
		X		X	X				X	S			X	X	X	X	X				U			X	X	S			U	U	X		
	X	X		X	X				X	X			X	S		S	X	X			U			X	S					X	U		
	X	X	X			X	S			X			X	S			X	X			X			X	X					X	U		
	X	U		X		S			X	X				X		U	X				X			X	X	X			U	U			
	X	U		X	X			X	X	X				X			X	X	U		X			X						U	U	U	
	X	U	X		X	X		U	X	X				X				X	X		X			U						U	U	U	
	X	X	X		X	X		U	X	X				X	U			X	U		X			S								U	
	X	S	X		X	X		S	X	X	S	U	X	X	X		X	X			U		U										
	X	U	X		X	X		U	X	X	X	U	S	X	X	X	U	X			S												
		X	X		X			U	X	X	S		X	X		X	S	X			U	S	U	X									
	X		X		X	X		X	X	X			X	X			S	X						X	S	S							
	31	22	28	18	43	31	7	13	32	39	10	1	34	36	9	14	36	31	1	4	0	2	11	6	0	25	10	2	5	0	0	4	1
	0	4	1	0	0	8	1	2	8	3	13	1	4	8	1	0	4	2	5	5	0	1	9	4	0	1	3	4	0	0	1	0	0
	1	10	5	0	0	4	1	19	1	0	2	3	0	0	1	16	1	3	1	9	2	2	9	3	7	1	3	2	2	3	5	4	5
	3	1	4	0	4	3	0	2	4	4	1	0	3	4	2	1	3	3	0	0	0	0	0	0	0	2	0	0	0	0	0	0	0
	0	1	0	0	0	0	0	0	1	0	0	2	0	1	0	0	1	1	0	0	0	0	0	1	1	0	0	1	1	0	0	0	0
	0	1	0	0	0	0	0	1	0	0	0	2	0	0	0	1	0	0	0	0	0	0	0	2	0	2	0	0	0	0	0	0	0
	0	0	2	0	0	9	0	0	1	16	1	0	17	5	1	0	3	0	0	0	0	1	0	1	0	0	0	1	3	0	0	0	0
	0	0	0	0	0	1	0	0	1	6	0	0	0	0	0	0	0	0	0	0	0	0	0	1	0	0	0	0	0	0	0	0	0

PLAYING SQUAD

Existing Players		SN	HT	WT	DOB	AGE	POB	Career	Apps	Goals
GOALKEEPERS										
Danny	Hurst	1			14/11/1980	30		Cheadle, Radcliffe 7/00, Sheff Wed (Trial) 2/03,		
								Fleetwood 5 fig 1/07 Rel 5/11, Barrow 7/11	31	0
Shaun	Pearson	21			16/08/1990	21	Bangor	Llangefni T, Barrow 8/10	14	0
DEFENDERS										
Tom	Anderson	16	6'04"		02/09/1993	19	Burnley	Burnley, Barrow (5ML) 8/12		
Dave	Bayliss		6'00"	12 11	08/06/1976	35	Liverpool	Rochdale, Luton 12/01 Rel c/s 05, Chester (2ML) 12/04,		
								Bristol R (Trial) 4/05, Oxford U (Trial) 5/05,		
								Wrexham 7/05 Rel c/s 06, Rochdale (L) 2/06, Lancaster 7/06,		
								Barrow 11/06 Joint Man		
Matty	Flynn	2	6'00"	11 08	10/05/1989	22	Preston	Warrington (Yth), Macclesfield 5/07, Warrington (L) 11/07,		
								Ashton U (L) 2/08, Rochdale (2WL) 8/09 Nominal 8/09 Rel c/s 11,		
								Fleetwood 8/11 Rel c/s 12, Altrincham (SL) 12/11, Barrow 5/12		
Sean	Hessey	4	5'11"	12 08	19/09/1978	33	Prescot	Liverpool (Trainee) Rel c/s 97, Leeds 9/97, Wigan 12/97,		
								Huddersfield 3/98, Kilmarnock 8/99, Blackpool 2/04 Rel c/s 04,		
								Chester 7/04 Rel c/s 08, Macclesfield (SL) 11/07,		
								Macclesfield 7/08 Rel c/s 10, Accrington 8/10 Rel c/s 12,		
								Barrow 7/12		
Michael	Pearson	5	5'11"	11 01	19/01/1988	23	Bangor	Liverpool (Sch), Oldham Rel c/s 08, Farsley Celtic (2ML) 10/07,		
								Barrow 7/08	10	1
Gavin	Skelton	3	5'10"	11 00	27/03/1981	30	Carlisle	Carlisle, Workington 10/00, Stoke (Trial) 11/00,		
								Gretna 10/01 Rel c/s 08, Kilmarnock 6/08 Rel c/s 10,		
								Hamilton 6/10 Rel c/s 11, Barrow 7/11	43	0
MIDFIELDERS										
Richie	Baker	8	5'10"	11 05	29/12/1987	23	Burnley	Man Utd (Yth), Preston (Scholar), Bury 7/06 Rel c/s 10,		
								Oxford U 7/10 Rel 1/11, Barrow 2/11	39	9
Aaron	Cole	20	6'02"		10/09/1992	19		Derby, Eastwood T (L) 8/11, Stockport (SL) 11/11, Barrow 8/12		
James	Owen	6	5'09"	10 07	14/01/1991	20	Caernarfon	Chester Rel 1/10, Barrow 3/10	33	0
Alex-Ray	Harvey	14	5'07"	10 09	04/04/1990	22	Burnley	Burnley Rel c/s 12, Fleetwood (SL) 3/11, Fleetwood (L) 8/11,		
								Barrow (3ML) 1/12, Barrow 7/12	13	1
Ben	Hoskin				08/10/1990	21	Accrington	Burnley Rel c/s 10, Padiham c/s 10, Barrow 8/12		
Garry	Hunter	15	5'07"	10 03	01/01/1985	27	Morecambe	Morecambe Rel c/s 12, Barrow 7/12		
Daniel	Rowe	11	6'00"	11 11	09/03/1992	19	Wythenshawe	Bolton (Yth), Stockport Rel c/s 12, Northwich (L) 11/10,		
								Barrow 8/12		
Paul	Rutherford	7	5'08"	10 11	10/07/1987	24	Moreton	Liverpool (Yth), Greenleas, Chester 10/05 Rel c/s 09,		
								Bournemouth (Trial) 7/08, Barrow 7/09	40	1
FORWARDS										
Obi	Anoruo	10	5'10"	11 06	28/08/1991	20	Nigeria	Wrexham Rel c/s 12, Newtown (4ML) 8/09,		
								Vauxhall Motors (SL) 8/10, Vauxhall Motors (L) 3/12,		
								Barrow 7/12		
Adam	Boyes	9	6'02"	11 08	01/11/1990	20	Lingdale	York C, Man Utd (Trial) 6/08, Scunthorpe Undisc 7/09 Rel 1/11,		
								York C (L) 10/09, Kidderminster (L) 2/10,		
								Boston U 1/11 Rel 5/11, Barrow 7/11	42	16
Joe	Jackson	12			03/02/1993	19	Barrow	Burnley, Barrow (SL) 1/12, Barrow (5ML) 8/12	6	3
Vinny	Mukendi	17	6'02"	12 00	12/03/1992	20	Manchester	Macclesfield Rel c/s 12, Southport (SL) 9/11, Southport (L) 1/12,		
								Barrow 8/12		

Loanees		SN	HT	WT	DOB	AGE	POB	From - To	APPS	GOA
(F)Louis	Almond		5'11"	12 00	15/08/1990	21	Blackburn	Blackpool (5ML) 8/11 - Lincoln C (SL) 1/12	23	1
(D)Adam	Quinn		6'02"	13 00	02/06/1983	28	Sheffield	Darlington (3ML) 8/11 - Alfreton (5WL) 11/11 Perm 1/12	18	0
(F)Ryan	Brooke		6'01"	11 07	04/10/1990	21	Congleton	Oldham 9/11 - AFC Telford (SL) 1/12, Rel c/s 12,		
								Altrincham 5/12	6	0
(D)Haydn	Hollis		6'04"	13 00	14/10/1992	20		Notts County 9/11 - Hinckley U 2/12, Darlington (L) 3/12	3	1
(M)Dominic	Rowe				23/04/1993	19	Leeds	Bradford C (3ML) 9/11 -	10	1
(D)Danny	Hone		6'02"	12 00	15/09/1989	20	Croydon	Lincoln C (SL) 11/11 - Rel c/s 12, Gainsborough 7/12	26	0
(G)Alex	Cairns				04/01/1993	19		Leeds 1/12 -	0	0
(D)Paul	Edwards		5'11"	10 12	01/01/1980	31	Manchester	Fleetwood (SL) 3/12 - Rel c/s 12	4	0
(G)Jack	Cudworth				11/09/1990	21	Preston	Macclesfield (SL) 3/12 - Rel c/s 12, AFC Telford 8/12	1	0

Departures		HT	WT	DOB	AGE	POB	From - To	APPS	GOA
(G)Zak	Jones	5'10"	12 08	24/11/1988	22	Darwen	Clitheroe NC 9/11 - Harrogate T NC 9/11, AFC Fylde 11/11,		
							Vauxhall Motors 5/12	0	0
(G)Kyle	Clancy						Burton 9/11 - AFC Fylde (Dual) 11/11, Eastwood T 12/11,		
							Bangor C 1/12	0	0
(M)Darren	Sheridan	5'05"	11 05	08/12/1967	43	Manchester	St Johnstone 1/07 Joint Man - Rel 2/12, Radcliffe B 2/12,		
							Droylsden 3/12, Salford C (Man) 5/12	2	0
(M)Chris	Turner	5'10"	11 10	26/08/1990	22	Burnley	Burscough 2/12 - Rel 3/12, Stocksbridge PS 3/12	5	0
(D)Phil	Bolland	6'02"	13 08	26/08/1976	35	Liverpool	Cambridge U 7/09 - Rel c/s 12, Droylsden 8/12	29	2
(D)Kelvin	Lomax	5'11"	12 03	12/11/1986	24	Bury	Shrewsbury 8/11 - Rel c/s 12, Hyde FC 8/12	26	0
(D)Cliff	Moyo			06/04/1993	19	Bulawayo, Zim	Stone Dominoes 8/11 - Rel c/s 12, Northwich (L) 8/11,		
							Northwich (2ML) 10/11, Droylsden (L) 2/12	9	0
(D)Andy	Nicholas	6'02"	12 08	10/10/1983	27	Liverpool	Rotherham 8/10 - Rel c/s 12,		
							Vauxhall Motors (3ML) 10/10	20	0
(M)Paul	Smith	5'09"	11 09	17/11/1991	19	Liverpool	Aigburth Peoples Hall 3/11 - Rel c/s 12	40	3
(M)Andy	Ferrell	5'08"	11 05	09/01/1984	27	Newcastle	Gateshead 6/11 - Rel c/s 12, Blyth (L) 3/12,		
							Bedlington 7/12	15	0
(M)Jack	Mackreth	5'09"		13/04/1992	19	Liverpool	Tranmere 7/11 - Macclesfield 5/12	44	5
(F)Andy	Cook	6'01"	11 04	18/10/1990	20	Bishop Auckland	Carlisle 1/11 - Grimsby 6/12	38	17
(M)Robin	Hulbert	5'10"	12 02	14/03/1980	31	Plymouth	Darlington 6/09 - Worcester 7/12	8	0
(G)Stuart	Dixon			19/05/1992	20	Kendal	Kendal T NC 2/12 -	1	0

Conference Action...

Luton Town's Andre Gray keeps his balance under a challenge from York City's Challinor during the Play-off final at Wembley.

Photo: Keith Clayton.

BRAINTREE TOWN

Chairman: Lee Harding
Secretary: Tom Woodley   **(T)** 07950 537 179   **(E)** tawoodley@talktalk.net
Additional Committee Members:
Barry Shepherd, Bird Luckin, Kim Cowell, Vic Dixon, Alan Stuckey, Terry Thorogood,
Christine Thorogood.
Manager: Alan Devonshire
Programme Editor: Lee Harding   **(E)** braintreetfc@aol.com

Club Factfile

Founded: 1898   **Nickname:** The Iron
Previous Names: Crittall Athletic > 1968, Braintree and Crittall Athletic > 1981, Braintree > 1983
Previous Leagues: N.Essex 1898-1925, Essex & Suffolk Border 1925-29, 55-64, Spartan 1928-35, Eastern Co. 1935-37, 38-39, 52-55, 70-91, Essex Co. 1937-38, London 1945-52, Gt London 1964-66, Met 1966-70, Southern 1991-96, Isthmian 1996-2006

Club Colours (change): Orange/blue/blue (White/orange/orange)

Ground: The Amlin Stadium, off Clockhouse Way, Braintree CM7 3RD   **(T)** 01376 345 617
Capacity: 4,000   **Seats:** 550   **Covered:** 1,769   **Clubhouse:** Yes   **Shop:** Yes
Directions: Leave M11 at junction 8A (for Stansted Airport) and follow A120 towards Braintree and Colchester for 17 miles. At Gallows Corner roundabout (with WestDrive Kia on your right) take first exit into Cressing Road. Clockhouse Way and the entrance to the ground are three quarters of a mile on the left and are clearly sign-posted.

Previous Grounds: The Fiar Field 1898-1903, Spalding Meadow and Panfield Lane

Record Attendance: 4,000 v Tottenham Hotspur - Testimonial May 1952
Record Victory: 12-0 v Thetford - Eastern Counties League 1935-36
Record Defeat: 0-14 v Chelmsford City (A) - North Essex League 1923
Record Goalscorer: Chris Guy - 211 (1963-90)
Record Appearances: Paul Young - 524 (1966-77)
Additional Records: Gary Bennett scored 57 goals during season 1997-98
Received £10,000 from Brentford for Matt Metcalf and from Colchester United for John Cheesewright
Senior Honours:
Eastern Counties League 1983-84, 84-85, Essex Senior Cup 1995-96. Isthmian League Premier Division 2005-06.
Conference South Champions 2010-11.
East Anglian Cup x3

10 YEAR RECORD

02-03		03-04		04-05		05-06		06-07		07-08		08-09		09-10		10-11		11-12	
Isth P	16	Isth P	23	Isth P	4	Isth P	1	Conf S	3	Conf S	5	Conf S	14	Conf S	7	Conf S	1	Conf	12

BRAINTREE TOWN

No.	Date	Comp	H/A	Opponents	Att:	Result	Goalscorers	Pos
1	Sat-13-Aug	BSP	A	Darlington	2268	L 0-1		22
2	Tue-16-Aug	BSP	H	Grimsby Town	1006	W 5-0	Davis 44, Marks 2 (45, 57), Yiadom 54, Quinton 90	9
3	Sat-20-Aug	BSP	H	Mansfield Town	875	D 1-1	Bailey-Dennis 54	9
4	Tue-23-Aug	BSP	A	Forest Green Rovers	1033	W 2-0	Wright 35, Yiadom 90	4
5	Sat-27-Aug	BSP	A	Luton Town	5703	L 1-3	Wright 20	9
6	Mon-29-Aug	BSP	H	Ebbsfleet United	810	L 2-3	Reason 2 (pen 15, 69)	12
7	Sat-03-Sep	BSP	H	Lincoln City	1182	W 1-0	Yiadom 31	11
8	Sat-10-Sep	BSP	A	Alfreton Town	656	W 1-0	Chilaka 18	8
9	Sat-17-Sep	BSP	H	Newport County	786	W 1-0	Wright 20	9
10	Tue-20-Sep	BSP	A	Hayes & Yeading United	209	W 2-1	Yiadom 22, Reason 55	6
11	Sat-24-Sep	BSP	A	Southport	938	W 4-0	Chilaka 27, Marks 45, Reason 56, Yiadom 66	3
12	Tue-27-Sep	BSP	H	Tamworth	840	W 3-1	Reason 2 (29, 89), Yiadom 62	2
13	Sat-01-Oct	BSP	H	Fleetwood Town	1005	L 1-2	Davis 21	4
14	Sat-08-Oct	BSP	A	York City	2640	L 2-6	Marks 45, Thomas 62	7
15	Tue-11-Oct	BSP	A	Kettering Town	1115	L 1-2	Marks 59	8
16	Sat-15-Oct	BSP	H	Bath City	703	D 3-3	Wright 19, McCammon 22, Paine 48	8
17	Tue-18-Oct	BSP	A	Kidderminster Harriers	1301	L 4-5	Marks 26, Wright 2 (33, pen 67), Thomas 63	11
18	Sat-22-Oct	BSP	A	Darlington	864	W 3-1	Stevens 44, Davis 51, Marks 58	9
19	Sat-05-Nov	BSP	A	Gateshead	745	D 2-2	Reason pen 47, Yiadom 55	9
20	Sat-19-Nov	BSP	H	Forest Green Rovers	1005	L 1-5	Marks 28	10
21	Sat-26-Nov	BSP	H	Wrexham	957	D 0-0		10
22	Tue-29-Nov	BSP	A	Tamworth	742	L 0-1		13
23	Sat-03-Dec	BSP	A	Mansfield Town	1790	L 1-4	Wright 8	14
24	Tue-06-Dec	BSP	H	Hayes & Yeading United	454	L 0-3		14
25	Sat-17-Dec	BSP	H	AFC Telford	605	W 2-0	Wright 2 (pen 45, 77)	13
26	Mon-26-Dec	BSP	A	Cambridge United	3717	L 0-2		14
27	Sun-01-Jan	BSP	H	Cambridge United	2029	W 3-2	Reason 51, Marks 55, Wright 77	14
28	Sat-07-Jan	BSP	A	Bath City	956	D 1-1	Marks 90	13
29	Sat-21-Jan	BSP	H	Stockport County	833	D 2-2	Thomas 58, Symons 61	13
30	Tue-24-Jan	BSP	A	Fleetwood Town	1791	L 1-3	Paine 5	13
31	Sat-28-Jan	BSP	H	Barrow	685	W 1-0	Thomas 79	13
32	Tue-14-Feb	BSP	A	Lincoln City	1616	D 3-3	Reason 2 (4, 54), Assombalonga 88	12
33	Sat-18-Feb	BSP	A	AFC Telford	1776	L 0-1		13
34	Tue-21-Feb	BSP	H	Kettering Town	730	W 2-1	Wright pen 15, Marks 45	13
35	Sat-03-Mar	BSP	A	Grimsby Town	3688	D 1-1	Marks 59	13
36	Tue-06-Mar	BSP	A	Newport County	1101	W 4-3	Assombalonga 2 (22, 49), Marks 32, Wright 35	12
37	Sat-10-Mar	BSP	H	Gateshead	650	W 3-1	Assombalonga 2 (5, 55), Wright 6	11
38	Sat-17-Mar	BSP	H	Kidderminster Harriers	610	L 1-4	Wright 6	12
39	Sat-24-Mar	BSP	A	Barrow	939	W 4-0	Thomas 25, Reason pen 29, Wright 45, Guy 90	12
40	Tue-27-Mar	BSP	H	Southport	637	D 0-0		11
41	Sat-31-Mar	BSP	H	Alfreton Town	620	L 1-2	Gibson 33	12
42	Sat-07-Apr	BSP	H	Luton Town	1703	W 3-1	Bailey-Dennis 5, Marks 70, Gibson pen 90	12
43	Mon-09-Apr	BSP	A	Ebbsfleet United	938	D 1-1	Wright pen 34	12
44	Sat-14-Apr	BSP	A	Stockport County	3199	D 1-1	Quinton 90	12
45	Sat-21-Apr	BSP	H	York City	1127	L 0-1		12
46	Sat-28-Apr	BSP	A	Wrexham	3303	L 1-5	Wright 52	12

CUPS

No.	Date	Comp	H/A	Opponents	Att:	Result	Goalscorers	Pos
1	Sat-29-Oct	FAC 4Q	A	Newport County	1234	L 3-4	Wright 9, Yiadom 66, Davis 86	
2	Sat-10-Dec	FAT 1	A	Gosport Borough	332	W 1-0	Wells 52	
3	Sat-14-Jan	FAT 2	A	Gateshead	605	D 2-2	Reason 42, Davis 90+2	
4	Tue-17-Jan	FAT 2R	H	Gateshead	261	D 1-1 aet (L 3-4 pens)	Marks 54	

		League
		Starts
		Substitute
		Unused Sub
		Cups
		Starts
		Substitute
		Unused Sub
		Goals (Lg)
		Goals (Cup)

Player appearance grid (X = start, S = used substitute, U = unused substitute)

MCDONALD	O'CONNOR	BAILEY-DENNIS	PAINE	THOMAS	SYMONS	REASON	DAVIS	JAMES-LEWIS	MARKS	WRIGHT	YIADOM	CHILAKA	QUINTON	A JONES	M JONES	CONSTANTINE	PETERS	MCLEAOD	POOLEY	JOHNSON	STEVENS	MCCAMMON	TAJBAKHSH	VOSE	WELLS	MUWANGA	KIERNAN	ASSOMBALONGA	GUY	BENTLEY	HAXELL	CLARK	APPIAH-KUBI	GREEN	GIBSON
16	4	5	3	7	6	8	23	9	10	17	19	15	22	12	18	2	24	25	18	21	14	20	26	24	32	26	14	11	37	31	18	20	22	18	8
X	X	X	X	X	X	X	X	X	X	X	X	S	S	S	U	U	U																		
X	X	X	X	X	X	X	X	U	X	X	X	S	S	S	U	S																			
X	X	X	X	X	X	X	X	U	X	X	X	S	S	S	U	U																			
X	U	X		X	X	X	X	X	X	X			S	S	U	U	X		X																
X	S	X	X	X	X	X	X	U		X		X	X	X	S	U	U																		
X	S	X	X	X	X	X	X	S	X	X	X	X	S	U	U	X																			
X	U	X	X	X	X	X	X	U	X	X	X	S	S	U	U	X																			
X		X	X	X	X	X	S	X	X	X	S	U		X	S	U																			
X	S	X	X	X	X	X	X		S	X	X	X	S	U	X	U																			
X	U	X	X	X	X	X	X		X	X	X	S	S	U	X	U																			
X	U	X	X	X	X	X	X		X	S	X	X	S	U	X			S	S																
X	U	X	X	X	X	X	X		X	S	X	X	S	U	X			S																	
X		X	X	X	X	X	X		X	X	X	S	U	X	U	S	S																		
X	X	X		X	X	X	X		X	X	S	S	U	X	X	X	S	U																	
X	X	X		X	X	X	X		X	X	U	U	X	X	S	U	S																		
X	U	X	X	X	X	X		X	S	U	X	X	U	X	S																				
X		X	X	X	X	X		X	X	S	U	X	S	U	S	X																			
X		U	X	X	S	X	X		X	U	X	X	S	U	X	S	S	S																	
X		U	X	X	X	X		X	X	X	S	X	U	X	U	S	X	S																	
X		X	X	S	X	X		X	X	X	S	X	U	X	U	S		X																	
X	X	X		X	X	X		X	X	X	S	U	U	S	S	X																			
X	X	X		X	X	X		U	X	X	X	S	U	S	S	X																			
X	U		X	X	X		X	X	X	S	X	U	U	X	X	X																			
X	U	X	X	X	X		X	X	X	S	S	U	X	U	X																				
X		X	X	X	X		X	X	X	S	X	U	S	U	S	S	X																		
X	X	X	X	X		X	X	X	X	S	X	U	S	U	U	S	X																		
X		U	X	X	X		X	X	X	S	S	U	X	S	X																				
X	S	U	X	X	X		X	X	X	S	S	U	X	X																					
X	X	X	S	X	X	X	X	X	X	S	S	U	U			X																			
X	X	X	X	X	X	X	X	X	X	S	S	U	S			X	U																		
X	U	X	X	X	X	X	X		S	X	S	U	U			X		X																	
X	S	X	X	X	X	X		S	U	U	U		X			X	X	X																	
X	X	X	X	X	U	X		X	S	U	X	S			X		X	X	U																
X	U	X	X	X	U	X		X	X	U	X	S	X			X	S	X																	
X	X	S	X	X	X	X		X	X	X	U		X			X		X	S	U															
X	X	S	X	X	X	X		X	X	X		U			X		X	S	U	U															
X	X	S	X	X	X	X		X	X	X		X			X		X	S	U	U	U	U												
X	X	U	X	X	X	X		X	X		X		S			X		S				S	U											
X	X	X	X	X	U	X		X	X		S	U			X		X				S		S	X										
X	X	X	X	U	X	X		X	X		S	U			X		U				U		U	X										
X	X	X	X	X	S	X		X	X		S		U			X		S			U		U	X										
X	X	X		X	X	X		X	X		S		S	U		X					U		U	X										
X	X	X		X	U	S	X	X	X		X	U			X	U				U		U	X											
X	X	X	X		S	X	X		X		S		X	U				S	U			X												
X	X	X	X	X	S	X	X		X		S		U					X	S	U			X											

X	U	S	X	X	S	X	X		X	X	X	S	X	U		X				U	X	U			X										
X	S	X	X	X	X			X	X	X	S	X	U			U				X	U				X										
X	X	X	X	X		S	X		X	X	S	U	S	U		X					U				X										
X	X	X	X	X	U	X	X		X	X	X	S	S	U				U						X											

Totals:

46	23	34	39	43	35	44	39	2	41	40	24	6	12	0	1	0	23	0	0	5	5	1	0	1	25	0	3	5	1	0	0	0	0	0	8
0	5	3	1	0	6	0	0	2	1	1	4	19	30	0	0	1	3	1	2	10	4	4	0	4	1	0	1	0	7	1	0	0	2	0	0
0	10	5	0	1	4	0	0	4	1	0	0	0	4	38	1	1	5	3	11	1	5	0	2	0	1	1	0	0	2	3	7	1	4	1	0

4	2	3	4	4	2	2	3	0	4	4	3	0	2	0	0	0	2	0	0	1	1	0	0	0	3	0	0	0	0	0	0	0	0	0	0
0	1	1	0	0	1	1	0	0	0	0	1	3	2	0	0	0	0	0	0	0	0	0	0	0	0	0	0	0	0	0	0	0	0	0	0
0	1	0	0	0	1	0	0	0	0	0	0	1	4	0	0	1	0	0	2	1	1	0	0	0	0	0	0	0	0	0	0	0	0	0	0

| 0 | 0 | 2 | 2 | 5 | 1 | 11 | 3 | 0 | 14 | 17 | 7 | 2 | 2 | 0 | 0 | 0 | 0 | 0 | 0 | 0 | 1 | 1 | 0 | 0 | 0 | 5 | 1 | 0 | 0 | 0 | 0 | 0 | 0 | 0 | 2 |
| 0 | 0 | 0 | 0 | 0 | 0 | 1 | 2 | 0 | 1 | 1 | 1 | 0 | 0 | 0 | 0 | 0 | 0 | 0 | 0 | 0 | 0 | 1 | 0 | 0 | 0 | 0 | 0 | 0 | 0 | 0 | 0 | 0 | 0 | 0 | 0 |

PLAYING SQUAD

Existing Players		SN	HT	WT	DOB	AGE	POB	Career	Apps	Goals
GOALKEEPERS										
Nathan	McDonald	1	6'00"	14 00	16/05/1991	21	Stevenage	Southend (Scholar) Rel c/s 09, Braintree c/s 09,		
								AFC Sudbury (Dual) 3/10	46	0
Danny	Naisbitt	22	6'01"	11 12	25/11/1978	33	Bishop Auckland	Middlesbrough (Trainee), Walsall, Bromsgrove (Trial) c/s 99,		
								Barnet 8/99 Rel 9/03, Carlisle (L) 8/02, Southend (Trial),		
								Harlow 9/03, Brentford 10/03, Cambridge C 11/03,		
								Dag & Red 12/03 Rel 2/04, Peterborough 3/04, Hendon 3/04,		
								Welling 3/04, AFC Wimbledon 6/04, Grimsby (Trial) 3/05,		
								Lewes (L) 3/05, Cambridge C 9/05, Histon 5/07,		
								Brighton (L) 3/10, Cambridge U 5/10 Rel c/s 12,		
								Cambridge C 7/12, Braintree 8/12		
DEFENDERS										
Adam	Bailey-Dennis	4			18/09/1990	21		Colchester, Felixstowe & W (WE) 1/09, Braintree 5/09,		
								Billericay (L) 11/09, Great Wakering (L) 1/10,		
								Aveley (L) 3/10	37	2
Kenny	Davis	8	5'07"	11 02	17/04/1988	24	London	Chelsea (Yth), Redbridge 3/05, Harlow c/s 05, Grays 8/08,		
								Braintree 6/10	39	3
Samuel	Habergham	3	6'00"	11 06	20/02/1992	20	Rotherham	Norwich Rel c/s 11, Lincoln C (Trial) 4/11, Tamworth 7/11,		
								Braintree 7/12		
Pat	O'Connor		6'01"	13 00	05/09/1990	21	Croydon	Millwall Rel c/s 11, Tooting & M (L) 9/10,		
								Hampton & R (10WL) 11/10, Hampton & R (6WL) 2/11,		
								Lewes (SL) 3/11, Braintree 8/11	28	0
Matthew	Paine	5	6'01"	12 12	22/12/1987	24	Bexley	Colchester Rel c/s 07, Staines (SL) 2/06, Thurrock (SL) 1/07,		
								Thurrock c/s 07, Braintree 6/10	40	2
Ryan	Peters	2			21/08/1987	25		Brentford (Sch), Windsor & E (2ML) 9/04, Gravesend (L) 12/04,		
								Crawley (L) 11/06, AFC Wimbledon (L) 3/07, Margate 1/08,		
								Braintree 5/09, Staines 6/10 Rel 8/10,		
								Braintree 9/10	26	0
David	Stevens				17/07/1987	25		Bracknell, Uxbridge 10/09, Hampton & R 8/10,		
								Luton (Trial) c/s 11, Braintree 7/11	9	1
Dean	Wells	19	6'01"	13 02	25/03/1985	26	Isleworth	Brentford Rel c/s 04, Hampton & R 6/04 Rel 4/11, Jail,		
								Staines 9/11, Braintree 11/11	26	0
MIDFIELDERS										
Josh	Dawkin	10	5'09"	10 12	16/01/1992	20	Huntingdon	Norwich Rel c/s 12, Kettering (3ML) 10/11,		
								Cambridge U (L) 3/12, Braintree 7/12		
Callum	McNish	18	6'02"	12 06	25/05/1992	20	Oxford	Watford (Jun), Southampton Rel c/s 11, Exeter 7/11 Rel c/s 12,		
								Braintree 7/12		
James	Mulley	17			30/09/1988	23	Edgware	Yeading/Hayes & Yeading Rel 10/10, Charlton (Trial) 7/10,		
								Dag & Red (Trial) 8/10, Chelmsford 10/10 Rel 12/10,		
								AFC Wimbledon 1/11 Rel c/s 12, Hayes & Yeading (L) 1/12,		
								Braintree 8/12		
Bradley	Quinton	6			07/09/1978	33		Tottenham (Jun), Hornchurch, Aveley, Romford c/s 98,		
								Bishops Stortford 1/99, Braintree 1/00 Temp Man 10/07	42	2
Daniel	Sparkes	11	6'04"	14 09	20/07/1991	21	Peterborough	Histon, Braintree 6/12		
Nicky	Symons	7			27/06/1984	28		Maldon T, Tilbury 11/06, Maldon T c/s 07, Redbridge 10/07,		
								Brentwood c/s 08, Aveley c/s 09, Braintree 6/10	41	1
FORWARDS										
Joel	Appiah-Kubi							Braintree	2	0
Lewis	Bentley							Braintree	1	0
Jamie	Guy		6'01"	13 00	01/08/1987	25	Barking	Colchester, Gravesend (L) 10/05, Staines (2ML) 10/05,		
								Staines (L) 1/06, Cambridge U (SL) 2/06, Oxford U (SL) 7/08,		
								Dag & Red (L) 3/09, Port Vale (L) 10/09, Grays 1/10 Rel 5/10,		
								Braintree 7/10, Thurrock (2ML) 11/11	8	1
Sean	Marks	9			25/11/1985	26	Essex	Heybridge, Braintree £1,000 5/08	42	14
Kane	Sheppard	14	6'01"		26/11/1993	18		L.Orient (Scholar) Rel c/s 12, St Albans (WE) 1/11,		
								Histon (WE) 8/11, Braintree 7/12		

Loanees	SN	HT	WT	DOB	AGE	POB	From - To	APPS	GOA
(M)Merrick James-Lewis				21/05/1992	20	Southend	Southend 8/11 - Bishops Stortford (2ML) 12/11,		
							Carshalton (L) 3/12	4	0
(M)Dominic Vose				23/11/1993	18		West Ham 10/11 -	5	0
(M)Brendan Kiernan				10/11/1992	19		AFC Wimbledon 1/12 -	4	0
(F)Brett Assombalonga		5'10"	11 13	06/12/1992	19	Kinshasa	Watford 2/12 -	5	5
(M)Billy Gibson		6'02"	11 07	30/09/1990	21	Harrow	Yeovil 3/12 - Rel c/s 12, Cambridge U 5/12	8	2

Departures	SN	HT	WT	DOB	AGE	POB	From - To	APPS	GOA
(D)Mark Jones				06/08/1979	33		Romford 2/00 - Rel 8/11, Boreham Wood 8/11	1	0
(M)Sam Lechmere				03/12/1990	21		Grays 7/10 - Boreham Wood 9/11, Billericay 3/12		
(D)Sean Francis				14/06/1984	28		Aveley - Billericay (L) 8/11, Bishops Stortford 9/11		
(F)Leon Constantine		6'02"	11 11	24/02/1978	34	Hackney	York C 8/11 - Rel 9/11, Lewes 10/11,		
							Tooting & M 11/11 Rel 11/11, Boston U 12/11 Rel 3/12	1	0
(D)Tobi Jinadu				14/07/1984	28		Kingstonian 9/11 - St Albans 9/11, Tooting & M 2/12		
(M)Kevin McLeod		5'11"	11 03	12/09/1980	31	Liverpool	Redbridge 8/11 - Maldon & Tiptree (Dual) 9/11, Thurrock 11/11,		
							Chelmsford 12/11, Brentwood 2/12	1	0
(F)Aryan Tajbakhsh		6'01"	11 07	20/10/1990	21		Billericay 9/11 - Harrow 11/11	0	0
(M)Matt Johnson				15/04/1990	22		Dover 9/11 - Bishops Stortford 1/12	15	0
(F)Chibuzor Chilaka		5'08"	13 00	21/10/1986	25	Nigeria	Bradford C 8/11 - Rel 1/12, Harrogate T 2/12	25	2
(M)Andy Yiadom				02/12/1991	20		Hayes & Yeading 8/11 - Barnet Undisc 1/12	28	7
(F)Mark McCammon		6'02"	14 05	07/08/1978	34	Barnet	Gillingham 10/11 - Sheffield FC 3/12,		
							Lincoln C (SL) 3/12	5	1
(M)Luke Clark							Braintree De-Registered 3/12	0	0
(G)Mike Green							Braintree, De-registered	0	0
(F)Ben Wright		6'02"	13 05	10/08/1988	24	Basingstoke	Crawley 6/11 - Forest Green 5/12	41	17
(M)Jai Reason		5'11"	13 01	09/01/1990	22	Southend	Crawley 9/10 - Eastleigh 5/12	44	11
(D)Aswad Thomas		5'10"	11 06	09/08/1989	23	Westminster	Woking 6/11 - Grimsby Undisc 7/12	43	5
(M)Matt Pooley				09/10/1991	20		Dag & Red 8/11 - Maldon & Tiptree (Dual) 12/11,		
							Walton Casuals (Dual) 2/12, Bishops Stortford 7/12	2	0
(G)Peter Haxell							Chelmsford (Yth), Braintree	0	0
(G)Ashlee Jones		6'01"	12 05	04/08/1987	25	Walthamstowe	Billericay 8/11 -	0	0
(D)Sibo Muwanga				23/06/1989	23	London	Braintree 1/12	0	0

Conference Action...

Alfreton's Jamie Mullan takes on Fleetwood's Steve McNulty.

Photo: Bill Wheatcroft.

CAMBRIDGE UNITED

Chairman: Paul Barry
Secretary: Claire Osbourn **(T)** 01223 566500 **(E)** claire.osbourn@cambridge-united.co.uk
Additional Committee Members:
Renford Sargent, Robert Smith, Dave Doggett, Jez George, Terry Baker, Colin Proctor, Robert Smith, Eddie Clark.
Manager: Jez George
Programme Editor: Mark Johnson **(E)** mark.johnson.6@btinternet.com

Back row L-R: Michael Wylde, Luke Allen, Ross Jarvis, Jack Eades, Scott Garner, Sam Smith, Billy Gibson, Tom Shaw, James Jennings, Harrison Dunk, Rory McAuley. Middle row L-R: Greg Reid (physiotherapist), Michael Gash, Ricky Wellard, Josh Coulson, Craig Ross, Jonathan Hedge, Will Norris, Blaine Hudson, Tom Elliott, Liam Hughes, Lance Key (GK coach) Front row L-R: Luke Berry, Adriano Moke, James Brighton, Andy Pugh, Jez George (Manager), Nolan Keeley (First Team Coach), Adam Marriott, Robbie Willmott, Kevin Roberts, Jonathon Thorpe

Club Factfile

Founded: 1912 **Nickname:** The U's
Previous Names: Abbey United 1919-51.
Previous Leagues: United Counties. Eastern Counties 1951-58. Southern 1958-70. Football League 1970-2005.

Club Colours (change): Amber/black/black & amber hoops (All white)

Ground: The R Costings Abbey Stadium, Newmarket Road, Cambridge CB5 8LN **(T)** 01223 566 500
Capacity: 9,217 **Seats:** 2,500 **Covered:** 5,000 **Clubhouse:** Yes **Shop:** Yes

Directions A14 towards Cambridge and Newmarket, leave A14 at Junction with B1047. Turn right at top of slip road, follow road through Fen Ditton to TJunction and traffic lights. Turn right at lights, and go straight over at roundabout. Ground is on left hand side approximately 1/2 mile from roundabout.

Previous Grounds:

Record Attendance: 14,000 v Chelsea - Friendly 01/05/1970
Record Victory: 5-1 v Bristol City - FA Cup 5th Round 1989-90
Record Defeat: 0-7 v Sunderland - League Cup 2nd Round 2002-03
Record Goalscorer: John Taylor - 86 (1988-92, 96-2001)
Record Appearances: Steve Spriggs - 416 (1975-87
Additional Records: Paid £192,000 to Luton Town for Steve Claridge 11/92. Received £1m from Manchester United for Dion Dublin 08/92 and from Leicester City for Trevor Benjamin 07/2000
Senior Honours: Football League Division Division Four 1976-77. Three 1990-91.

10 YEAR RECORD

02-03		03-04		04-05		05-06		06-07		07-08		08-09		09-10		10-11		11-12	
FL 3	12	FL 3	13	FL 2	24	Conf	12	Conf	17	Conf	2	Conf	2	Conf	10	Conf	17	Conf	9

CAMBRIDGE UNITED

No.	Date	Comp	H/A	Opponents	Att:	Result	Goalscorers	Pos
1	Sat-13-Aug	BSP	A	Wrexham	4206	D 1-1	Platt 90	11
2	Tue-16-Aug	BSP	H	AFC Telford	2482	W 1-0	Dunk 50	5
3	Sat-20-Aug	BSP	H	Kidderminster Harriers	2171	L 1-2	Gash 58	13
4	Tue-23-Aug	BSP	A	Grimsby Town	2616	L 1-2	Wylde 30	15
5	Sat-27-Aug	BSP	H	Hayes & Yeading United	1778	W 2-1	Platt 54, Berry 85	12
6	Mon-29-Aug	BSP	A	Kettering Town	2000	D 0-0		10
7	Sat-03-Sep	BSP	A	Newport County	1515	W 1-0	Charles 15	5
8	Sat-10-Sep	BSP	H	Forest Green Rovers	2408	D 1-1	Carew pen 78	10
9	Sat-17-Sep	BSP	A	Gateshead	904	D 1-1	Carew 16	12
10	Tue-20-Sep	BSP	H	Ebbsfleet United	1911	W 2-0	Winn 10, Shaw 32	10
11	Sat-24-Sep	BSP	H	Darlington	2300	W 2-0	Gash 23, Shaw 62	9
12	Tue-27-Sep	BSP	A	Luton Town	6274	W 1-0	McAuley 60	6
13	Sat-01-Oct	BSP	A	Southport	1104	L 0-1		9
14	Thu-06-Oct	BSP	H	Stockport County	2047	D 2-2	Berry 12, Patrick 74	9
15	Tue-11-Oct	BSP	A	Bath City	788	W 4-3	Gash 16, Carew 40, Berry 76, Shaw 84	7
16	Sat-15-Oct	BSP	H	Alfreton Town	2741	W 3-0	Berry 29, Dunk 2 (41, 52)	6
17	Tue-18-Oct	BSP	A	York City	2711	D 2-2	Dunk 8, Gash 31	6
18	Fri-21-Oct	BSP	H	Lincoln City	2875	W 2-0	Carew 2 (23, 90)	4
19	Sat-05-Nov	BSP	A	Mansfield Town	2046	W 2-1	Dunk 2 (57, 62)	3
20	Sat-19-Nov	BSP	H	Luton Town	4796	D 1-1	Hughes 77	4
21	Sat-26-Nov	BSP	A	Kidderminster Harriers	1899	D 0-0		4
22	Tue-29-Nov	BSP	H	Bath City	2267	D 1-1	Hughes 21	5
23	Tue-06-Dec	BSP	A	Ebbsfleet United	964	D 0-0		5
24	Sat-17-Dec	BSP	A	Darlington	1784	L 0-2		6
25	Mon-26-Dec	BSP	H	Braintree Town	3717	W 2-0	Gash 36, Berry 58	7
26	Sun-01-Jan	BSP	A	Braintree Town	2029	L 2-3	Jennings 88, Shaw 90	8
27	Thu-05-Jan	BSP	H	Southport	1840	W 3-0	Marriott 7, Roberts 29, Gash 72	6
28	Tue-10-Jan	BSP	H	Grimsby Town	2436	L 0-1		8
29	Sat-21-Jan	BSP	A	AFC Telford	1903	W 2-1	Roberts 45, Shaw 56	7
30	Sat-28-Jan	BSP	H	Tamworth	2281	L 0-1		10
31	Sat-18-Feb	BSP	A	Fleetwood Town	2068	L 0-1		10
32	Sat-03-Mar	BSP	A	Forest Green Rovers	1005	L 1-2	Berry 75	12
33	Tue-06-Mar	BSP	H	Mansfield Town	1738	L 1-2	Jennings 6	13
34	Sat-10-Mar	BSP	A	Stockport County	5957	W 1-0	Tiryaki 14	13
35	Tue-13-Mar	BSP	H	Barrow	1651	W 1-0	Pugh 88	10
36	Sat-17-Mar	BSP	H	Gateshead	2344	L 0-1		10
37	Tue-20-Mar	BSP	H	Newport County	1815	D 1-1	Dawkin 24	10
38	Sat-24-Mar	BSP	A	Alfreton Town	965	L 1-2	Pugh pen 30	11
39	Sat-31-Mar	BSP	H	Wrexham	3014	D 1-1	Shaw 48	11
40	Tue-03-Apr	BSP	A	Lincoln City	1978	W 1-0	Shaw 47	11
41	Sat-07-Apr	BSP	A	Hayes & Yeading United	336	D 0-0		11
42	Mon-09-Apr	BSP	H	Kettering Town	2578	W 2-0	Pugh 10, Pell 80	11
43	Sat-14-Apr	BSP	A	Barrow	870	W 3-1	Gash 16, Pell 38, Roberts 58	11
44	Tue-17-Apr	BSP	H	York City	2211	L 0-1		11
45	Sat-21-Apr	BSP	H	Fleetwood Town	2555	W 2-0	Eades 17, McAuley 31	10
46	Sat-28-Apr	BSP	A	Tamworth	1137	D 2-2	Marriott 2 (31, 49)	9

CUPS

No.	Date	Comp	H/A	Opponents	Att:	Result	Goalscorers	
1	Sat-29-Oct	FAC 4Q	A	Hayes & Yeading United	452	W 6-2	Berry 31, Carew 2 (44, 80), Dunk 46, Patrick 86, Charles 90	
2	Fri-11-Nov	FAC 1	H	Wrexham	2782	D 2-2	Coulson 2 (53, 90)	
3	Tue-22-Nov	FAC 1R	A	Wrexham	2606	L 1-2	Wylde 87	
4	Sat-10-Dec	FAT 1	A	Boreham Wood	401	W 1-0	Charles 75	
5	Sat-14-Jan	FAT 2	H	AFC Telford	1259	W 4-1	Og (Preston) 2, Roberts 46, Carew 73, Berry 90	
6	Tue-21-Feb	FAT 3	H	Guiseley	1118	W 1-0	Berry 25	
7	Sat-25-Feb	FAT 4	H	Wealdstone	2034	L 1-2	Jennings 70	

League
Starts
Substitute
Unused Sub

Cups
Starts
Substitute
Unused Sub

Goals (Lg)
Goals (Cup)

Appearance grid — players (shirt numbers below names):

	NAISBITT	ROBERTS	COULSON	WYLDE	KINNIBURGH	CAREW	SHAW	BERRY	DUNK	MARRIOTT	CHARLES	PLATT	GASH	JARVIS	BROWN	THORPE	MCAULEY	JENNINGS	PATRICK	EADES	HUDSON	WINN	MURTAGH	YAKUBU	HUGHES	CUFF	JOHNSON	PUGH	JACKSON	TIRYAKI	BRIGHTON	DAWKIN	PELL	AMBRUSICS	HURST	CORKER
No.	1	2	4	5	15	10	6	18	11	19	7	14	9	16	30	27	12	3	20	26	25	21	8	22	17	30	14	15	21	14	29	22	23	30	32	24
	X	X	X	X	X	X	X	X	X	X	X	X			S	S	S	U	U																	
	X	X	X	X	X	X	X	X	X	X	X	U			S	S	S	U	U																	
	X	X	X	X	S	X	X	X	X	X	X	X	S	S	U	U		X																		
	X	X	X	X	U	X	X	X	X		S	S	X	X	U		U	X																		
	X	X	X	X	X	X	X	X		X		X	X	S	U		S	X	S	U																
	X	X	X	X		X	X	X		U		X		X		S	U	X	S	X	U															
	X	X	X	X		X	X		U	X	U			X		S	U	X	S		X															
	X		X	X		X	X	S		X		X	X	U		X	X		X	S																
	X	X	X		X	X	X	S	U			X	X	U		X	X	S		X	U															
	X	X	X		X	X	X	S		U		X	X	U		X	X	U	U																	
	X	X	X		X	X	X	S				X	X			X	X	S			U	X														
	X	X	X	U		X	X	X	X	U	S		X	X			X	X	S					U												
	X	X	X		X	X	X	X	U	S			X	X			S	X	X	U					S	U										
	X		X	S	X	X	X	X			S		X	X			X	X	X			U			U	S										
	X	X	X	S		X	X	X	X		S		X	X			X	X				U			U	S										
	X	X	X	X		X	X	X	X	U	S		X	X			U	X	S				U	X												
	X	X	X	X		X	X	X		U			X	X			U		X	S		U	X			S										
	X		X	X		X	X			U	U		X	X			X	S	X	S		X	S			X										
	X	X	X	X		X	X	X			U	X		X	X			U	X	S			S			X										
	X	X	X	X		X	X	X	X				X	X			S	U	X	S			U			S										
	X	X	X	X		X	X	X	X		S		X	X			U		X	S						S										
	X	X	X	X		X	X	X	X	X	U		X	U			X		X				U			U										
	X	X	X	X		X	X	X	X	S			X	U			X		X	S			U			S										
	X	X	X	X		X	X	X	X				X	S			S		X	U			S			U										
	X	X	X		X	X	X	X				S		S			S	U	X		U		X	U		X	U									
	X	X	X		X	X	X	X	U				X	X			S	S	X		U	X			U											
	X	X	X		X	X	X		X				X	X			S	U	X		U	X					U									
	X	X			X	X	X						X	X			S	U	X		U	X			S		X	S								
	X	X			X	X	X	U					X	X			S	U	X	S	X	X			S		X	S	X							
	X	X		U		X	X						X			U	X	X	S	X	X			S		X	X	X	S							
	X	X	X			X	X		U				X			X	X	X	X		X	U		S		X		X		S						
	X	X	X			X	U			S			X	X			X	X	U		X	U		S		X		X		S						
	X	X	X		X		X	S					X	X			X	X	X		X	S		U		X	S	S	X							
	X	X				X	X						S	X			X	X	X	X		U	S			X	S	S	X	X	U					
	X	X		X		X	X						S	X			S	X	X	U	S			X		X		U	X	X	U					
	U	X		X		U	X						S	X			U	X	X		S	S		X		X		X		U	X					
	X	X				X	X						S	X	U		X	X	X		X			X		S		X		U	X	S	U			
	X	X				X	X						X	X	X		X	X	X		X			X		S		S	X	U	U	U	S			
	X					X	X		U				X	X	X		X	X	X	S	X	X		X		X			U		U	U	U			
	X					S	X	S	X				X	X	X	X	X	X	U	X			X		S				U							

(blank rows)

	X	X	X	U		X	X	X	X		S				X	X	U	U	X	X	S				S		U									
	X	X	X	U		X	X	X	X	S	S				X	X	U	U	X	X	S					U										
	X	X	X	X		X	X	S	X	U	S				X	X	U		U	X	S	U			X											
	X	X	X	X		S	X	X	X		X				S	U		U	X	X			X		S											
	X	X	X			X	X	X	X	X					S		S	U	X		U	X			X	U										
	X	X					X	X	X	X					X	S		S	U	X		U	X		S		X			X						
	X	X					X	X	X	X					S		U	S	X	S	U	X			X		X			X						

Totals:

	45	40	32	20	2	29	41	40	18	10	6	2	32	36	0	13	28	41	1	8	13	10	0	0	9	0	2	10	3	5	0	2	7	1	0	0
	0	0	0	2	1	0	1	3	5	1	13	3	8	5	0	13	3	0	18	2	5	3	7	0	12	0	0	3	2	1	3	3	0	0	1	1
	1	0	0	2	1	0	1	1	13	2	2	0	5	9	9	8	0	7	9	9	1	4	2	4	2	0	0	0	1	2	3	0	4	3	3	

	7	7	5	2	0	4	7	6	7	3	1	0	4	3	0	0	2	7	1	0	3	0	1	0	3	0	2	0	2	0	0	0	0	0	0	0
	0	0	0	0	0	1	0	1	0	1	3	0	0	4	0	2	1	0	4	0	0	0	1	0	2	0	0	0	0	0	0	0	0	0	0	0
	0	0	0	2	0	0	0	0	0	1	0	0	0	0	4	3	4	0	0	3	1	0	0	0	2	1	0	0	0	0	0	0	0	0	0	0

| | 0 | 3 | 0 | 1 | 0 | 5 | 7 | 6 | 6 | 3 | 1 | 2 | 7 | 0 | 0 | 0 | 2 | 2 | 1 | 1 | 0 | 1 | 0 | 0 | 2 | 0 | 0 | 3 | 0 | 1 | 0 | 1 | 2 | 0 | 0 | 0 |
| | 0 | 1 | 2 | 1 | 0 | 3 | 0 | 3 | 1 | 0 | 2 | 0 | 0 | 0 | 0 | 0 | 1 | 1 | 0 | 0 | 0 | 0 | 0 | 0 | 0 | 0 | 0 | 0 | 0 | 0 | 0 | 0 | 0 | 0 | 0 | 0 |

PLAYING SQUAD

Existing Players		SN	HT	WT	DOB	AGE	POB	Career	Apps	Goals
GOALKEEPERS										
Jonathan	Hedge	1	6'02"	13 00	19/07/1988	24	Rotherham	Rotherham Rel c/s 06, Halifax 4/07 Rel 5/07, Queensland Roar (Aust) c/s 07, Harrogate T 7/08, FC Halifax 7/09, Tamworth 7/11, Cambridge U 5/12		
Will	Norris							Royston, Cambridge U 7/12, Royston (SL) 7/12		
Craig	Ross	24			29/01/1990	22		Southampton (Yth), Arsenal (Yth), Reading (Yth), C.Palace (Yth), Colchester (Yth), Chertsey, Ashford T (Middx), Carshalton 5/10, Eastleigh (Trial), Hampton & R 9/11, Welling 10/11, Hampton & R 10/11		
DEFENDERS										
James	Brighton	26					Redditch	Birmingham C (Yth), Cambridge U 11/10, Hemel Hempstead (L) 11/11	3	0
Josh	Coulson	4	6'03"	11 11	28/01/1989	23	Cambridge	Cambridge C (Yth), Cambridge U c/s 06	32	0
Harrison	Dunk	11			25/10/1990	21		Fulham (Yth), Millfield School, Bromley c/s 09, Cambridge U 6/11	23	6
Scott	Garner	14	6'02"	13 02	20/09/1989	22	Coventry	Leicester, Ilkeston (L) 10/08, Mansfield 1/09, Grimsby 7/10 Rel c/s 12, Alfreton (2ML) 2/11, Cambridge U 6/12		
Blaine	Hudson	25			28/10/1991	20	Gorleston	Norwich (Yth), Cambridge U 5/08, Cambridge C (L) 11/11	18	0
James	Jennings	3	5'10"	11 02	02/09/1987	24	Manchester	Macclesfield, Altrincham (2ML) 1/08, Kettering 7/09, Cambridge U Undisc 5/10	41	2
Kevin	Roberts	2	6'02"	14 00	10/03/1987	25	Liverpool	Chester Rel 2/10, Cambridge U 2/10	40	3
Jonathon	Thorpe	20			12/02/1993	19		Cambridge U	26	0
Michael	Wylde	5	6'02"	13 02	06/01/1987	25	Birmingham	Cheltenham Rel c/s 08, Cirencester (WE) 12/05, Kidderminster (SL) 3/08, Tamworth 7/08, Cambridge U 5/11	22	1
MIDFIELDERS										
Luke	Allen	27			22/02/1993	19		Cambridge U		
Luke	Berry	18			12/07/1992	20	Bassingbourn	Cambridge U	43	6
Jack	Eades	23			30/10/1991	20		Notts Forest (Scholar), Cambridge U (CRC) c/s 08, Needham Market (L) 2/11, Hemel Hempstead (L) 11/11 10		1
Billy	Gibson	7	6'02"	11 07	30/09/1990	21	Harrow	Watford, Wealdstone (2ML) 12/09, Yeovil 8/10 Rel c/s 12, Braintree (SL) 3/12, Cambridge U 6/12		
Liam	Hughes	17			10/08/1992	20		Scunthorpe (Yth), Cambridge U (CRC) c/s 08	21	2
Rossi	Jarvis	16	6'00"	11 02	11/03/1988	24	Fakenham	Norwich Rel c/s 08, Torquay (L) 1/07, Rotherham (SL) 3/07, Luton 8/08 Rel 5/10, Barnet 7/10 Rel c/s 11, Cambridge U 8/11	41	0
Rory	McAuley	12	5'10"	12 06	16/10/1989	22	Blackpool	Cambridge U	31	2
Adam	Miller		5'11"	11 06	19/02/1982	30	Hemel Hempstead	Ipswich (Scholar), Southend (Trial) 8/00, Canvey Island 10/00, Southend (Trial), Grays PE 8/02, Gravesend 9/03, Aldershot 10/03, QPR £50,000 11/04, Peterborough (L) 9/05, Stevenage 1/06, Gillingham (6WL) 11/07 Undisc 1/08 Rel c/s 10, Dag & Red (2ML) 11/09, Cambridge U 6/10		
Adriano	Moke	21	5'09"	10 00	11/01/1990	22		Man Utd (Yth), Barnsley (Yth), Leeds (Yth), Notts Forest (Scholar), Glen Hoddle Academy 3/10, Sheff Wed (Trial) 7/10, Jerez Industrial (Spa), York C 6/11, Cambridge U 7/12		
Tom	Shaw	6	6'00"	12 00	01/12/1986	25	Nottingham	Notts Forest (Jun), Rushden & D (7/04) Rel 7/08, Mansfield 8/08 Rel 10/08, Tamworth 10/08, Kidderminster 6/10, Cambridge U 5/11	42	7
Ricky	Wellard	8	5'11"	09 13	09/05/1988	24	Hammersmith	Ashford T (Middx), AFC Wimbledon 7/09 Rel c/s 12, Cambridge U (2ML) 2/11, Cambridge U 5/12		
Robbie	Willmott	22	5'09"	12 01	16/05/1990	22	Harlow	Cambridge U, Luton £50,000 1/11 Rel c/s 12, Cambridge U 7/12		

Forwards

		SN	HT	WT	DOB	AGE	POB	From - To	APPS	GOA
Tom	Elliott	10	5'10"	11 00	09/09/1989	22	Leeds	Leeds, Macclesfield (L) 1/09, Bury (SL) 9/09, Rotherham (6ML) 7/10, Hamilton 1/11 Rel c/s 11, Bradford C (Trial) 6/11, Stockport 8/11, Cambridge U 5/12		
Michael	Gash	9	5'09"	12 01	03/09/1986	25	Cambridge	Cambridge C, Cambridge U 6/06, Cambridge C (L) 1/07, Cambridge C 5/07, Ebbsfleet £20,000 7/08, York C £55,000 7/09 Rel c/s 11, Rushden & D (SL) 1/11, Cambridge U 6/11	40	7
Adam	Marriott	19			14/04/1991	21	Brandon	Norwich (Yth), Cambridge C (Yth), Cambridge U (Yth) c/s 06 Pro c/s 09, Cambridge C (L) 3/12	11	3
Andy	Pugh	15	5'09"	12 02	28/01/1989	23	Gravesend	Gillingham Rel c/s 10, Welling (L) 10/07, Maidstone (L) 2/08, Folkestone I (L) 8/08, Grays (SL) 1/09, Dover (L) 9/09, Welling (2ML) 11/09, Histon (L) 3/10, Welling 7/10, L.Orient (Trial) 11/11, Cambridge U £15,000 1/12	13	3
Sam	Smith	28			20/05/1990	22	Corby	Corby (Yth), Rushden & D 2/07, Corby T (L) 10/09, Hinckley U (L) 12/09, Lincoln C 7/11, Cambridge U Undisc 8/12		

Loanees		SN	HT	WT	DOB	AGE	POB	From - To	APPS	GOA
(D)Steve	Kinniburgh		6'00"	11 02	13/06/1989	23	Glasgow	Oxford U 8/11 - Rel 2/12, AFC Telford 3/12	3	0
(M)Peter	Winn		6'00"	11 08	19/12/1988	23	Cleethorpes	Stevenage (3ML) 8/11 - Grimsby (SL) 3/12, Rel c/s 12, Macclesfield 7/12	13	1
(D)Ismael	Yakubu		6'01"	12 09	05/04/1985	27	Kano, Nig	Newport C 9/11 -	0	0
(G)Sean	Cuff				21/05/1993	19	Middlesbrough	Sheff Wed 1/12 - Worksop (SL) 3/12	0	0
(D)Brett	Johnson		6'01"	13 00	15/08/1985	27	Hammersmith	AFC Wimbledon 1/12 - Woking 8/12	2	0
(D)Ryan	Jackson				31/07/1990	22	Streatham	AFC Wimbledon (SL) 1/12 - Rel c/s 12, Macclesfield 6/12	5	0
(F)Mustafa	Tiryaki				02/03/1987	25	Hackney	Tranmere 3/12 - Rel c/s 12	6	1
(M)Josh	Dawkin		5'09"	10 12	16/01/1992	20	Huntingdon	Norwich 3/12 - Rel c/s 12, Tamworth 7/12	5	1
(M)Harry	Pell		6'03"	13 05	21/10/1991	20	Tilbury	Hereford 3/12 -	7	2

Departures		SN	HT	WT	DOB	AGE	POB	From - To	APPS	GOA
(F)Daryl	Clare		5'09"	11 00	01/08/1978	34	Jersey	Gateshead £10,000 6/10 - Rel 9/11, Alfreton (SL) 2/11, Gainsborough (L) 8/11, Louth T (Man) 6/12		
(M)Steve	Connors				05/01/1986	26	Liverpool	Fleetwood 6/11 - Rel 7/11 Reinstated 11/11 Rel 11/11, Witton (Trial) 7/12		
(G)Simon	Brown		6'02"	15 00	03/12/1976	35	Chelmsford	Northampton 2/10 - Rel 1/12, Welling 1/12	0	0
(M)Conal	Platt		5'09"	10 10	14/10/1986	25	Preston	Forest Green 6/10 - AFC Telford (L) 9/11, Lincoln C (2ML) 11/11 Perm 1/12	5	2
(G)Robert	Ambrusics		6'03"	13 00	22/01/1992	20	Hungary	Vasas SC (Hun) 3/12 - Rel c/s 12	1	0
(D)Ashley	Corker		5'11"	11 11	18/09/1990	21		Northampton Rel 1/12, Cambridge U 3/12 Rel c/s 12	1	0
(G)Danny	Naisbitt		6'01"	11 12	25/11/1978	33	Bishop Auckland	Histon 5/10 - Rel c/s 12, Cambridge C 7/12, Braintree 8/12	45	0
(M)Ashley	Carew		6'00"	11 00	17/12/1985	26	Lambeth	Ebbsfleet 7/11 - Rel c/s 12, Carshalton 5/12	29	5
(M)Jordan	Patrick				03/02/1991	21	Honolulu	Yth - Cambridge C 7/12	19	1
(M)Kieran	Murtagh		6'00"	12 00	29/10/1988	23	Wapping	Wycombe 6/11 - Woking (SL) 12/11, Macclesfield 7/12	7	0
(F)Ryan	Charles		6'00"	11 13	30/09/1989	22	Enfield	Rushden & D 6/11 - Rel c/s 12, Newport C (L) 1/12, Newport C 7/12	19	1
(M)Liam	Hurst							Leicester -	1	0

Conference Action...

Dartford's Elliott Bradbrook gets up highest to head his team into the lead against Basingstoke in the Conference South play-off semi-final.

Photo: Keith Clayton.

DARTFORD

Chairman: Bill Archer & David Skinner
Secretary: Peter Martin   **(T)** 07976 054 202   **(E)** peter@martinpe.freeserve.co.uk
Additional Committee Members:
Steve Irving, David Boswell, Bob Blair,Mark Brenlund,Tony Burman, Harry Extance, Dave Francis,
Norman Grimes, Jeremy Kit MBE, Jason Outram, Nicola Collett.
Manager: Tony Burman
Programme Editor: Tony Jaglo   **(E)** tonyjaglo@tiscali.co.uk

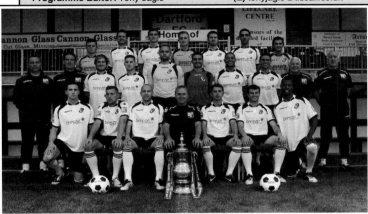

BACK ROW ; Jay Porter, Mark Arber, Tom Bonner, Ryan Sawyer, Elliot Bradbrook, Tom Champion, George Monger.
MIDDLE ROW; Steve Mosely (Coach), Paul Sawyer (Coach), Richard Rose, James Rogers, Louis Wells, Deren Ibrahim,
Jacob Erskine, Lee Burns, Dave Phillips (Physio) John Macrae (Goalkeeper Coach).
FRONT ROW ; Danny Harris, Ryan Hayes, Adam Green, Tony Burman (Manager), Lee Noble, Jon Wallis, Nathan Collier.

Club Factfile

Founded: 1888   **Nickname:** The Darts
Previous Names: None
Previous Leagues: Kent League 1894-96, 97-98, 99-1902, 09-14, 21-26, 93-96, Southern 1996-2006

Club Colours (change): White/black/white (Pale blue/red/blue)

Ground: Princes Park Stadium, Grassbanks, Darenth Road, Dartford DA1 1RT   **(T)** 01322 299 990
Capacity: 4,097   **Seats:** 640   **Covered:** Yes   **Clubhouse:** Yes   **Shop:** Yes

Directions: From M25 clockwise leave at Junction 1 B to roundabout controlled by traffic lights. Take third exit onto Princes Road, (A225) then second exit at next roundabout. Continue down hill to traffic lights (ground on your left), turn left into Darenth Road then second turning on your left into Grassbanks leading to car park. From M25 anti-clockwise leave at Junction 2 onto slip road A225 to roundabout, then first exit, second exit at next roundabout then down hill to traffic lights turn left into Darenth Road, then second turning on your left into Grassbanks leading to car park.

Previous Grounds: The Brent/Westgate House, Potters Meadow, Engleys Meadow, Summers Meadow, Watling Street

Record Attendance: 4,097 v Horsham YMCA - Isthmian Division 1 South 11/11/2006 and v Crystal Palace - Friendly 20/07/2007
Record Victory: Not known
Record Defeat: Not known
Record Goalscorer: Not known
Record Appearances: Steve Robinson - 692
Additional Records: Paid £6,000 to Chelmsford City for John Bartley
Received £25,000 from Redbridge Forest for Andy Hessenthaler
Senior Honours: Southern League Division 2 1896-97, Eastern Section 1930-31, 31-32, Southern Championship 30-31, 31-32, 73-74, 83-84, Southern Division 1980-81, League Cup 1976-77, 87-88, 88-89, Championship Shield 1983-84, 87-88, 88-89. Isthmian League Division 1 North 2007-08, Premier Division 2009-10. Kent Senior Cup 1929-30, 34-35, 38-39, 69-70.

10 YEAR RECORD

02-03		03-04		04-05		05-06		06-07		07-08		08-09		09-10		10-11		11-12	
SthE	17	SthE	16	SthE	16	SthE	7	Isth1S	7	Isth1N	1	Isth P	8	Isth P	1	Conf S	10	Conf S	2

DARTFORD

No.	Date	Comp	H/A	Opponents	Att:	Result	Goalscorers	Pos
1	Sat-13-Aug	BSS	A	Weston-Super-Mare	480	W 4-0	Bradbrook 15, Bonner 38, Sheringham 2 (65, 70)	2
2	Tue-16-Aug	BSS	H	Eastbourne Borough	1140	W 2-1	Sheringham 19, Green 60	5
3	Sat-20-Aug	BSS	H	Hampton & Richmond Borough	937	W 2-1	Sheringham pen 13, Bradbrook 20	1
4	Tue-23-Aug	BSS	A	Dover Athletic	1455	D 2-2	Sheringham 1, Bradbrook 45	1
5	Sat-27-Aug	BSS	A	Chelmsford City	1013	D 0-0		3
6	Mon-29-Aug	BSS	H	Bromley	1550	W 3-1	Bradbrook 7, Sheringham pen 82, Harris 84	3
7	Sat-03-Sep	BSS	A	Basingstoke Town	493	L 2-3	Sheringham pen 16, Green 32	3
8	Sat-10-Sep	BSS	H	Eastleigh	1079	W 3-0	Sheringham 2 (2, 69), Og (Breimyr) 90	3
9	Sat-17-Sep	BSS	A	Farnborough	679	W 2-1	Sheringham 22, Burns 45	3
10	Tue-20-Sep	BSS	H	Staines Town	1002	W 2-1	Hayes 54, Champion 74	2
11	Sat-24-Sep	BSS	H	Tonbridge Angels	1385	W 3-1	Bradbrook 10, Harris 64, Sheringham 77	2
12	Sat-08-Oct	BSS	A	Boreham Wood	441	L 1-3	Bradbrook 5	2
13	Sat-22-Oct	BSS	H	Truro City	1238	L 1-2	Bonner 77	4
14	Tue-25-Oct	BSS	A	Thurrock	642	W 3-0	Erskine 51, Rogers 56, Pallen 86	3
15	Sat-05-Nov	BSS	A	Salisbury City	769	W 2-1	Wallis 25, Erskine 62	4
16	Sat-12-Nov	BSS	H	Weston-Super-Mare	1149	D 1-1	Green 43	3
17	Sat-19-Nov	BSS	A	Eastleigh	604	D 2-2	Green pen 26, Wallis 36	4
18	Sat-03-Dec	BSS	A	Dover Athletic	1558	W 3-1	Green pen 7, Hayes 62, Bradbrook 88	3
19	Tue-13-Dec	BSS	H	Woking	1230	L 2-3	Rogers 65, Erskine 90	3
20	Sat-17-Dec	BSS	H	Dorchester Town	924	D 1-1	Harris 90	3
21	Mon-26-Dec	BSS	A	Welling United	1815	D 1-1	Noble 90	4
22	Mon-02-Jan	BSS	H	Welling United	2559	W 1-0	Harris 59	4
23	Sat-07-Jan	BSS	A	Havant & Waterlooville	802	W 4-1	Bradbrook 21, Harris 2 (29, 74), Noble 89	4
24	Sat-21-Jan	BSS	A	Hampton & Richmond Borough	656	W 3-1	Bradbrook 2 (32, 48), Erskine 52	4
25	Tue-24-Jan	BSS	A	Staines Town	378	W 4-1	Bonner 45, Essam 58, Harris 72, Green 83	2
26	Sat-28-Jan	BSS	H	Thurrock	1206	W 6-0	Bradbrook 2 (11, 79), Harris 30, Rogers 34, Burns 72, Garrod 77	2
27	Sat-18-Feb	BSS	A	Woking	2528	L 0-1		2
28	Sat-25-Feb	BSS	H	Salisbury City	941	W 2-0	Erskine 46, Rogers 52	2
29	Mon-27-Feb	BSS	H	Basingstoke Town	783	W 4-1	Harris 3 (53, 53, 81), Garrod 78	2
30	Sat-03-Mar	BSS	A	Tonbridge Angels	1139	W 1-0	Champion 18	2
31	Sat-10-Mar	BSS	A	Farnborough	1374	W 3-0	Erskine 2 (18, 52), Garrod 88	2
32	Tue-13-Mar	BSS	A	Maidenhead United	355	D 1-1	Harris 28	2
33	Sat-17-Mar	BSS	H	Havant & Waterlooville	1087	W 3-1	Noble 23, Harris 81, Wilkinson 87	2
34	Tue-20-Mar	BSS	H	Sutton United	1022	W 6-1	Noble 18, Green pen 22, Harris 47, Wilkinson 69, Bradbrook 82, Erskine 85	2
35	Sat-24-Mar	BSS	A	Dorchester Town	534	L 0-1		2
36	Sat-31-Mar	BSS	H	Maidenhead United	1069	W 2-1	Erskine 56, Wilkinson 62	2
37	Tue-03-Apr	BSS	A	Eastbourne Borough	823	W 1-0	Bradbrook 58	2
38	Sat-07-Apr	BSS	H	Chelmsford City	1616	D 0-0		2
39	Mon-09-Apr	BSS	A	Bromley	676	W 2-1	Harris 22, Wilkinson 26	2
40	Sat-14-Apr	BSS	A	Sutton United	756	W 1-0	Garrod 58	2
41	Sat-21-Apr	BSS	H	Boreham Wood	1309	D 2-2	Garrod 22, Erskine 79	2
42	Sat-28-Apr	BSS	A	Truro City	751	D 1-1	Erskine 90	2

CUPS

No.	Date	Comp	H/A	Opponents	Att:	Result	Goalscorers	Pos
1	Sat-01-Oct	FAC 2Q	H	Harrow Borough	803	W 5-0	Rogers 11, Bradbrook 14, Sheringham 25, Bonner 50, Burns 77	
2	Sat-15-Oct	FAC 3Q	A	Cray Wanderers	690	W 2-1	Hayes 72, Harris 80	
3	Sat-29-Oct	FAC 4Q	A	Bromley	1567	L 1-2	Pallen 31	
4	Sat-26-Nov	FAT 3Q	A	Eastbourne Borough	508	D 0-0		
5	Tue-29-Nov	FAT 3QR	H	Eastbourne Borough	611	W 2-1	Champion 57, Harris 66	
6	Sat-10-Dec	FAT 1	A	Brackley Town	291	W 3-0	Bradbrook pen 39, Erskine 2 (59, 62)	
7	Sat-14-Jan	FAT 2	H	Boston United	1166	W 4-2	Erskine 3 (4, 54, 90), Noble 61	
8	Tue-14-Feb	FAT 3	H	Wealdstone	770	D 2-2	Harris 28, Noble 51	
9	Tue-21-Feb	FAT 3R	A	Wealdstone	670	L 0-1		
10	Wed-02-May	PO SF1	A	Basingstoke Town	1691	W 1-0	Noble 46	
11	Sun-06-May	PO SF2	H	Basingstoke Town	2210	W 2-1	Bradbrook 56, Harris 71	
12	Sun-13-May	PO Final	H	Welling United	4088	W 1-0	Noble 4	

	League
	Starts
	Substitute
	Unused Sub
	Cups
	Starts
	Substitute
	Unused Sub
	Goals (Lg)
	Goals (Cup)

	YOUNG	JONES	GREEN	BONNER	GOODACRE	CHAMPION	HAYES	WALLIS	BRADBROOK	GRAHAM	SHERINGHAM	HARRIS	NOBLE	EVES	COOPER	IBRAHIM	BURNS	ROGERS	PALLEN	HAMMOND	ERSKINE	WELLS	GARROD	ESSAM	MONGER	WILKINSON
	X	X	X	X	X	X	X	X	X	X	X	S	S	S	U	U										
	X	X	X	X	X	X	X	X	X	X	X	S	S		U	U	S									
	X	X	X	X	X	X	X	X	X	X	X	S	S		U		S	U								
	X	X	X	X	X	X	X	X	X	X	X	S	S		U		S	U								
	X	X	X	X	X	X	X	X	X	X	X	S	S		U		S	U								
	X	X	X	X	X	X	X	X	X	X	X	S	S		U		S	U								
	X	X	X	X	X	X	X	X	X	X	X	S	S		X	U	U	U								
	X	X	X	X	X	X	X	X	U	X	X		S	X		U		S	S							
	X	X	X	X		X	S	X	X	X	X	S	X			U		X	S	U						
	X	X	X	X		X	X			X	X	X	S	S		U	U	X	S	S						
	X	X	X	X		X	X		S	X	X	X	S	X		U		X	S	U						
	X		X	X		X	X		S	X	X	X	S	X		U		X	S	U						
	X		X	X	X	X	X			X	X		X	S		U	U	X	X	S	S					
	U		X	X	X	X	X		U	X	S			X	S		X	X	X	S	X					
		U	X	X	X			U	X	X	U			X	X		U	X	X	U	X	X				
			X	X	X	U	S	X	X		S			X	X		U	X	X	S	X	X				
			X	X	X	X	S	X	X		S			X	X		U	X	U		S	X				
			X	X	X	X	X	X	X		S		S	S			U	X	X		U	X				
			X	X	X	X	X	X	X		S			U			U	X	X		S	X	S			
			X	X	X		X	X	X	X		S				U	U		S		X	X	S	X	U	
			X	X	X		X	X	X	X	S		X	S			U		U		S	X	X	X		
			X	X	X		X	X		X	U		X	U			U			X	X	U	X	U		
			X	X	X			X	U	U	X	U		X	X			U		X	X	X	S	X		
			X	X	X				S	X	X	X	S				U	U	X		X	X	S	X		
			X	X	X				S	X	X	X	S				U	X	X	U		X	X	S	X	
			X	X	X			U	S	X	X	X					U	X	X		X	X	S	X		
			U	X	X	X	X			S			X	X				X	X		X	X	S			X
			U	X	X	U	X	U		X			S				X	X			X	X	S			X
			X	X	X	U	X	X		S			X	X			U		X		X	X	S			X
			X	X	X	U	X	X	X		S			X	X			S	X		X	X	S			X
			X	X	X		X	S	X	S	X			X	X			U	S		X	X	U		U	X
			X	X	X		X	S	X		X			X	X			U	S	X	U	X	X	S		X
			U	X	X		X	X	U		X			X	X				X	X	U	X	X	S		X
			U	X	X	U	X	U			X			X	X				X	X	U	X	X	U		X
			U	X	X	U	X	S		X				X	X				X	X	U	X	X	S		X
				X	X			X	U		X	U		X	X				X	X		X	X	S	U	X
			S	X	X			X			X	S		X	X			S	X	X	S	X	X	X		X
			X	X	X	X	X	X			S	S		X	X				U	X	U	S	X	X		
			X	X	U	X	S			X	S			X	X				X	X	U	X	X	S		X
			X	X	X	X			X	X	S	X	U	X	X	U		S	U	X	X	S	U			
	X		X	X	X	X	X	X		X	X	X	S	S			U	U	X	X	U					
	U		X	X	X	X	X	U	X	S			X	S			U	X	X	X	X					
			X	X	X	X	X	U	X			U		X	X			U	X	S		X	X	S			
			X	X	X	X	X	X			U			X	U			U	X	X		U	X	U			
			X	U	X	X	X	X	S	X	X			X				U	S	X		X	X	S			
			X	X	X		X	U	U	X	S			X	X			U		X		X	X	S	X		
			X	X	X		X	U	X	X	X	S			X	X			U	X	X		X	X	S		
			U	X	X	X	X	S	X			U			X	X			U	X	X		X	X	S		
	U			X	X	U	X	U			X	U			X	X				X	X		X	X	U		X
	U			X	X	U	X	U			X	U			X	X				X	X		X	X	S		X
	U			X	X	U	X	U			X	U			X	X				X	X		X	X	S		X
	12	29	42	42	18	36	20	28	34	16	12	26	25	0	0	2	21	23	0	0	24	28	3	7	0	14
	0	1	0	0	0	0	16	1	3	16	0	14	12	1	0	1	9	7	5	0	5	0	18	0	0	0
	1	6	0	0	6	2	6	2	1	4	0	0	1	0	4	31	5	7	12	0	1	0	3	0	4	0
	2	6	11	12	6	12	5	4	9	2	2	11	6	0	0	1	10	11	1	0	8	9	0	1	0	3
	0	0	0	0	0	0	0	1	2	0	3	0	1	3	0	1	0	1	1	1	0	0	0	7	0	0
	4	1	1	0	3	0	6	2	0	7	0	0	2	0	2	0	2	8	0	0	1	1	0	2	0	0
	0	0	7	3	0	2	2	2	14	0	11	15	4	0	0	0	2	4	1	0	11	0	5	1	0	4
	0	0	0	1	0	1	0	1	1	0	3	0	1	4	4	0	0	0	1	1	1	0	5	0	0	0

PLAYING SQUAD

Existing Players		SN	HT	WT	DOB	AGE	POB	Career	Apps	Goals
GOALKEEPERS										
Deren	Ibrahim	23			09/03/1991	21		Gillingham (Trainee), Welling Rel 5/06, Beckenham, Ashford T, Dartford, Sittingbourne (L) 2/10, St Andrews (Mal) 8/10, Dartford 11/10, Margate (Dual) 3/11, Maidstone (Dual) 6/12	3	0
Louis	Wells	1	6'03"	13 05	22/02/1982	30	Hillingdon	Hayes, Aldershot 6/06, Maidenhead 8/07, Uxbridge 3/08, Staines c/s 08, Dartford 11/11	28	0
DEFENDERS										
Mark	Arber	16	6'01"	11 09	09/10/1977	34	Johannesburg, SA	Tottenham, Barnet (2ML) 9/98 £75,000 11/98, Peterborough 12/02, Oldham Bosman 7/04, Peterborough (L) 12/04 Perm 1/05, Dag & Red (SL) 3/07, Stevenage 6/07, Dag & Red (SL) 2/08, Dag & Red 7/08 Rel c/s 12, Dartford 7/12		
Tom	Bonner	6	6'00"	11 06	06/02/1988	24	Camden	Northampton Rel 1/07, Bedford (SL) 2/06, Nuneaton (L) 8/06, Rushden & D 1/07 Rel 8/07, Bedford (L) 2/07, Heybridge (L) 3/07, Corby T 8/07, Hinckley U 1/08, Solihull Moors 2/09, Corby T 6/09, Ilkeston 8/09, Dartford 8/10	42	3
Tom	Champion	4			15/05/1986	26	London	Watford (Yth), Barnet 8/04 Rel c/s 05, Wealdstone (L) 3/05, Bishops Stortford 7/05, Braintree 1/10, Dartford 5/10	36	2
Adam	Green	3	5'11"	10 11	12/01/1984	28	Hillingdon	Fulham Rel 5/06, Sheff Wed (L) 1/05, Bournemouth (L) 3/05, Bristol C (SL) 1/06, Grays 7/06 Rel 1/07, Woking 1/07 Rel c/s 08, Grimsby (Trial) 12/08, Hayes & Yeading 7/09, Dartford 6/11	42	7
Richard	Rose	2	6'00"	12 04	08/09/1982	29	Tonbridge	Gillingham Rel c/s 06, Bristol R (2ML) 12/02, Hereford 7/06 Rel c/s 11, Dag & Red 8/11 Rel 8/12, Dartford 8/12		
MIDFIELDERS										
Elliott	Bradbrook	10	6'01"	12 12	28/01/1985	27	Dartford	Maidstone, University (USA), Maidstone c/s 08, Dartford 5/09	37	14
Jake	Burman				05/07/1992	20		Dartford		
Nathan	Collier	15			15/08/1985	27	London	Hampton & R, Dartford 7/12		
Danny	Harris	11			07/07/1986	26	Newham	Tilbury, East Thurrock 12/04, Bishops Stortford 12/07, Dartford (Dual) 10/09 Perm	40	15
Ryan	Hayes	7			15/07/1985	27	Greenwich	Slade Green, Dartford 3/05	36	2
Lee	Noble	14			01/01/1988	24	Brentwood	Brentwood, Dartford 6/08, Concord R (2ML) 11/10	37	4
James	Rogers	13			09/12/1984	27		Dover, Margate (L) 9/10 Perm, Dartford 3/11	30	4
Jon	Wallis	8	5'07"	10 08	04/04/1986	28	Gravesend	Chelsea (Jun), Gilingham Rel 5/06, Hastings U (3ML) 8/04, Hastings U (L) 9/05 Hereford 6/06 Rel 3/07, Dover (2ML) 11/06, Dag & Red (L) 2/07, Dover 3/07, Dartford 5/11	29	2
Forwards										
Lee	Burns	20			17/07/1982	30		East Thurrock, Braintree 10/07, Dartford 6/09	30	2
Harry	Crawford	21	6'01"	12 04	10/12/1991	20	Watford	Southend, Maldon T (WE) 12/09, Dover (L) 8/10, Dartford 8/12		
Jacob	Erskine	9	6'01"	14 00	13/01/1989	23	Lambeth	Croydon A, Wingate & F 10/07, Dag & Red 10/07 Rel c/s 09, Tooting & M (L), 12/07, Maidstone (L) 1/08, Margate (L) 12/08, Sutton U (L) 1/09, Dorchester (6WL) 3/09, Bromley 6/09, Gillingham 8/09, Bromley (L) 10/09, Bishops Stortford (L) 2/10, Croydon Ath (SL) 3/10, Concord R 7/10, Forest Green 1/11, Swindon Supermarine (SL) 1/11, Ebbsfleet 2/11, Bromley (Trial) 7/11, Hampton & R 8/11 Rel 10/11, Dartford 10/11	29	11
Luke	Medlen							Dartford		
George	Monger							Dartford	0	0
Others										
Billy	Eves							Dartford	1	0
Ryan	Cooper							Dartford	0	0
Tom	Hammond							Dartford	0	0

Loanees		SN	HT	WT	DOB	AGE	POB	From - To	APPS	GOA
(D)Connor	Essam				09/07/1992	20		Gillingham 12/11 -	7	1
(D)Luke	Wilkinson		6'02"	11 08	02/12/1991	20	Wells	Dag & Red 2/12 -	14	4
(F)Sam	Higgins							East Thurrock (Dual) 3/12 -		
(F)Tony	Stokes							Concord R (Dual) 3/12 -		

Departures		SN	HT	WT	DOB	AGE	POB	From - To	APPS	GOA
(F)Charlie	Sheringham		6'01"	11 06	17/04/1988	24	Chingford	Bishops Stortford 6/10 - Bournemouth Undisc 10/11	12	11
(G)Andy	Young				28/02/1980	32		Thurrock 9/08 - Rel 11/11, Concord R	12	0
(D)Paul	Goodacre				15/07/1984	28		Braintree 5/10 - Rel c/s 12, AFC Hornchurch 6/12	18	0
(D)Matt	Jones				04/03/1985	27		Bishops Stortford 1/11 - Rel c/s 12	30	0
(M)Richard	Graham		5'10"	11 10	05/08/1979	33	Newry	Eastleigh 6/11 - Rel c/s 12, St Albans 7/12	32	0
(F)Tony	Garrod		6'02"	11 08	14/09/1991	20	Crawley	Farnborough 11/11 - Staines 7/12	21	5
(F)Jack	Pallen				16/12/1991	20		Dover 3/11 - VCD Ath (L) 11/11, Leatherhead (L) 12/11, Chatham 8/12	5	1

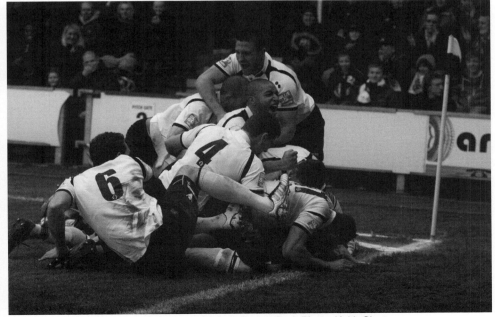

The Dartford players celebrate during their play-off semi-final. Photo: Keith Clayton.

Conference Action...

Wells, Dartford, puts in a challenge on Basingstoke's Sam-Yorke during the Conference South play-off semi-final which Dartford eventually won 3-1 on aggregate.

Photo: Keith Clayton.

EBBSFLEET UNITED

Chairman: Jessica McQueen
Secretary: Peter Danzey   **(T)** 07403 285 385   **(E)** peter@eufc.co.uk
Additional Committee Members:
Cheryl Wanless, Philip Sonsara.

Manager: Liam Daish
Programme Editor: TBA   **(E)**

Club Factfile

Founded: 1946   **Nickname:** The Fleet
Previous Names: Gravesend United and Northfleet United merged in 1946 to form Gravesend and Northfleet > 2007
Previous Leagues: Southern 1946-79, 80-96. Alliance 1979-80, Isthmian 1997-2001

Club Colours (change): Red/white/red (Yellow/black/yellow)

Ground: Stonebridge Road, Northfleet, Kent DA11 9EQ   **(T)** 01474 533 796
Capacity: 4,184   **Seats:** 500   **Covered:** 3,000   **Clubhouse:** Yes   **Shop:** Yes

Directions: A2 to Ebbsfleet/Eurostar International Junction.
Follow Brown signs to 'The Fleet'.

Previous Grounds: Gravesend United: Central Avenue

Record Attendance: 12,036 v Sunderland - FA Cup 4th Round 12/02/1963
Record Victory: 8-1 v Clacton Town - Southern League 1962-63
Record Defeat: 0-9 v Trowbridge Town - Southern League Premier DIvision 1991-92
Record Goalscorer: Steve Portway - 152 (1992-94, 97-2001)
Record Appearances: Ken Burrett - 537
Additional Records: Paid £8,000 to Wokingham Town for Richard Newbery 1996 and to Tonbridge for Craig Williams 1997
Senior Honours: Received £35,000 from West Ham United for Jimmy Bullard 1998
Southern League 1956-57, Division 1 South 1974-75, Southern Division 1994-95. Isthmian League Premier 2001-02.
FA Trophy 2007-08. Kent Senior Cup 1948-49, 52-53, 80-81, 99-00, 00-01, 01-02.

10 YEAR RECORD

02-03		03-04		04-05		05-06		06-07		07-08		08-09		09-10		10-11		11-12	
Conf	17	Conf	11	Conf	14	Conf	16	Conf	7	Conf	11	Conf	14	Conf	22	Conf S	3	Conf	14

EBBSFLEET UNITED

No.	Date	Comp	H/A	Opponents	Att:	Result	Goalscorers	Pos
1	Sat-13-Aug	BSP	H	York City	1522	L 1-2	Willock 80	21
2	Tue-16-Aug	BSP	A	Tamworth	921	L 0-1		23
3	Sat-20-Aug	BSP	A	Stockport County	3674	D 1-1	West 76	21
4	Tue-23-Aug	BSP	H	Newport County	992	D 1-1	West 90	21
5	Sat-27-Aug	BSP	H	Forest Green Rovers	889	D 1-1	Shakes 35	21
6	Mon-29-Aug	BSP	A	Braintree Town	810	W 3-2	Phipp pen 61, Ginty pen 87, Willock 90	16
7	Sat-03-Sep	BSP	H	Barrow	983	L 1-2	Enver-Marum 12	18
8	Sat-10-Sep	BSP	A	Kidderminster Harriers	1788	D 2-2	Enver-Marum 38, Herd 90	20
9	Sat-17-Sep	BSP	H	Fleetwood Town	974	L 1-3	Willock 40	20
10	Tue-20-Sep	BSP	A	Cambridge United	1911	L 0-2		22
11	Sat-24-Sep	BSP	A	Alfreton Town	661	D 2-2	Enver-Marum 5, Willock 45	22
12	Tue-27-Sep	BSP	H	Bath City	816	W 3-0	Willock 2 (24, 75), West 53	19
13	Sat-01-Oct	BSP	A	Wrexham	2849	L 0-1		20
14	Sat-08-Oct	BSP	H	Gateshead	947	L 0-1		21
15	Tue-11-Oct	BSP	H	Luton Town	1651	D 2-2	West 2 (77, 90)	21
16	Sat-15-Oct	BSP	A	AFC Telford	2004	W 2-0	Darvill 24, Willock 56	19
17	Tue-18-Oct	BSP	H	Grimsby Town	1143	W 3-1	West 14, Shakes 38, Willock 74	16
18	Sat-22-Oct	BSP	A	Kettering Town	1402	D 2-2	Willock pen 22, Darvill 33	16
19	Sat-05-Nov	BSP	A	Newport County	1412	W 1-0	Shakes 20	15
20	Sat-12-Nov	BSP	H	Stockport County	1119	W 2-1	Willock 81, Pinney 88	14
21	Sat-19-Nov	BSP	H	Darlington	1087	L 1-3	Willock 66	15
22	Sat-26-Nov	BSP	A	Lincoln City	2111	L 0-3		15
23	Tue-29-Nov	BSP	H	Kidderminster Harriers	731	D 3-3	Willock 2 (pen 55, 70), Pinney 72	16
24	Sat-03-Dec	BSP	A	Barrow	1047	D 1-1	Enver-Marum 87	16
25	Tue-06-Dec	BSP	H	Cambridge United	964	D 0-0		16
26	Sat-17-Dec	BSP	A	Grimsby Town	2818	L 3-4	Pinney 25, Mambo 28, Shakes 90	16
27	Mon-26-Dec	BSP	H	Hayes & Yeading United	1176	W 3-1	West 42, Phipp 2 (51, 61)	16
28	Tue-17-Jan	BSP	A	Hayes & Yeading United	266	W 2-1	Willock 2 (41, 77)	14
29	Sat-21-Jan	BSP	A	York City	2973	L 2-3	Pinney 50, Willock 87	14
30	Tue-24-Jan	BSP	H	Tamworth	746	W 3-0	Enver-Marum 54, Pinney 2 (61, 88)	14
31	Sat-28-Jan	BSP	H	Mansfield Town	1085	L 0-3		14
32	Sat-18-Feb	BSP	A	Bath City	693	W 3-2	Pinney 8, Shakes 79, Ugwu 90	14
33	Tue-21-Feb	BSP	A	Fleetwood Town	1411	L 2-6	Enver-Marum 2 (15, 86)	15
34	Sat-25-Feb	BSP	H	Southport	907	L 1-2	Ugwu 29	15
35	Sat-03-Mar	BSP	A	Gateshead	754	W 3-2	Barrett 55, Enver-Marum 78, Ugwu pen 88	14
36	Tue-13-Mar	BSP	H	Wrexham	990	L 0-5		14
37	Sat-17-Mar	BSP	A	Darlington	1796	W 2-0	Enver-Marum 49, Ugwu 50	14
38	Sat-24-Mar	BSP	H	Kettering Town	957	W 1-0	Shakes 20	14
39	Tue-27-Mar	BSP	H	Alfreton Town	687	L 1-2	Enver-Marum 7	14
40	Sat-31-Mar	BSP	A	Mansfield Town	2630	L 0-1		14
41	Fri-06-Apr	BSP	A	Forest Green Rovers	1058	L 1-3	Lorraine 20	15
42	Mon-09-Apr	BSP	H	Braintree Town	938	D 1-1	Willock pen 30	14
43	Sat-14-Apr	BSP	H	AFC Telford	875	W 3-2	West 27, Enver-Marum 2 (45, 62)	14
44	Tue-17-Apr	BSP	A	Luton Town	5526	L 0-3		14
45	Sat-21-Apr	BSP	A	Southport	1231	D 3-3	Shakes 15, Enver-Marum 89, Willock 90	14
46	Sat-28-Apr	BSP	H	Lincoln City	1217	L 2-3	Willock pen 24, Bellamy 66	14

CUPS

No.	Date	Comp	H/A	Opponents	Att:	Result	Goalscorers	
1	Sat-29-Oct	FAC 4Q	A	Ebbsfleet United	442	L 0-2		
2	Sat-10-Dec	FAT 1	A	Truro City	445	W 5-2	Enver-Marum 3 (2, 52, 90), West 20, Pinney 28	
3	Sat-14-Jan	FAT 2	H	Chester	1387	W 3-2	Willock 26, Mambo 55, Shakes 64	
4	Tue-14-Feb	FAT 3	A	York City	1419	L 0-1		

League
Starts
Substitute
Unused Sub

Cups
Starts
Substitute
Unused Sub

Goals (Lg)
Goals (Cup)

WELCH 17	STONE 2	SIMPEMBA 16	EASTON 5	HERD 3	PHIPP 11	FAKINOS 4	MARWA 8	WEST 7	SHAKES 10	ENVER-MARUM 15	STAVRINOU 20	WILLOCK 9	HOWE 14	EDWARDS 1	AZEEZ 18	WILLIAMS 19	GINTY 12	MCCARTHY 21	MAMBO 22	LORRAINE 6	DARVILL 23	MASROH-MCDOWELL 25	ROBERTSON 29	DEVINE 31	BARRETT 24	PINNEY 26	MCNEIL 12	ADAMS 27	SMITH 16	UGWU 23	CRONIN 30	BELLAMY 31
X	X	X	X	X	X	X	X	X	X	X	X	X	S	U	U	U																
X	X	X	X	X		S	X	X	X	X	X	X	S	U	S	U																
U	X	X	X	X		X	X	X	S	X	X	X	S	X	U		U															
U	X	X	X	X		X	X	X	S	X	X	X	S	X	U		S															
U	S	X	X	X	X	X	X	X	S	X	S	X	X	X			U															
U	X	X	X	X	X	U	X		X	X	U	X	X	X	S		S															
U	X	X		X	X	S	X		X	X	S	X	X	X	X	S		S	U													
U	X	X		X	X	S	X		X	X	X	X	X	X	X	S		S	U													
U	X	X		X	X	U	X	U	X	S	X	X	X	S	X			S			X											
U	X	X		X	X	S	X		X	X	S	X	X	X	X			S			X											
U	X	X		X	X	S	X		X	X	U	X		X	X			S			X	S										
U	X	X		S	X	X	X	S		X	X	X	U					S			X	X										
U	X	X		U	X	X	X	S		X	X	X	S					S			X	X										
U	X	X		X	X	U	X		U	X	X	X						S			X	X										
U	X	U			X	X	X	X		S	X	X	X	S				S			X	X	X									
U	X	U			X		X	X	X	S	X	X	X	S				S			X	X	X									
U	X	S			X		X	X	X	U	X	X	X	U				U			X	X	X									
U	X	S		U	X		X	X	X	S	X	X	X	U				S			X	X	X									
U	X	U			S		X	X	X	U	X	X	X								X	X	S		X	X						
U	X	U		U	X		X	X	X	S		X	X	X							X	X	U		X	X						
U	X	U			S		X	X	X	S		X	X	X							X	X	S		X	X						
U	X	S		U	S		X	X	X	S		X	X								X	X			X	X						
U	X	X		U	X		X	X	S	X		X	X	U							X	S				X						
U	U	X		X	X		X	X	S	X		X	X								X	S			S	X						
U	X	U		X			X	X	S	X		X	X								X	X	U		S	X						
U	X	X		U	X		X	X	S	X		X	X								X	S			S	X						
U	X	U			X		X	X	S	X		X	X	U							X	X	U		X	X						
	X			U	X		X	X	X	S		X	X	X	U			X	X						S	X	U					
	X			X	X			X		X	X	X	X	S			U	X		U					X	X	U	U				
	X			X			X	X		X	U	X	X	X	S			X	X						S	X	U	S				
	X			X			X	X	S	X	U	X	X	X	S			X	X						X	X	U		U			
	X			X		X		S	X	U	X	X	X	S				X	X						S	X	S		U	X		
	X			S			X	S		X	X	X			U			X	X						X	X	U		S	X	X	
	X			X			X		X	U	X			U				X							S	S	U		X	X	X	
	X	S		X			X	X	S	X		U						X							X	S	U		X		X	
	X	X		U	X		X	X	X			X	U	U				X							X	X	U	U		X		X
	X	U	X			X	X	X		X			S					X							X	S	U		X	X	X	S
	X		S		S	X	X	X		U	X							X							X	S	U		X	X	X	
	X		U		X	X	X	X		S	X							X							X	S	U		X	X	X	S
	X		U		X	X	X	X		S	X							X							X	X	U		X	S	X	S
	X	U	S		X	X	X	X		X	X							X							X	S	U			X	X	
	X	S	X			X	X	S	X		X							X							U	S	U		X	X		
	X	S	X		S	X	S	X		X	X		U					X							X		U			X	X	
	X	X			X	X	X	X		S	X		S			U				U					X		X	U	X			X
	X	S			X	X	X	X		X	X		U			U				U					X		X	U	X			X
	X	S			X	X	X	X		X	X		U							U					X	S	X	U	X			X
U	X	X		U	X		X	X		X	X	X	X		S		U		X	X	S	U	U									
U	X	U			X		X	X	S	X		X	X	X				X	X	S					S	X						
	X	U		U	X		X	X	S		X	X	X	U				X	X						X	X						
	X				X			X		S	X	U	X	X	X			X	X						U	X	U		U	X		
2	44	17	6	18	32	7	39	35	25	34	5	38	37	31	2	0	0	0	24	30	4	0	0	0	19	17	3	0	12	8	10	7
0	1	3	0	4	8	5	2	1	16	4	7	5	4	0	13	0	13	0	0	1	5	0	0	0	7	8	1	1	1	0	4	
25	1	7	0	9	2	3	0	0	0	0	10	1	1	2	12	4	3	6	0	0	3	1	0	0	1	0	15	5	2	0	0	0
0	4	1	0	0	4	0	3	3	1	2	1	4	4	4	0	0	0	3	4	1	0	0	0	1	3	0	0	0	1	0	0	
0	0	0	0	0	0	0	0	0	3	0	0	0	0	0	1	0	0	0	1	0	0	0	0	1	0	0	0	0	1	0	0	
2	0	2	0	2	0	0	0	0	0	0	1	0	0	0	1	0	0	1	0	0	1	0	1	1	1	0	1	0	1	0	0	0
0	0	0	0	1	3	0	0	8	7	13	0	19	0	0	0	0	1	0	1	1	2	0	0	0	1	7	0	0	0	4	0	1
0	0	0	0	0	0	0	0	1	1	3	0	1	0	0	0	0	0	0	1	0	0	0	0	0	0	1	0	0	0	0	0	0

PLAYING SQUAD

Existing Players		SN	HT	WT	DOB	AGE	POB	Career	Apps	Goals
GOALKEEPERS										
Preston	Edwards	1	6'00"	12 07	05/09/1989	22	Edmonton	Millwall Rel c/s 09, Dover (SL) 1/09, Grays 8/09 Rel 5/10, Ebbsfleet 8/10	31	0
Tom	McNeil	12						Wycombe (Yth), Walton & H, Windsor & E 8/09 Rel 8/10, Bracknell (L) 10/09, Beaconsfield SYCOB 8/10, Burnham 9/10, AFC Hayes 12/10, Slough, Flackwell Heath, Henley T, Ebbsfleet 1/12	4	0
DEFENDERS										
Patrick	Ada	4	6'00"	13 05	14/01/1985	27	Yaounde, Cam	Hornchurch, Ford U/Redbridge 12/03, Aldershot (Trial), Barnet 3/05, St Albans 7/05, Exeter 7/06, St Albans (2ML) 1/07, Histon 5/07, Crewe 7/09 Rel c/s 11, Kilmarnock 7/11 Rel 1/12, Burton 2/12 Rel c/s 12, Ebbsfleet 7/12		
Ryan	Blake	3	5'10"	10 10	08/12/1991	20	Weybridge	Brentford Rel c/s 12, Woking (L) 10/10, Ebbsfleet (3ML) 1/11, Farnborough (L) 10/11, Hampton & R (L) 1/12, Ebbsfleet 8/12		
James	Folkes	20			12/01/1990	22		Tottenham (Yth), QPR (Yth), Glen Hoddle Academy (Spa), Eastleigh 3/10, Glen Hoddle Academy, Hayes & Yeading 11/11 Rel 3/12, Ebbsfleet 8/12		
Joe	Howe	14	6'00"	11 04	21/01/1988	24	Sidcup	MK Dons Rel c/s 07, Walton & H (L) 8/06, Gravesend (WE) 1/07, Northampton 7/07 Rel 8/07, Kettering 8/07 Rel 12/07, Welling 12/07 Rel 7/08, Fisher 8/08, Croydon Ath 2/09, Ebbsfleet 10/10	41	0
Paul	Lorraine	6			12/10/1983	28		Welling, Dartford (L) 1/03, Erith & B 3/04, Braintree 5/04, Fisher 5/06, AFC Wimbledon (L) 12/06, Perm 1/07, Woking 5/07, AFC Wimbledon 5/09 Rel 4/10, Ebbsfleet 6/10	31	1
Paul	McCarthy		5'10"	13 10	04/08/1971	41	Cork	Brighton, Wycombe £100,000 7/96 Rel c/s 03, Oxford U (SL) 3/03, Oxford U 7/03, Rel c/s 04, Hornchurch 6/04, Gravesend/Ebbsfleet 11/04	0	0
MIDFIELDERS										
Lance	Azeez				07/01/1993	19		Ebbsfleet	15	0
Neil	Barrett	15	5'10"	11 00	24/12/1981	30	Tooting	Chelsea (Jun), Portsmouth (Trial) 3/01, Portsmouth 7/01, Dundee (3ML) 1/04, Dundee 7/04 Rel 9/05, Livingston 9/05 Rel 1/06, Exeter 9/06 Rel 12/06, Woking 1/07, Ebbsfleet 6/07, York C Undisc 6/09 Rel c/s 11, Luton (Trial) 7/11, Kingstonian (Trial) 7/11, Havant & W 9/11 Rel 10/11, Ebbsfleet 11/11	26	1
Liam	Bellamy	16	6'02"	12 05	16/10/1991	20	Whitechapel	Charlton Rel 3/10, Merstham 1/10, Cray W (WE) 2/10, Hastings U (WE) 3/10, Crawley 4/10, Chelmsford 8/10 Rel 9/10, Cray W 9/10, Welling 1/11, Brentford 7/11, Ebbsfleet (L) 3/12, Ebbsfleet 7/12	11	1
Ben	Greenhalgh	17						Corinthians, Welling 8/09, Inter Milan (Ita), Calcio Como (Ita), Welling 12/11, Ebbsfleet 8/12		
Rambir	Marwa				10/01/1980	32	Barkingside	L.Orient (Trainee), Erith & B 2/00, Ilford 7/00, Erith & B 1/01, Australia, L.Orient (Trial) 6/03, Grays 8/03, St Albans 8/04, Dag & Red 5/05, St Albans (L) 1/06 (Perm) 3/06, Hayes & Yeading (L) 11/07 Perm 12/07 Rel 5/10, Ebbsfleet 7/10	41	0
Tom	Phipp	11			03/08/1992	20		Ebbsfleet	40	3
Craig	Stone		6'00"	10 05	29/12/1988	23	Strood	Gillingham Rel 5/08, Brentford (2ML) 1/08, Ebbsfleet 6/08, Maidstone 3/10, Ebbsfleet 8/10	45	0

FORWARDS

		SN	HT	WT	DOB	AGE	POB	From - To	APPS	GOA
Moses	Ashikodi	10	6'00"	11 09	27/06/1987	25	Lagos, Nigeria	Millwall Rel 5/04, West Ham 8/04 Rel 1/06, Rushden & D (Trial) 7/05, Gillingham (3ML) 8/05, Rangers 1/06, Watford Undisc 1/07 Rel 2/09, Bradford C (SL) 3/07, Swindon (SL) 1/08, Hereford (5ML) 5/08, Luton (Trial) 2/09, Shrewsbury 2/09 Rel c/s 09, Kettering 9/09 Rel 12/09, Ebbsfleet 1/10, Kettering 6/10, York C (6WL) 11/11 Perm 1/12, Ebbsfleet 7/12		
Nathan	Elder	9	6'01"	13 12	05/04/1985	27	Hornchurch	Hornchurch, Ford U, Tilbury 9/03, Aveley 10/03, Billericay 12/04, Northampton (Trial) 11/05, Brighton Undisc 12/06, Brentford £35,000 1/08, Shrewsbury Undisc 8/09 Rel c/s 11, AFC Wimbledon (SL) 1/10, Hayes & Yeading 8/11, Hereford (3ML) 9/11 Perm 1/12 Rel c/s 12, Ebbsfleet 7/12		
Liam	Enver-Marum	7	6'03"	12 00	17/11/1987	24	London	Reading (Scholar) Rel c/s 06, Brighton (Trial) 7/06, Cambridge U 8/06, Woking 1/07 Rel 5/09, Eastbourne B 5/09 Rel 5/10, Crawley 6/10 Rel 12/10, Hayes & Yeading (L) 9/10, Forest Green (L) 10/10, Forest Green 1/11, Ebbsfleet 7/11, Stevenage (Trial) 6/12	38	13
Phil	Walsh	5	6'03"	13 04	04/02/1984	28	Hartlepool	Almondsbury T, Clevedon 1/03, Taunton 9/03, Clevedon 11/03, Almondsbury T 7/04, Bath C 8/05, Tiverton (L) 2/08, Newport C 6/08, Tiverton (3ML) 9/08 Undisc 12/08, Dorchester 3/09, Dag & Red Undisc 1/10 Rel c/s 12, Barnet (2ML) 8/10, Cheltenham (L) 1/11, Hayes & Yeading (SL) 1/12, Ebbsfleet 8/12		
Adam	Williams	19						Ebbsfleet, Erith T (L) 11/11	0	0

Loanees		SN	HT	WT	DOB	AGE	POB	From - To	APPS	GOA
(D)Yado	Mambo		6'03"	13 01	22/10/1991	20	Kilburn	Charlton (6ML) 9/11 -	24	1
(F)Nathaniel	Pinney		6'00"	12 05	16/11/1990	21	South Norwood	C.Palace (SL) 11/11 -	25	7
(F)Gozie	Ugwu				22/04/1993	19		Reading (2ML) 1/12 -	9	4
(G)Lance	Cronin		6'01"	12 00	11/09/1985	26	Brighton	Bristol R (2ML) 2/12 - Macclesfield 6/12	10	0

Departures		SN	HT	WT	DOB	AGE	POB	From - To	APPS	GOA
(F)Scott	Ginty		5'08"	11 11	17/05/1991	21		Peterborough (Scholar) 8/09 - Rel 11/11, Deeping R, Bishops Stortford 6/12	13	1
(D)Ian	Simpemba		6'02"	12 08	28/03/1983	29	Dublin	Havant & W 7/11 - Dover Nominal 1/12	20	0
(F)James	Darvill		5'11"	12 01	05/01/1988	24	London	Real Maryland Monarchs (USA) 10/11 - Rel 1/12, Sittingbourne, Cray W 3/12	9	2
(M)Alex	Stavrinou		5'09"	11 12	13/09/1990	21	Harlow	Charlton 8/11 - Rel 3/12, Lewes (2ML) 11/11	12	0
(G)Joe	Welch		6'02"	12 12	29/11/1988	23	Welwyn Garden	Histon 7/11 - Bromley (2ML) 1/12 Perm 3/12	2	0
(D)John	Herd		5'09"	12 00	03/10/1989	22	Huntingdon	Southend 8/11 - Rel c/s 12, Bishops Stortford 7/12	22	1
(M)Clint	Easton		5'11"	11 00	01/10/1977	34	Barking	Hereford 10/09 - Rel c/s 12	6	0
(F)Callum	Willock		6'01"	12 08	29/10/1981	30	Waterloo	Cambridge U 7/10 - Dover 6/12	43	19
(M)Ricky	Shakes		5'10"	12 00	26/01/1985	27	Brixton	Brentford 7/08 - Kidderminster 6/12	41	7
(M)Michael	West				09/02/1991	21		Yth - Crewe Nominal 7/12	36	8
(M)Ben	Adams							Glen Hoddle Academy - Eastbourne B 7/12	1	0
(D)Ross	Smith		6'00"	12 05	04/11/1980	31	Guelph, Can	Portland Timbers (USA) 1/12 -	13	0
(M)Liam	Devine							Yth -	0	0
(M)Giannoulis	Fakinos		5'08"		09/07/1989	23		ex Apollon Smyrni 3/11 -	12	0
(M)Ike	Robertson							Yth -	0	0
(F)Che	Masroh-McDowell							Staines (Yth) -	0	0

Conference Action...

Forest Green Rovers' number two prepares to take off with the ball as a Newport County player closes in during their First Round tie in the FA Trophy.

Photo: Peter Barnes.

FOREST GREEN ROVERS

Chairman: Dale Vince OBE
Secretary: Tom Cowling **(T)** 01453 761 402 **(E)** tom.cowling@ecotricity.co.uk
Additional Committee Members:
David Drew, Philip Catherall, Trevor Saunders, Mike Bullingham, Paul Wheatcroft,
David Drew, Chris Wintle.
Manager: David Hockaday
Programme Editor: Terry Brumpton **(E)** terrybrumpton@yahoo.co.uk

THE NON-LEAGUE CLUB DIRECTORY

Book Holiday Inn Hotels and Save today!

Home

Clubs

Steps 1 - 4

League Tables

35 Years of Non-League Football

The Non-League Club Directory has
developed into a comprehensive record
of competitions within the non-League
game, giving this level of football the

www.non-leagueclubdirectory.co.uk

Club Factfile

Founded: 1890   **Nickname:** Rovers

Previous Names: None

Previous Leagues: Stroud & District 1890-1922, Gloucestershire Northern Senior 1922-67, Gloucestershire Senior 1967-73, Hellenic 1973-82, Southern 1982-89.

Club Colours (change): Green/black/black (All white)

Ground: The New Lawn, Smiths Way, Nailsworth, Gloucestershire GL6 0FG   **(T)** 01453 834 860

Capacity: 5,141 **Seats:** 2,000 **Covered:** 1,000 **Clubhouse:** Yes **Shop:** Yes

Nailsworth is on the A46 between Stroud and Bath. At mini roundabout in town turn up Spring Hill towards Forest Green (signposted) and the stadium is at the top of the hill after the second roundabout.
Satnav users should enter GL6 0ET and not the mail post code. Please note on Matchdays there is a Temporary Traffic Order in place on the highway around the stadium. Car parking is available inside the stadium at £3 per vehicle.

Previous Grounds:

Record Attendance: 4,836 v Derby County - FA Cup 3rd Round 03/01/2009

Record Victory: 8-0 v Fareham Town - Southern League Southern Division 1996-97
Record Defeat: 0-7 v Moor Green - Southern League Midland Division 1985-86

Record Goalscorer: Karl Bayliss

Record Appearances: Alex Sykes

Additional Records: Paid £20,000 to Salisbury City for Adrian Randall. Received £35,000 from Nuneaton Borough for Marc McGregor and from Oxford United for Wayne Hatswell.

Senior Honours:
FA Vase 1981-82. Hellenic League 1981-82. Gloucestershire Senior Cup 1984-85, 85-86, 86-87.
Gloucestershire Senior Professional Cup 1984-85, 86-86, 87-87.

02-03		03-04		04-05		05-06		06-07		07-08		08-09		09-10		10-11		11-12	
Conf	9	Conf	18	Conf	20	Conf	19	Conf	14	Conf	8	Conf	18	Conf	21	Conf	20	Conf	10

FOREST GREEN ROVERS

No.	Date	Comp	H/A	Opponents	Att:	Result	Goalscorers	Pos
	Forest Green							
1	Fri-12-Aug	BSP	H	Stockport County	1848	D 1-1	Styche 21	1
2	Tue-16-Aug	BSP	A	Luton Town	6061	D 1-1	Griffin 52	14
3	Sat-20-Aug	BSP	A	Alfreton Town	686	W 6-1	Turley 4, Griffin 16, Styche 2 (22, 76), Og (Streete) 90, Klukowski 90	7
4	Tue-23-Aug	BSP	H	Braintree Town	1033	L 0-2		11
5	Sat-27-Aug	BSP	A	Ebbsfleet United	889	D 1-1	Styche 71	13
6	Mon-29-Aug	BSP	H	Bath City	1344	W 3-0	Styche 2 (14, 61), Stokes 31	7
7	Sat-03-Sep	BSP	H	Grimsby Town	1181	L 0-1		13
8	Sat-10-Sep	BSP	A	Cambridge United	2408	D 1-1	Griffin 9	13
9	Sat-17-Sep	BSP	H	Southport	873	L 2-3	Norwood 86, Klukowski 90	16
10	Tue-20-Sep	BSP	A	Tamworth	783	W 1-0	Og (Green) 4	12
11	Sat-24-Sep	BSP	A	Lincoln City	2076	D 1-1	McDonald 2	12
12	Tue-27-Sep	BSP	H	Newport County	1203	D 1-1	Griffin 66	14
13	Sat-01-Oct	BSP	H	Mansfield Town	893	D 1-1	Forbes 41	15
14	Sat-08-Oct	BSP	A	Fleetwood Town	1687	D 0-0		13
15	Tue-11-Oct	BSP	A	Hayes & Yeading United	251	L 0-2		16
16	Sat-15-Oct	BSP	H	Kettering Town	823	L 0-1		17
17	Tue-18-Oct	BSP	H	AFC Telford	632	W 2-1	Griffin 31, Og (Killock) 90	14
18	Sat-22-Oct	BSP	A	Stockport County	3391	W 1-0	Klukowski 36	13
19	Sat-05-Nov	BSP	H	Alfreton Town	764	W 4-1	Taylor 3 (49, 77, 80), Griffin 90	13
20	Sat-19-Nov	BSP	A	Braintree Town	1005	W 5-1	Klukowski 2 (6, 78), Griffin 27, Taylor 45, Henderson 80	13
21	Sat-26-Nov	BSP	H	York City	1157	D 1-1	Norwood 90	12
22	Tue-29-Nov	BSP	A	Southport	978	W 3-1	Turley 7, Klukowski 2 (pen 20, 31)	9
23	Sat-03-Dec	BSP	A	Darlington	1693	D 0-0		10
24	Tue-06-Dec	BSP	H	Tamworth	732	W 3-1	Thomson 15, Stokes 39, Klukowski pen 73	9
25	Sat-17-Dec	BSP	H	Lincoln City	969	L 0-2		9
26	Mon-26-Dec	BSP	A	Kidderminster Harriers	2491	L 0-1		11
27	Sun-01-Jan	BSP	H	Kidderminster Harriers	1542	D 1-1	Klukowski 35	10
28	Sat-07-Jan	BSP	A	Mansfield Town	2008	L 0-1		12
29	Sat-21-Jan	BSP	A	Newport County	1325	D 0-0		12
30	Tue-24-Jan	BSP	H	Wrexham	1109	W 1-0	Taylor 48	12
31	Sat-28-Jan	BSP	H	Fleetwood Town	922	L 1-2	Taylor 31	12
32	Sat-18-Feb	BSP	H	Gateshead	751	W 2-1	Wright 25, Henderson 79	12
33	Tue-21-Feb	BSP	A	Kettering Town	830	W 3-1	Collins 2 (2, 40), Klukowski 77	12
34	Sat-25-Feb	BSP	A	Barrow	1194	D 1-1	Klukowski 3	11
35	Sat-03-Mar	BSP	H	Cambridge United	1005	W 2-1	Uwezu 83, Wright 85	11
36	Sat-10-Mar	BSP	A	Grimsby Town	3294	L 1-2	Klukowski pen 18	12
37	Sat-17-Mar	BSP	H	Hayes & Yeading United	781	L 1-3	Uwezu 63	13
38	Tue-20-Mar	BSP	H	Luton Town	975	W 3-0	Klukowski 35, Taylor 2 (74, 89)	11
39	Sat-24-Mar	BSP	A	Wrexham	4451	W 2-1	Taylor 64, Norwood 90	10
40	Tue-27-Mar	BSP	A	AFC Telford	1674	L 0-2		10
41	Sat-31-Mar	BSP	H	Barrow	1070	W 3-0	Klukowski 3 (pen 49, 52, 90)	10
42	Fri-06-Apr	BSP	H	Ebbsfleet United	1058	W 3-1	Forbes 47, Taylor 62, Styche 90	8
43	Mon-09-Apr	BSP	A	Bath City	983	W 2-0	Klukowski 44, Styche 74	9
44	Sat-14-Apr	BSP	A	Gateshead	579	L 0-1		10
45	Sat-21-Apr	BSP	H	Darlington	1131	W 2-0	Forbes 4, Klukowski 67	8
46	Sat-28-Apr	BSP	A	York City	3391	L 0-1		10

CUPS

No.	Date	Comp	H/A	Opponents	Att:	Result	Goalscorers	Pos
1	Sat-29-Oct	FAC 4Q	A	Arlesey Town	343	L 1-2	Hodgkiss 62	
2	Sat-10-Dec	FAT 1	A	Newport County	724	D 0-0		
3	Tue-13-Dec	FAT 1R	H	Newport County	368	L 0-2		

League	
Starts	
Substitute	
Unused Sub	
Cups	
Starts	
Substitute	
Unused Sub	
Goals (Lg)	
Goals (Cup)	

BULMAN	IMUDIA	GRAHAM	TODD	HODGKISS	ROWE	ALLEN	FORBES	STYCHE	NORWOOD	GRIFFIN	KLUKOWSKI	TURK	HENRY	BITTNER	BARTLETT	TURLEY	STOKES	MATTHEWS	MCDONALD	TAYLOR	BANGURA	THOMSON	OSHODI	SANDELL	BOND	UWEZU	HENDERSON	LOCKE	PATERSON	RUSSELL	POOK	WRIGHT	COLLINS
13	12	16	6	2	19	18	11	9	7	10	8	4	15	1	14	5	3	21	17	14	20	21	22	28	30	23	24	30	27	30	4	29	28
X	X	X	X	X	X	X	X	X	X	X	S	S	S	U	U																		
X	U	X		X	X	X	X	X	X	X	S	S	U	U		X	X																
X	U	X		X	X	X	X	X		X	X		U	U		X	X	S	S														
X	S	X		X	X	X	X	X		X	X	S		U		X	X	S	U														
X	U	X		X	X	X	X	X		X	X	S		U		X	X	S	S														
	U	X		X	X	S	X	X	X	S	S	X		X		X	X	U	X														
	U	X		X	X	X	X	X	X	X	S	S		X		X	X	U	S														
		X		X	X	X	X	X	S	X	S	U	U	X		X	X		X	S													
	U	X		X	X	X	X		S	X	S	U		X		X	X		X	X	S												
	U	X		X	X	U	X	X	X	S	X	S		X		X	X		S		X												
U	U	X		X	X	S	X		X	S	X	S		X		X	X		X		X												
	U	X		X	S	U	X		X	X	X	X		X		X	X		X		U	S											
	U	X		X	X	S	X		X	X	X	U		X		X	X		S	S		X											
	U	X		X	U	U	X		X	X	X	S		X			X		X		X	S	X										
		X		X	X	U	X		X	S	S	U		X		S	X				X	X	X	X									
	U	S		X	X	S			X	X	X	U		X		X	X		U		X		X	X									
U	U	X		X	X	X			X	X	S	S		X			X				X	S	X	X									
	U	U		X	X		X		X	X	X	U		X		X	X			U	X	S	X										
	U	U		X	X		X			X	X			U		X	X			X	X	U	X		X	S							
		U		X	X		X			X	X			U		X	X			X	X	S	X		X	S	S						
		U		X	X		X		S	X	X			U		X	X			X	X	U	X		X	S							
		S		X	S				X	S	X			U		X	X			X	X	X	X		X	U	X						
		U		X	X		X		X	U	X			X		X	X			X	U	X	X			S	S						
	U	U		X	S		X			S	X			X		X	X			X		X	X			X	X	U					
		U		X	S		X		S	U	X			X		X	X			X		X	X			X	X	U					
U	U	X		X	X		X		X	S	X	S	U	X			X			X		X				X							
U		S		X		U	X		X	X	X	U		X		X	X			X		X	X			S							
		U		X		U	X		X	X	X	U		X		X	X					X	X			S	X		S				
U		U		X		S	X		X	S	X					X	X			X		X	X			S	X			X			
		U		X		S	X		X	S	X			U		X	X			X		X	X			S	X			X			
		U		X		X			X		X			S		X	X			X		X	X			S	X			X	U	U	
U		S		X					X		X					X	X			X		X	X			U	S			X	S	X	X
U		U		X			S		X		X					X	X			X		X	X				X			X	S	S	X
U		X	U	X			X		X		X					X	X					X				S	S			X	U	X	X
		U	U	X			X		X		X					X	X			X		X	X			S	X			X	S	S	
		X	U	X			X	U	X		X						X			X		X	X			S	X			X	S	S	
		U	U	X			X		X		X					X	X			X		X	X			S	X			X	S	S	
			U	X			X		X		X					X	X			X		S	X			S	X			X	S	U	X
			U	X			X	U	X		X					X	X			X			X			S	S			X	S	X	X
		S	X	X			X	S	X		X					X	X			X						X	S			X	U	U	X
		S		X	U		X	S			X					X	X			X		X	X			X	S			X		U	X
		S		X	U		X	S			X					X	X			X		S	X			X	X			X		U	X
		X		X	S		X	S	X		X						X			X		U	X			X	S			X	U		X
		X	U	X	U		X	S	X		X						X			X		S	X			S	X			X			X
			U	X	X		X	S	X		X					X	X			X		S	X			S				X	U		X
		U	U	X	S		X	S	X		X					X	X			X			X			X				X	U		X
X	U	U		X	X	U	X			S	X	S		S		X	X			X	X	X	X										
	S	X		X	X		X		S	S	X		U	X		X	X			X		X				X		U					
	U	U		X	X		X		S	S	X			X		X	X			X		X	X			X		U					
5	1	21	2	46	22	10	40	9	34	19	38	2	0	19	0	38	45	0	6	27	11	19	30	3	4	8	14	0	0	18	0	3	12
0	1	7	0	0	6	6	1	7	4	9	8	10	1	1	0	1	0	3	5	2	1	9	0	0	0	17	8	0	1	0	7	4	0
8	17	15	9	0	4	6	0	2	0	2	0	8	4	10	1	0	0	2	2	1	2	3	0	0	0	2	0	2	0	0	6	5	0
1	0	1	0	3	3	0	3	0	0	0	3	0	0	2	0	3	3	0	0	3	1	3	2	0	0	2	0	0	0	0	0	0	0
0	1	0	0	0	0	0	0	0	2	3	0	1	0	1	0	0	0	0	0	0	0	0	0	0	0	0	0	0	0	0	0	0	0
0	2	2	0	0	0	1	0	0	0	0	0	0	1	0	0	0	0	0	0	0	0	0	0	0	0	0	0	2	0	0	0	0	0
0	0	0	0	0	0	0	3	8	3	7	18	0	0	0	0	2	2	0	1	10	0	1	0	0	0	2	2	0	0	0	0	2	2
0	0	0	0	1	0	0	0	0	0	0	0	0	0	0	0	0	0	0	0	0	0	0	0	0	0	0	0	0	0	0	0	0	0

PLAYING SQUAD

Existing Players		SN	HT	WT	DOB	AGE	POB	Career	Apps	Goals
GOALKEEPERS										
Rob	Brown	13			23/04/1994	18		Forest Green		
Matt	Bulman	1	6'00"	11 05	14/10/1986	25	Swindon	Swindon Rel 6/06, Salisbury 8/06, Cirencester 7/07,		
								Swindon Supermarine 5/08, Cirencester 6/10,		
								Forest Green 5/11	5	0
Sam	Russell	23	6'00"	10 13	04/10/1982	29	Middlesbrough	Middlesbrough Rel c/s 04, Gateshead (SL) 2/02, Darlington (L) 12/02,		
								Scunthorpe (3ML) 8/03, Darlington 8/04 Rel c/s 07, MK Dons (Trial) 7/07,		
								Rochdale 8/07 Rel c/s 09, Wrexham 8/09, Darlington 5/10,		
								Forest Green 1/12	18	0
DEFENDERS										
Ed	Asafu-Adjaye	16	5'11"	12 04	22/12/1988	23	Southwark	Luton Rel c/s 12, Walton & H (L) 3/07, Salisbury (3ML) 1/08,		
								Histon (L) 3/11, Forest Green 7/12		
Paul	Green	22	5'08"	10 04	15/04/1987	25	Birmingham	Aston Villa, Lincoln C 1/07 Rel c/s 11, Tamworth 8/11,		
								Forest Green 7/12		
Eddie	Oshodi	15	6'00"	11 08	14/01/1992	20	Brent	Watford Rel 8/11, Dag & Red (6WL) 11/10, Rushden & D (3ML) 1/11,		
								Burton (Trial) 9/11, Forest Green 10/11	30	0
Aaron	Racine	21			30/10/1991	20	Littlehampton	Southampton Rel c/s 12, Forest Green 8/12		
Chris	Stokes	3	5'07"	10 02	08/03/1991	21	Trowbridge	Bolton Rel c/s 10, Crewe (L) 3/10, Crewe (Trial) 7/10, Walsall (Trial) 7/10,		
								Swindon Supermarine 10/10, Forest Green 11/10	45	2
Chris	Todd	6	6'01"	11 09	22/08/1981	31	Exeter	Swansea Rel c/s 02, Drogheda 8/02, Exeter 1/03,		
								Torquay £7,000 6/07 Rel 5/10, Salisbury (L) 2/09, Salisbury (5WL) 11/09,		
								Newport C (SL) 1/10, Newport C 5/10, Forest Green 5/11	2	0
Jamie	Turley	5	6'01"	14 00	07/04/1990	22		Wycombe Rel c/s 09, Hitchin (L) 2/08, Hendon (2ML) 11/08,		
								Salisbury 7/09, Forest Green 6/11	39	2
MIDFIELDERS										
Ali	Bangura	4	5'08"	10 07	24/01/1988	24	Freetown, S Leone	Chertsey (Yth), Watford Rel c/s 09, Brighton (L) 3/09,		
								Blackpool 8/09 Rel c/s 10, Mersin Idmanyurdu (Tur) 7/10,		
								FC Gabala (Azer) 1/11, Forest Green 7/11	12	0
Ashley	Brown	26			09/12/1994	17	Newent	Forest Green		
Jamie	Collins	12	6'03"	12 00	28/09/1984	27	Barking	Watford Rel 2/05, Havant & W 2/05, Hampton & R Undisc 7/09,		
								Newport C 10/09, Aldershot 6/11, Forest Green 1/12	12	2
Kieran	Forbes	11	5'04"	11 02	17/08/1990	22	Brent	Watford (Scholar) Rel c/s 08, Wealdstone 8/08,		
								Forest Green 1/11	41	3
Jared	Hodgkiss	2	5'06"	11 02	15/11/1986	25	Stafford	West Brom Rel c/s 09, Aberdeen (5ML) 8/08, Northampton (SL) 3/09,		
								Market Drayton 8/09, Forest Green 10/09	46	0
James	Rowe	19	5'11"	10 03	21/10/1991	20	Oxford	Southampton (Yth), Reading Rel c/s 11, Basingstoke (WE) 10/09,		
								Oxford C (L) 2/10, Lewes (L) 1/11, Forest Green 8/11	28	0
George	Washbourne	24	5'11"					Aston Villa (Yth), Walsall (Yth), Stratford, Nuneaton T c/s 10,		
								Atherstone T (L) 12/11, Forest Green 7/12		
FORWARDS										
Yan	Klukowski	8	6'00"	14 02	01/01/1987	25	Chippenham	Chippenham (Yth), Bath C, Reading (Trial) 4/05,		
								Central Connecticut State University (USA) 8/05, Chippenham (L) 12/06,		
								Ottawa Fury (Can), Cape Cod Crusaders (USA),		
								Western Mass Pioneers (USA) 4/09, Carlisle (Trial) 7/09,		
								Swindon (Trial) 8/09, Chippenham 8/09, Larkhall Ath,		
								Forest Green 8/10	46	18
Omar	Koroma	7	5'10"	12 00	22/10/1989	22	Banjul, Gam	Banjul Hawks (Gam), Watford (Trial) 10/07, Southampton (Trial),		
								Portsmouth 8/08 Rel c/s 09, Norwich (5ML) 8/08, Brondby (Den) (Trial),		
								Forest Green (Trial) 4/12, Forest Green 5/12		
Phil	Marsh	17	5'10"	11 13	15/11/1986	25	St Helens	Man Utd Rel c/s 07, Inverness Caledonian (Trial) 7/07,		
								Blackpool 9/07 Rel c/s 08, Bury (Trial) 7/08, Northwich 8/08 Rel 9/08,		
								Hyde U 10/08 Rel 11/08, Leigh Genesis 12/08, FCUM 3/09,		
								Stalybridge 8/10, Forest Green 5/12		
James	Norwood	20	5'09"	11 04	05/09/1990	21	Eastbourne	Brighton (Yth), C. Palace (Yth), Eastbourne T 7/08, Exeter 7/09 Rel c/s 11,		
								Sutton U (2ML) 11/09, Forest Green (2ML) 8/10, Eastbourne B (L) 1/11,		
								Forest Green 6/11	38	3

		SN	HT	WT	DOB	AGE	POB	From - To	APPS	GOA
Reece	Styche	9	6'01"	12 12	03/05/1989	23	Birmingham	Hednesford, Bromsgrove (L) 9/08, Chasetown 10/09, Forest Green 1/10	16	8
Matty	Taylor	14						Oxford U Rel 4/09, Abingdon U (L) 2/08, Cirencester (L) 3/08, Banbury U (2ML) 9/08, Brackley T (L) 2/09, Didcot T 5/09, North Leigh c/s 10, Cheltenham (Trial) 5/11, Forest Green 9/11	29	10
Magno	Vieira	10	5'09"	11 07	13/02/1985	27	Bahia, Bra	Wigan Rel c/s 05, Northampton (2ML) 1/04, Carlisle (SL) 8/04, Year out, Barnet 7/06 Rel c/s 07, Crawley 6/07 Rel 5/08, Cambridge U (SL) 3/08, Wycombe 6/08 Rel c/s 09, Ebbsfleet 8/09, Fleetwood 7/10, Forest Green 5/12		
Saul	Williams	25			26/05/1994	18		Tottenham (Yth), Watford (Yth), Forest Green 1/12		
Ben	Wright	18	6'02"	13 05	10/08/1988	24	Basingstoke	Basingstoke, Winchester (L) 12/06, Andover (L) 1/07, Carshalton (Dual) 10/07 Perm, Andover (Dual) 2/08, Fleet 3/08, Hampton & R 8/08, Peterborough £50,000 1/09, Kettering (6WL) 3/09, Luton (L) 9/09, Grimsby (2ML) 11/09, Barnet (L) 3/10, Hayes & Yeading (L) 8/10, Crawley Undisc 8/10, Newport C (2ML) 11/10, Hayes & Yeading (SL) 1/11, Braintree 6/11, Forest Green 5/12		

Loanees		SN	HT	WT	DOB	AGE	POB	From - To	APPS	GOA
(F)Robbie	Matthews				02/03/1982	30	Wiltshire	Newport C 8/11 - Salisbury (L) 9/11, Salisbury Undisc 1/12	3	0
(M)Andy	Sandell		5'11"	11 09	08/09/1983	28	Calne	Wycombe 10/11 - Rel 11/11, Chippenham 11/11, Chicago Fire (USA) (Trial) 12/11, Newport C 1/12	3	0
(G)Jonathan	Bond		6'04"	13 02	19/05/1993	19	Hemel Hempstead	Watford 11/11 - Dag & Red (L) 2/12, Bury (SL) 3/12	4	0
(F)Liam	Henderson		6'02"	12 02	28/12/1989	22	Gateshead	York C 11/11, (SL) 1/12 -	22	2
(G)Simon	Locke				15/10/1991	20	Newbury	Reading (2ML) 12/11 -	0	0
(F)Matthew	Paterson		5'10"	10 10	18/10/1989	22	Dunfermline	Southend 1/12 -	1	0

Departures		SN	HT	WT	DOB	AGE	POB	From - To	APPS	GOA
(D)Scott	Bartlett		5'10"	11 00	30/05/1979	32	Salisbury	Bath C 6/10 - Retired 8/11	0	0
(M)Wayne	Turk				21/01/1981	31	Swindon	Newport C (2ML) 10/10 Perm 1/11 - Rel 1/12, Salisbury (L) 11/11, Cirencester 1/12, North Leigh 7/12	12	0
(D)Jake	Thomson		5'11"	11 05	12/05/1989	23	Southsea	Kettering(3ML) 9/11 Perm 1/12 - Newport C 6/12	28	1
(G)James	Bittner		6'02"	13 01	02/02/1982	30	Devizes	Salisbury 6/10 - AFC Totton (SL) 2/11, Hereford 6/12	20	0
(D)Luke	Graham		6'03"	12 07	27/04/1986	26	Kettering	Kettering 7/11 - Hereford 6/12	28	0
(D)Callum	Henry		6'00"	12 10	10/06/1991	21	Cheltenham	Yth - Vauxhall Motors 7/12	1	0
(M)Michael	Pook		5'11"	11 10	22/10/1985	26	Swindon	Maidenhead 1/12 - Maidenhead 7/12	7	0
(F)Tommy	Wright		6'00"	11 12	28/09/1984	27	Kirby Muxloe	Luton 1/12 - Tamworth 7/12	7	2
(F)Charlie	Griffin		6'00"	12 07	25/06/1979	33	Bath	Stevenage 6/11 - Salisbury (SL) 2/12, Bath C 7/12	28	7
(M)Curtis	McDonald		5'10"	10 08	24/03/1988	24	Cardiff	Newport C (SL) 3/11, Perm 5/11 - Brackley (L) 3/12, Brackley 7/12	11	1
(D)Jeffrey	Imudia				19/04/1990	22		Injured 2/11 - Cirencester (Dual) 3/11, Staines (L) 3/12	2	0
(M)Chris	Allen		5'11"	11 10	03/01/1989	23	Bristol	Swindon Supermarine (Dual) 12/10 Perm 6/11 - Rel c/s 12, Staines (L) 12/11, Frome T (L) 3/12	16	0
(M)Adrian	Harvey							Yth -		
(F)Michael	Uwezu		5'06"	12 02	12/12/1990	21	Nigeria	Northampton 11/11 - Rel c/s 12	25	2

Conference Action...

Luton Town's Adam Watkins, shields the ball from Italy's Meduki, during England C's 1-1 draw in the Inter Challenge Trophy. It was Watkin's injury time goal that secured a crucial point.

Photo: Keith Clayton.

GATESHEAD

Chairman: Graham Wood
Secretary: Mike Coulson   **(T)** 07912 869 943   **(E)** mike.coulson@gateshead-fc.com
Additional Committee Members:
Brian Waites

Manager: Ian Bogie
Programme Editor: Jeff Bowron   **(E)** jeffbowron@hotmail.co.uk

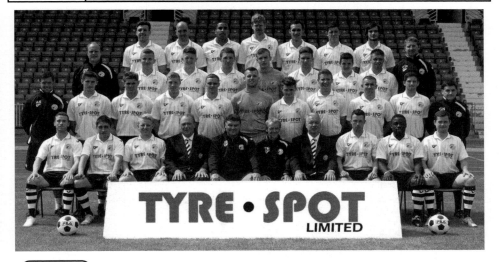

Club Factfile

Founded: 1930   **Nickname:** Tynesiders, The Heed
Previous Names: Gateshead Town, Gateshead United.
Previous Leagues: Football League 1930-60, Northern Counties east 1960-62, North Regional 1962-68, Northern Premier 1968-70, 73-83, 85-86, 87-90, Wearside 1970-71, Midland 1971-72, Alliance/Conf 1983-85, 86-87, 90-98

Club Colours (change): White/black/black & white (Maroon/maroon/maroon & sky blue)

Ground: International Stadium, Neilson Road, Gateshead NE10 0EF   **(T)** 0191 478 3883
Capacity: 11,795 **Seats:** 11,795 **Covered:** 3,300   **Clubhouse:** Yes   **Shop:** Yes

Directions: A1(M) to Washington Services, then A194(M) to first roundabout.
Turn left onto A184 and the ground is situated approximately 3 miles on the left.

Previous Grounds: Redheugh Park 1930-71

Record Attendance: 11,750 v Newcastle United - Friendly 07/08/95
Record Victory: 8-0 v Netherfield - Northern Premier League
Record Defeat: 0-9 v Sutton United - Conference 22/09/90
Record Goalscorer: Paul Thompson - 130
Record Appearances: Simon Smith - 501 (1985-94)
Additional Records: Record transfer fee paid; £9,000 - Paul Cavell, Dagenham & Redbridge 1994
Senior Honours: Record transfer fee received; £150,000 Lee Novak, Huddersfield Town 2009
Northern Premier League 1982-83, 85-86, Northern Premier League play-off 2007-8, Conference North play-off 2008-9,
Durham Challenge Cup 2010-11

10 YEAR RECORD

02-03		03-04		04-05		05-06		06-07		07-08		08-09		09-10		10-11		11-12	
NP P	21	NP P	6	NP P	17	NP P	17	NP P	9	NP P	3	Conf N	2	Conf	20	Conf	15	Conf	8

GATESHEAD

No.	Date	Comp	H/A	Opponents	Att:	Result	Goalscorers	Pos
1	Sat-13-Aug	BSP	A	Kidderminster Harriers	1636	W 3-2	Shaw pen 4, Cummins 19, Gate 80	3
2	Tue-16-Aug	BSP	H	Mansfield Town	825	W 3-0	Shaw 33, Odubade 41, Curtis 59	1
3	Sat-20-Aug	BSP	H	Kettering Town	661	D 1-1	Shaw pen 6	1
4	Tue-23-Aug	BSP	A	Southport	957	W 3-1	Moore 17, Turnbull 75, Shaw pen 84	1
5	Sat-27-Aug	BSP	A	Barrow	1291	W 2-1	Shaw 2 (22, 26)	2
6	Mon-29-Aug	BSP	H	Grimsby Town	1132	W 1-0	Shaw 58	2
7	Sat-03-Sep	BSP	H	Alfreton Town	991	W 2-0	Gate 2 (60, 81)	2
8	Sat-10-Sep	BSP	A	Fleetwood Town	1388	L 1-3	Odubade 90	2
9	Sat-17-Sep	BSP	H	Cambridge United	904	D 1-1	Gillies 33	1
10	Tue-20-Sep	BSP	A	Lincoln City	1587	L 0-1		3
11	Sat-24-Sep	BSP	A	Hayes & Yeading United	218	W 3-2	Shaw 3 (22, 34, 45)	2
12	Tue-27-Sep	BSP	H	York City	1604	W 3-2	Shaw 3 (3, 26, pen 69)	1
13	Sat-01-Oct	BSP	H	Tamworth	770	D 1-1	Curtis 23	1
14	Tue-04-Oct	BSP	H	Wrexham	1258	L 1-4	Gate 62	3
15	Sat-08-Oct	BSP	A	Ebbsfleet United	947	W 1-0	Henderson 40	1
16	Sat-15-Oct	BSP	A	Luton Town	6285	L 1-5	Shaw 77	5
17	Tue-18-Oct	BSP	H	Southport	737	L 2-3	Shaw 23, Odubade 27	7
18	Sat-22-Oct	BSP	A	AFC Telford	2484	W 2-1	Odubade 29, Shaw 84	6
19	Sat-05-Nov	BSP	A	Braintree Town	745	D 2-2	Cummins 35, Brittain 62	6
20	Sat-19-Nov	BSP	A	Alfreton Town	651	D 1-1	Moore 68	6
21	Sat-26-Nov	BSP	A	Fleetwood Town	768	D 1-1	Brittain 11	7
22	Tue-29-Nov	BSP	A	Mansfield Town	1513	D 1-1	Shaw 68	7
23	Tue-06-Dec	BSP	A	Stockport County	2366	W 1-0	Shaw 59	6
24	Sat-17-Dec	BSP	A	Wrexham	3161	L 1-2	Cummins 20	7
25	Mon-26-Dec	BSP	H	Darlington	1522	D 1-1	Brittain 53	8
26	Sun-01-Jan	BSP	A	Darlington	2581	W 1-0	Shaw 90	7
27	Sat-07-Jan	BSP	H	Stockport County	846	W 2-0	Shaw pen 61, Moore 64	7
28	Tue-10-Jan	BSP	H	Kidderminster Harriers	724	W 2-1	Cummins 25, Odubade 47	4
29	Sat-21-Jan	BSP	H	Lincoln City	870	D 3-3	Shaw 28, Odubade 2 (45, 53)	6
30	Tue-24-Jan	BSP	A	Kettering Town	804	L 1-2	Shaw 89	6
31	Sat-28-Jan	BSP	H	Newport County	704	L 2-3	Hatch 45, Shaw 53	8
32	Sat-18-Feb	BSP	A	Forest Green Rovers	751	L 1-2	Cummins 13	8
33	Wed-22-Feb	BSP	A	York City	2683	W 2-1	Cummins 2 (2, 57)	8
34	Sat-03-Mar	BSP	H	Ebbsfleet United	754	L 2-3	Cummins 15, Shaw 90	10
35	Tue-06-Mar	BSP	H	Hayes & Yeading United	465	W 2-0	Gate 34, Shaw 63	8
36	Sat-10-Mar	BSP	A	Braintree Town	650	L 1-3	Chandler 90	9
37	Sat-17-Mar	BSP	A	Cambridge United	2344	W 1-0	Hatch 47	8
38	Tue-20-Mar	BSP	H	Bath City	512	W 1-0	Shaw 67	7
39	Sat-24-Mar	BSP	A	Tamworth	968	D 1-1	Shaw 27	8
40	Sat-31-Mar	BSP	A	Newport County	1261	L 0-1		9
41	Sat-07-Apr	BSP	H	Barrow	701	W 2-0	Gate 37, Cummins 77	8
42	Mon-09-Apr	BSP	A	Grimsby Town	2938	L 0-2		10
43	Sat-14-Apr	BSP	H	Forest Green Rovers	579	W 1-0	Shaw 59	8
44	Sat-21-Apr	BSP	A	Bath City	649	L 2-4	Cummins 72, Hatch 79	11
45	Tue-24-Apr	BSP	H	Luton Town	703	D 0-0		8
46	Sat-28-Apr	BSP	H	AFC Telford	606	W 3-0	Hatch 48, Gillies 53, Gate 71	8

CUPS

No.	Date	Comp	H/A	Opponents	Att:	Result	Goalscorers	
1	Sat-29-Oct	FAC 4Q	H	Hebburn Town	1198	W 3-0	Shaw 2 (53, 61), Fisher 71	
2	Sat-12-Nov	FAC 1	A	Blyth Spartans	2763	W 2-0	Shaw 14, Cummins 54	
3	Sat-03-Dec	FAC 2	A	Tamworth	1163	L 1-2	Fisher 62	
4	Sat-10-Dec	FAT 1	H	Kettering Town	402	W 3-2	Shaw 2 (13, 37), Gate 30	
5	Sat-14-Jan	FAT 2	H	Braintree Town	605	D 2-2	Shaw 15, Chandler 90+1	
6	Tue-17-Jan	FAT 2R	A	Braintree Town	261	D 1-1 aet (W 4-3 pens) Cummins 59		
7	Tue-14-Feb	FAT 3	H	Alfreton Town	347	W 2-1	Shaw pen 38, Curtis 57	
8	Sat-25-Feb	FAT 4	A	Luton Town	2499	L 0-2		

League
Starts
Substitute
Unused Sub

Cups
Starts
Substitute
Unused Sub

Goals (Lg)
Goals (Cup)

FARMAN	ODHIAMBO	CLARK	CURTIS	CARRUTHERS	CUMMINS	GATE	TURNBULL	ODUBADE	SHAW	FISHER	MOORE	NIX	MULLIGAN	BAXTER	PORTER	DEASY	RENTS	GILLIES	ALNWICK	BRITTAIN	MOYES	HENDERSON	BRIGGS	MARWOOD	WILSON	CHANDLER	AIREY	HATCH	MAGNAY	O'BRIEN	DUMMETT
13	2	6	5	20	11	4	8	10	9	12	19	18	15	14	23	1	3	16	24	7	21	25	22	17	27	21	26	15	18	24	25
X	X	X	X	X	X	X	X	X	X	X	X		S	S	S	U															
X	X	X	X	X	X	X	X	X	X	X		S	S	S	U	U															
X	X	X	X	X	X	X	X	X	X	X		S	U	U	U	U	U														
X	X	X	X	X	X	X	X	X	X		S	X		U	U	U	S														
X	X	X	X	X	X	X	X	X	X		U	X		S	S	U	S														
X	X	X	X	X	X	X	X	X		S	X	S	S	S	U	U	X														
X	X	X	X	U	X	X	X	X	X		U	X		U		X	U														
X	X	X	X	U	X	X	X		S	X		X	U		X	U															
X	X	X	X		S	X	X	X	X	X	S		U		X	U															
X	X	X	X	X	X	X	X	X	X	U		S	S		S	X	U														
X	X	X	X	X	X	X	X	X		S		U	S		U	X	U														
X	X	X	X	X	X	X	X	X		U		S	S	U		X	U														
X	X	X	X		X	X	X	X	X	S			S	S		X	X	U	U												
X	X		X	X	X	X	X	X	S			U	S		X	X	U	S	X												
X	U		X	X	X	X	X	X	X	S				X		U	X	U	S		X										
X	U		X	X	X	X	X	X	X	S		S			X		X	U	S		X										
U	U		X	X	X	X	X	X	X	S		U		S		X	X	S		X											
U	X		X	X	U	X	X	X	X	U			X	X		S		X	S		X										
	X	X	X	X	X	X		X	X	S		S	X		U	U		X	X		U										
	X	X	X	X	X	X		X	X	S		S	X			X		U	U		X	X				S					
	X	X	S		X	X		X	X	S	X	X			X		U	X	U	X	U				S						
	X	X	X		X	X		X	X	X		U	U		X	X	X	X	U	S	U										
	X	X	X		X	X		X	X	X		S	U		X	X	X	U	U	S					S						
	X	X	X	X	X	X		X	S	X			X		X	S	U	U	X						S						
	U	X	X		X			X	S	X	X	X	U		X	X	X	S	U	X											
	U	X	X			X	X	X	X	U		X			X	X	X		U						S	U					
	S	X	X	U	X			X	X	X		X			X	X	X		S						S	U					
U	S		X	X	X			X	X		U				X	X	X		U						X		X	S				
U	U	X		X			X		X	X		S			X		X	X		S							X	X	S			
	S	X	X		S			X	X	X		U			X		X	X			U	X	U	X							
U	X	X			X	X	X			S					U		X	X	X		S						U	X			
U		X	X		X	X	X			S					U		X	X		S							U	X			
X		X	X		X	S	X		X						X		U	X	S		X					X		S	U	X	
X		X	X		X	X	S	X							X		U		S		X					X		U	X	X	X
X		X	X		S	X	S	X							X		U			S	X					X		U	X	X	X
X	S	X	X		X	U	X								X		U		U		X					X		S			X	X
X	U	X	X	X	X	S	X								X		U		S		X					X		X				
X		X	X			X		X				S			X		U		S		X					X		X	X	X	X	U
X	U	X		U	X	S		X							X		U		S		X					X		X	X	X	X	
X	X	X			X	X						S			X		U	U	X	X		U				S		X			X	X
X	U	X			X	X		S	X			S			X		U	X	X							S		X			X	X
U	U	X			X	X	S	X	X						X		X	X	S		U					U				S	X	X
U	S	X			X	X	S	X	X						X		X	X	X							U			S		X	X
U	X	X			X	X	X					U			U		X	X	U							S			X	X	X	X
U		X			X	X	X		X						U		X	X	U							S			X	X	S	X
U		S	X	X	U	X	X	X	X	S			S		X			X		X	X	U	X	U							
		X	X	X	X	X	X		X	S		S	U	X			U	U	U	X	X			S							
S		X	X	X		X	X		X	X	X	U	U	X		U	S		X	X	X	U									
X		X	X	S		X	X		X	X	X		S	U		X	X	X	U	S											
U		X	X			X		X	X			X			X		X	X	X	U					S	U	S				
S		X	X	S	X			X	X			S			X		X	X	X	U					X	U	X				
U		X	X			X	X	X	X			S			X		S		X	X	U							U			
U		X	X			X	X	X	X						X		X	X	U						S		S			U	X
25	20	40	38	19	41	36	38	27	43	7	13	2	2	24	0	15	24	19	6	10	1	5	0	5	0	13	1	8	3	11	10
0	5	0	0	2	2	3	3	2	0	13	11	6	12	3	0	0	5	8	0	10	0	1	0	16	0	0	1	3	1	1	0
10	10	0	0	4	1	1	0	0	0	5	3	5	5	13	1	19	6	5	13	8	1	1	0	1	3	0	1	1	4	0	1
0	2	7	8	3	5	6	8	5	7	3	3	0	0	6	0	5	6	4	3	3	0	1	0	1	0	1	0	0	0	1	0
0	2	1	0	2	0	0	0	0	1	3	2	1	1	0	0	1	0	1	0	2	0	2	0	0	0	0	0	2	0	0	0
3	1	0	0	0	1	0	0	0	0	0	0	1	2	1	0	2	1	2	1	3	1	1	0	2	0	0	0	2	0	0	
0	0	0	2	0	10	7	1	7	28	0	3	0	0	0	0	0	0	2	0	3	0	1	0	0	0	1	0	4	0	0	0
0	0	0	1	0	2	1	0	0	7	2	0	0	0	0	0	0	0	0	0	0	0	0	0	0	1	0	0	0	0	0	

PLAYING SQUAD

Existing Players		SN	HT	WT	DOB	AGE	POB	Career	Apps	Goals
GOALKEEPERS										
Adam	Bartlett	1	6'00"	11 11	27/02/1986	26	Newcastle	Newcastle Rel c/s 05, Leeds (Trial), Doncaster (Trial), Aberdeen (Trial), Boston U (Trial), Burton (Trial), Rushden & D (Trial), Rotherham (Trial), Dundee U (Trial), Dunston Fed, USA, Blyth 9/05, Skvastaras (Swe), Consett 7/06, Blyth 8/06, Kidderminster 5/08 Rel 5/09, Cambridge U (L) 5/09, Hereford 6/09, Gateshead 6/12		
Jordan	Nixon	19	5'11"	11 13	27/11/1993	18	Middlesbrough	Middlesbrough (Yth), Darlington 11/10, Gateshead 7/12		
DEFENDERS										
Patrick	Boyle	3	6'00"	12 09	20/03/1987	25	Glasgow	Livingston (Yth), Everton Rel c/s 08, Norwich (5WL) 9/06, Crewe (3ML) 1/08, Dumbarton 1/09, Partick 7/09, Clyde (L) 3/10, Dunfermline 6/11, Gateshead (6ML) 7/12		
Chris	Bush	16	6'03"	14 04	12/06/1992	20	Whipps Cross	Brentford, Salisbury (L) 3/10 (09/10 7,0), Woking (L) 9/10, AFC Wimbledon (4ML) 9/10, Thurrock (L) 3/11, AFC Wimbledon 6/11 Rel c/s 12, Gateshead 6/12		
Luke	Carr	21						Gateshead		
Ben	Clark	6	6'02"	13 00	24/01/1983	29	Consett	Man Utd (Trainee), Sunderland, Hartlepool Undisc 10/04 Rel c/s 10, Gateshead 7/10	40	0
James	Curtis	5	6'05"	13 05	13/04/1982	30	Sunderland	Kenneck Ryhope CA, Washington, Gateshead 6/03	38	2
Lewis	Galpin	22			18/11/1993	18	Hebburn	Middlesbrough (Scholar) Rel c/s 12, Workington (L) 3/12, Gateshead 8/12		
Jack	Lilley	23						Gateshead		
Carl	Magnay	2	6'00"	11 13	27/01/1989	23	Gateshead	Leeds (Yth), Chelsea 7/07 Rel 1/12, MK Dons (L) 1/09, Northampton (L) 3/09, Gateshead 1/12	4	0
Lance	McGlen	25			20/07/1994	18	Newcastle	Carlisle Rel c/s 12, Gateshead 8/12		
Lee	Mole	26						Gateshead		
Michael	Roberts	29			03/11/1993	18	Chester-le-Street	Middlesbrough (Scholar) Rel c/s 12, Workington (L) 3/12, Gateshead 8/12		
Glenn	Wilson	17	6'01"	12 09	16/03/1986	26	Lewisham	C.Palace Rel 5/06, AFC Wimbledon (L) 9/04, Bournemouth (Trial) 2/06, Rushden & D 6/06, Kidderminster (L) 3/07, Crawley 7/07 Rel c/s 12, Fleetwood T (3ML) 10/11, Woking (SL) 3/12, Gateshead 6/12		
MIDFIELDERS										
Jamie	Barton	20			20/11/1993	18	Stockton-on-Tees	Darlington, Gateshead 6/12		
Jamie	Chandler	4	5'07"	11 02	24/03/1989	23	South Shields	Sunderland, Darlington (4ML) 8/09, Darlington 7/10, Gateshead Undisc 1/12	13	1
Michael	Cummins	11	6'00"	12 06	01/06/1978	34	Dublin	Middlesbrough, Port Vale 3/00 Rel c/s 06, Darlington 7/06 Rel c/s 08, Rotherham 5/08 Rel c/s 10, Grimsby 6/10 Rel 5/11, Gateshead 5/11	43	10
Josh	Gilles	7	5'10"	11 06	12/06/1990	22	Sunderland	Sunderland Nissan, Newcastle Blue Star 1/09, Blyth 7/09, Whitley Bay 3/10, Gateshead 6/10	27	2
David	Luke	24						Gateshead		
James	Marwood	15	5'09"	11 05	21/05/1990	22	St Albans	Newcastle (Scholar) Rel c/s 09, Carlisle (Trial) 7/09, Blyth 11/09, Team Northumbria 2/10, Gateshead 6/10, FC Halifax (L) 10/1121		0
Rob	Ramshaw	28			12/11/1993	18	Durham	Darlington, Gateshead 8/12		
Phil	Turnbull	8	5'11"	11 08	07/01/1987	25	South Shields	Hartlepool Rel c/s 07, Gateshead (L) 12/05, Blyth (L) 3/07, York 7/07, Gateshead 2/08	41	1
FORWARDS										
James	Brown	14	5'11"	11 00	03/01/1987	25	Cramlington	Cramlington Jun, Hartlepool Rel c/s 12, Gateshead 6/12		
Nathan	Fisher	12	5'10"	11 06	06/07/1989	23	Northallerton	Middlesbrough (Scholar), Gretna Rel c/s 08, York C (Trial) 7/08, Durham C, Chester-le-Street 12/08, Consett c/s 09, Chester-le-Street, Gateshead 6/10	20	0
Liam	Hatch	9	6'02"	12 03	03/04/1982	30	Hitchin	Herne Bay, Gravesend 6/01, Ashford T (L) 2/02, Barnet £23,000 7/03, Peterborough £150,000 1/08, Darlington (SL) 8/08, Luton (SL) 6/09, Darlington (6ML) 7/10 Perm 1/11, Gateshead Undisc 1/12	11	4
Yemi	Odubade	10	5'07"	11 07	04/07/1984	28	Lagos	Eastbourne T, Yeovil 7/04, Eastbourne B 2/05, Oxford U 1/06 Rel 4/09, Stevenage 5/09 Rel c/s 11, Newport C (SL) 1/11, Gateshead 6/11	29	7
Callum	Patton	27						Chester-le-Street, Gateshead 8/12		
Peter	Ravenhill	30						Gateshead		

Loanees		SN	HT	WT	DOB	AGE	POB	From - To	APPS	GOA
(G)Jak	Alnwick		6'02"		17/06/1993	19	Prudhoe	Newcastle (4ML) 9/11, 1/12 -	6	0
(D)Jeff	Henderson		6'01"	12 01	09/12/1991	20	Ashington	Newcastle (2ML) 10/11 -	6	1
(G)Ben	Wilson		6'01"	11 08	09/08/1992	20	Stanley	Sunderland 1/12 -	0	0
(F)Philip	Airey		5'11"	10 05	14/11/1991	20	Newcastle	Newcastle 1/12 -	2	0
(D)Paul	Dummett		5'10"	10 02	26/09/1991	20	Newcastle	Newcastle (SL) 3/12 -	10	0
Peter	Jameson							Consett (Dual) 3/12		

Departures		SN	HT	WT	DOB	AGE	POB	From - To	APPS	GOA
(F)Gary	Mulligan		6'01"	12 03	23/04/1985	27	Dublin	Northampton 8/10 - Rel 1/12, Brackley 2/12	14	0
(M)Kyle	Nix		5'06"	09 10	21/01/1986	26	Sydney, Aust	Mansfield 7/11 - Rel 1/12, Tamworth 2/12	8	0
(D)Ewan	Moyes				30/03/1990	22		Hibernian 7/11 - Rel 1/12	1	0
(D)Craig	Baxter		5'10"	09 10	27/09/1986	25	Newcastle	Newcastle c/s 06 - Rel c/s 12, Bedlington 7/12	27	0
(M)Kris	Gate		5'07"	10 03	01/01/1985	27	Newcastle	Newcastle 9/07 - Rel c/s 12, Harrogate T 6/12 Rel 7/12 Work Related, Bedlington 7/12	39	7
(M)Chris	Moore		5'08"	11 13	17/01/1984	28	Newcastle	Darlington 7/11 - Rel c/s 12	24	3
(M)Alan	O'Brien		5'10"	10 10	20/02/1985	27	Dublin	Yeovil 2/12 - Rel c/s 12	12	0
(G)Tim	Deasy		6'01"	13 05	01/10/1985	26	Salford	Barrow 8/10 - Rel c/s 12	15	0
(G)Paul	Farman		6'05"	14 06	02/11/1989	22	North Shields	Blyth 6/09 - Rel c/s 12, Lincoln C (2ML) 11/11, Lincoln C 5/12	25	0
(D)Chris	Carruthers		5'10"	12 03	19/08/1983	29	Kettering	York C 7/11 - Rel c/s 12, Hereford 7/12	21	0
(D)Eddie	Odhiambo (Was Anaclet)		5'09"	10 00	31/08/1985	27	Arusha, Tanzania	Newport C 6/11 - Rel c/s 12	25	0
(D)Sam	Rents		5'09"	11 03	22/06/1987	25	Brighton	Crawley 5/11 - Rel c/s 12, Sutton U 7/12	29	0
(M)Rob	Briggs				29/12/1991	20		Yth - Rel c/s 12, Blyth (L) 11/11	0	0
(M)Martin	Brittain		5'08"	10 07	29/12/1984	27	Newcastle	Kidderminster 6/09 - Rel c/s 12	20	3
(F)Jon	Shaw		6'00"	13 01	10/11/1983	28	Sheffield	Mansfield 5/10 - Rel c/s 12, Luton 6/12	43	28
(G)Chris	Porter		6'02"	12 03	17/07/1979	32	Middlesbrough	Billingham Syn 11/10 - Darlington 6/12	0	0

Conference Action...

Grimsby's James McGowen saves Nathan Arnold's, Alfreton Town, shot during this high scoring Conference game which the Mariners won 5-2.

Photo: Bill Wheatcroft.

GRIMSBY TOWN

Chairman: John Fenty
Secretary: Ian Fleming   **(T)** 07711 188 542   **(E)** ian@gtfc.co.uk
Additional Committee Members:
John Elsom, Mike Chapman.

Manager: Paul Hurst & Rob Scott
Programme Editor: Jack Johnson   **(E)** jack@gtfc.co.uk

Club Factfile

Founded: 1878   **Nickname:** The Mariners
Previous Names: Grimsby Pelham 1878-79
Previous Leagues: Football League 1892-2010

Club Colours (change): Black & white stripes/black/red (All royal blue)

Ground: Blundell Park, Cleethorpes, North East Lincolnshire DN35 7PY   **(T)** 01472 605 050
Capacity: 10,033 **Seats:** Yes   **Covered:** Yes   **Clubhouse:** Yes   **Shop:** Yes

Directions: From the North/West All routes follow M180 onto the A180 to Grimsby. At first roundabout go straight on then follow signs for Cleethorpes (A180) onto Grimsby Road. Blundell Park is situated behind the Drive Thru' McDonalds. From the South A46 (Lincoln) Follow A46 into Grimsby, go straight on at roundabout after dual carriageway, following signs to Cleethorpes. At the 'Grimsby Institute' get in the right hand lane and keep following signs for Cleethorpes. At Isaac's Hill roundabout turn left onto Grimsby Road, the ground is on the right hand side behind the Drive Thru' at McDonalds.

Previous Grounds: Clee Park, Abbey Park

Record Attendance: 31,657 v Wolverhampton Wanderers - FA Cup 5th Round 20/02/1937
Record Victory: 9-2 v Darwen - Division 2 15/04/1899
Record Defeat: 1-9 v Arsenal - Division 1 28/01/1931
Record Goalscorer: Pat Glover - 180 (1930-39)
Record Appearances: John McDermott - 754 (1987-2007)
Additional Records: Paid £500,000 to Preston North End for Lee Ashcroft 11/08/1998
Senior Honours: Received £1.5m from Everton for John Oster July 1997
Football League Division 2 1900-01, 33-34, Division 3 North 1925-26, 55-56, Division 3 1979-80, Division 4 1971-72.
Division 2 Play-offs 1997-98.
League Group Cup 1982. Auto Windscreen Shield 1998.

10 YEAR RECORD

02-03		03-04		04-05		05-06		06-07		07-08		08-09		09-10		10-11		11-12	
FL 1	24	FL 2	21	FL 2	18	FL 2	4	FL 2	15	FL 2	16	FL 2	22	FL 2	23	Conf	11	Conf	11

GRIMSBY TOWN

No.	Date	Comp	H/A	Opponents	Att:	Result	Goalscorers	Pos
1	Sat-13-Aug	BSP	H	Fleetwood Town	4061	L 0-2		24
2	Tue-16-Aug	BSP	A	Braintree Town	1006	L 0-5		24
3	Sat-20-Aug	BSP	A	Newport County	1675	D 0-0		24
4	Tue-23-Aug	BSP	H	Cambridge United	2616	W 2-1	Thompson 28, Duffy 64	18
5	Sat-27-Aug	BSP	H	Darlington	2887	L 1-2	Makofo 51	20
6	Mon-29-Aug	BSP	A	Gateshead	1132	L 0-1		23
7	Sat-03-Sep	BSP	A	Forest Green Rovers	1181	W 1-0	Coulson 44	17
8	Sat-10-Sep	BSP	H	Hayes & Yeading United	2835	W 3-0	Duffy 2 (32, 47), Wood 86	15
9	Sat-17-Sep	BSP	A	Stockport County	3943	L 0-2		17
10	Tue-20-Sep	BSP	H	Kettering Town	2470	W 2-1	Elding 54, Coulson 84	16
11	Sat-24-Sep	BSP	H	Wrexham	3515	L 1-3	Hearn 29	17
12	Tue-27-Sep	BSP	A	Kidderminster Harriers	1807	D 1-1	Elding 90	16
13	Sat-01-Oct	BSP	H	Alfreton Town	2941	W 5-2	Hearn 4 (57, 60, 70, 86), Elding 90	14
14	Sat-08-Oct	BSP	A	Mansfield Town	2982	L 1-2	Coulson 31	15
15	Tue-11-Oct	BSP	H	Barrow	2675	W 5-2	Hearn 3 (5, 45, 76), Elding 2 (83, 85)	12
16	Sat-15-Oct	BSP	A	York City	3872	L 1-2	Disley 4	14
17	Tue-18-Oct	BSP	A	Ebbsfleet United	1143	L 1-3	Elding 1	15
18	Fri-21-Oct	BSP	H	Luton Town	3239	L 0-1		15
19	Sat-05-Nov	BSP	A	Bath City	993	D 2-2	Makofo 2 (11, 51)	16
20	Sat-19-Nov	BSP	H	Newport County	2701	D 2-2	Makofo 79, Elding pen 87	16
21	Sat-26-Nov	BSP	A	Kettering Town	1354	W 2-1	Hearn 2 (13, 63)	16
22	Tue-29-Nov	BSP	H	Stockport County	2254	W 7-0	Coulson 18, Hearn 3 (22, 45, 58), Elding 32, Green 35, I'Anson 64	15
23	Tue-06-Dec	BSP	H	Mansfield Town	2553	D 0-0		15
24	Sat-17-Dec	BSP	H	Ebbsfleet United	2818	W 4-3	Hearn 2 (2, 13), Antwi 11, Coulson 49	15
25	Mon-26-Dec	BSP	A	Lincoln City	5506	W 2-1	Garner 52, Hearn 61	13
26	Sun-01-Jan	BSP	H	Lincoln City	6672	W 3-1	Hearn 25, Coulson 45, Elding pen 52	11
27	Sat-07-Jan	BSP	A	Alfreton Town	1924	W 5-2	Hearn 2 (11, 40), Coulson 29, Garner 61, Duffy 90	10
28	Tue-10-Jan	BSP	A	Cambridge United	2436	W 1-0	Elding 24	9
29	Sat-21-Jan	BSP	H	Bath City	3836	W 6-0	Hearn 3 (21, 46, 57), Og (Gallinagh) 41, Hughes-Mason 77, Church 85	9
30	Tue-24-Jan	BSP	A	Barrow	1081	D 2-2	Hearn 10, Garner 73	9
31	Sat-28-Jan	BSP	H	AFC Telford	3704	W 2-1	Duffy 81, Artus 89	7
32	Fri-17-Feb	BSP	A	Southport	1934	W 2-1	Miller 45, Hearn 82	6
33	Sat-03-Mar	BSP	H	Braintree Town	3688	D 1-1	Hearn 65	8
34	Tue-06-Mar	BSP	A	Fleetwood Town	2447	L 1-2	Og (Cavanagh) 19	9
35	Sat-10-Mar	BSP	H	Forest Green Rovers	3294	W 2-1	Hearn 13, Townsend 90	7
36	Tue-13-Mar	BSP	H	York City	4250	L 2-3	Elding 74, Coulson 81	7
37	Sat-17-Mar	BSP	H	Tamworth	3206	D 0-0		9
38	Tue-20-Mar	BSP	A	Hayes & Yeading United	392	W 2-1	Duffy 30, Pearson 56	8
39	Sat-24-Mar	BSP	A	Luton Town	6419	D 1-1	Hughes-Mason 87	9
40	Tue-27-Mar	BSP	A	Tamworth	892	D 1-1	Hearn 61	7
41	Sat-31-Mar	BSP	H	Kidderminster Harriers	3194	L 1-2	Wright 39	8
42	Sat-07-Apr	BSP	A	Darlington	2212	D 0-0		9
43	Mon-09-Apr	BSP	H	Gateshead	2938	W 2-0	Pearson 2 (16, 56)	8
44	Sat-14-Apr	BSP	A	Wrexham	2917	D 2-2	Elding 64, Thanoj 82	9
45	Sat-21-Apr	BSP	A	AFC Telford	2676	D 0-0		9
46	Sat-28-Apr	BSP	H	Southport	3738	L 0-1		11

CUPS

No.	Date	Comp	H/A	Opponents	Att:	Result	Goalscorers	
1	Sat-29-Oct	FAC 4Q	H	Ashington	1540	W 5-0	Duffy 5, Hearn 2 (38, 40), Eagle 73, Southwell 78	
2	Sat-12-Nov	FAC 1	H	Port Vale	4450	D 0-0		
3	Sat-03-Dec	FAC 2	A	Salisbury City	2161	D 0-0		
4	Sat-10-Dec	FAT 1	H	Darlington	1527	W 3-0	Coulson 2 (21, 49), Elding 44	
5	Tue-13-Dec	FAC 2R	H	Salisbury City	1880	L 2-3 aet	Duffy 2 (90, 92)	
6	Sat-14-Jan	FAT 2	H	AFC Hornchurch	2415	W 4-0	Elding 3 (10, 28, 45), Townsend 71	
7	Tue-07-Feb	FAT 3	A	Bath City	546	W 2-1	Elding 53, Duffy 82	
8	Sat-25-Feb	FAT 4	H	York City	3662	L 0-1		

	League
	Starts
	Substitute
	Unused Sub

	Cups
	Starts
	Substitute
	Unused Sub

	Goals (Lg)
	Goals (Cup)

Player appearance and goals grid:

	MCKEOWN	SILK	I'ANSON	GARNER	RIDLEY	DISLEY	THANOJ	MAKOFO	ELDING	HEARN	COULSON	WOOD	ARTUS	SPENCER	PEARSON	EAGLE	KEMPSON	DUFFY	THOMPSON	CHURCH	FREEMAN	GREEN	SOUTHWELL	TOWNSEND	ARTHUR	PANTHER	ANTWI	MCCARTHY	MILLER	HUGHES-MASON	SOARES	CROUDSON	WINN	WRIGHT
Squad no.	13	2	26	6	3	8	21	18	39	10	7	19	11	9	15	29	5	12	16	4	27	17	20	22	1	23	28	25	32	33	40		36	34
	X	X	X		X	X	X	X	X	X	X		S	S	S	U	U																	
	X		X		X	U	X	X	X	X	X	X	S		S		U		U	S	S													
	X	U			X	X	U	S	X	X	X	X	S		X	X	X		X	X	X													
	X	U		X	X		X	S	X	X	X	X	U		X	X	X	U	X	X	X													
	X	S		X	X		X	U	X	X	X	X	S		X	X	X	U	X	X	X													
	X	X		X			S	S	X	X	X	X	S		X	X	X		U	X	U													
	X	U		X		X	S	X	X	X	X	U	X		S	X	S		U		X		X												
	X	U		X		X	S	X	X	X	U	X	S		X	X	S		X		X													
	X	U		X		X	S	X	X	X	X	X	S		X	X	S		X		X	U												
	X	U			X	U	X	X	X	S	X	U	X		X	X	U		X		X		X											
	X	U			X	X	U	X	X	S	X	S	U		X	X	X		S		X		X											
	X	S	X	U	X	U	X	X	S		X		U		X	U	X		X		X													
	X	S		U	X	X	X		S		X		U		X	U	X		S		X		X											
	X	S		X	X	X			S	S	X	X	X		U		X		X		X		X											
	X	X		X	X	X			X	S	X	X	U		U		S		U		X		X											
	X	X		X	X	X	U		X		X	X	U		U		X		U		X		X											
	X	X	X			X	X		X	X	S	X	U		U		S		X	S	X													
	X	X	X			X	X		X	X	X	U	S		U		S		X		X													
	X	U	X			X	X	X			X	U			U				X		X			U		X								
	X	X				X	X	X	S	X			X		U		S	S	X		X			U		X	X	X						
	X	X				X	U	X			X			U		U			S		X			X		X	X	S						
	X	X				X	S	X	X	X	X	U			S			U			X			X		X	X							
	X	U	X			X	S		X	X	X	X		U				U			X			X		X	X	X						
	X	U	X			X	S	U	X	X	X	X		S				U			X			X		X	X	X						
		X	S			X	S	U	X	X	X	X		S		X		U			X			X		X	X							
	X	U		X			X	S	U	X	X	X	X		U				U		X			X		X	U	X						
	X	X		X			X	X	U	X	X	X			X				S		X			X			U	X	S					
	X	X		X			X	X	X	X	X	X			X				U		X			X			U	X	U					
	X	X		X			X	X	X	X	U	X			X				S	S	X			X				X	S					
	X	X		X			X	X	X	X	X				X				S	U	X			X			U	X	U					
	X	X	U	X			X	X			X	X	U		X				S		X			X			X	S						
	X	X		X			X	X		X	U	X			S				S	S	X			X				X		U				
	X	X	U	U			X	X			X	X			X				X		X		U	X			X	S	X					
	X	X	U				X	S			X	X			U				X		X			X			X	X						
	X	X	U				X	S		X	X			X	U				S		X			U	X		X	U	X		S			
	X	X		U			X	X			X	X			X				S		X			X			X	U	X		X			
	X	X		U			X	X			X	S			X				S	S	X			X			X	S	S		X			
	X	X			U			X	U		X				X				X		X			X			X	S	U		X			
	X	U					X	S			X				X				X		X			X			X	S	S		X	X		
	X		U				X	X		X	X	S			X				S		X			X			X	S	X			U	X	
	X		U					X	X	X	X	X			X				S	S	X			X			X	S	U			X	X	
	X	X	U	X				X				X	S		X	S		S			X			X					U	X	X	X		
	X	U	X				X				X	S		X	X	X		X			X			X				U	X		S			
	X	X		U				X			X	S		X	X	X	X				X			X			X	X	S		U			
	X		U					X	X	X	X	X			X				S		X			X			X	U	X		X			
	X	X					X	X			X				S		X				X	X	U		U	X							S	

Reserves / lower block:

	MCKEOWN	SILK	I'ANSON	GARNER	RIDLEY	DISLEY	THANOJ	MAKOFO	ELDING	HEARN	COULSON	WOOD	ARTUS	SPENCER	PEARSON	EAGLE	KEMPSON	DUFFY	THOMPSON	CHURCH	FREEMAN	GREEN	SOUTHWELL	TOWNSEND	ARTHUR	PANTHER	ANTWI	MCCARTHY	MILLER	HUGHES-MASON	SOARES	CROUDSON	WINN	WRIGHT
	X	U	X			X	X	X	S	X	X	X	U				U	S	X	X					S	X	U							
	X	U	X			X	X	S	S	X	X	X	X	S	U	U			X	X		U		X		X								
	X	U	X			X	S		X	X	X	X	X	U	U	X		U	S			X			X		X		U					
	X	U	X			X	S		X	X	X	X	X	S		U		S				X			X		X	X						
	X	U	X	U		X	U	S	X	X	X	X	S	U	X		S					X		X			X							
	X	X	U	X			X	U	X	X	X	X	S	X		X			S					S	X		X							
	X	X	U	X			X	X	U	X	X	X		X				X		S		S		S	X									
	X	X	X				X	X	S			X	X	S				X	X	U		U	X							U				

Totals:

	MCKEOWN	SILK	I'ANSON	GARNER	RIDLEY	DISLEY	THANOJ	MAKOFO	ELDING	HEARN	COULSON	WOOD	ARTUS	SPENCER	PEARSON	EAGLE	KEMPSON	DUFFY	THOMPSON	CHURCH	FREEMAN	GREEN	SOUTHWELL	TOWNSEND	ARTHUR	PANTHER	ANTWI	MCCARTHY	MILLER	HUGHES-MASON	SOARES	CROUDSON	WINN	WRIGHT
	46	21	12	13	12	44	14	15	27	42	38	28	23	1	27	3	18	17	3	15	0	5	0	27	0	7	4	4	20	2	8	0	6	4
	0	3	1	1	0	0	9	3	16	0	5	4	6	6	3	8	1	18	0	6	0	1	1	0	0	0	0	0	1	0	9	3	0	4
	0	5	18	6	0	0	10	5	1	0	0	6	10	3	15	4	0	6	1	7	1	1	5	0	0	0	0	4	0	7	4	0	2	0
	8	3	6	2	0	7	5	1	5	8	8	5	2	0	5	0	2	3	0	1	0	1	0	8	0	4	1	3	0	0	0	0	0	0
	0	0	0	0	0	0	2	3	0	0	2	3	0	0	1	0	5	0	1	0	0	3	0	0	0	0	0	0	0	0	0	0	0	0
	0	5	2	1	0	0	1	2	0	0	0	0	2	3	3	0	1	0	0	0	1	1	1	0	1	0	1	0	0	0	1	0	0	0
	0	0	1	3	0	1	1	4	12	27	8	1	1	0	3	0	0	6	1	1	0	1	0	1	0	1	0	0	1	0	1	2	0	1
	0	0	0	0	0	0	0	0	5	2	2	0	0	0	1	0	4	0	0	0	0	1	1	0	0	0	0	0	0	0	0	0	0	0

PLAYING SQUAD

Existing Players		SN	HT	WT	DOB	AGE	POB	Career	Apps	Goals
GOALKEEPERS										
Steve	Croudson	34	6'00"	11 13	24/11/1980	31	Grimsby	Grimsby, Scunthorpe (L) 8/01, York C (Trial) 7/03, Boston U 8/03 Rel c/s 04, Grimsby (Trial) 7/04, Stevenage NC 8/04, Kettering 12/04, Halifax 3/05 Rel 4/05, Bangor C 8/05, Rhyl 12/06, Cammell Laird 7/07, Grimsby (Pl/Gk Coach)	0	0
Greg	Fleming	1	5'11"	12 09	27/09/1986	25	Dunfermline	Livingston, Gretna 6/05 Rel c/s 08, Oldham 6/08 Rel 1/11, Dunfermline (SL) 7/09, Galway U 1/11, Chesterfield 7/11 Rel c/s 12, Grimsby 7/12		
James	McKeown	13	6'01"	13 07	24/07/1989	23	Sutton Coldfield	Coventry (Yth), Walsall Rel c/s 07, Peterborough 7/07 Rel 1/11, Kettering (L) 8/07, Worcester (L) 10/07, Boston (5ML) 8/10, Alfreton 1/11, RKSV Leonidas (Holl) 1/11, Grimsby 7/11 46		0
DEFENDERS										
Simon	Ford	14	6'01"	12 04	17/11/1981	30	Newham	Charlton (Scholar), Grimsby 7/01 Rel c/s 04, Bristol R 8/04 Rel 8/04, Redbridge 8/04, Kilmarnock 10/04 Rel c/s 10, Chesterfield 7/10 Rel c/s 12, Grimsby 7/12		
Sam	Hatton	2	5'11"	11 02	07/02/1988	24	St Albans	St Albans (Yth), Stevenage, Northwood (L) 3/06, Yeading (2ML) 9/06, Maidenhead (L) 11/06, Yeading (L) 2/07, AFC Wimbledon 5/07 Rel c/s 12, Grimsby 6/12		
Ian	Miller	6	6'02"	12 01	23/11/1983	28	Colchester	Bury T, Ipswich 9/06, Boston U (2ML) 11/06, Darlington (2ML) 2/07, Darlington (6ML) 7/07 Perm 1/08 Rel 12/11, Grimsby 1/12	20	1
Shaun	Pearson	5			28/04/1989	23	York	Spalding U, Stamford 6/08, Boston U 8/09, Grimsby Undisc 6/11	30	3
Aswad	Thomas	3	5'10"	11 06	09/08/1989	23	Westminster	Charlton Rel c/s 09, Accrington (SL) 1/08, Barnet (L) 8/08, Lewes (3ML) 9/08, Woking 6/09, Braintree 6/11, Grimsby Undisc 7/12		
Bradley	Wood	19	5'08"	11 00	02/09/1991	20	Leicester	Grimsby	32	1
MIDFIELDERS										
Frankie	Artus	11	6'00"	12 10	27/09/1988	23	Bristol	Bristol C, Exeter (2ML) 8/07, Brentford (2ML) 8/08, Kettering (L) 1/09, Cheltenham (SL) 3/09, Cheltenham (L) 8/09, Cheltenham (L) 10/09, Chesterfield (6WL) 1/10, Cheltenham 7/10 Rel c/s 11, Grimsby 7/11	29	1
Joe	Colbeck	7	5'10"	10 12	29/11/1986	25	Bradford	Bradford C, Darlington (L) 10/07, Oldham Undisc 9/09, Hereford 7/10, Grimsby 6/12		
Craig	Disley	8	5'10	11 00	24/08/1981	31	Worksop	Mansfield, Bristol R 7/04 Rel c/s 09, Shrewsbury 7/09 Rel c/s 11, Grimsby 6/11	44	1
Derek	Niven	4	5'11"	12 05	12/12/1983	28	Falkirk	Stenhousemuir (Trainee), Raith 10/00, Bolton 11/01, Chesterfield (2ML) 12/03, Chesterfield 3/04 Rel c/s 12, Northampton (L) 10/11, Grimsby 7/11		
Nathan	Pond	22			05/01/1985	26		Lancaster, Fleetwood, Bamber Bridge (Trial) 7/05, Kendal T (L) 12/10, Grimsby (L) 8/12		
Louis	Soares	17	5'11"	13 05	08/01/1985	27	Reading	Reading Rel c/s 05, Tamworth (2ML) 2/05, Bristol R (L) 5/05, Barnet 8/05 Rel 5/06, Aldershot 5/06, Southend 7/10 Rel c/s 11, Hayes & Yeading 8/11, Grimsby 1/12	11	0
Andi	Thanoj	21			19/12/1992	19		Grimsby	23	1
FORWARDS										
Andy	Cook	12	6'01"	11 04	18/10/1990	21	Bishop Auckland	Carlisle, Workington (2ML) 2/09, Workington (L) 8/09, Barrow (3ML) 10/09, Barrow (2ML) 8/10, Barrow 1/11, Grimsby 6/12		
Anthony	Elding	9	6'01"	13 10	16/04/1982	30	Boston	Notts Forest (Yth), Lincoln C (Yth), Grimsby (Yth), Boston U, Bedford T (L) 9/01, Tottenham (Trial) 1/02, Bolton (Trial) 1/02, Gainsborough (L) 2/03, Stevenage 2/03, Kettering £20,000 + 1/06, Boston U 5/06, Stockport Undisc 1/07, Leeds Undisc 1/08, Crewe £175,000 7/08, Lincoln C (3ML) 1/09, Kettering (2ML) 11/09 (09/10 8,3), Ferncvaros (Hun) 1/10, Rochdale 7/10, Stockport (SL) 1/11, Grimsby Undisc 7/11	43	12
Liam	Hearn	10	5'10"		27/08/1985	27		Santos, Hucknall c/s 06, Eastwood T 10/07, Chasetown 1/08, Quorn 1/08, Alfreton 9/08, Grimsby Undisc 6/11	42	27
Greg	Pearson	18	6'00"	12 00	03/04/1985	27	Birmingham	West Ham, Barnet (SL) 2/04, Lincoln C (L) 8/04, Grimsby (Trial) 11/04, Canvey Island (L) 12/04, Rushden & D 7/05, Hucknall (L) 2/06, Bishops Stortford 2/07, Burton Undisc 7/08 Rel c/s 12, Aldershot T (6WL) 11/11, Crewe (3ML) 1/12, Grimsby 7/12		
Dayle	Southwell	20			20/10/1993	18		Grimsby	1	0

Loanees	SN	HT	WT	DOB	AGE	POB	From - To	APPS	GOA
(D)Conor Townsend							Hull C (SL) 10/11 -	27	1
(M)Manny Panther		6'00"	13 07	11/05/1984	28	Glasgow	Aldershot 11/11 -	7	0
(M)Luke McCarthy		5'09"	10 10	07/07/1993	19	Bolton	Bury (5WL) 11/11 -	5	0
(D)Will Antwi		6'02"	12 08	19/10/1982	29	Ashford, Kent	Luton (5WL) 11/11 - Rel 1/12, Staines 2/12	4	1
(M)Peter Winn		6'00"	11 08	19/12/1988	23	Cleethorpes	Stevenage (SL) 3/12 - Rel c/s 12, Macclesfield 6/12	10	0
(M)Andrew Wright		6'01"	13 07	15/01/1985	27	Formby	Scunthorpe 3/12 - Rel c/s 12, Morecambe 5/12	4	1

Departures	SN	HT	WT	DOB	AGE	POB	From - To	APPS	GOA
(M)Tyrone Thompson		5'09"	11 02	08/05/1981	31	Sheffield	Mansfield 8/11 - Rel 8/11, FC Halifax 10/11, Lincoln C 11/11	3	1
(D)Lee Ridley		5'10"	12 10	05/12/1981	30	Scunthorpe	Cheltenham 6/10 - Gainsborough 11/11	12	0
(D)Darran Kempson		6'02"	12 13	06/12/1984	26	Blackpool	Accrington 6/10 - Rel 12/11, Alfreton 1/12	19	0
(F)Sam Mulready				06/05/1993	19	Kings Lynn	Yth - North Ferriby (L) 9/11, Boston U (L) 10/11, Gainsborough (2ML) 11/11 Perm 1/12, Brigg T (L) 1/12, Brigg T (L) 3/12		
(F)Damian Spencer		6'01"	14 05	19/09/1981	30	Ascot	Aldershot 6/11 - Rel 1/12, Windsor 3/12	7	0
(M)Robert Eagle		5'08"	11 08	23/02/1987	25	Leiston	Inverness Caledonian 8/10 - Rel 1/12, Alfreton (2ML) 11/11, Lowestoft 1/12	11	0
(G)Kenny Arthur		6'04"	13 08	02/12/1978	33	Bellshill	Rochdale 6/10 - Rel 4/12, Gainsborough (2ML) 11/11	10	0
(M)Anthony Church				29/03/1987	25	Newham	Boston U Undisc 7/11 - Rel c/s 12, Alfreton (2ML) 11/11	21	1
(F)Kiernon Hughes-Mason		5'08"	10 05	22/10/1991	20	Hackney	Kettering 1/12 - Rel c/s 12, Welling 5/12	11	2
(D)Gary Silk		5'09"	13 07	13/09/1984	27	Newport, IOW	Mansfield 6/11 - Rel c/s 12, Boston U 8/12	24	0
(F)Robert Duffy		6'01"	12 04	02/12/1982	29	Swansea	Mansfield Undisc 1/11 - Rel c/s 12, Lincoln C 5/12	35	6
(D)Scott Garner		6'02"	13 02	20/09/1989	22	Coventry	Mansfield 7/10 Rel c/s 12 - Cambridge U 6/12	14	3
(M)Michael Coulson		5'10"	10 00	04/04/1988	24	Scarborough	Barnsley 5/10 - Rel c/s 12, York C 6/12	43	8
(D)Charlie I'Anson				01/07/1993	19		Yth - Rel c/s 12	13	1
(F)Serge Makofo		5'10"	12 05	22/10/1986	25	Kinshasa	Kettering 1/11 - Rel c/s 12	18	4
(D)Josh Freeman				08/09/1993	18	Grimsby	Yth -	0	0
(D)Jamie Green		5'07"	10 07	18/08/1989	22	Rossington	Rotherham 9/11 -	6	1

Conference Action...

Challinor, York City, does his best to stop the cross from Luton Town's Howells getting into the box during the Play-off Final.

Photo: Keith Clayton.

HEREFORD UNITED

Chairman: David Keyte
Secretary: Lee Symonds   **(T)** 0844 2761 939   **(E)** club@herefordunited.co.uk
Additional Committee Members:
Grenville Smith MBE, Linda Richards, Dave Preedy, Nick Nenadich, Terry Emmett.

Manager: Martin Foyle
Programme Editor: Jamie Griffiths&Mark Farmer   **(E)** webpages@herefordunited.co.uk

Club Factfile

Founded: 1924   **Nickname:** The Bulls
Previous Names: St Martins and RAOC amalgamated in 1924 to form Hereford United.
Previous Leagues: Birminham. Birmingham Combination. Southern 1939-72. Football League 1972-97, 2006-12. Conference 1997-2006.

Club Colours (change): White/black/white (Red & black stripes/white/red & black)

Ground: Edgar Street Athletic Ground, Blackfriars Street, Hereford HR4 9JU   **(T)** 0844 2761 939
Capacity: 8,843   **Seats:** 2,761   **Covered:** 6,082   **Clubhouse:** Yes   **Shop:** Yes

Directions

Edgar Street is in the heart of the City of Hereford.

The main road, Edgar Street, which lends it's name to the ground is the main A49 which runs directly through Hereford City Centre in a North-South direction.

Previous Grounds: None

Record Attendance: 18,114 v Sheffield Wednesday - FA Cup 3rd Round 04.01.1958
Record Victory: (League) 6-0 v Burnley (A) - Division Four 24.01.1987
Record Defeat: (League) 1-7 v Mansfield Town - Division Three
Record Goalscorer: (League) Stewart Phillips - 93, 1980-91. Goals in a Season - Dixie McNeil - 35, 1975-76.
Record Appearances: (League) Mel Pejic - 412, 1980-92.
Additional Records: Received £440,000 from Queen's Park Rangers for Darren Peacock 1990.
Senior Honours: Paid £80,000 to Walsall for Dean Smith 1994.
Football League Division Three 1974-76. Southern League Division One 1958-59. Welsh Cup 1989-90.

10 YEAR RECORD

02-03		03-04		04-05		05-06		06-07		07-08		08-09		09-10		10-11		11-12	
Conf	6	Conf	2	Conf	2	Conf	2	FL 2	16	FL 2	3	FL 1	21	FL 2	16	FL 2	21	FL 2	23

HEREFORD UNITED

No.	Date	Comp	H/A	Opponents	Result	
1	Sa 06Aug	LGE 2	A	Southend United	L	1 - 0
2	**Tu 09Aug**	**CC 1**	**H**	**Brentford**	**W**	**1 - 0**
3	Sa 13Aug	LGE 2	H	Morecambe	L	0 - 3
4	Tu 16Aug	LGE 2	H	Macclesfiedl Town	L	0 - 4
5	Sa 20Aug	LGE 2	A	AFC Wimbledon	D	1 - 1
6	**Tu 23Aug**	**CC 2**	**A**	**Aston Villa**	**L**	**2 - 0**
7	Sa 27Aug	LGE 2	A	Bristol R	D	0 - 0
8	**Tu 30Aug**	**JPT 1**	**A**	**Bournemouth**	**L**	**4 - 1**
9	Sa 03Sep	LGE 2	H	Dagenham & Redbridge	W	1 - 0
10	Sa 10Sep	LGE 2	A	Shrewsbury Town	L	3 - 1
11	Tu 13Sep	LGE 2	H	Aldershot Town	L	0 - 2
12	Sa 17Sep	LGE 2	H	Gillingham	L	1 - 6
13	Sa 24Sep	LGE 2	A	Cheltenham Town	D	0 - 0
14	Sa 01Oct	LGE 2	H	Oxford United	L	0 - 1
15	Sa 08Oct	LGE 2	A	Swindon Town	D	3 - 3
16	Sa 15Oct	LGE 2	H	Bradford City	W	2 - 0
17	Sa 22Oct	LGE 2	H	Barnet	W	1 - 0
18	Tu 25Oct	LGE 2	A	Northampton Town	W	1 - 3
19	Sa 29Oct	LGE 2	A	Torquay United	L	2 - 0
20	Sa 05Nov	LGE 2	H	Crawley Town	D	1 - 1
21	**Sa 12Nov**	**FAC 1**	**H**	**Yeovil Town**	**L**	**0 - 3**
22	Sa 19Nov	LGE 2	H	Burton Albion	L	2 - 3
23	Sa 26Nov	LGE 2	A	Crewe Alexandra	L	1 - 0
24	Sa 10Dec	LGE 2	H	Rotherham United	L	2 - 3
25	Sa 17Dec	LGE 2	A	Plymouth Argyle	D	1 - 1
26	Mo 26Dec	LGE 2	H	Port Vale	L	1 - 2
27	Fr 30Dec	LGE 2	H	Accrington Stanley	D	1 - 1
28	Mo 02Jan	LGE 2	A	Burton Albion	W	0 - 2
29	Tu 10Jan	LGE 2	H	Bristol Rovers	L	1 - 2
30	Sa 14Jan	LGE 2	A	Dagenham & Redbridge	W	0 - 1
31	Sa 21Jan	LGE 2	A	Oxford United	D	2 - 2
32	Sa 28Jan	LGE 2	H	Shrewsbury Town	L	0 - 2
33	Sa 11Feb	LGE 2	H	Cheltenham Town	D	1 - 1
34	Tu 14Feb	LGE 2	A	Aldershot Town	L	1 - 0
35	Sa 18Feb	LGE 2	H	Swindon Town	L	1 - 2
36	Sa 25Feb	LGE 2	A	Bradford City	D	1 - 1
37	Tu 28Feb	LGE 2	A	Gillingham	L	5 - 4
38	Sa 03Mar	LGE 2	H	AFC Wimbledon	W	2 - 1
39	Tu 06Mar	LGE 2	A	Macclesfield Town	D	2 - 2
40	Sa 10Mar	LGE 2	A	Morecambe	W	0 - 1
41	Sa 17Mar	LGE 2	H	Southend	L	2 - 3
42	Tu 20Mar	LGE 2	A	Port Vale	L	1 - 0
43	Sa 24Mar	LGE 2	H	Crewe Alexandra	L	0 - 1
44	Sa 31Mar	LGE 2	A	Rotherham United	L	1 - 0
45	Fr 06Apr	LGE 2	H	Plymouth Argyle	D	1 - 1
46	Mo 09Apr	LGE 2	A	Accrington Stanley	L	2 - 1
47	Fr 13Apr	LGE 2	A	Barnet	D	1 - 1
48	Sa 21Apr	LGE 2	H	Northampton Town	D	0 - 0
49	Sa 28Apr	LGE 2	A	Crawley Town	W	0 - 3
50	Sa 05May	LGE 2	H	Torquay United	W	3 - 2

PLAYING SQUAD 2012-13

Existing Players		SN	HT	WT	DOB	AGE	POB	Career	Apps	Goals
GOALKEEPERS										
James	Bittner	1	6'02"	13 01	02/02/1982	29	Devizes	Swindon (Trainee), Fulham 7/00, Salisbury 11/01, Bournemouth 3/02, Torquay (Trial) 7/02, Cheltenham (Trial) 7/02, Chippenham 8/02, Southend (Trial) 7/03, Exeter 8/03 Rel 4/05, Torquay 6/05 Rel 5/06, Woking 12/06 Rel 5/07, Salisbury 6/07, Chippenham (L) 11/07, Forest Green 6/10, AFC Totton (SL) 2/12, Hereford 6/12		
Dan	Hanford	12			06/03/1991	21	Rochdale	Rochdale, Clitheroe (WE) 3/09, Clitheroe c/s 09, Glen Hoddle Academy (Spa), Hereford 12/11		
DEFENDERS										
Chris	Carruthers	8	5'10"	12 03	19/08/1983	28	Kettering	Northampton, Hornchurch (L) 11/04, Kettering (L) 1/05, Bristol R (SL) 3/05, Bristol R Undisc 7/05 Rel c/s 08, Oxford U 7/08 Rel 1/10, Crawley (L) 8/09, York C (3ML) 9/09, York C 1/10 Rel 6/11, Gateshead 7/11 Rel c/s 12, Hereford 7/12		
Benoit	Dalibard	15	6'02"	12 08	26/03/1991	21	Landerneau, Fra	En Avant de Guingamp (Fra), Hereford 8/11		
Andy	Gallinagh	2	5'08"	11 08	16/03/1985	27	Sutton Coldfield	Stratford T, Cheltenham 9/04, Bath C (3ML) 9/11, Bath C 1/12, Hereford 7/12		
Luke	Graham	6	6'03"	12 07	27/04/1986	25	Kettering	Northampton, Aylesbury (L) 12/04, Kettering (2ML) 2/05, Forest Green (SL) 8/05, Kettering 5/06, Kings Lynn (SL) 10/08, Mansfield 5/09, York C (2ML) 11/09 Perm 1/10, Kettering 6/10, Luton (SL) 1/11, Forest Green 7/11, Hereford 6/12		
Joe	Heath	3	5'11"	11 11	04/10/1988	23	Birkenhead	Man Utd (Yth), Notts Forest Rel 1/10, Lincoln C (6ML) 7/09, Exeter (Trial) 2/10, Exeter 3/10 Rel c/s 11, Hereford (SL) 11/10, Hereford 6/11		
Stefan	Stam	14	6'02"	13 02	14/09/1979	32	Amersfoort (Holl)	VV Grasshoppers (Hol), AZ67 Alkmaar (Yth) (Hol), PSV (Yth), Eindhoven (Hol) 7/00, Huizen (Hol) 7/03, Oldham 2/05, Yeovil 7/09 Rel c/s 11, Hereford (SL) 3/11, Hereford 7/11		
Michael	Townsend	5	6'01"	13 12	17/05/1986	26	Walsall	Wolves (Scholar), Cheltenham 1/05 Rel c/s 10, Barnet (3ML) 10/08, Hereford 7/10		
MIDFIELDERS										
Simon	Clist	11	5'09"	11 09	13/06/1981	31	Bournemouth	Tottenham (Trainee) Rel 7/99, Bristol C, Torquay (2ML) 2/03, Barnet AL 1/04 Rel 5/06, Forest Green 5/06, Oxford U Undisc 2/09, Hereford (5ML) 8/11 Perm 1/12		
Sam	Clucas	18	5'09"	10 06	25/09/1990	21	Lincoln	Leicester (Trainee), Nettleham, Lincoln C 8/09 Rel c/s 10, Glen Hoddle Academy, Hereford 11/11		
Will	Evans	17			19/10/1991	20	Cricklade	Fairford, Swindon, Hereford (3ML) 8/11, Hereford 1/12		
James	McQuilken	16	5'08"	11 10	09/01/1989	23	Tipton	West Brom (Scholar), FC Tescoma Zlin (Cze) c/s 07, Weymouth 4/09, Hereford 8/09, Kidderminster (L) 1/12		
Harry	Pell	4	6'03"	13 05	21/10/1991	20	Tilbury	Charlton (Scholar), Hastings U (WE) 1/10, Bristol R 7/10, Hereford (2ML) 1/11, Hereford 7/11, Cambridge U (L) 3/12		
Ashley	Sammons	20	5'09"	11 02	10/11/1991	20	Solihull	Birmingham Rel c/s 12, Hereford 8/12		
Marley	Watkins	7	5'10"	10 04	17/10/1990	20	London	Swansea (Yth), Cheltenham Rel 1/11, Bath C (3ML) 9/10, Bath C 1/11, Hereford Trib 7/12		
Forwards										
Ryan	Bowman	19	6'02"	11 13	30/11/1991	19	Carlisle	Carlisle Rel c/s 11, Workington (WE) 2/10, Workington (L) 10/10, Darlington 8/11, Hereford 7/12		
Sean	Canham	10	6'01"	13 01	26/09/1984	27	Exeter	Exeter Rel 5/05, Tiverton (L) 12/04, Moor Green (L) 3/05, Team Bath 8/05, Notts County Nominal 8/08 Rel c/s 10, Hayes & Yeading (3ML) 9/09, Hereford 7/10, Kidderminster (SL) 2/11, Bath C (2ML) 9/11, Bath C (SL) 1/12		
Marlon	Jackson	9	5'11"	11 12	06/12/1990	21	Bristol	Bristol C Rel c/s 12, Hereford (L) 8/09, Aldershot (SL) 11/09, Aldershot (10WL) 9/10, Northampton (5WL) 9/11, Cheltenham (L) 11/11, AFC Telford (L) 1/12, AFC Telford (L) 3/12, Hereford 7/12		
Tom	Nichols	21	5'10"	11 11	01/09/1993	18	Taunton	Exeter, Dorchester (2ML) 1/12, Hereford (L) 8/12		

Conference Action...

Hyde's Scott Spencer shapes up to fire a shot in on goal whilst under pressure from D'Orsi, during England C's 1-1 draw in the International Challenge Trophy.

Photo: Keith Clayton.

HYDE FC

Chairman: Tahir Khan
Secretary: Andrew McAnulty   **(T)** 07866 165 957   **(E)** secretary@hydefc.co.uk
Additional Committee Members:
Jonathan Manship, Howard Eggleston, Joe Kitchen, Darren Mellor, Peter Ainger.

Manager: Scott McNiven
Programme Editor: Mark Dring   **(E)** mark@dring16.fsnet.co.uk

Club Factfile

Founded: 1885   **Nickname:** The Tigers
Previous Names: Hyde F.C., Hyde United > 2011.
Previous Leagues: Lancashire & Cheshire 1919-21, Manchester 1921-30, Cheshire County 1930-68, 1970-82,
Northern Premier 1968-70, 1983-2004

Club Colours (change): Red/navy/navy (Yellow with red flash/red/red)

Ground: Ewen Fields, Walker Lane, Hyde SK14 5PL   **(T)** 0161 367 7273
Capacity: 4,073   **Seats:** 550   **Covered:** 4,073   **Clubhouse:** Yes   **Shop:** Yes

Directions: M60 (Manchester Orbital Motorway) to Junction 24, take the M67 (towards Sheffield) to junction 3 (Hyde/Dukinfield/Stalybridge). Once on exit slipway, keep to the right-hand lane heading for Hyde town centre. At the traffic lights at end of the slipway turn right, then at the second set of lights turn left (Morrisons on left) onto Mottram Road. Turn right at next lights onto Lumn Road. Left at Give Way sign onto Walker Lane. Ground entrance is on left, just after Hyde Leisure Pool, and is clearly signposted. Please note for Satnav, use SK14 5PL

Previous Grounds: None

Record Attendance: 7,600 v Nelson - FA Cup 1952
Record Victory: 9-1 v South Liverpool 04/1991
Record Defeat: 0-26 v Preston North End - FA Cup 1887
Record Goalscorer: David Nolan - 117 in 404 appearances (1992-2003). Ged Kimmins - 117 in 274 appearances (1993-98)
Record Appearances: Steve Johnson - 623 (1976-1988)
Additional Records: Paid £8,000 to Mossley for Jim McCluskie 1989
Senior Honours: Received £50,000 from Crewe Alexandra for Colin Little 1995
Northern Premier League Division 1 2003-04, Premier Division 2004-05, League Cup x3. Conference North 2011-12.
Cheshire Senior Cup x6. Manchester Premier cup x6.

10 YEAR RECORD

02-03		03-04		04-05		05-06		06-07		07-08		08-09		09-10		10-11		11-12	
NP P	23	NP 1	1	NP P	1	Conf N	11	Conf N	8	Conf N	9	Conf N	20	Conf N	15	Conf N	19	Conf N	1

HYDE FC

No.	Date	Comp	H/A	Opponents	Att:	Result	Goalscorers	Pos
1	Sat-13-Aug	BSN	H	Worcester City	361	W 2-1	Crowther 24, Spencer pen 29	8
2	Tue-16-Aug	BSN	A	Colwyn Bay	394	W 1-0	Spencer 89	2
3	Sat-20-Aug	BSN	A	Corby Town	793	W 4-0	Spencer 4 (13, 50, 78, 90)	2
4	Mon-22-Aug	BSN	H	Hinckley United	323	W 4-0	Berkeley 2 (11, 52), Spencer pen 32, Crowther 39	1
5	Sat-27-Aug	BSN	H	Altrincham	745	W 2-1	Spencer 2 (10, 60)	1
6	Mon-29-Aug	BSN	A	Gloucester City	472	W 2-0	Berkeley pen 26, Broadbent 54	1
7	Sat-03-Sep	BSN	H	Harrogate Town	615	W 3-2	Crowther 13, Broadbent 45, Berkeley pen 90	1
8	Sat-10-Sep	BSN	A	Workington	383	W 3-0	Broadbent 13, Spencer 17, Crowther 60	1
9	Tue-13-Sep	BSN	A	Droylsden	625	W 3-2	Byrne 40, Spencer 57, Hall 77	1
10	Sat-17-Sep	BSN	H	Gainsborough Trinity	654	W 3-1	Crowther 2, Hall 17, Spencer 21	1
11	Sat-24-Sep	BSN	A	Eastwood Town	232	D 2-2	Spencer 30, Hall 90	1
12	Sat-08-Oct	BSN	H	Nuneaton Town	682	D 1-1	Crowther 36	1
13	Sat-22-Oct	BSN	A	Guiseley	789	L 0-2		2
14	Tue-25-Oct	BSN	A	FC Halifax Town	1534	L 2-3	Crowther 56, Og (Toulson) 90	2
15	Sat-29-Oct	BSN	H	Harrogate Town	420	W 3-0	Pearson 7, Hall 54, Havern 68	2
16	Sat-05-Nov	BSN	H	Histon	394	W 4-0	Payne 2 (19, 56), Havern 71, Berkeley 84	2
17	Mon-07-Nov	BSN	H	Blyth Spartans	351	W 1-0	Griffin 26	1
18	Sat-12-Nov	BSN	A	Boston United	1160	W 2-0	Payne 48, Broadbent 70	1
19	Mon-14-Nov	BSN	A	Hinckley United	365	D 0-0		1
20	Sat-19-Nov	BSN	H	Colwyn Bay	462	W 3-2	Pearson 22, Berkeley 61, Fisher 77	1
21	Sat-03-Dec	BSN	A	Worcester City	782	D 2-2	Poole 9, Pearson 32	1
22	Mon-05-Dec	BSN	H	Eastwood Town	302	W 4-1	Worsley 2 (36, 70), Poole 50, Spencer 52	1
23	Sat-17-Dec	BSN	H	Vauxhall Motors	357	W 4-2	Spencer 4 (5, 18, 56, 88)	1
24	Mon-26-Dec	BSN	H	Stalybridge Celtic	1868	D 1-1	Havern 80	1
25	Sun-01-Jan	BSN	A	Stalybridge Celtic	1806	W 3-1	Gray 65, Spencer 72, Og (Platt) 83	1
26	Sat-07-Jan	BSN	A	Gainsborough Trinity	683	L 0-2		1
27	Sat-14-Jan	BSN	H	Corby Town	537	D 2-2	Pearson 16, Berkeley 75	1
28	Sat-21-Jan	BSN	H	Gloucester City	509	D 0-0		1
29	Sat-28-Jan	BSN	A	Solihull Moors	365	L 0-1		1
30	Sat-25-Feb	BSN	H	Droylsden	546	W 4-0	Gray 32, Pearson 61, Spencer pen 66, Poole 73	1
31	Sat-03-Mar	BSN	A	Vauxhall Motors	242	W 2-0	Spencer 60, Abadaki 90	1
32	Mon-05-Mar	BSN	H	Workington	528	W 4-0	Byrne 39, Spencer 2 (64, 75), Gray 73	1
33	Sat-10-Mar	BSN	H	FC Halifax Town	1364	D 1-1	Worsley 46	1
34	Sat-17-Mar	BSN	A	Nuneaton Town	902	L 0-2		1
35	Sat-24-Mar	BSN	H	Guiseley	823	L 0-1		1
36	Tue-27-Mar	BSN	A	Bishops Stortford	314	W 1-0	Gray pen 82	1
37	Sat-31-Mar	BSN	H	Bishops Stortford	499	W 5-0	Spencer 3 (10, 61, 72), Crowther 2 (55, 88)	1
38	Sat-07-Apr	BSN	A	Altrincham	1290	W 3-1	Spencer 2 (pen 32, pen 49), Broadbent 38	1
39	Mon-09-Apr	BSN	H	Solihull Moors	591	W 3-0	Spencer 2 (51, 68), Abadaki 87	1
40	Sat-14-Apr	BSN	A	Blyth Spartans	321	W 1-0	Pearson 6	1
41	Sat-21-Apr	BSN	H	Boston United	1036	W 4-1	Poole 2, Broadbent 19, Spencer pen 83, Payne 90	1 Champions
42	Sat-28-Apr	BSN	A	Histon	667	D 1-1	Pearson 45	1

CUPS

No.	Date	Comp	H/A	Opponents	Att:	Result	Goalscorers
1	Sat-01-Oct	FAC 2Q	A	Staveley Miners Welfare	320	W 3-0	Berkeley 19, Crowther 2 (49, 69)
2	Sat-15-Oct	FAC 3Q	H	Bradford Park Avenue	560	L 0-1	
3	Sat-26-Nov	FAT 3Q	A	Matlock Town	367	W 1-0	Griffin 90
4	Sat-10-Dec	FAT 1	A	Boston United	710	L 1-2	Spencer 40

League
Starts
Substitute
Unused Sub
Cups
Starts
Substitute
Unused Sub
Goals (Lg)
Goals (Cup)

CARNELL	RICHARDSON	PEARSON	HAVERN	RENSHAW	BIRCH	WORSLEY	BYRNE	SPENCER	BERKELEY	CROWTHER	EVANS	BIRCHALL	BROADBENT	FALLON	WHITWELL	GRIFFIN	MACK	ASPIN	HALL	MOSES	MARTIN	FARRIMOND	JONES	WILLIAMS	BRIZELL	FISHER	PAYNE	POOLE	GRAY	WINTER	KELLY	ELLISON	ABADAKI	EDGHILL	JUDGE	FRITH
X	X	X	X	X	X	X	X	X	X	X	X	S	S	S	U	U																				
X	X	X	X	X	X	X	X	X	X	X	X	S	S	U	U	U																				
X	X	X	X	X	X	X	X	X	X	X	X	S	S	U	U	U																				
X	X	X	X		X	X	X	X	X	X	X	U	S	S		U	S	X																		
X	X	X		X	X	X	X	X	X	X		S	S	U	S	X	U																			
X		X	X	X	X	X	X	X	U	X	X		S	X	S	S	X	U																		
X		X	X	X	X	X	X		X	X		U	X	U	S	X	U	X	S																	
X		X	U		X	U	X	X	S	X		X	X			X	S	X	X	S																
X	U	X	U		X		X	X	S	X		X	X			X	S	X	X	U																
X	U	X	U		X		X	X	S	X		X	X			X	S	X	X	S																
X	U	X		X		X		X	S	X		X	X			X	S	X	X	U	U															
X	X			X	S	X	X	X	X			X	S			X	U	U	X	S																
X	U	X	X		X	X	X	X	S	X			X			X		S	X	S	U															
X	U	X	X		X	X	X	X	S	X			X			X		S	X	S	U															
X	U	X	X			X	U	X	X			X				X		X	X	U			S	U												
X	U	X	X		X	S	X		S			X				X		X	X	U			S		X	X										
X	U	X	X		X	S	X					X				X		X	X	U			S		X	X	X	S								
X	S	X	X		X	S	X					X				X		X	X	U			U		X	X	X	S								
X	X	X			X	X	X					X				X		X	U	U			U	S	X	X	X	S								
X	U	X			X	X	X		X			S				X		X					S	X	S	X	X									
X		X	U		X	X	X	X	S			S				X		X	S				U	X	X		X									
X		X	U		X	X	X	X	S			X				X		X	S	U			S	X		X										
X		X	X			X	X	X	U			X				X		X	X	U			S	X				X	S	S						
X		X	X			X	X	U				X				X		X	X	U			X	X				X	S	S	S					
X		X	X			X	X	U				S				X		X	X				S	X		S	X	U		X						
X		X	X				X	X				S				X		X	X	U			U	X		S	X	U		X						
X		X	X		U	S	X			S	X					X		X	X				U	X			S	X								
X		X	X		U	U	X	S	X	X						S		X	X				U	X			X									
X		X	X		X	X	S	X	X							S		X	X				U	U			S									
X		X	X		X	X	X		X							U		X	U					S			S	X				S				
X		X	X		X	X	X		X							U		X	S					U			S	X				S				
X		X	X		X	X	X		X							U		X	S					S			S	X				U				
X		X	X		X	X	X		X							U		X						U			S	X				S	U			
X		X	X		X	X	X		X							X		X	U					S			S	X				S		U		
X		X	X		X	X	X		X							X			S					X	S	S	X					U		U		
X		X	X			X	S	X		X						X		S	X					X	U	U	X					X	S			
X		X	X			X	X	U	X							X		S	S					X			S	X				X	U			
X		X	X			X	X		X			X				X		S	S					X	U	S	X					U				
X		X	X			X	S	X				X				X		U	X					X	U	X	X					S	S			
X		X	X		X	X	U	X		X						X		S	U					X			S	X				S				
X		X	X		X	X	U	X								X		U	S					X		S	X	X				S				
X		X	U		S	X	X	X								S		X	X					X			X					X	S		U	
X	S	X			X	U	X	X	X	X		X	S			X	U	X	X	S	U	U														
X	X		X		X	S	X	X	X	X		X	S			X		S	X	U	U		U													
X		X	U		X	X	X		X				S			X			X	S	U			S	X	X		X								
X		X	S		X	X	X	X	S				X			X			X	S	U			U	X		X									
42	7	41	32	6	32	27	35	32	12	28	0	5	21	0	0	38	0	5	28	14	0	0	0	1	17	5	5	7	17	0	0	2	3	0	0	0
0	1	0	0	0	1	5	3	1	10	0	3	6	12	1	4	0	4	2	5	13	0	0	0	7	4	1	2	16	0	2	2	1	7	3	0	0
0	9	0	6	0	2	2	3	2	3	0	1	1	5	6	3	0	4	1	2	6	13	0	0	7	4	0	3	1	0	2	0	0	3	2	2	1
4	1	3	1	0	4	2	4	3	3	2	0	2	1	0	0	4	0	1	4	0	0	0	0	0	2	1	0	2	0	0	0	0	0	0	0	0
0	1	0	1	0	0	1	0	0	1	0	0	0	3	0	0	0	0	1	0	3	0	0	0	1	0	0	0	0	0	0	0	0	0	0	0	0
0	0	0	1	0	0	1	0	0	0	0	0	0	0	0	0	1	0	0	1	4	1	1	1	0	0	0	0	0	0	0	0	0	0	0	0	0
0	0	7	3	0	0	3	2	31	7	9	0	0	6	0	0	1	0	0	4	0	0	0	0	0	0	1	4	4	4	0	0	0	2	0	0	0
0	0	0	0	0	0	0	0	1	1	2	0	0	0	0	0	1	0	0	0	0	0	0	0	0	0	0	0	0	0	0	0	0	0	0	0	0

PLAYING SQUAD

Existing Players		SN	HT	WT	DOB	AGE	POB	Career	Apps	Goals
GOALKEEPERS										
David	Carnell	1			18/04/1985	27		Man Utd (Yth), Oldham T, Hyde U c/s 06, Curzon Ashton (L) Perm, Stalybridge 11/09 Rel c/s 10, Curzon Ashton c/s 10, Hyde FC 6/11	42	0
Ashley	Frith	12						Blackburn (Yth), Man City (Yth), Glossop North End, Hyde FC 1/12, Woodley Sports (L) 3/12	0	0
DEFENDERS										
Luke	Ashworth	5	6'02"	12 08	04/12/1989	22	Bolton	Wigan, L.Orient (2ML) 8/08, L.Orient 1/09, Rotherham 7/10 Rel c/s 11, Harrogate T 9/11 Rel 12/11, FC Halifax NC 12/11 Rel c/s 12, Hyde FC 7/12		
Josh	Brizell	2	5'10"	12 04	15/10/1991	21	Liverpool	Rochdale, Hyde FC 10/11, Ossett T (L) 11/11	21	0
Adam	Griffin	3	5'07"	10 04	26/08/1984	28	Salford	Oldham, Chester (L) 1/03, Oxford U (2ML) 11/05, Stockport (SL) 1/06, Stockport Undisc 8/06, Darlington 7/08 Rel c/s 09, Stockport 8/09 Rel c/s 11, Hyde FC 8/11	38	1
Kelvin	Lomax	16	5'11"	12 03	12/11/1986	24	Bury	Oldham, Rochdale (2ML) 9/07, Chesterfield (5WL) 11/10, Shrewsbury 1/11 Rel c/s 11, Barrow 8/11 Rel c/s 12, Hyde FC 8/12		
Andrew	Pearson	4	6'00"	13 04	21/12/1989	22	Manchester	Bolton (Yth), Wigan Rel c/s 09, Salford C 8/09, Altrincham 8/09 Rel 1/10, Rhyl 1/10, Hyde FC 8/11	41	7
Robbie	Williams	15	6'05"		06/07/1987	24	Blackpool	TNS/The New Saints Rel c/s 09, Newtown (3ML) 11/06, Caersws (4ML) 9/08, Altrincham 7/09, AFC Telford 6/11 Rel c/s 12, Altrincham (3ML) 9/11, Lincoln C (SL) 1/12, Hyde U 8/12		
MIDFIELDERS										
Alex	Brown	6	5'08"	10 07	28/11/1984	27		Crewe (Scholar), Leek T 7/04, Witton 6/06, Droylsden 6/08, Chester FC 5/11, Hyde FC 5/12		
Callum	Byrne	8	5'07"	10 00	05/02/1992	20	Liverpool	Rochdale Rel c/s 11, Trafford (L) 9/10, Mossley (2ML) 11/10, Hyde FC (L) 3/11, Hyde FC 7/11	38	2
Matthew	Cassidy	17	6'00"	11 13	02/10/1988	23	Blackpool	Bolton Rel c/s 08, Enosi Neon Paralimniou (Cyp) 7/08, AEL Limassol (Cyp) 6/10, Othellos Atheniou (Cyp) 7/11, Hyde FC 8/12		
Stefan	Cox	11			17/09/1991	20		Luton (Yth), Lewes 1/08, Horsham (L) 2/08, C,Palace (Trainee) 7/09, Dulwich 8/09, Sutton U 9/09, Carshalton 11/09, Leyton c/s 10, Dulwich H 1/11, Horsham YMCA 3/11, Tooting & M 7/11, Fleetwood 8/11 Rel 3/12, Chester (L) 1/12, Hyde FC 7/12		
Tim	Marshall							Man City (Yth), Blackburn (Yth), Stalybridge (Yth), Hyde FC 6/12		
Tunji	Moses	13	5'10"	11 11	12/09/1983	28	Manchester	Oldham T, Rossendale, Salford C, FCUM 7/08, Time Out, Trafford 10/10, Curzon Ashton 2/11, Salford C, Hyde FC 9/11	27	0
David	Poole	7	5'08"	12 00	12/11/1984	27	Manchester	Man Utd Rel c/s 05, Yeovil 6/05, Stockport (3ML) 9/06 Stockport £10,000 1/07, Darlington 7/08 Rel c/s 09, Stockport 8/09 Rel c/s 11, Droylsden 8/11, Hyde FC 11/11	23	4
Grant	Spencer	18					Manchester	Stockport (Jun), Oldham (Jun), Bolton (Scholar), Ramsbottom 8/11, Hyde FC 7/12		
FORWARDS										
Dan	Broadbent		5'10"	12 00	02/03/1990	22	Leeds	Huddersfield Rel 5/09, Rushden & D (L) 1/09, Gateshead (L) 2/09, Harrogate T (SL) 3/09, Harrogate T 8/09, Frickley (SL) 3/10, Frickley 7/10, Curzon Ashton 9/10, Hyde FC 8/11, Radcliffe B (L) 3/12	33	6
Daniel	Douglas-Pringle	14	5'10"	10 09	08/12/1984	27	Manchester	Man City (Scholar), Bury (Scholar), Chorley (L) 10/04 Perm 11/04, Leigh RMI 1/05 Rel 2/05, Woodley Sports 2/05, Alfreton 7/07, Curzon Ashton Undisc 9/07, Chorley 2/08, Woodley Sports 8/08, Hyde U 11/08, New Mills 9/10, Hyde FC 8/12		
Phil	Jevons	10	5'11"	12 00	01/08/1979	33	Liverpool	Everton, Grimsby £150,000 7/01 Rel c/s 04, Hull C (SL) 9/02, Yeovil 7/04, Bristol C 7/06, Huddersfield (L) 12/07 Undisc 1/08 Rel c/s 10, Bury (SL) 3/09, Morecambe (SL) 7/09, Morecambe 7/10 Rel 4/12, Wrexham (Trial), Hyde FC 7/12		

		SN	HT	WT	DOB	AGE	POB	From - To	APPS	GOA
David	McNiven	19	5'10"	12 00	27/05/1978	33	Leeds	Oldham Rel c/s 00, Linfield (L) 3/97, Scarborough (L) 2/00, Southport (L) 3/00, York 8/00 Rel c/s 01, Chester 7/01, Hamilton 10/01, Northwich 7/02, Kidsgrove (L) 11/02, Leigh RMI 8/03, Q.O.South 7/04, Scarborough 1/06, Morecambe 6/06, Stafford R (L) 1/07, Stafford R 8/07, Farsley Celtic (L) 2/08, Hyde U 7/09, Droylsden 8/10 Rel 3/11, Hyde FC 3/11 Rel c/s 11, Workington 7/11, Bradford PA 3/12, Hyde FC 8/12		
Shelton	Payne							Cardiff (Yth), Blackburn (Yth), Trafford, Chorley 7/10, Hyde FC (L) 11/11, Colwyn Bay 1/12, Hyde FC 3/12, FC Halifax (Trial) 7/12	7	4
Scott	Spencer	9	5'11"	12 08	01/01/1989	23	Oldham	Oldham (Scholar), Everton 6/06 Rel c/s 09, Yeovil (L) 1/08, Macclesfield (L) 3/08, Rochdale 8/09 Rel 11/09, Southend 1/10, Lincoln C 1/11 Rel c/s 11, Southport (Trial) 7/11, Barrow (Trial), Hyde FC 8/11	33	31

Loanees		SN	HT	WT	DOB	AGE	POB	From - To	APPS	GOA
(F)Tom	Fisher		5'10"	11 07	28/06/1992	20	Wythenshawe	Macclesfield 11/11 - Droylsden (L) 1/12, Droylsden (L) 3/12	6	1
(F)Reece	Gray		5'07"	8 08	01/09/1992	19	Oldham	Rochdale 12/11, (2ML) 2/12 -	17	4
(F)Godwin	Abadaki							Rochdale (SL) 2/12 -	10	2
(M)Mark	Jones							Radcliffe B (Cover) 3/12 -		

Departures		SN	HT	WT	DOB	AGE	POB	From - To	APPS	GOA
(M)Joe	Fox		5'10"		03/12/1991	20	York	Hull C 8/11 - Worksop 9/11, Ossett A 11/11		
(F)Mike	Whitwell		6'00"	12 00	21/11/1991	20		Harrogate RA 8/11 - Worksop 9/11	4	0
(G)Andrew	Farrimond							Leigh Genesis 8/11 - FCUM 10/11	0	0
(F)Ryan	Crowther		5'11"	11 00	17/09/1988	23	Stockport	Ashton U 6/11 - Fleetwood Undisc 11/11, Hyde FC (3ML) 1/12	28	9
(D)Brett	Renshaw				23/12/1980	31	Barnsley	Bradford PA 6/11 - Rel 11/11, FC Halifax (L) 10/11 FC Halifax 11/11, Stocksbridge PS (L) 12/11, Worsborough Bridge (L) 2/12, Stocksbridge PS 2/12	6	0
(G)Will	Jones							Corby T 10/11 - Colwyn Bay 12/11	0	0
(D)Mike	Aspin				20/10/1989	22		Chester FC 8/11 - Rel 12/11	7	0
(D)Joel	Richardson		5'11"	11 00	22/09/1990	21	Liverpool	IK Hammerby (Swe) 6/11 - Skelmersdale 12/11, Colwyn Bay 7/12	8	0
(F)James	Ellison		5'10"	12 08	25/10/1991	20	Liverpool	Burton 12/11 - Southport 1/12, Skelmersdale (L) 3/12, Vauxhall Motors 8/12	3	0
(D)Nathan	Martin							Curzon Ashton 6/11 - Rel 1/12, Curzon Ashton 1/12	0	0
(M)Luke	Mack							Curzon Ashton 6/11 - Airbus UK 1/12	4	0
(F)Matthew	Berkeley		5'11"	10 10	03/08/1987	25	Manchester	The New Saints 8/11 - Workington 3/12, Colwyn Bay 6/12	22	7
(M)Thomas	Ingram							Corby T 8/11 - Corby T 3/12		
(M)Ashley	Kelly							Chester FC 12/11 - Radcliffe B 3/12, Northwich 8/12	2	0
(D)Danny	Hall		6'02"	12 07	14/11/1983	27	Ashton-under-Lyne	Stockport 9/11 - Altrincham 5/12	33	4
(M)David	Birch				14/01/1981	30		Curzon Ashton 8/11 - FCUM 6/12	33	0
(D)Gianluca	Havern		6'01"	13 00	24/09/1988	22	Gorton	Ashton U 6/11 - Altrincham 7/12	32	3
(M)Chris	Worsley							Curzon Ashton 8/11 - Skelmersdale (L) 1/12, FC Halifax 7/12	32	3
(M)Sean	Williams		5'07"		20/01/1992	20	Liverpool	Prescot Cables 10/11 - Skelmersdale (L) 3/12, Colwyn Bay 7/12	8	0
(M)Phil	Edghill							Curzon Ashton 3/12 - Ramsbottom 7/12	3	0
(F)Ben	Williamson		5'11"	11 13	25/12/1988	23	London	Bournemouth 6/11 - Port Vale (SL) 6/11 Perm 5/12		
(G)Adam	Judge							Chester 3/12 -	0	0
(M)Adam	Birchall							Skelmersdale 8/11 -	11	0
(M)Joseph	Evans				21/12/1990	21		Curzon Ashton 6/11 - Skelmersdale (Dual) 9/11	3	0
(M)Rory	Fallon							Loughborough University 8/11 -	1	0
(M)Harry	Winter		6'01"	12 00	16/06/1989	23		FC Halifax 12/11 - Matlock (Dual) 1/12, AFC Fylde (Dual) 2/12	2	0

Conference Action...

Watkins shoots wide for Luton Town against York City at Wembley during the Conference Play-off Final.

Photo: Keith Clayton.

KIDDERMINSTER HARRIERS

Chairman: Mark Serrell
Secretary: Graham Hill **(T)** 07786 992272 **(E)** info@harriers.co.uk
Additional Committee Members:
Ruth Serrell, John Davies, Joe Hancox, Ernie Lane, Kath Lane, Andrew Maidstone, Ken Rae, Gino Ruffinato, Wayne Allen.
Manager: Steve Burr
Programme Editor: Matt Wall **(E)** matt.wall@harriers.co.uk

Back Row (L-R): Keith Briggs, Kyle Storer, James Vincent, Callum Gittings, Jamille Matt, Justin Nisbett.
Middle Row: Gavin Crowe, Ade Ganderton, Mickey Demetriou, Ryan Austin, Daniel Lewis, Mike Williams, Danny Pilkington, Andy Fearn, Jerry Gill.
Front Row: Ryan Rowe, Ricky Shakes, Marvin Johnson, Anthony Malbon, Steve Burr, Lee Vaughan, Ricky Shakes, Jack Byrne, Exodus Geohaghon.

Club Factfile

Founded: 1886 **Nickname:** Harriers
Previous Names: Kidderminster > 1891
Previous Leagues: Birmingham 1889-90, 91-1939, 47-48, 60-62. Midland 1890-91. Southern 1939-45, 48-60, 72-83. Birmingham Comb. 1945-47. West Midlands 1962-72. Conference 1983-2000. Football League 2000-05.

Club Colours (change): Red & white/white & red/white & red (Yellow & royal blue/yellow/yellow & royal blue)

Ground: Aggborough Stadium, Hoo Road, Kidderminster DY10 1NB **(T)** 01562 823 931
Capacity: 6,419 **Seats:** 3,175 **Covered:** 3,062 **Clubhouse:** Yes **Shop:** Yes
Directions: From North M5 Junc 3 onto A456 to Kidderminster, From South M5 Junc 6 onto A449 to Kidderminster. Alternatively M40/42 Junc 1 onto A38 to Bromsgrove/A448 to Kidderminster. (All routes follow Brown signs to (SVR) Steam Railway then follow signs to Aggborough). Aggborough is signposted at either end of Hoo Road.

Previous Grounds:

Record Attendance: 9,155 v Hereford United - 27/11/48
Record Victory: 25-0 v Hereford (H) - Birmingham Senior Cup 12/10/1889
Record Defeat: 0-13 v Darwen (A) - FA Cup 1st Round 24/01/1891
Record Goalscorer: Peter Wassell - 432 (1963-74)
Record Appearances: Brendan Wassell - 686 (1962-74)
Additional Records: Paid £80,000 to Nuneaton Borough for Andy Ducros July 2000
Senior Honours: Recieved £380,000 from W.B.A. for Lee Hughes July 1997
FA Trophy 1986-87. Conference 1993-94, 1999-2000.

10 YEAR RECORD

02-03		03-04		04-05		05-06		06-07		07-08		08-09		09-10		10-11		11-12	
FL 3	11	FL 3	16	FL 3	23	Conf	15	Conf	10	Conf	13	Conf	6	Conf	13	Conf	6	Conf	6

KIDDERMINSTER HARRIERS

No.	Date	Comp	H/A	Opponents	Att:	Result	Goalscorers	Pos
1	Sat-13-Aug	BSP	H	Gateshead	1636	L 2-3	N Wright 20, Storer 25	19
2	Tue-16-Aug	BSP	A	Lincoln City	2448	W 1-0	Gittings 42	12
3	Sat-20-Aug	BSP	A	Cambridge United	2171	W 2-1	Guinan 2 (40, 44)	6
4	Tue-23-Aug	BSP	H	Stockport County	1886	D 1-1	Phelan 88	6
5	Sat-27-Aug	BSP	H	Southport	1763	W 2-0	Byrne 79, Marc Williams 81	4
6	Mon-29-Aug	BSP	A	Newport County	1672	W 3-1	Byrne 49, Og (Miller) 65, Jones 80	3
7	Sat-03-Sep	BSP	A	Wrexham	4102	L 0-2		3
8	Sat-10-Sep	BSP	H	Ebbsfleet United	1788	D 2-2	Jones 11, N Wright 74	4
9	Sat-17-Sep	BSP	H	Alfreton Town	1939	W 3-1	Marc Williams 39, Guinan 51, Vincent 89	5
10	Tue-20-Sep	BSP	A	Fleetwood Town	1316	L 2-5	L Vaughan 69, Matt 90	8
11	Sat-24-Sep	BSP	A	Mansfield Town	2522	W 3-0	Storer 6, N Wright 7, L Vaughan pen 23	7
12	Tue-27-Sep	BSP	H	Grimsby Town	1807	D 1-1	N Wright 16	7
13	Sat-01-Oct	BSP	A	Kettering Town	1301	W 1-0	Matt 42	5
14	Sat-08-Oct	BSP	H	Luton Town	3332	L 1-2	Sharpe 87	8
15	Tue-11-Oct	BSP	H	AFC Telford	2440	D 2-2	Matt 13, Og (Preston) 39	9
16	Sat-15-Oct	BSP	A	Darlington	1763	L 0-1		11
17	Tue-18-Oct	BSP	H	Braintree Town	1301	W 5-4	N Wright 2 (27, pen 77), Vincent 2 (51, 55), Gittings 58	9
18	Sat-22-Oct	BSP	A	Barrow	1246	L 1-3	Matt 35	12
19	Sat-05-Nov	BSP	H	Tamworth	1797	W 2-0	L Vaughan pen 6, Guinan 18	8
20	Sat-19-Nov	BSP	A	Hayes & Yeading United	289	W 3-1	L Vaughan pen 28, Gittings 2 (70, 87)	8
21	Sat-26-Nov	BSP	H	Cambridge United	1899	D 0-0		8
22	Tue-29-Nov	BSP	A	Ebbsfleet United	731	D 3-3	Hankin 5, N Wright 80, Matt 84	8
23	Tue-06-Dec	BSP	H	Bath City	1472	W 4-1	Guinan 33, Matt 2 (45, 66), Byrne 88	8
24	Mon-19-Dec	BSP	A	York City	2830	W 3-2	Byrne 5, Gittings 21, Matt 33	6
25	Mon-26-Dec	BSP	H	Forest Green Rovers	2491	W 1-0	Byrne 67	6
26	Sun-01-Jan	BSP	A	Forest Green Rovers	1542	D 1-1	Matt 90	6
27	Sat-07-Jan	BSP	H	Hayes & Yeading United	1732	W 3-1	Guinan 82, Matt 90+2, N Wright 90+8	5
28	Tue-10-Jan	BSP	A	Gateshead	724	L 1-2	N Wright pen 80	6
29	Sat-21-Jan	BSP	A	Alfreton Town	990	W 2-1	Malbon 90+2, Matt 90+4	5
30	Tue-24-Jan	BSP	H	York City	2417	D 1-1	McQuilken 85	5
31	Sat-28-Jan	BSP	A	Stockport County	3728	L 1-2	N Wright 56	5
32	Sat-18-Feb	BSP	H	Lincoln City	2081	D 1-1	Guinan 90	7
33	Tue-21-Feb	BSP	H	Wrexham	2492	L 0-1		7
34	Sat-25-Feb	BSP	A	Bath City	676	W 2-1	Byrne 2 (18, 54)	6
35	Sat-03-Mar	BSP	H	Barrow	2135	L 1-2	Malbon 31	7
36	Fri-09-Mar	BSP	H	Fleetwood Town	2341	L 0-2		7
37	Tue-13-Mar	BSP	A	AFC Telford	2192	L 1-2	Malbon 53	8
38	Sat-17-Mar	BSP	A	Braintree Town	610	W 4-1	Marshall 42, Byrne 2 (51, 69), Malbon 60	7
39	Tue-20-Mar	BSP	A	Tamworth	924	D 0-0		9
40	Sat-24-Mar	BSP	H	Darlington	1635	W 3-1	Hankin 26, Malbon 54, Rowe 89	7
41	Sat-31-Mar	BSP	A	Grimsby Town	3194	W 2-1	Malbon 55, Rowe 90	7
42	Sat-07-Apr	BSP	A	Southport	1544	W 2-1	Malbon 41, Jones 90	5
43	Mon-09-Apr	BSP	H	Newport County	2275	W 3-2	N Wright 3 (pen 86, 90+4, 90+6)	5
44	Sat-14-Apr	BSP	H	Kettering Town	1967	W 6-1	N Wright 2 (pen 25, 54), Malbon 72, Rowe 74, Jones 82, Mike Williams 89	4
45	Sat-21-Apr	BSP	A	Luton Town	8415	L 0-1		6
46	Sat-28-Apr	BSP	H	Mansfield Town	3565	L 0-3		6

CUPS

1	Sat-29-Oct	FAC 4Q	H	Corby Town	1281	D 0-0		
2	Wed-02-Nov	FAC 4QR	A	Corby Town	1026	L 1-4	Guinan 7	
3	Sat-10-Dec	FAT 1	A	Vauxhall Motors	253	D 4-4	Demetriou 4, Matt 26, Byrne 73, N Wright pen 90	
4	Tue-13-Dec	FAT 1R	H	Vauxhall Motors	746	W 2-0	Matt 13, Storer 24	
5	Sat-14-Jan	FAT 2	H	Droylsden	1104	W 5-1	Bradley 7, N Wright 34, Matt 49, Guinan 2 (54, 83)	
6	Tue-07-Feb	FAT 3	H	Luton Town	1186	L 1-2	Bradley 35	

League
Starts
Substitute
Unused Sub

Cups
Starts
Substitute
Unused Sub

Goals (Lg)
Goals (Cup)

Appearances / substitutes grid:

	LEWIS	L VAUGHAN	JONES	MARSHALL	MIKE WILLIAMS	STORER	VINCENT	GITTINGS	N WRIGHT	GUINAN	MARC WILLIAMS	MEDLEY	PHELAN	MATT	LYNESS	SHARPE	HANKIN	BYRNE	DEMETRIOU	BRISCOE	T WRIGHT	THOMPSON-BROWN	CRESSWELL	BIRD	BREEDEN	HENDRIE	N VAUGHAN	BRADLEY	MCQUILKEN	CHECKETTS	HURRELL	MALBON	JOHNSON	ROWE
	1	2	4	6	3	24	8	18	14	9	10	17	5	20	21	15	7	11	22	16	25	13	19	30	31	34	40	30	23	25	26	27	28	10
	X	X	X	X	X	X	X	X	X	X	X	X			S	S	S	U	U															
	X	X	X	X	X	X	X	X	X	X	X	X			S	S	S	U	U															
	X	X	X	X	X	X	X	X	X	X	X	X			S	S	S	U	U															
	X	X	X	X	X	X	X			S		X	X	X	X	U	U	S	S															
	X	X	X	X	X	X		S		X	X	X	S	X	U	U	S	X	X															
	X	X	X	X	X	X	X	S		X	X		S	X	S	U	U	X	X															
	X	X	X	X	X	X	S	X	X	X			X	S	U	U	S	X																
	X	X	X	X	X	X	S		X	X	X		X	S	U	U	U	X																
	X	X	X		X	X			X	X			S	X	S	X	U	X		X	S	U												
	X	X	X		X	X			X	X			S	X	S	X	U	X		X		U	S											
		X	X			S	X	X		X			S	X	S	X	X	X		X	U	U	S											
		X	X		X	X	X	X	X	U			S	X	S	X	X	X					S	U										
		X		U		X	X	X	X	S				U	X	X	X			X	X		S	U										
			X		X	X	X	X	S	U	U		X	X	X				X	X			S	S										
			X		X	X	X	X	S	S			S	X	X				X	X			U	U										
			X		X	X	X	X	S	S	U		X	X	X				X	X			U	S	X										
	X	U			S	X	S	X		X	U	U	X	X				X	X				X	X										
	X	U			X	X	X	S	X	S			X	U	X	X			X	X			S	X	X									
	X	U		S	X	X	X	S	X	U			X		X	X			X	X			X	X	S									
	X	S		U	X		X	S	X	U			X		X	X	X	S	X	X			X	X										
	X	X		U	X			X	X	S			X		X	X	X	S	X	U		S	X	X										
	X	X		U	X		X	S	S	S			X	U	X	X	X		X	X			X	X										
	X	X		U	X	S	X	U	S				X	U	X	X	X		X	X			X	X										
	X	X		U	X		X	X	S	S			X	U	X	X	X		X				X	X										
	X	X		U	X		X	X	S	S			X	U	X	X	X		X				X	X	S									
	X	X		U	X		X		X	S	X		X	U	X	X	X	S	X				X	X	X									
		X		U	X			S	X	S			X	U	X	X			X	U			X	X	X	X			S					
		X		X	X		U	X	U				X	U	X	X			X				X	X	X	S			S					
		X		X	X		U	X	X	U			X	U	X	S			X				X	X	X	S			S					
	X	X			X	X	S		X	S			X	U					X	U			X	X	X				X				X	S
	X	X			X	X			U	X	S	S	X	U					X				X	X	X							X		S
	X	X				X	X	U	X	S	S	X	X						U	X			X	X	X				X	S	X			
	X	X			X	X			S	S	S		X						U				X	X			U		X		X	X	X	S
	X	X	X	U	X				S	S	X		X						U				X	X	X	S			X		X	X	X	S
	X	X	X	U	X		U		X		S		X						U				X	X	X	S			S		X	X	X	S
	X	X	X	U	X				S		X		X						U				X	X	X				S		X	X	X	S
	X	X	X	U	X			S	S		X		X						U				X	X	X						X	X	X	S
	X	X	X		X		U		S		X		X						U				X	X	X						X	X	X	S
	X	X	X			X	U	S	S		X		X						U				X	X	X						X	X	X	S
	X	X	X	X		U	S		S		X		X						U				X	X	X				S		X	X	X	S
	X	X	X	X	X		X	U	S		X		X						U				X	X	X				S		X	X	X	S
	X	X	X	X	X		X		S		X		X						U				X	X	X				S		X	X	X	S
	X	X	X	X	X	X		X	S		X		X						S				X	X	X				S		X	X	X	S
	X	X	X	X	X	X		X	S		U		X						U				X	X	X				S		X	X	X	S
	X	X	X	X	X	X		S	U		U		X						X	S			X	X	X				X		X	X	X	X
	X	X	X			X	X			X	S	X		U	X	X	X	S				U	U			S	U	X						
	X	X	X				X	X	X	X				U	S	X	X	X				U	U			S	U	X						
	S	X			X	X			S	S	U	X		X	U	X	X	X	X				X						X					
	X	X			U	X			X	S	S	X		X	U	X	X	X	X	X	U							X						
			X	X					S	X	X	S		X	X	X	X		X	X									X	S	U	U		
	X	X			X	X			S	X	X	X	S		X	X	X		U			X	U						X	S				
	12	40	38	23	28	38	21	25	23	24	10	7	8	24	6	21	23	20	23	11	0	0	0	4	28	13	0	7	1	0	0	14	11	3
	0	0	1	0	0	1	7	5	20	14	12	6	7	8	0	1	4	6	3	1	2	3	3	0	0	2	0	8	2	0	0	3	1	12
	0	0	3	2	11	0	2	4	1	4	2	1	3	2	36	9	2	0	4	6	1	2	2	0	0	0	0	1	0	0	0	0	0	0
	0	4	5	2	3	5	2	3	4	3	3	0	0	5	4	5	4	2	4	2	0	0	0	2	0	0	2	2	0	0	0	0	0	0
	0	1	0	0	0	0	1	2	2	2	2	0	0	1	0	0	1	0	0	1	0	0	0	0	0	0	0	2	0	0	0	0	0	0
	0	0	0	0	1	0	0	0	0	1	0	0	2	0	2	0	1	0	2	4	0	0	2	0	0	0	0	0	1	1	0	0	0	0
	0	4	4	1	1	2	3	5	15	7	2	0	1	11	0	1	2	9	0	0	0	0	0	0	0	1	0	0	8	0	3			
	0	0	0	0	0	1	0	0	2	3	0	0	0	3	0	0	0	1	1	0	0	0	0	0	0	2	0	0	0	0	0			

PLAYING SQUAD

Existing Players		SN	HT	WT	DOB	AGE	POB	Career	Apps	Goals
GOALKEEPERS										
Danny	Lewis	1	6'01"	14 00	18/06/1982	30	Redditch	Alvechurch (Yth), Garringtons, Studley c/s 02,		
								Kidderminster 5/04 Rel 5/06, Moor Green 6/06, Redditch 6/07,		
								Kidderminster 5/10	12	0
Nathan	Vaughan	23			02/10/1981	30	Birmingham	Plymouth, Willenhall 7/00, Bradford C (Trial) 1/02, Newport C 3/05,		
								Chippenham (L) 10/05, Redditch 11/05, Evesham 3/06, Halesowen T 6/08,		
								Evesham 8/08, Romulus 11/11, Kidderminster NC 12/11, Leamington 1/12,		
								Kidderminster 8/12	0	0
DEFENDERS										
Ryan	Austin	16	6'02"	12 09	15/11/1984	27	Stoke	Crewe (Sch), Burton (3ML) 8/04, Burton 12/04 Rel c/s 12,		
								Kidderminster 7/12		
Ashley	Checketts							Kidderminster	0	0
Micky	Demetriou	3			12/03/1990	22	Durrington	Worthing, Leicester (Trial) 3/09, Bognor 8/09,		
								Glen Hoddle Academy (Spa) 8/10, Eastbourne B 1/11,		
								Kidderminster 6/11	26	0
Cheyenne	Dunkley	22	6'02"	13 06	13/02/1992	20	Wolverhampton	Crewe Rel c/s 10, Hednesford (2ML) 1/10, Hednesford (L) 4/10,		
								AFC Telford (Trial) 7/10, Hednesford 7/10, Birmingham (Trial) 2/12,		
								Kidderminster 5/12		
Exodus	Geohaghon	5	6'07"	11 11	27/02/1985	27	Birmingham	West Brom (Scholar), Sutton Coldfield, Bromsgrove Undisc 8/05,		
								Redditch U 7/06, Kettering (L) 7/08 Undisc 8/08,		
								Peterborough (5WL) 11/09 Perm 1/10 Rel c/s 11, Rotherham (3ML) 8/10,		
								Shrewsbury (L) 11/10, Port Vale (SL) 1/11, Barnet 8/11 Rel 9/11,		
								Darlington 10/11, Dag & Red (3ML) 11/11, Mansfield (SL) 2/12,		
								Kidderminster 7/12		
Tom	Sharpe	15	6'02"	13 04	12/10/1988	23	Nottingham	Notts Forest Rel 5/09, Bury (6WL) 11/07, Halifax (L) 1/08,		
								Stalybridge (3ML) 9/08, Kidderminster 7/09	22	1
Lee	Vaughan	2	5'07"	11 00	15/07/1986	26	Birmingham	Birmingham C (Yth), Portsmouth (Yth), Walsall 2/05, Willenhall (2ML) 8/05,		
								AFC Telford 2/06, Kidderminster 5/10	40	4
Mike	Williams	6	5'11"	12 00	27/10/1986	25	Rhos-on-Sea	Wrexham Rel 4/10, Kidderminster 7/10	28	1
MIDFIELDERS										
Keith	Briggs	21	5'10"	11 06	11/12/1981	30	Glossop	Stockport, Norwich £65,000 1/03, Crewe (L) 8/04, Stockport 1/05 Rel 1/08,		
								Shrewsbury 1/08 Rel 1/08, Mansfield 2/08 Rel c/s 08, Stalybridge 7/08,		
								Kidderminster 5/10, Fleetwood £5,000+ 5/11 Rel c/s 12,		
								Kidderminster 7/12		
Jack	Byrne	7			20/07/1989	23		Moor Green (Yth), Solihull B (Yth), Stratford T, Redditch 1/09,		
								Kidderminster 3/10, Chasetown (L) 2/12	26	9
Callum	Gittings	18			19/11/1985	26		Wolves (Yth), Redditch, Alvechurch (L) 12/03, Cinderford (L) 3/04,		
								Cinderford 7/04, Stourport 10/04, Tividale, Boldmere St Michaels 8/05,		
								Alvechurch 3/06, Kidderminster 8/10	30	5
Paul	Hurrell							Kidderminster	0	0
Danny	Pilkington	14	5'09"	11 08	25/05/1990	22	Blackburn	Myerscough College, Atherton Coll (Yth), Kendal T, Chorley,		
								Stockport 7/08 Rel 1/11, Chesterfield (Trial) 7/11, York C 8/11 Rel c/s 12,		
								Kidderminster 6/12		
Ricky	Shakes	17	5'10"	12 00	26/01/1985	27	Brixton	Bolton Rel c/s 05, Bristol R (L) 2/05, Bury (SL) 3/05,		
								Swindon 8/05 Rel c/s 07, Brentford (Trial) 7/07, Brentford 8/07 Rel 5/08,		
								Ebbsfleet 7/08, Kidderminster 6/12		
Kyle	Storer	4			30/04/1987	25	Nuneaton	Leicester (Jun), Bedworth 7/02, Tamworth 6/04, Hinckley U (L) 1/06,		
								Hinckley U 9/07, Atherstone 8/08, Nuneaton T 2/09,		
								Kidderminster £5,000 7/11	39	2
James	Vincent	8	5'11"	11 05	27/09/1989	22	Glossop	Stockport Rel c/s 11, Kidderminster 6/11	28	3

FORWARDS

		SN	HT	WT	DOB	AGE	POB	From - To	APPS	GOA
Stephen	Guinan	19	6'01"	13 02	24/12/1975	36	Birmingham	N.Forest, Greensboro Dynamo (L), Darlington (L) 12/95, Burnley (L) 3/97, Crewe (L) 3/98, Halifax (3ML) 10/98, Plymouth (SL) 3/99, Scunthorpe (L) 9/99, Cambridge U 12/99, Plymouth 3/00, Exeter (Trial) 2/02, Chester (Trial) 3/02, Shrewbury 3/02 Rel c/s 02, Hereford 8/02, Cheltenham 5/04, Hereford (3ML) 1/07, Hereford 7/07 Rel c/s 09, Northampton 7/09, Forest Green (6WL) 11/10 Perm 1/11 (10/11 18,5) Rel 5/11, Kidderminster 5/11	38	7
Marvin	Johnson	11			01/12/1990	22		Solihull Moors, Coleshill T (SL) 12/09, Romulus 7/10, Burton (Trial) 9/10, Burnley (Trial) 12/11, Kidderminster 1/12	12	0
Jamille	Matt	20			20/10/1989	22		Sutton Coldfield, Kidderminster 11/10	32	11
Anthony	Malbon	10	5'08"	11 00	14/10/1991	20	Sneyd Green	Derby (Yth), Port Vale Rel 11/10, Leek T (WE) 2/10, Newcastle T (L) 10/10, Leek T 11/10, Newcastle T 7/11, Kidderminster £7,000 1/12	17	8
Ryan	Rowe	9			11/06/1988	24		Cradley T, Stourbridge 7/09, Kidderminster 5 fig 2/12	15	3

Loanees		SN	HT	WT	DOB	AGE	POB	From - To	APPS	GOA
(M)David	Bird		5'09"	12 00	26/12/1984	27	Gloucester	Cheltenham 10/11 - Rel 1/12, Gloucester 3/12, Cinderford 8/124		0
(F)James	McQuilkin		5'08"	11 10	09/01/1989	23	Tipton	Hereford 1/12 -	3	1

Departures		SN	HT	WT	DOB	AGE	POB	From - To	APPS	GOA
(F)Tommy	Wright		6'00"	11 12	28/09/1984	27	Kirby Muxloe	Darlington NC 9/11 - Rel 10/11, Luton 10/11 Rel 1/12, Port Vale (Trial) 1/12, Forest Green 1/12, Tamworth 7/12	2	0
(F)Luke	Medley		6'01"	13 03	21/06/1989	23	Greenwich	Mansfield 6/11 - Rel 2/12, Lincoln C (2ML) 11/11, Woking (L) 1/12, Bromley 2/12	13	0
(F)Marc	Williams		5'09"	11 02	27/07/1988	24	Colwyn Bay	Wrexham 5/11 - Rel 2/12, Chester FC 2/12	22	2
(M)Scott	Phelan		5'07"	10 07	13/03/1988	24	Liverpool	FC Halifax 5/11 - Rel 2/12, Vauxhall Motors (2ML) 12/11, Vauxhall Motors 2/12, Altrincham 3/12	15	1
(M)Lee	Hendrie		5'10"	10 03	18/05/1977	35	Birmingham	Daventry T 11/11 - Rel 3/12, Chasetown 3/12, Redditch 3/1, Tamworth 7/12	15	0
(M)Jack	Cresswell		5'10"		18/11/1992	19	Redditch	Walsall (Scholar) 5/11 - Rel c/s 12, Redditch (L) 1/12, Chasetown (L) 2/12	3	0
(M)Dave	Hankin		6'03"		25/03/1985	27	Preston	Stalybridge 6/10 - Chester FC 5/12	27	2
(G)Tony	Breeden				31/01/1988	24		Leamington 11/11 - Rel c/s 12, Hednesford (L) 11/11, Tamworth 6/12	28	0
(D)Luke	Jones		5'09"	11 09	10/04/1987	25	Blackburn	Forest Green 5/11 - Mansfield 6/12	39	4
(F)Nick	Wright		6'02"	12 00	25/11/1987	24	Birmingham	Tamworth 7/10 - Mansfield 6/12	43	15
(D)Michael	Briscoe		5'11"	12 00	04/07/1983	29	Northampton	Tamworth 7/10 - AFC Telford 6/12	12	0
(D)Tom	Marshall		6'04"		16/11/1987	24	Lichfield	Tamworth 6/11 - Brackley (2ML) 12/11, Tamworth 6/12	23	1
(M)Daniel	Bradley		6'00"		13/05/1991	21	Stafford	Rushall O 1/12 - Alfreton 7/12	15	0
(G)Dean	Lyness		6'03"	12 00	20/07/1991	21	Halesowen	Hearts 6/11 - Burton 7/12	6	0
(F)Robert	Thompson-Brown	13			07/08/1992	20		Stratford T 10/10 - Solihull Moors (L) 9/11, Solihull Moors (2ML) 1/12, Nuneaton T 8/12	3	0

LINCOLN CITY

Chairman: Bob Dorrian
Secretary: Steve Prescott   **(T)** 07818 597 686   **(E)** steve.prescott@redimps.com
Additional Committee Members:
Bob Dorrian, David Parman, David Featherstone, Roger Bates, Kevin Cooke, Stuart Mitchell, Jane Powell, David Beck, Fran Martin.
Manager: David Holdsworth
Programme Editor: John Vickers   **(E)** jv@redimps.com

Back: Graham Hutchison, Andrew Boyce, Vadaine Oliver, Nick Draper, Paul Farman, Jake Turner,
Josh Gowling, Dan Gray, Elliot Green.
Middle: Mike Jolley (coach), Karl Cunningham, Jake Sheridan, Conner Robinson, Tom Miller, Gary Mills, Rob Duffy, Conal Platt,
Bradley Barraclough, Geoffrey Gouveia, Dan Coupland, Will Ferry (training assistant).
Front: Sam Rees (physiotherapist), Paul Robson, Peter Bore, Alan Power, Adam Smith, David Holdsworth (first team manager),
John Nutter, Jamie Taylor, Nicky Nicolau, Frazer Cobb, John Vickers (media manager).

Club Factfile

Founded: 1884   **Nickname:** Imps
Previous Names: None
Previous Leagues: Midland (Founder Member) 1889-91, 1908-09, 1911-12, 1920-21, Football Alliance 1891-92,
Football League (Founder Member) 1892-1908, 1909-11, 1912-20, 1921-86, 1988-2011, Conference 1986-88.

Club Colours (change): Red & white stripes/black/red & white (All white)

Ground: Sincil Bank Stadium, Lincoln LN5 8LD   **(T)** 01522 880 011
Capacity: 9,800   **Seats:** Yes   **Covered:** Yes   **Clubhouse:**   **Shop:** Yes

Directions
From South: Exit A1 at s/p 'Lincoln A46, Sleaford A17' onto the A46. At roundabout after 9.4 mile take 3rd exit (s/p Lincoln South A1434). Keep on A1434, following 'Lincoln and City Centre' signs for 4.3 miles. Then get into inside lane (s/p City Centre, Worksop A7) and go straight on (1st exit) at r'about into the High St. After 0.5 miles get in outside lane, and go straight on at lights (s/p City Ctre, Worksop A57). After 0.1 miles turn right into Scorer Street. **From North:** Exit A1(M) at the r'about after the Fina and Shell garages (s/p Lincoln A57, E. Markham) onto the A57. At junc. after 9.9 miles turn right (s/p Lincoln A57), remaining on A57 which here runs alongside the Foss Dyke. At r'about after 5.9 miles turn right (Lincoln South, Newark A46, Grantham A1) onto the A46. Straight on at r'about after 1.8 miles. At next r'about after 1.6 miles (by BP station) turn left (s/p Lincoln South B1190, Doddington Ind.Est., into Doddington Rd, Sraight on for 2 miles to T-junction. Here, turn left (no signpost) onto Newark Rd A1434. Keep on A1434 following City Centre signs. Go straight on (1st exit) at r'about into the High St. After (0.5 miles get in outside lane, and go straight on at lights (s/p City Ctre, Worksop A57). After 0.1 miles turn right into Scorer St. Tip: Have some change ready for a small toll bridge (Dunham) en route.
Previous Grounds: John O'Gaunt's 1883-94.

Record Attendance: 23,196 v Derby County, League Cup 4th Round 15/11/1967
Record Victory: 11-1 v Crewe Alexandra, Division Three North 29/09/1951.
Record Defeat: 3-11 v Manchester City, Division Two 23/03/1895.
Record Goalscorer: (League) Andy Graver - 143, 1950-55, 58-61.
Record Appearances: (League) Grant Brown - 407, 1989-2002.
Additional Records: Paid, £75,000 for Tony Battersby from Bury, 08/1998.
Senior Honours: Received, £500,000 for Gareth Ainsworth from Port Vale, 09/1997.
Midland League 1908-09, 20-21. Football League Division Three North 1931-32, 47-48, Division Four 1975-76.
Football Conference 1987-88.

10 YEAR RECORD

02-03		03-04		04-05		05-06		06-07		07-08		08-09		09-10		10-11		11-12	
FL 3	6	FL 3	7	FL 2	6	FL 2	7	FL 2	5	FL 2	15	FL 2	13	FL 2	20	FL 2	23	Conf	17

LINCOLN CITY

No.	Date	Comp	H/A	Opponents	Att:	Result	Goalscorers	Pos
	Lincoln							
1	Sat-13-Aug	BSP	A	Southport	1687	D 2-2	S Smith 29, Perry 50	7
2	Tue-16-Aug	BSP	H	Kidderminster Harriers	2448	L 0-1		17
3	Fri-19-Aug	BSP	H	Wrexham	2211	L 1-2	S Smith 45	17
4	Tue-23-Aug	BSP	A	AFC Telford	2323	W 2-1	Perry 2 (75, 80)	14
5	Fri-26-Aug	BSP	H	Stockport County	2152	D 1-1	Power 8	14
6	Mon-29-Aug	BSP	A	Darlington	2252	L 1-3	Power 71	18
7	Sat-03-Sep	BSP	A	Braintree Town	1182	L 0-1		21
8	Sat-10-Sep	BSP	H	Kettering Town	2269	L 0-2		22
9	Sat-17-Sep	BSP	A	Luton Town	6316	L 0-1		22
10	Tue-20-Sep	BSP	H	Gateshead	1587	W 1-0	Fuseini 77	19
11	Sat-24-Sep	BSP	H	Forest Green Rovers	2076	D 1-1	Hone 60	19
12	Tue-27-Sep	BSP	A	Barrow	1181	L 0-1		21
13	Sat-01-Oct	BSP	H	Bath City	2244	W 2-0	S Smith 19, McCallum 30	19
14	Sat-08-Oct	BSP	A	Tamworth	1232	L 0-4		19
15	Tue-11-Oct	BSP	A	Alfreton Town	1232	W 3-1	S Smith 2 (11, 13), McCallum 24	19
16	Fri-14-Oct	BSP	H	Fleetwood Town	2332	L 1-3	O'Keefe 42	19
17	Tue-18-Oct	BSP	H	Mansfield Town	2944	D 1-1	McCallum 76	21
18	Fri-21-Oct	BSP	A	Cambridge United	2875	L 0-2		21
19	Sat-05-Nov	BSP	H	Barrow	2090	W 2-1	S Smith 20, Christophe 22	18
20	Sat-19-Nov	BSP	A	Wrexham	3424	L 0-2		20
21	Sat-26-Nov	BSP	H	Ebbsfleet United	2111	W 3-0	Platt 38, Russell 74, Nutter 80	18
22	Tue-29-Nov	BSP	A	York City	3155	L 0-2		18
23	Sat-03-Dec	BSP	A	Newport County	1270	L 0-1		19
24	Tue-06-Dec	BSP	H	Luton Town	2049	D 1-1	Hinds 77	18
25	Sat-17-Dec	BSP	A	Forest Green Rovers	969	W 2-0	Power pen 42, Laurent 72	17
26	Mon-26-Dec	BSP	H	Grimsby Town	5506	L 1-2	Platt 33	17
27	Sun-01-Jan	BSP	A	Grimsby Town	6672	L 1-3	Taylor 59	17
28	Sat-07-Jan	BSP	H	York City	3048	L 0-2		18
29	Sat-21-Jan	BSP	A	Gateshead	870	D 3-3	Pacquette 2 (7, 82), S Smith 87	18
30	Tue-24-Jan	BSP	H	Southport	1615	W 2-0	Christophe 7, Pacquette 53	16
31	Sat-28-Jan	BSP	A	Kettering Town	1417	L 0-1		16
32	Tue-14-Feb	BSP	H	Braintree Town	1616	D 3-3	Louis 1, T Thompson 56, Almond 90	16
33	Sat-18-Feb	BSP	A	Kidderminster Harriers	2081	D 1-1	Louis 21	17
34	Sat-25-Feb	BSP	H	AFC Telford	2438	D 1-1	Og (Blackburn) 32	17
35	Sat-03-Mar	BSP	A	Mansfield Town	4830	L 1-2	McCammon 90	18
36	Sat-10-Mar	BSP	H	Alfreton Town	2253	L 0-1		19
37	Sat-17-Mar	BSP	A	Bath City	760	L 1-2	Lloyd-McGoldrick 76	20
38	Sat-24-Mar	BSP	H	Newport County	1951	W 2-1	McCammon 25, Nutter 33	19
39	Tue-27-Mar	BSP	A	Hayes & Yeading United	327	W 2-1	Louis 68, Miller 73	18
40	Sat-31-Mar	BSP	H	Tamworth	2213	W 4-0	Bore 7, Og 2 (D Thomas 30, 82), Power pen 48	17
41	Tue-03-Apr	BSP	H	Cambridge United	1978	L 0-1		17
42	Sat-07-Apr	BSP	A	Stockport County	3975	L 0-4		19
43	Mon-09-Apr	BSP	H	Darlington	2274	W 5-0	Lloyd-McGoldrick 2 (21, 39), Taylor 33, Louis 2 (37, 74)	17
44	Fri-13-Apr	BSP	A	Fleetwood Town	4511	D 2-2	Taylor 8, Louis 20	16
45	Sat-21-Apr	BSP	H	Hayes & Yeading United	2585	L 0-1		19
46	Sat-28-Apr	BSP	A	Ebbsfleet United	1217	W 3-2	Og (Howe) 15, Bore 27, Taylor 33	17

CUPS

No.	Date	Comp	H/A	Opponents	Att:	Result	Goalscorers	Pos
1	Sat-29-Oct	FAC 4Q	A	Alfreton Town	1000	D 1-1	S Smith 10	
2	Tue-01-Nov	FAC 4QR	H	Alfreton Town	1728	L 1-2	S Smith 20	
3	Sat-10-Dec	FAT 1	A	Colwyn Bay	383	W 3-1	Taylor 2 (10, 71), Platt 31	
4	Sat-14-Jan	FAT 2	H	Carshalton Athletic	1743	D 0-0		
5	Wed-18-Jan	FAT 2R	A	Carshalton Athletic	488	L 1-3	Sheridan 89	

League
Starts
Substitute
Unused Sub

Cups
Starts
Substitute
Unused Sub

Goals (Lg)
Goals (Cup)

ANYON	WATTS	HONE	GOWLING	NUTTER	MCCALLUM	FUSEINI	POWER	RUSSELL	PERRY	S SMITH	BARRACLOUGH	TAYLOR	O'KEEFE	SINCLAIR	NICOLAU	CHRISTOHE	NELSON	ARNAUD	CUNNINGHAM	DRAPER	THOMAS	C THOMPSON	LAURENT	FARMAN	HINDS	PLATT	MEDLEY	T THOMPSON	SHERIDAN	BEARDSLEY	WILLIAMS	WATSON	LLOYD-MCGOLDRICK	PACQUETTE	A SMITH	PEARSON	ROBSON	BORE	LOUIS	ALMOND	RODNEY	MCCAMMON	MILLER	COBB
1	4	6	5	3	30	10	8	15	9	14	19	7	23	13	17	27	16	18	25	21	29	26	11	28	2	12	32	34	36	10	4	2	18	16	31	32	26	31	10	28	43	33	35	20
38	11	9	36	46	17	15	42	17	14	18	4	10	4	23	14	22	9	0	2	0	0	5	8	9	14	0	26	12	0	10	3	3	9	0	0	16	11	14	3	2	2	8	0	
0	0	0	1	0	1	2	0	9	10	7	8	14	6	1	5	5	1	1	0	0	1	1	9	0	0	0	6	0	8	1	1	2	9	4	0	0	0	0	0	2	4	0	1	
6	5	9	1	0	1	1	0	0	0	2	4	3	1	21	4	2	1	0	25	0	0	0	0	1	0	0	0	0	2	5	1	1	1	4	0	0	0	0	0	0	0	0	1	
4	2	0	1	5	1	0	4	3	0	4	0	2	2	3	2	5	2	0	0	1	0	1	0	1	3	0	3	0	0	0	0	0	2	0	0	0	0	0	0	0	0	0	0	
0	0	0	1	0	0	0	1	1	2	0	0	1	0	0	1	0	0	0	0	1	1	0	2	0	0	0	0	0	0	0	0	0	0	0	2	0	0	0	0	0	0	0	0	
0	0	2	2	0	1	0	0	0	1	0	0	1	0	0	2	0	0	0	1	1	1	0	0	0	0	0	0	0	0	0	0	0	0	2	0	0	0	0	0	0	0	0	0	
0	0	1	0	2	3	1	4	1	3	7	0	4	1	0	0	2	0	0	0	0	0	0	1	0	1	2	0	1	0	0	0	0	3	3	0	0	0	2	6	1	0	2	1	0
0	0	0	0	0	0	0	0	0	0	2	0	2	0	0	0	0	0	0	0	0	0	0	0	0	0	0	0	1	0	0	0	0	0	0	0	0	0	0	0	0	0	0	0	0

ALSO PLAYED: LINDBERG U (6). WILSON U (9, 14). ROBINSON S (45). R THOMPSON S (C5).

PLAYING SQUAD

Existing Players		SN	HT	WT	DOB	AGE	POB	Career	Apps	Goals
GOALKEEPERS										
Nick	Draper	21			10/12/1993	18	Grimsby	Lincoln C, Sheffield FC (SL) 7/12	0	0
Paul	Farman	1	6'05"	14 06	02/11/1989	22	North Shields	Newcastle (Scholar). Blyth c/s 08, Mansfield (Trial) 1/09, Newcastle Blue Star (Dual) 1/09, Gateshead 6/09 Rel c/s 12, Lincoln C (2ML) 11/11, Lincoln C 5/12	8	0
Jake	Turner	27	6'01"	11 13	19/01/1993	19	Retford	Scunthorpe Rel 1/12, Brigg T (L) 8/11, Winterton R 1/12, Lincoln C 7/12		
DEFENDERS										
Andrew	Boyce	5			05/11/1989	22	Doncaster	Doncaster Rel c/s 09, Worksop (WE) 3/08, Worksop (SL) 8/08, Mansfield (Trial) 4/09, Kings Lynn 7/09, Gainsborough 12/09, Lincoln C 5/12		
Dan	Coupland	25					Harrogate	Lincoln C, Goole AFC (5ML) 8/12		
Josh	Gowling	6	6'03"	12 08	29/11/1983	28	Coventry	West Brom (Scholar) Rel c/s 03, Herfølge Boldklub (Den) 7/03 Rel c/s 05, Bournemouth 8/05, Carlisle 7/08, Hereford (SL) 11/08, Gillingham (5WL) 7/09 Perm 8/09, Rel c/s 11, Lincoln C (L) 10/10, Crewe (Trial) 7/11, Lincoln C 7/11	37	0
Dan	Gray	15	6'00"	11 00	23/11/1989	22	Mansfield	Chesterfield Rel c/s 12, Alfreton (SL) 3/08, Macclesfield (SL) 1/11, Macclesfield (L) 11/11, Lincoln C 7/12		
Elliott	Green	23					Lincoln	Lincoln C		
Graham	Hutchison	19			17/01/1993	19	Bellshill	Lincoln C (Scholar) Rel 4/10, Birmingham (Scholar) 6/10, Lincoln C (6MYthL) 7/12		
John	Nutter	3	6'02"	12 10	13/06/1982	30	Burnham	Blackburn (Sch), Wycombe Rel c/s 01, Aldershot 5/01, St Albans (L) 2/02, Gravesend (L) 11/02, Grays (L) 1/03, Grays 6/04, Stevenage 5/06, Gillingham (2ML) 11/07 Undisc 1/08 Rel c/s 11, Lincoln C 7/11	46	2
Paul	Robson	2	5'08"	11 05	04/08/1983	29	Hull	Doncaster (Scholar), Charlton Rel c/s 03, Bridlington T 8/04, Long Island Rough Riders (USA) 7/05, Crystal Palace Baltimore (USA) 2/08, C.Palace (Trial) 1/09, Newport C 7/11 Rel 10/11, Lincoln C 1/12	16	0
MIDFIELDERS										
Peter	Bore	18	6'00"	12 02	04/11/1987	24	Grimsby	Grimsby Rel 5/11, York C (L) 9/08, Harrogate T 8/11, Lincoln C 1/12	11	2
Frazer	Cobb	22			05/09/1993	18	Newark	Lincoln C	1	0
Karl	Cunningham	24			04/11/1993	18	Lincoln	Lincoln C, Worksop (L) 1/12, Goole AFC (5ML) 5/12	2	0
Geoffrey	Gouveia	26			22/12/1990	21	Boston (USA)	Boston State Team (USA), Pontassolense (Port), Lincoln C 7/12		
Tom	Miller	20			29/06/1990	22	Ely	Littleport (Yth), Ipswich (Yth), Norwich (Scholar) Rel c/s 4/08, Rangers 4/08, Brechin (L) 12/09, Dundalk 2/10, Newport C 1/11 Rel 1/12, Lincoln C 3/12	8	1
Gary	Mills	4	5'09"	11 06	20/05/1981	31	Sheppey	Rushden & D, Yeovil (Trial) 6/06, Crawley 8/06, Rushden & D 1/07 Rel 5/07, Tamworth 6/07, Kettering 10/07, Stevenage 5/08, Mansfield 6/09 Rel 1/11, Forest Green (L) 10/10, Rushden & D 1/11, Bath C 5/11, Nuneaton 9/11, Lincoln C 5/12		
Nicky	Nicolau	16	5'08"	10 03	12/10/1983	28	Camden	Arsenal Rel c/s 04, Southend (SL) 3/04, Southend 5/04 Rel c/s 05, Swindon 7/05 Rel 5/06, Hereford (3ML) 1/06, Barnet 7/06 Rel c/s 08, Weymouth (Trial) 7/08, Brighton (Trial) 7/08, Grimsby (Trial) 8/08, Barnet 9/08 Rel c/s 09, Maidenhead 8/09, Woking 9/09, Dover 8/10, Boreham Wood 12/10, Lincoln C 7/11	19	0
Conal	Platt	11	5'09"	10 10	14/10/1986	25	Preston	Liverpool, Bournemouth 5/06 Rel c/s 07, Morecambe (L) 11/06, Weymouth (SL) 2/07, Weymouth 8/07, Rushden & D (SL) 2/08, Forest Green 5/08, Cambridge U 6/10, AFC Telford (L) 9/11, Lincoln C (2ML) 11/11 Perm 1/12	14	2
Alan	Power	8	5'07"	11 06	23/01/1988	23	Dublin	Notts Forest Rel 5/08, Grays (3ML) 11/07, Hartlepool 7/08 Rel c/s 10, Rushden & D 6/10, Lincoln C 7/11	42	4
Jake	Sheridan	12	5'09"	11 06	08/07/1986	26	Nottingham	Notts County (Yth), Dunkirk, Notts County 8/05 Rel c/s 07, Tamworth 7/07, Eastwood T 7/11, Lincoln C (2ML) 11/11 Perm 1/12	20	0

FORWARDS

		SN	HT	WT	DOB	AGE	POB	From - To	APPS	GOA
Bradley	Barraclough	17			26/05/1989	23	Nuneaton	Bellarmine University Knights (USA), Cincinatti Knights (USA), Lincoln C 8/11, Buxton (L) 12/11	12	0
Luke	Daley	35	5'11"	11 00	10/11/1989	22	Northampton	Norwich, Stevenage (L) 1/11, Plymouth 7/11 Rel c/s 12, Lincoln C 8/12		
Robert	Duffy	9	6'01"	12 04	02/12/1982	29	Swansea	Rushden & D Rel c/s 05, Stamford (L) 1/05, Peterborough (Trial) 7/05, Cambridge U 8/05, Kettering 9/05, Gainsborough 1/06, Stevenage 3/06 Rel 5/06, Oxford U 8/06 Rel 4/08, Wrexham (SL) 1/08, Mansfield (Trial) c/s 07, Newport C 7/08, Mansfield 1/09, Grimsby Undisc 1/11 Rel c/s 12, Lincoln C 5/12		
Vadaine	Oliver	14			21/10/1991	20	Sheffield	Sheff Wed Rel c/s 12, Lincoln C 8/12		
Conner	Robinson							Lincoln C	1	0
Adam	Smith	7	5'11"	12 00	20/02/1985	27	Huddersfield	Chesterfield Rel 6/08, Lincoln C (L) 1/08, Gainsborough 8/08, York C (2ML) 11/08, York C Undisc 1/09, Mansfield 5/10 Rel c/s 12, Aldershot (L) 10/11, Aldershot (2ML) 11/11, Lincoln C 6/12		
Jamie	Taylor	10	5'07"	11 11	16/12/1982	28	Crawley	Broadbridge H, Horsham c/s 01, Aldershot 8/02 Rel 2/04, Horsham (L) 2/03, Carshalton (L) 12/03, Oakwood 2/04, AFC Wimbledon 3/04, Horsham 10/04, Woking 12/06, Dag & Red 3/07, Grays (SL) 2/08, Grays 5/08, Eastbourne B 7/09, Lincoln C 6/11	24	4
Jordan	Thomas						Grantham	Lincoln C	1	0
Reece	Thompson							Lincoln C	0	0

Loanees

		SN	HT	WT	DOB	AGE	POB	From - To	APPS	GOA
(D)Mitchell	Nelson		6'03"		31/08/1989	23	Lambeth	Bournemouth 8/11, 10/11, 11/11 - Rel 12/11, Eastleigh 12/11	10	0
(M)Curtis	Thompson							Notts County 10/11 -	1	0
(F)Luke	Medley		6'01"	13 03	21/06/1989	23	Greenwich	Kidderminster (2ML) 11/11 - Woking (L) 1/12, Rel 2/12, Bromley 2/12	6	0
(D)Robbie	Williams		6'05"		06/07/1987	25	Blackpool	AFC Telford (SL) 1/12 - Rel c/s 12, Hyde FC 8/12	11	0
(G)Adam	Smith				23/01/1992	20	Sunderland	Leicester (SL) 1/12 -	0	0
(D)Matthew	Pearson				03/08/1993	19		Blackburn 1/12 -	0	0
(F)Louis	Almond		5'11"	12 00	15/08/1990	22	Blackburn	Blackpool (SL) 1/12 -	5	1
(F)Mark	McCammon		6'02"	14 05	07/08/1978	34	Barnet	Sheffield FC (SL) 3/12 -	6	2

Departures

		SN	HT	WT	DOB	AGE	POB	From - To	APPS	GOA
(G)Doug	Lindberg		6'04"	14 13	27/03/1988	24	Australia	Fawkner Blues 8/11 - Rel 11/11, Sleaford T (L)	0	0
(M)Ali	Fuseini		5'06"	09 10	07/12/1988	23	Accra, Ghana	Lewes 1/11 - Rel 11/11, Eastleigh 12/11, Bromley 1/12	17	1
(D)Jean	Arnaud		6'02"	12 03	07/04/1987	25	Brou-sur-Chantereine (France)	Libourne (Fra) 9/11 - Rel 12/11	1	0
(D)Adam	Watts		6'01"	11 09	04/03/1988	24	London	Fulham (3ML) 10/09 Undisc 1/10 - Rel 12/11, Gainsborough 1/12 Rel c/s 12	11	0
(M)Josh	O'Keefe		6'01"	11 05	22/12/1988	23	Whalley	Walsall 7/10 - Rel 12/11, Luton (Trial) 2/12, Southport 3/12	10	1
(D)Richard	Hinds		6'02"	12 02	22/08/1980	32	Sheffield	Sheff Wed 11/11 - Rel 1/12, Yeovil 2/12	9	1
(D)Jason	Beardsley		6'00"	11 00	12/07/1989	23	Uttoxeter	Stafford R 12/11 - Rel 1/12	1	0
(F)Gavin	McCallum		5'09"	12 00	24/08/1987	25	Mississauga, Can	Hereford 7/10 - Rel 1/12, Barnet (L) 11/11, Woking 8/12	18	3
(G)Joe	Anyon		6'02"	12 03	29/12/1986	25	Poulton-le-Fylde	Port Vale 7/10 - Rel c/s 12	38	0
(D)Danny	Hone		6'02"	12 00	15/09/1989	22	Croydon	Yth - Rel c/s 12, Barrow (SL) 11/11, Gainsborough 7/12	9	1
(D)Tony	Sinclair				05/03/1985	27		Gillingham 7/11 - Rel c/s 12	24	0
(D)Karlton	Watson				30/04/1992	20	Peterborough	Notts Forest 1/12 - Rel c/s 12	5	0
(M)Jean-Francois	Christophe		6'01"	13 00	13/06/1982	30	Creil, Fra	AFC Compiegne (Fra) 8/11 - Rel c/s 12	27	2
(M)Francis	Laurent		6'02"	13 13	06/01/1986	26	Paris, Fra	Northampton 7/11 - Rel c/s 12	14	1
(M)Nialle	Rodney		6'01"	11 11	28/02/1991	21	Nottingham	Bradford C 1/12 - Rel c/s 12	6	0
(M)Simon	Russell		5'07"	10 06	19/03/1985	27	Hull	Cambridge U 7/11 - Rel c/s 12, Alfreton 7/12	26	1
(F)Andy	Hutchinson		5'10"	10 07	10/03/1992	20	Lincoln	Yth - Rel c/s 12		
(F)Jefferson	Louis		6'02"	13 02	22/02/1979	34	Harrow	Brackley T 1/12 - Rel c/s 12, Newport C 6/12	14	6
(F)Richard	Pacquette		6'00"	12 06	23/01/1983	29	Paddington	Maidenhead 1/12 - Rel c/s 12	13	3
(F)Kyle	Perry		6'04"	14 05	05/03/1986	26	Birmingham	Tamworth 7/11 - Rel c/s 12, AFC Telford (SL) 1/12, Nuneaton 7/12	24	3
(F)James	Wilson						Lincoln	Yth - Rel c/s 12, Worksop (6WL) 11/11, Holbeach U (L) 1/12	0	0
(M)Dan	Lloyd-McGoldrick				03/12/1991	20	Liverpool	Colwyn Bay 1/12 - Rel c/s 12, Colwyn Bay 7/12	12	3
(D)Ashley	Westwood	15	5'11"	11 02	31/08/1976	36	Bridgnorth	Kettering 5/12 - Portsmouth (Coach) 7/12		
(F)Sam	Smith	14			20/05/1990	22	Corby	Rushden & D 7/11 - Cambridge U Undisc 8/12	25	7
(M)Tom	Richardson				10/06/1993	19	York	Sheffield FC 1/12 - Blyth (L) 1/12, North Ferriby (L) 3/12, Bridlington T 8/12		
(M)Tyrone	Thompson		5'09"	11 02	08/05/1981	31	Sheffield	FC Halifax 11/11 - Rel c/s 12	26	1

Conference Action...

More action from the Conference Play-off between Luton Town and York City.

Photo: Peter Barnes.

LUTON TOWN

Chairman: Nick Owen
Secretary: Kevan Platt **(T)** 01582 411 622 **(E)** kevan.platt@lutontown.co.uk
Additional Committee Members:
Gary Sweet, David Wilkinson, David Blakeman, Bob Curson, Paul Ballantyne.

Manager: Paul Buckle
Programme Editor: Andrew Barringer **(E)** andrew.barringer@lutontown.co.uk

Back row (left to right): Jon Shaw, Scott Rendell, Alex Lacey, Dan Walker, Lewis Kidd, Mark Tyler, Dean Brill, Dean Beckwith,
Lathaniel Rowe-Turner, Alasan Ann, Janos Kovacs
Middle row (left to right): Paul Driver (Youth Team Coach) Stuart Fleetwood, Jake Howells, JJ O'Donnell, Danny Spiller, James Dance,
Yaser Kasim, Alex Lawless, Jake Woolley, Matt Robinson, Garry Richards, Simon Parsell (Physiotherapist)
Front row (left to right): Andre Gray, Dmitri Kharine (Goalkeeper Coach), Alan Neilson (Assistant Manager), Ronnie Henry,
Paul Buckle (Manager), Greg Taylor, Carl Emberson (First Team Development Coach),
Paul Carden (First Team Coach), Adam Watkins

Club Factfile

Founded: 1885 **Nickname:** The Hatters
Previous Names: None
Previous Leagues: Football League 1897-1900, 1920-2009. Southern 1900-20.

Club Colours (change): Orange/navy/white (Navy/white/white)

Ground: Kenilworth Stadium, 1 Maple Road, Luton LU4 8AW **(T)** 01582 411 622
Capacity: 10,226 **Seats:** 10,226 **Covered:** All **Clubhouse:** Yes **Shop:** Yes
Directions From the North: Exit the M1 at Junction 11, and join the A505 towards Luton. Follow the A505 for approximately 1.5 miles and Kenilworth Road is on your right as you leave the one-way system along Dunstable Road. To park, follow the one-way around, turning left, right and right again all in about 100 yards so that you do a complete U-turn and then take the second left into Ash Road. Continue down to the bottom, turn left at the end and the club is in front of you. Continue straight past the club and the road bends immediately over a dual carriageway bridge. Beyond this is plenty of street parking (and a great fish shop) if you are early. From the South: You can join the M1 from the M25 at Junction 21A, which is Junction 6 of the M1. Exit at Junction 11 and follow directions above in From the North. From the East: If you are on the A1, leave at Junction 8 of the A1(M) and take the A602 towards Hitchin, then follow the signs to Luton along the A505. When you come into Luton, head for the City Centre and once you reach the one-way system, follow signs to Dunstable and you will see Kenilworth Road on your left. From the West: Come in on the A505 and follow the directions above in From the North.
Previous Grounds: Excelsior, Dallow Lane 1885-97, Dunstable Road 1897-1905

Record Attendance: 30,069 v Blackpool - FA Cup 6th Round Replay 04/03/59
Record Victory: 12-0 v Bristol Rovers - Division 3 South 13/04/36
Record Defeat: 0-9 v Small Heath - Division Two 12/11/1898
Record Goalscorer: Gordon Turner - 243 (1949-64)
Record Appearances: Bob Morton - 495 (1948-64)
Additional Records: Paid £850,000 to Odense for Lars Elstrup
Senior Honours: Recieved £2,500,000 from Arsenal for John Hartson
Football League Division 3 South 1936-37, Division 4 1967-68, Division 2 1981-82, Division 1 2004-05. League Cup 1988.
League Trophy 2008-09

10 YEAR RECORD

02-03		03-04		04-05		05-06		06-07		07-08		08-09		09-10		10-11		11-12	
FL 2	9	FL 2	10	FL 1	1	FLCh	10	FLCh	23	FL 1	24	FL 2	24	Conf	2	Conf	3	Conf	5

LUTON TOWN

No.	Date	Comp	H/A	Opponents	Att:	Result	Goalscorers	Pos
1	Tue-16-Aug	BSP	H	Forest Green Rovers	6061	D 1-1	Beckwith 70	16
2	Sat-20-Aug	BSP	H	Southport	5681	W 5-1	Watkins 41, Antwi 71, Morgan-Smith 73, Willmott 77, Crow 78	10
3	Tue-23-Aug	BSP	A	Mansfield Town	2592	D 1-1	Antwi 78	10
4	Sat-27-Aug	BSP	A	Braintree Town	5703	W 3-1	Morgan-Smith 2 (12, 44), Howells 45	6
5	Tue-30-Aug	BSP	A	Hayes & Yeading United	1015	D 2-2	Morgan-Smith 26, Crow 28	9
6	Fri-02-Sep	BSP	A	Stockport County	3389	D 1-1	Lawless 5	6
7	Sat-10-Sep	BSP	H	Darlington	5952	W 2-0	Crow 31, Fleetwood 71	7
8	Tue-13-Sep	BSP	A	AFC Telford	2640	W 2-0	Morgan-Smith 2 (8, 46)	3
9	Sat-17-Sep	BSP	H	Lincoln City	6316	W 1-0	Fleetwood 84	2
10	Tue-20-Sep	BSP	A	Bath City	1158	D 1-1	Morgan-Smith 45	1
11	Sat-24-Sep	BSP	A	York City	3570	L 0-3		6
12	Tue-27-Sep	BSP	H	Cambridge United	6274	L 0-1		9
13	Sat-01-Oct	BSP	H	Barrow	5613	W 5-1	Willmott 2 (12, 46), Watkins 55, Dance 61, Morgan-Smith 75	6
14	Sat-08-Oct	BSP	A	Kidderminster Harriers	3332	W 2-1	Willmott 2 (39, 82)	5
15	Tue-11-Oct	BSP	H	Ebbsfleet United	1651	D 2-2	Morgan-Smith 44, Dance 71	5
16	Sat-15-Oct	BSP	H	Gateshead	6285	W 5-1	Howells 2 (34, 44), O'Connor 70, Hand 2 (79, 90)	3
17	Tue-18-Oct	BSP	H	Wrexham	7270	L 0-1		5
18	Fri-21-Oct	BSP	A	Grimsby Town	3239	W 1-0	Wright 73	3
19	Sat-05-Nov	BSP	H	Fleetwood Town	6361	L 1-2	Kovacs 90	7
20	Sat-19-Nov	BSP	A	Cambridge United	4796	D 1-1	Fleetwood 18	7
21	Sat-26-Nov	BSP	A	Newport County	1511	W 1-0	Crow 90	6
22	Tue-29-Nov	BSP	H	AFC Telford	5399	D 1-1	Willmott 41	6
23	Tue-06-Dec	BSP	A	Lincoln City	2049	D 1-1	Crow 36	7
24	Sat-17-Dec	BSP	A	Tamworth	1467	W 3-1	Crow 2 (38, 53), Dance 56	5
25	Mon-26-Dec	BSP	H	Kettering Town	7164	W 5-0	Howells 20, O'Connor 27, Lawless 49, Fleetwood 80, Willmott 85	5
26	Sun-01-Jan	BSP	A	Kettering Town	3247	W 5-0	Howells 4, Watkins 9, Kovacs 62, Taylor 74, Fleetwood 90	3
27	Sat-07-Jan	BSP	H	Newport County	6108	W 2-0	O'Connor 35, Crow 66	3
28	Tue-10-Jan	BSP	A	Stockport County	5588	W 1-0	O'Connor pen 73	3
29	Sat-21-Jan	BSP	A	Southport	1665	D 3-3	Crow 39, Watkins 45, O'Connor 47	3
30	Wed-25-Jan	BSP	H	Mansfield Town	5261	D 0-0		3
31	Sat-28-Jan	BSP	H	Alfreton Town	5658	W 1-0	G Pilkington pen 39	3
32	Sat-18-Feb	BSP	H	Tamworth	5833	W 3-0	Fleetwood 14, Kovacs 63, Og (F Francis) 81	3
33	Tue-21-Feb	BSP	A	Barrow	925	L 0-1		3
34	Sat-03-Mar	BSP	H	Bath City	5745	W 2-0	Kovacs 17, Watkins 81	3
35	Wed-07-Mar	BSP	A	Wrexham	4206	L 0-2		3
36	Tue-13-Mar	BSP	A	Darlington	1382	D 1-1	Fleetwood 90	3
37	Tue-20-Mar	BSP	A	Forest Green Rovers	975	L 0-3		4
38	Sat-24-Mar	BSP	H	Grimsby Town	6419	D 1-1	Gray 60	5
39	Fri-30-Mar	BSP	H	York City	5925	L 1-2	Gray 5	6
40	Sat-07-Apr	BSP	A	Braintree Town	1703	L 1-3	Gray 7	7
41	Mon-09-Apr	BSP	H	Hayes & Yeading United	6003	W 4-2	Fleetwood 2 (13, 44), Keane 53, Gray 71	7
42	Sat-14-Apr	BSP	A	Alfreton Town	1654	D 0-0		7
43	Tue-17-Apr	BSP	H	Ebbsfleet United	5526	W 3-0	Fleetwood 2 (45, 46), McAllister 90	6
44	Sat-21-Apr	BSP	H	Kidderminster Harriers	8415	W 1-0	Willmott 67	5
45	Tue-24-Apr	BSP	A	Gateshead	703	D 0-0		5
46	Sat-28-Apr	BSP	A	Fleetwood Town	4446	W 2-0	Og (Pond) 10, Gray 70	5

CUPS

No.	Date	Comp	H/A	Opponents	Att:	Result	Goalscorers
1	Sat-29-Oct	FAC 4Q	H	Hendon	2329	W 5-1	O'Connor pen 7, Dance 13, Wright 25, Fleetwood 70, Kissock 71
2	Sat-12-Nov	FAC 1	H	Northampton Town	4799	W 1-0	Watkins 80
3	Sat-03-Dec	FAC 2	H	Cheltenham Town	4516	L 2-4	O'Connor 2 (40, 51)
4	Sat-10-Dec	FAT 1	H	Swindon Supermarine	1298	W 2-0	Fleetwood 37, Wright 65
5	Wed-18-Jan	FAT 2	A	Hinckley United	754	D 0-0	
6	Mon-23-Jan	FAT 2R	H	Hinckley United	1004	W 3-0	Og (Bragoli) 14, Morgan-Smith 44, Fleetwood 65
7	Tue-07-Feb	FAT 3	A	Kidderminster Harriers	1186	W 2-1	Howells 24, Fleetwood 45
8	Sat-25-Feb	FAT 4	H	Gateshead	2499	W 2-0	Kissock 7, Keane 59
9	Sat-10-Mar	FAT SF1	A	York City	3365	L 0-1	
10	Sat-17-Mar	FAT SF2	H	York City	5796	D 1-1	Willmott 43
11	Thu-03-May	PO SF1	H	Wrexham	9012	W 2-0	Gray 22, Fleetwood 30
12	Mon-07-May	PO SF2	A	Wrexham	9087	L 1-2	G Pilkington pen 26
13	Sun-20-May	PO Final	N	York City	39265	L 1-2	Gray 2

	League
	Starts
	Substitute
	Unused Sub
	Cups
	Starts
	Substitute
	Unused Sub
	Goals (Lg)
	Goals (Cup)

Football appearance grid (X = start, S = substitute, U = unused substitute).

	K PILKINGTON	OSANO	ASAFU-ADJAYE	HOWELLS	ANTWI	BECKWITH	LAWLESS	KEANE	DANCE	O'CONNOR	BARNES-HOMER	WILLMOTT	KIDD	MORGAN-SMITH	CROW	WATKINS	TYLER	GLEESON	WALKER	POKU	KISSOCK	FLEETWOOD	CARDEN	HAND	SAMUEL	KOVACS	G PILKINGTON	BLACKETT	WRIGHT	HENRY	TAVERNIER	TAYLOR	BRUNT	LACEY	O'DONNELL	MCADAMS	SMITH	ANN	WOOLLEY	NASH	LONGDEN	MCALLISTER	MAGURAUSHE	BOUCAUD	GRAY
No.	30	18	16	15	17	5	7	4	19	14	9	11	31	8	10	28	1	2	29	25	20	13	22	27	23	34	6	12	39	21	36	3	23	24	26	40	41	37	44	43	42	9	45	17	27

P	12	28	7	42	12	8	38	33	21	21	1	29	0	15	23	20	34	8	0	5	7	22	1	11	0	37	33	5	1	0	0	15	0	0	0	0	0	0	0	0	0	4	0	4	9
S	0	0	2	0	0	0	0	0	5	13	0	10	0	2	6	14	0	2	1	5	14	15	0	2	1	0	0	4	3	2	0	2	5	0	0	0	0	1	0	0	10	0	3	0	
U	20	1	4	0	3	1	0	1	1	4	2	2	3	1	4	10	11	2	1	5	11	2	1	2	1	0	0	5	1	0	0	2	0	1	0	0	0	0	0	0	0	4	0	2	0

Gls	3	10	4	10	1	3	9	9	2	3	0	9	0	2	4	6	10	2	0	0	7	9	0	2	0	7	8	2	1	2	0	5	1	3	2	2	0	1	0	1	0	0	0	0	3
	0	1	0	0	0	0	0	0	0	2	0	1	0	2	2	3	0	0	0	3	1	0	0	0	0	1	1	2	1	1	0	0	2	1	1	0	0	1	0	2	0	1	0	1	0
	1	0	0	0	0	2	0	0	1	1	0	1	5	0	0	1	3	3	0	0	0	1	1	1	1	1	0	5	1	1	0	1	0	0	1	0	1	0	2	0	1	0	1	0	0

| | 0 | 0 | 0 | 5 | 2 | 1 | 2 | 1 | 3 | 5 | 0 | 8 | 0 | 9 | 9 | 5 | 0 | 0 | 0 | 0 | 0 | 11 | 0 | 2 | 0 | 4 | 1 | 0 | 1 | 0 | 0 | 1 | 0 | 1 | 0 | 0 | 0 | 0 | 0 | 0 | 0 | 1 | 0 | 0 | 5 |
| | 0 | 0 | 0 | 1 | 0 | 0 | 0 | 1 | 1 | 3 | 0 | 1 | 0 | 1 | 0 | 1 | 0 | 0 | 0 | 0 | 0 | 2 | 5 | 0 | 0 | 0 | 1 | 0 | 2 | 0 | 0 | 0 | 0 | 0 | 0 | 0 | 0 | 0 | 0 | 0 | 0 | 0 | 0 | 0 | 2 |

PLAYING SQUAD

Existing Players		SN	HT	WT	DOB	AGE	POB	Career	Apps	Goals
GOALKEEPERS										
Dean	Brill	33	6'02"	14 05	02/12/1985	26	Luton	Luton Rel c/s 05, Gillingham (6WL) 11/06, Oldham 7/09 Rel c/s 11, Barnet 8/11 Rel c/s 12, Luton 8/12		
Lewis	Kidd	21			28/10/1992	19		Luton, Swindon Supermarine (L) 12/11, Dunstable T (5ML) 8/12	0	0
Mark	Tyler	1	6'00"	12 09	02/04/1977	35	Norwich	Peterborough, Billericay (3ML) 1/96, Yeovil (L) 11/96, Hull C (L) 1/08, Watford (2ML) 9/08, Bury (2ML) 1/09, Luton 6/09	34	0
DEFENDERS										
Dean	Beckwith	5	6'03"	13 02	18/09/1983	28	Southwark	Gillingham Rel c/s 05, Tonbridge A (L) 8/02, Dag & Red (L) 10/03, Margate (L) 9/04, Hereford 7/05 Rel c/s 09, Northampton 7/09 Rel 5/11, Luton 6/11	8	1
Michael	Cain							Luton		
Ronnie	Henry	25	5'11"	11 10	02/01/1984	28	Hemel Hempstead	Tottenham Rel 11/03, Southend (L) 3/03, Fisher 2/04, Dublin C 8/04, Stevenage 1/05 Rel c/s 12, Luton 6/12		
Janos	Kovacs	6	6'04"	14 11	11/09/1985	26	Budapest, Hun	MTK Hungaria (Hun), Bodajk (Hun) (SL) 8/04, Chesterfield 8/05, York C (L) 3/07, Lincoln C £17,500 6/08 Rel 1/10, Luton 1/10, Hereford 6/10, Luton (4ML) 9/11 Perm 1/12	37	4
Alex	Lacey	16			31/05/1993	19		Luton, Cambridge C (2ML) 8/11, Thurrock (L) 11/11, Thurrock (L) 12/11, Eastbourne B (L) 2/12	0	0
Alex	Lawless	7	5'11"	10 08	05/02/1983	29	Llwynupion	Fulham, Torquay 7/05 Rel 5/06, Forest Green 8/06, York C 6/09, Luton (2ML) 11/10 Undisc 1/11	38	2
Brett	Longden							Luton	0	0
Garry	Richards	4	6'03"	13 00	11/06/1986	26	Romford	Colchester, Brentford (SL) 2/07, Southend Undisc 8/07, Gillingham £70,000 1/08 Rel c/s 12, Luton 6/12		
Lathaniel	Rowe-Turner	2	6'01"	13 00	12/11/1989	22	Leicester	Leicester, Cheltenham (L) 10/08, Redditch (SL) 2/09, Kings Lynn (3ML) 9/09, Torquay Undisc 2/10 Rel c/s 12, Luton 7/12		
Greg	Taylor	3	6'01"	12 01	15/01/1990	22	Bedford	Rushden & D (Yth), Northampton Rel c/s 09, Kettering 6/09, Darlington Undisc 1/11, Luton (2ML) 11/11 Perm 1/12	17	1
MIDFIELDERS										
Alasan	Ann	32			01/12/1993	18		Luton, Hitchin (L) 12/11	0	0
Andre	Boucaud	26	5'10"	10 02	09/10/1984	27	Enfield	Reading Rel c/s 04, Peterborough (SL) 3/03, Peterborough (2ML) 8/03, Walsall (Trial) 2/04, Peterborough 7/04, Aldershot (3ML) 9/05, Kettering 5/06, Wycombe 8/07 Rel c/s 08, Kettering 8/08, York C (6WL) 11/10 Perm 1/11, Luton £25,000 1/12, Notts County (5ML) 8/12	7	0
Paul	Carden		5'09"	11 10	29/03/1979	32	Liverpool	Blackpool, Rochdale (Trial) 2/98 Perm 3/98, Hull C (Trial), Chester 3/00, Doncaster £10,000 7/01, Chester 11/01 Rel c/s 05, Peterborough 7/05 Rel 10/06, Burscough 10/06, Burton (3ML) 10/06 Perm 1/07, Accrington 5/07 Rel 5/08, Cambridge U (6WL) 11/07, Cambridge U (SL) 1/08, Cambridge U 5/08, Luton (SL) 2/11, Luton (Pl/Coach) 8/11	1	0
Newman	Carney	31	5'10"		23/03/1994	18		Luton		
James	Dance	19			15/03/1987	25	Coleshill	Birmingham (Yth), Cheltenham (Scholar), Coleshill, Rushall O 6/09, Redditch 8/09, Kettering 11/09, Crawley Undisc 1/11, Luton Undisc 7/11	26	3
Ryan	Dasilva							Luton		
Jake	Howells	11	5'09"	11 08	18/04/1991	21	St Albans	Luton	42	5
Yaser	Kasim	18	5'11"	11 06	10/05/1991	21	Baghdad, Iraq	Tottenham (Scholar) Rel c/s 10, C.Palace (Trial) 4/10, C.Palace (Trial) 7/10, Brighton 10/10, Luton (6ML) 7/12		
Colby	McAdams							Luton, Hitchin (L) 12/11	0	0
Jerry	Nash							Luton	0	0
Jonathan	O'Donnell	17			29/10/1991	20		Watford (Yth), MK Dons (Yth), Hemel Hempstead, St Albans 7/09, Luton (Trial) 12/09, Luton 1/10, St Albans (L) 1/10, St Albans (L) 3/11, Cambridge C (2ML) 8/11, Hampton & R (6WL) 10/11, Hampton & R (L) 12/11, Thurrock (SL) 3/12	0	0
Matt	Robinson							Leicester (Scholar) Rel c/s 12, Luton 7/12		
Charlie	Smith				07/09/1995	16		Luton	0	0
Danny	Spiller	8	5'08"	11 00	10/10/1981	30	Maidstone	Gillingham, Longford T (Ire) (L) 1/02, Millwall 6/07 Rel c/s 09, Wycombe 8/09 Rel 8/09, Welling 9/09, Dag & Red 9/09, Gillingham 7/10 Rel c/s 12, Luton 6/12		
Adam	Watkins	15			08/09/1991	20	Luton	Luton, Arlesey T (WE) 2/10, Arlesey T (L) 9/10, Arlesey T (L) 12/10, Harrow (L) 3/11	34	5

FORWARDS

		SN	HT	WT	DOB	AGE	POB	From - To	APPS	GOA
Stuart	Fleetwood	13	5'10"	12 07	23/04/1986	26	Chepstow	Cardiff, Hereford 1/06 Rel c/s 07, Accrington (L) 1/07, Forest Green 6/07, Charlton Tribunal 6/08, Cheltenham (L) 9/08, Brighton (3ML) 10/08, Exeter (SL) 3/09, Exeter (SL) 9/09, Hereford Undisc 7/10, Luton Undisc 8/11	37	11
Andre	Gray	12	5'11"	12 06	26/06/1991	21	Wolverhampton	Shrewsbury Rel c/s 10, AFC Telford (2ML) 11/09, Hinckley U (L) 3/10, Hinckley U 6/10, Luton (SL) 3/12 £30,000 7/12	9	5
Jon-Paul	Kissock		5'05"	10 09	02/12/1989	22	Liverpool	Everton Rel c/s 09, Gretna (SL) 1/08, Accrington (L) 1/09, Hamilton 8/09 Rel 12/09, Brighton (Trial) c/s 10, MK Dons (Trial) c/s 10, Newton 8/10, Formby 10/10, Southport 12/10, Luton 8/11, Macclesfield (6ML) 7/12	21	0
Leeroy	Maguraushe							Luton	0	0
Scott	Rendell	10	6'01"	13 00	21/10/1986	25	Ashford, Middx	Aldershot (Yth), Reading (Sch), Aldershot (2ML) 2/05, Forest Green (5ML) 8/05, Hayes (SL) 3/06, Crawley (L) 8/06 Perm 1/07 (06/07 43,11), Cambridge U 5/07, Peterborough (SL) 2/08, £115,000 7/08, Yeovil (L) 10/08, Cambridge U (6WL) 11/08, Cambridge U (SL) 1/09, Torquay (SL) 7/09, Wycombe Undisc 7/10, Bristol R (L) 10/11, Oxford U (SL) 1/12, Luton Undisc 6/12		
Jon	Shaw	9	6'00"	13 01	10/11/1983	28	Sheffield	Sheff Wed Rel 11/04, York (2ML) 11/03, Burton 11/04, Cheltenham (Trial) 11/04, Halifax 8/07, Rochdale £60,000 7/08 Rel 1/10, Crawley (L) 1/09, Barrow (3ML) 8/09, Gateshead (5WL) 11/09, Mansfield 1/10 Rel 5/10, Gateshead 5/10 Rel c/s 12, Luton 6/12		
Dan	Walker	29			15/08/1990	22		Stony Stratford, Bedford T, Leighton T (SL) 10/09, Luton 8/10, Eastbourne B (L) 1/11, Cambridge U (L) 2/11, Southport (5ML) 8/11	1	0
Jake	Woolley				11/09/1993	18		Rushden & D, Luton	1	0

Loanees		SN	HT	WT	DOB	AGE	POB	From - To	APPS	GOA
(M)Jamie	Hand		6'00"	11 08	07/02/1984	28	Uxbridge	Hayes & Yeading (3ML) 9/11 - Rel c/s 12, Mansfield 7/12	13	2
(F)Ryan	Brunt				26/05/1993	19	Birmingham	Stoke (2ML) 11/11 - Tranmere (L) 1/12, L.Orient (6ML) 7/12	5	0
(F)Craig	McAllister		6'01"	12 07	28/06/1980	32	Glasgow	Newport C (SL) 1/12 -	14	1

Departures		SN	HT	WT	DOB	AGE	POB	From - To	APPS	GOA
(F)Collin	Samuel		5'09"	11 13	27/08/1981	31	North Manzanilla	St Johnstone 8/11 - Rel 11/11, Arbroath 1/12	1	0
(D)Fred	Murray		5'10"	11 12	22/05/1982	30	Clonmel	Grays (6ML) 8/09 Perm 1/10 - De-Registered 11/11		
(D)Ashley	Deeney				25/11/1991	20	Milton Keynes	Yth - Rel 11/11 St Neots (L) 9/11		
(F)Matthew	Barnes-Homer		5'11"	12 05	25/01/1986	26	Dudley	Kidderminster (5WL) 11/09 £75,000 1/10 - Rel 1/12, Rochdale (5ML) 8/11, Nuneaton T 2/12, Ostersunds SK (Swe) 3/12, Macclesfield 6/12	1	0
(D)Will	Antwi		6'02"	12 08	19/10/1982	29	Ashford, Kent	Dag & Red 7/11 - Rel 1/12, Grimsby (5WL) 11/11, Staines 2/1212		2
(F)Tommy	Wright		6'00"	11 12	28/09/1984	27	Kirby Muxloe	Kidderminster 10/11 - Rel 1/12, Port Vale (Trial) 1/12, Forest Green 1/12, Tamworth 7/12	4	1
(G)Kevin	Pilkington		6'01"	13 00	08/03/1974	38	Hitchin	Notts County 5/10 - Mansfield (3ML) 10/10, Notts County (Gk Coach) 2/12	12	0
(F)Charlie	Henry				01/07/1987	25	Stevenage	Newport C (5WL) 11/10 Undisc 1/11 - Rel c/s 12, Aldershot T (2ML) 11/11, Macclesfield 7/12	2	0
(D)Ed	Asafu-Adjaye		5'11"	12 04	22/12/1988	23	Southwark	Yth - Rel c/s 12, Forest Green 7/12	9	0
(M)Christian	Tavernier							Yth - Rel c/s 12, Tooting & M (L) 11/11, Arlesey (L) 3/12	0	0
(D)Curtis	Osano		5'11"	11 04	08/03/1987	25	Nakuru, Kenya	Rushden & D 7/11 - AFC Wimbledon 5/12	28	0
(D)Shane	Blackett		6'00"	12 11	03/10/1982	29	Luton	Peterborough 7/09 - Rel c/s 12	9	0
(D)Dan	Gleeson		6'03"	13 02	17/02/1985	27	Cambridge	Cambridge U 5/10 - Rel c/s 12, Lowestoft T 7/12	10	0
(F)Danny	Crow		5'09"	11 00	26/01/1986	26	Great Yarmouth	Cambridge U 5/10 - Rel c/s 12, Newport C 6/12	29	9
(M)Keith	Keane		5'09"	11 01	20/11/1986	25	Luton	Yth - Preston 7/12	33	1
(M)Godfrey	Poku				22/07/1990	22		St Albans 1/10 - Southport (5ML) 8/11, Mansfield 7/12	10	0
(D)George	Pilkington		5'11"	11 06	07/11/1981	30	Rugeley	Port Vale 8/08 - Mansfield 7/12	33	1
(M)Robbie	Willmott		5'09"	12 01	16/05/1990	22	Harlow	Cambridge U £50,000 1/11 - Rel c/s 12, Cambridge U 7/12	39	8
(F)Amari	Morgan-Smith		6'00"	13 06	03/04/1989	23	Wolverhampton	Ilkeston 9/10 - Rel c/s 12, Doncaster (Trial) 7/12	17	9
(F)Aaron	O'Connor	14	5'10"	12 00	09/08/1983	29	Nottingham	Rushden & D 6/11 - Newport C 7/12	34	5

Conference Action...

Luton Town take the lead thanks to a Andre Gray goal in the Play-off Final.

Photo: Peter Barnes.

MACCLESFIELD TOWN

Chairman: Mike Rance
Secretary: Julie Briggs   **(T)** 01625 264 686   **(E)** juliebriggs@mtfc.co.uk
Additional Committee Members:
Andy Scott, Barrie Darcey, Jon Harris, Amar Alkadhi, Bashar Alkadhi, Jeremy Turner.

Manager: Steve King
Programme Editor: Richard Stanton   **(E)** richard.stanton.t21@btinternet.com

THE NON-LEAGUE CLUB DIRECTORY

Book Holiday Inn Hotels and Save today!

Home

Clubs

Steps 1 - 4

League Tables

35 Years of Non-League Football

The Non-League Club Directory has developed into a comprehensive record of competitions within the non-League game, giving this level of football the

www.non-leagueclubdirectory.co.uk

Club Factfile

Founded: 1874   **Nickname:** The Silkmen

Previous Names: None

Previous Leagues: Manchester. Cheshire County. Northern Premier. Conference 1987-97. Football League 1997-2012.

Club Colours (change): All blue (Yellow/navy/navy)

Ground: Moss Rose Ground, London Road, Macclesfield SK11 7SP   **(T)** 01625 264 686

Capacity: 6,208   **Seats:** Yes   **Covered:** Yes   **Clubhouse:** Yes   **Shop:** Yes

Directions
From North (M6), Exit Junction 19, Knutsford. Follow the A537 to Macclesfield. Follow signs for the Town Centre. The follow signs A523 Leek, the ground is a mile out of town. The ground is sign-posted from the Town Centre
From South (M6), Exit Junction 17 Sandbach. Follow A534 to Congleton. Then A536 to Macclesfield. After passing the Rising Sun on the left, less than a mile, turn right into Moss Lane. Follow this around and it will bring you to the rear of the ground.

Previous Grounds: Rostron Field 1874-1891.

Record Attendance: 9,008 v Winsford United - Cheshire Senior Cup 04.02.1948.

Record Victory: 15-0 v Chester St Marys - Cheshire Senior Cup Second Round 16.02.1886.
Record Defeat: 1-13 v Tranmere Rovers Reserves - 03.05.1929.

Record Goalscorer: Not known

Record Appearances: Not known

Additional Records:

Senior Honours:
Manchester League 1908-09, 10-11. Cheshire County League 1931-32, 32-33, 53-54, 60-61, 63-64, 67-68.
Northern Premier League 1968-69, 69-70, 86-87. Bob Lord Trophy 1993-94. Conference 1994-95, 96-97, Championship Shield 1996, 1997, 1998. FA Trophy 1969-70, 95-96. Cheshire Senior cup x20 most recently 1999-2000.

02-03		03-04		04-05		05-06		06-07		07-08		08-09		09-10		10-11		11-12	
FL 3	16	FL 3	20	FL 2	5	FL 2	17	FL 2	22	FL 2	19	FL 2	20	FL 2	19	FL 2	15	FL 2	24

MACCLESFIELD TOWN

No.	Date	Comp	H/A		Opponents		Result
1	LGE 2		Sa 06Aug	H	Dagenham & Redbridge	L	0 - 1
2	CC 1		Tu 09Aug	A	Hull City	W	0 - 2
3	LGE 2		Sa 13Aug	A	Crawley Town	L	2 - 0
4	LGE 2		Tu 16Aug	A	Hereford United	W	0 - 4
5	LGE 2		Sa 20Aug	H	Bristol Rovers	D	0 - 0
6	CC 2		We 24Aug	A	Bolton Wanderers	L	2 - 1
7	LGE 2		Sa 27Aug	H	AFC Wimbledon	W	4 - 0
8	LGE 2		Sa 03Sep	A	Torquay United	L	3 - 0
9	LGE 2		Sa 10Sep	A	Cheltenham Town	L	2 - 0
10	LGE 2		Tu 13Sep	H	Morecambe	D	1 - 1
11	LGE 2		Sa 17Sep	H	Northampton Town	W	3 - 1
12	LGE 2		Sa 24Sep	A	Plymouth Argyle	L	2 - 0
13	LGE 2		Fr 30Sep	H	Swindon Town	W	2 - 0
14	JPT 1		We 05Oct	A	Crewe Alexandra	L	1 - 0
15	LGE 2		Sa 08Oct	A	Aldershot Town	W	1 - 2
16	LGE 2		Sa 15Oct	H	Oxford United	D	1 - 1
17	LGE 2		Sa 22Oct	A	Crewe Alexandra	W	0 - 1
18	LGE 2		Tu 25Oct	H	Bradford City	W	1 - 0
19	LGE 2		Sa 29Oct	H	Southend United	L	0 - 2
20	LGE 2		Sa 05Nov	A	Burton Albion	L	1 - 0
21	FAC 1		Sa 12Nov	A	East Thurrock	W	0 - 3
22	LGE 2		Sa 19Nov	H	Accrington Stanley	D	1 - 1
23	LGE 2		Fr 25Nov	A	Barnet	L	2 - 1
24	FAC 2		Sa 03Dec	A	Chelmsford City	D	1 - 1
25	LGE 2		Sa 10Dec	H	Gillingham	D	0 - 0
26	FAC 2r		We 14Dec	H	Chelmsford City	W	1 - 0
27	LGE 2		Sa 17Dec	A	Shrewsbury Town	L	1 - 0
28	LGE 2		Mo 26Dec	H	Rotherham United	D	0 - 0
29	LGE 2		Sa 31Dec	H	Port Vale	W	2 - 1
30	LGE 2		Mo 02Jan	A	Accrington Stanley	L	4 - 0
31	FAC 3		Sa 07Jan	H	Bolton Wanderers	D	2 - 2
32	LGE 2		Sa 14Jan	H	Torquay United	L	1 - 2
33	FAC 3r		Tu 17Jan	A	Bolton Wanderers	L	2 - 0
34	LGE 2		Sa 21Jan	A	Swindon Town	L	1 - 0
35	LGE 2		Tu 24Jan	A	AFC Wimbledon	L	2 - 1
36	LGE 2		Sa 28Jan	H	Cheltenham Town	L	1 - 3
37	LGE 2		Tu 14Feb	A	Morecambe	L	1 - 0
38	LGE 2		Sa 18Feb	H	Aldershot Town	L	0 - 1
39	LGE 2		Tu 21Feb	A	Northampton Town	L	3 - 2
40	LGE 2		Sa 25Feb	A	Oxford United	D	1 - 1
41	LGE 2		Tu 28Feb	H	Plymouth Argyle	D	1 - 1
42	LGE 2		Sa 03Mar	A	Bristol Rovers	D	0 - 0
43	LGE 2		Tu 06Mar	H	Hereford United	D	2 - 2
44	LGE 2		Sa 10Mar	H	Crawley Town	D	2 - 2
45	LGE 2		Sa 17Mar	A	Dagenham & Redbridge	L	2 - 0
46	LGE 2		Tu 20Mar	A	Rotherham United	L	4 - 2
47	LGE 2		Fr 23Mar	H	Barnet	D	0 - 0
48	LGE 2		Sa 31Mar	A	Gillingham	L	2 - 0
49	LGE 2		Fr 06Apr	H	Macclesfield	L	1 - 3
50	LGE 2		Mo 09Apr	A	Port Vale	L	1 - 0
51	LGE 2		Sa 14Apr	H	Macclesfield	D	2 - 2
52	LGE 2		Sa 21Apr	A	Bradford	L	1 - 0
53	LGE 2		Sa 28Apr	H	Macclesfield	L	0 - 2
54	LGE 2		Sa 05May	A	Southend	L	2 - 0

PLAYING SQUAD 2012-13

Existing Players		SN	HT	WT	DOB	AGE	POB	Career	Apps	Goals
GOALKEEPERS										
Lance	Cronin	1	6'01"	12 00	11/09/1985	26	Brighton	Brighton (Jun), C.Palace, Wycombe (L) 3/05, Oldham 11/05 Rel 2/06, Shrewsbury 2/06, MK Dons (Trial) 4/06, Gravesend/Ebbsfleet 8/06, Gillingham 7/10 Rel c/s 11, Bristol R 7/11 Rel c/s 12, Ebbsfleet (2ML) 2/12, Macclesfield 6/12		
Andrew	Mills	13			15/07/1994	18		Macclesfield, Witton (WE) 12/11		
DEFENDERS										
James	Bolton	24						Macclesfield		
Nat	Brown	5	6'02"	12 05	15/06/1981	31	Sheffield	Huddersfield Rel c/s 05, Lincoln C 8/05 Rel 6/08, Wrexham 6/08 (08/09 7,0), Macclesfield (SL) 11/08, Macclesfield 7/09		
Kieran	Charnock	6	6'01"	13 07	03/08/1984	28	Preston	Wigan Rel 3/03, Southport 3/03, Northwich 8/03, Peterborough Undisc 7/07, Accrington (SL) 10/08, Torquay 8/09, Morecambe (L) 11/10 Perm, Fleetwood (6WL) 11/11 Perm 1/12, Macclesfield (5ML) 8/12		
Tony	Diagne	14	6'01"	11 11	17/09/1990	21	Aubergenville (Fra)	Notts Forest Rel c/s 10, CM Aubervilliers (Fra) 6/10, Macclesfield 1/11		
Ryan	Jackson	2			31/07/1990	21	Streatham	AFC Wimbledon Rel c/s 12, Fleetwood (L) 10/11, Cambridge U (SL) 1/12, Macclesfield 6/12		
Carl	Martin		5'08"	10 07	24/10/1986	25	Camden	Wealdstone, Dag & Red (Trial) 9/09, Crewe Nominal 10/09 Rel c/s 12, Macclesfield 8/12		
Carl	Tremarco	3	5'08"	11 11	11/10/1985	26	Liverpool	Tranmere, Wrexham 1/08, Darlington (2ML) 1/09, Macclesfield 6/09		
MIDFIELDERS										
Harry	Agombar	25			12/07/1992	20	London	Arsenal (Yth), Tottenham (Yth), Grays, Barnet NC c/s 11, Grays 7/11, Partizan Belgrade (Ser) 4/12, West Ham (Trial), Macclesfield 7/12		
Euloge	Ahodikpe	4	5'08"	10 05	01/05/1983	29	Paris, Fra	Lille (Fra), Amiens (Fra), Creteil (Fra), Lombard Papa (Hun) 7/07, Diósgyőri VTK (Hun) (SL) 7/08, Diyarbakırspor (Tur) 8/09, Creteil B (Fra) 7/11, Macclesfield 7/12		
Craig	Braham-Barrett	22			01/09/1988	23		Charlton (Yth), Sheff Wed (Yth), Aveley, Dulwich H 7/07, Potters Bar 10/07, Eastleigh, East Thurrock 2/08, Welling 5/08, Peterborough £10,000 + 10/08 Rel 7/09, Kettering (L) 1/09, Grays 8/09 Rel 1/10, Farnborough 1/10, Havant & W 6/11, Sutton U 2/12 Rel c/s 12, Macclesfield 7/12		
Andre	Costa	15						Hayes & Yeading, Bournemouth (Trial) 7/09, Poole T 9/09, Dorchester 10/09, Sutton U 11/09, Walton & H (L) 1/10, AFC Hayes (L) 3/10, Uxbridge 10/10, Nea Salamis (Cyp), Dulwich H 7/11, Macclesfield 7/12		
Jack	Mackreth	7	5'09"	11 00	13/04/1992	19	Liverpool	Tranmere Rel c/s 11, Burscough (2ML) 9/10, Colwyn Bay (L) 12/10, Hyde FC (L) 2/11, Chester FC (L) 3/11, Barrow 7/11, Macclesfield 5/12		
Arnaud	Mendy	12	6'03"	13 10	10/02/1990	22	Evreux, Fra	Rouen (Fra), Derby c/s 08 Rel c/s 11, Grimsby (L) 10/09, Tranmere (3ML) 8/10, Macclesfield 7/12		
Kieran	Murtagh	8	6'00"	12 00	29/10/1988	22	Wapping	Charlton (Scholar) Rel c/s 07, Fisher 10/07, Fulham (Trial) 5/08, Yeovil 6/08, Wycombe 7/10 Rel c/s 11, Woking (2ML) 1/11, Cambridge U 6/11, Woking (SL) 12/11, Macclesfield 7/12		
Sam	Wedgbury	17	6'00"	12 08	26/02/1989	23	Oldbury	Worcester, Sheff Utd 1/06 Rel c/s 10, Mansfield (L) 10/08 (08/09 1,0), Ferencvaros (Hun) (SL) 1/09, Ferencvaros (Hun) (6ML) 7/09, Macclesfield 7/10, Altrincham (L) 1/11		
Peter	Winn	11	6'00"	11 08	19/12/1988	23	Cleethorpes	Scunthorpe Rel 5/10, Northwich (3ML) 10/08, Barrow (L) 2/09, Gateshead (2ML) 10/09, Gateshead (SL) 2/10, Stevenage 7/10 Rel c/s 12, Cambridge U (3ML) 8/11, Grimsby (SL) 3/12, Macclesfield 7/12		
Junior	Yiadom (Konadu)	16						Barking, Eton Manor, Barking 1/08, Eton Manor, Leyton, Ilford, Hemel Hempstead, Dag & Red, St Neots, Peterborough (Trial), Macclesfield 7/12		

PLAYING SQUAD

FORWARDS

Matthew	Barnes-Homer	9	5'11"	12 05	25/01/1986	25	Dudley

Wolves (Sch) Rel c/s 04, Aldershot 9/04 Rel 11/04, Hednesford 2/05, Bromsgrove 3/05, Sracuse (USA), Virginia Beach Mariners (USA), Tividale 7/06, Willenhall 8/06, Wycombe 3/07 Rel 5/07, Kidderminster 7/07, Luton (5WL) 11/09 £75,000 1/10 Rel 1/12, Rochdale (5ML) 8/11, Nuneaton T 2/12, Ostersunds SK (Swe) 3/12, Macclesfield 6/12

Rob	Edmans	30	6'07"		25/01/1987	25	Greenwich

Loughborough Univ, Virginia Tech Hokies (USA), Tiptree, Maldon T, Loughborough D, Witham T, Chelmsford (L) 8/09 Perm 8/09, Dag & Red Undisc 7/11, Dover (SL) 3/12

Wade	Fairhurst	20	5'10"	10 07	07/05/1989	23	Sheffield

Sheff Utd (Jun), Doncaster, Retford U (WE) 3/08, Solihull Moors (L) 1/09, Shrewsbury (3ML) 10/09, Southend (L) 10/10, Hereford (3ML) 2/11, Macclesfield 7/11

Charlie	Henry	18			01/07/1987	24	Stevenage

Luton (Yth), Buntingford, Arlesey, Wycombe 11/05, Grays 3/06 Rel c/s 06, Haverhill R 7/06, Cambridge C 10/06, Dorchester 6/07, Havant & W 11/07, Newport C 6/09, Luton (5WL) 11/10 Undisc 1/11 Rel c/s 12, Aldershot T (2ML) 11/11, Macclesfield 7/12

Jon-Paul	Kissock	19	5'05"	10 09	02/12/1989	21	Liverpool

Everton Rel c/s 09, Gretna (SL) 1/08, Accrington (L) 1/09, Hamilton 8/09 Rel 12/09, Brighton (Trial) c/s 10, MK Dons (Trial) c/s 10, Newton 8/10, Formby 10/10, Southport 12/10, Luton 8/11, Macclesfield (6ML) 7/12

Ben	Mills	29	6'02"		23/03/1989	23	Stoke

Leek T, Newcastle T 7/07, Leek T 9/08, Stafford R 7/09, Alfreton 11/09, Stafford R 6/10, Nantwich 6/11, Macclesfield 5 fig 1/12

MANSFIELD TOWN

Chairman: John Radford
Secretary: Keith Burnard   **(T)** 01623 482 482   **(E)** keith.burnand@mansfieldtown.net
Additional Committee Members:
Carolyn Radford, Mark Hawkins, James Beachill.

Manager: Paul Cox
Programme Editor: Mark Stevenson   **(E)** mark.Stevenson@mansfieldtown.net

Club Factfile

Founded: 1897   **Nickname:** The Stags
Previous Names: Mansfield Wesleyans 1897-1906, Mansfield Wesley 1906-10
Previous Leagues: Mansfield & District Am. 1902-06, Notts & Dist. 1906-11, Central Alliance 1911-14, 15-21,
Notts & Derbys' 1914-15, Midland 1921-26, Midland Combination 1926-31, Football League 1931-2008

Club Colours (change): All yellow with two blue stripes (White/blue/blue)

Ground: One Call Stadium, Quarry Lane, Mansfield NG18 5DA   **(T)** 01623 482 482
Capacity: 10000 **Seats:**   **Covered:** All   **Clubhouse:** Yes   **Shop:** Yes

Directions From the North: Take the M1 exiting at junction 29, then join the A617 to Mansfield, after around 6 miles turn right into Rosemary Street, then proceed to Quarry Lane where you should turn right to the ground. From the South: Take the M1 exiting at junction 28, then take the A38 to Mansfield, after around 6 miles turn right into Belvedere Street (at crossroads), then after a quarter of a mile turn right into Quarry Lane. From the East: Take the A617 to Rainworth, at the crossroads turn left, after 3 miles turn right into Nottingham Road, a left turn will take you into Quarry Lane where you find the ground. From the West: Take the M1 exiting at junction 28, then take the A38 to Mansfield, after around 6 miles turn right into Belvedere Street (at crossroads), then after a quarter of a mile turn right into Quarry Lane.

Previous Grounds: West Field Lane 1897-99, Ratcliffe Gate 1899-1901, 12-16, Newgate Lane 1901-12.

Record Attendance: 24,467 v Nottingham Forest - FA Cup 3rd Round 10/01/53
Record Victory: 9-2 v Rotherham United - Division 3 South 29/08/31
Record Defeat: 1-8 v Walsall - Division 3 North 19/01/33
Record Goalscorer: Harry Johnson - 104 (1931-36)
Record Appearances: Ron Arnold - 440 (1970-83)
Additional Records: Paid £150,000 to Carlisle United for Lee Peacock
Senior Honours: Received £655,000 from Tottenham Hotspur for Colin Calderwood
Football Division 4 1974-75, Division 3 1976-77. League Trophy 1987.

10 YEAR RECORD

02-03		03-04		04-05		05-06		06-07		07-08		08-09		09-10		10-11		11-12	
FL 3	23	FL 3	5	FL 2	13	FL 2	16	FL 2	17	FL 2	23	Conf	12	Conf	9	Conf	13	Conf	3

MANSFIELD TOWN

No.	Date	Comp	H/A	Opponents	Att:	Result	Goalscorers	Pos
1	Sat-13-Aug	BSP	H	Bath City	3997	D 1-1	Connor 3	13
2	Tue-16-Aug	BSP	A	Gateshead	825	L 0-3		21
3	Sat-20-Aug	BSP	A	Braintree Town	875	D 1-1	Briscoe 47	18
4	Tue-23-Aug	BSP	H	Luton Town	2592	D 1-1	Green 26	20
5	Sat-27-Aug	BSP	H	Kettering Town	2051	W 3-0	Briscoe 11, Green 51, Dyer 64	14
6	Mon-29-Aug	BSP	A	Stockport County	3571	W 1-0	O'Neill 67	8
7	Sat-03-Sep	BSP	A	Darlington	2647	W 2-0	Green 2 (5, 15)	4
8	Sat-10-Sep	BSP	H	Newport County	2324	W 5-0	Green 11, Briscoe 2 (33, 72), Dyer 56, O'Neill 75	3
9	Sat-17-Sep	BSP	A	Barrow	1244	W 3-2	Green 4, Futcher 29, Meikle 81	4
10	Tue-20-Sep	BSP	H	AFC Telford	2481	D 1-1	Green 72	5
11	Sat-24-Sep	BSP	H	Kidderminster Harriers	2522	L 0-3		8
12	Tue-27-Sep	BSP	A	Wrexham	3478	W 3-1	Og (Wright) 41, Green pen 67, Connor 90	5
13	Sat-01-Oct	BSP	A	Forest Green Rovers	893	D 1-1	Dyer 1	8
14	Sat-08-Oct	BSP	H	Grimsby Town	2982	W 2-1	O'Neill 72, Connor 78	6
15	Sat-15-Oct	BSP	H	Southport	2406	L 1-3	Connor 76	9
16	Tue-18-Oct	BSP	A	Lincoln City	2944	D 1-1	Green 86	10
17	Sat-22-Oct	BSP	H	Alfreton Town	2982	W 3-2	Green pen 75, Meikle 86, Todd 90	8
18	Sat-05-Nov	BSP	H	Cambridge United	2046	L 1-2	Green 55	10
19	Sat-19-Nov	BSP	A	AFC Telford	2203	D 0-0		9
20	Sat-26-Nov	BSP	A	Bath City	816	D 1-1	Meikle 24	9
21	Tue-29-Nov	BSP	H	Gateshead	1513	D 1-1	Dyer 10	10
22	Sat-03-Dec	BSP	H	Braintree Town	1790	W 4-1	Dempster 24, Green 2 (49, 67), Meikle 60	8
23	Tue-06-Dec	BSP	A	Grimsby Town	2553	D 0-0		10
24	Sat-17-Dec	BSP	A	Southport	1006	L 1-3	Dempster 48	10
25	Mon-26-Dec	BSP	H	York City	3551	D 1-1	Green 11	9
26	Sun-01-Jan	BSP	A	York City	4284	D 2-2	Green 14, Verma 72	9
27	Sat-07-Jan	BSP	H	Forest Green Rovers	2008	W 1-0	Meikle 64	9
28	Sat-21-Jan	BSP	H	Hayes & Yeading United	1872	W 3-2	Dyer 38, Green 67, Hutchinson pen 90	10
29	Wed-25-Jan	BSP	A	Luton Town	5261	D 0-0		10
30	Sat-28-Jan	BSP	A	Ebbsfleet United	1085	W 3-0	Green 22, Roberts 2 (38, 90)	9
31	Sat-18-Feb	BSP	A	Newport County	1285	L 0-1		9
32	Tue-21-Feb	BSP	H	Darlington	1697	W 5-2	Dempster 15, Green 3 (44, 70, pen 75), Briscoe 86	8
33	Sat-25-Feb	BSP	H	Tamworth	2221	W 2-1	Smith 76, Green 87	7
34	Sat-03-Mar	BSP	H	Lincoln City	4830	W 2-1	Dyer 47, Roberts 58	6
35	Tue-06-Mar	BSP	A	Cambridge United	1738	W 2-1	Dyer 10, Briscoe 57	5
36	Sat-10-Mar	BSP	A	Tamworth	1600	W 1-0	Green 13	4
37	Tue-13-Mar	BSP	H	Fleetwood Town	3132	D 1-1	Geohaghon 90	4
38	Sat-17-Mar	BSP	H	Barrow	2510	W 7-0	Briscoe 3 (9, 17, 67), Howell 28, Meikle 41, Green 54, Rhead 77	3
39	Tue-20-Mar	BSP	A	Alfreton Town	3354	W 6-3	Howell 2 (17, 43), Briscoe 31, Green 2 (33, 90), Geohaghon 89	3
40	Sat-24-Mar	BSP	A	Fleetwood Town	3106	L 0-2		3
41	Sat-31-Mar	BSP	H	Ebbsfleet United	2630	W 1-0	Green 82	3
42	Sat-07-Apr	BSP	A	Kettering Town	1818	W 3-0	Meikle 14, Green 63, Rhead 86	3
43	Mon-09-Apr	BSP	H	Stockport County	3883	W 2-1	Smith 47, Briscoe 53,	3
44	Sat-14-Apr	BSP	A	Hayes & Yeading United	487	W 3-1	Howell 5, Dyer 67, Green 71	3
45	Fri-20-Apr	BSP	H	Wrexham	3665	W 2-0	Howell 13, Marriott 61	3
46	Sat-28-Apr	BSP	A	Kidderminster Harriers	3565	W 3-0	Stevenson 56, Briscoe 78, Green 87	3

CUPS

No.	Date	Comp	H/A	Opponents	Att:	Result	Goalscorers	Pos
1	Sat-29-Oct	FAC 4Q	H	Fleetwood Town	1725	D 1-1	Dyer 70	
2	Tue-01-Nov	FAC 4QR	A	Fleetwood Town	1159	L 0-5		
3	Sat-10-Dec	FAT 1	A	Droylsden	335	L 1-2	Green 84	
4	Wed-02-May	PO SF1	H	York City	6057	D 1-1	Dyer 26	
5	Mon-07-May	PO SF2	H	York City	7295	L 0-1 ae		

League	
Starts	
Substitute	
Unused Sub	
Cups	
Starts	
Substitute	
Unused Sub	
Goals (Lg)	
Goals (Cup)	

	MARRIOTT	BELL	RILEY	NAYLOR	O'NEILL	TODD	WORTHINGTON	MURRAY	BRISCOE	CONNOR	GREEN	DYER	MEIKLE	REDMOND	STEVENSON	WOOD	KENDRICK	SMITH	FUTCHER	HOWELL	SUTTON	BOLLAND	DAY	MOULT	SOMES	THOMPSON	FREEMAN	HEGARTY	VERMA	RODNEY	DEMPSTER	KELLY	ROBERTS	HUTCHINSON	EDWARDS	RHEAD	GEOHAGHON	ANDREW
	1	18	6	2	16	20	4	11	7	9	10	15	24	23	8	25	3	19	26	21	17	14	22	28	27	5	30	29	34	32	31	33	35	28	2	9	26	29
1	X	X	X	X	X	X	X	X	X	X	X	X	S	S	U	U	U	U																				
2	X		X	X	X			X	X	X	X	X	X	S	U	U	U	X	S	X	S																	
3	X		X		X		U	X	X	X	X	X	U	U	U	X		X	X																			
4	X		X		X		U	X	U	X	U	X	X	X	X	U	U	X	X																			
5	X		X		X			S	X	X	S	X	X	X	U	U		X	X	X	S																	
6	X							S	X	X	S	X	X	X	U	U	U	X	X	X																		
7	X			U	X			S	X	X	S	X	X	X	U	U		X	S	X	X																	
8	X			U	X			S	X	X	S	X	X	X	U		X	S	X	X	X																	
9	X			U	X			S	X	X	S	X	X	X	U		X		X	X	X	S																
10	X			U	X			U	X	X	X	X	X	X	U		X		X	X	X																	
11	X			U	X				S	X	X	X	U	X	X	U		X		X	X	X	S															
12	X	U	X	X	X	X	X		S	X	X	U	U			X	X	X	S																			
13	X		X						S	X	X	X	S	U			X		X	U																		
14	X	U	X	X	X	X	X		S	X	X	S	U	U			X		X	U																		
15	X	S	X	X	X	X	X		S	X	X	S	U			X		X	U																			
16	X		X		X	S	U	X	S	X	X	X	X	U			X		X	X	U																	
17	X		X		X	S	U	X		X	X	X	X	U			X		X	X	X	U																
18	X			X				X		U	X	X	X	U		X	X	X	U			S			U	X	X											
19	X			X					S	X	X	X	X	U			X	X	U	U	U				X	X	X											
20	X			X				U		X	S	X	X	X	U	X			X	S						X	X		X	S	S							
21	X			X				U		X	S	X	X	X	U	X			X	S						X	X		X	U	X							
22	X			X				U		X	S	X	X	X					X	X						X	X		U	X	U							
23	X			X						X	X	X	X	X	U	U			X	X						S	X		U		X	S						
24	X	X		X				X	S	X	X	X	X	U	U				X		U					X			X		X	U						
25	X	X		X			S	X	U		X	X	X	U	S				X	X						X			X		S							
26	X	S		X				X	X		X	X	X	U	U				S	X									X		X	S						
27	X	U		X				X	S		X	X	X	U		X	X		S	X									X		X	S						
28	X			X			U	X	S		X	X	S	U			X		U	X									X		X	X						
29	X			X				X	S		X	X	S	U			X		S	X									X		X	X	U					
30	X	U		X				X	S		X	X	S	U			X		S	X									X		X	X	S	S				
31	X	U		X				X		S		X	X	S			S		S	X									X		X	S	X					
32	X	X		X			S		X		X	X	X	S	U			X		X									X	U		U	X					
33	X	X		X		U		U	X		X	X	X	X	U	U				X									X	S		S	X					
34	X	X		X			X	X	S		X	X	X	X	U					X									U			S	X	U				
35	X	X		X				X	X		X	X	X	X	U					X									S			S	X	S				
36	X	X		X			U	X	S		X	X	X	X	U					X										U	U		S	X	U				
37	X	X		X				X	X		X	X	X	S	U			X		U	X									X			S	X	S				
38	X	X		X			S		X		X	X	S	S	U			X		X	X									S			X	X	X				
39	X	X		X		U			S		X	X	X	U						X										X		X	X	S	U				
40	X	X		X				X	X			X	X	U	X					X										U	U		S	X	S				
41	U		X		X	X			X			S		U	X	X				S							X					X	S		X		X	

<small>(blank separator rows)</small>

42	X	U	X		X	U		X			U	X	X	X	U						X	X	X	X	U	S	U											
43	X	U	X		X	U		X			U		X	X							X	X	X	X	S	X	S	U										
44	X			S				X	S		X	X	X	X	U	X					X	S				X				X	U	X	X					
45	X	X		X				X	S		X	X	X	X	U	U					X	X								X					S	X	S	
46	X	X		X				X	X		X	X	U	S							X	X				U				X					S	X	U	

Totals (appearances as X):

| | 45 | 1 | 26 | 5 | 43 | 6 | 8 | 39 | 25 | 4 | 44 | 42 | 33 | 1 | 6 | 0 | 15 | 8 | 13 | 28 | 39 | 4 | 0 | 0 | 6 | 9 | 2 | 4 | 0 | 11 | 0 | 16 | 5 | 2 | 2 | 13 | 1 | |

Sub appearances (S):

| | 0 | 0 | 2 | 0 | 0 | 2 | 9 | 0 | 13 | 11 | 1 | 3 | 9 | 0 | 1 | 1 | 0 | 4 | 0 | 5 | 2 | 6 | 0 | 1 | 0 | 1 | 0 | 0 | 1 | 2 | 1 | 1 | 1 | 7 | 1 | 13 | 0 | 4 |

Unused (U):

| | 1 | 0 | 5 | 5 | 3 | 1 | 10 | 1 | 1 | 4 | 0 | 0 | 4 | 44 | 12 | 4 | 0 | 0 | 0 | 3 | 0 | 4 | 5 | 1 | 0 | 1 | 0 | 0 | 1 | 2 | 0 | 2 | 2 | 4 | 1 | 1 | 0 | 5 |

Goals — competition 1:

	5	0	4	0	4	0	0	5	1	0	3	5	5	0	1	0	0	0	2	4	5	2	0	1	0	1	0	0	1	0	1	1	2	0	0	0	2	0
	0	0	0	0	0	1	0	0	0	2	0	0	0	0	0	0	0	1	0	0	0	0	0	0	0	1	1	1	1	0	0	0	0	0	0	0	2	1
	0	2	0	0	0	2	0	0	0	2	0	0	0	4	1	0	0	0	0	0	0	0	1	0	1	2	0	0	0	1	0	0	0	0	0	0	0	1

Goals — competition 2:

| | 1 | 0 | 0 | 0 | 3 | 1 | 0 | 0 | 12 | 4 | 29 | 8 | 7 | 0 | 1 | 0 | 0 | 2 | 1 | 5 | 0 | 0 | 0 | 0 | 0 | 0 | 0 | 0 | 0 | 1 | 0 | 3 | 0 | 3 | 1 | 0 | 2 | 2 |
| | 0 | 0 | 0 | 0 | 0 | 0 | 0 | 0 | 0 | 0 | 1 | 2 | 0 | 0 | 0 | 0 | 0 | 0 | 0 | 0 | 0 | 0 | 0 | 0 | 0 | 0 | 0 | 0 | 0 | 0 | 0 | 0 | 0 | 0 | 0 | 0 | 0 | 0 |

PLAYING SQUAD

Existing Players		SN	HT	WT	DOB	AGE	POB	Career	Apps	Goals
GOALKEEPERS										
Alan	Marriott	1	6'01"	12 05	03/09/1978	33	Bedford	Tottenham Rel c/s 99, Lincoln C 8/99 Rel c/s 08, Rushden & D 7/08, Mansfield 1/09	45	1
Shane	Redmond	23	6'02"	12 10	23/03/1989	23	Rathcole	Cherry Orchard (Ire) (Yth), Notts Forest Rel c/s 10, Eastwood T (SL) 9/08, Burton (6ML) 7/09, Darlington (3ML) 1/10, Chesterfield 8/10, Mansfield 7/11	1	0
DEFENDERS										
Lee	Beevers	17	6'02"	11 07	04/12/1983	28	Doncaster	Ipswich Rel c/s 03, Boston U (Trial) 1/03, Colchester (Trial) 2/03, Boston U (SL) 3/03, Boston U 6/03, Lincoln C £50,000 2/05 Rel c/s 09, Colchester 7/09 Rel c/s 11, Walsall 7/11 Rel c/s 12 Mansfield 7/12		
John	Dempster	4	6'00"	11 07	01/04/1983	29	Kettering	Rushden & D, Oxford U 1/06 Rel 2/07, Kettering (L) 1/07 Kettering 3/07, Crawley Undisc 1/11 Rel c/s 12, Kettering (L) 9/11, Mansfield (3ML) 11/11, Mansfield 7/12	12	3
Luke	Jones	5	5'09"	11 09	10/04/1987	25	Blackburn	Blackburn Rel c/s 06, Cercle Brugge (SL) c/s 05, Ashton U 9/06, Shrewsbury 11/06 Rel 4/08, Kidderminster (2ML) 1/08, Kidderminster 5/08 Rel 5/09, Mansfield 5/09 Rel 4/10, Forest Green 6/10, Kidderminster 5/11, Mansfield 6/12		
Andy	Owens	15	6'03"	13 05	15/10/1989	22	Liverpool	Liverpool (Yth), Stoke (Scholar) Rel c/s 08, Leek T (WE) 2/08, Glen Hoddle Soccer Academy, Stafford R 8/09, Altrincham 11/09 Rel 1/10, Rhyl 1/10, Accrington 8/10, Northwich (L) 3/11, Southport 7/11, Mansfield 6/12		
George	Pilkington	6	5'11"	11 06	07/11/1981	30	Rugeley	Everton Rel c/s 03, Exeter (2ML) 11/02, Port Vale 7/03 Rel c/s 08, Luton 8/08, Mansfield 7/12		
Jobe	Shaw	30						Mansfield		
Ritchie	Sutton	2	6'00	11 04	29/04/1986	26	Stoke	Crewe Rel 5/07, Leek T (2ML) 11/05, Stafford R (L) 3/06, Stafford R (SL) 8/06, Stafford R 7/07, Northwich 5/08, FC Halifax (L) 12/08 Perm 1/09, Nantwich 6/09, Port Vale 7/10, Mansfield 6/11	41	0
John	Thompson	3	6'00"	11 11	12/10/1981	30	Dublin	River Valley Rangers (Yth), Home Farm (Yth), Notts Forest Rel c/s 07, Tranmere (6WL) 10/06, Tranmere (SL) 1/07, Oldham 7/07, Notts County (10WL) 10/08 Perm 1/09 Rel c/s 11, Mansfield 7/11	7	0
MIDFIELDERS										
Paul	Bolland		6'00"	12 06	23/12/1979	32	Bradford	Bradford C, Notts County (L) 1/99 £75,000 4/99 Rel c/s 05, Grimsby 8/05 Rel c/s 09, Macclesfield 7/09, Mansfield 6/11, Harrogate T (SL) 12/11	10	0
Chris	Clements	14	5'09"	10 05	06/02/1990	22	Birmingham	Crewe Rel c/s 10, Nantwich (WE) 3/08, Leigh Genesis (L) 12/08, Stafford R (L) 3/09, Hednesford (L) 3/10, Hednesford 7/10, Mansfield 5/12		
Colin	Daniel	31	5'11"	11 06	15/02/1988	24	Eastwood	Eastwood T, Crewe Undisc 5/07 Rel c/s 09, Grays (L) 1/08, Leek T (L) 3/08, FC Halifax (L) 10/08, Macclesfield (SL) 3/09, Macclesfield 7/09, Mansfield 8/12		
Jamie	Hand	19	6'00"	11 08	07/02/1984	28	Uxbridge	Watford, Oxford U (2ML) 8/04, Livingston (3ML) 1/05, Peterborough (3ML) 9/05, Fisher 1/06, Northampton (SL) 2/06, Chester 7/06, Lincoln C 8/07 Rel 5/08, Oxford U (SL) 2/08, Ebbsfleet 8/08 Rel 2/09, Chelmsford 2/09 Rel 9/09, Woking 9/09 Rel 5/10, Hemel Hempstead (L) 3/10, Hayes & Yeading 8/10 Rel c/s 12, Luton (3ML) 9/11, Mansfield 7/12		
Joel	Holland	28						Mansfield		
Anthony	Howell	13			27/05/1986	26	Nottingham	Carlton T, Shepshed D 9/05, Carlton T 11/06, Grantham 3/07, Notts County (Trial) c/s 07, Eastwood T 6/07, Worksop 9/07, Eastwood (L) 1/08 Perm, Ilkeston 8/08, Mansfield 1/09 Rel 5/09, Alfreton (SL) 3/09, Alfreton 5/09, Mansfield 6/11	33	5
Adam	Murray	21	5'09"	10 00	30/09/1981	30	Birmingham	Derby, Mansfield (SL) 2/02, Kidderminster (L) 8/03, Solihull 11/03, Burton 11/03, Notts County 11/03, Kidderminster 1/04, Mansfield 6/04, Carlisle Nominal 3/05, Torquay £10,000 8/06, Macclesfield £17,500 1/07, Oxford U Undisc 1/08, Luton 7/10, Mansfield (3ML) 10/10 Perm 1/11 Pl/Ass Man 6/12	39	0
Godfrey	Poku	22			22/07/1990	22	Newham	Redbridge College, St Albans 8/09, Luton (Trial) 12/09, Luton 1/10, St Albans (L) 1/10, Southport (5ML) 8/11, Mansfield 7/12		
Gary	Roberts	18	5'08"	10 05	04/02/1987	25	Chester	Crewe, Yeovil (5ML) 8/08 Undisc 1/09 Rel 8/09, Brighton (Trial), Rotherham 11/09 Rel 4/10, Port Vale 7/10 Rel 12/11, Mansfield 1/12	17	3
Scott	Rogers	29						Mansfield		
Lee	Stevenson	26	5'10"		01/06/1984	28	Sheffield	Sheff Wed (Scholar), Kings Lynn 3/03, Belper 11/06, Eastwood T 5/10, Mansfield Undisc 5/11, Alfreton (L) 10/11	7	1
Andy	Todd	24	6'00"	11 03	22/02/1979	33	Nottingham	Eastwood T, N.Forest 2/96, Scarborough 2/99, Eastwood T 5/99, Ilkeston 3/00, Eastwood T 7/01, Worksop 10/01, Hucknall 12/03, Burton 7/05, Accrington (SL) 1/06, Accrington Undisc 6/06, Rotherham 8/07 Rel c/s 09, Accrington (SL) 1/08, Eastwood T (SL) 10/08, Alfreton 8/09, Eastwood T 5/10, Mansfield (Pl/Coach) 6/11	8	1

		SN	HT	WT	DOB	AGE	POB	From - To	APPS	GOA
Jamie	Tolley	20	6'00"	11 02	12/05/1983	29	Ludlow	Shrewsbury Rel c/s 06, Macclesfield 8/06 Rel c/s 09, Hereford 7/09 Rel 3/10, Wrexham 8/10, Mansfield 7/12		

FORWARDS

		SN	HT	WT	DOB	AGE	POB	From - To	APPS	GOA
Louis	Briscoe	11	6'00"	11 13	02/04/1988	24	Burton	Port Vale Rel 1/07, Stafford R (Trial), Moor Green 3/07, Leek T 7/07, Huston Dynamoes (USA) (Trial) 3/08, Hednesford 6/08, Gresley R 9/08, Stafford R 11/08, Ilkeston 12/08, Mansfield 1/09	38	12
Ross	Dyer	9	6'02"	13 02	12/05/1988	24	Stafford	Hednesford, Forest Green 5/10, Mansfield 6/11	45	8
Matt	Green	10	5'08"	10 05	02/01/1987	25	Bath	Bristol C (Yth), Cirencester, Newport C 6/05, Cardiff C £10,000 1/07 Rel 5/08, Darlington (L) 10/07, Oxford U (L) 11/07, Oxford U (SL) 1/08, Torquay 5/08, Oxford U (SL) 6/09, Oxford U Undisc 6/10, Cheltenham (SL) 1/11, Mansfield (6ML) 7/11 Undisc 1/12	45	29
Ben	Hutchinson	25	5'11"	12 08	27/11/1987	24	Nottingham	Derby (Jun), Notts County (Jun), Eastwood T c/s 05, Arnold T, Middlesbrough 1/06, Billingham Syn (L) 10/06, Celtic Nominal 1/08 Rel c/s 11, Swindon (5ML) 8/09, Dundee (SL) 1/10, Lincoln C (SL) 8/10, Kilmarnock 7/11, Mansfield 1/12	12	1
Lindon	Meikle	7			21/03/1988	24	Nottingham	Vernon Colts, Eastwood T 7/04, Mansfield Undisc 5/11	42	7
Matt	Rhead	16	6'04"		31/05/1984	28	Stoke	Stallington, Kidsgrove Ath c/s 04, Eastwood T Undisc 10/07, Kidsgrove Ath (L) 9/08, Nantwich 6/09, Congleton (L) 12/09 Perm, Eastwood T 6/10, Corby T 7/11, Mansfield 1/12	15	2
Adam	Somes	27						Mansfield	0	0
Jake	Speight	8	5'07"	11 02	28/09/1985	26	Sheffield	Sheff Utd, Leigh RMI (L) 3/05, Bury (Trial) c/s 05, Scarborough (L) 8/05 Perm 9/05, Bury (6WL) 12/05 Nominal 1/06 Rel 4/07, Northwich 6/07 Rel 5/08, Farsley Celtic 9/08, Droylsden 2/09, Mansfield 5/09, Bradford C £25,000 6/10, Port Vale (2ML) 10/10, Wrexham Undisc 7/11, Mansfield Undisc 7/12		
Nick	Wright	12	6'02"	12 00	25/11/1987	24	Birmingham	Birmingham, Tamworth (L) 1/06, Bristol C (L) 10/06, Northampton (6WL) 11/06, Ashford T (L) 3/07, Halesowen T 8/07, Tamworth 10/07, Kidderminster 7/10, Mansfield 6/12		

Loanees		SN	HT	WT	DOB	AGE	POB	From - To	APPS	GOA
(D)Ben	Futcher		6'07"	12 05	20/02/1981	31	Manchester	Bury (3ML) 8/11 - AFC Telford (L) 1/12, Macclesfield (3ML) 2/12, FC Halifax (SL) 7/12	13	1
(F)Louis	Moult		6'00"	13 05	14/05/1992	20	Stoke	Stoke 10/11 - Alfreton (L) 1/12	1	0
(D)Kieron	Freeman				21/03/1992	20	Bestwood	Notts Forest (2ML) 11/11 - Notts County (L) 1/12	9	0
(M)Aman	Verma		6'01"	13 00	03/01/1987	25	Birmingham	Kettering (6WL) 11/11 - Hinckley U 7/12	5	1
(M)Marcus	Kelly		5'07"	10 00	16/03/1986	26	Kettering	Kettering (6WL) 11/11 - Tamworth 7/12	1	0
(M)Nialle	Rodney		6'01"	11 11	28/02/1991	21	Nottingham	Bradford C 11/11 - Rel 1/12, Lincoln C 1/12 Rel c/s 12	2	0
(D)Paul	Edwards		5'11"	10 12	01/01/1980	32	Manchester	Fleetwood 1/12 - Barrow (SL) 3/12, Rel c/s 12	3	0
(D)Exodus	Geohaghon		6'07"	11 11	27/02/1985	27	Birmingham	Darlington (SL) 2/12 - Kidderminster 7/12	13	2
(D)Danny	Andrew		5'11"	11 06	23/12/1990	21	Holbeach	Cheltenham (SL) 3/12 -	5	0

Departures		SN	HT	WT	DOB	AGE	POB	From - To	APPS	GOA
(D)Nick	Wood		6'01"	12 02	09/11/1990	21	Ossett	Tranmere 8/11 - Rel 9/11, FC Halifax 9/11, Mickleover Sports 10/11	1	0
(F)Paul	Connor		6'02"	11 08	12/01/1979	33	Bishop Auckland	Lincoln C 7/10 - Gainsborough 12/11	15	4
(M)Nick	Hegarty		5'10"	11 00	25/06/1986	26	Hemsworth	Wakefield 11/11 - Rel 12/11, Australia	2	0
(D)Tom	Naylor		5'11"	11 04	28/06/1991	21	Sutton-in-Ashfield	Yth - Burnley (Trial) 10/11, Derby (6WL) 11/11 Undisc 1/12	5	0
(D)Rhys	Day		6'02"	13 06	31/08/1982	30	Bridgend	Oxford U (3ML) 10/10 Perm 1/11 - Retired c/s 12	0	0
(D)Matt	Bell		5'10"	11 03	03/01/1992	20	Stoke	Port Vale 6/11 - Rel c/s 12, Solihull Moors (L) 8/11, Stafford R (L) 12/11, Leek T (SL) 3/12, Leek T 7/12	1	0
(D)Sam	Craven		6'01"	12 01	27/09/1988	23	Nottingham	FC New York (USA) 1/12 - Rel c/s 12, Hednesford (Dual) 3/12		
(D)Joe	Kendrick		6'00"	11 04	26/06/1983	29	Dublin	Bray W (Ire) 7/11 - Rel c/s 12, Blyth (SL) 1/12, Blyth 7/12	15	0
(M)Jon	Worthington		5'09"	11 05	16/04/1983	29	Dewsbury	Bradford C 6/11 - Rel c/s 12, FC Halifax 7/12	17	0
(F)Danny	Mitchley		5'10"	10 08	07/10/1989	22	Liverpool	Burscough 11/10 - Rel c/s 12, Nuneaton T (3ML) 9/11, Nuneaton T (SL) 1/12, Altrincham 3/12		
(F)Adam	Smith		5'11"	12 00	20/02/1985	27	Huddersfield	York C 5/10 - Rel c/s 12, Aldershot (L) 10/11, Aldershot (2ML) 11/11, Lincoln C 6/12	12	2
(G)Neil	Collett				02/10/1989	22	Coventry	Nuneaton T 1/10 - Nuneaton T (SL) 7/11, Nuneaton T 5/12		
(D)Luke	O'Neill		6'00"	11 04	20/08/1991	21	Slough	Leicester 7/11 - Burnley Undisc 6/12	43	3
(D)Martin	Riley		6'00	12 01	05/12/1986	25	Wolverhampton	Cheltenham 7/11 - Wrexham 7/12	28	0

Conference Action...

Newport County's Jarvis fires in a shot during the FA Trophy final at Wembley Stadium.

Photo: Peter Barnes.

NEWPORT COUNTY AFC

Chairman: (Acting) David Hando
Secretary: Mike Everett   **(T)** 07889 359 100   **(E)** mike.everett3@googlemail.com
Additional Committee Members:
John Allison, Howard Greenhaf, Tim Harris, Jackie Tutton, Steve Dance.

Manager: Justin Edinburgh
Programme Editor: Phil Tanner   **(E)** phil.tanner1@btopenworld.com

Newport County's skipper Gary Warren challenges York City's
Lanre Oyebanjo during the FA Trophy Final at Wembley. Photo: Roger Turner.

Club Factfile

Founded: 1998   **Nickname:** The Exiles
Previous Names: Newport AFC after demise of Newport County in 1988-89, changed to Newport County AFC in 1999
Previous Leagues: Hellenic 1989-90, Southern 1990-2004

Club Colours (change): Amber/black/black (All red)

Ground: Rodney Parade, Newport, South Wales NP19 0UU   **(T)** 01633 670 690
Capacity: **Seats:** Yes   **Covered:** 3,236   **Clubhouse:** Yes   **Shop:** Yes

Directions: FROM THE WEST: Take Junction 26 from the M4. Take 3rd Exit off Roundabout onto Malpas Road. Take 2nd Exit off Roundabout at Next Roundabout take 1st Exit across River Usk, at Next Traffic Lights bear Right onto Chepstow Road. Take 1st Right onto Cedar Road. Take 1st Right onto Corporation Road. Take 1st Left onto Grafton Road. Rodney Parade is on your Left Hand Side.
FROM THE EAST: Take Junction 25a from the M4. Take 1st Exit off Roundabout onto Heidenheim Way. Take 1st Exit off Flyover Take 2nd Exit off Roundabout, at Next Roundabout take 1st Exit across River Usk, at Next Traffic Lights bear Right onto Chepstow Road. Take 1st Right onto Cedar Road. Take 1st Right onto Corporation Road. Take 1st Left onto Grafton Road. Rodney Parade is on your Left Hand Side.

Previous Grounds: Newport Stadium > 2012.

Record Attendance: 4,616 v Swansea City - FA Cup 1st Round 11/11/2006
Record Victory: 9-0 v Pontlottyn Blast Furnace (A) - Welsh Cup 01/09/90
Record Defeat: 1-6 v Stafford Rangers (A) - 06/01/96
Record Goalscorer: Chris Lillygreen - 93
Record Appearances: Mark Price - 275
Additional Records: Paid £5,000 to Forest Green Rovers for Shaun Chapple
Senior Honours: Received £5,000 from Merthyr Tydfil for Craig Lima
Hellenic League 1989-90. League Cup 1989-90. Gloucestershire Senior Cup 1993-94.
Southern League Midland Division 1994-95. Gwent FA Senior Cup 1996-97, 97-98, 99-2000, 00-01, 01-02, 03-04, 04-05.
Conference South 2009-10.

10 YEAR RECORD

02-03	03-04	04-05	05-06	06-07	07-08	08-09	09-10	10-11	11-12
SthP 10	SthP 7	Conf S 18	Conf S 18	Conf S 6	Conf S 9	Conf S 10	Conf S 1	Conf 9	Conf 19

NEWPORT COUNTY

No.	Date	Comp	H/A	Opponents	Att:	Result	Goalscorers	Pos
1	Sat-13-Aug	BSP	A	Kettering Town	2047	L 2-3	Buchanan 6, D Rose 61	20
2	Tue-16-Aug	BSP	H	Hayes & Yeading United	1519	W 4-0	Rogers 14, Buchanan 53, D Rose 2 (62, 66)	10
3	Sat-20-Aug	BSP	H	Grimsby Town	1675	D 0-0		11
4	Tue-23-Aug	BSP	A	Ebbsfleet United	992	D 1-1	Buchanan 4	12
5	Sat-27-Aug	BSP	A	AFC Telford	2147	L 1-2	D Rose 41	16
6	Mon-29-Aug	BSP	H	Kidderminster Harriers	1672	L 1-3	Foley 50	17
7	Sat-03-Sep	BSP	H	Cambridge United	1515	L 0-1		19
8	Sat-10-Sep	BSP	A	Mansfield Town	2324	L 0-5		21
9	Sat-17-Sep	BSP	A	Braintree Town	786	L 0-1		21
10	Tue-20-Sep	BSP	H	Stockport County	1205	D 1-1	D Rose 31	23
11	Sat-24-Sep	BSP	H	Barrow	1315	D 2-2	Jarvis 9, D Rose 73	23
12	Tue-27-Sep	BSP	A	Forest Green Rovers	1203	D 1-1	Jarvis 38	23
13	Sat-01-Oct	BSP	A	Darlington	1785	L 0-2		23
14	Sat-08-Oct	BSP	H	Southport	1576	L 0-3		23
15	Tue-11-Oct	BSP	A	Fleetwood Town	1277	W 4-1	Foley 3 (15, 29, 59), D Rose pen 23	22
16	Sat-15-Oct	BSP	A	Tamworth	1310	L 1-2	Knights 74	22
17	Tue-18-Oct	BSP	H	Kettering Town	1249	W 3-1	D Rose 3 (pen 34, 53, 61)	22
18	Sat-22-Oct	BSP	A	Wrexham	4232	D 0-0		22
19	Sat-05-Nov	BSP	H	Ebbsfleet United	1412	L 0-1		22
20	Sat-19-Nov	BSP	A	Grimsby Town	2701	D 2-2	Hatswell 2, Jarvis 17	22
21	Sat-26-Nov	BSP	H	Luton Town	1511	L 0-1		22
22	Tue-29-Nov	BSP	A	Hayes & Yeading United	303	W 4-0	D Rose 22, Foley 38, Yakubu 2 (45, 75)	20
23	Sat-03-Dec	BSP	H	Lincoln City	1270	W 1-0	Yakubu 24	18
24	Tue-06-Dec	BSP	A	Alfreton Town	579	L 2-3	Buchanan 4, Warren 60	19
25	Sat-17-Dec	BSP	H	Fleetwood Town	1011	L 0-1		19
26	Tue-03-Jan	BSP	A	Bath City	1147	L 2-3	Jarvis 13, Warren 54	20
27	Sat-07-Jan	BSP	A	Luton Town	6108	L 0-2		20
28	Sat-21-Jan	BSP	H	Forest Green Rovers	1325	D 0-0		20
29	Sat-28-Jan	BSP	A	Gateshead	704	W 3-2	Buchanan 57, Foley 90, Harris 90+4	21
30	Sat-11-Feb	BSP	A	Stockport County	3565	D 2-2	Sandell 50, Harris 87	21
31	Tue-14-Feb	BSP	H	Bath City	847	W 1-0	Minshull 12	17
32	Sat-18-Feb	BSP	H	Mansfield Town	1285	W 1-0	Foley 33	16
33	Tue-21-Feb	BSP	A	Tamworth	815	L 1-2	Foley pen 6	16
34	Sat-03-Mar	BSP	A	Southport	1105	D 1-1	Yakubu 40	17
35	Tue-06-Mar	BSP	H	Braintree Town	1101	L 3-4	Foley 29, Warren 44, Charles 90	17
36	Tue-20-Mar	BSP	A	Cambridge United	1815	D 1-1	Sandell pen 86	18
37	Sat-24-Mar	BSP	A	Lincoln City	1951	L 0-2		20
38	Sat-31-Mar	BSP	H	Gateshead	1261	W 1-0	Charles 12	20
39	Tue-03-Apr	BSP	H	York City	1241	W 2-1	Jarvis 33, R Rose 70	18
40	Fri-06-Apr	BSP	H	AFC Telford	1540	D 0-0		17
41	Mon-09-Apr	BSP	A	Kidderminster Harriers	2275	L 2-3	Reid 1, Foley 37	19
42	Sat-14-Apr	BSP	A	York City	2824	D 1-1	Jarvis 4	19
43	Tue-17-Apr	BSP	H	Darlington	1249	D 0-0		20
44	Sat-21-Apr	BSP	H	Alfreton Town	1239	W 1-0	R Rose 38	17
45	Tue-24-Apr	BSP	H	Wrexham	1431	L 0-1		17
46	Sat-28-Apr	BSP	A	Barrow	900	L 1-3	Yakubu 15	19

CUPS

No.	Date	Comp	H/A	Opponents	Att:	Result	Goalscorers	
1	Sat-29-Oct	FAC 4Q	H	Braintree Town	1234	W 4-3	Foley 25, McAllister 55, Jarvis 75, Rodgers 89	
2	Sat-12-Nov	FAC 1	H	Shrewsbury Town	2362	L 0-1		
3	Sat-10-Dec	FAT 1	H	Forest Green Rovers	724	D 0-0		
4	Tue-13-Dec	FAT 1R	A	Forest Green Rovers	368	W 2-0	McAllister 32, Knights 68	
5	Tue-24-Jan	FAT 2	A	Worksop Town	538	W 3-1	Buchanan 58, Harris 2 (86, 90)	
6	Tue-07-Feb	FAT 3	H	Carshalton Athletic	975	W 4-0	Foley 4, Buchanan 38, Chapman 46, R Rose 86	
7	Sat-25-Feb	FAT 4	A	Northwich Victoria	601	W 3-2	Harris 2 (60, 85), Jarvis 90	
8	Sat-10-Mar	FAT SF1	H	Wealdstone	2209	W 3-1	Buchanan 6, Jarvis 21, Knights 78	
9	Sat-17-Mar	FAT SF2	A	Wealdstone	2092	D 0-0		
10	Sat-12-May	FAT Final	N	York City	19844	L 0-2		

League	
Starts	
Substitute	
Unused Sub	
Cups	
Starts	
Substitute	
Unused Sub	
Goals (Lg)	
Goals (Cup)	

	POTTER	ROBSON	MILLER	YAKUBU	BAKER	DOHERTY	D ROSE	ROGERS	VELEZ	JARDIM	BUCHANAN	MCALLISTER	FOLEY	HUGHES	RODGERS	HARRISON	THOMPSON	HATSWELL	GILLIGAN	WARREN	GREENING	NEWMAN	JARVIS	PIPE	KNIGHTS	SWAN	MATTHEWS	HARRIS	PROSSER	SANDELL	CHARLES	MINSHULL	CHAPMAN	R ROSE	REID	PORTER	EVANS	DARLOW	FRANKS
	1	2	4	6	3	14	7	8	29	27	26	9	10	16	25	40	18	17	12	5	24	22	15	19	11	39	21	23	33	28	20	30	32	31	41	42	36	43	44
	X	X	X	X	X	X	X	X	X	X	X	X	S	S	U	U	U																						
	X		X	X	X	X	X	X	S	X	X	X	S	S	X				U	U																			
	X		X	X	X	X	X	X	U	X	X	X	U	U	S				U	U	S																		
	X		X	X	X	X	X	S	U	S	X	X	S	X	X				U		X																		
	X		X	X	U	X	X	S	U	X	X	X	S	X	X				S				X																
			X	X			X			X	S	X	X	X	X	X	X	X	U		X	U	X	U															
		X		S	X				X	S	X	X	X	X	X	U	X	U	X	U																			
	X	X	X	X	X				S	X	X	X	U	X	U	X	U	X		S																			
		X		X	X	X	X			S	X	X	U	X	U	X	U	X																					
		X	X	X	X				S	X	X	X	U	X	U	S	X		X	X																			
		X	X	X	X				S	X	X	X	U	X	U	S	X		X	X	S																		
		X	X		X			X		S	X	X	X		U	X	U	S	X		X	X	S																
		X	X		X			X		S	S	X			U	X	U	S	X		X	X	S																
		X	X			X	S		U	X	S	S		U	X			X			X	X	X																
		X		X	X	X			X	X	S	S	X		X	X	U	X		X	X	U	X																
		S		X	X	X	S		U	X	X	X	X	X	X			X		X	X	U	X																
	X	U		X	X	U		U		X	X	X	X					X		S	X	X																	
	X	S		X	X	X	U			X	X	X	X					X		S	X	X																	
	X	S		X	X	U	U			X	X	X	X					X		S	X	X																	
	X	S	X	X	X	U				X	X	X	X					X		S	X	X	S																
	X		X	X	X		S			X	S	X	X	X				X		X	X		X																
	X		X	X	X	U				X	S	X	X	X				U		X	U		U																
	X		X	X		X				S	X	X	X					U		U	U		S	S															
	X		X	X						S	X	X	X					U		U	U		S	S															
	X		X	X	U	X				U	X		X					U		X	U	X	U	X															
	X		X	X	S	X					S	X	X					U		X	X	U	X	U															
	X	X	X	U						S		X	X	X				U		X	X	U	S	S															
	U		X	S							X	X	X	X				X		X	X	U	S	S	X	X													
	U		X	U	U						X	X	X	X				X		X	X	U	S	S	U	X	X												
	U		X								X	X	X	X				X		X	U		S		X	X	X	X	U										
	U		X								X	X	X	X				X		X	U		U		X	X	X	U	S										
	U		X								X	X	X	S				X		X	X		S		X	X	X	U	S										
	U	X	X								X	X	X	U				X		S	X		U		X	X	S	X											
	U		X	X							U	X	X	X				X		X	S		S		X	S	X									X			
			X								X		X	X	X	S		X	U	X			X		X							X	S	X	S	X	X	U	
											X	X	X	U				U		X			X	X	U					X	X	X		S		X	U	U	X
			U								X		X	X				U		U			X	X	U					X	X	X		S	U	S		X	
		U									X		X	X	X			U		U			X	X	S					X	X	X		S	S	S		X	
		X	X								X		X	X	S			U	S				X	X	X		U			X	X	X			X	S	X		
		X	X								U		X	X	U				U				X	X	X					X	X	X		U		X	X	X	
		X									X		X	X				U					X	X	S		U			X	X		U		X	X	X	U	X
		X									U		X	X	U				U				X	X	X		S			X	X		S		X	X	X		X
		X									X		X	X	S		U	S					X	X	X		X		U		X				X	X	X	U	X
		X	S								X				S	X	X						X	X	S		S				X				X	X	X	X	
	X		X	X				X	X	S	U	U		X	X	X	X					U	X				U	U	S										
	X		U	X				X	X	U				S	X	X	X	X			S		S	X	X				U										
	X		X	X					X				U	X	S	X						X		X	U		X			U									
	X		X	X			S	X			U	X	X		X						U	U		X	X		X		S										
	U			X	U						X		X	X	X			X	U		X	U		X	X				S					X					
	U			X							X			X	X	X		X	U		X	U			S	X	X		S					X	X	S			
	U		X	X							X		X	X	S			X				U			X	X	S		S					X	X	X			
			X	X							X		X	S	X			X			X	X	X		X	X	S	U	S						X		X	X	
			X								X			X	S	X		X			X	S			X	X	X	U	U	S						X		X	X
			X								X			X	X	U		X			X				X	X	S	U	S					X		X		X	X

PLAYING SQUAD

Existing Players		SN	HT	WT	DOB	AGE	POB	Career	Apps	Goals
GOALKEEPERS										
Alan	Julian	1	6'02"	13 07	11/03/1983	29	Ashford	Brentford Rel 2/05, Stevenage 2/05, Gillingham 5/08 Rel c/s 11, Stevenage 7/11 Rel c/s 12, Newport C 6/12		
Joe	Perry	22	6'00"	12 05	29/03/1992	20	Caerphilly	Cheltenham (Scholar) Rel c/s 10, Evesham (WE) 7/09, Bracknell (L) 9/09, Merthyr T 8/10, Newport C 7/12		
Lenny	Pideley	40	6'04"	14 09	07/02/1984	28	Twickenham	Chelsea, Watford (SL) 9/03, Millwall (L) 11/05, Millwall 6/06 Rel 5/09, Woking (3ML) 8/08, Carlisle 7/09 Rel c/s 10, Woking 8/10 Rel 9/10, Bradford C 10/10 Rel 5/11, Exeter 6/11 Rel c/s 12, Newport C 8/12		
Matthew	Swan							Newport C	0	0
DEFENDERS										
Mike	Flynn	17	5'10"	13 04	17/10/1980	31	Newport	Newport C, Barry T c/s 00, Wigan £15,000 6/02, Blackpool (2ML) 8/04, Gillingham 2/05 Rel c/s 07, Blackpool 7/07 Rel c/s 08, Huddersfield 7/08, Darlington (5WL) 11/08, Bradford C 8/09 Rel c/s 12, Newport C 7/12		
Andrew	Hughes	3			05/06/1992	20	Cardiff	Cardiff (Yth), Newport C, Mangotsfield (2ML) 10/10	38	0
Tony	James	5	5'10"	13 06	09/10/1978	33	Abergavenny	WBA Rel 5/98, Hereford c/s 98 Rel 5/06, Weymouth 5/06, Burton 5/07 Rel c/s 12, Hereford (L) 10/10, Newport C 6/12		
Jake	Thomson	14	5'11"	11 05	12/05/1989	23	Southsea	Southampton, Bournemouth (5WL) 1/09, Torquay (SL) 10/09, Exeter 7/10 Rel c/s 11, Cheltenham (L) 2/11, Southend (Trial) 7/11, Kettering 8/11, Forest Green (3ML) 9/11, Forest Green 1/12, Newport C 6/12		
Ismael	Yakubu	6	6'01"	12 09	05/04/1985	27	Kano, Nig	Barnet Rel c/s 10, AFC Wimbledon 7/10 Rel 5/11, Newport C 6/11, Cambridge U (L) 9/11	26	5
MIDFIELDERS										
Lee	Evans	16						Newport C	3	0
Lee	Minshull	8	6'02"	14 06	11/11/1985	26	Chatham	Ramsgate, Tonbridge 2/09, AFC Wimbledon 5/10 Rel c/s 12, Newport C (SL) 1/12, Newport C 7/12	17	1
David	Pipe	2	5'09"	12 01	05/11/1983	28	Caerphilly	Coventry, Notts County (3ML) 1/04 Perm 4/04, Bristol R £50,000 7/07 Rel c/s 10, Cheltenham (10WL) 11/09, Jail 6/10, Newport C 9/11	34	0
Max	Porter	4	5'11"	13 00	29/06/1987	25	Hornchurch	Brighton (Yth), Gillingham (Yth), Southend (Sch), Cambridge U (6WL) 11/05 Perm 1/06, Bishops Stortford 6/06, Barnet Undisc 5/07 Rel c/s 09, Rushden & D 7/09, AFC Wimbledon 6/11 Rel c/s 12, Newport C (SL) 2/12, Newport C 6/12	13	0
Andy	Sandell	13	5'11"	11 09	08/09/1983	28	Calne	Forest Green (Yth), Bristol C (Trainee), Malmesbury, Melksham, Paulton R 7/03, Bath C £1,500 7/05, Bristol R 5/06, Salisbury (L) 8/07 Undisc 8/07, Aldershot (6WL) 11/08 £10,000 1/09, Wycombe 7/10 Rel 11/11, Forest Green (L) 10/11, Chippenham 11/11, Chicago Fire (USA) (Trial) 12/11, Newport C 1/12	10	2
FORWARDS										
Ryan	Charles	11	6'00"	11 13	30/09/1989	22	Enfield	Luton Rel 5/10, Hitchin (SL) 3/07, Hinckley U (WE) 12/07, Kettering (L) 3/09, Kidderminster (5WL) 11/09, Rushden & D 6/10, Cambridge U 6/11 Rel c/s 12, Newport C (L) 1/12, Newport C 7/12	14	2
Danny	Crow	9	5'10"	11 00	26/01/1986	26	Great Yarmouth	Norwich, Northampton (2ML) 2/05, Peterborough 8/05 Rel 9/08, Notts County (L) 10/08, Notts County (SL) 2/09, Cambridge U 9/08, Luton 5/10 Rel c/s 12, Newport C 6/12		
Jake	Harris	15			28/10/1990	21	Weston-Super-Mare	Weston-Super-Mare, Newport C 7/10, Gloucester (SL) 8/10, Gloucester (L) 9/11, Frome T (L) 11/11	10	2
Jefferson	Louis	10	6'02"	13 02	22/02/1979	33	Harrow	Chesham, Aylesbury 7/00, Thame U 3/01, Oxford U 3/02, Woking (L) 8/03, Gravesend (L) 8/04, Forest Green Free 9/04, Woking 12/04 Rel 5/05, Bristol R 5/05, Hemel Hempstead 11/05, Lewes 11/05, Worthing 11/05, Stevenage 12/05 Rel c/s 06, Eastleigh 7/06, Yeading 9/06 Rel 12/06, Havant & W 12/06, Weymouth 6/07 Rel 1/08, Maidenhead 1/08, Mansfield 1/08 Rel 5/08, Wrexham 6/08 Rel 5/09, Crawley 5/09 Rel 5/10, Rushden & D (SL) 11/09, Gainsborough 6/10 Rel 1/11, Darlington (3ML) 10/10, Hayes & Yeading 1/11, Maidenhead 3/11, Brackley T 7/11, Lincoln C 1/12 Rel c/s 12, Newport C 6/12		
Aaron	O'Connor	7	5'10"	12 00	09/08/1983	29	Nottingham	Ilkeston, Scunthorpe 12/02 Rel 2/03, Ilkeston 3/03, Nuneaton c/s 03, Ilkeston, Gresley R 7/04, Rushden & D (Trial) 6/06 Grays 1/07, Mansfield 8/08, Rushden & D 6/09, Luton 6/11, Newport C 7/12		

Loanees		SN	HT	WT	DOB	AGE	POB	From - To	APPS	GOA
(M)Ryan	Gilligan		5'10"	11 07	18/01/1987	25	Swindon	Watford (Scholar) Rel c/s 05, Northampton 8/05, Torquay (L) 2/11,		
								Newport C (6ML) 8/11	6	0
(F)Nat	Jarvis		6'00"	12 06	20/10/1991	20	Cardiff	Cardiff (2ML) 9/11, (SL) 1/12 -	31	6
(D)Luke	Prosser		6'02"	12 04	28/05/1988	24	Waltham Cross	Southend 12/11 -	0	0
(M)Adam	Chapman		5'10"	11 00	29/11/1989	22	Doncaster	Oxford U 1/12 -	5	0
(G)Karl	Darlow		6'01"	12 05	08/10/1990	21	Northampton	Notts Forest 3/12 -	8	0
(D)Fraser	Franks		6'00"	10 11	22/11/1990	21		AFC Wimbledon 3/12 -	1	0

Departures		SN	HT	WT	DOB	AGE	POB	From - To	APPS	GOA
(D)Paul	Robson		5'08"	11 05	04/08/1983	29	Hull	Crystal Palace Baltimore (USA) 7/11 - Rel 10/11,		
								Lincoln C 1/12	7	0
(M)Scott	Rogers		5'11"	11 00	23/05/1979	33	Bristol	Bath C 4/09 - Eastleigh 12/11 Rel c/s 12, Chippenham 6/12	13	1
(M)Daniel	Rose		5'07"	10 01	21/02/1988	24	Bristol	Oxford U 7/08 - C.Palace (Trial) 10/11,		
								Fleetwood Undisc 1/12	24	11
(F)Robbie	Matthews				02/03/1982	30	Wiltshire	Kidderminster 7/10 - Forest Green (L) 8/11, Salisbury (L) 9/11,		
								Salisbury Undisc 1/12	9	0
(M)Tommy	Doherty		5'08"	09 13	17/03/1979	33	Bristol	Bradford C 6/11 - Rel 1/12, Bath C NC 2/12, Exeter 7/12	19	0
(M)Tom	Miller				29/06/1990	22	Ely	Dundalk 1/11 - Rel 1/12, Lincoln C 3/12	24	0
(G)Danny	Potter		5'11"	13 00	18/03/1979	33	Ipswich	Torquay 5/11 - Rel 3/12, Staines 3/12,		
								Eastbourne B (Pl/Coach) 6/12	16	0
(G)Glyn	Thompson		6'02"	13 01	24/02/1981	31	Telford	Hereford 7/07 - Rel c/s 12, Worcester 7/12	23	0
(D)Lee	Baker		5'10"	12 01	20/01/1989	23	Redditch	Kidderminster 6/10 - Rel c/s 12, Worcester 7/12	20	0
(F)Elliott	Buchanan		5'11"		17/07/1989	23		Hayes & Yeading 7/11 - Rel c/s 12, Boreham Wood 6/12	37	5
(D)Paul	Rodgers		5'10"	10 10	06/10/1989	22	Edmonton	Northampton 8/11 - Rel c/s 12	37	0
(M)Troy	Greening				17/04/1993	19		Yth - Rel c/s 12	1	0
(M)Guillaume	Velez		5'10"	11 06	13/05/1991	21	Toulouse, Fra	Toulouse 8/11 - Rel c/s 12	4	0
(F)Darryl	Knights		5'07"	10 01	01/05/1988	24	Ipswich	Kidderminster 7/10 - Rel c/s 12	23	1
(M)Sam	Foley		6'00"	10 08	17/10/1986	25	Upton	Kidderminster (SL) 2/09 Perm 7/09 - Yeovil 7/12	41	10
(D)Gary	Warren				16/04/1984	28	Bristol	Team Bath 5/09 - Inverness Caledonian 6/12	35	3
(F)Craig	McAllister		6'01"	12 07	28/06/1980	32	Glasgow	Crawley 5/11 - Luton (SL) 1/12, Eastleigh 6/12	25	0
(F)Jake	Reid				22/06/1987	25	London	Salisbury 1/12 Rel c/s 12 - AFC Telford 7/12	12	1
(G)Lee	Harrison		6'02"	12 07	12/09/1971	40	Billericay	Hayes & Yeading as (Ass Coach) 5/11 (Temp Man) 9/11 - Rel 10/11,		
								Wycombe (GK Coach) 8/12	0	0
(M)Romone	Rose		5'09"	11 05	19/01/1990	22	Reading	Muangthong Utd (Tha) 1/12 - Rel c/s 12	12	2
(F)Felino	Jardim		5'09"	11 08	10/08/1985	27	Rotterdam	RBC Roosendaal (Holl) 7/11 - Rel c/s 12	8	0
(M)Ryan	Newman							Yth - Merthyr T (L) 2/12 Perm	0	0
(D)Wayne	Hatswell		6'00"	13 10	08/02/1975	37	Swindon	Dundalk (Pl/Coach) 1/11 (Temp Man) 9/11 - Brackley T 8/12	12	1

Conference Action...

Andrew Hughes - Newport County - gets in a shot before the Forest Green defender can make a challenge during their First Round Trophy tie which County won 2-0.

Photo: Peter Barnes.

NUNEATON TOWN

Chairman: Ian Neale
Secretary: Richard Dean   **(T)** 02476 385738   **(E)** richard.dean1955@o2.co.uk
Additional Committee Members:
Neil Hodgson, Dave Allen, Kevin Harris-James, Mary Mills.

Manager: Kevin Wilkin
Programme Editor: Liz Robbins   **(E)** liz.robbins@nuneatontownfc.com

Club Factfile

Founded: 2008   **Nickname:** The Boro
Previous Names: Nuneaton Borough 1937-2008
Previous Leagues: Central Amateur 1937-38, Birmingham Combination 1938-52, West Midlands 1952-58, Southern 1958-79
81-82, 88-90, 2003-04, 08-10, Conference 1979-81, 82-88, 99-03, 04-08

Club Colours (change): Blue & white stripes/blue or white/blue or white (Claret & sky blue/blue/blue)

Ground: Triton Showers Community Arena, Liberty Way, Nuneaton CV11 6RR   **(T)** 02476 385 738
Capacity: **Seats:**   **Covered:**   **Clubhouse:**   **Shop:**
Directions From the South, West and North West, exit the M6 at Junction 3 and follow the A444 into Nuneaton. At the Coton Arches roundabout turn right into Avenue Road which is the A4254 signposted for Hinckley. Continue along the A4254 following the road into Garrett Street, then Eastboro Way, then turn left into Townsend Drive. Follow the road round before turning left into Liberty Way for the ground. From the North, exit the M1 at Junction 21 and follow the M69. Exit at Junction 1 and take the 4th exit at roundabout onto A5 (Tamworth, Nuneaton). At Longshoot Junction turn left onto A47, continue to roundabout and take the 1st exit onto A4254, Eastboro Way. Turn right at next roundabout into Townsend Drive, then right again into Liberty Way, CV11 6RR.

Previous Grounds: Manor Park

Record Attendance: 22,114 v Rotherham United - FA Cup 3rd Round 1967 (At Manor Park)
Record Victory: 11-1 - 1945-46 and 1955-56
Record Defeat: 1-8 - 1955-56 and 1968-69
Record Goalscorer: Paul Culpin - 201 (55 during season 1992-93)
Record Appearances: Alan Jones - 545 (1962-74)
Additional Records: Paid £35,000 to Forest green Rovers for Marc McGregor 2000
    Received £80,000 from Kidderminster Harriers for Andy Ducros 2000
Senior Honours:
Southern League Midland Division 1981-82, 92-93, Premier Division 1988-99, Premier Division Play-offs 2009-10.
Conference North Play-offs 2011-12.
Birmingham Senior Cup x7.

10 YEAR RECORD

02-03		03-04		04-05		05-06		06-07		07-08		08-09		09-10		10-11		11-12	
Conf	20	SthP	4	Conf N	2	Conf N	3	Conf N	10	Conf N	7	SthE	2	SthP	2	Conf N	6	Conf N	5

NUNEATON TOWN

No.	Date	Comp	H/A	Opponents	Att:	Result	Goalscorers	Pos - 6 points Mar
1	Sat-13-Aug	BSN	H	Stalybridge Celtic	786	L 1-2	Smith 86	15
2	Tue-16-Aug	BSN	H	Gloucester City	626	D 0-0		19
3	Sat-20-Aug	BSN	A	Droylsden	328	L 1-2	Burns 24	19
4	Tue-23-Aug	BSN	H	Boston United	765	W 2-0	Smith 27, Burns 51	14
5	Sat-27-Aug	BSN	H	Bishops Stortford	645	W 2-0	Glover pen 66, Moore 86	9
6	Mon-29-Aug	BSN	A	Worcester City	947	D 1-1	Moore 11	9
7	Sat-03-Sep	BSN	H	Gainsborough Trinity	753	L 0-1		12
8	Sat-10-Sep	BSN	A	Vauxhall Motors	239	W 2-1	Smith 76, G Dean 80	8
9	Sat-17-Sep	BSN	H	Eastwood Town	675	W 4-0	Walker 9, Armson 2 (28, 63), Pugh 48	7
10	Tue-20-Sep	BSN	H	Histon	572	W 3-2	Smith pen 21, Pugh 43, Glover 82	5
11	Sat-24-Sep	BSN	A	Altrincham	775	L 0-2		6
12	Sat-08-Oct	BSN	A	Hyde FC	682	D 1-1	Thornton 25	8
13	Sat-22-Oct	BSN	H	Solihull Moors	733	L 0-1		11
14	Mon-24-Oct	BSN	H	Droylsden	539	W 2-1	Thornton 36, G Dean 90	9
15	Sat-05-Nov	BSN	A	Harrogate Town	394	W 2-0	Hadland 45, Glover 90	7
16	Sat-12-Nov	BSN	H	Workington	712	W 2-1	Moore 49, York 88	6
17	Sat-19-Nov	BSN	A	Corby Town	820	W 2-0	Moore 85, York 90	6
18	Tue-22-Nov	BSN	A	Guiseley	397	D 1-1	Pugh 4	4
19	Sat-03-Dec	BSN	A	Eastwood Town	415	W 5-0	York 18, Forsdick 58, Marsden 70, Noon 86, Pugh 88	4
20	Tue-06-Dec	BSN	A	Gloucester City	302	W 2-1	York 61, Glover pen 66	4
21	Sat-17-Dec	BSN	H	Harrogate Town	689	W 2-0	Glover pen 45, Walker 56	4
22	Mon-26-Dec	BSN	A	Hinckley United	1334	D 1-1	Moore 55	4
23	Sun-01-Jan	BSN	H	Hinckley United	1372	L 2-5	G Dean 47, Walker 86	4
24	Sat-07-Jan	BSN	A	Workington	466	D 1-1	Hadland 86	4
25	Sat-14-Jan	BSN	H	Blyth Spartans	768	D 2-2	G Dean 36, Forsdick 61	5
26	Sat-21-Jan	BSN	A	Boston United	1070	D 0-0		5
27	Sat-28-Jan	BSN	H	Vauxhall Motors	622	W 2-1	Glover 2 (pen 67, pen 83)	6
28	Sat-18-Feb	BSN	A	Colwyn Bay	453	W 6-1	Glover 4 (6, 26, 39, 65), Brown 7, Noon 23	4
29	Tue-21-Feb	BSN	A	FC Halifax Town	1309	W 3-0	G Dean 5, Glover 70, Brown 90	2
30	Sat-25-Feb	BSN	H	FC Halifax Town	1051	W 1-0	Brown 30	2
31	Sat-03-Mar	BSN	H	Corby Town	775	W 2-0	Hadland 10, Walker 29	2
32	Mon-05-Mar	BSN	H	Guiseley	785	D 1-1	Walker 60	2
33	Sat-10-Mar	BSN	A	Gainsborough Trinity	624	L 2-3	G Dean 79, Brown 83	2
34	Sat-17-Mar	BSN	H	Hyde FC	902	W 2-0	York 14, Glover 75	2
35	Sat-24-Mar	BSN	A	Histon	487	D 1-1	Brown 19	3
36	Tue-27-Mar	BSN	A	Stalybridge Celtic	419	L 1-4	Glover 32	3
37	Sat-31-Mar	BSN	A	Altrincham	765	W 2-1	Glover 34, Forsdick 57	3
38	Sat-07-Apr	BSN	A	Bishops Stortford	538	W 3-0	Albrighton 36, Brown 55, G Dean 77	3
39	Mon-09-Apr	BSN	H	Worcester City	958	W 3-0	Forsdick 3, Glover 29, Brown 35	3
40	Sat-14-Apr	BSN	A	Solihull Moors	517	D 0-0		4
41	Sat-21-Apr	BSN	H	Colwyn Bay	856	D 1-1	Nisevic 67	5
42	Sat-28-Apr	BSN	A	Blyth Spartans	363	W 3-2	Armson 5, Forsdick 30, Glover pen 37	5

CUPS

No.	Date	Comp	H/A	Opponents	Att:	Result	Goalscorers	
1	Sat-01-Oct	FAC2Q	A	Needham Market	319	W 3-0	Mitchley 2 (13, 17), Pugh 54	
2	Sat-15-Oct	FAC 3Q	A	Daventry Town	605	W 2-1	Nisevic 52, Glover 80	
3	Sat-29-Oct	FAC 4Q	A	Nantwich Town	1011	L 0-1		
4	Sat-26-Nov	FAT 3Q	A	Sheffield FC	426	W 4-0	G Dean 18, Hadland 37, Walker 48, Nisevic 85	
5	Sun-11-Dec	FAT 1	A	AFC Telford	945	L 0-2		
6	Wed-02-May	PO SF1	H	Guiseley	1476	D 1-1	Glover 2	
7	Sun-06-May	PO SF2	A	Guiseley	1676	W 1-0 aet	Brown 117	
8	Sun-13-May	PO Final	A	Gainsborough Trinity	3890	W 1-0	Brown 16	

League
Starts
Substitute
Unused Sub

Cups
Starts
Substitute
Unused Sub

Goals (Lg)
Goals (Cup)

COLLETT	HADLAND	ALBRIGHTON	G DEAN	SMITH	NOON	LAVERY	ARMSON	NISEVIC	MARSDEN	MOORE	JAMES	BURNS	WALKER	BELCHER	GUDGER	TAYLOR	GLOVER	WARD	FORSDICK	PUGH	MILLS	MITCHLEY	THORNTON	BAKER	WASHBOURNE	ALCOCK	YORK	A DEAN	BROWN	CARTWRIGHT	BARNES-HOMER
X	X	X	X	X	X	X	X	X	X	X	S	S	S	U	U																
X	X	X	X	X	X	X	X	S	S	X	X	S	X	U		U															
X	X	X	X	X	X	X	X	U	U	S	X	X	X	X	S			S													
X	U	X	X	X	X	S		S	U	X	X	X	X	U			X	X													
X	S	X	X	X	X	X	U	S			X	X	U	S			X	X													
X	S	X	X	X	X	X	S	X			X	U	U				X	X	U												
X	X	X	X	X	X		X	X			S						X	X	U												
X	X	X	X	X	X	U	S	U			S						X	X	X	S											
X	X	U	X	X	X		X	X			S			U	X	S			X			X	X	S							
X	X	U	X	X	X		X	X			S			U	X	U			X			X	X	X	S						
X	X	X	X	X			X	X			S				S				X	X	X	S		X		U		U	S		
X	X	X	X	X			X	S	S	S	U		X						X	X	X	X		X	X	S					
X	X	U	X		X			U	S	U	S		X						X	X	X	X		X	X						
X	X	X			X			U	X	X			X						X	X	X	S		X		U		U	S		
X	X	X	X	U			X			S	S	U		X					X	X	X	X				U	S				
X	X	U	X		X			S	U	X	X			X					X	X	X			U	X						
X	X		X		X			S	S	X	X			X			U	X	X	X			U	X							
X	U	X			X			X	S	X	X			X					X	S	X		U	U	S						
X	U	X			X			X	S	X	S			X					X	X	X	U		X	X	X	S				
X	U	X			X			S	X			X		U					X	X	X	U		X	X	X	U				
X	U	X			X			S	X	U	S			X	U				X	X	S	U		X	X	X					
U	X	U	X		X			S	X			X	U						X	X		U		X	X	X					
U	X	U	X		X			S	X			X	U						X	X		S		X	X	X					
X	S	X			X			S	S			X	U						X	X		X		X	X	U	X				
X	U	X			X			U	S			X						X	S		X		X	X	U	X					
U	X	X			X			S			X							S	X		X	X		X	X	U	X				
U	X	X	U		X			X			X		U				S	X		X	X		X	S		X	X				
X	S	X			X			S			U						X	U	X		X	S		X	X		X	X			
U	X	U	X		X			U			S						X	S	X		X			X	X		X	X			
X	X	U	X		X			U			S						X	U	X		X			X	X		X	X	X	S	
X	X	U	X		X			U			S						X	U	X		X	S		X			X	X	X	S	
X	X	U	X		X			S			S						X		X	U		X	U				X	X	X	S	
X	X	U	X		X			U			S						X		X		X	U					X	X	X	U	
X	U	X	X		X			S			X		U				X	U	X		X	S					X	X	X		
X	S	X	X		X			S			X		U				X	U	X		X	S					X	X	X		
X	U	X	X				X	X		U			X		U		X	U	X		X	U					X	X			
X	S	X	X				X	X		S			X		U		X	U	X		X	S					X	X			
X	S	X	X	U			X	X		U			X		S		X		X		X	S					X	X			
X	X	X		U			X	X		S			X		U		X	U	X		X	U					X	X			
X	X	X		U			X	X		S			X				X	U	X		X	S					X	X			
X	U	X		X			X	X		U			U				X		X		X	S					X	X			
X	X	U	X		X			S		U	S			X			X	X	X	X		X	X	S	U	U					
X	X	U	X		X		X	X	S	S	X			X			X	X	X	X			X	S	U						
X	X	U	X		X		S	S	U	S	X			X			X	X	X	X		X	X	U	U						
U	X	S	X		X		X	S	X	X				S			X	X						X	X						
U	X	U	X		X		X	U	X	X				X			X	S	U			X	X								
X	X	U	X		X		X	X		U			S				X	U	X		X	U					X	X			
X	X	X			X		S	S		X			U				X	U	X		X	S					X	X			
X	X	U	X		X		S	U		X							X	U	X		X	U					X	X			
30	34	19	36	11	37	6	19	12	8	17	4	6	37	0	0	35	10	35	10	19	6	2	0	0	12	19	3	19	16	0	
0	5	2	0	0	0	1	12	9	6	18	2	3	2	3	2	0	3	1	0	4	4	9	0	1	0	0	3	1	0	0	4
5	3	18	2	0	3	1	8	4	3	5	2	1	3	7	12	1	1	9	2	0	4	5	0	1	0	5	0	4	0	0	1
6	8	0	8	0	7	0	4	2	2	4	0	0	7	0	0	0	8	3	8	3	3	3	2	0	0	2	2	0	3	3	0
0	0	1	0	0	0	0	4	3	1	3	0	0	1	0	1	0	0	1	0	1	0	2	0	0	0	0	0	0	0	0	0
2	0	6	0	0	0	0	0	3	1	1	0	0	0	1	0	0	3	0	0	1	2	0	1	2	2	0	0	0	0	0	0
0	3	1	7	4	2	0	3	1	1	5	0	2	5	0	0	0	17	0	5	4	0	0	2	0	0	0	5	0	7	0	0
0	1	0	1	0	0	0	0	2	0	0	0	0	1	0	0	0	2	0	0	1	0	2	0	0	0	0	0	0	2	0	0

PLAYING SQUAD

Existing Players		SN	HT	WT	DOB	AGE	POB	Career	Apps	Goals
GOALKEEPERS										
Neil	Collett	1	6'01"		02/10/1989	22	Coventry	Mansfield, Nuneaton T (SL) 7/11, Nuneaton T 5/12	30	0
Ben	McNamara	19			29/10/1988	23		Newcastle Jets (Aus), Manly United (Aus) 7/09,		
								Rockdale City Suns (Aust) 1/10, Bonnyrigg (Aus) 9/11,		
								AFC Wimbledon (Trial), Doncaster (Trial), Nuneaton T 8/12		
Sam	Slater							Nuneaton T, Nuneaton Griff (SL) 8/11		
DEFENDERS										
Gavin	Cowan	4	6'04"	14 04	24/05/1981	31	Hanover(Ger)	Exeter (Trainee), Braintree 7/99, Canvey Island 12/02, Nuneaton (L) 12/04,		
								Nuneaton (L) 2/05, Shrewsbury £5,000 + 3/05, Kidderminster (L) 8/06,		
								Grays 1/07 Rel 6/07, Nuneaton (L) 3/07, Nuneaton 6/07,		
								AFC Telford 5/08 Rel 1/10, Fleetwood 1/10, Gainsborough 3/10 Rel c/s 12,		
								Nuneaton T 6/12		
Gareth	Dean	5	6'00"		25/01/1990	22	Nuneaton	Nuneaton T	36	7
Ben	Ford	16						Kettering, Nuneaton 6/12		
Delroy	Gordon	15	6'01"	11 08	16/08/1984	28	Northampton	Rushden & D (Trainee), Kettering 1/03, Stamford 6/04, Rugby T c/s 05,		
								Oxford C 3/10, Banbury U 8/10, Corby T 6/11, Nuneaton T 6/12		
Tom	James	18	5'11"	11 08	19/11/1988	23		Stratford T, Kidderminster (Trial) 7/11, Watford 8/11 Rel c/s 12,		
								Nuneaton 7/12		
Eddie	Nisevic	3	6'00"		19/05/1991	21		Nuneaton T, Shepshed D (L) 9/09, Brackley (SL) 12/11	21	1
Stephen	O'Halloran	21	6'00"	11 06	29/11/1987	24	Cork, Ire	Aston Villa Rel c/s 10, Wycombe (3ML) 10/06, Southampton (L) 1/08,		
								Leeds (L) 2/08, Swansea (3ML) 11/08, Coventry 7/10 Rel c/s 11,		
								Carlisle 7/11 Rel c/s 12, Nuneaton T 8/12		
MIDFIELDERS										
Jon	Adams	11			08/01/1985	27		Leamington, AFC Telford c/s 07 Rel c/s 12, Leamington (L) 1/12,		
								Nuneaton 5/12		
James	Armson	12	6'00"		22/01/1990	22	Nuneaton	Nuneaton T	31	3
Robbie	Burns		6'00"	11 12	15/11/1990	21	Milton Keynes	Leicester Rel c/s 10, Tranmere (SL) 3/09, Ipswich (Trial) 7/10,		
								Nuneaton T 9/10, Hemel Hempstead (Dual) 3/12	9	2
Neil	Cartwright	2	5'10"		25/06/1982	30	Wrexham	Hinckley U, Corby T 6/10, Worcester 8/10 Rel 1/12,		
								Nuneaton T 1/12	16	0
Simon	Forsdick	14	5'10"		27/04/1983	29	Cambridge	Coventry (Ass Sch), Stratford, Loughborough Univ, Shepshed D,		
								Halesowen T 1/04, Hednesford T 7/07, AFC Telford 9/07,		
								Nuneaton T (L) 8/08, Bloxwich U (L) 8/08, Rushall O (Dual) 2/09,		
								Stratford T (Dual) 3/09, Nuneaton T (L) 3/09 Perm 6/09	35	5
Mark	Noon	8	5'10"	12 04	23/09/1983	28	Leamington Spa	Coventry, Tamworth 3/04, Nuneaton B/T 7/04	37	2
Kyle	Patterson	22	5'08"	10 00	06/01/1986	26	Birmingham	West Brom (Scholar), TP-47 Torino (Fin) 1/05, Saint Louis Lions (USA) 7/05,		
								LA Galaxy (USA) 7/08 Rel 11/09, GAIS (Swe) 2/10, Hednesford 8/10,		
								Tamworth 6/11, Nuneaton T 8/12		
Danny	Sleath	13	5'08"	11 05	14/12/1986	25	Matlock	Mansfield Rel 5/08, Gresley (L) 10/06, Alfreton (L) 2/07,		
								Boston U (L) 11/07, Gainsborough (SL) 3/08, Eastwood T 9/08,		
								Ilkeston 3/09, Boston U 7/09, Nuneaton T 6/12		
Adam	Walker	6	5'06"	09 00	22/01/1991	21	Coventry	Coventry Rel 4/10, Nuneaton T (3ML) 10/09, Nuneaton T 4/1039		5
Graham	Ward		5'08"	11 09	25/02/1983	29	Dublin	Wolves, Cambridge U (Trial) 3/03, Bournemouth (Trial) 4/03,		
								Kidderminster Free 8/03 Rel c/s 04, Cheltenham 8/04, Rel c/s 05,		
								Burton (L) 3/05, Tamworth 5/05, Worcester (L) 10/06 Perm Rel 5/11,		
								Nuneaton T 5/11	11	0

FORWARDS

		SN	HT	WT	DOB	AGE	POB	From - To	APPS	GOA
Andy	Brown	10			03/03/1986	26	Lincoln	Scunthorpe (Scholar), Harrogate T (L) 3/05, Hinckley 5/05, Nuneaton 7/07, AFC Telford 6/08, Nuneaton T (2ML) 1/12 Perm 3/12	19	7
Daniel	Newton	17			18/03/1991	21		Hinckley Downes, Hinckley U (Dual) 12/09, Hinckley U 6/10, Nuneaton T 6/12		
Kyle	Perry	9	6'04"	14 05	05/03/1986	25	Birmingham	Walsall Rel c/s 05, Moor Green (L) 8/04, AFC Telford (SL) 9/04, AFC Telford c/s 05 Rel 7/06, Hednesford 7/06, Willenhall 9/06, Chasetown 6/07, Port Vale (Nominal) 1/08 Rel c/s 09, Northwich (L) 3/09, Mansfield 7/09, Tamworth 7/10, Lincoln C 7/11 Rel c/s 12, AFC Telford (SL) 1/12, Nuneaton 7/12		
Robert	Thompson-Brown	20			07/08/1992	20		Kidderminster (Yth), Redditch 8/10, Stratford T 9/10, Kidderminster 10/10, Solihull Moors (L) 9/11, Solihull Moors (2ML) 1/12, Nuneaton T 8/12		
Wes	York	7	5'11"				Leicester	Derby (Yth), Leicester (Yth), Notts Forest (Yth), Anstey Nomads, Nuneaton T 11/11	22	5

Loanees		SN	HT	WT	DOB	AGE	POB	From - To	APPS	GOA
(F)Danny	Mitchley		5'10"	10 08	07/10/1989	22	Liverpool	Mansfield (3ML) 9/11, (SL) 1/12 - Rel c/s 12, Altrincham 6/12	15	0
(D)Joe	Henderson							Coventry (WE) 3/12 -		

Departures		SN	HT	WT	DOB	AGE	POB	From - To	APPS	GOA
(M)Luke	Taylor						Nuneaton	Yth - Rel 9/11	0	0
(M)Sam	Belcher		5'11"		05/01/1992	20	Nuneaton	Wycombe 6/11 - Rel 9/11, Hinckley U 9/11	3	0
(F)Lee	Smith		5'06"	13 02	08/09/1983	28	Coney Hill	Forest Green 7/11 - Worcester 9/11 Rel c/s 12, Cirencester (L) 1/12, Cinderford 6/12	11	4
(M)Richard	Lavery				28/05/1977	35	Coventry	Corby T 3/11 - Rel 9/11, Hinckley U 9/11	7	0
(M)Kevin	Thornton		5'07"	11 00	09/07/1986	26	Drogheda, Ire	Northampton 9/11 - Rel 11/11	2	2
(D)Aaron	James							Stirling Univ 8/11 - Rugby T (2ML) 10/11, Bedford T 12/11	6	0
(F)Connor	Baker							Bedworth - Rel 12/11	1	0
(F)Ben	Pugh							Forest Green 8/11 - Evesham 12/11, Hungerford 8/12	14	4
(D)Alex	Dean				25/01/1990	22		Bedworth 11/11 - Bedworth (Dual) 1/12 Perm	4	0
(F)Justin	Marsden				07/03/1984	28	Coventry	Brackley 9/08 - Rel 1/12, Solihull Moors 1/12	14	1
(G)Danny	Alcock		5'11"	11 03	15/02/1984	28	Salford	Tamworth 8/10 - Rel 2/12, Stoke C (Academy Coach) 2/12	12	0
(F)Matthew	Barnes-Homer		5'11"	12 05	25/01/1986	26	Dudley	Luton 2/12 - Ostersunds SK (Swe) 3/12, Macclesfield 6/12	4	0
(M)Gary	Mills		5'09"	11 06	20/05/1981	31	Sheppey	Bath C 9/11 - Lincoln C 5/12	23	0
(F)Danny	Glover		6'00"	11 02	24/10/1989	22	Crewe	Worcester 6/11 - Rel c/s 12, Worcester 7/12	38	17
(D)Guy	Hadland		6'01"	12 11	23/01/1979	33	Nuneaton	Brackley 6/08 - Rel c/s 12, Barwell 5/12	39	3
(D)Mark	Albrighton		6'01"	12 07	06/03/1976	36	Nuneaton	Kidderminster 5/11 - Barwell 6/12	21	1
(M)George	Washbourne		5'11"					Stratford c/s 10 - Forest Green	0	0
(D)Alex	Gudger							Yth - Bedworth (L) 8/11, Nuneaton Griff (L) 10/11, Rugby T 8/12	2	0
(F)Lee	Moore				09/11/1985	26	Bathgate	Coventry (Jun), Bedworth 7/02, Tamworth 7/06, AFC Telford (3ML) 9/06 £5,000 12/06, Nuneaton 6/09 Rel c/s 12	35	5
(F)Chris	Dillon		6'00"		13/01/1984	28	Middlesbrough	Arlesey (Dual) 3/12 -		
(F)Kurtis	Mewies							Bedworth 8/11 -		

Conference Action...

Alfreton's Ant Wilson jinks into the box surrounded by Southport players.

Photo: Bill Wheatcroft.

SOUTHPORT

Chairman: Charles Clapham
Secretary: Ken Hilton **(T)** 07802 661 906 **(E)** secretary@southportfc.net
Additional Committee Members:
Sam Shrouder, Andrew Pope, Tim Medcroft, Stephen Porter, Gordon Medcroft, Wes Hall, Hayden Preece.
Manager: Liam Watson
Programme Editor: Rob Urwin **(E)** programme@southportfc.net

Back Row L to R: Steve Akrigg, Tony McMillan, Karl Ledsham, Matt Nemes, Chris Lever.
Middle Row L to R: Charlie Joyce, Russell Benjamin, Darren Stephenson, Steve Tames, Chris Almond, Andy Parry, Chris Lynch, Michael Bakare, Aaron Chalmers, Louis Barnes
Front Row L to R: Shaun Whalley, Chris Roberts (Physio), Alan Moogan, Dominic Morley (Asst Manager), Simon Grand (Capt), Liam Watson (Manager), James Smith (Vice Capt), Kevin Lee (Coach), Tony Gray

Club Factfile

Founded: 1881 **Nickname:** The Sandgrounders
Previous Names: Southport Central, Southport Vulcan
Previous Leagues: Preston & District, Lancashire 1889-1903, Lancashire comb. 1903-11, Central 1911-21,
Football League 1921-78, Northern Premier 1978-93, 2003-04, Conference 1993-2003

Club Colours (change): Yellow & black stripes/yellow/yellow (All sky blue)

Ground: Haig Avenue, Southport, Merseyside PR8 6JZ **(T)** 01704 533 422
Capacity: 6,008 **Seats:** 1,660 **Covered:** 2,760 **Clubhouse:** Yes **Shop:** Yes
Directions: Leave M6 at junction 26. Join M58 to junction 3. Join A570 signposted Southport, follow A570 through Ormskirk Town Centre following signs for Southport. At the big roundabout (McDonalds is on the left) take the fourth exit. Proceed along this road until you reach the 2nd set of pedstrian lights and take the next left into Haig Avenue.

Previous Grounds: Sussex Road Sports Ground, Scarisbrick New Road, Ash Lane (later named Haig Avenue)

Record Attendance: 20,010 v Newcastle United - FA Cup 1932
Record Victory: 8-1 v Nelson - 01/01/31
Record Defeat: 0-11 v Oldham Athletic - 26/12/62
Record Goalscorer: Alan Spence - 98
Record Appearances: Arthur Peat - 401 (1962-72)
Additional Records: Paid £20,000 to Macclesfield Town for Martin McDonald

Senior Honours:
Lancashire Senior Cup 1904-05. Liverpool Senior Cup 1930-31, 31-32, 43-44, 62-63, 74-75, 90-91, 92-93, 98-99,
Shared 57-58, 63-64. Football League Division 4 1972-73. Northern Premier League Challenge Cup 1990-91.
Northern Premier League Premier Division 1992-93. Conference North 2004-05, 2009-10.

10 YEAR RECORD

02-03		03-04		04-05		05-06		06-07		07-08		08-09		09-10		10-11		11-12	
Conf	21	NP P	6	Conf N	10	Conf	18	Conf	23	Conf N	4	Conf N	5	Conf N	1	Conf	21	Conf	7

SOUTHPORT

No.	Date	Comp	H/A	Opponents	Att:	Result	Goalscorers	Pos
1	Sat-13-Aug	BSP	H	Lincoln City	1687	D 2-2	Kissock 41, Whalley 51	8
2	Tue-16-Aug	BSP	A	Alfreton Town	777	D 0-0		15
3	Sat-20-Aug	BSP	A	Luton Town	5681	L 1-5	Brown 8	19
4	Tue-23-Aug	BSP	H	Gateshead	957	L 1-3	Gray 15	23
5	Sat-27-Aug	BSP	A	Kidderminster Harriers	1763	L 0-2		23
6	Mon-29-Aug	BSP	H	Barrow	1204	W 2-1	Gray 57, Lee 80	19
7	Sat-03-Sep	BSP	H	AFC Telford	1123	W 3-2	Whalley 14, Walker 17, Lee 20	15
8	Sat-10-Sep	BSP	A	Bath City	663	W 2-1	Walker 3, Gray 77	12
9	Sat-17-Sep	BSP	A	Forest Green Rovers	873	W 3-2	Davis 33, Grand 48, Whalley 73	10
10	Tue-20-Sep	BSP	H	Wrexham	1710	D 0-0		11
11	Sat-24-Sep	BSP	H	Braintree Town	938	L 0-1		11
12	Tue-27-Sep	BSP	A	Darlington	1637	W 3-0	Grand 7, Lee 52, Gray 64	11
13	Sat-01-Oct	BSP	H	Cambridge United	1104	W 1-0	Owens 3	10
14	Sat-08-Oct	BSP	A	Newport County	1576	W 3-0	Grand 30, Ledsham 40, Gray 44	9
15	Tue-11-Oct	BSP	H	York City	1107	D 1-1	Mukendi 81	10
16	Sat-15-Oct	BSP	A	Mansfield Town	2406	W 3-1	Og (Todd) 25, Whalley 38, Gray 48	7
17	Tue-18-Oct	BSP	A	Gateshead	737	W 3-2	Whalley 2 (67, 75), Mukendi 89	4
18	Sat-22-Oct	BSP	H	Tamworth	1310	D 1-1	Gray 14	7
19	Sat-05-Nov	BSP	A	Kettering Town	1368	W 3-2	Grand 18, Gray 2 (pen 24, 88)	5
20	Sat-19-Nov	BSP	H	Bath City	1021	W 2-1	Gray 2 (87, 89)	3
21	Sat-26-Nov	BSP	A	Stockport County	4540	W 1-0	Ledsham 74	3
22	Tue-29-Nov	BSP	H	Forest Green Rovers	978	L 1-3	Owens 64	3
23	Sat-03-Dec	BSP	H	Alfreton Town	1061	W 2-1	Guthrie 71, Gray 72	3
24	Tue-06-Dec	BSP	A	Wrexham	3256	L 0-2		4
25	Sat-17-Dec	BSP	H	Mansfield Town	1006	W 3-1	Lever 2 (50, pen 90+1), Brown 90+3	3
26	Mon-26-Dec	BSP	A	Fleetwood Town	3029	D 2-2	Gray 2 (13, 50)	3
27	Sun-01-Jan	BSP	H	Fleetwood Town	2589	L 0-6		4
28	Thu-05-Jan	BSP	A	Cambridge United	1840	L 0-3		4
29	Sat-21-Jan	BSP	H	Luton Town	1665	D 3-3	Gray 10, Mukendi 33, Og (K Pilkington) 59	8
30	Tue-24-Jan	BSP	A	Lincoln City	1615	L 0-2		8
31	Sat-28-Jan	BSP	A	Hayes & Yeading United	294	W 2-0	Akrigg 22, Sheridan 67	6
32	Tue-14-Feb	BSP	H	Darlington	1130	W 2-0	Ledsham 8, Whalley 49	4
33	Fri-17-Feb	BSP	H	Grimsby Town	1934	L 1-2	Og (Elding) 28	4
34	Sat-25-Feb	BSP	A	Ebbsfleet United	907	W 2-1	Gray 2 (pen 38, pen 89)	4
35	Sat-03-Mar	BSP	H	Newport County	1105	D 1-1	Og (Warren) 18	5
36	Sat-10-Mar	BSP	A	AFC Telford	2025	W 1-0	Ledsham 50	5
37	Tue-13-Mar	BSP	H	Kettering Town	753	D 0-0		6
38	Sat-17-Mar	BSP	H	Stockport County	1648	W 5-0	Gray 2 (41, pen 73), Whalley 3 (64, 70, 76)	5
39	Sat-24-Mar	BSP	A	York City	3465	W 2-1	Owens 64, Gray 69	4
40	Tue-27-Mar	BSP	A	Braintree Town	637	D 0-0		4
41	Sat-31-Mar	BSP	H	Hayes & Yeading United	1147	L 1-2	Gray pen 59	5
42	Sat-07-Apr	BSP	H	Kidderminster Harriers	1544	L 1-2	Moogan 16	6
43	Mon-09-Apr	BSP	A	Barrow	918	D 2-2	Stephenson 33, Gray pen 90	6
44	Sat-14-Apr	BSP	A	Tamworth	830	D 2-2	Whalley 11, Gray pen 23	6
45	Sat-21-Apr	BSP	A	Ebbsfleet United	1231	D 3-3	Owens 16, Ellison 22, Gray pen 59	7
46	Sat-28-Apr	BSP	A	Gateshead	3738	W 1-0	Stephenson 87	7

CUPS

No.	Date	Comp	H/A	Opponents	Att:	Result	Goalscorers	
1	Sat-29-Oct	FAC 4Q	H	Stockport County	1358	W 1-0	Owens 80	
2	Sat-12-Nov	FAC 1	H	Barnet	1939	L 1-2	Akrigg 71	
3	Sat-10-Dec	FAT 1	A	Alfreton Town	394	L 0-4		

	League
	Starts
	Substitute
	Unused Sub
	Cups
	Starts
	Substitute
	Unused Sub
	Goals (Lg)
	Goals (Cup)

MCMILLAN	SMITH	AKRIGG	GRAND	OWENS	WHALLEY	LEE	LEDSHAM	BROWN	GRAY	KISSOCK	DALY	BENJAMIN	LEVER	DAVIS	NEMES	ORDISH	OSBORNE	MOOGAN	WALKER	POKU	CARDEN	MUKENDI	ALEY	PARRY	GUTHRIE	ELLISON	SHERIDAN	PALMER	O'KEEFE	PUTTERILL	STEPHENSON	FARRAN	
1	14	4	6	15	7	2	17	12	10	21	9	20	3	5	13	22	18	8	24	19	23	18	9	11	9	9	24	21	21	25	24	27	
X	X	X	X	X	X	X	X	X	X	X	S	S	S	U	U																		
X	X	X	X	U	X	X	X	U	X	X	S	X	X		U	U																	
X	X	X	X	S	X	X	X	X	X	X		S	X		U	U	S																
X	X		X	U	X	X	X	S	X	X		S	X	X	U		S	X															
		S	X	U	X	X	X	U	X			X	X	X	X		X	X	S	S													
U		X		X	X	X		X	X			S	S	X	X	S	U	X	X	X													
U		X		X	X	X		X	X			S	S	X	X	U	S	X	X	X													
X		X		X	X	X	S	X	X		S		U	X	U	S		X	X	X													
X		U	X		X	X	X	S	X		S		X	X	U			X	X	X	S												
X		S	X		X	X	S	X	X		S		X	X	U			X	X	X	U												
X	X	X	X	S	X	X	X	X	X		S			X	U				X		U	S											
X	X	X	X	X	X	X	X	X	X				U	U	U				S		S	X											
X	X	X	X	X	X	X	X	U	X						U			S	S	X	S	X											
X	X	X	X	X	X	X	X	S	X						U			U	S	X	S	X											
X	X	X	X	X	X		X	U	X				S		U			X	X	X	U	S											
X		X	X	X	X	X	X	U	X				U		U			X	S	X	U	X											
X		X	X	X	X	X	X	U	X				S		U			X	U	X	S	X											
X		X	X		X	X	X	S	X				X	S	U				U	X	U	X	X										
X	X	X	X	X	X		X	U	X				S	U	U			X		X	U		X										
X	X	X	X	X	X		X	X	X			X	S	U	U					X	S		S										
X	X	X	X	X	X		X	S	X				X	U	U			X		X	S			S									
X	X	X	X	X			X	X				S	X	U	U			X		X	S			S	X								
X	X	X	X	X				U	X			S	X	S	U			X		X	X			S	X								
X	X	X	X	X			X	X	X				X	U	U			X		X	S			S	S								
X	X	X	X	X	X		X	S					X	S	U			X		X	X			U	S								
X	X		X	X	X			U	X			U	X	X	U			X		X	U			X	S								
X	X	X	X	X	X			S	X			S		X	U			X		X	S			X	U								
X	X	S	X	X	X			S	X			S	X	X	U			X		X	U			X									
X	X	X	X	X	X		X	U	X			S	X		U						U	X		X		S							
X	X	X	X	X	X		X	S	X			X		U	U						S	X		X		S							
X	X	X	X	X	X		X		X			S			U						S	X		X		S	X	U					
X	X	X	X	X	X		X		X			S			U						S	X		X		S	X	U					
X	X	X	X	X	X		X		X				U		U			X			U	X		X		S	S						
X	X	X	X	X	X		X		X			S		U	U	U		X			S			X		X							
X	X	X	X	X	X		X		X			U		U	U						U			X		X			X	S			
X	X	X	X	X	X		X		X			S		U	U						S			X		X			X	S			
X	X	X	X	X	X		X		X			U		U	U						S			X		X			X		S		
X	X	X	X	X	X		X		X			S	X	U	U						S			X		X					S		
X	X	X	X	X			X		X			X	X	X	U						S			X		U					U	U	
X	X	X	X	X			X		X			X	X	X	U						U			X		U					U	U	
X	X	X	X	X	X		X		X			S	X	U	U						U			X					X		S		
X	X	X	X	X	X		X		X			S	X	U	U			X			U			X		S							
X	X	X	X		X		X		X			S	X	S	U			X								S			X		X	U	
X	X	X	X	X	X		X		X			U	S	X	U			X			U			X		S							
X	X	X	X	X	X		U		X				X		U			X			S			X		X			S		S		
X	X	X		X	X		X		X			X	X		U			X			U			X		S			S		S		
X	X	X		X	X		X	S	X				S	X	U	U		X	X		S		X										
X	U	X	X	X	X		X	S	X				X	S	U	U		X	U	X	S		X										
X	X	X	X	X	X		X	S				U	X	S	U			X		X	S				X								
43	37	40	42	37	41	17	37	11	44	4	0	7	23	14	3	0	1	26	7	21	2	11	2	20	2	6	2	0	5	0	1	0	0
0	0	3	0	2	0	0	2	9	0	0	6	18	8	4	0	2	3	1	5	1	19	2	1	4	3	9	1	0	2	2	5	0	0
2	0	1	0	3	0	0	1	10	0	0	0	4	4	15	43	4	1	1	2	0	16	0	0	1	1	2	0	2	0	0	2	3	0
3	2	3	2	3	3	0	3	0	2	0	0	0	2	1	0	0	0	3	1	2	0	0	2	0	1	0	0	0	0	0	0	0	0
0	0	0	0	0	0	0	0	3	0	0	0	0	1	2	0	0	0	0	0	0	3	0	0	0	0	0	0	0	0	0	0	0	0
0	1	0	0	0	0	0	0	0	0	0	0	1	0	0	3	2	0	0	1	0	0	0	0	0	0	0	0	0	0	0	0	0	0
0	0	1	4	4	11	3	4	2	24	1	0	0	2	1	0	0	0	1	2	0	0	3	0	0	1	1	1	0	0	0	2	0	0
0	0	1	0	1	0	0	0	0	0	0	0	0	0	0	0	0	0	0	0	0	0	0	0	0	0	0	0	0	0	0	0	0	0

PLAYING SQUAD

Existing Players		SN	HT	WT	DOB	AGE	POB	Career	Apps	Goals
GOALKEEPERS										
Anthony	McMillan	1			19/02/1982	30	Wigan	Preston (Scholar), Wigan, Runcorn, Lancaster 3/05, Burscough 6/06, Lancaster (2ML) 11/06, Ashton U (L) 2/07, Colwyn Bay (L) 3/07, Southport 7/08	43	0
Matthew	Nemes	13	5'10"	12 01	02/04/1987	25	Sydney	Central Coast Mariners (Aus), Spirit FC (Aust), Blacktown City (Aust), Trafford 3/11, AFC Telford (Trial) 3/11, Southport 8/11, Skelmersdale (L) 3/12	3	0
DEFENDERS										
Steve	Akrigg	4			02/01/1987	25	Liverpool	Warrington, Skelmersdale 1/07, Southport 5/11	43	1
Louis	Barnes	14			16/10/1991	20	Liverpool	Stockport (Scholar) Rel c/s 10, Man U (Trial) 8/10, Northwich 9/10, Marine c/s 11, Southport 7/12		
Earl	Davis		6'01"	13 02	17/05/1983	29	Manchester	Burnley, Southport (SL) 3/03, Southport 12/03, Swansea NC 1/04 Rel 2/04, Southport 2/04, Hyde U c/s 06, Burscough (3ML) 11/07 Perm 2/08, Southport 7/08	18	1
Simon	Grand	6	6'00"	10 03	23/02/1984	28	Chorley	Rochdale Rel c/s 04, Carlisle 8/04, Grimsby (L) 1/07 Undisc 1/07 Rel c/s 07, Morecambe 8/07 Rel c/s 08, Northwich 9/08, Chester (Trial) 9/08, Fleetwood 3/10 Rel 5/11, Mansfield (3ML) 10/10, Aldershot (SL) 1/11, Southport 6/11	42	4
Chris	Lever	3	5'10"	11 02	13/02/1987	25	Oldham	Oldham Rel c/s 07, Stalybridge (SL) 3/07, Southport c/s 07	31	2
Chris	Lynch	17	6'03"	15 06	31/01/1991	21	Blackburn	Burnley Rel c/s 11, Chester (5ML) 8/09, Hyde FC (L) 8/10, Stalybridge 8/11, Southport 7/12		
Andy	Parry	5			13/09/1991	20	Liverpool	Blackburn Rel c/s 11, Hartlepool (Trial) 4/11, Kettering 8/11 Rel 9/11, Accrington (Trial), Radcliffe B 11/11, Southport (6WL) 11/11 Perm 1/12	24	0
James	Smith	2	5'10"	11 08	17/10/1985	26	Liverpool	Everton (Sch), Liverpool, Ross County (3ML) 1/07, Stockport (3ML) 8/07 Stockport 1/08, Altrincham (Trial) 9/08, Vauxhall Motors 10/08, Altrincham 11/08 Rel c/s 11, Southport 7/11	37	0
MIDFIELDERS										
Russell	Benjamin	12			20/10/1991	20	Liverpool	Rochdale (Scholar) Rel c/s 11, Southport (WE) 2/09, Southport 8/11, Colwyn Bay (L) 9/11	25	0
Aaron	Chalmers	15	5'10"	12 08	02/02/1991	21	Manchester	Oldham Rel 12/08, Macclesfield NC 3/09, Hibernian c/s 09, Mossley 6/10, Droylsden (SL) 3/11, Woodley Sports/Stockport Sports Undisc 8/11, Southport 7/12		
Charlie	Joyce	20						Morecambe Rel c/s 12, Southport 8/12		
Karl	Ledsham	8	6'03"	12 12	17/11/1987	24	Huyton	St Helens, Skelmersdale 9/09, Southport (6WL) 11/10 Perm 1/11	39	4
Alan	Moogan	16	5'10"	11 04	22/02/1984	28	Liverpool	Everton Rel c/s 04, Injured, Burscough c/s 06, Southport 7/08, Skelmersdale (Dual) 3/11	27	1
Aaron	Turner				05/05/1984	28	Rotherham	Ashton T, Skelmersdale c/s 06, Southport 1/11		
FORWARDS										
Chris	Almond	11						Ashton Ath, Skelmersdale 2/08, Southport 6/12		
Michael	Bakare	19	5'11"		01/12/1986	25	Hackney	Waltham Forest, Haringey, Hertford 10/06, Edgware, Welwyn Garden, Leyton 11/08, Maidenhead (Trial) 2/09, Welling 9/09, Thurrock 8/10, Bishops Stortford 10/10, Chelmsford 10/11, Macclesfield 1/12 Rel c/s 12, Southport 8/12		
Tony	Gray	10			06/04/1984	28	Liverpool	Newton, Bangor C 9/04, Burscough 7/05, Southport 6/06, Droylsden 12/08, Southport 5/10	44	24
Darren	Stephenson	9			09/06/1993	19	St Catherine	Bradford C, Hinckley U (L) 8/11, Woodley Sports (2ML) 10/11, Stocksbridge PS (L) 1/12, Southport (SL) 3/12, Southport 8/12	6	2
Steven	Tames	18						Prescot Cables, Southport 7/12		
Shaun	Whalley	7	5'09"	10 07	07/08/1987	25	Prescot	Southport, Chester 9/04 Rel c/s 05, Runcorn Halton 8/05, Witton 3/06, Accrington (2ML) 11/06 Perm 1/07 Rel c/s 08, Wrexham 6/08 Rel 5/09, Southport (SL) 2/09, Droylsden 8/09, Hyde FC 8/10, Southport 1/11, Skelmersdale (Dual) 3/11	41	11

Loanees		HT	WT	DOB	AGE	POB	From - To	APPS	GOA
(F)Leon	Osborne	5'10"	10 10	28/10/1989	22	Doncaster	Bradford C 8/11 -	4	0
(M)Godfrey	Poku			22/07/1990	22		Luton (5ML) 8/11 - Mansfield 7/12	22	0
(F)Dan	Walker			15/08/1990	22		Luton (5ML) 8/11 -	12	2
(F)Vinny	Mukendi	6'02"	12 00	12/03/1992	20	Manchester	Macclesfield 9/11, 1/12 - Barrow 8/12	13	3
(M)Zach	Aley	5'11"	11 02	17/08/1991	21	Fazackerley	Blackburn 10/11 - Macclesfield (SL) 3/12	3	0
(F)Kurtis	Guthrie			21/04/1993	19	Peterborough	Accrington 11/11 -	5	1
(M)Sam	Sheridan	5'11"	11 10	30/11/1989	22	Trafford	Stockport 1/12 -	3	1
(D)Ashley	Palmer	6'01"	11 13	09/11/1992	19	Pontefract	Scunthorpe 1/12 - Harrogate T (L) 3/12	0	0
(G)Sam	Ashton						Skelmersdale (Cover) 3/12 -		
(D)Rob	McIntosh						Skelmersdale (Cover) 3/12 -		

Departures		HT	WT	DOB	AGE	POB	From - To	APPS	GOA
(F)Jon-Paul	Kissock	5'05"	10 09	02/12/1989	22	Liverpool	Formby 12/10 - Luton 8/11	4	1
(M)Matty	McGinn			27/06/1983	29	Fazackerley	Burscough 7/08 - Chester FC (L) 8/11 Perm 9/11		
(F)Steve	Daly			10/12/1981	30	Fazackerley	Burscough 7/08 - Retired 9/11	6	0
(M)Michael	Ordish			03/12/1992	19	Liverpool	Celtic 8/11 - Vauxhall Motors (L) 9/11, Skelmersdale (L) 11/11, Marine (L) 1/12, Hednesford (L) 3/12, Marine 6/12	2	0
(M)Adam	Carden			24/07/1985	27	Southport	Kendal T 7/11 - AFC Fylde 6/12	21	0
(D)Andy	Owens	6'03"	13 05	15/10/1989	22	Liverpool	Accrington 7/11 - Mansfield 6/12	39	4
(F)Ross	Farran						Warrington 3/12 - Northwich 8/12	0	0
(M)Ray	Putterill	5'08"	12 03	02/03/1989	23	Liverpool	ex Accrington 3/12 - Vauxhall Motors (L) 3/12, Rochdale 8/12	2	0
(D)Kevin	Lee	6'00"	11 10	04/11/1985	26	Liverpool	Wigan 7/06 - Retired, Southport Coach c/s 12	17	3
(F)Jonathan	Brown	5'11"	11 04	17/04/1990	22	Bridgend	Bath C 7/11 - AFC Telford (SL) 1/12, AFC Telford 7/12	20	2
(F)James	Ellison	5'10"	12 08	25/10/1991	20	Liverpool	Hyde FC 1/12 - Skelmersdale (L) 3/12, Vauxhall Motors 8/12	15	1
(M)Josh	O'Keefe	6'01"	11 05	22/12/1988	23	Whalley	ex Lincoln C 3/12 - Rel c/s 12	7	0

Conference Action...

Stockport's Carl Piergianni gets up highest to clear the danger during their League match against Alfreton Town.

Photo: Bill Wheatcroft.

STOCKPORT COUNTY

Chairman: Lord Peter Snape
Secretary: Tony Whiteside   **(T)** 0161 286 8888 x257   **(E)** tony.whiteside@stockportcounty.com
Additional Committee Members:
Kevan Taylor, Spencer Feam, John Fitzpatrick, James Gannon.

Manager: James Gannon
Programme Editor: Phil Brennan   **(E)** phil.brennan@stockportcounty.com

Back Row (L to R): Jon Routledge, Cameron Darkwah, Kyle Brownhill, Ben Chu-Say, Alex Kenyon, Euan Holden, Dane Smith,
Ian Ormson, Sean Newton, Andy Halls, Jon Nolan, Sean McConville, Danny Whitehead, Andy Graham, Sam Sheridan.
Front Row (L to R): Danny Hattersley, Carl Piergianni, Craig Hobson, Joe Connor, Rodger Wylde (Physio), Alan Lord (asst Manager),
James Gannon (Manager), Grace Conroy (PA to JG), Richard Landon (kit manager), Danny O'Donnell, James Tunnicliffe,
Deji Omoboye, Tom Collins.

Club Factfile

Founded: 1883   **Nickname:** County or Hatters
Previous Names: Heaton Norris Rovers 1883-88, Heaton Norris 1888-90.
Previous Leagues: Football League 1900-2011.

Club Colours (change): Blue/blue/white (White/black/black)

Ground: Edgeley Park, Hardcastle Road, Stockport SK3 9DD   **(T)** 0161 286 8903
Capacity: 10,800 **Seats:** Yes   **Covered:** Yes   **Clubhouse:**   **Shop:** Yes

Directions: **From The South** (M6): Exit the M6 at Junction 19 (sign-posted 'Manchester Airport, Stockport A55, M56 East') and at the r'about turn right onto the A556. At the Bowden r'about after 4.2 miles, turn right (sign-posted 'Manchester M56') onto the M56. Exit the M56 after 6.9 miles (sign-posted 'Stockport M60, Sheffield M67') onto the M60. Exit the M60 at Junction 1 ('sign-posted 'Stockport Town Centre and West'). At the r'about turn right and continue through to the second set of lights and turn left (ignoring the sign directing you to Stockport Co.) and follow the road to the left, which is Chestergate. At the lights turn right up King Street, past the fire station on the right to the top of the hill, turn right at the r'about signed Edgeley. Continue down Hardcastle street turning left after the bus stop signed Caroline Street. **From the North** (M62 from Leeds): Follow the M62 onto the M60 and continue south. Exit the M60 at Junction 1 ('sign-posted Stockport Town centre') At the roundabout turn right and continue through to the second set of lights and turn left (ignoring the sign directing you to Stockport Co.) and follow the road to the left, which is Chestergate. At the traffic lights turn right up King Street, past the fire station on the right to the top of the hill, turn right at the roundabout signed Edgeley. Continue down Hardcastle street turning left after the bus stop signed Caroline Street. At the end of Caroline St turn right where you will see the main car park on the left. (not available on Match Days)
Previous Grounds: Nursery Inn, Green Lane 1889-1902.

Record Attendance: 27,833 v Liverpool, FA Cup 5th Round 11/02/1950.
Record Victory: 13-0 v Halifax Town, Division Three North 06/01/1934.
Record Defeat: 1-8 v Chesterfield, Division Two 19/04/1902.
Record Goalscorer: (League) Jack Connor - 132, 1951-56.
Record Appearances: (League) Andy Thorpe - 489, 1978-86, 88-92.
Additional Records: Paid, £800,000 for Ian Moore from Nottingham Forest, 07/1998.
Senior Honours: Received, £1,600,000 for Alun Armstrong from Middlesbrough, 02/1998.
League Division Three North 1921-22, 36-37, Division Four 1966-67.

10 YEAR RECORD

02-03		03-04		04-05		05-06		06-07		07-08		08-09		09-10		10-11		11-12	
FL 2	14	FL 2	19	FL 1	24	FL 2	22	FL 2	8	FL 2	4	FL 1	18	FL 1	24	FL 2	24	Conf	16

STOCKPORT COUNTY

No.	Date	Comp	H/A	Opponents	Att:	Result	Goalscorers	Pos
1	Fri-12-Aug	BSP	A	Forest Green Rovers	1848	D 1-1	Chadwick 78	2
2	Tue-16-Aug	BSP	H	Kettering Town	3429	W 1-0	Holden 60	6
3	Sat-20-Aug	BSP	H	Ebbsfleet United	3674	D 1-1	Chadwick 68	8
4	Tue-23-Aug	BSP	A	Kidderminster Harriers	1886	D 1-1	Elliott 27	9
5	Fri-26-Aug	BSP	A	Lincoln City	2152	D 1-1	Elliott 44	8
6	Mon-29-Aug	BSP	H	Mansfield Town	3571	L 0-1		15
7	Fri-02-Sep	BSP	H	Luton Town	3389	D 1-1	McConville 90	11
8	Sat-10-Sep	BSP	A	AFC Telford	2375	D 1-1	German 51	16
9	Sat-17-Sep	BSP	H	Grimsby Town	3943	W 2-0	McConville 23, Elliott 61	13
10	Tue-20-Sep	BSP	A	Newport County	1205	D 1-1	Elliott 82	14
11	Sat-24-Sep	BSP	A	Tamworth	1381	D 1-1	Chadwick 48	14
12	Tue-27-Sep	BSP	H	Fleetwood Town	3023	L 2-4	German 2 (30, 71)	15
13	Sat-01-Oct	BSP	H	York City	3753	L 1-2	Paton 90	17
14	Thu-06-Oct	BSP	A	Cambridge United	2047	D 2-2	Chadwick 3, Whitehead 63	17
15	Tue-11-Oct	BSP	H	Darlington	2671	L 3-4	Chadwick 3, Paton 2 (12, 52)	18
16	Sat-15-Oct	BSP	A	Wrexham	3874	L 0-4		20
17	Tue-18-Oct	BSP	A	Bath City	919	W 2-0	Chadwick 63, Paton 90	17
18	Sat-22-Oct	BSP	H	Forest Green Rovers	3391	L 0-1		18
19	Sat-05-Nov	BSP	H	Hayes & Yeading United	2804	D 3-3	Elliott 27, Piergianni 2 (30, 57)	17
20	Sat-12-Nov	BSP	A	Ebbsfleet United	1119	L 1-2	Chadwick pen 21	17
21	Sat-19-Nov	BSP	A	Fleetwood Town	3021	L 1-2	McConville pen 59	18
22	Sat-26-Nov	BSP	H	Southport	4540	L 0-1		20
23	Tue-29-Nov	BSP	A	Grimsby Town	2254	L 0-7		21
24	Tue-06-Dec	BSP	H	Gateshead	2366	L 0-1		22
25	Sat-17-Dec	BSP	H	Alfreton Town	2802	D 0-0		22
26	Mon-26-Dec	BSP	A	Barrow	2103	L 0-1		23
27	Sun-01-Jan	BSP	H	Barrow	3301	W 3-2	Sheridan 2 (10, pen 84), Connor 32	19
28	Sat-07-Jan	BSP	A	Gateshead	846	L 0-2		19
29	Tue-10-Jan	BSP	A	Luton Town	5588	L 0-1		19
30	Sat-21-Jan	BSP	A	Braintree Town	833	D 2-2	Connor 67, Danny L Rowe 90	19
31	Tue-24-Jan	BSP	H	AFC Telford	2831	D 2-2	O'Donnell 67, Piergianni 82	19
32	Sat-28-Jan	BSP	H	Kidderminster Harriers	3728	W 2-1	McConville 21, Danny L Rowe 55	19
33	Sat-11-Feb	BSP	H	Newport County	3565	D 2-2	Danny L Rowe 2 (8, 60)	17
34	Sat-18-Feb	BSP	A	York City	3370	L 1-2	Danny L Rowe 52	19
35	Sat-25-Feb	BSP	H	Wrexham	4518	W 1-0	Og (Mayebi) 27	19
36	Sat-03-Mar	BSP	A	Darlington	2202	W 1-0	Danny L Rowe pen 60	16
37	Tue-06-Mar	BSP	A	Alfreton Town	1115	L 1-6	Rose 90	16
38	Sat-10-Mar	BSP	H	Cambridge United	5957	L 0-1		16
39	Sat-17-Mar	BSP	A	Southport	1648	L 0-5		18
40	Sat-24-Mar	BSP	H	Bath City	3744	W 4-0	Hattersley 14, Elliott 2 (55, 82), Piergianni 61	17
41	Sat-31-Mar	BSP	A	Kettering Town	1281	W 3-1	Hattersley 29, Newton 45, Darkwah 90	19
42	Sat-07-Apr	BSP	H	Lincoln City	3975	W 4-0	Hattersley 6, Danny L Rowe 2 (11, 55), Darkwah 90	17
43	Mon-09-Apr	BSP	A	Mansfield Town	3883	L 1-2	Rose 89	18
44	Sat-14-Apr	BSP	H	Braintree Town	3199	D 1-1	Hattersley 15	18
45	Sat-21-Apr	BSP	H	Tamworth	6393	W 2-0	O'Donnell 48, Hattersley 77	16
46	Sat-28-Apr	BSP	A	Hayes & Yeading United	654	W 2-1	Hattersley 7, Connor 70	16

CUPS

No.	Date	Comp	H/A	Opponents	Att:	Result	Goalscorers	
1	Sat-29-Oct	FAC 4Q	A	Southport	1358	L 0-1		
2	Sat-10-Dec	FAT 1	H	Stalybridge Celtic	1690	D 2-2	Elliott 5, McConville 50	
3	Tue-13-Dec	FAT 1R	A	Stalybridge Celtic	1149	L 1-2	McConville 12	

League
Starts
Substitute
Unused Sub

Cups
Starts
Substitute
Unused Sub

Goals (Lg)
Goals (Cup)

GLENNON	BRAHIM-BOUNAB	MCCANN	HALL	HOLDEN	FRAUGHAN	SHERIDAN	MILES	ROUTLEDGE	CHADWICK	GRITTON	ELLIOTT	PIERGIANNI	ORMSON	HALLS	PARKER	O'DONNELL	CHAMBERLAIN	DANIEL M ROWE	NOLAN	MCCONVILLE	BLACKBURN	GERMAN	PATON	WHITEHEAD	EDWARDS	LYNCH	DARKWAH	SMITH	HALSTEAD	COLE	CHU SAY	CONNOR	BROWNHILL	DANNY L ROWE	MAINWARING	TURNBULL	HIRMER	ROSE	HATTERSLEY	AMIS	KING	NEWTON
1	21	16	6	3	11	14	10	4	19	9	20	22	12	17	23	5	24	18	8	7	25	6	23	15	24	2	13	27	28	29	31	32	30	6	19	23	1	2	10	9	28	16
X	X	X	X	X	X	X	X	X	X	X	X	S	U	U	U																											
X	X	X		X	X	X		X	X	X	U	X	X	U		S	S	S																								
X	U			X	X	X		X	X	X	S	X	U	X		X	S	X	U																							
X	S	X		X		X	X	X	X	U	X	X	U			X	S	S		X																						
X	X	S		X		X	X	X	U	X	X	U			X	S	X	X																								
X		X		X	X	S		S	X	X	X	U	U		X	S	X	X	X																							
X		X	X	S		X	X		S	X	U		X	S	X	X	X	U																								
X	U		X		X	U		S	X	X	U	X		X	S	X	X	X	X																							
X	U	S			S		S	X	X	X	U	X		X	X	X	X	X																								
X		S	S		U		U	X	X	X	U	X		X	X	X	X	X																								
X	U	X		X		X		X	X	X	U		X	S	X	S	X	S	X																							
X	U	X			S	S		X		X	X	U		X	X	X	X	X	S																							
X	X	U		X		S	X		S	X	U		X	X	X	S	X																									
X	X	S		X	X		X	X		X	U		X	S	U	X	S	X																								
X	X	S		X	X		X		X	U	X	X	S	S	X	U	X																									
X	U			X	X	S	X		S	X	U		X	X	X	X	S	X																								
X		X		U		X	X	X	X	U		X	S	S	X	S	X	S	X	X																						
X		X		S		X	X	X	X	U		U	S	X	S	X	X																									
X		S		X	X	X	X	X	U		X	X	X	U	X	X	X	S																								
U	X	X		X	S		X	X		X	X		X	U	X	S	S	X	X	X	S																					
	X	U		X		X		X	U		X		U	X	X	X		S	U	X	X	X		X																		
	X	X		X			S	S	X		U	X	S	U	X	X	X	X	X	U		X	S																			
	X	X		X			U		X	S		X	S	U	X	X	X	X	S		S	X	X																			
X				X	S	U		X		X	X	U	X	X	X	X	S		X	U	X	S																				
X				X		S		X	X	X	U	X	X	X	U	X	X		S			X	U	X	U																	
X		S		X	X	X		S	X	X	U	X	X	U	X	U			X			S	X																			
X		S		X	X	X		X	S	X	U	X	X	S	U			X	U	X		X		X																		
U			X	U	X		X	S	X	X	X	X		X	S				X	X	S			X	U	X		S														
U			X			X	U	X	X	X	X	X		X	X	S			X	X			S		X			S	X													
U			X			U	X	X	X	X	X			X	S			S			X		X	X	X																	
U			X			U	X	X	U	X	X			X	U		S	X			S		X	X	X																	
			X					X	S	X	S	X	X	X	U			X				S		X	X	X	X	U														
			S	U				X	X	X	X	X		X	X	X		X		S		U	X	X	X	X	U	X														
			S					X	S	X	X	X		X	X		X	X		S		S		X	X	X	U	X														
			X					S	X	X	X	X		X	X			U				S		X	X	X	U	X														
			S		U			X	X	X	X			X	S			X				U		X	X	X	U	X														
					X					X	X	X				S	X							S				S		X	U	X	X	X	X	S	X	X	U		
					X					X	X	X				S	S							S				U		X			X	X	X	X	U	X	X		X	X
			X							X	X	U	X			S	U							S				S		X			X	X	X	S	X		U	X	X
			X							X	X	U	X			S	X					U		S				S		X			X	X	X	S	X		U	X	X
			X							X	X	U	X		S		U			X				X				S	X	S		X	X		X			S	X	U	X
			X							X	X	X	X		X		S			X				X				U	X	S			X	X		S	X		U	X	
			X							X	X	X	X		S		X			X				X				S		U		X	X	X		S	X		U	X	
U	X		X		U	X	X			X	X	U			X			U			U	X	X		X	S	U															
X		X			X		X	U	X	S		X			X		S	X	X	X	X			X			S			U	S											
X		X		S				U	X	X		X			X		X	X	X	X			X			S		U	S													
24	10	11	1	29	6	24	11	12	17	6	33	39	13	29	0	32	0	15	18	21	12	10	15	4	11	5	0	0	4	7	0	19	0	13	15	14	0	6	8	0	5	7
0	1	8	0	4	4	3	3	2	2	5	9	2	0	0	1	2	5	11	13	2	3	6	0	13	0	1	7	0	0	9	1	2	2	0	0	1	4	0	0	0	0	0
5	5	3	0	0	2	4	1	1	2	6	0	0	30	3	1	0	0	5	5	0	2	2	1	3	0	1	1	0	1	4	1	0	2	0	0	0	7	1	0	1	2	0
2	0	2	0	2	0	0	1	2	1	0	2	2	1	2	0	3	0	1	2	2	2	1	1	1	2	1	0	0	0	0	0	0	0	0	0	0	0	0	0	0	0	0
0	0	0	0	0	0	0	0	1	0	0	0	0	0	0	0	1	0	0	0	0	0	0	0	0	0	0	2	0	0	2	0	0	0	0	0	0	0	0	0	0	0	0
0	1	0	0	0	0	1	0	0	0	2	0	0	0	1	0	0	0	0	0	1	0	0	1	0	0	0	0	0	0	1	2	0	0	0	0	0	0	0	0	0	0	0
0	0	0	0	1	0	2	0	0	7	0	7	4	0	0	0	2	0	0	0	4	0	3	4	1	0	0	2	0	0	0	0	0	0	3	0	8	0	0	0	2	6	0
0	0	0	0	0	0	0	0	0	0	0	1	0	0	0	0	0	0	0	0	0	2	0	0	0	0	0	0	0	0	0	0	0	0	0	0	0	0	0	0	0	0	0

PLAYING SQUAD

Existing Players		SN	HT	WT	DOB	AGE	POB	Career	Apps	Goals
GOALKEEPERS										
Lewis	King	21			08/05/1993	19	Derby	Derby (Scholar) Rel 10/09, Sunderland (Scholar) 11/09 Pro 7/11 Rel c/s 12, Stockport (SL) 3/12, Stockport 8/12	5	0
Ian	Ormson	1	5'10"	11 04	16/05/1994	18	Liverpool	Stockport	13	0
Dane	Smith							Stockport	0	0
Tom	Whitehurst							Stockport		
DEFENDERS										
Kyle	Brownhill	16						Stockport	2	0
Ben	Chu Say	17			22/09/1993	18	Warrington	Stockport	1	0
Joe	Connor	4	6'01"	12 08	01/02/1986	26	Stockport	Lee Flames (USA), Fort Wayne Fever (USA), Charlotte Eagles (USA) c/s 08, Stockport 12/11	21	3
Jordan	Fagbola	20	6'03"	11 11	01/12/1993	18	Manchester	Rochdale Rel c/s 12, Stockport 7/12		
Andy	Halls	2	6'00"	12 01	20/04/1992	20	Urmston	Stockport	29	0
Euann	Holden		6'00"	12 01	02/02/1988	24	Aberdeen	Aberdeen (Yth), Conneticut Huskies (USA), New Mexico Lobos (USA), Austin Aztec (USA), Vejle BK (Den) 1/10 Rel 6/10, Crewe (Trial) 9/10, Derby (Trial) 10/10, Oldham (Trial) 2/11, FC Hjorring (Den) 4/11, Stockport 7/11, Southend (Trial) 7/12	33	1
Daniel	O'Donnell	5	6'02"	11 11	10/03/1986	26	Liverpool	Liverpool, Crewe (SL) 8/06, Crewe Undisc 6/07 Rel c/s 10, Rochdale (Trial) 7/10, Shrewsbury 8/10 Rel 12/10, Stockport 1/11	34	2
Sean	Newton	3	6'02"	13 00	23/09/1988	23	Liverpool	Chester, Southport (3ML) 8/07, Droylsden (SL) 2/08, Droylsden 8/08, Barrow 7/09, AFC Telford (2ML) 8/09 Perm 10/09, Stockport (SL) 3/12 Nominal 5/12	7	1
Carl	Piergianni	15	6'01"	13 05	03/05/1992	20	Peterborough	Peterborough, Spalding U (WE) 12/09, Altrincham (SL) 1/11, Stockport 8/11	41	4
James	Tunnicliffe	6	6'04"	12 03	17/01/1989	23	Denton	Stockport, Liverpool (Trial) 10/05, Northwich (L) 10/07, Brighton Undisc 7/09, MK Dons (2ML) 2/10, Bristol R (SL) 7/10, Wycombe 7/11 Rel c/s 12, Crewe (L) 2/12, Stockport 7/12		
Brandon	Windsor							Stockport		
MIDFIELDERS										
Andy	Graham							Stockport		
Alex	Kenyon	8			01/07/1992	20	Preston	Everton (Yth), Preston (Yth), Chorley, Lancaster c/s 09, Stockport 5/12		
John	Nolan	18	5'09"	11 04	22/04/1992	20	Huyton	Everton Rel c/s 11, Watford (Trial) 4/10, Stockport 7/11	31	0
Deji	Omoboye							Stockport		
Sam	Sheridan	14	5'11"	11 10	30/11/1989	22	Trafford	Bolton Rel c/s 11, Altrincham (L) 9/09, Stockport 7/11, Southport (L) 1/12	27	2
FORWARDS										
Josh	Amis							Stockport	0	0
Tom	Collins	10			24/08/1992	20		Stevenage, Hayes & Yeading 8/11, Stockport 6/12		
Cameron	Darkwah	13	5'09"		02/09/1992	19	Manchester	Stockport, Mossley (2ML) 8/11, FC Halifax (2ML) 1/12	7	2
Danny	Hattersley	9	6'03"		08/04/1992	20	Bradford	Lancaster, Stockport 3/12	8	6
Craig	Hobson	11			25/02/1988	24		Kendal T, Stalybridge 9/09, Stockport 5/12		
Sam	Mitten							Stockport		
Danny L	Rowe	19			29/01/1989	23		Preston (Yth), Man Utd (Yth) Undisc, Kendal T c/s 08, Fleetwood 12/10, Droylsden (4ML) 8/11, Stockport (SL) 1/12, Stockport (6ML) 7/12	15	8
Danny	Whitehead	7			23/10/1993	18	Salford	Stockport	17	1

Loanees		SN	HT	WT	DOB	AGE	POB	From - To	APPS	GOA
(M)Elliott	Chamberlain				29/04/1992	20	Paget, Ber	Leicester 8/11 - AFC Telford (L) 11/11	5	0
(F)Michael	Paton		5'10"	11 00	25/03/1989	23	Greenock	Aberdeen (5ML) 8/11 -	15	4
(D)Joe	Edwards		5'08"	11 06	31/10/1990	21	Gloucester	Bristol C 9/11, (2ML) 11/11 - Yeovil (L) 1/12	11	0
(G)Mark	Halstead		6'03"	14 00	01/01/1990	22	Blackpool	Blackpool (6WL) 11/11 -	4	0
(M)Aaron	Cole							Derby (SL) 11/11 - Barrow 8/12	16	0
(M)Matty	Mainwaring		5'11"	12 02	28/03/1990	21	Salford	Preston (Scholar), Stockport 6/08 Rel 9/11, Hull C 1/12,		
								Stockport (2ML) 1/12	15	0
(M)Paul	Turnbull		6'00"	12 07	23/01/1989	23	Handforth	Northampton 1/12 -	14	0

Departures		SN	HT	WT	DOB	AGE	POB	From - To	APPS	GOA
(F)Keigan	Parker		5'07"	10 05	08/06/1982	30	Livingston	Mansfield 8/11 - Rel 8/11, AFC Blackpool 8/11, AFC Fylde 9/11,		
								Ayr U 2/12	1	0
(D)Danny	Hall		6'02"	12 07	14/11/1983	28	Ashton-under-Lyne	Crawley 8/11 - Rel 8/11, Hyde FC 9/11, Altrincham 5/12	1	0
(F)Nick	Chadwick		6'00"	12 08	26/10/1982	29	Market Drayton	Barrow 7/11 - Plymouth (2ML) 11/11 Perm 1/12	19	7
(F)Antonio	German		5'10"	12 03	26/12/1991	20	Wembley	QPR 8/11 - Rel 1/12, Bromley 1/12, Brentford 1/12	16	3
(D)Chris	Blackburn		5'07"	10 06	02/08/1982	30	Crewe	Wrexham 8/11 - AFC Telford 1/12	15	0
(G)Matt	Glennon		6'02"	14 09	08/10/1978	33	Stockport	Bradford C 9/10 - Rel 1/12, Chester 2/12 Rel c/s 12,		
								FC Halifax 7/12	24	0
(D)Mark	Lynch		5'11"	11 03	02/09/1981	30	Manchester	Rotherham 7/10 - Rel 1/12, Altrincham 2/12 Rel c/s 12	6	0
(M)Ryan	McCann		5'08"	11 02	21/09/1981	30	Bellshil	Ayr 7/11 - Rel 1/12	19	0
(F)John	Miles		5'10"	12 09	28/09/1981	30	Bootle	Fleetwood 7/11 - Rel 1/12, Altrincham 2/12 Rel c/s 12	14	0
(F)Martin	Gritton		6'00"	12 05	01/06/1978	34	Glasgow	Yeovil 7/11 - Rel 3/12, Truro C 3/12	11	0
(G)Bernhard	Hirmer				06/12/1967	44		Bristol R (Coach) - Rel c/s 12	1	0
(D)Jordan	Rose				22/11/1989	22	Southampton	Hayes & Yeading 2/12 - Rel c/s 12	10	2
(M)Daniel	Rowe		6'00"	11 11	09/03/1992	20	Wythenshawe	Bolton (Yth) - Rel c/s 12, Barrow 8/12	26	0
(M)Nabil	Brahim-Bounab		6'00"	11 11	28/04/1988	24	Frejus, Fra	Frejus St-Raphael (Fra) 8/11 - Rel, Buxton (L) 2/12	11	0
(F)Tom	Elliott		5'10"	11 00	09/09/1989	22	Leeds	Hamilton 8/11 - Cambridge U 5/12	42	7
(M)Ryan	Fraughan		5'06"	11 02	11/02/1991	21	Liverpool	Tranmere 7/11 - The New Saints (SL) 1/12,		
								The New Saints 5/12	10	0
(M)Jon	Routledge		6'00"	13 07	23/11/1989	22	Liverpool	Hamilton 8/11 - Hamilton (SL) 1/12, Hamilton 8/12	14	0
(F)Sean	McConville		5'10"	11 08	06/03/1989	23	Burscough	Burscough, Skelmersdale 7/07, Stockport (Trial) 1/09,		
								Accrington Undisc 2/09 Rel c/s 11, Stockport 7/11 Rel c/s 12,		
								Rochdale (SL) 3/12	23	4

Conference Action...

The Tamworth defender looks favourite to get to the ball first but Alfreton's Ant Wilson isn't going to make it easy.

Photo: Bill Wheatcroft.

TAMWORTH

Chairman: Bob Andrews
Secretary: Rod Hadley   **(T)** 01827 657 98   **(E)** clubsec@thelambs.co.uk
Additional Committee Members:
Stephen Lathbury, Brian Whitehouse, John Holcroft, Martin Newbold, Nick, Lunn.

Manager: Marcus Law
Programme Editor: Terry Brumpton   **(E)** terrybrumpton@yahoo.co.uk

2011-12 Squad - Back Row (L-R): Patrick Kanyuka, Liam Francis, Danny Mills, Joe Collister, Jonathan Hedge, Sam Andrew, Francino Francis, Callum Reynolds, Daniel Bradley, Rico Taylor.
Middle Row: Dale Belford (Goalkeeper Coach) Buster Belford (Kit Manager), Nabil Shariff, Samuel Habergham, Liam McDonald, Kieron St.Aimie, Richard Tait, Scott Barrow, Lee Weemes, Kyle Patterson, Paul O'Brian (Coach), Huseyin Torgut (Therapist).
Front Row: Danny Thomas, Ashley Cain, Connor Gudger, Paul Green, Marcus law (Manager), Duane Courtney, Jay Smith, Iyseden Christie, Troy Wallen

Club Factfile

Founded: 1933   **Nickname:** The Lambs
Previous Names: None
Previous Leagues: Birmingham Combination 1933-54, West Midlands (originally Birmingham League) 1954-72, 84-88, Southern 1972-79, 83-84, 89-2003, Northern Premier 1979-83

Club Colours (change): All red (All sky blue)

Ground: The Lamb Ground, Kettlebrook, Tamworth, Staffordshire B77 1AA   **(T)** 01827 657 98
Capacity: 4,100   **Seats:** 518   **Covered:** 1,191   **Clubhouse:** Yes   **Shop:** Yes
Directions M42 Junction 10. Take A5/A51 to Town centre, then follow the signs for Kettlebrook and Tamworth FC.

Previous Grounds: Jolly Sailor Ground 1933-34

Record Attendance: 5,500 v Torquay United - FA Cup 1st Round 15/11/69
Record Victory: 14-4 v Holbrook Institue (H) - Bass Vase 1934
Record Defeat: 0-11 v Solihull (A) - Birmingham Combination 1940
Record Goalscorer: Graham Jessop - 195
Record Appearances: Dave Seedhouse - 869
Additional Records: Paid £7,500 to Ilkeston Town for David Hemmings December 2000
Senior Honours: Received £7,500 from Telford United for Martin Myers 1990
Birmingham Senior Cup 1960-61, 65-66, 68-69. West Midlands League 1964-65, 65-66, 71-72, 87-88. FA Vase 1988-89. Southern League Premier Division 2002-03. Conference North 2008-09.

10 YEAR RECORD

02-03		03-04		04-05		05-06		06-07		07-08		08-09		09-10		10-11		11-12	
SthP	1	Conf	17	Conf	15	Conf	20	Conf	22	Conf N	15	Conf N	1	Conf	16	Conf	19	Conf	18

TAMWORTH

No.	Date	Comp	H/A	Opponents	Att:	Result	Goalscorers	Pos
1	Sat-13-Aug	BSP	A	Barrow	1371	D 1-1	Christie pen 31	15
2	Tue-16-Aug	BSP	H	Ebbsfleet United	921	W 1-0	Bradley 71	7
3	Sat-20-Aug	BSP	H	Darlington	977	W 1-0	Christie pen 83	4
4	Tue-23-Aug	BSP	A	Wrexham	3353	L 0-3		8
5	Sat-27-Aug	BSP	A	Bath City	656	W 2-0	Thomas 31, Shariff 90	5
6	Mon-29-Aug	BSP	H	AFC Telford	1316	D 2-2	St Aimie 2 (41, 67)	5
7	Sun-04-Sep	BSP	A	Hayes & Yeading United	359	L 0-1		7
8	Sat-10-Sep	BSP	H	York City	1012	W 2-1	St Aimie pen 53, Christie pen 73	5
9	Sat-17-Sep	BSP	A	Kettering Town	1955	W 2-0	Thomas 30, Christie 80	6
10	Tue-20-Sep	BSP	H	Forest Green Rovers	783	L 0-1		9
11	Sat-24-Sep	BSP	H	Stockport County	1381	D 1-1	Christie 90	10
12	Tue-27-Sep	BSP	A	Braintree Town	840	L 1-3	McDonald 30	10
13	Sat-01-Oct	BSP	A	Gateshead	770	D 1-1	Christie pen 77	11
14	Sat-08-Oct	BSP	H	Lincoln City	1232	W 4-0	St Aimie 2 (12, 87), Christie pen 61, F Francis 64	11
15	Sat-15-Oct	BSP	A	Newport County	1310	W 2-1	St Aimie 47, Christie 59	10
16	Tue-18-Oct	BSP	H	Hayes & Yeading United	742	W 2-1	St Aimie 83, Patterson 90	8
17	Sat-22-Oct	BSP	A	Southport	1310	D 1-1	Christie pen 50	10
18	Sat-05-Nov	BSP	A	Kidderminster Harriers	1797	L 0-2		11
19	Fri-18-Nov	BSP	H	Kettering Town	1197	D 2-2	Patterson pen 41, Mills 55	11
20	Sat-26-Nov	BSP	A	Darlington	1752	L 0-2		13
21	Tue-29-Nov	BSP	H	Braintree Town	742	W 1-0	Mills 56	11
22	Tue-06-Dec	BSP	A	Forest Green Rovers	732	L 1-3	Shariff 19	12
23	Sat-17-Dec	BSP	H	Luton Town	1467	L 1-3	Mills 76	14
24	Mon-26-Dec	BSP	A	Alfreton Town	1012	L 2-5	McDonald 78, Tait 86	15
25	Sun-01-Jan	BSP	H	Alfreton Town	1241	D 2-2	Courtney 17, Christie 49	15
26	Sat-14-Jan	BSP	H	Wrexham	1923	L 1-2	Wilson 54	14
27	Sat-21-Jan	BSP	H	Barrow	1222	L 2-3	Patterson 2 (7, 49)	15
28	Tue-24-Jan	BSP	A	Ebbsfleet United	746	L 0-3		15
29	Sat-28-Jan	BSP	A	Cambridge United	2281	W 1-0	McDonald 50	15
30	Sat-04-Feb	BSP	A	Fleetwood Town	1911	D 2-2	Patterson 9, Barrow 40	14
31	Sat-18-Feb	BSP	A	Luton Town	5833	L 0-3		15
32	Tue-21-Feb	BSP	H	Newport County	815	W 2-1	Barrow 83, Thomas 85	14
33	Sat-25-Feb	BSP	A	Mansfield Town	2221	L 1-2	Marna 54	14
34	Sat-03-Mar	BSP	H	Fleetwood Town	958	L 0-3		15
35	Tue-06-Mar	BSP	A	York City	2249	D 0-0		15
36	Sat-10-Mar	BSP	H	Mansfield Town	1600	L 0-1		15
37	Sat-17-Mar	BSP	A	Grimsby Town	3206	D 0-0		15
38	Tue-20-Mar	BSP	H	Kidderminster Harriers	924	D 0-0		15
39	Sat-24-Mar	BSP	H	Gateshead	968	D 1-1	Marna pen 44	15
40	Tue-27-Mar	BSP	H	Grimsby Town	892	D 1-1	C Taylor 87	15
41	Sat-31-Mar	BSP	A	Lincoln City	2213	L 0-4		16
42	Fri-06-Apr	BSP	H	Bath City	957	L 0-1		16
43	Sat-14-Apr	BSP	H	Southport	830	D 2-2	Christie 53, Gudger 63	16
44	Tue-17-Apr	BSP	A	AFC Telford	3477	L 0-1		16
45	Sat-21-Apr	BSP	A	Stockport County	6393	L 0-2		18
46	Sat-28-Apr	BSP	H	Cambridge United	1137	D 2-2	Marna 2 (16, 54)	18

CUPS

1	Sat-29-Oct	FAC 4Q	H	King's Lynn Town	966	W 2-1	Patterson 22, St Aimie 43	
2	Sat-12-Nov	FAC 1	A	Hinckley United	1906	D 2-2	Christie pen 83, Patterson 90	
3	Tue-22-Nov	FAC 1R	H	Hinckley United	1583	W 1-0	St Aimie 90	
4	Sat-03-Dec	FAC 2	A	Gateshead	1163	W 2-1	F Francis 29, Patterson 90	
5	Sat-10-Dec	FAT 1	A	Worksop Town	343	L 0-1		
6	Sat-07-Jan	FAC 3	A	Everton	27564	L 0-2		

League
Starts
Substitute
Unused Sub

Cups
Starts
Substitute
Unused Sub

Goals (Lg)
Goals (Cup)

HEDGE	TAIT	GREEN	KANYUKA	BARROW	CAIN	THOMAS	MCDONALD	SMITH	CHRISTIE	PATTERSON	ST AIMIE	SHARIFF	BRADLEY	L FRANCIS	MILLS	F FRANCIS	COLLISTER	REYNOLDS	HABERGHAM	VALENTIM	COURTNEY	ANDREW	HEALY	R TAYLOR	FARAH	GROCOTT	GUDGER	WILSON	ISAAC	QUI	MOKOY	WALLEN	HUBBINS	HEADLEY	BELFORD	REECE	MARNA	NIX	C TAYLOR	BALDOCK	COLLINS	GRAYSON
1	2	16	24	19	8	11	12	7	23	14	10	22	18	6	9	5	21	20	3	15	4	13	31	26	32	25	17	15	18	6	33	27	34	35	30	8	7	15	9	25	24	26
X	X	X	X	X	X	X	X	X	X	X	X	S	S	S	U	U																										
X	X	X		X	X	X	U	X	X	X	S	S	X		S	U																										
X	X	X			X	X	S	X	S	X	S	X	U	X	X		X	X	U																							
X	X				X		X	S	X	U	X	X	X	S	S	X		X	X	U																						
X	X	X		X	S	X	U	X	X	X	S	S	X		X	X		U																								
X	X	X		X	X	X	X	X	U	S	X	X	S		S	X		U																								
X	X	X			S	S		X	S	X	X	X	X		X	X	U		X	U																						
X	X	X			S	X	S	X	S		X	X	X		X	X	U		X	U																						
X	X	X			X	X	U	X	X	S	S	X	X		X	X	U		X	S																						
X	X	X			X	X	U	X	S	S	X	X		S	X		X		U																							
X	X	X			U	X	X	X	X	X	S	S	X		S	X		X		U																						
X	X	X		U	X		U	X	X	U	S	X		X	X	U		X	U																							
X	X	X	S	S	X		X		X		X	X	X		S	X		X		U	U																					
X	X	X	S	U	X		X	S	X		X	X	X		U	X		X		S																						
X	X	X	X	X	S		X	X	S	X		U		U	X		X		S																							
X	X	X			S	X		X	X	S	X		U		X	X	U		X	X																						
X	S	X	X	U	X	X	S	X	X	X	X	S		U	X		X		X																							
X	X	X	U	X		X	X		S	X	S	X	X		X	X	U		S																							
X	X	X	X	U		X	X		S	X	S	X	X		S	U		X							S																	
X	X	X	X	U		X	S		S	X	S	U		X		X		X							X																	
X	X	X	X		X	X	U		S	X	X	X		X		X		U							S																	
X	X		X	X		X	U		X	X	S		X		S		U	X	X		X																					
X		X	X		X		U			X	S	U	X		X			X		X								S														
U	X	X			X	U		X	X		X		S		X	X		X										S	X	S	X											
U	X	X			S	U		X	X		X		X		X	U		X										S	X	X	X	X										
X		X			S	X		X			X		X		X	U	U		X									X		X	U	X		X	S							
X		X		X			X			U			X		X		U		X									X	X	X	X	X	U		U	U						
X			X			X			X		S	X	U		X		U		X									S	X	X	X			U			X	X				
X	X	X		X		S	X		S	X	S			X			X		U									X	X	X						S	X	X				
X	X	X		X		S	X		X	X	X			U			X		X									X		X						S	X	U				
X	X	X		X		S	X		X	X	S			U			S		X									X		X						U	X	S	X			
X	X	X		U		X	X			X	S			S			X		X									X	U	X	X					X	U	X	X			
X	X	X		X		S		X	S					S			X		X		X							U					X	X		U	U	X				
X	X	X		X		X	S		X	U				X			X		X		X							U					X	X		S	X	U				
X	X	X		X		X	S		S					X			X		X									U			U					X	X	U	X	X	X	S
X	X		X			X	S		S					X			X		X									U			U		X			X	X	S	X	X	U	
X	X		X			X	S		S					X			X		X		U							U			X					X	X	X	X	X	X	S
X	X	X		X		X	S		S	S							X		X		U							X		X						X	U	X		X		
X	X	X		X		U	X		X	X							S		X									X		X						S	X	U		X	S	
X		X	S		X	S	X		X	X					X		U		X		X	U						X		X				U		X	S				X	
X		X	X		X	S	X		X	X					X		U		X		X		S					X		X						S	X					U
X	X	X		X		X	X		X	S							X		U		X							S									U	X	X	U		X
X		X	X	U	X	X	U	X	S	X	X		S	X	S		U				X																					
X	X	X	X	X	X	X	X	S	X	X	X		S	U		S	X	U		U	U																					
X	X		X		X	S		X	X		X	X	X		S	X	X	U		X					U	U																
X	X	X	X	S		X	S		X	X			X	X	U	S	X	X	U		X					U	U															
U	X	X		X		X			X	S			S		S	X	X	X			X					U	X	X	U													
U	X		X	X		X			X	S			X	X	S	S	X	X			X					U											X	U				
43	40	40	11	26	12	24	22	15	22	26	18	13	15	0	9	35	3	2	28	0	18	0	0	0	1	0	6	3	8	12	14	0	1	0	0	4	10	9	6	3	6	1
0	1	0	2	4	4	13	9	2	11	15	12	11	2	0	11	1	0	1	2	1	2	0	1	0	2	0	5	0	2	1	0	0	0	1	0	3	1	2	2	0	0	3
2	0	0	1	5	1	3	11	0	3	1	3	4	2	2	4	4	11	6	2	2	8	1	1	0	0	0	4	0	2	1	0	1	0	2	3	1	2	4	4	0	0	2
4	5	4	5	3	2	6	1	2	3	5	3	1	2	0	2	5	2	0	4	0	4	0	0	0	1	1	0	0	0	0	1	0	0	0	0	0	0	0	0	0	0	0
0	0	0	0	2	0	0	3	0	2	1	1	4	1	1	1	0	0	0	0	0	0	0	0	0	0	0	0	0	0	0	0	0	0	0	0	0	0	0	0	0	0	0
2	0	0	0	1	0	0	1	0	0	0	0	1	1	0	0	0	4	0	1	0	1	0	1	4	1	0	1	0	0	1	0	1	0	0	0	0	0	0	0	0	0	0
0	1	0	0	2	0	3	3	0	11	5	7	2	1	0	3	1	0	0	0	1	0	0	0	0	1	1	0	0	0	0	0	0	0	4	0	1	0	0	0			
0	0	0	0	0	0	0	0	0	1	3	2	0	0	0	0	1	0	0	0	0	1	0	0	0	0	0	0	0	0	0	0	0	0	0	0	0	0	0	0			

PLAYING SQUAD

Existing Players		SN	HT	WT	DOB	AGE	POB	Career	Apps	Goals
GOALKEEPERS										
Dale	Belford		5'10"	13 00	11/07/1967	45	Tamworth	Tamworth (Ass Man)	0	0
Tony	Breedon	13			31/01/1988	24		Sutton Coldfield, Tamworth 2/06 (05/06 1,0), Stourport 3/06, Solihull B 8/06, Rushall O 6/07, Sutton Coldfield 6/09, Leamington 11/09, Rushall O (L) 3/10, Loughborough D (L) 10/10, Birmingham (Trial) 10/11, Kidderminster 11/11, Hednesford (L) 12/11, Tamworth 6/12		
James	Wren	1			26/06/1993	19	Walsall	Walsall (Scholar) Rel c/s 11, Burton 9/11 Rel c/s 12, Tamworth 7/12		
DEFENDERS										
Scott	Barrow	19	5'08"	11 00	19/10/1988	23	Swansea	Swansea (Yth), Briton Ferry, Port Talbot 8/06, Tamworth 8/10	30	2
Duane	Courtney	15	5'11"	11 03	07/01/1985	27	Oldbury	Derby (Yth), Birmingham (Scholar) Rel c/s 04, AFC Telford 9/04, Burnley £25,000 8/05 Rel 8/06, The New Saints 9/06 Rel c/s 09, Kidderminster 7/09, York C 5/10 Rel 1/11, Tamworth 2/11	20	1
Graeme	Law	24	5'10"	11 08	06/10/1984	27	Kirkcaldy	York, Dundee 2/06, Tamworth 7/06, Farsley Celtic 7/07, Tamworth (L) 10/07 Perm 11/07 Rel c/s 09, Stalybridge 8/09, Northwich 12/10, Tamworth (Pl/Ass Man) 7/12		
Tom	Marshall	6	6'04"		16/11/1987	24	Lichfield	Hednesford, Eastwood T 5/09, Chasetown (L) 10/09, Tamworth 6/10 Rel 5/11, Kidderminster 6/11, Brackley (2ML) 12/11, Tamworth 6/12		
Scott	Meer	25			16/02/1994	18	Burton			
Sam	Oji	30	6'00"	14 05	09/10/1985	26	Westminster	Arsenal (Scholar), Birmingham Rel 1/08, Doncaster (6WL) 11/05, Bristol R (2ML) 2/07, Southend (Trial) c/s 07, L.Orient (3ML) 8/07, L.Orient 1/08 Rel c/s 08, Hereford 8/08 Rel 2/09, Ljungskile SK (Swe) 3/09 Rel 6/09, Tranmere (Trial) 8/09, L.Orient (Trial) 9/09, Injured, Tamworth 12/11	13	0
Jamie	Smith	26			29/10/1994	17	Worksop	Mansfield (Yth), Tamworth c/s 12		
Richard	Tait	2	5'11"	11 13	02/12/1989	22	Galashiels	Curzon Ashton, Notts Forest 12/07 Rel 5/09, Tamworth (L) 3/09 Tamworth 5/09	41	1
MIDFIELDERS										
Luke	Bottomer	16	5'08"		05/09/1992	19	Walsall	Coventry (Scholar) Rel c/s 11, Worcester (L) 3/11, Tamworth 8/11, Solihull Moors (L) 8/11, Rushall O (3ML) 9/11, Rushall O (L) 1/12		
Conor	Gudger	17	5'08"		23/09/1992	19	Nuneaton	Coventry Rel c/s 11, Hinckley U (SL) 1/11, Hinckley U 5/11, Tamworth 7/11, Hinckley U (2ML) 8/11	11	1
Lee	Hendrie	8	5'10"	10 03	18/05/1977	35	Birmingham	Aston Villa Rel c/s 07, Stoke (3ML) 9/06, Stoke (SL) 1/07, Sheff Utd 7/07, Leicester (SL) 2/08, Blackpool (6WL) 11/08, Derby 8/09 Rel c/s 10, Brighton (SL) 3/10, Bradford C 9/10 Rel 12/10, Bandung FC (Ind) 1/11 Rel c/s 11, Daventry T 10/11, Kidderminster 11/11 Rel 3/12, Chasetown 3/12, Redditch 3/12		
Marcus	Kelly	3	5'07"	10 00	16/03/1986	26	Kettering	Rushden & D, Oxford U 5/09, Kettering (6WL) 11/09, Perm 1/10, Mansfield (6WL) 11/11, Tamworth 7/12		
Lloyd	Kerry	11	6'02"	12 04	22/01/1988	24	Chesterfield	Sheff Utd Rel c/s 08, Torquay (2ML) 2/07, Chesterfield (SL) 2/08, Chesterfield 8/08 Rel c/s 10, Alfreton (L) 11/09, Kidderminster (L) 3/10, Hinckley U 7/10, Tamworth 7/12		
Peter	Till	18	5'11"	11 04	07/09/1985	26	Walsall	Birmingham, Scunthorpe (3ML) 10/05, Boston U (SL) 1/06, L.Orient (L) 10/06, Grimsby (3ML) 11/06 Perm 1/07 Rel c/s 09, Chesterfield (SL) 1/09, Walsall 7/09 Rel c/s 10, York C 6/10, Fleetwood 7/11, Tamworth 7/12		
FORWARDS										
Charlie	Collins	28	6'00"	11 11	22/11/1991	20	Hammersmith	MK Dons, Aylesbury (L) 10/10, Kettering (L) 1/11, Aylesbury U (L) 10/11, Aldershot (L) 1/12, Tamworth (SL) 3/12, Tamworth (SL) 8/12	6	0
Adam	Cunnington	7	6'03"	12 10	07/10/1987	24	Leighton Buzzard	Coventry (Yth), Barton R, Leighton T, Hitchin 3/07, Aylesbury 10/07, Barton R 11/07, Rothwell T 2/08, Stamford 7/08, Barwell (L), Barwell c/s 09, Solihull Moors 7/10, Kettering Undisc 1/11, Dag & Red (6WL) 11/11 Undisc 1/12 Rel c/s 12, Alfreton (SL) 3/12, Tamworth 7/12		
Jordan	Ivey-Ward	5			20/10/1993	18	Milton Keynes	MK Dons, Tamworth (6ML) 8/12		
Jan	Llado	20	5'08"	10 07	22/01/1992	20	Barcelona	Gimnàstic de Tarragona (Spa), Pobla de Mafumet (Spa), Tamworth 8/12		
Jean-Paul	Marna	10	6'03"	13 09	21/02/1981	31	Cannes, Fra	Paris St Germain (Fra), Berkhamsted, Kettering 7/06 Rel 1/12, Corby T (2ML) 11/11, Tamworth 1/12	11	4
Troy	Wallen	27			18/11/1992	19	Birmingham	Tamworth, Dudley T (L) 11/10, Heather St Johns (4ML) 8/11	0	0
Tommy	Wright	9	6'00"	11 12	28/09/1984	27	Kirby Muxloe	Leicester, Brentford (10WL) 9/03, Brentford (4ML) 12/03, Blackpool (4ML) 8/05, Barnsley £50,000 1/06, Walsall (7WL) 11/06, Darlington (L) 1/07 Undisc 1/07, Aberdeen £75,000 8/08 Rel 1/10, Grimsby 1/10, Darlington 5/10 Rel 8/11, Kidderminster NC 9/11 Rel 10/11, Luton 10/11 Rel 1/12, Port Vale (Trial) 1/12, Forest Green 1/12, Tamworth 7/12		

Loanees		HT	WT	DOB	AGE	POB	From - To	APPS	GOA
(F)Danny	Mills	6'04"	13 00	27/11/1991	20	Peterborough	Peterborough (5ML) 8/11 - Kettering (L) 1/12	20	3
(M)Ibrahim	Farah			24/01/1992	20	Cardiff	Cardiff 11/11 -	3	0
(M)Callum	Wilson	5'11"	10 06	27/02/1992	20	Coventry	Coventry 1/12 -	3	1
(M)Chez	Isaac	5'10"	11 13	16/11/1992	19	Hatfield	Watford (2ML) 1/12 - Boreham Wood 5/12	10	0
(M)Luke	Hubbins	5'09"	10 07	11/09/1991	20	Birmingham	Birmingham 1/12 - Rel c/s 12, AFC Telford 5/12	1	0
(M)Charlie	Reece	5'11"	11 03	08/09/1988	23	Birmingham	Bristol R 1/12 - Worcester 7/12	7	0
(F)Connor	Taylor			05/09/1992	19	Coventry	Aston Villa 3/12 - Rel c/s 12, Walsall 8/12	8	1
(M)George	Baldock	5'09"	10 07	26/01/1993	19	Buckingham	MK Dons (SL) 3/12	3	0

Departures		HT	WT	DOB	AGE	POB	From - To	APPS	GOA
(D)Evangelino	Valentim	6'07"		24/12/1984	27		Maidenhead 8/11 - Rel 12/11	1	0
(M)Daniel	Bradley	6'00"		13/05/1991	21	Stafford	Aston Villa (Scholar) 8/10 - Rel 12/11, Rushall O 12/11, Kidderminster 1/12	17	1
(D)Liam	Francis	6'03"	11 04	27/09/1989	22	Birmingham	Hednesford 6/11 - Solihull B (L) 8/11, Rushall O (L) 10/11, Eastwood T (L) 11/11, Leamington 12/11	0	0
(D)Patrick	Kanyuka	6'00"	12 06	19/07/1987	25	Kinshasa, Con	Lincoln C 8/11 - Rel 1/12, Leeds (Trial) 3/12, CD Chivas (USA) (Trial) 3/12	13	0
(M)Ashley	Cain	6'02"	12 06	27/09/1990	21	Nuneaton	Mansfield 6/11 - AFC Telford (6WL) 11/11 Perm 1/12 Rel c/s 12	16	0
(M)Jay	Smith	5'07"	12 00	24/09/1981	30	Lambeth	Eastwood T 1/10 - AFC Telford (6WL) 11/11 Perm 1/12	17	0
(F)Lee	Weemes			14/10/1992	19		Wycombe (Scholar) 8/11 - Barwell (L) 9/11, Shepshed D (2ML) 10/11, Farnborough 3/12		
(G)Jonathan	Hedge	6'02"	13 00	19/07/1988	24	Rotherham	FC Halifax 7/11 - Cambridge U 5/12	43	0
(D)Paul	Green	5'08"	10 04	15/04/1987	25	Birmingham	Lincoln C 8/11 - Forest Green 7/12	40	0
(D)Samuel	Habergham	6'00"	11 06	20/02/1992	20	Rotherham	Norwich 7/11 - Braintree 7/12	30	0
(M)Liam	McDonald			19/02/1985	27		Kettering 8/11 - Redditch 7/12	31	3
(F)Kieron	St Aimie	6'01"	13 00	04/05/1989	23	Brent	Kettering 6/11 - AFC Telford 8/12	30	7
(F)Iyseden	Christie	5'10"	12 02	14/11/1976	35	Coventry	Kettering 8/11 - Alfreton 8/12	33	11
(G)Joe	Collister	6'00"	13 10	15/12/1991	20	Holyoak	Tranmere 8/11 - Rel c/s 12, Barwell (L) 9/11, Altrincham (L) 1/12, Fleetwood (L) 3/12	3	0
(F)Harvey	Headley	5'11"		05/10/1988	23	Coventry	Longwood University 1/12 - Solihull Moors (L) 3/12, Hinckley U 8/12	1	0
(F)Jake	Healy						Yth - Atherstone T (L) 11/11	1	0
(F)Nabil	Shariff			19/04/1992	20	Milton Keynes	Rushden & D 7/11 - Hemel Hempstead (L) 3/12	24	2
(M)Danny	Thomas	5'07"	11 05	01/05/1981	31	Leamington Spa	Kettering 6/10 - FH (Ice) 5/12	37	3
(D)Francino	Francis	6'03"	14 02	18/01/1987	25	Kingston, Jam	Barwell 6/11 - Rel c/s 12, Hednesford 7/12	36	1
(M)Kyle	Nix	5'06"	09 10	21/01/1986	26	Sydney, Aust	Gateshead 2/12 - UR La Louvière (Bel) c/s 12	11	0
(M)Ashley	Grayson						Carlton T 3/12 -	4	0
(M)Will	Grocott			27/01/1992	20	Cambridge	Aston Villa - Loughborough D (L) 8/11, Bedworth (L) 1/12, Loughborough D (L) 3/12	0	0
(M)Nick	McKoy	6'00"	12 04	03/09/1986	25	Newham	Northampton 1/12 - Sutton U 8/12	14	0
(M)Luke	Shearer						Torquay (Yth) - Barwell (L) 9/11		
(M)Rico	Taylor			16/04/1994	18	Birmingham	Sutton Coldfield 7/11 - Stafford R (L) 8/11, Sutton Coldfield (L) 3/12	0	0
(D)Callum	Reynolds			10/11/1989	22		Basingstoke 8/11 - Hinckley U (L) 8/11, Corby T (10WL) 10/11, Boreham Wood (L) 3/12, Boreham Wood 5/12	3	0
(G)Sam	Andrew			07/01/1993	19	Barnsley	Sheff Utd (Scholar) 8/11 - Shepshed D (2ML) 10/11, Ilkeston FC (L) 1/12, Eastwood T (L) 2/12	0	0
(M)Kyle	Patterson 14	5'08"	10 00	06/01/1986	26	Birmingham	Hednesford 6/11 - Nuneaton T 8/12	41	5

Conference Action...

Greg Young - Alfreton Town - manages to block this Tamworth player in his tracks.

Photo: Bill Wheatcroft.

WOKING

Chairman: Mike Smith
Secretary: Derek Powell   **(T)** 01483 772 470   **(E)** derek.powell@wokingfc.co.uk
Additional Committee Members:
James Aughterson, Peter Jordan, James Aughterson, Geoff Chapple, Rosemary Jonhson, David Holmes, John Moore.
Manager: Garry Hill
Programme Editor: David Horncastle   **(E)** raetec.david@btinternet.com

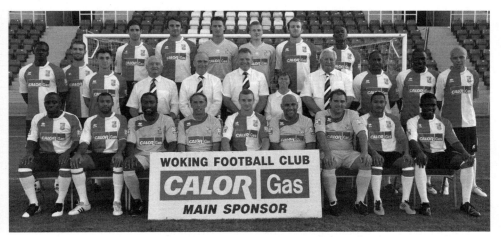

2011-12 Squad.

Club Factfile

Founded: 1889   **Nickname:** The Cards
Previous Names: None
Previous Leagues: Isthmian 1911-92.

Club Colours (change): Red and white/black/white (All yellow)

Ground: Kingfield Stadium, Kingfield Road, Woking, Surrey GU22 9AA   **(T)** 01483 772 470
Capacity: 6,000   **Seats:** 2,500   **Covered:** 3,900   **Clubhouse:** Yes   **Shop:** Yes
Directions: Exit M25 Junction 10 and follow A3 towards Guildford. Leave at next junction onto B2215 through Ripley and join A247 to Woking. Alternatively exit M25 junction 11 and follow A320 to Woking Town Centre. The ground is on the outskirts of Woking opposite the Leisure Centre.

Previous Grounds: Wheatsheaf, Ive Lane (pre 1923)

Record Attendance: 6,000 v Swansea City - FA Cup 1978-79 and v Coventry City - FA Cup 1996-97
Record Victory: 17-4 v Farnham - 1912-13
Record Defeat: 0-16 v New Crusaders - 1905-06
Record Goalscorer: Charlie Mortimore - 331 (1953-65)
Record Appearances: Brian Finn - 564 (1962-74)
Additional Records: Paid £60,000 to Crystal Palace for Chris Sharpling
Received £150,000 from Bristol Rovers for Steve Foster
Senior Honours:
Surrey Senior Cup 1912-13, 26-27, 55-56, 56-57, 71-72, 90-91, 93-94, 95-96, 99-2000, 2003-04. FA Amateur Cup 1957-58. Isthmian League Cup 1990-91, Premier Division 1991-92. FA Trophy 1993-94, 94-95, 96-97. Vauxhall Championship Shield 1994-95. GLS Conference Cup 2004-05. Conference South 2011-12.

10 YEAR RECORD

02-03	03-04	04-05	05-06	06-07	07-08	08-09	09-10	10-11	11-12
Conf 19	Conf 9	Conf 8	Conf 11	Conf 15	Conf 17	Conf 21	Conf S 5	Conf S 5	Conf S 1

WOKING

No.	Date	Comp	H/A	Opponents	Att:	Result	Goalscorers	Pos
1	Sat-13-Aug	BSS	A	Sutton United	1200	W 5-0	Binns 2, Hammond 50, Sole 3 (60, 88, 90)	1
2	Tue-16-Aug	BSS	H	Hampton & Richmond Boro'1467		W 2-1	Ademola 63, King pen 84	2
3	Sat-20-Aug	BSS	H	Boreham Wood	1196	D 0-0		3
4	Tue-23-Aug	BSS	A	Eastleigh	665	D 0-0		5
5	Sat-27-Aug	BSS	H	Basingstoke Town	1207	W 1-0	Hammond 4	2
6	Mon-29-Aug	BSS	A	Tonbridge Angels	922	W 6-3	King pen 4, McNerney 17, Ademola 42, Hammond 61, Gray 2 (82, 87)	2
7	Sat-03-Sep	BSS	A	Welling United	1214	L 2-3	Cowan-Hall 18, Sole 76	2
8	Sat-10-Sep	BSS	H	Eastbourne Borough	1203	W 3-1	Cowan-Hall 6, Ademola 24, King pen 90	2
9	Sat-17-Sep	BSS	H	Dover Athletic	1306	W 3-1	Ademola 5, Cowan-Hall 81, Davies 86	2
10	Tue-20-Sep	BSS	A	Bromley	478	W 4-2	Ademola 2 (38, 80), Gray 50, Hammond 87	1
11	Sat-24-Sep	BSS	A	Dorchester Town	628	W 1-0	Ademola 63	1
12	Sat-08-Oct	BSS	H	Salisbury City	1634	D 0-0		1
13	Sat-22-Oct	BSS	A	Staines Town	1019	W 1-0	Hammond 26	1
14	Mon-24-Oct	BSS	H	Weston-Super-Mare	1462	W 4-1	King pen 45, Hammond 73, Ademola 75, Sole 80	1
15	Sat-29-Oct	BSS	A	Truro City	664	W 4-1	Cowan-Hall 2 (8, 17), Ademola 44, Inns 84	1
16	Sat-05-Nov	BSS	H	Havant & Waterlooville	1655	W 3-0	Gray 2 (46, 52), Cowan-Hall 73	1
17	Sat-19-Nov	BSS	A	Dover Athletic	1061	W 3-0	Binns 9, King pen 45, Hammond 90	1
18	Tue-22-Nov	BSS	H	Chelmsford City	1558	D 1-1	Doyle 21	1
19	Sat-03-Dec	BSS	H	Eastleigh	1610	W 1-0	Gray 47	1
20	Sat-10-Dec	BSS	H	Sutton United	1730	W 4-1	Cowan-Hall 1, Gray 7, Binns 43, Ademola 63	1
21	Tue-13-Dec	BSS	A	Dartford	1230	W 3-2	Inns 4, Doyle 42, Hammond 86	1
22	Sat-17-Dec	BSS	A	Thurrock	380	D 1-1	Hammond 75	1
23	Mon-26-Dec	BSS	H	Farnborough	3014	W 1-0	Smith 11	1
24	Sun-01-Jan	BSS	A	Farnborough	2017	W 1-0	King 3	1
25	Sat-07-Jan	BSS	H	Staines Town	2104	L 0-1		1
26	Sat-14-Jan	BSS	H	Bromley	1612	W 3-2	Gray 20, Cowan-Hall 47, McNerney 90	1
27	Sat-21-Jan	BSS	A	Salisbury City	1034	L 0-2		1
28	Sat-28-Jan	BSS	A	Boreham Wood	413	W 2-1	Hammond 23, Ademola 84	1
29	Sat-18-Feb	BSS	H	Dartford	2528	W 1-0	Inns 3	1
30	Sat-25-Feb	BSS	A	Hampton & Richmond Boro'1069		D 1-1	Cowan-Hall 65	1
31	Sat-03-Mar	BSS	H	Maidenhead United	1777	L 0-2		1
32	Sat-10-Mar	BSS	A	Havant & Waterlooville	1009	W 4-3	Sole 23, Cowan-Hall 2 (37, 45), Ademola 53	1
33	Tue-13-Mar	BSS	H	Dorchester Town	1268	W 4-1	Murtagh 31, Sole 2 (pen 50, pen 52), McNerney 75	1
34	Sat-17-Mar	BSS	H	Welling United	1926	W 2-1	Davis 36, Sole 46	1
35	Tue-20-Mar	BSS	A	Weston-Super-Mare	361	W 3-0	Sole 2 (6, 41), Betsy 43	1
36	Sat-24-Mar	BSS	A	Eastbourne Borough	1037	L 1-2	Sole 54	1
37	Sat-31-Mar	BSS	H	Thurrock	1754	W 5-1	Inns 8, Sole 2 (19, 30), King 63, Betsy pen 79	1
38	Fri-06-Apr	BSS	A	Basingstoke Town	1198	W 3-0	Sole 2 (14, 38), Betsy 56	1
39	Mon-09-Apr	BSS	H	Tonbridge Angels	2430	W 2-1	Ademola 42, Sole 83	1
40	Sat-14-Apr	BSS	A	Maidenhead United	1192	W 1-0	Sole 23	1 Champions
41	Sat-21-Apr	BSS	H	Truro City	4048	D 3-3	Cowan-Hall 2 (22, 53), Sole 32	1
42	Sat-28-Apr	BSS	A	Chelmsford City	1080	W 3-2	King 10, Sole 45, Murtagh 60	1

CUPS

No.	Date	Comp	H/A	Opponents	Att:	Result	Goalscorers	Pos
1	Sat-01-Oct	FAC 2Q	A	Wells City	410	W 7-0	Og (Higgins) 5, Cowan-Hall 6, Gray 15, King 2 (pen 20, 60), Hammond 68, Sole 90	
2	Sat-15-Oct	FAC 3Q	A	Maidenhead United	625	L 1-4	King pen 23	
3	Sat-26-Nov	FAT 3Q	A	Chelmsford City	740	L 0-2		

	League
	Starts
	Substitute
	Unused Sub
	Cups
	Starts
	Substitute
	Unused Sub
	Goals (Lg)
	Goals (Cup)

LITTLE	NEWTON	DUNCAN	RICKETTS	MCNERNEY	DOYLE	SOLE	KING	ADEMOLA	HAMMOND	BINNS	COWAN-HALL	GRAY	KORANTENG	TURNBULL	HOWE	DAVIES	CESTOR	GRIFFITHS	KENNEDY	SOGBANMU	INNS	FRITH	SMITH	PEGLER	MURTAGH	MEDLEY	SHARIF	BETSY	DAVIS	WILSON
X	X	X	X	X	X	X	X	X	X	X	S	S	S	U	U															
X	X	X	X	X	X	X	X	X	X	X	S	S	S		U	U														
X	X	X	X	X	X	X	X	X	X	X	S	S	U		U	S	X													
X	X		X	X	X	X	X	X	X	X	S	S	U		U	U	X													
X	X		X	X	X	X	X	X	X	X	U	S	S		U	S	X													
X	X		X	X	U	X	X	X	X	X	S	S			U	S	X													
U	X	U	X	X	X	S	X	X	X	X	S				X	U	X													
X	X		X	X	X	S	X	X	X	X	S	U			U	S	X													
X	X		X	X	S	X	X	S	X	X	X				U	S		U												
	X	X	X	X	U	X	X	X	S	S	X	X		S	X	X		U												
U		X	X		X	S	X	X	X	X					X	X		X	S	U										
U	X	S	X	S	X	S	X	X	X	X			U		X	X			X											
U	X	X	X	U	X	S	X	X	X	X				S	X	X			S											
U	X	S	X	S	X	S	X	X	X			X	U	X	X	X			X											
U	X	S	X	S	X	S	X	X			X	X	X	U	X	X			X											
U	X	U	X		X	U	X	X	S	X					X	X		S	X						X					
U	X	S	X		X	U	X	X	S	X					X	X		S	X						X					
U	X		X		S	X	X	S	X	X					X	X	S		U	X		X								
U	X		X	U	X	S	X	S	X	X					X	S			X			X								
U	X		X		X	S	X	X	X	X					X	S		S	X			U								
X	X	U		X	X	S	X	X	X	X					X		S		X		X	U								
U	X	X		X	X	X	X		X	S	U				X	X			S		X				X					
X	X	S		X		U	X	X	S						X	X	X	U		X					X	S				
S	X	X		X		U	X	X	S						X		X	U		X					X	S				
U	X	S		X			X	X	X						X	U	X	S		X					X	S	X			
U	X			U	X			X	X	X					S	X			X		X				X		S	X		
U	X	U		X			X	X	X						X	X		S	X		X				X		S	X		
U	X	U		X	X	S	X	X	S	S	X	X			X				X		X				X			X		
U	X	X			S	X	X		X	S	S	X	U		X				X		X				X			X	X	
U	X	X			S	X	X		X	S	S	X	U		X				X		X				X			X	X	
U	X	X			U	X	X		X	S					X			U			X				X			X	X	
U	X	X			U	X	X	X	S	X	S				X			S			X				X			X	X	
U		X			X	X	U	X	S						X		S				X				X			X	X	X
U		S			X	X	X	S	X	S		U			X		X				X				X			X	X	X
U	U	X		X		X		X	X	S	S				X		S				X				X			X	X	X
U	X	X			X		X	S	X	S	X	S	X		X		U				X				X				X	X
U	X	S		X			X	X	X	X	S	S	X		X		X				X				X				X	U
U	X	X			X	S	X	X	X	X	S	U	X		X						X				X			X	S	
X	X	U			X	X	X	X	X	S	U	X	S		U										X			X	X	
	X	X	X	X		X	X	X	S	U	X	X			X	X		S	U	S	U									
U		X	X	X	X	S	X	X	X	S	X				X	X		X		S	U	U								
U	X	X	X		X	X	X	X	X	S		S			X			U		S	X		X							
12	38	17	21	24	33	18	35	39	20	24	28	17	1	0	30	13	14	1	0	0	28	0	4	0	19	0	1	12	10	3
1	0	8	0	7	1	16	2	2	19	7	8	13	5	1	0	9	2	4	0	8	1	0	0	0	3	2	0	1	0	0
28	1	7	0	5	1	4	1	0	1	1	5	6	1	11	4	1	4	1	1	1	1	1	0	0	0	0	0	0	0	2
0	2	3	3	2	2	3	3	2	0	2	1	0	0	3	2	0	1	0	0	1	0	1	0	0	0	0	0	0	0	0
0	0	0	0	0	0	0	1	0	0	1	2	0	1	0	0	0	0	0	1	0	3	0	0	0	0	0	0	0	0	0
2	0	0	0	0	0	0	0	0	0	0	1	0	0	0	0	0	0	1	1	0	2	1	0	0	0	0	0	0	0	0
0	0	0	0	3	2	20	8	13	10	3	13	8	0	0	0	1	0	0	0	0	4	0	1	0	2	0	0	3	1	0
0	0	0	0	0	0	1	3	0	1	0	1	1	0	0	0	0	0	0	0	0	0	0	0	0	0	0	0	0	0	0

PLAYING SQUAD

Existing Players		SN	HT	WT	DOB	AGE	POB	Career	Apps	Goals
GOALKEEPERS										
Sam	Beasant	18	6'05"		08/04/1988	24		Chelsea (Yth), Wycombe (Scholar), Amersham, Olympiakos Nicosia (Cyp), Glen Hoddle Academy 11/09, Birmingham (Trial), Maidenhead 9/11, Woking 8/12		
Aaron	Howe	1			05/10/1987	24		Woking Rel 5/07, Carshalton (L) 2/07, Carshalton c/s 07, Hayes & Yeading 8/08, Havant & W 7/09, Woking 7/11	30	0
DEFENDERS										
Mike	Cestor	3			30/04/1992	20	Paris, Fra	AC Pisa (Ita) (Yth), L.Orient Rel c/s 12, Boreham Wood (SL) 1/11, Woking (L) 8/11, Woking (10WL) 1/12, Woking (SL) 3/12, Woking 7/12	16	0
Adam	Doyle				23/03/1986	26		Alton T, Bisley T, Farnborough (Dual) 10/07 Perm 1/08, Woking 8/10	34	2
Brett	Johnson	16	6'01"	13 00	15/08/1985	27	Hammersmith	Ashford T (Midd), Reading (Trial), Aldershot 2/04, Northampton £30,000 6/05 Rel c/s 08, Gravesend (L) 11/05, Grays (6ML) 1/06, Luton (Trial) 3/08, Brentford 8/08 Rel c/s 09, AFC Wimbledon 8/09, Cambridge U (L) 1/12, Woking 8/12		
Joseph	McNerney	5			24/01/1990	22		Woking, Corinthian Casuals (L) 10/09, Ashford T (Middx) (L) 3/10	31	3
MIDFIELDERS										
Kevin	Betsy	11	6'01"	12 00	20/03/1978	34	Woking	Woking, Fulham £80,000 9/98, Bournemouth (L) 9/99, Hull C (L) 11/99, Barnsley (L) 2/02 £200,000 3/02, Hartlepool (L) 8/04, Oldham 9/04 Rel c/s 05, Wycombe 7/05, Bristol C £150,000 1/07, Yeovil (L) 10/07, Walsall (SL) 1/08, Southend Nominal 8/08, Wycombe (4ML) 9/09, Wycombe 1/10 Rel 12/11, Woking 2/12	12	3
Jay	Davies		5'07"	11 02	26/12/1991	20	Dagenham	Peterborough, Woking (6WL) 2/11, Farnborough 3/11, Woking 6/11	22	1
George	Frith							Woking	0	0
Josh	Griffiths				27/03/1992	20		Croydon Ath (Yth), Woking	5	0
Adam	Newton	2	5'10"	11 06	04/12/1980	31	Grays	West Ham Rel c/s 02, Portsmouth (2ML) 7/99, Notts County (SL) 11/00, L.Orient (6WL) 3/02, Peterborough 7/02, Brentford 6/08 Rel c/s 09, Luton 7/09 Rel c/s 11, Woking 6/11	38	0
Jack	Parkinson	8			23/07/1989	23		Tonbridge A (Yth), VCD Ath, Welling 7/08, Margate (L) 10/08, Bournemouth (Trial) 3/10, Southend (Trial) 7/11, Woking 5/12		
Loick	Pires	7	6'03"	13 02	20/11/1989	22	Lisbon, Port	Stoke (Yth), L.Orient Rel c/s 10, Welling 7/10, Crewe (Trial) 7/11, Woking 5/12		
Mark	Ricketts	4	6'00"	11 02	07/10/1984	27	Sidcup	Charlton Rel c/s 06, MK Dons (3ML) 11/05, Gravesend/Ebbsfleet 8/06, Woking 6/09	21	0
Lee	Sawyer	15	5'10"	10 03	10/09/1989	22	Leytonstone	Chelsea Rel 12/09, Southend (3ML) 8/08, Coventry (L) 1/09, Wycombe (SL) 3/09, Southend (3ML) 7/09, Barnet 1/10 Rel 2/10, Woking 11/10, Southend 1/11 Rel c/s 12, Woking 7/12		
Dean	Sinclair	17	5'10"	11 03	17/12/1984	27	St Albans	Norwich Rel 4/04, Barnet 8/04, Charlton £125,000 8/07, Cheltenham (L) 10/07, Cheltenham (L) 8/08, Grimsby (2ML) 1/09, Barnet (L) 11/09, Grimsby (SL) 1/10, Grimsby 12/10 Rel 5/11, Cambridge U (SL) 3/11, Arlesey T 8/11, Hayes & Yeading 11/11, Arlesey T (L) 11/11, Lowestoft T 2/12, Woking 8/12		

FORWARDS

Bradley	Bubb	9	5'07"	12 03	30/05/1988	24	Harrow	Hendon, QPR (Yth), Hendon (L) 1/06, Chalfont St Peter c/s 06, Beaconsfield SYCOB c/s 08, Farnborough 7/09, Aldershot 6/11, Basingstoke (2ML) 11/11, Eastleigh (SL) 1/12, Woking (SL) 7/12		
Jack	Mazzone							Woking		
Gavin	McCallum	19	5'09"	12 00	24/08/1987	25	Mississauga, Can	Oakville YC (Can), Yeovil 1/06 Rel c/s 07, Tamworth (2ML) 8/06, Recalled 10/06, (L) 10/06, Crawley (L) 11/06, Dorchester (SL) 3/07, Weymouth 8/07, Havant & W 2/08 Rel 5/08, Sutton U 8/08, Hereford 8/09, Lincoln C 7/10 Rel 1/12, Barnet (L) 11/11, Hereford 8/12		
Giuseppe	Sole	10			08/01/1988	24	Woking	Woking, Basingstoke (L) 3/06, Ebbsfleet(SL) 1/09, Newport C 5/10, Dorchester (L) 9/10, Havant & W (3ML) 10/10 Perm 1/11 Rel c/s 11, Woking 6/11, Basingstoke (L) 1/12	34	20
Brett	Williams	14	6'02"	12 05	01/12/1987	24	Southampton	Eastleigh (Yth), Winchester, Eastleigh 11/08, AFC Totton (2ML) 8/09 Undisc 10/09, Eastleigh (L) 8/10 Perm, Reading £50,000 1/11, Rotherham (6ML) 8/11, Northampton (L) 2/12, St Johnstone (Trial) 7/12, Woking (L) 8/12		

Loanees		HT	WT	DOB	AGE	POB	From - To	APPS	GOA
(M)Ben	Smith	5'08"	11 06	23/11/1978	33	Chelmsford	Crawley 11/11 - Aldershot (3ML) 1/12, Rel c/s 12	4	1
(M)Kieran	Murtagh	6'00"	12 00	29/10/1988	23	Wapping	Cambridge U (SL) 12/11 - Macclesfield 7/12	19	2
(F)Luke	Medley	6'01"	13 03	21/06/1989	23	Greenwich	Kidderminster 1/12 - Rel 2/12, Bromley 2/12	3	0
(F)Mo	Sharif					Burundi	QPR 1/12 -	3	0
(M)Tom	Davis			17/02/1984	28		Carshalton (SL) 3/12 - Tonbridge A 6/12	11	1
(D)Glenn	Wilson	6'01"	12 09	16/03/1986	26	Lewisham	Crawley (SL) 3/12 - Rel c/s 12, Gateshead 6/12	3	0

Departures		HT	WT	DOB	AGE	POB	From - To	APPS	GOA
(F)Oliver	Palmer			21/01/1992	20		Yth - Boreham Wood (2ML) 7/11, Havant & W 9/11		
(M)Nathan	Koranteng	6'02"	12 08	26/05/1992	20	London	Peterborough 3/11 - Rel 12/11, Boreham Wood (L) 9/11, Boreham Wood 12/11, Tonbridge A 12/11	6	0
(G)Matt	Pegler			12/08/1991	21		Aldershot (Yth) c/s 09 - Rel 2/12, Badshot Lea (L) 7/11, Injured, Havant & W 7/12	0	0
(F)Ola	Sogbanmu			06/03/1992	20		Yth - Farnborough (L) 1/12, Carshalton (L) 3/12, Carshalton Undisc 5/12	8	0
(M)Dale	Binns			08/07/1981	31	London	Farnborough 6/11 - Eastleigh 5/12	31	3
(F)Paris	Cowan-Hall	5'08"	11 08	05/10/1990	21	Hillingdon	Scunthorpe 8/11 - Plymouth 5/12	36	13
(F)Wayne	Gray	5'10"	11 05	07/11/1980	31	Dulwich	Chelmsford 7/11 - Carshalton 5/12	30	8
(D)Alan	Inns			05/06/1982	30	Reading	AFC Wimbledon 5/10 - Farnborough 5/12	29	4
(D)Derek	Duncan	5'10"	10 11	23/04/1987	25	Newham	Ebbsfleet 7/11 - Maidenhead 6/12	25	0
(F)Elvis	Hammond	5'10"	10 10	06/10/1980	31	Accra, Gha	Sutton U 10/10 - Rel c/s 12	39	10
(F)Moses	Ademola	5'06"	10 08	18/07/1989	23	Bermondsey	Brentford (6ML) 7/09 Perm 1/10 - Eastleigh 7/12	41	13
(M)Jack	King			20/08/1985	27		Farnborough 6/11 - Preston 7/12	37	8
(M)Charlie	Turnbull			08/12/1990	21		Yth -	1	0
(F)Anson	Cousins			22/11/1991	20		Yth -		
(G)Jordan	Kennedy						Yth -	0	0
(D)Josh	Watkins						Yth -		
(G)Andy	Little	6'03"	13 10	03/10/1974	37	Sheffield	Croydon Ath 9/10 - Reired c/s 12	13	0

Conference Action...

Luton Town's Osano puts in a good tackle against York City's Blair during the Play-off Final at Wembley.

Photo: Keith Clayton.

WREXHAM

Chairman: TBC
Secretary: Geraint Parry   **(T)** 07801 749 021   **(E)** geraint.parry@wrexhamfc.tv
Additional Committee Members:
Gavin Jones, David Roberts, Don Bircham, Spencer Harris, Barry Horne, Gavin Jones,
Alan Watkin, Mark Williams.
Manager: Andy Morrell
Programme Editor: TBC   **(E)**

Back Row (L-R): Anthony Stephens, Stephen Wright, Joe Clarke, Glen Little, Mark Creighton, Martin Riley, Danny Wright, Chris Westwood.
Middle Row (L-R): Aman Hansra (asst physio), Michael Oakes (coach), Nick Rushton, John Hunt, Jay Colbeck, Andy Coughlin, Joslain Mayebi, Rob Ogleby, Steve Tomassen, Declan Walker, Riston Lloyd (physio), Alan Jones (kitman).
Front Row (L-R): Jamie Morton, Adrian Cieslewicz, Dean Keates, Billy Barr (asst man), Andy Morrell (man), Neil Ashton, Jay Harris, Brett Ormerod

Club Factfile

Founded: 1872   **Nickname:** The Robins
Previous Names: Wrexham Athletic for the 1882-83 season only
Previous Leagues: The Combination 1890-94, 1896-1906, Welsh League 1894-96, Birmingham & District 1906-21, Football League 1921-2008

Club Colours (change): Red/white/red (All green)

Ground: Racecourse Ground, Mold road, Wrexham LL11 2AN   **(T)** 01978 262 129
Capacity: 15,500 **Seats:** 10,100 **Covered:** 15,500 **Clubhouse:** Yes **Shop:** Yes

Directions
From Wrexham by-pass (A483) exit at Mold junction (A451).
Follow signs for Town Centre and football ground is half a mile on the left hand side.

Previous Grounds: Rhosddu Recreation Ground during the 1881-82 and 1882-83 seasons.

Record Attendance: 34,445 v Manchester United - FA Cup 4th Round 26/01/57
Record Victory: 10-1 v Hartlepool United - Division Four 03/03/62
Record Defeat: 0-9 v v Brentford - Division Three
Record Goalscorer: Tommy Bamford - 201 (1928-34)
Record Appearances: Arfon Griffiths - 592 (1959-79)
Additional Records: Paid £800,000 to Birmingham City for Bryan Hughes March 1997
Received £210,000 from Liverpool for Joey Jones October 1978
Senior Honours:
Welsh FA Cup 1877-78, 81-82, 92-93, 96-97, 1902-03, 04-05, 08-09, 09-10, 10-11, 13-14, 14-15, 20-21, 23-24, 24-25, 30-31, 56-57, 57-58, 59-60, 71-72, 74-75, 77-78, 85-86, 94-95. Welsh Lge 1894-95, 95-96. Combination 1900-01, 01-02, 02-03, 04-05. Football Lge Div. 3 1977-78. FAW Prem. Cup 1997-98, 99-2000, 00-01, 02-03, 03-04. F. Lge Trophy 2004-05

10 YEAR RECORD

02-03	03-04	04-05	05-06	06-07	07-08	08-09	09-10	10-11	11-12
FL 3 3	FL 2 13	FL 1 22	FL 2 13	FL 2 19	FL 2 24	Conf 10	Conf 11	Conf 4	Conf 2

WREXHAM

No.	Date	Comp	H/A	Opponents	Att:	Result	Goalscorers	Pos
	Wrexham							
1	Sat-13-Aug	BSP	H	Cambridge United	4206	D 1-1	Morrell 17	16
2	Tue-16-Aug	BSP	A	Bath City	1075	W 2-0	Morrell 2 (78, 79)	3
3	Fri-19-Aug	BSP	A	Lincoln City	2211	W 2-1	Tolley 28, Harris 56	1
4	Tue-23-Aug	BSP	H	Tamworth	3353	W 3-0	Og (Reynolds) 18, Tolley 78, Cieslewicz 82	2
5	Sat-27-Aug	BSP	A	Alfreton Town	1165	W 4-1	Speight 3 (13, 32, pen 57), Pogba 90	1
6	Mon-29-Aug	BSP	H	Fleetwood Town	4283	W 2-0	Speight 2, Morrell 59	1
7	Sat-03-Sep	BSP	H	Kidderminster Harriers	4102	W 2-0	Tolley 24, D Wright 48	1
8	Sat-10-Sep	BSP	A	Barrow	1463	L 1-3	Speight 40	1
9	Sat-17-Sep	BSP	H	York City	3872	L 0-3		3
10	Tue-20-Sep	BSP	A	Southport	1710	D 0-0		2
11	Sat-24-Sep	BSP	A	Grimsby Town	3515	W 3-1	Pogba 16, Harris 62, Fowler 68	1
12	Tue-27-Sep	BSP	H	Mansfield Town	3478	L 1-3	Fowler 64	4
13	Sat-01-Oct	BSP	H	Ebbsfleet United	2849	W 1-0	Speight pen 78	3
14	Tue-04-Oct	BSP	A	Gateshead	1258	W 4-1	D Wright 4, Clarke 49, Og (Moyes), 59, Keates pen 78	1
15	Sun-09-Oct	BSP	A	Hayes & Yeading United	625	W 2-0	Knight-Percival 59, Pogba 61	1
16	Sat-15-Oct	BSP	H	Stockport County	3874	W 4-0	Knight-Percival 2 (3, 46), Morrell 23, Speight 75	1
17	Tue-18-Oct	BSP	A	Luton Town	7270	W 1-0	Pogba 73	1
18	Sat-22-Oct	BSP	H	Newport County	4232	D 0-0		1
19	Sat-05-Nov	BSP	A	York City	4295	D 0-0		1
20	Sat-19-Nov	BSP	H	Lincoln City	3424	W 2-0	Pogba 2 (11, pen 61)	1
21	Sat-26-Nov	BSP	A	Braintree Town	957	D 0-0		1
22	Wed-30-Nov	BSP	H	Darlington	3171	W 2-1	Cieslewicz 78, Speight 81	1
23	Tue-06-Dec	BSP	H	Southport	3256	W 2-0	Speight pen 44, Cieslewicz 78	1
24	Sat-17-Dec	BSP	H	Gateshead	3161	W 2-1	Pogba 3, D Wright 35	1
25	Mon-26-Dec	BSP	A	AFC Telford	4591	W 2-0	Clarke 13, Speight 67	1
26	Sun-01-Jan	BSP	H	AFC Telford	5812	W 4-0	Og (Killock) 34, Creighton 35, Speight 74, Cieslewicz 86	1
27	Sat-14-Jan	BSP	A	Tamworth	1923	W 2-1	Tolley 5, Speight 29	1
28	Sat-21-Jan	BSP	H	Kettering Town	4066	W 4-1	Morrell 5, Creighton 53, Colbeck 2 (77, 90)	1
29	Tue-24-Jan	BSP	A	Forest Green Rovers	1109	L 0-1		2
30	Sat-28-Jan	BSP	A	Bath City	3583	W 2-0	Obeng 13, Speight pen 48	2
31	Sat-18-Feb	BSP	H	Hayes & Yeading United	3845	W 4-1	Speight 16, Creighton 44, Harris 58, Pogba 74	2
32	Tue-21-Feb	BSP	A	Kidderminster Harriers	2492	W 1-0	Morrell 45	2
33	Sat-25-Feb	BSP	A	Stockport County	4518	L 0-1		2
34	Sat-03-Mar	BSP	A	Kettering Town	1377	W 1-0	Tolley 24	2
35	Wed-07-Mar	BSP	H	Luton Town	4206	W 2-0	D Wright 6, Keates 39	2
36	Sat-10-Mar	BSP	H	Barrow	3432	W 2-0	D Wright 34, Speight 52	2
37	Tue-13-Mar	BSP	A	Ebbsfleet United	990	W 5-0	Pogba 27, Morrell 2 (44, 68), Leslie 57, Speight pen 78	2
38	Sat-24-Mar	BSP	H	Forest Green Rovers	4451	L 1-2	Speight pen 20	2
39	Tue-27-Mar	BSP	A	Darlington	1401	W 4-2	Speight 2 (44, pen 90), Knight-Percival 65, Pogba 86	2
40	Sat-31-Mar	BSP	A	Cambridge United	3014	D 1-1	Ogleby 90	2
41	Fri-06-Apr	BSP	H	Alfreton Town	4673	L 0-1		2
42	Tue-10-Apr	BSP	A	Fleetwood Town	4994	D 1-1	Speight 53	2
43	Sat-14-Apr	BSP	H	Grimsby Town	2917	D 2-2	Og (Pearson) 23, Westwood 72	2
44	Fri-20-Apr	BSP	A	Mansfield Town	3665	L 0-2		2
45	Tue-24-Apr	BSP	A	Newport County	1431	W 1-0	Cieslewicz 10	2
46	Sat-28-Apr	BSP	H	Braintree Town	3303	W 5-1	Morrell 19, Cieslewicz 42, Pogba 59, D Wright 88, Ashton pen 90	2

CUPS

No.	Date	Comp	H/A	Opponents	Att:	Result	Goalscorers	Pos
1	Sat-29-Oct	FAC 4Q	H	York City	2252	W 2-1	Knight-Percival 50, Og (McGurk) 81	
2	Sat-12-Nov	FAC 1	H	Cambridge United	2782	D 2-2	Morrell 2 (20, 60)	
3	Tue-22-Nov	FAC 1R	H	Cambridge United	2606	W 2-1	Pogba 59, D Wright 76	
4	Sat-03-Dec	FAC 2	A	Brentford	3452	W 1-0		
5	Sat-10-Dec	FAT 1	H	Hinckley United	1101	L 1-2	Little 54	
6	Sat-07-Jan	FAC 2	A	Brighton & Hove Albion	18573	D 1-1	Cieslewicz 62	
7	Wed-18-Jan	FAC 2R	H	Brighton & Hove Albion	8316	D 1-1 aet (L 4-5 pens) Morrell 23		
8	Thu-03-May	PO SF1	A	Luton Town	9012	L 0-2		
9	Mon-07-May	PO SF2	H	Luton Town	9087	W 2-1	Cieslewicz 63, Morrell 76	

League	
Starts	
Substitute	
Unused Sub	
Cups	
Starts	
Substitute	
Unused Sub	
Goals (Lg)	
Goals (Cup)	

Player appearance grid (X = started, S = substitute, U = unused substitute):

	MAXWELL	OBENG	CREIGHTON	KNIGHT-PERCIVAL	ASHTON	HARRIS	FOWLER	TOLLEY	SPEIGHT	D WRIGHT	MORRELL	CIESLEWICZ	POGBA	TOMASSEN	MAYEBI	TAYLOR	CLARKE	KEATES	LITTLE	WESTWOOD	ANORUO	WARD	HUNT	CLOWES	MOSS	PARLE	MORTON	STEPHENS	COLBECK	ALFEI	LESLIE	S WRIGHT	OGLEBY	WALKER	EVANS	GRAY
No.	21	2	4	20	3	6	8	18	10	9	11	7	24	15	25	14	26	12	15	23	19	13	16	14	33			36	27	2	30	34	31	22	35	1
	X	X	X	X	X	X	X	X	X	X	X	S	S	S	U	U																				
	X	X	X	X	X	X	X	X	X	X	X	S	S	U	U	U																				
	X	X	X	X	X	X	X	X	X	X	X	S	U	U	U	S																				
	X	X	X	X	X	X	X	X	X	X	X	S	S		S	U	U																			
	X	X	X	X	X	X	X	X	X	X	X	S	S		S	U	U																			
		X		X	X	X	X	X	X	X	S			X	U		S	U																		
		X	S	X	X	X	X	X	X	X	S			X	U	X	U																			
	X	X	X	X	X	X	X	U	X		X	S	X		X	S	U	S																		
	X		X	X	X	X	X	U	X		S	X	X		U	X	U	X																		
		X	X	X	X	X		X	X	X	S	S		X	X	S	X	U																		
		X	X	X	X			X	X	X	X	S		X	X	S	U	U	U	S																
		X	X	X			X	S	X	X	X	X	S		X	X	X	U	U	S																
	U	X	X	X	X	X		X	S	S	X	X		X		S	X			U																
	U	X	X	X	X	X		X	X	U	S	X	X		X		U			U																
	U	X	X	X	X	X		X	S	S	X	X		X		S	X			U																
	U	X	X	X	X	X	S	X		X	S	X	X	X		X	X	U			S															
	U	X	X	X	X	X	X	X	X	S	S	X	X		X		U	U	U	S																
	U	X	X	X	X	X	X	X	S	S	X	X		X		X		U	U																	
	U	X	X	X	X	X		X	X	X		X		S	X		X	S	S		U															
	U	X	X	X	X	X	X	X	S	X	X		X		X	X	S	S		U																
	U	X	X	X	X	X	X	X	S	X	X		X		X		X	S	S		U															
	U	X	X	X	X	X		X	X		X	X	X		X		X	X	X	S		S														
	U	X	X	X	X	X		X	X		X	X	X		X		X	X	X	S	U	S														
	U	X	X	X	X	X		X	X		X	X		X	U	X		X	X	S	S	S														
	U		X	X	X	X		X	X	X	S	X	X		X		X	U	U		S						X	X								
	U		X	X	X	X		X	X	X	S	X		X		X		U	S		S						X	X								
	U		X	X	X			X	S	X	S	X		X		X		S	X		U						X	X								
	U		X	X		X	X	X	X	S	S	X		X		X		S	X		U							X	X							
	U		X	X		X	X	X	X	S	S	X		X		X		U	X		X								U	X						
	U		X	X		X	X	X	X	S	S	X		X		X		S	X		X							X	X	S						
	U	X	X	X	X		X	X		X	S	X		X		X		S	S	U							X	X								
	U	X	X	X	X		X		X		S	X		X	X	S			X	S	U			X			X	X								
	U	X	X	X		X		X		X		X	X	S	X		X	S	U			X					S	X	S							
	U	X	X	X		X		X		X		X	X	S	X		X	S	U			X					S	X	S							
	U		X	X	X		S	X		X	X		U		X		X	X	X	S			X				X					S				
	U		X	X	X			X	X		S	X		S	X		X	X	X						X	S	S	U								
	X						S		X		X	S	X		X			X		X		X	X		U	X	X	S	X	U	U	U				
	U		X	X	X	X		X		S	X	X	X	S	X		X		X		U		S				X				X					
	U	X	X	X	X	X	S		X	S	S	X	X		X		X		U	U					X	U										
		X	X	X			X	X	S	X	X	S	X		X		X		U	X	U	U	U	S	U											
	U	X	X	X	X	X	S	X	S	X	X	X	U	X		X		X		U	U				U											
	U	X	X	X	X	X	X	X	X	X	S	X	S	X		X			U	U					U									X		
	X						X		X		X		X				X	X	X	U	X	X	S	X	U	U	U									
	U	X	X	X	X	X		X	X		X	X	S	S	X		X	S	S		U			S	U											
	U	X	X	X	X	X		X	X		X	S	S	S	X		X	S	S		U			S	U							X				
	U		X	X	X	X		X			S	X	X	X	X		U	X		U			S													
	U		X	X	X	X		S	X	X	S	S	X		X		X	X	U					X												
	10	29	38	43	43	38	14	29	33	26	31	18	27	0	36	0	19	23	3	12	0	0	4	1	0	0	0	0	1	5	10	10	2	1	0	0
	0	0	1	0	0	0	3	5	5	6	11	26	10	2	0	1	8	6	14	2	3	0	9	0	1	0	0	0	3	0	3	1	4	0	1	0
	30	0	0	0	0	0	0	2	0	1	0	2	0	1	6	7	8	2	10	13	4	3	10	2	0	0	0	1	0	0	1	0	1	0	0	0
	1	5	8	8	8	7	3	6	5	5	5	6	5	0	8	0	6	2	2	2	1	0	2	1	0	1	0	0	0	1	0	1	0	0	0	0
	0	0	0	0	0	0	2	1	2	2	3	2	1	0	0	0	0	2	2	0	0	0	4	0	1	0	0	0	0	0	0	0	0	0	0	0
	7	0	0	0	0	0	0	0	0	0	0	1	0	0	0	0	1	0	4	5	3	2	2	4	0	0	1	1	1	0	0	0	0	0	0	0
	0	1	3	4	1	3	2	5	20	6	10	6	11	0	0	0	2	2	0	1	0	0	0	0	0	0	0	2	0	1	0	1	0	0	0	0
	0	0	0	1	0	0	0	0	0	1	4	2	1	0	0	0	0	1	0	0	0	0	0	0	0	0	0	0	0	0	0	0	0	0	0	0

PLAYING SQUAD

Existing Players		SN	HT	WT	DOB	AGE	POB	Career	Apps	Goals
GOALKEEPERS										
Andy	Coughlin	13	6'03"	14 04	31/01/1993	19	Bootle	Tranmere Rel c/s 12, Fleetwood (WE) 11/10, Wrexham 7/12		
Louis	Gray							Wrexham	0	0
Joslain Leon	Mayebi	1	6'02"	14 02	14/10/1986	25	Douala, Cam	FC Metz (Fra), AEK Larnaca (Cyp) 7/08, Hakoah Ramat Gan (Isr) 1/09, Beitar Jerusalem (Isr) (5ML) 7/09, Maccabi Ahi Nazareth (SL) 1/10, Dinamo Bucharest II (Rom) 7/10, Preston (Trial) 12/10, Wrexham 1/11	36	0
DEFENDERS										
Neil	Ashton	3	5'08"	12 06	15/01/1985	27	Liverpool	Tranmere, Shrewsbury (SL) 12/04, Shrewsbury 6/05 Rel c/s 09, Macclesfield (SL) 1/08, Chester 7/09 Rel 2/10, Wrexham 6/10	43	1
Leon	Clowes	20	5'10"	11 13	27/02/1992	20	Chester	Wrexham, Technogroup Welshpool (L) 8/09, Airbus UK (SL) 8/10, Prescot Cables (L) 9/11	1	0
Mark	Creighton	5	6'04"	12 01	08/10/1981	30	Birmingham	Kidderminster (Yth), Moor Green, Paget R, Halesowen T, Redditch 8/01, Bromsgrove, Willenhall 1/02, Redditch 8/05, Kidderminster 6/06, Oxford U Small Fee 5/09, Wrexham (2ML) 11/10 Perm 1/11	39	3
Johnny	Hunt	16	5'10"	10 03	23/08/1990	22	Liverpool	Wrexham, Droylsden (L) 2/11	13	0
Jamie	Morton				03/11/1993	18		Wrexham, Prescot Cables (WE) 9/11, Colwyn Bay (WE) 3/12	0	0
Matty	Owen				23/06/1994	18		Wrexham		
Kyle	Parle							Wrexham	0	0
Martin	Riley	6	6'00	12 01	05/12/1986	25	Wolverhampton	Wolves Rel 12/07, Shrewsbury 3/08 Rel c/s 08, Kidderminster 8/08 Rel 7/10, Cheltenham 7/10 Rel c/s 11, Mansfield 7/11, Wrexham 7/12		
Anthony	Stephens				21/01/1994	18		Wrexham	0	0
Steve	Tomassen				03/09/1993	18		Wrexham	2	0
Declan	Walker	18	5'10"	10 05	01/03/1992	20	Warrington	Wrexham, Droylsden (L) 2/11	1	0
Chris	Westwood	23	6'00"	12 02	13/02/1977	35	Dudley	Wolves Rel c/s 98, Injured, Reading (Trial), Telford (Trial), Hartlepool 3/99, Walsall 7/05 Rel c/s 07, Peterborough 5/07 Rel c/s 09, Cheltenham (2ML) 1/09, Wycombe 7/09 Rel c/s 11, Wrexham 6/11	14	1
Stephen	Wright	2	6'00"	12 06	08/02/1980	32	Liverpool	Liverpool, Crewe (5WL) 8/99, Crewe (SL) 11/99, Sunderland £3,000,000 8/02 Rel c/s 08, Stoke (5ML) 8/07, Coventry 8/08 Rel c/s 10, Brentford 10/10 Rel c/s 11, Hartlepool 9/11 Rel 1/12, Wrexham 3/12	11	0
MIDFIELDERS										
Adrian	Cieslewicz	7	5'10"		16/11/1990	21		Man City, Wrexham 6/09	44	6
Joe	Clarke	14			28/07/1988	24		Redditch, Sollihull Moors 7/10, Darlington 8/10 Rel 2/11, Solihull Moors (2ML) 12/10, Solihull Moors 2/11, Wrexham 8/11	27	2
Rob	Evans							Wrexham	1	0
Jay	Harris	8	5'07"	11 06	15/04/1987	25	Liverpool	Everton Rel c/s 06, Accrington 8/06 Rel c/s 08, Chester 7/08 Rel 8/09, Banned, Wrexham 7/10	38	3
Dean	Keates	12	5'06"	10 10	30/06/1978	34	Walsall	Walsall Rel c/s 02, Hull C 8/02, Kidderminster Undisc 2/04 Rel c/s 05, Lincoln C 8/05, Walsall 1/06 Rel c/s 07, Peterborough 7/07 Rel 12/09, Wycombe 1/10 Rel c/s 10. Wrexham 7/10	29	2
Glen	Little	17	6'03"	13 00	15/10/1975	36	Wimbledon	C.Palace, Derry (L) 11/94, Glentoran 11/94, Burnley 11/96, Reading (SL) 3/03, Bolton (2ML) 9/03, Reading 7/04, Portsmouth 7/08 Rel c/s 09, Reading (SL) 3/09, Sheff Utd 8/09 Rel c/s 10, Aldershot T 7/10 Rel 1/11, Wrexham (Trial) 3/11, Wrexham 8/11	17	0
Louie	Moss				23/10/1993	18	Chester	Wrexham	1	0

FORWARDS

		SN	HT	WT	DOB	AGE	POB	From - To	APPS	GOA
James	Colbeck	21			05/08/1993	19		Wrexham	4	2
Max	Fargin							Wrexham		
Andy	Morrell	11	5'11"	12 00	28/09/1974	37	Doncaster	Newcastle Blue Star, Wrexham 12/98, Coventry 7/03,		
								Blackpool 8/06 Rel c/s 08, Bury 8/08, Wrexham 6/10	42	10
Rob	Ogleby	15	6'01"	12 12	05/01/1992	20	Coventry	Coventry (Scholar), Hearts c/s 10 Rel 1/12, East Fife (6ML) 7/11,		
								Wrexham 1/12	6	1
Brett	Ormerod	10	5'11"	11 12	18/10/1976	35	Blackburn	Blackburn (Trainee), Accrington c/s 95, Blackpool £50,000 3/97,		
								Southampton £1,750,000 12/01, Leeds (5WL) 9/04, Wigan (5WL) 3/05,		
								Preston 1/06, Notts Forest (SL) 3/08, Oldham (L) 10/08,		
								Blackpool 1/09 Rel c/s 12, Rochdale (L) 1/12, Wrexham 7/12		
Nick	Rushton	19			03/02/1992	20		Wrexham, Airbus UK (SL) 8/10, Newtown (SL) 8/11		
Rob	Salathiel				28/08/1994	18		Wrexham		
Danny	Wright	9	6'02"	13 08	10/09/1984	27	Southampton	Attleborough, Dereham c/s 05, Grimsby (Trial) 12/05, Histon 3/07 Rel 4/10,		
								Peterborough (Trial) 11/09, Cambridge U 5/10,		
								Wrexham Undisc 6/11	32	6

Loanees		SN	HT	WT	DOB	AGE	POB	From - To	APPS	GOA
(D)Daniel	Alfei		5'11"	12 02	23/02/1992	20	Swansea	Swansea (SL) 1/12 -	5	0

Departures		SN	HT	WT	DOB	AGE	POB	From - To	APPS	GOA
(D)Chris	Blackburn		5'07"	10 06	02/08/1982	30	Crewe	Swindon 5/08 - Wrexham 5/10 Rel 8/11 Stockport 8/11, AFC Telford 1/12		
(F)Gareth	Taylor		6'02"	13 08	25/02/1973	39	Weston-Super-Mare	Doncaster 6/09, - Man C (Yth Coach) 9/11	1	0
(M)Lee	Fowler		5'07"	10 00	10/06/1983	29	Cardiff	Forest Green 1/11 - Fleetwood Undisc 1/12	17	2
(G)Danny	Ward				22/06/1993	19	Wrexham	Yth - Liverpool Undisc 1/12	0	0
(D)Curtis	Obeng		5'09"	11 00	14/02/1989	23	Manchester	Man City 8/09 - Swansea Undisc 1/12	29	1
(D)Lee	Roberts							Yth - Prescot Cables (WE) 9/11, Colwyn Bay 3/12		
(M)Nathaniel	Knight-Percival		6'00"	11 07	31/03/1987	25	Cambridge	Histon 6/10 - Peterborough 7/12	43	4
(G)Chris	Maxwell				30/07/1990	22	Wrexham	Yth - Fleetwood 7/12	10	0
(D)Max	Penk				17/02/1993	19	Tarporley	Yth - Rel c/s 12, Newtown (SL) 8/11		
(M)Steven	Leslie		5'10"	11 02	05/11/1987	24	Glasgow	Shrewsbury 1/12 - Rel c/s 12, AFC Telford 8/12	13	1
(F)Obi	Anoruo		5'10"	11 06	28/08/1991	21	Nigeria	Yth - Rel c/s 12, Vauxhall Motors (L) 3/12, Barrow 7/12	3	0
(M)Jamie	Tolley		6'00"	11 02	12/05/1983	29	Ludlow	Hereford 8/10 - Mansfield 7/12	34	5
(F)Jake	Speight		5'07"	11 02	28/09/1985	26	Sheffield	Bradford C Undisc 7/11 - Mansfield Undisc 7/12	38	20
(F)Mathias	Pogba		6'02"	13 09	19/08/1990	22		FC Quimper (Gui) 9/10 - Crewe 7/12	37	11

FLEETWOOD TOWN - BLUE SQUARE PREMIER CHAMPIONS

No.	Date	Comp	H/A	Opponents	Att:	Result	Goalscorers	Pos
1	Sat-13-Aug	BSP	A	Grimsby Town	4061	W 2-0	Mangan 57, Donnelly 90	2
2	Tue-16-Aug	BSP	H	Darlington	1811	D 0-0		4
3	Sat-20-Aug	BSP	H	Hayes & Yeading United	1376	W 1-0	Milligan 85	3
4	Tue-23-Aug	BSP	A	Barrow	1482	L 0-4		7
5	Fri-26-Aug	BSP	H	York City	2111	D 0-0		4
6	Mon-29-Aug	BSP	A	Wrexham	4283	L 0-2		11
7	Sat-03-Sep	BSP	A	Kettering Town	1209	W 3-2	Vardy 2 (1, 40), Seddon 38	8
8	Sat-10-Sep	BSP	H	Gateshead	1388	W 3-1	Mangan 51, Vardy 2 (79, 90)	6
9	Sat-17-Sep	BSP	A	Ebbsfleet United	974	W 3-1	Vieira 2 (49, 70), Vardy 82	7
10	Tue-20-Sep	BSP	H	Kidderminster Harriers	1316	W 5-2	Seddon 45, Vieira 2 (46, 67), Mangan 57, Brodie 77	4
11	Sat-24-Sep	BSP	H	AFC Telford	1686	D 2-2	Brodie 2 (76, 90)	4
12	Tue-27-Sep	BSP	A	Stockport County	3023	W 4-2	Vieira 2, Clancy 49, Cox 57, Mangan 90	3
13	Sat-01-Oct	BSP	A	Braintree Town	1005	W 2-1	Milligan pen 20, Clancy 65	2
14	Sat-08-Oct	BSP	H	Forest Green Rovers	1687	D 0-0		3
15	Tue-11-Oct	BSP	H	Newport County	1277	L 1-4	Seddon 1	3
16	Fri-14-Oct	BSP	A	Lincoln City	2332	W 3-1	Jackson 2 (53, 72), Mangan 65	2
17	Tue-18-Oct	BSP	A	Alfreton Town	625	W 4-1	Brodie pen 37, Vardy 3 (47, 58, 61)	2
18	Sat-22-Oct	BSP	H	Bath City	1451	W 4-1	McGuire 43, Vardy 2 (45, 90), Seddon 83	2
19	Sat-05-Nov	BSP	A	Luton Town	6361	W 2-1	Vardy 11, Milligan pen 67	2
20	Sat-19-Nov	BSP	H	Stockport County	3021	W 2-1	Mangan 53, Vardy 66	2
21	Sat-26-Nov	BSP	A	Gateshead	768	D 1-1	Vardy 72	2
22	Tue-29-Nov	BSP	H	Kettering Town	1221	W 3-0	Charnock 24, Mangan 32, Clancy 69	1
23	Sat-17-Dec	BSP	A	Newport County	1011	W 1-0	Cavanagh 75	2
24	Tue-20-Dec	BSP	A	Hayes & Yeading United	264	W 3-1	Briggs 14, Vieira 74, Mangan pen 82	2
25	Mon-26-Dec	BSP	H	Southport	3029	D 2-2	Mangan pen 18, Brodie 88	2
26	Sun-01-Jan	BSP	A	Southport	2589	W 6-0	Brodie 2 (4, 29), Milligan pen 28, Vardy 2 (52, 90), Mangan 79	2
27	Tue-10-Jan	BSP	H	Barrow	2091	W 4-1	Till 5, Vardy 2 (48, 84), Rose 54	1
28	Sat-21-Jan	BSP	A	Darlington	5638	W 1-0	Rose 44	2
29	Tue-24-Jan	BSP	H	Braintree Town	1791	W 3-1	Vieira 2 (pen 34, 51), Vardy 44	1
30	Sat-28-Jan	BSP	A	Forest Green Rovers	922	W 2-1	Vieira 44, Atkinson 90	1
31	Sat-04-Feb	BSP	H	Tamworth	1911	D 2-2	Mangan 1, Vardy 55	1
32	Sat-18-Feb	BSP	H	Cambridge United	2068	W 1-0	Mangan 3	1
33	Tue-21-Feb	BSP	H	Ebbsfleet United	1411	W 6-2	Seddon 16, Cavanagh 23, Vardy 3 (29, 48, 58), Mangan pen 43	1
34	Sat-25-Feb	BSP	H	Alfreton Town	1929	W 4-0	Pond 18, Seddon 2 (37, 56), Og (Lowson) 84	1
35	Sat-03-Mar	BSP	A	Tamworth	958	W 3-0	Mangan 2 (pen 25, 90), Vardy 88	1
36	Tue-06-Mar	BSP	H	Grimsby Town	2447	W 2-1	Mangan pen 77, Vardy 90	1
37	Fri-09-Mar	BSP	A	Kidderminster Harriers	2341	W 2-0	Mangan 53, Og (Vaughan) 61	1
38	Tue-13-Mar	BSP	A	Mansfield Town	3132	D 1-1	Vardy 81	1
39	Sat-17-Mar	BSP	A	AFC Telford	2313	W 4-1	Mangan 2 (4, 15), Vardy 2 (83, 90)	1
40	Sat-24-Mar	BSP	H	Mansfield Town	3106	W 2-0	Beeley 50, Vardy 64	1
41	Sat-31-Mar	BSP	A	Bath City	762	W 4-1	Vardy 11, Cavanagh 36, Og (Gallinagh) 72, Brodie 76	1
42	Sat-07-Apr	BSP	A	York City	4048	W 1-0	Brodie 73	1
43	Tue-10-Apr	BSP	H	Wrexham	4994	D 1-1	Seddon 59	1
44	Fri-13-Apr	BSP	H	Lincoln City	4511	W 2-0	Vardy 2 (45, 49)	1
45	Sat-21-Apr	BSP	A	Cambridge United	2555	L 0-2		Champions 1
46	Sat-28-Apr	BSP	H	Luton Town	4446	L 0-2		1

CUPS

No.	Date	Comp	H/A	Opponents	Att:	Result	Goalscorers	
1	Sat-29-Oct	FAC 4Q	A	Mansfield Town	1725	D 1-1	Milligan 43	
2	Tue-01-Nov	FAC 4QR	H	Mansfield Town	1159	W 5-0	Brodie 22, Clancy 45, Milligan 56, Seddon 76, Mangan 90	
3	Sat-12-Nov	FAC 1	H	Wycombe Wanderers	2711	W 2-0	Mangan 25, Vardy 80	
4	Fri-02-Dec	FAC 2	H	Yeovil Town	3319	D 2-2	Charnock 82, Milligan pen 89	
5	Sat-10-Dec	FAT 1	A	Northwich Victoria	484	L 1-3	Seddon 45	
6	Tue-13-Dec	FAC 2R	A	Yeovil Town	3276	W 2-0	McGuire 29, Vardy 90	
7	Sat-07-Jan	FAC 3	H	Blackpool	5092	L 1-5	Vardy 70	

League
Starts
Substitute
Unused Sub

Cups
Starts
Substitute
Unused Sub

Goals (Lg)
Goals (Cup)

Appearance grid (player columns with squad numbers; X = start, S = substitute, U = unused substitute).

DAVIES	BARRY	FLYNN	MCNULTY	EDWARDS	ATKINSON	GOODALL	S BROWN	MCGUIRE	VIEIRA	MANGAN	BRODIE	SEDDON	DONNELLY	ST LOUIS-HAMILTON	COX	BRIGGS	MILLIGAN	HARVEY	HUGHES	HOLMES	VARDY	LINWOOD	BEELEY	J BROWN	CLANCY	POND	WILSON	WASSMER	JACKSON	CAVANAGH	TILL	CROWTHER	CHARNOCK	WYN	STEVENSON	ROSE	FOWLER	ALLEN	ROWE
1	4	28	5	3	25	13	29	18	10	14	9	19	27	16	17	15	8	31	24	32	33	20	2	12	7	6	31	32	36	26	11	39	23	22	34	31	27	29	30
X	X	X	X		X	X	X	X	X	X		X	S	S	S	U	U																						
X	X	X	X			X	X	X	X	U		X	S	S		X	U	X	S																				
X		X	X	X	X	X	X	X	S			X	X	S	X	U		U	X	S																			
X			X	X	X	S	U	X	S			X	X	X	S	U		X	X	X	X																		
X			X	X	X	U	X	X	X				X	U	U			U	S	X		X	X																
X			X	X	X	X	U		X	X			S	X	U	S	X	S	X	S		X	X	X															
X			X	X	U		X	X	S	S	X		U	X	S	X		X	X	X		X	X																
X		X		X	U		X	X	X	U	X		U	X	S	X		X	X	X	S																		
X		X		X	S		X	X	X	S	X		U	S	X	X		X	X	U																			
X		X		X	U	S		X	X	X	S	X		U	S	X	X		X	X	X																		
X		X		X	U	X		X	X	X	S		U		X			X	S	S	X	X	X																
X		X			U		X		X	X	S		U		S			X	S	X	X	X	X																
X		X			U	U	X		X	X	S		U		X			X	S	X	X	X	X	X															
X		X					X	U	S	X	S		S	X				X	X	X	X		X																
X		X				X		X	U	X		S						X	S	X	X	X		X	S														
X				X			S	X	X		S			X				X	U	X	X		U	X	X	U	X	X	U	X									
X				X			S		X	X		S			X			U	U	X	X		X	S	X			X	S	X									
X		X				X		X	U	X			S				X			X	S		X	U	X		U	X	X						U				
X		X				X		X	S	X		S				X				S	X	S	X	U			X	X	U				U						
X		X				X		X	X	X	S	X				S				X	S	X	U				X	X					U						
X		X				U			X	X	X	S				X X				X	X	X					X						U	S					
X		X				X		S	U	X	X	S								X		X					X	X					U	X	X	S			
X		X		S	X		U	X	X	S	S								X		X					X						U	X	X					
X		X		S	X		U	X	X	S	U								X		X					X						U	X	X					
X		X		U	X			U	X	X	S	U							X		X X	U				X						U	X	X					
X		X					S	X	X	S	X				S				X		X					X						U	U	S X					
X		X		U		X	S	X	U	X									X		X	S				X				X	S		U	X					
X		X		U	X	X	S	X	U									X	X U		X	X	S			X				X	S		U	X					
X		X		U		X	U	X	S	X								X		X					X	S	U	U	S									
X		X				X	U	X	X	S								X		X					X	S	U	U	X									
X		X				X	U	X	X	U								X		S					X	S	X	X	U	U	X								
X		X				X	S	X	S	X								X		X					X	S	X	S	U	U	X								
X		X				X	S	X	S	X								X		X					X	S	X	S	U	U	X								
X		X				X	S	X	U	X					S X				X		X					X	S		U	X	X								
X		X				X	S	X	S	X								X		X					X	S	S	U	U X										
X		X				X		X	X	S					S S				X		X					U		X	S	X	U								
X		X				X		X		X					S S				X		X					U		X	X X	S S								

46	2	3	39	7	15	29	8	34	16	39	16	22	2	0	3	8	19	3	1	34	3	32	13	7	29	5	3	4	23	9	0	4	0	0	8	17	0	0	
0	0	0	0	0	2	1	4	8	2	18	16	3	0	3	8	6	2	0	0	2	0	1	3	4	5	0	0	0	9	3	0	0	0	2	2	2			
0	0	0	0	0	3	14	4	2	11	0	2	3	1	22	1	3	0	0	2	1	0	1	3	4	1	2	1	0	0	1	1	9	0	23	3	0	0	0	

6	0	0	6	1	0	5	0	7	0	5	4	4	0	1	0	2	5	0	0	6	0	6	2	3	6	1	1	0	2	2	1	1	0	0	0	0	0	0	
0	0	0	1	0	0	1	0	0	3	1	1	0	0	0	0	2	0	0	0	0	0	0	3	0	0	0	0	2	0	2	1	0	0	0	0	0			
1	0	0	0	0	1	2	0	3	0	1	2	0	4	3	0	0	0	0	0	0	1	1	0	0	2	0	1	1	0	1	0	1	0	2	0	0	0	0	

| 0 | 0 | 0 | 0 | 0 | 1 | 0 | 0 | 1 | 9 | 19 | 9 | 8 | 1 | 0 | 1 | 1 | 4 | 0 | 0 | 0 | 31 | 0 | 1 | 0 | 3 | 1 | 0 | 0 | 2 | 3 | 1 | 0 | 1 | 0 | 0 | 2 | 0 | 0 | |
| 0 | 0 | 0 | 0 | 0 | 0 | 0 | 0 | 1 | 0 | 2 | 1 | 2 | 0 | 0 | 0 | 3 | 0 | 0 | 0 | 3 | 0 | 0 | 0 | 1 | 0 | 0 | 0 | 0 | 0 | 1 | 0 | 0 | 0 | 0 | 0 | 0 | | | |

YORK CITY - BLUE SQUARE PREMIER PLAY-OFF WINNERS

No.	Date	Comp	H/A	Opponents	Att:	Result	Goalscorers	Pos
	York							
1	Sat-13-Aug	BSP	A	Ebbsfleet United	1522	W 2-1	Walker 2 (pen 83, 90)	5
2	Tue-16-Aug	BSP	H	Barrow	3075	W 3-1	Walker 7, McLaughlin 45, Blair 90	2
3	Sat-20-Aug	BSP	H	AFC Telford	2723	L 0-1		5
4	Tue-23-Aug	BSP	A	Kettering Town	1595	W 5-1	Boucaud 20, Walker 2 (21, 31), Moke 39, Pilkington 90	3
5	Fri-26-Aug	BSP	A	Fleetwood Town	2111	D 0-0		2
6	Mon-29-Aug	BSP	H	Alfreton Town	3166	L 0-1		6
7	Sat-10-Sep	BSP	A	Tamworth	1012	L 1-2	Walker 84	14
8	Tue-13-Sep	BSP	H	Bath City	2030	W 1-0	Reed 88	9
9	Sat-17-Sep	BSP	A	Wrexham	3872	W 3-0	McLaughlin 4, Chambers 21, Reed 24	8
10	Tue-20-Sep	BSP	H	Darlington	2844	D 2-2	Reed 2, Walker 79	7
11	Sat-24-Sep	BSP	H	Luton Town	3570	W 3-0	Chambers 2 (9, 45), Walker 31	5
12	Tue-27-Sep	BSP	A	Gateshead	1604	L 2-3	Walker 23, Og (Curtis) 87	8
13	Sat-01-Oct	BSP	A	Stockport County	3753	W 2-1	Blair 52, Walker 86	7
14	Sat-08-Oct	BSP	H	Braintree Town	2640	W 6-2	Chambers 15, McLaughlin 2 (28, 41), Fyfield 37, Walker pen 72, Moke 85	4
15	Tue-11-Oct	BSP	H	Southport	1107	D 1-1	Chambers 62	4
16	Sat-15-Oct	BSP	H	Grimsby Town	3872	W 2-1	Walker 34, Chambers 86	4
17	Tue-18-Oct	BSP	H	Cambridge United	2711	D 2-2	Walker 2 (21, 89)	3
18	Sat-22-Oct	BSP	A	Hayes & Yeading United	525	W 4-2	Walker 14, Challinor 19, McLaughlin 61, Chambers 76	3
19	Sat-05-Nov	BSP	H	Wrexham	4295	D 0-0		4
20	Sat-19-Nov	BSP	A	Barrow	2190	D 0-0		5
21	Sat-26-Nov	BSP	A	Forest Green Rovers	1157	D 1-1	Reed pen 83	5
22	Tue-29-Nov	BSP	H	Lincoln City	3155	W 2-0	Pilkington 4, McLaughlin 56	4
23	Sat-03-Dec	BSP	A	Kettering Town	2899	W 7-0	Reed 2 (6, 12), Challinor 30, Blair 45, McLaughlin 50, Chambers 65, Ashikodi 77	4
24	Tue-06-Dec	BSP	A	AFC Telford	1601	D 0-0		3
25	Mon-19-Dec	BSP	H	Kidderminster Harriers	2830	L 2-3	Blair 20, McGurk 68	4
26	Mon-26-Dec	BSP	H	Mansfield Town	3551	D 1-1	Henderson 62	4
27	Sun-01-Jan	BSP	A	Mansfield Town	4284	D 2-2	Blair 77, Fyfield 90	5
28	Sat-07-Jan	BSP	A	Lincoln City	3048	W 2-0	Blair 2 (64, 72)	4
29	Sat-21-Jan	BSP	H	Ebbsfleet United	2973	W 3-2	Blair 2 (10, 53), Meredith 67	4
30	Tue-24-Jan	BSP	A	Kidderminster Harriers	2417	D 1-1	Smith 57	4
31	Sat-28-Jan	BSP	A	Darlington	6413	D 2-2	Smith 60, Chambers 61	4
32	Sat-18-Feb	BSP	H	Stockport County	3370	W 2-1	Reed 84, Blinkhorn 90	4
33	Wed-22-Feb	BSP	H	Gateshead	2683	L 1-2	Reed 65	4
34	Sat-03-Mar	BSP	H	Hayes & Yeading United	2603	W 2-0	Oyebanjo 57, Walker pen 90	4
35	Tue-06-Mar	BSP	H	Tamworth	2249	D 0-0		4
36	Tue-13-Mar	BSP	A	Grimsby Town	4250	W 3-2	Reed 19, Smith 47, Fyfield 90	5
37	Sat-24-Mar	BSP	H	Southport	3465	L 1-2	Reed 84	6
38	Tue-27-Mar	BSP	A	Bath City	565	W 1-0	McLaughlin 50	5
39	Fri-30-Mar	BSP	A	Luton Town	5925	W 2-1	McLaughlin 81, Meredith 86	4
40	Tue-03-Apr	BSP	A	Newport County	1241	L 1-2	McLaughlin 39	4
41	Sat-07-Apr	BSP	H	Fleetwood Town	4048	L 0-1		4
42	Mon-09-Apr	BSP	A	Alfreton Town	1603	W 2-0	Blair 69, Oyebanjo 76	4
43	Sat-14-Apr	BSP	H	Newport County	2824	D 1-1	Walker 59	5
44	Tue-17-Apr	BSP	A	Cambridge United	2211	W 1-0	Walker 64	4
45	Sat-21-Apr	BSP	A	Braintree Town	1127	W 1-0	Tonne 75	4
46	Sat-28-Apr	BSP	H	Forest Green Rovers	3391	W 1-0	Moke 82	4

CUPS								
1	Sat-29-Oct	FAC 4Q	A	Wrexham	2252	L 1-2	McLaughlin 57	
2	Sat-10-Dec	FAT 1	H	Solihull Moors	1116	D 2-2	Blair 6, Challinor pen 90	
3	Tue-13-Dec	FAT 1R	A	Solihull Moors	275	W 3-0	Smith 12, Blair 2 (61, 76)	
4	Sat-14-Jan	FAT 2	A	Salisbury City	827	W 6-2	Blair 2 (19, 21), Reed 25, McLaughlin 2 (34, 86), Blinkhorn 69	
5	Tue-14-Feb	FAT 3	H	Ebbsfleet United	1419	W 1-0	Blair 49	
6	Sat-25-Feb	FAT 4	A	Grimsby Town	3662	W 1-0	Kerr 83	
7	Sat-10-Mar	FAT SF1	A	Luton Town	3365	W 1-0	Reed 18	
8	Sat-17-Mar	FAT SF2	A	Luton Town	5796	D 1-1	Blair 90	
9	Wed-02-May	PO SF1	H	Mansfield Town	6057	D 1-1	Og (Geohoghon) 42	
10	Mon-07-May	PO SF2	A	Mansfield Town	7095	W 1-0 aet	Blair 111	
11	Sat-12-May	FAT Final	N	Newport County	19844	W 2-0	Blair 66, Oyebanjo 74	
12	Sun-20-May	PO Final	N	Luton Town	39265	W 2-1	Chambers 26, Blair 47	

League
Starts
Substitute
Unused Sub

Cups
Starts
Substitute
Unused Sub

Goals (Lg)
Goals (Cup)

INGHAM	OYEBANJO	SMITH	MCGURK	MEREDITH	MOKE	MCLAUGHLIN	BOUCAUD	BLAIR	WALKER	CHAMBERS	PARSLOW	REED	POTTS	FYFIELD	HENDERSON	KERR	PILKINGTON	CHALLINOR	MUSSELWHITE	ASHIKODI	BROWN	BLINKHORN	DOIG	SWALLOW	TONNE	GIBSON	BOPP	KELLY	WHITE
24	2	4	5	3	18	26	15	17	9	10	6	7	14	16	11	8	12	20	1	28	19	21	23	22	15	27	13	25	29
X	X	X	X	X	X	X	X	X	X	X	X	U	U	U	U	U													
X	X	X	X	X	X	X	X	X	X	X	U	S	S	U	U														
X	X	X	X	X	X	X	X	X	X	X	U	S	U	S		S													
X	X	X	X	X	X	X	X		X	X	U	S	U	S		X	S												
X	X	X	X	X	X	X		X	X	U	U		S		X	S	S												
X	X	X	X	X	X		X	X	X	U	S		X	U	S														
X	X	X	X	X		S	U	X	X	X	U	S		S	X		X												
X		U	X	X		U	X	S	X	X	X	S		X	S	X	X												
X		U	X	X		X	X	S	X	X	U	S	X	U	X		X												
X		X	X	S	X	X	U	X	X	U	X	U	X	U	X		X												
X	U	X	X	S	X	X	S	X	X	U	X	X	S	X	X		X												
X	U	X	X	S	X	X	S	X	X	U	X	X	S	X	X		X												
X		X	X	U	X	X	X	X	X	S	U	S	X	U	X		X												
X	U	X	S	X	X	X	X	X	X	S	S	U	X		X	U	X												
X	U	X	X	X	U	X	X	X		U	U	S	X	U	X		X												
X	U	X	S	X	X	X	X		X	S	U	U	X	X		X													
X	X	U	X	S	X	X	X	X	X	U	S	S	X		X		X												
X	U	S	X	X	X	X	X	X	X	U	U	S	X		X		X												
X	S	X	U	X	X	X	X	X	X	U	X		S	X		X		X											
X	X	X	U	X	U	X		X	S	S		X	S	X		X	S	X		X									
X	S	U	X	X	U	X		X	U	X		X	X	X		X	X		S										
X	S	U	X	S	X		X	U	X		X	X	X	X		X	X		S										
X	U	U	X	X		X	X	X	X		X	S		X	X	X	X		S										
X	U	U	X	X	S	X	X	X		X	S		X	X	X	X		S											
X	X	X	X	X		X	U	X		S	U	S	U	X	X	X		U											
X	X		X	X	U	X	X		X	X	S	U	X	X	S	U													
X		X		X		X	U	X	U	X	X	X	X	X	U	U	X												
X		X	X	U	X	U	X		X	X	X		S	X	X	X	X	U	X	S									
X		X	U	X	X	X	S	X		S	X	X	X	U	X	X	X		S										
X		X	U	X		X	X	X		S	X	S	U	S	X	X	X		X										
X		X		X		X	X	X	U	S		X		X	X	S	X	S	U	X									
X	X		X		U	X		X	X	U	S		X		X	X	S	X	S		X								
X	X		X	S	X		X	X	X	S	U		X	U	X		S	X		X									
X	X		X	U	X		X	X	S	U	X		X	S	X		S		U	U									
X	X	X		X	S	S		X	X	X		X	S	X		X		U	X	S									
X	X	X		X	U	X		X	X	S	S	X		X		X	X	X	X	X									
X	X	X		X		X		X	X	U	S			X		S	X	U	X										
X	X	X		X	X		S	S	X	X			X	S		X	S	X	U										
X	X		X	X		S	X	X		S	U	S		X	X	X	S	X											
X		X		X		X	X	X	S	U	X	X		X	X	S	S	U	S										
		X	U			X	S	X	X		S	X	X	X	X	X	X		S		U								
X	X	U	X	X	X	X	U	S		S	X	X	X	U	X	X			S	U									
X		U	X	X	S	X	X	X		S		U	X		X	X	X		S										
X	X	X	X	X	S	U	X	X		X		U	X		X	S	X		U										
X		X		X	S	X	U	X			X	X	U		S	X	S		X	S									
X		X			X		X	X	S	S			X	U	X		U	X	X	X									
X	X	X		X	S	X		X	X	U	U		X		S	X		S	X		X								
X	X	X			U		U	X	X	S	X	S	X		X	S	X		X		X								
X		X		X		X	X	X	S	X		X		X	U	S	S	U											
X		X		X	S	X	X	X	X	U	X	X		X	U	U		X											
X	X	X		X	S	X	X	X	X	U	S	S		X	U		X					X							
X	X	X		X	U	S	X	X	X	X	S	U	S		X	U		X											

43	19	31	18	43	11	42	23	37	29	34	17	17	2	25	2	33	10	35	3	2	6	3	10	0	2	8	1	0	0
0	2	0	1	0	15	2	1	4	1	8	10	18	8	8	4	1	8	4	0	6	1	12	0	2	1	0	1	1	0
0	2	8	9	1	9	2	3	1	0	0	18	10	12	5	0	3	2	1	3	3	2	2	0	6	1	2	0	1	

12	6	10	3	12	1	10	1	10	9	5	9	4	1	5	1	8	2	10	0	1	1	1	5	1	1	3	0	0	0
0	0	0	0	0	7	1	0	1	0	4	2	3	2	2	0	0	2	2	0	2	2	3	0	0	0	0	0	0	0
0	0	2	0	0	1	1	3	1	0	0	1	3	4	2	0	0	1	0	6	1	1	1	1	0	0	0	0	0	0

| 0 | 2 | 3 | 1 | 2 | 3 | 10 | 1 | 10 | 18 | 9 | 0 | 10 | 0 | 3 | 1 | 0 | 2 | 2 | 0 | 1 | 0 | 1 | 0 | 0 | 1 | 0 | 0 | 0 | 0 |
| 0 | 1 | 1 | 0 | 0 | 0 | 3 | 0 | 10 | 0 | 1 | 0 | 2 | 0 | 0 | 0 | 1 | 0 | 1 | 0 | 1 | 0 | 0 | 0 | 1 | 0 | 0 | 0 | 0 | 0 |

Blue Square Premier Statistics 2011-12

	Games Played	& Goals Scored & Conceded	Top Goalscorers League, FAC & FAT	Number of Scorers per Club	Hat Tricks Scored	Penalties Scored	Best Individual Consecutive Scoring Run	Number of Clean Sheets	Number of Games in which club failed to score	Number of players with 10+ goals in League FAC & FAT	Scorers with 10+
AFC Telford United	P50	F53-A74	Sharp 11-2-2=15	20	0	2	Sharp 4	14	16	1	Sharp 15
Alfreton Town	52	76-94	Jarman 12-2-3=17	17+2	0	2	Moult 3	11	15		Jarman 17 (5p), Brown 10 & Clayton 10
Barrow	52	71-82	Boyes 15-4-2=21	14+2	Boyes 2	5	Boyes 2x3	10	10(7)	3	Boyes 3 (1pen), Cook 17 & Baker 10 (4pen)
Bath City	51	50-94	M.Canham 7-0-2=9	15	0	7	Murray 5	5	19	0	
Braintree Town	50	83-87	Wright 17-1-0-18	17	0	8	Reason 3	11	8	3	Wright 18 (4pens), Marks 15 & Reason 12 (3pens)
Cambridge United	53	73-50	Berry 6-1-1-8 Carew 5-2-1=8	21	0	2	Berry 3	17	10	0	
Darlington	49	48-80	Bowman 10-1-0=11	19+2ogs	0	5	Bowman 3	11	22	1	Bowman 11 (1pen)
Ebbsfleet United	50	77-91	Willock 19-0-1=20	15	Enver-Marum 1	7	Willock 3	7	12	3	Willock (4pens), Enver-Marum 15 & West 10
Fleetwood Town	53	116-59	Vardy 31-3-0=34	19+3ogs	Vardy 2	12	Vardy 2 x 4	18	7	4	Vardy 34 (1pen), Mangan 21 (5 pens), Brodie 10 (1pen) & Seddon 10
Forest Green R	56	67-49	Klukowski 18-0-0=18	15+3ogs	Klukowski & Taylor 2	3	5 x 2	12	15(4)	2	Klukowski 18 (3pens) & Taylor 10
Gateshead	56	83-69	Shaw 28-3-4=35	13	Shaw 2	6	Shaw 6	16	5	2	Shaw 35 (6pens) & Cummins 11
Grimsby Town	56	96-62	Hearn 26-2-0=28	22+2ogs	Hearn 4	1	Hearn 4	19(4)	14	4	Hearn 28, Elding 16 (1pen), Duffy 11&Coulson 10
Hayes & Yeading	48	60-98	Soares 15-1-0=16	18	0	4	Soares 5	7	11	1	Soares 16 (1pen)
Kettering Town	49	45-104	Mama 8-0-2=10	17	0	6	Cunnington 3	7	18(4)		Mama 10 (1pen)
Kidderminster H	52	95-74	Wright 15-0-2-17	21+2ogs	Wright 1	9	Malbon 3	11	9		Wright 17 (5 pens), Matt 13, Guinan 10 & Byrne 10
Lincoln City	51	62-73	Smith 7-2-0=9	23+4ogs	0	2	Smith 3	9	17	0	
Luton Town	59	98-52	Fleetwood 12-1-3=16	21+2ogs	Crow 1	3	Gray 3	24 (5&6)	11	3	Fleetwood 16, Crow 10 & Morgan-Smith 10
Mansfield Town	51	90-58	Green 28-0-1=29	18+1og	Briscoe & Green 2	3	Green 4	15 (4)	9	3	Green 29 (2pens), Briscoe 12 & Dyer 10
Newport County	56	72-70	Rose 13-0-1-14	16	Foley & Rose 2	3	Buchanan 3	16	17	2	Rose 14 (2pens) 7 Foley 12 (1pen)
Southport	49	74-75	Gray 24-0-2=26	18+4ogs	Whalley 1	9	Gray 3	14	11	2	Gray 26 (8 pens) & Whalley 11
Stockport County	49	61-82	Elliott 7-0-1-8 D.Rowe 8-0-0-8	17+1og	0	3	Hattersley 3 D.L.Rowe 3	9	13	0	
Tamworth	51	54-76	Christie 11-1-0-12 16	16	0	8	St Aimie 3	11	16(5)	1	Christie 12 (6 pens)
Wrexham (1pen)	55	74-71	Speight 20-0-0=20	19+4ogs	Speight 1	5	Speight 4	23(2x4)	10	3	Speight 20 (5pens), Morrell 13 & Pogba 12
York City	58	99-53	Walker 18-0-0-18	19-1og	0	5	Blair 4 Walker 4	21(4)	8	4	Walker 18 (3pens), Blair 17, McLaughlin 12 & Reed 12(1pen)

ALTRINCHAM

Chairman: Grahame Rowley
Secretary: Derek Wilshaw   **(T)** 07833 636 381   **(E)** dwilshaw@altrinchamfootball.co.uk
Additional Committee Members:
George Heslop, Andrew Shaw, Paul Daine, Brian Flynn.

Manager: Lee Sinnott
Programme Editor: Grahame Rowley.   **(E)** altrinchamprog@yahoo.co.uk

 Altrincham Football Club
2011/2012 Players & Staff

Club Factfile

Founded: 1903   **Nickname:** The Robins
Previous Names: Broadheath FC 1893-1903.
Previous Leagues: Manchester 1903-11. Lancashire C. 1911-19. Cheshire C. 1919-68. Northern Premier 1968-79,97-99. Conference 1979-97, 99-

Club Colours (change): Red & white stripes/red/red. (Aqua/grey/aqua)

Ground: Moss Lane, Altrincham, Cheshire WA15 8AP   **(T)** 0161 928 1045
Capacity: 6,085   **Seats:** 1,154   **Covered:** Yes   **Clubhouse:** Yes   **Shop:** Yes

Directions: From M6 junction19, turn right towards Altrincham into town centre (approx 15 minutes). Turn down Lloyd Street, past Sainsburys on the right. Tesco Extra on left. Then follow signs for Altrincham F.C.

Previous Grounds: Pollitts Field 1903-10.

Record Attendance: 10,275 - Altrincham Boys v Sunderland Boys English Schools Shield 1925.
Record Victory: 9-2 v Merthyr Tydfil - Conference 1990-91.
Record Defeat: 1-13 v Stretford (H) - 04.11.1893.
Record Goalscorer: Jack Swindells - 252 (1965-71).
Record Appearances: John Davison - 677 (1971-86).
Additional Records: Transfer fee paid - £15k to Blackpool for Keith Russell. Received - £50k from Leicester for Kevin Ellison.

Senior Honours:
Cheshire Senior Cup Winners 1904-05, 33-34, 66-67, 81-82. F.A. Trophy Winners 1977-78, 85-86.
Football Alliance Champions 1979-80, 80-81. N.P.L. Premier Champions 1998-99.
Conference North & South Play-off Winners 2004-05.

10 YEAR RECORD

02-03	03-04	04-05	05-06	06-07	07-08	08-09	09-10	10-11	11-12
NP P 14	NP P 12	Conf N 5	Conf 22	Conf 21	Conf 21	Conf 15	Conf 14	Conf 22	Conf N 8

ALTRINCHAM

No.	Date	Comp	H/A	Opponents	Att:	Result	Goalscorers	Pos
1	Sat-13-Aug	BSN	A	Harrogate Town	587	L 2-3	Twiss 60, Reeves 69	14
2	Tue-16-Aug	BSN	H	Workington	774	D 1-1	Densmore 41	17
3	Sat-20-Aug	BSN	H	Histon	686	W 3-0	Clee 35, Reeves 61, Richman 90	9
4	Tue-23-Aug	BSN	A	Vauxhall Motors	382	D 2-2	Densmore 20, Reeves 46	12
5	Sat-27-Aug	BSN	A	Hyde FC	745	L 1-2	Lees 26	16
6	Mon-29-Aug	BSN	H	Guiseley	749	D 2-2	Reeves 7, Twiss 25	16
7	Sat-03-Sep	BSN	A	Gloucester City	360	D 1-1	Clee 53	15
8	Sat-10-Sep	BSN	H	Worcester City	771	W 4-1	Lawrie 38, Reeves 2 (46, 68), Twiss 63	13
9	Sat-17-Sep	BSN	A	Solihull Moors	343	L 0-2		14
10	Tue-20-Sep	BSN	A	Colwyn Bay	444	W 6-1	Reeves 2 (21, 65), Clee 2 (32, 88), Lawrie 68, Williams 76	11
11	Sat-24-Sep	BSN	H	Nuneaton Town	775	W 2-0	Reeves 2 (pen 62, 76)	10
12	Sat-08-Oct	BSN	H	Boston United	804	W 6-1	Reeves 3 (15, 46, 75), Lawrie 27, Twiss 84, Mulholland 87	6
13	Sat-15-Oct	BSN	H	Vauxhall Motors	706	W 3-2	Reeves 4, Lawrie 26, Richman 90	5
14	Sat-22-Oct	BSN	A	Stalybridge Celtic	1005	L 1-5	Reeves 37	7
15	Sat-05-Nov	BSN	H	Eastwood Town	761	W 2-0	Reeves 3, Williams 71	6
16	Sat-12-Nov	BSN	A	Worcester City	824	L 0-3		8
17	Sat-19-Nov	BSN	H	Gloucester City	773	L 1-2	Reeves 73	11
18	Sat-03-Dec	BSN	A	FC Halifax Town	1414	W 4-2	Reeves 2 (11, 14), Redshaw 2 (43, 72)	8
19	Tue-06-Dec	BSN	H	Corby Town	649	D 1-1	Reeves 13	9
20	Mon-26-Dec	BSN	H	Droylsden	846	W 5-1	Reeves 3 (11, 33, 77), Lawrie 24, Twiss 82	8
21	Sun-01-Jan	BSN	A	Droylsden	601	L 1-3	Reeves 71	9
22	Sat-07-Jan	BSN	H	Colwyn Bay	816	L 3-4	Redshaw 2 (20, 49), Reeves 28	11
23	Mon-09-Jan	BSN	A	Hinckley United	434	W 4-1	Hawes 43, Lawrie 44, Reeves 47, Redshaw 58	8
24	Sat-14-Jan	BSN	A	Workington	473	W 2-1	Lawrie 25, Reeves pen 61	7
25	Sat-21-Jan	BSN	H	Harrogate Town	773	W 5-2	Reeves 4 (14, 24, 60, 75), Redshaw 58	7
26	Tue-24-Jan	BSN	A	Blyth Spartans	356	D 1-1	Reeves pen 90	7
27	Sat-28-Jan	BSN	A	Gainsborough Trinity	668	L 0-2		7
28	Sat-18-Feb	BSN	H	Blyth Spartans	840	W 2-1	Broomes 33, Reeves pen 47	7
29	Tue-21-Feb	BSN	H	Hinckley United	625	D 2-2	Reeves 12, Redshaw 41	7
30	Sat-25-Feb	BSN	A	Bishops Stortford	485	L 0-1		7
31	Sat-03-Mar	BSN	A	Histon	388	W 3-2	Lawrie 2 (14, 34), Reeves 26	7
32	Tue-06-Mar	BSN	H	Stalybridge Celtic	791	W 2-1	Reeves 62, M Flynn 87	6
33	Sat-10-Mar	BSN	H	Bishops Stortford	844	L 0-2		7
34	Sat-17-Mar	BSN	A	Boston United	1204	D 1-1	Lawrie 51	7
35	Sat-24-Mar	BSN	H	Solihull Moors	801	D 1-1	Reeves pen 73	7
36	Wed-28-Mar	BSN	A	Corby Town	280	W 3-1	Reeves 2 (9, 49), McGivern 54	7
37	Sat-31-Mar	BSN	A	Nuneaton Town	765	L 1-2	Reeves 54	8
38	Sat-07-Apr	BSN	H	Hyde FC	1290	L 1-3	Reeves pen 8	8
39	Mon-09-Apr	BSN	A	Guiseley	776	L 2-3	Clee 13, Reeves 45	8
40	Sat-14-Apr	BSN	H	FC Halifax Town	1291	D 1-1	Reeves 19	8
41	Sat-21-Apr	BSN	A	Eastwood Town	239	W 6-1	Phelan 2 (32, 48), Reeves pen 37, McGivern 3 (44, 78, 90)	8
42	Sat-28-Apr	BSN	H	Gainsborough Trinity	989	L 2-3	Clee 34, Watmore 43	8

CUPS

No.	Date	Comp	H/A	Opponents	Att:	Result	Goalscorers	
1	Sat-01-Oct	FAC 2Q	H	Witton Albion	628	L 0-2		
2	Sun-27-Nov	FAT 3Q	A	FC United of Manchester	1945	L 1-2	Redshaw 52	

League
Starts
Substitute
Unused Sub

Cups
Starts
Substitute
Unused Sub

Goals (lg)
Goals (Cup)

Appearance grid (X = played, S = substitute, U = unused substitute)

COBURN	LAWTON	BROWN	C LYNCH	JONES	A FLYNN	DENSMORE	DANYLYK	TWISS	REEVES	CLEE	SUMMERSKILL	LEES	MULHOLLAND	OLLERENSHAW	RICHMAN	COOMBES	LAWRIE	WILLIAMS	FEARON	REID	REDSHAW	WATMORE	M FLYNN	HAWES	DODD	TOMSETT	WALMSLEY	BROOMES	HOLDEN	TOLSON	COLLISTER	M LYNCH	MILES	MCGIVERN	PHELAN	SMART	GRIMSHAW
X	X	X	X	X	X	X	X	X	X	X	X	S	U	U	U																						
X	X	X	X	X	X	X	X	X	X	X	X	S	U	S	U																						
X	X	X	X	X	X	X	X	X	X	X	X	U	S	S	U	S																					
X	X	X	X	X		X	X	X	X	X	X	S	X	U	U	U	S	U																			
X	X	X	X	X		X	X	X	X	X	X	U	X	S	U	S	U																				
X	X	X	S	X	S	X	X	X	X	X	X	S	X	U	U	X		S																			
X		X	X			X	X	X	X	X	X	S	X	S	U		U	X	X	U																	
X		X	X	U		X	X	X	X	X	X	S	U		X	S	U		U	X	X	S															
X		X		U		X	X	X	X	X	X	X	X	S	X	S	U		U	X	X	X															
X		X	X		X	X	X	X	X	X	X	X	X	U			X	X	U	U																	
X		X	U		X	X	X	X	X	X	X	U	X	S		S		X	X		U																
X		X	U		X	X	X	X	X	X	X	U	X		S		X	X		U	S																
X		X	S		X	X	X	X	X	X	X	U	X		S		X	X		U	S																
X	U	S	X		X	X	X	X	X	X	X		X		S		X	X		U	S																
X	S	S	X		X	X	X	X	X	X	X		X				U	X	X		U	S															
X	U	X	X		X	X	X	X	X	S		X			X	S	S		U	X																	
X		X		X	X	X	U	X	X		U		X		U	X	X	X	S																		
X		X	S		X	X	X	U	X	X		S		X	U	X	X	X	S																		
X		X	S		X		X	X	X		S		X	U	X	X	X	X	X																		
X		U	X		X	X	U	X	X		U	X	X	U	X	X	U	X	X	S																	
X		X		U	X	X	X	X	S	X	U	X		X	X	U	X	U	S	X		X	X	X													
		X	U	X		X	X	X	S	X			X		X	X	U	U	U	S	X		X	X													
		X	U	X		X	X	X	X	U	X			X		X	X	U	X	S	X	X	X														
		X		X	U	X	X		X			X		X	X	U	X	X	X	X			X	X	S												
		X		X	U	S		X	X			S		X	X	U	X	U	S	X		X	X														
			U	X		X		S	X			S		X	X	U	X	X	S	X	X	X		X	X	S											
			U	X		X		S	X			S		X	X	U	X	X	S	X	X	X		X	X	X											
X			U	X		X		X	X				X		X	X	U	X	U	U	U		X	X													
X		X		X		S	X	S	X		U		X		X	X	U	X		X		X	X	X	S												
X	U		X		X	X		U		X		X		X	X	U		S	X	S	X		X		X	X	X	X									
X		X		X		S	X	X		X			X		X	X	U		S	X	U		X	S	X	X	X										
X		X		X		U	X				X		X		X	X	U		S	X	S		S	U	X	X	X	X									
X		X		X		S	X				X		X		X	X	U		S	X	S		U	S	X	X	X										
X		X		X		X	X	X					X		X	X	U		X	U	S	X	X					U	S	X	U						
X		X		X		X	X	X				U		X		X	X	U		S	X	S	U									X	X				
X		X		X		X	X	X					X		X	X	U		S	X	X		X					U	U	S	X	X	X				
X		S		X		U	X						X		X	X	U		X	X		X						U	S	X	X	X					
X		U		X		U	X	X					X		X	X	U		X	X		X							U		X	X	U				

| X | | X | X | | S | X | X | X | X | X | U | X | S | | U | X | X | | U | | | | | | | | | | | | | | | | | | |
| X | | X | | | X | X | X | S | X | X | | X | | X | U | S | X | | U | X | S | | | | | | | | | | | | | | | | |

Totals

36	7	17	29	7	14	37	18	23	42	32	1	21	0	0	19	0	32	9	1	2	12	2	21	10	3	5	11	9	0	0	4	6	8	7	10	7	0
0	1	3	5	0	0	1	0	10	0	3	8	3	8	0	11	0	3	1	1	0	5	9	1	0	2	0	3	0	4	0	0	1	3	2	1	0	0
0	2	1	4	0	8	1	0	6	0	0	11	9	4	10	4	6	0	1	2	30	0	2	0	0	0	1	0	4	3	0	6	3	0	0	1	1	

2	0	2	1	0	1	2	2	1	2	2	0	2	0	0	1	0	1	2	0	0	1	0	0	0	0	0	0	0	0	0	0	0	0	0	0	0	0
0	0	0	0	0	0	1	0	0	1	0	0	0	0	1	0	0	0	1	0	0	0	1	0	0	0	0	1	0	0	0	0	0	0	0	0	0	0
0	0	0	0	0	0	0	0	0	0	0	1	0	0	0	1	1	0	0	0	2	0	0	0	0	0	0	0	0	0	0	0	0	0	0	0	0	0

0	0	0	0	0	0	2	0	5	44	6	0	1	1	0	2	0	10	2	0	0	7	1	1	0	0	0	1	0	0	0	0	4	2	0	0		
0	0	0	0	0	0	0	0	0	0	0	0	0	0	0	0	0	1	0	0	0	0	0	0	0	0	0	0	0	0	0	0	0	0	0	0	0	0

PLAYING SQUAD 2012/13

Existing Players		SN	HT	WT	DOB	AGE	POB	Career	Apps	Goals
GOALKEEPERS										
Stuart	Coburn		6'01"	14 00	05/05/1975	37	Manchester	Maine Road, Irlam, Trafford 94/95, Altrincham 3/97, Leigh RMI 5/02, Altrincham 10/03	36	0
Adam	Reid				29/06/1994	18		Altrincham, Buxton (Dual) 10/11	2	0
Defenders										
Matt	Doughty		5'11"	11 00	02/11/1981	30	Warrington	Chester, Rochdale 7/01 Rel 5/04, Halifax 5/04, Altrincham 6/08, Curzon Ashton (L) 10/10, Nantwich (2ML) 10/10, Witton (Dual) 12/10, Hyde FC 3/11 Rel c/s 11, Warrington 8/11, Altrincham 7/12		
Sam	Grimshaw				24/10/1993	18		Altrincham, Radcliffe B (Dual) 3/12	0	0
Danny	Hall		6'02"	12 07	14/11/1983	28	Ashton-under-Lyne	Oldham Rel c/s 06, Scarborough (L) 2/03, Shrewsbury 5/06, Gretna 1/08 Rel 5/08, Chesterfield 7/08 Rel c/s 10, Darlington (L) 11/09, Crawley 5/10 Rel 5/11, Forest Green (3ML) 1/11, Ashton U (Trial) 7/11, Stockport 8/11 Rel 8/11, Hyde FC 9/11, Altrincham 5/12		
Gianluca	Havern		6'01"	13 00	24/09/1988	23	Gorton	Stockport Rel 1/09, Radcliffe B (L) 2/07, Ashton U (L) 11/07, Mansfield 2/09 Rel 5/09, Stockport 8/09 Rel 8/10, Mossley 9/10, Ashton U 10/10, Hyde FC 6/11, Altrincham 7/12		
Scott	Leather		6'01"	10 12	30/09/1992	19	Manchester	Crewe (Yth), Preston Rel c/s 12, Barrow (Trial) 7/12, Altrincham 7/12		
MIDFIELDERS										
Nicky	Clee				30/08/1983	29	Huddersfield	Local, Ossett A 12/02, Ashton U 8/04, Hyde U 6/05, Altrincham 7/09	35	6
Shaun	Densmore		6'03"	14 09	11/11/1988	23	Liverpool	Everton Rel c/s 08, Bradford C (Trial) 7/08, Altrincham 9/08	38	2
Patrick	Lacey				16/03/1993	19	Liverpool	Sheff Wed (Scholar) Rel c/s 11, Bradford C 7/11 Rel 1/12, Vauxhall Motors (L) 9/11, Vauxhall Motors (L) 12/11, Droylsden 3/12, Altrincham 7/12		
Scott	Phelan		5'07"	10 07	13/03/1988	24	Liverpool	Everton Rel c/s 07, Bradford C Rel c/s 08, FC Halifax 9/08, Kidderminster 5/11 Rel 2/12, Vauxhall Motors (2ML) 12/11, Vauxhall Motors 2/12, Altrincham 3/12	11	2
Simon	Richman		5'11"	11 12	02/06/1990	22	Ormskirk	Bolton (Yth), Port Vale Rel c/s 10, Southport (Trial) 7/10, Worcester 8/10, Altrincham 5/11	30	2
Carl	Rodgers				26/03/1983	29	Chester	Chester (Yth), Caernarfon c/s 02, TNS 3/04, Colwyn Bay 5/04, AFC Telford 5/06 Rel c/s 12, Altrincham 5/12		
FORWARDS										
Ryan	Brooke		6'01"	11 07	04/10/1990	21	Congleton	Oldham Rel c/s 12, Barrow (L) 9/11, AFC Telford (SL) 1/12, Altrincham 5/12		
James	Lawrie		6'00"	12 05	18/12/1990	21	Belfast	Port Vale Rel c/s 10, Kidderminster (SL) 2/10, Exeter (Trial) 7/10, Stevenage (Trial) 7/10, Morecambe (Trial) 7/10, AFC Telford 8/10 Rel 12/11, Altrincham (3ML) 8/11, Altrincham 12/11	35	10
Danny	Mitchley		5'10"	10 08	07/10/1989	22	Liverpool	Blackpool, Southport (SL) 3/09, Burscough (L) 8/09, Wrexham (SL) 3/10, Burscough 10/10, Mansfield NC 11/10 Rel c/s 12, Nuneaton T (3ML) 9/11, Nuneaton T (SL) 1/12, Altrincham 6/12		
Damien	Reeves		5'09"	11 10	18/12/1985	26	Doncaster	Leeds Rel c/s 05, Scarborough (Trial) c/s 05, Barnsley (Trial) 9/05, Wakefield & Emley 10/05, Farsley Celtic 1/06, Histon 6/08, Northwich 1/09, Farsley Celtic 3/09, Alfreton 7/09, Guiseley (L) 9/09, AFC Telford 11/09, Bradford PA 3/10, Altrincham 6/10, Gillingham (Trial) 7/12	42	44
Neil	Tolson		6'02"	12 04	25/10/1973	38	Wordsley	Walsall, Oldham £150,000 3/92, Bradford C £50,000 12/93, Chester (L) 1/95, York £60,000 7/96 Rel c/s 99, Southend 7/99 Rel c/s 01, Retired, Leigh RMI 10/02, Kettering 1/03 Rel 1/03, Halifax 3/03, Hyde 7/03 Pl/Ass Man c/s 07 Rel 4/11, Radcliffe B (L) 2/06, Altrincham (Ass Man) 6/11	0	0
Duncan	Watmore				08/03/1994	18		Altrincham, Clitheroe (Dual) 1/12, Curzon Ashton (L) 3/12	11	1

BISHOP'S STORTFORD

Chairman: Luigu Del Basso
Secretary: Ian Kettridge   **(T)** 07904 169 017   **(E)** ianket@aol.com
Additional Committee Members:
Franco Del Basso, John Turner.

Manager: Rod Stringer
Programme Editor: John Allington   **(E)** j.allington@bsfc.co.uk

Club Factfile

Founded: 1874   **Nickname:** Blues or Bishops
Previous Names:
Previous Leagues: East Herts 1896-97, 1902-06, 19-21, Stansted & District 1906-19, Herts County 1921-25, 27-29, Herts & Essex Border 1925-27, Spartan 1929-51, Delphian 1951-63, Athenian 1963-73, Isthmian 1974-2004

Club Colours (change): All blue (White/black/black)

Ground: Woodside Park, Dunmow Road, Bishop's Stortford, Herts CM23 5RG   **(T)** 01279 306 456
Capacity: 4,000   **Seats:** 298   **Covered:** 700   **Clubhouse:** Yes   **Shop:** Yes

Directions: Woodside Park is situated 1/4 mile from Junction 8 of M11.
Follow A1250 towards Bishop's Stortford Town Centre, entrance to the ground is signposted through Woodside Park Industrial Estate.

Previous Grounds:

Record Attendance: 6,000 v Peterborough Town - FA Cup 2nd Round 1972-73 and v Middlesbrough - FA Cup 3rd Round replay 1982-83
Record Victory: 11-0 v Nettleswell & Buntwill - Herts Junior Cup 1911
Record Defeat: 0-13 v Cheshunt (H) - Herts Senior Cup 1926
Record Goalscorer: Post 1929 Jimmy Badcock - 123
Record Appearances: Phil Hopkins - 543
Additional Records:

Senior Honours:
Athenian League 1969-70. FA Amateur Cup 1973-74. Isthmian League Division 1 1980-81. FA Trophy 1980-81. London Senior Cup 1973-74. Premier Inter League Cup 1989-90. Herts Senior Cup x9.

10 YEAR RECORD

02-03	03-04	04-05	05-06	06-07	07-08	08-09	09-10	10-11	11-12
Isth P 13	Isth P 11	Conf S 10	Conf S 15	Conf S 5	Conf S 10	Conf S 9	Conf S 18	Conf S 16	Conf N 10

BISHOP STORTFORD

No.	Date	Comp	H/A	Opponents	Att:	Result	Goalscorers	Pos
1	Sat-13-Aug	BSN	H	Colwyn Bay	363	L 0-2		20
2	Wed-17-Aug	BSN	A	Corby Town	827	L 1-6	Bakare 40	22
3	Sat-20-Aug	BSN	A	Blyth Spartans	469	L 1-3	Bakare 14	22
4	Tue-23-Aug	BSN	H	Solihull Moors	251	W 1-0	Gayle 12	19
5	Sat-27-Aug	BSN	A	Nuneaton Town	645	L 0-2		21
6	Mon-29-Aug	BSN	H	Hinckley United	303	W 5-0	Gayle 3 (6, 20, 90), Essam 29, Bakare 30	17
7	Sat-03-Sep	BSN	H	Boston United	661	L 0-1		18
8	Sat-10-Sep	BSN	A	Gainsborough Trinity	465	L 2-4	Bakare 2 (65, 80)	20
9	Sat-17-Sep	BSN	H	Stalybridge Celtic	358	L 0-3		21
10	Tue-20-Sep	BSN	A	Eastwood Town	176	W 4-3	Bakare 1, Craig 43, Gayle 2 (85, 88)	19
11	Sat-24-Sep	BSN	A	Worcester City	696	L 1-2	Bakare 89	18
12	Sat-08-Oct	BSN	H	Gloucester City	401	W 3-2	Whiteley 11, Gayle 42, Bakare 47	17
13	Sat-22-Oct	BSN	A	Vauxhall Motors	149	L 3-4	Subuola 54, Shulton 74, Gayle pen 80	18
14	Tue-25-Oct	BSN	H	Corby Town	313	L 0-2		19
15	Sat-05-Nov	BSN	H	Gainsborough Trinity	351	D 1-1	Francis 25	20
16	Sat-12-Nov	BSN	A	Solihull Moors	260	L 1-3	Gayle pen 77	20
17	Tue-15-Nov	BSN	A	Harrogate Town	216	D 1-1	Gayle 63	20
18	Sat-19-Nov	BSN	H	Worcester City	333	D 1-1	Gayle 79	20
19	Sat-03-Dec	BSN	H	Blyth Spartans	297	D 3-3	Prestedge 2 (44, 90), Adedipe 54	20
20	Sat-17-Dec	BSN	A	Gloucester City	225	W 2-0	Gayle 35, Dadson 50	19
21	Mon-26-Dec	BSN	H	Histon	629	L 0-2		19
22	Sun-01-Jan	BSN	A	Histon	649	W 3-2	Francis 10, Prestedge 2 (22, 60)	19
23	Sat-07-Jan	BSN	H	Guiseley	392	W 4-1	Prestedge 10, Wickham 19, Gayle 84, Dadson 90	19
24	Tue-10-Jan	BSN	A	Boston United	811	W 2-0	Prestedge 47, Gayle pen 90	15
25	Sat-14-Jan	BSN	H	Harrogate Town	433	L 3-4	Prestedge 27, Gayle 2 (pen 45, 69)	17
26	Sat-21-Jan	BSN	H	Workington	466	D 1-1	Gayle pen 90	16
27	Sat-18-Feb	BSN	A	Droylsden	271	D 2-2	Gayle 2 (48, 85)	18
28	Sat-25-Feb	BSN	H	Altrincham	485	W 1-0	Pavett 70	18
29	Sat-03-Mar	BSN	H	Droylsden	401	W 5-0	Sappleton 19, Odubajo 3 (30, 52, 54), Gayle 42	16
30	Tue-06-Mar	BSN	A	Colwyn Bay	141	L 1-4	Gayle 40	18
31	Sat-10-Mar	BSN	A	Altrincham	844	W 2-0	Gayle 32, Sappleton 51	15
32	Tue-13-Mar	BSN	A	FC Halifax Town	1008	W 1-0	Francis 66	13
33	Sat-17-Mar	BSN	A	Workington	377	D 1-1	Sappleton 3	13
34	Sat-24-Mar	BSN	H	FC Halifax Town	667	L 1-3	Gayle 44	15
35	Tue-27-Mar	BSN	H	Hyde FC	314	L 0-1		15
36	Sat-31-Mar	BSN	A	Hyde FC	499	L 0-5		16
37	Tue-03-Apr	BSN	A	Stalybridge Celtic	352	W 3-2	Gayle 3 (4, 11, 76)	15
38	Sat-07-Apr	BSN	H	Nuneaton Town	538	L 0-3		16
39	Mon-09-Apr	BSN	A	Hinckley United	427	W 3-1	Johnson 8, Francis 54, Melaugh 78	13
40	Sat-14-Apr	BSN	H	Vauxhall Motors	378	W 2-0	Prestedge 38, Sappleton 51	12
41	Sat-21-Apr	BSN	A	Guiseley	926	W 1-0	Johnson 45	10
42	Sat-28-Apr	BSN	H	Eastwood Town	502	W 4-0	Dunbar 10, Gayle 3 (59, 73, pen 77)	10

CUPS

No.	Date	Comp	H/A	Opponents	Att:	Result	Goalscorers	
1	Sat-01-Oct	FAC 2Q	A	Canvey Island	316	W 1-0	Bakare 55	
2	Sat-15-Oct	FAC 3Q	A	Burnham	182	W 5-2	Shulton 5, Jones 10, Gayle pen 35, Bakare 2 (65, 75)	
3	Sat-29-Oct	FAC 4Q	A	Salisbury City	501	L 1-2	Shulton 90	
4	Sat-26-Nov	FAT 3Q	H	Tonbridge Angels	297	D 1-1	Subuola 65	
5	Tue-29-Nov	FAT 3QR	A	Tonbridge Angels	274	W 2-1	Subuola 28, Gayle 73	
6	Sat-10-Dec	FAT 1	A	Carshalton Athletic	243	L 0-5		

League
Starts
Substitute
Unused Sub

Cups
Starts
Substitute
Unused Sub

Goals (Lg)
Goals (Cup)

Player appearance grid (X = start, S = substitute, U = unused substitute). Column headers left to right:

EYRE, LETTEJ/ALLOW, ANDERSON, HABU, ESSAM, ABDULLAHI, COLE, RANCE, GAYLE, SHULTON, BAKARE, DADSON, READ, HAHN, PRESTEDGE, JEFFRIES, WRIGHT, JONES, GAISIE, CRAIG, QUAINOO, SUBUOLA, FRANCIS, DUNBAR, WHITELEY, ARCHER, GODWIN-GREEN, GILL, ADEDIPE, JAMES-LEWIS, WICKHAM, ARTEMI, SAPPLETON, MILTON, HAINES, JOHNSON, STEWART, ODUBAJO, LAMPE, PAVETT, SEYMOUR-SHOVE, MELAUGH, HAXHIA, HUNT, DAVISON

Totals rows (appearances, substitute appearances, unused substitute):

EYRE	LETTEJ/ALLOW	ANDERSON	HABU	ESSAM	ABDULLAHI	COLE	RANCE	GAYLE	SHULTON	BAKARE	DADSON	READ	HAHN	PRESTEDGE	JEFFRIES	WRIGHT	JONES	GAISIE	CRAIG	QUAINOO	SUBUOLA	FRANCIS	DUNBAR	WHITELEY	ARCHER	GODWIN-GREEN	GILL	ADEDIPE	JAMES-LEWIS	WICKHAM	ARTEMI	SAPPLETON	MILTON	HAINES	JOHNSON	STEWART	ODUBAJO	LAMPE	PAVETT	SEYMOUR-SHOVE	MELAUGH	HAXHIA	HUNT	DAVISON
7	6	36	9	7	25	9	3	41	28	12	13	0	2	38	8	4	24	1	17	0	8	30	24	5	25	2	2	1	3	2	0	12	9	2	17	1	2	12	0	0	10	2	3	0
0	5	0	0	0	2	6	5	1	1	0	14	5	12	1	0	0	1	6	5	1	7	0	2	2	0	0	0	1	2	1	0	0	0	0	0	1	0	1	12	3	0	0	2	0
0	18	1	0	0	12	1	0	0	4	0	8	5	3	1	8	0	4	2	4	2	1	0	4	1	0	0	3	0	1	1	4	0	5	0	0	3	0	0	0	1	0	0	2	3

Additional goal/card totals:

EYRE	LETTEJ/ALLOW	ANDERSON	HABU	ESSAM	ABDULLAHI	COLE	RANCE	GAYLE	SHULTON	BAKARE	DADSON	READ	HAHN	PRESTEDGE	JEFFRIES	WRIGHT	JONES	GAISIE	CRAIG	QUAINOO	SUBUOLA	FRANCIS	DUNBAR	WHITELEY	ARCHER	GODWIN-GREEN	GILL	ADEDIPE	JAMES-LEWIS	WICKHAM	ARTEMI	SAPPLETON	MILTON	HAINES	JOHNSON	STEWART	ODUBAJO	LAMPE	PAVETT	SEYMOUR-SHOVE	MELAUGH	HAXHIA	HUNT	DAVISON
0	1	5	0	0	3	2	0	6	3	2	3	0	0	6	3	0	5	0	3	0	3	5	4	2	6	0	0	2	1	0	0	0	0	0	0	0	0	0	0	0	0	0	0	0
0	0	0	0	0	2	2	0	0	2	0	3	0	2	0	1	0	0	4	0	0	0	0	0	0	0	0	0	1	0	0	0	0	0	0	0	0	0	0	0	0	0	0	0	0
0	3	0	0	0	1	0	0	0	0	0	0	0	2	0	2	0	0	0	0	0	0	0	2	0	0	1	0	0	0	0	0	0	0	0	0	0	0	0	0	0	0	0	0	0
0	0	0	0	1	0	0	0	29	1	8	2	0	0	8	0	0	0	0	1	0	1	4	1	1	0	0	0	1	0	1	0	4	0	0	2	0	3	0	1	0	1	0	0	0
0	0	0	0	0	0	0	0	2	2	3	0	0	0	0	0	0	1	0	0	0	2	0	0	0	0	0	0	0	0	0	0	0	0	0	0	0	0	0	0	0	0	0	2	3

ALSO PLAYED: CALVER S (2). DAWSON U (8) U (C2). IVES U (20, 21) S (C6). REDGRAVE U (39, 40, 42) S (41).

PLAYING SQUAD 2012/13

Existing Players		SN	HT	WT	DOB	AGE	POB	Career	Apps	Goals
GOALKEEPERS										
Ross	Kitteridge		6'02"	13 11	28/12/1989	22	Reading	Arsenal (Yth), Reading (Scholar) 7/06 Rel c/s 09, Basingstoke (Trial) c/s 07, Stevenage (Trial) c/s 07, Dover (Trial) 7/07, Eastleigh (L) 11/07, Basingstoke (SL) 7/08, Basingstoke 7/09 Rel 5/10, Aldershot T 8/10, Bishops Stortford 10/10, Dover 6/11 Rel 12/11, Hemel Hempstead 12/11, Thurrock 3/12, Bishops Stortford (Trial) 7/12		
DEFENDERS										
Phil	Anderson				01/03/1987	25		Southend, Aldershot 7/06 Rel 5/07, Thurrock c/s 07, Billericay 1/11, Bishops Stortford 3/11	36	0
Lynvall	Duncan				22/07/1982	30		Clapton, Ashford T (Kent), Leatherhead 12/05, Billericay 9/08, Braintree 5/09, Bishops Stortford 2/10, Thurrock 2/11, Kingstonian 8/11 Rel 11/11, Leatherhead 11/11, Thurrock 12/11, Aveley (Dual) 12/11 Perm, Bishops Stortford 7/12		
Sean	Francis				14/06/1984	28		Aveley, Braintree, Aveley (SL) 8/10, Billericay (L) 8/11, Bishops Stortford 9/11	30	4
John	Herd		5'09"	12 00	03/10/1989	22	Huntingdon	Southend Rel c/s 11, Ebbsfleet 8/11 Rel c/s 12, Bishops Stortford 7/12		
Ritchie	Jones				06/03/1990	22		Northampton Rel 11/08, Cheshunt 12/08, Gillingham (Trial) 3/09, Dag & Red (Trial), Bishops Stortford 3/09	25	0
Jack	Lampe				24/02/1992	20		Harlow, West Ham 7/09, Glen Hoddle Academy, Jerez Industrial (Spa), Bishops Stortford 2/12	13	0
Harry	Milton				15/09/1993	18	Romford	MK Dons Rel 1/12, Aveley (3ML) 9/11, Bishops Stortford 1/12	9	0
David	Obaze		6'04"		24/10/1989	22		Southend Rel c/s 08, Harlow (WE) 2/08, Bromley 8/08, Rel 5/09, Histon (Trial) 7/09, Weymouth 8/09, Grays 12/09, Leyton 1/10, Sutton U 1/10, Carshalton 9/10, Bishops Stortford 7/12		
Matt	Redgrave							Colchester (Scholar), Bishops Stortford (L) 3/12, Bishops Stortford 6/12	1	0
MIDFIELDERS										
Ali	Abdullahi				19/05/1991	21		Dulwich H, Bishops Stortford 11/09	27	0
Steve	Cawley							Hoddesdon T, Waltham Abbey 7/10, Bishops Stortford 6/12		
Nathan	Gordon							Tilbury, Ilford 3/11, Redbridge, Grays 2/12, Bishops Stortford 6/12		
Matt	Johnson				15/04/1990	22		Aveley, Rushden & D 6/10, Dover 6/11 Rel 9/11, Braintree 9/11, Bishops Stortford 1/12	17	2
Baimass	Lettejallow		5'09"	10 12	16/04/1984	28	London	Barnet, Braintree 10/03, Harlow 1/04, Dag & Red 1/05, Aveley (L) 2/07, Thurrock (SL) 9/07, Thurrock (3ML) 8/08, Bishops Stortford (SL) 1/09, Bishops Stortford c/s 09, Thurrock 9/10, Hampton & R 11/10, Bishops Stortford 3/11	11	0
Matt	Pooley				09/10/1991	20		Dag & Red Rel c/s 11, Braintree 8/11, Maldon & Tiptree (Dual) 12/11, Walton Casuals (Dual) 2/12, Bishops Stortford 7/12		
Reece	Prestedge				25/12/1985	26		Bishops Stortford, Dag & Red, Brimsdown, Cheshunt 6/08, Bishops Stortford 2/09, Thurrock 10/09, AFC Hornchurch 10/09, Billericay 12/09, Bishops Stortford 3/10	39	8
Lewwis	Spence		5'11"	13 03	29/10/1987	24	Lambeth	C.Palace Rel c/s 08, C.Palace Baltimore (L) 4/07, Wycombe 6/08 Rel c/s 10, Forest Green (L) 9/09, Rushden & D 7/10, Dover (2ML) 1/11, Dover 3/11 Rel 5/11, Bishops Stortford 6/12		
FORWARDS										
Scott	Ginty		5'08"	11 11	17/05/1991	21		Peterborough (Scholar) Rel c/s 09, Stamford (WE) 3/09, Ebbsfleet 8/09 Rel 11/11, Deeping R, Bishops Stortford 6/12		
Jordan	Pavett				16/12/1991	20	Maldon	Colchester, Chelmsford (WE) 2/10, Bishops Stortford (L) 3/10, Histon 8/10 Rel 10/10, Redbridge, Swindon 1/11 Rel 1/12, Heybridge (L) 12/11, Bishops Stortford 2/12	12	1
Ricky	Sappleton		5'10"	11 13	08/12/1989	22	Kingston, Jam	QPR (Scholar) Rel c/s 07, Leicester 10/07, Bournemouth (L) 8/08, Oxford U (L) 1/09, AFC Telford (SL) 3/09, Macclesfield (5ML) 8/09 Perm 1/10 Rel c/s 11, Bishops Stortford 1/12	12	4

BOSTON UNITED

Chairman: David Newton
Secretary: John Blackwell   **(T)** 07860 663 299   **(E)** admin@bufc.co.uk
Additional Committee Members:
Neil Kempster, Chris Cook, Craig Singleton.

Manager: Jason Lee
Programme Editor: Craig Singleton   **(E)** craig.singleton@bufc.co.uk

BACK ROW (left-to-right): Gary Silk, Mark Jones, Nathan Stainfield, Tom Ward, Travis Munn, Matt Wilson, Kern Miller.
MIDDLE ROW: Jason Hatfield (kit man), Spencer Weir-Daley, Joe French, Dan Haystead, Gareth Jelleyman, Ricky Drury,
Marc Newsham, Jason Field, Katie Cooper (sports therapist).
FRONT ROW: Conor Marshall, Ben Fairclough, James Reed, Graham Hyde (assistant manager), Jason Lee (manager),
Ian Freeman (fitness coach), Jason Stokes, Ben Milnes, Kallum Smith.

Club Factfile

Founded: 1933   **Nickname:** The Pilgrims
Previous Names: Reformed as Boston United when Boston Town folded in 1933
Previous Leagues: Midland 1933-58, 62-64, Southern 1958-62, 98-2000, United Counties 1965-66, West Midlands 1966-68, Northern Premier
1968-79, 93-98, 2008-10, Alliance/Conference 1979-93, 2000-02, 07-08, Football League 2002-07

Club Colours (change): Amber and black stripes/black/black (White & red/red/red and white hoops)

Ground: Jakemans Stadium, York Street, Boston PE21 6JN   **(T)** 01205 364 406
Capacity: 6,645   **Seats:** 1,323   **Covered:** 6,645   **Clubhouse:** Yes   **Shop:** Yes
Directions: A1 to A17 Sleaford to Boston-Over Boston Railway Station crossing, bear right at the Eagle Public House-To light over Haven
Bridge-straight along John Adams Way(Dual Carriageway) -Turn right at traffic lights into main ridge, then right again into York Street
(This is opposite Eagle Fisheries)-Ground is signposted after Railway crossing.

Previous Grounds:

Record Attendance: 10,086 v Corby Town - Floodlights inauguration 1955
Record Victory: 12-0 v Spilsby Town - Grace Swan Cup 1992-93
Record Defeat: Not known.
Record Goalscorer: Chris Cook - 181
Record Appearances: Billy Howells - 500+
Additional Records: Paid £30,000 to Scarborough for Paul Ellender, 08/2001
Received £50,000 from Bolton Wanderers for David Norris 2000
Senior Honours:
Central Alliance League 1961-62. United Counties League 1965-66. West Midlands League 1966-67, 67-68.
Northern Premier League 1972-73, 73-74, 76-77, 77-78. League Cup 1973-74, 75-76. Southern League 1999-2000. Conference 2001-02.

10 YEAR RECORD

02-03		03-04		04-05		05-06		06-07		07-08		08-09		09-10		10-11		11-12	
FL 3	15	FL 3	11	FL 2	16	FL 2	11	FL 2	23	Conf N	10	NP P	16	NP P	3	Conf N	3	Conf N	11

BOSTON UNITED

No.	Date	Comp	H/A	Opponents	Att:	Result	Goalscorers	Pos
1	Sat-13-Aug	BSN	A	Workington	585	W 2-1	Holsgrove 2 (pen 42, 90)	7
2	Tue-16-Aug	BSN	H	Histon	1222	D 1-1	Newsham 26	6
3	Sat-20-Aug	BSN	H	Vauxhall Motors	1114	L 1-2	Og (Hannigan) 89	12
4	Tue-23-Aug	BSN	A	Nuneaton Town	765	L 0-2		15
5	Sat-27-Aug	BSN	A	Harrogate Town	522	W 2-0	Newsham 10, Lee 88	11
6	Mon-29-Aug	BSN	H	FC Halifax Town	1596	L 0-1		11
7	Sat-03-Sep	BSN	A	Bishops Stortford	661	W 1-0	Newsham 90	9
8	Sat-10-Sep	BSN	H	Solihull Moors	1175	L 0-1		12
9	Sat-17-Sep	BSN	A	Blyth Spartans	456	L 0-1		11
10	Tue-20-Sep	BSN	H	Hinckley United	813	W 2-0	Stainfield 51, Sleath 60	10
11	Sat-24-Sep	BSN	H	Droylsden	1127	W 2-1	Ward 48, Burrow 79	8
12	Sat-08-Oct	BSN	A	Altrincham	804	L 1-6	Lee 65	12
13	Sat-15-Oct	BSN	A	Histon	417	W 3-1	Newsham pen 16, Sleath 62, Lee 67	7
14	Sat-22-Oct	BSN	H	Workington	1114	W 2-1	Lee 43, Burrow 85	6
15	Sat-29-Oct	BSN	H	Colwyn Bay	1076	D 2-2	Lee 10, Milnes 90	6
16	Sat-05-Nov	BSN	A	Solihull Moors	301	L 0-1		9
17	Sat-12-Nov	BSN	H	Hyde FC	1160	L 0-2		11
18	Sat-19-Nov	BSN	A	Gainsborough Trinity	793	W 3-1	Newsham 2 (18, 76), Milnes 40	10
19	Sat-03-Dec	BSN	A	Stalybridge Celtic	506	L 0-3		12
20	Tue-13-Dec	BSN	H	Corby Town	736	D 1-1	Kirk 87	11
21	Sat-17-Dec	BSN	A	Guiseley	508	L 1-2	Newsham 7	11
22	Mon-26-Dec	BSN	H	Eastwood Town	1247	W 4-2	Sleath 19, Ward 38, Newsham 58, Lee 60	10
23	Sun-01-Jan	BSN	A	Eastwood Town	596	D 2-2	Ross 18, Newsham 70	10
24	Sat-07-Jan	BSN	H	Blyth Spartans	986	D 1-1	Semple 80	10
25	Tue-10-Jan	BSN	H	Bishops Stortford	811	L 0-2		11
26	Sat-21-Jan	BSN	H	Nuneaton Town	1070	D 0-0		12
27	Sat-28-Jan	BSN	A	Corby Town	552	W 2-1	Ross 53, B Fairclough 90	11
28	Tue-07-Feb	BSN	A	Colwyn Bay	244	L 2-3	Sleath 31, Newsham 54	11
29	Tue-21-Feb	BSN	A	Vauxhall Motors	173	W 4-0	Weir-Daley 5, Ward 23, Newsham 2 (27, 41)	10
30	Sat-25-Feb	BSN	H	Gloucester City	1077	W 2-0	B Fairclough 32, Ward 65	10
31	Sat-03-Mar	BSN	A	Worcester City	756	L 0-3		10
32	Sat-10-Mar	BSN	H	Stalybridge Celtic	1000	W 3-2	Newsham 2 (23, pen 76), Weir-Daley 72	10
33	Mon-12-Mar	BSN	A	Hinckley United	441	W 2-1	Weir-Daley 2 (26, 70)	9
34	Sat-17-Mar	BSN	A	Altrincham	1204	D 1-1	B Fairclough 35	9
35	Sat-24-Mar	BSN	A	Droylsden	315	L 1-2	Ross 62	9
36	Tue-27-Mar	BSN	H	Worcester City	841	L 2-3	Newsham 2 (pen 33, pen 46)	9
37	Sat-31-Mar	BSN	A	Gloucester City	315	W 3-1	Newsham 2 (42, pen 43), Milnes 61	9
38	Sat-07-Apr	BSN	H	Harrogate Town	1049	L 0-2		9
39	Mon-09-Apr	BSN	A	FC Halifax Town	1584	L 2-3	Newsham 45, Burge 72	10
40	Sat-14-Apr	BSN	H	Gainsborough Trinity	1164	L 1-2	Stainfield 60	10
41	Sat-21-Apr	BSN	A	Hyde FC	1036	L 1-4	Ross 30	11
42	Sat-28-Apr	BSN	H	Guiseley	1087	D 3-3	Weir-Daley 15, Newsham 42, Reed 71	11

CUPS

No.	Date	Comp	H/A	Opponents	Att:	Result	Goalscorers	
1	Sat-01-Oct	FAC 2Q	H	Kidsgrove Athletic	817	D 0-0		
2	Tue-04-Oct	FAC 2QR	A	Kidsgrove Athletic	280	L 0-2		
3	Sat-26-Nov	FAT 3Q	H	Workington	743	W 1-0	Newsham 58	
4	Sat-10-Dec	FAT 1	H	Hyde FC	710	W 2-1	Austin 60, B Fairclough 77	
5	Sat-14-Jan	FAT 2	A	Dartford	1166	L 2-4	Weir-Daley 21, Constantine 82	

League
Starts
Substitute
Unused Sub

Cups
Starts
Substitute
Unused Sub

Goals (Lg)
Goals (Cup)

	BASTOCK	CANOVILLE	JELLEYMAN	HALL	PARKER	AUSTIN	MILNES	WILKINSON	SUAREZ	HOLSGROVE	NEWSHAM	JOACHIM	WARD	J FAIRCLOUGH	DEANE	MILLSON	DUDFIELD	SEMPLE	STONES	OGDEN	LEE	WHITE	SLEATH	FIELD	HEWITT	STAINFIELD	B FAIRCLOUGH	BURROW	ARMSTRONG	MULREADY	DRURY	KIRK	ROSS	EDWARDS	JOYCE	CONSTANTINE	WEIR-DALEY	MARSHALL	REED	SMITH	BURGE
	X	X	X	X	X	X	X			X	X	X	S	S	U	U	U																								
	X	X	X	X	X	X				X	X		U	S	U	X	X	S	U	U																					
	X		X	X	X	X				X	X		U	X	U	X		S	X	U	S																				
	X		X	X	X	U		S					X	U	U			X			X		S	X	X																
	X		X	X	X	U		U	S	X	X		X	S	U			X			X	X																			
	X		X	X		U	S	S	S	X	X		X	X				X	X			X	X	U																	
	X		X	X		U	S	U	X	S	X		X	X				X	X			X	X	U																	
	X			X		X	X	X	X	S	X		X				U		X			S	X	X	X	U	U														
	X			X		X	X	X	S		X		X				U		X			X	X	X	X	U		S	S												
	X			X			X	X	U		X		X	U			U		X			X	X	X				S	S												
	X			X		X	U	X			S			X					S			S		S				X	X	X	X	X	U								
	X	X	X			U	S	U			X			X								X	X	X				X	S	S	S	X									
	X	X	X	U		S	U	X			X			X								X	X	X				X	S	S	X	X									
	X	X	X	X			X	X	U		S			X								X		X				U	X	S	X		U								
	X	X	X	X			X	X			S	S		X								X	X	X					S	X		U	U								
	X		X	X			X	X			X			X								X	X	X					U	S			S								
	X		X	X			X	X			X			U	S							X	X	X					S	S		U	S								
	X		X	S			X	X			X			U	X							X	X	X					S			U		X	S						
	X	U		U			X	X			X			X	X							X	X	X					X			S	X	U							
	X	X		U			X	X			X			X	X							X		X	S		S		X	X	U	U									
	X	X		S			X	X			X			X	X					S		X		U			U		X	X					S						
	X	X		S			X	X			X			X	X					S		X		U			U		X	X					U						
	X	X		X			X				X			X	X					S		X	X	S		U			S	X	U		X								
	X		X	S			X				X			X	X					X		X	U			X	U	U	S				S		X						
	X	X	X	U		U	X			X			X									X			U	X			U			X		S	X	X					
	X	X	X	S		U	X			X			X									X			U	X			X	U			S	X	X						
	X	X	X	U			S	X			X			X								X			U	X				U	X		S	X	X						
	X		X	S							X			X							U		X			X	X					S	U	S	X						
	X		X	U		U	X			X			X								U		X			X	X					S	X		S	X					
	X	U	X	S		S	X			X			X								U		X			X	X					X	X		S		X				
	X	U	X	S		U	X			X			X										X			X	X					X	X				S	X	U		
	X	U	X	S		U	X			X			X							S			X			X	X					U	X				X	X			
	X	U	X	U			U	X			X			X						S		S		X			X	X						X				X	X			
	X	U	X				U	X			X			X						S				X			X	X						X				X	X	S	U	
	X	U	X				X	X			X			U						S				X			X	X						X				X	X		U	S
		S	X	U			X	X			X			U						S				X		X			X				S		X				X	X	S	U X
		X	X	U			X	X			X			S						X							X	S			X							X	X	X	U S
		S	X	U			X				X			X						S		S		X			X	X						X				X	U	U	X
	X	X	X				S	X			X			U						S		S		X			X	X						X				X	U	U	X
	X	X	X				U	X			X			U						S				X			X	S						X				X	X	U	X X
	X	X	X				U	X			X			U						U							X	S						X				X	X	X	X S
	X		X	X			S	X	X		X			X	U		U		X			S	X	X				U	U	S	X										
	X		X				X	X	X		X			S		S		X			X		X	U	X	U	X	X	S												
	X		X	S			X	X			X			U	X				X			X	X	X				U	S				X	X							
	X		X	U			X	X			X			S	X				X			X	X	X					S				S	X	U						
	X	X	X	S			X				X			X					X			X		X	U		U	X						X	U		S	X			
39	**39**	**18**	**35**	**17**	**6**	**21**	**33**	**6**	**3**	**6**	**37**	**0**	**24**	**13**	**1**	**2**	**19**	**4**	**0**	**14**	**13**	**31**	**0**	**0**	**18**	**16**	**3**	**3**	**3**	**5**	**23**	**0**	**0**	**2**	**15**	**16**	**2**	**2**	**4**	
	0	2	0	9	0	4	3	2	3	2	4	1	3	3	0	1	0	13	0	0	7	0	1	2	0	1	13	5	0	0	0	7	0	1	0	7	1	0	1	1	3
	0	7	0	10	0	14	2	4	1	0	0	0	10	3	6	4	0	1	2	2	3	0	0	7	2	5	3	0	0	2	6	2	0	4	1	1	0	1	3	3	1
	5	1	5	1	0	4	4	2	0	0	5	0	2	2	0	0	0	3	0	0	4	3	5	0	0	1	2	1	0	0	0	1	3	0	0	0	1	0	0	0	0
	0	0	0	2	0	1	0	0	0	0	0	0	0	1	1	0	1	0	1	0	0	1	0	0	0	0	0	0	2	2	0	0	0	1	0	0	0	1	0	0	0
	0	0	0	1	0	0	0	0	0	0	0	0	0	1	1	0	1	0	1	0	0	0	0	0	0	0	0	0	2	2	2	1	0	0	0	0	0	0	2	0	0
	0	0	0	0	0	0	3	0	0	2	20	0	4	0	0	0	0	1	0	0	6	0	4	0	0	2	3	2	0	0	1	4	0	0	0	5	0	1	0	1	
	0	0	0	0	0	1	0	0	0	0	1	0	0	0	0	0	0	0	0	0	0	0	1	0	0	0	0	0	0	0	0	0	0	0	0	1	1	0	0	0	

PLAYING SQUAD 2012/13

Existing Players		SN	HT	WT	DOB	AGE	POB	Career	Apps	Goals
GOALKEEPERS										
Ricky	Drury				30/10/1989	22		Boston U (Yth), Sleaford, Boston U 7/10, Quorn (L) 12/11, Holbeach (L) 3/12	3	0
Danny	Haystead		6'01"	11 09	13/02/1986	26	Chesterfield	Sheff Utd Rel c/s 05, Scarborough (L) 11/04, Hinckley U 8/05 Rel c/s 07, Moor Green (L) 8/05, Quorn (SL) (06/07), Quorn c/s 07, Sheffield FC 2/08, Ilkeston 6/08, Hucknall 6/09, Hinckley U 6/10, Boston U 12/10 Rel 5/11, Hinckley U 5/11, Boston U 5/12		
DEFENDERS										
Jason	Field				21/04/1993	19		Boston U, Spalding U (Dual) 10/11	2	0
Gareth	Jelleyman		5'10"	10 06	14/11/1980	31	Holywell	Norwich (Yth), Peterborough, Boston U (L) 12/98, Boston U (L) 8/04, Mansfield (L) 1/05 Perm 1/05, Rushden & D 7/08 Rel 5/09, Barrow (SL) 3/09, AFC Telford NC 7/09, Barrow 8/09 Rel 5/10, Boston U 7/10	35	0
Conor	Marshall							Grimsby (Scholar) Rel 8/11, Brigg T 8/11, Boston U 1/12	16	0
Kern	Miller		5'09"	11 03	02/09/1991	20	Skegness	Lincoln C Rel 12/10, Barnsley 1/11 Rel 1/12, Accrington (4ML) 7/11, Hereford 1/12 Rel 2/12, Gainsborough 3/12, Boston U 7/12		
Travis	Munn							Boston U		
Gary	Silk		5'09"	13 07	13/09/1984	26	Newport, IOW	Portsmouth Rel c/s 06, Barnet (L) 12/03, Wycombe (8ML) 7/04, Boston U (SL) 1/06, Notts County 7/06 Rel c/s 08, Mansfield 7/08, Grimsby 6/11 Rel c/s 12, Boston U 8/12		
Nathan	Stainfield							Swineshead Institute, Boston T c/s 11, Boston U 9/11, Hucknall (L) 11/11	19	2
Tom	Ward				30/08/1990	22		Sleaford T, Boston U c/s 10	27	4
MIDFIELDERS										
Joe	French							Boston U		
Ben	Milnes				12/09/1991	20		Leicester Rel c/s 11, Boston U 7/11	36	3
James	Reed							Boston U	3	1
Ian	Ross		5'10"	11 00	23/01/1986	26	Sheffield	Sheff Utd, Boston U (3ML) 8/05, Bury (SL) 3/06, Notts County (SL) 7/06, Rotherham (2ML) 11/07 Perm 1/08 Rel c/s 08, Gainsborough 8/08, Alfreton 3/09, Harrogate T 5/11, Boston U 11/11	23	4
Kallum	Smith							Lincoln U, Boston U 3/12	3	0
Jason	Stokes							Boston U		
Matt	Wilson		6'02"		10/03/1987	25		Darlington (Yth), Mackinlay Park, Sheffield Hallam Univ, Diddington T, Grantham 3/07, Alfreton 8/07, Worksop (3ML) 8/08, Guiseley (SL) 3/12, Boston U (3ML) 8/12		
FORWARDS										
Ben	Fairclough		5'06"	09 10	18/04/1989	22	Nottingham	Notts Forest (Scholar), Notts County 8/08 Rel c/s 10, Ilkeston (L) 8/09, Hinckley U 8/10, Eastwood T 6/11, Boston U 9/11	29	3
Mark	Jones							Bourne T, Blackstones 1/08, Peterborough Northern Star 6/10, Deeping R 2/11, Corby T 12/11, Boston U 5/12		
Jason	Lee		6'03"	13 08	09/05/1971	41	Forest Gate	Charlton, Fisher (L) 8/89, Stockport (L) 2/91, Lincoln C £35,000 3/91, Southend (L) 8/93 £150,000 9/93, N.Forest £200,000 3/94, Charlton (2ML) 2/97, Grimsby (L) 3/97, Watford £200,000 6/97, Chesterfield £250,000 8/98, Peterborough (2ML) 1/00 £50,000 3/00 Rel c/s 03, Scarborough (Trial) 7/03, Falkirk 8/03, Boston U 8/04, Northampton 1/06 Rel c/s 06, Notts County 6/06 Rel c/s 08, Mansfield 7/08, Kettering 1/09, Corby 3/09, Ilkeston 3/10, Boston U 9/10 Retired 11/10, Arnold T 3/11, Boston U (Jt Coach) 3/11 Pl/Man 5/11	21	6
Marc	Newsham		5'10"	09 11	24/03/1987	25	Hatfield, Yor	Rotherham Rel c/s 09, Gainsborough (L) 10/08, Sheffield FC (L) 12/08, Ilkeston (SL) 1/09, Boston U 6/09	41	20
Spencer	Weir-Daley		5'09"	10 11	05/09/1985	26	Leicester	Notts Forest Rel c/s 07, Macclesfield (2ML) 8/06, Lincoln C (3ML) 1/07, Bradford C (SL) 3/07 Notts County 7/07 Rel 1/09, Mansfield (Trial) 3/09, Ilkeston 9/09, Boston U 10/09 Rel c/s 11, AFC Telford 8/11, Buxton (Dual) 9/11, Boston U 1/12	16	5

BRACKLEY TOWN

Chairman: Sara Crannage
Secretary: Pat Ashby   **(T)** 07969 825 636   **(E)** pat.ashby55@btinternet.com
Additional Committee Members:
Phil Hedges, Francis Oliver, Tim Carroll.

Manager: Jon Brady
Programme Editor: Brian Martin   **(E)** brianmartin2905@aol.com

Back Row L/R: Gary Mulligan, Stephen Diggin, Elliot Sandy, Glenn Walker, Josh Green, Brett Solkhon, Billy Turley, Will Green, Marvin Robinson, Michael Corcoran, Eddie Odihambo, Curtis Davis.
Front Row. L/R: Tommy Jaszczun, James Clifton, Owen Story, Jon Brady (Manager), Darren Collins (Assistant Manager), Ellis Myles, Tom Winters, Wayne Hatswell.
Trophies: Southern League Premier Division Championship Shield, The Northamptonshire Hillier Senior Cup and Maunsell Cup.
Missing. Jamie Grimes, Chris Zyricki, Carl Palmer, Karl Ballard (Physio).
Photo: Brian Martin.

Club Factfile

Founded: 1890   **Nickname:** Saints
Previous Names: None
Previous Leagues: Banbury & District, North Buckinghamshire, Hellenic 1977-83, 94-97, 99-2004, United Counties 1983-84, Southern 1997-99

Club Colours (change): Red and white/red/white and red (All yellow)

Ground: St James Park, Churchill Way, Brackley NN13 7EJ   **(T)** 01280 704 077
Capacity: 3,500   **Seats:** 300   **Covered:** 1,500   **Clubhouse:** Yes   **Shop:** Yes

Directions: Take A43 from Northampton or Oxford, or A422 from Banbury to large roundabout south of town. Take exit marked Brackley and follow towards the town (Tesco store on left). Pass the Locomotive public house and take first turning right, signposted Football Club, into Churchill Way - road leads into Club car park.

Previous Grounds: Banbury Road, Manor Road, Buckingham Road > 1974

Record Attendance: 960 v Banbury United - 2005-06
Record Victory: Not known
Record Defeat: Not known
Record Goalscorer: Paul Warrington - 320
Record Appearances: Terry Muckelberg - 350
Additional Records: Received £2,000 from Oxford City for Phil Mason 1998

Senior Honours:
Hellenic League Premier Division 1996-97, 2003-04, Division 1 Cup 1982-83. Southern League Division 1 Midlands 2006-07.
Southern Premier Division 2011-12. Northamptonshire Senior Cup 2011-12.

10 YEAR RECORD

02-03		03-04		04-05		05-06		06-07		07-08		08-09		09-10		10-11		11-12	
Hel P	7	Hel P	1	SthW	7	SthW	3	SthM	1	SthP	8	SthP	11	SthP	5	SthP	9	SthP	1

BRACKLEY TOWN

No.	Date	Comp	H/A	Opponents	Att:	Result	Goalscorers	Pos
1	Aug 13	Sth P	A	Swindon Supermarine	205	W 2 - 0	Green 81 Sandy 90	
2	16		H	Chesham United	203	W 3 - 2	Sandy 11 Solkhon 43 (pen) Winters 57	
3	20		H	Bedford Town	205	W 7 - 1	Sandy 21 Louis 42 44 Chennells 56 Winters 72 81 Diggin 79	2
4	23		A	Arlesey Town	113	L 0 - 2		
5	27		A	Chippenham Town	251	W 1 - 0	Story 73	2
6	29		H	Evesham United	302	W 2 - 0	Louis 35 36	
7	Sept 3		A	Frome Town	253	D 1 - 1	Winters 20	
8	10		H	AFC Totton	285	L 0 - 3		4
9	13		A	Barwell	109	L 4 - 5	Story 8 Winters15 Louis 43 (pen) Sandy 50	
10	17	FAC 1Q	A	Thame United	217	L 0 - 2		
11	24		H	Cirencester Town	221	D 0 - 0		8
12	Oct 1		H	Redditch United	193	W 2 - 0	Story 38 Diggin 51	
13	8		A	Leamington	612	D 0 - 0		7
14	15		H	Hitchin Town	242	W 3 - 0	Winters 3 Sandy 20 Story 64	4
15	22	FAT 1Q	H	Mickleover Sports	167	W 1 - 0	Louis 90 (pen)	
16	29		A	Weymouth	542	W 1 - 0	Sandy 30	3
17	Nov 5	FAT 2Q	A	Hemel Hempstead	210	W 3 - 2	Diggin 46 Louis 49 May 85 (og)	
18	12		H	Bashley	208	W 3 - 2	Diggin 2 8 Kemp 67	2
19	15		A	Cambridge City	256	W 3 - 2	Louis 21 Winters 45 Kemp 75	2
20	19		A	St Albans City	377	D 1 - 1	Green 6	2
21	26	FAT 3Q	H	Chertsey Town	136	W 2 - 0	Sandy 67 J.Green 90	
22	Dec 3		A	Bedford Town	273	L 2 - 5	Winters 38 Diggin 80	3
23	6		H	Oxford City	217	W 5 - 2	Kemp 45 Story 46 Stanley 49 Louis 57 67	
24	10	FAT 1	H	Dartford	291	L 0 4		2
25	17		A	Chesham United	342	W 3 - 2	Louis 16 53 Winters 66	
26	26		H	Banbury United	603	D 1 - 1	Story 70	1
27	31		A	Hemel Hempstead	262	D 1 - 1	Louis 53	
28	Jan 2		A	Evesham United	121	W 2 - 0	Daniel 60 (og) Louis 90	1
29	7		H	Stourbridge	278	L 0 - 2		
30	10		H	Arlesey Town	146	W 2 - 1	Louis 33 77	
31	14		A	AFC Totton	654	D 2 - 2	Walker 40 Sandy 64	1
32	21		H	Frome Town	210	D 1 - 1	Sandy 47	1
33	28		A	Reddiitch United	221	W 3 - 2	Myles 41 Story 60 Diggin 68 (pen)	1
34	Feb 18		H	Leamington	407	W 3 - 0	Robinson 60 Diggin 72 (pen) 79	
35	21		H	Barwell	146	W 2 - 1	Diggin 7 Solkhon 22	1
36	25		A	Hitchin Town	344	L 1 - 2	Sandy 66 (pen)	1
37	March 3		H	Cambridge City	348	W 4 - 2	Diggin 37 (pen) 58 Marshall 38 Clifton 74	1
38	10		A	Bashley	259	D 1 - 1	Robinson 86	1
39	13		H	Weymouth	257	W 3 - 1	Sandy 18 Diggin 49 51 (pen)	
40	20		A	Cirencester Town	73	W 2 - 0	Walker 19 Robinson 83	1
41	24		H	Chippenham Town	272	W 5 - 1	Mulligan 7 Diggin 46 78 Walker 63 Robinson 69	
42	31		A	Stourbridge	623	L 0 - 1		1
43	Apr 7		H	Hemel Hempstead	275	W 3 - 0	Sandy 12 (pen) Mulligan 44 Robinson 61	
44	9		A	Banburu United	483	W 2 - 0	Sandy 40 Solkhon 48	1
45	14		H	Swindon Supermarine	290	W 4 - 0	Solkhon 3 Walker 15 Sandy 31 (pen) Robinson 53	
46	21		A	Oxford City	535	D 1 1	Story 13	Champions
47	28		H	St Albans City	535	W 6 0	Solkhon 21 SANDY 3 (30 43 54) Robinson 62 Diggin 81	

PLAYING SQUAD 2012/13

Existing Players		SN	HT	WT	DOB	AGE	POB	Career	Apps	Goals
GOALKEEPERS										
Billy	Turley		6'04"	15 07	15/07/1973	39	Wolverhampton	Evesham U, Northampton 7/95, Kettering (SL) 1/97, L.Orient (3ML) 2/98, Rushden & D £130,000 6/99 Rel 2/05, Oxford U 7/05, Brackley T 5/10		
DEFENDERS										
James	Clifton				28/11/1991	20		Aston Villa (Scholar), Brackley 8/10		
Josh	Green							Luton, Brackley 5/06, Woodford U 8/06, Brackley 5/07, Aveley, Romford 10/09, Brackley, Oxford C 6/11, Brackley T 9/11		
Jamie	Grimes		6'02"	13 00	22/12/1990	21	Nottingham	Swansea Rel c/s 11, Haverfordwest (SL) 7/09, Forest Green (2ML) 8/10, Redditch 7/11, Brackley 7/12		
Wayne	Hatswell		6'00"	13 10	08/02/1975	37	Swindon	Cinderford T, Witney T, Cinderford, Forest Green 7/99, Oxford U £35,000 12/00 Rel 4/02, Chester Free 5/02, Kidderminster £15,000 10/03, Rushden & D 1/06, Cambridge U Undisc 1/08, Dundalk (Pl/Coach) 1/10, Newport C (Pl/Coach) 1/11 (Temp Man) 9/11, Brackley T 8/12		
Tommy	Jaszczun		5'11"	11 02	16/09/1977	34	Kettering	Aston Villa, Blackpool £30,000 1/00 Rel c/s 04, Northampton 7/04, Rochdale 7/05, Cambridge U (SL) 1/06, Cambridge U 7/06 Retired 3/07, Kettering 5/07, Corby T 3/09 Rel 5/10, Kettering (Pl/Ass Man) 5/10 Rel 12/10, Corby T 1/11 Rel 2/11, Corby T 3/11 Rel 5/11, Brackley T 7/11		
Eddie	Odhiambo (Was Anaclet)		5'09"	10 00	31/08/1985	27	Arusha, Tanzania	Southampton Rel 5/06, Chester (L) 12/04, Tamworth (3ML) 11/05, Oxford U 7/06, Stevenage 5/08, Newport C 7/10 Rel c/s 11, Gateshead 6/11 Rel c/s 12, Brackley 8/12		
Ellis	Myles							Leicester (Scholar), Brackley c/s 11		
MIDFIELDERS										
Michael	Corcoran		5'10"	11 04	28/12/1987	23	Coalisland	Cardiff, Oxford U (3ML) 1/07, Oxford U 7/07 Rel 1/08, Rushden & D 1/08, Dover 6/11, Brackley 7/12		
Curtis	McDonald		5'10"	10 08	24/03/1988	23	Cardiff	Cardiff Rel c/s 07, Accrington (L) 11/06, Hereford (Trial) 7/07, Carmarthen 8/07, MKS Swit (Pol) 10/07, Forest Green (Reserves) 11/07, Forest Green 8/08, Newport C 1/11, Forest Green (SL) 3/11, Forest Green 5/11, Brackley (L) 3/12, Brackley 7/12		
Carl	Palmer				02/11/1978	33		Wednesfield, Sandwell B c/s 98, Wednesfield 12/98, Rushall O c/s 99, Bilston T (Dual) 10/99, Hednesfield 8/03, Redditch 5/05, Nuneaton 6/07, Stafford R 6/08, Rushall O 12/08, Hednesford c/s 09, Kings Lynn 9/09, Alfreton T (Dual), Halesowen T (Dual) 12/09 Perm, Brackley T 3/10		
Elliott	Sandy							Cogenhoe, Brackley, Corby (L) 12/09, Oxford C, Brackley 1/11		
Brett	Solkhon		5'11"	12 06	12/09/1982	29	Canvey Island	Ipswich (Yth), Arsenal (Yth), Rushden & D 7/00 Rel 1/03, Kettering 2/03 Rel 4/09, Corby 5/09, Brackley 3/10, Kettering 7/10, Brackley T 7/11		
FORWARDS										
Steve	Diggin				02/11/1987	24		Aston Villa (Yth), Wycombe (Yth), Cogenhoe, Kings Lynn 2/07, Cogenhoe 3/07, Corby 6/07 Rel 6/11, Brackley 6/11		
Will	Green				02/09/1992	19		Northampton (Scholar), Banbury U (WE) 3/11, Banbury U c/s 11, Brackley 12/11		
Gary	Mulligan		6'01"	12 03	23/04/1985	26	Dublin	Wolves, Rushden & D (3ML) 10/04, Sheff Utd 7/05 Rel c/s 06, Port Vale (3ML) 9/05, Gillingham (L) 1/06, Gillingham (SL) 3/06, Gillingham 7/06 Rel c/s 09, Northampton 7/09 Rel c/s 10, Cheltenham (Trial) 7/10, Gateshead 8/10 Rel 1/12, Brackley 2/12		
Marvin	Robinson		6'00"	12 08	11/04/1980	32	Crewe	Derby Rel c/s 03, Stoke (L) 9/00, Tranmere (2ML) 11/02, Barnsley (Trial) 7/03, Chesterfield 9/03 Rel c/s 04, Mansfield (Trial) 7/04, Notts County 9/04, Rushden & D 11/04, Walsall 12/04, Stockport 3/05 Rel c/s 05, Lincoln C 8/05, Macclesfield 7/06, Oxford U 8/06 Rel 1/08, Cambridge U (L) 9/07, Injured, Kettering 1/09, Redditch 1/09, Massey Ferguson c/s 09, Nantwich 12/09, Hednesford 10/10, Brackley 2/12		
Owen	Storey		5'11"	10 10	03/08/1984	28	Burton	Rushden & D Rel c/s 04, Team Bath c/s 04, Torquay 12/04, Bath C 3/05 Hinckley U 8/05, Redditch 6/08, Kings Lynn 6/09, Brackley 12/09		
Glenn	Walker				03/08/1986	26		Sileby, Long Buckby c/s 09, Banbury U 11/09, Corby T 1/10, Banbury U 8/11, Brackley 1/12		
Tom	Winters		5'09"	10 09	11/12/1985	26	Banbury	Oxford U, Brackley (L) 12/05, Brackley 8/06		

Conference Action...

Corby forward, Jordan Smith, tries to shake off Hinckley United defender, Haydn Hollis in their 3-0 away win.

Photo: Jonathan Holloway.

BRADFORD PARK AVENUE

Chairman: Dr. John Dean
Secretary: Trevor Jowett   **(T)** 07863 180 787   **(E)** tjj@21thirlmere.freeserve.co.uk
Additional Committee Members:
Robert Blackburn, Kevin Hainsworth, Gary Choppin.

Manager: John Deacey
Programme Editor: Tim Parker   **(E)** timparker79@yahoo.co.uk

THE NON-LEAGUE CLUB DIRECTORY

Book Holiday Inn Hotels and Save today!

Home

Clubs

Steps 1 - 4

League Tables

35 Years of Non-League Football

The Non-League Club Directory has developed into a comprehensive record of competitions within the non-League game, giving this level of football the

www.non-leagueclubdirectory.co.uk

Club Factfile

Founded: 1907   **Nickname:** Avenue

Previous Names: Reformed in 1988

Previous Leagues: Southern 1907-08, Football League 1908-70, Northern Premier 1970-74, West Riding Co.Am. 1988-89, Central Midlands 1989-90, North West Counties 1990-95

Club Colours (change): White with red, amber & black diagonal stripes/black/black (All green & white)

Ground: Horsfall Stadium, Cemetery Road, Bradford, West Yorkshire BD6 2NG   **(T)** 01484 400 007

Capacity: 5,000 **Seats:** 1,247 **Covered:** 2,000 **Clubhouse:** Yes **Shop:** Yes

Directions: M62 to junction 26. Join M606 leave at second junction. At the roundabout take 2nd exit (A6036 signposted Halifax) and pass Odsal Stadium on the left hand side. At next roundabout take the 3rd exit (A6036 Halifax, Horsfall Stadium is signposted). After approximately one mile turn left down Cemetery Road immediately before the Kings Head Public House. Ground is 150 yards on the left.

Previous Grounds: Park Ave. 1907-73, Valley Parade 1973-74, Manningham Mills 1988-89, McLaren Field 1985-93, Batley 1993-96

Record Attendance: 2,100 v Bristol City - FA Cup 1st Round 2003

Record Victory: 11-0 v Derby Dale - FA Cup 1908
Record Defeat: 0-7 v Barnsley - 1911

Record Goalscorer: Len Shackleton - 171 (1940-46)

Record Appearances: Tommy Farr - 542 (1934-50)

Additional Records: Paid £24,500 to Derby County for Leon Leuty 1950
Received £34,000 from Derby County for Kevin Hector 1966

Senior Honours:
Football League Division 3 North 1928. North West Counties League 1994-95.
Northern Premier League Division 1 2000-01, Division 1 North 2007-08. Premier Division Play-offs 2011-12.
West Riding Senior Cup x9. West Riding County Cup x2.

02-03		03-04		04-05		05-06		06-07		07-08		08-09		09-10		10-11		11-12	
NP P	7	NP P	17	Conf N	22	NP P	21	NP 1	4	NP1N	1	NP P	7	NP P	2	NP P	3	NP P	4

BRADFORD PARK AVENUE

No.	Date	Comp	H/A	Opponents	Att:	Result	Goalscorers	Pos
1	Aug 7	NPL P	H	Hednesford Town	442	L 0 - 1		
2	15		A	Whitby Town	346	W 4 - 1	James 55 Savory 67 O'Brien 85 Marshall 90	
3	20		A	Nantwich Town	292	W 3 - 0	Clayton 24 Marshall 35 O'Brien 45	4
4	22		H	Worksop Town	354	W 1 - 0	Savory 44	1
5	27		H	Burscough	291	W 3 - 0	BOSHELL 3 (5 40 45)	2
6	29		A	F.C.United	1831	L 2 - 5	Duckworth 36 Marshall 66	
7	Sept 3		H	Chasetown	338	W 2 - 1	Daly 3 O'Brien 65 (pen)	4
8	7		A	Marine	281	W 2 - 0	Drury 34 Savory 78	4
9	10		A	Matlock Town	398	W 1 - 0	Hotte 5	1
10	12		H	North Ferriby United	298	W 1 - 0	Savory 70	1
11	17	FAC 1Q	H	**Harrogate Railway**	265	W 8 - 0	GREAVES 3 (1 51 87) SAVORY 3 (35 53 75) O'Brien 68 Drury 90	
12	24		H	Northwich Victoria	473	L 1 - 2	Savory 24	4
13	27		A	Stocksbridge Park Steels	168	D 2 - 2	Riley 75 Boshell 77	
14	Oct 1	FAC 2Q	H	**Warrington Town**	268	W 3 - 1	Marshall 42 60 Law 82	
15	8		A	Mickleover Sports	231	L 0 - 4		5
16	15	FAC 3Q	A	**Hyde United**	560	W 1 - 0	Greaves 90	
17	22	FAT 1Q	H	**Worksop Town**	269	D 1 - 1	Marshall 36	
18	26	FAT 1Qr	A	**Worksop Town**	281	L 1 - 4	Deacey 55	
19	29	FAC 4Q	A	**Kidgrove Athletic**	1140	W 2 - 0	Beadle 56 86	
20	Nov 2		H	Chester	604	W 2 - 1	Marshall 41 Ahmed 90	5
21	5		H	Stocksbridge PS	329	W 2 - 0	O'Brien 6 Riley 86	5
22	12	FAC 1	A	**AFC Totton**	2315	L 1 - 8	Clayton 30	
23	19		A	Ashton United	182	W 1 - 0	Savory 88	5
24	21		H	Marine	288	L 0 - 1		
25	26		A	Chasetown	242	W 4 - 0	O'Brien 1 27 (pen) Deacey 77 Greaves 84	
26	Dec 3		H	Matlock Town	282	D 2 - 2	Duckworth 61 Clayton 90	5
27	10		A	Frickley Athletic	208	W 2 - 1	O'Brien 45 52	5
28	13		A	North Ferriby United	180	L 1 - 2	Marshall 44	
29	26		A	Rushall Olympic	241	D 0 - 0		6
30	Jan 2		H	FCUnited	1288	L 2 - 5	Bernard 16 Hotte 80	6
31	7		A	Hednesford Town	529	D 1 - 1	Greaves 32	6
32	21		H	Nantwich Town	257	W 3 - 1	Greaves 2 McDonald 4(og) Hotte 20	6
33	28		A	Worksop Town	401	W 2 - 0	James 10 Matthews 71	6
34	Feb 18		H	Mickleover Sports	322	W 3 - 1	Knowles 14 Davidson 50 75	6
35	20		H	Whitby Town	220	W 3 - 0	Duckworth 13 Hotte 21 Marshall 86	
36	25		A	Kendal Town	329	D 1 - 1	Davidson 70	5
37	March 3		H	Stafford Rangers	532	W 3 - 1	Marshall 54 77 Greaves 72	5
38	10		A	Stafford Rangers	432	L 1 - 3	James 86	5
39	12		H	Buxton	315	W 3 - 1	Marshall 34 Hotte 51 Riley 53	
40	17		A	Chester	2781	L 2 - 3	Riley 67 O'Brien 80	5
41	24		H	Ashton United	395	W 4 - 0	Hotte 7 72 Knowles 24 Marshall 27	4
42	26		H	Kendal Town	303	W 4 - 1	Matthews 44 Greaves 46 58 O'Brien 60	
43	31		A	Buxton	379	W 3 - 1	Greaves 20 Marshall 22 Daly 90	
44	Apr 2		H	Chorley	502	W 1 - 0	Marshall 65 (pen)	
45	7		A	Burscough	167	D 1 - 1	Clayton 30	3
46	9		H	Rushall Olympic	331	L 0 - 2		
47	14		H	Frickley Athletic	398	W 3 - 0	Mathews 2 South 24 (og) Greaves 85	3
48	17		A	Northwich Victoria	230	L 0 - 1		
49	21		A	Chorley	1277	L 1 - 3	Marshall 47	4
50	28	Play-Off SF	H	**Hednesford Town**	609	W 5 - 0	Marshall 26 (pen) 89 Clayton 41 Drury 63 Knowles 74	
51	May 6	Play-Off F	H	**FC United**	1897	W 1 - 0*	Greaves 118	

PLAYING SQUAD 2012/13

Existing Players		SN	HT	WT	DOB	AGE	POB	Career	Apps	Goals
GOALKEEPERS										
Simon	Eastwood	6'02"	13 13		24/07/1989	22	Luton	Huddersfield, Woking (3ML) 11/08, Bradford C (5ML) 7/09, Oxford U 6/10 Rel c/s 11, FC Halifax 6/11 Rel c/s 12, Bradford PA 7/12, Portsmouth (Trial) 7/12		
John	Lamb				12/11/1982	29		Halifax, Guiseley, Leigh RMI 7/05, Eccleshill Utd, Bradford PA 3/08, Ossett T, Harrogate T 6/09, Bradford PA 3/10		
DEFENDERS										
Matt	Dempsey				06/02/1990	22		Bradford C (Jun), Eccleshall U, Sheff Utd, Glen Hoddle Academy, Eccleshall U, Garforth T, Bradford PA 2/12		
Martin	Drury				10/04/1986	26		Sheff Utd (Yth), Rotherham (Yth), Doncaster (Yth), Sheff Wed (Yth), Stocksbridge PS, Gainsborough, Belper T c/s 06, Gainsborough 7/07, Bradford PA 6/09		
Aaron	Hardy	5'08"	11 04		26/05/1986	25	South Emsall	Huddersfield Rel c/s 08, Harrogate T 7/08, FC Halifax 7/09 Rel c/s 12, Bradford PA 6/12		
Mark	Hume	6'02"	13 02		21/05/1978	34	Barnsley	Barnsley Rel c/s 98, Doncaster 8/98, Gainsborough (L) 10/99, Barrow (L) 11/99, Barrow 1/00, Scunthorpe (Trial) 10/01, Alfreton £4,000 2/04, Stalybridge 7/06, Harrogate T 6/07, Buxton 6/08, Eastwood T 9/08, Bradford PA 11/09, Retford U, Gainsborough 8/10, Bradford PA 11/10		
Amjad	Iqbal				23/09/1980	31		Bradford C (Jun), Farsley Celtic, Thackley, Farsley Celtic 7/01, Harrogate T, Farsley Celtic 10/02, Bradford PA Undisc 3/09, Farsley FC, Bradford PA 10/11		
James	Knowles				21/05/1983	29		Blackburn, Garforth, Harrogate T, Glasshoughton W, Harrogate RA, Farsley Celtic 12/03, Bradford PA 1/09, Farsley 10/10, Bradford PA 12/10		
James	Riley				02/05/1985	27		Thackley, Harrogate RA 7/07, FC Halifax 3/09, Bradford PA 3/11		
MIDFIELDERS										
Simon	Baldry	5'10"	11 06		12/02/1976	35	Huddersfield	Huddersfield Rel c/s 03, Bury (L) 9/98, Notts County 8/03 Rel c/s 04, Injured, Ossett T 1/08, Bradford PA 7/09 (Pl/Ass Man) c/s 10, Guiseley 12/10 Rel c/s 12, Bradford PA 7/12		
Adam	Clayton				20/07/1986	26		Liversedge, Ossett T, Stocksbridge PS 1/10, Garforth T 3/10, Bradford PA 7/10		
Ross	Daly				03/05/1989	23		Thackley, Bradford PA 7/12		
Jordan	Deacey				31/03/1994	18		Bradford PA		
Michael	Duckworth				28/04/1992	20		York C (Yth), Glen Hoddle Academy, Harrogate RA 10/10, Bradford PA 7/11		
Nathan	Hotte				24/03/1988	24		Hull C (Jun), North Ferriby, Farsley Celtic 7/06, North Ferriby, Frickley 7/07, North Ferriby 10/07, Bridlington T, Scarborough Ath 7/10, Bradford PA 1/11		
Matty	James				15/01/1986	26		Local, Farsley Celtic 8/08, Bradford PA 12/08, Garforth, Harrogate RA 3/10, Guiseley 8/10, Bradford PA 1/11		
Rob	O'Brien				28/11/1983	28		Doncaster (Jun), Gainsborough, Ossett T 7/05, Bradford PA 7/09		
FORWARDS										
Alex	Davidson				18/12/1988	23		North Ferriby, Guiseley 6/11, North Ferriby 10/11, Bradford PA 2/12		
Tom	Greaves				15/11/1986	25		Bradford PA, Bridlington T (L) 1/07 Perm, Guiseley 1/08, Woodley Sports 3/08, Bridlington (L), Ossett T c/s 08, Garforth T, Bradford PA 7/10, Garforth (L) 12/11		
Danny	Holland				18/02/1983	28	Mansfield	Sheff Utd (Yth), Chesterfield (Yth), Staveley MW, Matlock 8/02, Grimsby (Trial) 7/04, Hucknall 8/04, Harrogate T (L) 11/04 Perm 12/04, Eastwood T Undisc 2/09, FC Halifax 7/10 Rel c/s 12, Bradford PA 6/12		
Jamie	Jackson	5'06"	10 01		01/10/1986	25	Sheffield	Chesterfield Rel c/s 08, Matlock (2ML) 11/07, Gainsborough (L) 2/08, Matlock (L) 3/08, Matlock 8/08, Sheffield FC 11/09, Worksop 2/10, Bradford PA 6/12		
Billy	Law				15/04/1994	18		Doncaster (Yth), Yorkshire Am, Bradford PA, Tadcaster (Dual), Ossett T (Dual) 8/12		
Richard	Marshall				01/05/1986	26		Liversedge, Harrogate RA 12/06, Liversedge, Harrogate RA 8/07, FC Halifax, Harrogate T (SL) 3/11, Bradford PA 7/11		
Nicky	Matthews				24/03/1988	24		Thackley, Bradford PA 1/12		
Paul	Walker							Buxton, Liversedge, Garforth 1/10, Bradford PA 7/12		

Conference Action...

Worcester City centre-forward, Mike Symons homes in on the Solihull goal during their 0-0 draw at Damson Park.

Photo: Jonathan Holloway.

CHESTER

Chairman: Chris Pilsbury
Secretary: Calvin Hughes   **(T)** 07739 351 711   **(E)** info@chesterfc.com
Additional Committee Members:
Chris Pilsbury, Mike Vickers, Jane Hipkiss, Mark Howell, David Evans, Campbell Smith, Pat Cluskey, Alan Tarbuck, Jeff Banks, Russell Hughes, Noel O'Neill, Bill Smith, Paul Baker.
Manager: Neil Young
Programme Editor: Rob Ashcroft   **(E)** ashcazrob@aol.com

Back Row: Alex Hay (Chief Scout), Levi Mackin, Michael Powell, Michael Taylor, Paul Linwood, Dave Hankin, Adam Proudlock, Lee Worrall (Goalkeeping Coach)
Middle Row:Jimmy Soul (Kit Man), Dom Collins, Robbie Booth, Martin Fearon, John Danby, George Horan (Captain), Matty McGinn, Will Osbourne (Physio), Calvin Hughes (Football Secretary)
Front Row: Sean Clancy, Antoni Sarcevic, Wes Baynes, Gary Jones (Assistant Manager), Neil Young (Manager), Gary Powell (First Team Coach), Ashley Williams, Iain Howard, Nathan Jarman, Marc Williams

Club Factfile

Founded: 1885   **Nickname:** Blues
Previous Names: Chester > 1983, Chester City 1983-2010
Previous Leagues: Cheshire 1919-31, Football League 1931-2000, 2004-09, Conference 2000-04, 09-10 (Did not finish the season)

Club Colours (change): Blue and white stripes/blue/blue and white hoops (Green/black/black)

Ground: Exacta Stadium, Bumpers Lane, Chester. CH1 4LT   **(T)** 01244 371 376
Capacity: 6,012   **Seats:** 3,284   **Covered:** Yes   **Clubhouse:** Yes   **Shop:** Yes

Directions: Stay on the M56 until you reach a roundabout at the end of the motorway. Follow the signs to North Wales & Queensferry A5117. After around one and a half miles you will reach a set of traffic lights where you need to bear left on to the A550 (signposted North Wales & Queensferry). Then from the A550, take the A548 towards Chester. Head straight through the first set of traffic lights and after passing a Vauxhall and then a Renault garage on your left, turn right at the next lights into Sovereign Way. Continue to the end of Sovereign Way and then turn right into Bumpers Lane and the entrance to the Club car park is just down on the right.

Previous Grounds: Faulkner Street 1885-98, The Old Showground 98-99, Whipcord Lane 1901-06, Sealand Road 06-90, Macclesfield FC 90-92

Record Attendance: 20,378 v Chelsea - FA Cup 3rd Round replay 16/01/1952
Record Victory: 12-0 v York City - 01/02/1936
Record Defeat: Not known
Record Goalscorer: Stuart Rimmer - 135
Record Appearances: Ray Gill - 406 (1951-62)
Additional Records: Paid £100,000 to Rotherham for Gregg Blundell.
Received £300,000 from Liverpool for Ian Rush
Senior Honours:
Conference 2003-04.
Cheshire Senior Cup 1894-95, 96-97, 1903-04, 07-08, 08-09, 30-31, 31-32. Herefordshire Senior Cup 1991-92 (shared).
Welsh Cup 1907-08, 32-33, 46-47. NPL Division One North 2010-11. Premier Division 2011-12.

10 YEAR RECORD

02-03		03-04		04-05		05-06		06-07		07-08		08-09		09-10		10-11		11-12	
Conf	4	Conf	1	FL 2	20	FL 2	15	FL 2	18	FL 2	22	FL 2	23	Conf	dnf	NP1N	1	NP P	1

CHESTER

No.	Date	Comp	H/A	Opponents	Att:	Result	Goalscorers	Pos
1	Aug 7	NPL P	H	Rushall Olympic	2326	D 1 - 1	McNeil 12	
2	17		A	Burscough	774	W 4 - 1	Rainford 3 (pen) Wright 62 McNeil 83 Horan 90	
3	20		A	Hednesford United	1009	L 0 - 1		9
4	24		H	F.C.United	3219	W 2 - 1	McGinn 16 (pen) McNeil 45	
5	27		H	Stocksbridge P.S.	2040	W 5 - 1	Howard 8 McGinn 33 Powell 55 73 Wright 90	4
6	29		A	Nantwich Town	1561	L 1 - 4	Smith 76	
7	Sept 3		H	North Ferriby United	2150	W 6 - 0	Simm 15 52 Howard 26 Barnes 76 Booth 79 McGinn 86	6
8	7		A	Ashton United	528	W 2 - 0	Simm 1 McGinn 38 (pen)	
9	10		A	Worksop Town	570	W 3 - 0	Powell 58 McGinn 83 (pen) Baynes 90	4
10	13		H	Kendal Town	2029	W 4 - 0	Smith 1 McGinn 3 (pen) McNeil 32 Howard 90	
11	24		A	Stafford Rangers	1098	W 3 - 0	Howard 14 Powell 21 78	3
12	28		H	Chorley	3310	W 3 - 0	Powell 53 McNeill 61 Baynes 84	
13	Oct 8		H	Chasetown	2930	W 1 - 0	Wilde 88	2
14			A	Buxton	602	D 1 - 1	Powell 42	
15	15		A	FC United	3112	W 3 - 2	Simm 2 79 Horan 90	2
16	**22**	**FAT 1Q**	**H**	**Ashton United**	**1624**	**W 2 - 1**	**Howard 2 Wilde 61**	
17	29		H	Frickley Athletic	2485	D 2 - 2	Rainford 36 McGinn 72	2
18	Nov 2		A	Bradford PA	604	L 1 - 2	Booth 50	2
19	**5**	**FAT 2Q**	**H**	**Stafford Rangers**	**1551**	**W 2 - 0**	**McGinn 45 (pen) Booth 49**	
20	12		A	Whitby Town	652	W 4 - 0	Holden 14 McGinn 27 (pen) 36 Howard 86	2
21	19		H	Matlock	2605	W 4 - 0	McNeil 23 55 Holden 89 Wilde 90	2
22	23		H	Ashton United	2247	W 1 - 0	Brownhill 38	1
23	**26**	**FAT 3Q**	**A**	**Stourbridge**	**1481**	**W 2 - 0**	**Howard 67 McNeil 79**	
24	Dec 3		H	Worksop Town	1850	W 2 - 0	Powell 32 72	1
25	**10**	**FAT 1**	**A**	**North Ferriby United**	**510**	**W 5 - 1**	**Wilde 39 48 McNeil 45 Sarcevic 60 Howard 72**	
26	17		A	Marine	1288	W 2 - 1	Baynes 43 McGinn 53 (pen)	1
27	26		A	Northwich Victoria	2664	D 1 - 1	Baynes 13	1
28	Jan 2		H	Nantwich Town	3560	D 1 - 1	Sarcevic 53	1
29	7		A	Rushall Olympic	714	W 4 - 0	McNeill 29 Powell 49 McGinn 57 (pen) Mackin 90	1
30	14	FAT 2	A	Ebbsfleet United	1387	L 2 - 3	McNeil 61 Loraine 72 (og)	
31	21		H	Hednesford Town	3343	L 1 - 2	McGinn 45 (pen)	1
32	28		H	Mickleover Sports	2085	W 2 - 1	Brown 10 McNeill 19	1
33	Feb 11		H	Stafford Rangers	2381	W 2 - 0	Brown 48 Smith 80	1
34	18		A	Chasetown	679	D 1 - 1	Sarcevic 49	1
35	25		H	Buxton	2470	W 4 - 0	Simm 4 54 Baynes 32 63	1
36	March 3		A	Frickley Athletic	720	W 3 - 1	Smith 63 Howard 71 Horan 79	1
37	7		H	Ashton United	2527	W 4 - 0	Sarcevic 17 Smith 23 Simm 68 Howard 88	
38	17		H	Bradford PA	2781	W 3 - 2	Taylor 32 Williams 38 40	1
39	24		A	Matlock Town	1036	W 1 - 0	Wilde 66	
40	27		A	North Ferriby United	459	W 3 - 0	Horan 9 Wilde 60 Simm 87	1
41	31		H	Whitby Town	3126	W 2 - 0	Wilde 45 McGinn 53 (pen)	1
42	Apr 2		A	Kendal Town	701	W 3 - 0	Simm 11 Smith 71 Williams 90	
43	7		A	Stocksbridge PS	1009	W 2 - 1	Simm 6 Booth 18	1
44	9		H	Northwich Victoria	5009	D 1 - 1	McGinn 84	
45	14		A	Mickleover Sports	660	W 3 - 1	Simm 16 Booth 71 Howard 90	1
46	17		A	Chorley	2213	W 2 - 0	Simm 7 Williams 67	Champions
47	21		H	Marine	3686	W 4 - 0	Williams 24 SIMM 3 (39 45 79)	1

PLAYING SQUAD 2012/13

Existing Players		SN	HT	WT	DOB	AGE	POB	Career	Apps	Goals
GOALKEEPERS										
John	Danby		6'02"	12 09	20/09/1983	28	Stoke	Kidderminster Rel 5/06, Stourport (2ML) 2/03, Chester 5/06 Rel 3/10, Eastwood T 3/10, Chester FC 6/11		
Martin	Fearon		6'02"	12 02	30/10/1988	23	Liverpool	Burnley, Accrington 5/07 Rel c/s 08, Clitheroe 7/08, Lancaster 7/09, Chester FC 6/12		
DEFENDERS										
Wes	Baynes		5'11"	10 10	12/10/1988	23	Chester	Wrexham, Altrincham (SL) 10/10, Chester FC 6/11		
Dominic	Collins		6'02"		15/04/1991	21	Preston	Preston Rel c/s 11, Crawley (L) 9/09, Northwich (L) 12/10, Northwich (SL) 1/11, Northwich 7/11, Chester FC 5/12		
Jordan	Grace							Chester FC		
George	Horan				18/02/1982	30	Chester	Bangor C, Connahs Quay c/s 00, Rhyl c/s 05, Droylsden 2/10, Chester FC 7/10		
Paul	Linwood		6'02"	12 08	24/10/1983	27	Birkenhead	Tranmere, Wrexham (2ML) 8/05, Chester £15,000 8/06 Rel 5/09, Grimsby 7/09, Fleetwood 6/10 Rel c/s 12, Chester FC 5/12		
Michael	Taylor		6'02"	13 10	21/11/1982	29	Liverpool	Blackburn Rel c/s 04, Carlisle (3ML) 9/02, Rochdale (L) 3/03, Reading (Trial) 12/03, Wycombe (Trial) 3/04, Cheltenham 7/04, Forest Green (2ML) 3/06, Halifax 7/06 Rel 7/06, Lancaster 7/06 Rel 10/06, Barrow 10/06, Hyde U 10/06, TNS Undisc 8/07, Fleetwood 1/09 Rel 5/10, Hyde FC 7/10, Chester FC 12/10		
MIDFIELDERS										
Robbie	Booth		5'07"	11 08	30/12/1985	26	Liverpool	Everton (Scholar), Chester (Sch) (Pro) 3/05 Rel c/s 05, Southport 7/05, Burscough (L) 1/06, Burscough 9/06, Southport 7/08, Vauxhall Motors (2ML) 8/09, Droylsden 7/10, Chester FC 9/10		
Sean	Clancy		5'08"	09 12	16/09/1987	23	Liverpool	Blackpool, Southport 8/06, Burscough (L) 3/07, USA, Shrewsbury NC 8/07, Altrincham 8/07 Rel 9/07, Burscough 9/07, Fleetwood Undisc 3/09 Rel c/s 12, FC Halifax (SL) 3/12, Chester FC 6/12		
Dave	Hankin		6'03"		25/03/1985	26	Preston	Preston (Yth), Bamber Bridge, Squires Gate, Clitheroe 2/08, Stalybridge 6/09 Rel 4/10, Kidderminster 6/10, Chester FC 5/12		
Iain	Howard				27/11/1987	24		Flixton, Ashton U, Chester FC 6/10		
Levi	Mackin		6'01"	12 00	04/04/1986	25	Chester	Wrexham Rel 5/09, Droylsden (3ML) 1/08, York C (SL) 1/09, York C 5/09 Rel 6/11, Alfreton 7/11 Rel 1/12, Chester FC 1/12		
Matty	McGinn				27/06/1983	29	Fazackerley	Southport, Runcorn 8/02, Southport 7/05 Rel 9/06, Burscough 9/06, Southport 7/08, Skelmersdale (L) 2/11, Chester FC (L) 8/11 Perm 9/11		
Joe	Ormrod							Chester FC		
Michael	Powell				10/09/1985	26	Ormskirk	Southport, Chester FC 3/11		
Antoni	Sarcevic		6'00"	13 05	13/03/1992	20	Manchester	Man City (Yth), Woodley Sports, Crewe 5/10, Chester FC (L) 10/10, Chester FC Undisc 11/11		
Ashley	Williams				08/10/1987	24		Man C Rel c/s 07, Upton AAA, Vauxhall Motors 1/08, Airbus UK Broughton 7/08, Chester FC 1/11		
FORWARDS										
Nathan	Jarman		5'11"	11 03	19/09/1986	24	Scunthorpe	Barnsley Rel c/s 07, Bury (L) 1/06, Worksop (SL) 2/07, Grimsby (Trial) 7/07, Grimsby 9/07 Rel c/s 10, Harrogate T (Trial) c/s 10, Corby T 8/10, Alfreton Undisc 3/11, Chester FC 5/12		
Adam	Proudlock		6'00"	13 07	09/05/1981	30	Wellington	Wolves, Clyde (L) 8/00, Notts Forest (L) 3/02, Tranmere (L) 10/02, Sheff Wed (L) 12/02, Sheff Wed £150,000 9/03 Rel 9/05, Ipswich 10/05 Rel c/s 06, Walsall (Trial) 7/06, Stockport 8/06 Rel c/s 08, Darlington 7/08, Grimsby (2ML) 11/08 Perm 1/09 Rel c/s 10, Kidderminster (Trial) 8/10, AFC Telford 9/10, Chester FC 6/12		
Marc	Williams		5'09"	11 02	27/07/1988	23	Colwyn Bay	Wrexham Rel 5/11, Kidderminster (3ML) 8/10, Kidderminster 5/11 Rel 2/12, Chester FC 2/12		

Conference Action...

Worcester City winger, Greg Mills, tracks back to tackle this Solihull player in their away 0-0 League game.

Photo: Jonathan Holloway.

COLWYN BAY

Chairman: Robert Paton
Secretary: Grant McIndoe   **(T)** 07769 538 012   **(E)** egmcindoe@yahoo.co.uk
Additional Committee Members:
Roger Skinner, Bill Murray, Allan Ham, David Messon, David Rhodes.

Manager: Jon Newby
Programme Editor: David Jones   **(E)** dai1974@sky.com

Club Factfile

Founded: 1885   **Nickname:** Seagulls
Previous Names:
Previous Leagues: North Wales Coast 1901-21, 33-35, Welsh National 1921-30, North Wales Combination 1930-31, Welsh League (North) 1945-84, North West Counties 1984-91

Club Colours (change): Sky blue and claret/claret/sky blue (White & claret/white/white)

Ground: Llanelian Road, Old Colwyn, North Wales LL29 8UN   **(T)** 01492 514 581
Capacity: 2,500   **Seats:** 250   **Covered:** 700   **Clubhouse:** Yes   **Shop:** Yes

Directions From Queensferry take the A55 and exit at Junction 22 signposted Old Colwyn at end of slip road turn left, up the hill to the mini roundabout, straight across onto Llanelian Road, ground is approx half mile on the right.

Previous Grounds: Eirias Park

Record Attendance: 5,000 v Borough United at Eirias Park 1964
Record Victory: Not known
Record Defeat: Not known
Record Goalscorer: Peter Donnelly
Record Appearances: Bryn A Jones
Additional Records:
Senior Honours:
Northern League Division 1 1991-92, Division 1 Play-off 2009-10

10 YEAR RECORD

02-03	03-04	04-05	05-06	06-07	07-08	08-09	09-10	10-11	11-12
NP P 22	NP 1 16	NP 1 13	NP 1 12	NP 1 5	NP1S 7	NP1N 4	NP1N 4	NP P 2	Conf N 12

COLWYN BAY

No.	Date	Comp	H/A	Opponents	Att:	Result	Goalscorers	Pos
1	Sat-13-Aug	BSN	A	Bishops Stortford	363	W 2-0	McKenna 32, Doherty 49	4
2	Tue-16-Aug	BSN	H	Hyde FC	394	L 0-1		10
3	Sat-20-Aug	BSN	H	Eastwood Town	370	W 2-0	Lloyd-McGoldrick 68, Hopley 78	6
4	Tue-23-Aug	BSN	A	FC Halifax Town	1406	D 1-1	Newby pen 16	6
5	Sat-27-Aug	BSN	A	Guiseley	328	L 0-2		10
6	Mon-29-Aug	BSN	H	Workington	390	W 1-0	Newby 71	8
7	Sat-03-Sep	BSN	A	Droylsden	349	L 1-2	Lea 45	11
8	Sat-10-Sep	BSN	H	Histon	318	W 2-1	Lloyd-McGoldrick 51, Denson 55	7
9	Sat-17-Sep	BSN	A	Gloucester City	280	W 1-0	Newby 78	5
10	Tue-20-Sep	BSN	H	Altrincham	444	L 1-6	Hopley 56	6
11	Sat-24-Sep	BSN	H	Solihull Moors	321	D 0-0		9
12	Sat-08-Oct	BSN	A	Hinckley United	419	L 1-3	Newby pen 25	13
13	Sat-15-Oct	BSN	H	Stalybridge Celtic	403	W 2-0	Lea 1, Davey pen 85	8
14	Sat-22-Oct	BSN	H	Corby Town	385	L 0-2		10
15	Sat-29-Oct	BSN	A	Boston United	1076	D 2-2	McEvilly 2 (45, pen 45+2)	10
16	Sat-05-Nov	BSN	A	Blyth Spartans	451	D 2-2	Noon 40, Newby 90	11
17	Sat-12-Nov	BSN	H	Gainsborough Trinity	436	W 2-1	McEvilly 49, Noon 72	10
18	Sat-19-Nov	BSN	A	Hyde FC	462	L 2-3	Meadowcroft 37, Evans 71	13
19	Sat-03-Dec	BSN	H	Droylsden	272	W 6-3	Lloyd-McGoldrick 3 (7, 40, 89), Hopley 2 (27, 48), Lea 53	10
20	Tue-06-Dec	BSN	A	Harrogate Town	180	L 0-4		11
21	Sat-17-Dec	BSN	H	Worcester City	295	L 0-2		12
22	Mon-26-Dec	BSN	A	Vauxhall Motors	343	L 0-1		12
23	Sat-07-Jan	BSN	A	Altrincham	816	W 4-3	Hopley 2 (17, 56), Evans 22, Sinclair 90	13
24	Sat-14-Jan	BSN	A	Eastwood Town	238	W 1-0	McLachlan 79	11
25	Tue-17-Jan	BSN	H	Vauxhall Motors	170	D 0-0		10
26	Sat-21-Jan	BSN	A	Worcester City	791	W 1-0	Hopley 13	10
27	Sat-28-Jan	BSN	A	Stalybridge Celtic	529	W 4-0	Hopley 3 (41, 45, 50), Denson 69	8
28	Tue-07-Feb	BSN	H	Boston United	244	W 3-2	Noon 2 (51, 87), Payne 59	7
29	Sat-11-Feb	BSN	H	FC Halifax Town	634	L 0-1		7
30	Sat-18-Feb	BSN	H	Nuneaton Town	453	L 1-6	McLachlan 89	8
31	Sat-25-Feb	BSN	A	Histon	379	D 0-0		8
32	Sat-03-Mar	BSN	H	Blyth Spartans	279	L 0-2		9
33	Tue-06-Mar	BSN	H	Bishops Stortford	141	W 4-1	Evans 7, Noon 21, Newby 56, Hopley 70	8
34	Sat-10-Mar	BSN	A	Solihull Moors	242	L 0-1		9
35	Sat-17-Mar	BSN	H	Hinckley United	237	L 0-5		10
36	Sat-24-Mar	BSN	A	Corby Town	318	L 0-1		11
37	Sat-31-Mar	BSN	A	Gainsborough Trinity	533	L 0-2		11
38	Sat-07-Apr	BSN	H	Guiseley	386	L 1-2	McKenna 36	12
39	Mon-09-Apr	BSN	A	Workington	514	L 1-3	Noon 17	14
40	Sat-14-Apr	BSN	H	Harrogate Town	284	D 2-2	Lea 34, Sinclair 81	14
41	Sat-21-Apr	BSN	A	Nuneaton Town	856	D 1-1	Hopley 15	16
42	Sat-28-Apr	BSN	H	Gloucester City	476	W 4-2	Hopley 3, McLachlan 17, Evans 18, McKenna 44	12

CUPS

No.	Date	Comp	H/A	Opponents	Att:	Result	Goalscorers	Pos
1	Sat-01-Oct	FAC 2Q	A	Stocksbridge Park Steels	128	L 1-3	Barnes 14	
2	Sat-26-Nov	FAT 3Q	H	FC Halifax Town	420	D 0-0		
3	Tue-29-Nov	FAT 3QR	A	FC Halifax Town	717	W 2-1	McLachlan pen 43, Og (Anderson) 64	
4	Sat-10-Dec	FAT 1	H	Lincoln City	383	L 1-3	McLachlan pen 60	

League
Starts
Substitute
Unused Sub

Cups
Starts
Substitute
Unused Sub

Goals (Lg)
Goals (Cup)

Appearance grid (X = start, S = substitute, U = unused substitute)

	SANNA	DENSON	LEA	MCDONALD	MEADOWCROFT	MCLACHLAN	EVANS	MCKENNA	HOPLEY	NEWBY	DOHERTY	LLOYD-MCGOLDRICK	NOON	SHEEHAN	S WILLIAMS	DAVEY	ALLEN	BENSON	ROUSE	BENJAMIN	KING	BARNES	HUGHES	MCEVILLY	CHALLINOR	JONES	CUDWORTH	PARKINSON	SINCLAIR	METCALF	PAYNE	MCKERNAN	BARLOW	C ROBERTS	ENNIS	COLLINS	MORTON	L ROBERTS
	X	X	X	X	X	X	X	X	X	X	X	X	S	S	S	U	U																					
	X	X	X	X	X	X	X	X	X	X	X	X	S	S	U	U		S																				
	X	X	X	X	X	S	X	X	X	X	U	S	X		U	S	X																					
	X	X	X	X	X	U	S	X	X	X	X	U	U		U	X	X																					
	X	X	X	X	X	S	X	X		X	U	X		S	U	X	X	S																				
	X	X	X	X	X	S	X	X		X	X	S	X		U	X	X	U																				
	X	X	X	X	X	U	X	X			X	S	U	X	X	X	U	S																				
	X	X	X	X	X		X	X		X		X	S	U	S	X	U	X	S																			
	X	X	X	X		S	X	S	X		X	U	U	S	X		X	X																				
	X	X	X	X		X	X	X	X		S	X	U	U	X	S	S	X																				
	X	X	X	X		S	X	S	X		X	S	X	U	X	X	S	X																				
	X			S	X		U	X	S	X		X	U		S	X	X	X	X	X																		
	X	X	X	U	X		X	S	X			S	S		X		X		X	X	X																	
	X	X	X	X		X	U	X			U	S		X	U		X		X	U	X	X																
	X	X	X	X	X	X		S	S		X	X		X		U		X	X	U																		
	X	X	X	X	X	X		U	S		X	X		S	X	U	U		X	X																		
	X	X	X	U	X		X	X	S	X		X	X		S		U		X	X																		
	X	X	X	U	X	X	X	X	S	S		X	X		U	U		X	X																			
	X	X	X		X	X	X	X	U		X	X		S		U		S	X	S																		
	X	X		X	X	X	X	X	S		X	X		S		U		U	X	S		X																
	X	X		X	X	X	X	X	S		X		U	S		U		X	S			X	X															
	X	X		X	X	X	X	U		X	S		U		U		X		X	X																		
	X	X		X	X	S	X	X		X		X		U	U		U		X		X	S	X	U														
	X	X		X	X	X	X	X		X		X	U		X		U		X		U			U		S												
	X	X		X	X	S	X	X		X		S			X		S		X	S		X	U	X														
	X	X		X	X	X	X	X		S		S			S		U		X	U		X	U	X														
	X	X		U	X	X	X	X		S		S			S		S		X	U		X																
	X	X		X	X	X	X	X		S		X			X		U		X	S		X	U															
	X	X		U	X	X	X	X		S		X			S		U		X	X	X	U																
	X	X		S	X	X	X	X	S		X			U		U		X	X	X																		
	X	X		X	X	X	X	X		S		U			U		U		X	X	U	U																
	X	X		X	X	X	X	X		S		U			U		U		X	X	S	U																
	X	X		X	X	X	X	X		S		X			S		U		X	X	S	S	U															
	X	X		S	X	X	X	X		S		X			S		U		X	X	S	U	U															
	X	X		X	X	X	X	X		S		X			S		S		X	X	S	U																
	X	X		X	X	X		X		S		X			S			X	X	U		X	X	S	U													
	X	X		X		X		X		X		X			U		S		U	X		X	U	X	X	X	X	U										
	X	X		S	X		X	X		X		S			U		U		X			X		X	X	X	U											
	X	X		S	X		X	X		X		S			U		U		X			X		X	X	X	U											
	X	X		X	X	X	X	X		U		U			U		X		X	X		U	U															
	X	X		X	X	X	X	X		S		U			U		X		X	X		S	U															
	X	X		X	X	X	X	X		S		S			U		X		X	X		U	S															
	X			X	X			U	S			S	S	X		U	X	X	X	X	X	X																
	X	X	X	U	X	X	X	X	S	U		X	X		U	S		X	X																			
	X	U	X	X	X	X	U	X	X	X		S	X		X		U		X	S																		
	X	X			X	X	X	X	X		X	S	U	S		U		U	X	X			X															

Appearances / totals

	SANNA	DENSON	LEA	MCDONALD	MEADOWCROFT	MCLACHLAN	EVANS	MCKENNA	HOPLEY	NEWBY	DOHERTY	LLOYD-MCGOLDRICK	NOON	SHEEHAN	S WILLIAMS	DAVEY	ALLEN	BENSON	ROUSE	BENJAMIN	KING	BARNES	HUGHES	MCEVILLY	CHALLINOR	JONES	CUDWORTH	PARKINSON	SINCLAIR	METCALF	PAYNE	MCKERNAN	BARLOW	C ROBERTS	ENNIS	COLLINS	MORTON	L ROBERTS
	24	41	40	14	28	26	35	33	32	29	4	13	23	0	0	13	12	1	5	3	2	3	25	4	0	1	3	2	18	10	6	0	0	4	4	3	1	0
	0	0	0	1	4	3	3	4	5	6	0	6	13	2	0	18	1	8	3	1	2	0	0	5	0	0	1	0	0	4	2	0	0	2	1	0	0	
	0	0	0	3	2	2	1	1	1	2	2	2	5	1	12	10	1	23	2	0	13	0	0	4	1	0	0	1	0	4	1	7	3	1	1	2	3	1
	3	2	3	2	3	3	2	3	2	2	0	2	3	0	0	2	1	1	1	1	1	1	3	2	0	0	1	0	0	0	0	0	0	0	0	0	0	0
	0	0	0	0	0	0	0	0	2	0	1	2	1	0	0	2	0	0	0	0	0	0	0	1	0	0	1	0	0	0	0	0	0	0	0	0	0	0
	0	1	0	1	0	0	1	1	0	1	0	0	0	0	3	0	0	2	0	0	1	0	0	1	0	0	0	0	0	0	0	0	0	0	0	0	0	0
	0	2	4	0	1	3	4	3	13	6	1	5	6	0	0	1	0	0	0	0	0	0	0	3	0	0	0	0	2	0	1	0	0	0	0	0	0	0
	0	0	0	0	0	2	0	0	0	0	0	0	0	0	0	0	0	0	0	0	0	0	0	1	0	0	0	0	0	0	0	0	0	0	0	0	0	0

PLAYING SQUAD 2012/13

Existing Players		SN	HT	WT	DOB	AGE	POB	Career	Apps	Goals
GOALKEEPERS										
Andy	Metcalf							Colwyn Bay, Union College (USA), Colwyn Bay 12/11	10	0
Chris	Sanna				02/07/1987	25		Stoke, Watford (L) 10/05, Wrexham (Trial), Shrewsbury (Trial), Colwyn Bay 1/07, Stamford 2/07, Nuneaton (Trial) 7/07, Worcester (SL) 3/08, Halesowen T c/s 08, Colwyn Bay 12/08, Chester FC 11/10, Colwyn Bay 1/11	24	0
DEFENDERS										
Luke	Denson		6'00"	11 00	26/02/1991	21	Wirral	Tranmere (Scholar) Rel c/s 09, Colwyn Bay 7/09, Inverness Caledonian (Trial) 5/12	41	2
Danny	Meadowcroft		6'04"	12 05	22/05/1985	27	Macclesfield	Stockport, Mossley (L) 10/04 Perm 11/04, Morecambe 7/06 Rel 5/07, Mossley (L) 11/06, Bradford PA 7/07, Ossett T 10/07, Northwich 1/08 Rel 5/08, Droylsden c/s 08, FC Halifax 10/08, Northwich 3/09, Salford C (L) 12/09, Colwyn Bay (L) 1/10, Chester FC 5/10, Bamber Bridge (L) 10/10, Colwyn Bay 1/11	32	1
Joel	Richardson		5'11"	11 00	22/09/1990	21	Liverpool	Tranmere (Scholar) Rel c/s 09, Aberystwyth 12/09, IK Hammerby (Swe), Hyde FC 6/11, Skelmersdale 12/11, Colwyn Bay 7/12		
Lee	Roberts							Wrexham, Prescot Cables (WE) 9/11, Colwyn Bay 3/12	0	0
Frank	Sinclair		5'08"	12 09	03/12/1971	40	Lambeth	Chelsea, West Brom (L) 12/91, Leicester £2 million 8/98 Rel c/s 04, Burnley 7/04 Rel c/s 07, Huddersfield (SL) 2/07, Huddersfield 7/07 Rel c/s 08, Lincoln C 7/08 Rel c/s 09, Wycombe (SL) 3/09, Wrexham 8/09 Rel c/s 11, Hendon 11/11, Colwyn Bay 1/12	18	2
Tom	Smyth		5'11"	12 08	18/03/1991	21	Southport	Preston Rel 2/10, Northwich 4/10, Accrington 6/10 Rel c/s 11, Workington (3ML) 12/10, Workington 8/11, Northwich 10/11, Colwyn Bay 5/12		
MIDFIELDERS										
Liam	Benson				14/04/1993	19		Tranmere Rel c/s 11, Colwyn Bay 8/11	9	0
Allan	Collins				07/02/1990	22		Southport, Warrington (L) Perm, Skelmersdale c/s 11, Warrington 9/11, Colwyn Bay 3/12	4	0
Paul	Ennis		5'06"	11 02	01/02/1990	22	Stockport	Stockport Rel c/s 09, Salford C (L) 9/08, Wrexham (Trial) 7/09, Stalybridge 9/09 Rel 11/09, Bala T 1/10, Stalybridge 3/10, Bala T 8/10, Droylsden 2/11, Witton 3/11, Northwich c/s 11, Colwyn Bay 3/12	6	0
Gareth	Evans				29/04/1987	25		Chester (Yth), Bangor C, Mochdre, Llandudno, Colwyn Bay 9/10	38	4
Mike	Lea		6'00"	12 00	04/11/1987	24	Salford	Man Utd, Royal Antwerp (4ML) 8/07, Scunthorpe Undisc 7/08, Chester 7/09 (09/10 19,0) Rel 3/10, Hyde U 3/10, Rochdale 3/10 Rel c/s 10, Hyde FC 7/10, Colwyn Bay 8/10	40	4
Dan	Lloyd-McGoldrick				03/12/1991	20	Liverpool	Southport, Marine (Dual) 9/09, Chorley (SL) 11/09, Skelmersdale (3ML) 8/10, Skelmersdale (3ML) 12/10, Chasetown (L) 3/11, Colwyn Bay 8/11, Lincoln C 1/12 Rel c/s 12, Colwyn Bay 7/12	19	5
John	McKenna				15/05/1990	22		The New Saints Rel c/s 11, Ipswich (Trial) 1/08, Preston (Trial), Newtown (5ML) 8/10, AFC Telford (Trial) 7/11, Colwyn Bay 8/11	37	3
Sean	Williams		5'07"		20/01/1992	20	Liverpool	Stockport (Scholar) Rel c/s 11, Vauxhall Motors 8/11 Rel 10/11, Prescot Cables 10/11, Hyde FC 10/11, Skelmersdale (L) 3/12, Colwyn Bay 7/12		
FORWARDS										
Matthew	Berkeley		5'11"	10 10	03/08/1987	25	Manchester	Fletcher Moss, Burnley, Gretna 6/04, Workington (2ML) 2/06, Rel c/s 07, Altrincham 8/07 (07/08 2,0) Rel 9/07, Workington 10/07, Droylsden 6/08, Leigh Genesis 8/08, Mossley 11/08, Hyde U 11/08, The New Saints 1/09, Hyde FC 8/11, Workington 3/12, Colwyn Bay 6/12		
Lee	Davey				20/02/1987	25		Heswall, Colwyn Bay 11/08, Buckley Ath (L) 11/09	31	1
Kevin	Holsgrove				09/01/1988	24		Everton (Yth), NEWI Cefn Druids 8/07, Colwyn Bay 8/09, Hyde U 9/09, Kidderminster (Trial) 7/10, Altrincham 8/10, Hyde FC (L) 10/10, Hyde FC (3ML) 1/11, Boston U 7/11 Rel 9/11, FC Halifax NC 9/11 Rel 10/11, Vauxhall Motors 10/11, Colwyn Bay 8/12		
Rob	Hopley		6'04"		02/01/1985	27		Macclesfield (Yth), Winsford 12/04, Leek T 7/07, Colwyn Bay 6/08, Chester FC 5/10, Colwyn Bay (L) 12/10, Colwyn Bay 3/11	37	13
Jon	Newby		6'00"	12 04	28/11/1978	33	Warrington	Liverpool, Carlisle (L) 12/99, Crewe (2ML) 3/00, Sheff Utd (3ML) 8/00, Bury (2ML) 2/01 £100,000 3/01 Rel c/s 03, Huddersfield 8/03, York C (L) 3/04, Bury 8/04 Rel 5/06, Kidderminster (L) 3/06, Wrexham 8/06 Rel 12/06, Southport 1/07 Rel 5/07, Morecambe 8/07 Rel c/s 08, Morton c/s 08 Rel 5/09, Burton (SL) 9/08, Northwich 7/09, Colwyn Bay 7/10 (Pl/Man) 11/11	35	6

CORBY TOWN

Chairman: Kevin Ingram
Secretary: Gerry Lucas   **(T)** 07932 6333 43   **(E)** gerry21@gmail.com
Additional Committee Members:
David Mallinger, Graham Stamer, Ian Hopewell, Chris Rivett, Martin Harris, John Laws.

Manager: Ian Sampson
Programme Editor: Chris Rivett   **(E)** crivett@corbytownfc.co.uk

Back: left to right: Nathan Fox, Nethaniel Wedderburn, Greg Kaziboni, Sam Ives, Ryan Semple, Tom McGowan
Middle: left to right: Kenny Williams, Lewis Webb, Avelino Vieira, Josh Moreman, Paul Walker, Paul Malone, Liam Richardson, George, James McCafferty, Scott Tomkins.
Front: left to right: Leon McKenzie, Ricky Miller, Ian Sampson, Chris Plummer, Tom Ingram, Jason Crowe.
Missing: Nathan Horne, Jon Stead, Pierrick Briand

Club Factfile

Founded: 1947   **Nickname:** The Steelmen
Previous Names: Stewart & Lloyds (Corby) > 1947
Previous Leagues: United Counties 1935-52. Midland 1952-58. Southern 1958-2009

Club Colours (change): White/black/black (All maroon)

Ground: Steel Park, Jimmy Kane Way, Rockingham Road, Corby NN17 2FB   **(T)** 01536 406 640
Capacity: 6,000   **Seats:** 300   **Covered:** 1,000   **Clubhouse:** Yes   **Shop:** Yes

Directions: From A14, Exit at Jnc 7, Keep left, at first roundabout take A6003 Oakham/Uppingham stay on this road for approx. 7 miles (ignore signs for Corby to your right en route) straight over two roundabouts at second B.P. petrol station on right. At next roundabout approx 1 mile ahead turn right onto A6116 for 300 yards entrance to Ground between Rugby Club and Rockingham Forest Hotel (Great Western).

Previous Grounds: Not known.

Record Attendance: 2,240 v Watford - Friendly 1986-87
Record Victory: Not known
Record Defeat: Not known
Record Goalscorer: David Holbauer - 159 (1984-95)
Record Appearances: Derek Walker - 601
Additional Records: Paid £2,700 to Barnet for Elwun Edwards 1981
Senior Honours: Received £20,000 from Oxford United for Matt Murphy 1993
United Counties League 1950-51, 51-52. Southern League Premier Division 2008-09.
Northants Senior Cup x6.

10 YEAR RECORD

02-03		03-04		04-05		05-06		06-07		07-08		08-09		09-10		10-11		11-12	
SthE	19	SthE	15	SthW	12	SthE	2	SthP	20	SthP	16	SthP	1	Conf N	6	Conf N	13	Conf N	17

CORBY TOWN

No.	Date	Comp	H/A	Opponents	Att:	Result	Goalscorers	Pos
1	Sat-13-Aug	BSN	A	FC Halifax Town	1738	W 3-1	Og (L Hogan) 58, J Smith 80, Ives 90	2
2	Wed-17-Aug	BSN	H	Bishops Stortford	827	W 6-1	Ozmen 20, J Smith 2 (25, 41), Rhead 2 (34, 58), Burgess 60	1
3	Sat-20-Aug	BSN	H	Hyde FC	793	L 0-4		5
4	Tue-23-Aug	BSN	A	Gainsborough Trinity	462	L 0-1		10
5	Sat-27-Aug	BSN	A	Histon	302	D 1-1	Gordon 30	8
6	Mon-29-Aug	BSN	H	Eastwood Town	555	W 5-0	Malone 20, Rogan 2 (26, pen 90), Rhead 2 (pen 28, 80)	6
7	Sat-03-Sep	BSN	A	Worcester City	921	W 2-0	Gulliver 63, Rogan 72	5
8	Sat-10-Sep	BSN	H	Guiseley	580	L 0-1		6
9	Sat-17-Sep	BSN	A	Workington	372	D 1-1	Malone 9	6
10	Tue-20-Sep	BSN	A	Gloucester City	201	D 0-0		7
11	Sat-24-Sep	BSN	H	Blyth Spartans	543	W 4-0	Rhead pen 42, Malone 45, J Smith 78, Hibbert 84	5
12	Sat-08-Oct	BSN	H	Stalybridge Celtic	532	L 1-2	Hall 14	7
13	Sat-22-Oct	BSN	A	Colwyn Bay	385	W 2-0	Rhead 70, J Smith 74	8
14	Tue-25-Oct	BSN	A	Bishops Stortford	313	W 2-0	Rogan 25, Rhead pen 78	5
15	Sat-05-Nov	BSN	H	Vauxhall Motors	620	W 1-0	Gulliver 9	5
16	Wed-16-Nov	BSN	H	Droylsden	458	W 5-2	Og (S Holden) 10, Hall 25, Mullarkey 53, Rhead 65, Towers 88	4
17	Sat-19-Nov	BSN	H	Nuneaton Town	820	L 0-2		5
18	Sat-03-Dec	BSN	H	Gainsborough Trinity	553	L 1-3	Spruce 70	6
19	Tue-06-Dec	BSN	A	Altrincham	649	D 1-1	Mullarkey 81	7
20	Tue-13-Dec	BSN	A	Boston United	736	D 1-1	Marna pen 78	7
21	Mon-26-Dec	BSN	H	Solihull Moors	588	L 0-3		9
22	Sun-01-Jan	BSN	A	Solihull Moors	362	W 2-1	M Jones 2 (27, 90)	8
23	Sat-07-Jan	BSN	H	FC Halifax Town	739	L 2-4	Beeson 73, J Smith 88	8
24	Sat-14-Jan	BSN	A	Hyde FC	537	D 2-2	Ozmen 45, Mullarkey 51	9
25	Sat-21-Jan	BSN	A	Blyth Spartans	305	W 2-1	M Jones 45, Mullarkey 83	8
26	Sat-28-Jan	BSN	H	Boston United	552	L 1-2	Gordon 38	9
27	Wed-15-Feb	BSN	H	Hinckley United	286	L 0-2		10
28	Sat-18-Feb	BSN	H	Histon	287	L 0-2		10
29	Sat-25-Feb	BSN	A	Hinckley United	503	W 3-0	Gordon 32, King 86, Hall 87	11
30	Sat-03-Mar	BSN	A	Nuneaton Town	775	L 0-2		11
31	Tue-06-Mar	BSN	A	Harrogate Town	175	L 2-6	Gordon 16, Amory 27	11
32	Sat-10-Mar	BSN	H	Worcester City	343	L 2-3	Hall 18, King pen 90	11
33	Sat-17-Mar	BSN	A	Stalybridge Celtic	449	D 2-2	J Smith 53, King 75	11
34	Tue-20-Mar	BSN	A	Droylsden	176	L 1-2	M Jones 10	13
35	Sat-24-Mar	BSN	H	Colwyn Bay	318	W 1-0	Gordon 21	12
36	Wed-28-Mar	BSN	H	Altrincham	280	L 1-3	M Jones 34	12
37	Sat-31-Mar	BSN	A	Guiseley	589	L 0-3		13
38	Sat-07-Apr	BSN	H	Gloucester City	277	L 0-1		15
39	Mon-09-Apr	BSN	A	Eastwood Town	189	W 4-1	Hibbert 10, Og (Benjamin) 42, Malone 2 (47, 84)	11
40	Sat-14-Apr	BSN	A	Workington	290	D 3-3	Hibbert 21, King 50, Gordon 60	13
41	Sat-21-Apr	BSN	A	Vauxhall Motors	189	L 1-2	Malone 47	13
42	Sat-28-Apr	BSN	H	Harrogate Town	460	L 0-5		17

CUPS

No.	Date	Comp	H/A	Opponents	Att:	Result	Goalscorers
1	Sat-01-Oct	FAC 2Q	A	Histon	427	D 1-1	Hall 46
2	Wed-05-Oct	FAC 2QR	H	Histon	642	W 3-1 aet	Malone 2 (23, 94), Rhead 111
3	Sat-15-Oct	FAC 3Q	A	Hednesford Town	602	W 4-2	Rhead 3 (pen 57, 67, 90), Hall 60
4	Sat-29-Oct	FAC 4Q	A	Kidderminster Harriers	1281	D 0-0	
5	Wed-02-Nov	FAC 4QR	H	Kidderminster Harriers	1026	W 4-1	Mayo 61, Reynolds 2 (66, 73), Hall 80
6	Sat-12-Nov	FAC 1	A	Bristol Rovers	3787	L 1-3	Reynolds 62
7	Sat-26-Nov	FAT 3Q	H	North Ferriby United	519	D 1-1	Ozmen 20
8	Tue-29-Nov	FAT 3QR	A	North Ferriby United	170	L 2-3	Hibbert 67, Rhead 83

League
Starts
Substitute
Unused Sub

Cups
Starts
Substitute
Unused Sub

Goals (Lg)
Goals (Cup)

MACKENZIE	MCDONALD	MAYO	MALONE	GULLIVER	OZMEN	HALL	TOWERS	RHEAD	ROGAN	BURGESS	GORDON	J SMITH	IVES	HIBBERT	W JONES	SPRUCE	G SMITH	LAND	FARDEN	DRURY	DOSSOU	FAIRLAMB	FOX	REYNOLDS	BEESON	MULLARKEY	MARNA	BEXFIELD	M JONES	TARRY	EKINS	R JONES	WALTON	MCGOWAN	KING	BOLT	SPEISS	AMORY	LOUIS	BENNION
X	X	X	X	X	X	X	X	X	X	X	S	S	S	U																										
X	X	X	S	X	X	X	X	X	X	U	X	X	X	X	S	S	U																							
X	X	X	U	X	S	X	X	X	X	X	S	X	X	X	S	S	U																							
X	X	X	U	X	S	X	X	X	X	X	S	X	X	X	S	X	U																							
X	U	X	X	X	X	X	X	X	X	X		S	U		S	U																								
X	U	X	X	S	X	X	X	X	X		X	X	X		S	U	S																							
X	X	X	X	S	X	X	X	X	U		X	X	X		S	U	U																							
X		X	X	S	X	X	X	X	S	X	X	X	X	U		S	U																							
X		X	X	S	X	X	X	X	X	S	X	U	X		S	U																								
X		X	X	S	X	X	X	X	S	X	X	U	X		S	U																								
X	S	X		X	S	X	X	X	X	X	X	X	X		S	U																								
X		X		X	X	X	X	X	X		X	X	U		S		S		U		S																			
X		X		X	X	X	X	X	X		X	X	U		S		U	S	U	X																			
X		X		X	X	X	X	X	X		X	X	U		S		U	S	X	X																			
X		X	S	X	X	X	X	X	S	U	X	S			X		U	S	X	X	X																		
X		X	S	X	X	X	X	X	S	U	X	S		U			U	X	X	X																			
X		X	X	X	X	X	X		X	S		U		S			U	X	S	X																			
X		X	X	X	X	X	X		X	S		U	X		U		S	S	X																				
X	X	X		X	X	S	X	X		X	S		S	U		X	U	X	X	S																			
X	S	X		X	X	S	X		X	X	S		X	U		X	S	X	U																				
X	X	X		X	X	X	X		X	X	S		X	U		U	X		U	X																			
X	X	U	X		X	X	X		X	X	S		X	S		S	X		X	U																			
X	X	X		X	X	X			X	X			X			U		U		X	X	U	S	U															
X	U	X	X	X	X	X			X	X			S				X	S	X			U																	
X	S	X	X	X	X	X			X	X			S				X	S	X			U	U																
X		X	X	X	X	X			X	S			S			S	U	X			X	U																	
X	X	X	X	X	S	X			X	X			S			X	U				S	U	X																
X	X	X	X	X	S	X			X	X			S			S					U		S	X	U														
		X	X	X	S	X			X	X			U			X					U	X	S	X	S	X	X	S											
		X	X	X		X			X	X			S			X					S	X	U	X	X	S													
		X	X		S	X			X	X			S	U			U				X	X	S	X	X	U													
		X	X	X	S	X		S			X	X			S					U	X	U		U	X	S	X												
		X	X	U	X	X		X			X	X			U						X	S	X	S		S		X											
		X	X	S	X			X			X	X			X					U	X	S	X	U			S	X											
		X	S	X				X			X	X			U					S	X	U	X	S	U			S	X										
		X	X	U	X			X			X	X			X					S	X	S	X	X	U			S	X										
		X	S	X	X			X			X	S			X	U				S	X	U	X	X	U			S	X										
		X	X	U	X			X			X	S			X	X				S	X	X	S	X				U	X										
		X	X	X	S	X			X	X			U				U				X	S																	

Second block:

X	U	X			X	S	X	X	X	X	X	X	S	U	X		S	X																						
X			X	X	S	X	X	X			X	X	X	S	X		X	U	S		U																			
X	X		X	X	S	X	X	X	S		X	X	U	X	X		X	U			U	U																		
X		X	U	X	X	X	X	X		X	X	U	U		S	U			U	U		X																		
X		X	U	X	X	X	X	X		X	X	U	S	S		U	S		U	S		X																		
X		X	S	X	X			X	X	U	X	X	S	X	S		U	U				X																		
X		X	U	X	X	X	X	S	X	X	S	S	U		U		X				X					X														
		X	X	X	S	X	X	S			X	X	X		S	X	U			X					X															

Totals:

28	10	40	31	39	25	41	41	22	11	7	40	27	4	15	0	4	2	0	0	1	3	0	0	4	6	10	2	0	13	0	0	1	0	4	14	0	5	4	0	8
0	3	0	4	0	13	1	0	0	4	2	1	14	5	6	0	11	2	2	8	0	4	0	1	1	3	7	1	2	3	0	1	1	0	6	0	3	0	5	2	0
0	3	1	2	0	3	0	0	0	1	3	0	0	5	6	2	4	2	12	10	1	5	1	2	1	1	3	0	3	0	1	2	3	1	6	1	3	0	3	0	0

7	1	6	3	8	4	8	7	7	4	3	8	6	0	5	0	2	0	1	0	1	0	0	0	5	0	0	2	0	0	0	0	0	0	0	0	0	0	0	0	0
0	0	0	1	0	4	0	0	1	2	0	0	2	2	2	0	5	0	1	0	0	1	0	0	0	0	0	0	0	0	0	0	0	0	0	0	0	0	0	0	0
0	1	0	3	0	0	0	0	0	0	1	0	0	4	1	0	0	1	4	0	3	5	2	0	0	0	0	0	0	0	0	0	0	0	0	0	0	0	0	0	0

| 0 | 0 | 0 | 6 | 2 | 2 | 4 | 1 | 8 | 4 | 1 | 6 | 7 | 1 | 3 | 0 | 1 | 0 | 0 | 0 | 0 | 0 | 0 | 0 | 1 | 4 | 1 | 0 | 5 | 0 | 0 | 0 | 0 | 0 | 4 | 0 | 0 | 1 | 0 | 0 | |
| 0 | 0 | 1 | 2 | 0 | 1 | 3 | 0 | 5 | 0 | 0 | 0 | 0 | 1 | 0 | 0 | 0 | 0 | 0 | 0 | 0 | 0 | 0 | 3 | 0 | 0 | 0 | 0 | 0 | 0 | 0 | 0 | 0 | 0 | 0 | 0 | 0 | 0 | 0 | 0 | |

PLAYING SQUAD 2012/13

Existing Players		SN	HT	WT	DOB	AGE	POB	Career	Apps	Goals
GOALKEEPERS										
Paul	Walker		5'10"	10 10	18/04/1992	20	Wales	Northampton Rel 1/12, Brackley (L) 12/09, Brackley (L) 9/11, Brackley 2/12, Corby T 6/12		
DEFENDERS										
Pierrick	Briand							AC Arles Avignon (Fra), Dover 11/10, Maidstone (Dual) 1/11, France, Corby T 7/12		
Jason	Crowe		5'09"	10 09	30/09/1978	33	Sidcup	Arsenal, C.Palace (3ML) 11/98, Portsmouth 7/99 Rel c/s 03, Brentford (3ML) 9/00, Grimsby 8/03 Rel c/s 05, Northampton 7/05 Rel c/s 09, Leeds 7/09, L.Orient 1/11 Rel c/s 11, Northampton 11/11 Rel c/s 12, Corby T 7/12		
Andy	Holt		6'01"	12 07	21/05/1978	34	Stockport	Oldham, Hull C (SL) 3/01, Hull C 5/01 Rel c/s 04, Barnsley (2ML) 8/02, Shrewsbury (SL) 3/03, Wrexham 7/04 Rel c/s 06, Northampton 7/06 Rel c/s 12, Corby T 7/12		
Nathan	Horne							Yaxley, Alconbury, Peterborough Northern Star, Corby T 6/12		
Paul	Malone							Corby T (Yth), Desborough (L) 10/07 Perm, S & L Corby c/s 08, Stamford 7/09, Corby T (Small Fee) 3/11	35	6
MIDFIELDERS										
Nathan	Fox		5'10"	12 02	14/11/1992	19	Leicester	Notts County (Scholar) Rel c/s 11, Derby (Trial) 7/11, Corby T 10/11, Corby T 7/12	1	0
Sam	Ives				24/06/1991	21	Cambridge	Cambridge C (Yth), Cambridge U Rel 5/11, Bury T (L) 12/10, Corby T 6/11 Rel 11/11, Cambridge C 11/11, Bishops Stortford 12/11, Stamford 3/12, Corby T 7/12	9	1
Ryan	Semple		5'11"	10 11	04/07/1985	27	Belfast	Peterborough, Man Utd (Trial) 2/03, Farnborough (3ML) 11/03, Lincoln C 7/06 Rel 1/08, Chester (6WL) 11/06, Rushden & D (L) 8/07, Oxford U NC 2/08, Brackley T 3/08, Boston U (Trial) c/s 08, Deeping R 8/08, Haverhill R (Dual) 3/09, Gainsborough 6/09, Boston U 3/10 Rel c/s 12, Corby T 6/12		
Jon	Stead							Bedford T, Spalding U 8/08, Blackstones, Peterborough Northern Star 6/10, Corby T 6/12		
Lewis	Webb				13/03/1991	21		Yaxley (Yth), Peterborough, Stamford (L) 3/08, Aylesbury (L) 11/08, Stamford (WE) 3/09, Kings Lynn 6/09, St Neots 12/09, Corby T 6/12		
FORWARDS										
Leon	McKenzie		5'11"	12 11	17/05/1978	34	Croydon	C.Palace, Fulham (L) 10/97, Peterborough (L) 8/98, Peterborough (2ML) 10/98, Peterborough 10/00, Norwich 12/03, Coventry £600,000 8/06, Charlton 9/09 Rel c/s 10, Northampton 9/10 Rel c/s 11, Luton (Trial) 7/11, Kettering 8/11 Retired 12/11, Jail, Corby T 7/12		
Josh	Moreman							Peterborough Northern Star, Deeping R 8/11, Corby T 6/12		
Avelino	Vieira							Blackstones, Peterborough Northern Star £750 8/10, Corby T 6/12		

DROYLSDEN

Chairman: David Pace
Secretary: Alan Slater   **(T)** 07989 024 777   **(E)** alans83@btinternet.com
Additional Committee Members:
Bryan Pace, Stella Quinn

Manager: David Pace
Programme Editor: TBA   **(E)**

Club Factfile

Founded: 1892   **Nickname:** The Bloods
Previous Names: None
Previous Leagues: Manchester, Lancashire Combination 1936-39, 50-68, Cheshire County 1939-50, 68-82,
North West Counties 1982-87, Northern Premier 1986-2004

Club Colours (change): All red (All royal blue)

Ground: The Butchers Arms Ground, Market Street, Droylsden, M43 7AY   **(T)** 0161 370 1426
Capacity: 3,500   **Seats:** 500   **Covered:** 2,000   **Clubhouse:** Yes   **Shop:** Yes
Directions From junction 23 M60 follow signs A635 Manchester, then A662 signed Droylsden, at town centre traffic lights turn right into Market Street, through next set of lights and the main entrance to the ground is 75 yards on your left.

Previous Grounds:

Record Attendance: 4,250 v Grimsby
Record Victory: 13-2 v Lucas Sports Club
Record Defeat: Not known
Record Goalscorer: E. Gillibrand - 275 (1931-35)
Record Appearances: Paul Phillips - 326
Additional Records: Received £11,000 from Crewe Alexandra for Tony Naylor 1990

Senior Honours:
Northern Premier League Division 1 1998-99. Conference North 2006-07.
Manchester Premier Cup x3. Manchester Senior Cup x3.

10 YEAR RECORD

02-03		03-04		04-05		05-06		06-07		07-08		08-09		09-10		10-11		11-12	
NP P	9	NP P	2	Conf N	3	Conf N	4	Conf N	1	Conf	24	Conf N	7	Conf N	5	Conf N	8	Conf N	9

DROYLSDEN

No.	Date	Comp	H/A	Opponents	Att:	Result	Goalscorers	Pos
1	Sat-13-Aug	BSN	A	Eastwood Town	309	D 2-2	Jones 15, Rouse 49	11
2	Tue-16-Aug	BSN	H	Guiseley	322	W 2-0	P Brown 70, Rowe 75	3
3	Sat-20-Aug	BSN	H	Nuneaton Town	328	W 2-1	Rowe 77, C Brown 84	4
4	Tue-23-Aug	BSN	A	Harrogate Town	350	D 0-0		4
5	Sat-27-Aug	BSN	A	Workington	308	L 1-3	Gardner 53	7
6	Mon-29-Aug	BSN	H	Gainsborough Trinity	285	L 1-2	Poole 85	10
7	Sat-03-Sep	BSN	H	Colwyn Bay	349	W 2-1	Hardiker 7, Kilheeney 78	8
8	Sat-10-Sep	BSN	A	Blyth Spartans	488	W 3-1	Hall 56, Rowe 2 (87, 90)	5
9	Tue-13-Sep	BSN	H	Hyde FC	625	L 2-3	Logan 25, Poole 90	5
10	Sat-17-Sep	BSN	H	Hinckley United	265	L 2-3	Kilheeney 4, Johnson 13	8
11	Sat-24-Sep	BSN	A	Boston United	1127	L 1-2	Kilheeney 57	11
12	Sat-08-Oct	BSN	A	Solihull Moors	260	W 2-0	Rowe 37, Gardner pen 56	10
13	Sat-22-Oct	BSN	H	FC Halifax Town	683	W 2-1	Gardner 2 (57, pen 72)	9
14	Mon-24-Oct	BSN	A	Nuneaton Town	539	L 1-2	Gardner 72	10
15	Sat-05-Nov	BSN	H	Stalybridge Celtic	656	D 3-3	Gardner 50, Logan 71, Rowe 90	12
16	Tue-08-Nov	BSN	H	Worcester City	225	W 4-1	Logan 4, Johnson 21, Rowe 2 (26, 56)	8
17	Sat-12-Nov	BSN	A	Vauxhall Motors	189	D 1-1	Rowe 89	9
18	Wed-16-Nov	BSN	A	Corby Town	458	L 2-5	Marshall 37, Rowe 75	9
19	Sat-19-Nov	BSN	H	Solihull Moors	191	W 1-0	Kilheeney 16	7
20	Sat-03-Dec	BSN	A	Colwyn Bay	272	L 3-6	Kerr 15, C Brown 75, Rowe 87	9
21	Mon-26-Dec	BSN	A	Altrincham	846	L 1-5	Kilheeney 88	11
22	Sun-01-Jan	BSN	H	Altrincham	601	W 3-1	Kilheeney 2 (pen 6, 69), Johnson 34	11
23	Sat-07-Jan	BSN	A	Stalybridge Celtic	802	W 3-1	Kilheeney 2 (7, 32), Johnson 9	9
24	Sat-21-Jan	BSN	A	Guiseley	468	L 3-4	Johnson 24, Kilheeney 35, Gardner 45	11
25	Tue-24-Jan	BSN	H	Eastwood Town	175	D 3-3	Johnson 2 (32, 62), Gardner 90	11
26	Sat-18-Feb	BSN	H	Bishops Stortford	271	D 2-2	Kilheeney 53, Rouse 75	13
27	Sat-25-Feb	BSN	A	Hyde FC	546	L 0-4		15
28	Sat-03-Mar	BSN	A	Bishops Stortford	401	L 0-5		17
29	Tue-06-Mar	BSN	H	Gloucester City	185	W 3-1	Kilheeney 14, Killeen 64, Johnson 90	13
30	Sat-10-Mar	BSN	H	Histon	192	L 2-3	Gardner 59, Hall 62	16
31	Tue-13-Mar	BSN	H	Blyth Spartans	170	D 3-3	Johnson 44, Gardner 2 (57, pen 71)	16
32	Sat-17-Mar	BSN	A	Worcester City	895	W 2-0	Fisher 37, Johnson 84	14
33	Tue-20-Mar	BSN	H	Corby Town	176	W 2-1	Logan 49, Gardner pen 55	11
34	Sat-24-Mar	BSN	H	Boston United	315	W 2-1	Hall 10, Johnson 76	10
35	Sat-31-Mar	BSN	A	Hinckley United	354	D 1-1	Nsangou 42	10
36	Tue-03-Apr	BSN	A	Harrogate Town	169	D 1-1	Gardner pen 13	10
37	Sat-07-Apr	BSN	H	Workington	245	D 1-1	Gardner 58	10
38	Mon-09-Apr	BSN	A	Gainsborough Trinity	629	W 2-1	Johnson 41, Lacey 69	9
39	Sat-14-Apr	BSN	H	Gloucester City	220	L 1-2	Johnson 72	9
40	Tue-17-Apr	BSN	A	Histon	313	D 5-5	Nsangou 34, Kerr 43, Logan 44, Hall 50, Johnson 90	9
41	Sat-21-Apr	BSN	A	FC Halifax Town	1815	L 1-2	Johnson 14	9
42	Sat-28-Apr	BSN	H	Vauxhall Motors	401	W 5-2	Gardner 3 (20, 63, pen 88), C Brown 59, Johnson 90	9

CUPS

No.	Date	Comp	H/A	Opponents	Att:	Result	Goalscorers
1	Sat-01-Oct	FAC 2Q	A	Workington	316	W 2-1	Kilheeney 2 (23, 36)
2	Sat-15-Oct	FAC 3Q	H	Stocksbridge Park Steels	230	W 4-1	Gardner 2 (11, pen 55), Rowe 13, Kilheeney 49
3	Sat-29-Oct	FAC 4Q	H	Blyth Spartans	393	D 0-0	
4	Tue-01-Nov	FAC 4QR	A	Blyth Spartans	678	L 1-2	Hall 63
5	Sat-26-Nov	FAT 3Q	H	Witton Albion	304	W 2-1	Rowe 2 (23, 76)
6	Sat-10-Dec	FAT 1	H	Mansfield Town	335	W 2-1	Johnson 2 (20, 58)
7	Sat-14-Jan	FAT 2	A	Kidderminster Harriers	1104	L 1-5	Hall 41

League
Starts
Substitute
Unused Sub

Cups
Starts
Substitute
Unused Sub

Goals (Lg)
Goals (Cup)

PHILLIPS	ANANE	LOGAN	C BROWN	HARDIKER	P BROWN	GARDNER	KILLEEN	ROWE	JOHNSON	JONES	VAUGHAN	ROUSE	HALL	LAKE	GERRARD	POOLE	KILHEENEY	ROBINSON	LANGFORD	PEYTON	L HOLDEN	KERR	MARSHALL	S HOLDEN	LYNCH	D THOMPSON	T THOMPSON	OWEN	FISHER	MOYO	ST LOUIS-HAMILTON	LACEY	MCKENZIE	SHERIDAN	NSANGOU	DAVIES
X	X	X	X	X	X	X	X	X	X	X		S	S		S	U	U																			
X	X	X	X	X	X	X	X	X	X	X		S	X		S	U	U	S	S																	
X	X	X	X	X	X	X	X	X	X	X		U	X		S	U	S	S																		
X	X	X	X	X	X	X	X	X	X	X		S			S	U	S	U	X																	
X			X	X	X	X	X	X	X		X				S	U	S	U	X	X	S															
X			X	X	X	X	X	X	X		X				S	U	S	S	X				X	X	U											
X	X			X		X	S	X	S		S		U					X	X		U		X	X	X	X										
X	X	X	S	X		X	X	X	S		S		X	U				X	X		U			X												
U	X	X	X	X		S	X	X	X		U		X	X			S	X	X	X				S												
X	X	X	S	X		X	X	X	X		U		X	X	S	X	X		X																	
X		X	X	X		X	X	X		X	U	X			U			S		S	S															
X		X	X	X		X	X		X	X	U	X		S		S	X		X	U																
X		X	X		X		X	S	S	U			S	X		S	X		X	U																
X		X		U		X	X	X		X		X	U	S		X	S		X	U																
X		X	S	X		X	X	X		X		U	S	S		X	X		X	S	X															
X		X		X		X	X	X		X		U	S		S	X	U		X	X																
	X		X		X	S	X	S		X	X	X			X	S		X	U	U																
	X	X		X	X	X	X		X	X	S		X	S	U	X	X	X	U																	
X		X		X	X	X		S	U			S	X	S	X	X	X	U																		
X		X	X		X	S	S	X			X	X		X	X	X	U	U																		
X	S			X	X		X		X	X	S		U		X	X		X	S	X		X														
U		X	X		X	X		X		X	U		X	X	U		U		S		X	X	X													
	X	X		X	X	X		S	U	X	X	X		U	S	X	X	X					U													
	X	U		X	X	X		X	U		X	X	U		X	X	X	X	U	U			S													
	X		X	X	X		S	U		X		X	X		X		X	X	X	S	U	X	S													
X	S		X	X		X		U	U		X		U	X	X	X	X		X	X	X	U														
U	X		X	X		X	U		X	X	U	U	S		X	X		X				S		X	X	X										
X	X		X	X		S	U		X	X		U	S	X	X	X	U	U					X	X	X	U	U									
X	U		X	X		U		X	X	U		X	S		X	X		X	X	S	U	X														
X		X	X	X		S	U		X	X		X		X	X	X	U	X	S					X	X	X	S									
X	S		X		X	U		X	X	U	U		X	X	X		X	X	X	S																
U	X		X		X	X	X		U	U		X	X		X	X		S		X	X	S	U				X	U								
U	X	S	X	X		S		X	U		X	X		X		X		X	X	X							X	S								
U	X	X	X		X	X	S		X		X	S		X		X		U		X	X	U	X	S												
U	X	X	X		X		X		X		X	X		X		X		U		X	X	S	U	S												
U	X	X	X	U		X	X		X		X	S		X		X		S		X	S	U	U	X												
	X	X	X	X		X		X		X		U		X	U	X	S	S	X	S																
X		X	X	X		X	X	X	U		U		X	U	X	S	X		U	U	U	X														
X		X	X	X		X	X	X	S		U		X	U	U		X		U	U		X		S	S											
X		X	U	X		X	X	X	S		X		X	U	S		X		U	S		X		X	U											
X		X	S	X		X	S	X	X		X		X	U	S		U	X	X	X		U	U													
	X	X				X	S	X	X		X		X	X			X		U	U		X	X	X	U											
X		X				X	X	X	X		X	S	X	U	U	S		X	X		X	X	X													
X						X	X		X		X	S	X	U	S	X		X	X		X	X	X				U		S							

25	9	35	25	16	6	39	31	21	37	1	9	3	21	3	3	3	19	1	23	16	2	29	10	24	0	3	0	0	8	10	14	7	0	6	3	0
0	0	3	7	0	0	1	5	1	5	0	4	6	11	2	12	4	4	0	5	11	1	0	1	3	2	0	0	5	1	0	0	5	2	0	6	1
8	0	1	2	2	0	0	1	0	0	0	3	0	3	27	4	2	2	0	5	5	0	2	0	4	5	4	1	6	0	0	0	1	10	2	1	1
6	0	5	4	4	0	7	5	6	3	0	3	0	7	1	2	0	5	0	2	2	1	7	3	4	0	0	0	0	0	0	0	0	0	0	0	0
0	0	0	1	0	0	0	2	0	3	0	0	2	0	0	3	1	1	0	0	2	0	0	0	1	1	0	0	1	0	0	0	0	0	0	0	0
0	0	0	1	0	0	0	0	0	1	0	2	0	0	6	1	0	0	0	5	3	1	0	0	1	3	1	0	0	0	0	0	0	0	0	0	0
0	0	5	3	1	1	17	1	11	16	1	0	2	4	0	0	2	12	0	0	0	2	1	0	0	0	0	0	0	1	0	0	1	0	0	2	0
0	0	0	0	0	0	2	0	3	2	0	0	0	2	0	0	0	3	0	0	0	0	0	0	0	0	0	0	0	0	0	0	0	0	0	0	0

PLAYING SQUAD 2012/13

Existing Players		SN	HT	WT	DOB	AGE	POB	Career	Apps	Goals
GOALKEEPERS										
Paul	Phillips				15/11/1978	33	Manchester	Man Utd, Bury, Buxton, Curzon Ashton, Droylsden 12/99, Stalybridge 5/08, Droylsden 11/09	25	0
DEFENDERS										
Phil	Bolland		6'02"	13 08	26/08/1976	36	Liverpool	Altrincham, Salford C 10/95, Trafford 3/96, Knowsley U 8/96, Southport c/s 97, Oxford U 7/01, Chester (2ML) 1/02 £15,000 3/02, Peterborough 1/06 Rel c/s 06, Chester 6/06, Wrexham 1/08, Cambridge U 7/08 Rel 6/09, Barrow 7/09 Rel c/s 12, Droylsden 8/12		
Chris	Brown		6'05"	12 04	21/02/1992	20	Hazel Grove	Rochdale Rel c/s 11, Bamber Bridge (WE) 2/10, Droylsden (WE) 3/10, Ashton U (L) 8/10, Bamber Bridge (L) 1/11, Hyde FC (L) 3/11, Droylsden 7/11	32	3
Shaun	Holden				12/12/1991	20		Southport, Burscough (L) 12/09 Perm, Droylsden 9/11	27	0
Nat	Kerr		6'00"	10 10	31/10/1987	24	Manchester	Crewe, Rotherham 1/07 Rel c/s 08, Northwich (SL) 11/07, Woodley Sports 8/08 Rel 9/08, Barrow 10/08 Rel 5/09, Northwich 7/09, Droylsden 8/10	29	2
Andrew	Langford		5'11"	12 05	03/07/1988	24	Manchester	Morecambe Rel c/s 08, Leek T (L) 11/07, Workington 12/08 Rel 5/11, Droylsden 8/11	28	0
MIDFIELDERS										
Tom	Baker		5'06"	11 00	28/03/1985	27	Salford	Barnsley Rel c/s 05, Gainsborough 7/05, Scarborough 1/06 Rel 5/06, Bradford PA c/s 06, FC Halifax 10/08 Rel c/s 12, Droylsden 7/12		
Michael	Connor				10/09/1989	22		Man City (Scholar), Sunday Football, Mossley 9/08, Salford C, Woodley Sports, Northwich 7/09, Droylsden 12/10 Rel 9/11, Droylsden 8/12		
Stephen	Hall							New Mills, Ashton U 11/10, Altrincham (Trial), Droylsden 8/11	32	4
Lewis	Killeen		5'09"	10 07	23/09/1982	29	Peterborough	Sheff Utd Rel c/s 03, Halifax (3ML), Halifax 6/03, Crawley 5/08 Rel 5/10, Droylsden 7/10	36	1
Carlos	Logan		5'07"	11 00	07/11/1985	26	Wythenshawe	Man City Rel c/s 05, Chesterfield (SL) 3/05, Darlington 8/05 Rel c/s 07, Bradford C (L) 1/07, Altrincham 8/07 Rel 2/08, Drogheda U (Trial) 2/08, Flixton 3/08, Barrow 8/07 Rel 5/10, Hyde FC 8/10 Rel 9/10, AFC Telford 12/10, Northwich 1/11, Droylsden 3/11	38	5
Martin	Ormesher				12/11/1982	29		Ashton T, Ashton Ath 1/07, AFC Liverpool 9/08, Leigh Genesis, Burscough 12/09, Ashton T, Ashton Ath 1/11, Middlewich T, Newtown 1/12, Droylsden 8/12		
Joe	Reidy							Rochdale (Scholar) Rel c/s 11, Coaching,Droylsden 8/12		
Lee	Rick				18/06/1989	23		Macclesfield (Yth), Hyde U/FC, Mossley 3/11, Droylsden 8/12		
FORWARDS										
Antonio	Bryan				04/10/1989	22	Manchester	Man Utd Rel c/s 09, Altrincham 10/09 Rel 11/09, Witton 10/10, Droylsden 8/12		
Tom	Fisher		5'10"	11 07	28/06/1992	20	Wythenshawe	Stockport Rel c/s 11, Macclesfield 7/11 Rel c/s 12, Hyde (L) 11/11, Droylsden (L) 1/12, Droylsden (L) 3/12, Droylsden 8/12	9	1
Joe	O'Neill		6'00"	10 05	28/10/1982	29	Blackburn	Preston, Bury (SL) 7/03, Mansfield (3ML) 8/04, Chester (3ML) 1/05, York 7/05 Rel 5/06, Altrincham 6/06 Rel 5/09, Stalybridge 6/09, Guiseley 6/10 Rel c/s 12, Droylsden 8/12		

FC HALIFAX TOWN

Chairman: David Bosmworth
Secretary: Hayley Horne   **(T)** 01422 341 222   **(E)** hayleyhorne@halifaxafc.co.uk
Additional Committee Members:
D Paul Anderson, Bobby Ham, Stuart Peacock

Manager: Neil Aspin
Programme Editor: Greg Stainton   **(E)** marketing@sandalbmw.net

THE NON-LEAGUE CLUB DIRECTORY

Book Holiday Inn Hotels and Save today!

Home

Clubs

Steps 1 - 4

League Tables

35 Years of Non-League Football

The Non-League Club Directory has developed into a comprehensive record of competitions within the non-League game, giving this level of football the

www.non-leagueclubdirectory.co.uk

Club Factfile

Founded: 1911   **Nickname:** Shaymen

Previous Names: Halifax Town 1911-2008 then reformed as F.C. Halifax Town

Previous Leagues: Yorkshire Combination 1911-12, Midland 1912-21, Football League 1921-93, 98-2002, Conference 1993-98, 2002-08

Club Colours (change): Blue & white/white & blue/blue & white (Red/black & red/black & red)

Ground: The Shay Stadium, Shay Syke, Halifax HX1 2YT   **(T)** 01422 341 222

Capacity: 6,561   **Seats:** 2,330   **Covered:** 4,231   **Clubhouse:** Yes   **Shop:** Yes

Directions: M62, junction 24, head towards Halifax on A629 and the Town Centre.
After 3-4 miles, ground is on the right (Shaw Hill) sign posted The Shay.

Previous Grounds: Sandhall Lane 1911-15, Exley 1919-20

Record Attendance: 36,885 v Tottenham Hotspur - FA Cup 5th Round 14/02/1953

Record Victory: 12-0 v West Vale Ramblers - FA Cup 1st Qualifying Road 1913-14
Record Defeat: 0-13 v Stockport County - Division 3 North 1933-34

Record Goalscorer: Albert Valentine

Record Appearances: John Pickering

Additional Records:

Senior Honours:
Conference 1997-98. Northern Premier League Division 1 North 2009-10, Premier Division 2010-11.

02-03		03-04		04-05		05-06		06-07		07-08		08-09		09-10		10-11		11-12	
Conf	8	Conf	19	Conf	9	Conf	4	Conf	16	Conf	20	NP1N	8	NP1N	1	NP P	1	Conf N	3

FC HALIFAX TOWN

No.	Date	Comp	H/A	Opponents	Att:	Result	Goalscorers	Pos
1	Sat-13-Aug	BSN	H	Corby Town	1738	L 1-3	Holland 59	18
2	Tue-16-Aug	BSN	A	Blyth Spartans	736	W 3-2	Baker 31, Dean 55, Vardy 75	13
3	Sat-20-Aug	BSN	A	Worcester City	927	D 1-1	Vardy 11	14
4	Tue-23-Aug	BSN	H	Colwyn Bay	1406	D 1-1	Vardy 68	13
5	Sat-27-Aug	BSN	H	Stalybridge Celtic	1476	D 2-2	Gregory 7, Baker 90	15
6	Mon-29-Aug	BSN	A	Boston United	1596	D 0-0		13
7	Sat-03-Sep	BSN	H	Workington	1433	W 3-1	Gregory 15, Baker 2 (pen 19, 73)	10
8	Sat-10-Sep	BSN	A	Hinckley United	571	L 2-3	Gregory 35, Winter 64	14
9	Sat-17-Sep	BSN	H	Vauxhall Motors	1265	L 1-5	Dean 50	16
10	Tue-20-Sep	BSN	A	Guiseley	897	W 4-3	Gregory 2 (25, 65), Og (Ellis) 51, Dixon 54	12
11	Sat-24-Sep	BSN	A	Harrogate Town	1107	D 0-0		12
12	Sat-08-Oct	BSN	H	Eastwood Town	1320	W 2-1	Gregory 2 (5, 52)	11
13	Sat-22-Oct	BSN	A	Droylsden	683	L 1-2	Gregory 67	13
14	Tue-25-Oct	BSN	H	Hyde FC	1534	W 3-2	Marwood 10, Garner 18, Gregory 42	11
15	Sat-05-Nov	BSN	A	Gloucester City	505	W 3-1	Dean 2 (17, 80), Garner 86	10
16	Wed-16-Nov	BSN	H	Solihull Moors	1140	D 0-0		11
17	Sat-19-Nov	BSN	A	Histon	513	W 4-1	Walshaw 2 (38, 60), Gregory pen 52, Rainford 90	9
18	Sat-03-Dec	BSN	H	Altrincham	1414	L 2-4	Rainford 17, Garner 41	11
19	Tue-06-Dec	BSN	A	Workington	410	W 2-1	Gregory 38, Dean 80	8
20	Sat-10-Dec	BSN	H	Blyth Spartans	1059	W 3-0	Rainford 25, Walshaw 34, St Juste 82	6
21	Sat-17-Dec	BSN	H	Hinckley United	1267	W 6-1	Rainford 2 (9, 62), Walshaw 3 (34, 37, 60), Gregory 85	6
22	Mon-26-Dec	BSN	A	Gainsborough Trinity	1201	W 1-0	Dean 90	5
23	Sat-07-Jan	BSN	A	Corby Town	739	W 4-2	Holland 2 (17, 43), Dean 75, St Juste 84	5
24	Sat-14-Jan	BSN	A	Worcester City	1556	W 2-1	Darkwah 90, Gregory 90+3	3
25	Sat-21-Jan	BSN	A	Vauxhall Motors	532	W 3-1	Holland 3 (32, 44, 45)	3
26	Tue-24-Jan	BSN	H	Gainsborough Trinity	1300	D 2-2	Gregory 7, Garner 72	3
27	Sat-11-Feb	BSN	A	Colwyn Bay	634	W 1-0	Holland 43	2
28	Sat-18-Feb	BSN	A	Eastwood Town	579	D 2-2	L Hogan 5, Holland 8	2
29	Tue-21-Feb	BSN	H	Nuneaton Town	1309	L 0-3		3
30	Sat-25-Feb	BSN	A	Nuneaton Town	1051	L 0-1		3
31	Sat-03-Mar	BSN	H	Harrogate Town	1398	W 3-1	Wint 30, Holland 32, Dean 75	3
32	Sat-10-Mar	BSN	A	Hyde FC	1364	D 1-1	Dean 11	3
33	Tue-13-Mar	BSN	H	Bishops Stortford	1008	L 0-1		4
34	Sat-17-Mar	BSN	H	Gloucester City	1662	D 0-0		4
35	Sat-24-Mar	BSN	A	Bishops Stortford	667	W 3-1	Hannah 3 (4, 11, 69)	4
36	Tue-27-Mar	BSN	H	Guiseley	1772	L 1-2	Gregory 11	4
37	Sat-31-Mar	BSN	H	Histon	1338	W 4-0	Gregory 25, Hannah 2 (29, 55), Crooks 61	4
38	Fri-06-Apr	BSN	A	Stalybridge Celtic	1647	L 1-2	Clancy 34	5
39	Mon-09-Apr	BSN	H	Boston United	1584	W 3-2	Hannah 2 (5, 34), Dean 39	4
40	Sat-14-Apr	BSN	A	Altrincham	1291	D 1-1	Dean 45	5
41	Sat-21-Apr	BSN	H	Droylsden	1815	W 2-1	Clancy 38, Gregory 55	3
42	Sat-28-Apr	BSN	A	Solihull Moors	711	W 2-1	Gregory 39, Clancy 50	3

CUPS

No.	Date	Comp	H/A	Opponents	Att:	Result	Goalscorers	
1	Sat-01-Oct	FAC 2Q	H	Tadcaster Albion	1002	W 2-1	Dean 82, McManus 90	
2	Sat-15-Oct	FAC 3Q	A	Lancaster City	646	W 3-0	Renshaw 3, Garner 33, Gregory 85	
3	Sat-29-Oct	FAC 4Q	A	Solihull Moors	551	W 1-0	Holland 74	
4	Sun-13-Nov	FAC 1	H	Charlton Athletic	4621	L 0-4		
5	Sat-26-Nov	FAT 3Q	A	Colwyn Bay	420	D 0-0		
6	Tue-29-Nov	FAT 3QR	H	Colwyn Bay	717	L 1-2	Baker 62	
7	Wed-02-May	PO SF1	A	Gainsborough Trinity	2380	D 2-2	Gregory 2 (44, 85)	
8	Sun-06-May	PO SF2	H	Gainsborough Trinity	3468	L 0-1		

League
Starts
Substitute
Unused Sub

Cups
Starts
Substitute
Unused Sub

Goals (Lg)
Goals (Cup)

EASTWOOD	HARDY	LOWE	L HOGAN	HAGGERTY	MCMANUS	VARDY	BAKER	DEAN	HOLLAND	NEEDHAM	GRAY	GREGORY	WINTER	SENIOR	GARNER	FOSTER	ANDERSON	TOULSON	S HOGAN	DIXON	WOOD	ST JUSTE	HOLSGROVE	RENSHAW	MARWOOD	GIBSON	THOMPSON	RAINFORD	WALSHAW	ASHWORTH	DARKWAH	HATFIELD	TAYLOR	WINT	CROOKS	CLANCY	HANNAH
X	X	X	X	X	X	X	X	X	X	X		S	S	S		S	U	U																			
X	X	X	X	X	X	X	X	X	X	X					S	X	X	S																			
X	X	X	X			X	X	X	X						U	U	U	S	X	X	S																
X	X	X	X		X	X	X	S	X			X	X	X	U	S	S	U																			
X	X	X	X	U	X		X	X	X	S	S	X	X	U	X		S																				
X	X	X	X	U	X		X	X		X	U	X	U	U	S		X		S																		
X	X	X	X	S	X		X	S	X	X		X	X	U	S		X		U																		
X	X	X	X	S	X		X		S	S		X	X	U	X		X	U	X																		
X	U	X	X		X	X		X	X			X	X	U	X		X		U	X	S																
X	S	X	X		X		X	S	X	X		X		U	U	X		X		X		U															
X	S	X	X	U	X		X	U	X	X		X		U		X		X		X			S														
	S	X		X			X		S	S		X	X	X	X	X	U		X			X	X	X	U												
U	X	X	X		X		X			U		X	X	X	X		X			S			S	X	S												
U		X		X			X	X		S		X	X	X	X		U	X	X			S			X	S											
X	S	X		X			X	X	S			X	U	X		U	X			S				X			X										
X	X	X		X			X		S	U		X		U	X		U	X		S							X	X									
X	X	X		X			X		X	S		X		U	X		U			U							S	X									
X		X		X			X	X	U			X	U	U	X	S	X	X		S							X	X									
X		X		X			X	X	S	S		X	S	U	X		X			U							X	X									
X		X		X			X	X	S	S		U	U	U	X		X			S							X	X									
X	X	X		X			X	X	S	X		S		U	X	U		X		X							X	X	S								
X	S	X		X			X	X	U	X		S		U	X		X			X							X	X	X								
X	U	X		X			X	X	X	X		X		U	X	S		S		S								X									
X		X		X			X	X	X	X		X		U	X	U		S		S								X	S								
X		X		X			X	X	X	X		X		U	X	U		S		S								X	S	U							
X		X		X			X	X	X	X		X		U	X	U		X		S								X	S	S							
X	S	X		X			X	X	X	X		X			X		U			U						S		X	S		U						
X	S	X		X			X		X	X		U		U	X		X			S							X	X	S								
X	X	X		X			S	X	X					U	X		X			S							X	X	S								
X	S	X		X			X	X	X	X		X		U	X		X			S								U	S								
X	U	X		X			X	X	X					U	X		X			S							S	U				X					
X	X	X		X			X	X	X					U	X		X			X							X	U					S	S			
X	X	X		X			X	X	X					U	X		S			X							X	U					S	S			
X		X		X			X	X	X					U	U		X			S							S	U					S	X	X		
X		X	X				S	S	X	X		X		U			X			S							U	X					X	X	X		
X	U	X	X				S	X	S	X		X		U			X			S								X					X	X	X		
X	U	X	X		X		S	S		X		X		U	S		X			X							S						X	X	X		
X	U	X	X		X		S	X		X		X		U	S		X			S							U						X	X	X		
X	S	X	X		X		S	X		X		X		U	X		X			S													X	X	X		
X	U	X	X		X		X	X	S			X		U	X		X			S							S	X					S	X	X		
X	U	X	X		X		X	X	S			X		U	S		X			U							X						X	X	X		
X		X	X		X		X	X	S			X		U	X		X			U							U						U	X	X		
X	U	X	X	U	X			S	X	X		X	X	U	U	X		X	S			S	X														
	X	X	X	S	S		X		U	U		X	X	X	X				X	S		X	X	U		U											
X	X	X	X		X		X	X	S	U		X	X	U	X			U	X			S	U		S												
X	X	X	X		X		X		X	U		X	S	U	X	U	S	X	U			S				X											
X	X	X	X		X		X		X	S		X	U	U	X		U	X	U			S						X									
X	X		X		X		X	X		X		X	S	U	X		X	X	U			S						X									
X		X	X		X		X	X		X		X		U	U		X			U							S						U	X	S		
X		X	X		X		X	X		X		X		U	U		X			S							X						U	X	S		
39	15	40	40	3	38	4	32	30	22	23	1	29	10	3	28	4	5	29	1	4	0	3	0	1	4	0	0	11	7	10	1	0	0	1	6	9	9
0	9	0	0	2	0	0	5	6	11	6	2	3	2	0	8	5	2	4	1	0	1	0	20	1	1	0	0	2	5	0	1	6	1	0	2	4	0
2	8	0	0	3	0	0	0	1	2	2	1	4	4	38	3	4	5	0	2	1	0	6	0	0	0	1	0	2	0	6	0	1	1	0	1	0	0
7	5	7	8	0	7	0	7	3	4	3	0	8	3	1	6	1	1	8	0	0	0	1	1	1	0	0	0	1	2	1	0	0	0	0	0	2	0
0	0	0	0	1	1	0	0	1	1	1	0	0	2	0	0	0	1	0	2	0	0	5	0	0	0	0	1	0	0	1	0	0	0	0	0	0	2
0	1	0	0	1	0	0	0	0	1	4	0	0	1	7	2	1	2	0	3	0	0	1	0	1	0	1	0	0	0	0	0	0	0	0	2	0	0
0	0	0	1	0	0	3	4	11	9	0	0	18	1	0	4	0	0	0	1	0	2	0	0	1	0	0	5	6	0	1	0	0	1	1	3	7	
0	0	0	0	0	0	1	0	1	1	1	0	0	3	0	0	1	0	0	0	0	0	0	0	1	0	0	0	0	0	0	0	0	0	0	0	0	0

PLAYING SQUAD 2012/13

Existing Players		SN	HT	WT	DOB	AGE	POB	Career	Apps	Goals
GOALKEEPERS										
Matt	Glennon		6'02"	14 09	08/10/1978	33	Stockport	Bolton, Port Vale (2ML) 9/99, Stockport (L) 1/00, Bristol R (L) 9/00, Carlisle (SL) 11/00, Hull £50,000 6/01, Carlisle 10/02 Rel c/s 05, Falkirk 7/05, St Johnstone 1/06 Rel c/s 06, Huddersfield 6/06, Bradford C 1/10 Rel c/s 10, Stockport 9/10 Rel 1/12, Chester 2/12 Rel c/s 12, FC Halifax 7/12		
Phil	Senior		5'11"	10 12	30/10/1982	29	Huddersfield	Huddersfield Rel 5/06, Northwich 6/06, Droylsden 6/07, Alfreton 12/07, Ilkeston 2/08, FC Halifax 7/08	3	0
DEFENDERS										
Ben	Futcher		6'07"	12 05	20/02/1981	31	Manchester	Oldham Rel 1/02, Stalybridge (3ML) 8/01, Stalybridge 1/02, Doncaster 3/02, Lincoln C 5/02 Rel c/s 05, Boston U 7/05, Grimsby 1/06, Peterborough Undisc 8/06, Bury 6/07, Oxford U (2ML) 11/10, Mansfield (3ML) 8/11, AFC Telford (L) 1/12, Macclesfield (3ML) 2/12, FC Halifzx (SL) 7/12		
Liam	Hogan		6'00"	12 00	08/02/1989	23		Irlam FC, Flixton, Woodley Sports 3/08, FC Halifax 5/10	40	1
Danny	Lowe		5'11"	12 00	12/01/1984	28	Barnsley	Northampton Rel c/s 03, Harrogate T 7/03, Harrogate RA (L) 8/03, Liversedge, Harrogate RA 12/06, Harrogate T 3/08 Rel c/s 09, FC Halifax 8/09	40	0
Scott	McManus		6'00"	11 00	28/05/1989	23	Prestwich	Man Utd (Yth), Prestwich Heys, Ashton U (Trial) 10/07, Curzon Ashton c/s 08, Notts Forest (Trial) 7/08, Crewe Undisc 8/08 Rel 12/09, Curzon Ashton (2ML) 9/09, FCUM c/s 10, FC Halifax 5/11	38	0
Connor	Qualter							FC Halifax		
MIDFIELDERS										
Dan	Gardner		6'01"	12 08	30/11/1989	22	Manchester	Celtic Rel 5/09, Flixton 7/09, Crewe 2/10 Rel c/s 10, Droylsden 8/10, FC Halifax 7/12		
Jason	Jarrett		6'01"	13 10	14/09/1979	32	Bury	Blackpool, Wrexham 10/99, Bury 6/00, Wigan 3/02 Rel c/s 05, Stoke (L) 1/05, Norwich 7/05, Plymouth (6WL) 11/05, Preston (SL) 3/06, Preston 5/06, Hull C (L) 11/06, Leicester (SL) 2/07, QPR (3ML) 10/07, Oldham (3ML) 1/08, Brighton 1/09 Rel c/s 09, Port Vale 9/09 Rel 12/09, Oldham 7/10 Rel 1/11, Rochdale (Trial) 7/11, FC Halifax 7/12		
Paul	Marshall		6'01"	12 03	09/07/1989	23	Manchester	Man City Rel c/s 10, Blackpool (L) 1/09, Rochdale, Port Vale (SL) 3/09, Walsall 7/10 Rel c/s 11, Rochdale 8/11 Rel 9/11, Droylsden 9/11, Port Vale (Trial) 1/12, Port Vale 2/12 Rel c/s 12, FC Halifax 7/12		
Liam	Needham		5'11"	12 02	19/10/1985	26	Sheffield	Sheff Wed Rel c/s 05, Notts County (Trial) 8/05, Gainsborough 8/05, Notts County 11/05 Rel 12/06, Gainsborough (L) 11/06, Gainsborough 12/06 Rel 5/09, Guiseley c/s 09, FC Halifax 6/11	29	0
Jason	St Juste		5'06"	10 05	21/09/1985	26	Leeds	Garforth, Darlington 10/04, Southampton 9/05, Garforth 11/06, Sandes Ulf (Nor) 3/09, Chester FC (L) 2/11, Darlington (Trial), Bradford PA (Trial), FC Halifax 9/11	23	2
Ryan	Toulson				18/11/1985	26		Halifax, Stocksbridge (L) 9/05, Altrincham (SL) 1/08, Harrogate T 6/08, Gainsborough 5/09, Guiseley 5/10 Rel c/s 11, FC Halifax 7/11	33	0
Chris	Worsley							Curzon Ashton, Hyde FC 8/11, Skelmersdale (L) 1/12, FC Halifax 7/12		
Jon	Worthington		5'09"	11 05	16/04/1983	29	Dewsbury	Huddersfield Rel c/s 09, Yeovil (2ML) 1/09, Oldham 7/09, Fleetwood (L) 11/10, Bradford C 1/11, Mansfield 6/11 Rel c/s 12, FC Halifax 7/12		
FORWARDS										
Lee	Gregory				26/08/1988	24	Sheffield	Sheff Utd (Scholar), Staveley MW, Mansfield 9/09, Glapwell (3ML) 9/09, Harrogate T (3ML) 12/09, FC Halifax (L) 3/10, FC Halifax 12/10	32	18
Dale	Johnson		6'00"	11 08	03/05/1985	27	Ashton	Woodley Sports, Hyde U 2/04, Droylsden (6WL) 3/08, Altrincham 6/08 Rel 9/10, Hyde FC 9/10, Altrincham 3/11 Rel c/s 11, Droylsden 7/11, FC Halifax 7/12		
Jamie	Rainford							Marine, Prescot Cables 10/08, Marine 3/09, Chester FC Undisc 5/11, FC Halifax (L) 11/11, FC Halifax Undisc 2/12	16	5
Gareth	Seddon		5'11"	12 00	23/05/1980	32	Burnley	Accrington, Atherstone, RAF Codsall, Everton (Trial), Bury 8/01 Rel c/s 04, Northwich (L) 1/03, Rushden & D 5/04 Retired 1/05, Padiham 8/05, Worcester 3/06, Hyde 6/06, Kettering Undisc 7/08, Fleetwood Undisc 9/09 Rel c/s 12, FC Halifax 7/12		

GAINSBOROUGH TRINITY

Chairman: Peter Swann
Secretary: Pete Wallace   **(T)** 07841 163 110   **(E)** petewallace@aol.com
Additional Committee Members:
Karin Swann

Manager: Steve Housham
Programme Editor: Pete Wallace   **(E)** petewallace@aol.com

Club Factfile

Founded: 1873   **Nickname:** The Blues
Previous Names: None
Previous Leagues: Midland Counties 1889-96, 1912-60, 61-68, Football League 1896-1912, Central Alliance 1960-61, Northern Premier 1968-2004

Club Colours (change): All blue (All yellow)

Ground: The Northolme, Gainsborough, Lincolnshire DN21 2QW   **(T)** 01427 613 295 (office) 613 688 (Social C)
Capacity: 4,340   **Seats:** 504   **Covered:** 2,500   **Clubhouse:** Yes   **Shop:** Yes
Directions: The Northolme is situated on the A159, Gainsborough to Scunthorpe road, approximately a third of a mile north of the Town Centre. Public Car Park on the right 150 yards before the Ground. Any person parked illegally in the Streets around the Ground will be issued with a ticket from the Police.

Previous Grounds:

Record Attendance: 9,760 v Scunthorpe United - Midland League 1948
Record Victory: 7-0 v Fleetwood Town and v Great Harwood Town
Record Defeat: 1-7 v Stalybridge Celtic - Northern Premier 2000-01 and v Brentford - FA Cup 03-04.
Record Goalscorer: Not known
Record Appearances: Not known
Additional Records: Paid £3,000 to Buxton for Stuart Lowe
Senior Honours: Received £30,000 from Lincoln City for Tony James
Midland Counties League 1890-91, 1927-28, 48-49, 66-67
Lincolnshire Senior Cup x12

10 YEAR RECORD

02-03	03-04	04-05	05-06	06-07	07-08	08-09	09-10	10-11	11-12
NP P 15	NP P 10	Conf N 11	Conf N 16	Conf N 12	Conf N 11	Conf N 13	Conf N 14	Conf N 18	Conf N 4

GAINSBOROUGH TRINITY

No.	Date	Comp	H/A	Opponents	Att:	Result	Goalscorers	Pos
1	Sat-13-Aug	BSN	H	Solihull Moors	408	W 3-1	Cowan 2 (47, 57), Stamp 90	3
2	Mon-15-Aug	BSN	A	Hinckley United	413	L 0-3		11
3	Sat-20-Aug	BSN	A	Stalybridge Celtic	457	L 0-4		17
4	Tue-23-Aug	BSN	H	Corby Town	462	W 1-0	Boyce 8	11
5	Sat-27-Aug	BSN	H	Blyth Spartans	407	W 2-0	Kendall 60, R Williams 75	6
6	Mon-29-Aug	BSN	A	Droylsden	285	W 2-1	Mettam 71, R Williams 81	4
7	Sat-03-Sep	BSN	A	Nuneaton Town	753	W 1-0	Boyce 7	4
8	Sat-10-Sep	BSN	H	Bishops Stortford	465	W 4-2	Cowan 19, Stamp 2 (52, 90), R Williams 75	4
9	Sat-17-Sep	BSN	A	Hyde FC	654	L 1-3	Kendall 57	4
10	Tue-20-Sep	BSN	H	Workington	472	W 2-0	Kendall 31, Boyce 74	4
11	Sat-24-Sep	BSN	H	Guiseley	629	W 1-0	Cowan 78	3
12	Sat-08-Oct	BSN	A	Harrogate Town	360	L 1-2	Yates 44	4
13	Sat-22-Oct	BSN	A	Hinckley United	639	W 2-1	Kendall 28, Stamp 55	4
14	Tue-25-Oct	BSN	A	Eastwood Town	321	W 6-1	McMahon 2 (pen 4, 69), Nelthorpe 7, Kendall 3 (18, 30, 37)	3
15	Sat-05-Nov	BSN	A	Bishops Stortford	351	D 1-1	Mettam 41	3
16	Sat-12-Nov	BSN	A	Colwyn Bay	436	L 1-2	Mettam 5	3
17	Tue-15-Nov	BSN	H	Gloucester City	373	L 1-4	Leary 2	3
18	Sat-19-Nov	BSN	H	Boston United	793	L 1-3	Clarke 24	4
19	Sat-03-Dec	BSN	A	Corby Town	553	W 3-1	J Williams 44, Kendall 47, Mettam 90	5
20	Tue-06-Dec	BSN	H	Stalybridge Celtic	438	W 3-1	Kendall 3, Mettam 2 (52, 54)	5
21	Sat-17-Dec	BSN	A	Histon	342	D 1-1	Stamp 78	5
22	Mon-26-Dec	BSN	H	FC Halifax Town	1201	L 0-1		7
23	Sat-07-Jan	BSN	H	Hyde FC	683	W 2-0	Kendall 15, Cowan 52	6
24	Sat-14-Jan	BSN	A	Solihull Moors	272	L 3-5	Waterfall 47, Mettam 86, R Williams 88	6
25	Sat-21-Jan	BSN	H	Histon	507	W 3-2	Connor 2 (23, 79), Boyce 90	6
26	Tue-24-Jan	BSN	A	FC Halifax Town	1300	D 2-2	Boyce 45, Connor 58	5
27	Sat-28-Jan	BSN	H	Altrincham	668	W 2-0	Mettam 28, R Williams 50	5
28	Sat-18-Feb	BSN	H	Harrogate Town	596	L 0-1		6
29	Tue-21-Feb	BSN	A	Workington	250	W 2-0	Kendall 33, D'Laryea 47	5
30	Sat-25-Feb	BSN	H	Vauxhall Motors	414	D 1-1	Leary 64	5
31	Sat-03-Mar	BSN	A	Guiseley	571	L 0-2		6
32	Sat-10-Mar	BSN	H	Nuneaton Town	624	W 3-2	J Williams 32, Godden 60, D'Laryea 77	5
33	Mon-12-Mar	BSN	A	Worcester City	693	L 1-2	Kendall 29	5
34	Sat-17-Mar	BSN	A	Vauxhall Motors	171	L 1-3	Stamp 15	6
35	Sat-24-Mar	BSN	H	Eastwood Town	471	W 2-0	D'Laryea 72, Godden 82	5
36	Tue-27-Mar	BSN	A	Gloucester City	205	W 2-0	Stamp 49, Kendall 69	5
37	Sat-31-Mar	BSN	H	Colwyn Bay	533	W 2-0	Waterfall 7, Boyce 27	5
38	Sat-07-Apr	BSN	A	Blyth Spartans	392	W 3-2	Kendall 16, Mettam 76, Clarke 86	4
39	Mon-09-Apr	BSN	H	Droylsden	629	L 1-2	Stamp 40	5
40	Sat-14-Apr	BSN	A	Boston United	1164	W 2-1	Mettam pen 43, Stamp 62	3
41	Sat-21-Apr	BSN	H	Worcester City	390	D 2-2	Mettam 38, Waterfall 44	4
42	Sat-28-Apr	BSN	A	Altrincham	989	W 3-2	Mettam 3 (14, 45, 73)	4

CUPS

No.	Date	Comp	H/A	Opponents	Att:	Result	Goalscorers	
1	Sat-01-Oct	FAC 2Q	A	AFC Fylde	282	D 2-2	Kendall 16, Stamp 22	
2	Tue-04-Oct	FAC 2QR	H	AFC Fylde	525	W 2-1 aet	Leary 19, Boyce 120	
3	Sat-15-Oct	FAC 3Q	H	Frickley Athletic	644	W 2-0	Stamp 55, Kendall 65	
4	Sat-29-Oct	FAC 4Q	A	AFC Telford	1075	L 0-5		
5	Sat-26-Nov	FAT 3Q	H	Hinckley United	321	L 0-1		
6	Wed-02-May	PO SF1	H	FC Halifax Town	2380	D 2-2	Connor 2 (6, 13)	
7	Sun-06-May	PO SF2	A	FC Halifax Town	3468	W 1-0	Clarke 62	
8	Sun-13-May	PO Final	H	Nuneaton Town	3890	L 0-1		

League
Starts
Substitute
Unused Sub

Cups
Starts
Substitute
Unused Sub

Goals (Lg)
Goals (Cup)

Player appearance grid (X = start, S = substitute, U = unused substitute). Reading across columns as listed in the header.

BARNES	ROMA	SANDWITH	COWAN	BOYCE	LEARY	D'LARYEA	R WILLIAMS	KENDALL	STAMP	YATES	CLARE	WATERFALL	MCMAHON	PACZKOWSKI	WARLOW	COLEMAN	CLARKE	NELTHORPE	GRAY	METTAM	PETTINGER	J WILLIAMS	ARTHUR	EVTIMOV	MULREADY	EMERY	RIDLEY	CONNOR	WATTS	REID	THEWLIS	WHITE	MILLER	GODDEN	HOLDEN
X	X	X	X	X	X	X	X	X	X	X	X	S	U	U	U	U																			
X	X	X	X	X	X	X	X	X		X	X	U	S	S	U	S																			
X	X	X	X	X	X	X	X	X		X	S	S	U	U	U		X																		
X	X	X	X	X	X	X	X	X		X	S		S	X		U		S	U																
X	X	X	X	X	X	X	X	X		X			S	X		U		S	U	S															
X	X	X	X	S	X	X	X			X			S		S		U	X	U	X															
X	X	X	X	X	X	X	X	X		X			S		S		U	U	U	X															
X	X	X	X	X	X	X	X	X					U		S			U	U	S															
X	X	X	X	X	X	X	X	X		X		U			S		U		S	X															
	X	U	X		S	X	X	X	X	X		U	X	S		X			S	X															
X	X	X	X	X	X	X	X	X		X		U	S	U		S			S	X															
X	S	X		X	X	X	S	X	X			U	S			X			X	X	X	U													
X	X		X		X	X		X		X		X	S	S		U		X	U		X	S													
X	X		X	U	X		X	U		X	X		X	X		S		X	U	S	X	X													
X	X	X	X		X	X		X	S		X	S	U	X	S		U	S	U	S	X		U	X											
X	X	X	X	X	U	X	S		S		X	U	X		X	X		X		U		X													
X	U	S	X	X	X	X	S	X	S	X		X	X			X		X		U		X													
X	X	X	X	X	X	S			X		U	S	X		X		X		U		X	S													
X	X	X	S	S	X	X	X	U	U		X								S		X	X				X	X								
X	X	X	X	U	S	X	X	X	U	S		X							S		X	X				X	X								
X	X	X	U	U	X	X		S	S		X				S				S		X	X				X	X								
X	X	X	U	U	X	X		X	X		X								S		U	X				S	X								
X	X	U			X	U	X	U	S		X								S							X	X	X	X	X					
X	X	U	X			S	X		U		X								S		U					X	X	X	X	X					
X	X			S	U	X	X	X			X		X	U					X		S					X	U	X	X						
U	X	X	X	S	X	X	X	X			U			U					X		S					X	X	X	X						
X	X			X	U	X	X			X		X	S						X		X	U				X	U	X	U						
X	X			X	U	X	X	S		X		X	U						X		X					X	X	S			S				
X	X			X	X	X	X	U	X		X		X	U					X		S	U				X	U	X			U				
X	X			X	X	X	X	X	X	X	S	S	X		U				X		S					X	X	U							
X			X	X	X	X	X	S			X			U					X							U	X	X				X	S	S	
X			X	X	X	X	X	S			X			U					X							X	X				S	X	U	S	
X			X	X	X	X	S	X	X			U				S			U							S	X				X		X		
X	X			X	X	X		X	U	S							U		S		X					S		U				S	X		
X	X			X	S	X		X	X	X	X							S	X		U					U						S	X		
X	X			X	U	X		X	X	X	X								X		U		X		X							S	X		
X	X			X	X	U	X	X									S		X		U							U				S	X		
X	X			X	X	X	X	X	X		X								X		S							U				S	X		
X	X			X	S	X	X	X	X	X								S	X		S		X					U				X			
X	X			X	X	X	X	X	X										X		X							U			X				

Second section:

X	X	X	X	S	X			X	X	X			U	X	U	X	U				U	U	S	X											
X	X	X	X	X	X	X	X	X	U	S			U	X			U	U			S	U	X	X											
X	X	X	X	S	X	X	X	X	X	X			U	S	S		U	X	U		X	U													
X	X	X	X	X	X	X	X	X	X	X			U	S	U		U	S	S		S														
X	X	X	U	X		X			X	X			X	X				X							S	X		S	U	U					
X	X		X		X			X	X				X	U					X		X	S		U			X	U			S	X			
X	X		X				S	X	X	X			X	U					X		X							S	U			X			
X	X		X	S	X	X	X	X	X				X	U					X		S							S	U			X			

Totals / statistics (bottom section):

9	39	36	22	34	24	41	30	31	16	28	1	26	5	4	0	3	17	5	1	12	5	7	5	3	0	10	6	17	7	2	0	10	0	1	5
0	0	1	1	2	7	0	4	3	7	6	3	1	12	5	3	3	6	3	0	21	0	3	0	0	1	0	2	5	1	0	2	0	1	7	0
0	1	2	0	5	8	0	2	0	5	3	0	9	7	8	3	4	3	2	7	1	0	15	0	0	0	1	3	2	5	0	3	0	1	0	0

1	8	8	5	7	3	7	6	6	7	0	4	3	0	1	0	4	1	0	2	3	1	1	0	0	0	0	1	0	0	0	3	0	0	0	0
0	0	0	0	0	3	0	1	0	0	1	0	0	2	1	0	0	0	2	0	4	0	2	0	0	1	0	0	2	0	0	1	0	0	0	0
0	0	0	0	1	0	0	0	0	1	0	0	4	3	2	1	4	0	1	3	0	0	2	0	0	1	1	1	0	3	0	0	0	0	0	0

| 0 | 0 | 0 | 5 | 6 | 2 | 3 | 5 | 14 | 9 | 1 | 0 | 3 | 2 | 0 | 0 | 0 | 2 | 1 | 0 | 14 | 0 | 2 | 0 | 0 | 0 | 0 | 0 | 3 | 0 | 0 | 0 | 0 | 0 | 2 | 0 |
| 0 | 0 | 0 | 0 | 1 | 1 | 0 | 0 | 2 | 2 | 0 | 0 | 0 | 0 | 0 | 0 | 0 | 1 | 0 | 0 | 0 | 0 | 0 | 0 | 0 | 0 | 0 | 0 | 2 | 0 | 0 | 0 | 0 | 0 | 0 | 0 |

PLAYING SQUAD 2012/13

Existing Players		SN	HT	WT	DOB	AGE	POB	Career	Apps	Goals
GOALKEEPERS										
Jan	Budtz		6'05"	13 05	20/04/1979	33	Hillerod, Den	B1909 (Den), FC Nordsjaelland (Den) 1/05 Rel c/s 05, Doncaster 7/05, Wolves (3ML) 1/07, Hartlepool 9/07 Rel c/s 09, Oldham (L) 2/09, Eastwood T 9/09 Rel 3/10, Stalybridge 8/10 Rel c/s 12, Buxton (Trial) 6/12, Gainsborough 7/12		
Jason	White		6'02"	12 01	28/01/1983	29	Suton-in-Ashfield	Notts Forest (Yth), Mansfield Rel 5/09, Kings Lynn 8/09, Shirebrook T, Gainsborough 3/12	10	0
DEFENDERS										
Danny	Hone		6'02"	12 00	15/09/1989	22	Croydon	Lincoln C Rel c/s 12, Darlington (6ML) 7/10, Barrow (SL) 11/11, Gainsborough 7/12		
Lee	Ridley		5'10"	12 10	05/12/1981	30	Scunthorpe	Scunthorpe Rel c/s 07, Cheltenham 7/07 Rel c/s 10, Darlington (6WL) 11/07, Lincoln C (SL) 1/08, Grimsby 6/10, Gainsborough 11/11	8	0
Dominic	Roma		5'10"	11 11	29/11/1985	26	Sheffield	Sheff Utd Rel c/s 07, Boston U (L) 2/05, Notts County (Trial) 7/05, Tamworth (SL) 2/06, Hinckley U 7/07, Alfreton 5/09, Harrogate T 6/10, Gainsborough 5/11	39	0
Luke	Waterfall		6'02"	12 11	30/07/1990	22	Sheffield	Barnsley (Scholar), Tranmere 7/08 Rel c/s 09, Altrincham (L) 10/08, Oxford U (Trial) 7/09, York C (Trial) 7/09, Ilkeston 8/09, Gainsborough 5/10	27	3
Josh	Wilde							Buxton, Gainsborough 5/12		
Greg	Young		6'02"	12 03	24/04/1983	29	Doncaster	Sheff Wed (Scholar), Shrewsbury (Trial) 3/02, Grimsby 7/02, Northwich (L) 10/04, Northwich (L) 12/04, Halifax 2/05, Northwich (L) 11/06, Alfreton (L) 8/07, Altrincham 1/08, York C 5/10, Altrincham (SL) 2/11, Alfreton 6/11, Gainsborough 6/12		
MIDFIELDERS										
Shane	Clarke		6'01"	13 03	07/11/1987	24	Lincoln	Lincoln C Rel 8/10, Stamford (WE) 1/06, Gateshead 10/10 Rel 11/10, Boston U 11/10, Chicago Fire (USA) (Trial) 2/11, Gainsborough 6/11	23	2
Jonathan	D'Laryea		5'10"	12 02	03/09/1985	26	Manchester	Man City, Mansfield (3ML) 10/05, Mansfield 1/06, Northwich (3ML) 8/09 Perm 11/09, Eastwood T Undisc 2/10, Gainsborough 6/11	41	3
Terry	Hawkridge				23/02/1990	22		Carlton T, Hucknall 6/09, Carlton T 9/10, Gainsborough 6/12		
Michael	Leary		5'11"	12 03	17/04/1983	29	Ealing	Luton Rel c/s 07, Bristol R (3ML) 8/05, Walsall (SL) 1/06, Torquay (L) 11/06, Brentford (SL) 1/07, Barnet 7/07 Rel c/s 09, Grimsby 7/09 Rel 5/11, Gainsborough 7/11	31	2
Jonathan	Williams				26/03/1992	20		Scunthorpe Rel c/s 11, Boston U (L) 11/10, Brigg T (L) 3/11, Gainsborough 5/11, Stocksbridge PS (L) 9/11	10	2
Ryan	Williams		5'04"	11 02	31/08/1978	34	Chesterfield	Mansfield, Tranmere £70,000 + 8/97, Chesterfield (3ML) 11/99 £80,000 2/00, Hull C £150,000 7/01, Bristol R (2ML) 10/03 Perm 12/03, Forest Green (2ML) 12/04, Aldershot (L) 8/05, Aldershot 1/06 Rel 4/08, Weymouth 5/08 Rel 2/09, Mansfield 2/09 Rel 1/11, Gainsborough (2ML) 10/10, Gainsborough 1/11	34	5
Jamie	Yates		5'07"	10 11	24/12/1988	23	Sheffield	Rotherham Rel 5/09, Burton (3ML) 1/09, Kettering 7/09 Rel 9/09, Retford U 9/09, Alfreton 9/09, Boston U (2ML) 9/09 Perm 11/09, Gainsborough 5/11	34	1
FORWARDS										
Paul	Connor		6'02"	11 08	12/01/1979	33	Bishop Auckland	Middlesbrough Rel c/s 99, Gateshead (L) 8/97, Hartlepool (L) 2/98, Stoke (SL) 3/99, Stoke 5/99, Cambridge U (3ML) 11/00, Rochdale £100,000 3/01, Swansea £35,000 3/04, L.Orient £40,000 1/06, Cheltenham £25,000 1/07 Rel c/s 09, Lincoln C 7/09 Rel c/s 10, Mansfield 7/10, Gainsborough 12/11	22	3
Sam	Mulready				06/05/1993	19	Kings Lynn	Grimsby, North Ferriby (L) 9/11, Boston U (L) 10/11, Gainsborough (2ML) 11/11 Perm 1/12, Brigg T (L) 1/12, Brigg T (L) 3/12	1	0
Darryn	Stamp		6'01"	11 10	21/09/1978	33	Beverley	Hessle, Scunthorpe 7/97 Rel c/s 01, Halifax (L) 2/00, Scarborough (L) 3/01, Scarborough 5/01, Northampton £30,000 5/02, Chester 8/03, Kidderminster (L) 11/04, Stevenage 1/05, York C (3ML) 10/06, Halifax 1/07, Northwich (SL) 3/08, Northwich 8/08, Gateshead (SL) 3/09, Gainsborough 6/09 Rel c/s 10, Guiseley 7/10, Gainsborough 6/11	23	9
Jordan	Thewlis		5'09"	11 00	24/10/1992	19	Scunthorpe	Scunthorpe Rel 1/12, Corby T 1/12 Rel 2/12, Gainsborough 2/12	2	0

GLOUCESTER CITY

Chairman: Nigel Hughes
Secretary: Shaun Wetson   **(T)** 07813 931 781   **(E)** swgcfc@gmail.com
Additional Committee Members:
Phil Warren, Eamonn McGurk, Jenni Silver.

Manager: David Mehew
Programme Editor: Mike Dunstan   **(E)** mikedunstan@blueyonder.co.uk

Club Factfile

Founded: 1889   **Nickname:** The Tigers
Previous Names: Gloucester Y.M.C.A.
Previous Leagues: Bristol & District (now Western) 1893-96, Gloucester & Dist. 1897-1907, North Gloucestershire 1907-10,
Gloucestershire North Senior 1920-34, Birmingham Combination 1935-39, Southern 1939-2000

Club Colours (change): Amber & black/black/black (Sky blue/navy blue/sky blue)

Ground: Cheltenham Tn FC, The Abbey Business Stad., Whaddon Rd GL52 5NA   **(T)** 01242 573558 (Cheltenham Town No.)
Capacity: 7,289   **Seats:** Yes   **Covered:** Yes   **Clubhouse:** Yes   **Shop:** Yes

Directions: From the North (M5) leave at Jnctn 10, follow road A4019 towards Cheltenham, keep going straight through traffic lights until you reach a roundabout, PC World will be on your left and McDonalds on your right. Turn left here, after 500 yards you will then come to a double roundabout, go straight over, keep going for another 300 yards then turn right into Swindon Lane, follow the road over the level crossing and 2 mini roundabouts until you come to a large roundabout, go straight over, signposted Prestbury, continue past Racecourse and turn right into Albert Road, follow this to the end then turn left at roundabout into Prestbury Road, 200yards turn into Whaddon Rd.

Previous Grounds: Longlevens 1935-65, Horton Road 1965-86, Meadow Park 1986-2007, Corinium Stadium Cirencester 2007-10

Record Attendance: Longlevens: 10,500 v Tottenham - Friendly 1952. Meadow Park: 4,000 v Dagenham & Red. - FAT 3rd Q Rnd 12/04/97
Record Victory: 10-1 v Sudbury Town (H) - FA Cup 3rd Qualifying Round 17/10/98
Record Defeat: 1-12 v Gillingham - 09/11/46
Record Goalscorer: Reg Weaver - 250 (1930s)
Record Appearances: Stan Myers & Frank Tredgett - (1950s)
Additional Records: Paid £25,000 to Worcester City for Steve Ferguson 1990-91
Senior Honours: Received £25,000 from AFC Bournemouth for Ian Hedges 1990
Southern League Cup 1955-56, Midland Division 1988-89, Premier Division Play-off 2008-09.
Gloucestershire Senior Cup x19

10 YEAR RECORD

02-03		03-04		04-05		05-06		06-07		07-08		08-09		09-10		10-11		11-12	
SthW	5	SthW	2	SthP	15	SthP	13	SthP	10	SthP	6	SthP	3	Conf N	18	Conf N	14	Conf N	14

GLOUCESTER CITY

No.	Date	Comp	H/A	Opponents	Att:	Result	Goalscorers	Pos
1	Sat-13-Aug	BSN	A	Vauxhall Motors	179	W 2-0	Edwards 26, Davies 50	5
2	Tue-16-Aug	BSN	A	Nuneaton Town	626	D 0-0		5
3	Sat-20-Aug	BSN	H	Workington	345	W 2-0	Edwards 2 (34, 89)	3
4	Tue-23-Aug	BSN	A	Eastwood Town	262	L 1-2	Rawlings 37	7
5	Sat-27-Aug	BSN	A	Hinckley United	455	W 3-2	Edwards 2 (19, 58), Morford 62	5
6	Mon-29-Aug	BSN	H	Hyde FC	472	L 0-2		7
7	Sat-03-Sep	BSN	H	Altrincham	360	D 1-1	Davies 90	7
8	Sat-10-Sep	BSN	A	Harrogate Town	329	L 0-2		11
9	Sat-17-Sep	BSN	H	Colwyn Bay	280	L 0-1		10
10	Tue-20-Sep	BSN	H	Corby Town	201	D 0-0		13
11	Sat-24-Sep	BSN	A	Stalybridge Celtic	448	D 2-2	Morford 11, Davies 81	13
12	Sat-08-Oct	BSN	A	Bishops Stortford	401	L 2-3	Morford 70, Webb 86	16
13	Sat-22-Oct	BSN	H	Blyth Spartans	302	W 4-0	Weir 26, Morford 50, Mullings 67, Jake Harris 90	14
14	Tue-25-Oct	BSN	A	Solihull Moors	330	L 1-1		14
15	Sat-05-Nov	BSN	H	FC Halifax Town	505	L 1-3	Weir 55	15
16	Sat-12-Nov	BSN	H	Harrogate Town	275	W 1-0	Edwards 74	13
17	Tue-15-Nov	BSN	A	Gainsborough Trinity	373	W 4-1	Davies 54, Reece 55, Hamblin 59, Edwards 66	13
18	Sat-19-Nov	BSN	A	Altrincham	773	W 2-1	Webb 2, Edwards 30	12
19	Sat-03-Dec	BSN	H	Hinckley United	325	D 2-2	Og (Oddy) 44, Edwards 51	13
20	Tue-06-Dec	BSN	H	Nuneaton Town	302	L 1-2	Morford 25	13
21	Sat-17-Dec	BSN	H	Bishops Stortford	225	L 0-2		13
22	Mon-26-Dec	BSN	A	Worcester City	1501	L 1-2	Edwards 21	15
23	Sun-01-Jan	BSN	H	Worcester City	802	W 3-1	Edwards 2 (14, 24), Morford 68	12
24	Sat-07-Jan	BSN	H	Solihull Moors	305	W 1-0	Webb 14	12
25	Sat-14-Jan	BSN	A	Histon	313	L 3-4	Morford 3 (8, 28, 34)	13
26	Sat-21-Jan	BSN	A	Hyde FC	509	D 0-0		13
27	Sat-28-Jan	BSN	H	Eastwood Town	289	W 2-0	Morford 55, Mann 58	12
28	Sat-18-Feb	BSN	H	Vauxhall Motors	303	W 2-1	Morford 37, Mann 70	11
29	Sat-25-Feb	BSN	A	Boston United	1077	L 0-2		12
30	Sat-03-Mar	BSN	A	Workington	375	L 0-3		12
31	Tue-06-Mar	BSN	H	Droylsden	185	L 1-3	Edwards pen 40	12
32	Sat-10-Mar	BSN	H	Guiseley	285	W 2-1	Lewis 53, Edwards 89	12
33	Sat-17-Mar	BSN	A	FC Halifax Town	1662	D 0-0		12
34	Sat-24-Mar	BSN	A	Blyth Spartans	452	W 1-0	Lock pen 50	13
35	Tue-27-Mar	BSN	H	Gainsborough Trinity	205	L 0-2		13
36	Sat-31-Mar	BSN	H	Boston United	315	L 1-3	Bird 59	14
37	Tue-03-Apr	BSN	A	Guiseley	487	L 2-3	Mullings 3, Edwards 70	14
38	Sat-07-Apr	BSN	A	Corby Town	277	W 1-0	Lock 51	11
39	Mon-09-Apr	BSN	H	Histon	320	L 0-1		12
40	Sat-14-Apr	BSN	A	Droylsden	220	W 2-1	Edwards 6, Lewis 61	11
41	Sat-21-Apr	BSN	H	Stalybridge Celtic	320	L 1-2	Mullings 47	12
42	Sat-28-Apr	BSN	A	Colwyn Bay	476	L 2-4	Edwards 2 (72, 90)	14

CUPS

No.	Date	Comp	H/A	Opponents	Att:	Result	Goalscorers
1	Sat-01-Oct	FAC 2Q	A	Whitchurch United	400	W 2-0	Edwards 50, Morford 54
2	Sat-15-Oct	FAC 3Q	H	Truro City	385	W 7-2	Rose 2, Webb 22, Morford 35, Mullings 2 (70, 88), Lock 77, Edwards 90
3	Sat-29-Oct	FAC 4Q	A	Chelmsford City	928	D 1-1	Morford 45
4	Tue-01-Nov	FAC 4QR	H	Chelmsford City	490	L 0-1	
5	Sat-26-Nov	FAT 3Q	H	Truro City	300	D 1-1	Reece 51
6	Tue-29-Nov	FAT 3QR	A	Truro City	228	L 2-3	Wilson 85, Mullings 86

League
Starts
Substitute
Unused Sub

Cups
Starts
Substitute
Unused Sub

Goals (Lg)
Goals (Cup)

	SAWYER	MIKE GREEN	RAWLINGS	COUPE	HAMBLIN	WEBB	WEIR	MULLINGS	EDWARDS	DAVIES	MANN	ROSE	CLARIDGE	JACK HARRIS	MUSTOE	MORFORD	MICHAEL GREEN (G)	BLOOM	JAMES	LIDDIARD	LOCK	JAKE HARRIS	CAREY	LLOYD	REECE	HUNT	WILSON	LEWIS	BIRD	MACE	HUMPHRIES
	X	X	X	X	X	X	X	X	X	X	X	S	S	S	U																
	X	X	X	X	X	X	X	X	X	U	X	U	S	U	X																
		X	U	X	X	X	X	X	X			X	U	S	S	S	X	X	X												
		X	X	X	X	X	X	X	X			X	U	S	S	S	X	X													
	X	X	X	X	X			X	X	X	X	X	S	S		S	X			U	U										
	X	X	S	X	X	X	X			X	X	S	X	S			S	X				X									
	X	X	S	X	X	X	X				X	X	X	S			S	X			X										
	X	X	U	X	X	X	X				X	S			S	X	U	X			X	S									
		X	X	X	X			X	X			S	X			U	S	U	X			X	X	X	U						
		X	X	X	X				S	X	X	S	X	U		S	U	X			X	X	X								
		X	U	X				X	X	X	X	X	S			X	U	S			X	X	X								
	U	X	X	S	X	X	X	X			X	X				X	U				X	S	X		S						
	U	X	X	U	X	X	X			S	X					U	X	X			X	S			X						
	X	U	X	X	X	X	X	X	S	X	S				S	X	U					X			X						
	X	S	X	X	X	S	X	X	X	X	S	X	U			U	X	X			X				X						
	X	S	X	X	X		X	X	X	X	X				S		X				X				X						
	X	U	X	X	X	X	X	X	S	X	S				U	X	X								X						
		X	X	X	X	X	X	X	X	S	S				U	X	X			S					X						
		X	X	X	X		X	X	X	S	S		U			X				S		X			X	U					
		X		X	X	X	S	X	X	S	X		S	U		X				S		X			X	U					
	S	U		X	X	X	X	X	S	X	X			X		X				S		X			S						
	S	X	X	X	X	X	X	X	U	X	U					X				S		X			U						
	U	X	X	X	X	X	X	X	S	X	S					X				S		X			U						
		X	X	X	X		X	X	S	X	U		U			X				S		X			S						
		X	S	X	X		X	X	S	X	U		X			X				S		X			U						
		X	U	X	X		X	X	S	X	S		X	U		X				X		X			S						
		X	U	X	X		X	X	S	X	S		X	U		X				X		U			U						
		X	S	X	X		X	X	S	X	U		X	U		X				S		X			S						
		X	S	X			X	X	X	S	X		X	U		X				X		X			S						
		X	S	X	S	X	X	X	X	X	X		X	U		X				X		U			U						
		X	S	X		X	X	X	X		X		X	U		X				X		X	U			S					
		X	S	X	X		X		X	S	X		X			X				X		X	U	U		X					
		X		X	X		X			S	X		X	S		X				X		X	U		S	X	X	X			
		X		X	X		X		X	S	S		X			X				X		X	U		X	X	X	X			
		X	S	X	X			X			X		X	U	X		S			X		X	S	X	X	U					
		X	X	X	S	X		X	X			X		S	U	S				X		X		U	X	X					
		X	X	X	X		X	X		S	S		X			X				X		X		U	S	X					
		X		X	X		X	X		X	S		X	U	S					X		X		U	X	S					
		X	S		X	X		X	X			X		X	U	X				S			U		U	X	X		X		
	U	X		X	S	X	X			X			X	U			S	X				S		U	X	X	X		X		
			U	S	X	X		X	X			S	X		X	X	X				S	X			X				U		X
	X	S	X	X	S	X	X	X		X				U	X	S	X				X		X								
		X	S	X	U	X	X	X	X			X		X	U	U	X				X	U	X								
	X	U	X	X	X	X	X	X	U	X	U			U	U	X					X		X		U	U					
	X	U	X	X	X	X	X	X	S	X	U			U	U	X					X		X		S	U					
		X	X	X	X	X	X	S	X	S				U	X	X				U			X								
		X	X	X	X	X	X	S	X					S	X	X				U			X	S							
6	32	17	37	35	33	23	39	35	14	26	15	0	19	1	34	8	1	0	0	30	3	25	1	8	0	3	7	7	0	3
0	2	13	1	3	2	1	1	0	13	12	15	7	8	7	4	0	0	0	3	4	3	0	3	1	0	6	2	1	0	0
0	4	9	0	1	0	0	0	0	2	0	8	3	2	26	0	2	0	1	1	0	0	0	5	0	0	12	0	0	1	0
0	4	2	6	5	5	6	6	6	0	6	1	0	1	0	6	2	0	0	0	4	0	4	0	2	0	0	0	0	0	0
0	0	2	0	0	1	0	0	0	3	0	1	0	0	0	2	0	0	0	0	0	0	0	0	1	0	1	0	0	0	0
0	0	2	0	1	0	0	0	0	1	0	2	2	2	4	0	0	0	0	0	2	0	1	0	0	1	2	0	0	0	0
0	0	1	0	1	3	2	3	18	4	2	0	0	0	0	11	0	0	0	0	2	1	0	0	1	0	0	2	1	0	0
0	0	0	0	0	1	0	3	2	0	0	1	0	0	0	3	0	0	0	0	1	0	0	0	1	0	1	0	0	0	0

PLAYING SQUAD 2012/13

Existing Players		SN	HT	WT	DOB	AGE	POB	Career	Apps	Goals
GOALKEEPERS										
Mike (Michael)	Green		6'01"	13 01	23/07/1989	23	Bristol	Bristol R Rel c/s 11, Mangotsfield (L) 9/06, Clevedon T (L) 3/09, Gloucester (SL) 7/09, Cheltenham (Trial) 7/11, Eastleigh NC 8/11, Gloucester 8/11, Cirencester 8/11, Gloucester 9/11	8	0
DEFENDERS										
Matt	Coupe				07/10/1978	33	St Asaph	Bristol C, Forest Green, Gloucester c/s 99, Clevedon T 9/99, Bath C c/s 01, Aberystwyth, Forest Green 1/02, Chippenham (L) 1/03, Bath C 2/03 Rel 9/10, Gloucester 9/10	38	0
Mike	Green		5'09"	11 04	18/12/1984	27	Gloucester	Southampton, Chippenham (L) 12/03 (L) 3/04, Forest Green 3/04 Rel 4/05, Cinderford c/s 05, Bath C 6/06, Clevedon (3ML) 8/07 Dual 11/07, Weston-Super-Mare 12/07, Gloucester 6/10	34	0
Tom	Hamblin		6'01"		15/09/1986	25		Mangotsfield (Yth), Bristol Manor Farm, Gloucester 5/06	38	1
Keiron	Mace							Gloucester	0	0
Neil	Mustoe		5'09"	12 10	05/11/1976	35	Gloucester	Man Utd, Wigan Undisc 1/98 Cambridge U 7/98 Rel c/s 02, Hartlepool (Trial) 7/01, Cambridge C (L) 9/01, Gloucester 8/02, Stevenage 1/03, Yeovil 2/03 Rel c/s 03, Gloucester 8/03 Temp Man 1/06	8	0
MIDFIELDERS										
Steve	Davies		5'09"	12 03	27/04/1989	23	Swansea	Afan Lido, Cirencester 7/08, Forest Green 7/09 Rel 5/11, Gloucester (3ML) 9/10, Gloucester 5/11	27	4
Jack	Harris				07/06/1989	23	Bristol	Avonmouth, Hallen, Gloucester c/s 08, Cirencester (L) 11/11	27	0
Lewis	Hogg		5'09"	11 11	13/09/1982	29	Bristol	Bristol R Rel c/s 03, Barnet 8/03, Weston-s-Mare 12/03, Bath C 5/06, Gloucester 6/12		
Matt	Liddiard							Gloucester	3	0
Adam	Mann							Shortwood, Gloucester	38	2
Darren	Mullings		6'01"	12 00	03/03/1987	25	Bristol	Bristol R, Clevedon (L) 12/06, Torquay 6/07 Rel 5/08, Tiverton (L) 11/07, Weston-Super-Mare 8/08, Gloucester 7/10	40	3
Sam	Rawlings							Cheltenham (Scholar) Rel c/s 11, Gloucester 8/11	30	1
Tom	Webb				02/05/1984	28		Luton (Yth), Gloucester 7/00, Viney St Swithens (L), Highworth T (L), Yate T (L) 8/09	35	3
FORWARDS										
Darren	Edwards				04/08/1980	32	Bristol	Bristol Manor Farm, Mangotsfield 98, Bristol R (Trial) 4/02,, Tiverton 1/04, Mangotsfield 9/04, Yate T 1/05, Bath C 12/06 Rel 11/10, Cinderford (L) 11/10, Gloucester 11/10	35	18
Ben	Hunt		6'01"	11 00	23/01/1990	22	Southwark	West Ham (Scholar), Bristol R c/s 08, Kingstonian (L) 10/09, Gloucester (3ML) 12/09, Newport C (L) 3/10, Dover 7/10, Lewes (SL) 2/11 Perm 3/11, Weston-Super-Mare 8/11, Gloucester 10/11, Cirencester (Dual) 11/11, Thurrock 1/12, Bishops Stortford 3/12, Gloucester 7/12	0	0
Will	Morford				28/04/1986	26		Staunton & Corse, Tuffley Rovers, Slimbridge, Gloucester 10/07	38	11
Joe	Parker				11/03/1995	17		Gloucester		
Scott	Wilson							Bristol C, Gloucester (SL) 11/11, Gloucester c/s 12	9	0

GUISELEY

Chairman: Steve Parkin
Secretary: Adrian Towers   **(T)** 07946 388 739   **(E)** admin@guiseleyafc.co.uk
Additional Committee Members:
Neil Shackleton, Stuart Allen, Gary Douglas, John Gill, Phil Rogerson.
Matthew Rogerson.
Manager: Steve Kittrick
Programme Editor: Rachel O'Connor   **(E)** rachel.football@hotmail.co.uk

2011-12 Squad - Back Row (L-R): Adrian Towers (General Manager),Gavin Rothery, Danny Boshell, Lee Ellington, Danny Ellis, Gavin Allott, Jacob Giles (gk) Steve Drench(gk), Jamie Clarke, Mark Bower, Simon Ainge, Peter Davidson, Joe O'Neill, Joey Spivack.
Front Row: Alex Davidson, Ciaran Toner, Michael Burns, Chris Holland (Ass't Mgr), SteveKittrick (Mgr) Martin Stringfellow (Therapist), Dave Merris, James Booker, Danny Forrest.

Club Factfile

Founded: 1909   **Nickname:** The Lions
Previous Names: Not known
Previous Leagues: Wharfedale, Leeds, West Riding Counties, West Yorkshire, Yorkshire 1968-82, Northern Counties East 1982-91, Northern Premier 1991-2010

Club Colours (change): White/navy/navy (All yellow)

Ground: Nethermoor Park, Otley Road, Guiseley, Leeds LS20 8BT   **(T)** 01943 873 223 (Office) 872 872 (Club)
Capacity: 3,000 **Seats:** 427 **Covered:** 1,040 **Clubhouse:** Yes **Shop:** Yes

Directions: From the West M62, M606 then follow signs to A65 through Guiseley to Ground on Right. From South and East M1 and M621 towards Leeds City Centre. Continue on M621 to Junction 2, follow Headingly Stadium signs to A65 towards Ilkley then as above. From North West From Skipton, A65 Ilkley, via Burley By-pass A65 towards Leeds, Ground quarter of a mile on left after Harry Ramsden's roundabout From North/NE A1M, leave at A59, towards Harrogate, then A658 signed Leeds Bradford Airport, at Pool turn right onto A659 Otley, continue towards Bradford/Leeds, to Harry Ramsden roundabout then A65 Leeds ground quarter of a mile on left.

Previous Grounds:

Record Attendance: 2,486 v Bridlington Town - FA Vase Semi-final 1st Leg 1989-90
Record Victory: Not known
Record Defeat: Not known
Record Goalscorer: Not known
Record Appearances: Not known
Additional Records:

Senior Honours:
Northern Counties East 1990-91. FA Vase 1990-91.
Northern Premier League Division 1 1993-94, Premier Division 2009-10, Challenge Cup 2008-09.

10 YEAR RECORD

02-03		03-04		04-05		05-06		06-07		07-08		08-09		09-10		10-11		11-12	
NP 1	14	NP 1	9	NP P	10	NP P	14	NP P	6	NP P	6	NP P	3	NP P	1	Conf N	5	Conf N	2

GUISELEY

No.	Date	Comp	H/A	Opponents	Att:	Result	Goalscorers	Pos
1	Sat-13-Aug	BSN	H	Hinckley United	361	W 3-0	Boshell 30, Toner 85, Allott 87	1
2	Tue-16-Aug	BSN	A	Droylsden	322	L 0-2		8
3	Sat-20-Aug	BSN	A	Solihull Moors	230	W 1-0	Toner 90	7
4	Tue-23-Aug	BSN	H	Blyth Spartans	476	W 5-0	Forrest 32, Boshell 37, Ellington 2 (47, 83), Ainge 67	3
5	Sat-27-Aug	BSN	H	Colwyn Bay	328	W 2-0	Rothery 38, Ellington 76	3
6	Mon-29-Aug	BSN	A	Altrincham	749	D 2-2	Toner 35, Rothery 39	3
7	Sat-03-Sep	BSN	H	Vauxhall Motors	522	W 4-1	Ellington 18, Forrest 33, Baldry 2 (76, 82)	3
8	Sat-10-Sep	BSN	A	Corby Town	580	W 1-0	Rothery 78	3
9	Sat-17-Sep	BSN	H	Worcester City	461	W 4-1	Rothery 2 (25, pen 47), Baldry 68, A Davidson 89	3
10	Tue-20-Sep	BSN	H	FC Halifax Town	897	L 3-4	A Davidson 2, Rothery 2 (8, 45)	3
11	Sat-24-Sep	BSN	A	Gainsborough Trinity	629	L 0-1		4
12	Sat-08-Oct	BSN	A	Workington	349	W 3-1	Rothery 2 (21, 38), Allott 86	3
13	Sat-22-Oct	BSN	H	Hyde FC	789	W 2-0	Ellington 43, Allott 87	3
14	Sat-05-Nov	BSN	A	Worcester City	745	D 2-2	Boshell 72, Rothery pen 90	4
15	Sat-12-Nov	BSN	A	Eastwood Town	292	D 2-2	Holdsworth 11, Baldry 85	4
16	Sat-19-Nov	BSN	H	Stalybridge Celtic	738	D 1-1	Brough 52	3
17	Tue-22-Nov	BSN	H	Nuneaton Town	397	D 1-1	Rothery pen 90	3
18	Sat-03-Dec	BSN	H	Workington	384	W 2-1	Senior 23, Rothery 80	3
19	Tue-06-Dec	BSN	A	Blyth Spartans	301	W 2-1	Ainge 19, Forrest 67	3
20	Sat-17-Dec	BSN	H	Boston United	508	W 2-1	Holdsworth 2 (17, 77)	3
21	Mon-26-Dec	BSN	A	Harrogate Town	661	W 4-0	Clarke 32, Senior 2 (56, 69), Burns 67	3
22	Sat-07-Jan	BSN	A	Bishops Stortford	392	L 1-4	Ellington 72	3
23	Sat-21-Jan	BSN	H	Droylsden	468	W 4-3	Senior 77, Walshaw 3 (pen 79, 82, 86)	4
24	Tue-24-Jan	BSN	A	Vauxhall Motors	204	D 1-1	Senior 57	4
25	Sat-28-Jan	BSN	A	Histon	328	D 2-2	Walshaw 2 (70, pen 81)	2
26	Sat-18-Feb	BSN	A	Hinckley United	469	W 1-0	Baldry 46	3
27	Sat-25-Feb	BSN	H	Eastwood Town	484	L 1-2	Ellis 85	4
28	Sat-03-Mar	BSN	H	Gainsborough Trinity	571	W 2-0	Ellis 14, Baldry 24	4
29	Mon-05-Mar	BSN	A	Nuneaton Town	785	D 1-1	Holdsworth 5	3
30	Sat-10-Mar	BSN	A	Gloucester City	285	L 1-2	Walshaw 47	4
31	Tue-13-Mar	BSN	H	Solihull Moors	344	W 3-1	Ellis 52, Ainge 55, Toner 59	3
32	Sat-17-Mar	BSN	H	Histon	518	D 2-2	Boshell 42, Ellington 90	3
33	Tue-20-Mar	BSN	H	Harrogate Town	519	W 2-1	Price 48, Ainge 63	3
34	Sat-24-Mar	BSN	A	Hyde FC	823	W 1-0	Walshaw 42	2
35	Tue-27-Mar	BSN	A	FC Halifax Town	1772	W 2-1	Ellington 49, Baldry 65	2
36	Sat-31-Mar	BSN	H	Corby Town	589	W 3-0	Walshaw 2 (24, pen 50), Holdsworth 65	2
37	Tue-03-Apr	BSN	H	Gloucester City	487	W 3-2	Boshell 46, Ellington 59, Toner 61	2
38	Sat-07-Apr	BSN	A	Colwyn Bay	386	W 2-1	Ainge 2 (61, 63)	2
39	Mon-09-Apr	BSN	H	Altrincham	776	W 3-2	Ainge 50, Walshaw 52, Senior 90	2
40	Sat-14-Apr	BSN	A	Stalybridge Celtic	710	W 3-0	Ainge 41, Walshaw 42, Wilson 55	2
41	Sat-21-Apr	BSN	H	Bishops Stortford	926	L 0-1		2
42	Sat-28-Apr	BSN	A	Boston United	1087	D 3-3	Senior 2 (54, 78), Wilson 87	2

CUPS

No.	Date	Comp	H/A	Opponents	Att:	Result	Goalscorers
1	Sat-01-Oct	FAC 2Q	A	Stalybridge Celtic	493	W 2-1	Ellington 24, O'Neill 90
2	Sat-15-Oct	FAC 3Q	A	Ashington	731	L 0-1	
3	Sat-26-Nov	FAT 3Q	H	Eastwood Town	323	W 7-0	Rothery 3 (8, 36, 85), Forrest 2 (30, 45), Toner 41, Baldry 52
4	Sat-10-Dec	FAT 1	H	FC United of Manchester	810	W 2-0	Rothery 71, Ellington 86
5	Sat-14-Jan	FAT 2	H	Stalybridge Celtic	630	W 2-0	Senior 33, Ellington 64
6	Tue-21-Feb	FAT 3	A	Cambridge United	1113	L 0-1	
7	Wed-02-May	PO SF1	A	Nuneaton Town	1476	D 1-1	Wilson 90
8	Sun-06-May	PO SF2	H	Nuneaton Town	1676	L 0-1 aet (L 1-2 agg)	

League
Starts
Substitute
Unused Sub

Cups
Starts
Substitute
Unused Sub

Goals (Lg)
Goals (Cup)

	DRENCH	CLARKE	MERRIS	TONER	ELLIS	AINGE	O'NEILL	BOSHELL	ELLINGTON	FORREST	ROTHERY	ALLOTT	BURNS	BOOKER	BOWER	GILES	P DAVIDSON	HOLLAND	A DAVIDSON	BALDRY	HOLDSWORTH	GALL	BROUGH	SENIOR	WALSHAW	LISLES	WILSON	HALVORSEN	PRICE
	X	X	X	X	X	X	X	X	X	X	X	S	S	S	U	U													
	X	X	X	X	X	X	X	X	X	X	X	S	S	S	U	U													
	X	X	X	X	X	X	X	X	X	X	X	S	S	U	U	U													
	X	X	X	X	X	X		X	S	X	X	X	X	U	S	U	S												
	X	X	X	X	X	X		X	X	X	X		X	U	U	U	U	U											
	X	X	X	X	X			X	X	X	X		X	U	U	U	U	U	U										
	X	X	X	X		X		X	X	X	X		X	U	X	U	S		S	S									
	X	X	X	X	X	X	S		X	X	X		X		X	U	U		S	X									
		X	X	X	X	X	S	S		X		U	X	U	X	X	X		S	X									
	X	X	X	X	X	X	S	S		X		X	S	X		X	U	U		S	X	X							
	X	X	X	X	X	X	S	X	X		X	S	U			U	S		X	X									
	X	X	X	X		X			X	X	X		X	S	U	U	U	U		U	X	X	X						
	X	X	X	X			X		X	X		X	S	U	U	U	X	U		U		X	X						
	X	X	X			X	S	X	X	S	X		U				U			X	X	X	X						
	U	X	X	X			X	S	X	S	X		U	U			X			X	X	X	X						
	X	X	X	X		X	U	X	U	X	S		U				U			X	X	X	X						
	X	X	X	X			X	X	X	S	X		U	U			U			X	X	S							
	X		X	X	S	X	U		X	X	X		U	U			U			X	X			X	X				
	X	X	X	S	X	S		X	X	X			U	U			U			X	X			X	X				
	X	X	X	X	X	U		X		X			U	U	S	U				X	X			X					
	X	X	X	X	X	X	S		X				X	S	S	U		U		X	X			X					
	X	X	X	X	X	X	U	S	S		X			U	U					X	X			X	X				
	X	X	X	X	X	X		X	X	S				U	U					X	X			X	S				
	X	X	X	X	X	X	X	X	S					U	U					X	X			X					
	X	U	X	X	X	X		X	S	X				U		X	U			X	X			S	X				
	X	X	X		X	X	S	X	S	X				X			U			S	X			X	X	X	U		
	X	X	X	X			S	X	S					U			U			X	X			X	X	S	X		
	X	X	X	X	X	X		X						S	X		U			S	X			X		U	X	U	
	X			X	X	X	X	U	X			U		S						X	X			X	X	U	X		
	X	X	X	X	X	X	X	X		S							U			S	X			S	X	U	X		
	X	S	X	X	X	X	S	X	S								U			X	X			X	U	X		X	
	X	S	X	X	X	X	X	X	X					U			U			X				S	S		X		X
	X	X	X	X	X	X		X	X					X			U				S			X	X	U			S
	X	X	X	X	X	X		X	X					U			U			X	X			U	X	U			S
	X	X	X	X	X	X		X	X	S				U			U			X	X			X		S		S	S
	X	X	X	X	X	X		X	S	X				U			U			S	X			X		S		X	
	X	X	X	X	X	X		X	X	X				U			U			S	X			S	X		U		
	X	X	X	X	X	X		X	S	X				U			U			X	X			S	X		S		
	X	X	X	X	X	X	X	X	S					S			U			S	X			U	X		X		
	X	X	X	X	X	X	X	X	S					U			U			S	X			S	X		X		
	U	X			S		X			S	S				X	X				X	X			X		X	X	U	X
	X	X	X	X	X	X	S		X		X	S	S	U	X	U	U		X	X									
	X	X	X	X		X		S	X		X	S	X	U	X	U		U		X	X								
	X	X	X	X		X	S	X	X	X	X		S	S		U			X	X	U								
	X	X	X	X	X	X	S	X	X	X	X		S		U	U			X		U								
	X	X	X	X	X	S	X	X	S	X			U						S	X			X						
	X	S	X	X	X	S	X	X	X				U	X	U				X	X			S						
	X	X	X	X	X	X	X	U	X				U						X	X			S		S				
	X	X	X	X	X	X	S	S	X				S		U				X				X		X		U		
	39	37	42	40	32	38	10	31	25	19	19	1	9	1	8	3	1	0	2	24	29	4	5	14	15	1	9	0	4
	0	2	0	0	3	2	12	1	13	7	1	7	7	3	3	1	3	0	3	8	1	1	0	6	3	1	3	0	3
	2	1	0	0	0	0	5	0	1	1	0	1	22	12	9	37	5	4	1	1	0	0	0	2	0	7	1	2	0
	8	7	8	8	6	8	2	5	6	5	5	0	1	0	3	0	0	0	1	5	7	0	0	2	0	0	1	0	0
	0	1	0	0	0	0	5	2	1	1	0	2	4	1	0	0	0	0	0	0	1	0	0	0	2	0	0	1	0
	0	0	0	0	0	0	0	0	1	0	0	0	3	2	1	8	1	1	0	0	0	1	1	0	0	0	0	0	1
	0	1	0	5	3	8	0	5	9	3	12	3	1	0	0	0	0	0	0	2	7	5	0	1	8	11	0	2	0	1
	0	0	0	1	0	0	1	0	3	2	4	0	0	0	0	0	0	0	0	1	0	0	0	1	0	0	0	0	0

PLAYING SQUAD 2012/13

Existing Players		SN	HT	WT	DOB	AGE	POB	Career	Apps	Goals
GOALKEEPERS										
Steven	Drench				11/09/1985	26		Blackburn Rel 5/06, Morecambe (SL) 11/05, Morecambe c/s 06, Southport (L) 1/08, Southport 6/08, Cambridge U (4ML) 8/08, Leigh Genesis 3/09, Guiseley 8/10	39	0
Jacob	Giles				12/10/1985	26	Huddersfield	Huddersfield (Yth), Team Bath, Taunton 9/05, Newport C 6/06 Rel 8/07, Gloucester (L) 10/06, Bradford PA 10/07, Harrogate RA 12/07, Leeds Carnegie, Guiseley 8/11	4	0
DEFENDERS										
Simon	Ainge	6'01"	12 02		18/02/1988	24	Shipley	Bradford C Rel c/s 09, Halifax (SL) 1/08, Cambridge U (SL) 3/09, Bradford PA c/s 09, Guiseley (L) 11/09 Perm 12/09	40	8
Mark	Bower	5'10"	11 00		23/01/1980	32	Bradford	Bradford C Rel c/s 09, York C (SL) 2/00, York C (SL) 11/00, Luton (3ML) 1/09, Darlington 7/09, FC Halifax 6/10, Guiseley 5/11	11	0
Danny	Ellis	6'00"	12 00		23/11/1985	26	Bradford	Bradford C Rel c/s 06, Guiseley c/s 06	35	3
Andy	McWilliams	5'08"			05/11/1989	22	Stockton	York C, Stalybridge (SL) 8/10, Stalybridge 6/11, Guiseley 6/12		
Rhys	Meynell	5'11"	12 03		17/08/1988	24	Barnsley	Barnsley Rel c/s 08, Ossett A (L) 3/07, Gretna (SL) 1/08, Barnet (Trial) c/s 08, Stalybridge 8/08, AFC Telford (Trial) 6/09, Chester 7/09 Rel 2/10, Galway U 2/10, Stalybridge 12/10, Guiseley 5/12		
Macauley	Parkinson							Sheff Utd (Jun), Guiseley 8/12		
MIDFIELDERS										
Danny	Boshell	5'11"	11 10		30/05/1981	31	Bradford	Oldham, Bury (L) 3/05, Stockport 8/05 Rel c/s 06, Grimsby 8/06 Rel 2/10, Chesterfield 2/10 Rel c/s 10, Guiseley 8/10	32	5
Nicky	Boshell				11/08/1986	26		Huddersfield, Liversedge, Harrogate RA c/s 08, Mossley 9/08, Ossett A 1/09, Liversedge, Wibsey, Brighouse T, Bradford PA 1/11, Guiseley 7/12		
Jamie	Clarke	6'02"	12 03		18/09/1982	29	Sunderland	Mansfield Rel c/s 04, Rochdale 7/04, Boston U 1/06 Rel c/s 07, Grimsby Rel 2/10, York C 2/10 Rel 5/10, Darlington (Trial) 7/10, Gateshead (Trial) 8/10, St Johnstone (Trial) 8/10, Gainsborough 8/10, Guiseley 7/11	39	1
Zack	Dale							Blackburn (Yth), Preston (Yth), Everton (Yth), Padiham, Guiseley 7/12		
Andy	Holdsworth	5'09"	11 02		29/01/1984	28	Pontefract	Huddersfield Rel c/s 09, Oldham 7/09, Morecambe 1/11 Rel c/s 11, Alfreton 8/11, Guiseley 10/11	30	5
Chris	Holland	5'09"	11 05		11/09/1975	36	Whalley	Preston, Newcastle £100,000 1/94, Birmingham (2ML) 9/96 £600,000 10/96, Huddersfield £150,000 2/00, Boston U 3/04, Southport 1/07, Leigh Genesis 7/08, Fleetwood 11/08, Burscough 3/09, Guiseley 7/09 (Pl/Coach) 8/10	0	0
Gavin	Rothery	5'09"	10 10		22/09/1987	24	Leeds	Leeds Rel 4/08, York C 10/08, Harrogate T 12/08, Carlisle 3/09 Rel c/s 10, Barrow (6WL) 11/09, Guiseley 7/10	20	12
FORWARDS										
Wayne	Brooksby				24/04/1990	22		Scarborough, Scarborough T, Pickering (L), Sunshine George Cross (Aust), North Ferriby, Guiseley 7/12		
Danny	Forrest	5'10"	11 07		23/10/1984	27	Keighley	Bradford C Rel 5/06, Halifax (SL) 8/05, Halifax 6/06, Hucknall (L) 1/08, Crawley 5/08 Rel 5/10, Barrow 6/10 Rel 5/11, Guiseley (3ML) 1/11, Guiseley 5/11	26	3
Chris	Mason	5'09"	11 08		28/11/1990	21	Blackburn	Bury (Scholar) Rel c/s 09, Harrogate T (L) 3/09, Chorley c/s 09 Rel c/s 10, Floriana (Mal) (Trial) c/s 09, Ange IF (Swe), Bala T 7/10, Guiseley 7/12		
James	Walshaw				12/02/1984	28	Dewsbury	Thornhill, Ossett T, Lincoln C (Trial) 11/05, Bradford PA 3/07, Ossett T, Leek T 3/08 Farsley Celtic 7/08, Wakefield 11/08, Guiseley 3/09, Darlington 5/11, FC Halifax (6WL) 11/11, Guiseley 1/12	18	11
Josh	Wilson				05/07/1988	24	Liverpool	Stoke (Scholar) Rel 6/06, Abroad, Northwich 7/07 Rel 5/08, Leigh RMI/Leigh Genesis 5/08, Burscough 11/08, Vauxhall Motors 8/09, Guiseley 5/12		

HARROGATE TOWN

Chairman: Irving Weaver
Secretary: Kay Barnes Forster   **(T)** 01423 880675   **(E)** kaybarnesforster@harrogatetown.com
Additional Committee Members:
Howard Matthews, David Bolton, Peter Arnett, Richard Crabb, Tad Nowakowski,
Clive Dunnington.
Manager: Simon Weaver
Programme Editor: Peter Arnett   **(E)** htafcpressofficer@btinternet.com

Club Factfile

Founded: 1919   **Nickname:** Town
Previous Names:
Previous Leagues: West Riding 1919-20, Yorkshire 1920-21, 22-31, 57-82, Midland 1921-22, Northern 1931-32,
Harrogate & Dist. 1935-37, 40-46, W. Riding Co.Am. 1937-40, W. Yorks. 1946-57, N.C.E. 1982-87, N.P.L. 1987-2004

Club Colours (change): Yellow & black/black/black (Blue/white/blue)

Ground: The CNG Stadium, Wetherby Road, Harrogate HG2 7SA   **(T)** 01423 880 675
Capacity: 3,291   **Seats:** 502   **Covered:** 1,300   **Clubhouse:** Yes   **Shop:** Yes
Directions: A61 to Harrogate, turn right on to A658, and at roundabout take A661, proceed through second set of lights (Woodlands pub) ground approx. 500 mtrs on the right. From A1 Wetherby. Leave A1 at Wetherby on to A661 to Harrogate. Stay on this road and when reaching Harrogate at Woodland pub lights, ground 500mtrs on the right.

Previous Grounds:

Record Attendance: 4,280 v Railway Athletic - Whitworth Cup Final 1950
Record Victory: 13-0 v Micklefield
Record Defeat: 1-10 v Methley United - 1956
Record Goalscorer: Jimmy Hague - 135 (1956-58 and 1961-76)
Record Appearances: Paul Williamson - 428 (1980-81, 1982-85, and 1986-93)
Additional Records:

Senior Honours:
West Riding County Cup 1962-63, 72-73, 85-86. Northern Premier League Division 1 2001-02.
West Riding Challenge Cup x2.

10 YEAR RECORD

02-03		03-04		04-05		05-06		06-07		07-08		08-09		09-10		10-11		11-12	
NP P	6	NP P	5	Conf N	6	Conf N	5	Conf N	6	Conf N	6	Conf N	9	Conf N	21	Conf N	12	Conf N	15

HARROGATE TOWN

No.	Date	Comp	H/A	Opponents	Att:	Result	Goalscorers	Pos
	Harrogate							
1	Sat-13-Aug	BSN	H	Altrincham	587	W 3-2	Brayson 2 (12, 34), L Wilson pen 90	6
2	Tue-16-Aug	BSN	A	Stalybridge Celtic	417	L 2-3	Hassan 61, Brayson 69	11
3	Sat-20-Aug	BSN	A	Hinckley United	330	W 2-1	Bore 70, Brayson 72	8
4	Tue-23-Aug	BSN	H	Droylsden	350	D 0-0		8
5	Sat-27-Aug	BSN	H	Boston United	522	L 0-2		13
6	Mon-29-Aug	BSN	A	Blyth Spartans	559	D 3-3	Bore 4, Hassan 6, L Wilson 70	12
7	Sat-03-Sep	BSN	A	Hyde FC	615	L 2-3	Brayson 6, Nowakowski 19	13
8	Sat-10-Sep	BSN	H	Gloucester City	329	W 2-0	Turnbull 86, Brayson 90	10
9	Sat-17-Sep	BSN	A	Histon	316	L 0-4		13
10	Sat-24-Sep	BSN	H	FC Halifax Town	1107	D 0-0		15
11	Tue-27-Sep	BSN	A	Vauxhall Motors	169	W 1-0	Elam 78	11
12	Sat-08-Oct	BSN	H	Gainsborough Trinity	360	W 2-1	Meechan 20, Pell 79	9
13	Sat-22-Oct	BSN	A	Worcester City	782	L 2-3	Allan 46, Dean 74	12
14	Tue-25-Oct	BSN	A	Workington	322	L 1-2	Bore 11	13
15	Sat-29-Oct	BSN	H	Hyde FC	420	L 0-3		14
16	Sat-05-Nov	BSN	H	Nuneaton Town	394	L 0-2		14
17	Sat-12-Nov	BSN	A	Gloucester City	275	L 0-1		16
18	Tue-15-Nov	BSN	H	Bishops Stortford	216	D 1-1	Brayson 48	16
19	Sat-19-Nov	BSN	H	Eastwood Town	314	W 2-1	Turnbull 3, Ashworth 54	14
20	Sat-03-Dec	BSN	A	Solihull Moors	209	L 1-5	Brayson 77	15
21	Tue-06-Dec	BSN	H	Colwyn Bay	180	W 4-0	Pell 2 (2, 35), Allan 45, Bloomer 53	14
22	Sat-17-Dec	BSN	A	Nuneaton Town	689	L 0-2		14
23	Mon-26-Dec	BSN	H	Guiseley	661	L 0-4		16
24	Sat-07-Jan	BSN	H	Histon	393	D 0-0		17
25	Sat-14-Jan	BSN	A	Bishops Stortford	433	W 4-3	Og (Abdullahi) 19, Brayson 35, Allan 2 (67, 73)	16
26	Sat-21-Jan	BSN	A	Altrincham	773	L 2-5	Brayson 2 (pen 34, 51)	17
27	Sat-28-Jan	BSN	H	Hinckley United	354	W 2-1	Youhill 12, Pell 17	16
28	Sat-18-Feb	BSN	A	Gainsborough Trinity	596	W 1-0	Youhill 51	16
29	Sat-25-Feb	BSN	H	Stalybridge Celtic	438	L 2-1	Brayson 90	16
30	Sat-03-Mar	BSN	A	FC Halifax Town	1398	L 1-3	Chilaka 22	18
31	Tue-06-Mar	BSN	H	Corby Town	175	W 6-2	Platt 14, Meechan 17, Chilaka 3 (19, 39, pen 58), Bolland 44	14
32	Sat-10-Mar	BSN	H	Vauxhall Motors	430	L 1-2	Allan 90	17
33	Sat-17-Mar	BSN	A	Eastwood Town	173	W 1-0	Allan 90	16
34	Tue-20-Mar	BSN	A	Guiseley	519	L 1-2	Turl 43	16
35	Sat-24-Mar	BSN	H	Workington	430	L 0-1		18
36	Sat-31-Mar	BSN	H	Worcester City	319	L 0-2		18
37	Tue-03-Apr	BSN	A	Droylsden	169	D 1-1	Meechan 9	18
38	Sat-07-Apr	BSN	A	Boston United	1049	W 2-0	White 42, Nowakowski 62	17
39	Mon-09-Apr	BSN	H	Blyth Spartans	425	D 0-0		19
40	Sat-14-Apr	BSN	A	Colwyn Bay	284	D 2-2	Meechan 61, Chilaka 84	19
41	Sat-21-Apr	BSN	H	Solihull Moors	604	D 1-1	Elam 7	19
42	Sat-28-Apr	BSN	A	Corby Town	460	W 5-0	Pell 2 (48, 71), Bolland 52, Allan 86, Platt 90	15

CUPS

No.	Date	Comp	H/A	Opponents	Att:	Result	Goalscorers	
1	Sat-01-Oct	FAC 2Q	A	Frickley Athletic	285	D 1-1	Turl 10	
2	Tue-04-Oct	FAC 2QR	H	Frickley Athletic	275	L 1-2	Elam 54	
3	Sat-26-Nov	FAT 3Q	A	Worcester City	676	W 1-0	Brayson 17	
4	Sat-10-Dec	FAT 1	A	Barrow	868	L 2-3	Turl 8, L Wilson 11	

League
Starts
Substitute
Unused Sub

Cups
Starts
Substitute
Unused Sub

Goals (Lg)
Goals (Cup)

Appearance grid — player columns:

	COOK	BLOOMER	RADCLIFFE	ROSS	NOWAKOWSKI	PICTON	L WILSON	TAIT	BRAYSON	HASSAN	TURNBULL	PELL	HECKINGBOTTOM	ELAM	HARDY	TURL	BORE	WRIGHT	ELLIOT	DARVILLE	ASHWORTH	JONES	COHEN	ALLAN	MEECHAN	DEAN	MCDERMOTT	BEESLEY	EMMETT	B WILSON	BROUGH	CLAYTON	WHITE	YOUHILL	BOLLAND	LIBURD	CHILAKA	LYNN	PLATT	BURNS	PALMER
	X	X	X	X	X	X	X	X	X	X	X	S	S	U	U	U																									
	X	X	X	X	X	X	X	U	X	X	X	U	S	S	U			X																							
	X	X	X	X	X	X	X	U	X	X	X	U	X	S	S				S																						
	X	U	X		X	X	X	U	X	X	X	U	X	X	S	U	X																								
	X	U	X	S	X	X	X		X	X	X	U	X	X	S	S	X																								
	X		X	X	U	X		X	X	X	S	X	S		U	S	X	X																								
	X	U	X		X	X	X		X	X	X	U	X	S	S	S	X	X																								
		U	X	S	X	X	X		S	X		U		X	X							X	X	X																	
		U	X		X	X	X		X			U		U	S							X	X	X																	
		U	X	S	X	X	X		X		X	X	S	X		S	X					X		X	U																
		U	X	S	X	X	X		X		X	X		X		X	S	X				X	U	X	U																
		S	X	X		X	X				X	X	U	S		X	X					X		X	U	S	X														
		X	X						S			X			X			X				X	X	X	U	X	X	U	U	U											
		X	X	S		U			S		U		X	S		X	S	X	X			X	X	X		X	X	X													
		X	U			X	X		X			X		X	S		S	S				X	U	X		X	X	X													
			S	S		X			X			X	X	U		X	X					X	X			S	X	S		U		X									
	U	U	X			X	X		X			X	X	X	U	X		S				X				X	S			X											
		X	X			X	X		X			X	X	U	X		S					X	S			X	S			U	X										
	X	X	X			X			X			X		U	X	U						X	X			X	S			U											
	X	X	X			X			X			X	U	U	X		S	X				X	X		X	S	U	X	X		U										
	X	X	X						X	S	S			X			X	X	X							X				S		X	U								
	X	X	X			U		X	X					X	S		X	X								S	X		S			X		X	U						
	X	U	X			X	U		S						U	X	X	U								X				X			X	X	X	X					
	X		X			X						U	X	X	U		U	S								X				U			X	X	X	X					
	X		X				S		X			S	U	X	S		U	X								X				X			X	X	X	X	X				
	X	S	X			X			X			X	X	X	U		S	U							X	U							X	X	X						
	X	S	X			X	X		X			X	X	U	U															U	X	X	X	X			X				
	X	S	X			X	X		X			X	X	X	S													U		X		U	X	X	X		X	U			
	X	S	X				X	X			X		X	X	S		S								U			U		X	X	X	X	X		X					
	X	X	X				X				X		X		S		U								X			U	U		U	X	X	X	X			X			
	X	X	X				X						X		S		S								S	X				X			X	S	X	X		X	X	X
	X	X	X				X						X		X		U								S	X		X		S	X	X			X	X		X	X	U	U
	X	X	X				X					X			X										S	U	X			S	S				X			X	X	X	X
	X	X	X				X				X				U										S	U	X				S				X			X	X	X	X
	X		X		S	X					X				X		U									X	U		S		S			X	X	X		X	X	X	
	X	X	X				X				U				U			X		X						X	X		X					X	U	X		X	U	X	U
	X	X	X				X				U				S			X								X	X		X					X	S	X		S	U	X	U
	X	X	X		U						U				X		X		U							X								X	X	X		X		X	U
	X	X	X				U				U				X			S		X						X	X	U						X	S	X		X		S	X
	X	X	X		U						U				X											X	X	X						X	U	X		U		X	U

Substitutes / additional block:

		S	X	X			X	X				X	X	U	X	S	X	X						X	U	X	U	S													
		U	X	X			X	X				X	X	U	X		X	X						X	U	X	U	S													
	X	X	X				X	X			X				U	X					S				X	X			X	S					U						
	X	X	X				X	X			X				X	X	S	S						X						U						U						

Totals:

	31	22	40	7	14	29	21	3	29	7	18	22	18	14	0	10	18	2	2	13	7	6	0	14	18	10	0	4	0	3	5	0	17	10	18	1	11	0	8	7	3
	0	5	1	6	1	1	0	2	6	0	1	3	3	20	4	14	4	0	0	0	2	0	0	7	4	0	0	1	3	0	1	0	0	5	0	0	2	0	2	1	0
	0	9	1	1	3	2	1	3	6	0	2	8	6	6	3	11	1	0	0	1	2	0	5	0	4	2	1	4	6	1	1	4	0	5	0	0	1	1	1	2	4

Goals blocks:

	2	2	4	2	0	4	4	0	2	0	4	3	0	3	0	2	3	0	0	3	1	2	0	2	1	0	0	0	0	0	0	0	0	0	0	0	0	0	0	0	0
	0	1	0	0	0	0	0	0	0	0	0	0	1	1	1	0	1	0	0	0	0	0	0	2	1	0	0	0	0	0	0	0	0	0	0	0	0	0	0	0	0
	0	1	0	0	0	0	0	0	0	0	0	3	0	0	0	0	0	0	1	2	0	2	0	0	0	0	0	2	0	0	0	0	0	0	0	0	0	0	0	0	0

| | 0 | 1 | 0 | 0 | 2 | 0 | 2 | 0 | 12 | 2 | 2 | 6 | 0 | 2 | 0 | 1 | 3 | 0 | 0 | 1 | 0 | 0 | 7 | 4 | 1 | 0 | 0 | 0 | 0 | 0 | 1 | 2 | 2 | 0 | 5 | 0 | 2 | 0 | 0 | | |
| | 0 | 0 | 0 | 0 | 0 | 0 | 1 | 0 | 1 | 0 | 0 | 0 | 1 | 0 | 2 | 0 | 0 | 0 | 0 | 0 | 0 | 0 | 0 | 0 | 0 | 0 | 0 | 0 | 0 | 0 | 0 | 0 | 0 | 0 | 0 | 0 | 0 | 0 | 0 | 0 | 0 |

PLAYING SQUAD 2012/13

Existing Players		SN	HT	WT	DOB	AGE	POB	Career	Apps	Goals
GOALKEEPERS										
Mark	Cook		6'00"	12 01	07/09/1988	23	North Shields	Newcastle (Scholar) Rel c/s 08, Hartlepool 7/08 Rel c/s 10, Gateshead 8/10, Harrogate T 10/10	31	0
Jose	Veiga		6'02"	12 13	18/12/1976	35	Lisbon, Port	Benfica (Port), Levante (Spain), Valladolid (Spain), Estrela da Amadora (Port), Sporting Club Olhanense (Port), Tamworth 10/06 Rel c/s 08, Atherstone, Hereford NC 12/08, Macclesfield 8/09 Rel c/s 12, Harrogate T 7/12		
DEFENDERS										
Matt	Bloomer		6'00"	13 00	03/11/1978	33	Grimsby	Grimsby Rel c/s 01, Hull C (Trial) 4/01, Hull C 7/01, Lincoln C (L) 3/02, Telford (3ML) 8/02, Lincoln C 12/02 Rel 5/06, Grimsby (L) 1/06, Cambridge U (2ML) 3/06, Cambridge U 7/06 Rel 1/07, Grimsby 1/07 Rel c/s 07, Boston U 7/07, Harrogate T 6/09	27	1
Shane	Killock		6'00"	12 04	12/03/1989	23	Huddersfield	Ossett A (Yth), Huddersfield, Hyde U (SL) 2/08, Harrogate T (L) 9/08, Oxford U (L) 1/09 Perm 2/09, AFC Telford (2ML) 8/09 Perm 10/09 Rel c/s 12, Harrogate T 5/12		
Dave	Merris		5'07"	10 06	13/10/1980	31	Rotherham	Rotherham (Scholar), Guiseley 7/98, Harrogate T 9/99, York 8/03 Rel 5/06, Harrogate T 6/06, Guiseley 3/08 Rel c/s 12, Harrogate T 5/12		
Craig	Racliffe				12/04/1989	23		Athletic Bilbao (Sp) (Yth), Middlesbrough (Yth), Durham C, Cambridge C c/s 06, Mildenhall T (L) 10/08, Bury T 11/09, Biggleswade T, Harrogate T 8/11	41	0
Dwayne	Samuels		5'08"	11 00	11/10/1990	21	Wolverhampton	West Brom, Grimsby 8/10 Rel 6/11, Redditch (L) 1/11, AFC Telford 7/11, Worcester 3/12, Harrogate T 5/12		
Danny	Stimpson		6'03"	13 07	27/02/1990	22		Huddersfield (Yth), York C (Yth), Ange IF (Swe), Luton (Trial), Harrogate T 7/11		
Alan	White		6'01"	13 02	22/03/1976	36	Darlington	Derby (Sch), Middlesbrough, Luton £40,000 9/97 Rel c/s 00, Colchester (6WL) 11/99, Colchester 7/00 Rel c/s 04, L.Orient 7/04, Boston U 3/05, Notts County 7/06, Peterborough (SL) 3/07, Darlington 7/07, Luton 7/09 Rel 8/10, Darlington (SL) 1/10, Stalybridge 10/10, Gateshead 11/10 Rel 2/11, Blyth 2/11 Rel c/s 11, Boston U 8/11, Harrogate T 12/11	17	1
MIDFIELDERS										
Adam	Bolder		5'09"	10 08	25/10/1980	31	Bolton	Hull C, Derby 4/00, QPR 1/07, Sheff Wed (SL) 2/08, Millwall (2ML) 11/08, Millwall 1/09, Bradford C (SL) 3/10, Burton 7/10 Rel c/s 12, Harrogate T 7/12		
Dan	Clayton							Boroughbridge, Northallerton, Harrogate T 12/11	0	0
Luke	Dean		5'09"	11 00	01/06/1989	23	Cleckheaton	Bradford C Rel c/s 12, FC Halifax (L) 12/09, Ossett T (L) 3/11, Hinckley U (L) 8/11, Harrogate T (L) 10/11, Harrogate T (L) 3/12, Harrogate T 7/12	10	1
Lee	Elam		5'08"	10 12	24/09/1976	35	Bradford	Guiseley, Southport 11/98, Morecambe 8/02, Halifax 5/03, Yeovil (L) 10/03 Perm 11/03, Chester (L) 3/04, Hornchurch 5/04, Burton 11/04, Morecambe 11/04 Rel 5/05, Crawley 7/05 Rel 9/05, Weymouth 9/05, Exeter 1/07 Rel 5/08, Altrincham 7/08 Rel 1/09, Northwich 1/09, Bradford PA 3/10, Stalybridge 8/10, Harrogate T 8/11	34	2
Jack	Emmett				22/11/1993	18		Harrogate T, Ripon T (Dual)	3	0
Adam	Nowakowski				22/10/1986	25		Ripon C, Harrogate T	15	2
Robbie	Youhill				28/09/1986	25		Tadcaster A, USA Scholarship, New Jersey (USA), Harrogate T 12/11	15	2
FORWARDS										
Jonny	Allan		6'00"	11 03	24/05/1983	29	Penrith	Carlisle Rel c/s 02, Workington 8/02, Oxford U (Trial) 8/02 Northwich 8/02, Tranmere (Trial) 7/03, Lancaster 11/03, Halifax 12/03, Northwich 8/04, Gateshead 5/10 Rel 5/11, Harrogate T 5/11	21	7
Paul	Beesley				13/03/1984	28		Boroughbridge, Harrogate RA c/s 11, Harrogate T 10/11, Harrogate RA (L)	5	0
Chibuzor	Chilaka		5'08"	13 00	21/10/1986	25	Nigeria	Rushden & D (Yth), Notts County Rel c/s 06, Hinckley U (6WL) 12/05, Grimsby (Trial) 7/06, Hull University, Hull C (Trial) 7/07, Bridlington T c/s 08, Leeds Carnegie 7/09, Guiseley (Trial) 7/10, Bradford C 8/10 Rel c/ 11, Bradford PA (L) 11/10, Harrogate T (6WL) 2/11, Braintree 8/11 Rel 1/12, Harrogate T 2/12	13	5
Liam	Hardy				21/12/1987	24		Armthorpe Welfare, Harrogate T 6/10	4	0
Alex	Meechan		5'08"	10 10	29/01/1980	32	Plymouth	Swindon, Bristol C 7/98, Forest Green (2ML) 8/00, Yeovil (L) 11/00, Forest Green NC 12/00, Dag & Red 6/03, Forest Green (3ML) 11/03 Perm 2/04 Rel 6/04, Luton (Trial) 7/04, Leigh RMI 8/04 Rel 11/04, Halifax 11/04 Rel 4/05, Forest Green 7/05 Rel 1/07, Chester 1/07 Rel c/s 07, York C 7/07, Stalybridge 11/07, Altrincham 6/08 Rel 3/09, Stalybridge (L) 1/09, Stalybridge 3/09, Droylsden 7/09, AFC Telford 7/10 Rel 12/11, Harrogate T (10WL) 10/11, Harrogate T 1/12	22	4

HINCKLEY UNITED

Chairman: Kevin Downes
Secretary: Ray Baggott   **(T)** 07802 355 249   **(E)** raybaggott@yahoo.co.uk
Additional Committee Members:
Robert Mayne, Ku Akeredolu, A Dyer, P Moss, D Newman, D Radburn, M Sutton,
K Thompson.
Manager: Dean Thomas
Programme Editor: TBA   **(E)**

2011-12 Squad - Back Row (L-R): Jay-Lee Hodgson, Andre Gray, Tobias Dingwall, Ben Richards-Everton, Jermaine Clarke,
Craig McAughtrie, Keenen Meakin-Richards.
Middle Row: Sam Palmer (Ass. Physio), Dave Radburn (Kit Manager), Joseph Hull, Paul Lister, Robert Oddy, Daniel Haystead,
Denham Hinds, Jake Holt, Mark Dudley, Nicky Platnauer (Ass. Manager), Stuart Storer (Coach), Andy Keeley (Physio).
Front Row: Lloyd Kerry, Stuart Hendrie, Andrew Gooding, Dean Thomas (Manager), Tom Byrne, David Kolodynski, Daniel Newton.

Club Factfile

Founded: 1997   **Nickname:** United
Previous Names: Today's club was formed when Hinckley Athletic and Hinckley Town merged in 1997
Previous Leagues: As United: Southern 1997-2004

Club Colours (change): Red & navy/navy/red (All orange)

Ground: The Greene King Stadium, Leicester Road, Hinckley LE10 3DR   **(T)** 01455 840 088
Capacity: 4,329   **Seats:** 630   **Covered:** 2,695   **Clubhouse:** Yes   **Shop:** Yes
Directions: M1 J21 take M69 (Coventry) or M6 J2 take M69 (Leicester). M69 J2 take A5 North. At 3rd roundabout (Dodwells). Take 2nd exit
A47 Earl Shilton & Industrial Estates, follow A47 over three roundabouts & a set of traffic lights at next roundabout take 3rd exit
B4668. Stadium is 100 yards on right.

Previous Grounds:

Record Attendance: 2,278 v Nuneaton Borough - 10/12/2005
Record Victory: 9-1 v Rocester (A) - 28/08/2000
Record Defeat: 1-7 v Stalybridge Celtic (A) - Conference North 03/03/2009
Record Goalscorer: Jamie Lenton - 74
Record Appearances: Jamie Lenton - 280
Additional Records:

Senior Honours:
Southern League Division 1 Western 2000-01

10 YEAR RECORD									
02-03	03-04	04-05	05-06	06-07	07-08	08-09	09-10	10-11	11-12
SthP 13	SthP 6	Conf N 12	Conf N 10	Conf N 4	Conf N 19	Conf N 10	Conf N 7	Conf N 15	Conf N 20

HINCKLEY UNITED

No.	Date	Comp	H/A	Opponents	Att:	Result	Goalscorers	Pos
1	Sat-13-Aug	BSN	A	Guiseley	361	L 0-3		22
2	Mon-15-Aug	BSN	H	Gainsborough Trinity	413	W 3-0	Hendrie 36, Gray 2 (37, 52)	10
3	Sat-20-Aug	BSN	H	Harrogate Town	330	L 1-2	Gray 43	15
4	Mon-22-Aug	BSN	A	Hyde FC	323	L 0-4		16
5	Sat-27-Aug	BSN	H	Gloucester City	455	L 2-3	Jermaine Clarke 14, Gray 77	19
6	Mon-29-Aug	BSN	A	Bishops Stortford	303	L 0-5		21
7	Sat-03-Sep	BSN	A	Solihull Moors	358	W 2-1	Dean 39, Horne 45	20
8	Sat-10-Sep	BSN	H	FC Halifax Town	571	W 3-2	Gray 68, Newton 78, Dean 87	15
9	Sat-17-Sep	BSN	A	Droylsden	265	W 3-2	Jermaine Clarke 42, Holt 76, Newton 90	9
10	Tue-20-Sep	BSN	A	Boston United	813	L 0-2		14
11	Sat-24-Sep	BSN	H	Histon	438	L 0-3		16
12	Sat-08-Oct	BSN	H	Colwyn Bay	419	W 3-1	Newton 2 (45, 57), Gray 71	14
13	Sat-22-Oct	BSN	A	Gainsborough Trinity	639	L 1-2	Byrne 90	16
14	Sat-05-Nov	BSN	A	Workington	360	L 1-3	Gray 21	17
15	Mon-14-Nov	BSN	H	Hyde FC	365	D 0-0		17
16	Sat-19-Nov	BSN	A	Blyth Spartans	364	D 3-3	Raglan 23, Newton 2 (45, 73)	19
17	Sat-03-Dec	BSN	A	Gloucester City	325	D 2-2	Byrne 17, Gray 21	18
18	Mon-05-Dec	BSN	H	Worcester City	377	L 2-3	Byrne 5, Newton 10	18
19	Sat-17-Dec	BSN	A	FC Halifax Town	1267	L 1-6	Gray 44	20
20	Mon-26-Dec	BSN	H	Nuneaton Town	1334	D 1-1	Newton 4	20
21	Sun-01-Jan	BSN	A	Nuneaton Town	1372	W 5-2	Lavery 1, Gooding 14, Belcher 2 (22, pen 71), Gray 59	20
22	Sat-07-Jan	BSN	H	Eastwood Town	405	W 4-0	Gooding 11, Newton 84, Lister 2 (88, 90)	20
23	Mon-09-Jan	BSN	A	Altrincham	434	L 1-4	Newton 65	20
24	Sat-21-Jan	BSN	H	Stalybridge Celtic	401	D 5-5	Farrell 45, Deards 47, Newton 50, Gray 2 (57, 67)	20
25	Sat-28-Jan	BSN	A	Harrogate Town	354	L 1-2	Gray 55	20
26	Wed-15-Feb	BSN	A	Corby Town	286	W 2-0	Lavery 55, Farrell 61	19
27	Sat-18-Feb	BSN	H	Guiseley	469	L 0-1		19
28	Tue-21-Feb	BSN	H	Altrincham	625	D 2-2	Belcher 2 (pen 8, pen 69)	19
29	Sat-25-Feb	BSN	H	Corby Town	503	L 0-3		19
30	Sat-03-Mar	BSN	A	Eastwood Town	284	W 3-0	Gray 23, Kerry 50, Belcher 71	19
31	Sat-10-Mar	BSN	A	Workington	435	W 4-2	Newton 7, Lavery 72, Lister 83, Gooding 90	19
32	Mon-12-Mar	BSN	H	Boston United	441	L 1-2	Kerry 31	19
33	Sat-17-Mar	BSN	A	Colwyn Bay	237	W 5-0	Gooding 9, Kerry 53, Flanagan 74, Lavery 79, Gray 88	19
34	Mon-19-Mar	BSN	H	Solihull Moors	401	L 1-2	Gray 18	19
35	Sat-24-Mar	BSN	H	Vauxhall Motors	407	D 2-2	Bogle 23, Bragoli 82	19
36	Sat-31-Mar	BSN	H	Droylsden	354	D 1-1	Bragoli 5	19
37	Tue-03-Apr	BSN	A	Vauxhall Motors	232	W 2-1	Newton 6, Og (Wilson) 18	16
38	Sat-07-Apr	BSN	A	Histon	354	W 3-2	Farrell 2 (57, 63), Kerry 86	14
39	Mon-09-Apr	BSN	H	Bishops Stortford	427	L 1-3	Bogle 84	17
40	Sat-14-Apr	BSN	A	Worcester City	813	D 1-1	Bogle 76	18
41	Sat-21-Apr	BSN	H	Blyth Spartans	624	L 1-3	Farrell 86	20
42	Sat-28-Apr	BSN	A	Stalybridge Celtic	670	L 2-4	Og (Lynch) 24, Farrell 65	20

CUPS

No.	Date	Comp	H/A	Opponents	Att:	Result	Goalscorers	
1	Sat-01-Oct	FAC 2Q	A	Matlock Town	411	W 3-1	Gray 2 (43, 89), Byrne 54	
2	Sat-15-Oct	FAC 3Q	H	Leek Town	436	D 3-3	Lavery 26, Joyce 2 (27, 45)	
3	Tue-18-Oct	FAC 3QR	A	Leek Town	488	W 2-1 aet	Gray 13, Byrne 94	
4	Sat-29-Oct	FAC 4Q	A	Darlington	1175	D 1-1	Belcher 9	
5	Tue-01-Nov	FAC 4QR	H	Darlington	837	W 3-0	Belcher 2 (32, 79), Gray 70	
6	Sat-12-Nov	FAC 1	H	Tamworth	1906	D 2-2	Gray 78, Kerry 88	
7	Tue-22-Nov	FAC 1R	A	Tamworth	1583	L 0-1		
8	Sat-26-Nov	FAT 3Q	A	Gainsborough Trinity	321	W 1-0	Gray 29	
9	Sat-10-Dec	FAT 1	A	Wrexham	1101	W 2-1	Belcher 24, Gray 76	
10	Wed-18-Jan	FAT 2	H	Luton Town	754	D 0-0		
11	Mon-23-Jan	FAT 2R	A	Luton Town	1004	L 0-3		

League
Starts
Substitute
Unused Sub

Cups
Starts
Substitute
Unused Sub

Goals (Lg)
Goals (Cup)

	HAYSTEAD	DUDLEY	MEAKIN-RICHARDS	MCLAUGHTRIE	RICHARDS-EVERTON	LISTER	KERRY	GRAY	BYRNE	HENDRIE	ODDY	HODGSON	KOLODYNSKI	NEWTON	HOLT	HORNE	JERMAINE CLARKE	DEAN	STEPHENSON	HULL	REYNOLDS	GUDGER	JAMAL CLARKE	PORTER	LAVERY	RAGLAN	BELCHER	JOYCE	YATES	GOODING	HINDS	FLANAGAN	BEVAN	BRAGOLI	COBB	THOMSON	DEENEY	LANGHAM	FARRELL	DEARDS	DARIKWAH	LANE	HOLLIS	BROWN	BOGLE
	X	X	X	X	X	X	X	X	X	X	X				S	S	S	S	U																										
	X	X		X	X	U	X	X	U	X	X		S	X	U	U	X	X																											
	X	X	U	X	X	S	X	X	U	X	X		S	X	X	U	X																												
	X	X		X	X	S	X	X	S	X	X		X	U	S	X	S	X	X	X	X	U																							
	X	X	U		S	X	X	X		X	S	X	X	X	S		X	X		X																									
	X			U	X	X	X		X	X			S	S	U	X	X				X	X																							
	X				X	X	X	X		X	X			S	S	X	X	X		X	X	U																							
	X	S			X	X	X		X	X			X	S		X	X		X	X	U																								
	X	X			X	X	X		U	X			X			X	X	X	X	U	S																								
	X	X	U		X	X	X		U	X			X		S	X	X	U	S																										
	X			U	X	X	X	U	S	X			X			S		X	U	X	X	X	X																						
	X	U		S	X	X	X	X		S			X			S	X	X	X	X	U	X																							
	X	X		S	X	X	X	X		X			S	U		X	X	X	U	X	U	X			U																				
	X			U	X	X	X		X				X	S		X	X	X	S	U	X	X	S			U		X	X	S	S														
	X			S	X	X	X	U		X			X	S		X		X	S		X	X	X	X	U	X																			
	U			X	X	X	X		X	X			X	S		S		X	X		X	X	X	U	X	S				X	S														
	X			X	X	X	S		X	X			X	U		X		X	X		X	X	X	U	U	X																			
	X			X	X	X	X	S		U			X	S		X		X	X		X	X	X	S	U	S																			
	X			X	X	X	X		U	U			X			X		X	X		X	X	X	X	S																				
	X			X	X	X	X		U	S			X	U		X		X			X	U		X				S	X	X									X	S	X			
	X			X	X	X	X		S				X	U		X		X			X	U		S				X	S	X									X	S				
	X			X	X	X	X		U				S	U		X		X			X			X				S		X	X	S	X						X	X	X			
				X	X	X	X	U					S	S		S		X			X			X				X		X	X								X	X	X	X		
	U			X	X	X	X	S					S	S		X		X			X			X				X		X	U								X	X	X	X		
	X			X	X	X	X	S					X	S		X		X			X			X				X		X	U								X	X	X			
	X			S	X	X	X	S					X	U		X		X			X				U			X		U	S	X	S	X						X			X	
	X	X		U	X	X	X	X					X	U		X		X			X			X				S		S	S	S								X	X		X	
	X	X		U	X	X	X	S					X	X		X		X			X			X				S		X	X	U								X	X		X	
	X	U		U	X	X	X	X					X	S		X		X			X			S				X		X	X	X								X	X		X	
	X	U		U	X	X	X	X					X	S		X		X			S			S				X		X	X	X								X	X		X	
	X	X		X	X			S					S	X		X		X			U			X				X		X	X	X								S	X			X
	X	X		X	X			S	U				S	U		X		X			X	S		X				X		X	X	X								X			X	X
	X	X		X	X			X	U				S	U	S	X		X			X	S		U				X	U	X	X								S			X	X
	X	X		X	X			U					X	X	U	X		X			X	U		X				X		X	X								S				X
	X	X		X	X			U					X	X		X		X	S		X	U		X				X		X	X			S					X				X
	X	X		X	X			X					X	U		X		X			X	U		X				X		S	X								U				X
	X	X		X	X			S					X	U	X	X		X			X			X				U		X	X								S				X
	X	X		X	X			S					S	S	U	X		X			X			X				X		U	X								X				X
	X	S				X	X	X	S	S	X			X			X				X			X	U	X	X	X	X	U															
	X					U	X	X	U	S	X			X			X		S		X			X	X	X	X	X	S																
	X					U	X	X	S	U	X			X			X		S		X			X	X	X	X	S																	
	X	S				U	X	X	X		X			S	U		X		S		X			X	X	X	X	X																	
	X	X				U	X	X	X		X			S	S		S		S		X			X	X	X	X	X	U																
	X	X				U	X	X	X		X			S	S		S				X			X	X	X	X	U	X	S	U														
	X					U	X	X	X		X			X	U		X		U		X			X	X	S	X	X	U																
	X		U			U	X	X	X		X			X	S		X		U		X				X	U	X									X	U	U	X						
	S					X	X	X	U		X			X	S		X				X			X	X	X	X					X	U	U	X										
	X					X	X	X	U		U			X	S		X				X			X	X	X	S												X						
	X					X	X	X	S		U			X	X		X				X			X	X		X												X						

ALSO PLAYED: FORDE S (7). HICKS U (20, 28), S (C11). JOHNSON S(34). KNIGHT U (C7). CANAVAN S (C11).

	HAYSTEAD	DUDLEY	MEAKIN-RICHARDS	MCLAUGHTRIE	RICHARDS-EVERTON	LISTER	KERRY	GRAY	BYRNE	HENDRIE	ODDY	HODGSON	KOLODYNSKI	NEWTON	HOLT	HORNE	JERMAINE CLARKE	DEAN	STEPHENSON	HULL	REYNOLDS	GUDGER	JAMAL CLARKE	PORTER	LAVERY	RAGLAN	BELCHER	JOYCE	YATES	GOODING	HINDS	FLANAGAN	BEVAN	BRAGOLI	COBB	THOMSON	DEENEY	LANGHAM	FARRELL	DEARDS	DARIKWAH	LANE	HOLLIS	BROWN	BOGLE
	30	31	1	4	12	34	40	34	11	7	18	0	4	29	4	5	11	7	1	1	5	7	0	0	23	6	23	3	0	21	8	24	2	11	0	1	1	13	1	5	2	8	6	7
	0	1	0	0	5	3	0	0	15	1	0	4	3	12	13	1	3	0	0	0	0	0	3	2	0	3	5	0	4	0	2	0	6	1	2	0	2	3	3	0	0	0	0	1
	1	3	2	1	9	2	0	0	8	2	5	2	0	1	18	0	2	0	0	1	0	0	4	1	0	0	4	5	2	1	0	2	0	8	4	1	0	0	1	0	0	0	0	0
	6	6	0	0	0	6	11	11	5	0	9	0	0	8	1	0	0	0	0	4	0	0	8	8	10	7	0	7	5	4	0	2	0	0	1	0	2	0	0	0	0	0	0
	0	3	0	0	0	0	0	0	3	2	0	0	3	5	0	4	0	0	0	0	0	0	0	1	0	2	1	0	1	0	0	0	0	0	0	0	0	0	0	0	0	0	0
	0	0	0	1	6	1	0	0	3	1	2	0	0	2	0	0	0	0	0	0	0	0	1	0	0	1	0	2	0	1	2	0	0	1	1	0	0	0	0	0	0	0	0
	0	0	0	0	3	4	16	3	1	0	0	0	13	1	1	2	2	0	0	0	0	0	4	1	5	0	0	4	0	1	0	2	0	0	0	0	6	1	0	0	0	3
	0	0	0	0	0	0	1	7	2	0	0	0	0	0	0	0	0	0	0	0	0	0	1	0	4	2	0	0	0	0	0	0	0	0	0	0	1	0	4	2	0	0	0	0

PLAYING SQUAD 2012/13

Existing Players		SN	HT	WT	DOB	AGE	POB	Career	Apps	Goals
GOALKEEPERS										
Scott	Furlong				27/12/1993	18		Notts Forest (Scholar) Rel c/s 12, Hinckley U 6/12		
Rob	Peet				11/10/1992	19		Leicester, Grimsby 8/10, Man Utd (Trial) 2/11, Hull C 10/11, Hinckley U 7/12		
DEFENDERS										
Sol	Davis	5'07"	12 04		04/09/1979	32	Cheltenham	Swindon, Luton £600,000 8/02 Rel c/s 09, Peterborough (2ML) 9/07, Grimsby (Trial) 7/09, MK Dons 8/09 Rel c/s 10, Kettering (5WL) 11/09, Kettering 5/10, Hinckley U 8/12		
Mark	Dudley	5'10"	12 02		29/01/1990	22	Doncaster	Derby Rel c/s 10, Tamworth (L) 3/09, Alfreton (L) 10/09, Hinckley U (L) 11/09, Hinckley U (L) 2/10, St Paricks (Ire) 6/10, Stafford R 8/10, Hinckley U 8/11	32	0
Paul	Lister				03/12/1989	22	Sheffield	Chesterfield (Jun), Burton, Grantham (SL) 11/08, Hinckley U 7/09, Alfreton 12/10 Rel 5/11, Frickley (2ML) 3/11, Hinckley U 5/11	37	3
Charlie	Raglan	6'00"	11 13		28/04/1993	19		Port Vale Rel c/s 12, Hinckley U (2ML) 9/11, Chasetown (L) 3/12, Hinckley U 7/12	6	1
Ben	Richards-Everton				17/10/1991	20	Birmingham	Romulus, Carlisle (Scholar) 9/09, Romulus 1/10, Cradley T, Kettering (Trial) 4/11, Kidderminster (Trial) 4/11, Hinckley U 8/11, Sutton Coldfield (L) 9/11, Romulus (L) 12/11	17	0
Declan	Towers							Oadby T, Hinckley U 6/12		
MIDFIELDERS										
Indy	Aujla							Bradford C Rel c/s 06, Chester C, Longford T. Bacup B, Guiseley, CCBC Essex (USA), Buxton 7/09, Garforth T, Royal Racing FC Montegnee (Bel) (Pl/Coach), Inverness Caledonian (Trial) 7/12, Hinckley U 8/12		
Danny	Bragoli							Shrewsbury, Stourport (L), Wilmington Hammerheads (USA), Stourport 7/05, Willenhall, Rushall O 7/06, Tipton T, Chasetown 6/09, Tipton T, Rushall O 6/11, Hinckley U 11/11	17	2
Jack	Lane							Oadby T, Hinckley U 6/12		
Aman	Verma	6'01"	13 00		03/01/1987	25	Birmingham	Leicester (Yth), FC Khalsa, Ellistown, Bedworth c/s 07, Redditch 8/08, Leicester 12/08 Rel 5/11, Crewe (3ML) 8/09, Histon (L) 3/10, Kidderminster (L) 8/10, Darlington (SL) 11/10, Kettering 7/11, Mansfield (6WL) 11/11, Hinckley U 7/12		
FORWARDS										
Omar	Bogle							Birmingham, Celtic c/s 11 Rel 12/11, Luton (Trial), Hinckley U 3/12	8	3
Jason	Bradley	6'03"	13 00		16/03/1989	23	Sheffield	Sheff Wed Rel c/s 08, Buxton (L) 10/07, Darlington 7/08, Buxton (L) 9/08, Blyth (L) 11/08, Gainsborough (SL) 2/09, Mansfield 7/09 Rel 4/10, Newport (L) 8/09, Kings Lynn (L) 9/09, Harrogate T (SL) 12/09, Brackley T 6/10, Tamworth 1/11, Eastwood T 6/11, Sheffield FC 2/12, Hinckley U 7/12		
Phil	Green				10/03/1988	24		Aston Villa, Ecesham (L), Kings Lynn 7/08 Rel 8/08, Redditch 9/09 Rel 2/11, Stourport 2/11, Hednesford 3/11, Worcester 1/12, Hinckley U 7/12		
Jake	Holt							Hinckley U	17	1

HISTON

Chairman: Russell Hands
Secretary: Howard Wilkins   **(T)** 01223 237 373   **(E)** secretary@histonfc.co.uk
Additional Committee Members:
John Hall, David Humm, Neil Davies, Colin Pettit, Joy Mansfield, Brenda Soar,
Graham Eales.
Manager: Brian Page
Programme Editor: Howard Wilkins   **(E)** secretary@histonfc.co.uk

2011-12 Squad - Back Row (l-r): Daniel Sparkes, Zak Mills, Harri Hawkins, Jorg Stadelmann, David Knight, Jim Stevenson, Remy Clerima, Ollie Cleaver
Middle: Lewis Taaffe, Grant Roberts, Dan Holman, Dallas Moore, Danny Fitzsimons, Omer Riza, Matt Breeze, Jay Dowie
Front: Joe Asensi, Jack Sessions, Nick Whitehouse (Physio), Brian Page (Asst Manager), David Livermore (Manager), Howard Willmott (Academy Director), Charlie Day, Eugene Libertucci

Club Factfile

Founded: 1904   **Nickname:** The Stutes
Previous Names: Histon Institute
Previous Leagues: Cambridgeshire 1904-48, Spartan 1948-60, Delphian 1960-63, Eastern Counties 1966-2000, Southern 2000-05.

Club Colours (change): Red and black stripes/black/black (All blue)

Ground: The Glassworld Stadium, Bridge Road, Impington, Cambridge CB24 9PH   **(T)** 01223 237 373
Capacity: 3,250   **Seats:** 450   **Covered:** 1,800   **Clubhouse:** Yes   **Shop:** Yes

Directions: From the M11 (Northbound) Junc 14, take the A14 eastbound signed towards Newmarket. Take the first exit off the A14 and at the roundabout, take the first exit onto the B1049. Go straight over the traffic lights, past the Holiday Inn Hotel (on your right) and the entrance to the club is half a mile on your right.

Previous Grounds:

Record Attendance: 6,400 v King's Lynn - FA Cup 1956
Record Victory: 11-0 v March Town - Cambridgeshire Invitation Cup 15/02/01
Record Defeat: 1-8 v Ely City - Eastern Counties Division One 1994
Record Goalscorer: Neil Kennedy - 292
Record Appearances: Neil Andrews and Neil Kennedy
Additional Records: Paid £6,000 to Chelmsford City for Ian Cambridge 2000. Received £30,000 from Manchester United for
Senior Honours: Guiliano Maiorana.
Eastern Counties League Cup 1990-91, Eastern Counties League 1999-2000, Southern League Premier 2004-05, Conference South 2006-07.

10 YEAR RECORD

02-03		03-04		04-05		05-06		06-07		07-08		08-09		09-10		10-11		11-12	
SthE	10	SthE	2	SthP	1	Conf S	5	Conf S	1	Conf	7	Conf	3	Conf	18	Conf	24	Conf N	16

HISTON

No.	Date	Comp	H/A	Opponents	Att:	Result	Goalscorers	Pos
1	Sat-13-Aug	BSN	H	Blyth Spartans	428	D 2-2	Holman 38, Breeze 57	13
2	Tue-16-Aug	BSN	A	Boston United	1222	D 1-1	Holman 4	15
3	Sat-20-Aug	BSN	A	Altrincham	686	L 0-3		18
4	Tue-23-Aug	BSN	H	Worcester City	342	L 1-5	Holman 90	20
5	Sat-27-Aug	BSN	H	Corby Town	302	D 1-1	Hawkins 63	20
6	Mon-29-Aug	BSN	A	Solihull Moors	203	W 2-0	Mills 4, Riza 41	18
7	Sat-03-Sep	BSN	H	Stalybridge Celtic	362	L 0-1		19
8	Sat-10-Sep	BSN	A	Colwyn Bay	318	L 1-2	Sparkes 14	18
9	Sat-17-Sep	BSN	H	Harrogate Town	316	W 4-0	Holman 2 (5, 58), Sparkes 68, Riza 80	17
10	Tue-20-Sep	BSN	A	Nuneaton Town	572	L 2-3	Taaffe 29, Sparkes 53	17
11	Sat-24-Sep	BSN	A	Hinckley United	438	W 3-0	Og (Reynolds) 14, Taaffe 53, Holman 90	14
12	Sat-08-Oct	BSN	H	Vauxhall Motors	363	D 3-3	Holman 52, Taaffe 65, Breeze 89	15
13	Sat-15-Oct	BSN	H	Boston United	417	L 1-3	Sparkes 8	16
14	Sat-22-Oct	BSN	A	Eastwood Town	214	W 2-1	Fitzsimons 35, Riza 67	15
15	Sat-29-Oct	BSN	H	Workington	360	W 2-0	Sparkes 48, Holman 82	13
16	Sat-05-Nov	BSN	A	Hyde FC	394	L 0-4		13
17	Sat-12-Nov	BSN	A	Stalybridge Celtic	601	L 0-2		14
18	Sat-19-Nov	BSN	H	FC Halifax Town	513	L 1-4	Taaffe 74	16
19	Sat-03-Dec	BSN	A	Vauxhall Motors	177	D 1-1	Sparkes 88	16
20	Tue-06-Dec	BSN	H	Solihull Moors	203	W 3-0	Sparkes 26, Holman 35, Stevenson 49	15
21	Sat-17-Dec	BSN	H	Gainsborough Trinity	342	D 1-1	Sparkes 45	15
22	Mon-26-Dec	BSN	A	Bishops Stortford	629	W 2-0	Riza 2, Clerima 84	13
23	Sun-01-Jan	BSN	H	Bishops Stortford	649	L 2-3	Fitzsimons 37, Holman 90	14
24	Sat-07-Jan	BSN	A	Harrogate Town	393	D 0-0		14
25	Sat-14-Jan	BSN	H	Gloucester City	313	W 4-3	Holman 2 (2, 13), Sparkes 66, Taaffe 89	14
26	Sat-21-Jan	BSN	A	Gainsborough Trinity	507	L 2-3	Holman 47, Stevenson 59	14
27	Sat-28-Jan	BSN	H	Guiseley	328	D 2-2	Holman 2 (38, 54)	15
28	Mon-30-Jan	BSN	A	Worcester City	916	D 1-1	Holman pen 49	15
29	Sat-18-Feb	BSN	A	Corby Town	287	W 2-0	Holman 49, Breeze 82	14
30	Sat-25-Feb	BSN	H	Colwyn Bay	379	D 0-0		14
31	Sat-03-Mar	BSN	H	Altrincham	388	L 2-3	Taaffe 23, Sparkes 48	15
32	Tue-06-Mar	BSN	A	Blyth Spartans	343	L 1-2	Sparkes 23	17
33	Sat-10-Mar	BSN	A	Droylsden	192	W 3-2	Holman 2 (34, 86), Sparkes 45	14
34	Sat-17-Mar	BSN	A	Guiseley	518	D 2-2	Holman 2 (25, 61)	17
35	Sat-24-Mar	BSN	H	Nuneaton Town	487	D 1-1	Taaffe 1	16
36	Sat-31-Mar	BSN	A	FC Halifax Town	1338	L 0-4		17
37	Sat-07-Apr	BSN	H	Hinckley United	354	L 2-3	Holman 15, Taaffe 75	20
38	Mon-09-Apr	BSN	A	Gloucester City	320	W 1-0	Holman 42	20
39	Sat-14-Apr	BSN	H	Eastwood Town	310	W 3-0	Holman 39, Taaffe 54, Sparkes 90	15
40	Tue-17-Apr	BSN	H	Droylsden	313	D 5-5	Holman 2 (3, 45), Gomez 2 (33, 52), Stevenson 89	14
41	Sat-21-Apr	BSN	A	Workington	649	D 0-0		14
42	Sat-28-Apr	BSN	H	Hyde FC	667	D 1-1	Holman pen 55	16

CUPS

No.	Date	Comp	H/A	Opponents	Att:	Result	Goalscorers
1	Sat-01-Oct	FAC 2Q	H	Corby Town	427	D 1-1	Holman 70
2	Wed-05-Oct	FAC 2QR	A	Corby Town	642	L 1-3 aet	Taaffe 56
3	Sat-26-Nov	FAT 3Q	A	Uxbridge	150	L 1-2	Holman 10

	League
	Starts
	Substitute
	Unused Sub
	Cups
	Starts
	Substitute
	Unused Sub
	Goals (Lg)
	Goals (Cup)

STADELMANN	MILLS	HAWKINS	SALT	MOORE	FITZSIMONS	BREEZE	STEVENSON	HOLMAN	RIZA	SPARKES	ROBERTS	TAAFFE	CLEAVER	KITSCHA	DAY	DOWIE	SHEPPARD	CLERIMA	LIVERMORE	CROOK	LIBERTUCCI	SESSIONS	MCDONALD	ASENSI	GOMEZ	ACHEAMPONG	LOGAN
X	X	X	X	X	X	X	X	X	X	X	X	S	S	U	U	U											
X	X	X		X	X	X	X	X	X	X	X	X	S	S	U	U	S	S	S								
X	X			X	X	X	X	X	X	X	U	S	U	U		X	S	X									
X	X	X		X	X	X	X	X	X	X	X	S	S	U	U	U	X										
X	X	X		X	X	X	X	X	X	X	X	X	S	U	U	U	U										
X	X	X		X	X	X	X	X	X	X	X	X	S	U	S	U	S										
X		X		X	X	X	X	X	X	X	X	S	X	U	X	S	X										
	X			X	X	S	X	X	X	X	S	X	U	X	S	X			X	U							
X	X			X	X	S	X	X	X	X		X	S	X	U	X	S	X									
X	X	X			X		X	X			X	U	X	X	U	U	X				U	U					
X	X	X		X			X	X			X	X	U	X	X						S	S	U	U			
X		X		X			X	X	X	X	S	S	X	U	U	X		X					U		X		
X		X		X			X	X	X	X	S	X	U	U			X						U	X	S		
X	X	X		X			X	X	X	X	S	X	U	U		S							X	X	S		
X	X	S		X			X	X	X	X	S	X		U				X	X		U		U		X		
X	X	U		X			X	X	X	X	U	X		U				X	X		U				U		
X	X	U		X	X	X	X	X			S	X		U	S	X		X	X		U						
X		S		X	X	X	X	X			X	X		U	S	X		X	X						U		
X		S		X	S	X	X	X	X	X	X			U	U	X		X	X						S		
X		U		X	U	X	X	X	X		X		U	U	X			X	X		U				X		
X		U		X	S	X	X	X	X		X				U	X		X	X	U					X		S
X		U		X	S	X	X	X	X		X				U	X		X	X	U					S		
X		X		X	X	X	X	X	X				U	X		X	X	U		U		S		U			
X		U		X			X	X	X	X			U	X		X	X	U					S		U		
X		U		X	X	X	X	X			X		U	X		X	X	U						U			
X		U		X	X	X	X	X			S	S	X	X		S	X		X	X					X		
X		U		X	X	X	X	X			X	X	X	S		U		X	X	U	U				X		
X		U		X	X	X	X	X			U	U	S			X	X				U				X		
X		U		X	X	X	X	X			U	U	S			X	X				U				X		
X	S	U		X	X	X	X	X			U	S				X	X				U				X		
X	S	U		X	X	X	X	X			U	U				X	X				U				X		
X	X	U		X	X	X	X	X			U	U	U			X	X				U						
X	X	U		X	X	X	X	X			U	U				X	X				U				S		
X	X	U		X	X	X	X	X			U	S				X	X				S				S		
X	X	U		X			X	X	X	X	U	U	U			X	X				U				X		
X	X	U		X			X	X	X			U	U			X	X				S	S			X		
X	X	U		X			X	X	X			U	S			X	X				S	S			X		
X	X	U		X			X	X	X			U	U			X	X				U	S			X		
X	X	U		X			X	X	X			U	U			X	X				U	U			X		
X	X	U		X			X	X	X			U	U			X	X				S	U			X		
X	X	X		X	X	X	X			X	U	X	S	U	U	X						U	U				
X	X	X		X	X	X	X			X	U	X	X	U	S	X						S	U	U	U		
X	X	X		X	X	S	X			X	S	X			U	X	X	S	X							U	
41	26	13	1	11	41	22	42	42	20	41	27	32	5	1	1	19	0	30	29	0	0	0	0	0	18	0	0
0	2	3	0	0	0	5	0	0	0	1	11	8	2	1	9	8	3	0	1	0	4	5	0	0	6	2	1
0	0	22	0	0	0	1	0	0	0	0	3	0	14	34	26	0	0	0	0	7	10	9	5	2	1	2	2
3	3	3	0	1	3	3	2	3	0	3	0	3	1	0	1	3	0	1	0	0	0	0	0	0	0	0	0
0	0	0	0	0	0	0	0	1	0	0	0	1	0	1	0	1	0	1	0	1	0	0	0	1	0	0	0
0	0	0	0	0	0	0	0	0	0	0	2	0	0	3	1	0	0	0	0	0	1	2	1	1	0	1	0
0	1	1	0	0	2	3	3	27	4	13	0	9	0	0	0	0	1	0	0	0	0	0	0	0	2	0	0
0	0	0	0	0	0	0	0	2	0	0	0	1	0	0	0	0	0	0	0	0	0	0	0	0	0	0	0

PLAYING SQUAD 2012/13

Existing Players		SN	HT	WT	DOB	AGE	POB	Career	Apps	Goals
GOALKEEPERS										
Calum	Kitscha						Edmonton	Bishops Stortford (Yth), Histon 7/11	2	0
DEFENDERS										
Remy	Clerima				20/09/1990	21		L'Orient (Fra), Histon 8/10	30	1
Danny	Fitzsimons		6'00"	11 02	05/05/1992	20		Millwall (Scholar), QPR 7/10 Rel 12/10, Histon (L) 9/10,		
								Boreham Wood 1/11, Yeovil 2/11 Rel c/s 11, Histon 8/11	41	2
Harri	Hawkins							Histon	16	1
Sam	Hearn							Histon, Harborough (L)		
Zak	Mills				28/05/1992	20		Histon	28	1
MIDFIELDERS										
Jay	Dowie				28/12/1991	20		Histon	27	0
Claudiu	Hoban	24	5'08"	11 04	23/11/1991	20		Leicester (Yth), Holbeach 7/10, Northampton Spencer.		
								Kettering 11/10 (10/11), Rugby T, Daventry T 7/11, Histon 8/12		
Theo	Ola							Thurrock (Yth), Histon 8/12		
Grant	Roberts							Leeds (Yth), Sheff Utd (Scholar), Ossett T 11/09,		
								Guiseley (Reserves) c/s 10, Histon 8/11	38	0
Adrian	Sear							Beaconsfield SYCOB, Burnham, St Neots c/s 11, Histon 8/12		
James	Stevenson				17/05/1992	20		Histon	42	3
George	Thomson		5'08"	11 05	19/05/1992	20		Notts Forest (Scholar) Rel c/s 10, Glen Hoddle Academy,		
								Hinckley U 12/11, Histon 8/12		
FORWARDS										
Dan	Holman							Long Buckby, Oxford C 8/10, Long Buckby 9/10, Histon 7/11	42	27
Deakan	Napier							Needham Market, Histon 7/12		
Lewis	Taaffe				18/10/1991	20		Histon	40	9
Tom	Wright							Histon		

OXFORD CITY

Chairman: Brian Cox
Secretary: John Shepperd   **(T)** 07748 628 911   **(E)** shepoxf@tiscali.co.uk
Additional Committee Members:
Peter Knapton, Paul Cotterell, Colin Taylor, Paul Townsend, Sharon Smith.

Manager: Mike Ford
Programme Editor: Colin Taylor   **(E)** ctoxford@btinternet.com

2011-12 Squad.

Club Factfile

Founded: 1882   **Nickname:** City
Previous Names:
Previous Leagues: Isthmian 1907-88, 94-2005, South Midlands 1990-93, Spartan South Midlands 2005-06

Club Colours (change): Blue and white hoops/blue/blue (All yellow)

Ground: Court Place Farm, Marsh Lane, Marston, Oxford OX3 0NQ   **(T)** 01865 744 493
Capacity: 3,000 **Seats:** 300   **Covered:** 400   **Clubhouse:** Yes   **Shop:** Yes

Directions: Ground lies off A40 ring road, northern by-pass.
Follow signs for J.R. Hospital in yellow and small green signs to Court Place Farm Stadium.

Previous Grounds: The White House 1882-1988, Cuttleslowe Park 1990-91, Pressed Steel 1991-93

Record Attendance: 9,500 v Leytonstone - FA Amateur Cup - 1950
Record Victory: Not known
Record Defeat: Not known
Record Goalscorer: John Woodley
Record Appearances: John Woodley
Additional Records: Paid £3,000 to Woking for S Adams
Received £15,000 from Yeovil Town for Howard Forinton
Senior Honours:
FA Amateur Cup 1905-06. Oxford Senior Cup x3
Spartan South Midlands League Premier Division 2005-06. Southern Premier Play-offs 2011-12.

10 YEAR RECORD

02-03		03-04		04-05		05-06		06-07		07-08		08-09		09-10		10-11		11-12	
Isth1N	15	Isth1N	19	SthW	21	SSM P	1	SthW	12	SthW	4	SthP	6	SthP	13	SthP	14	SthP	2

OXFORD CITY

No.	Date	Comp	H/A	Opponents	Att:	Result	Goalscorers	Pos
1	Aug 13	Sth P	H	Redditch United	208	D 1 - 1	Basham 23	
2	16		A	AFC Totton	354	L 0 - 6		
3	20		A	Cirencester Town	125	W 1 - 0	Barcelos 60	13
4	23		H	Bashley	182	W 3 - 0	Barcelos 14 Basham 44 Ballard 74	
5	27		A	Evesham United	109	W 1 - 0	Ballard 60	7
6	29		H	Banbury United	418	L 0 - 1		
7	Sept 3		H	Leamington	366	W 2 - 1	Steele 29 (pen) Barcelos 58	6
8	10		A	Barwell	116	W 2 - 0	Benjamin 18 Blossom 89	5
9	13		H	Frome Town	120	W 2 - 0	Basham 23 (pen) Blossom 31	
10	17	FAC 1Q	H	Didcot Town	259	D 1 - 1	Steele 13	
11	20	FAC 1Qr	A	Didcot Town	162	W 3 - 0	Basham 49 79 Barcelos 85	
12	24		A	Bedford Town	259	W 2 - 1	Bossom 14 Barcelos 75	2
13	Oct 1	FAC 2Q	A	Thame United	462	W 3 - 1	Basham 50 Barcelos 52 Pond 68	
14	8		H	Swindon Supermarines	182	W 7 - 1	BASHAM 4 (2 36 39 42) STEELE 3 (50 75 83)	2
15	15	FAC 3Q	A	Eastleigh	325	W 3 - 1	Basham 19 Pond 61 68	
16	22	FAT 1Q	H	Mangotsfield Town	196	L 0 - 3		
17	25		A	Weymouth	622	L 0 - 1		5
18	29	FAC 4Q	A	Weston-s-Mare	630	W 3 - 2	Pond 3 Basham 34 Barcellos 74	
19	Nov 5		H	St Albans City	241	W 3 - 1	Steele 20 73 Ballard 54	3
20	9		A	Arlesey	101	W 4 - 1	Basham 10 Barcelos 34 83 Pond 66	
21	12	FAC 1	A	Redbridge	465	D 0 - 0		
22	19		H	Hitchin Town	241	D 0 - 0		3
23	22	FAC 1r	H	Redbridge	1175	L 1 - 2*	Steele 19	
24	Dec 3		H	Cirencester Town	235	D 0 - 0		4
25	6		A	Brackley Town	217	L 2 - 5	Ballard 64 Barcelos 75 (pen)	
26	10		A	Bashley	234	W 2 - 0	Whitby 1(og) Lyon 62	
27	13		A	Chesham United	206	D 1 - 1	Ballard 77	
28	17		H	AFC Totton	243	D 2 - 2	Blossom 15 Steele 45	4
29	26		H	Hemel Hempstead	191	D 1 - 1	Wilmot 60	4
30	31		A	Cambridge City	450	L 0 - 2		6
31	Jan 2		A	Banbury United	339	D 1 - 1	Pond 27	5
32	7		H	Chippenham Town	194	W 2 - 1	Benjamin 15 B Barcelos 37 (pen)	3
33	21		A	Leamington	552	D 1 - 1	Haysham 45	5
34	28		H	Weymouth	260	W 2 - 0	Wilmot 65 Ballard 71	4
35	Feb 18		A	Swindon Supermarine	123	W 4 - 2	Benjamin 4 9 Basham 32 Wilmott 38	4
36	21		H	Stourbridge	175	L 1 - 2	Basham 31	
37	25		A	Arlesey Town	153	W 3 - 0	Blossom 34 Basham 43 Woodley 63	4
38	March 3		A	StAlbans City	414	L 2 - 3	Blossom 20 Woodley 58	4
39	6		H	Barwell	116	W 2 - 0	Pond 66 Barcellos 88	
40	10		H	Chesham United	283	W 2 - 0	Basham 36 (pen) Barcelos 90	3
41	17		A	Stourbridge	421	L 0 - 2		4
42	24		H	Evesham United	165	W 2 - 0	Basham 36 Lyon 57	4
43	27		H	Bedford Town	178	W 1 - 0	Basham 48	
44	31		A	Chippenham Town	370	W 1 - 0	Woodley 80	2
45	Apr 7		H	Cambridge City	367	D 0 - 0		3
46	14		A	Redditch United	251	D 1 - 1	Willmott 6	4
47	21		H	Brackley Town	535	D 1 - 1	Basham 3	5
48	24		A	Hemel Hempstead	212	L 0 - 2		
49	25		A	Frome Town	146	W 3 - 0	Benjamin 34 Basham 37 Malone 86	
50	28		A	Hitchin Town	387	W 3 - 0	Barcelos 24 37 McDonough 76	2
51	May 3	Play-Off SF	H	Cambridge City	564	W 1 - 0	Willmott 72	
52	May 7	Play-Off F	H	AFC Totton	1280	W 4 - 2	Barcelos 39 Basham 59 (pen) Isaac 73 Skendl 84	

PLAYING SQUAD 2012/13

Existing Players		SN	HT	WT	DOB	AGE	POB	Career	Apps	Goals
GOALKEEPERS										
Christian	Lawrence							Oxford C		
Keith	McLoughlin							Oxford C		
DEFENDERS										
Wayne	Blossom							Banbury U, Brackley 6/08, Leamington 10/09, Daventry T (L) 11/09 Perm, Oxford C 9/10		
James	Clarke							Oxford U, Oxford C 2/09, Yeovil (Trial) 7/12		
Kynan	Isaac							Oxford C		
Adam	Learoyd							Wantage, Didcot T, Abingdon U 7/07, Banbury, Oxford C 6/11		
Marvin	Martin							Oxford U (Scholar), Kidlington (L) 1/09, Banbury U (L) 8/09, Banbury U c/s 10, Oxford C 3/11		
Paul	Stonehouse	5'07"	11 03		13/07/1987	24	Wegberg	Forest Green, Yate T (2ML) 10/05, Cinderford (L) 1/06, Gloucester (7WL) 2/06, Gloucester (L) 1/07, Mansfield Undisc 6/10 Rel 5/11, Bath C 5/11, Oxford C 7/12		
Chris	Willmott	6'02"	11 13		30/09/1977	34	Bedford	Luton, Wimbledon £350,000 7/99 Rel c/s 03, Luton (4ML) 1/03, Northampton 7/03, Oxford U 7/05 Rel 4/09, Brackley 8/09, Oxford C 12/11		
MIDFIELDERS										
Andy	Ballard							Oxford C, Banbury U 7/05, Slough 9/05, Abingdon U 7/06, Eastbourne B 8/07, Eastbourne T (Dual) 10/07, Hastings U (Dual) 9/08, Oxford C 11/08		
Declan	Benjamin				04/02/1991	21		Oxford U Rel 1/10, Abingdon U (L), Banbury U (L) 8/09, Banbury U 1/10, Oxford C 6/11		
Michael	Lyon							Bedford T, Oxford C 2/08		
Darren	Pond							Banbury U, Oxford C 6/07		
Nick	Stanley							Cirencester, Chippenham 12/05, Devizes 8/06, Swindon Supermarine, Leamington 3/11, Oxford C 6/11, Swindon Supermarine, Oxford C 6/12		
FORWARDS										
Felipe	Barcelos							Oxford C		
Steve	Basham	6'00"	12 00		02/12/1977	34	Southampton	Southampton, Wrexham (L) 2/98, Preston (SL) 2/99, Preston £200,000 7/99 Rel c/s 02, Oxford U 8/02 Rel 5/07, Exeter 7/07 Rel c/s 09, Luton 8/09 Rel 5/10, Hayes & Yeading (SL) 11/09, Brackley 7/10, Oxford C 6/11		
Jamie	Cook	5'10"	10 09		02/09/1979	31	Oxford	Oxford U Rel 1/01, Darlington (Trial) 1/01, Boston U 2/01, Stevenage 2/03, Bath C (3ML) 2/04, Maidenhead 7/04, Witney U 9/05, Rushden & D (NC) 1/07, Havant & W 3/07, Crawley 7/07, Oxford U Undisc 9/09, Crawley 6/10 Rel 5/11, Bath C 5/11, Oxford C 6/12		

Conference Action...

Solihull Moors forward, Richard Walker, shoots at the Worcester City goal in their league clash at Damson Park.

Photo: Jonathan Holloway.

SOLIHULL MOORS

Chairman: Nigel Collins
Secretary: Robin Lamb   **(T)** 07976 752 493   **(E)** robin.lamb5@btinternet.com
Additional Committee Members:
Graham Davison, Margaret Smith, Trevor Stevens, Geoff Hood, Ray Bird, Danny Thomas, Steve Shipway, Ronald Crane.
Manager: Marcus Bignot
Programme Editor: John Clothier   **(E)** solihullmoors@aol.com

Club Factfile

Founded: 2007   **Nickname:**
Previous Names: Today's club was formed after the amalgamation of Solihull Borough and Moor Green in 2007
Previous Leagues: None

Club Colours (change): White/black/black & white (Yellow/blue/yellow & blue)

Ground: Damson Park, Damson Parkway, Solihull B91 2PP   **(T)** 0121 705 6770
Capacity: 3,050   **Seats:** 280   **Covered:** 1,000   **Clubhouse:** Yes   **Shop:** Yes
Directions: M42 junction 6 take the A45 towards Birmingham after approximately 1.5 miles take the left filter lane at the traffic lights onto Damson Parkway. Ground approximately 1 mile on the right.

Previous Grounds: None

Record Attendance: 1,076 v Rushden & Diamonds - FA Cup 4th Qualifying Round 27/10/2007
Record Victory: 4-1 v Southport - Conference South 05/04/2008
Record Defeat: 1-6 v Kettering Town - Conference South 01/01/2008
Record Goalscorer: Not known
Record Appearances: Carl Motteram - 71 (2007-09)
Additional Records:

Senior Honours:
None

10 YEAR RECORD

02-03	03-04	04-05	05-06	06-07	07-08	08-09	09-10	10-11	11-12
					Conf N 17	Conf N 16	Conf N 17	Conf N 7	Conf N 19

SOLIHULL MOORS

No.	Date	Comp	H/A	Opponents	Att:	Result	Goalscorers	Pos
1	Sat-13-Aug	BSN	A	Gainsborough Trinity	408	L 1-3	English 10	19
2	Tue-16-Aug	BSN	H	Eastwood Town	240	L 0-2		21
3	Sat-20-Aug	BSN	H	Guiseley	230	L 0-1		21
4	Tue-23-Aug	BSN	A	Bishops Stortford	251	L 0-1		22
5	Sat-27-Aug	BSN	A	Vauxhall Motors	181	L 1-2	Adkins 51	22
6	Mon-29-Aug	BSN	H	Histon	203	L 0-2		22
7	Sat-03-Sep	BSN	H	Hinckley United	358	L 1-2	Langdon 5	22
8	Sat-10-Sep	BSN	A	Boston United	1175	W 1-0	Thompson-Brown 51	22
9	Sat-17-Sep	BSN	H	Altrincham	343	W 2-0	Walker 11, Fitzpatrick 70	20
10	Mon-19-Sep	BSN	A	Worcester City	669	L 0-3		20
11	Sat-24-Sep	BSN	A	Colwyn Bay	321	D 0-0		22
12	Sat-08-Oct	BSN	H	Droylsden	260	L 0-2		22
13	Sat-22-Oct	BSN	A	Nuneaton Town	733	W 1-0	Spencer 78	19
14	Tue-25-Oct	BSN	H	Gloucester City	330	W 1-0	Midworth 50	18
15	Sat-05-Nov	BSN	H	Boston United	301	W 1-0	Morris 66	16
16	Sat-12-Nov	BSN	H	Bishops Stortford	260	W 3-1	Walker 5, English 14, Blackwood 67	15
17	Wed-16-Nov	BSN	A	FC Halifax Town	1140	D 0-0		14
18	Sat-19-Nov	BSN	A	Droylsden	191	L 0-1		15
19	Sat-03-Dec	BSN	H	Harrogate Town	209	W 5-1	Langdon 37, Morris 56, Pierpoint 70, Fitzpatrick 2 (84, 90)	14
20	Tue-06-Dec	BSN	A	Histon	203	L 0-3		16
21	Sat-17-Dec	BSN	H	Stalybridge Celtic	450	D 1-1	Hurren 76	16
22	Mon-26-Dec	BSN	A	Corby Town	588	W 3-0	Beswick 22, English 51, Fitzpatrick 64	14
23	Sun-01-Jan	BSN	H	Corby Town	362	L 1-2	Walker pen 90	15
24	Sat-07-Jan	BSN	A	Gloucester City	305	L 0-1		15
25	Sat-14-Jan	BSN	H	Gainsborough Trinity	272	W 5-3	Beswick 3 (5, 44, pen 54), Spencer 67, Morris 77	15
26	Sat-28-Jan	BSN	H	Hyde FC	365	W 1-0	Beswick pen 89	14
27	Sat-18-Feb	BSN	H	Worcester City	398	D 0-0		17
28	Tue-21-Feb	BSN	A	Eastwood Town	184	D 1-1	Pierpoint 32	15
29	Sat-25-Feb	BSN	H	Workington	220	W 2-1	Thompson-Brown 20, Spencer 33	13
30	Sat-03-Mar	BSN	A	Stalybridge Celtic	471	L 0-3		14
31	Sat-10-Mar	BSN	H	Colwyn Bay	242	W 1-0	English 79	13
32	Tue-13-Mar	BSN	A	Guiseley	344	L 1-3	Marsden 30	14
33	Sat-17-Mar	BSN	H	Blyth Spartans	245	D 2-2	Langdon 27, Blackwood 82	15
34	Mon-19-Mar	BSN	A	Hinckley United	401	W 2-1	Pierpoint 20, A Francis 52	11
35	Sat-24-Mar	BSN	A	Altrincham	801	D 1-1	Fitzpatrick 5	14
36	Sat-31-Mar	BSN	A	Workington	382	D 1-1	Hurren 31	12
37	Tue-03-Apr	BSN	A	Blyth Spartans	238	L 1-2	Morris 32	12
38	Sat-07-Apr	BSN	H	Vauxhall Motors	266	L 2-3	Morris 2 (9, 18)	13
39	Mon-09-Apr	BSN	A	Hyde FC	591	L 0-3		16
40	Sat-14-Apr	BSN	H	Nuneaton Town	517	D 0-0		17
41	Sat-21-Apr	BSN	A	Harrogate Town	604	D 1-1	Pierpoint 79	18
42	Sat-28-Apr	BSN	H	FC Halifax Town	711	L 1-2	Hinton pen 72	19

CUPS

No.	Date	Comp	H/A	Opponents	Att:	Result	Goalscorers	
1	Sat-01-Oct	FAC2Q	H	Loughborough Dynamo	152	W 2-0	Spencer 2 (32, 56)	
2	Sat-15-Oct	FAC 3Q	H	Grantham Town	308	W 3-2	Melligan 10, Walker 30, Blackwood 71	
3	Sat-29-Oct	FAC 4Q	H	FC Halifax Town	551	L 0-1		
4	Sat-26-Nov	FAT 3Q	H	Ossett Town	152	D 2-2	Morris 15, English 76	
5	Thu-29-Sep	FAT 3QR	A	Ossett Town	137	W 1-0	Spencer 90	
6	Sat-10-Dec	FAT 1	A	York City	1116	D 2-2	Fitzpatrick 3, Walker 40	
7	Tue-13-Dec	FAT 1R	H	York City	275	L 0-3		

League
Starts
Substitute
Unused Sub

Cups
Starts
Substitute
Unused Sub

Goals (Lg)
Goals (Cup)

	SINGH	MIDWORTH	A FRANCIS	PRICE	BROADHURST	RICHARDS	JOHNSON	FITZPATRICK	J MCPIKE	ENGLISH	ADKINS	GRANDISON	FELLOWS	RACHEL	JACKSON	PIERPOINT	SPENCER	BUSWELL	MILLAR	HINTON	BLACKWOOD	BOTTOMER	KIMBERLEY	LANGDON	BUTLIN	AGBOR	L FRANCIS	BELL	TOMCZAK	THOMPSON-BROWN	WALKER	BESWICK	KALONJI	M MCPIKE	MELLIGAN	HURREN	MORRIS	ACTON	BENNETT	LEWIS	CONNOLLY	MARTINEZ	MARSDEN	HEADLEY	BYFIELD
	X	X	X	X	X	X	X	X	X	X	X	X	S		U		U																												
	X	X	X	U	X		X	X	X	X	X	X	U	S			X	X	S	U																									
	X	X	X	X			X	X	X	X	X	S	S	S	U		X	X			S																								
	X		X	U	X			X	X	X	X	X	S	S	U		X	X			X	X	X	U																					
	X		X	U				X	X	X	X	X	S		U			X			X	X	X	U	X	S																			
			S	U		X	S	X	X	X	X		X					X			X	X	X	U	X	S	X																		
	X	X	S	X	U	S	X			X										U		X	X			X	S		X	X	X														
	X	X	X	X	U			X	S								U	S			X				X			X	X	U	X	X													
	X	X	X	U			U	X	U								S	S			X				X			X	X		X	X													
	X	X	X	U		S	X	S									U	S			X				X			X	X		X	X													
	X	X	X	U	X			S	X	U	X						U	S			X	X			X			X			X	X													
	X	X	U		X			X	X	X	X					S	S	S	X			X			X			X			X														
	X	X					U	X	U	X		X						X	X			X			X		S				X			X	X	S	S								
	X	X	S				U	X	U	X								X	X			X			X						X				S	X	X	S							
	X			U			S	X		X					U			X	X			X	X			X					X				U	S	X	X	X						
	X	X	U				S	X	S	X								X	X			X			X						X					X	S	X	X						
	X	X	S			S	U	S			X							U	X			X			X						X					X	X	X	X						
	X	X	S			U	U	S	X		X							S	X	X		X			X						X					X	X	X	X						
	X	X	S			U			S		X							S	X	X		X			X						X				U	X	X	X			X					
	X	X	S			U			S		X							S	X	X	U		X		X						X					S	X	X	X						
	X		X				X	X		X								U	X	X		U	X	X							X	S	S			X				U					
	X		X			S		U	X		X							U	X	X			X								X	X				X	S		X	S		X			
	X		X				X	S		X									X	X			X		S						X	X				X	S		X	X		U	U		
	X		X			S		S	U		X								X	X			X								X	X				X	S		X	X		U	U		
	X		X			S		S	U		X								X	X			X		S						X	X	X			X				S		X		U	
	X	X				U		S			X								X	X			X								X	X	X				U	X		X		U	U	S	
	X	X				U		S			X								X	X			X								X	X	X				U	X		X		U	U	S	
	X	X						X			X								X	X				X							U	U	X				X	X	U			U	U		
	X	X	S			U			X										X	X				X							X		X				X	S				S	U	X	
	X	X			X		S			X									X	X			S								X		X									S	U	X	U
	X	X	S			U			X										X	X				X							X		X						U	U		S	S	X	S
	X	S	S			S			U										X	X				X								U					X		U	X		X	X	X	X
	X		U			X			S		X								X	X				X								S		S			X		U	X		X	X	X	S
	X		X			U			U		X								X	X				X								S		S			U					X	U	X	U
	X	S	X			U					X								X	X				X								U		S			X	U	U	X	U	X		X	
	X	X	X						X											X			U									S		X			X	S	U	X		X	X		
	X	X	X					X		X									U	X				X								S		X			S	X	U	X		S	X		
	X	U				S			S		X								X	X				X										X			X	X	U	X		X		S	X
	X		X			X			X		X								X	X			X	S										X			X	X	U	U		S			X
	X	X							X		X								X	X			X	X								U		X			X	S	U	X		U	S		
	X	X	X						X		X								X				X	X								U		S			S	U	X	X		S			
	X	X	X		X		X	X	S	X							U	S	U	X			U	X							X					X	S	U							
	X	X	U		X		S	X	U	X							U	S	U	X			U	X							X			X	X		X								
	X	X	S			U	X	X	X	X							U	S	X				X	X							S	U		X											
	X	X	S		U	U			X								X	X	X		U		X								X			S		X	X								
	X	X	U		U	U			S	X							X	X	X				X								X			S			S	X	X	U					
	X	X	S			U			S	X							X	X			U		X								X						S	X	X						
	X		X			S			X	X							S	X	X		U		X								X	S	X				X	X	U						
	42	27	21	6	10	1	6	31	6	37	5	0	0	0	0	31	31	0	0	11	30	4	0	34	0	1	4	4	1	10	19	15	0	1	5	20	13	0	16	0	7	0	9	2	2
	0	2	9	1	6	1	8	7	3	0	1	4	2	0	4	2	4	1	0	3	1	0	0	1	3	0	1	0	5	1	0	4	1	2	2	4	9	0	1	0	6	0	5	3	0
	0	1	3	4	16	2	4	2	5	0	0	1	2	4	4	4	0	1	4	1	0	0	2	0	0	0	0	3	1	1	2	1	0	1	2	0	11	2	2	7	6	1	1	0	
	7	6	3	0	2	0	3	5	1	6	0	0	0	0	2	5	6	0	0	1	6	0	0	6	0	0	0	0	0	0	6	0	1	1	2	4	4	0	0	0	0	0	0	0	0
	0	0	3	0	1	0	2	0	2	0	0	0	0	0	4	0	0	0	0	0	0	0	0	0	0	0	0	0	0	0	0	3	2	0	1	0	0	0	0	0	0	0	0	0	0
	0	0	1	0	3	3	0	0	1	0	0	0	0	0	3	0	2	0	0	2	3	0	0	0	0	0	0	0	0	0	0	2	0	0	0	2	0	0	0	0	0	0	0	0	0
	0	1	1	0	0	0	0	5	0	4	1	0	0	0	0	4	3	0	0	1	2	0	0	3	0	0	0	0	0	0	2	3	5	0	0	2	6	0	0	0	0	0	1	0	0
	0	0	0	0	0	0	0	1	0	1	0	0	0	0	0	0	3	0	0	1	0	0	0	1	0	0	0	0	0	0	0	0	0	0	0	2	0	0	0	2	0	0	0	0	0

PLAYING SQUAD 2012/13

Existing Players		SN	HT	WT	DOB	AGE	POB	Career	Apps	Goals
GOALKEEPERS										
Sheridon	Martinez							Solihull Moors	0	0
Jasbir	Singh		6'02"	13 05	12/03/1990	22		Shrewsbury Rel c/s 09, Bridgnorth (L) 8/08, Hinckley U (L) 10/08, Sutton Coldfield (L) 1/09, Kidderminster 8/09 Rel 5/10, Solihull Moors 7/10	42	0
DEFENDERS										
Karl	Broadhurst		6'00"	11 07	18/03/1980	32	Portsmouth	Bournemouth Rel c/s 07, Hereford 7/07 Rel c/s 09, Bournemouth (Trial) 7/08, Crawley 8/09 Rel 4/10, AFC Telford 8/10 Rel 8/10, Solihull Moors 8/11	16	0
Andre	Francis				25/04/1985	27	Birmingham	Stafford R, Rushall O, Halesowen T 6/07, Romulus 1/08, Stafford R 7/08, Solihull Moors 5/11	30	1
Tom	Kemp		6'03"		16/01/1987	25	Ashby	Derby (Jun), Lincoln C Rel 11/06, Tamworth (3ML) 8/06, Tamworth 12/06, Grays 2/07, Kettering 6/07, Halesowen T (L) 8/08 Perm, Worcester 11/08, Brackley 6/10, Solihull Moors 6/12		
Dominic	Langdon		6'02"	11 00	14/09/1988	23	Kettering	Rushden & D Rel c/s 07, Tamworth 7/07, Atherstone (L) 11/09, Brackley 1/10, Solihull Moors 8/10	35	3
Stuart	Pierpoint				17/02/1982	30	Halesowen	Oldbury U, Sutton Coldfield, Halesowen T 8/05, Stafford R 7/08, Nuneaton T 6/09 Rel 5/11, Solihull Moors 6/11	33	4
Danny	Spencer				29/11/1981	30		St Andrews, Atherstone U, St Andrews, Rothwell 1/04, Barwell, Brackley, Redditch 11/07, Brackley 2/08, Kings Lynn 9/09, Oadby T 11/09, Nuneaton T 3/10, Solihull Moors 6/11	35	3
MIDFIELDERS										
Dean	Bennett		5'10"	11 00	13/12/1977	34	Wolverhampton	Aston Villa (Jun), WBA 12/96, Bromsgrove 9/98, Kidderminster £30,000 1/99, Wrexham Bosman 7/04 Rel c/s 06, Chester 7/06 Rel 5/08, Kidderminster (3ML) 8/07 (SL) 1/08, Kidderminster c/s 08 Rel c/s 10, Dundalk 8/10, Solihull Moors 11/11	17	0
Junior	English				08/10/1985	26		Moor Green/Solihull Moors	37	4
Jordan	Fitzpatrick		6'00"	12 00	15/06/1988	24	Stourbridge	Wolves (Scholar), Hereford 9/06 Rel c/s 08, Bromsgrove (L) 3/08, Worcester 8/08 Rel 2/10, Redditch 7/10, Corby T 2/11 Rel 6/11, Solihull Moors 7/11	38	5
Andy	Gooding		5'07"	10 05	30/04/1988	24	Coventry	Coventry Rel 1/08, Burton (2ML) 8/07, Rushden & D 1/08 Rel 5/08, Hinckley U 7/08, Corby T 5/10, Solihull Moors (L) 10/10, Hinckley U (SL) 12/10, Hinckley U 5/11, Solihull Moors 6/12		
Alex	Price				15/04/1991	21		Solihull Moors, Stratford T (L) 3/09	7	0
FORWARDS										
Ryan	Beswick				12/01/1988	24	Walton-on-Thames	Leicester, Redditch (SL) 1/09, Kettering 5/09, Kings Lynn (2ML) 8/09, Solihull Moors 10/09	19	5
Gary	Birch		6'00"	12 08	08/10/1981	30	Birmingham	Walsall, Exeter (L) 3/01, Exeter (3ML) 8/01, Nuneaton (L) 12/01, Barnsley (SL) 3/04, Kidderminster 12/04 Rel c/s 05, Lincoln C 8/05, Tamworth (L) 8/06, Hucknall (L) 10/06, AFC Telford 1/07, Rushall O (2ML) 9/07, Chasetown 5/08, Solihull Moors 6/12		
Michael	Blackwood		5'10"	11 04	30/09/1979	32	Birmingham	Aston Villa Rel c/s 00, Chester (2ML) 9/99, Wrexham 6/00 Rel c/s 02, Worcester 8/02, Stevenage 9/02, Halesowen 3/03, Telford 8/03, Lincoln C 7/04 Rel c/s 05, Kidderminster 7/05 Rel c/s 08, Oxford U (L) 1/08, Mansfield 7/08 Rel 5/09, Tamworth (SL) 3/09, Tamworth 5/09, Brackley T 6/10, Solihull Moors (3ML) 10/10, Solihull Moors 8/11	31	2
Steve	Jackson							Solihull Moors	4	0
David	Kalonji				20/06/1989	23		Royal Boussu Dour Borinage (Bel), Solihull Moors 9/11, Alvechurch (L) 2/12	1	0
Alando	Lewis							Tamworth (10/11) Rel 3/11, Dudley T (L) 11/10, Darlaston T, Solihull Moors 11/11	0	0
Justin	Marsden				07/03/1984	28	Coventry	Rugby U, Solihull B 7/05, AFC Telford 5/06, Bedworth U (L) 2/08, Leamington (L) 3/08, Brackley 6/08, Nuneaton T 9/08 Rel 1/12, Solihull Moors 1/12	14	1

STALYBRIDGE CELTIC

Chairman: Rob Gorski
Secretary: John Hall   **(T)** 07813 864 492   **(E)** celticblueblood@hotmail.com
Additional Committee Members:
Syd White, Gerald Crossley, Gordon Greenwood, Bill McCallum, Les Taylor, Keith Trudgeon.

Manager: Jim Harvey
Programme Editor: Nick Shaw   **(E)** nick@newimage.co.uk

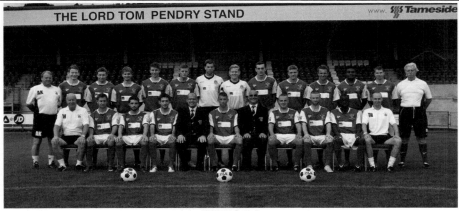

THE LORD TOM PENDRY STAND   www. ⚡⚡ Tameside

2011-12 Squad

Back row (L-R): Alan Keeling (U21 Pro manager), Connor Jennings, Phil Marsh, Adam Kay, Greg Wilkinson, Lloyd Ellams, Jan Budtz, Ashley Woodhouse, Craig Hobson, Chris Lynch, Kristian Platt, Joel Bembo - Leta, Mitchell Austin, David Pover (Sports Therapist).
Front Row: Jim Harvey (Manager), Tom Buckley, Jack Rea, Andy McWilliams, Syd White (Chief Executive), Rhys Meynell (Captain), Rob Gorski (Chairman), Callum Warburton, Dennis Sheriff, Arthur Gnahoua, Tim Ryan (Assistant Manager).

Club Factfile

Founded: 1909   **Nickname:** Celtic
Previous Names:
Previous Leagues: Lancashire Combination 1911-12, Central League 1912-21, Southern 1914-15, Football League 1921-23, Cheshire Co. 1923-82, North West Co. 1982-87, N.P.L. 1987-92, 98-2001, Conference 1992-98, 01-02

Club Colours (change): Royal blue & white/white/blue (All yellow)

Ground: Bower Fold, Mottram Road, Stalybridge, Cheshire SK15 2RT   **(T)** 0161 338 2828
Capacity: 6,108   **Seats:** 1,200   **Covered:** 2,400   **Clubhouse:** Yes   **Shop:** Yes

Directions: Leave the M6 at junction 19 (Northwich). At the roundabout at the end of the slip road turn right (exit 3 of 4) to join the A556 towards Altrincham. Stay on the A556 for 5 miles to a roundabout with the M56. Turn right at the roundabout (exit 3 of 4) onto the M56. Stay on the M56 for 6 1/2 miles to junction 3 (M60 signposted Sheffield, M67) Stay on the M60 for 7 miles to junction 24 (M67, Denton) At the roundabout turn right (exit 4 of 5) to join the M67. Stay on the M67 to the very end, Junction 4. At the roundabout turn left (exit 1 of 4) onto the A57 (Hyde Road). After 1/2 a mile you will reach a set of traffic lights (signposted Stalybridge). Turn left onto B6174 (Stalybridge Road). Almost immediately, there is a mini roundabout. Turn left (exit 1 of 5) onto Roe Cross Road (A6018). Follow this road for 1 3/4 miles passing the Roe Cross Inn on the right and through the cutting (the road is now called Mottram Road). When you pass the Dog and Partridge on the right, you will be almost there. Bower Fold is on the left opposite a sharp right turn next to the Hare and Hounds pub. If the car park is full (it usually is), parking can be found on the streets on the right of Mottram Road.

Previous Grounds:

Record Attendance: 9,753 v West Bromwich Albion - FA Cup replay 1922-23
Record Victory: 16-2 v Manchester NE - 01/05/1926 and v Nantwich - 22/10/1932
Record Defeat: 1-10 v Wellington Town - 09/03/1946
Record Goalscorer: Harry Dennison - 215
Record Appearances: Kevan Keelan - 395
Additional Records: Cecil Smith scored 77 goals during the 1931-32 season
Paid £15,000 to Kettering Town for Ian Arnold 1995. Received £16,000 from Southport for Lee Trundle.
Senior Honours:
Manchester Senior Cup 1922-23.
Northern Premier League Premier Division 1991-92, 2000-01.
Cheshire Senior Cup x2.

10 YEAR RECORD

02-03		03-04		04-05		05-06		06-07		07-08		08-09		09-10		10-11		11-12	
NP P	4	NP P	11	Conf N	19	Conf N	7	Conf N	18	Conf N	2	Conf N	6	Conf N	9	Conf N	10	Conf N	6

STALYBRIDGE CELTIC

No.	Date	Comp	H/A	Opponents	Att:	Result	Goalscorers	Pos
1	Sat-13-Aug	BSN	A	Nuneaton Town	786	W 2-1	Marsh 2 (44, pen 88)	9
2	Tue-16-Aug	BSN	H	Harrogate Town	417	W 3-2	Hobson 45, Ellams 47, Jennings 90	1
3	Sat-20-Aug	BSN	H	Gainsborough Trinity	457	W 4-0	Marsh 2 (pen 35, 70) Warburton 60, Wilkinson 74	1
4	Tue-23-Aug	BSN	A	Workington	406	W 5-2	Kay 39, Marsh 2 (62, 84), Jennings 2 (63, 89)	2
5	Sat-27-Aug	BSN	A	FC Halifax Town	1476	D 2-2	Marsh pen 4, Jennings 17	2
6	Mon-29-Aug	BSN	H	Vauxhall Motors	508	W 4-2	Marsh 3 (5, 68, 80), Jennings 18	2
7	Sat-03-Sep	BSN	A	Histon	362	W 1-0	Ellams 56	2
8	Sat-10-Sep	BSN	H	Eastwood Town	540	W 2-1	Jennings 5, Wilkinson 66	2
9	Sat-17-Sep	BSN	A	Bishops Stortford	358	W 3-0	Ellams 14, Jennings 42, Marsh 65	2
10	Tue-20-Sep	BSN	H	Blyth Spartans	440	W 2-0	Wilkinson 43, Kay 74	2
11	Sat-24-Sep	BSN	H	Gloucester City	448	D 2-2	Ellams 43, Jennings 55	2
12	Sat-08-Oct	BSN	A	Corby Town	532	W 2-1	Jennings 45, Marsh 58	2
13	Sat-15-Oct	BSN	A	Colwyn Bay	403	L 0-2		2
14	Sat-22-Oct	BSN	H	Altrincham	1005	W 5-1	Jennings 2 (6, 63), Wilkinson 36, Marsh 39, Og (Williams) 54	1
15	Sat-29-Oct	BSN	H	Worcester City	604	W 2-0	Jennings 2 (36, 77)	1
16	Sat-05-Nov	BSN	A	Droylsden	656	D 3-3	Jennings 40, Ellams 49, Brogan 63	1
17	Sat-12-Nov	BSN	H	Histon	601	W 2-0	Marsh 2 (16, 85)	2
18	Sat-19-Nov	BSN	A	Guiseley	738	D 1-1	Brogan 80	2
19	Sat-03-Dec	BSN	H	Boston United	506	W 3-0	Gnahoua 34, Hobson 2 (87, 90)	2
20	Tue-06-Dec	BSN	A	Gainsborough Trinity	438	L 1-3	Marsh 56	2
21	Sat-17-Dec	BSN	A	Solihull Moors	450	D 1-1	Marsh pen 90	2
22	Mon-26-Dec	BSN	A	Hyde FC	1868	L 1-3	Marsh 2	2
23	Sun-01-Jan	BSN	H	Hyde FC	1806	L 1-3	Jennings pen 90	2
24	Sat-07-Jan	BSN	H	Droylsden	802	L 1-3	Marsh pen 45	2
25	Sat-21-Jan	BSN	A	Hinckley United	401	D 5-5	Platt 2, Og (Flanagan) 6, Hobson 2 (20, 41), N Rogan 79	2
26	Sat-28-Jan	BSN	H	Colwyn Bay	529	L 0-4		3
27	Sat-18-Feb	BSN	H	Workington	501	L 1-3	Marsh 62	5
28	Tue-21-Feb	BSN	A	Blyth Spartans	339	D 1-1	Austin 65	6
29	Sat-25-Feb	BSN	A	Harrogate Town	438	D 1-1	Brogan 75	6
30	Sat-03-Mar	BSN	H	Solihull Moors	471	W 2-0	Hobson 41, Brogan 89	5
31	Tue-06-Mar	BSN	A	Altrincham	791	L 1-2	Hobson 14	5
32	Sat-10-Mar	BSN	A	Boston United	1000	L 2-3	Brogan 41, Hobson 90	6
33	Sat-17-Mar	BSN	H	Corby Town	449	D 2-2	Hobson 2 (36, 64)	5
34	Sat-24-Mar	BSN	A	Worcester City	774	D 0-0		6
35	Tue-27-Mar	BSN	H	Nuneaton Town	419	W 4-1	Wilkinson 25, Brogan 44, Meynell 66, Hobson 77	6
36	Sat-31-Mar	BSN	A	Eastwood Town	243	W 1-0	Brogan 60	6
37	Tue-03-Apr	BSN	H	Bishops Stortford	352	L 2-3	Platt 13, Wilkinson 28	6
38	Fri-06-Apr	BSN	H	FC Halifax Town	1647	W 2-1	Lynch 27, Wilkinson 85	5
39	Mon-09-Apr	BSN	A	Vauxhall Motors	254	L 0-1		6
40	Sat-14-Apr	BSN	H	Guiseley	710	L 0-3		6
41	Sat-21-Apr	BSN	A	Gloucester City	320	W 2-1	Rea 3, Sherriff 71	6
42	Sat-28-Apr	BSN	H	Hinckley United	670	W 4-2	Brogan 2 (27, 75), Wilkinson 45, Sherriff 53	6

CUPS

No.	Date	Comp	H/A	Opponents	Att:	Result	Goalscorers	
1	Sat-01-Oct	FAC 2Q	H	Guiseley	493	L 1-2	Marsh 90	
2	Sat-26-Nov	FAT 3Q	A	Blyth Spartans	324	W 3-1	Brogan 6, Jennings 50, Marsh 51	
3	Sat-10-Dec	FAT 1	A	Stockport County	1690	D 2-2	Jennings 2 (34, 39)	
4	Tue-13-Dec	FAT 1R	H	Stockport County	1149	W 2-1	Wilkinson 58, Jennings 89	
5	Sat-14-Jan	FAT 2	A	Guiseley	630	L 0-2		

League
Starts
Substitute
Unused Sub

Cups
Starts
Substitute
Unused Sub

Goals (Lg)
Goals (Cup)

	BUDTZ	J BEMBO-LETA	MEYNELL	PLATT	REA	WILKINSON	MARSH	MCWILLIAMS	ELLAMS	HOBSON	KAY	LYNCH	JENNINGS	AUSTIN	RYAN	GNAHOUA	WARBURTON	SHERRIFF	BUCKLEY	BROGAN	JACKSON	MACGILLIVRAY	ROGAN	BANKS	D BEMBO-LETA	LEES
	X	X	X	X	X	X	X	X	X	X	X	S	S	S	U	U										
	X	X	X	X	X	X	X	X	X	X	X	U	S	U			S									
	X	X	X	X	X	X	X	X	X	X	X	S	S	U		U	S									
	X	X	X	X	X	X	X	X	X	X	X	S	S	U		U	S									
	X	X			X	X	X	X	X	X		X	X	X	U	U	S	S	U							
	X	X	X	S	X	X	X	X	X	X		U	S	X	X		U	S	X							
	X	U	X	X	X	X	X	X	X	X		X	S	X	X		S	S		U						
	X	S	X	X	X	X	X	X	X	X		U	X	X			U	S		U						
	X	U	X	X	X	X	X	X	X	X		S	S	X	X		U	X		U						
	X	U	X	X	X	X	X	X	X	X		S	U	X	X		U	S	X							
	X	U	X	X	X	X	X	X	X		S	S		X	X	U		S	X			X				
	X	U	X	X	X	X	X	X	X	X	S	U		X	X	U		S	X			X				
	X	X	X		X	X	X	X	X	U		X	X	S	U	U	S		X							
	X	X	X		X	X	X	X	X	U		X	X	U		S	S	U		X						
	X	X	X	U	X	X	X	X	S		X	X	X	S		U	U		X							
	X	X	X		X	X	X	X	S		X	X	X	S		U	U		X	U						
	X	X	X		X	X	X	X	S	U		X	X	S		X	S		X	U						
	X	X	X	U	X	X	X	X	U	S		X	X	S		X	S		X							
	X	X		X	X	X	S	X	X	X		X	X	S		U	U	S	X							
	X	X		X	X	X	X	X	U	S		X	X	X	S	U		U	X		U					
	X	X	X	X	X	X	X	S		X	X	X	S		U		U	X		S						
	X	X	X	X	X	X	X	U	X	X	X	S		X		X		U	X		U	S				
	X	X	U	X	X	S	X	U	X		X		S		X		X	S	X	X						
	X	X	X	X	X	X	X		X		S			X	U	X	X		X		U	U	S			
	X	X	X	X	X	X	X		S		U		X	U	X	X		X			U	S				
	X	X	X	X	X	X	X		X		U		S	U	U	X		X			X	U				
	X	S	X	X	X	X	X		X		U		S		S	X		X			X	U				
	X	S	X	X	X	X	X	X	U	X		S		S		X	X		X			X	U			
	X	S	X	X	X	X	X	X		X		U		S		S	X		X			X	U			
	X	X	X	X	X	X	S	X	U	X		U		X		X	S					X	S			
	X	S	X		S	X		U	X		X		X	X	U	X		X				X	S	X		
	X		X	S	X	X		U	X		X		X	X	U	X		S				X	S	X		
	X	U	X	U	X	X			X		X	X	X	S	X		X		S	S	X					
	X	S	X	X	X	X	X		U		X		X		U	X		U	S	X						
	X	U	X	X	X	X	X		S		X		S	X	X	X		U		X						
	X	U	X	X	X	X	S	X		X		S		X	U	X		S		X						
	X	U	X	U	X	X		S	X		X		X	X		S	X		X	S	X					
	X		X	X	X	X		X	U	X		X		U		S		S	X		U	X	X			
	X		X	S	X	X		X	U	X		X		S	U	S	X	X		X						
	X	X	X		X	X	X	X	S	U	X	X	S		U	S		U	X	U						
	U	X	X		X	X	X	X		S	U	X	X	S		X	S		X		X					
	X	X	X		X	X	S	X	X	X		X	X	S		U	S	U	X							
	X	X	X		X	X		X	X	X		X	X	U		U	S	S	X		U					
	X	X	X	X	X	X	X	U	X	X		X			U	S	S		X			S				
	41	24	38	27	42	41	33	32	21	21	6	29	19	9	5	9	16	1	0	28	0	1	2	7	1	9
	0	6	0	3	0	1	3	2	3	13	4	6	4	18	0	15	16	3	0	0	0	0	2	3	9	0
	0	9	0	6	0	0	1	0	10	3	3	6	0	7	9	17	3	6	5	0	0	4	1	5	4	0
	4	5	5	1	5	5	3	4	4	3	0	5	4	0	0	1	0	0	0	5	0	1	0	0	0	0
	0	0	0	0	0	0	0	1	0	0	2	0	0	0	3	0	0	5	2	0	0	0	0	1	0	0
	1	0	0	0	0	0	0	0	1	0	0	2	0	0	1	0	4	0	1	1	0	1	1	0	0	0
	0	0	1	2	1	8	20	0	5	11	2	1	15	1	0	1	1	2	0	9	0	0	1	0	0	0
	0	0	0	0	0	1	2	0	0	0	0	0	4	0	0	0	0	0	0	0	0	1	0	0	0	0

PLAYING SQUAD 2012/13

Existing Players		SN	HT	WT	DOB	AGE	POB	Career	Apps	Goals
GOALKEEPERS										
Andy	Ralph				28/05/1983	29		Liverpool (Yth),Tranmere (Scholar) Rel c/s 02, Chester (Trial) c/s 02, Kidsgrove, Vauxhall Motors 7/02, Northwich 10/03 Rel 5/05, Stalybridge (L) 3/04, Witton (L) 3/05, Bangor C 7/05, Marine 8/05, Metro FC (NZ) 2/07, Marine 1/08, Altrincham 7/08, Abbey Hey (L) 9/08, Trafford (Dual) 1/09, Redland City Devils (Aust) 2/09, Stalybridge 8/12		
Ashley	Woodhouse							Stockport (Yth), Glossop NE, Stalybridge 1/11		
DEFENDERS										
Sam	Egerton							Lancaster, Stalybridge 8/12		
Mark	Lees				23/07/1988	24		Mossley (Yth), Curzon Ashton (Yth), Stalybridge (Yth), New Mills, Buxton 1/08, Ashton U 2/09, Hyde U/FC 7/09, Altrincham 6/11, Stalybridge 3/12	9	0
Jonny	Lindsay				16/10/1992	19	Bellshill	Celtic (Jun), St Johnstone, Dumbarton (L) 12/10, Partick 7/11 Rel c/s 12, Brechin (SL) 1/12, Stalybridge 8/12		
Kristian	Platt		6'02"	11 13	15/12/1991	30	Rock Ferry	Chester Rel 2/10, Stalybridge 7/10	30	2
Tim	Ryan		6'00"	11 07	10/12/1974	37	Stockport	Scunthorpe, Buxton 11/94, Doncaster 8/96 Rel c/s 97, Altrincham (2ML) 3/97, Southport 8/97, Doncaster 5/00 Rel 1/06, Peterborough 3/06 Rel c/s 06, Boston U 7/06, Darlington Undisc 1/07 Rel c/s 09, Harrogate T (L) 8/08, Chester 7/09 Rel 3/10, Stalybridge 3/10 (Pl/Ass Man) 6/10	5	0
Callum	Warburton				25/02/1989	23		Rochdale Rel 12/07, Northwich (L) 3/07, Kendal (4ML) 8/07, Kendal 12/07, Stalybridge 8/10	32	1
MIDFIELDERS										
Mitchell	Austin		6'02"	11 10	03/04/1991	21	Rochdale	Rotherham (Scholar) Rel c/s 10, Stalybridge 10/10, Worksop (L) 8/11	27	1
Jordan	Barrow				18/10/1993	18		Everton (Scholar) Rel c/s 12, Stalybridge 8/12		
Jamie	Mullan		5'06"	11 13	10/02/1988	24	Nottingham	Notts County (Yth), Man Utd Rel c/s 07, Leeds (Trial) 5/07, Huddersfield (Trial) 8/07, Carlisle (Trial) 9/07, Rochdale 11/07, Northwich 1/08, Fleetwood £5,000 5/09, Alfreton 7/11 Rel c/s 12, Stalybridge 6/12		
Adam	Pepper		5'06"	09 04	02/12/1991	20	Liverpool	Liverpool Rel c/s 10, Aberwystwyth 9/10, Stalybridge 7/12		
Greg	Wilkinson				03/10/1989	22		East Manchester, Stalybridge 2/08	42	8
FORWARDS										
Joel	Bembo-Leta				15/02/1992	20		Oldham (Yth), Stalybridge	30	0
Corey	Gregory				23/02/1993	19		Sheff Utd (Scholar) Rel c/s 12, Belper (WE) 9/11, Hucknall (WE) 10/11, Leicester (2ML) 2/12, Stalybridge 8/12		
Jack	Laird							Oldham (Scholar) Rel c/s 12, Tranmere (Trial), Stalybridge 8/12		
Dennis	Sherriff		6'01"	11 03	22/01/1992	20		Rochdale (Scholar) Rel c/s 10, Woodley Sports (SWE) 1/10, Woodley Sports 6/10, Stalybridge 9/10, Worksop (L) 8/11, Radcliffe B (L) 11/11, Nantwich (L) 1/12	4	2

VAUXHALL MOTORS

Chairman: Alan Bartlam
Secretary: Mike Harper   **(T)** 07817 400 202   **(E)** mike.harper@sky.com
Additional Committee Members:
Stephen McInerney, A Woodley, L Jones, D Mathers, Mrs L Bartlam, A Harper, N Kelly,
P Jarvis, A Marley, Mrs L Edmunds, Miss M Jones, Mrs C Mathers, C Wheelwright, Mrs T Wheelwright
Manager: Carl Macauley
Programme Editor: Ceri Richards   **(E)** ceririchards@ntlworld.com

Club Factfile

Founded: 1963   **Nickname:** The Motormen
Previous Names: Vauxhall Motors 1963-87, Vauxhall GM 1995-99
Previous Leagues: Ellesmere Port, Wirral Combination, West Cheshire 1966-87, 92-95, North West Co. 1987-92, 95-2000,
Northern Premier 2000-04

Club Colours (change): White/blue/blue (Yellow/green/green)

Ground: Rivacre Park, Rivacre Road, Ellesmere Port, South Wirrall CH66 1NJ   **(T)** 0151 328 1114 (Club) 327 2294 (Social)
Capacity: 3,500 **Seats:** 266 **Covered:** 1,000 **Clubhouse:** Yes **Shop:** Yes
Directions: Leave M53 at junction 5 and take A41 towards North Wales. At first set of traffic lights (Hooton Crossroads) turn left into Hooton Green. At 'T' junction turn left into Hooton Lane. At next 'T' junction turn right into Rivacre Road. Ground is 200 yards on right.

Previous Grounds: Not known

Record Attendance: 1,500 - FA XI fixture for the opening of Rivacre Park 1987
Record Victory: Not known
Record Defeat: Not known
Record Goalscorer: Terry Fearns - 111
Record Appearances: Carl Jesbitt - 509
Additional Records:

Senior Honours:
North West Counties League Division 2 1988-89, 95-96, Division 1 1999-2000.
Wirral Senior Cup 1987.

10 YEAR RECORD

02-03	03-04	04-05	05-06	06-07	07-08	08-09	09-10	10-11	11-12
NP P 3	NP P 9	Conf N 15	Conf N 18	Conf N 15	Conf N 21	Conf N 11	Conf N 20	Conf N 17	Conf N 18

VAUXHALL MOTORS

No.	Date	Comp	H/A	Opponents	Att:	Result	Goalscorers	Pos
1	Sat-13-Aug	BSN	H	Gloucester City	179	L 0-2		21
2	Mon-15-Aug	BSN	A	Worcester City	620	L 0-2		22
3	Sat-20-Aug	BSN	A	Boston United	1114	W 2-1	Jackson 20, Wilson 84	16
4	Tue-23-Aug	BSN	H	Altrincham	382	D 2-2	McGivern 82, Wilson pen 87	17
5	Sat-27-Aug	BSN	H	Solihull Moors	181	W 2-1	Wilson 5, Mannix 67	14
6	Mon-29-Aug	BSN	A	Stalybridge Celtic	508	L 2-4	Jackson 39, Williams 73	14
7	Sat-03-Sep	BSN	A	Guiseley	522	L 1-4	Wilson pen 89	16
8	Sat-10-Sep	BSN	H	Nuneaton Town	239	L 1-2	Wilson 55	17
9	Sat-17-Sep	BSN	A	FC Halifax Town	1265	W 5-1	Wilson pen 9, Mahon 36, McGivern 3 (39, 52, 79)	15
10	Sat-24-Sep	BSN	H	Workington	158	L 0-1		17
11	Tue-27-Sep	BSN	H	Harrogate Town	169	L 0-1		17
12	Sat-08-Oct	BSN	A	Histon	363	D 3-3	McGivern 7, Mahon 31, Wilson pen 40	18
13	Sat-15-Oct	BSN	A	Altrincham	706	L 2-3	Dames 11, McGivern pen 34	18
14	Sat-22-Oct	BSN	H	Bishops Stortford	149	W 4-3	McGivern 3 (3, 49, 82), Hannigan 72	17
15	Sat-29-Oct	BSN	H	Eastwood Town	201	L 1-2	McGivern pen 51	17
16	Sat-05-Nov	BSN	A	Corby Town	620	L 0-1		18
17	Sat-12-Nov	BSN	H	Droylsden	189	D 1-1	Lawless pen 24	17
18	Tue-15-Nov	BSN	H	Blyth Spartans	358	W 2-1	McGivern 2 (37, 81)	17
19	Sat-19-Nov	BSN	A	Workington	406	L 1-2	McGivern pen 48	17
20	Sat-03-Dec	BSN	H	Histon	177	D 1-1	Hannigan 83	17
21	Sat-17-Dec	BSN	A	Hyde FC	357	L 2-4	Lacey 22, McGivern 87	18
22	Mon-26-Dec	BSN	H	Colwyn Bay	343	W 1-0	Holsgrove 90	18
23	Sat-07-Jan	BSN	H	Worcester City	228	W 3-2	Wilson 5, Mahon 40, Stockton 72	18
24	Tue-17-Jan	BSN	A	Colwyn Bay	170	D 0-0		19
25	Sat-21-Jan	BSN	H	FC Halifax Town	532	L 1-3	Phelan 51	19
26	Tue-24-Jan	BSN	H	Guiseley	204	D 1-1	Wynn 26	19
27	Sat-28-Jan	BSN	A	Nuneaton Town	622	L 1-2	McGivern 25	19
28	Sat-18-Feb	BSN	A	Gloucester City	303	L 1-2	Mahon 5	20
29	Tue-21-Feb	BSN	H	Boston United	173	L 0-4		20
30	Sat-25-Feb	BSN	A	Gainsborough Trinity	414	D 1-1	Hannigan 17	20
31	Sat-03-Mar	BSN	H	Hyde FC	242	L 0-2		20
32	Tue-06-Mar	BSN	A	Eastwood Town	151	W 4-2	Wilson 3 (23, 27, 54), Holsgrove 29	20
33	Sat-10-Mar	BSN	A	Harrogate Town	430	W 2-1	Hannigan 85, Wilson pen 90	20
34	Sat-17-Mar	BSN	H	Gainsborough Trinity	171	W 3-1	Wilson 2 (pen 48, 85), Holsgrove 74	20
35	Sat-24-Mar	BSN	A	Hinckley United	407	D 2-2	Wilson 45, Holsgrove 54	20
36	Sat-31-Mar	BSN	A	Blyth Spartans	209	W 2-1	Parkinson 26, Wynn 55	20
37	Tue-03-Apr	BSN	H	Hinckley United	232	L 1-2	Fearnehough 45	20
38	Sat-07-Apr	BSN	A	Solihull Moors	266	W 3-2	Hannigan 28, Wilson 63, Parkinson 76	19
39	Mon-09-Apr	BSN	H	Stalybridge Celtic	254	W 1-0	Wilson 55	18
40	Sat-14-Apr	BSN	A	Bishops Stortford	378	L 0-2		20
41	Sat-21-Apr	BSN	H	Corby Town	189	W 2-1	Wilson 13, Jones 77	15
42	Sat-28-Apr	BSN	A	Droylsden	401	L 2-5	Holsgrove 74, Fearnehough 90	18

CUPS

1	Sat-01-Oct	FAC 2Q	A	Ashington	262	D 3-3	Mahon 13, Wilson 14, McGivern 73	
2	Tue-04-Oct	FAC 2QR	H	Ashington	221	L 0-1		
3	Sat-26-Nov	FAT 3Q	H	Marine	329	W 3-2	McGivern 2 (8, 78), Og (Rey) 67	
4	Sat-10-Dec	FAT 1	H	Kidderminster Harriers	253	D 4-4	McGivern 9, Stockton 2 (15, 53), Hannigan 44	
5	Tue-13-Dec	FAT 1R	A	Kidderminster Harriers	746	L 0-2		

League
Starts
Substitute
Unused Sub

Cups
Starts
Substitute
Unused Sub

Goals (Lg)
Goals (Cup)

Appearance grid (X = start, S = substitute used, U = unused substitute)

TYNAN	GROCOTT	DAMES	HIGHDALE	JACKSON	TAYLOR	WHEELER	MANNIX	MCGIVERN	WILSON	MAHON	FIELD	NETHERCOTE	HANNIGAN	BENNETT	O'CONNELL	WILLIAMS	BECK	WRIGHT	MURPHY	JONES	ORDISH	LACEY	FEARNEHOUGH	SPOTSWOOD	MARTINDALE	OVERSON	BURKE	LAWLESS	HOLSGROVE	SAXTON	BENN	STOCKTON	NOONE	GLOVER	KASBARIAN	PHELAN	WYNN	WINSLADE	ABLETT	HORNE	EGERTON	PARKINSON	OGDEN	ANORUO
X	X	X	X	X	X	X	X	X	X	X			S	S	S	U																												
X	S	X	S	X	X		X	X	X	X	X	S		U	U	X																												
X	S	X	X	X	X		X	X	X	X		X	S	U	U	X	U																											
X	S	X	X	X	X		X	X	X	X		X	S	U	S	X	U																											
X	S	X		X	X	U	X	X	X	X		X	S	U	X	U																												
X	X	X	X	S		X		X	X	X		X	X	X			S																											
X		X	U	X	X		X	X	X	X		S	X	X	U	X	X	U	X	X	U	S																						
X	S	X		X		X	X	X	X	X		S	X	S	U	X	X			U	X																							
X	S		U		X		X	X	X	X		S	X	X	U		X			X	X	S																						
X	X		S		X		X	X	X	X		U	X		U		X			S	X	X	S																					
X		X	S		X		X	X	X	X		S	X	U	U		X			S	X		X																					
X		X					X	X	X	X		X	U			U		X			X		X	U		X	X	S																
X		X		S			X	X	S	X		X			U			X			X		X			X	X	S	X	U														
X		X		U			X	X	S	X		X			U			X			X		U			X	X	U	X	U														
X		X		X			X	X	S	X		X	U					X			X		S			X	S	X	U	S														
U		X					X	X		X		X	X		U			X			X		X	U		X	X	X	U	S														
U		X					X	X		X		X	X			S	U				X		X		U	X	X	X	X	U														
U		X					X	X		X		X	U		S	U		X			X		X		U	X	X	X	X	U														
X							X	X		X		X	X		S		X				X		X		U	X	X	U	S		S													
X								X		X		X	U				X	X			X		X			X	X		S	X		U	U											
X	U						S			X		X					X	X		U		X			S	X	X		X	X		S	U	X										
X	X			S		X	X		X	X		X						X			X		S	X			X	X		U	X		S	U	X									
X	X			U		X	X	X	X	X		X						X			X				U	X	S	S		X			U	X										
X	X						X	X	X	X		X						X	U		X		S	X	U		X			S			X	X	S									
X	X					S	X	X	X	X		X						X	U		X	U		X	U		X			S			X	X	S									
X						X	X	X	X			X						X	U		X	U			S	U				X		X		X	X	U				X	X	U		
X							X	X	X			X						X	U		X				X				X		S	X	S	S	X									
X	U						X	X	X			X						X	U		X								X		X	U	X	S	X									
X	S						X	X	X			X						X	U		X		S		S	X			X			X	U	S										
X							X	X	X			X						X	U		X		X	X					S			U	U	S	S									
X							X	X	X			X						X	U		X		X	X					U			U	U	X	U									
X							X	X	X			X						X	U		X		X	X					S			U	U	X										X
X							X	X	X			X						X	U		X		X	X					S			U	S	X										U
X							X	X	X									U		X		X	U	U		X			X			X		U	X	S								
X							X	X	X									U		X		X	U	U		X			S			U	U	X										
X							X	X	X									U		X		X	U	U		X			U			U	U	X	U									
X							X	X	X									U		X		X	U	U		X			S			S	X											
X							X	X	X									U		X		X	U			X			U			U	X											
X							X	X	X									U		X		X	S	U		X	X					S												

X	X	U		X			X	X	X	X		S	X			X	X	U	X		S	U	U																					
X	X			X			X	X	X	X		S	X	U		X	X	U	X		S	U	U																					
X							X	X		X		X	X		S			X			X				X	X	X	U	U	S	U													
X							X	X		X		X	U					X			X			X	U	X		S	X		S	U												
X							X	X		X		X	U					X		U		X			X	S	X		X	X		S	U											

Totals:

39	3	32	4	7	11	1	38	22	32	41	1	0	39	6	0	5	13	0	0	32	2	3	28	0	0	3	23	10	21	3	3	7	0	0	7	7	0	1	4	0	13	0	1
0	6	1	3	0	3	0	2	0	3	0	1	6	1	5	0	1	2	1	3	2	0	3	1	1	0	0	4	5	3	0	4	1	1	3	0	1	6	2	1	0	6	0	3	0
3	0	2	2	0	2	1	0	0	0	0	0	1	0	7	11	1	1	18	1	0	0	0	1	17	9	0	1	1	1	4	5	0	1	1	5	0	3	0	1	5	9	0	2	1

5	0	2	0	0	2	0	5	5	2	5	0	0	5	2	0	2	2	0	5	0	0	3	0	0	0	3	1	3	0	1	2	0	0	0	0	0	0	0	0	0	0	0	0
0	0	0	0	0	0	0	0	0	0	0	0	2	0	0	0	1	0	0	0	2	0	0	0	0	0	2	0	0	0	1	1	0	2	0	0	0	0	0	0	0	0	0	0
0	0	0	1	0	0	0	0	0	0	0	0	0	0	2	0	0	3	0	0	0	0	0	2	2	0	0	1	0	1	1	0	1	0	2	0	0	0	0	0	0	0	0	0

| 0 | 0 | 1 | 0 | 2 | 0 | 0 | 1 | 15 | 18 | 4 | 0 | 0 | 5 | 0 | 0 | 1 | 0 | 0 | 0 | 1 | 0 | 1 | 2 | 0 | 0 | 0 | 0 | 1 | 5 | 0 | 0 | 1 | 0 | 0 | 0 | 1 | 2 | 0 | 0 | 0 | 0 | 2 | 0 |
| 0 | 0 | 0 | 0 | 0 | 0 | 0 | 0 | 4 | 1 | 1 | 0 | 0 | 1 | 0 | 0 | 0 | 0 | 0 | 0 | 0 | 0 | 0 | 0 | 0 | 0 | 0 | 2 | 0 | 0 | 0 | 0 | 0 | 0 | 0 | 0 | 0 | 0 | 0 | 0 | 0 | 0 | 0 | 0 |

ALSO PLAYED: FARRAN U (30). OWENS S (C2).

PLAYING SQUAD 2012/13

Existing Players		SN	HT	WT	DOB	AGE	POB	Career	Apps	Goals
GOALKEEPERS										
Zak	Jones		5'10"	12 08	24/11/1988	23	Darwen	Blackburn Rel c/s 10, Southampton (3ML) 11/05, Stockport (L) 9/07, Forest Green 8/10 Rel 5/11, Clitheroe, Barrow NC 9/11, Harrogate T NC 9/11, AFC Fylde 11/11, Vauxhall Motors 5/12		
Gary	Spotswood							Everton Deaf Team, Vauxhall Motors 9/11	1	0
DEFENDERS										
Lee	Dames				21/01/1986	26	Liverpool	Tranmere (Yth), Burscough, Vauxhall Motors 6/06	33	1
Jonathan	Egerton				19/09/1988	23		Vauxhall Motors	6	0
Tom	Hannigan				30/06/1988	24		Vauxhall Motors	40	5
Callum	Henry		6'00"	12 10	10/06/1991	21	Cheltenham	Forest Green, Frome T (L) 9/09, Frome T (L) 8/10, Cirencester (3ML) 9/10, Cirencester (L) 1/11, Evesham (L) 3/12, Vauxhall Motors 7/12		
David	Thompson				27/02/1991	21	Liverpool	Everton (Yth), Oldham (Yth), Bury Rel 1/10, Colwyn Bay, Northwich, Marine 3/11, Colwyn Bay 12/11, Droylsden 12/11, Vauxhall Motors 8/12		
Steve	Wainwright							Tranmere (Scholar) Rel c/s 12, Vauxhall Motors 8/12		
MIDFIELDERS										
Michael	Burns		5'10"	11 07	04/10/1988	23	Huyton	Liverpool (Scholar), Bolton 7/07, Gillingham (Trial) c/s 08, Carlisle 1/09, Stafford R (2ML) 1/10, Runcorn Linnets, Newport C 1/11 Rel 2/11, Guiseley 6/11, Vauxhall Motors 6/12		
Danny	Fearnehough		5'10"	11 00	23/11/1991	20	Liverpool	Barnsley Rel 9/11, Vauxhall Motors 9/11	29	2
Craig	Mahon		5'07"	09 10	21/06/1989	23	Dublin	Lourdes Celtic (Yth), Wigan Rel c/s 09, Accrington (L) 11/08, Salford C c/s 09, Burscough 2/10, Vauxhall Motors 9/10	41	4
Conor	Roberts							Tranmere (Scholar), Burscough, Racing Club Portunse (Spa), Vauxhall Motors 8/12		
FORWARDS										
James	Ellison		5'10"	12 08	25/10/1991	20	Liverpool	Burton Rel 12/11, Alfreton (3ML) 8/11, Chester FC (L) 11/11, Rel 12/11, Hyde FC 12/11, Southport 1/12, Skelmersdale (L) 3/12, Vauxhall Motors 8/12		
Gary	Martindale				24/06/1971	41		Vauxhall Motors (Ass Man) 6/11	0	0
Chris	Noone		6'02"	12 00	25/10/1984	27	Liverpool	Everton, Vauxhall Motors, La Nucia (Spa), Caernarfon c/s 07 Rel 9/07, Banned, Vauxhall Motors c/s 08	1	0
Dan	Parkinson				02/11/1992	19		Morecambe, Vauxhall Motors (SL) 2/12, Vauxhall Motors (2ML) 8/12	13	2
Tom	Rutter							Northwich, Chorley, Witton 10/07, Radcliffe B, Warrington 2/10, Runcorn T, Knutsford, Vauxhall Motors 7/12		
Mark	Winslade							Vauxhall Motors	2	0
Anthony	Wright		5'11"	11 00	06/03/1978	34	Liverpool	Wrexham, Barrow, Droylsden 9/98, TNS, Aberystwyth, Hyde (L) 8/03, Vauxhall Motors 8/04, Colwyn Bay 1/08, Vauxhall Motors 5/08 (Pl/Man) 5/11 (Player) 11/11	1	0

WORCESTER CITY

Chairman: Anthony Hampson
Secretary: Joe Murphy   **(T)** 07837 086 205   **(E)** joemurphy77@yahoo.co.uk
Additional Committee Members:
Colin Layland, John Jordan, Anthony Hampson, Mike Davis, Richard Widdowson, Mark Wilson Phil Williamson.
Manager: Carl Heeley
Programme Editor: Rob Bazley   **(E)** r.bazley@sky.com

Back Row: Shab Khan, Rob Elvins, Mike Symons, Jacob Rowe, Lee Ayres, Danny Edwards.
Middle Row: Joe Murphy (Secretary), Pete O'Connell (Chiropodist), Martyn Obrey (Assistant Physiotherapist), Stuart Whitehead,
Danny Glover, Glyn Thompson, Matt Sargeant, Charlie Reece, Jay Denny, Lawson Mayor (Physiotherapist),
Ashley Kingdon (Goalkeeper Coach), Kevin Gardiner (Kit Manager).
Front Row: Dan Polan, Matt Breeze, Tyler Weir, Carl Heeley (Manager), Matt Gardiner (Assistant Manager), Greg Mills, Ellis Deeney,
Tom Thorley. Photo: Worcester News.

Club Factfile

Founded: 1902   **Nickname:** City
Previous Names:
Previous Leagues: West Midlands, Birmingham, Southern 1938-79, 85-2004, Alliance 1979-85

Club Colours (change): Blue & white stripes/blue with white trim/blue with white trim (Green with white trim/black/black)

Ground: St George's Lane, Barbourne, Worcester WR1 1QT   **(T)** 01905 23003
Capacity: 4,004   **Seats:** 1,125   **Covered:** 2,000   **Clubhouse:** Yes   **Shop:** Yes

Directions: Leave the M5 at Junction 6 (Worcester North) and take the A449 dual-carriageway towards Kidderminster. At the first island take the 2nd exit towards Worcester. After around 3 miles, at traffic lights/T-junction turn right towards Worcester City Centre. Take the 3rd turning on the left - St. George's Lane North. Ground on the left.

Previous Grounds: Severn Terrace, Thorneloe, Flagge Meadow

Record Attendance: 17,042 v Sheffield United - FA Cup 4th Round 24/01/1959
Record Victory: 18-1 v Bilston - Birmingham League 21/11/1931
Record Defeat: 0-10 v Wellington - Birmingham League 29/08/1920
Record Goalscorer: John Inglis - 189 (1970-77)
Record Appearances: Bobby McEwan - 596 (1959-75)
Additional Records: Paid £8,500 to Telford United for Jim Williams 1981
Senior Honours: Received £27,000 from Everton for John Barton
Birmingham League 1913-14, 24-25, 28-29, 29-30.
Southern League Cup 1939-40, 2000-01, Division 1 1967-68, 76-77, Premier 1978-79.
Birmingham Senior Cup 1975-76. Worcestershire Senior Cup x26 (last win 1996-97)

10 YEAR RECORD

02-03		03-04		04-05		05-06		06-07		07-08		08-09		09-10		10-11		11-12	
SthP	6	SthP	5	Conf N	7	Conf N	8	Conf N	9	Conf N	12	Conf S	16	Conf S	20	Conf N	16	Conf N	7

WORCESTER CITY

No.	Date	Comp	H/A	Opponents	Att:	Result	Goalscorers	Pos
1	Sat-13-Aug	BSN	A	Hyde FC	361	L 1-2	Symons 62	16
2	Mon-15-Aug	BSN	H	Vauxhall Motors	620	W 2-0	Birley 10, Corbett pen 67	6
3	Sat-20-Aug	BSN	H	FC Halifax Town	927	D 1-1	Carey-Bertram 85	11
4	Tue-23-Aug	BSN	A	Histon	342	W 5-1	Elvins 2 (18, 65), Symons 3 (19, 39, 75)	5
5	Sat-27-Aug	BSN	A	Eastwood Town	311	W 1-0	Corbett 89	4
6	Mon-29-Aug	BSN	H	Nuneaton Town	947	D 1-1	Taylor 90	5
7	Sat-03-Sep	BSN	H	Corby Town	921	L 0-2		6
8	Sat-10-Sep	BSN	A	Altrincham	771	L 1-4	Symons pen 90	9
9	Sat-17-Sep	BSN	A	Guiseley	461	L 1-4	Naylor 87	12
10	Mon-19-Sep	BSN	H	Solihull Moors	669	W 3-0	O'Connor 39, Birley 43, Symons 84	9
11	Sat-24-Sep	BSN	H	Bishops Stortford	696	W 2-1	Brown pen 4, Symons 12	7
12	Sat-08-Oct	BSN	A	Blyth Spartans	485	W 2-1	Symons 2, Corbett 26	5
13	Sat-22-Oct	BSN	H	Harrogate Town	782	W 3-2	Corbett 19, Symons 58, Birley 90	5
14	Sat-29-Oct	BSN	A	Stalybridge Celtic	604	L 0-2		7
15	Sat-05-Nov	BSN	H	Guiseley	745	D 2-2	Ayres 36, Symons 42	8
16	Tue-08-Nov	BSN	A	Droylsden	225	L 1-4	Edwards 78	9
17	Sat-12-Nov	BSN	H	Altrincham	824	W 3-0	Brown pen 9, Thorley 2 (40, 81)	7
18	Sat-19-Nov	BSN	A	Bishops Stortford	333	D 1-1	Carey-Bertram 33	8
19	Sat-03-Dec	BSN	H	Hyde FC	782	D 2-2	Thorley 2 (pen 29, pen 79)	7
20	Mon-05-Dec	BSN	A	Hinckley United	377	W 3-2	L Smith 12, O'Connor 41, Brown pen 59	6
21	Sat-17-Dec	BSN	A	Colwyn Bay	295	W 2-0	Cartwright 9, Symons 90	7
22	Mon-26-Dec	BSN	H	Gloucester City	1501	W 2-1	Taylor 70, Brown pen 78	6
23	Sun-01-Jan	BSN	A	Gloucester City	802	L 1-3	Symons 36	6
24	Sat-07-Jan	BSN	A	Vauxhall Motors	228	L 2-3	Og (Jones) 14, Symons 80	7
25	Sat-14-Jan	BSN	A	FC Halifax Town	1556	L 1-2	Symons 43	8
26	Sat-21-Jan	BSN	H	Colwyn Bay	791	L 0-1		9
27	Sat-28-Jan	BSN	A	Workington	366	D 0-0		10
28	Mon-30-Jan	BSN	H	Histon	916	D 1-1	Thorley pen 61	9
29	Sat-18-Feb	BSN	A	Solihull Moors	398	D 0-0		9
30	Sat-25-Feb	BSN	H	Blyth Spartans	643	W 2-1	Birley 40, Taylor 50	9
31	Sat-03-Mar	BSN	H	Boston United	756	W 3-0	Elvins 10, Birley 30, Thorley pen 49	8
32	Sat-10-Mar	BSN	A	Corby Town	343	W 3-2	Taylor 8, Thorley pen 63, Green 78	8
33	Mon-12-Mar	BSN	H	Gainsborough Trinity	693	W 2-1	Symons 69, Mills 71	7
34	Sat-17-Mar	BSN	H	Droylsden	895	L 0-2		8
35	Sat-24-Mar	BSN	A	Stalybridge Celtic	774	D 0-0		8
36	Tue-27-Mar	BSN	A	Boston United	841	W 3-2	Taylor 19, Symons 34, Birley pen 67	7
37	Sat-31-Mar	BSN	A	Harrogate Town	319	W 2-0	Elvins 35, Green 90	7
38	Sat-07-Apr	BSN	H	Eastwood Town	857	W 1-0	Symons 76	7
39	Mon-09-Apr	BSN	A	Nuneaton Town	958	L 0-3		7
40	Sat-14-Apr	BSN	H	Hinckley United	813	D 1-1	Symons 45	7
41	Sat-21-Apr	BSN	A	Gainsborough Trinity	390	D 2-2	Mills 42, Thorley 83	7
42	Sat-28-Apr	BSN	H	Workington	818	L 0-1		7

CUPS

No.	Date	Comp	H/A	Opponents	Att:	Result	Goalscorers
1	Sat-01-Oct	FAC 2Q	A	Godalming Town	334	L 1-2	Corbett 90
2	Sat-26-Nov	FAT 3Q	H	Harrogate Town	676	L 0-1	

League
Starts
Substitute
Unused Sub

Cups
Starts
Substitute
Unused Sub

Goals (Lg)
Goals (Cup)

Player appearances / substitutes grid:

DORMAND	WILSON	CHARLTON	CARTWRIGHT	ELVINS	CLARKE	BIRLEY	O'CONNOR	SYMONS	CAREY-BERTRAM	EDWARDS	CORBETT	EMERY	TAYLOR	AYRES	SARGEANT	MCGREGOR	ROWE	NWADIKE	THORLEY	NAYLOR	LAKE-GASKIN	BROWN	L SMITH	J SMITH	DEENEY	WEIR	WHITEHEAD	GREEN	MILLS	SAMUELS
X	X	X	X	X	X	X	X	X	X	X	X	S	S	U	U															
X	X		X	X	X	X	X	X	S	X	X	S	U	X	U	S														
X	X		X	X	X	X	X	S	X	X	S		X	U	S	U														
X	U		X	X	X	X	X	X	X	X	S		X	U	S	X	S													
X	U	U	X	X		X	X	X			S		S	X	U		X	X	X											
X	U	X		X	X	S	X	X				U	S	X	U		X	X	X											
X	U	X	S	X	X	X	X	X	S				S	X	U		X	X	X											
X	X	X		X	X	X	X						S	X	U	U	X	S	X	S										
X	X		X	X	X	X	X						S	X	U		U	S	X	X	X	S								
X		X		X	X	X	X	X					U	U	S	X	U	X	X	S	X									
X		X		X	X	X	X	S					U	U	S	X	S	X	X		X									
X		X	S	X	X	X	X	S		X			X	U		U	X	U	X			X								
X			S	X	X	X		X	U	X	X		X	U		S	X	X	X		U	X								
X		X	U	X		X	X			S	X		X	U		U	X	X	X		S	X								
X		X	S	X		X	X	U	S	S			X	U			X	X	X		S	X								
X		X	S	X		X		U	S	X			X	U		S	X	X	X		X	X								
X		X	X	X	S	X		X	S	S			X	U		U		X	X		X	X								
		X	X	X	S	X	X	X	X				S	X	X		X		X	S		U	U							
		X		X	X	X		X	S				S	U	X		X		X	X		X	X	U						
X		X		X	X	X	S	X	X				S	X	U		X		X			X	S							
X		X		X	X	X	X	X	U				S	X	U		X		X	U		X	U	U						
X		X		X	X	X	S	X	X				S	X	U		X		S			X	S	U						
X		X		X	S	X	X	U	X				S	X	U		S		X	X		X	X							
X		X		X	X	X	X	U	X				S		U		X		X	S			U	X	X					
X			X	X	X	X	U	X					S	U	S		X		X				X	X	X	S				
		U	U	X	X	X	X						S	X	X		X		X			U			X	X	U	X		
		S	U	X	X	X	X			X			U	X	X		X		X			S			X	X	S	X		
		X	U	X	X	X	S	S					X	U	X		X		X			U			X	X		U	X	
U		X	U	X	X	X	X		S				X	S	X		X		X						X	X		S	X	
U		X		X	X	X	S						X	S	X		X		X						X	X	U	S	X	
U		X		X	X	X	S	U					X	S	X		X		X						X	X	U	X	X	
U		X		X	X	X	U	S					X	S	X		X		X						X	X	U	X	X	
X		S		X	X	X	S	S					X		U		X		X						X	X	X	U	X	X
X		X		X	X	X	S	S					X	U	U		X		X						X	X	X	S	X	X
X		X		X	X	X	X						U	U		X		S			U			X	X	X	S		X
X		X		U	X	X	X	S						U	U		X		X			S			X	S	X	U	X
X		X		X	X	U	S						S		X		X		X			U			X	X	X	X	X	S
X		X	U	X	X	S	X						U	X		X		X			S		S		X	X		X	X

| X | X | S | X | X | X | X | U | S | | S | | | U | U | X | X | U | X | X | | | X | | | | | | | | |
| X | | X | X | X | S | X | X | X | S | | | | U | | X | | X | X | | | | S | U | | | | | | | |

30	5	6	18	25	26	25	39	37	13	17	6	0	7	22	12	0	30	8	34	12	1	13	8	0	15	17	11	4	15	6
0	0	0	1	6	1	5	0	2	14	14	6	3	16	4	2	5	3	4	1	3	1	5	2	1	0	1	0	7	0	1
4	3	2	0	2	4	3	0	0	9	1	0	1	2	11	28	1	6	1	1	1	0	6	2	4	0	0	3	4	0	1

2	0	1	2	2	1	2	1	1	0	0	0	0	0	1	2	0	2	2	0	0	1	0	0	0	0	0	0	0	0	0
0	0	0	1	0	0	1	0	0	1	0	2	0	0	0	0	0	0	0	0	1	0	0	0	1	0	0	0	0	0	0
0	0	0	0	0	0	0	0	1	0	0	0	0	1	2	0	0	1	0	0	0	0	1	0	0	0	0	0	0	0	0

| 0 | 0 | 0 | 1 | 4 | 0 | 6 | 2 | 18 | 2 | 1 | 4 | 0 | 5 | 1 | 0 | 0 | 0 | 8 | 1 | 0 | 4 | 1 | 0 | 0 | 0 | 0 | 2 | 2 | 0 | |
| 0 | 0 | 0 | 0 | 0 | 0 | 0 | 0 | 0 | 0 | 0 | 1 | 0 | 0 | 0 | 0 | 0 | 0 | 0 | 0 | 0 | 0 | 0 | 0 | 0 | 0 | 0 | 0 | 0 | 0 | 0 |

PLAYING SQUAD 2012/13

Existing Players		SN	HT	WT	DOB	AGE	POB	Career	Apps	Goals
GOALKEEPERS										
James	Dormand		6'01"	14 09	13/06/1986	26	Birmingham	Birmingham Rel 5/06, Bromsgrove (L) 8/03, Stafford R (3ML) 9/04, Tamworth (3ML) 8/05, Boston U (Trial) 7/06, Tamworth 7/06 (06/07 1,0), Rel 9/06, Halesowen T 10/06, Stratford T (L) 12/07, Stratford T (2ML) 1/08, Bromsgrove 6/08, Halesowen T 1/09, Redditch 12/10 Rel 2/11, Solihull Moors 3/11, Worcester 6/11	30	0
Matt	Sargeant								14	0
Glyn	Thompson		6'02"	13 01	24/02/1981	31	Telford	Shrewsbury, Fulham £50,000 10/99, Mansfield (3ML) 1/00, Shrewsbury (L) 1/01, Northampton (2ML) 11/02, Northampton 3/03 Rel c/s 04, Walsall 8/04, Koge (Den), Rushden & D (Trial) 2/05, Waterford U (Trial) 2/05, Stafford R 1/05, Chesterfield 3/05 Rel c/s 05, Shrewsbury 7/05 Rel 5/06, Koje Boldklub (Den), Hereford 6/06 Rel c/s 07, Newport C 7/07 Rel c/s 12, Worcester 7/12		
DEFENDERS										
Lee	Ayres		6'02"	12 06	28/08/1982	30	Birmingham	Walsall (Yth), Evesham, Kidderminster 6/01, Stourport (L) 02, Tamworth (L) 9/03, Tamworth 11/03, Notts County (Trial) 7/04, Burton £10,000 8/04 Rel 4/06, Bristol R (Trial) c/s 06, Moor Green/Solihull Moors c/s 06, Bristol R (Trial) 10/06, Redditch 7/08, Forest Green 12/08, Halesowen T 8/10, Redditch 10/10, Solihull Moors 2/11, Worcester 7/11	26	1
Lee	Baker		5'10"	12 01	20/01/1989	23	Redditch	West Brom, Kidderminster (5ML) 8/08, Kidderminster 1/09, Newport C 6/10 Rel c/s 12, Worcester 7/12		
Ellis	Deeney				19/10/1991	20		Aston Villa, Kettering 11/11, Hinckley U 12/11, Worcester 1/12	15	0
Rob	Elvins		6'02"	12 04	17/09/1986	25	Alvechurch	West Brom, Cheltenham (L) 9/06, York C (2ML) 1/07, Aldershot 6/07 Rel c/s 09, Woking (2ML) 2/09, Worcester 7/09	31	4
Shabir	Khan				10/11/1985	26		Worcester, Gloucester (L) 12/06, Stourport (L) 8/11		
Jacob	Rowe				09/12/1990	21		Derby (Yth), Solihull Moors (Yth), Birmingham, Redditch (L) 12/09, Rochdale (Trial) 7/10, Tamworth (Trial) 8/10 AFC Telford 8/10, Redditch 10/10, Worcester 6/11	33	0
Stuart	Whitehead		6'00"	12 02	17/07/1976	36	Bromsgrove	Bromsgrove, Bolton 9/95 Rel c/s 98, Carlisle 7/98, Darlington 10/02, Telford 6/03, Shrewsbury 6/04, Kidderminster 5/06, AFC Telford 1/08 Rel 1/12, Worcester 1/12	11	0
MIDFIELDERS										
Matt	Birley		5'08"	11 01	26/07/1986	26	Bromsgrove	Birmingham Rel c/s 07, Lincoln C (L) 11/06, Bournemouth (Trial) 5/07, Bromsgrove c/s 07, Tamworth 10/08, Kings Lynn 6/09 Rel 9/09, Worcester 9/09	30	6
Matt	Breeze				06/02/1993	19	Peterborough	Peterborough Rel c/s 12, Shepshed D (WE) 12/10, Histon (5ML) 8/11, (SL) 1/12, Worcester 8/12		
Jay	Denny		5'11"	10 09	06/01/1986	26	Los Angeles, USA	Stoke Rel c/s 05, Shrewsbury 7/05 Rel 4/06, Nuneaton c/s 06, Halesowen T 6/07, Leamington 6/09, Halesowen T 10/09, Hednesford 7/10, Worcester 8/12		
Danny	Edwards				27/10/1983	28	Wellington	Shrewsbury, Stafford R (SL) 3/03, Stafford R 8/03, Redditch 6/07, AFC Telford 11/08, Halesowen T (L) 11/09, Leamington 7/10, Chasetown 9/10, Stafford R 1/11, Worcester 6/11	31	1
Kyonn	Evans							Worcester, Stourport (L) 8/11		
Robin	Hulbert		5'10"	12 02	14/03/1980	32	Plymouth	Swindon, Newcastle (SL) 2/98, Bristol C £25,000 3/00, Shrewsbury (SL) 3/03, Telford 11/03, Port Vale 7/04 Rel c/s 08, Darlington 8/08 Rel c/s 09, Barrow 6/09, Worcester 7/12		
Greg	Mills		6'02"	13 01	18/09/1990	21	Derby	Derby Rel c/s 11, Solihull Moors (L) 9/09, Solihull Moors (6WL) 11/09, Macclesfield (L) 1/10, AFC Telford (5ML) 8/10, AFC Telford (SL) 1/11, AFC Telford 8/11 Rel 1/12, Worcester 1/12	15	2
Charlie	Reece		5'11"	11 03	08/09/1988	23	Birmingham	Aston Villa (Yth), Bristol R Rel c/s 12, Solihull Moors (L) 1/09, Gloucester (2ML) 10/11, Tamworth (L) 1/12, Worcester 7/12		
Tom	Thorley		5'10"	11 08	05/04/1990	22	Stafford	Stoke Rel 6/09, Stafford R (3ML) 7/08, Burscough (L) 10/08, Stafford R (SL) 1/09, Stafford R 7/09, Worcester 6/10	35	8
Tyler	Weir		5'10"	11 10	21/12/1990	21	Hereford	Hereford, Gloucester (SL) 3/11, Gloucester (5ML) 8/11, Worcester (SL) 1/12, Worcester 7/12	18	0
FORWARDS										
Danny	Carey-Bertram		5'11"	13 00	14/06/1984	28	Birmingham	WBA, Hereford 9/03 Rel 6/06, Cambridge U 6/06 Rel 1/07, Forest Green Rovers 1/07 Rel 4/08, Bath C 8/08, AFC Telford 10/08 Rel 5/11, Worcester (L) 12/09, Hednesford (L) 10/10, Worcester 6/11	27	2
Danny	Glover		6'00"	11 02	24/10/1989	22	Crewe	Port Vale Rel c/s 10, Salisbury (L) 8/09, Rochdale (L) 11/09, Stafford R (L) 3/10, Worcester 8/10, Nuneaton 6/11 Rel c/s 12, Worcester 7/12		
Michael	Symons				22/07/1986	26	Gloucester	Ilfracombe, Barnstaple 7/04, Slimbridge (Dual) 12/04, Bideford 9/05, Cirencester 1/06, Clevedon T 3/07, Forest Green 8/08, Gloucester (L) 8/08, Gloucester (SL) 2/09, Gloucester 5/09 Rel 5/11, Worcester 6/11	39	18
Michael	Taylor							Earlswood, Worcester 8/11, Stourport (L) 9/11	23	5

WORKINGTON

Chairman: Humphrey Dobie
Secretary: Steve Durham **(T)** 07899 938 156 **(E)** sbj.durham@btinternet.com
Additional Committee Members:
Colin Doorbar, Alec Graham, Thex Johnston, Dave Wilson, Paul Armstrong.

Manager: Darren Edmondson
Programme Editor: Paul Armstrong **(E)** paul@workingtonafc.com

Back row (left to right) Sue Pollock, Kyle May, Jordan Connerton, Gareth Arnison, Niall Cowperthwaite, Aaran Taylor,
David Hewson (captain), Shaun Routledge, Jonny Wright, Stefan Scott, Dan Wordsworth, Chris Wraighte, Lee Andrews, Alan Clark.
Front row (left to right) Phil McLuckie, Mark Boyd, Jake Simpson, Darren Edmondson (manager), Humphrey Dobie (chairman),
Tony Elliott (assistant manager), Gari Rowntree, Anthony Wright, Mark Sloan.

Club Factfile

Founded: 1884 **Nickname:** Reds
Previous Names: None
Previous Leagues: Cumberland Assoc. 1890-94, Cumberland Senior 1894-1901, 03-04. Lancashire 1901-03,
Lancashire Comb. 1904-10, North Eastern 1910-11, 21-51, Football League 1951-77, N.P.L. 1977-2005

Club Colours (change): Red/white/red (Cream/red/cream)

Ground: Borough Park, Workington, Cumbria CA14 2DT **(T)** 01900 602 871
Capacity: 2,500 **Seats:** 500 **Covered:** 1,000 **Clubhouse:** Yes **Shop:** Yes
Directions: A66 into Workington. At traffic lights at bottom of hill (HSBC opposite), turn left towards town centre. Approach traffic lights in centre lane (Washington Central Hotel on your right) and turn right. Continue on this road, passing over a mini roundabout, a pedestrian crossing and a further set of traffic lights. You will come to the Railway Station (facing you), carry on through the junction and bear right, passing the Derwent Park Stadium (Rugby League/speedway), then left and Borough Park becomes visible ahead of you.

Previous Grounds: Various 1884-1921, Lonsdale Park 1921-37

Record Attendance: 21,000 v Manchester United - FA Cup 3rd round 04/01/1958
Record Victory: 17-1 v Cockermouth Crusaders - Cumberland Senior League 19/01/1901
Record Defeat: 0-9 v Chorley (A) - Northern Premier League 10/11/1987
Record Goalscorer: Billy Charlton - 193
Record Appearances: Bobby Brown - 419
Additional Records: Paid £6,000 to Sunderland for Ken Chisolm 1956
Received £33,000 from Liverpool for Ian McDonald 1974
Senior Honours:
North West Counties League 1998-99
Cumberland County Cup x23

10 YEAR RECORD									
02-03	03-04	04-05	05-06	06-07	07-08	08-09	09-10	10-11	11-12
NP 1 10	NP 1 7	NP P 2	Conf N 13	Conf N 3	Conf N 14	Conf N 12	Conf N 4	Conf N 11	Conf N 13

WORKINGTON

No.	Date	Comp	H/A	Opponents	Att:	Result	Goalscorers	Pos
1	Sat-13-Aug	BSN	H	Boston United	585	L 1-2	Arnison pen 70	17
2	Tue-16-Aug	BSN	A	Altrincham	774	D 1-1	McNiven 28	18
3	Sat-20-Aug	BSN	A	Gloucester City	345	L 0-2		20
4	Tue-23-Aug	BSN	H	Stalybridge Celtic	406	L 2-5	Simpson 31, Hewson 35	21
5	Sat-27-Aug	BSN	H	Droylsden	308	W 3-1	Arnison 15, J Wright 2 (59, 88)	17
6	Mon-29-Aug	BSN	A	Colwyn Bay	390	L 0-1		20
7	Sat-03-Sep	BSN	A	FC Halifax Town	1433	L 1-3	Green 1	21
8	Sat-10-Sep	BSN	H	Hyde FC	383	L 0-3		21
9	Sat-17-Sep	BSN	H	Corby Town	372	D 1-1	Andrews 51	22
10	Tue-20-Sep	BSN	A	Gainsborough Trinity	472	L 0-2		22
11	Sat-24-Sep	BSN	A	Vauxhall Motors	158	W 1-0	Green 73	21
12	Sat-08-Oct	BSN	H	Guiseley	349	L 1-3	Simpson 77	21
13	Sat-22-Oct	BSN	A	Boston United	1114	L 1-2	Arnison 20	22
14	Tue-25-Oct	BSN	H	Harrogate Town	322	W 2-1	A Wright 46, Hewson 65	20
15	Sat-29-Oct	BSN	A	Histon	360	L 0-2		21
16	Sat-05-Nov	BSN	H	Hinckley United	360	W 3-1	McLuckie 2 (3, 63), Simpson 90	19
17	Sat-12-Nov	BSN	A	Nuneaton Town	712	L 1-2	J Wright 20	19
18	Sat-19-Nov	BSN	H	Vauxhall Motors	406	W 2-1	Johnson 7, Andrews 12	18
19	Sat-03-Dec	BSN	A	Guiseley	384	L 1-2	Arnison 75	19
20	Tue-06-Dec	BSN	H	FC Halifax Town	410	L 1-2	Arnison 45	19
21	Sat-17-Dec	BSN	A	Eastwood Town	209	W 3-0	Og (Caines) 36, Arnison 2 (41, 50)	17
22	Mon-26-Dec	BSN	H	Blyth Spartans	590	W 2-0	Arnison 66, McLuckie 69	17
23	Mon-02-Jan	BSN	A	Blyth Spartans	641	W 3-0	McLuckie 35, McNiven 2 (57, 60)	16
24	Sat-07-Jan	BSN	H	Nuneaton Town	466	D 1-1	Simpson 50	16
25	Sat-14-Jan	BSN	H	Altrincham	473	L 1-2	McNiven 70	18
26	Sat-21-Jan	BSN	A	Bishops Stortford	466	D 1-1	Hewson 16	18
27	Sat-28-Jan	BSN	H	Worcester City	366	D 0-0		17
28	Sat-11-Feb	BSN	H	Eastwood Town	319	W 3-0	Hewson 4, McLuckie 60, J Wright 73	16
29	Sat-18-Feb	BSN	A	Stalybridge Celtic	501	W 3-1	J Wright 2 (6, 45), Arnison 44	15
30	Tue-21-Feb	BSN	H	Gainsborough Trinity	250	L 0-2		16
31	Sat-25-Feb	BSN	A	Solihull Moors	220	L 1-2	Hewson 90	17
32	Sat-03-Mar	BSN	H	Gloucester City	375	W 3-0	Arnison pen 11, Boyd 24, J Wright 84	13
33	Mon-05-Mar	BSN	A	Hyde FC	528	L 0-4		14
34	Sat-10-Mar	BSN	A	Hinckley United	435	L 2-4	Boyd 18, Arnison 20	18
35	Sat-17-Mar	BSN	H	Bishops Stortford	377	D 1-1	Scott 18	18
36	Sat-24-Mar	BSN	A	Harrogate Town	430	W 1-0	McLuckie 8	17
37	Sat-31-Mar	BSN	H	Solihull Moors	382	D 1-1	Connerton 14	15
38	Sat-07-Apr	BSN	A	Droylsden	245	D 1-1	Beck 68	18
39	Mon-09-Apr	BSN	H	Colwyn Bay	514	W 3-1	Arnison 12, May 50, McLuckie 52	15
40	Sat-14-Apr	BSN	A	Corby Town	290	D 3-3	McLuckie 34, Boyd 69, A Wight 77	16
41	Sat-21-Apr	BSN	H	Histon	649	D 0-0		17
42	Sat-28-Apr	BSN	A	Worcester City	818	W 1-0	Connerton 75	13

CUPS

No.	Date	Comp	H/A	Opponents	Att:	Result	Goalscorers	
1	Sat-01-Oct	FAC 2Q	H	Droylsden	316	L 1-2	May 90	
2	Sat-26-Nov	FAT 3Q	A	Boston United	743	L 0-1		

League
Starts
Substitute
Unused Sub

Cups
Starts
Substitute
Unused Sub

Goals (Lg)
Goals (Cup)

	TAYLOR	HOPPER	A WRIGHT	MAY	ANDREWS	BOYD	GREEN	DILLON	J WRIGHT	ARNISON	MCLUCKIE	MCNIVEN	SIMPSON	MAIN	TUCKER	BLAKE	M SLOAN	HEWSON	MURRAY-JONES	WORDSWORTH	SMYTH	GALL	ROWNTREE	JOHNSON	SNAITH	MCLELLAN	SCOTT	HALL	BERKELEY	FLYNN	CONNERTON	BECK	ROBERTS	ROUTLEDGE
	X	X	X	X	X	X	X	X	X	X	X	S	S		S	U		U																
	X	X	X	X	X	X			X	X	X	X	X		S	U	S		U		S													
	X	X	X	X	X	X			X	X	X	X	X		S	U			U	S	U													
	X	S	X	X	X	X			X	X	X	X			U			U		S	X	S												
	X	S	X	X	X	X			X	X	X	X	U	X				U		X			S	S										
	X	X	X	X	X	X	S	S	X	X	X		S		X			U		X			X	X										
	X	X	X			X	X	X		X	X			X	S	S	U	S		U			X											
	X		X			X	X	X	X	X	X	X	U	S	S			X			X	U	S											
	X		X		X	X		S	X	X	X	X	U	S	S			U			X	X	X											
	X	U	X	X		X		S	X	X	X	S	S	U				X			X	X	X											
	X	U	X		X	X			X	X	X		S	S			U	U		X			X											
	X	X	X	X	X	X	X			X	X	S	X	S	U			U			X		X											
	X	X	X	X	X	X		S		X	X	X	S	S			U	U			X			X										
	X		X	X	X	U				X	X	X	S	S	S		U	S			X			X										
	X		X	X	S	S				X	X	X			X	X	U	S			X			X										
	X		X	X	X	U				X	X	X	S	S	U			X					X	X	S									
	X		X	X	X	X				X	X		U		X	X		U	U				X	X	S									
	X		X	X	X	U				X	X	S	U	U	X			X					X	X	S									
	X		X	X		U	X			X	X		S	X	X			X					X	X		S								
	X		X	X	X	U				X	X		X	X	X			X					X	X		S	S							
	X		X	X	X					X	X		U	S	X			X					X	X		S	S	S						
	X		X	X	X					X	X			X	U	S		X		U			X	X	S	S	S							
	X		X	X	X					X	X		X	S	X			S	X				X	U			S							
	X		X	X	X	U				X	X		X	X	X	S		U	X				U	X			U							
	X		X	X	X	S				X	X		X	X	U			S	X		X			U			X							
	X		X	X	X	S				X	X		X	X	S			U	X		X			S			U							
	X		X	X	S	X				X	X		X	X	U			U	X		X			S			S							
	X		X	X	S	X				X	X		X	X	S			S	X		X			S			U	U						
	X		X	X	X	U				X	X			U				S	X		X			X			S	S						
	X		X	U	X	X				X	X		X	U				S	X		X			X			S	S						
	X		X	X	X	U				X	X		X	U	S	S		X	X		X			X				S						
	X		X	X	X	S				X	X		S	U	S		U	X	X		X			X			X							
	X		X	X	X	X				X	X			S	U		U	X	X		X								X	X	S	S		
	X		X	X	X	X				X	X			S	U		U	X	X		X								U	X	X	S		
	X		X	X	X	U				X	X			S	U		U	X	X		X								S	X	X	X		
	X		X	X	X	X	U			X	X				X	X		U	X		X		U						S	X	X	S		
	X		X	X	X	X	S			X	X			X	X			S	X		X		U				U		S	X	X			
	X		X	X	X	X				X	X			X	X			S	X		X			S			S		S	X	X		U	
	X		X	X	X	X				X	X				X			S	X		X						S		S	U	X	X		U
	X	X	X	X	X	X	X			X	X	S	S				S	X					X											
	X		X	X		S			X	X	X	X	S	S	X			X								X	X	U						
Apps	42	7	42	39	39	32	11	7	24	39	38	12	9	12	0	0	0	37	0	20	4	4	17	12	0	0	1	0	1	6	6	1	0	0
Subs	0	2	0	0	0	7	10	0	1	2	1	9	19	11	2	0	13	1	1	1	1	4	0	6	5	6	2	5	0	1	3	0	0	
	0	1	0	0	1	3	7	0	0	0	0	9	5	12	1	9	18	0	1	3	1	0	5	0	1	0	5	1	2	0	0	0	1	1
	2	1	2	2	2	1	1	0	1	2	2	0	0	1	0	0	0	2	0	0	0	1	1	1	0	0	0	0	0	0	0	0	0	0
	0	0	0	0	0	0	0	1	0	0	0	0	0	2	2	0	0	0	1	0	0	0	0	0	0	0	0	0	0	0	0	0	0	0
	0	0	0	0	0	0	0	0	0	0	0	0	0	0	0	0	0	0	0	0	0	0	0	1	0	0	0	0	0	0	0	0	0	0
	0	0	1	1	2	3	2	0	7	12	8	4	4	0	0	0	5	0	0	0	0	1	0	0	1	0	0	1	0	0	2	1	0	0
	0	0	0	1	0	0	0	0	0	0	0	0	0	0	0	0	0	0	0	0	0	0	0	0	0	0	0	0	0	0	0	0	0	0

PLAYING SQUAD 2012/13

Existing Players		SN	HT	WT	DOB	AGE	POB	Career	Apps	Goals
GOALKEEPERS										
Shaun	Routledge				30/12/1992	19		Oldham (Scholar), Morecambe Rel 2/12, Workington 3/12	0	0
Aaron	Taylor				20/11/1986	25		Annan Ath, Penrith, Workington c/s 07, Barrow 7/08 Rel 9/08, Penrith,		
								Workington (Trial) 2/09, Workington 3/09	42	0
DEFENDERS										
Lee	Andrews	6'00"	11 06		23/04/1983	29	Carlisle	Carlisle Rel 5/06, Rochdale (L) 2/03, York (2ML) 11/05, Torquay (L) 3/06,		
								Torquay 5/06 Rel c/s 07, Newcastle Blue Star 9/07,		
								Workington 1/08	39	2
Niall	Cowperthwaite	5'11"	11 00		28/01/1992	20	Barrow	Morecambe Rel c/s 12, Workington 7/12		
Kyle	May				07/09/1982	29	Doncaster	Carlisle Rel c/s 02, Gretna 8/02, Workington (5ML) 8/04,		
								Workington 1/05	39	1
Phil	McLuckie				13/04/1989	23		Morecambe, Workington (3ML) 12/07 Perm 3/08	39	8
Gari	Rowntree				05/10/1986	25		Carlisle (Yth), Blackburn, Workington 3/07	21	0
Dan	Wordsworth						Carlisle	Carlisle Rel 1/09, Kendal T (L) 9/08, Kendal T (L) 11/08, Kendal T 1/09,		
								Workington (Trial) c/s 10, Harraby Catholic Club,		
								Workington 7/11	21	0
MIDFIELDERS										
Marc	Boyd	5'10"	12 04		22/10/1981	30	Carlisle	Newcastle Rel c/s 02, Carlisle (Trial) 3/02, Port Vale 7/02,		
								Carlisle 3/04 Rel c/s 04, Gretna 7/04 Rel 1/06, Macclesfield (SL) 1/05,		
								Accrington 2/06, Southport 6/06, Sligo R c/s 07, Barrow 1/08,		
								Droylsden (L) 1/11 Perm 1/11, Workington 6/11	39	3
David	Hewson				05/05/1983	29		Gretna, Workington, Harraby CC (L)	38	5
Jake	Simpson	5'11"	12 03		27/10/1990	21	Oxford	Blackburn (Scholar), Shrewsbury 7/09 Rel c/s 10, Carlisle (Trial) c/s 10,		
								Morecambe (Trial) c/s 10, Wrexham (Trial) c/s 10, Tranmere (Trial) c/s 10,		
								Stockport 9/10 Rel c/s 11, Hyde FC (L) 3/11, Workington 8/11	28	4
Chris	Wraighte				08/03/1992	20		Morecambe Rel c/s 11, Kendal (L) 11/10, Crookland Casuals,		
								Workington 7/12		
Anthony	Wright				13/04/1986	26		Penrith, Workington 6/06	42	1
FORWARDS										
Gareth	Arnison				18/09/1986	25		Morecambe, Workington 8/05, Kendal (L) 12/06 Perm 1/07,		
								Workington 8/08	41	12
Jordan	Connerton	5'11"	12 08		02/10/1989	22	Lancaster	Lancaster, Marsh U, Chorley, Kendal T 1/09, Lancaster 6/09,		
								Crewe Undisc 3/10 Rel c/s 12, Lancaster (SL) 3/10, Nantwich (L) 9/10,		
								IBV (Ice) (2ML) 5/11, Kendal T (2ML) 11/11, Nantwich (L) 1/12,		
								Workington (SL) 3/12, Workington 7/12	7	2
Ryan	Hall							Workington	2	0
Stefan	Scott							Workington	7	1
Mark	Sloan	5'09"			07/09/1992	19		Carlisle U (Scholar) Rel c/s 11, Workington (SL) 3/11,		
								Workington 7/11	13	0
Johnny	Wright				31/10/1985	26		Whitehaven Amateurs, Workington 8/07	25	7

AFC HORNCHURCH

Chairman: Colin McBride
Secretary: Peter Butcher   **(T)** 07918 645109   **(E)** peter.butcher5@btinternet.com
Additional Committee Members:
Ken Hunt, David Crown, Tony Bowditch, Wayne Slade, Colin Burford.

Manager: Jim McFarlane
Programme Editor: Peter Butcher   **(E)** peter.butcher5@btinternet.com

The Eastside Stand.

Club Factfile

Founded: 2005   **Nickname:** The Urchins
Previous Names: Formed in 2005 after Hornchurch F.C. folded
Previous Leagues: Hornchurch F.C. Athenian, Isthmian, Conference. Since 2005: Essex Senior

Club Colours (change): Red and white stripes/black/black (Purple & white/black/black)

Ground: The Stadium, Bridge Avenue, Upminster, Essex RM14 2LX   **(T)** 01708 220 080
Capacity: 3,500   **Seats:** 800   **Covered:** 1,400   **Clubhouse:** Yes   **Shop:** Yes
Directions Bridge Avenue is off A124 between Hornchurch and Upminster.

Previous Grounds:

Record Attendance: 3,500 v Tranmere Rovers - FA Cup 2nd Round 2003-04
Record Victory: Not known
Record Defeat: Not known
Record Goalscorer: Not known
Record Appearances: Not known
Additional Records: Won the Essex League with a record 64 points in 2005-06

Senior Honours:
Since reformation in 2005: Essex Senior League, League Cup and Memorial Trophy 2005-06.
Isthmian League Division 1 North 2006-07, Premier Division Play-offs 2011-12.

10 YEAR RECORD

02-03		03-04		04-05		05-06		06-07		07-08		08-09		09-10		10-11		11-12	
Isth1N	2	Isth P	5	Conf S	17	ESen	1	Isth1N	1	Isth P	4	Isth P	6	Isth P	9	Isth P	10	Isth P	2

A.F.C. HORNCHURCH

No.	Date	Comp	H/A	Opponents	Att:	Result	Goalscorers	Pos
1	21	Isth P	A	Cray Wanderers	173	W 5 - 2	Spencer 39 Tuohy 45 49 Black 83 Flack 90	
2	23		H	Canvey Island	270	L 1 - 2	Styles 18	
3	27		H	Horsham	200	L 0 - 2		14
4	29		A	Lowestoft Town	727	L 1 - 2	Gayle 78	
5	Sept 3		A	Met Police	171	W 2 - 0	Tuohy 72 Flack 78	12
6	10		H	Tooting & Mitcham U	221	W 6 - 0	TUOHY 3 (3 30 85) Hunt 29 Smith 49 Spencer 90	8
7	13		A	Aveley	301	W 3 - 2	Styles 2 Smith 50 Tuohy 81	6
8	17	FAC 1Q	H	Concord Rangers	280	L 1 - 3	Eyong 42	
9	24		H	Wealdstone	267	D 1 - 1	Smith 64	8
10	27		A	Margate	254	W 2 - 0	Spencer 46 76	
11	Oct 1		H	Wingate & Finchley	221	W 1 - 0	Hayles 50	5
12	4		H	Bury Town	197	L 0 - 1		
13	8		A	East Thurrock	255	W 1 - 0	L.Smith 18	6
14	15		H	Kingstonian	281	W 3 - 0	Tuohy 68 Smith 71 Curley 80	1
15	22	FAT 1Q	A	Wingate & Finchley	162	W 2 - 1	L.Smith 30 89	
16	29		A	Lewes	642	W 4 - 0	Tuohy 49 66 Smith 78 Anderson 90	1
17	Nov 5	FAT 2Q	A	Harrow Borough	123	D 1 - 1	Styles 12	
18	8	FAT 2Qr	H	Harrow Borough	176	W 1 - 0	Thompson 29	
19	14		A	Concord Rangers	182	W 2 - 1	Curley 76 Smith 79	2
20	19		A	Hastings United	399	W 3 - 1	Tuohy 22 Smith 23 Hunt 71	
21	22		H	Carshalton Athletic	219	D 1 - 1	Curley 62	2
22	26	FAT 3Q	A	Thurrock	211	W 5 - 0	Hunt 7 Tuohy 36 Glover 48 L.Smith 69 Spencer 90	
23	20		H	Hendon	187	L 0 - 1		
24	Dec 3		A	Leatherhead	305	W 1 - 0	Tuohy 90	3
25	10	FAT 1	H	Farnborough	302	D 0 - 0		
26	14	FAT 1r	A	Farnborough	204	W 3 - 2	Tuohy 11 49 L.Smith 73	
27	17		H	Aveley	266	W 2 - 1	Tuohy 24 Noel 47	3
28	27		A	Billericay Town	1106	W 1 - 0	Black 59	4
29	31		A	Canvey Island	428	L 1 - 4	Tuohy 75	
30	Jan 2		H	Lowestoft Town	450	W 3 - 0	Tuohy 26 L.Smith 63 Anderson 76	3
31	7		A	Wingate & Finchley	150	W 2 - 1	Tuohy 5 L.Smith 50	2
32	10		H	Harrow Borough	232	D 0 - 0		
33	14	FAT 2	A	Grimsby Town	2415	L 0 - 4		
34	21		A	Bury Town	456	L 1 - 2	Hunt 83	2
35	28		H	East Thurrock United	357	W 1 - 0	Smith 90	2
36	Feb 18		H	Lewes	298	W 1 - 0	Tuohy 32	2
37	25		A	Kingstonian	299	W 2 - 0	Tuohy 7 62	2
38	March 3		H	Concord Rangers	328	W 2 - 0	Tuohy 20 Orilonishe 48	2
39	6		H	Hastings United	209	L 0 - 1		
40	10		A	Hendon	209	L 0 - 2		2
41	13		A	Carshalton Athletic	138	W 2 - 1	L.Smith 27 61	
42	17		H	Cray Wanderers	287	L 1 - 2	Tuohy 71	2
43	24		A	Horsham	199	W 3 - 0	Tuohy 37 Smith 62 McKenzie 77	
44	27		H	Margate	220	W 3 - 0	Tuohy 11 78 Smith 33	2
45	31		H	Met Police	265	W 1 - 0	Tuohy 44	
46	Apr 6		A	Tooting & Mitcham U	262	W 2 - 1	Tuohy 83 86 (pen)	
47	9		H	Billericay Town	1095	D 0 - 0		
48	14		A	Wealdstone	538	L 1 - 2	Smith 59	2
49	21		A	Harrow Borough	203	L 0 - 1		2
50	28		H	Leatherhead	247	W 2 - 1	Rook 19 McKenzie 46	
51	May 2	Play Off SF	H	Bury Town	646	W 3 1	Smith 48 Tuohy 52 Rook 71	
52	7	Play Off F	H	Lowestoft Town	1411	W 2 1*	Mackenzie 94 Spencer 119	

PLAYING SQUAD 2012/13

Existing Players		SN	HT	WT	DOB	AGE	POB	Career	Apps	Goals
GOALKEEPERS										
Michael	Bowditch							AFC Hornchurch		
Joe	Woolley				20/09/1989	22		Charlton (Yth), Grays c/s 08 Rel 8/08, Thurrock 10/08, Harlow (Dual) 3/11, Chelmsford 8/11 Rel 9/11, AFC Hornchurch 9/11		
DEFENDERS										
Joe	Anderson		5'11"	11 05	13/10/1989	22	Stepney	Fulham, Woking (SL) 2/09, Lincoln C Undisc 1/10 Rel c/s 11, AFC Hornchurch 8/11		
Alex	Bentley							Millwall, Fisher (WE) 10/08 Perm, Dag & Red 8/09 Rel c/s 10, Aveley (L) 12/09, Bishops Stortford (L) 1/10, Cray W 7/10, AFC Hornchurch 6/12		
Paul	Goodacre				15/07/1984	28		Burnham Ramblers, Maldon T 8/02, Bishops Stortford 6/06 Rel 10/09, Braintree 10/09, Dartford 5/10 Rel c/s 12, AFC Hornchurch 6/12		
Dave	McSweeney		5'11"	11 07	28/12/1981	30	Basildon	Southend Rel c/s 04, Welling (L) 3/04, Billericay 8/04, Grays 6/09 Rel 8/09, Billericay Rel 3/10, AFC Hornchurch c/s 10		
Reiss	Noel				19/10/1989	22		Southend, St Albans 7/07 Rel 5/08, Potters Bar 11/08, Enfield T 1/09, Eastleigh, Aveley, Brentwood 10/09, Woking 12/10, AFC Hornchurch 6/11		
Elliot	Styles							Ilford, Redbridge, AFC Hornchurch		
MIDFIELDERS										
Tommy	Black		5'07"	11 10	26/11/1979	32	Chigwell	Arsenal, Carlisle (L) 8/99, Bristol C (L) 12/99, C.Palace £250,000 7/00 Rel c/s 07, Sheff U (L) 9/04, Gillingham (SL) 1/06, Bradford C (L) 11/06, Southend 7/07 Rel c/s 08, Stevenage 10/08 Rel 1/09, Barnet 1/09 Rel 2/09, Grays NC 3/09 Rel c/s 09, Grays 8/09 Rel 8/09, Hemel Hempstead 9/09, AFC Hornchurch 4/10		
Sam	Cutler				11/02/1990	21	Sidcup	Cambridge U, Weymouth 5/08, Grays 8/09, Torquay (Trial), Welling 11/09, Dover 7/10 Rel 12/11, Thurrock 12/11, AFC Hornchurch 6/12		
Frankie	Curley							Redbridge, AFC Hornchurch 11/07, Time Out, Aveley, AFC Hornchurch 10/10		
Tambeson	Eyong		6'00"		21/09/1989	22	Denmark Hill	West Ham (Yth), Dag & Red, Gretna, Aveley, Harlow, AFC Hornchurch 3/10		
Simon	Glover				03/05/1982	30		Wycombe (Yth), Faversham, Ashford T 2/00, Welling c/s 00, Ashford T (L) 10/01, Fisher 1/02, Dover 3/02 (01/02 1,0), Ashford T (2ML) 1/04, Folkestone I 5/04, Heybridge 10/05, Ashford T c/s 06, Bromley 6/07 Rel 3/08, Tonbridge A 3/08, Chelmsford 7/09, Maidstone 6/10, AFC Hornchurch c/s 11		
Jonathan	Hunt		5'10"	11 11	02/11/1971	40	Camden	Barnet, Southend 7/93, Birmingham 9/94, Derby 5/97, Sheff Utd (L) 8/98, Ipswich (L) 10/98, Sheff Utd 3/99, Cambridge U (SL) 3/00, Wimbledon 9/00 Rel c/s 01, Reading (Trial) 10/01, Peterborough 9/02 Rel 10/02, Out of football, St Albans 2/08, Harrow c/s 09, AFC Hornchurch 10/09		
FORWARDS										
Aaron	Gayle							Eton Manor, Clapton, Redbridge, Barking 3/08, Potters Bar, Waltham Abbey 12/08, Bromley 3/10, Waltham Abbey, Chesham 11/10, AFC Hornchurch c/s 11		
James	Love							Heybridge, Brentwood 1/11, AFC Hornchurch 1/12		
Leon	McKenzie				18/10/1984	27		L.Orient, Waltham Forest, Thurrock 6/06 Rel 12/08, Luton (Trial) 12/08, Grays 12/08 Rel 1/09, Bishops Stortford 6/09, Thurrock 9/09, Bromley 8/10, Billericay 8/10, Boreham Wood 9/10 Rel 10/10, Bromley 10/10, Grays (Dual) 11/11 Perm Rel 1/12, AFC Hornchurch 2/12		
Lewis	Smith				27/10/1989	22		Fulham Rel 3/09, Bishops Stortford (SL) 12/08 Perm 3/09, Gillingham (Trial) 3/09, Bournemouth 4/09, Bishops Stortford 8/09, Chelmsford 1/10 Rel 2/10, Thurrock 2/10, AFC Hornchurch 8/10		
Martin	Tuohy				04/05/1984	28		Barking, Redbridge, East Thurrock, Aveley (L) 8/06 Perm, Great Wakering 1/07, East Thurrock 6/08, Aveley c/s 09, Braintree 6/10, AFC Hornchurch 8/10		

Conference Action...

Conference South side Basingstoke Town in action during their
FA Trophy First Round match against Didcot Town which the
'Dragons' won 1-0..

Photo: Peter Barnes.

BASINGSTOKE TOWN

Chairman: Rafi Razzak
Secretary: Richard Trodd   **(T)** 07887 507 447   **(E)** richard.trodd@ntlworld.com
Additional Committee Members:
Ian Halloway, David Knight, Sarah Parsons, Geoff Yates, David Partridge, Paul Waller,
Lee Atkins, Martin Beckingham, Dean Coombs.
Manager: Jason Bristow
Programme Editor: David Knight & Sam Morris   **(E)** d.knight@barrelfield.co.uk

Back Row L-R: Alex Charlick, Nathan Campbell, Chris Paterson, Stefan Brown, Delano Sam-Yorke, Shaun McAuley, Joe McDonnell, Ross Adams, Ashley Bayes, Stuart Lake, Jay Gasson, Tim Sills, Rob Rice, Nathan Smart, Matthew Warner.
Front Row L-R: Kieron Maylen, Jordace Holder-Spooner, Wes Daly, Jason Bristow (Manager), Kevin Braybrook (Ass Manager), Jide Ogunbote, Toby Little, Simon Dunn.

Club Factfile

Founded: 1896   **Nickname:** Dragons
Previous Names: None
Previous Leagues: Hampshire 1900-40, 45-71, Southern 1971-87, Isthmian 1987-2004

Club Colours (change): Blue and yellow/blue/yellow (All red)

Ground: Camrose Ground, Western Way, Basingstoke RG22 6EZ   **(T)** 01256 327 575
Capacity: 6,000   **Seats:** 651   **Covered:** 2,000   **Clubhouse:** Yes   **Shop:** Yes

Directions: Leave M3 at junction 6 and turn left onto South Ringway which is the A30.
Straight over first roundabout. At second roundabout turn left into Winchester Road.
Proceed past ground on right to roundabout.
Take fifth exit into Western Way. Ground on right.

Previous Grounds: Castle Field 1896-1947

Record Attendance: 5,085 v Wycombe Wanderers - FA Cup 1st Round replay 1997-98
Record Victory: 10-1 v Chichester City (H) - FA Cup 1st Qualifying Round 1976
Record Defeat: 0-8 v Aylesbury United - Southern League April 1979
Record Goalscorer: Paul Coombs - 159 (1991-99)
Record Appearances: Billy Coomb
Additional Records: Paid £4,750 to Gosport Borough for Steve Ingham

Senior Honours:
Hampshire League 1967-68, 69-70, 70-71. Southern League Southern Division 1984-85.
Hampshire Senior Cup 1970-71, 89-90, 95-96, 2007-08.

10 YEAR RECORD

02-03		03-04		04-05		05-06		06-07		07-08		08-09		09-10		10-11		11-12	
Isth P	5	Isth P	14	Conf S	6	Conf S	19	Conf S	19	Conf S	15	Conf S	18	Conf S	15	Conf S	13	Conf S	5

BASINGSTOKE TOWN

No.	Date	Comp	H/A	Opponents	Att:	Result	Goalscorers	Pos
1	Sat-13-Aug	BSS	A	Eastleigh	611	W 2-0	Sam-Yorke 2 (13, 28)	5
2	Tue-16-Aug	BSS	H	Weston-Super-Mare	374	W 4-1	Lake 5, Pratt 2 (7, 29), Warner 90	3
3	Sat-20-Aug	BSS	H	Sutton United	424	L 1-2	Sam-Yorke 90	7
4	Mon-22-Aug	BSS	A	Boreham Wood	202	D 1-1	Sam-Yorke 68	4
5	Sat-27-Aug	BSS	A	Woking	1207	L 0-1		11
6	Mon-29-Aug	BSS	H	Hampton & Richmond Boro'	415	D 2-2	Daly 25, Dunn 73	11
7	Sat-03-Sep	BSS	H	Dartford	493	W 3-2	Sam-Yorke 6, Little 34, McAuley 53	10
8	Sat-10-Sep	BSS	A	Dover Athletic	861	D 0-0		10
9	Sat-17-Sep	BSS	H	Dorchester Town	336	W 1-0	Sills 45	7
10	Tue-20-Sep	BSS	A	Salisbury City	731	D 1-1	Sills 84	8
11	Sat-24-Sep	BSS	H	Farnborough	614	W 4-3	McAuley 2 (32, 88), Sam-Yorke 55, Sills 70	5
12	Sat-08-Oct	BSS	A	Truro City	521	W 5-2	Sam-Yorke 13, Sills 2 (18, 53), Lake 30, McAuley 83	5
13	Sat-22-Oct	BSS	A	Tonbridge Angels	579	W 3-2	McAuley 2 (26, 84), Smart 54	5
14	Tue-25-Oct	BSS	H	Staines Town	341	D 1-1	McAuley 55	5
15	Sat-05-Nov	BSS	A	Dorchester Town	491	L 1-2	Sills 63	6
16	Sat-19-Nov	BSS	A	Eastbourne Borough	628	W 2-0	Bubb 20, Sills 71	6
17	Tue-22-Nov	BSS	H	Boreham Wood	309	D 1-1	Little 60	6
18	Tue-13-Dec	BSS	H	Welling United	336	L 0-1		8
19	Sat-17-Dec	BSS	H	Chelmsford City	434	D 1-1	Daly pen 44	8
20	Mon-26-Dec	BSS	A	Maidenhead United	314	D 1-1	Ogunbote 74	7
21	Sat-31-Dec	BSS	H	Maidenhead United	362	L 1-3	Bubb 51	7
22	Sat-07-Jan	BSS	A	Bromley	423	W 3-1	Warner 12, Og (Harwood) 25, Daly 83	9
23	Tue-10-Jan	BSS	A	Weston-Super-Mare	304	L 1-2	MacDonald 38	9
24	Sat-21-Jan	BSS	H	Eastleigh	404	W 1-0	Sills 75	9
25	Sat-28-Jan	BSS	A	Farnborough	411	L 0-1		9
26	Tue-14-Feb	BSS	A	Salisbury City	407	D 2-2	Sam-Yorke 2 (16, 69)	9
27	Sat-18-Feb	BSS	A	Sutton United	502	L 0-1		10
28	Sat-25-Feb	BSS	H	Thurrock	391	W 3-1	Sills 18, Daly pen 27, McAuley 29	9
29	Mon-27-Feb	BSS	A	Dartford	783	L 1-4	Lake 56	9
30	Sat-03-Mar	BSS	A	Staines Town	411	W 2-0	Sills 4, Pratt 87	7
31	Tue-06-Mar	BSS	H	Tonbridge Angels	312	L 0-2		7
32	Sat-10-Mar	BSS	H	Dover Athletic	438	D 1-1	McAuley 58	7
33	Sat-17-Mar	BSS	H	Bromley	312	W 1-0	Sam-Yorke 51	7
34	Tue-20-Mar	BSS	H	Truro City	318	W 2-1	Og (Pugh) 6, Sam-Yorke 45	7
35	Sat-24-Mar	BSS	A	Chelmsford City	865	W 1-0	Daly 23	7
36	Sat-31-Mar	BSS	H	Havant & Waterlooville	481	W 3-2	Ogunbote 18, Og (Dolan) 33, Smart 54	7
37	Fri-06-Apr	BSS	A	Woking	1198	L 0-3		7
38	Sat-14-Apr	BSS	A	Thurrock	211	W 2-1	Pratt 21, Sills 47	7
39	Mon-16-Apr	BSS	A	Havant & Waterlooville	724	W 1-0	Sam-Yorke 21	7
40	Sat-21-Apr	BSS	H	Eastbourne Borough	458	W 3-0	Sam-Yorke 10, Daly 57, McAuley 58	6
41	Tue-24-Apr	BSS	A	Hampton & Richmond Boro'	569	W 2-0	Sam-Yorke 25, Sills 56	5
42	Sat-28-Apr	BSS	A	Welling United	632	D 1-1	Old 26	5

CUPS

No.	Date	Comp	H/A	Opponents	Att:	Result	Goalscorers	
1	Sat-01-Oct	FAC 2Q	A	Frome Town	300	D 0-0		
2	Sat-04-Oct	FAC 2QR	H	Frome Town	262	W 3-0	Daly 13, Sam-Yorke 76, McAuley 83	
3	Sat-15-Oct	FAC 3Q	H	Hartley Wintney	577	W 4-0	Daly 9, Pratt 12, McAuley 20, Sills 27	
4	Sat-29-Oct	FAC 4Q	H	Staines Town	545	W 2-1	Gasson 37, McAuley 45	
5	Sat-12-Nov	FAC 1	A	Brentford	3553	L 0-1		
6	Sat-26-Nov	FAT 3Q	A	Sutton United	460	W 2-1	Bubb 7, Lake 84	
7	Sat-10-Dec	FAT 1	A	Didcot Town	259	W 1-0	McAuley 69	
8	Sat-14-Jan	FAT 2	A	Bath City	633	L 0-1		
9	Wed-02-May	PO SF1	H	Dartford	1691	L 0-1		
10	Sun-06-May	PO SF2	A	Dartford	2210	L 1-	McAuley 67	

	League
	Starts
	Substitute
	Unused Sub

	Cups
	Starts
	Substitute
	Unused Sub

	Goals (Lg)
	Goals (Cup)

BAYES	RICE	LITTLE	R ADAMS	GASSON	LAKE	DALY	MCAULEY	SILLS	SAM-YORKE	PRATT	OGUNBOTE	SMART	WARNER	GRADWELL	MORRIS	DUNN	GONDWE	EAGLE	CHARLICK	PARMENTER	DANSIE	T ADAMS	LOCKYER	BUBB	MACDONALD	MEKKI	ROUGA	BONDON	SOLE	OLD	MCDONNELL
X	X	X	X	X	X	X	X	X	X	X	X	S	U	U	U																
X	X	X	X	X	X	X	X	X	X	X	U	U	S	U	U																
X	X	X	X	X	X	X	X	X	X	X	U	S	U	S	S	U															
X	X	X	X	X	X	X	X	X	X	X	U	U	S	S	U																
X	X	X	X	X	X	X	X	X		X	S	S	X	S	X																
X	S	X	X	X		X	S	X		X	X	X	X	X	U	S		U													
X	S	X	X	X	X	X	X	X	X		X	U	S	U	U																
X	U	X	X	X	X	X	X	X	X	X		X	U	S	S	S															
X	S	X	X	X	X	X	X	X	X	X	U	X	S	S		U															
X	X	X		X	X	X	X	X	X	U	X	S	X	S	U	U															
X	X	X		X	X	X	X	X	X	U	X	S	X	S	U	U															
X		X	X	X	X	X	X	S		X	X	S	X	S	U	S	U			X											
X	U	X		X	X	X	X		S	X	U	X	X	X	U					X											
X	U	X		X	X	X	X	S		X	X	U	X	X	U	U				X											
X	X	X		X	X	X	X	X	S	X	S	X	X	S	U					U											
X	X	X		X	X	X	X			S	U	X	U	X	U	U								X							
X	X	X		X	X	X	X			X	U	X	S	U	U	U								X							
X		X		X	X	X	X			S	S	X	X	S										X	X	U	U				
X		X		X	X	X			S	S	X	X	U	U	U									X	X	X					
X	U	X		X	X	X			X	X	S	S	X	U		S								X	X	X					
U	X	U		X	X	X			X		X	X	S	X	S	X								X	X						
	X	U		X	X	X			X		X	X	X	X	S	X								X	X		U	U			
	X	X		X	X			X		S	X	X	X	X	S	X	S								X		U	U			
X	X	X		X	X	X	X		X	X	X	U	U		U	U	S								X						
X	X	X		X	X		X		X		U	X		X	U	S									X		U	U	X		
X	X	X		X	X		X			X	X	U	S	X	U	U			U									X	X		
X	X	U		X	X	X	X	X		X		U	U	X	S													X	X		
X	X	U		X	X	X	X	X	X	X	S	S	X	X	S		U											X			
X	X			X	X	X	X	X	X	X	S	X	X	U	S													X			
X		U		X	X	X	X	X	X	X	S	X	X	U	U													X	U		
X	U	S		X	X	X	X	X	X	X	U	X	X	X	U	U												X			
X	X	X		X	X	X	X	X	X	U	X	X	X	U	U		S												U		
X	X	S		X	X	X	X	X	X	X	U	X	X	U		S													U		
	X	U		X	X	X	X	X		U	X	X	U	X	U														U		
	X	U		X	X	X	X			X	S	X	X	U	X	U													S		
X	X	U		X	X	X	X	X	X	X	S	X	X	U															U	U	
X	X	U	S	X	X	X	X			X	X	X	X	S	U														U		
X	X	S	S	X	X	X	X			X	X	X	X	S		U													U		
X	X	U	X	X	X	X	X	X	X	X	S	S	X	X	U														U		
X	X	S	X	X		X	X	X	X	X	X	S	X	X	S														U	U	
X	X	X	X		X	X	X	X	X	X	S	X	X	U	U														U		
X	X	U	X	X		X	X	X	X	X	S	X	X	U															S	U	
X		X		X	X	X	X	X	X	S	X	S	X	S	X	U	U	U	U	U											
X		X		X	X	X	X	X	X	X	U	X	X	U	U	S	U	U	U												
X		X		X	X	X	X	X	X		X	S	X	X	U	S	U	S	U		X	U									
X	X	X		X	X		X		X	X	X	X	U	X	U	U	U	U			U										
X	X	X		X	X		X		X	X	X	S	X	X	X	U	U	U	U		U		S								
X	X			X	X	X	X			S	U	X	S	U	U										X	X	X				
X		X		X	X	X	X			U	U	X	U	U	U										X	X	X				
X	X	X		X	X	X	X	S	U			X	X	U	U	U	S								X						
X	X	U		X	X	X	X	X	X	X	U	X	X	U	U					U											
X	X	U	X	X	X	X	X	X	X	X	S	S	X	X						U										U	

37	29	25	13	42	36	40	37	38	29	20	18	33	27	4	5	0	0	0	0	3	0	0	0	7	8	2	0	0	3	6	0
0	3	4	2	0	0	0	1	1	4	16	9	2	8	20	2	10	0	0	0	0	0	0	0	0	0	0	0	0	0	2	0
1	5	13	0	0	0	0	0	0	0	3	12	7	5	16	23	14	2	1	1	1	0	0	0	0	0	0	4	4	0	7	6

10	6	7	1	10	10	9	10	10	5	3	3	10	7	1	0	0	0	0	1	0	0	0	2	3	2	0	0	0	0	0	0
0	0	0	0	0	0	0	0	0	1	3	3	0	2	1	0	3	0	0	0	0	0	0	1	0	0	0	0	0	0	0	0
0	0	2	0	0	0	0	0	0	4	3	0	1	7	10	3	5	2	4	1	1	0	0	0	0	0	0	0	0	0	1	0

| 0 | 0 | 2 | 0 | 0 | 3 | 6 | 10 | 12 | 14 | 4 | 2 | 2 | 2 | 0 | 0 | 1 | 0 | 0 | 0 | 0 | 0 | 0 | 2 | 1 | 0 | 0 | 0 | 1 | 0 | | |
| 0 | 0 | 0 | 0 | 1 | 1 | 2 | 5 | 1 | 1 | 1 | 0 | 0 | 0 | 0 | 0 | 0 | 0 | 0 | 0 | 0 | 0 | 0 | 1 | 0 | 0 | 0 | 0 | 0 | 0 | | |

PLAYING SQUAD 2012/13

Existing Players		SN	HT	WT	DOB	AGE	POB	Career	Apps	Goals
GOALKEEPERS										
Ashley	Bayes	6'01"	13 05		19/04/1972	40	Lincoln	Brentford Rel c/s 93, Torquay 8/93 Rel c/s 96, Exeter 7/96 Rel c/s 99,		
								L.Orient 7/99 Rel c/s 02, Bohemians (Ire) c/s 02, Woking 3/03,		
								Hornchurch 5/04, Grays 11/04 Rel 5/07, Crawley 6/07 Rel 5/08,		
								Stevenage 5/08, Basingstoke 6/11	37	0
Joe	McDonnell							Basingstoke, Benfica (Trial) 12/10	0	0
Chay	Morris							Wycombe (Scholar), Beaconsfield SYCOB 2/05, Arlesey, Burnham 8/09,		
								Hemel Hempstead 7/10, Burnham 8/10, Beaconsfield SYCOB 2/11,		
								Basingstoke 2/11, Hungerford (SL) 3/12	7	0
DEFENDERS										
Ross	Adams	5'11"	12 04		11/03/1983	29	Birmingham	Swindon (Sch), Highworth T, Chippenham 7/05, Basingstoke 5/10,		
								Swindon Supermarine (L) 2/12	15	0
Jay	Gasson				29/12/1984	27		Fulham (Yth), Croydon A, Whyteleafe 10/03, Croydon A 2/04,		
								Corinthian Casuals 7/04, Farnborough 6/05, Woking 6/07 Rel 5/08,		
								Havant & W 5/08, Basingstoke 5/10	42	0
Chris	Paterson							Hartley Wintney, Basingstoke 7/12		
Robert	Rice	5'08"	11 11		23/02/1989	23	Hendon	Fulham (Yth), Wycombe Rel c/s 09, Wealdstone (L) 1/08,		
								Basingstoke 6/09	32	0
Nathan	Smart				18/04/1985	27		Fleet T, Basingstoke 7/10	35	2
MIDFIELDERS										
Nathan	Campbell	6'03"						Chipstead, Croydon Ath, AFC Totton, Basingstoke 6/12		
Wes	Daly				07/03/1984	28		QPR, Gravesend (L) 10/03, Barnet (Trial) 12/03, Grays (L) 1/04,		
								Raith (L) 8/04, Grays 2/05, AFC Wimbledon c/s 05,		
								Maidenhead 7/07 Rel 5/08, Boreham Wood c/s 08, Carshalton c/s 09,		
								Hendon 10/09, Bromley 12/09, Basingstoke 7/11	40	6
Simon	Dunn							Southampton (Yth), Basingstoke, Whitchurch U (Dual) 1/12	10	1
Jordace	Holder-Spooner				05/11/1992	19	Reading	Southampton (Scholar) Rel c/s 11, Bournemouth (Trial) 7/11,		
								Eastleigh 8/11, Basingstoke 6/12		
Stuart	Lake				17/11/1979	32	London	Wimbledon, Walton & Hersham, Farnborough 10/98, Northwood 3/99,		
								Yeading, Northwood, Marlow 2/03, Uxbridge 7/04, Ashford T (Middx),		
								Hampton & R 2/07, Basingstoke 6/10	36	3
Toby	Little				19/02/1989	23		Hayes/Hayes & Yeading, Woking NC 8/10, Staines 2/11,		
								Basingstoke 7/11	29	2
Shaun	McAuley				16/02/1987	25		Hayes & Yeading, Hampton & R c/s 07, Walton Casuals (Dual) 10/07,		
								Eastleigh 7/09 Rel 5/11, Basingstoke 7/11	38	10
Jide	Ogunbote				17/08/1988	24		Woking, Corinthian C (L) 9/07, Basingstoke 8/08	27	2
Matt	Warner				12/05/1985	27	Farnham	Wycombe, Baingstoke (2ML) 10/03, Team Bath, Farnborough 6/05,		
								Basingstoke 7/06	35	2
FORWARDS										
Stefan	Brown							Thatcham, AFC Totton 5/10, Basingstoke 7/12		
Delano	Sam-Yorke	6'01"	13 04		20/01/1989	23		Woking Rel 5/10 Cray W (L) 11/09, AFC Wimbledon 7/10 Rel 5/11,		
								Basingstoke (L) 9/10, Basingstoke (SL) 1/11,		
								Basingstoke 6/11	33	14
Tim	Sills	6'02"	12 02		10/09/1979	32	Romsey	Millwall (Yth), Camberley 7/97, Basingstoke 7/99, Staines (L) 9/00,		
								Kingstonian (L) 1/02, Kingstonian 3/02, Aldershot 5/03,		
								Oxford U £50,000 1/06 Rel c/s 06, Hereford 6/06, Torquay 6/07,		
								Stevenage Undisc 1/10, Rushden & D (3ML) 9/10, Aldershot 1/11 Rel 5/11,		
								Basingstoke T 7/11	39	12

BATH CITY

Chairman: Manda Rigby
Secretary: Quentin Edwards   **(T)** 07785 795 532   **(E)** qcath@blueyonder.co.uk
Additional Committee Members:
Paul Williams, Geoff Todd, Phil Weaver, Andrew Pierce, Andy Weeks, Shane Morgan.

Manager: Adie Britton
Programme Editor: Shane Morgan   **(E)** slmorgan@live.co.uk

Back row (L-R): Cameron Brown, Luke Cummings, Danny Ball, Kerry Morgan, Noah Keats, Brad Norris.
Middle row: Aaron Brown, Adie Harris, Josh Low, Glyn Garner, Jason Mellor, Lewis Pierre, Mark Preece, Charlie Griffin.
Front row: Adam Connolly, Joe Burnell, Jim Rollo, Gethin Jones, Marc Canham.

Club Factfile

Founded: 1889   **Nickname:** The Romans
Previous Names: Bath AFC 1889-92. Bath Railway FC 1902-05. Bath Amateurs 1913-23 (Reserve side)
Previous Leagues: Western 1908-21. Southern 1921-79, 88-90, 97-2007. Alliance/Conference 1979-88, 90-97.

Club Colours (change): Black & white stripes/black/black (Yellow with blue trim/yellow/yellow)

Ground: Twerton Park, Twerton, Bath, Somerset BA2 1DB   **(T)** 01225 423 087
Capacity: 8,840   **Seats:** 1,017   **Covered:** 4,800   **Clubhouse:** Yes   **Shop:** Yes
Directions: Take Junction 18 off M4. 3rd exit off roundabout and follow A46 (10 miles) to Bath City Centre. Along Pulteney Road then right into Claverton Street and then follow A36 Lower Bristol Road (1.5 miles). Left under Railway bridge (signs Bath City FC) into Twerton High Street and ground is 2nd turning on left.

Previous Grounds: The Belvoir Ground 1889-92 & 1902-15. Lambridge Show Ground 1919-32.

Record Attendance: 18,020 v Brighton & Hove Albion - FA Cup
Record Victory: 8-0 v Boston United - 1998-99
Record Defeat: 0-9 v Yeovil Town - 1946-47
Record Goalscorer: Paul Randall - 106
Record Appearances: David Mogg - 530
Additional Records: Paid £15,000 to Bristol City for Micky Tanner. Received £80,000 from Southampton for Jason Dodd.

Senior Honours:
Southern Lge Western Div.2 1928-29. Southern Lge Western Division 1933-34. Southern League 1959-60, 77-78, 2006-07.
Southern League Cup 1978-79. Somerset Premier Cup 1951-52, 52-53, 57-58, 59-60, 65-66, 67-68, 69-70, 77-78, 80-81,
81-82, 83-84, 84-85, 85-86, 88-89, 89-90, 93-94, 94-95, 2007-08.

10 YEAR RECORD

02-03		03-04		04-05		05-06		06-07		07-08		08-09		09-10		10-11		11-12	
SthP	14	SthP	16	SthP	6	SthP	2	SthP	1	Conf S	8	Conf S	8	Conf S	4	Conf	10	Conf	23

BATH CITY

No.	Date	Comp	H/A	Opponents	Att:	Result	Goalscorers	Pos
	Bath							
1	Sat-13-Aug	BSP	A	Mansfield Town	3997	D 1-1	Connolly 35	10
2	Tue-16-Aug	BSP	H	Wrexham	1075	L 0-2		20
3	Sat-20-Aug	BSP	H	Barrow	781	L 0-1		22
4	Tue-23-Aug	BSP	A	Hayes & Yeading United	172	D 1-1	Murray 90	22
5	Sat-27-Aug	BSP	H	Tamworth	656	L 0-2		22
6	Mon-29-Aug	BSP	A	Forest Green Rovers	1344	L 0-3		24
7	Sat-10-Sep	BSP	H	Southport	663	L 1-2	Watkins 79	24
8	Tue-13-Sep	BSP	A	York City	2030	L 0-1		24
9	Sat-17-Sep	BSP	A	AFC Telford	2093	L 1-2	Watkins 22	24
10	Tue-20-Sep	BSP	H	Luton Town	1158	D 1-1	Phillips 72	24
11	Sat-24-Sep	BSP	H	Kettering Town	734	L 0-1		24
12	Tue-27-Sep	BSP	A	Ebbsfleet United	816	L 0-3		24
13	Sat-01-Oct	BSP	A	Lincoln City	2244	L 0-2		24
14	Sat-08-Oct	BSP	H	Darlington	1156	W 2-0	S Canham 69, Phillips 71	24
15	Tue-11-Oct	BSP	H	Cambridge United	788	L 3-4	Clough 12, M Canham 2 (pen 25, pen 79)	24
16	Sat-15-Oct	BSP	A	Braintree Town	703	D 3-3	Jones 3, Watkins 71, Phillips 90	24
17	Tue-18-Oct	BSP	A	Stockport County	919	L 0-2		24
18	Sat-22-Oct	BSP	A	Fleetwood Town	1451	L 1-4	Stonehouse 74	24
19	Sat-05-Nov	BSP	H	Grimsby Town	993	D 2-2	M Canham pen 57, S Canham 72	24
20	Sat-19-Nov	BSP	H	Southport	1021	L 1-2	S Canham 76	24
21	Sat-26-Nov	BSP	H	Mansfield Town	816	D 1-1	Watkins 19	24
22	Tue-29-Nov	BSP	A	Cambridge United	2267	D 1-1	Hogg 53	24
23	Sat-03-Dec	BSP	H	AFC Telford	761	W 3-1	Murray 26, M Canham pen 55, Bryan 83	24
24	Tue-06-Dec	BSP	A	Kidderminster Harriers	1472	L 1-4	Murray 6	24
25	Sat-17-Dec	BSP	A	Kettering Town	1096	D 1-1	Murray 51	24
26	Tue-03-Jan	BSP	H	Newport County	1147	W 3-2	Connolly 23, S Canham 30, Murray 47	24
27	Sat-07-Jan	BSP	H	Braintree Town	956	D 1-1	S Canham 5	24
28	Sat-21-Jan	BSP	A	Grimsby Town	3836	L 0-6		24
29	Tue-24-Jan	BSP	H	Alfreton Town	739	L 0-3		24
30	Sat-28-Jan	BSP	A	Wrexham	3583	L 0-2		24
31	Tue-14-Feb	BSP	A	Newport County	847	L 0-1		24
32	Sat-18-Feb	BSP	H	Ebbsfleet United	693	L 2-3	Jones 61, S Canham 90	24
33	Tue-21-Feb	BSP	H	Hayes & Yeading United	512	L 0-1		24
34	Sat-25-Feb	BSP	H	Kidderminster Harriers	676	L 1-2	S Canham 88	24
35	Sat-03-Mar	BSP	A	Luton Town	5745	L 0-2		24
36	Tue-06-Mar	BSP	A	Barrow	1190	W 1-0	S Canham 27	24
37	Sat-17-Mar	BSP	H	Lincoln City	760	W 2-1	M Canham pen 2, Watkins 4	24
38	Tue-20-Mar	BSP	A	Gateshead	512	L 0-1		24
39	Sat-24-Mar	BSP	A	Stockport County	3744	L 0-4		24
40	Tue-27-Mar	BSP	H	York City	565	L 0-1		24
41	Sat-31-Mar	BSP	H	Fleetwood Town	762	L 1-4	Connolly 81	24
42	Fri-06-Apr	BSP	A	Tamworth	957	W 1-0	Cook 78	Relegated 24
43	Mon-09-Apr	BSP	H	Forest Green Rovers	983	L 0-2		24
44	Sat-14-Apr	BSP	A	Darlington	1420	D 2-2	Russell 83, Murray 89	24
45	Sat-21-Apr	BSP	H	Gateshead	649	W 4-2	Connolly 4, M Canham pen 8, Gallinagh 13, S Canham 55	23
46	Sat-28-Apr	BSP	A	Alfreton Town	786	L 1-2	Murray pen 25	23

CUPS

No.	Date	Comp	H/A	Opponents	Att:	Result	Goalscorers	
1	Sat-29-Oct	FAC 4Q	A	Dover Athletic	922	W 1-0	Gallinagh 46	
2	Sat-12-Nov	FAC 1	A	Dagenham & Redbridge	1225	D 1-1	S Canham 11	
3	Wed-23-Nov	FAC 1R	H	Dagenham & Redbridge	1704	L 1-3 aet	Connolly 71	
4	Sat-10-Dec	FAT 1	A	Chelmsford City	635	W 3-2	M Canham pen 49, Murray 64, Cook 88	
5	Sat-14-Jan	FAT 2	H	Basingstoke Town	633	W 1-0	S Canham 23	
6	Tue-07-Feb	FAT 3	H	Grimsby Town	546	L 1-2	Shephard 34	

	League
	Starts
	Substitute
	Unused Sub

	Cups
	Starts
	Substitute
	Unused Sub

	Goals (Lg)
	Goals (Cup)

	GARNER	STONEHOUSE	PREECE	JONES	SIMPSON	RUSSELL	CONNOLLY	BURNELL	WATKINS	HOGG	PHILLIPS	MURRAY	COOK	MATTHEWS	ROLLO	WEBB	MILLS	M CANHAM	EGAN	CARVALHO-LANDELL	SWALLOW	CLOUGH	AGDESTEIN	GALLINAGH	S CANHAM	BRYAN	AMADI-HOLLOWAY	SHEPHARD	DOHERTY	SMITH
	1	3	15	5	2	21	8	19	18	11	10	7	9	17	4	14	6	16	20	22	23	24	25	26	27	28	35	36	40	41
	X	X	X	X	X	X	X	X	X	X	X	X	S	S	U	U	U													
	X	X	X	X	X	X	X	S	X	X	X	X	S	U	U	U	S													
	X	X	X	X	X	X	X	X	U	X	X	X	S	X	U	S	U	X												
	X	X	X	X	X	X	S	X	X	X	X	X	S	S	U	U	U	X												
	X	X	X	X	X	S	X	X	X	X	X	S	X	U		U	S	S												
	X	X	X	X	X	S	X	X	X	X	X	S	U		U		S			X										
	X	X	S	X	X		X	X	X		X		U	U	U		X		S		X	X								
	X	X	U	X	X	S		X	X	S	X		U		X	U	X	X	X											
	X	X	S	X	U	X	X		S	X	X	S			U		X		U		X	X	X							
	X		X		X		X	X	S	X	X	S		U	S		X	U		X	X									
	X	X	U		X		X	X	X	X	S	S	U	X			X		X	X	U	X								
	X	S	U	X		X			X	X	X			S			X		X	X		X	S							
	X	X		X		X	S	X	X	U	X	X	U	S			X			X		X	X							
	X	X		X		S	X	X	S	X	X	X	U	U			X			X		X	X							
	X	X		X	X	S	X		S	X	X	U	U				X			X		X	X							
	X	X	S	X	X	X		X		X	U	U		X			X		S			X	X							
	X	X	U		X	X	X		X		S	U		X	U		X		S			X	X							
	X	S		X	X	X		X	X	X	S	U		X			X			U		X	X							
	X	S		X	X	X	X	X	X	S	U	X		U			X			X		X	X							
		U		X	X	U	X		X	X	S	S		X			X			X		X	X	X	S					
		U		X	X	S	X	X	X	X	S	U		X			X			X		X	X	U	X					
		S		X	X	X	X	X		X	X	X		U			X				S	X		S	X					
		U		X	X	U	X	S	X	X	X			X			X				S	X		S	X					
		X		X	X	U	X	X	X	U	X	X		U			X							S	S					
		X	U	X	X	S	X	X	X	X	X	S	X	S	X	U		X							X					
	U	X	S	X	X	X	X	X	X	X	S		U	X	S	X	U		X					X						
		X	U	X	X	X	X	X	X		X	S	X	S	X	U		X						X	X					
	X	U	U	X	X	X	X	X			X	S	X	U		U		X						X	X					
	X	X	X		X	X	X	X		S		X	X	S	U	S		X						X						
	X	X	X			X	S	X	X	X	S	X		U	U			X	U					X			X			
	X	U	X	X	X		X	X	X	X				U				S						X	X		S	U		
		X	X		X		X	S	X	S	X		U	X	U	S		X						X	X		S	U		
		X	X		X	X	S	X	U	X	S	X			U			U						X	X		S	X		
	X	X	X	X			X	X	X	X		S	U		U			X						X	X		S	U		
	X	X	X	X		U	X	X	X		S	X		S				X	S					X	X					
	X	X	X	X		S	X	X	X	S		S	X	U				X	U					X	X					
	X	X	X	X			X	X		X		S	X	S				X	S					X	X					S
	X	X	X	X	U		X	X		X		X	S					X	S					X	X					S
	X	X	X		X	X	X	X	S	S		X	X					X	U					X						U
	X	X	X	S	X	X	X	X		S		X	S					X	U					X						
	X	X	X	X	S	X	S		S	X		X	X					X	U					X						U
	X	X	X	X	S	X		X	X		S	X		X				U	S					U						U
	X	S	X	X	U	X	X		X	X		S	X		U			X	U					X	S					
	X	U	X	X	X	X		X	S		X	U		S				X						X	X				S	
	X	S	X	X	S	X	X		X	X			X		U			X	S					X						U
	X	U	S	X	X	X	X		X	X	X	U	S	U	X	U		X			U			X						
	X	S	U	X	X	X	X			S	U	X	U	X							U	S		X	X					
	X	X	U		X	X	X	X	X	X	S	S	U	U	S			X			U		X	X	X					
		S		X	X	S	X	X		X	X	X	X	U				X					U	X		S	X			
	U	X		X	X	X	X	X	X		X	S	X	S	X	U		X							X					
	X	X			X	X	X	X	X		X		S	U	S			X	S					X			X			
36	32	25	39	34	17	41	32	28	34	24	15	13	10	7	0	2	36	0	1	7	10	3	32	22	1	3	1	1	0
0	6	4	1	2	14	2	1	9	8	7	20	11	0	9	0	2	2	8	0	2	2	0	0	2	3	2	4	0	3
1	6	7	0	2	6	0	1	1	0	2	5	12	7	26	5	1	2	7	0	0	2	1	1	0	1	0	0	3	4
4	3	0	4	6	5	6	5	4	4	2	2	2	2	2	0	0	4	0	0	0	1	0	5	3	0	1	1	0	0
0	2	1	0	0	1	0	0	0	0	3	1	3	0	2	0	0	0	1	0	0	1	0	0	1	0	0	0	0	0
1	1	2	0	0	0	0	0	0	0	0	2	1	4	2	1	0	0	0	2	1	1	0	0	0	0	0	0	0	0
0	1	0	2	0	1	4	0	5	1	3	7	1	0	0	0	6	0	0	0	1	0	1	9	1	0	0	0	0	0
0	0	0	0	0	0	1	0	0	0	1	1	0	0	0	0	1	0	0	0	0	0	1	2	0	0	1	0	0	0

PLAYING SQUAD

Existing Players		SN	HT	WT	DOB	AGE	POB	Career	Apps	Goals
GOALKEEPERS										
Glyn	Garner		6'02"	13 11	09/12/1976	35	Pontypool	Cwmbran, Llanelli, Bury 7/00, L.Orient 5/05 Rel c/s 07, Shrewsbury 8/07, Rel 1/10, Grays 2/10 Rel 5/10, Newport C 7/10, Bath C 5/11	36	0
Jason	Mellor							Nailsea T, Clevedon T 8/10, Bath C 5/12		
DEFENDERS										
Danny	Ball				21/11/1991	20		Bristol C Rel c/s 12, Bath C 7/12		
Luke	Cummings				25/10/1991	20		Cardiff C Rel c/s 10, Neath c/s 10, Bath C 6/12		
Gethin	Jones		5'11"	12 04	08/08/1981	31	Llanbyther	Carmarthen, Cardiff 8/00 Rel c/s 03, Weymouth (L) 9/02, Bath C (Trial) c/s 03, Merthyr 8/03, Bath C 6/05	40	2
Mark	Preece		6'02"	13 07	03/06/1987	25	Bristol	Bristol R Rel c/s 06, Gloucester (SL) 1/06, Kidderminster (Trial) 7/06, Forest Green 7/06, Weston-super-Mare (L) 1/07, Mansfield 7/10 Rel 5/11, Eastwood T (L) 9/10, AFC Telford (L) 2/11, Bath C 8/11, Weston-Super-Mare (L) 11/11	29	0
Jim	Rollo		6'00"	11 00	22/05/1976	36	Wisbech	Walsall Rel c/s 96, Yate T 4/96, Cardiff 8/96 Rel c/s 98, Bath C (L) 1/97, Ebbw Vale (L) 3/98, Yate T (Trial) c/s 98, Forest Green 6/98 Rel c/s 99, Cirencester (L) 10/98, Bath C (L) 1/99, Clevedon 8/99, Merthyr 6/01, Bath C 5/02	16	0
Sekani	Simpson		5'10"	11 10	11/03/1984	28	Bristol	Bristol C Rel c/s 05, Forest Green (L) 3/04, Tamworth (SL) 9/04, Forest Green 7/05 Rel 5/06, Weston-Super-Mare 8/06 Rel 9/06, Bath C 10/06	36	0
MIDFIELDERS										
Joe	Burnell		5'10"	11 01	10/10/1980	31	Bristol	Bristol C, Wycombe 7/04 Rel c/s 06, Northampton 8/06 Rel c/s 08, Oxford U 7/08 Rel 7/09, Exeter 7/09 Rel c/s 10, Bath C 7/10	33	0
Marc	Canham		5'11"	12 03	11/09/1982	29	Wegburg, Ger	Colchester Rel 6/03, Bournemouth (Trial) c/s 03, Team Bath 8/03, Yeovil (Trial) 2/05, Hayes & Yeading 7/09 Rel 5/10, Bath C 6/10	38	6
Danny	Collins							Bath C		
Adam	Connolly		5'09"	12 04	10/04/1986	26	Manchester	Cheltenham Rel c/s 08, Newport C (Trial) 7/08, Hednesford 8/08, Bath C 9/08	43	4
Adie	Harris				21/02/1981	31	Cardiff	Cardiff, Llanelli, Merthyr, Haverfordwest, Hornchurch 7/04, Haverfordwest c/s 05, Bath C 7/05, Haverfordwest 6/06 Rel 11/06, Bath C 12/06, Newport C 6/08, Weston-Super-Mare 4 fig 1/09 Rel 1/10, Bath C 1/10, Neath 6/11, Bath C 6/12		
Josh	Low		6'02"	14 03	15/02/1979	33	Bristol	Bristol R, Farnborough (L) 11/98 (98/99 4,2), L.Orient 5/99, Cardiff C 11/99, Oldham 8/02, Northampton 7/03 Rel c/s 06, Leicester 6/06, Peterborough 1/07, Cheltenham 8/08 Rel c/s 12, Forest Green (L) 11/08, Bath C 6/12		
Alex	Russell		5'10"	11 07	17/03/1973	39	Crosby	Liverpool (Scholar), Stockport, Morecambe, Burscough, Rochdale £4,000 7/94 Rel c/s 98, Glenavon (L) 11/95, Cambridge U 8/98 Rel c/s 01, Torquay 8/01, Bristol C 7/05 Rel c/s 08, Northampton (3ML) 8/07, Cheltenham (SL) 1/08, Cheltenham 6/08, Exeter (SL) 2/09, Exeter 7/09 Rel c/s 10, Bath C NC 9/10, Yeovil 1/11 Rel c/s 11, Bath C 7/11	31	1
FORWARDS										
Charlie	Griffin		6'00"	12 07	25/06/1979	33	Bath	Bristol R (Ass Sch), Melksham, Chippenham T 7/98, Swindon £10,000 1/99, Yeovil (L) 10/99, Woking (L) 10/00 £15,000 11/00, Havant (L) 11/01, Chippenham T (L) 2/02, Chippenham 9/02, Forest Green 5/04, Wycombe 5/05, Forest Green (5ML) 7/06, Newport C 2/07 Rel 6/08, Salisbury NC 8/08, Stevenage 5/09 Rel c/s 11, Newport C (SL) 1/11, Forest Green 6/11, Salisbury (SL) 2/12, Bath C 7/12		
Kerry	Morgan		5'10"	11 03	31/10/1988	23	Merthyr	Swansea Rel c/s 11, Clevedon (L) 3/08, Newport C (3ML) 10/09, Newport C (5ML) 8/10, Newport C (SL) 1/11, Neath 5/11, Bath C 8/12		

BILLERICAY TOWN

Chairman: Steve Kent
Secretary: Ian Ansell   **(T)** 0795 897 8154   **(E)** secretary@billericaytownfc.co.uk
Additional Committee Members:
Jim Green, Simon Williams

Manager: Craig Edwards
Programme Editor: Gary Clark   **(E)** programme.editor@billericaytownfc.co.uk

THE NON-LEAGUE CLUB DIRECTORY

Book Holiday Inn Hotels and Save today!

Home

Clubs

Steps 1 - 4

League Tables

35 Years of Non-League Football

The Non-League Club Directory has
developed into a comprehensive record
of competitions within the non-League
game, giving this level of football the

www.non-leagueclubdirectory.co.uk

Club Factfile

Founded: 1880   **Nickname:** Town or Blues

Previous Names:

Previous Leagues: Romford & District 1890-1914, Mid Essex 1918-47, South Essex Combination 1947-66, Essex Olympian 1966-71, Essex Senior 1971-77, Athenian 1977-79

Club Colours (change): Royal blue/white/royal blue (All sky blue)

Ground: New Lodge, Blunts Wall Road, Billericay CM12 9SA   **(T)** 01277 652 188

Capacity: 3,500   **Seats:** 424   **Covered:** 2,000   **Clubhouse:** Yes   **Shop:** Yes

Directions: From the M25 (J29) take the A127 to the Basildon/Billericay (A176) turn-off, (junction after the Old Fortune of War r'about). Take second exit at r'about (Billericay is signposted). Then straight over (2nd exit) at the next roundabout. Continue along that road until you enter Billericay. At the first r'about take the first available exit. At the next r'about (with Billericay School on your left) go straight over (1st exit). At yet another r'about!, turn left into the one-way system. Keep in the left-hand lane and go straight over r'about. At first set of lights, turn left. Blunts Wall Road is the second turning on your right.

Previous Grounds:

Record Attendance: 3,841 v West Ham United - Opening of Floodlights 1977

Record Victory: 11-0 v Stansted (A) - Essex Senior League 05/05/1976
Record Defeat: 3-10 v Chelmsford City (A) - Essex Senior Cup 04/01/1993

Record Goalscorer: Freddie Claydon - 273

Record Appearances: J Pullen - 418

Additional Records: Leon Gutzmore scored 51 goals during the 1997-98 season.
Received £22,500+ from West Ham United for Steve Jones November 1992

Senior Honours:

FA Vase 1975-76, 76-77, 78-79. Essex Senior Cup 1975-76. Athenian League 1978-79. Isthmian Premier Division 2011-12.
Essex Senior Trophy x2.

02-03		03-04		04-05		05-06		06-07		07-08		08-09		09-10		10-11		11-12	
Isth P	12	Isth P	22	Isth P	2	Isth P	7	Isth P	4	Isth P	10	Isth P	11	Isth P	13	Isth P	11	Isth P	1

BILLERICAY TOWN

No.	Date	Comp	H/A	Opponents	Att:	Result	Goalscorers	Pos
1	Aug 20	Isth P	H	Leatherhead	325	W 2 - 1	Kpaka 30 Luke 72	
2	23		A	Harrow Brough	160	D 1 - 1	May 68	
3	27		A	Lewes	483	L 1 - 2	May 83	11
4	29		H	Bury Town	339	D 4 - 4	Berry 27 Knight 42 66 Semakula 73	
5	Sept 3		H	Kingstonian	429	W 6 - 0	Semakula 18 Swaine 24 32 May 82 White 84 Chatting 89	7
6	10		A	Carshaltobn Athletic	134	W 1 - 0	May 80	7
7	13		H	Concord Rangers	282	D 0 - 0		
8	17	FAC 1Q	H	**Stotfold**	**260**	**W 4 - 0**	**Swaine 2 30 Knight 32 Boot 60**	
9	24		A	East Thurrock	249	W 2 - 1	Knight 47 Wild 64	7
10	27		A	Wingate & Finchley	128	W 4 - 1	Kpaka 18 Knight 18 Luke 30 Berry 65	
11	Oct 1	FAC 2Q	A	**Chipstead**	**175**	**W 3 - 0**	**Swaine 34 Knight 69 (pen) Chatting 76**	**6**
12	4		H	Hastings United	273	W 2 - 0	Ray (og) 13 Swaine 37	
13	8		A	Metropolitan Police	132	W 1 - 0	Chatting 89	1
14	15	FAC 3Q	H	**Leatherhead**	**384**	**L 0 - 3**		
15	22	FAT 1Q	H	**Whitehawk**	**272**	**W 1 - 0**	**Halle 81 (pen)**	
16	29		H	Canvey Island	601	W 4 - 2	May 4 51 Knight 78 Swaine 84	2
17	Nov 1		H	Tooting & Mtcham U	306	W 5 - 1	May 5 Luke 6 Swaine 35 Knight 78 Wild 82	
18	5	FAT 2Q	H	**St Neots Town**	**315**	**W 2 - 0**	**Swaine 17 Knight 42**	
19	12		H	Wealdstone	474	D 0 - 0		1
20	19		A	Hendon	240	W 2 - 1	Halle 11 (pen) Onwubiko 14	3
21	22		A	Horsham	197	W 5 - 0	Edwards 8 22 May 62 Onwubiko 74 76	1
22	26	FAT 3Q	A	**Maidenhead United**	**235**	**L 0 - 1**		
23	29		A	Cray Wanderers	172	W 3 - 2	Chatting 22 Onwubiko 45 Swaine 55	1
24	Dec 3		A	Lowestoft Town	812	L 0 - 1		1
25	10		H	Margate	388	D 1 - 1	Kpaka 20	1
26	13		H	Aveley	233	W 2 - 1	Onwubiko 34 60	1
27	17		A	Concord Rangers	290	D 0 - 0		1
28	27		H	AFC Hornchurch	1106	L 0 - 1		1
29	31		H	Harrow Borough	429	W 3 - 0	Halle 2 55 Swaine 58	1
30	Jan 2		A	Bury Town	560	D 1 - 1	May 36	1
31	7		A	Tooting & Mitcham U	302	L 2 - 4	Sobers 21 Cousins 32	3
32	14		H	Wingate & Finchley	419	W 2 - 0	Halle 12 (pen) Swaine 60	1
33	21		A	Hastings United	368	D 0 - 0		1
34	28		H	Met Police	533	W 2 - 1	Halle 17 Collis 76	1
35	Feb 13		H	Hendon	301	W 2 - 1	Chatting 59 80	1
36	18		A	Canvey Island	506	W 2 - 0	Swaine 4 Poole 72	1
37	25		H	Cray Wanderers	488	W 3 - 1	White 13 23 Wild 27	1
38	March 3		A	Wealdstone	617	D 1 - 1	Poole 7	1
39	10		H	Horsham	539	D 2 - 2	White 45 May 64	1
40	17		A	Leatherhead	309	W 2 - 0	May 45 Chatting 70	1
41	19		A	Aveley	304	W 6 - 0	MAY 3 (41 78 86) Poole 40 (pen) 80 Wild 47	
42	24		H	Lewes	651	W 1 - 0	Chatting 90	1
43	31		A	Kingstonian	383	W 2 - 0	Poole 29 (pen) White 63	
44	Apr 6		H	Carshalton Athletic	876	D 1 - 1	Murphy (og) 3	
45	9		A	AFC Hornchurch	1095	D 0 - 0		
46	14		H	East Thurrock United	648	W 1 - 0	Chatting 45	1
47	21		A	Margate	536	D 2 - 2	Poole 75 (pen) Swaine 85	Champions
48	28		H	Lowestoft Town	1145	L 1 - 4	Cockrill 12 (og)	1

PLAYING SQUAD

Existing Players		SN	HT	WT	DOB	AGE	POB	Career	Apps	Goals
GOALKEEPERS										
Dale	Brightly							AFC Hornchurch, Concord R 2/09, Billericay 11/11		
Harry	Ricketts							Cheshunt, Potters Bar 12/08, Enfield T 1/09, Ware 3/09,		
								Waltham Abbey 1/10, Billericay 3/12		
DEFENDERS										
Dave	Collis							Billericay, AFC Hornchurch, Billericay		
Greg	Oates							Norwich (Yth), Ipswich (Yth), Arsenal Rel c/s 02,		
								Colchester (Trial) 1/02, Sheff Wed (Trial) 3/02,		
								L.Orient (Trial) 3/02, Margate 8/02 (02/03 39,3, 03/04 36,1),		
								Maldon T c/s 07, Chelmsford 1/08, Billericay		
Rob	Swaine				28/02/1988	24		Billericay, Thurrock 9/07, Chelmsford 3/11,		
								Billericay (Dual) 3/11, Billericay 8/11		
Chris	Wild							St Albans, Braintree c/s 05, Maidenhead, Margate 8/06,		
								Hemel Hempstead, Enfield T 11/08, Billericay 11/09		
MIDFIELDERS										
Harrison	Chatting							Billericay, Heybridge (L) 2/10		
Richard	Halle							Grays, East Thurrock (L) 9/02, Redbridge, Chelmsford 7/05,		
								East Thurrock 8/06, Aveley, Canvey Island 3/07,		
								AFC Hornchurch 5/07, Canvey Island 1/08, Concord R,		
								Billericay 10/11		
Sam	Lechmere				03/12/1990	20		Thurrock, West Ham (Trial) 11/08, Aveley 7/09,		
								Yeovil 12/09 Rel 2/10, Grays 2/10, Braintree 7/10,		
								Boreham Wood 9/11, Billericay 3/12		
Junior	Luke				24/05/1990	22		Potters Bar, Dulwich Hamlet 11/07, Leyton 12/07, Potters Bar,		
								Leyton 1/09, Waltham Forest 7/09, Thurrock 8/09, Leyton 9/09,		
								Waltham Forest 11/09, Maldon T, Brentwood 2/10 Rel 5/10,		
								Billericay, Waltham Forest 1/11, Billericay,		
								Maldon & Tiptree (L) 3/12		
Glenn	Poole	5'07"	11 04		03/02/1981	31	Barking	Tottenham (Trainee), Witham T 99/00, Yeovil 11/99,		
								Bath C (L) 9/01, Ford U/Redbridge 2/02, Thurrock 11/04,		
								Grays 7/05, Rochdale (SL) 3/07, Brentford 5/07 Rel c/s 09,		
								Grays 8/09, AFC Wimbledon 1/10 Rel 4/10, Barnet 6/10,		
								Braintree 2/11, Thurrock 7/11, Billericay 12/11		
FORWARDS										
Jay	May							Tonbridge A, Dartford 7/06, Bromley Tribunal 6/08,		
								Ramsgate (L) 9/08, Ramsgate 10/08, Dartford 3/09, Ramsgate,		
								Tonbridge A 3/10, Croydon Ath 7/10, Tonbridge A,		
								Billericay 6/11		
Emeka	Onwubiko							Bray Wan, Athlone, Solihull Moors 12/10,		
								Sutton Coldfield (Dual) 2/11, Billericay		
Courtney	White							Castle U, Billericay 6/11, Waltham Forest (L) 11/11		

Conference Action...

This Basingstoke player gets set to take on the incoming Didcot defender during the Conferecne South side's 1-0 win in the FA Trophy First Round.

Photo: Peter Barnes.

BOREHAM WOOD

Chairman: Danny Hunter
Secretary: Peter Smith **(T)** 07711 745987 **(E)** peter.s.smith@royalmail.com
Additional Committee Members:
Bill Hunter, Matthew Hunter, John Gill

Manager: Ian Allinson
Programme Editor: John Gill **(E)** johndgill2002@yahoo.co.uk

Club Factfile

Founded: 1948 **Nickname:** The Wood
Previous Names: Boreham Wood Rovers and Royal Retournez amalgamated in 1948 to form today's club
Previous Leagues: Mid Herts 1948-52, Parthenon 1952-57, Spartan 1956-66, Athenian 1966-74, Isthmian 1974-2004, Southern 2004-10

Club Colours (change): White/black/white (All sky blue)

Ground: Meadow Park, Broughinge Road, Boreham Wood WD6 5AL **(T)** 0208 953 5097
Capacity: 4,502 **Seats:** 600 **Covered:** 1,568 **Clubhouse:** Yes **Shop:** Yes
Directions: Leave A1 at A5135 and follow A5135 towards Borehamwood.
Cross two mini roundabouts then at large roundabout turn right (second exit) into Brook Road then take first right after car park for Broughinge Road.

Previous Grounds: Eldon Avenue 1948-63

Record Attendance: 4,030 v Arsenal - Friendly 13/07/2001
Record Victory: Not known
Record Defeat: Not known
Record Goalscorer: Mickey Jackson
Record Appearances: Dave Hatchett - 714
Additional Records: Received £5,000 from Dagenham & Redbridge for Steve Heffer

Senior Honours:
Athenian League 1973-74. Isthmian League Division 2 1976-77, Division 1 1994-95, 2000-01.
Southern League East 2005-06, Premier Division Play-off 2009-10.
Herts Senior cup 1971-72, 98-99, 2001-02. London Challenge Cup 1997-98.

10 YEAR RECORD

02-03		03-04		04-05		05-06		06-07		07-08		08-09		09-10		10-11		11-12	
Isth P	22	Isth1N	9	SthE	7	SthE	1	Isth P	7	Isth P	19	Isth P	18	Isth P	4	Conf S	14	Conf S	8

BOREHAM WOOD

No.	Date	Comp	H/A	Opponents	Att:	Result	Goalscorers	Pos
1	Sat-13-Aug	BSS	H	Havant & Waterlooville	201	L 0-1		16
2	Tue-16-Aug	BSS	A	Bromley	337	L 0-4		20
3	Sat-20-Aug	BSS	A	Woking	1196	D 0-0		19
4	Mon-22-Aug	BSS	H	Basingstoke Town	202	D 1-1	Bryant 77	18
5	Sat-27-Aug	BSS	H	Thurrock	162	W 2-1	Wilkinson 25, Bryant 42	17
6	Mon-29-Aug	BSS	A	Staines Town	255	L 1-2	Akinola 90	19
7	Sat-03-Sep	BSS	A	Weston-Super-Mare	341	L 1-4	Bryant 90	20
8	Sat-10-Sep	BSS	H	Truro City	290	L 1-2	Effiong 53	20
9	Sat-17-Sep	BSS	A	Eastbourne Borough	604	L 2-3	Wilkinson 57, Palmer 74	20
10	Mon-19-Sep	BSS	H	Welling United	273	W 2-1	Currie 2 (pen 12, pen 55)	19
11	Sat-24-Sep	BSS	A	Chelmsford City	1042	D 0-0		20
12	Sat-08-Oct	BSS	H	Dartford	441	W 3-1	Isaac 1, Thalassitis 17, Koranteng 56	17
13	Sat-15-Oct	BSS	A	Hampton & Richmond Boro'	401	W 1-0	Bryant 44	16
14	Sat-22-Oct	BSS	A	Dorchester Town	443	W 1-0	Bryant 36	13
15	Mon-24-Oct	BSS	H	Maidenhead United	210	W 1-0	Hutton pen 42	7
16	Sat-05-Nov	BSS	A	Bromley	231	W 2-1	Bryant 30, Wilkinson 45	8
17	Sat-12-Nov	BSS	H	Dover Atletic	261	W 4-2	Thalassitis 3 (5, 45, 57), Bryant 11	7
18	Sat-19-Nov	BSS	A	Welling United	688	L 0-2		10
19	Tue-22-Nov	BSS	A	Basingstoke Town	309	D 1-1	Garrard 71	8
20	Sat-17-Dec	BSS	A	Eastleigh	490	L 0-2		11
21	Mon-19-Dec	BSS	H	Chelmsford City	251	L 1-3	Cox 6	12
22	Mon-26-Dec	BSS	H	Sutton United	232	D 1-1	Thalassitis 5	13
23	Sat-14-Jan	BSS	A	Farnborough	403	L 2-3		13
24	Sat-21-Jan	BSS	H	Weston-Super-Mare	201	W 3-0	Lobjoit 2 (47, 65), Lechmere 90	12
25	Sat-28-Jan	BSS	H	Woking	413	L 1-2	Noto 55	13
26	Tue-14-Feb	BSS	A	Sutton United	513	L 1-2	Noto 29	14
27	Sat-18-Feb	BSS	H	Eastbourne Borough	202	D 1-1	Noto 34	14
28	Sat-25-Feb	BSS	A	Maidenhead United	242	W 3-0	Bryant 24, Riza 26, Sankofa 86	14
29	Mon-27-Feb	BSS	A	Tonbridge Angels	391	D 1-1	Bryant 9	13
30	Sat-03-Mar	BSS	A	Havant & Waterlooville	580	W 4-2	Vilhete 2 (3, 37), Noto 2 (44 pen 62)	12
31	Sat-10-Mar	BSS	H	Dorchester Town	201	D 2-2	Riza 37, Noto pen 42	13
32	Tue-13-Mar	BSS	A	Truro City	299	L 2-1	Bryant 19	13
33	Sat-17-Mar	BSS	A	Salisbury City	525	W 2-0	Vilhete 32, Riza 47	12
34	Mon-19-Mar	BSS	H	Salisbury City	255	D 1-1	Riza 64	12
35	Sat-24-Mar	BSS	H	Eastleigh	201	W 6-1	Reynolds 7, Bryant 47, Montgomery 49, Riza pen 53, Garrard 68, Cox 90	10
36	Sat-31-Mar	BSS	A	Dover Atletic	575	W 2-0	Bryant 20, Riza 88	10
37	Mon-02-Apr	BSS	H	Hampton & Richmond Boro'	251	W 2-1	Vilhete 2 (63, 90)	8
38	Fri-06-Apr	BSS	A	Thurrock	214	L 0-1		9
39	Mon-09-Apr	BSS	H	Staines Town	174	L 1-2	Montgomery 79	9
40	Sat-14-Apr	BSS	H	Farnborough	175	W 4-0	Riza 6, Akinola 63, Effiong 65, O'Loughlin 85	8
41	Sat-21-Apr	BSS	A	Dartford	1309	D 2-2	Montgomery 30, O'Loughlin 88	8
42	Sat-28-Apr	BSS	H	Tonbridge Angels	275	W 4-2	Montgomery 8, Jones 45, Og (T Olurunda) 78, Effiong 81	8

CUPS

No.	Date	Comp	H/A	Opponents	Att:	Result	Goalscorers	
1	Sat-01-Oct	FAC 2Q	A	Slough Town	277	L 2-3	Bryant 2 (55, 57)	
2	Sat-26-Nov	FAT 3Q	H	Dover Athletic	181	W 1-0	Bryant 15	
3	Sat-10-Dec	FAT 1	H	Cambridge United	401	L 0-1		

League
Starts
Substitute
Unused Sub

Cups
Starts
Substitute
Unused Sub

Goals (Lg)
Goals (Cup)

	PUTNINS	SANKOFA	BRAITHWAITE	HUNTER	WILKINSON	O'LOUGHLIN	RUDDOCK	GARRARD	EFFIONG	MCMAHON	CURRIE	CHABAN	PALMER	YALA	LAWAL	JORDAN	BRYANT	NOTO	HURRELL	O'LEARY	AKINOLA	SMITH	JONES	SCOTT-MORRIS	BAKER-OWENS	LECHMERE	ISAAC	BECKFORD	KORANTENG	COCHRANE	THALASSITIS	COX	HUTTON	MARTIN	JOHNSON	BECKLES	CLEMENTS	LOBJOIT	VILHETE	RIZA	LEWIS	MONTGOMERY	REYNOLDS	CLOSE	RUBINIA
	X	X	X	X	X	X	X	X	X	X	X	S	S	U	U	U	U																												
	X	X	X	X			X	S		X	X	X	X	X	X	S	U	X																											
	X	X	X	S	X	X	X		X	X			U				U	X	X	X	S	S																							
	X	X	X	S	X	X	X		X				S				U	X	X	X	X	S	U																						
	X	X	X	U	X	X	S		X	X			S				X	X	X	U	X	U																							
		X		S	X	X		X	X	X	X		S				X	X	X	U		S	U	X																						
		X		S	X	X			S	X			X				X	X	X	X		U	X	X	S	U																				
U		X	X	X	X			S		U			U				X	X		X		X	X	X	U		X																			
	X	X	X	S		X		U		S			X				X	X		S	X	X	U	X	X	X																			
	X	X	X	S		X		X				U				X	X		U				X	X	U	X	X																		
U	U	X	X	X		X		S		X						X	X		S				X	X	U	X	X																		
X		X	U	X	X			S								U	X		U		X		X	X	S	X	X	X																	
X		X	X	X	S			S							S	U	X		U		X		X	X		X	X	X																	
X	X		S	X	X	S										X			U		X		U	X	X		X	X	X	U															
X	X		S	X	X	S										X			S		X		U	X	X		X	X	X	U															
	X		U	X	X	S										X	X		U		X		U	X	X		S	X	X	X															
X	X		U	X	X	S	S									U	X		X		X		X	X		S	X	X	X			S													
X	X			X			X										X		X		X		U	X		S	S	X	X	X		S	U											
	X	U		X	X		X	S								X	S						X		U		X	X	X			X	U											
	X			X	X	X		X								X	X						X		U	S	X	X	X			X	U											
	X	S		X	X			X								X	X						X		U	S	X	X	X			U	U											
	X	X	U	X	X			X								X	X		U					S		X		X	X	X	U			S	X									
	X	U	X	X	X							S				X	X		X		U			X	X	U		X	S	X	S													
	X	U	U	X	X			X		X						X	X	X		X		U		S			X	S			X			X		X								
	X	U	X	U	X		X									X	X	X		U		X		S			X				X	U			X			X						
	X	S	U		X											X	X	X		S		X	U		S			X				X	X			X			X					
X	X	X	X	U		X										U	X	X		U							S				X	X			X			X		X	S			
X	X	X	X			X										X	X						U				S				X	U			X			U	X	U				
X	X	X				X										X	X										U				X	U			X			S	X	X		X		
X	X	X	U			X									S	U	X	X									U				S	S			X			U	X	X		X	X	
X	X					X										U	X										S					X	S			X			X	X	X	X	X	X	S
X	X					X										U	X						U				S					X	S			X			S	X	X	X	U	U	
X	X		U			X										U	X						X				S					X	S			X			U	X	X	X	U	U	
X	X					X										U	X			U	S						S					X	U			X			X	X	X	S			
	X	X				X									S	X	X	X					X									X	U			X			U	X	X	U	U	U
X	X			X											U	U	X	X					X				S					X				X			U	X	X	U	U	
X	X			X											S	U	X	X			X		X	S			X					X				U			X	X	X	U	S	
U		X				X		X	X						U	X	X				X		X	U			S					U				X	X			X	X			
X	X		S			X		X	X						U	S	U				X		X				X	X				X				X			X	S				
X	X					X		X	S						U	X	U			S	X		X				X					X				U			X	X	X			
X	X					X		X	X						U	X	S			S	S						X					X				U			X	X	X			
U	X	X	X	X			S		X						X	X				S			S			X	X	U	X	X														
	X	X				X		X	U						X	X							U				X	X			X	X				S	U							
	X	U		X	X			X				S				X	X				X	U				X	X	S	S	X			X											
25	36	16	13	23	37	4	20	8	9	5	1	2	1	0	17	38	14	5	1	6	3	25	0	0	15	11	1	5	4	11	23	16	0	1	15	1	4	9	13	0	12	11	1	0
0	0	1	8	0	0	9	1	10	1	0	1	5	4	2	0	2	1	0	1	11	0	0	4	0	7	0	1	0	4	0	1	9	1	2	4	0	1	1	0	0	1	0	1	3
3	1	4	10	1	0	0	0	0	0	2	1	0	5	1	20	0	2	1	1	9	3	3	4	6	1	0	2	2	1	0	0	4	2	2	6	0	2	1	0	2	0	0	5	3
0	3	2	1	2	2	0	2	0	0	1	0	0	0	0	3	3	0	0	0	0	0	1	0	0	3	3	0	1	2	1	1	2	0	0	0	0	0	0	0	0	0	0	0	0
0	0	0	0	0	0	0	0	1	1	0	0	0	0	0	0	0	0	0	0	0	1	0	1	0	0	0	0	0	0	1	1	0	0	0	0	1	0	0	0	0	0	0	0	0
1	0	1	0	0	0	0	0	0	1	0	0	0	0	0	0	0	0	0	0	0	0	0	2	0	0	1	0	0	0	0	0	0	0	0	1	0	0	0	0	0	0	0	0	0
0	1	0	0	3	2	0	2	3	0	2	0	1	0	0	12	6	0	0	2	0	1	0	0	1	1	0	1	0	5	2	1	0	0	0	0	2	5	7	0	4	1	0	0	
0	0	0	0	0	0	0	0	0	0	0	0	0	0	0	3	0	0	0	0	0	0	0	0	0	0	0	0	0	0	0	0	0	0	0	0	0	0	0	0	0	0	0	0	0

ALSO PLAYED: WALKER U (2). WILTON U (C2). MCCANN U (28). DOOLAN U (32).

PLAYING SQUAD 2012/13

Existing Players		SN	HT	WT	DOB	AGE	POB	Career	Apps	Goals
GOALKEEPERS										
Cameron	Baker-Owens				17/01/1993	19		Boreham Wood	0	0
Daniel	Lewis				05/12/1989	22		Boreham Wood	0	0
James	Russell		6'00"		19/09/1987	24	Welwyn	Chelsea Rel c/s 07, Walton & H (L) 2/07, Kettering (Trial) 7/07, Stevenage 8/07, Canvey Island (3ML) 1/08, Halesowen T (L) 8/08, Arlesey (SL) 11/08, Canvey Island 7/09, Boreham Wood 5/12		
DEFENDERS										
Lee	Close							Boreham Wood	2	0
Sam	Doolan							Boreham Wood	0	0
Luke	Garrard		5'10"	10 09	22/09/1985	26	Barnet	Tottenham (Scholar), Swindon 7/02 Rel c/s 05, Bishops Stortford 7/05, Boreham Wood 10/05, Northwood 11/05, AFC Wimbledon 3/06, Boreham Wood (3ML) 10/09 Perm 1/10 (Ass Man) 3/12	21	2
Mark	Jones				06/08/1979	33		Burnham Ramblers, Billericay Rel 8/99, Romford 8/99, Braintree 2/00 Rel 8/11, Boreham Wood 8/11	25	1
Ben	Nunn				25/10/1989	22		Boston U, Rushden & D Rel 7/08, Cambridge C 8/08 Rel 6/09, Bishops Stortford c/s 09, Chelmsford 3/10 Rel c/s 12, Boreham Wood 7/12		
Charlie	O'Loughlin		6'01"	13 02	17/03/1989	23	Birmingham	Port Vale Rel 4/08, Nantwich (L) 11/07, Hinckley U (L) 1/08, Nantwich 6/08, Ilkeston 6/09, Solihull Moors 7/10, Boreham Wood 5/11	37	2
Callum	Reynolds				10/11/1989	22		Rushden & D, Rugby T (WE) 3/07, Portsmouth 7/07, Basingstoke (L) 3/09, Luton (6ML) 7/09, Basingstoke 10/10, Tamworth 8/11, Hinckley U (L) 8/11, Corby T (10WL) 10/11, Boreham Wood (SL) 3/12, Boreham Wood 5/12	11	1
Lewis	Wallace							Boreham Wood		
MIDFIELDERS										
Robert	Hastings							Boreham Wood		
David	Hutton		5'05"	10 10	04/12/1989	22	Enfield	Tottenham Rel c/s 09, Cheltenham (L) 3/09, Cheltenham 5/09 Rel c/s 10, Grimsby (Trial), L.Orient (Trial), St Albans 10/10, Glen Hoddle Academy (Spa), Jerez Industrial (Spa), Boreham Wood 10/11	25	1
Chez	Isaac		5'10"	11 13	16/11/1992	19	Hatfield	Watford Rel c/s 12, Boreham Wood (3ML) 9/11, Tamworth (2ML) 1/12, Boreham Wood 5/12	11	1
Graeme	Montgomery		6'01"	12 00	03/03/1988	24	Dagenham	Wealdstone, Dag & Red 1/09 Rel 5/11, Hayes & Yeading (L) 11/10, Newport C (SL) 1/11, Aldershot T 8/11 Rel 12/11, Eastleigh (3ML) 9/11, Eastleigh 12/11 Rel 2/12, Boreham Wood 3/12	13	4
Mario	Noto				24/10/1984	27	Enfield	Tottenham (Scholar), Reading (Scholar), Wycombe (Trial) 2/04, Southend (Trial) 4/04, C.Palace (Trial) c/s 04, Darlington (Trial) 12/04, Canvey Island 1/05, Chelmsford 7/06 Rel 7/08, Boreham Wood c/s 08	15	6
FORWARDS										
Simeon	Akinola							Boreham Wood, Billericay (L) 11/11	17	2
Elliott	Buchanan		5'11"		17/07/1989	23		Northwood, Stevenage 1/08 Rel 5/09, AFC Wimbledon (SL) 3/08, Boreham Wood (L) 8/08, Concord R (SL) 1/09, Slough 9/09 Rel c/s 10, Hayes & Yeading 8/10, Newport C 7/11 Rel c/s 12, Boreham Wood 6/12		
Inih	Effiong				02/03/1991	21		St Albans, Northwood (L) 10/08, Boreham Wood 8/09, St Albans c/s 10, Boreham Wood 7/11, Hitchin (L) 12/11, Chesham (L) 3/12	18	3
Omer	Riza		5'08"	11 02	08/11/1979	32	Edmonton	Arsenal, Den Haag (Holl) (SL) 2/99, West Ham £20,000 12/99 Rel c/s 02, Barnet (3ML) 10/00, Cambridge U (SL) 3/01, Aberdeen (Trial) 7/02, Cambridge U 8/02 Rel c/s 03, Denizlispor (Tur) 7/03, Trabzonspor (Tur) 1/06 Rel 1/08, Shrewsbury 4/09 Rel 1/10, Aldershot T 2/10 Rel c/s 10, Stevenage (Trial) c/s 10, Histon 8/10 Rel 1/12, Boreham Wood 2/12	13	7
Harvey	Scott-Morris							Boreham Wood	4	0
Donovan	Simmonds		5'10"	11 00	12/10/1988	23	Walthamstow	Charlton (Scholar), Coventry 7/07 Rel c/s 09, Gillingham (SL) 3/08, Kilmarnock (SL) 8/08, Floriana (Mal) 8/09, Morton 2/10 Rel c/s 10, Rushden & D 8/10, Nuneaton T 9/10, Dover 12/10 Rel c/s 12, Boreham Wood 6/12		

BROMLEY

Chairman: Ashley Reading
Secretary: Colin Russell   **(T)** 07970 031 511   **(E)** colin@bromleyfc.co.uk
Additional Committee Members:
Paul Greenwood, Michael Coles, Jeremy Dolke, Paul Greenwood, Jeff Hutton.

Manager: Mark Goldberg
Programme Editor: Jeff Hutton   **(E)** jeff@bromleyfc.net

Club Factfile

Founded: 1892   **Nickname:** The Lillywhites
Previous Names:
Previous Leagues: South London, Southern, London, West Kent, South Surburban, Kent, Spartan 1907-08,
Isthmian 1908-11, 52-2007, Athenian 1919-1952

Club Colours (change): White/black/black (All red)

Ground: The Stadium, Hayes Lane, Bromley, Kent BR2 9EF   **(T)** 020 8460 5291
Capacity: 5,000   **Seats:** 1,300   **Covered:** 2,500   **Clubhouse:** Yes   **Shop:** Yes

Directions: From M25 Motorway: Leaving the M25 at Junction 4, follow the A21 to Bromley and London, for approximately 4 miles and then fork left onto the A232 signposted Croydon/Sutton. At the 2nd set of traffic lights turn right into Baston Road (B265), following it for about 2 miles as it becomes Hayes Street and then Hayes Lane. Bromley FC is on right hand side of road just after a mini roundabout. From the Croydon/Surrey areas use the A232, turn left into Baston Road (B265), following it for about 2 miles as it becomes Hayes Street and then Hayes Lane. From West London use the South Circular Road as far as West Dulwich and then via Crystal Palace, Penge, Beckenham and Bromley South areas. From North and East London use the Blackwall Tunnel and then the A20 road as far as Sidcup. Then use the A232 to Keston Common, turn right into Baston Road (B265), following it for about 2 miles as it becomes Hayes Street and then Hayes Lane.

Previous Grounds:

Record Attendance: 10,798 v Nigeria - 1950
Record Victory: 13-1 v Redhill - Athenian League 1945-46
Record Defeat: 1-11 v Barking - Athenian League 1933-34
Record Goalscorer: George Brown - 570 (1938-61)
Record Appearances: George Brown
Additional Records: Received £50,000 from Millwall for John Goodman

Senior Honours:
Isthmian League 1908-10, 53-54, 60-61. Athenian League 1922-23, 48-49, 50-51.
Kent Senior Cup x5. Kent Amateur Cup x12. London Senior Cup x4

10 YEAR RECORD

02-03		03-04		04-05		05-06		06-07		07-08		08-09		09-10		10-11		11-12	
Isth1S	6	Isth1S	8	Isth1	4	Isth P	11	Isth P	2	Conf S	11	Conf S	13	Conf S	12	Conf S	11	Conf S	17

BROMLEY

No.	Date	Comp	H/A	Opponents	Att:	Result	Goalscorers	Pos
1	Sat-13-Aug	BSS	A	Hampton & Richmond Boro'	539	W 2-1	Smith 42, Jones 90	6
2	Tue-16-Aug	BSS	H	Boreham Wood	337	W 4-0	Araba 22, Hockton 53, Smith 66, Williams 78	4
3	Sat-20-Aug	BSS	H	Maidenhead United	417	L 0-1		8
4	Tue-23-Aug	BSS	A	Eastbourne Borough	605	L 0-5		11
5	Sat-27-Aug	BSS	H	Sutton United	509	W 3-0	Harding 22, Waldren 26, Araba 27	4
6	Mon-29-Aug	BSS	A	Dartford	1550	L 1-3	Waldren 63	8
7	Sat-03-Sep	BSS	A	Eastleigh	568	W 2-0	Harding pen 51, Waldren 68	9
8	Sat-10-Sep	BSS	H	Salisbury City	605	D 2-2	Williams 27, Ibrahima 41	8
9	Sat-17-Sep	BSS	A	Staines Town	308	L 1-4	Williams 10	12
10	Tue-20-Sep	BSS	H	Woking	478	L 2-4	Araba 5, McKenzie 68	14
11	Sat-24-Sep	BSS	H	Welling United	648	D 1-1	Harwood 85	13
12	Sat-08-Oct	BSS	A	Havant & Waterlooville	766	W 2-1	Araba 2 (56, 57)	10
13	Sat-22-Oct	BSS	A	Maidenhead United	405	D 3-3	McKenzie 2, McBean 73, Araba 79	12
14	Tue-25-Oct	BSS	H	Dover Athletic	554	L 0-1		14
15	Sat-05-Nov	BSS	A	Boreham Wood	231	L 1-2	Waldren 75	17
16	Sat-19-Nov	BSS	A	Chelmsford City	1008	L 1-6	Taylor 80	17
17	Tue-22-Nov	BSS	H	Hampton & Richmond Boro'	298	L 1-2	Araba 45	17
18	Sat-03-Dec	BSS	H	Eastbourne Borough	363	L 1-3	Ibrahima 50	18
19	Sat-10-Dec	BSS	A	Dover Athletic	625	L 1-4	Araba 86	18
20	Tue-13-Dec	BSS	H	Dorchester Town	223	D 0-0		18
21	Sat-17-Dec	BSS	A	Farnborough	409	L 1-2	Smith 33	19
22	Mon-26-Dec	BSS	H	Tonbridge Angels	771	D 2-2	Smith 7, Araba pen 61	19
23	Sun-01-Jan	BSS	A	Tonbridge Angels	905	L 1-3	Rhule 81	19
24	Sat-07-Jan	BSS	H	Basingstoke Town	423	L 1-3	Gillman 90	20
25	Sat-14-Jan	BSS	A	Woking	1612	L 2-3	Waldren pen 74, Smith 87	20
26	Sat-21-Jan	BSS	H	Truro City	435	D 1-1	Joseph-Dubois 63	21
27	Sat-28-Jan	BSS	A	Weston-Super-Mare	343	W 3-0	Araba 2 (2, 76), Joseph-Dubois 80	19
28	Tue-14-Feb	BSS	A	Thurrock	218	D 1-1	Malcolm 85	19
29	Sat-18-Feb	BSS	A	Salisbury City	701	W 2-0	Thomas 50, Joseph-Dubois 54	18
30	Sat-25-Feb	BSS	H	Chelmsford City	636	W 1-0	Araba 64	18
31	Sat-03-Mar	BSS	A	Welling United	788	L 1-2	Araba 50	18
32	Tue-06-Mar	BSS	H	Staines Town	233	D 1-1	Malcolm 22	18
33	Sat-10-Mar	BSS	H	Eastleigh	432	D 0-0		17
34	Sat-17-Mar	BSS	A	Basingstoke Town	312	L 0-1		18
35	Tue-20-Mar	BSS	H	Havant & Waterlooville	303	D 0-0		18
36	Sat-24-Mar	BSS	H	Farnborough	448	D 1-1	Joseph-Dubois 15	18
37	Sat-31-Mar	BSS	H	Weston-Super-Mare	676	W 1-0	Fuseini 62	17
38	Sat-07-Apr	BSS	A	Sutton United	749	D 1-1	Araba 74	17
39	Mon-09-Apr	BSS	H	Dartford	676	L 1-2	Malcolm 77	18
40	Sat-14-Apr	BSS	A	Truro City	537	W 2-1	Malcolm 56, Waldren 75	18
41	Sat-21-Apr	BSS	H	Thurrock	688	D 0-0		18
42	Sat-28-Apr	BSS	A	Dorchester Town	500	D 1-1	Waldren 24	17

CUPS

No.	Date	Comp	H/A	Opponents	Att:	Result	Goalscorers	
1	Sat-01-Oct	FAC 2Q	H	Welling United	716	W 2-1	Waldren 2 (pen 56, pen 79)	
2	Sat-15-Oct	FAC 3Q	A	Margate	515	W 3-2	McBean 2 (70, 71), Waldren pen 88	
3	Sat-29-Oct	FAC 4Q	A	Dartford	1567	W 2-1	Araba pen 27, Williams 75	
4	Sat-12-Nov	FAC 1	A	Leyton Orient	4452	L 0-3		
5	Sat-26-Nov	FAT 3Q	H	Didcot Town	277	L 1-3	Waldren pen 26	

League
Starts
Substitute
Unused Sub

Cups
Starts
Substitute
Unused Sub

Goals (Lg)
Goals (Cup)

Appearances / substitutes grid:

	SANTANEGLO	ADAMS	PATTERSON	WALDREN	DOLAN	HARWOOD	SMITH	HENRIQUES	ARABA	HOCKTON	DOLBY	HARDING	MCKENZIE	JONES	GILLMAN	UDOJI	WILLIAMS	HENLY	GREENE	RHULE	IBRAHIMA	LOCKETT	FORECAST	MCBEAN	AGU	HILL	TAYLOR	GOLDBERG	MAYNARD	PARMENTER	WARREN	SWAIBU	SEKAJJA	ANDERSON	WELCH	GERMAN	JOSEPH-DUBOIS	FUSEINI	THOMAS	JARRETT	MALCOLM	MEDLEY	SOBERS
	X	X	X	X	X	X	X	X	X	X	X	X	S	S	S	U	U																										
	X	X	X	X	X	X	X	X	X	X	X	X	S	S	S	U	U		S																								
	X	X	X	X	X	X	X	X	S	X	X	X	S	X	X	S	X		U	U							S	X															
	X		X	X	X		X	X	S	U	X	S	X	U	X	X			X	S																							
	X		X	U	X		X	S	X	X	X		U	X	S	U	X		X	X				U																			
	X		U	X	X			U	X	S	X	X		U	X	S	X		X	X				U																			
	X		S	X		X	X		S	X	S	X		X	X		X		U	X	U																						
	X		X	X	X	S	X	X		U	X	S	U		X	X			X	S																							
	X		U	X	X	X		X	X		U	S	X	X		X	X		X																								
			X	X	X	X	X	S				U	S	X	U		X			S	X		X																				
			X	X	S		X	X			X	S	X	X		X			X	U	X		X	U		S																	
			X	X	X		S	X			U	X	X		X	X			S	X			X	S	U	X																	
			X	S	U	X			X		S	X	X	S					X	X			X	X	X					X	X												
			S				X	X	U		S	X		X	X				S	X	U	S			X			X	X	X			U										
					U	X	X	S	X			X	X		U	X				S	X				X			X	X	X	U												
			S				X	X	X	X			U	X						U	X				U	X		X		X	X	S											
		X	U			X	X	U	X						S						S							X	X	U		X	X	X	X	X							
		X	S			X	X	U	X						X						S							X		U		X	X	X	X	S	X						
		X	X			X	X	U	X						U	S					X							X	X	S					X	X		X						
		X	U			X	X	X	S						S					X								S	U				U		X	X		X	X	X	X			
		X	X			X	X	X	S						X					S								U					X		X			X	X	X	X	X		
		X	X			X	X	X							U					U								U					X		X			X	X	X	X	S	S	
		X	X			X	X	X							U					U								U					X		X			X	X	X	X	S	S	
		X	X			X	X	X							U					U								U					X		X			X	X	X	X	S	S	
		X	X			X	X	X						U			S			U			U					S					X		X			X	X	X	X	X		
		X	X			X	X	S						U						X			S					S					X		X			X	X	S	X	S		
		X	X			X	X	X						U			X			S								U					X		X			X	X	S	X	S		
		X				X	X	S						X			X			U			U	U				X							X			X	X	X	X	X		
		X				X	X	S						X			U			S	U							U							X			X	X	X	X	X		X
		X	U			X	S	X	X						X					U								U					X		X			X	X	S	X	X		
		X	X			X	X	X						X			U			S			U					S					X		X			X	X	X	S			
		X	X			X	X	X						U						S			X	U				S					X		X			X	X	S	S	S		
		X	X			X		X	S						U					U			U										X		X			X	X	X	X	X		
		X	X			X		X	S						U					S			U	U									X		X			X	X	X	X	X		
		X	X			X		X	X						U					U			S	U									X		X			X	X	U	X	X		
			X	X			S	X	X				U	S	X	X	X	X		X	U	X				X	S	U	U														
		X	X			X	U	X	X				X	U	X	X	X	X		U	S					U	S	U	S														
		X				X	X	S	X	X			U	U	U	X	S	X		X	X				X	X		X	S	U	X												
		X	X	X	X	X	S			X			U		X	X	X			U	X	U			X	S	U	X			S												
		X	X	X	S			X					S	U	X	X				X		S		X		U	X	X	X														

Totals

	SANTANEGLO	ADAMS	PATTERSON	WALDREN	DOLAN	HARWOOD	SMITH	HENRIQUES	ARABA	HOCKTON	DOLBY	HARDING	MCKENZIE	JONES	GILLMAN	UDOJI	WILLIAMS	HENLY	GREENE	RHULE	IBRAHIMA	LOCKETT	FORECAST	MCBEAN	AGU	HILL	TAYLOR	GOLDBERG	MAYNARD	PARMENTER	WARREN	SWAIBU	SEKAJJA	ANDERSON	WELCH	GERMAN	JOSEPH-DUBOIS	FUSEINI	THOMAS	JARRETT	MALCOLM	MEDLEY	SOBERS
	9	3	32	32	15	40	13	34	31	5	5	7	6	9	10	11	13	1	9	4	10	0	11	1	0	9	13	4	0	4	7	23	1	3	18	2	18	17	11	14	6	0	1
	0	0	3	2	0	1	7	1	9	1	1	6	9	8	1	1	13	0	1	15	0	0	0	2	0	3	3	2	1	0	1	0	2	0	0	0	0	0	4	1	9	3	0
	0	0	3	3	1	0	4	1	0	5	1	0	17	6	3	9	0	1	11	14	1	0	1	0	2	7	2	0	0	2	0	2	0	0	0	0	1	0	0	0	0	0	0
	0	0	4	4	4	3	0	3	5	0	0	1	0	2	5	4	4	0	2	2	2	0	5	0	0	3	1	1	0	0	0	0	0	0	0	0	0	0	0	0	0	0	0
	0	0	0	0	0	1	3	0	0	0	0	0	2	0	0	1	0	0	0	1	1	0	0	4	0	1	0	1	0	0	0	0	0	0	0	0	0	0	0	0	0	0	0
	0	0	0	0	0	0	1	0	0	0	0	2	3	2	0	0	0	0	2	1	1	0	0	0	5	1	0	0	0	0	0	0	0	0	0	0	0	0	0	0	0	0	0
	0	0	0	7	0	1	5	0	14	1	0	2	2	1	1	0	3	0	0	1	2	0	0	1	0	0	1	0	0	0	0	0	0	0	4	1	1	0	4	0	0		
	0	0	4	0	0	0	0	0	1	0	0	0	0	0	0	0	1	0	0	0	0	2	0	0	0	0	0	0	0	0	0	0	0	0	0	0	0	0	0	0	0		

PLAYING SQUAD 2012/13

Existing Players		SN	HT	WT	DOB	AGE	POB	Career	Apps	Goals
GOALKEEPERS										
George	Howard							Charlton (Scholar), Bromley 7/12		
Joe	Welch		6'02"	12 12	29/11/1988	23	Welwyn Garden	Southend Rel c/s 07, Diss T (L) 3/07, Bishops Stortford c/s 07 Rel 8/08, Cheshunt 8/08, Histon 10/08, Weymouth (2ML) 2/10, Stevenage (SL) 3/11, Ebbsfleet 7/11, Bromley (2ML) 1/12 Perm 3/12	18	0
DEFENDERS										
Tony	Finn				27/11/1982	29		Hayes, Gravesend Rel 2/04, Edgware, Northwood 8/04, Colliers Wood, Met Police 3/06, AFC Wimbledon 6/07 Rel 5/09, Welling 6/09, Chelmsford 3/10 Rel c/s 10, Bromley 7/10, Met Police c/s 11, Carshalton 11/11, Bromley 7/12		
Liam	Harwood				10/03/1988	24		Chipstead, Carshalton 7/06, Bristol R Undisc 9/08, Margate (2ML) 12/08, Carshalton 3/09, Margate 10/09, Tonbridge A 11/09, Bromley 11/10, Dulwich H 11/10, Thurrock 1/11, Bromley 2/11	41	1
Marlon	Patterson		5'09"	11 10	24/06/1983	29	London	Millwall (Trainee), Chelsea (Trainee), Crawley 8/02, Fisher 1/03, Billericay, Fisher 12/03, Carshalton 3/04, Dulwich Hamlet 12/04, Carshalton 7/05, Hayes & Yeading 7/06, Dag & Red NC 8/07, Welling (3ML) 9/07, Grays (SL) 2/08, Bishops Stortford (L) 11/08, Histon 1/09, Bishops Stortford (SL) 2/09, Staines (Trial) 8/09, Bishops Stortford 8/09, Chelmsford 12/09, Bromley 9/10, Thurrock 2/11, Billericay 3/11, Bromley 8/11	35	0
Jerome	Sobers				18/04/1986	26		Ford U, Ipswich 2/04 Rel c/s 05, Brentford (L) 3/05, Chelmsford 7/05, Bromley 10/06, Braintree 7/07 Rel 10/07, Bromley 10/07, Billericay, Bromley 3/12	1	0
Moses	Swaibu		6'02"	11 11	09/05/1989	23	Southwark	C.Palace Rel c/s 08, Weymouth (L) 2/08, Gillingham (Trial), Bromley NC 9/08, Lincoln C 1/09 Rel c/s 11, Kettering 10/11 Rel 12/11, Bromley 12/11	23	0
MIDFIELDERS										
Ali	Fuseini		5'06"	09 10	07/12/1988	23	Accra, Ghana	Millwall Rel c/s 10, Leeds (Trial) 7/10, C.Palace (Trial) 7/10, L.Orient (Trial) 9/10, Lewes 1/11, Lincoln C 1/11 Rel 11/11, Eastleigh 12/11, Bromley 1/12	17	1
Bradley	Goldberg							Charlton (Scholar) Rel c/s 12, Bromley (2ML) 11/11, Hastings U (WE) 2/12, Bromley c/s 12, Hastings U (Dual)	6	0
Albert	Jarrett		6'01"	10 07	23/10/1984	27	Sierra Leone	Arsenal (Jun), Dulwich H, Wimbledon 4/03 Rel c/s 04, Brighton 7/04, Stevenage (L) 3/05, Swindon (2ML) 1/06, Watford 8/06 Rel c/s 07, Boston U (L) 2/07, MK Dons (SL) 3/07, Southend (Trial) 8/07, Injured, Yeovil (Trial) 8/08, Gillingham 9/08 Rel c/s 09, Barnet 7/09 Rel c/s 10, Lincoln C 7/10 Rel 3/11, Aldershot T (L) 2/11, Port Vale (Trial) 9/11, Lewes 11/11, Bromley 1/12	15	0
Sanchez	Ming				26/03/1990	22		Fisher, Welling 10/08 Rel 9/09, Dulwich H, Chipstead, Bishops Stortford 8/10 Rel c/s 11, Dulwich H c/s 11, Bromley c/s 12	19	1
Aaron	Rhule							Bromley		
Danny	Waldren							Waltham Forest, Croydon A 12/06, Tooting & M 9/10, Croydon A 12/10, Bromley 8/11	34	7
FORWARDS										
Hakeem	Araba				12/02/1990	22		Peterborough, Boston U (SL) 2/08, Dag & Red 8/08 Rel 6/10, Thurrock (3ML) 8/08, Redbridge (L) 11/08, Redbridge (L) 1/09, Bishops Stortford 8/10, Billericay 9/10, East Thurrock 10/10, Bromley 8/11	40	14
Ali	Chaaban				16/03/1982	30	Lebanon	Dorking, Leatherhead 7/02, Farnborough 6/03 Rel 1/05, Lewes 3/04, Farnborough 8/04, Exeter 2/05 Rel 2/05, Sutton U 8/05 Rel 9/05, Break, Sutton U 12/05, Staines 1/06, Bromley 6/07 Rel, Break, Bromley 1/09 Rel c/s 09, Staines (Dual) 4/09, Gillingham (Trial) c/s 09, Bromley 8/09, Staines 9/09, Boreham Wood 11/10, Chelmsford 2/11, Boreham Wood 7/11, Kingstonian 9/11, Staines 11/11, Bromley c/s 12 Bromley	17	1
Mike	Jones									
Pierre	Joseph-Dubois				12/02/1988	24	Paris, Fra	Reading, Tooting & Mitcham (L) 8/06, Grays 1/07, Crawley 8/07 Rel 5/08, Weymouth 5/08 Rel 2/09, Histon NC 9/09 Rel 10/09, Weymouth 12/09, Hayes & Yeading (Trial) c/s 10, Hayes & Yeading 3/11, Bromley 1/12	18	4
Michael	Malcolm		5'10"	11 07	13/10/1985	26	Harrow	Wycombe (Yth), Tottenham £10,000 Rel c/s 05, Stockport 7/05 Rel c/s 07, Kettering 8/07 Rel 9/07, Rushden & D 9/07, Thurrock 12/07, Weymouth 1/08, Crawley (2ML) 11/08 Perm 1/09 Rel 12/09, Hayes & Yeading (3ML) 8/10, Farnborough 12/10, Lewes 7/11, Bromley 2/12	15	4
Warren	McBean				13/02/1986	26	London	Watford (Jun), Broxbourne B, Barnet 7/04, Waltham Forest (L) 3/05, Farnborough 8/05 Rel 8/06, Braintree 8/06 Rel 10/06, St Albans 10/06 Rel 10/06, Sutton U 10/06, Eastleigh (2ML) 2/08, Bromley 6/08, Chelmsford (SL) 3/10, Lewes 7/11, Havant & W 8/11 Rel 9/11, Bromley 9/11 Rel 11/11, Margate 12/11, Welling 1/12, Bromley 7/12	3	1
Gareth A	Williams		5'10"	11 13	10/09/1982	29	Germiston	C.Palace, Colchester (2ML) 1/03, Cambridge U (L) 10/03, Bournemouth (L) 2/04, Colchester (SL) 3/04, Colchester P/E 9/04 Rel 5/06, Blackpool (SL) 3/06, Yeovil (Trial) 8/06, Bromley 9/06, Weymouth 9/06, Basingstoke 10/06, Bromley 10/06, Braintree 5/08 Rel 5/09, Bromley 6/09, Croydon Ath 1/10, Ebbsfleet 9/10 Rel 6/11, Bromley 8/11	26	3

CHELMSFORD CITY

Chairman: Mansell Wallace
Secretary: Alan Brown　　　(T) 07963 626 381　　(E) algbrown@blueyonder.co.uk
Additional Committee Members:
David Selby, Mansell Wallace, Trevor Smith, Martyn Gard, Martin Bissett.

Manager: Glenn Pennyfather
Programme Editor: TBA　　　　　　　　(E)

2011-12 Squad.

Club Factfile

Founded: 1938　　　**Nickname:** City or Clarets
Previous Names:
Previous Leagues: Southern League 1938-2004. Isthmian 2004-08

Club Colours (change): All claret (All white)

Ground: Melbourne Park Stadium, Salerno Way, Chelmsford CM1 2EH　　　(T) 01245 290 959
Capacity: 3,000　**Seats:** 1,300　**Covered:** 1,300　**Clubhouse:** Yes　**Shop:** Yes

Directions: Leave A12 at J15 and head towards Chelmsford. At the roundabout turn left into Westway. Turn left onto the A1060 signposted Sawbridgeworth. At the second set of traffic lights turn right into Chignal Road. Turn right into Melbourne Avenue. Salerno Way is on your left. At the end of the football pitches and immediately before the block of flats, turn left at the mini roundabout in Salerno Way to enter the Stadium car park.

Previous Grounds: New Writtle Street 1938-97, Maldon Town 1997-98, Billericay Town 1998-2005

Record Attendance: 16,807 v Colchester United - Southern League 10/09/1949. Salerno Way: 2,998 v Billericay Town - Isthmian Jan. 2006
Record Victory: 10-1 v Bashley (H) - Southern League 26/04/2000
Record Defeat: 1-10 v Barking (A) - FA Trophy 11/11/1978
Record Goalscorer: Tony Butcher - 287 (1957-71)
Record Appearances: Derek Tiffin - 550 (1950-63)
Additional Records: Paid £10,000 to Dover Athletic for Tony Rogers 1992
Received £50,000 from Peterborough United for David Morrison
Senior Honours:
Southern League 1945-46, 67-68, 71-72, Southern Division 1988-89, League Cup 1945-46, 59-60, 90-91.
Essex Professional Cup 1957-58, 69-70, 70-71, 73-74, 74-75. Non-League Champions Cup 1971-72.
Essex Senior Cup 1985-86, 88-89, 92-93, 2002-03. Isthmian League Premier Division 2007-08.

10 YEAR RECORD

02-03		03-04		04-05		05-06		06-07		07-08		08-09		09-10		10-11		11-12	
SthP	9	SthP	18	Isth P	8	Isth P	10	Isth P	3	Isth P	1	Conf S	5	Conf S	3	Conf S	4	Conf S	6

CHELMSFORD CITY

No.	Date	Comp	H/A	Opponents	Att:	Result	Goalscorers	Pos
1	Sat-13-Aug	BSS	H	Truro City	808	L 0-1		17
2	Sat-20-Aug	BSS	A	Havant & Waterlooville	692	W 3-2	Og (Newton) 6, Akurang 16, Cornhill 85	13
3	Mon-22-Aug	BSS	H	Farnborough	764	D 2-2	Cornhill 41, Akurang 69	12
4	Sat-27-Aug	BSS	H	Dartford	1013	D 0-0		15
5	Mon-29-Aug	BSS	A	Eastbourne Borough	781	W 3-1	Modeste 6 Og (Cole) 8, Clark 19	12
6	Sat-03-Sep	BSS	H	Dover Athletic	1031	L 2-3	Rainford 8, Clark 90	14
7	Sat-10-Sep	BSS	A	Hampton & Richmond Boro'	489	W 4-0	Palmer 3, Rainford pen 22, Haines 23, Akurang 68	13
8	Tue-13-Sep	BSS	A	Staines Town	264	D 1-1	Rainford 3	10
9	Sat-17-Sep	BSS	A	Weston-Super-Mare	431	W 2-1	Cornhill 2, Ibe 87	6
10	Mon-19-Sep	BSS	H	Tonbridge Angels	938	D 2-2	Rainford pen 8, Modeste 11	5
11	Sat-24-Sep	BSS	H	Boreham Wood	1042	D 0-0		8
12	Sat-08-Oct	BSS	A	Maidenhead United	355	D 1-1	Ibe 5	9
13	Sat-22-Oct	BSS	A	Salisbury City	763	W 1-0	Tann 90	6
14	Mon-24-Oct	BSS	H	Eastleigh	937	W 3-0	Morgan 8, Tann 12, Palmer 20	6
15	Sat-05-Nov	BSS	A	Farnborough	505	W 3-1	Akurang 2, Ibe 52, Bakare 60	5
16	Mon-07-Nov	BSS	H	Dorchester Town	813	D 0-0		5
17	Sat-19-Nov	BSS	H	Bromley	1008	W 6-1	Ibe 16, Rainford pen 21, Cornhill 30, Bakare 52, Benjamin 84, Parker 90	5
18	Tue-22-Nov	BSS	A	Woking	1558	D 1-1	Parker 36	5
19	Mon-05-Dec	BSS	H	Maidenhead United	704	W 2-0	Bakare 49, Whitely 80	4
20	Sat-17-Dec	BSS	A	Basingstoke Town	434	D 1-1	Ibe 10	5
21	Mon-19-Dec	BSS	A	Boreham Wood	251	W 3-1	Parker pen 68, Bakare 72, Ibe 74	3
22	Mon-26-Dec	BSS	H	Thurrock	1064	W 1-0	Rainford pen 15	3
23	Sun-01-Jan	BSS	A	Thurrock	729	W 2-0	Bakare 35, Parker86	2
24	Sat-07-Jan	BSS	H	Sutton United	1168	L 2-3	Parker 28, Akurang 80	3
25	Sat-14-Jan	BSS	A	Truro City	505	W 2-0	Cornhill 78, Ibe 88	2
26	Sat-21-Jan	BSS	H	Staines Town	901	L 0-1		3
27	Sat-28-Jan	BSS	A	Welling United	779	D 1-1	Cornhill 14	4
28	Sat-18-Feb	BSS	H	Havant & Waterlooville	859	W 3-1	Miller 20, Modeste 67, Akurang 89	3
29	Mon-20-Feb	BSS	H	Weston-Super-Mare	701	W 3-2	Rainford 58, Ibe 67, Whitely 89	2
30	Sat-25-Feb	BSS	A	Bromley	636	L 0-1		4
31	Sat-03-Mar	BSS	H	Hampton & Richmond Boro'	821	W 1-0	Rainford pen 60	4
32	Tue-06-Mar	BSS	A	Dover Athletic	625	L 1-2	Akurang 59	5
33	Sat-10-Mar	BSS	H	Welling United	1003	L 1-2	Rainford pen 13	5
34	Sat-17-Mar	BSS	A	Sutton United	654	L 2-3	Whitely 12, Rainford 80	5
35	Tue-20-Mar	BSS	A	Dorchester Town	384	W 2-1	Slabber 32, Tann 45	5
36	Sat-24-Mar	BSS	H	Basingstoke Town	865	L 0-1		5
37	Sat-31-Mar	BSS	A	Tonbridge Angels	728	D 0-0		5
38	Sat-07-Apr	BSS	A	Dartford	1616	D 0-0		5
39	Mon-09-Apr	BSS	H	Eastbourne Borough	835	W 1-0	Akurang 78	5
40	Sat-14-Apr	BSS	H	Salisbury City	777	L 2-3	Slabber 6, Akurang 45	5
41	Sat-21-Apr	BSS	A	Eastleigh	831	D 1-1	Rainford pen 88	5
42	Sat-28-Apr	BSS	H	Woking	1080	L 2-3	Akurang 16, Slabber 42	6

CUPS

No.	Date	Comp	H/A	Opponents	Att:	Result	Goalscorers	
1	Sat-01-Oct	FAC 2Q	H	Tonbridge Angels	653	W 3-0	Ibe 2 (45, 50), Og (Judge) 73	
2	Sat-15-Oct	FAC 3Q	A	Lowestoft Town	1065	W 5-2	Akurang 37, Cornhill 40, Ibe 2 (51, 86), Og (Fisk) 59	
3	Sat-29-Oct	FAC 4Q	H	Gloucester City	928	D 1-1	Clark 90	
4	Tue-01-Nov	FAC 4QR	A	Gloucester City	490	W 1-0	Akurang 85	
5	Sat-12-Nov	FAC 1	H	AFC Telford	1430	W 4-0	Palmer 11, Parker 45, Rainford 2 (pen 63, 87)	
6	Sat-26-Nov	FAT 3Q	H	Woking	740	W 2-0	Palmer 77, Ibe 81	
7	Sat-03-Dec	FAC 2	H	Macclesfield Town	2919	D 1-1	Cornhill 35	
8	Sat-10-Dec	FAT 1	H	Bath City	635	L 2-3	Parker 2 (pen 52, 90)	
9	Wed-14-Dec	FAC 2R	A	Macclesfield Town	1607	L 0-1		

League
Starts
Substitute
Unused Sub

Cups
Starts
Substitute
Unused Sub

Goals (Lg)
Goals (Cup)

This page is a player appearances and goals grid (season record). Player surnames run across the top as column headers; each row is a match, with X = start, S = substitute used, U = unused substitute. The figures at the foot are totals.

SEARLE	NUNN	PALMER	TANN	CLARK	RAINFORD	MODESTE	CORCORAN	IBE	CORNHILL	BENJAMIN	WHITELY	AKURANG	BROWN	HAINES	WOOLLEY	MORGAN	SCARLETT	MILLER	PENTNEY	COOK	BAKARE	HARRISON	PARKER	BATCHFORD	LAMB	POPO	MCLEOD	OSBORN	ROSSIS	WELSH	BRYAN	GOUGH	SLABBER	HAMILTON	DIEDHIOU	MENSAH
X	X	X	X	X	X	X	X	X	X	S	S	S	U	U																						
	X	X	X	X	X	X	S	S	X	U	S	X	X	S	U																					
X	X	X	X	X	X	X	U	S	X		S	X	X	S	U	X																				
X	X	X		X		X	X	X	X	S	X		X	X	X	U	S	U	U																	
X	X	X		X	X	X	U	S	X	S	X	S	X	X	X	U	S																			
X	X	X		X	X	X	U	S	X	S	X	X	X	X		S		U																		
X	U	X		X	X	X	S	S	X	S	X	S	X	X	X		U	X																		
	U	X		X	X	X	U	S	X	S	X	S	X	X	X		S	X	X																	
	X	X		X	X		X	S	X	U	X	U	X	U	X		X		S	X	S															
	X	X		X	X	X	X	X	X	X	U	X	U	S	X		S		X	S	X															
		X	X	X	X	X	X	X	X	U		X	U	U	U		S		X	X	X	S														
X	U	X	X		X	X	X	X	X	U	X	U	U			S		X																		
X	U	X	X			X	X	X	X		S	X	U	U		X		X		S																
X	X	X	X	X	U	X	X	X	X	S	X	X	U	U				S																		
X	X	X	X	S	X	X		X	X	X	S	X	X	U	U			U		X																
X	U	X	X	X			X	X	X	X	S	X		U	S			X		X	S															
X	U	X	X	X	X		X	X	X	U	X		U	U				X		U	X															
X	S	X	X	X			X	X	X	X		U	U			U	X		X		X															
X	S	X	X	X	X		X	X	X	S		U				X		X		S		X		U												
X	U	X	X	X			X	X	X	U	X	X	S					X		S		X		S												
X	U	X	X	X	X		X	X	X	X	U							X		X	S			X	S											
X	U	X	X	X	X		X	X	X	X	S		U					X		S	X			X	U											
X	U	X	X	X	X	S		X	X		S	U						X		X	X			X	U											
X	S	X	X	X	X		X	X		U	X				U		X			S		X		S	X											
X	X	X		X	X	X		X	X	X	U		U					X				X		U	S	U										
X	X	X		X	X	S	X	X		U	S							X				X		S	U	X										
X	X	X		X	X	X	X	X		S	S							X				X		S	U	U										
X	X	X		X	X	X	X	X		U	S	U						S				X		X	U	S										
X	X	X	X	X	X	X	X			U	S	U						X						U		S			S							
X	X	X	X	X	X	X		X		S	X	U						X						U	U	S										
X	X	X	X	X	X	U	X	X			X	X	U					U						S		X	S									
X	X	X	X	X	S			X			X	X	U					U						S	X	U	X									
X	X	X	X	X	X	S	U	S	X			X	U					U						X		S	U	X								
X	X	X	X	X		U	S	X			X	X	U					X						S		S	X	X								
X	X	X		X		X	X	X	X		X	S	X					U						S		U		X	U							
X	X	X		X		X	X	X	X		X	S	X					U						S		U		X	U							
X	X	X	X			X	U	S	X		U	X		X				X						X		X		X	U							
X	X	X	X			X	S	S	X		S	X	X					U						X		X	U		X		U					
X	X	X	X	X			X		X			X	X					X						U		S		U	U	U	U					
X		X	X	X	X			S	X			X	X					X						U		S		X		U	X		U			
X	U	X	X	X	X	X	X	X	S	U	X	U	U			S		X		S																
X	U	X	X			X	X	X	X	X	S	X	S	U				U	X																	
X	S	X	X			X	X	X	X	S	U	X	U	U		X	U	X					U													
X	X	X	X			X	X	X	X	U	X	U	U			U							U	U												
X	U	X	X	X			X	X	X	S	X			U		X	U	X					U	S	U											
X	U	X	X			X	X	X	U	X	X	U	U					X	U		X															
X	U	X	X			X	X	X	U	X	X	U	U				U	X			U	X														
X	X	X	X		X		X		S			U	X			S	U	X			X		X													
X	U	X	X	X	S	X	X	X	X	U		X	U			S	U	X			U	X														
34	**25**	**42**	**28**	**40**	**29**	**26**	**26**	**26**	**41**	**2**	**25**	**24**	**8**	**12**	**1**	**5**	**0**	**21**	**5**	**0**	**5**	**0**	**16**	**0**	**2**	**1**	**3**	**0**	**6**	**0**	**2**	**7**	**0**	**0**	**0**	
0	3	0	0	0	2	3	3	12	0	11	8	9	3	2	0	6	0	2	0	4	5	0	5	0	0	4	1	9	0	3	4	0	0	0	0	
0	12	0	0	0	1	1	7	0	0	6	7	5	9	17	4	3	2	4	0	0	2	0	5	0	0	1	4	1	7	4	0	1	0	4	3	1
9	2	9	9	9	2	6	8	9	8	1	4	7	0	1	0	2	0	8	0	0	1	0	4	0	0	0	0	0	0	0	0	0	0	0	0	0
0	1	0	0	0	1	0	0	0	0	4	1	0	1	0	0	3	0	0	0	1	0	0	1	0	0	1	0	0	0	0	0	0	0	0	0	0
0	6	0	0	0	0	0	0	0	0	4	2	0	7	7	0	0	7	0	0	0	1	4	1	1	0	0	0	0	0	0	0	0	0	0	0	0
0	0	2	3	2	11	3	0	8	6	1	3	10	0	1	0	1	0	1	0	0	5	0	5	0	0	0	0	0	0	0	0	3	0	0	0	
0	0	2	0	1	2	0	0	5	2	0	0	2	0	0	0	0	0	0	0	0	0	0	3	0	0	0	0	0	0	0	0	0	0	0	0	

PLAYING SQUAD 2012/13

Existing Players		SN	HT	WT	DOB	AGE	POB	Career	Apps	Goals
GOALKEEPERS										
Stuart	Searle		6'03"	12 04	27/02/1979	33	Wimbleson	Tooting & Mitcham (Yth), Wimbledon Rel c/s 97, Woking c/s 97, Carshalton 8/98, Aldershot 12/99, Molesey (L) 3/00, Molesey (L) 9/00, Carshalton (L) 3/01, Carshalton £2,500 7/01, Basingstoke 11/05 (Also Chelsea Academy coach), Chelsea (Pl/Coach) 7/07, Walton & H (Dual) 7/07, Carshalton 7/08, Watford 1/09, MK Dons 7/09 Rel c/s 11, Chelmsford 8/11	34	0
DEFENDERS										
Kenny	Clark				12/08/1988	24		Dag & Red, Heybridge (L) 3/06, Thurrock 6/06, Chelmsford 6/11	40	2
Anthony	Cook		5'07"	11 02	10/08/1989	23	London	Cardiff (Yth), Croydon Ath, Dag & Red 8/07, Carshalton (L) 10/08, Concord R (L) 12/08 Perm, Braintree (Dual) 3/09, Chelmsford 7/09, Canvey Island (L) 9/11	4	0
Mark	Haines		6'03"		28/09/1989	22		Northampton, Cheshunt (WE) 2/08, Grays (WE) 3/08, Grays 5/08, East Thurrock (L) 9/08, Chelmsford 7/09, Bishops Stortford (L) 1/12	14	1
Justin	Miller		6'00"	11 10	16/12/1980	31	Johannesburg, SA	Ipswich, L.Orient (3ML) 9/02, L.Orient 1/03 Rel c/s 07, Port Vale 7/07 Rel 4/08, Chelmsford 7/08 Rel 1/09, Bidvest Wits (SA) 1/09, Rushden & D 6/10, Chelmsford 5/11	23	1
Aiden	Palmer		5'08"	10 10	02/01/1987	25	Enfield	L.Orient Rel c/s 09, Dag & Red (L) 1/09, Prison, Bishops Stortford 12/09, Cambridge U 1/10 Rel 4/10, Bishops Stortford 7/10, Chelmsford 6/11	42	2
Adam	Tann		6'00"	12 08	12/05/1982	30	Fakenham	Norwich (Yth), Cambridge U Rel c/s 05, Cambridge C (SL) 3/01, Reading (Trial) 7/05, Ipswich (Trial) 8/05, Rushden & D (Trial), Gravesend 10/05, Notts County 11/05, L.Orient 1/06 Rel c/s 07, Notts County 8/07 Rel c/s 09, Histon 7/09, Chelmsford 7/10	28	3
MIDFIELDERS										
David	Bridges		6'00"	12 00	22/09/1982	29	Huntingdon	Cambridge U, New England Rev (USA) (Trial) c/s 04, Chesterfield (Trial) 7/04, Northampton (Trial) 8/04, Latvia c/s 04, Braintree 1/05, Rushden & D 2/05, Histon 3/05, Cambridge U 8/05 Rel 5/07, Kettering 7/07, Stevenage 5/08, Kettering 8/11, Chelmsford 8/12		
Max	Cornhill							Local, Romford, East Thurrock 9/06, Chelmsford 5/11	41	6
Greg	Morgan				30/09/1987	24		Boreham Wood Rel 5/11, Chelmsford 6/11	11	1
Craig	Parker							Bury T, Needham Market, Chelmsford 5/11	21	5
Jordan	Parkes		6'00"	12 00	26/07/1989	23	Watford	Watford, Stevenage (L) 11/08, Barnet 7/10 Rel c/s 12, Farnborough (L) 1/12, Chelmsford 8/12		
Dave	Rainford		6'00"	11 11	21/04/1979	33	Stepney	Colchester Rel c/s 99, Scarborough (L) 12/98, Slough 6/99, Grays c/s 01, Heybridge S 7/02, Slough 11/02, Ford U 1/03, Bishops Stortford 3/03, Dag & Red 5/06, Chelmsford 6/08	31	11
Ishmael	Welsh		5'07"	10 10	04/09/1987	24	Deptford	West Ham Rel c/s 06, Yeovil 7/06 Rel 5/08, Weymouth (L) 3/07, Torquay (5ML) 8/07, Forest Green (SL) 2/08, Grays 5/08, Ebbsfleet 7/09, Grays 8/10, Lewes 1/11, Chelmsford 2/12	9	0
Warren	Whitely				11/09/1985	26		Croydon, Three Bridges, Harrow 9/08, Northwood (Dual) 11/10 Perm, Ashford T (Middx) 3/11, Chelmsford 8/11	33	3
FORWARDS										
Cliff	Akurang		6'02"	12 03	27/02/1981	31	Ghana	Chelsea (Jun), Luton (Trainee), Chesham, Hitchin 8/00 Rel 12/01, Purfleet/Thurrock 12/01, Heybridge Swifts 2/05, Dag & Red (L) 11/05, Dag & Red 1/06, Thurrock (SL) 1/07, Histon 5/07, Barnet Undisc 1/08 Rel c/s 10, Weymouth (SL) 3/09, Rushden & D (SL) 7/09, Thurrock 7/10, Maidenhead 11/10, Braintree 2/11, Chelmsford 6/11	33	10
Craig	Calver		5'10"	12 00	20/01/1991	21	Cambridge	Cambridge C (Yth), Ipswich (Scholar) Rel 3/08, Southend Rel c/s 10, Harlow (L) 12/08, St Albans (L) 8/09, Braintree (L) 2/10, AFC Sudbury (L) 3/10, Yeovil 7/10, Braintree (L) 3/11, Histon (Trial) 6/11, Bishops Stortford 8/11, Kings Lynn T 9/11, AFC Sudbury 9/11, Haverhill R (Dual) 11/11, Chelmsford 7/12		
Jamie	Slabber		6'02"	11 10	31/12/1984	27	Enfield	Tottenham, AB Copenhagen (L) 3/04, Swindon (L) 12/04, Aldershot 3/05 Rel 5/05, Grays 7/05, Oxford U (L) 11/06, Stevenage 12/06 Rel 5/07, Rushden & D (Trial) 7/07, Havant & W 8/07 Rel 10/08, Grays NC 10/08, Woking 12/09 Rel 5/10, Eastleigh 5/10, Chelmsford 3/12	7	3

DORCHESTER TOWN

Chairman: Shaun Hearn
Secretary: David Martin   **(T)** 07971 172 795   **(E)** dorchdave@gmail.com
Additional Committee Members:
David Martin, Adam Robertson, David Diaz, Paul Harris, Dan Steadman, Matthew Lucas, Keith Kellaway.
Manager: Phil Simkin
Programme Editor: Keith Kellaway   **(E)** manager@dorchestertownfc.co.uk

Club Factfile

Founded: 1880   **Nickname:** The Magpies
Previous Names: None
Previous Leagues: Dorset, Western 1947-72

Club Colours (change): Black & white/black/black & white (All yellow)

Ground: The Avenue Stadium, Weymouth Avenue, Dorchester DT1 2RY   **(T)** 01305 262 451
Capacity: 5,009   **Seats:** 710   **Covered:** 2,846   **Clubhouse:** Yes   **Shop:** Yes

Directions: The stadium is located at the junction of A35 Dorchester Bypass and the A354 to Weymouth, adjacent to Tesco. There is a coach bay for the team coach at the front of the stadium. Any supporters coach should park on the railway embankment side of the stadium.

Previous Grounds: Council Recreation Ground, Weymouth Avenue 1908-1929, 1929-90, The Avenue Ground 1929

Record Attendance: 4,159 v Weymouth - Southern Premier 1999
Record Victory: 7-0 v Canterbury (A) - Southern League Southern Division 1986-87
Record Defeat: 0-13 v Welton Rovers (A) - Western League 1966
Record Goalscorer: Not known
Record Appearances: Derek 'Dinkie' Curtis - 458 (1950-66)
Additional Records: Denis Cheney scored 61 goals in one season. Paid £12,000 to Gloucester City for Chris Townsend 1990.
Senior Honours: Received £35,000 from Portsmouth for Trevor Sinclair.
Western League 19954-55. Southern League 1985-86, Division 1 East 2002-03. Dorset Senior Cup x7

10 YEAR RECORD

02-03		03-04		04-05		05-06		06-07		07-08		08-09		09-10		10-11		11-12	
SthE	1	SthP	17	Conf S	8	Conf S	11	Conf S	17	Conf S	21	Conf S	19	Conf S	17	Conf S	17	Conf S	11

DORCHESTER TOWN

No.	Date	Comp	H/A	Opponents	Att:	Result	Goalscorers	Pos
1	Sat-13-Aug	BSS	A	Dover Athletic	937	L 0-4		19
2	Tue-16-Aug	BSS	H	Maidenhead United	410	W 4-0	Flood pen 6, Critchell 61, N Walker 76, Moss 90	9
3	Sat-20-Aug	BSS	H	Eastbourne Borough	432	L 0-3		15
4	Fri-26-Aug	BSS	H	Eastleigh	505	L 1-3	Moss 32	16
5	Mon-29-Aug	BSS	A	Truro City	701	W 1-0	Crittenden 73	17
6	Sat-03-Sep	BSS	A	Sutton United	645	L 1-3	Critchell 32	18
7	Sat-10-Sep	BSS	H	Welling United	508	W 3-2	Flood pen 15, Dickenson 33, Bowles 47	15
8	Tue-13-Sep	BSS	A	Hampton & Richmond Boro'	260	W 2-0	Dovell 15, Crittenden 76	14
9	Sat-17-Sep	BSS	A	Basingstoke Town	336	L 0-1		14
10	Tue-20-Sep	BSS	H	Weston-Super-Mare	367	L 1-3	Moss 89	16
11	Sat-24-Sep	BSS	H	Woking	628	L 0-1		16
12	Sat-08-Oct	BSS	A	Staines Town	298	W 2-0	Moss 33, Devlin 90	15
13	Sat-15-Oct	BSS	A	Welling United	502	L 2-3	Flood pen 30, Dovell pen 82	15
14	Sat-22-Oct	BSS	H	Boreham Wood	443	L 0-1		16
15	Tue-25-Oct	BSS	A	Havant & Waterlooville	539	L 2-4	Bowles 8, Dickenson 15	17
16	Sat-29-Oct	BSS	H	Tonbridge Angels	417	W 3-1	Dickenson 8, Moss 2 (11, 89)	16
17	Sat-05-Nov	BSS	H	Basingstoke Town	491	W 2-1	Dickenson 14, Martin 51	11
18	Mon-07-Nov	BSS	A	Chelmsford City	813	D 0-0		10
19	Sat-12-Nov	BSS	H	Hampton & Richmond Boro'	447	W 1-0	Critchell 90	9
20	Sat-19-Nov	BSS	H	Sutton United	552	D 0-0		11
21	Sat-03-Dec	BSS	A	Maidenhead United	269	W 1-0	Wilson 18	7
22	Tue-06-Dec	BSS	H	Farnborough	334	D 3-3	Wilson 2 (2, 42), Dickenson 87	7
23	Tue-13-Dec	BSS	A	Bromley	223	D 0-0		7
24	Sat-17-Dec	BSS	A	Dartford	924	D 1-1	Symes 70	7
25	Mon-26-Dec	BSS	H	Salisbury City	981	L 0-3		8
26	Mon-02-Jan	BSS	A	Salisbury City	1003	W 1-0	Wilson 39	7
27	Sat-07-Jan	BSS	H	Thurrock	493	W 3-0	White 14, Wilson 48, Nichols 90	7
28	Sat-14-Jan	BSS	A	Eastbourne Borough	564	W 4-1	Wilson 39, Nichols pen 45, Crittenden 66, N Walker 80	7
29	Sat-21-Jan	BSS	H	Dover Athletic	579	D 1-1	Nichols 83	7
30	Sat-25-Feb	BSS	H	Havant & Waterlooville	469	L 3-6	Malsom 33, Nichols 2 (pen 57, pen 85)	10
31	Sat-03-Mar	BSS	A	Weston-Super-Mare	303	W 4-0	Nichols 13, Critchell 22, Malsom 45, Dovell 73	8
32	Sat-10-Mar	BSS	A	Boreham Wood	201	D 2-2	N Walker 22, Nichols pen 77	8
33	Tue-13-Mar	BSS	A	Woking	1268	L 1-4	N Walker 78	9
34	Sat-17-Mar	BSS	A	Thurrock	176	L 0-2		11
35	Tue-20-Mar	BSS	H	Chelmsford City	384	L 1-2	Dovell 61	11
36	Sat-24-Mar	BSS	H	Dartford	534	W 1-0	Dovell 54	9
37	Sat-31-Mar	BSS	A	Farnborough	452	W 2-1	Dovell 1, Nichols pen 82	9
38	Fri-06-Apr	BSS	A	Eastleigh	513	W 1-0	Og (Elphick) 90	8
39	Mon-09-Apr	BSS	H	Truro City	504	L 2-3	Critchell 63, Dovell 90	8
40	Sat-14-Apr	BSS	H	Staines Town	413	L 0-3		9
41	Sat-21-Apr	BSS	A	Tonbridge Angels	756	L 1-2	Malsom 24	10
42	Sat-28-Apr	BSS	H	Bromley	500	D 1-1	Malsom 47	11

CUPS

No.	Date	Comp	H/A	Opponents	Att:	Result	Goalscorers	
1	Sat-01-Oct	FAC 2Q	H	Weston-Super-Mare	329	L 0-1		
2	Sat-26-Nov	FAT 3Q	H	Gosport Borough	381	L 1-2	Dickenson 71	

League
Starts
Substitute
Unused Sub

Cups
Starts
Substitute
Unused Sub

Goals (Lg)
Goals (Cup)

EVANS	CRITCHELL	MARTIN	JERMYN	N WALKER	PEPRAH-ANNAN	CRITTENDEN	NICHOLLS	MOSS	FLOOD	DEVLIN	DICKENSON	WILSON	DOVELL	BELL	WALKER-HARRIS	SYMES	GLEESON	BOWLES	VICKERS	TAYLOR	JORDAN	TALLACK	SMEETON	MEKKI	JONES	GODFREY	FLOYD	WAY	S WALKER	WHITE	BROOMFIELD	CARLILE	NICHOLS	MALSOM	WORSFOLD	BUCKLER	TENNANT	GOODLAND
X	X	X	X	X	X	X	X	X	X	X		S	S	S	U	U																						
X	X	X	X	X	X	X	X	X	X	X		U	S	U	U	U																						
X	X	X	X	X	X	X	X	X	X	X		S	S		U	U																						
X	X	X	X	X	X		X	X	X	X		S		U	U	U																						
X	X	X	X		S	X	X	X	X	X			X	U	U	U	S																					
X	X	X	X		X	X	X	X				X	U	U	U	S	X																					
U	X	X	X		S		X	X	X	X		X	X	U	X	U	X	X																				
	X	X		X		X	S	X	X		X	S	X	X	X	X	U	U																				
	X	X		X		X	U	X	X	S	S	X	X	U	U		X	X		X																		
	X	X		X		X	S	X	X	S	S	X	X	U	U		X	X		X																		
		X				X	X	X	X	S	S	U	X	S	X	X	U		X		X																	
	X	S		X			X	U	S	X		X	X	X	S	X		U	X	X	X																	
	X	S		X			X	X	X		S	X	S	X	X			U	X	X	X																	
	X	X		X		S		X	S	S		X	X	X	U	X	U		X	X	X																	
	X	U		X		X	X	X	S	S	X	U	S		X			X	X																			
	X	S	X	X		X	X	X	U	S	X		U			X		U	X	X																		
U	X	X	X	X		X	X	X		S	X		S			X	U	X																				
	X	X	X	X		X	X	X		S	X	U	X	U	U			U	X																			
	X	X	X	X		X	X	X		U	X	S	U		X	U	X		U	X																		
		X	X	X			X	X		U	X	X	S	U	X	U	X	X		U	X																	
	X	U	X	X				X	X		X	X	X	X	X	X			U						U	U	U											
	X	U	X	X		S	S	S	X	X	X	U	X	U	X	X									X													
	X	X	X	X			X	X		X	X	X	S	U	X	U	X								U		U											
	X	X	X	X			X	X		X	X	S	U	X	X									U			U			X	U	U						
	X	X	X	X			X	X		X	X	S	U	X	X	S								U			X											
	X	U	X	X			X	X		X	X	S	U	X		X								U			S											
	X	S	X	X			X			X		X	S	U	X	U	X							X				S										
		X	X	X			X			X		X	S	X	X	U								X			U	U	U		X							
	X	U	X	X			X			X		X	U	U	X	U	X							X					U		X							
	X	U	X	X			X			X		X	U	U	X	S	X							X	U						X	X						
	X	X	X	X			U	X				U	X	X		U								X	X	U				U	X	X						
	X	X	X	X			X						X	X										X	U	S		U	U		X	X	X					
	X	S	X	X			X	X				U	X	X		S								X	U				U		X	X	X	S				
	X	S	X	X			X	X				X	U	X		S								X	U						S	X	X	X				
	X	X	X	X			X					X	U	X		X		X						X			U	U			X	S	U					
	X	S	X	X			X	X				X	U	X		X								X	S			U			X	X	U					
	X	S	X	X			X					X	S	U	X									X	X						X	U	X		U			
	X	X	X	X			X	X				U		U	X									X	X			U			U	X	X	S				
	X	X	X	X			X					X	U		X	X								X	X			U	U			X	S	U				
	X	X	X	X			X	S				X	X		X	X								X	U		U			S		X	U					
		S	X	X			X	X				X	X		X									X	U		X			S		X	X	X	U			
	X	X	X	X			X	X				X			X									X	U		U			X	X		X	X	U	U		
X	X		X				X	X	X	X	S	X	U	X	U	X		U		U	X	U																
X	X	X	X			X	X	X		S	X		S	U	X	S	X								X	U												
6	38	27	34	42	4	31	30	18	12	16	17	13	17	11	27	6	29	8	1	0	2	4	27	5	4	0	2	0	0	3	0	0	11	11	6	0	0	0
0	0	9	0	0	0	4	4	2	2	8	5	6	13	4	0	4	4	0	0	0	0	0	0	1	1	0	0	0	1	0	3	1	1	2	1	0	0	0
2	0	6	0	0	0	1	1	0	2	2	1	4	7	22	8	17	0	2	3	3	2	3	1	0	10	2	2	5	9	2	1	4	0	1	2	2	3	1
0	2	2	1	2	0	1	1	2	1	1	2	0	1	0	2	0	2	0	0	0	0	1	1	0	0	0	0	0	0	0	0	0	0	0	0	0	0	0
0	0	0	0	0	0	0	0	0	0	1	0	1	1	0	0	1	0	0	0	0	0	0	0	0	0	0	0	0	0	0	0	0	0	0	0	0	0	0
0	0	0	0	0	0	0	0	0	0	0	0	0	2	0	1	0	0	1	0	1	0	1	0	1	0	1	0	0	0	0	0	0	0	0	0	0	0	0
0	5	1	0	4	0	3	0	6	3	1	5	6	7	0	0	1	0	2	0	0	0	0	0	0	0	0	1	0	0	8	4	0	0	0	0	0	0	0
0	0	0	0	0	0	0	0	0	0	1	0	0	0	0	0	0	0	0	0	0	0	0	0	0	0	0	0	0	0	0	0	0	0	0	0	0	0	0

PLAYING SQUAD 2012/13

Existing Players		SN	HT	WT	DOB	AGE	POB	Career	Apps	Goals
GOALKEEPERS										
Dan	Floyd							Dorchester	2	0
Nic	Jones				13/05/1987	25	Poole	Dorchester, Weymouth, Basingstoke 3/08, New Milton 11/08, Hamworthy U, Poole T, Dorchester NC 11/11	5	0
Jason	Matthews	6'00"	12 02		15/03/1975	37	Paulton	Bristol R (Yth), Mangotsfield, Welton R, Westbury, Bath C, Paulton, Salisbury, Nuneaton, Taunton 8/98, Exeter 8/99 Rel c/s 00, Aberystwyth c/s 00, Cleveden 6/01, Weymouth 8/02, Eastleigh 3/08 Rel 5/11, Bath C 6/11, Dorchester 5/12		
Alan	Walker-Harris				06/10/1981	30	London	Southampton (Jun), Bashley, Brockenhurst, Lymington & New Milton 7/02, Bashley, Salisbury, Winchester 2/05, Eastleigh, Brockenhurst 5/06, Wimborne, Dorchester 8/11	27	0
DEFENDERS										
Harrison	Bell						Poole	Bournemouth (Scholar) Rel c/s 11, Dorchester 8/11	15	0
Neil	Martin				05/04/1989	23		Exeter, Hayes & Yeading (L) 8/08 Perm 9/08 Rel 10/08, Salisbury 1/09 Rel c/s 09, Dorchester 8/09	36	1
Jake	Smeeton	5'08"	11		09/08/1988	24	Yeovil	Yeovil Rel c/s 07, Dorchester 8/07, Gillingham T (L) 11/09, Poole T (2ML) 8/10, Poole T (L) 8/11	27	0
Ashley	Vickers	6'03"	13 10		14/06/1972	40	Sheffield	Sheff Utd, Worcester, Malvern T, 61 Club, Heybridge Swifts, Peterborough £5,000 12/97, St Albans 8/98, Dag & Red 3/00, Weymouth 5/06, Eastleigh 3/08, Newport C (L) 8/08 Perm 9/08, Dorchester (Pl/Coach) 3/09 (Pl/Man) 3/10	1	0
Nathan	Walker				03/10/1986	25		Weymouth, Portland U (L), Dorchester, Hamworthy U, Wimborne T 1/09, Dorchester 12/09	42	4
Steve	Walker							Poole T, Dorchester 6/11	0	0
Jacob	Wannell							Exeter, Dorchester (L) 8/12		
Daniel	Way							Dorchester	0	0
MIDFIELDERS										
Anthony	Carlile							Dorchester	3	0
Nick	Crittenden	5'08"	10 11		11/11/1978	33	Ascot	Chelsea Rel 6/00, Plymouth (L) 11/98, Yeovil 8/00 Rel c/s 03 Re-signed, Rel c/s 04, Aldershot 6/04, Weymouth 5/06 Rel 5/08, Dorchester 6/08	35	3
Jamie	Gleeson	6'00"	12 03		15/01/1985	27	Poole	Southampton Rel c/s 04, Kidderminster 7/04 Rel c/s 05, Eastleigh (L) 10/04, Dorchester 8/05	33	0
Mark	Jermyn	6'00"	11 05		16/04/1981	31	Germany	Torquay Rel 2/00, Dorchester 8/00	34	0
Andy	Masson							Hamworthy, Dorchester 7/12		
Ashley	Nicholls	5'11"	11 11		30/10/1981	30	Ipswich	Ipswich Wan, Ipswich 7/00 Rel c/s 02, Canvey Island (L) 2/02, Hereford (Trial) 7/02, Darlington 8/02, Cambridge U (SL) 2/04, Cambridge U 7/04, Rushden & D (3ML) 8/05, Rushden & D 1/06, Grays 8/06, Boston U 7/07, Maidenhead 4/08 Rel 5/09, Bishops Stortford 5/09, Newport C (2ML) 12/09, Eastleigh 3/10, Maidenhead 6/10, Dorchester 5/11	34	0
Jamie	Symes				17/06/1993	19		Yeovil (Scholar), Bridport c/s 09, Dorchester 10/09, Bridport (Dual) 10/09, Blackpool (Trial) 2/10, Bridport c/s 10, Dorchester 3/11	10	1
Adam	Taylor				21/05/1992	20	Dorchester	Dorchester (Yth), Weymouth, Dorchester 2/11	0	0
FORWARDS										
Ryan	Dovell							Dorchester Rel 5/05, Hamworthy, Poole T, Bridport 7/10, Dorchester 6/11	30	7
Alex	Godfrey							Dorchester	1	0
Matt	Goodland							Dorchester	0	0
Sam	Malsom	5'10"	11 11		10/01/1987	25	Teignmouth	Torquay (Yth), Bishopsteighnton, Plymouth, Tiverton (L) 2/07, B36 (Far), Prottur (Ice), Dundalk 3/10, Motala FC (Swe), Hereford 7/10 Rel c/s 11, Gloucester (L) 2/11, Redditch (L) 10/10, Truro C (Trial) 8/11, Weymouth 9/11, Dorchester 1/12	12	4
Jamie	Reid							Exeter, Dorchester (L) 8/12		
Josh	Tennant							Dorchester	0	0
Ben	Watson	5'10"	11 02		06/12/1985	26	Shoreham	Brighton, Bognor Regis (L) 3/04, Bognor Regis 7/04, Grays 7/07, Exeter (SL) 3/08, Exeter 6/08 Rel c/s 11, Forest Green (2DL) 12/09, Forest Green (L), Bath C (L) 1/11, Eastbourne B 6/11, Dorchester 6/12		

DOVER ATHLETIC

Chairman: Jim Parmenter
Secretary: Franke Clarke   **(T)** 07794 102 664   **(E)** frank.clarke@doverathletic.com
Additional Committee Members:
Chris Oakley, Scott Rutherford, Frank Clarke, Roger Knight, Alistair Bayliss, Neil Cook, Steve Parmenter.
Manager: Nicky Forster
Programme Editor: Chris Collings   **(E)** chris.collings@doverathletic.com

Club Factfile

Founded: 1983   **Nickname:** The Whites
Previous Names: Dover F.C. until club folded in 1983
Previous Leagues: Southern 1983-93, 2002-04, Conference 1993-2002, Isthmian 2004-2009

Club Colours (change): White/black/black (All light blue)

Ground: Crabble Athletic Ground, Lewisham, Dover, Kent CT17 0JB   **(T)** 01304 822 373
Capacity: 6,500   **Seats:** 1,000   **Covered:** 4,900   **Clubhouse:** Yes   **Shop:** Yes

Directions From outside of Kent, find your way to the M25, then take the M2/A2 (following the signs to Canterbury, then from Canterbury follow signs to Dover) as far as the Whitfield roundabout (there is a McDonald's Drive-Thru on the left). Take the fourth exit at this roundabout, down Whitfield Hill. At the bottom of the hill turn left at the roundabout and follow this road until the first set of traffic lights. At the lights turn right (180 degrees down the hill) and follow the road under the railway bridge, the ground is a little further up the road on the left. There is no parking for supporters within the ground, although parking is available in the rugby ground, which is just inside the main entrance - stewards will direct you. If you have to take the M20/A20 leave the A20 in Folkestone (the exit immediately after the tunnel through the hill) and travel through the Alkham Valley (turn left at the roundabout at the end of the slip-road and then left again, following the signs for Alkham) which will eventually take you near Kearsney train station (turn right into Lower Road just before the railway bridge, before you get to the station).

Previous Grounds: None.

Record Attendance: 4,186 v Oxford United - FA Cup 1st Round November 2002
Record Victory: 7-0 v Weymouth - 03/04/1990
Record Defeat: 1-7 v Poole Town
Record Goalscorer: Lennie Lee - 160
Record Appearances: Jason Bartlett - 359
Additional Records: Paid £50,000 to Farnborough Town for David Lewworthy August 1993
Senior Honours: Received £50,000 from Brentford for Ricky Reina 1997
Southern League Southern Division 1987-88, Premier Division 1989-90, 92-93, Premier Inter League Cup 1990-91.
Kent Senior Cup 1990-91. Isthmian League Division 1 South 2007-08, Premier Division 2008-09.

10 YEAR RECORD

02-03		03-04		04-05		05-06		06-07		07-08		08-09		09-10		10-11		11-12	
SthP	3	SthP	19	Isth P	21	Isth1	5	Isth1S	3	Isth1S	1	Isth P	1	Conf S	2	Conf S	7	Conf S	7

DOVER ATHLETIC

No.	Date	Comp	H/A	Opponents	Att:	Result	Goalscorers	Pos
1	Sat-13-Aug	BSS	H	Dorchester Town	937	W 4-0	Bricknell 2 (15, 61), Purcell 2 (18, 23)	3
2	Tue-16-Aug	BSS	A	Thurrock	443	W 4-0	Baker 2 (44, 56), Bricknell 47, Purcell 57	1
3	Sat-20-Aug	BSS	A	Truro City	1017	L 0-1		5
4	Tue-23-Aug	BSS	H	Dartford	1455	D 2-2	Purcell 20, Bricknell 61	6
5	Sat-27-Aug	BSS	H	Tonbridge Angels	1003	D 0-0		8
6	Mon-29-Aug	BSS	A	Sutton United	714	D 0-0		7
7	Sat-03-Sep	BSS	A	Chelmsford City	1031	W 3-2	Baker 2, Purcell 12, Bricknell 70	7
8	Sat-10-Sep	BSS	H	Basingstoke Town	861	D 0-0		7
9	Sat-17-Sep	BSS	A	Woking	1306	L 1-3	Watt 37	10
10	Tue-20-Sep	BSS	H	Farnborough	785	D 0-0		12
11	Sat-24-Sep	BSS	H	Havant & Waterlooville	735	D 1-1	Simmonds 77	12
12	Sat-08-Oct	BSS	A	Welling United	851	D 0-0		12
13	Sat-22-Oct	BSS	H	Thurrock	793	W 3-1	Simmonds 2 (41, 69), Walker pen 44	9
14	Tue-25-Oct	BSS	A	Bromley	554	W 1-0	Simmonds 4	7
15	Sat-05-Nov	BSS	H	Weston-Super-Mare	725	W 1-0	Cogan 90	7
16	Tue-08-Nov	BSS	A	Maidenhead United	359	W 4-1	Simmonds 45, Walker 2 (73, 77), Baker 90	5
17	Sat-12-Nov	BSS	A	Boreham Wood	261	L 2-4	Baker 3, Walker pen 66	6
18	Sat-19-Nov	BSS	H	Woking	1061	L 0-3		7
19	Sat-03-Dec	BSS	A	Dartford	1558	L 1-3	Battipiedi 13	8
20	Sat-10-Dec	BSS	H	Bromley	625	W 4-1	Walker 2, Purcell 3 (12, 26, 31)	6
21	Sat-17-Dec	BSS	A	Staines Town	308	W 3-0	Bricknell 14, Purcell 57, Og (Gordon) 73	6
22	Mon-26-Dec	BSS	H	Eastbourne Borough	1027	D 1-1	Cogan 61	6
23	Mon-02-Jan	BSS	A	Eastbourne Borough	879	D 2-2	Corcoran 5, Dixon 77	6
24	Sat-07-Jan	BSS	H	Eastleigh	751	W 2-0	Purcell 2 (1, 54)	6
25	Sat-21-Jan	BSS	A	Dorchester Town	579	D 1-1	Simmonds 81	8
26	Sat-28-Jan	BSS	A	Salisbury City	825	D 1-1	Southam 57	8
27	Sat-18-Feb	BSS	H	Truro City	751	W 3-1	Purcell 19, J Johnson 34, Bricknell 90	6
28	Sat-25-Feb	BSS	H	Welling United	950	L 0-1		7
29	Sat-03-Mar	BSS	A	Salisbury City	695	W 1-0	Bricknell 86	6
30	Tue-06-Mar	BSS	H	Chelmsford City	625	W 2-1	Bricknell 30, Walker 86	6
31	Sat-10-Mar	BSS	A	Basingstoke Town	438	D 1-1	Bricknell 79	6
32	Tue-13-Mar	BSS	A	Hampton & Richmond Boro'	369	D 2-2	Simpempa 39, Bricknell 86	6
33	Sat-17-Mar	BSS	A	Eastleigh	513	W 3-2	Bricknell 2 (21, 48), Cogan 29	6
34	Wed-21-Mar	BSS	A	Farnborough	402	W 2-0	Simpemba 3, Bricknell 29	6
35	Sat-24-Mar	BSS	H	Staines Town	759	L 0-4		6
36	Tue-27-Mar	BSS	H	Hampton & Richmond Boro'	525	L 0-1		6
37	Sat-31-Mar	BSS	H	Boreham Wood	575	L 0-2		6
38	Sat-07-Apr	BSS	A	Tonbridge Angels	940	W 3-2	Dixon 16, Bricknell pen 24, Huke 89	6
39	Mon-09-Apr	BSS	H	Sutton United	675	L 0-2		6
40	Sat-14-Apr	BSS	A	Havant & Waterlooville	792	W 1-0	Edmans 22	6
41	Sat-21-Apr	BSS	H	Maidenhead United	725	D 2-2	Cogan 21, Corcoran 35	7
42	Sat-28-Apr	BSS	A	Weston-Super-Mare	325	D 1-1	Edmans 50	7

CUPS

No.	Date	Comp	H/A	Opponents	Att:	Result	Goalscorers	
1	Sat-01-Oct	FAC 2Q	H	Carshalton Athletic	639	W 3-0	Bricknell 2 (44, 68), Cutler 82	
2	Sat-15-Oct	FAC 3Q	H	Wroxham	635	W 3-1	Harris 52, Walker 83, Simmonds 89	
3	Sat-29-Oct	FAC 4Q	H	Bath City	922	L 0-1		
4	Sat-26-Nov	FAT 3Q	A	Boreham Wood	181	L 0-1		

League
Starts
Substitute
Unused Sub

Cups
Starts
Substitute
Unused Sub

Goals (Lg)
Goals (Cup)

	HOOK	STARKEY	WYNTER	CUTLER	HARRIS	HUKE	SIMMONDS	M JOHNSON	PURCELL	BRICKNELL	COGAN	I'ANSON	BAKER	WALKER	ASHTON	KITTERIDGE	CORCORAN	SOUTHAM	JAIMEZ-RUIZ	WATT	SCHULZ	REDWOOD	BATTIPIEDI	VASSELL	RAGGETT	DIXON	SIMPEMBA	J JOHNSON	NOONE	RANCE	GREEN	EVISON	WARREN	EDMANS	HARRINGTON
	X	X	X	X	X	X	X	X	X	X	X	S	S	S	U	U																			
	X		X	X	U	X	S	S	X	X	X	X	X	S	X	U																			
	X	X	X		X	X	S	X	X	X	X		X	U	S	S	X	U																	
		X	X		U	X	S		X	X	X	U		X		S	U	X	X	X															
	X	U	X	X	X		X	X	X	S		S	X	X	U	U	X	X																	
	X	X	U		X	S		X		X	X	X	U	U	X	S	X	X																	
	X	X	X	U	X		S	X	X		X	X	S	U	X	U	X	X																	
	X	X	X	U	X		X	X	U	X	X	S	S		X	S	X	X																	
	X	X	X	U	X		X	X	S	U	X	S		U	X	X	X	X																	
	X	X	X	U	X		X	X	X	U	X	S		U	X	X	X	X																	
	X	X	X	S	X	S	X	X			S	X	U	U	X	X	X	X																	
	U	X	X	X	X	S		X	X		S		U	U	X	X	X	X			X	X													
	U	X		X	X	X		S		X		S	X	U		X	X	X			X	X	X	S											
	S	X		X	X	X		S		X		S	X	U	U	X	X	X			X	X	X												
	X	X		X	U	X		X		X		S	U		S	X	X	X			X	X	X	S											
	X	X		X	X		X		X	S	S	X		U		X	X	X			X	S	X		U										
	X	X	U	X		X		X	S	X	X	X	U	U	X	X					U	X													
	U	X	X	U	X		X		S		X	S	X	X			X	X			X	S	X												
	U	X	X		U	X			X	S	X		S	X			U	X	X	X	X	X													
	U	X	X		X	X			X	X	X		S	X			X	X	X		S	U	U												
	U	X	X		X	X	S		X	X	X			X			X	X			U			S											
	U	X	X		X	X			X	X	S		X	X			X	X			U			S											
	U	X	X		X	X			X	X	X	U		X			X	X			U	U		X											
	U	X	X		X	X	S		X	S	X			S			X	X			U	S		X											
	U	X	X		X	X	S		X	S	X			X			X	X			U			X	U										
	U	X			S	X	S		X	X	X			S			X	X			U			X	X										
	U	X			X	X	X		X	S	X			S			X	X			X			X	X	X	U								
	U	X			X	X	X		X	S	X			S			X	X						X	X	X	X	U	S						
		S	X		X	X	U		X	S	X				S			X			X			X	X	X	U	S							
		X	X		X	S	U		X	X	X			S				U	S	X				X	X	X		X							
		X	X		X	S	S		X	X	X			S				X	X					U	X	X			X	U					
		X	X		U	X	S		X	X	X			S				X	X					X	X	U		X		U					
		X			X	X	X		X	X	X			S			S	X	X					X	X	S		U		U					
		X			X	X	X		X	X	X			S			S	X	X					S	X	S		U		U					
		X	U		X	X	X		X	X	X			S				X						X	S			S		U	X				
		X	X		U	X	X		X	X	X			X				X						X	U			U		U	S				
		X	X		S	X	X		U	X	X			X				X	X					X	X	S				U	S				
		X			U	X	X			X	X			U				X	U					X	X	X						U	S	X	
		X			U	X	X			X	X			U				X	S	X				X	X	X						U	U	X	
	U	X			U	X	X		S	X	X			S				X	X							X		S					X	X		
	U	X	U		U	X			X	X	X							X	X					U	S	X							X	X		
	X	U	X		U	X			X	X	X			U				X	U					X	X			S					X	X		
		X	X	X	X	X			S	X	U	S	X	U	X	U	X	X	X		S														
	U	X	X	X	X	S			X	X	S		S		S		U	U	X		X	X	X												
		U	X	U	X	X				X		X	U	S	X	S	U		X	X		X	X	X	S										
	U	S	X		X	X	X			S			X	X	S	X			X	X		X	X	U												
	4	36	32	9	24	36	15	3	34	28	36	4	10	19	3	0	25	28	38	7	7	5	9	0	0	13	17	8	0	1	2	0	0	4	5
	0	2	0	0	3	2	14	2	4	7	2	5	10	15	3	1	2	6	0	0	1	2	2	2	0	4	0	4	2	1	1	0	0	3	0
	13	3	3	3	14	1	2	0	1	0	3	1	4	4	15	5	3	1	0	5	2	5	0	2	1	1	1	3	0	3	1	8	1	0	
	0	0	4	2	4	4	2	0	2	2	2	1	1	2	1	0	1	4	4	0	3	3	2	0	0	0	0	0	0	0	0	0	0	0	0
	0	1	0	0	0	0	1	0	2	0	1	1	2	1	1	0	0	0	0	0	1	0	0	1	0	0	0	0	0	0	0	0	0	0	0
	1	2	0	1	0	0	0	0	0	0	1	2	0	1	0	3	1	0	0	0	0	0	1	0	0	0	0	0	0	0	0	0	0	0	0
	0	0	0	0	0	1	6	0	12	15	4	0	5	6	0	0	2	1	0	1	0	0	1	0	0	2	1	1	0	0	0	0	0	2	0
	0	0	0	1	1	0	1	0	0	2	0	0	0	1	0	0	0	0	0	0	0	0	0	0	0	0	0	0	0	0	0	0	0	0	0

PLAYING SQUAD 2012/13

Existing Players		SN	HT	WT	DOB	AGE	POB	Career	Apps	Goals
GOALKEEPERS										
Lee	Hook		5'09"	08 11	11/03/1979	33	Margate	Wolves (Yth), Exeter, Ramsgate, Whitstable, Sittingbourne 9/02, Eastbourne B 6/03 Rel 5/09, Dover 5/09	4	0
Mitch	Walker		6'02"	13 00	24/09/1991	20	St Albans	Brighton (Pro 6/10), Eastbourne B (L) 2/10, Welling (L) 1/11, Eastbourne B (SL) 2/12, Dover 5/12		
DEFENDERS										
Lloyd	Harrington							Dover	5	0
Sean	Raggett							Dover, Sittingbourne (Dual), C. Palace (Trial) 11/10	0	0
Ian	Simpemba		6'02"	12 08	28/03/1983	29	Dublin	Wycombe, Woking (3ML) 10/02, Woking (L) 9/03, Crawley Undisc 7/04, Aldershot (SL) 3/06, Lewes 6/06, Havant & W 5/08, Ebbsfleet 7/11, Dover Nominal 1/12	17	1
Steven	Watt		6'03"	14 00	01/05/1985	27	Aberdeen	Chelsea, Barnsley (L) 10/05, Swansea 1/06 Rel c/s 08, Inverness Cal (L) 8/07, Ross County 8/08 Rel c/s 10, Grimsby 8/10 Rel 5/11, Dover (Trial) 7/11, Mansfield (Trial) 7/11, Dover 7/11	7	1
Danny	Webb		6'01"	11 08	02/07/1983	29	Poole	Southampton (Scholar), Southend 12/00, Brighton (SL) 12/01, Brighton (L) 11/02, Hull C 12/02, Lincoln C (L) 3/03, Cambridge U (2ML) 12/03 Perm 2/04 Rel c/s 05, Weymouth 6/05, Yeovil 12/05, Rushden & D (L) 1/07, Woking (L) 3/07, Marsaxlokk (Mal) 7/07, AFC Wimbledon 7/07 Rel 5/08, Chelmsford 7/08 Rel 9/08, Havant & W 10/08, Salisbury 11/08, Bath C 5/10, Salisbury (L) 11/11, Salisbury 12/11, Dover 5/12		
Tom	Wynter		5'07"	11 11	20/06/1990	22	Lewisham	Gillingham, Ramsgate (3ML) 11/08, Dover (2ML) 10/09, Dover 7/10	32	0
MIDFIELDERS										
Tom	Axford							Dover		
Barry	Cogan		5'09"	09 00	04/11/1984	27	Sligo	Millwall, Barnet Undisc 8/06 Rel 5/07, Gillingham 7/07, Grays (SL) 3/08, Grays 7/08, Crawley 6/09 Rel 11/10, Dover 11/10	38	4
Shane	Huke		5'11"	12 07	02/10/1985	26	Reading	Rochedale Rangers (Aust), Peterborough Rel c/s 07, Kings Lynn (L) 8/03, Bedford T (L) 12/03, Heybridge (L) 3/04, Cambridge C (L) 9/04, Hornchurch (L) 11/04, Dag & Red 1/07 Rel 1/09, Central Coast Mariners (Aust) 1/09, Rushden & D 3/10, Dover 5/11	38	1
Ricky	Modeste				20/02/1988	24		Chelmsford, Dover 5/12		
Dean	Rance				14/05/1991	21	Maidstone	Gillingham Rel c/s 12, Maidstone (L) 3/10, Maidstone (L) 1/11, Bishops Stortford (SL) 3/11, Bishops Stortford (L) 8/11, Dover (L) 3/12, Dover 5/12	2	0
Chris	Sessegnon		5'10"		10/08/1993	19		Norwich C (Yth), Sutton U, Kingstonian (L), Tooting & M (L), Whyteleafe 3/12, Dover 8/12		
Jamie	Smith		5'06"	10 05	16/09/1989	22	Leytonstone	C.Palace Rel c/s 09, Brighton 8/09 Rel 12/11, L.Orient 3/12 Rel c/s 12, Dover 7/12		
Steven	Thomson		5'08"	10 09	23/01/1978	34	Glasgow	C.Palace Rel c/s 03, Bournemouth (Trial) 7/03, L.Orient (Trial) 8/03, Peterborough 9/03 Rel c/s 05, Falkirk 7/05, Brighton 1/08, St Mirren 1/09, Dover 5/12		
FORWARDS										
Billy	Bricknell		5'11"		24/07/1988	24	Enfield	Tottenham (Yth), Waltham Abbey, Leyton c/s 07, Billericay 1/08, Barnet (Trial) c/s 10, Chelmsford Undisc 8/10, Dover 7/11	35	15
Terry	Dixon		6'01"	11 13	15/01/1990	22	Holloway	Tottenham Rel 3/08, Injured, West Ham 2/09 Rel 4/10, Stevenage 10/10 Rel 1/11, Ware 2/11, Tooting & M 3/11, Bradford C 8/11, FC Halifax (L) 8/11, Dover 12/11	17	2
Nicky	Forster		5'09"	11 05	08/09/1973	38	Caterham	Horley T, Gillingham 5/92, Brentford 6/94, Birmingham 1/97, Reading 6/99 Rel c/s 05, Ipswich 8/05, Hull 8/06, Brighton 6/07 Rel c/s 09, Charlton (SL) 3/10, Brentford 7/10 Pl/Man 3/11 Rel c/s 11, Lingfield c/s 11, Dover (Pl/Man) 9/11		
Ben	May		6'00"	12 12	10/03/1984	28	Gravesend	Millwall, Colchester (SL) 3/03, Brentford (SL) 8/03, Brentford (3ML) 12/04, Scunthorpe (5WL) 9/07, Scunthorpe 1/08 Rel c/s 10, Stevenage 10/10 Rel c/s 12, Barnet (SL) 3/12, Dover 8/12		
Callum	Willock		6'01"	12 08	29/10/1981	30	Waterloo	ADT College, Fulham 7/00, QPR (L) 11/02, Bristol R (L) 8/03, Peterborough (2ML) 10/03 £25,000 12/03, Brentford £50,000 1/06 Rel c/s 07, Port Vale 8/07 Rel 12/07, Stevenage 1/08 Rel 5/09, AFC Wimbledon (Trial) 7/09, Crawley 9/09 Rel 2/10, Cambridge U NC 2/10 Rel 4/10, Ebbsfleet 7/10, Dover 6/12		

EASTBOURNE BOROUGH

Chairman: Len Smith
Secretary: Mrs Jan Field   **(T)** 07749 572 693   **(E)** janfield38@sky.com
Additional Committee Members:
Mick Grimer, Mike Spooner, Angus Scott, Steve Carter, Tim Cobb, Tim Firth, Paul Maynard, Paul Robinson, Geoffrey Smith.
Manager: Tommy Widdrington
Programme Editor: David Bealey   **(E)** programme@ebfc.co.uk

Back: Nick Redman (Goalkeeper coach), Ethan Strevett, James Walker, Danny Potter, Anwar Uddin, Nick Jordan, Marvin Hamilton, Matt Turpin, H.Silva (Analyst)
Middle: Damian Karchinski (Kitman), Jake McPherson, Darren Baker, Charlie Gorman, Darren Lok, Tim Gilbert, Gary Hart, Sam Cole, Ben Adams, Dave Funnell (Kitman), Ray Tuppen (Sports Therapist)
Front: Chris Morgan, David Knight, Tommy Widdrington (Manager), Ollie Rowe, Alan Kimble (Coach), Simon Johnson, Chris Shepherd

Club Factfile

Founded: 1966   **Nickname:** Borough
Previous Names: Langney Sports > 2001
Previous Leagues: Eastbourne & Hastings, Sussex County, Southern

Club Colours (change): Red with navy stripe/navy/red (All yellow)

Ground: Langney Sports Club, Priory Lane, Eastbourne BN23 7QH   **(T)** 01323 766 265
Capacity: 4,151   **Seats:** 542   **Covered:** 2,500   **Clubhouse:** Yes   **Shop:** Yes
Directions: From M25 take M23/A23 eastbound to A27 Polegate by pass pick up and follow signs for crematorium 50yds past crematorium turn right at mini roundabout into Priory Road Stadium 100yds on left.

Previous Grounds: None

Record Attendance: 3,770 v Oxford United - FA Cup 1st Round 05/11/05
Record Victory: 10-1 v Haywards Heath Town - Sussex County Division One 1991-92
Record Defeat: 0-8 v Sheppey United (A) - FA Vase 09/10/93 and v Peachaven & Tels (A) - Sussex Co. Div.1 09/11/93
Record Goalscorer: Nigel Hole - 146
Record Appearances: Darren Baker - 689
Additional Records: Paid £1,800 to Yeovil Town for Yemi Odoubade.
Senior Honours: Received £15,000 from Oxford United for Yemi Odoubade.
Sussex County League 1999-2000, 02-03. Sussex Senior Cup 2001-02.

10 YEAR RECORD

02-03	03-04	04-05	05-06	06-07	07-08	08-09	09-10	10-11	11-12
SthE 2	SthP 11	Conf S 5	Conf S 17	Conf S 7	Conf S 2	Conf 13	Conf 19	Conf 23	Conf S 18

EASTBOURNE BOROUGH

No.	Date	Comp	H/A	Opponents	Att:	Result	Goalscorers	Pos
1	Sat-13-Aug	BSS	H	Farnborough	751	D 1-1	Elphick 90	9
2	Tue-16-Aug	BSS	A	Dartford	1140	L 1-2	Strevett 90	15
3	Sat-20-Aug	BSS	A	Dorchester Town	432	W 3-0	Rowe 21, Watson 31, Brinkhurst 64	10
4	Tue-23-Aug	BSS	H	Bromley	605	W 5-0	Watson 7, Hutchinson 33, Cole 2 (36, 67), Strevett 84	7
5	Sat-27-Aug	BSS	A	Welling United	541	L 0-3		10
6	Mon-29-Aug	BSS	H	Chelmsford City	781	L 1-3	Crabb 21	13
7	Sat-03-Sep	BSS	H	Havant & Waterlooville	668	W 2-1	Brinkhurst 2 (48, 59)	11
8	Sat-10-Sep	BSS	A	Woking	1203	L 1-3	Elphick 49	14
9	Sat-17-Sep	BSS	H	Boreham Wood	604	W 3-2	Og (Hunter) 1, Crabb 9, Hutchinson 45	11
10	Tue-20-Sep	BSS	A	Thurrock	284	W 4-1	Hutchinson 33, Rowe 45, Hart 71, Watson 86	7
11	Sat-24-Sep	BSS	A	Salisbury City	667	L 0-3		9
12	Sat-08-Oct	BSS	H	Eastleigh	663	W 3-0	Rowe 10, Watson 21, Crabb 88	6
13	Sat-22-Oct	BSS	A	Weston-Super-Mare	326	D 3-3	Johnson 38, Elphick 52, Rook 85	7
14	Tue-25-Oct	BSS	H	Tonbridge Angels	924	L 1-3	Watson 21	10
15	Sat-05-Nov	BSS	A	Hampton & Richmond Boro'	441	L 1-3	Watson 31	12
16	Sat-12-Nov	BSS	A	Havant & Waterlooville	783	D 0-0		13
17	Sat-19-Nov	BSS	H	Basingstoke Town	628	L 0-2		14
18	Sat-03-Dec	BSS	A	Bromley	363	W 3-1	Brinkhurst 16, Austin 69, Treleaven 81	13
19	Tue-06-Dec	BSS	H	Truro City	463	D 2-2	Rook 8, Watson 82	13
20	Sat-17-Dec	BSS	H	Weston-Super-Mare	519	L 1-2	Johnson 89	14
21	Mon-26-Dec	BSS	A	Dover Athletic	1027	D 1-1	Rook 17	14
22	Mon-02-Jan	BSS	H	Dover Athletic	879	D 2-2	Hart 2 (21, 90)	14
23	Sat-07-Jan	BSS	A	Maidenhead United	301	L 0-1		15
24	Sat-14-Jan	BSS	H	Dorchester Town	564	L 1-4	Hart 68	16
25	Sat-21-Jan	BSS	A	Tonbridge Angels	734	L 1-5	Crabb 23	17
26	Sat-28-Jan	BSS	H	Maidenhead United	572	L 0-2		18
27	Sat-18-Feb	BSS	A	Boreham Wood	202	D 1-1	Smart 6	19
28	Sat-25-Feb	BSS	H	Staines Town	672	L 0-1		19
29	Sat-03-Mar	BSS	A	Truro City	493	W 2-0	Hart 36, Crabb 44	19
30	Tue-06-Mar	BSS	A	Farnborough	400	L 0-1		19
31	Sat-10-Mar	BSS	H	Sutton United	802	D 0-0		19
32	Wed-14-Mar	BSS	A	Sutton United	475	D 1-1	Watson 43	19
33	Sat-17-Mar	BSS	A	Staines Town	269	W 2-1	Watson 40, Brinkhurst 50	17
34	Sat-24-Mar	BSS	H	Woking	1037	W 2-1	Lacey 12, Watson 15	16
35	Tue-27-Mar	BSS	H	Thurrock	557	W 2-1	Rowe 16, Watson pen 87	15
36	Sat-31-Mar	BSS	A	Eastleigh	439	L 1-2	Remy 68	16
37	Tue-03-Apr	BSS	H	Dartford	823	L 0-1		16
38	Sat-07-Apr	BSS	H	Welling United	751	L 0-3		16
39	Mon-09-Apr	BSS	A	Chelmsford City	835	L 0-1		16
40	Sat-14-Apr	BSS	H	Hampton & Richmond Boro'	633	W 2-0	Lacey 27, Ademeno 79	16
41	Sat-21-Apr	BSS	A	Basingstoke Town	458	L 0-3		17
42	Sat-28-Apr	BSS	H	Salisbury City	705	L 1-3	Hart 87	18

CUPS

No.	Date	Comp	H/A	Opponents	Att:	Result	Goalscorers	
1	Sun-02-Oct	FAC 2Q	A	Waltham Forest	175	W 3-0	Elphick 71, Watson 85, Rook 90	
2	Sat-15-Oct	FAC 3Q	H	AFC Sudbury	529	W 1-0	Elphick 84	
3	Sat-29-Oct	FAC 4Q	H	East Thurrock United	603	L 1-2	Elphick 81	
4	Sat-26-Nov	FAT3Q	H	Dartford	508	D 0-0		
5	Tue-29-Nov	FAT 3QR	A	Dartford	611	L 1-2	Rook pen 79	

League
Starts
Substitute
Unused Sub

Cups
Starts
Substitute
Unused Sub

Goals (Lg)
Goals (Cup)

BANKS	BAKER	COBBS	SMART	CHARMAN	ELPHICK	BRINKHURST	JOHNSON	PULMAN	COLE	CRABB	WATSON	HUTCHINSON	STREVETT	ROWE	SMITH	MEDLOCK	NORRIS	ROOK	CAMARA	GILBERT	HART	SHAW	BATTIPIEDI	MASTERS	TRELEAVEN	AUSTIN	GOUGH	LACEY	BULL	HAMILTON-OMOLE	ANDERSON	REMY	WALKER	MASON	ADEMENO
X	X	X	X	X	X	X	X	X	X	X	S	S	S	U																					
X	X	X	S		X	X	X	S	X	X	X	X	S	X		U	U																		
X	X		X		X	X	X	S	X	X	X	X	S	X		S																			
X	X		X		X	X	X	S	X	X	X			S	X	U	U	S																	
X	X		X		X	X	X	S	X	X	X			S	X	S	U	X																	
X	X	X		X	X	U	X	X	X			S	X		U	U	X	S																	
X	X		X	U	X	X	X	X	S	X	X			X	S	X		U	X																
X		X	U	X	X	X	X			X	X	U	X	U	X		U	U	S		X														
X		X	X	X	X	X			X	X	U	X	U	X		U	U	S		X															
X	U		X	X	X	X			X	X	S	X	S	X		S	U		X																
X	S			X	X	X	X			X	X	S	X	X		U	S		X	U															
X	X		S		X	X	X			X	X	X	X	U	X		S	S		X	U		U												
X	X		U	U	X	X			X	X	X	X	X	U	X		X	U					U												
X	X		U	S	X	X			X	X	X	X	X	S	X		X	S																	
U	U		X	X	X	X			X	X	X	X	X	S	X		S	S					X												
U	X		U	X	X	X			X	X	X	X	X	S	X		U						X	S											
	X		S	X	X	X			X	X	X	X	U	X		U			S				X	S											
	X		X	S	U	X		S		X	X	S	U	X		X		U			X	X	X												
	X		X		X	S		X		X	X	X	X	U	X		X	U			X		X	X	X										
	X		S	S	X	S	X			X	X	X	U	X		X					X		U	X	X										
	X		U	X		X	X			X	U		U	X	X		X	S			X		X	U	X										
	X		S	X		X	X			X	X		U	X	X		X	S			X		S	X	X										
	X		U	X		X	X		S	X			U	X	X		X	S			X		X	U	X										
	X		X	U	U	X	X			X	S	X		X		U	S				X		X	X	X										
	X		S	X		S	X			X	X	X	U	U	X		S		X		X		X												
	X		X	X		S	X			X	X	X	S	S	X		U		X		X		X	X											
X	X			X			S	X		X	X	X	X	S	X	X			X		S					U	X	U							
X	U			X			S	S		X	X	X		U	X			X			X							X		X	X	S			
U	U			X			S	X		X	X	S		U	X			X			X							X		X	X	X	X		
	X			U	X			X		X	X	U		U	X			X			X							X		X	S	X	X		
	S		X	S				X		X	X	S		U	X			U			X							X		X	X	X	X		
	X		X	S			X	X		X	X	X		U	X						X		U					X		X	U	X			
	X			X			S	X		X	X	X		U	X						X							X		X	S	X	S		
	X		X	S			U	X		X	X	S			X						S				S			X		X	X	X	U	S	
	X		U	X				X		X	X	X			X						S				X	U		X		X	S		S	S	
U		X	U				X		X	X	S			X							S			X	X			X		X	X	X	S	X	
	X		U		S	X		X		X	X	X			X						S				X	U		X		X	X	X	U	X	
	X		U					X		X	X	S			X						S				X	U		X		X	X	X	U	X	
X		X					X		X	X	X			U	X						X				U			X		S	X	S	X		S
X		X					X		X	X	X			U	X						X					U				X	X	S	X	U	U
X		X	X				X		X	X	S			S	X				U	X		X								S	X	X		U	
X	X		X			X	X	X			X	X	S	X	U	X			S	U		X	U	U											
X	X		S	U	X	X	X			X	X	X	X	U	X			S	S		X			U											
X	X		S	S	X	X	X			X	X	X	X	U	X			X	U			U	S												
	X		X	X	X	X				X	S	X		X	X			S	U		X			X	S	U									
	X			X	X					X	S	U	U	X	X			X	S		X			X	X	S									
16	32	3	29	14	17	23	39	1	38	40	25	14	2	41	3	0	0	14	2	0	25	0	0	13	4	9	1	14	0	6	15	6	12	0	4
0	2	0	6	6	0	9	3	5	1	1	10	5	13	0	0	3	0	4	11	0	5	0	0	0	3	1	0	0	3	0	8	0	4	3	
3	5	0	6	6	2	3	0	2	0	0	4	1	19	1	1	4	7	5	5	3	0	3	0	3	3	4	1	0	1	0	0	1	0	5	1
3	5	0	3	1	5	5	3	0	5	3	3	3	2	5	0	0	0	2	0	0	4	0	0	2	1	0	0	0	0	0	0	0	0	0	0
0	0	0	2	1	0	0	0	0	0	2	1	0	0	0	0	0	0	3	2	0	0	0	0	0	0	2	1	0	0	0	0	0	0	0	0
0	0	0	0	1	0	0	0	0	0	0	1	1	3	0	0	0	0	3	0	0	1	1	2	0	1	0	0	0	0	0	0	0	0	0	0
0	0	0	1	0	3	5	2	0	2	5	11	3	2	4	0	0	0	3	0	0	6	0	0	0	1	1	0	2	0	0	0	1	0	0	1
0	0	0	0	0	3	0	0	0	0	0	1	0	0	0	0	0	0	2	0	0	0	0	0	0	0	0	0	0	0	0	0	0	0	0	0

PLAYING SQUAD 2012/13

Existing Players		SN	HT	WT	DOB	AGE	POB	Career	Apps	Goals
GOALKEEPERS										
Nick	Jordan		6'02"	13 01	13/11/1989	22	Aldershot	Portsmouth (Scholar) Rel c/s 08, Exeter 8/08 Rel c/s 09, Crawley 8/09 Rel 5/11, Weymouth (L) 2/11, Weymouth c/s 11, Dorchester (L) 9/11, Eastbourne B 6/12		
Danny	Potter		5'11"	13 00	18/03/1979	33	Ipswich	Chelsea (Trainee), Colchester 10/97 Rel c/s 98, Exeter 8/98 Rel c/s 00, Weymouth (L) 11,99, Salisbury (L) 1/00, Weymouth 6/00, Chelmsford 2/02, Canvey Island 8/02, Stevenage 6/06, Cambridge U 5/07 Rel 4/10, Torquay 5/10, Newport C 5/11 Rel 3/12, Staines 3/12, Eastbourne B (Pl/Coach) 6/12		
DEFENDERS										
Darren	Baker		5'10"	09 06	23/11/1974	37	Eastbourne	Brighton (Ass Sch), Littlehampton (Yth), Eastbourne B 6/92	34	0
Tom	Gilbert							Eastbourne B	0	0
Marvin	Hamilton-Omole		6'00"	11 02	08/10/1988	23	Leytonstone	Gillingham Rel 3/08, Folkestone I (L) 1/08, Dover 3/08, Lincoln C (Trial) 8/08, Enfield T 10/08, Leyton 11/08, APEP Pitsilia (Cyp) 1/10, Hemel Hempstead, Eastbourne B 2/12	9	0
Jack	MacFarlane							Southampton (Yth), Brighton (Scholar), Eastbourne B 8/12		
Ollie	Rowe		6'01"	11 02	22/05/1991	21	Eastbourne	Brighton (Scholar) Rel c/s 09, Ringmer c/s 09, Eastbourne T, Eastbourne B 11/09, Eastbourne T (Dual) 11/09, Lewes (L) 9/10, Chelmsford 10/10, Hastings U 1/11, Eastbourne B 5/11	41	4
Matt	Turpin							Hertford, Ware, Cheshunt 7/11, Billericay 9/11, Redbridge 10/11, Eastbourne B 6/12		
Anwar	Uddin		5'11"	11 10	01/11/1981	30	Whitechapel	West Ham, Cheltenham (Trial) 10/01, Sheff Wed 2/02 Rel c/s 02, Bristol R 7/02 Rel 5/04, Hereford (2ML) 12/03, Telford (L) 3/04, Dag & Red 7/04, Grays (3ML) 9/09, Barnet 6/10 Rel 2/12, Sutton U 2/12, Eastbourne B 6/12		
MIDFIELDERS										
Ben	Adams							Leicester, Glen Hoddle Academy, Ebbsfleet, Eastbourne B 7/12		
Sam	Cole							Hailsham, Rye U c/s 09, Eastbourne B 7/11	39	2
Charlie	Gorman							Leverstock Green, Chesham 11/10, Leverstock Green, Hemel Hempstead 6/11, Eastbourne B 7/12		
Simon	Johnson		5'08"	11 11	14/04/1991	21	Hailsham	Eastbourne B	42	2
Chris	Morgan							Eastbourne B		
Chris	Shephard		6'03"	13 03	25/12/1988	23	Exeter	Exeter Rel c/s 12, Weston-Super-Mare (L) 11/09, Salisbury (L) 3/10 (09/10 9,2), Bath C (L) 1/12, Eastbourne B 7/12		
FORWARDS										
Charles	Ademeno		5'10"	11 13	12/12/1988	23	Milton Keynes	Southend Rel 6/09, Bishops Stortford (2ML) 9/06, Cambridge U (L) 1/07, Welling (2ML) 11/07, Rushden & D (2ML) 2/08, Salisbury (5WL) 11/08, Salisbury (SL) 2/09, Crawley 7/09, Grimsby £10,000 7/10 Rel 6/11, AFC Wimbledon 6/11 Rel 1/12, Eastbourne B 3/12	7	1
Gary	Hart		5'09"	12 08	21/09/1978	33	Harlow	Stansted, Brighton £1,000 6/98 Rel c/s 11, Havant & W (L) 12/07, Eastbourne B 7/11	30	6
David	Knight				13/09/1990	21		Thurrock Rel 11/09, Aveley 12/09, Thurrock 11/10, Aveley, Thurrock 2/12, Eastbourne B 6/12		
Darren	Lok							Eastbourne B, Ringmer, Eastbourne B 8/11		
Ethan	Strevett				30/11/1989	22		Eastbourne B, Eastbourne T 10/08, Eastbourne B 8/10	15	2
James	Walker		5'11"	11 13	25/11/1987	24	Hackney	Charlton, Hartlepool (L) 1/06, Luton (Trial) 2/06, Derby (Trial) 3/06, Bristol R (L) 9/06, L.Orient (3ML) 11/06, Notts County (SL) 3/07, Yeovil (3ML) 10/07, Southend (SL) 2/08, Southend £200,000 5/08 Rel 2/10, Hereford (L) 9/09, Gillingham 2/10 Rel c/s 10, L.Orient 9/10 Rel 1/11, Grimsby (Trial), Woking 3/11, Dover 7/11 Rel c/s 12, Eastbourne B 8/12		

EASTLEIGH

Chairman: Stewart Donald
Secretary: Ray Murphy   **(T)** 07801 638 158   **(E)** raymurphy@ntlworld.com
Additional Committee Members:
Mike Andrews, Derik Brooks, Stephen Brookwell, Mick Budny, Stewart Deas, John Dunn, Neil Fox,
Mick Geddes, Alan Harding, Peter McIntosh, Allen Prebble, John Russell, Peter Vickery
Manager: Ian Baird
Programme Editor: Mike Denning   **(E)** mike.denning@talk21.com

Back Row L to R – Osei Sankofa, Lee Peacock, Craig McAllister, Wayne Shaw, Daryl McMahon, Tom Jordan, Jack Dovey,
Gary Elphick, Mitchell Nelson, Michael Green, Andy Forbes.
Front Row L to R – Ken Kudjodji, Glen Southam, Chris Flood, Marvin Williams, Jai Reason, Moses Ademola, Adam Everitt,
Damian Scannell.

Club Factfile

Founded: 1946   **Nickname:** The Spitfires
Previous Names: Swaythling Athletic 1946-59, Swaythling 1973-80
Previous Leagues: Southampton Junior & Senior 1946-59, Hampshire 1950-86, Wessex 1986-2003, Southern 2003-04, Isthmian 2004-05

Club Colours (change): Sky blue/navy/navy (Yellow/royal blue/royal blue)

Ground: Silverlake Stadium 'Ten Acres', Stoneham Lane, Eastleigh SO50 9HT   **(T)** 02380 613 361
Capacity: 2,300   **Seats:** 175   **Covered:** 385   **Clubhouse:** Yes   **Shop:** Yes
Directions: From junction 13 of M3, turn right into Leigh Road, turn right at Holiday Inn, at mini roundabout take second exit, at the next mini roundabout take second exit, then next mini roundabout take first exit. Then take the first turning right (signposted) ground 200 metres on the left.

Previous Grounds:

Record Attendance: 2,589 v Southampton - Friendly July 2005
Record Victory: 12-1 v Hythe & Dibden (H) - 11/12/1948
Record Defeat: 0-11 v Austin Sports (A) - 01.01.1947
Record Goalscorer: Johnnie Williams - 177
Record Appearances: Ian Knight - 611
Additional Records: Paid £10,000 to Newport (I.O.W.) for Colin Matthews
Senior Honours:
Southampton Senior League (West) 1950.
Wessex League Cup 1992,2003, Division One 2002-03.

10 YEAR RECORD

02-03		03-04		04-05		05-06		06-07		07-08		08-09		09-10		10-11		11-12	
Wex1	1	SthE	4	Isth P	3	Conf S	8	Conf S	15	Conf S	6	Conf S	3	Conf S	11	Conf S	8	Conf S	12

EASTLEIGH

No.	Date	Comp	H/A	Opponents	Att:	Result	Goalscorers	Pos
1	Sat-13-Aug	BSS	H	Basingstoke Town	611	L 0-2		18
2	Tue-16-Aug	BSS	A	Truro City	713	L 1-2	White 45	19
3	Sat-20-Aug	BSS	A	Tonbridge Angels	464	L 0-4		22
4	Tue-23-Aug	BSS	H	Woking	665	D 0-0		20
5	Fri-26-Aug	BSS	A	Dorchester Town	505	W 3-1	Holder-Spooner 53, White 2 (58, 82)	16
6	Mon-29-Aug	BSS	H	Weston-Super-Mare	426	W 2-1	Holder-Spooner 17, Slabber 23	15
7	Sat-03-Sep	BSS	H	Bromley	568	L 0-2		16
8	Sat-10-Sep	BSS	A	Dartford	1079	L 0-3		18
9	Sat-17-Sep	BSS	H	Hampton & Richmond Boro'	463	D 1-1	Slabber 36	19
10	Tue-20-Sep	BSS	A	Sutton United	517	L 0-2		20
11	Sat-24-Sep	BSS	H	Staines Town	401	W 2-1	Slabber 18, Brown 25	18
12	Sat-08-Oct	BSS	A	Eastbourne Borough	663	L 0-3		19
13	Sat-22-Oct	BSS	H	Welling United	391	W 3-0	Mike Green 29, Gillespie 80, Montgomery 82	17
14	Mon-24-Oct	BSS	A	Chelmsford City	937	L 0-3		17
15	Sat-29-Oct	BSS	A	Thurrock	196	W 3-1	Slabber 2 (25, 90), Og (Hughes) 88	18
16	Sat-05-Nov	BSS	H	Maidenhead United	503	W 4-1	Slabber 2 (10, 36), Montgomery 22, Flood 90	14
17	Sat-12-Nov	BSS	A	Farnborough	471	W 3-1	White 17, Forbes 74, Brown 79	11
18	Sat-19-Nov	BSS	H	Dartford	604	D 2-2	Smith 42, Jordan 53	13
19	Sat-03-Dec	BSS	A	Woking	1610	L 0-1		14
20	Sat-10-Dec	BSS	H	Thurrock	317	W 3-2	Montgomery 28, Tsovolos 39, Brown 43	12
21	Sat-17-Dec	BSS	H	Boreham Wood	490	W 2-0	Slabber 36, Scannell 68	10
22	Mon-26-Dec	BSS	A	Havant & Waterlooville	938	D 0-0		11
23	Sat-07-Jan	BSS	A	Dover Athletic	751	L 0-2		12
24	Sat-21-Jan	BSS	A	Basingstoke Town	404	L 0-1		13
25	Tue-24-Jan	BSS	H	Salisbury City	903	D 1-1	Montgomery 85	11
26	Sat-28-Jan	BSS	H	Sutton United	859	W 4-0	Bubb 3 (32, 50, 62), Scannell 82	10
27	Tue-07-Feb	BSS	H	Havant & Waterlooville	526	W 3-2	McMahon 4, Scannell 39, Bubb 69	10
28	Tue-14-Feb	BSS	A	Staines Town	202	D 2-2	Bubb 2 (pen 75, pen 80)	10
29	Sat-18-Feb	BSS	A	Hampton & Richmond Boro'	371	W 4-0	Slabber 6, Bubb 65, Forbes 70, McMahon 87	8
30	Tue-21-Feb	BSS	A	Salisbury City	647	L 0-2		8
31	Sat-25-Feb	BSS	H	Truro City	535	W 3-1	Bubb 2 (16, 87), Brown 20	6
32	Sat-03-Mar	BSS	H	Farnborough	652	L 0-1		9
33	Sat-10-Mar	BSS	A	Bromley	432	D 0-0		9
34	Sat-17-Mar	BSS	H	Dover Athletic	513	L 2-3	Flood 26, Peacock 69	10
35	Tue-20-Mar	BSS	H	Tonbridge Angels	307	L 1-2	Bubb 50	10
36	Sat-24-Mar	BSS	A	Boreham Wood	201	L 1-6	McMahon 57	12
37	Sat-31-Mar	BSS	H	Eastbourne Borough	439	W 2-1	Elphick 20, Jordan 60	11
38	Fri-06-Apr	BSS	H	Dorchester Town	513	L 0-1		11
39	Mon-09-Apr	BSS	A	Weston-Super-Mare	201	D 0-0		11
40	Sat-14-Apr	BSS	A	Welling United	454	W 1-0	Smith 39	11
41	Sat-21-Apr	BSS	H	Chelmsford City	831	D 1-1	Forbes 82	12
42	Sat-28-Apr	BSS	A	Maidenhead United	495	L 3-4	Peacock 41, S Wilson 61, Nelson 65	12

CUPS

No.	Date	Comp	H/A	Opponents	Att:	Result	Goalscorers	
1	Sat-01-Oct	FAC 2Q	H	Cinderford Town	274	W 3-1	Jordan 25, Forbes 33, White 80	
2	Sat-15-Oct	FAC 3Q	H	Oxford City	325	L 1-3	Slabber pen 66	
3	Sat-26-Nov	FAT 3Q	A	Chippenham Town	421	D 1-1	Gillespie 88	
4	Tue-29-Nov	FAT 3QR	H	Chippenham Town	214	D 1-1	(aet L 7-8 pens) Brown 11	

League
Starts
Substitute
Unused Sub

Cups
Starts
Substitute
Unused Sub

Goals (Lg)
Goals (Cup)

MICHAEL GREEN (G)	FORBES	B WILSON	BROWN	JORDAN	BOTTOMLEY	WHITE	SMITH	SLABBER	GILLESPIE	O'HARA	ROSE	HOLDER-SPOONER	S WILSON	BARFOOT	TSOVOLOS	VALLIS	CASHIN-MURRAY	RAYMOND	PRYDE	BREIMYR	FITZHORSEWELL	COLLINS	COOPER	GETESKI	MONTGOMERY	WILKINSON	SMALLPIECE	HERRING	MIKE GREEN	WILLSHER	DOVEY	FLOOD	HIBBERD	ROGERS	FUSEINI	SCANNELL	NELSON	APPIAH	BUBB	ELPHICK	MCMAHON	PHILLIPS	PEACOCK	AIMSON	CASSON
X	X	X	X	X	X	X	X	X	X	X	S	S	S	U																															
U	X	U	X	X	X	X	X	X	X	X		X	S	X	U	U																													
	X	U	X	X	X	X	X	X	X	X		X	S	X	S		U	U	X	U																									
	X	U	X	X	X	X	X	X	X	X		S	S	X		U	U	U		X				X																					
	X		X	X		X	X	X	X	X		X	S	X	U	U		X		X	S	U																							
	X	U		X			X	X	X	X		X	X	X	X	X	U	S		U	U	X	S																						
	X	U		X	X	X		X	X	X	S	X	S	X	X	X	U		U		X		X	S																					
	X	U		X	X	X		X	X			S	S	X	X		U		X				X	S		X	S	U																	
	X	U		X	X	X	X	X	S			S		X	X		U		X							X	S	U																	
	X	U		X	X	X	S	X	X			X	S	X	U				X							X	S	X																	
	X			X	X	X		X				S		X	U	U			X							X		U	U																
	X			X	X		S	X				S	X	X	U			S								X		X	X	U															
		U	X	X	X	S	X	X	X			S	X	X	S											X		X	X	U															
	X	U	X	X	X	S	X	X	X					U	U	U										X		X	X	X															
	X	U			X	X	X	X				S	S	U	U											X		X	X	X	X														
	X		S	X	X	X	X					S	S	U	U											X		X	X	X	X														
	X		S	X	X	X	X	X	S			S	U	U												X		X	X	X	X														
	X			X	X	X	S	X	S			S		U	U											X		X	X	X		X	X												
	X		X	X	X	U						X	S	U	X											X		X	X	S	X	U	X												
	X		X	X	S		S	X				X		U	U											X		X	X	S	X		X	X											
	X		X	X	S		X	X				S		U												X	U	X	X	S	X		X	X	X										
	X		X	X			S	X				U		U												X	U	X	X	S	X		X	X	X										
	X		X	X		U		S						U												U		X	X	X	X		X	X	X	X	S								
	X		X	X		U								U												S		X	X	S	X		X	X	X	X	U	X							
	X		S	X		S	X							U												S		X	X		X		X	X	X	X	U	X							
	X		S	X		X	X	S				S		U												S		X	X	U	X		X	X		X		X							
	X		S	X		X	X					S		U												S		X	U		X		X	X	S	X	U	X							
	X		S	X		X	X	S				U														S		U	X				X	X	S	X	X	X							
	X		X	X		X	X						S	U														S	X		U		X	X	S	X	X	X							
	X		X	X		X	S						U	U														X	X		S	S	X	S	X	X	X		X						
	X		X	X		X	S						U	U														S	X	X	S	X	X	X	X		X				X	S			
	X	S	X			X							U	U											X	X		X	X	U		X		X	X	X	X			X	S			
	X	X	X										U	U	U										X			X	X	X		X		X	X	X	X	S	X						
	X	X	X	S		U								U										U				X	X	X				X	X	X	X	S	X						
	X	U	S	X		X								U												S		X	X					X	X	X	X	S	X						
	X	U	X	X		X						S	U															X	X					X	S	X	X	X				U			
	X	U	X	X		X						X	U												X		S	X	X					X	X		U	X		S					
	X		X			X						S		U													S	X	X					X	X	X	X	X				X	S	U	
	X		X			X						U	S	S													U	X	X		S			X	X	X	X	X				X			
	X	U	X	X	X	S	X	X	X	S		X	U	X	X										X		U	S																	
	X	X	X	X	X	X	X	X	X	U		S	S	X	U		U								X	U	U	X																	
	X	S	X	X	X	X	X	X	S			S	U	U											X		X	X	X	X															
	X	X	X	X	S	X		X				S	U	U											X		X	X	X	X	U														
1	41	3	25	39	16	15	29	15	1	0	9	4	13	5	0	0	4	0	9	0	0	2	0	16	1	0	9	22	0	28	11	0	11	1	15	22	10	18	13	16	3	6	0	0
0	0	1	9	1	2	3	5	2	6	2	1	13	15	1	2	0	3	0	0	0	2	1	0	1	5	3	0	3	2	0	0	5	0	3	0	1	0	5	0	1	0	4	2	1	0
1	0	14	0	0	0	1	3	0	0	0	0	4	6	27	12	4	5	0	3	0	0	1	0	0	1	0	3	5	2	2	0	1	0	3	1	0	0	0	4	0	0	1	0	1
0	4	0	3	4	4	2	4	3	3	0	0	1	0	2	1	0	0	0	0	0	0	0	0	4	0	0	3	2	0	2	2	0	0	0	0	0	0	0	0	0	0	0	0	0
0	0	0	1	0	0	2	0	0	1	1	0	3	1	0	0	0	0	0	0	0	0	0	0	0	0	0	0	1	0	0	0	0	0	0	0	0	0	0	0	0	0	0	0	0
0	0	1	0	0	0	0	0	0	0	1	0	0	2	2	2	0	1	0	0	0	0	0	0	0	0	0	0	1	2	0	0	0	0	1	0	0	0	0	0	0	0	0	0	0
0	3	0	4	2	0	4	2	9	1	0	0	2	1	0	1	0	0	0	0	0	0	0	0	4	0	0	0	1	0	2	0	0	0	3	1	0	10	1	3	0	2	0	0	
0	1	0	1	1	0	1	0	1	1	0	0	0	0	0	0	0	0	0	0	0	0	0	0	0	0	0	0	0	0	0	0	0	0	0	0	0	0	0	0	0	0	0	0	

PLAYING SQUAD 2012/13

Existing Players		SN	HT	WT	DOB	AGE	POB	Career	Apps	Goals
GOALKEEPERS										
Jack	Dovey				23/10/1992	19	Totton	Southampton Rel c/s 12, Eastleigh (SL) 10/11, Eastleigh 5/12	28	0
Wayne	Shaw				29/10/1970	41	Southampton	Southampton (Jun), Reading (Trainee), Basingstoke, Bashley, Wimborne, Gosport, AFC Lymington, Bournemouth FC, Fleet, BAT Sports, Lymington & New Milton, AFC Totten, Eastleigh (Pl/Coach) 6/03, Sutton U (Pl/Coach) c/s 09, Eastleigh (Pl/Coach) 7/12		
DEFENDERS										
Gary	Elphick	6'01"	13 02		17/10/1985	26	Brighton	Brighton, Eastbourne B (L) 9/04, St Albans (SL) 12/04, Aldershot (2ML) 1/06, St Albans 3/06 Rel 12/07, Havant & W 12/07, Eastbourne B 5/09, Eastleigh Undisc 1/12	14	1
Adam	Everitt				28/06/1982	30	Hemel Hempstead	Hemel Hempstead, Harrow c/s 00, Luton, Harrow 10/01, Hayes 6/03 Rel 5/05, Yeading (Trial) c/s 05, Yeading 9/05, Cambridge C 5/07, Eastleigh Undisc 10/07 Rel 5/08, AFC Hornchurch 8/08, Bromley 8/08, St Albans 11/08, Staines 6/11, Eastleigh 7/12		
Mike	Green	6'00"	13 02		12/05/1989	23		Christchurch, New Milton T 10/07, Christchurch, Eastleigh 5/09, AFC Totton (2ML) 8/09 Undisc 10/09, Port Vale 6/11, Eastleigh (L) 10/11 Perm 11/11	24	1
Tom	Jordan	6'04"	12 04		24/05/1981	31	Manchester	Bristol C Rel c/s 02, Huddersfield (Trial) 3/02, Carlisle (Trial) 7/02, Exeter (Trial) 7/02, Southend 8/02 Rel c/s 03, Tamworth 8/03, Forest Green 3/04, Havant & W 8/04, Eastleigh 6/08	40	2
Mitchell	Nelson	6'03"			31/08/1989	23	Lambeth	Colchester Rel c/s 09, Heybridge (WE) 8/08, Tooting & M 7/09, Bournemouth 5/10 Rel 12/11, Eastbourne B (3ML) 10/10, Lewes (SL) 3/11, Crewe (Trial) 8/11, Lincoln C (L) 8/11, Lincoln C (L) 10/11, Lincoln C (L) 11/11, Eastleigh 12/11	22	1
Osei	Sankofa	6'00"	12 04		19/03/1985	27	London	Charlton Rel c/s 08, Bristol C (2ML) 9/05, Brentford (SL) 1/08, Southend 7/08 Rel c/s 10, Farnborough 9/10, Boreham Wood 7/11, Eastleigh 5/12		
MIDFIELDERS										
Dale	Binns				08/07/1981	31	London	Hendon, Cambridge C 8/04, Stevenage 6/06 Rel 5/07, Lewes 7/07, Maidenhead 5/08, Hayes & Yeading 2/09 Rel 5/10, Farnborough 6/10 Rel 6/11, Woking 6/11, Eastleigh 5/12		
Chris	Flood				28/11/1989	22		Andover (Yth), Winchester (Yth), Farnborough 6/07, Brentford, Thatcham (WE) 12/07, QPR 8/08 Rel 1/09, Eastleigh 3/09, Salisbury 8/09, Crawley £10,000 7/10, Forest Green (L) 9/10, Dorchester (L) 1/11 Perm 2/11, Eastleigh (L) 11/11 Perm 11/1116		2
Mark	Hughes	5'10"	12 05		16/09/1983	28	Dungannon, NI	Tottenham, Northampton (L) 8/04, Oldham (3ML) 11/04 Perm 2/05, Thurrock 10/06, Chesterfield (2ML) 11/06, Stevenage 1/07 (06/07 10,2) Rel 5/07, Chester 7/07, Barnet 2/09 Rel c/s 12, Eastleigh 8/12		
Darryl	McMahon	5'11"	12 02		10/10/1983	28	Dublin	West Ham Rel c/s 04, Torquay (L) 3/04, Port Vale 9/04, L.Orient 11/04, Notts County (2ML) 11/06, Stevenage 1/07, Cambridge U 1/09, Farnborough 7/09 Rel 6/11, Boreham Wood 6/11, Eastleigh Undisc 1/12	16	3
Jai	Reason	5'11"	13 01		09/01/1990	22	Southend	Ipswich Rel 5/09, Cambridge U (SL) 2/09, Cambridge U 7/09 Rel 4/10, Crawley 8/10 Rel 9/10, Braintree 9/10, Eastleigh 5/12		
Damian	Scannell	5'10"	11 07		28/04/1985	27	Croydon	Thames Poly, Greenwich B, Fisher 7/04, Luton (Trial) 11/04, Millwall (L) 1/07, Dulwich H (L) 3/07, Eastleigh 5/07, Southend £5,000 1/08, Brentford (L) 11/08, Dag & Red 7/10, Eastleigh 12/11	16	3
Glen	Southam	5'07"	11 10		27/08/1980	32	Enfield	Fulham (Jun), Tottenham (Jun), Enfield, Bishops Stortford 7/00, Boreham Wood (L), Dag & Red 5/04, Hereford 7/09, Bishops Stortford 10/09, Histon 2/10 Rel 4/10, Barnet 6/10 Rel c/s 11, Dover 8/11, Eastleigh 5/12		
FORWARDS										
Moses	Ademola	5'06"	10 08		18/07/1989	23	Bermondsey	Cray W (Yth), Croydon A, Brentford Undisc 7/08, Welling (L) 11/08 Recalled 1 day, Welling (L) 12/08, Welling (2ML) 2/09, Woking (6ML) 7/09, Woking 1/10, Eastleigh 7/12		
Andy	Forbes				28/05/1979	33	Reading	Reading, Basingstoke, Andover, Winchester 8/02, Eastleigh 8/04 Rel 5/10, Woking 5/10, Sutton U (3ML) 10/10 Perm 1/11 Rel 5/11, Eastleigh 6/11	41	3
Craig	McAllister	6'01"	12 07		28/06/1980	32	Glasgow	Eastleigh, Basingstoke 3/02, Stevenage 5/04 Rel 6/05, Gravesend (L) 12/04, Eastleigh (3ML) 2/05, Woking 7/05, Grays 5/07, Rushden & D 10/07, Rushden & D (2ML) 11/07, Oxford U 1/08 Rel 4/08, Exeter 5/08 Rel c/s 10, Barnet (5WL) 11/09, Rotherham (SL) 3/10, Crawley 6/10 Rel 5/11, Newport C 5/11, Luton (SL) 1/12, Eastleigh 6/12		
Lee	Peacock	6'00"	12 08		09/10/1976	35	Paisley	Carlisle, Mansfield £90,000 10/97, Man City £500,000 11/99, Bristol C £600,000 8/00, Sheff Wed 7/04 Rel 1/06, Swindon 1/06, Grimsby 1/10 Rel 5/11, Havant & W 6/11 Rel 1/12, Eastleigh 3/12	8	2
Marvin	Williams	5'11"	11 06		12/08/1987	25	Lincoln	Millwall, Torquay (L) 3/07, Yeovil 7/07 Brentford 6/08, Torquay 9/09 Rel 12/09, IFK Ostursund (Swe) 3/10 Rel 8/10, Stevenage 10/10 Rel 10/10, Hemel Hempstead 2/11, Salisbury 11/11, Eastleigh 5/12		

FARNBOROUGH

Chairman: Brian Berger
Secretary: Steve Duly　　　**(T)** 07922 666621　　　**(E)** steve.duly@farnboroughfc.co.uk
Additional Committee Members:
Robert Prince, Marcus Jones.

Manager: Spencer Day
Programme Editor: Marcus Jones　　　**(E)** marcus.jones@farnboroughfc.co.uk

Club Factfile

Founded: 1967　　　**Nickname:** Boro
Previous Names: Farnborough Town 1967-2007
Previous Leagues: Surrey Senior 1968-72, Spartan 1972-76, Athenian 1976-77, Isthmian 1977-89, 99-2001,
　　　　Alliance/Conference 1989-90, 91-93, 94-99, Southern 1990-91, 93-94, 2007-10

Club Colours (change): All yellow (All white)

Ground: Rushmoor Stadium, Cherrywood Road, Farnborough, Hants GU14 8UD　　　**(T)** 01252 541 469
Capacity: 4,163　**Seats:** 627　　**Covered:** 1,350　　**Clubhouse:** Yes　**Shop:** Yes
Directions: Leave the M3 at Junction 4 and take the A331 signed to Farnham, after a few hundred yards exit at the second slip road- signed A325 Farnborough, turn right at the roundabout and cross over the dual carriageway and small roundabout, passing the Farnborough Gate shopping centre on your left hand side, at the next roundabout turn left (first exit) onto the A325. Go over a pelican crossing and at the next set of lights take the right filter into Prospect Avenue. At the end of this road turn right at the roundabout into Cherrywood Road, the ground is half a mile on the right hand side.

Previous Grounds: None as Farnborough. Queens Road as Farnborough Town

Record Attendance: 2,230 v Corby Town - Southern Premier 21/03/2009
Record Victory: 7-0 v Newport (I.O.W.) (A) - Southern League Division 1 South & West 01/12/2007
Record Defeat: 0-4 v Hednesford Town (A) - Southern League Premier Division 04/03/2010
Record Goalscorer: Dean McDonald - 35 (in 53+3 Appearances 2009-10)
Record Appearances: Nic Ciardini - 147 (2007-10)
Additional Records:

Senior Honours:
Southern League Division 1 South & West 2007-08, Premier Division 2009-10.
Farnborough Town: Southern League Premier Division 1990-91, 93-94. Isthmian League Division 1 1984-85, Premier Division 2000-01.
Hampshire Senior Cup 1974-75, 81-82, 83-84, 85-86, 90-91, 2003-04.

10 YEAR RECORD

02-03		03-04		04-05		05-06		06-07		07-08		08-09		09-10		10-11		11-12	
Conf	13	Conf	20	Conf	21	Conf S	3	Conf S	11	SthW	1	SthP	2	SthP	1	Conf S	2	Conf S	16

FARNBOROUGH

No.	Date	Comp	H/A	Opponents	Att:	Result	Goalscorers	Pos
1	Sat-13-Aug	BSS	A	Eastbourne Borough	751	D 1-1	Murphy 24	10
2	Wed-17-Aug	BSS	H	Salisbury City	788	W 1-0	Connolly 36	8
3	Sat-20-Aug	BSS	H	Welling United	534	L 1-4	Connolly 78	12
4	Mon-22-Aug	BSS	A	Chelmsford City	764	D 2-2	Bygrave 37, Bergqvist 57	10
5	Sat-27-Aug	BSS	A	Hampton & Richmond Boro'	420	D 1-1	Murphy 79	16
6	Mon-29-Aug	BSS	H	Maidenhead United	538	L 0-3		20
7	Sat-03-Sep	BSS	A	Tonbridge Angels	612	W 5-1	Woodyard 6, Murphy 15, Garrod 3 (45, 58, 83)	12
8	Sat-10-Sep	BSS	H	Staines Town	515	W 1-0	Og (Gordon) 31	11
9	Sat-17-Sep	BSS	H	Dartford	679	L 1-2	Merriman 63	13
10	Tue-20-Sep	BSS	A	Dover Athletic	785	D 0-0		13
11	Sat-24-Sep	BSS	A	Basingstoke Town	614	L 3-4	Connolly 57, Woodyard 80, Appiah 90	14
12	Sat-08-Oct	BSS	H	Thurrock	504	L 0-2		16
13	Sat-22-Oct	BSS	H	Sutton United	603	L 0-3		18
14	Tue-25-Oct	BSS	A	Truro City	434	L 2-8	Holland 5, Bygrave 72	19
15	Sat-29-Oct	BSS	A	Havant & Waterlooville	799	L 0-5		19
16	Sat-05-Nov	BSS	H	Chelmsford City	505	L 1-3	Connolly 30	19
17	Sat-12-Nov	BSS	H	Eastleigh	471	L 1-3	Connolly 56	19
18	Sat-19-Nov	BSS	A	Salisbury City	804	W 3-1	Blake 52, Bennett 2 (60, 72)	19
19	Sat-03-Dec	BSS	H	Truro City	427	W 2-1	Page 2 (6, 73)	17
20	Tue-06-Dec	BSS	A	Dorchester Town	334	D 3-3	Bennett 8, Connolly 2 (27, 83)	17
21	Sat-17-Dec	BSS	H	Bromley	409	W 2-1	Bergqvist 38, Connolly pen 80	16
22	Mon-26-Dec	BSS	A	Woking	3014	L 0-1		17
23	Sun-01-Jan	BSS	H	Woking	2017	L 0-1		18
24	Sat-07-Jan	BSS	A	Weston-Super-Mare	422	L 2-5	Connolly 15, Bennett 44	18
25	Sat-14-Jan	BSS	H	Boreham Wood	403	W 4-0	Connolly 3 (3, 25, pen 39), Webb 45	18
26	Sat-21-Jan	BSS	A	Welling United	555	L 0-1		18
27	Sat-28-Jan	BSS	H	Basingstoke Town	411	W 1-0	Page 90	17
28	Sat-18-Feb	BSS	A	Staines Town	415	W 2-1	Charles 2 (82, 90)	16
29	Tue-21-Feb	BSS	A	Thurrock	218	W 1-0	Ciardini 79	14
30	Sat-25-Feb	BSS	H	Tonbridge Angels	608	W 3-2	Charles 12, Jeffrey 15, Page 45	11
31	Sat-03-Mar	BSS	H	Eastleigh	652	W 1-0	Page pen 67	11
32	Tue-06-Mar	BSS	H	Eastbourne Borough	400	W 1-0	Page 90	10
33	Sat-10-Mar	BSS	A	Dartford	1374	L 0-3		12
34	Sat-17-Mar	BSS	H	Weston-Super-Mare	460	L 0-1		13
35	Wed-21-Mar	BSS	H	Dover Athletic	402	L 0-2		13
36	Sat-24-Mar	BSS	A	Bromley	448	D 1-1	Page pen 63	13
37	Sat-31-Mar	BSS	H	Dorchester Town	452	L 1-2	Bennett 68	13
38	Sat-07-Apr	BSS	H	Hampton & Richmond Boro'	593	L 0-2		14
39	Mon-09-Apr	BSS	A	Maidenhead United	339	W 4-3	Ciardini 53, Page 2 (69, 83), Og (Behzadi) 75	13
40	Sat-14-Apr	BSS	A	Boreham Wood	175	L 0-4		14
41	Sat-21-Apr	BSS	H	Havant & Waterlooville	789	W 1-0	Bennett 3	16
42	Sat-28-Apr	BSS	A	Sutton United	1321	L 0-2		16

CUPS

No.	Date	Comp	H/A	Opponents	Att:	Result	Goalscorers	
1	Sat-01-Oct	FAC 2Q	A	Maidenhead United	352	D 1-1	Bygrave 51	
2	Wed-05-Oct	FAC 2QR	H	Maidenhead United	395	L 2-3	Merriman 86, Bygrave 90	
3	Sat-26-Nov	FAT 3Q	H	Bury Town	312	D 2-2	Merriman 2 (62, 63)	
4	Tue-29-Nov	FAT 3QR	A	Bury Town	255	W 2-0 aet	Connolly 91, Pearson 120	
5	Sat-10-Dec	FAT 1	A	AFC Hornchurch	302	D 0-0		
6	Wed-14-Dec	FAT 1R	H	AFC Hornchurch	204	L 2-3	Appiah 23, Connolly 45	

League
Starts
Substitute
Unused Sub

Cups
Starts
Substitute
Unused Sub

Goals (Lg)
Goals (Cup)

TOKARCZYK	WEBB	PEARSON	APPIAH	BYGRAVE	BERGQVIST	MURPHY	WINN	GARROD	PATTISON	CONNOLLY	JAMES	COBB	FRASER	MYERS	SOMERVILLE	JACOBS	ASARE-ADDAI	WOODYARD	MERRIMAN	CHANDLER	G SMITH	NEWBY	SANTANGELO	HOLLAND	BLAKE	MATIC	LOVELOCK	BENNETT	FERGUSON	M SMITH	PAGE	BROWN	GURUNG	TREACHER	JEFFREY	MOODY	ORLU	BRADSHAW	SOGBANMU	PARKES	CIARDINI	CHARLES	LAIDLER	WEEMES	WALLACE
X	X	X	X	X	X	X	X	X	X	X	X	S	S	S	U	U																													
X	X	X	X	X	X	X	X	X	X	X	X	S	U		U	U	U																												
X	X	X	X	X	X	X	X	X	X	X	X	S	S	S	U	U																													
X	X	X	X	X	X	S	X	X	X	X	X	X	U	U	U	U																													
X	X	X		X	X	X	X	X	X	X	X	X	U	U	U	U		S																											
X	X	X		X	X	X	X	X	X	X	X	S	S	U	S		U																												
U	X	X		X	X	X	X	X	X		X	X	S		U	X		S	X	S																									
U	X		X	X	X	X	X	X		X	S	U		X			X	S	X	S																									
U	X	X	X	X	X	X		X	S	X		X		X			X	U	X	S	S																								
U	X	X	X	X	X	X		S	X	X		S		X			X	X	U	S																									
U	X	X	X	X	X	X		S	X	X	X	U		X			S	X		S																									
	X	X	X	X	X	S	X	X		X	X	S	S		X			X	X		U	U																							
U	X	X	X	X	X	X	X	X		X	S	U		X			X	S					X																						
U	X	X	X	X	X	X	X	S		X	U	S		X			X	U					X																						
U	X	S	X	X		X	X	U		X	X	S		X			X	S				X	X																						
	X	S	X		X	X	X		X	S	X		X		U	U		S			X	X	X																						
	X		X		X	X	X		X	S	U		U		U	X	S			X	X	X																						
	X		X	X	X	X		X	S	U		U				X	X		X	X	X	S	S																					
U			X	U		X			S							U	U			X		X	X	X	X	X																		
U	X		X		X	U		X		S						U				X		X	X	X	X	X		X	X	X														
	X		S	X	X		X		X											X		X	X	S	S	X		X	U	X		U												
U		X	X		X		X		X						U					U		X	X	S	X	X		X	X	X		U												
S		X			X		X		X						U					S		X	X	S	X	X		X	X	X	X	U												
U		X	X		X		X		X													X	X	S	X	S		X	X	X	X	U	U	S									
	X		X		X		X		X											S		X	X	S	X	S		X	X	X	U	U	U	X									
U		X	X		X		X		X						U							X	X		X	X		X	X	S		U	S	X										
X		X			X		X		X						U							X	X		X	X		X	X	S		U	S	X										
U	U		X			X			X													X	S	X	X		X	S	X	X		X	X	S										
U	S		X			X			U													X	X	X	X		X	X	S	X	X		S	X										
U	U		X			X			S													X	U	X	X		X	X	S	X	X		X	X										
U	U		X	X		X																X	U	X	X		X	X	S	U	X		X	X										
U	S		X	X		X																X	S	U	X		X	X	X	U	X		X	X	S									
S			X	X		X																X	X	U	X		X	X	X		X		X	X	S									
	S		X	X		X								U								X	X	U	X		X	X	U	X			X	X	S	S								
U	X		X	X		X								X			S					X		U	X		X	X	U				X	X	X	S	X							
	S		X	X		X								X								X		U	X		U	X					X	S	X	U	X							
	U		X	X		X								X								X		S	X		X	X				S		X	S	X	U	X						
U			X	X		X								U								X		X	X		X	X	U	X			X	X	X	S	X							
U			X			X					S			U								X		X	X		X	X	X				X	X	X	S	X	X						
U			X			X					U	S		U								X	S	X	X		X	X	X				X	X	X		S	X						
U			X			X					S	X		U								X	S	X	X		X	X	X				X	X	X	X		X					S	
			X			X						U		U			U					X	U	X	X		X	X	X				X	X	X	X		X				X		X
			X									X	S				S		X			X	X	X	X		U	X	X	U										X				
U	X	X	X	X	X	S	X	X	U	X	X	U			X			X																										
X	X	X	X	X	X	X	X	S	X	X	X	U	U		X			X	S	U		U																						
X		X		X	X	X		X	X	X		U						S				X	X		X			U	U															
X	S	U		X	X	U		X	X	X		U						X	X			X			X				X	S														
X		X	X	X	X			X		S		U						X	X			X			X			S									X	U						
X	U	X	X	X	S	X		X		S		U						X	X			X			X													X	S						
6	23	13	16	36	32	16	27	12	8	27	6	3	1	0	12	0	0	10	3	1	0	0	0	9	4	2	10	25	4	19	23	0	0	19	20	18	8	11	1	3	10	9	8	0	6
1	5	2	1	0	0	2	0	3	1	0	9	13	5	0	1	0	4	0	0	0	0	0	0	0	0	0	0	10	3	2	0	0	0	1	5	0	0	3	0	3	3	3	4	0	
16	10	0	0	0	0	2	0	2	0	0	1	14	3	7	13	1	4	0	4	3	0	1	1	0	0	0	0	3	1	0	0	0	0	2	1	7	8	0	0	0	0	0	0	2	0
0	6	2	5	4	6	3	4	2	0	6	4	2	0	0	2	0	0	2	3	3	0	0	0	4	1	0	4	0	0	0	0	1	0	0	0	2	0	0	0	0	0	0	0	0	0
0	0	1	0	0	0	3	0	0	1	0	0	2	0	0	0	0	0	0	2	0	0	0	0	2	0	0	0	0	0	0	0	0	0	0	0	1	1	0	0	1	0	0	0	0	0
1	0	1	1	0	0	0	1	0	1	0	0	2	1	0	4	0	0	0	1	0	1	0	0	0	0	0	0	0	1	1	0	0	0	1	0	0	0	0	0	0	0	0	0	0	0
0	1	0	1	2	2	3	0	3	0	12	0	0	0	0	0	0	2	1	0	0	0	1	0	0	6	0	0	9	0	0	0	1	0	0	0	0	2	3	0	0	
0	0	1	1	2	0	0	0	0	2	0	0	0	0	0	0	0	0	2	0	0	0	0	0	0	0	0	0	0	0	0	0	0	0	0	0	0	0	0	0	0	0	0	0	0	0

ALSO PLAYED: VINER U (36,37), X (42). HARKNESS S (41).

PLAYING SQUAD 2012/13

Existing Players		SN	HT	WT	DOB	AGE	POB	Career	Apps	Goals
GOALKEEPERS										
Craig	Bradshaw							Cove, Walton Casuals 10/07, Leatherhead 6/09, Horsham 12/09,		
								Kingstonian (L) 2/10 Perm, Walton Casuals 3/10, Bedfont T,		
								Farnborough 12/11	11	0
DEFENDERS										
Alfredo	Bosch							Spain, Farnborough 6/12		
Adam	Bygrave		5'09"	12 02	24/02/1989	23	Walthamstow	Reading Rel c/s 08, Gillingham (SL) 11/07, Weymouth 5/08,		
								Histon £5,000 1/09, Hayes & Yeading 8/10,		
								Farnborough 6/11	36	2
Alan	Inns				05/06/1982	30	Reading	Oxford C (Jun), Wokingham, Hampton & R 9/02,		
								AFC Wimbledon 5/08 Rel 4/10, Woking 5/10,		
								Boreham Wood (SL) 2/11, Farnborough 5/12		
MIDFIELDERS										
Nic	Ciardini				01/09/1988	23		Farnborough (Yth), Southampton (Yth), Swindon (Yth),		
								Bournemouth (Yth), Farnborough Rel 6/11, Lewes 6/11,		
								Farnborough 2/12	13	2
Callum	Cobb							Farnborough	16	0
Steve	Laidler				10/10/1983	28	Reading	Reading (Scholar) Rel c/s 03, Basingstoke 8/03, Farnborough 11/03,		
								Dorking 1/04, Dumbarton 3/04 Rel c/s 04, Year Out,		
								Farnborough 7/05, Woking (Trial) c/s 06, Basingstoke 5/07,		
								Farnborough 5/08 Rel 9/09, Basingstoke (L) 8/09 Perm 9/09,		
								Australia 2/11, Farnborough NC 3/12	11	0
Ollie	Treacher							Chertsey, Farnborough 11/11	19	0
FORWARDS										
Dan	Bennett				23/07/1988	24		Weymouth, Chesham, Chertsey T, Farnborough 11/11	25	6
Jordan	Merriman							Farnborough	13	1
Phillip	Page							Chertsey, Farnborough 11/11	25	9
David	Tarpey				14/11/1988	23		C.Palace (Yth), Basingstoke 8/06 Rel 5/09, Hampton & R 7/09,		
								Walton & H (Dual) 9/09, Farnborough 5/12		

HAVANT AND WATERLOOVILLE

Chairman: Derek Pope
Secretary: Trevor Brock   **(T)** 07768 271 143   **(E)** trevor.brock52@yahoo.com
Additional Committee Members:
James Fallon, Ray Jones, Adrian Hewett , Kevin Moore, Adrian Aymes.

Manager: Stuart Ritchie
Programme Editor: Adrian Aymes   **(E)** aaymes2125@aol.com

Club Factfile

Founded: 1998   **Nickname:** Hawks
Previous Names: Havant Town and Waterlooville merged in 1998
Previous Leagues: Southern 1998-2004

Club Colours (change): All white (Yellow & blue/blue/yellow)

Ground: Westleigh Park, Martin Road, West Leigh, Havant PO7 8EJ   **(T)** 02392 787 822
Capacity: 4,800   **Seats:** 562   **Covered:** 3,500   **Clubhouse:** Yes   **Shop:** Yes
Ground is a mile and a half from Havant Town Centre. Take A27 to Havant then turn onto B2149 (Petersfield Road). Turn right at next junction after HERON pub into Bartons Road then take first right into Martin Road.

Previous Grounds: None

Record Attendance: 4,400 v Swansea City - FA Cup 3rd Round 05/01/2008
Record Victory: 9-0 v Moneyfields - Hampshire Senior Cup 23/10/2001
Record Defeat: 0-5 v Worcester City - Southern Premier 20/03/2004
Record Goalscorer: James Taylor - 138
Record Appearances: James Taylor - 297
Additional Records: Paid £5,000 to Bashley for John Wilson
Senior Honours: Received £15,000 from Peterborough United for Gary McDonald
Southern League Southern Division 1998-99. Russell Cotes Cup 2003-04

10 YEAR RECORD

02-03		03-04		04-05		05-06		06-07		07-08		08-09		09-10		10-11		11-12	
SthP	8	SthP	12	Conf S	13	Conf S	6	Conf	4	Conf S	7	Conf S	15	Conf S	6	Conf S	9	Conf S	19

HAVANT & WATERLOOVILLE

No.	Date	Comp	H/A	Opponents	Att:	Result	Goalscorers	Pos
1	Sat-13-Aug	BSS	A	Boreham Wood	201	W 1-0	Peacock 2	7
2	Wed-17-Aug	BSS	H	Welling United	599	L 1-2	Braham-Barrett 44	11
3	Sat-20-Aug	BSS	H	Chelmsford City	692	L 2-3	Ramsey 2 (pen 83, pen 88)	14
4	Tue-23-Aug	BSS	A	Weston-Super-Mare	313	L 1-3	Woodford 36	16
5	Sat-27-Aug	BSS	H	Truro City	502	W 4-1	Fogden 3, Jones 2 (35, 71), Ryan 82	14
6	Mon-29-Aug	BSS	A	Salisbury City	845	L 1-4	Fogden 40	16
7	Sat-03-Sep	BSS	A	Eastbourne Borough	668	L 1-2	Igoe pen 54	17
8	Sat-10-Sep	BSS	H	Sutton United	789	D 2-2	Woodford 19, Braham-Barrett 34	17
9	Tue-13-Sep	BSS	A	Maidenhead United	224	L 0-2		17
10	Sat-17-Sep	BSS	H	Thurrock	607	W 3-0	Fogden 2 (43, 85), Woodford 47	17
11	Sat-24-Sep	BSS	A	Dover Athletic	735	D 1-1	Fogden 37	17
12	Sat-08-Oct	BSS	H	Bromley	766	L 1-2	Palmer 24	18
13	Sat-22-Oct	BSS	A	Hampton & Richmond Boro'	475	D 3-3	Peacock 4, Jones 2 (31, 59)	19
14	Tue-25-Oct	BSS	H	Dorchester Town	539	W 4-2	Palmer 2 (49, 59), Igoe 65, Woodford 82	16
15	Sat-29-Oct	BSS	H	Farnborough	799	W 5-0	Palmer 2 (38, 53), Igoe 62, Ramsey 2 (78, 90)	13
16	Sat-05-Nov	BSS	A	Woking	1655	L 0-3		16
17	Sat-12-Nov	BSS	H	Eastbourne Borough	783	D 0-0		15
18	Sat-19-Nov	BSS	A	Staines Town	274	D 1-1	Palmer 65	15
19	Sat-03-Dec	BSS	H	Weston-Super-Mare	586	D 1-1	Cashman 45	15
20	Sat-17-Dec	BSS	A	Tonbridge Angels	599	W 2-1	Ramsey 10, Palmer 81	15
21	Mon-26-Dec	BSS	H	Eastleigh	938	D 0-0		15
22	Sat-07-Jan	BSS	H	Dartford	802	L 1-4	Jones 65	16
23	Sat-14-Jan	BSS	H	Maidenhead United	584	W 2-1	Woodford 74, Jones 88	14
24	Sat-21-Jan	BSS	A	Thurrock	194	D 0-0		14
25	Sat-28-Jan	BSS	H	Hampton & Richmond Boro'	645	D 2-2	Ramsey 35, Holland 76	16
26	Tue-07-Feb	BSS	A	Eastleigh	526	L 2-3	Pearce 2 (44, 89)	16
27	Sat-18-Feb	BSS	A	Chelmsford City	859	L 1-3	Jones 90	17
28	Tue-21-Feb	BSS	A	Welling United	384	L 1-3	Ryan 2	17
29	Sat-25-Feb	BSS	A	Dorchester Town	469	W 6-3	Ramsey 4 (3, 17, 61, 68), Palmer 2 (27, 52)	16
30	Sat-03-Mar	BSS	H	Boreham Wood	580	L 2-4	Jones 33, Ramsey 53	17
31	Tue-06-Mar	BSS	A	Sutton United	409	L 0-2		17
32	Sat-10-Mar	BSS	H	Woking	1009	L 3-4	Palmer 2 (3, 77), Ramsey 49	18
33	Sat-17-Mar	BSS	A	Dartford	1087	L 1-3	Jones 8	19
34	Tue-20-Mar	BSS	A	Bromley	303	D 0-0		19
35	Sat-24-Mar	BSS	H	Tonbridge Angels	708	D 1-1	Nanetti 70	19
36	Sat-31-Mar	BSS	A	Basingstoke Town	481	L 2-3	Nanetti 70, Og (Ogunbote) 90	21
37	Sat-07-Apr	BSS	A	Truro City	698	W 1-0	Nanetti pen 70	20
38	Tue-10-Apr	BSS	H	Salisbury City	743	W 2-1	Jones 12, Nanetti pen 25	17
39	Sat-14-Apr	BSS	H	Dover Athletic	792	L 0-1		19
40	Mon-16-Apr	BSS	H	Basingstoke Town	724	L 0-1		19
41	Sat-21-Apr	BSS	A	Farnborough	789	L 0-1		19
42	Sat-28-Apr	BSS	H	Staines Town	949	W 3-2	Jones 22, Palmer 42, Dolan 90	19

CUPS

No.	Date	Comp	H/A	Opponents	Att:	Result	Goalscorers	
1	Sat-01-Oct	FAC 2Q	H	Sholing	370	W 4-1	Ramsey 26, Peacock 41, Fogden 51, Braham-Barrett 64	
2	Sat-15-Oct	FAC 3Q	A	Weston-Super-Mare	333	L 2-3	Ramsey pen 3, Palmer 45	
3	Sat-26-Nov	FAT 3Q	A	Weymouth	462	D 0-0		
4	Tue-29-Nov	FAT 3QR	H	Weymouth	238	L 0-2		

League
Starts
Substitute
Unused Sub

Cups
Starts
Substitute
Unused Sub

Goals (Lg)
Goals (Cup)

ASHMORE	NEWTON	MCDONALD	HINSHELWOOD	HOLLAND	PEARCE	FOGDEN	RAMSEY	PEACOCK	IGOE	BRAHAM-BARRETT	NWOKEJI	SCOTT	BEAZLEY	WOODFORD	EBERENDU	MCBEAN	JONES	RYAN	WHYTE	OKUS	ARHTUR	GADD	N BARRETT	HOPKINSON	PALMER	PERICARD	GETESKI	NORTON	CASHMAN	THOMPSON	FENELON	DOLAN	HUTCHINSON	THOMAS	NANETTI
X	X	X	X	X	X	X	X	X	X	X		S	S	U	U	U																			
X	X	X	X	X	X	X	X		X	X	X	U	U	U	U	S																			
X	X	X	X	X	X	X	X			X	X	U	U	U		S	S																		
X	X	X	X	X	X	X			X	X	U	U	S	U	X	S																			
X	X		X	X	S	X	X			X	S	S	U	X	U	X	X	X																	
X		X	X	X		X	X	X			U	U	X	S	S	X	X	X	X																
U			X	X	X		X	X	X		X	X	U		X	X	S	X	S	U															
U	X	S		X	U	X		X	X	X		X	X		S	X	U	X		X															
U	X	X		X	X	X		X	X	S		X			S	X	U	X		X	U														
U	X	X		X	X	X		X	X	X		X			S	X		S	X		X	U													
U	X			U	X	X		U	X	X		X			U	X		S	X		U	X													
U		X	S	S	X		X	X	X			X	X		U	X	X			X			X		S										
	X	X	S	X	U		S	X	X	X		X	X		X	X	U						X		S										
	X	S	S	X	U		X	S	X	X		X	X		X	X	U						X		X										
	S	X	X	X	U		X	S	X	X		X	X		X	X	S						X			U									
	U	X	X	X	U		X	S	X	X		X	X		X	X	S						X		S										
		X	X	S	X		X	X		X		X	X		X			X		X			U	X	U	S	S								
	S	X	X	X	X		X	X	X			X	X		X	U		U	X	X	X	S	U												
	X		X	X	U		X		X			X	X		S	X	U				U	U	X												
	X	U	X	X	X		X		X	S		X	U		X	S			X			X		X	S					X					
	X	X	X		X		X	S	X	X		X	S		X	S			U	S		X		U	S					X					
	X	X	U		X		X		X	X		X	U		X	U			X	U		X		S			U	X							
	X	X	X	X		X		U	U			X	S		X	U			X			X		X				U	S						
	X	X	X	X		X		S	U			X	U		X	U	U		X			X		S					X						
	X	X	X	X		X		U	S			X	U		X	U			X	X		X		S	U				S						
	X	X	X	U	X		X		X	S		X	X		X	X	U		X			X		S	X				S						
	X	U	X	U	X		X		X	S		X	X		X	X			X			X		S	X		U		X						
		X	X	X	U		X		S			X	X		X	X	S		X			X		S	X			U		X					
U	X	X	X	U		X		S				X	X		X	X			X			X		S	X				X	S					
S	U	X		X		X		S				X	X		X	X			X	X		X		X	X		U		S	U	X				
X	U	U		X		S						X	U		X	X			X	X		X		X	X			S		X	X				
X		U		X		X		U				U	U		X	X			X	X		X			X			S		X	X	X	X		
X		S		X		X		U				U	U		X	X			X	X		X			X			S		X	X	X	X		
X		U		X		X		U				X	U		X	X			X			X			X			S		X	X	U	X		
X	U	S		X		X		S				X	S		X				X			X			X			X		X	X	U	X		
X	U	X	U	X		X		X				X			U				X			X			U			S		X	X	X	X		
X	U	X		X		U		X				X			U				S	S		X			S			U		X	X	X	X		
X	U	X		U		X		X				X	U		X				U	X		X			S			S		X	X	X	X		
X	S	X		X		X		X				U			X	U			X	U		X			S			S		X	X	X	X		
X		X		X		X		S							U				X	S		X			U				U			X	X	X	X	

U	X		U	U	X	X	X	X	X			X	X					S	X	U	S			X		S									
U	X	X	S	X	U		X	X	X	X		X	X					S	S	U				X		X			U						
	U	X	X	X	X		X	X	X	X		X	S					X	S					U	X		U			U						
X	X	X	X				X	S	X			X	X					X	X	U				S	X		S	U								

6	32	21	28	22	30	11	36	12	26	17	2	0	28	20	0	2	30	27	2	2	26	0	5	6	20	2	0	0	4	2	0	13	12	8	10
0	3	3	5	2	2	0	1	4	7	6	2	2	0	4	1	3	7	2	4	1	1	0	0	7	7	3	2	1	0	10	2	0	1	0	0
6	2	9	4	4	10	0	0	0	5	2	0	5	8	16	5	0	1	4	9	2	0	1	0	8	1	1	3	5	1	2	0	1	0	2	0

0	3	3	2	3	2	1	4	3	4	3	0	0	4	3	0	0	1	3	0	0	0	2	0	3	0	0	0	0	0	0	0	0	0	0	0
0	0	0	1	0	0	0	0	1	0	0	0	0	0	1	0	0	2	1	1	1	0	0	0	1	1	0	1	0	0	0	0	0	0	0	0
2	1	0	1	1	1	0	0	0	0	0	0	0	0	0	0	0	0	0	3	0	0	0	0	1	0	0	2	1	0	0	0	0	0	0	0

| 0 | 0 | 0 | 0 | 1 | 2 | 5 | 12 | 2 | 3 | 2 | 0 | 0 | 0 | 5 | 0 | 0 | 11 | 2 | 0 | 0 | 0 | 0 | 0 | 12 | 0 | 0 | 0 | 1 | 0 | 0 | 1 | 0 | 0 | 4 | |
| 0 | 0 | 0 | 0 | 0 | 0 | 1 | 2 | 1 | 0 | 1 | 0 | 0 | 0 | 0 | 0 | 0 | 0 | 0 | 0 | 0 | 0 | 0 | 0 | 0 | 1 | 0 | 0 | 0 | 0 | 0 | 0 | 0 | 0 | 0 | 0 |

PLAYING SQUAD 2012/13

Existing Players		SN	HT	WT	DOB	AGE	POB	Career	Apps	Goals
GOALKEEPERS										
Clark	Masters		6'03"	13 12	31/05/1987	25	Hastings	Brighton (Yth), Gillingham (Yth), Brentford, Redbridge (2ML) 8/05, Slough (SL) 11/05, AFC Wimbledon (L) 3/07, Welling (L) 8/07, Southend 1/08 Rel c/s 09, Stevenage (SL) 1/08, Welling (L) 11/08, Grimsby (Trial) 1/09, Aldershot Undisc 7/09, Hayes & Yeading 2/10 Rel c/s 10, Hastings U 8/10 Rel 11/10, Barrow NC 11/10 Rel 5/11, Millwall (Trial) 11/10, Eastbourne B 6/11, Havant & W 7/12		
Matt	Pegler				12/08/1991	21		Fulham (Yth), QPR (Yth), Aldershot (Yth), Woking c/s 09 Rel 2/12, Fleet T (L) 3/11, Badshot Lea (L) 7/11, Injured, Havant & W 7/12		
Dan	Thomas		6'02"	13 01	01/09/1991	20	Poole	Brockenhurst College, Bournemouth Rel 3/12, Dorchester (L) 2/11, Dorchester (L) 3/11, Welling (5ML) 8/11, AFC Totton (L) 1/12, Havant & W 3/12	8	0
DEFENDERS										
Ed	Harris		6'01"	13 05	03/11/1990	21	Roehampton	QPR, AFC Wimbledon 7/10 Rel 5/11, Dover (L) 3/11, Dover 6/11 Rel c/s 12, Havant & W 7/12		
Paul	Hinshelwood		6'02"	14 00	11/10/1987	24	Chatham	Brighton Rel c/s 07, Burgess Hill (L) 8/06, Torquay 6/07 Rel 5/08, Tiverton (L) 11/07, Bognor 8/08, Havant & W 1/09	33	0
Jake	Newton				09/06/1984	28	Hammersmith	Hampton & R (Yth), Kingston Academy, Staines c/s 03, Chalfont St Peter (L) 2/04, Bashley 2/05, Staines 7/05, Havant & W 7/09	35	0
Sam	Page		6'04"	13 02	30/10/1987	24	Croydon	C.Palace (Yth), MK Dons Rel 1/08, Aylesbury (L) 8/06, Hendon (L) 9/06, Cambridge U (SL) 2/07, Walton & H (L) 9/07, Hendon (3ML) 10/07, Rushden & D (Trial) 1/08, Hendon 1/08, Horsham 6/08, Sutton U 7/10 Rel c/s 12, Havant & W 6/12		
Sam	Pearce				11/02/1987	25	Portsmouth	Havant & W, Fleet T 3/06, South Africa, Bognor Regis 8/08, Salisbury 3/09, Havant & W 6/09	32	2
Perry	Ryan				10/04/1992	20		Portsmouth Rel c/s 11, Bognor Regis (2ML) 12/10, Havant & W 8/11	29	2
Harvey	Whyte				24/08/1991	21		Havant & W, Bognor Regis (2ML) 3/12	6	0
Ryan	Woodford		5'11"	11 08	14/08/1991	21		Portsmouth (Scholar) Rel c/s 09, Havant & W 7/09	24	5
MIDFIELDERS										
Chris	Arthur		5'10"	12 01	25/01/1990	22	Enfield	QPR Rel 6/09, Hayes & Yeading (WE) 12/07, Kettering (3ML) 11/08, Rushden & D (L) 2/09, Turkey, Bishops Stortford 9/10, Rotherham 12/10, Bishops Stortford 1/11, Turkey, Havant & W 9/11, Northampton 9/11 Rel 12/11, Havant & W 12/11	27	0
Stefan	Bailey		5'11"	12 08	10/11/1987	24	Brent	QPR Rel 5/08, Oxford U (L) 10/07, Grays 6/08, Farnborough (L) 2/09, Ebbsfleet 8/09 Rel c/s 10, AFC Telford 9/10, Kettering 3/11, Banbury U (Trial) 7/11, Hemel Hempstead, Banbury U 9/11, Havant & W 8/12		
Bobby	Hopkinson		5'08"	13 07	03/07/1990	22	Plymouth	Plymouth (Scholar),Tiverton 3/08, Aldershot Undisc 8/09 Rel 3/10, Farnborough (Dual) 1/10, Havant & W 3/10, Horndean (Dual) 8/11	13	0
Eddie	Hutchinson		6'01"	13 00	23/02/1982	30	Kingston	Sutton U, Brentford £75,000 8/00, Oxford U 7/06 Rel 4/09, Crawley 5/09 Rel 11/10, Eastbourne B 1/11 Rel 2/12, Havant & W 3/12	13	0
Christian	Nanetti						Bologna	QPR (Scholar) Rel 5/10, Raith 9/10, Ashford T (Middx), Bradford C (Trial), Charlton (Trial), Lewes 10/11, Havant & W 3/12	10	4
Steven	Ramsey (was Walker)				23/11/1989	22		Portsmouth (Scholar), Rel c/s 08 Havant & W 5/08	37	12
Lewis	Stockford				01/10/1992	19	Portsmouth	Portsmouth Rel c/s 12, Salisbury (L) 9/11, Salisbury (L) 10/11, AFC Totton (L) 2/12, Havant & W 7/12		
Tony	Taggart		5'10"	11 02	07/10/1981	30	London	Brentford Rel c/s 00, Farnborough c/s 00, Barnet 6/03, Farnborough 8/04, Weymouth 6/05, Havant & W 12/05, Eastleigh 7/08, Newport C 5/10, Eastleigh (2ML) 10/10 Perm 12/10, Sutton U 5/11 Rel c/s 12, Havant & W 6/12		
FORWARDS										
Alex	Balacchino				06/01/1991	21		Havant & W, Milton T (Dual), Poole T (Dual) 3/12, Poole T (Dual) 7/12		
Scott	Jones							Brading T, Havant & W 8/11	37	11
Sahr	Kabba				13/04/1989	23		Bristol R (Yth), Almondsbury T, Weston-Super-Mare 7/10, Havant & W Undisc 7/12		
Ryan	Moss		5'11"	12 04	14/11/1986	25	Dorchester	Bournemouth Rel c/s 05, Dorchester 8/05, Bashley 7/06, Dorchester Undisc 6/08 Rel 2/09, Bashley 2/09, Dorchester c/s 09 Rel 12/11, Bashley 12/11, AFC Totton 1/12, Havant & W 6/12		
Oliver	Palmer				21/01/1992	20		Woking, Sevenoaks (L) 9/10, St Albans (2ML) 11/10, Boreham Wood (2ML) 7/11, Havant & W 9/11	27	12

HAYES & YEADING

Chairman: Derek Goodall
Secretary: Bill Gritt   **(T)** 07710 102 004   **(E)** secretary@hyufc.com
Additional Committee Members:
Trevor Griffiths, John Bond, Derrick Matthews, Nick Griffith, Dean Goodall,
Trevor Gorman, Avril Radford, Simon East, Eric Stevens, Colin Hanlon.
Manager: Nas Bashir
Programme Editor: Andy Corbett   **(E)** programme@hyufc.com

Photo courtesy: www.hyufc.com

Club Factfile

Founded: 2007   **Nickname:**
Previous Names: Hayes - Botwell Mission 1909-29. Hayes and Yeading merged to form today's club in 2007
Previous Leagues: Isthmian

Club Colours (change): Red/black/black (Blue/white/white)

Ground: Woking FC, Kingfield Stadium, Kingfield Road, Woking GU22 9AA   **(T)** 0208 573 2075
Capacity: 6,000   **Seats:** 2,500   **Covered:** 3,900   **Clubhouse:** Yes   **Shop:** Yes

Directions
The ground is situated on the A247, opposite the entrance to Woking Park, midway between the town centre and Old Woking. Leave the M25 at either junctions 10 (Wisley) or 11 (Chertsey) and follow the signs towards Woking. When nearing the town centre follow the brown signs showing Heathside car park. The ground is about 15 minutes' walk from the car park. Come out of the car park and follow the signs for Woking FC (the first route described below for rail travellers). Travelling supporters are requested to use Heathside car park as there are no parking areas around Kingfield Stadium.
It has been brought to our notice that cars parking in Westfield Avenue have been subjected to parking tickets, this also applies to cars parking on the grass verge near the ground. We therefore suggest that you try to park elsewhere to avoid this happening to you.

Previous Grounds: Beaconsfield Road > 2012.

Record Attendance: 1,881 v Luton Town - Conference Premier 06/03/2010
Record Victory: 8-2 v Hillingdon Borough (A) - Middlesex Senior Cup 11/11/08
Record Defeat: 0-8 v Luton Town (A) - Conference Premier 27/03/10
Record Goalscorer: Josh Scott - 40 (2007-09)
Record Appearances: James Mulley - 137 (2007-10)
Additional Records:

Senior Honours:
Conference South Play-offs 2008-09

10 YEAR RECORD										
02-03	03-04	04-05	05-06	06-07	07-08	08-09	09-10	10-11	11-12	
					Conf S 13	Conf S 4	Conf 17	Conf 16	Conf 21	

HAYES & YEADING UNITED

No.	Date	Comp	H/A	Opponents	Att:	Result	Goalscorers	Pos
1	Sat-13-Aug	BSP	H	Alfreton Town	262	W 3-1	McClure 9, Pacquette 30, Crockford 73	1
2	Tue-16-Aug	BSP	A	Newport County	1519	L 0-4		13
3	Sat-20-Aug	BSP	A	Fleetwood Town	1376	L 0-1		17
4	Tue-23-Aug	BSP	H	Bath City	172	D 1-1	Pacquette 45	16
5	Sat-27-Aug	BSP	A	Cambridge United	1778	L 1-2	Bentley 49	18
6	Tue-30-Aug	BSP	H	Luton Town	1015	D 2-2	Soares 2 (4, 45)	19
7	Sun-04-Sep	BSP	H	Tamworth	359	W 1-0	Pacquette 49	15
8	Sat-10-Sep	BSP	A	Grimsby Town	2835	L 0-3		19
9	Sat-17-Sep	BSP	A	Darlington	1809	D 1-1	Soares 68	18
10	Tue-20-Sep	BSP	H	Braintree Town	209	L 1-2	Joseph-Dubois 13	18
11	Sat-24-Sep	BSP	H	Gateshead	218	L 2-3	Soares pen 72, Collins 83	20
12	Tue-27-Sep	BSP	A	Kettering Town	1119	W 5-3	Collins 7, Soares 2 (pen 17, 83), Joseph-Dubois 22, Mackie 55	18
13	Sat-01-Oct	BSP	A	AFC Telford	1941	D 1-1	Pacquette 85	18
14	Sun-09-Oct	BSP	H	Wrexham	625	L 0-2		18
15	Tue-11-Oct	BSP	H	Forest Green Rovers	251	W 2-0	Collins 2 (61, 83)	17
16	Sat-15-Oct	BSP	A	Barrow	1074	L 1-3	Soares pen 58	18
17	Tue-18-Oct	BSP	A	Tamworth	742	L 1-2	Soares pen 15	20
18	Sat-22-Oct	BSP	H	York City	525	L 2-4	Soares 45, Williams 90	20
19	Sat-05-Nov	BSP	A	Stockport County	2804	D 3-3	Sinclair 13, Soares 2 (75, 88)	21
20	Sat-19-Nov	BSP	H	Kidderminster Harriers	289	L 1-3	Cadmore 65	21
21	Sat-26-Nov	BSP	A	Alfreton Town	600	L 2-3	Og (Arnold) 90+2, Soares 90+5	21
22	Tue-29-Nov	BSP	A	Newport County	303	L 0-4		22
23	Tue-06-Dec	BSP	A	Braintree Town	454	W 3-0	Williams 2 (56, 88), Collins 63	21
24	Sat-17-Dec	BSP	H	Barrow	313	D 1-1	Wishart 40	21
25	Tue-20-Dec	BSP	H	Fleetwood Town	264	L 1-3	Collins 36	21
26	Mon-26-Dec	BSP	A	Ebbsfleet United	1176	L 1-3	Collins 80	21
27	Sat-07-Jan	BSP	A	Kidderminster Harriers	1732	L 1-3	Williams 28	23
28	Sat-17-Jan	BSP	H	Ebbsfleet United	266	L 1-2	Soares 46	23
29	Sat-21-Jan	BSP	A	Mansfield Town	1872	L 2-3	J Owusu 31, Soares 55	23
30	Tue-24-Jan	BSP	H	Darlington	550	W 3-2	Soares pen 4, Wishart 6, Collins 60	22
31	Sat-28-Jan	BSP	H	Southport	294	L 0-2		23
32	Sat-18-Feb	BSP	A	Wrexham	3845	L 1-4	Thalassitis 88	23
33	Tue-21-Feb	BSP	A	Bath City	512	W 1-0	Thalassitis 38	23
34	Sat-03-Mar	BSP	A	York City	2603	L 0-2		22
35	Tue-06-Mar	BSP	A	Gateshead	465	L 0-2		22
36	Sat-10-Mar	BSP	H	Kettering Town	253	W 1-0	Wishart 84	21
37	Sat-17-Mar	BSP	A	Forest Green Rovers	781	W 3-1	Cadmore 40, Thalassitis 68, Wishart 81	21
38	Tue-20-Mar	BSP	H	Grimsby Town	392	L 1-2	Hand pen 87	21
39	Sat-24-Mar	BSP	H	AFC Telford	307	D 0-0		21
40	Tue-27-Mar	BSP	H	Lincoln City	327	L 1-2	Pele 70	21
41	Sat-31-Mar	BSP	A	Southport	1147	W 2-1	Hand pen 14, J Owusu 90	21
42	Sat-07-Apr	BSP	H	Cambridge United	336	D 0-0		21
43	Mon-09-Apr	BSP	A	Luton Town	6003	L 2-4	Wishart 21, Og (Kovacs) 56	21
44	Sat-14-Apr	BSP	H	Mansfield Town	487	L 1-3	Mingoia 37	21
45	Sat-21-Apr	BSP	A	Lincoln City	2585	W 1-0	Mingoia 50	21 Relegated
46	Sat-28-Apr	BSP	H	Stockport County	654	L 1-2	J Owusu 15	21

CUPS

No.	Date	Comp	H/A	Opponents	Att:	Result	Goalscorers	Pos
1	Sat-29-Oct	FAC 4Q	H	Cambridge United	452	L 2-6	Crockford 29, Soares pen 88	
2	Sat-10-Dec	FAT 1	A	Hampton & Richmond Boro'	242	L 0-2		

League
Starts
Substitute
Unused Sub

Cups
Starts
Substitute
Unused Sub

Goals (Lg)
Goals (Cup)

ARNOLD	ARGENT	CADMORE	BENTLEY	JOHN	CROCKFORD	HAND	JOSEPH-DUBOIS	McCLURE	PACQUETTE	SOARES	ELDER	FEDERICO	WISHART	SAVILLE	PREDDIE	WILLIAMS	BAYLEY	UAH	MACKIE	COLLINS	NOBLE	FRANKS	SPENCE	MARSAUD	LEGG	LEE	BETTAMER	BASSELE	HARRIOTT	SINCLAIR	L OWUSU	PENTNEY	FOLKES	MORRIS	WYNTER	GAMEIRO	BEASANT	AJALA	MOUTAOUAK	GLADWIN	PICKFORD	J OWUSU	WALSH	ROSE
1	2	5	12	3	8	4	9	14	7	16	11	6	21	10	22	24	23	27	28	29	30	26	20	17	33	29	6	31	22	23	3	15	31	25	3	6	39	38	18	29	23	19	38	8

PLAYING SQUAD 2012/13

Existing Players		SN	HT	WT	DOB	AGE	POB	Career	Apps	Goals
GOALKEEPERS										
James	Beasant		6'02"	14 11	16/03/1989	23	London	Watford, Glen Hoddle Academy, Hayes & Yeading 12/11	3	0
Delroy	Preddie		6'00"		14/07/1976	36	Berkshire	Northampton (Trainee), Slough c/s 94, Walton & H (L) 3/96,		
								Walton & H 8/96, Chesham 7/99, Yeading 5/03, Maidenhead 11/06,		
								Staines 8/07, Hayes & Yeading 8/07 Rel 9/09, Walton & H 10/09,		
								Windsor & E 8/10, Godalming 12/10, Hayes & Yeading 1/11	7	0
DEFENDERS										
Tom	Cadmore		6'00"	13 01	26/01/1988	24	Rickmansworth	Watford (Yth), Wycombe Rel 5/08, Yeading (3ML) 8/07,		
								Hayes & Yeading 7/08	46	2
Sam	Cox		5'07"	10 00	10/10/1990	21	Edgware	Tottenham Rel c/s 10, Cheltenham (2ML) 9/09, Histon (L) 11/09,		
								Torquay (L) 1/10, Barnet 7/10 Rel c/s 12, Boreham Wood (3ML) 10/11,		
								Boreham Wood (SL) 1/12, Hayes & Yeading 8/12		
Jay	Kalama							AFC Wimbledon (Yth), Kingstonian, Walton & H 1/12, Whyteleafe,		
								Hayes & Yeading 8/12		
Elliott	Legg							Hayes & Yeading	1	0
Pedro	Monteiro (Pele)		6'01"	13 07	02/05/1978	34	Albufeira	Desportivo Clube (Por), SC Farense (Por) c/s 02, Belenenses (Por) c/s 03,		
								Southampton 7/06, West Brom c/s 07, Falkirk 11/09, MK Dons 8/10,		
								Shrewsbury (Trial), Northwich 2/11, Hednesford c/s 11,		
								Hayes & Yeading 1/12	19	1
Dan	Spence		5'10"	12 06	22/10/1989	22	Reading	Reading, Woking (2ML) 10/08, Salisbury (L) 1/09, Salisbury 7/09,		
								Glen Hoddle Football Academy 10/09, Mansfield 1/11 Rel 5/11,		
								Hayes & Yeading 9/11	20	0
MIDFIELDERS										
Mark	Bentley		6'02"	13 04	07/01/1978	34	Hertford	Enfield, Aveley, Enfield, Aldershot 8/99, Southampton (Trial) 9/99,		
								Crewe (Trial) 3/00, Gravesend 5/02, Dag & Red 6/03,		
								Southend Undisc 1/04, Gillingham 5/06 Rel c/s 11, Cambridge U (L) 3/11,		
								Hayes & Yeading 8/11	34	1
Darryl	McLean				04/05/1992	20		Southampton, Hayes & Yeading 8/10 Rel c/s 11, Hayes & Yeading 8/12		
Luke	Williams				27/11/1989	22		Reading (Scholar), Woodley T, Binfield 2/11,		
								Hayes & Yeading 7/11	39	4
FORWARDS										
Aristede	Bassele				15/06/1994	18		Bromley (Yth), Hayes & Yeading	4	0
Tobi	Joseph				04/12/1992	19		Stevenage, AFC Hornchurch, Nike Academy, Hayes & Yeading 8/12		
Kudus	Oyenuga		5'10"	12 01	18/03/1993	19	Walthamstow	Tottenham Rel c/s 12, MyPa (Fin) (4ML) 4/11, Bury (L) 8/11,		
								St Johnstone (SL) 1/12, Hayes & Yeading 8/12		
Manny	Williams				13/11/1981	30	London	Notts County (Yth), Millwall (Yth), Concord R, Bowers Utd, Leyton 7/01,		
								Yeading 9/05, Leyton 7/06, Maidenhead 8/07, Woking 5/08 Rel 5/09,		
								Maidenhead (2ML) 11/08, Weston-Super-Mare (3ML) 1/09,		
								Havant & W 6/09, Maidenhead 6/11, Hayes & Yeading 8/12		
Daniel	Wishart				28/05/1992	20		Hayes & Yeading, Hendon (2ML) 10/10, Burnham (L) 10/11	36	5

MAIDENHEAD UNITED

Chairman: Peter Griffin
Secretary: Ken Chandler   **(T)** 07726 351 286   **(E)** kenneth.chandler@btinternet.com
Additional Committee Members:
Robert Hussey, Una Loughrey, Robert Hussey, Mark Stewart, Steve Jinman,
Suzanne Loughrey, Graham Alfred, Mark Smith.
Manager: Johnson Hippolyte
Programme Editor: Mark Roach   **(E)** markroachonline@yahoo.co.uk

Back row, left to right: Aryan Tajbakhsh, Devante McKain, Leon Solomon, Alec Wall, Marcus Rose, Leigh Henry
Middle row, left to right: Jon Urry, Max Bangura, Ashley Watson, Joe Crook, James Regis, Jonathan Hippolyte, Alex Tokarczyk,
Billy Lumley, Michael Pearce, Harry Pritchard, Jamie Connor Martel Powell, Paul Semakula, Stefan Powell, Jordan Chandler
Front row, left to right: Michael Pook, David Pratt, Lee Barney, Mark Nisbet, Simon Lane, Johnson Hippolyte, Dereck Brown,
Bobby Behzadi, Reece Tison-Lascaris Derek Duncan, Daniel Brown.
Photo: Stefan Baisden.

Club Factfile

Founded: 1870   **Nickname:** Magpies
Previous Names: Maidenhead F.C and Maidenhead Norfolkians merged to form today's club
Previous Leagues: Southern 1894-1902, 2006-07, West Berkshire 1902-04, Gr. West Suburban 1904-22, Spartan 1922-39,
Gr. West Comb. 1939-45, Corinthian 1945-63, Athenian 1963-73, Isthmian 1973-2004, Conf. 2004-06

Club Colours (change): Black & white stripes/black/white (Yellow/blue/yellow)

Ground: York Road, Maidenhead, Berkshire SL6 1SF   **(T)** 01628 636 314
Capacity: 4,500   **Seats:** 400   **Covered:** 2,000   **Clubhouse:** Yes   **Shop:** Yes

Directions
The Ground is in the town centre.
200 yards from the station and two minutes walk from the High Street.
Access from M4 Junctions 7 or 8/9.

Previous Grounds: Kidwells Park (Norfolkians)

Record Attendance: 7,920 v Southall - FA Amateur Cup Quarter final 07/03/1936
Record Victory: 14-1 v Buckingham Town - FA Amateur Cup 06/09/1952
Record Defeat: 0-14 v Chesham United (A) - Spartan League 31/03/1923
Record Goalscorer: George Copas - 270 (1924-35)
Record Appearances: Bert Randall - 532 (1950-64)
Additional Records: Received £5,000 from Norwich City for Alan Cordice 1979

Senior Honours:
Corinthian League 1957-58, 60-61, 61-62.
Berks & Bucks Senior Cup x19.

10 YEAR RECORD

02-03		03-04		04-05		05-06		06-07		07-08		08-09		09-10		10-11		11-12	
Isth P	10	Isth P	12	Conf S	20	Conf S	22	SthP	4	Conf S	17	Conf S	6	Conf S	16	Conf S	19	Conf S	20

MAIDENHEAD UNITED

No.	Date	Comp	H/A	Opponents	Att:	Result	Goalscorers	Pos
	Maidenhead							
1	Sat-13-Aug	BSS	H	Tonbridge Angels	385	L 0-4		20
2	Tue-16-Aug	BSS	A	Dorchester Town	410	L 0-4		22
3	Sat-20-Aug	BSS	A	Bromley	417	W 1-0	Thomas 9	17
4	Tue-23-Aug	BSS	H	Thurrock	221	W 4-0	Powell 2 (12, 45), Thomas pen 28, Wall 29	13
5	Sat-27-Aug	BSS	H	Staines Town	305	D 1-1	Williams 21	13
6	Mon-29-Aug	BSS	A	Farnborough	538	W 3-0	Thomas 34, Powell 60, Wall 84	5
7	Sat-03-Sep	BSS	A	Truro City	576	W 2-1	Powell 47, Thomas 87	5
8	Sat-10-Sep	BSS	H	Weston-Super-Mare	375	L 1-3	Williams 69	9
9	Tue-13-Sep	BSS	H	Havant & Waterlooville	224	W 2-0	Wall 2 (25, 65)	4
10	Sat-17-Sep	BSS	A	Welling United	640	L 0-4		5
11	Tue-20-Sep	BSS	H	Truro City	301	L 1-3	Og (Brooks) 20	9
12	Sat-24-Sep	BSS	A	Sutton United	1332	L 1-4	Thomas 59	11
13	Sat-08-Oct	BSS	H	Chelmsford City	355	D 1-1	Holgate 90	11
14	Sat-22-Oct	BSS	H	Bromley	405	D 3-3	Powell 3, Brown 24, Thomas 66	14
15	Mon-24-Oct	BSS	A	Boreham Wood	210	L 0-1		14
16	Sat-05-Nov	BSS	A	Eastleigh	503	L 1-4	Brown 53	18
17	Tue-08-Nov	BSS	H	Dover Athletic	359	L 1-4	Holgate 64	18
18	Tue-15-Nov	BSS	H	Hampton & Richmond Boro'	227	L 0-2		18
19	Sat-19-Nov	BSS	A	Weston-Super-Mare	307	L 2-4	Williams 55, Quamina 90	18
20	Sat-03-Dec	BSS	H	Dorchester Town	269	L 0-1		19
21	Mon-05-Dec	BSS	A	Chelmsford City	704	L 0-2		19
22	Sat-17-Dec	BSS	A	Salisbury City	647	W 2-0	Powell 26, Pacquette 28	18
23	Mon-26-Dec	BSS	H	Basingstoke Town	314	L 0-1	Wall 60	18
24	Sat-31-Dec	BSS	A	Basingstoke Town	362	W 3-1	Tison-Lascaris 28, Pacquette 2 (83, 88)	17
25	Sat-07-Jan	BSS	H	Eastbourne Borough	301	W 1-0	Wall 90	14
26	Sat-14-Jan	BSS	A	Havant & Waterlooville	584	L 1-2	Wall 60	15
27	Sat-21-Jan	BSS	A	Sutton United	313	D 1-1	Williams 6	16
28	Sat-28-Jan	BSS	A	Eastbourne Borough	572	W 2-0	Henry 14, Williams 15	14
29	Sat-18-Feb	BSS	A	Thurrock	156	D 1-1	Williams 63	15
30	Sat-25-Feb	BSS	H	Boreham Wood	242	L 0-3		17
31	Sat-03-Mar	BSS	A	Woking	1777	W 2-0	Behzadi pen 71, Strutton 73	16
32	Sat-10-Mar	BSS	A	Tonbridge Angels	591	L 0-1		16
33	Tue-13-Mar	BSS	H	Dartford	355	D 1-1	Wall 13	16
34	Sat-17-Mar	BSS	A	Hampton & Richmond Boro'	296	D 0-0		16
35	Tue-20-Mar	BSS	H	Welling United	260	L 0-4		16
36	Sat-24-Mar	BSS	H	Salisbury City	434	L 0-1		17
37	Sat-31-Mar	BSS	A	Dartford	1069	L 1-2	Semakula 63	18
38	Sat-07-Apr	BSS	A	Staines Town	327	D 0-0		19
39	Mon-09-Apr	BSS	H	Farnborough	339	L 3-4	Semakula 14, Powell 18, Behzadi pen 88	20
40	Sat-14-Apr	BSS	H	Woking	1192	L 0-1		21
41	Sat-21-Apr	BSS	A	Dover Athletic	725	D 2-2	McKain 41, Brown 46	20
42	Sat-28-Apr	BSS	H	Eastleigh	495	W 4-3	Wall 16, Tison-Lascaris 2 (20, 67), Semakula 67	20

CUPS

No.	Date	Comp	H/A	Opponents	Att:	Result	Goalscorers
1	Sat-01-Oct	FAC 2Q	H	Farnborough	352	D 1-1	Powell 30
2	Wed-05-Oct	FAC 2QR	A	Farnborough	395	W 3-2	Tison-Lascaris 58, Thomas 59, Kamara 84
3	Sat-15-Oct	FAC 3Q	H	Woking	624	W 4-1	Holgate 2 (17, 33), Tison-Lascaris 2 (28, 43)
4	Sat-29-Oct	FAC 4Q	A	Godalming Town	703	W 5-0	Powell 32, Soloman 2 (39, 77), Thomas 46, Williams 88
5	Sat-12-Nov	FAC 1	H	Aldershot Town	2283	D 1-1	Thomas 7
6	Tue-22-Nov	FAC 1R	A	Aldershot Town	2181	L 0-2	
7	Sat-26-Nov	FAT 3Q	H	Billericay Town	235	W 1-0	Tison-Lascaris 23
8	Sat-10-Dec	FAT 1	A	Staines Town	201	D 0-0	
9	Tue-13-Dec	FAT 1R	H	Staines Town	154	L 1-2	Tison-Lascaris 54

League
Starts
Substitute
Unused Sub

Cups
Starts
Substitute
Unused Sub

Goals (Lg)
Goals (Cup)

	BUSSEY	SOLOMAN	BEHZADI	TAYLOR	HENDRY	SCARBOROUGH	POWELL	HENRY	WILLIAMS	WORSFOLD	HOLGATE	BROWN	WALL	THOMAS	FAGAN	CLEMENT	SAROYA	TISON-LASCARIS	LUMLEY	SILVER	NYDELL	DAVIES	S BEASANT	BARNEY	ROSE	MCKAIN	JONES	AHMIDI	KAMARA	HIPPOLYTE	QUAMINA	CROOK	SEMAKULA	STANISLAUS	HINDS	NISBET	PACQUETTE	POOK	N BEASANT	WALKER	PRITCHARD	LENNOX	STRUTTON	MENDY	OPARA	LUCAS
	X	X	X	X	X	X	X	X	X	X	X	X	S	S	S	U	U	U																												
	U	X	U	X		X	S	U	X	X		X	X	X	X	X	X	S																												
	U	S	X	X	S	X	S	U	X	X		X	X	X	X	X		X																												
	U	X	X	S	X	X	X	X	X	X	S	X	X	X	X			X		U		X																								
		X	X	X	X	U	X	X	X	X	S	S	U	X	X			X		X	U																									
		X	S	X	S	X	X	X	S	X	X	X	X	X				U		X	U																									
		X	X		X	X	X	X	X	X	S	X	X	S				S	U	U																										
		X	X			X	X	X	X	S	X	X	X	X		S	S		U	X	U																									
		X	X		S	X	X	X	X	S	X	X	U			X	S		U	X	U	U																								
		X	X		X	X	X		X	S	U	X	S	U		X	S		X	X																										
		X	X		X	X			X	S	U	X				X		X	S			U		X	S																					
		X	X		X				X	X	X					X	S		X			U		X			X	S	S																	
		X	S		X	X	X	X	X				X		U	U	X					X						S																		
		S	X		U		S	X	X	X	X	S				X		U	X	X				X								X														
		X	S		U		S	X	X	X	S	X	X			X		X	U	X				X														X								
		X	X				X	X	X	X	S	X	X			X		X	U	U				X		U	U																			
		X	X				X	X	X		X		X			U	X		X					X		U			S				S													
			X				X	X	X	X	X		X	S	X	X			U					X		X	S					S														
		X	X				X	S	X	X	X	X	S					X						X		X	U						X		S											
		X	S		X		S		S		X	X				U	X	X	X					U		X	S								S	X										
		X	X				X		S	X		X	X	U		U		X	X					X		X	S						X		S	X										
		X	X				X	X	U			X	X	S				X	S	X						U							X		S	X	X	X	S							
		X	X				X	X			S		U	X				X	X					U									X		S	X	X	X	X	X	S					
		X	X				X	X					S	S	S	X		X	X					U									X		U	X	X	X	X							
		X	X		U		X	X			S	X	S	X				X	X					U									X		S	X	X	X								
		X	X				S	X	X	X	S	S						X	X					U									X		U	X	X	X		X						
		X	X				X	S	X	X	U	S	X					X	X					U									X		U	X	X		X							
		X	X				X	X	X	X		S	X					X	X					U									X		S	X					U						
		X	X				X	X	X	X		S	X					X	X					U		U							X		U	X	S			S	U					
		X	X				X	X	X	X		S	X					X						U									X		U	S	X			U	S	X				
		X	X				X	X		U		X	S	X					U								S						X		X	X	X				X	X	S		
		X	X				X	X	U	S		X	S	S					U													X		X	X	X				X	X	X			
		X	X				X	X	U			X	X				X	X						U								X		X			S			X	U	S			
		X	X				X	X	S			U	X	X				X	X								S					S		X			S			X	U	X			
		X	X				X	X					X	X			S		X					U									X		X		X				U	U			
		X	X				X	X					X	X	S				X					U									X		X		X				U	U			
		X	X				X	X	U	X			X	X					X		U						S		S				X		X		S	X			X			S	
		X	X				X	X	U	X			X	X					X		S					S			S				X		X		S	X			X				U
		X	X				X	X	S				X	X					X		X			U			U						X		X		X				X			S	S
		X	X				X	X	S	S			X	X					X		X						X		X				S		X		X				X				U
		X	X				X	X		S			X	X					X		X						S		X						X		X				U		S		U
	X	S				X	X	U	X	X	X	X					X	X	S	X				X					U		S	U	U												
	X					X	X	X	X	X		X	X	X			X	X	U	X		U	S						U		S	U													
		X				X	X	X	X			S	X	X	S		X	X	X	X	U	X							U		S														
	X	X				X	X	X	X			S	S	X	X			X	S	U	U	X							U		U														
	X	X				X	X	X	X	S		X	X				X	S	U	U	X							U		U			U												
	X	X				X	X	X	S			X	X	S	X	S		U	X	U			X					U		S		U			X										
	X							S		S	X	X	X	X	U		X	X	X				X	X				X					X												
		X						X		S	X	X	X	S	X				X				X													X			X	X	X				
		X			U				S	X	X	X	S	S		U		X	X				X												X			X	X	X				
1	39	37	5	10	30	36	26	25	15	19	33	26	12	7	2	10	21	26	0	3	0	7	3	4	0	0	0	0	2	0	7	0	13	17	3	5	0	0	9	3	2	0	0	0
0	2	4	1	3	1	6	1	8	10	12	6	6	4	2	0	2	5	0	0	0	0	3	0	6	1	0	2	0	0	2	13	0	4	2	0	1	1	1	1	0	3	3	0	1
3	0	1	0	1	2	0	5	3	0	3	2	0	3	1	7	6	1	3	6	2	2	8	1	4	7	0	0	0	1	0	0	3	0	1	1	0	0	0	2	3	4	0	0	4	0
0	6	6	0	5	6	7	4	1	4	9	9	1	7	3	1	3	5	3	0	0	0	5	0	3	1	0	0	0	0	1	2	0	1	2	2	2	0	0	0	0	0	0	0	0
0	0	1	0	0	0	0	1	0	6	3	0	0	5	1	2	1	0	1	0	0	0	0	0	0	1	0	1	2	0	0	0	0	1	0	0	0	0	0	0	0	0	0	0	0
0	0	0	0	0	1	0	1	0	0	0	1	0	0	0	0	0	1	0	4	4	0	2	0	1	3	0	0	0	5	0	1	2	3	0	1	0	0	0	0	0	0	0	0	0
0	0	2	0	0	0	7	1	6	0	2	3	9	6	0	0	0	3	0	0	0	0	0	0	0	0	0	1	0	0	0	1	0	0	0	1	0	3	0	0	0	3	0	0	0	1
0	2	0	0	0	0	2	0	1	0	2	0	0	3	0	0	0	5	0	0	0	0	0	0	0	0	1	0	0	0	0	0	0	0	1	0	0	0	0	0	0	0	0	1	0	0

PLAYING SQUAD 2012/13

Existing Players		SN	HT	WT	DOB	AGE	POB	Career	Apps	Goals
GOALKEEPERS										
Billy	Lumley		6'05"	14 13	28/12/1989	22	Loughton	Wolves (Scholar), Glen Hoddle Academy 11/08, Brentford (Trial) 7/09, Grays 8/09 Rel 9/09, Stafford R 9/09 Rel 11/09, Northampton 12/09, Eastleigh 3/10, Billericay 7/10, Jerez Industrial CF (Spa) 8/10, Bournemouth (Trial) 4/11, Maidenhead 8/11	26	0
Jonathan	Nydell							Seacoast Utd (USA), Maidenhead 8/11	3	0
Emmanuel	Opara							Maidenhead	0	0
DEFENDERS										
Bobby	Behzadi				08/02/1981	31	London	Stevenage, Wealdstone (L) 1/00, Hayes 3/00, Yeading 8/01, Maidenhead 1/07	41	2
Derek	Duncan		5'10"	10 11	23/04/1987	25	Newham	L.Orient Rel 5/07, Lewes (L) 9/06, Grays 5/07, Wycombe 7/07, Lewes (2ML) 11/07, Ebbsfleet 1/09, AFC Wimbledon 6/09 Rel 4/10, Ebbsfleet 7/10, Woking 7/11, Maidenhead 6/12		
Leigh	Henry		5'10"	11 11	29/09/1986	25	Swindon	Swindon Rel 12/06, Bath C (WE) 3/05, Weston-Super-Mare (2ML) 8/06, Swindon Supermarine 2/07, Bath C 2/11 Rel 5/11, Swindon Supermarine (Dual) 3/11, Maidenhead 6/11	27	1
Mark	Nisbet				29/11/1986	25		Flackwell Heath, Maidenhead 7/06	19	0
Bradley	Quamina		5'11"		28/06/1985	26		Yeading Rel 8/05, USA Scholarship, Yeading/Hayes & Yeading 1/06, Woking 5/07 Rel 5/09, Maidenhead 6/09	2	1
Marcus	Rose				04/06/1990	22		QPR (Yth), Barnet (Scholar), Hitchin (2ML) 11/08, Leyton c/s 09, Maidenhead 11/09, Beaconsfield SYCOB (L) 8/11	4	0
John	Scarborough		6'01"		13/03/1979	33	Gravesend	Gravesend, Ashford T, Herne Bay, Eastbourne B, Tilbury, Billericay c/s 03, Tilbury 2/04, Chelmsford (Trial) c/s 04, Dover 9/04, Sutton U 9/04, Hampton & R 6/08, Bromley 8/10 Rel 12/10, Lewes 12/10, Maidenhead 3/11	31	0
Leon	Soloman				18/02/1986	26		Millwall (Junior), Gillingham (Scholar) 7/02, Hastings U (L) 8/04, Worthing (L) 12/04, Welling 9/05, Hayes & Yeading 8/08, Walton Casuals (L) 12/08, Bracknell 1/09, Hemel Hempstead c/s 09, Harrow 8/10, Windsor & E 10/10, Maidenhead 2/11	41	0
MIDFIELDERS										
Wadah	Ahmidi							Molten, Kingsbury London Tigers, Maidenhead 9/11	0	0
Daniel	Brown				28/10/1988	23		Northwood, Maidenhead 8/09	39	3
Jermaine	Hinds							Fleet, Kingstonian, Croydon, Dorking, Carshalton, Walton Casuals, Dulwich H, Maidenhead, Leyton, Maidenhead 2/11, Farleigh R, Maidenhead 11/11	17	0
Marcel	Jones							Maidenhead	1	0
Michael	Pook		5'11"	11 10	22/10/1985	26	Swindon	Swindon Rel c/s 09, Cheltenham 7/09 Rel 8/11, Forest Green (Trial), Brackley 10/11, Maidenhead 12/11, Forest Green 1/12, Maidenhead 7/12	6	0
Martel	Powell				28/09/1991	20		MK Dons (Scholar) Rel c/s 10, Maidenhead 8/10	42	7
Harry	Pritchard							Flackwell Heath, Burnham, Maidenhead 2/12, Burnham (Dual) 2/12	10	0
Paul	Semakula							L.Orient, St Albans 7/07, Tonbridge A, Sittingbourne (L) 9/10, Billericay 6/11, Maidenhead 11/11	20	3
Chris	Taylor		5'08"	10 05	30/10/1985	26	Swindon	Swindon Rel c/s 06, Newport C (L) 3/05, Newport C (L) 8/05, Swindon Supermarine 8/06, Dandedong Thunder (Aust) 1/11, Maidenhead 7/11	6	0
FORWARDS										
Lee	Barney				01/04/1992	20		Maidenhead, Walton & H (Dual) 2/11, Beaconsfield SYCOB (Dual) 8/11	6	0
Joe	Crook							Eastleigh, Maidenhead 8/11	2	0
Ashan	Holgate		6'02"	12 00	09/11/1986	25	Swindon	Swindon Rel c/s 07, Salisbury (L) 3/06, Newport C (L) 10/06, Macclesfield (SL) 1/07, Weston-Super-Mare 8/07, Eastleigh 4 fig 12/07, Cirencester (L) 2/08, Weston-Super-Mare 3/08, Newport C 10/09 Rel 1/10, Swindon Supermarine 3/10, Maidenhead 6/11	31	2
Ishmail	Kamara							Ivory Coast, Thailand, Motala AIF (Swe), Margate 8/10 Rel c/s 11, Leeds (Trial) 9/10, Maidenhead 9/11	2	0
Kyle	Lucas							Maidenhead	1	0
Devante	McKain							Maidenhead	10	1
Marcus	Mealing							Marlow, Maidenhead 11/11		
Anthony	Mendy							Maidenhead	3	0
David	Pratt				01/08/1987	25		Swindon Supermarine, Chippenham 6/07, Basingstoke 5/09 Rel c/s 12, Maidenhead 6/12		
Reis	Stanislaus				17/03/1989	23		Maidenhead 11/11	0	0
Reece	Tison-Lascaris							Boreham Wood, Maidenhead 7/11	26	3
Alex	Wall				22/09/1990	21		Thatcham, Maidenhead 8/09	32	9
Johnson	Hippolyte							Maidenhead (Man)	0	0

SALISBURY CITY

Chairman: W. Harrison-Allen
Secretary: Peter Matthiae   **(T)** 07784 303035   **(E)** peter.matthiae@salisburycity-fc.co.uk
Additional Committee Members:
Jeff Hooper, Geoff Cain.

Manager: Darrell Clarke
Programme Editor: Paul Osborn   **(E)** info@sarumgraphics.co.uk

Salisbury City FC 'THE WHITES'

Cameron Hough, Jamie White, Callum Hart, Dan Fitchett, Will Puddy, Mark Scott, Rhys Baggridge, Theo Lewis, Matt Clark, Stuart Sinclair

Chris McPhee, Ryan Brett, Brian Dutton, Mikey Harris (Ass. Manager), Darrell Clarke (Manager), Michael Cooper (Coach), Chris Giles (Captain), Robbie Matthews, Ugo Udoji

Club Factfile

Founded: 1947   **Nickname:** The Whites
Previous Names: Salisbury F.C.
Previous Leagues: Western 1947-68, Southern 1968-2004, 2010-11, Isthmian 2004-05, Conference 2005-10.

Club Colours (change): All white with black trim (Yellow/blue/yellow)

Ground: Raymond McEnhill Stadium, Partridge Way, Old Sarum SP4 6PU   **(T)** 01722 776 655
Capacity: 5,000   **Seats:** 500   **Covered:** 2,247   **Clubhouse:** Yes   **Shop:** Yes

Directions
Situated A345 Salisbury/Amesbury Road.
From North/East/West: Leave A303 at Countess roundabout at Amesbury and take A345 towards Salisbury until Park and Ride roundabout from where the ground is signposted.
From South: Proceed to A345 and then follow directions to Amesbury until Park
and Ride roundabout from where the ground is signposted.

Previous Grounds: Victoria Park

Record Attendance: 3,100 v Nottingham Forest - FA Cup 2nd Round 2006
Record Victory: 11-1 v RAF Colerne (H) - Western League Division 2 1948
Record Defeat: 0-7 v Minehead (A) - Southern League 1975
Record Goalscorer: Royston Watts - 180 (1959-65)
Record Appearances: Barry Fitch - 713 (1963-75)
Additional Records: Paid £15,000 to Bashley for Craig Davis
Senior Honours: Received £20,000 from Forest Green Rovers for Adrian Randall
Western League 1957-58, 60-61. Southern League Premier Division 1994-95, 2005-06.

10 YEAR RECORD

02-03		03-04		04-05		05-06		06-07		07-08		08-09		09-10		10-11		11-12	
SthE	4	SthE	6	Isth P	12	SthP	1	Conf S	2	Conf	12	Conf	16	Conf	12	SthP	3	Conf S	10

SALISBURY CITY

No.	Date	Comp	H/A	Opponents	Att:	Result	Goalscorers	Pos
1	Sat-13-Aug	BSS	H	Thurrock	738	D 1-1	Knight 70	11
2	Wed-17-Aug	BSS	A	Farnborough	788	L 0-1		15
3	Sat-20-Aug	BSS	A	Staines Town	1002	W 1-0	Wright 51	11
4	Tue-23-Aug	BSS	H	Truro City	899	W 2-1	Adelsbury 15, Reid 34	9
5	Sat-27-Aug	BSS	A	Weston-Super-Mare	390	L 0-2		12
6	Mon-29-Aug	BSS	H	Havant & Waterlooville	845	W 4-1	Fitchett 4, Reid 45, Dutton 48, D Clarke 89	4
7	Sat-03-Sep	BSS	H	Hampton & Richmond Boro'	803	W 4-2	Reid pen 47, Giles 2 (55, 72), Wright 90	4
8	Sat-10-Sep	BSS	A	Bromley	605	D 2-2	Reid pen 35, Wright 90	5
9	Sat-17-Sep	BSS	A	Tonbridge Angels	511	L 1-3	Giles 81	9
10	Tue-20-Sep	BSS	H	Basingstoke Town	731	D 1-1	Reid 69	10
11	Sat-24-Sep	BSS	H	Eastbourne Borough	667	W 3-0	Fitchett 45, Matthews 52, Brett 83	6
12	Sat-08-Oct	BSS	A	Woking	1634	D 0-0		7
13	Sat-22-Oct	BSS	H	Chelmsford City	763	L 0-1		10
14	Tue-25-Oct	BSS	A	Sutton United	718	L 0-5		12
15	Sat-05-Nov	BSS	H	Dartford	769	L 1-2	Anderson 2	15
16	Tue-15-Nov	BSS	A	Welling United	440	L 3-4	Reid 8, Williams 2 (51, 89)	16
17	Sat-19-Nov	BSS	H	Farnborough	804	L 1-3	Reid 45	16
18	Tue-06-Dec	BSS	H	Tonbridge Angels	448	W 2-0	Anderson 2 (pen 45, 53)	15
19	Sat-17-Dec	BSS	H	Maidenhead United	647	L 0-2		17
20	Mon-26-Dec	BSS	A	Dorchester Town	981	W 3-0	Kelly 12, Williams 23, Anderson pen 42	16
21	Mon-02-Jan	BSS	H	Dorchester Town	1003	L 0-1		16
22	Tue-10-Jan	BSS	A	Thurrock	186	D 1-1	Giles 36	16
23	Sat-21-Jan	BSS	H	Woking	1034	W 2-0	Matthews 45, Dutton 61	15
24	Tue-24-Jan	BSS	A	Eastleigh	903	D 1-1	Matthews 16	14
25	Sat-28-Jan	BSS	A	Dover Athletic	825	D 1-1	Matthews 45	15
26	Sat-11-Feb	BSS	A	Truro City	590	D 2-2	Williams 2 (30, 66)	13
27	Tue-14-Feb	BSS	A	Basingstoke Town	407	D 2-2	Og (Rice) 23, Losasso 88	13
28	Sat-18-Feb	BSS	H	Bromley	701	L 0-2		13
29	Tue-21-Feb	BSS	H	Eastleigh	647	W 2-0	Sinclair 32, Bell-Baggie 83	13
30	Sat-25-Feb	BSS	A	Dartford	941	L 0-2		13
31	Sat-03-Mar	BSS	H	Dover Athletic	695	L 0-1		14
32	Sat-10-Mar	BSS	H	Staines Town	563	W 1-0	Fitchett 37	14
33	Sat-17-Mar	BSS	H	Boreham Wood	525	L 0-2		14
34	Mon-19-Mar	BSS	A	Boreham Wood	255	D 1-1	Losasso 58	14
35	Sat-24-Mar	BSS	A	Maidenhead United	434	W 1-0	Sinclair 20	14
36	Sat-31-Mar	BSS	H	Welling United	610	D 0-0		14
37	Sat-07-Apr	BSS	H	Weston-Super-Mare	605	D 0-0		13
38	Tue-10-Apr	BSS	A	Havant & Waterlooville	743	L 1-2	Griffin 15	15
39	Sat-14-Apr	BSS	A	Chelmsford City	777	W 3-2	Griffin pen 85, Williams 90+2, Bell-Baggie 90+6	13
40	Tue-17-Apr	BSS	A	Hampton & Richmond Boro'	469	W 2-1	Losasso 39, Webb 45	12
41	Sat-21-Apr	BSS	H	Sutton United	892	W 3-1	Williams 3 (49, 81, 90)	11
42	Sat-28-Apr	BSS	A	Eastbourne Borough	705	W 3-1	Williams 60, Griffin 66, Fitchett 78	10

CUPS

No.	Date	Comp	H/A	Opponents	Att:	Result	Goalscorers
1	Sat-01-Oct	FAC 2Q	H	Swindon Supermarine	598	W 3-0	Dutton 45, Kelly 90, Fitchett 90
2	Sat-15-Oct	FAC 3Q	H	Poole Town	961	W 6-1	Fitchett 3 (12, pen 42, 45), Kelly 40, Reid 77, Knight 90
3	Sat-29-Oct	FAC 4Q	A	Bishops Stortford	501	W 2-1	Brett 41, Knight 45
4	Sat-12-Nov	FAC 1	H	Arlesey Town	1298	W 3-1	Fitchett 12, Reid pen 55, Kelly 90
5	Sat-26-Nov	FAT 3Q	H	Weston-Super-Mare	552	W 2-0	Anderson 23, Dutton 42
6	Sat-03-Dec	FAC 2	H	Grimsby Town	2161	D 0-0	
7	Sat-10-Dec	FAT 1	H	Lowestoft Town	494	W 4-1	Fitchett 3 (19, 90, 90), Giles 32
8	Tue-13-Dec	FAC 2R	A	Grimsby Town	1880	W 3-2 aet	Fitchett 46, Dutton 100, Anderson pen 113
9	Sat-07-Jan	FAC 3	A	Sheffield United	10488	L 1-3	Macklin 86
10	Sat-14-Jan	FAT 2	H	York City	827	L 2-6	Reid 2 (35, pen 79)

		League
		Starts
		Substitute
		Unused Sub
		Cups
		Starts
		Substitute
		Unused Sub
		Goals (Lg)
		Goals (Cup)

Player appearance grid (X = started, S = substitute, U = unused substitute):

	GOUGH	RUDDICK	CASEY	ADELSBURY	DUTTON	C HART	KELLY	ANDERSON	WRIGHT	REID	KNIGHT	GILES	HERBERT	D CLARKE	BRETT	SMITH	FITCHETT	HARRIS	STOCKFORD	MATTHEWS	COOPER	NEISH	LOSASSO	WEBB	ALEXIS	WILLIAMS	R HART	MCCAULEY	SCOTT	TURK	MACKLIN	ARTHUR	PUDDY	SINCLAIR	O'DONNELL	M CLARK	BELL-BAGGIE	UDOJI	GRIFFIN	LYSKOV
	X	X	X	X	X	X	X	X	X	X	X	X	S	S	S	U	U																							
	X	X	X	X	X	X	S	X	S	X	X	X	S	X	U	U	U																							
	X	X	S	X	X	X	X	X	X	X	X	X	S	U	U	U																								
	X	X	S	X	X	X	X	X	U	X	X	X	S	S	U	X																								
	X	X	U	X	X	X	X	X	X	X	X	S	X	U	U	U	X																							
	X	X	U	X	X	X	X	X	S	X	X	X	S	X	U	X																								
	X	X	S	X	X	X	X	S	X	X	X	S	X	U	U	X																								
	X	X	X	X		X	X		S	X	S	X	U	X	X	U	X		S																					
	X	X	X	X		X	X		S	X	S	X	U	X	U	X		S																						
	X	X	S	X		X	X		U	X	X	X	U	S	X	U	X		X																					
	X		X	X		X	X		S	S	X	X	S		X	U	X		X	X	U																			
	X		X	X		X	X		U	S	X		S	U	X	U	X		X	X																				
	X		X		X		X	X	U	S	X	X	S	X	U	X		X	X																						
	X		X	S	X		X	X	S	X	S	X	S	U	X	X	U	X		X																				
	X				X		X	X	S	X	S	X	U	X	X		U																							
			X	X			X	X			X	S		U	X	X	X					S			X		X	S	U											
			X		X		X	X			X	S		S	X	X	X					U			X		X	X	U	U										
			X	X			U	X			S	S	X		X	U	S								X		X			X	X	X								
			U	X	X		S	X			X	S	X		X		S								X		X			X	X	X	U							
			S	X	X		X	X			X		X	X	U		X	U			U				X		X			X	X		S	U						
			X	X			X	X			U	X	X		X	X	U		U						X		X			X		U	U							
	U			X	X			S			S	S	X		X	X								X	X		X		U			X	X	U						
	X		S	X				S			S		X		X	X			U					X	X		X					X	X		S	U				
	X		X	X				X			X		X		X	X			S			X		X	X		X					X	X		U	U				
	X		X	X			U	X			U		X		X	X			X			X		S	X		X					X	X		S	S				
	X		X	X				X	S	U			X		X	X			X			X		S	X		X					X	X		U	U				
			X	X			X	S					X	S		X			X			X		X	X		X				U	X	X		U	S				
			X	X			S	S					X			X			X	X		X		X	X		X			U		X		U	S					
			X	X				X					X	U	S				S			S		X	X		X			X			X	U	S	X	X			
			X					U			X		X		X				U			X		X	X		X			X			X	S	U	X				
			X					U			X		X	S		X			X			U		X			X			X			X	S	X	S				
			X										X	X	X		X			X					X	X		X			X			U	X	U	U	X	X	S	
			X					S					X		X			X			X					X	X		X			X			U	X	U	S	X	S	
			X										X	X	X			X			X					X	X		X			U	X		U	U	U	X	X	
			X	X									X		X			S			X					X	X		U			X		U	X	U	U	X	X	
	S			X									X		X			S			X					X	X	U				X		U	X		S	X	X	X	
				X									X		X	U		S			X	X					X							U	X	X	U	X	X	X	X	U
				X									X		U	U		X			X	X				U	X		X					U	X	X	U	X		U	
			X	X									X		X	U		X			S					X	X		X					X	X		U	X	U	X	U
			X	X									X		X			U			U					S	X		X					X	X	U	X		X	X	S
			X	X					X	S	S	X		X			U	S	X	X	X	X	U	X	X				U											
	X		S	X	X			S	X	U	S	X	X	X	U	X	X	U	X	X	U	X			U	X			X											
	X	X	S	X	X			X	X	S	X	X	X	X	S	U	X	U	X			U		U																
		X	S	X	X			S	S	X	X	X	X		X	X	X	X	X	U		U	U			X														
		U	X	X				S	X			X	X			U	X	U	X			U				X	X			X	X									
		U	X	X				U	X			X	S	X			U	X	U	X			U			X	X	X		X		S	U							
		S		X				S	X			X	X	X	X		U	X		X					U	X	S			X	X	X								
		U	X	X				S	X			X	S	X			U	X	U	X		U	U			X	X	X		X		S								
		U	X	X				U	X			X	X	S	X		X	X			U					S	X		X			X		S	U					
	X	S	X	X				S	X			X					X	X		U			U			X	X										X			

Totals:

15	18	11	34	32	11	18	17	2	15	14	31	0	12	32	3	31	0	5	15	0	0	10	27	3	24	0	0	12	2	2	0	12	21	0	8	3	12	10	0
0	1	5	2	0	0	2	4	11	7	7	1	9	7	1	1	6	0	2	5	0	1	9	0	0	1	0	0	0	0	0	0	3	9	0	4	1			
0	1	3	0	0	0	2	0	7	2	0	0	5	3	5	16	2	7	1	3	3	1	2	0	0	1	2	2	0	0	1	8	5	0	4	9	7	1	0	4

2	3	1	9	9	0	2	9	0	9	6	7	0	4	10	2	10	0	1	2	0	0	2	7	3	3	0	0	4	2	1	2	0	0	0	0	0	0	0	0
0	0	5	0	0	0	6	1	3	1	3	0	1	1	0	0	0	0	1	0	1	0	0	0	0	0	3	0	0	0	0	0	0	0	0	0	0	0	0	0
0	0	4	0	0	0	2	0	1	0	0	0	2	5	0	3	0	4	3	0	6	4	0	0	0	0	0	2	0	0	0	0	0	0	0	0	0	0	0	0

| 0 | 0 | 0 | 1 | 2 | 0 | 1 | 4 | 3 | 7 | 1 | 4 | 0 | 1 | 1 | 0 | 4 | 0 | 0 | 4 | 0 | 0 | 3 | 1 | 0 | 10 | 0 | 0 | 0 | 0 | 0 | 0 | 2 | 0 | 0 | 2 | 0 | 3 | 0 | |
| 0 | 0 | 0 | 0 | 3 | 0 | 3 | 3 | 2 | 0 | 4 | 2 | 1 | 0 | 1 | 0 | 1 | 0 | 9 | 0 | 0 | 0 | 0 | 0 | 0 | 0 | 0 | 0 | 1 | 0 | 0 | 0 | 0 | 0 | 0 | 0 | 0 | 0 | 0 | |

PLAYING SQUAD 2012/13

Existing Players		SN	HT	WT	DOB	AGE	POB	Career	Apps	Goals
GOALKEEPERS										
Simon	Arthur							Salisbury Rel 5/06, Winchester, Andover 7/06, Farnborough 6/07, AFC Totton, Salisbury (Gk Coach) 11/11	0	0
Will	Puddy		5'10"	11 07	04/10/1987	24	Warminster	Bristol C (Yth), Cheltenham Rel c/s 10, Mangotsfield (L) 10/06, Yate (L) 2/07, Stafford R (L) 10/07, Tamworth (4ML) 7/08, Bath C (3ML) 7/09, Oxford C (L) 11/09, Salisbury 10/10, Swindon Supermarine 11/10, Chippenham 8/11, Salisbury 1/12	12	0
Mark	Scott		6'03"	12 04	03/01/1991	21	Fleet	Swindon Rel c/s 12, Banbury (L) 3/10, Swindon Supermarine (2ML) 9/10, Salisbury (6WL) 11/11, Salisbury (2ML) 2/12, Salisbury 7/12	12	0
DEFENDERS										
Ryan	Brett				11/11/1990	21		Plymouth Rel 12/09, Glen Hoddle Academy (Trial), Plymouth Parkway 2/10, Salisbury 7/10	33	1
Michael	Cooper				13/08/1982	30		Yeovil, Exeter 7/97, Weston-Super-Mare (L) 99/00, Yeovil 7/00, Salisbury 2/02, Taunton (L) 12/05, Rel 5/06, Salisbury (Coach) 0		0
Brian	Dutton		5'11"	12 00	12/04/1985	27	Malton	Pickering T, Scarborough (Trial), Swindon (Trial), Cambridge U 11/03 Rel c/s 04, Pickering T 6/04, Weymouth 3/05, Eastleigh 5/06 Rel 10/06, Weymouth 1/07 Rel c/s 07, York C (Trial) c/s 07, Mangotsfield (Trial), Dorchester 9/07 Rel 10/07, Pickering T 3/08, Salisbury 8/08, Harrogate T 7/09, Northwich 12/09, Salisbury c/s 10	32	2
Chris	Giles		6'02"	13 00	16/04/1982	30	Milborne Port	Sherborne, Yeovil 7/99, Weston-S-Mare (2ML) 3/01, Weymouth (L) 8/02, Gravesend (L) 12/02, Woking (L) 2/04, Aldershot 3/04 Rel 5/05, Crawley 7/05, Forest Green 7/06 Rel 7/06 Injured, Forest Green 11/06 Rel 4/08, Crawley 5/08 Rel 1/10, Salisbury 1/10	32	4
Callum	Hart		6'00"	11 00	21/12/1985	26	Cardiff	Bristol C (Scholar) Rel c/s 05, Bournemouth 8/05 Rel c/s 07, Weymouth NC 11/07 Rel 1/08, Newport C 10/08, Farnborough 2/09, Weymouth 3/09 Rel c/s 09, Bath C 9/09 Rel 10/09, Weston-Super-Mare 10/09, Bath C c/s 10, Paulton R (Dual) 9/10, Salisbury 3/11	11	0
Luke	Ruddick		6'00"		03/03/1990	22	Ashford	Brentford, Ashford T (Middx), Walton Casuals 9/08, Hampton & R 10/08 Harrow 11/08, Salisbury 11/08, Bath C 6/10, Salisbury 8/11	19	0
Emmanuel (Udo)	Udoji		6'00"	13 05	09/01/1989	23		Rushden & D, Portsmouth, Glen Hoddle Soccer Academy, Stafford R 9/09, Bromley 3/10, Aveley 8/10, Ebbsfleet 8/10 Rel 10/10, Havant & W 11/10, Aveley, Bromley 3/11 Rel 1/12, Bishops Stortford 1/12, Salisbury NC 2/12	12	0
MIDFIELDERS										
Matt	Clark				16/11/1992	19	Swindon	Swindon, Oxford C (L) 9/11, Salisbury 1/12	11	0
Darrell	Clarke		5'10"	10 11	16/12/1977	34	Mansfield	Mansfield, Hartlepool Undisc 7/01 Rel c/s 07, Stockport (L) 1/05, Port Vale (L) 9/05, Rochdale (5ML) 7/06, Salisbury 7/07 (Pl/Man) 7/10	19	1
Mikey	Harris				23/09/1984	27		Salisbury (Pl/Ass Man)	0	0
Stuart	Sinclair		5'07"	10 07	09/11/1987	24	Houghton Conquest	Luton Rel c/s 06, Cambridge C 8/06 Rel 5/07, Bedford T, Dunstable, Arlesey 7/11, Salisbury (SL) 1/12, Salisbury c/s 12	21	2
FORWARDS										
Danny	Fitchett				28/03/1991	21		Reading (Yth), Wycombe Rel c/s 11, Badshot Lea (L) 2/10, Oxford C (L) 9/10, Salisbury (SL) 11/10, Salisbury 6/11	37	4
Theo	Lewis		5'10"	10 12	10/08/1991	21	Oxford	Cheltenham Rel c/s 12, Gloucester (L) 3/12, Salisbury 7/12		
Robbie	Matthews				02/03/1982	30	Wiltshire	Bournemouth (Yth), Swindon (Yth), Salisbury, Bemerton Heath Harlequins 11/01, Eastleigh c/s 02, Southampton (Trial), Bristol R (Trial) 2/03, Salisbury 9/04, Havant & W (6WL) 11/08, Crawley (SL) 1/09, Kidderminster 8/09 Rel 7/10, Newport C 7/10, Forest Green (SL) 3/11, Forest Green (L) 8/11, Salisbury 9/11, Salisbury Undisc 1/12	20	4
Chris	McPhee		5'11"	11 09	20/03/1983	29	Eastbourne	Brighton Rel 5/06, Aldershot (3ML) 8/05, Swindon (SL) 3/06, Torquay 7/06, Ebbsfleet 8/07, Weymouth 7/08 Rel 2/09, Kidderminster 2/09, Torquay 6/11, Salisbury (Pl/Coach) 7/12		
Jamie	White		5'08"	10 07	17/11/1989	22	Southampton	Southampton Rel 5/10, Shrewsbury (2ML) 11/08, Eastleigh (L) 10/09, Eastleigh 12/10, Totton & Eling 1/11, Winchester 9/11, Salisbury 6/12		

STAINES TOWN

Chairman: Matthew Boon
Secretary: Steven Parsons   **(T)** 07850 794 315   **(E)** steve@stainestownfootballclub.co.uk
Additional Committee Members:
C Boon, D & V Cox, H Denning, G Gould, G Gulyas, J & M Hanson, M Holland, A Jones, S Moore, B Moss, S Parsons, A Payne, S Payne, J Richards, K & R Sherwood, Ch & K Wainwright, K Williams.
Manager: Marcus Gayle
Programme Editor: Steve Parsons   **(E)** steve@stainestownfootballclub.co.uk

Back row (left to right) - Roy Lewis (team attendant), Martyn Spong (Academy Director / Reserve Team Manager), Hanif Boyle, Louis Hollingsworth, Louis-Rae Beadle, Jordaan Brown, Jack Turner, Kyle Merson, Teddy Ngoy, Tony Garrod, Osa Obamwonyi, Chan Quan, Mark Fabian (Youth Team Manager), Thiago Melo (Physiotherapist). Front (l—r) - Reece Hall, Ade Osifuwa, Max Worsfold, Scott Taylor (Player/Coach), Marcus Gayle (Manager), Gus Hurdle (Assistant Manager), David Wheeler, Troy Ferguson, Sam Bates. Insets (l—r) - Elliott Godfrey (captain), Dominic Ogun, Emmanuel Shosanya, Bajram Pashaj. Not pictured - Matt Drage, Lewis Ferrell.

Club Factfile

Founded: 1892   **Nickname:** The Swans
Previous Names: Staines Albany & St Peters Institute merged in 1895. Staines 1905-18, Staines Lagonda 1918-25, Staines Vale (WWII)
Previous Leagues: Great Western Suburban, Hounslow & District 1919-20, Spartan 1924-35, 58-71, Middlesex Senior 1943-52, Parthenon 1952-53, Hellenic 1953-58, Athenian 1971-73, Isthmian 1973-2009

Club Colours (change): Old gold & blue/blue/blue (All white)

Ground: Wheatsheaf Park, Wheatsheaf Lane, Staines TW18 2PD   **(T)** 01784 225 943
Capacity: 3,000   **Seats:** 300   **Covered:** 850   **Clubhouse:** Yes   **Shop:** Yes

Directions: Leave M25 at Junction 13. If coming from the North (anticlockwise), bear left onto A30 Staines By-Pass; if coming from the South (clockwise), go round the roundabout and back under M25 to join By-Pass. Follow A30 to Billet Bridge roundabout, which you treat like a roundabout, taking last exit, A308, London Road towards Town Centre. At 3rd traffic lights, under iron bridge, turn left into South Street, passing central bus station, as far as Thames Lodge (formerly Packhorse). Turn left here, into Laleham Road, B376, under rail bridge. After 1km, Wheatsheaf Lane is on the right, by the traffic island. Ground is less than 100 yds on left. Please park on the left.

Previous Grounds:

Record Attendance: 2,750 v Banco di Roma - Barassi Cup 1975 (70,000 watched the second leg)
Record Victory: 14-0 v Croydon (A) - Isthmian Division 1 19/03/1994
Record Defeat: 1-18 - Wycombe Wanderers (A) - Great Western Suburban League 27/12/1909
Record Goalscorer: Alan Gregory - 122
Record Appearances: Dickie Watmore - 840
Additional Records:

Senior Honours:
Spartan League 1959-60. Athenian League Division 2 1971-72, Division 1 1974-75, 88-89.
Middlesex Senior cup 1975-76, 76-77, 77-78, 88-89, 90-91, 94-95, 97-98, 2009-10. Barassi Cup 1975-76.
Isthmian Full Members Cup 1994-95, Premier Division Play-off 2008-09.

10 YEAR RECORD

02-03		03-04		04-05		05-06		06-07		07-08		08-09		09-10		10-11		11-12	
Isth1S	15	Isth1S	6	Isth P	9	Isth P	6	Isth P	12	Isth P	2	Isth P	2	Conf S	8	Conf S	15	Conf S	15

STAINES TOWN

No.	Date	Comp	H/A	Opponents	Att:	Result	Goalscorers	Pos
1	Sat-13-Aug	BSS	A	Welling United	500	D 1-1	Taylor 80	12
2	Sat-20-Aug	BSS	H	Salisbury City	1002	L 0-1		18
3	Tue-23-Aug	BSS	A	Sutton United	505	L 0-1		19
4	Sat-27-Aug	BSS	A	Maidenhead United	305	D 1-1	Butler 25	21
5	Mon-29-Aug	BSS	H	Boreham Wood	255	W 2-1	Wheeler 2 (6, 17)	18
6	Sat-03-Sep	BSS	H	Thurrock	276	L 2-3	Newton 38, Everitt pen 90	19
7	Sat-10-Sep	BSS	A	Farnborough	515	L 0-1		19
8	Tue-13-Sep	BSS	H	Chelmsford City	264	D 1-1	Everitt 67	19
9	Sat-17-Sep	BSS	H	Bromley	308	W 4-1	Butler pen 36, Wheeler 2 (44, 46), Nwokeji 90	18
10	Tue-20-Sep	BSS	A	Dartford	1002	L 1-2	Everitt 19	18
11	Sat-24-Sep	BSS	A	Eastleigh	401	L 1-2	Everitt 6	19
12	Sat-08-Oct	BSS	H	Dorchester Town	298	L 0-2		20
13	Sat-22-Oct	BSS	H	Woking	1019	L 0-1		20
14	Tue-25-Oct	BSS	A	Basingstoke Town	341	D 1-1	Charles-Smith 88	20
15	Sat-05-Nov	BSS	H	Sutton United	378	L 1-4	Dunne 63	20
16	Sat-12-Nov	BSS	A	Tonbridge Angels	517	L 2-3	Taylor 2 (5, 57)	20
17	Tue-15-Nov	BSS	A	Weston-Super-Mare	220	L 1-2	Nwokeji 42	21
18	Sat-19-Nov	BSS	H	Havant & Waterlooville	274	D 1-1	Chaaban pen 58	22
19	Sat-03-Dec	BSS	A	Thurrock	219	W 2-1	Goodman 28, Everitt 90	21
20	Sat-17-Dec	BSS	A	Dover Athletic	308	L 0-3		21
21	Mon-26-Dec	BSS	A	Hampton & Richmond Boro'	629	W 2-1	Charles-Smith 28, Og (Ross) 31	21
22	Sun-01-Jan	BSS	H	Hampton & Richmond Boro'	592	L 1-4	Chaaban pen 78	21
23	Sat-07-Jan	BSS	A	Woking	2104	W 1-0	Chaaban 50	21
24	Sat-21-Jan	BSS	A	Chelmsford City	901	W 1-0	Wheeler 73	19
25	Tue-24-Jan	BSS	H	Dartford	378	L 1-4	Chaaban 11	19
26	Sat-28-Jan	BSS	A	Truro City	512	L 1-2	Nwokeji 57	21
27	Tue-14-Feb	BSS	H	Eastleigh	202	D 2-2	Wheeler 22, Nwokeji 55	20
28	Sat-18-Feb	BSS	H	Farnborough	415	L 1-2	Taylor 29	20
29	Sat-25-Feb	BSS	A	Eastbourne Borough	672	W 1-0	Charles-Smith 6	20
30	Mon-27-Feb	BSS	H	Welling United	301	W 4-2	Antwi 8, Butler 45, Nwokeji 76, Everitt 87	19
31	Sat-03-Mar	BSS	H	Basingstoke Town	411	L 0-2		20
32	Tue-06-Mar	BSS	A	Bromley	233	D 1-1	Chaaban 90	20
33	Sat-10-Mar	BSS	A	Salisbury City	563	L 0-1		20
34	Tue-13-Mar	BSS	H	Tonbridge Angels	228	D 1-1	Wheeler 22	20
35	Sat-17-Mar	BSS	H	Eastbourne Borough	269	L 1-2	Nwokeji 11	20
36	Sat-24-Mar	BSS	A	Dover Athletic	759	W 4-0	Wheeler 24, Antwi pen 31, Chaaban 2 (85, 90)	20
37	Sat-31-Mar	BSS	H	Truro City	304	D 1-1	Wheeler 86	20
38	Sat-07-Apr	BSS	H	Maidenhead United	327	D 0-0		21
39	Mon-09-Apr	BSS	A	Boreham Wood	174	W 2-1	Nwokeji 27, Vassell 51	17
40	Sat-14-Apr	BSS	A	Dorchester Town	413	W 3-0	Og 2 (N Walker 43, Martin 64), Risbridger 86	17
41	Sat-21-Apr	BSS	H	Weston-Super-Mare	283	W 2-1	Chaaban 22, Antwi pen 28	15
42	Sat-28-Apr	BSS	A	Havant & Waterlooville	949	L 2-3	Chaaban 19, Vassell 23	15

CUPS

No.	Date	Comp	H/A	Opponents	Att:	Result	Goalscorers	
1	Sat-01-Oct	FAC 2Q	H	Beaconsfield SYCOB	213	D 0-0		
2	Mon-03-Oct	FAC 2QR	A	Beaconsfield SYCOB	175	W 2-0	Orlu 19, Wheeler 32	
3	Sat-15-Oct	FAC 3Q	A	Worthing	468	W 2-0	Charles-Smith 87, Newton 90	
4	Sat-29-Oct	FAC 4Q	A	Basingstoke Town	545	L 1-2	Charles-Smith 50	
5	Sat-26-Nov	FAT 3Q	A	Folkestone Invicta	342	W 3-1	Risbridger 34, Goodman 37, Charles-Smith 64	
6	Sat-10-Dec	FAT 1	H	Maidenhead United	201	D 0-0		
7	Tue-13-Dec	FAT 1R	A	Maidenhead United	154	W 2-1	Allen 10, Everitt pen 90	
8	Sat-14-Jan	FAT 2	A	Northwich Victoria	517	L 0-1		

League
Starts
Substitute
Unused Sub

Cups
Starts
Substitute
Unused Sub

Goals (Lg)
Goals (Cup)

Squad appearance grid (X = start, S = substitute appearance, U = unused substitute)

	L WELLS	JACKSON	SMITH	GORDON	IFURA	SCARLETT	HARRIS	RISBRIDGER	BUTLER	TAYLOR	WHEELER	SANKOH	PATTISON	MASKELL	NEWTON	AITE-OUAKRIM	THOMPSON	ALLAWAY	OGUN	ORLU	EVERITT	CHARLES-SMITH	TYRELL	NWOKEJI	KEWLEY-GRAHAM	MERSON	DUNNE	D WELLS	DUFFY	BOYLE	CHAABAN	JEAN-ZEPHIRIN	GOODMAN	EVANS	ALLEN	O'BRIEN	DOLAN	KAVANAGH	ANTWI	GALLAGHER	COURTNAGE	IMUDIA	POTTER	VASSELL	PLUMMER
1	X	X	X	X	X	X	X	X	X	X	X	S	U		U																														
2	X	X	X	X	X	X	X	X			X		U		X	S	S	U	U																										
3	X	X	X	X	X	X	X	S	X	X		X			X	X	S	U	U	S																									
4	X	X	X	X	U	X		X	X		X				S	U	U			X	X	X	U																						
5	X	X	X	X	X	U	U	X	X		X				X	U	S			U	X	X																							
6	X	X	X	X	X	X	S		X	S	X				X	S				U	X	X	U																						
7	X	X	S	X	X	X			S	S	X				X		U			X	X	X	U	X																					
8	X	X	X	X				X	X	X					S	U		U		X	X	X	U	S																					
9	X	X	X	X	U			X	S	X					X		U			X	X	X	S	S																					
10	X	X	X	X	S			X	X	S	X				S					X	X	X	U	S																					
11	X	X	X	X	U	X		X	X	S	X				S						X	X	S	U	X																				
12	X		S	X	X		U	X	X	X							U				S	X	X	X	U																				
13	X	X		X				X		S	S				X						X	X	S	X	X	U	X	U																	
14	X	X		X				X	X	S	X				X		U				X	S	U	X	S		X	X																	
15		X		X		X		X	U	X					X						X	S	X	X	U	X	X	S	S		X														
16		X		X		X		X		X					X	X	U				X	S	X	U	U	X	X	S	X																
17			X		X		X		X					U							S	X	X	S	U	X	X	U		X															
18			X		X			X	S	X					X						X	S	U	X		U			U	X	X	X													
19			X		X		S	S		X					X						X	S	S	X		U				X	X	X													
20		X		S	S		X	X		U	X				X						X		U							X	X	X													
21		X		S	U		X	X			S				X						X	X	S			U				X	X	X		X											
22		X		X	X	S	X				U				X						X	S		S						X	X	X	X												
23		X		X	X	S	U	X							X						S	X	X		U					X	X	X		X											
24		X		X	U		S	X	U	X					X						X	U	S							X	X	X	X												
25		X		S			U	X	X						X						U	U		X						X	X	X		X						X	X	U			
26		X		U			S	X	X						X						S	S		X						X	X	X		X						X	X	U			
27		X		X	S	X	S								S						X	X	X							X	X			X						X	X				
28	S	X		X	X	X									X						X	U		X		U				S	X	X		S	X	X									
29	X	X		X	X	S									S						X	X		S		U				X	X			X	X	U	X								
30	X	X		X	X	X	U								X						S	S		X						S	X			X	X										
31	X	X		S	U	X	X								X						X	X		X		U				X	U			S	X	X	X								
32	X	X		S	X	X	S								X						X		X							S	X			X			U	U	X						
33		X		X	X	U	X								X							S		X						S				X	X	X		U	U	X					
34		X		X	X	S	X								S							S								X	X			X					U	X	X	U			
35		X		X	X	X									U	S														X	X			X			X	X	U	X	X	U			
36		X		X	X	X									U	S														X				S	X	X	X	U	U	X	X	U			
37		X		X	U	X							X	X							S									S		U			S	X			U	X	X	U			
38		X		X	X	S							X	S							X	S								X	U			S	X			U	X	X	U				
39		X		X	U	X							X	X							X	S								X				X			X	X	U	X	X	U			
40		X		X	X	U	S							X							X	S								X				X			X	X	U	X	X	U			
41		X		X	X	X	S							X							X	S	S							X				X			X	X	U	X	X	X	S		

ALSO PLAYED: PHILLIPS U (1). QUAN U (1, C4). DOUGLAS U (36, 37). ONIEVA-MONTALBAN U (36, 37).

Summary totals:

	L WELLS	JACKSON	SMITH	GORDON	IFURA	SCARLETT	HARRIS	RISBRIDGER	BUTLER	TAYLOR	WHEELER	SANKOH	PATTISON	MASKELL	NEWTON	AITE-OUAKRIM	THOMPSON	ALLAWAY	OGUN	ORLU	EVERITT	CHARLES-SMITH	TYRELL	NWOKEJI	KEWLEY-GRAHAM	MERSON	DUNNE	D WELLS	DUFFY	BOYLE	CHAABAN	JEAN-ZEPHIRIN	GOODMAN	EVANS	ALLEN	O'BRIEN	DOLAN	KAVANAGH	ANTWI	GALLAGHER	COURTNAGE	IMUDIA	POTTER	VASSELL	PLUMMER
	14	36	10	38	7	26	2	33	19	13	28	0	0	11	2	19	3	0	8	26	18	3	21	3	0	5	4	0	21	2	15	11	3	2	4	17	14	1	3	5	9	6	0
	0	1	2	0	0	7	5	0	10	9	1	1	0	0	4	2	5	0	0	1	2	16	6	10	2	0	0	0	2	1	5	0	0	0	0	0	3	0	0	0	0	1	1
	0	0	0	0	2	5	3	2	9	5	1	0	2	3	1	3	1	7	4	2	1	4	12	0	1	15	0	1	2	0	0	2	0	0	2	0	0	2	0	0	3	5	4	0	0	5

Goals:

	4	4	1	8	2	1	0	8	7	5	3	0	0	4	0	4	0	0	2	8	5	1	4	2	0	2	1	0	0	1	4	3	2	1	0	1	0	0	0	0	0	0	0	0
	0	0	0	0	0	0	3	0	0	0	0	0	0	1	0	0	1	1	0	2	1	2	2	1	0	1	0	0	0	0	0	0	0	0	0	0	0	0	0	0	0	0	0	0
	0	2	1	0	0	4	0	0	1	2	1	0	0	1	0	0	4	1	0	0	1	6	0	0	3	0	0	2	0	0	0	0	0	0	0	0	0	0	0	0	0	0	0	0	0
	0	0	0	0	0	0	1	3	4	9	0	0	1	0	0	0	0	6	3	0	7	0	0	1	0	0	0	9	0	1	0	0	0	0	3	0	0	0	0	2	0
	0	0	3	0	0	0	0	1	0	0	1	0	0	0	0	0	1	1	3	0	0	0	0	0	0	0	0	0	1	0	0	1	0	1	0	0	0	0	0	0	0

PLAYING SQUAD 2012/13

Existing Players		SN	HT	WT	DOB	AGE	POB	Career	Apps	Goals
GOALKEEPERS										
Kyle	Merson							Staines, St Albans (L) 8/11, Godalming T (L) 3/12	0	0
Jack	Turner		6'02"	13 07	17/09/1992	19	Ashford	AFC Wimbledon Rel c/s 12, Bedfont Green (SL) 2/10 Staines 6/12		
DEFENDERS										
Sam	Bates							Staines		
Jordaan	Brown				13/03/1992	20		AFC Wimbledon, Chipstead (L), Staines 7/12		
Louis	Hollingsworth							Chipstead, Merstham Horsham 2/12, Staines 7/12		
Teddy	Ngoy							Standard Liege (Bel), Staines 6/12		
Ade	Osifuwa							Southend, Maldon & Tiptree (WE) 10/10, AFC Wimbledon 12/11, Staines 7/12		
MIDFIELDERS										
Louis-Ray	Beadle				07/08/1990	22		Hampton & R, Kingstonian 3/12, Staines 7/12		
Adam	Cashin-Murray				11/11/1990	21	Reading	Reading T, Hungerford T 1/11, Eastleigh c/s 11, Staines c/s 12		
Troy	Ferguson							Walton & H, Walton Casuals 11/09, Merstham 3/10, Chertsey, Farnborough 11/11, Staines 7/12		
Elliott	Godfrey		5'09"	11 13	22/02/1983	29	Toronto, Can	Watford Rel c/s 04, Colchester (Trial) 7/04, Hampton & R 9/04, AFC Wimbledon 6/08 Rel 4/10, Staines (L) 3/10, Boreham Wood 8/10, Hendon 8/11, Staines 6/12		
Reece	Hall							C.Palace (Jun), Tooting & M, Staines 7/12		
David	Wheeler				04/10/1990	21		Lewes, Staines 6/11	29	9
Max	Worsfold		5'09"	12 06	25/10/1992	19	Chertsey	Aldershot, Wealdstone (WE) 1/11, Maidenhead (L) 2/11, Maidenhead (6ML) 7/11, Dorchester (SL) 1/12, Staines 7/12		
FORWARDS										
Hanif	Boyle							Cambridge U (Jun), Staines, Burnham (L) 10/11	1	0
Tony	Garrod		6'02"	11 08	14/09/1991	19	Crawley	Southampton Rel c/s 11, Bishops Stortford (L) 2/11, Farnborough 7/11 Rel 11/11, Dartford 11/11, Staines 7/12		
Dominic	Ogun							Staines	0	0
Chan	Quan							Fisher FC, Staines 8/11	0	0
Scott	Taylor		5'10"	11 06	05/05/1976	36	Chertsey	Staines, Millwall £15,000 2/95, Bolton £150,000 3/96, Rotherham (2ML) 12/97, Blackpool (L) 3/98, Tranmere £50,000 10/98 Rel c/s 01, Stockport 8/01, Blackpool 1/02, Plymouth £100,000 12/04, MK Dons £100,000 1/06, Brentford (L) 3/07, Rochdale (L) 10/07, Grays 1/08 Rel c/s 08, Lewes 7/08, Staines 11/08	22	4

SUTTON UNITED

Chairman: Bruce Elliott
Secretary: Gerard Mills   **(T)** 0793 270 2375   **(E)** honsec@suttonunited.net
Additional Committee Members:
Dave Farebrother, Graham Starns, Lee Wallis, David Mathers, Adrian Barry, Michael Bidmead,
Tony Holland, Steve Moore, Brian Williams, Graham Baker.
Manager: Paul Doswell
Programme Editor: Lyall Reynolds   **(E)** suttoneditor@hotmail.com

THE NON-LEAGUE CLUB DIRECTORY

Book Holiday Inn Hotels and Save today!

Home

Clubs

Steps 1 - 4

League Tables

35 Years of Non-League Football

The Non-League Club Directory has developed into a comprehensive record of competitions within the non-League game, giving this level of football the

www.non-leagueclubdirectory.co.uk

Club Factfile

Founded: 1898   **Nickname:** The U's

Previous Names: None

Previous Leagues: Sutton Junior, Southern Suburban, Athenian 1921-63, Isthmian 1963-86, 91-99, 2000-04, 2008-11, Conference 1999-2000, 04-08

Club Colours (change): All amber (All white)

Ground: Borough Sports Ground, Gander Green Lane, Sutton, Surrey SM1 2EY   **(T)** 0208 644 4440

Capacity: 7,032   **Seats:** 765   **Covered:** 1,250   **Clubhouse:** Yes   **Shop:** Yes

Directions: Travel along the M25 to junction 8. Then north on the A217 for about 15-20 minutes. Ignoring signs for Sutton itself, stay on the A217 to the traffic lights by the Gander Inn (on the left), turn right into Gander Green Lane. The Borough Sports Ground is about 200 yards up this road on the left hand side, if you reach West Sutton station you have gone too far.

Previous Grounds: Western Road, Manor Lane, London Road, The Find

Record Attendance: 14,000 v Leeds United - FA Cup 4th Round 24/01/1970

Record Victory: 11-1 v Clapton - 1966 and v Leatherhead - 1982-83 both Isthmian League
Record Defeat: 0-13 v Barking - Athenian League 1925-26

Record Goalscorer: Paul McKinnon - 279

Record Appearances: Larry Pritchard - 781 (1965-84)

Additional Records: Received £100,000 from AFC Bournemouth for Efan Ekoku 1990

Senior Honours:

Anglo Italian Cup 1979. Isthmian League (x4) 2010-11. Athenian League x3.
London Senior Cup x2. Surrey Senior Cup x2.

02-03		03-04		04-05		05-06		06-07		07-08		08-09		09-10		10-11		11-12	
Isth P	6	Isth P	2	Conf S	15	Conf S	13	Conf S	13	Conf S	22	Isth P	5	Isth P	2	Isth P	1	Conf S	4

SUTTON UNITED

No.	Date	Comp	H/A	Opponents	Att:	Result	Goalscorers	Pos
1	Sat-13-Aug	BSS	H	Woking	1200	L 0-5		22
2	Tue-16-Aug	BSS	A	Tonbridge Angels	683	W 4-1	Beautyman 8, Orilonishe 2 (13, 76), Riviere 87	10
3	Sat-20-Aug	BSS	A	Basingstoke Town	424	W 2-1	Page 45, Dundas 78	9
4	Tue-23-Aug	BSS	H	Staines Town	505	W 1-0	Kavanagh 37	4
5	Sat-27-Aug	BSS	A	Bromley	509	L 0-3		7
6	Mon-29-Aug	BSS	H	Dover Athletic	714	D 0-0		6
7	Sat-03-Sep	BSS	H	Dorchester Town	645	W 3-1	Bray 36, Watkins 2 (61, 85)	6
8	Sat-10-Sep	BSS	A	Havant & Waterlooville	789	D 2-2	Taggart 51, Page 80	6
9	Sat-17-Sep	BSS	A	Truro City	558	W 3-0	Beautyman 28, Watkins 57, Kavanagh 90	4
10	Tue-20-Sep	BSS	H	Eastleigh	517	W 2-0	Og (Brown) 7, Taggart 36	4
11	Sat-24-Sep	BSS	H	Maidenhead United	1332	W 4-1	Watkins 3 (7, 17, pen 37), Griffiths 43	4
12	Sat-08-Oct	BSS	A	Weston-Super-Mare	395	D 0-0		4
13	Sat-22-Oct	BSS	A	Farnborough	603	W 3-0	Griffiths 2 (45, 81), Watkins 79	3
14	Tue-25-Oct	BSS	H	Salisbury City	718	W 5-0	Watkins 2 (21, 32), Dundas 49, Beautyman 58, Kavanagh 79	2
15	Sat-05-Nov	BSS	A	Staines Town	378	W 4-1	Griffiths 2 (35, pen 68), Orilonishe 2 (66, 77)	2
16	Tue-15-Nov	BSS	H	Tonbridge Angels	737	L 0-1		3
17	Sat-19-Nov	BSS	A	Dorchester Town	552	D 0-0		3
18	Sat-10-Dec	BSS	A	Woking	1730	L 1-4	Beautyman 32	5
19	Sat-17-Dec	BSS	H	Welling United	609	W 4-3	Kavanagh 12, Beautyman 16, Page 74, Watkins 77	4
20	Tue-20-Dec	BSS	H	Truro City	567	D 2-2	Beautyman 2 (76, 90)	5
21	Mon-26-Dec	BSS	A	Boreham Wood	232	D 1-1	McCrae 90	5
22	Sat-07-Jan	BSS	A	Chelmsford City	1168	W 3-2	Watkins 2 (47, 67), Dundas 82	5
23	Tue-10-Jan	BSS	H	Hampton & Richmond Boro'	529	D 2-2	Ledgister 2 (24, 66)	5
24	Sat-14-Jan	BSS	H	Thurrock	517	D 1-1	Downer 90	5
25	Sat-21-Jan	BSS	A	Maidenhead United	313	D 1-1	Riviere 8	5
26	Sat-28-Jan	BSS	A	Eastleigh	859	L 0-4		5
27	Tue-14-Feb	BSS	H	Boreham Wood	513	W 2-1	Dundas 35, Beautyman 84	5
28	Sat-18-Feb	BSS	H	Basingstoke Town	502	W 1-0	Beautyman 23	5
29	Sat-25-Feb	BSS	H	Weston-Super-Mare	656	W 3-2	Vassell 50, Beautyman 56, Dundas 75	5
30	Sat-03-Mar	BSS	A	Thurrock	299	W 1-0	Vassell 85	5
31	Tue-06-Mar	BSS	H	Havant & Waterlooville	409	W 2-0	Taggart 7, Griffiths 43	4
32	Sat-10-Mar	BSS	H	Eastbourne Borough	802	D 0-0		4
33	Wed-14-Mar	BSS	H	Eastbourne Borough	475	D 1-1	Watkins pen 45	4
34	Sat-17-Mar	BSS	H	Chelmsford City	654	W 3-2	Dundas 1, Telfer 45, Griffiths 70	4
35	Tue-20-Mar	BSS	A	Dartford	1022	L 1-6	Beautyman 29	4
36	Sat-24-Mar	BSS	A	Welling United	748	D 0-0		4
37	Sat-31-Mar	BSS	A	Hampton & Richmond Boro'	669	D 0-0		4
38	Sat-07-Apr	BSS	H	Bromley	749	D 1-1	Payne 33	4
39	Mon-09-Apr	BSS	H	Dover Athletic	675	W 2-0	Taggart 12, Watkins 23	4
40	Sat-14-Apr	BSS	H	Dartford	756	L 0-1		4
41	Sat-21-Apr	BSS	A	Salisbury City	892	L 1-3	Watkins 2	4
42	Sat-28-Apr	BSS	H	Farnborough	1321	W 2-0	Payne 29, Watkins 34	4

CUPS

No.	Date	Comp	H/A	Opponents	Att:	Result	Goalscorers	
1	Sat-01-Oct	FAC 2Q	H	Dulwich Hamlet	494	W 5-1	Griffiths 4 (16, 51, 54, 71), Taggart 90	
2	Sat-15-Oct	FAC 3Q	H	Bognor Regis Town	622	W 4-0	Dundas 22, Taggart 2 (26, 40), Griffiths 74	
3	Sat-29-Oct	FAC 4Q	H	Leatherhead	882	D 3-3	Dundas 2 (29, 36), Watkins 60	
4	Tue-01-Nov	FAC 4QR	A	Leatherhead	940	W 3-2 aet	Watkins 2 (2, 77), Orilonishe 98	
5	Sat-12-Nov	FAC 1	H	Kettering Town	1532	W 1-0	Watkins 64	
6	Sat-26-Nov	FAT 3Q	H	Basingstoke Town	460	L 1-2	Gasson 5	
7	Sun-04-Dec	FAC 2Q	H	Notts County	3704	L 0-2		
8	Wed-02-May	PO SF1	H	Welling United	1255	L 1-2	Og (Holloway) 67	
9	Sun-06-May	PO SF2	A	Welling United	1408	D 0-0		

League
Starts
Substitute
Unused Sub

Cups
Starts
Substitute
Unused Sub

Goals (Lg)
Goals (Cup)

Player appearance grid (X = start, S = substitute, U = unused substitute).

SCRIVEN	DOWNER	BRAY	MURRAY	EL-SALAHI	PAGE	RIVIERE	DAVIS	GRIFFITHS	DUNDAS	TAGGART	ORILONISHE	KAVANAGH	WATKINS	CONROY	MCCRAE	BEAUTYMAN	MCKIMM	SHAW	PIPER	TELFER	LEDGISTER	TAYLOR	SESSEGNON	JENKINS	WOODS-GARNESS	VASSELL	BOATENG	OBAMWONYI	ODUBAJO	UDDIN	HUNT	BRAHAM-BARRETT	REECE	PAYNE
X	X	X	X	X	X	X	X	X	X	X	X	S	S	S	U	U																		
X		X	X	X	X		X	S	X	X		U	X	S	X	U	U																	
X		X	X	X	X		X	S	X	X	X	S		S	X	U	U																	
X		X	X	X	X		X		X	X	X	S	X	S	X	U	S	U																
X		X	X	X	X		X	X	X		S	S	U	S	U		X	X																
X	U	X		X	X	X		X	X	X	X	S	S	S	U	X	X																	
X	X	X			X	X		X	X	X	X	U	S	X	X	U	S	X																
X	X	X			X	X		X	X	X	U	S	X	S	X	U	S	X																
X	X		S		X	X		X	X	X	S	S	X	U	X	U	X	X																
X	X		S		X	X		X	U	X	X	X	X	X	S	U	X	X																
X	X	U	S		X	X		X	S	X	X	S	X	X	X		X	X		U														
X	X	X	S		X	X		X	X	X	X	S	S	X		X			X	U		U												
X	X	X	X		X	X		X	X		S	S	X		X	U	S	X	U															
X	U	X	X	X			X	S	X	X	S	X	S	X		U	X								X									
X	X		X	S	X	X		X	X	S	U	U	X		S	X		X							X									
X	X		X	X		X	X	S	X	U	X	S	X		U	X	U	X	X						S									
X	X		X	X		X	S	X	S	X	S	X		U	X	U	X	X							S									
X	X		X	X		S	X	X	S	X	X		U	X			S		X	U	X				S									
X	X		X	X		X	S	S	U	X		X	X		X			X			X	X	U		S									
X	S		X		X	X	U		X	X	U	X	X		U	X		X		U	X	X			S									
X	X		X			X	X		X	X	X	X		U	X		U	X			X	X	U	X										
X	X			U	X		X	S	X			X	X	U	X		U	X			X	X	U	X										
X	X			U	X		S	X		X	X		X		U	X		X			S	X	X		X									
X	X		X	X		X	X	U		X			X		U	X		U	X		S	X	X	X										
X			X		X	X	X		X	X		U	X		U	S		X			X	X	X	X										
X	U			X		X	X	U			X	S	X		U	S		X	X		X	X	X											
X	X			X		X	X	S			X	X		U	S		X	X			S		X	X	X									
X	X			S		X	X	X				X		U	U	S		X			X	X	X	X	S									
X	X		U	X		X	S	X	S		S	X		U	U		S				X	X	X	S	X									
X	X		S	X		X	X	X	S		U		X			X					S	X	X	X	U						X			
X	X		X	X		S	S	X	X		X	S		X		X					X	X	U	X	X	U					X			
X	X		X	S	U	X	X	S			X	X		S				X			S	X	X	X		U	X							
X			X	X	S	X	U		X		U	X	S		X						S	X	X								X	X		
X	X		X	X		X	S	X		X		S	X			X					S		X								U	U		X

X	X	U	S		X	X		X	S	X	X	X	X		S	U	U	X	X															
X	X	S	S		X	X		X	X	X	X	X	S	U	X	U		X	X	U	U													
X	X	X	X		X	X		X	X	S	U	S	X	U	U	S	X	U																
X	X	U	S	U	X		X	X	X	S	S	X	X	U	U	X																		
X	X	X		S	X	X		X	X	S	X	U	X		X		U	S		X		U												
X	X		X	X	X		X	S	X	S	U	X		X		U	U	X																
X	X		S	X	X		X	X	S	S	U	X		U	X		U	X	X						U									
X	X			X	X		X	X	U		X			S	X		X								S	U	X			U			X	
X				X	X		U	X	X		X			X		X									S		X	U				S	S	

42	29	12	9	9	33	36	1	32	30	22	7	12	27	1	7	36	0	0	9	24	7	0	0	9	1	5	21	3	3	10	11	10	0	4
0	1	0	4	1	1	2	0	9	10	10	8	6	11	1	18	5	0	1	6	4	3	0	0	1	6	6	2	0	0	0	1	1	1	1
0	3	1	1	0	3	0	0	1	1	5	4	2	2	1	10	0	8	22	0	4	2	1	1	0	1	3	0	4	0	2	2	2	0	1

8	9	2	2	2	9	9	0	8	7	5	3	1	8	0	1	8	0	1	5	8	0	0	0	0	0	2	0	0	0	0	0	0	1	
0	0	1	4	1	0	0	0	0	2	3	3	3	0	0	1	1	0	0	2	0	0	0	0	0	2	0	0	0	0	0	0	1	0	1
0	0	2	0	1	0	0	0	1	0	1	1	3	1	0	1	0	5	6	0	0	2	1	1	0	1	1	0	1	0	1	0	0	0	

| 0 | 1 | 1 | 0 | 0 | 3 | 2 | 0 | 7 | 6 | 4 | 4 | 4 | 16 | 0 | 1 | 11 | 0 | 0 | 0 | 1 | 2 | 0 | 0 | 0 | 2 | 0 | 0 | 0 | 0 | 0 | 0 | 0 | 2 | |
| 0 | 0 | 0 | 0 | 0 | 0 | 0 | 0 | 5 | 3 | 3 | 1 | 0 | 4 | 0 | 0 | 0 | 0 | 0 | 0 | 0 | 0 | 0 | 0 | 0 | 0 | 0 | 0 | 0 | 0 | 0 | 0 | 0 | 0 | |

PLAYING SQUAD 2012/13

Existing Players		SN	HT	WT	DOB	AGE	POB	Career	Apps	Goals
GOALKEEPERS										
Tom	Lovelock				14/05/1993	19	Harlow	L.Orient Rel c/s 12, Welling (L) 2/11, Bromley (SL) 3/11, Chertsey (L) 9/11, Farnborough (SL) 11/11		
Kevin	Scriven				27/11/1984	27	Bournemouth	Bournemouth Rel c/s 05, Bournemouth FC (L) 8/03, Farnborough 6/05, Havant & W 6/07, Sutton U 6/09	42	0
DEFENDERS										
Michael	Abnett				22/12/1990	21		C.Palace, Dover (L) 2/10, Glen Hoddle Academy (Spa), Havant & W 11/10, Lewes 1/11, Horsham YMCA 2/11, Bl/Bolungarvik (Ice), Whyteleafe, Sutton U 7/12		
Simon	Downer	5'11"	12 08		19/10/1981	30	Romford	L.Orient Rel 5/04, Newcastle (Trial) 2/01, Aldershot (SL) 3/04, Retired, Hornchurch 11/04 Rel c/s 05, Weymouth 7/05, Grays 1/07 Rel 10/08, Wivenhoe 10/08, Sutton U 11/08, Rushden & D 1/09 Rel 6/10, Sutton U 7/10	30	1
Gareth	Gwillim	6'00"	12 05		09/02/1983	29	Farnborough	Welling (Yth), C.Palace, Ashford T 3/02, Farnborough 9/02, B.Stortford (SL) 11/02, Bishops Stortford 5/03, Histon 6/07, Dag & Red 6/10, AFC Wimbledon (SL) 1/11, AFC Wimbledon 7/11Rel c/s 12, Sutton U 7/12		
Osa	Obamwonyi							Fisher, Dulwich H, Leyton 10/10, Welling 11/10, Aveley (L) 12/10 Perm, Waltham Forest 1/11, Tooting & M 2/11, Sutton U 12/11, Bognor Regis (L) 2/12, Bognor Regis (L) 3/12	3	0
Sam	Rents	5'09"	11 03		22/06/1987	25	Brighton	Brighton Rel 5/08, Worthing (L) 11/05, Crawley 5/08 Rel 5/11, Hayes & Yeading (SL) 3/11, Gateshead 5/11 Rel c/s 12, Sutton U 7/12		
Jamie	Stuart	5'10"	11 00		15/10/1976	35	Southwark	Charlton cc 12/97, Millwall 9/98 Rel c/s 01, Cambridge U (Trial) 7/01, Bury 10/01, Southend 6/03 Rel c/s 04, Hornchurch 7/04, Grays 11/04, Rushden & D 6/09, AFC Wimbledon Undisc 1/11 Rel c/s 12, Sutton U 5/12		
Paul	Telfer	5'09"	11 06		21/10/1971	40	Edinburgh	Luton, Coventry 7/95, Southampton 11/01, Celtic 7/05 Rel c/s 07, Bournemouth 7/07 Rel 12/07, Leeds 8/08 Rel 2/09, Slough 4/09, Sutton U (Pl/Coach) 8/11	28	1
MIDFIELDERS										
Harry	Beautyman				01/04/1992	20	Newham	L.Orient (Pro 5/10) Rel c/s 11, St Albans (L) 10/10, Hastings U (L) 1/11, Sutton U 8/11	41	11
Reece	Jones	6'00"	11 08		22/12/1992	19	Kingston	Fulham, AFC Wimbledon 8/10 Rel c/s 12, Lewes (L) 11/10, Kingstonian (L) 1/11, Hampton & R (L) 2/12, Sutton U 7/12		
Tom	Kavanagh							Sutton U, Staines (SL) 1/12	18	4
Romone	McCrae	6'01"	12 07		01/08/1990	21	Southwark	Crawley, Peterborough Undisc 7/09 Rel c/s 11, Histon (5ML) 7/10, Kettering (SL) 2/11, Sutton U 7/11, Kingstonian (3ML) 9/11	25	1
Nick	McKoy	6'00"	12 04		03/09/1986	25	Newham	Wimbledon/MK Dons, Cardiff 7/06 Rel c/s 07, Torquay (SL) 1/07, Darlington (Trial) 1/07, Shrewsbury (Trial) 12/07, Potters Bar 8/08, St Johnstone 8/08 Rel 12/08, Enfield T 1/09, Grays 6/09 Rel 8/09, Bishops Stortford (Trial) 8/09, Sutton U Rel 1/10, Kettering 10/10 (10/11 30,3), Northampton 7/11, Tamworth 1/12, Sutton U 8/12		
Jamie	O'Connell							Notts County (Scholar), Injury, Sutton U 7/12		
Anthony	Riviere				09/11/1978	33	Kent	Faversham, Welling 11/98, Fisher 6/04 Rel 5/07, Eastleigh 7/07 Rel 5/11, Sutton U 5/11	38	2
Kyle	Vassell				07/02/1993	19		Brentford (Scholar) Rel c/s 11, Woking (WE) 10/10, St Albans (WE) 2/11, Crewe (Trial), Dover 10/11, Sutton U 11/11, Tooting & M (Dual) 12/11, Whitehawk (Dual) 1/12, Staines (L) 3/12	11	2
FORWARDS										
Craig	Dundas				16/02/1981	31		Local, Croydon, Dulwich H 1/04, Cyprus c/s 04, Dulwich H c/s 05, Carshalton 11/05, Sutton U 11/07 Rel c/s 09, Carshalton (Trial) 7/09, Tooting & M (Trial) 8/09, Hampton & R 8/09, Sutton U 5/10	40	6
Kezie	Ibe	5'10"	12 00		06/12/1982	29	London	Arsenal (Jun), Bournemouth (Jun), Leatherhead 9/01, Hampton & R 12/01, Aylesbury c/s 02, Staines 6/03, Yeovil 8/04, Tiverton (L) 10/04, Exeter (L) 12/04, Weymouth (L) 2/05, St Albans (L) 3/05, Canvey Island 8/05, Chelmsford 8/06 Rel 7/08, Ebbsfleet 8/08, AFC Wimbledon (L) 3/09, Farnborough c/s 09, Chelmsford 6/11, Sutton U 7/12		
Stefan	Payne	5'10"			10/08/1991	21	Lambeth	Sutton U, Fulham £25,000 + 9/09, Gillingham 7/10, Braintree (L) 2/11, Aldershot 1/12, Sutton U 2/12	5	2
Matt	Reece							Sutton U	1	0
Craig	Watkins				04/05/1986	26	Croydon	Epsom & E, Sutton U 7/04, Exeter 8/05 Rel 2/06, Sutton U (L) 10/05, Lewes (L) 12/05, Staines (L) 1/06, Havant & W 3/06, Sutton U 7/07, Havant & W 10/07 Rel c/s 09, Woking 8/09 Rel 10/09, Hayes & Yeading 11/09 Rel 5/10, Met Police 6/10, Sutton U 6/11	38	16

TONBRIDGE ANGELS

Chairman: Steve Churcher
Secretary: Keith Masters   **(T)** 07770 578 222   **(E)** keith.master@yahoo.co.uk
Additional Committee Members:
John Gibbons, Chris Drew, Colin Fry, Darren Apps.

Manager: Tommy Warrilow
Programme Editor: TBA   **(E)**

Back Row (Left to Right): Melvin Slight (Physio), Rob Churcher (Kit man), Nathan Koranteng, Sonny Miles, Ollie Schulz, Lee Worgan, Mikel Suarez, Ben Judge, George Crimmen, Ryan Waterman, Terry Sedge (Coach), Simon Balsdon (Coach), Tina Jenner (Physio). Front Row (Left to Right): Robbie Kember, George Purcell, Tom Davis, Alex O'Brien (Coach), Tommy Warrilow (Manager), Frannie Collin, Lee Browning, Rory Hill Chris Piper.
Photo: David Couldridge

Club Factfile

Founded: 1948   **Nickname:** Angels
Previous Names: Tonbridge Angels, Tonbridge F.C., Tonbridge A.F.C.
Previous Leagues: Southern 1948-80, 93-2004, Kent 1989-93, Isthmian 2004-11.

Club Colours (change): Blue/white/blue (White/red/white)

Ground: Longmead Stadium, Darenth Avenue, Tonbridge, Kent TN10 3LW   **(T)** 01732 352 417
Capacity: 2,500   **Seats:** 707   **Covered:** 1,500   **Clubhouse:** Yes   **Shop:** Yes

Directions: From M25. Take A21 turning at Junction 5 to junction with A225/b245 (signposted Hildenborough). After passing Langley Hotel on left thake slightly hidden left turn into Dry Hill Park Road. Left again at mini roundabout into Shipbourne Road (A227) and then left again at next roundabout into Darenth Avenue' Longmead stadium can be found at the bottom of the hill at the far end of the car park.

Previous Grounds: The Angel 1948-80

Record Attendance: 8,236 v Aldershot - FA Cup 1951
Record Victory: 11-1 v Worthing - FA Cup 1951
Record Defeat: 2-11 v Folkstone - Kent Senior Cup 1949
Record Goalscorer: Jon Main scored 44 goals in one season including seven hat-tricks
Record Appearances: Mark Giham
Additional Records:

Senior Honours:
Kent Senior Cup 1964-65, 74-75

10 YEAR RECORD

02-03		03-04		04-05		05-06		06-07		07-08		08-09		09-10		10-11		11-12	
SthE	9	SthE	3	Isth P	20	Isth1	3	Isth P	11	Isth P	8	Isth P	3	Isth P	8	Isth P	2	Conf S	9

TONBRIDGE ANGELS

No.	Date	Comp	H/A	Opponents	Att:	Result	Goalscorers	Pos
1	Sat-13-Aug	BSS	A	Maidenhead United	385	W 4-0	Henry 21, Beecroft 37, Main 70, A Olorunda 78	4
2	Tue-16-Aug	BSS	H	Sutton United	683	L 1-4	Collin 84	7
3	Sat-20-Aug	BSS	H	Eastleigh	464	W 4-0	Collin 2 (pen 17, 87), Beecroft 55, Browning 84	6
4	Tue-23-Aug	BSS	A	Welling United	545	L 2-3	Collin 2 (6, 39)	10
5	Sat-27-Aug	BSS	A	Dover Athletic	1003	D 0-0		9
6	Mon-29-Aug	BSS	H	Woking	922	L 3-6	Collin 2 (pen 40, 89), Andrews 75	14
7	Sat-03-Sep	BSS	H	Farnborough	612	L 1-5	A Olorunda 19	15
8	Sat-10-Sep	BSS	A	Thurrock	358	D 0-0		16
9	Sat-17-Sep	BSS	H	Salisbury City	511	W 3-1	Collin 2 (pen 26, 35), Browning 90	16
10	Mon-19-Sep	BSS	A	Chelmsford City	938	D 2-2	Henry 76, Collin 90	13
11	Sat-24-Sep	BSS	A	Dartford	1385	L 1-3	Collin pen 86	15
12	Sat-08-Oct	BSS	H	Hampton & Richmond Boro'	523	W 1-0	Collin pen 88	14
13	Sat-22-Oct	BSS	H	Basingstoke Town	579	L 2-3	Collin 53, Miles 89	15
14	Tue-25-Oct	BSS	A	Eastbourne Borough	924	W 2-1	McLaggon 44, Browning 75	13
15	Sat-29-Oct	BSS	A	Dorchester Town	417	L 1-3	McLaggon 25	15
16	Sat-05-Nov	BSS	H	Thurrock	478	W 3-2	Walder pen 20, Kinch 85, Boateng 89	10
17	Sat-12-Nov	BSS	H	Staines Town	517	W 3-2	Kinch 7, Collin 2 (8, 79)	10
18	Tue-15-Nov	BSS	A	Sutton United	737	W 1-0	Collin 77	7
19	Sat-19-Nov	BSS	A	Truro City	662	L 0-2		9
20	Sat-03-Dec	BSS	H	Welling United	631	D 1-1	Og (Parkinson) 4	10
21	Tue-06-Dec	BSS	A	Salisbury City	448	L 0-2		11
22	Sat-17-Dec	BSS	H	Havant & Waterlooville	599	L 1-2	T Olorunda 48	12
23	Mon-26-Dec	BSS	A	Bromley	771	D 2-2	Miles 49, Suarez 87	12
24	Sun-01-Jan	BSS	H	Bromley	905	D 1-1	Henry 77	12
25	Sat-07-Jan	BSS	A	Hampton & Richmond Boro'	524	D 1-1	Koranteng 30	10
26	Sat-21-Jan	BSS	H	Eastbourne Borough	734	W 5-1	Collin 4 (1, 46, pen 66, 76), Piper 10	10
27	Sat-18-Feb	BSS	H	Weston-Super-Mare	642	W 3-0	Collin 2 (58, 69), Main pen 90	11
28	Sat-25-Feb	BSS	A	Farnborough	608	L 2-3	Suarez 1, Hill 70	12
29	Mon-27-Feb	BSS	H	Boreham Wood	391	D 1-1	Collin 89	11
30	Sat-03-Mar	BSS	H	Dartford	1139	L 0-1		13
31	Tue-06-Mar	BSS	A	Basingstoke Town	312	W 2-0	Collin 2 (14, 71)	12
32	Sat-10-Mar	BSS	H	Maidenhead United	591	W 1-0	Schulz 53	10
33	Tue-13-Mar	BSS	A	Staines Town	228	D 1-1	Schulz 28	10
34	Sat-17-Mar	BSS	H	Truro City	639	W 3-0	Collin 40, Suarez 50, Browning 85	8
35	Tue-20-Mar	BSS	A	Eastleigh	307	W 2-1	Browning 81, Suarez 90	8
36	Sat-24-Mar	BSS	A	Havant & Waterlooville	708	D 1-1	Browning 90	8
37	Sat-31-Mar	BSS	H	Chelmsford City	728	D 0-0		8
38	Sat-07-Apr	BSS	H	Dover Athletic	940	L 2-3	T Olorunda 9, Collin pen 27	10
39	Mon-09-Apr	BSS	A	Woking	2430	L 1-2	Collin 40	10
40	Sat-14-Apr	BSS	A	Weston-Super-Mare	327	D 2-2	Piper 1, Collin 55	10
41	Sat-21-Apr	BSS	H	Dorchester Town	756	W 2-1	Suarez 48, Og (Bell 53)	9
42	Sat-28-Apr	BSS	A	Boreham Wood	275	L 2-4	Piper 17, Collin 66	9

CUPS

No.	Date	Comp	H/A	Opponents	Att:	Result	Goalscorers
1	Sat-01-Oct	FAC 2Q	A	Chelmsford City	653	L 0-3	
2	Sat-26-Nov	FAT 3Q	A	Bishops Stortford	297	D 1-1	Boateng 73
3	Tue-29-Nov	FAT 3QR	H	Bishops Stortford	274	L 1-2	Browning 7

League
Starts
Substitute
Unused Sub

Cups
Starts
Substitute
Unused Sub

Goals (Lg)
Goals (Cup)

WORGAN	MILES	HEATH	BROWNING	JUDGE	ANDREWS	BEECROFT	STOREY	MAIN	A.OLORUNDA	HENRY	WALDER	COLLIN	JONES	T.OLORUNDA	HAGAN	KINCH	TAYLOR	KEMBER	BOATENG	MCLAGGON	SUAREZ	CRIMMEN	KORANTENG	PIPER	BENJAMIN	HILL	SCHULZ	BEWICK	ROOK	SMELT
X	X	X	X	X	X	X	X	X	X	X	S	S	S	U	U															
X	X	X	X	X	X	X	X	X	X	X	S	S	S	U	U															
X	X	X	X	X	X	X	X	X	S	X	S	X	X	U	S	U														
X	X	X	X	X	X	X	X	X	S	X	S	X	X	U	U	U														
X	X	X	X	X	X	X	X	X	S	X	S	X	X		U	U	U													
X	X	X	X	X	X	X	X	X	S	X	S	X	X		U	U	U													
X	X		X		X	X	X	X	X	S	X	S	X		S	U	U	X	S											
X	X		X	X	X	X	X	X		U			X	S	X		U	X	U											
X	X	X	X			X	X	U	X	U	S	X	S			X	X	S												
X	X	X	X	X	S	X	X	U	X	U	S	U	X			X	X	S												
X	X	X		X	X	X	X	X	U	X	S	S	X	S	U		X	X												
X	X	X	X		X	X	X	X		X	X	X	X	S	U	U	U													
X	X	X			X	X	X			X	S				X		X	S	X	X	S									
X	X	X	X	X	U	S	X		X	U	X	X			X			S	X	X	S									
X	X	X	X	X	S	S	X		S	U	X	X		U			X	X	X											
X	S	X	X	X	S	X				X	X			X	U	S		X	X	X										
X		X	X	X	U	X	X		S	S			X	U	X		X	S	X	X										
X	X	X		X	S	S	X		X	U	S	X		X	U		X	X	X											
X	X	X	U	X		X	X		S	S	S	X		U			X	X	X											
X	X	X	X		X			U	U	X		X	U	X	X		U	X	X	S										
X	X	X	X		X			S	S	U	X			X		S	X	X	X	S										
X	X		U	X		U	X		X	S	X	X		X		S	X	X	X	S										
X	X	U	X	X		X	X		X	S	X	X		S			X		S	U										
X	X	X	X		S	S		X	S	X	X		X	U			X	U	X											
X	X	X	X	X	U			S	X	X	X		U			X		X	S	S										
X	X		X	X		X		X	S	X	X		S						S	X	X	X								
X	X	X	X	X		X		S			X	X		U	U			S			X	X	X	S						
X	X	X	X	X		X		S			X	X		X	X		X			X	X	X	X	X						
X	X	X	X	X		U		X		S			U		U		X			S	X	X	X							
X	X		X	X		U		S		X	X		S			U		U		S	X	X	X	X						
X	X	U	X	X				X	X		S		X				X			S	X	X	U	X	X					
X	X	S	U	X				X	X		S		X				X			S	X	X	S	X	X					
X	X	U	X					X	X		U						S			S	X	X	S	X	X					
X	X	X	X						S		X		U				S			X	X	X	S	X						
X	X	X	X						S		X		S				S			X	X	X	S	X						
X	X	X							X		X		U				S			X	X	S	X	X						
X	X	U	X	U					X		X		S				X			X	X	S	X	X						
X	X	X	X						X		X		X							X	U	X	S	X		S	S	U		
X	X	X	X						X		S									X	X	S	X	X						
X	X	X	X				S		S	X										X	S	X	X	X		X				
X	X	S	X	X			S		X	X		U								X	U	X	X	X		X				
X	X	S		X			S		X	X		X								X	S	X	X	X		X				
X	X	X	X	X	X	X	U	X	S	S	X		S		U	X														
X	X	U	X	X		U			X	S	X	X		X		X		S	X	X	S									
X	X		X	X				S	X		S	S	X	X		U		X		U	X	X	X							
42	41	29	35	37	10	22	19	5	17	6	25	37	0	11	1	9	4	11	10	10	19	1	17	17	8	12	11	0	0	0
0	0	4	0	0	5	4	1	7	9	14	9	3	6	9	0	2	0	11	0	0	7	3	2	1	9	1	0	1	1	0
0	0	4	3	1	2	4	0	3	0	6	3	0	2	15	15	5	0	4	0	0	0	4	0	0	1	0	0	0	0	1
3	3	1	3	3	1	1	2	0	2	0	2	3	0	1	0	2	1	0	2	2	1	0	0	0	0	0	0	0	0	0
0	0	0	0	0	0	0	1	0	0	1	3	1	0	0	1	0	0	0	1	0	0	1	0	0	0	0	0	0	0	0
0	0	1	0	0	0	1	0	1	0	0	0	0	0	1	0	1	0	1	0	0	0	0	0	0	0	0	0	0	0	0
0	2	0	6	0	1	2	0	2	2	3	1	30	0	2	0	2	0	0	1	2	5	0	1	3	0	1	2	0	0	0
0	0	0	1	0	0	0	0	0	0	0	0	0	0	0	0	0	0	0	1	0	0	0	0	0	0	0	0	0	0	0

PLAYING SQUAD 2012/13

Existing Players		SN	HT	WT	DOB	AGE	POB	Career	Apps	Goals
GOALKEEPERS										
Lee	Worgan		6'01"	13 10	01/12/1983	28	Eastbourne	Wimbledon Rel c/s 04, Aylesbury (SL) 12/02, Wycombe (L) 4/04, Rushden & D 8/04 Rel c/s 05, Eastbourne B 8/05, Cardiff C 10/05 Rel c/s 06, Merthyr (L) 1/06, Eastbourne B 7/06, Hastings U 10/06, Tonbridge A 5/08	42	0
DEFENDERS										
Jon	Heath							Tonbridge A	33	0
Ben	Judge				22/05/1977	35	Redhill	C.Palace (Jun), Croydon (94), Crawley 11/01 Rel 8/07, Bromley 9/07 Rel 3/08, AFC Wimbledon 3/08 Rel 4/10, Croydon Ath 7/10, Tonbridge A 10/10	37	0
Sonny	Miles							Tonbridge A	41	2
Ollie	Schulz				25/05/1985	27		Ramsgate, Dover 5/08, Tonbridge A 3/12	11	2
Danny	Walder				03/09/1989	22	Chatham	Gillingham Rel 1/09, Ramsgate (3ML) 10/08 Perm 1/09, Dover 8/09 Rel 5/10, Tonbridge A 5/10	34	1
MIDFIELDERS										
George	Crimmen							Tonbridge A	4	0
Tom	Davis		5'10"	11 06	17/02/1984	28	Bromley	Fulham Rel c/s 04, Gravesend 9/04, St Albans (L) 11/04, St Albans 2/05, Lewes 4 fig 7/07, AFC Wimbledon 5/08 Rel 5/09, Dover 6/09 Rel 1/10, Croydon Ath (L) 12/09, Croydon Ath 1/10, Bromley 2/10, Dorking Wanderers 3/10, Sutton U 5/10, Carshalton 8/11, Woking (L) 3/12, Tonbridge A 6/12		
Rory	Hill				28/03/1990	22		Gillingham Rel 1/09, Salisbury (L) 11/08, Bishops Stortford 3/09, Croydon Ath, Tonbridge A 9/10, Lewes 1/11, Bromley 9/11, Tonbridge A 2/12	13	1
Robbie	Kember				21/08/1981	31	Wimbledon	C.Palace, Bournemouth (Trial) 7/02, Woking 8/02 Rel c/s 03, L.Orient (Trial) 7/03, Basingstoke 8/03 Rel 2/04, Crawley 3/04, Lewes (3ML) 2/06, Tonbridge A c/s 06, Eastbourne B 2/08 Rel 6/08, Hampton & R 7/08 Rel 8/09, Bromley 8/09, Whyteleafe 11/09, Folkestone I 7/10, Carshalton 3/11, Tonbridge A 8/11	22	0
Nathan	Koranteng		6'02"	12 08	26/05/1992	20	London	Peterborough Rel 3/11, Tamworth (L) 9/09, Spalding U (WE) 12/09, Boston U (WE) 1/10, Rushden & D (L) 8/10, Boston U (2ML) 1/11, Woking 3/11 Rel 12/11, Boreham Wood (L) 9/11, Boreham Wood 12/11, Tonbridge A 12/11	19	1
Chris	Piper				20/10/1981	30	London	Charlton, St Albans, Farnborough 2/01, Dag & Red 6/03, Fisher 6/04 Rel 5/07, Eastleigh 7/07 Rel 5/08, Braintree 7/08 Rel 5/09, Croydon Ath c/s 09, Tonbridge A 10/10, Sutton U 8/11, Tonbridge A 1/12	18	3
FORWARDS										
Lee	Browning				06/05/1987	25		Gillingham (Jun), Aston Villa (Trial), Derby (Trial), Sittingbourne 7/03, Dover 9/07 Rel 3/10, Tonbridge A 5/10	35	6
Frannie	Collin		5'11"	11 11	20/04/1987	25	Chatham	Chatham, Gillingham c/s 05 Rel c/s 07, Dover 6/07 Rel 5/10, Tonbridge A 5/10	40	30
George	Purcell		5'11"	11 09	08/04/1988	24	Gravesend	Gillingham, Gravesend/Ebbsfleet 8/06, Heybridge (L) 9/07, Ramsgate (L) 2/09, Braintree 5/09, York C Undisc 7/10, Dartford (L) 11/10, Eastbourne B (SL) 1/11, Dover Undisc 7/11 Rel c/s 12, Tonbridge A 5/12		
Mikel	Suarez				28/09/1986	25	Bilbao, Spa	Loughborough University, Nuneaton T (Trial) 7/09, Boston U 7/09, Worksop 1/11, Boston U 6/11 Rel 9/11, Quorn 9/11, Tonbridge A 10/11	26	5

TRURO CITY

Chairman: Kevin Heaney
Secretary: Mark Woolcock   **(T)** 07811 455858   **(E)** mark@tigermedical.co.uk
Additional Committee Members:
Chris Webb, Julia Sincock, Shaun Lawrence.

Manager: Lee Hodges
Programme Editor: Shaun Lawrence   **(E)** shaunlawrence@cornishpropertiesltd.com

Photo: Keith Clayton.

Club Factfile

Founded: 1889   **Nickname:** City
Previous Names: None
Previous Leagues: Cornwall County, Plymouth & District, South Western, Western 2006-08, Southern 2008-11.

Club Colours (change): All white (All blue)

Ground: Treyew Road, Truro, Cornwall TR1 2TH   **(T)** 01872 225 400 / 278 853 (Social Club)
Capacity: **Seats:** 750   **Covered:** Yes   **Clubhouse:** Yes   **Shop:**

Directions: On arriving at Exeter, leave the M5 at junction 31 and join the A30. Travel via Okehampton, Launceston, and Bodmin.. At the end of the dual carriageway (windmills on right hand side) take left hand turning signposted Truro. After approximately 7 miles turn right at traffic lights, travel downhill crossing over three roundabouts, following signs for Redruth. Approximately 500 metres after third roundabout signed 'Arch Hill', ground is situated on left hand side.

Previous Grounds: None

Record Attendance: 1,400 v Aldershot - FA Vase
Record Victory: Not known
Record Defeat: Not known
Record Goalscorer: Not known
Record Appearances: Not known
Additional Records: Most League points and goals in a season:
Senior Honours: 115 points & 185 goals, Western League Division One (42 games) 2006-07.
South Western League 1960-61, 69-70, 92-93, 95-96, 97-98. Western League Division 1 2006-07, Premier Division 07-08.
FA Vase 2006-07. Southern League Division 1 South & West 2008-09, Premier Division 2010-11.
Cornwall Senior Cup x15

10 YEAR RECORD

02-03		03-04		04-05		05-06		06-07		07-08		08-09		09-10		10-11		11-12	
SWest	16	SWest	15	SWest	6	SWest	2	West1	1	WestP	1	Sthsw	1	SthP	11	SthP	1	Conf S	14

TRURO CITY

No.	Date	Comp	H/A	Opponents	Att:	Result	Goalscorers	Pos
1	Sat-13-Aug	BSS	A	Chelmsford City	808	W 1-0	Smith 80	8
2	Tue-16-Aug	BSS	H	Eastleigh	713	W 2-1	Watkins 10, Walker pen 58	6
3	Sat-20-Aug	BSS	H	Dover Athletic	1017	W 1-0	Martin 58	2
4	Tue-23-Aug	BSS	A	Salisbury City	899	L 1-2	Walker 7	3
5	Sat-27-Aug	BSS	A	Havant & Waterlooville	502	L 1-4	Walker pen 90	6
6	Mon-29-Aug	BSS	H	Dorchester Town	701	L 0-1		10
7	Sat-03-Sep	BSS	H	Maidenhead United	576	L 1-2	Hayles 65	13
8	Sat-10-Sep	BSS	A	Boreham Wood	290	W 2-1	Martin 3, Walker 90	12
9	Sat-17-Sep	BSS	H	Sutton United	558	L 0-3		15
10	Tue-20-Sep	BSS	A	Maidenhead United	301	W 3-1	Walker 64, Hayles 72, Afful 90	11
11	Sat-24-Sep	BSS	A	Thurrock	201	D 1-1	Hayles 30	10
12	Sat-08-Oct	BSS	H	Basingstoke Town	521	L 2-5	Walker 2 (pen 20, pen 88)	13
13	Sat-22-Oct	BSS	A	Dartford	1238	W 2-1	Watkins 5, Og (Goodacre) 7	11
14	Tue-25-Oct	BSS	H	Farnborough	434	W 8-2	Walker 14, Yetton 2 (15, 37), Afful 2 (22, 28), Watkins 2 (33, 54), Hayles 45	8
15	Sat-29-Oct	BSS	H	Woking	664	L 1-4	Afful 1	8
16	Sat-05-Nov	BSS	H	Welling United	542	L 2-3	Hayles 9, McConnell 89	9
17	Sat-19-Nov	BSS	H	Tonbridge Angels	662	W 2-0	Afful 18, Palmer 90	12
18	Sat-03-Dec	BSS	A	Farnborough	427	L 1-2	Yetton 80	12
19	Tue-06-Dec	BSS	A	Eastbourne Borough	463	D 2-2	Walker pen 48, Ash 52	12
20	Sat-17-Dec	BSS	H	Hampton & Richmond Boro'	250	D 3-3	Ash 2 (7, 90), Walker 58	13
21	Tue-20-Dec	BSS	A	Sutton United	567	D 2-2	Cooke 2 (59, 78)	11
22	Mon-26-Dec	BSS	A	Weston-Super-Mare	620	W 1-0	Ash 67	10
23	Sun-01-Jan	BSS	H	Weston-Super-Mare	616	L 0-1		10
24	Sat-07-Jan	BSS	A	Welling United	649	L 1-5	Walker pen 78	11
25	Sat-14-Jan	BSS	H	Chelmsford City	505	L 0-2		12
26	Sat-21-Jan	BSS	A	Bromley	435	D 1-1	Watkins 45	11
27	Sat-28-Jan	BSS	H	Staines Town	512	W 2-1	Watkins 2 (73, 88)	11
28	Sat-11-Feb	BSS	H	Salisbury City	590	D 2-2	Hayles 4, Walker pen 90	11
29	Sat-18-Feb	BSS	A	Dover Athletic	751	L 1-3	Walker pen 10	12
30	Sat-25-Feb	BSS	A	Eastleigh	535	L 1-3	Ash 64	15
31	Sat-03-Mar	BSS	H	Eastbourne Borough	493	L 0-2		15
32	Sat-10-Mar	BSS	A	Hampton & Richmond Boro'	369	L 3-4	Watkins 2 (27, 60), Afful 61	15
33	Tue-13-Mar	BSS	H	Boreham Wood	299	W 2-1	Martin 11, Yetton 56	15
34	Sat-17-Mar	BSS	A	Tonbridge Angels	639	L 0-3		15
35	Tue-20-Mar	BSS	A	Basingstoke Town	318	L 1-2	Yetton 58	15
36	Sat-24-Mar	BSS	H	Thurrock	492	W 3-0	Martin 13, Gritton 46, Kelly 79	15
37	Sat-31-Mar	BSS	A	Staines Town	304	D 1-1	Yetton 44	15
38	Sat-07-Apr	BSS	H	Havant & Waterlooville	698	L 0-1		15
39	Mon-09-Apr	BSS	A	Dorchester Town	504	W 3-2	Pugh 38, Gritton 66, Watkins 78	14
40	Sat-14-Apr	BSS	H	Bromley	537	L 1-2	Watkins 47	15
41	Sat-21-Apr	BSS	A	Woking	4048	D 3-3	Watkins 36, Pugh 57, Afful 86	14
42	Sat-28-Apr	BSS	H	Dartford	751	D 1-1	Hayles 87	14

CUPS

No.	Date	Comp	H/A	Opponents	Att:	Result	Goalscorers	
1	Sat-01-Oct	FAC 2Q	A	Bournemouth FC	238	D 0-0		
2	Tue-04-Oct	FAC 2QR	H	Bournemouth FC	182	W 3-2	Hayles 49, Walker pen 83, Martin 84	
3	Sat-15-Oct	FAC 3Q	A	Gloucester City	385	L 2-7	Watkins 2 (13, 68)	
4	Sat-26-Nov	FAT 3Q	A	Gloucester City	300	D 1-1	Ash 71	
5	Tue-29-Nov	FAT 3QR	H	Gloucester City	228	W 3-2	Pugh 3 (46, 52, 88)	
6	Sat-10-Dec	FAT 1	H	Ebbsfleet United	445	L 2-5	Afful 2 (19, 55)	

League
Starts
Substitute
Unused Sub

Cups
Starts
Substitute
Unused Sub

Goals (Lg)
Goals (Cup)

SANDERCOMBE	MCCONNELL	WALKER	PUGH	ADAMS	ASH	TAYLOR	MARTIN	WATKINS	HAYLES	AFFUL	SMITH	CLAY	E PALMER	BROAD	YETTON	BROOKS	HODGES	COOKE	CONIBEAR-TRATHEN	NIXON	S PALMER	CARNE	CHENOWETH	KELLY	VASSELL	GRITTON
X	X	X	X	X	X	X	X	X	X	X	S	S	U	U	U	U										
X	X	X	X	X	X	X	X	X	X	X		S	U	S	U	U										
X	X	X	X	X	X	X	X			X		X	S	S	X	U	U	S								
X	X	X	X	X	X	X	X	S		X		X	S	S	X	U		U								
X	U	X	X	X	U	X	X		U	X		X	X	X	X	U		S								
X	X	U	X	X	X	X	S	X	X			X	X	U	S	U										
X	X	X	X	X	X	X	X	X	X	X	U	U	S	U	U											
X	X	X	X	X	X	X	X	X	X	X	S	S	U		U	U										
X	X	X	X	X	X	X	X	X	X	X	S	U	U	S	S											
	X	X	X	X	X	S	X		X	S	X	X		S	X	X										
X	X	X	X	X	X	S	X	S	X	S	X	S	X	X	U	U	X									
X	X	X	X	U		X	X	X	X	X	S	U	X	X	S			U								
X	X	X		X	U	U		X	X	X	U	X	X	X	X		U	U								
X	X	X		X			S		X	X	X	S	X	X	X	X			S							
X	X	X	U	X		S	X		X	X	X		X	X	X	U	U	U								
X	X	X	X			U	X	S	X	X	X	U		X	U	U										
X	X	X	X	X			X	X	X	X	S	S	S		X	U	U									
X	X	X	X	X			X		X	S		X	X	X	U	S	U	U								
X	X	X	X	X		U	X		X	X		X	S	X	U	S										
X	X	X	X	X			X		X	X		X	X		X	S	U	U								
X	X	X	X	X					X	X		X			X	X	X		U							
X	X	X	X	X		U	U		X	X		X			X	X	X									
X	X	X	X	X		S	X		X	X		X	U		X	X	U									
X	X	X	X	X		S	X		X	X		X			X	X	S									
X	X	X	X	X		S	X	S	X	S		X			X	X	X									
X	X	X	X	X		X	X	S	X			X		X		X				U	U					
X	X	X	X	X		S	X	X				X				X				S	S	X				
X	X	X	X	X		S	X	X				X				U				S	S	X	X			
X	X	X	X	X		X	X	X				X		U		U				U	X	S				
X	X	X	X	X		S	X	X				X				U				U	X	X				
X	X	X	X	X		S	X	X				X	S			S				U	X	X				
S	X		X	X		S	X	X				X	S		X	X				S	X	X				
X	S		X	X		X	X					X	X		X	X					X	U	U			
X	X	S	X	X		X	X	S	X			X	X		X	X					X	U	S			
X	X	X	X	X		S		X	S			X	X		S						X	X	X			
X	X	X		X		X	U	X	X			X	X		S						X	S	S	X		
X	X	X	X	X		X	S	X	X			S	X		S						X	U	U	X		
X	X	X	X	X			S	X	X			X	X		U						X	S	S	X		
X	X	X	X	X		U	X	S	S			S	X		X						X	X	X			
X	X	X	X	X			U	X	S			S	X		X						X	U	X			
X	X	X	X	X	U		X	S	S			X			X						X	X	X			
X	X	X	X	X	S		X	S	S			X			X						X	X	X			
X		X	X		U	X		X		X	X	X	X	X	X			U	S							
X	X	X	X		U	X	S	X	X	X		X	X	X	S			U	U							
X	X	X	X	X		X	X	X	U	X	X	X	S	S	S			U								
X	X	X	X	X	X		X	X	X	X	S		S		X	U	U	U								
X	X	X	X	X	X		X	X		X	S		X		X	U	U	U	U							
X	X	X	X	X			X		X	X		X	X	U	U	S	X	U								

21	40	40	36	40	34	10	22	28	23	35	10	9	11	24	19	9	7	12	0	0	0	0	12	9	3	8
0	1	1	0	1	4	8	6	7	6	8	4	4	8	6	0	3	8	0	0	2	3	0	3	3	0	
0	1	1	1	1	3	2	3	2	1	1	2	3	6	6	4	12	5	11	2	1	1	4	0	3	3	0

6	5	6	6	4	2	3	3	6	2	6	3	3	4	3	3	0	0	1	0	0	0	0	0	0	0	0
0	0	0	0	0	0	0	1	0	0	0	2	0	2	1	2	0	1	1	0	0	0	0	0	0	0	0
0	0	0	0	0	2	0	0	0	1	0	0	0	0	0	1	3	5	3	2	0	0	0	0	0	0	0

| 0 | 1 | 13 | 2 | 0 | 5 | 0 | 4 | 12 | 7 | 7 | 1 | 0 | 0 | 0 | 6 | 0 | 0 | 2 | 0 | 0 | 0 | 0 | 0 | 1 | 0 | 2 |
| 0 | 0 | 1 | 3 | 0 | 1 | 0 | 1 | 2 | 1 | 2 | 0 | 0 | 0 | 0 | 0 | 0 | 0 | 0 | 0 | 0 | 0 | 0 | 0 | 0 | 0 | 0 |

PLAYING SQUAD 2012/13

Existing Players		SN	HT	WT	DOB	AGE	POB	Career	Apps	Goals
GOALKEEPERS										
Tom	Brooks							Plymouth (Scholar), Truro C 7/09 Rel 2/12, Turo C 3/12	9	0
Timothy	Sandercombe		6'04"	13 12	15/06/1989	23	Plymouth	QPR (Yth), Plymouth (Scholar) Rel c/s 07, Tiverton (L) 11/06,		
								Notts County 7/07 Rel c/s 08, Torquay (Trial), Stafford R 9/08,		
								Mansfield 5/09, Weymouth 2/10, Worcester 7/10 Rel 4/11,		
								Truro C 7/11	21	0
DEFENDERS										
Steve	Adams		6'00"	12 04	25/09/1980	31	Plymouth	Plymouth, Sheff Wed 3/05 Rel c/s 07, Swindon 8/07,		
								Torquay 1/08 Rel c/s 10, Forest Green (L) 8/09, Truro C (SL) 10/09,		
								Truro C 7/10	40	0
Jake	Ash		6'01"	13 04	26/07/1983	29		Exeter (Trainee), Falmouth, Truro C	35	5
Arran	Pugh		6'06"					Dorchester (Yth), Dawlish T, Tiverton T 7/08, Truro C 7/09	37	2
Martin	Watts		5'11"	10 08	20/11/1988	23	Truro	Plymouth, Truro 3/08		
Danny	Carne							Truro C	3	0
Scott	Palmer							Truro C	2	0
Tim	Nixon							Truro C	0	0
MIDFIELDERS										
Ben	Adelsbury				20/10/1990	21		Plymouth (Yth), Swansea, Salisbury 12/09 Rel c/s 12, Truro C 7/12		
Les	Afful		5'06"	10 00	04/02/1984	28	Liverpool	Exeter Rel 5/06, Torquay (SL) 1/06, Forest Green 5/06,		
								Truro C 7/09	41	7
Joe	Broad		5'11"	12 07	24/08/1982	30	Bristol	Plymouth, Weymouth (Trial) c/s 01, Yeovil (L) 11/01,		
								Torquay 9/03 Rel c/s 04, Walsall 8/04, Redditch (L) 9/05,		
								Redditch (6WL) 11/05, Truro 1/06	32	0
Cody	Cooke							Penryn Ath, Truro C 12/10	20	2
Lee	Hodges		6'00"	12 01	04/09/1973	38	Epping	Tottenham Rel c/s 94, Plymouth (L) 2/93, Wycombe (L) 12/93, Barnet 5/94,		
								Reading £100,000 7/97 Rel c/s 01, Plymouth 8/01 Rel 5/08, Torquay 6/08,		
								Truro C (SL) 10/09, Truro C (Pl/Man) 5/10	10	0
Adam	Kelly				11/02/1988	24		Tiverton, Winchester, Bashley 3/09, Salisbury c/s 10 Rel 2/12,		
								Truro C 2/12	12	1
Marcus	Martin				09/02/1985	27	Torquay	Plymouth (Sch), Exeter (SL) 8/04, Truro C 1/06	30	4
FORWARDS										
Andy	Watkins							Bodmin, Bideford 7/05, Truro C 7/06	34	12
Stewart	Yetton		5'08"	10 03	27/07/1985	27	Plymouth	Plymouth, Weymouth (L) 1/04, Weymouth (L) 11/04, Tiverton 2/05,		
								Truro C 10/05	25	6

WELLING UNITED

Chairman: Paul Websdale
Secretary: Barrie Hobbins   **(T)** 07782 347 432   **(E)** wellingutdfcsecretary@hotmail.co.uk
Additional Committee Members:
Steve Pain, George Evans, Dan Chapman, Matthew Mein, Matthew Panting.

Manager: Jamie Day
Programme Editor: Paul Carter   **(E)** paul_carter40@yahoo.co.uk

Club Factfile

Founded: 1963   **Nickname:** The Wings
Previous Names: None
Previous Leagues: Eltham & District 1963-71, London Spartan 1971-77, Athenian 1978-81, Southern 1981-86, 2000-04, Conference 1986-2000

Club Colours (change): Red/red/white (All blue)

Ground: Park View Road Ground, Welling, Kent DA16 1SY   **(T)** 0208 301 1196
Capacity: 4,000   **Seats:** 1,070   **Covered:** 1,500   **Clubhouse:** Yes   **Shop:** Yes

Directions
M25 to Dartford then A2 towards London.
Take Bexleyheath/Blackfen/Sidcup,turn off (six miles along A2) then follow A207 signed welling.
Ground is 1 mile From A2 on main road towards Welling High Street.

Previous Grounds: Butterfly Lane, Eltham 1963-78

Record Attendance: 4,100 v Gillingham - FA Cup
Record Victory: 7-1 v Dorking - 1985-86
Record Defeat: 0-7 v Welwyn Garden City - 1972-73
Record Goalscorer: Not known
Record Appearances: Not known
Additional Records: Paid £30,000 to Enfield for Gary Abbott
Senior Honours: Received £95,000 from Birmingham City for Steve Finnan 1995
Southern League 1985-86. Kent Senior Cup 1985-86, 98-99, 2008-09.
London Senior Cup 1989-90. London Challenge Cup 1991-92.

10 YEAR RECORD

02-03		03-04		04-05		05-06		06-07		07-08		08-09		09-10		10-11		11-12	
SthP	15	SthP	9	Conf S	16	Conf S	9	Conf S	8	Conf S	16	Conf S	7	Conf S	9	Conf S	6	Conf S	3

WELLING UNITED

No.	Date	Comp	H/A	Opponents	Att:	Result	Goalscorers	Pos
1	Sat-13-Aug	BSS	H	Staines Town	500	D 1-1	Pugh 60	14
2	Wed-17-Aug	BSS	A	Havant & Waterlooville	599	W 2-1	Clarke 43, Pugh 82	7
3	Sat-20-Aug	BSS	A	Farnborough	534	W 4-1	Pugh 2 (4, 48), Cumbers 11, Pires 58	4
4	Tue-23-Aug	BSS	H	Tonbridge Angels	545	W 3-2	Pires 45, Pugh 70, Parkinson 74	2
5	Sat-27-Aug	BSS	H	Eastbourne Borough	541	W 3-0	Pugh 5, Pires 60, Fazackerley 67	1
6	Mon-29-Aug	BSS	A	Thurrock	397	W 4-1	Clarke pen 40, Og (Bruce) 42, Pires 57, Pugh 61	1
7	Sat-03-Sep	BSS	H	Woking	1214	W 3-2	Martin 13, Parkinson 2 (28, 71)	1
8	Sat-10-Sep	BSS	A	Dorchester Town	508	L 2-3	Parkinson 2 (59, 85)	1
9	Sat-17-Sep	BSS	H	Maidenhead United	640	W 4-0	Pugh 3 (18, 29, 84), Clarke pen 26	1
10	Mon-19-Sep	BSS	A	Boreham Wood	273	L 1-2	Martin 70	1
11	Sat-24-Sep	BSS	A	Bromley	648	D 1-1	Cumbers 63	3
12	Sat-08-Oct	BSS	H	Dover Athletic	851	D 0-0		3
13	Sat-15-Oct	BSS	H	Dorchester Town	502	W 3-2	Day 11, Pugh 44, Pires 66	2
14	Sat-22-Oct	BSS	A	Eastleigh	391	L 0-3		2
15	Sat-29-Oct	BSS	H	Hampton & Richmond Boro'	572	W 2-1	Acheampong 6, Pugh 37	3
16	Sat-05-Nov	BSS	A	Truro City	542	W 3-2	Pugh 5, Pires 65, Day 71	3
17	Tue-15-Nov	BSS	H	Salisbury City	440	W 4-3	Day 30, Parkinson 36, Pugh 74, Pires 90	2
18	Sat-19-Nov	BSS	H	Boreham Wood	688	W 2-0	Clarke 2 (23, pen 29)	2
19	Sat-03-Dec	BSS	A	Tonbridge Angels	631	D 1-1	Pugh 15	2
20	Tue-13-Dec	BSS	A	Basingstoke Town	336	W 1-0	Clarke pen 8	2
21	Sat-17-Dec	BSS	A	Sutton United	609	L 3-4	Pugh 13, Cumbers 2 (25, 73)	2
22	Mon-26-Dec	BSS	H	Dartford	1815	D 1-1	Clarke pen 38	2
23	Mon-02-Jan	BSS	A	Dartford	2559	L 0-1		3
24	Sat-07-Jan	BSS	H	Truro City	649	W 5-1	Clarke pen 40, Cracknell 2 (50, 74), Cumbers 2 (68, 70)	2
25	Sat-14-Jan	BSS	A	Weston-Super-Mare	422	L 0-2		3
26	Sat-21-Jan	BSS	A	Farnborough	555	W 1-0	Cumbers 74	2
27	Sat-28-Jan	BSS	H	Chelmsford City	779	D 1-1	Pires 43	3
28	Tue-21-Feb	BSS	H	Havant & Waterlooville	384	W 3-1	Baker 86, Greenhalgh 87, Cumbers 90	4
29	Sat-25-Feb	BSS	A	Dover Athletic	950	W 1-0	Parkinson 78	3
30	Mon-27-Feb	BSS	H	Staines Town	301	L 2-4	Flack 2 (72, 78)	3
31	Sat-03-Mar	BSS	H	Bromley	788	W 2-1	Kinch 25, Cracknell 77	3
32	Tue-06-Mar	BSS	H	Weston-Super-Mare	387	W 2-0	Parkinson 35, Pires 50	3
33	Sat-10-Mar	BSS	A	Chelmsford City	1003	W 2-1	Day 5, Cumbers 62	3
34	Sat-17-Mar	BSS	A	Woking	1926	L 1-2	Parkinson 17	3
35	Tue-20-Mar	BSS	A	Maidenhead United	260	W 4-0	Cumbers 2 (27, 62), Og (Scarborough) 48, Baker 71	3
36	Sat-24-Mar	BSS	H	Sutton United	748	D 0-0		3
37	Sat-31-Mar	BSS	A	Salisbury City	610	D 0-0		3
38	Sat-07-Apr	BSS	A	Eastbourne Borough	751	W 3-0	Healy pen 15, Pires 2 (25, 72)	3
39	Mon-09-Apr	BSS	H	Thurrock	511	W 1-0	Baker 15	3
40	Sat-14-Apr	BSS	H	Eastleigh	454	L 0-1		3
41	Sat-21-Apr	BSS	A	Hampton & Richmond Boro'	519	W 2-0	Day 42, Healy 90	3
42	Sat-28-Apr	BSS	H	Basingstoke Town	632	D 1-1	Parkinson pen 43	3

CUPS

No.	Date	Comp	H/A	Opponents	Att:	Result	Goalscorers	
1	Sat-01-Oct	FAC 2Q	A	Bromley	716	L 1-2	Pires 16	
2	Sat-26-Nov	FAT 3Q	A	Thamesmead Town	273	D 2-2	Pugh 60, Clarke pen 72	
3	Tue-29-Nov	FAT 3QR	H	Thamesmead Town	288	W 3-1	Parkinson 54, Pugh 79, Pires 81	
4	Sat-10-Dec	FAT 1	A	East Thurrock United	224	L 1-2	Pugh 30	
5	Wed-02-May	PO SF1	A	Sutton United	1255	W 2-1	Clarke 25, Healy 71	
6	Sun-06-May	PO SF2	H	Sutton United	1408	D 0-0		
7	Sun-13-May	PO Final	A	Dartford	4088	L 0-1		

League
Starts
Substitute
Unused Sub

Cups
Starts
Substitute
Unused Sub

Goals (Lg)
Goals (Cup)

WHITEHOUSE	FAZACKERLEY	OBERSTELLER	DAY	ACHEAMPONG	MARTIN	PARKINSON	CLARKE	CUMBERS	PUGH	HEALY	PIRES	ATTWOOD	MEHMET	JOHNSON	POOLE	CAMACHO	CONTEH	THOMAS	HEFFERNAN	SAMBROOK	TUNA	SIDIBEH	DAVISSON	DOLBY	HUDSON	TAYLOR	EVANS	POPE	CRACKNELL	BROWN	MCBEAN	GREENHALGH	KINCH	HOLLOWAY	BAKER	CULLUM	KESSINGTON	FLACK	MCLAREN	TURNER
X	X	X	X	X	X	X	X	X	X	X	S	S	U	U	U																									
X	X		X	X	X	X	X	X	X	X	X	U		U	U	U																								
X	X		X	X	X	X	X	X	X	X	S		U	U	U	U	X	U																						
X	X		X	X	X	X	X	X	X	X	S		U	U	U	U	X																							
X	X	U		X	X	X	X	X	X	X	X			S	S	S	X	U																						
X	X		X	X	X	X	X	X	X	X	S		S	U	U	U		X																						
X	X	U	X	X	X	X	X	X	X	X	S		U		U	X	U																							
X	X		X	X	X	X	X	X	X	X	S	S	U		X	U	S																							
X	X	U	X	X	X	X	X	X	X	S	S		U	X	U	S																								
X	U	X	X			X	X	X	X	X	X	X	U		U	X	U	U																						
X	X	U	X	X		X	X	X	X	U	S			X	X	S	S	S																						
U	X	X	X			X	X	S	X	X	X	X	U		X	U	S	S																						
X	X	X	S	X	X	X	X	X	X	U		X	U	S	S																									
X	X	X	S	X		X	X	X	X	U	U	U		X	U	U	U																							
X	X	X	S	X		X	X	X	X	S	U		X	U		U																								
X	X	X		X	S	X	X	X	X	U		X	U	U		U																								
X	X	X	X		X	X	X	X	S		X	U	U	U	S																									
X	X	U	X	X	X	X	X	X		X	U		X	U	S	U																								
U	X	X	X	X	X	X	X	X	X	U		X	U	U	X																									
U	X	X	X	X	X	X	X	S	U		X	S	U	X																										
X	X	U	X	X	X	X	X	X	S		U	U	U	X	X																									
U	X	U	X	X	X	X	X	U		X	U	S	X	X	X																									
S	X	X	U	X	X	X	X	X		X	S	S	X	X	X	U																								
X	X	U	X	X	X	X	X		X	X	X	X	S	S																										
X	U	X	U	X	X	X	X		X	U	X	X	X	S	S																									
X	X	X	X	X	X		X	X		X	X	S	S	U																										
X	X		X	X		X	X		S	X	S	X	S	X	S	U	U	U																						
X	X	X	X	X	X		S	S	X	X	X	X	U	U	U																									
X	X	X	X	X	X		X	X	X	X	U	U	U																											
X	S	X	X	X	X	X	X	X	X	S		U	U																											
X	X	X	U	X	S	X	X	X	X	S	X	U																												
S	X	X	X	X		X	S	X	X	X		U	X	X	U																									
X	X	X	X		X	S	X	U	X	X	S	U	X	X																										
X	X	U	X	X	S	X	X	S	X	X	S	X	X	X	S			U																						
X	X	S	X	X	X	X	X	S	X	X	U	X	X	X			S																							
U	X	X	U	X	S	X	X	X		S	X	X	X		S	X	X		U	X	U																			
X	U	X	X	X	U	X	S	X	X	X		X	S	X	S	X			U	U																				
X	U	X	X	X	X	U		X	X	X	S	X	S	X		U	X	U																						
X	X	X	S	X	X	X	X		X	X	S	X			U	U	X	X	S																					
X	X	X	X	X	X	S	S	X	X	X	S		U			X		X	U	U	U																			
X	X	U	X	X	X	X	S	S	X		X		X		X	X	S		U	X																				
X	X	X	X	X	S	X	X		X	X		X		X	X	S	U																							
U	S	X	X	X	X	X	X	S	X	X		X		X		U	U																							
X	X	X	U	X	X		X	X		S		X	U	X	S			U																						
X	X	X	U	X	X		X		X		X	U	S	X	S			U	U																					
X	X	X	S	X	X	X		X	X		U		X	U	X	S			U																					
3	29	36	23	29	34	38	34	37	22	28	32	4	0	2	0	0	0	19	0	21	0	0	0	1	0	0	8	4	13	1	0	7	11	12	9	0	0	0	2	3
0	2	0	1	3	2	0	5	2	0	4	3	7	0	5	1	3	3	0	1	5	3	0	3	4	0	0	0	5	0	2	9	2	0	4	0	0	4	3	0	
1	4	3	4	6	3	1	0	0	0	2	1	1	1	12	8	5	4	0	5	5	11	0	2	7	1	0	0	0	2	0	2	2	3	0	2	3	3	8	3	1
0	4	6	7	3	7	7	4	5	3	5	7	0	0	3	0	0	0	4	0	4	1	0	0	1	0	0	0	3	0	0	0	0	3	0	0	0	0	0	0	0
0	0	1	0	1	0	0	2	2	1	1	0	1	0	0	0	0	0	0	0	1	2	0	0	0	0	0	0	0	0	0	0	0	0	1	0	3	0	0	0	0
0	1	0	0	3	0	0	0	0	0	0	0	0	0	0	0	0	0	1	1	3	1	0	1	0	0	0	0	0	0	0	0	0	1	2	0	0	0	0	0	3
0	1	0	5	1	2	10	8	11	16	2	11	0	0	0	0	0	0	0	0	0	0	0	0	0	0	0	0	0	3	0	0	1	1	0	3	0	0	2	0	0
0	0	0	0	0	0	1	2	0	3	1	2	0	0	0	0	0	0	0	0	0	0	0	0	0	0	0	0	0	0	0	0	0	0	0	0	0	0	0	0	0

PLAYING SQUAD 2012/13

Existing Players		SN	HT	WT	DOB	AGE	POB	Career	Apps	Goals
GOALKEEPERS										
Sam	Mott				01/08/1988	24		Gravesend, Whitstable (L) 1/06, Croydon A (L) 11/07, Croydon A (L) 12/08, Ramsgate, Thamesmead 6/10, Welling 5/12		
Jamie	Turner							Welling, Horsham 8/98, Greenwich B, Welling (Trial) c/s 99, Welling (Cover) 11/99, Deal T, Gravesend, Tonbridge A 6/03, Welling 7/05, Ramsgate (L) 12/08 Perm 1/09, Maidstone U 5/09, Margate 3/10 Rel c/s 11, Welling 4/12	3	0
DEFENDERS										
Anthony	Acheampong		6'03"	12 05				Cardiff (Trainee) Rel c/s 08, Aldershot (Trial) 8/08, Horsham 10/08, Welling (Trial) c/s 10, Welling 9/10, Aveley (Dual) 9/10	32	1
Fraser	Franks	29	6'00"	10 11	22/11/1990	21	Hammersmith	Brentford Rel c/s 10, Basingstoke (L) 9/09, AFC Wimbledon 7/10 Rel c/s 12, Hayes & Yeading (L) 9/11, Newport C (L) 3/12, Welling 6/12		
Ben	Martin		6'07"	13 08	25/11/1982	29	Harpenden	Harpenden, Aylesbury 3/03, Swindon 8/03 Rel c/s 04, Lincoln C (L) 10/03, Farnborough (L) 1/04, St Albans 8/04, Staines (L) 11/06, Leighton (L) 1/07, Wealdstone (L) 1/07, Chelmsford 7/09, St Albans 8/10, Welling 3/11	36	2
Jack	Obersteller		6'02"	13 00	10/10/1988	23	Newham	Millwall, Crawley (L) 3/07, Wycombe 7/07 Rel 5/08, Grays (SL) 10/07, Exeter 5/08, Grays NC 8/09, Welling 11/09, Gillingham (Trial) 7/11	36	0
MIDFIELDERS										
Harry	Baker		5'10"	11 13	20/09/1990	21	Bexleyheath	L.Orient Rel c/s 10, Grays (L) 1/10, Dover 8/10, Welling 2/12	13	3
Jamie	Day		5'10"	11 04	13/09/1979	32	Bexley	Arsenal, Bournemouth £20,000 3/99 Rel c/s 01, Dover 7/01, Welling 5/04, Grays 5/07, Eastbourne (L) 9/07, Havant & W (SL) 3/08, Dartford 8/08, Welling (Pl/Man) 11/09	24	5
Theo	Fairweather-Johnson							Fisher, Thamesmead, Welling c/s 12		
Louis	Fazackerley				24/07/1984	28	Winchester	Fulham Rel c/s 04, Northampton (Trial) c/s 04, Farnborough (Trial) c/s 04, Sutton U 8/04, Eastbourne B 11/04, Leyton 7/06, Bishops Stortford 8/07, Bromley 5/08, Welling 10/08	31	1
Scott	Kinch							Carshalton, Tooting & M 8/03, Tonbridge A 5/06, Cray W 6/08, Concord R 12/09, Tonbridge A 1/10 Rel 1/12, Kingstonian (Dual) 10/11, Welling 1/12	13	1
FORWARDS										
Lee	Clarke		5'11"	10 08	28/07/1983	29	Peterborough	Yaxley, Peterborough Undisc 10/01, Kettering (SL) 3/03, Kettering (2ML) 8/03, St Albans (SL) 1/04, St Albans 7/04 Rel 4/09, Welling 5/09, Cambridge C (L) 9/09	39	8
Luis	Cumbers		6'00"	11 10	06/09/1988	23	Chelmsford	Gillingham Rel c/s 10, Maidstone (L) 9/07, Grays (L) 11/07, AFC Wimbledon (SL) 3/08, Ebbsfleet (L) 3/09, Ebbsfleet (L) 9/09, AFC Wimbledon (2ML) 11/09, Dover (L) 2/10, Welling 7/10	39	11
Ryan	Flack							Welling	4	2
Joe	Healy		6'00"	12 04	26/12/1986	25	Sidcup	Millwall, Crawley (L) 2/05, Walton & H (L) 2/06, Fisher 8/06, Yeading (SL) 3/07, Beckenham c/s 07, Welling 7/08 Rel 10/08, Beckenham 10/08, Margate 12/08 Rel 2/10, Welling 3/10	32	2
Kiernon	Hughes-Mason		5'08"	10 05	22/10/1991	20	Hackney	Millwall Rel c/s 11, Cheltenham (L) 3/10, Swindon (Trial) 7/10, Tooting & M (L) 8/10, Tooting & M (6WL) 11/10, Chelmsford (L) 2/11, Burton (Trial) 7/11, Grimsby (Trial) 8/11, Tooting & M 8/11, Kettering 9/11, Grimsby 1/12 Rel c/s 12, Welling 5/12		
Ross	Lafayette							Chesham, Aylesbury 3/09, Wealdstone, Burnham (Dual) 2/10, Hemel Hempstead c/s 10, Welling c/s 12		
Jon	Main		5'10"	12 01	07/03/1981	31	Greenwich	VCD Ath, Cray W, Tonbridge A 1/06, Wolves (Trial) 3/07, Norwich (Trial) 3/07, AFC Wimbledon Undisc 11/07 Rel 5/11, Dartford (3ML) 1/11, Dover (SL) 3/11, Tonbridge A 6/11 Rel c/s 12, Welling 5/12		

WESTON-SUPER-MARE

Chairman: Paul Bliss
Secretary: Richard Sloane   **(T)** 0771 107 8589   **(E)** wsmsecretary@hotmail.co.uk
Additional Committee Members:
Dennis Usher, Oliver Bliss, Phil Sheridan, Richard Sloan, Ryan Northmore.

Manager: Craig Laird
Programme Editor: Phil Sheridan   **(E)**

Back Row: Martin Slocombe; Dayle Grubb; Kane Ingram; Ashley Kington; Owen Irish; Jamie Price; Callum Laird; Robbie Maggs; Ross Stearn; Nabi Diallo
Middle Row: Jamie Laird; Brett Trowbridge; Chas Hemmings; Nat Pepperell; Lloyd Irish; Matt Villis; Chris Young; Marc McGregor; Pete Monks
Front Row: Dave Callow Physio; Ben Kirk (Captain); Jon Haile Assistant Manager; Richard Sloane Director; Craig Laird Manager; Any Callow Physio; Barrie Neale Kitman

Club Factfile

Founded: 1899   **Nickname:** Seagulls
Previous Names: Borough or Weston-super-Mare
Previous Leagues: Somerset Senior, Western League

Club Colours (change): All white (All sky blue and white)

Ground: Woodspring Stadium, Winterstoke Road, Weston-super-Mare BS24 9AA   **(T)** 01934 621 618
Capacity: 3,000   **Seats:** 278   **Covered:** 2,000   **Clubhouse:** Yes   **Shop:** Yes

Directions: Leave the M5 at Junction 21, take the dual carriageway A370 and continue straight until the 4th roundabout with ASDA on the right. Turn left into Winterstoke Road, bypassing a mini roundabout and continue for 1/2 mile. Woodspring Stadium is on the right.

Previous Grounds: Langford Road, Winterstoke Road

Record Attendance: 2,623 v Woking - FA Cup 1st Round replay 23/11/1993 (At Winterstoke Road)
Record Victory: 11-0 v Paulton Rovers
Record Defeat: 1-12 v Yeovil Town Reserves
Record Goalscorer: Matt Lazenby - 180
Record Appearances: Harry Thomas - 740
Additional Records: Received £20,000 from Sheffield Wednesday for Stuart Jones

Senior Honours:
Somerset Senior Cup 1923-24, 26-67.
Western League 1991-92.

10 YEAR RECORD

02-03		03-04		04-05		05-06		06-07		07-08		08-09		09-10		10-11		11-12	
SthW	2	SthP	10	Conf S	11	Conf S	14	Conf S	21	Conf S	20	Conf S	17	Conf S	21	Conf S	12	Conf S	13

WESTON-SUPER-MARE

No.	Date	Comp	H/A	Opponents	Att:	Result	Goalscorers	Pos
1	Sat-13-Aug	BSS	H	Dartford	480	L 0-4		21
2	Tue-16-Aug	BSS	A	Basingstoke Town	374	L 1-4	Huxley 67	21
3	Sat-20-Aug	BSS	A	Thurrock	156	W 3-0	Ingram 2 (21, 23), Mackay 76	16
4	Tue-23-Aug	BSS	H	Havant & Waterlooville	313	W 3-1	Pepperell 46, Price pen 53, Kabba 88	12
5	Sat-27-Aug	BSS	H	Salisbury City	390	W 2-0	Pepperell pen 59, Kabba 90	5
6	Mon-29-Aug	BSS	A	Eastleigh	426	L 1-2	Young 9	9
7	Sat-03-Sep	BSS	H	Boreham Wood	341	W 4-1	Young 18, Cleverley 71, Price 90, Grubb 90	8
8	Sat-10-Sep	BSS	A	Maidenhead United	375	W 3-1	Kirk 21, Ingram 2 (65, 90)	4
9	Sat-17-Sep	BSS	H	Chelmsford City	431	L 1-2	Pepperell 90	8
10	Tue-20-Sep	BSS	A	Dorchester Town	367	W 3-1	Hunt 19, Ingram 57, Price 60	5
11	Sat-24-Sep	BSS	A	Hampton & Richmond Boro'	391	L 1-3	Grubb 89	7
12	Sat-08-Oct	BSS	H	Sutton United	395	D 0-0		8
13	Sat-22-Oct	BSS	H	Eastbourne Borough	326	D 3-3	Kabba 2 (6, 12), Pepperell pen 61	8
14	Mon-24-Oct	BSS	A	Woking	1462	L 1-4	Pepperell pen 90	9
15	Sat-05-Nov	BSS	A	Dover Athletic	725	L 0-1		13
16	Sat-12-Nov	BSS	A	Dartford	1149	L 0-1	Pepperell 29	14
17	Tue-15-Nov	BSS	H	Staines Town	220	W 2-1	Grubb 75, Kabba 81	11
18	Sat-19-Nov	BSS	H	Maidenhead United	307	W 4-2	Pepperell 18, Grubb 2 (19, 90), McGregor 83	8
19	Sat-03-Dec	BSS	A	Havant & Waterlooville	586	D 1-1	Trowbridge 33	9
20	Sat-17-Dec	BSS	A	Eastbourne Borough	519	L 2-1	Young 28, Grubb 63	9
21	Mon-26-Dec	BSS	H	Truro City	620	L 0-1		9
22	Sun-01-Jan	BSS	A	Truro City	616	W 1-0	Og (Pugh) 88	7
23	Sat-07-Jan	BSS	H	Farnborough	422	W 5-2	Kabba 3 (24, 25, 33), Pepperell pen 32, Kirk 45	8
24	Tue-10-Jan	BSS	H	Basingstoke Town	304	W 2-1	Kabba 2, Ingram 59	6
25	Sat-14-Jan	BSS	A	Welling United	422	W 2-0	Kabba 14, Pepperell pen 35	6
26	Sat-21-Jan	BSS	A	Boreham Wood	201	L 0-3		6
27	Sat-28-Jan	BSS	H	Bromley	343	L 0-3		6
28	Sat-18-Feb	BSS	A	Tonbridge Angels	642	L 0-3		7
29	Mon-20-Feb	BSS	A	Chelmsford City	701	L 2-3	Kabba pen 39, Pepperell pen 90	7
30	Sat-25-Feb	BSS	A	Sutton United	656	L 2-3	Kabba 2 (19, 64)	8
31	Sat-03-Mar	BSS	H	Dorchester Town	303	L 0-4		10
32	Tue-06-Mar	BSS	A	Welling United	387	L 0-2		11
33	Sat-10-Mar	BSS	H	Thurrock	208	D 2-2	Kabba 4, Price 81	11
34	Sat-17-Mar	BSS	A	Farnborough	460	W 1-0	Trowbridge 69	9
35	Tue-20-Mar	BSS	H	Woking	361	L 0-3		9
36	Sat-24-Mar	BSS	H	Hampton & Richmond Boro'	249	L 1-2	Kabba 5	11
37	Sat-31-Mar	BSS	A	Bromley	676	L 0-1		12
38	Sat-07-Apr	BSS	A	Salisbury City	605	D 0-0		12
39	Mon-09-Apr	BSS	H	Eastleigh	201	D 0-0		12
40	Sat-14-Apr	BSS	H	Tonbridge Angels	327	D 2-2	Duharty 33, Ingram 75	12
41	Sat-21-Apr	BSS	A	Staines Town	283	L 1-2	Ingram 50	13
42	Sat-28-Apr	BSS	H	Dover Athletic	325	D 1-1	Price 65	13

CUPS

No.	Date	Comp	H/A	Opponents	Att:	Result	Goalscorers	
1	Sat-01-Oct	FAC 2Q	A	Dorchester Town	329	W 1-0	Villis 80	
2	Sat-15-Oct	FAC 3Q	H	Havant & Waterlooville	333	W 3-2	Price 19, Pepperell pen 29, Mackay 53	
3	Sat-29-Oct	FAC 4Q	H	Oxford City	630	L 2-3	Pepperell pen 55, Ingram 90	
4	Sat-26-Nov	FAT 3Q	A	Salisbury City	552	L 0-2		

League
Starts
Substitute
Unused Sub

Cups
Starts
Substitute
Unused Sub

Goals (Lg)
Goals (Cup)

Appearance grid (X = started, S = substitute, U = unused substitute):

IRISH	PRICE	SLOCOMBE	TROWBRIDGE	MARTIN	J LAIRD	INGRAM	KIRK	YOUNG	DIALLO	PEPPERELL	GRUBB	KABBA	MACKAY	BOOTH	HUXLEY	VILLIS	HUNT	CLEVERLEY	SEERY	CURETON	MCGREGOR	PREECE	JACKSON	DUHARTY	C LAIRD	CAMM	MAWFORD
X	X	X	X	X	X	X	X	X	X	X	S	S	S	U	U	U											
X	X	X		X	U	X	X	U	X	X		S			U	X	X	X	U								
X	X	X		U	X	X	X	X	S	X	X		S	X		U	X	U									
X	X	X		X	U	X	X	X	S	X	X	S		X		X	X	U									
X	X	X		X	S	X	X	X	U	X	X	S	S			U	X	X									
X	X	X		X	U	X	X	X	U	X	X	S	X			U	X										
X	X	X		U	X	X	X	X	S	X	X	S			X	X	U	U									
X	X	X		X	X	X	U	X	X	X	X	S	X	U	U	U		S									
X	X	X		U	X	U	X	X	X	X	X	S	U		U	X	X										
X	X		X	X	X	X	X	X	X	X	S	U		S	X	X	S										
X	X		X	X	X	X	X	X	X	X	S		U	X		S		X									
X	X		X	X	X	X	U	U	X	X	S	S	U		X	X		X									
X	X	X	U	X	X	X			U	X	X	X			S	X			S								
X	X	X	S	U	X	X	X	X	X	S	X	X	S			U				X	X	U					
X		X	S	X	X	X	X	X	S	X	X	S			U				X	X	U	U	S				
X		X	X		X	X	X	X	U	X	X	S				X			X	X		U	U				
X		X	X	U		X	X	X	X	X	S					X			S	X		U					
X	S	X	X	U	X	S	X	X	X	X	S					X			X	X			U				
X	X	X	X	U	X	X	X	S		X	U	X				X			X	X		S		U				
X	X	X	X	U	X	X	X	S	S	X		X				X			X	X		U		U			
X	X	X	X	U	X	X	X	S	U	X		X				X			X	X		S		U			
X	X	X	X	U	X	X	X	S	U	X		X				X			X	X		S		S			
X	X	X	X	U	X	X	X	S	X			U	X			X			X	X		S		S			
X	X	X	X		X	X	X	X	S	S			X			X			X	U		S		X	U		
X	X	X	X		X		X	X	X	X						X			X	X		U				S	U
X	X	X	X		X		X	X	X	S	S					X			X	X		S		U			
X	X		X		S	X	X	X	X	S	X					X			X	U		S		U			
X	X	X	X			X	X	X	X	S	X					X			X	X				U	S		
X	X	X	X			X	X	U		X	X	X				X			X	U			S			S	
X	X	X	X			X	X	X	U	U	X	X	X			X			X	U		U		S			
X	X	X	X			X	X	X	U	S	X	X	U			X			X	U		U		X			
X	X		S			X	X	X	U	X	X	X	X			X			X	X		U		S	S	U	
X	X		S			X	X	X	S	X	X	X	X			X			X	X		U		S	U		
X	X	X	X			X	X	X	X	U	S	X	X			X			X	U				U			
X	X	X	U			X	U	X	U	X	X	X	S			X			X	X				X	U		
X	X	X	X			X	S	X	U	X	X	X	S			X			X	U		U		X			
X		X	S			X	X	X	X	X	X	X	S			X			X	X		S		U			
X	X	X				X	X		X	X	X	X	U			X			X			X		U	U	S	

X	X		U	X	X		X	X	X	X	X	S	U	U	X	X	U	S									
X	X	U	U	X	X	X	X	S	X	X	X	S	X		U	X		U									
X	X	U	S	X	X	X	X	X	X	U	X	X	X	U		U	X		U								
X			U	X	X	X	X	X	U	X	X	S				X		X		U	S	X					

42	34	37	23	12	37	32	35	25	21	40	29	16	3	1	4	38	4	22	1	0	1	1	0	4	0	0	0
0	1	0	6	0	1	4	0	8	10	1	7	22	3	0	2	0	1	4	0	0	12	0	0	6	0	2	2
0	0	0	1	13	3	1	4	8	8	0	2	2	7	3	11	0	4	8	1	2	7	1	1	8	2	4	1

4	3	0	0	4	4	3	4	3	2	4	4	1	1	0	1	4	0	1	0	0	0	1	0	0	0	0	0
0	0	0	1	0	0	0	0	1	0	0	0	3	0	0	0	0	0	1	0	0	1	0	0	0	0	0	0
0	0	2	3	0	0	0	0	0	2	0	0	0	2	1	2	0	1	2	0	1	0	0	0	0	0	0	0

| 0 | 5 | 0 | 2 | 0 | 0 | 8 | 2 | 3 | 0 | 10 | 6 | 15 | 1 | 0 | 1 | 0 | 1 | 1 | 0 | 0 | 1 | 0 | 0 | 1 | 0 | 0 | 0 |
| 0 | 1 | 0 | 0 | 0 | 0 | 1 | 0 | 0 | 0 | 2 | 0 | 0 | 1 | 0 | 0 | 1 | 0 | 0 | 0 | 0 | 0 | 0 | 0 | 0 | 0 | 0 | 0 |

PLAYING SQUAD 2012/13

Existing Players		SN	HT	WT	DOB	AGE	POB	Career	Apps	Goals
GOALKEEPERS										
Lloyd	Irish				07/09/1988	23		Yeovil Rel 10/09, Chard T (Dual) c/s 07, Taunton (Dual) c/s 08, Bridgwater, Weston-Super-Mare 7/10	42	0
DEFENDERS										
Jory	Cureton				03/05/1993	19		Weston-Super-Mare, Wellington (L) 1/11	0	0
Craig	Laird							Plymouth (Yth), Bridgwater, Weston-Super-Mare, Exeter (Trial)0		0
Jamie	Laird				18/06/1989	22		Plymouth (Yth) Rel c/s 07, Ange IF (Swe), Bridgwater 10/07, Teramo Calcio (Ita) (Trial) 11/07, Bath C NC 4/08 Rel c/s 08, Bridgwater 11/08, Weston-Super-Mare 7/10	38	0
Jak	Martin							Exeter, Taunton, Willand R, Tiverton, Bridgwater 11/07, Weston-Super-Mare, Tiverton (6ML) 8/10	12	0
Jamie	Price				13/05/1987	25		Yeovil (Trainee), Taunton c/s 05, Bridgwater c/s 06, Taunton 7/08, Bridgwater 12/08, Weston-Super-Mare 8/10	35	5
Martin	Slocombe				08/11/1988	23	Weston-Super-Mare	Bristol C Rel c/s 08, Bath C 8/08, Weymouth 7/09, Chippenham 3/10, Bath C (Dual) 3/10, Weston-Super-Mare 8/10	37	0
Matt	Villis		6'03"	12 07	13/04/1984	28	Bridgwater	Bridgwater, Plymouth 9/02 Rel c/s 05, Torquay (SL) 7/04, Torquay 7/05 Rel c/s 07, Bridgwater (Trial) 7/07, Tiverton 7/07, Bridgwater 10/09, Weston-Super-Mare 7/10	38	0
MIDFIELDERS										
George	Booth		5'08"		18/02/1992	20		Bristol R Rel c/s 11, Longwell Green Sports (L) 1/11, Weston-Super-Mare (L) 3/11, Weston-Super-Mare 8/11	1	0
Jack	Camm							Bristol R (Scholar) Rel c/s 11, Weston-Super-Mare 8/11	2	0
Ben	Cleverley				12/09/1981	30		Bristol C Rel c/s 03, Forest Green (L) 12/02, Cheltenham 8/03 5/04, Forest Green 7/04 Rel 4/05, Bath C (L) 12/04, Paulton R 7/05, Tiverton 6/09, Weston-Super-Mare 10/09, Paulton R 6/10, Weston-Super-Mare 9/11	26	1
Dayle	Grubb				24/07/1991	21		Weston-Super-Mare	36	6
Kane	Ingram				15/09/1987	24		Bristol C (Yth), Bath C, Taunton 9/06, Almondsbury T, Paulton 10/09, Cinderford 1/10, Weston-Super-Mare 7/10	36	8
Ashley	Kington				26/11/1990	21		Bristol C Rel c/s 10, Oxford C, Mangotsfield 3/11, Clevedon 8/11, Weston-Super-Mare 6/12		
Ben	Kirk				30/09/1984	27		Bridgwater, Chippenham 8/04, Weston-Super-Mare 6/06, Bridgwater Undisc 8/06, Weston-Super-Mare 7/10	35	2
Jake	Mawford				07/06/1993	19		Weston-Super-Mare, Wellington (L) 1/11, Street (L) 1/11, Mangotsfield (L) 11/11, Bridgwater (SL) 3/12	2	0
Ross	Stearn				17/09/1990	21		Bristol C (Scholar) Rel c/s 09, Cheltenham (Trial) 3/09, Yeovil (Trial) 7/09, Forest Green NC 8/09 (09/10 7,1) Rel 9/09, Weston-Super-Mare 9/09, Almondsbury T 10/09, Chippenham, Weston-Super-Mare 6/12		
Brett	Trowbridge				19/07/1986	26		Bridgwater, Weston-Super-Mare 8/10	29	2
FORWARDS										
Nabi	Diallo				27/12/1990	21		Bristol R (Yth), Minehead, Gloucester 11/09, Weston-Super-Mare, Bridgwater (Dual) 8/10	31	0
Chas	Hemmings							Bristol R (Trainee), Clevedon T, Weston-Super-Mare 6/12		
Matt	Huxley							Oldland Abbotonians, Weston-Super-Mare 6/11, Cadbury Heath 12/11	6	1
Michael	Mackay						Taunton	Bristol C, Australia, Bridgwater, Weston-Super-Mare 8/11	6	1
Marc	McGregor		5'09"	11 10	30/04/1978	34	Southend	Oxford U Rel c/s 97, Endsleigh c/s 97, Forest Green 8/98, Cirencester (L) 10/98, Nuneaton £35,000 6/00, Weston Super-Mare (L) 8/02, Macclesfield (Trial) 1/03, Tamworth 8/03, Chippenham (L) 9/03, Weston-Super-Mare (L) 10/03, Weston-Super-Mare (L) 12/03, Weston-Super-Mare 3/04, Hinckley U 5/05, Weston-Super-Mare 5/06, Worcester 10/09 (Pl/Coach) 8/11, Bishops Cleeve (L) 10/11, Weston-Super-Mare 11/11	13	1
Nat	Pepperell				08/02/1988	24		Bridgwater, Swansea, Bath C 8/04, Tiverton 10/06, Taunton (L) 3/07, Bridgwater, Weston-Super-Mare 8/10	41	10
Chris	Young							Bridgwater T, Lunn University (USA), Bridgwater T 12/06, Tiverton 6/07, Bridgwater T (L) 2/08, Bridgwater T 7/08, Weston-Super-Mare 6/11	33	3
Dan	Jackson							Weston-Super-Mare	0	0

DIVISION ONE SOUTH

		P	W	D	L	F	A	GD	Pts
1	(C) Grantham Town (-1)	42	29	7	6	92	44	48	93
2	Carlton Town	42	26	5	11	101	52	49	83
3	(R) Ilkeston FC	42	26	5	11	93	44	49	83
4	Sheffield FC	42	22	9	11	93	62	31	75
5	Leek Town	42	22	8	12	77	60	17	74
6	Belper Town	42	23	5	14	74	57	17	74
7	Stamford	42	20	8	14	77	75	2	68
8	Loughborough Dynamo	42	18	11	13	80	61	19	65
9	New Mills	42	17	12	13	79	76	3	63
10	Goole AFC	42	18	8	16	72	78	-6	62
11	Hucknall Town	42	16	9	17	54	61	-7	57
12	Sutton Coldfield Town	42	16	7	19	72	63	9	55
13	Kidsgrove Athletic	42	13	16	13	62	59	3	55
14	Coalville Town	42	15	10	17	69	72	-3	55
15	Newcastle Town	42	14	10	18	59	70	-11	52
16	Market Drayton Town	42	11	14	17	61	84	-23	47
17	Brigg Town	42	11	12	19	52	76	-24	45
18	Lincoln United	42	10	13	19	65	85	-20	43
19	Rainworth Miners Welfare	42	10	11	21	38	55	-17	41
20	Romulus	42	7	15	20	56	85	-29	36
21	(R) Quorn	42	6	9	27	48	85	-37	27
22	(R) Shepshed Dynamo	42	5	10	27	45	115	-70	25

PLAY-OFFS
Semi-Finals
Carlton Town 2-2 Leek Town (Leek Town won 7-6 on penalties)
Ilkeston 7-0 Sheffield

Final (@ Ilkeston, 28/4/12)
Ilkeston 2-0 Leek Town

		1	2	3	4	5	6	7	8	9	10	11	12	13	14	15	16	17	18	19	20	21	22
1	Belper Town		2-2	0-2	0-2	2-0	0-3	1-5	3-1	3-1	2-1	1-0	3-1	3-2	1-1	3-1	2-1	1-0	2-1	1-3	3-1	2-3	1-2
2	Brigg Town	1-2		3-2	0-0	1-2	2-3	1-2	1-1	0-4	0-3	2-1	0-3	3-0	1-4	1-1	5-2	0-4	1-0	0-2	3-2	2-2	2-1
3	Carlton Town	3-2	2-0		4-2	3-0	2-1	3-1	2-0	2-2	7-1	1-2	2-1	5-2	1-1	2-3	2-1	0-0	4-0	3-1	1-0	4-2	0-2
4	Coalville Town	1-3	1-1	1-3		3-1	1-2	2-0	0-0	1-1	2-4	1-2	0-2	2-2	0-0	1-0	2-0	1-5	4-2	1-3	2-0	0-2	2-0
5	Goole	0-3	1-3	2-2	4-2		3-4	3-1	3-0	1-2	1-1	2-4	3-1	0-0	0-4	4-2	2-0	2-1	5-4	1-1	3-1	1-1	0-1
6	Grantham Town	2-0	1-1	4-2	0-0	3-0		1-1	2-1	3-0	1-3	3-3	1-0	4-2	2-0	2-3	1-0	0-1	4-0	2-0	2-0	1-0	2-1
7	Hucknall Town	0-3	0-1	3-2	2-2	0-2	1-2		0-2	1-0	0-0	3-0	0-3	2-2	1-0	0-1	1-0	2-0	2-3	2-2	0-2	3-1	
8	Ilkeston	0-1	2-0	2-0	0-0	4-0	1-3	3-1		1-2	3-4	3-1	2-2	1-0	3-1	3-0	2-0	2-0	4-1	4-1	5-0	1-2	2-1
9	Kidsgrove Athletic	2-0	1-0	0-0	2-2	1-2	1-2	1-1	0-0		2-2	3-3	1-0	0-0	0-2	1-1	2-0	1-1	2-2	2-1	1-2	3-2	2-1
10	Leek Town	0-3	3-0	1-0	2-1	2-2	1-3	0-2	0-1	0-1		1-0	3-1	1-2	4-0	1-0	4-2	1-0	3-0	2-3	5-0	2-0	0-5
11	Lincoln United	1-1	1-1	1-4	3-2	3-4	1-1	0-1	2-5	1-1	1-2		1-1	1-4	1-2	0-2	0-0	0-0	1-1	2-2	2-3	4-5	3-1
12	Loughborough Dynamo	2-2	2-1	2-4	1-3	2-1	3-1	3-0	2-4	2-1	1-1	3-3		1-1	3-3	1-2	1-0	1-0	1-1	3-4	6-2	2-0	2-1
13	Market Drayton Town	3-0	1-1	1-0	0-2	1-3	1-5	3-0	0-6	2-1	1-1	2-3	1-7		1-4	0-2	1-1	1-1	2-1	2-4	4-1	2-2	0-3
14	New Mills	1-4	3-1	2-3	4-2	3-0	0-4	2-2	0-3	0-6	0-2	3-0	1-1	2-2		4-2	5-3	3-2	2-5	2-1	4-2	2-1	3-1
15	Newcastle Town	2-0	2-1	0-2	1-5	4-4	0-0	2-4	0-2	2-2	2-3	3-0	1-5	2-1	1-1		1-0	1-1	1-1	2-1	0-1	1-2	0-1
16	Quorn	1-2	1-3	0-8	2-1	1-2	0-5	0-0	3-2	3-3	0-1	1-3	1-3	0-0	2-2	2-3		3-2	1-1	1-2	5-0	1-2	1-0
17	Rainworth Miners Welfare	0-2	0-0	2-1	0-2	1-3	1-2	0-4	1-4	1-1	2-1	1-0	0-1	1-1	0-2	0-1	1-0		0-0	0-2	2-1	3-0	0-2
18	Romulus	2-1	1-1	1-3	4-1	0-2	2-3	0-1	0-4	4-1	2-2	1-3	2-0	1-2	2-1	1-0	3-3	1-1		1-1	2-2	0-0	1-1
19	Sheffield	0-2	1-0	2-1	2-3	4-0	2-0	1-0	1-3	3-0	4-2	2-3	0-0	4-2	2-2	1-1	0-0	2-0	4-1		7-1	6-0	3-2
20	Shepshed Dynamo	0-6	2-3	0-6	2-5	0-2	1-2	1-2	0-0	1-1	0-3	0-1	2-2	2-2	1-0	1-1	2-2	1-0	1-1	2-2	1-1		1-4
21	Stamford	1-1	2-2	0-1	4-2	1-0	1-3	1-1	2-4	3-2	1-4	4-0	2-1	0-1	1-1	3-2	3-2	2-1	4-1	4-3	3-0		3-2
22	Sutton Coldfield Town	2-0	6-1	1-2	2-0	1-1	2-2	5-1	2-1	0-2	1-2	2-2	2-2	1-4	1-0	0-2	0-3	0-1	3-1	3-3	4-1	3-0	

LEAGUE CHALLENGE CUP

PRELIMINARY ROUND

Ossett Town 0–2 Brigg Town

Rainworth Miners Welfare 1–2 Stamford

Romulus 3–5 (AET) Kidsgrove Athletic

Warrington Town 4–2 (AET) Cammell Laird

ROUND 1

AFC Fylde 0–3 Bamber Bridge

Carlton Town 2–4 (AET) Belper Town

Coalville Town 2–1 Ilkeston

Farsley 1–0 Durham City

Goole 5–0 Lincoln United

Harrogate Railway Athletic 1–5 Garforth

Kidsgrove Athletic 5–2 Market Drayton Town

Lancaster City 4–2 Skelmersdale United

Loughborough Dynamo 3–2 Hucknall Town

Mossley 2–0 Curzon Ashton

(Curzon Ashton reinstated after Mossley played an

ineligible player)

New Mills 3–4 Salford City

Ossett Albion 1–2 Brigg Town

Prescot Cables 1–2 Warrington Town

Quorn 2–0 (AET) Grantham Town

Radcliffe Borough 1–3 Woodley Sports

Sheffield 4–2 Wakefield

Shepshed Dynamo 0–3 Stamford

Sutton Coldfield Town 0–3 Newcastle Town

Trafford 1–1 2-4p Clitheroe

Witton Albion 4–0 Leek Town

ROUND 2

Brigg Town 3–0 Farsley

Curzon Ashton 0–3 Woodley Sports

Goole 1–2 Garforth

Lancaster City 2–1 Clitheroe

Newcastle Town 2–0 (AET) Warrington Town

Quorn 1–2 Loughborough Dynamo

Salford City 2–1 Bamber Bridge

Sheffield 1–2 Belper Town

Stamford 5–3 (AET) Coalville Town

Witton Albion 2–0 Kidsgrove Athletic

ROUND 3

Ashton United 1–4 Lancaster City

Belper Town 1–3 (AET) Worksop Town

Brigg Town 0–1 Buxton

Burscough 0–2 F.C. United of Manchester

Woodley Sports 0–2 Kendal Town

Frickley Athletic 4–2 Garforth Town

Hednesford Town 3–1 Chester

Loughborough Dynamo 3–1 (AET) Stamford

Matlock Town 4–1 Mickleover Sports

Newcastle Town 2–2 4-3p Nantwich Town

North Ferriby United 1–0 Whitby Town

Northwich Victoria 4–0 Marine

Rushall Olympic 1–0 Chasetown

Salford City 1–2 Chorley

Stocksbridge Park Steels 1–1, 3-4p Bradford Park Ave.

Witton Albion 3–1 Stafford Rangers

ROUND 4

Bradford Park Avenue 4–0 Loughborough Dynamo

Chorley 2–3 F.C. United of Manchester

Lancaster City 3–3 4-5p Kendal Town

Matlock Town 0–1 Frickley Athletic

Newcastle Town 2–3 Northwich Victoria

North Ferriby United 4–2 Worksop Town

Rushall Olympic 2–1 Hednesford Town

Witton Albion 4–1 Buxton

QUARTER FINALS

Frickley Athletic 3-1 F.C. United of Manchester

Kendal Town 2-1 Witton Albion

North Ferriby United 2-1 Bradford Park Avenue

Northwich Victoria 4-5 Rushall Olympic

SEMI-FINALS

Rushall Olympic 2-1 (AET) Frickley Athletic

North Ferriby United 3-0 Kendal Town

FINAL

North Ferriby United 4-1 (AET) Rushall Olympic

Northern Premier Premier Division Statistics 2011-12

	Games Played & Goals Scored & Conceded	Top Goalscorers League, FAC & FAT	Number of Scorers per Club	Hat Tricks Scored	Penalties Scored	Best Individual Consecutive Scoring Run	Number of Clean Sheets	Number of Games in which club failed to score	Scorers with 10+
Ashton United	46-67/74	Burns 16-0-0=16	16+2ogs	0	8	Burns & Wright 3	8	12	Burns 16 and Amadi 11
Bradford PA	51-100/63	Marshall 13-2-1=16	19+2ogs	Boshell,Greaves & Savoury 3	3	Savory 3	19 (4)	6	Marshall 18 (1p) Greaves 13 & O'Brien 11(1p)
Burscough	45-58/112	Beesley 13-1-0=14	17+2ogs	Cummins 1	4	Beesley 3	3	12	Beesley 14 and Jones 11
Buxton	46-70/84	Reed 18-0-1=19	16	Reed 1	3	Barraclough 5	8	11	Reed 18 (2p),Lugsden15 & Barrowclough11
Chasetown	46-64/83	Perrow 8-2-4=14	20+1og	Perrow 1	7	3 x 2	6	14(4)	Perrow 14 (3 pens)
Chester	47-114/34	McGinn 14-0-1=15	20	Simm 1	10	McGinn & Simm 3	22(7&6)	1	McGinn 15 (10p), Simm 14, McNeil 12 Howard 11 & Powell 10
Chorley	46-77/53	Foster 20-0-0=20	18+2ogs	Foster & Walwyn 2	7	Foster 3	13	13	Foster 20 (5 pens)
F.C.United	52-100/60	Norton 18-1-3=22	17+7ogs	Wolfenden 1	5	Norton 4	14	9	Norton 22 Wolfenden 18 and Roca 10 (4pens)
Frickley Athletic	47-53/78	Ashmore 11-1-0=12	16+2ogs	0	7	None	6	16	Ashmore 12 (4 pens)
Hednesford T	49-74/60	Clements 13-3-0=16	20+1og	Robinson 1	6	Clements 6	16	12	Clements 16 (5pens)
Kendal Town	48-88/94	Jackson 13-1-1=15	22+4ogs	McEvatt & Williams 2	4	Jackson & Leadbetter 3	6	10	Jackson 15, Leadbetter 14 (4p) & McEvatt 10
Marine	46-64/57	Harvey 16-0-1=17	14+5ogs	0	3	Harvey 3	16	10	Harvey 17 (1pen) and Rey 12
Matlock Town	48-60/59	Holmes 14-1-1=16	15+1og	Joynes 1	2	4 x 2	12(4)	12	Holmes 16 (1pen)
Mickleover Sp	45-72/92	Ashton 15-3-0=18	17+1og	Ashton 1	2	Steadman 3	5	8	Ashton 18 and Steadman 14 (1pen)
Nantwich Town	48-72/72	Lennon 13-0-0=13	20	McPherson 1	5	Lennon & Mills 3	12	12	Lennon 13, Cooke 11 (1p) and Mills 11
N.Ferriby Utd	49-69/82	Bradshaw 17-1-1=19	13+1og	Bradshaw & Davidson 2	3	Bolder 4	13	14(5)	Bradshaw 19 Brooksby 11
Northwich Vic	56-96/53	Riley 11-0-3=14	19+1og	0	8	Budrys, Clarke 3	20	4	Riley 14, Clarke 11 and Wade 10
Rushall Olympic	47-58/58	Obeng 10-2-0=12	20+2og	Bannister 1	9	6 x 2	16	15	Obeng 12
Stafford R	46-71/76	Thompson 8-1-2=11	18+3ogs	Street 1	3	Kinsella 3	5	10	Thompson 11 Kinsella 10 (1pen)
Stocksbridge PS	48-69/87	Muldoon 12-2-2=16	18	0	5	Muldoon 4	7	13	Muldoon 16 Cusworth 11
Whitby Town	46-64/87	Clarke 11-0-0=11	18+2ogs	0	4	Beadle 5	6	12	Clarke 11
Worksop Town	50-69/84	Jackson 13-0-1=14	18	18	6	Burbeary & Hudson (2) 3	11	15	Jackson 13 and Hudson 13 (6pens)

A click away from memory lane!

Over 35 years of publishing the Non-League Club Directory has filled a room full of information and photographs covering the game we know and love.

What we intend, over time, is to create a website that shares with you everything we have accumulated, which we hope will bring back some fond memories of season's gone by.

Log on to **www.non-leagueclubdirectory.co.uk** today and see how many faces from teams gone by you recognise

A.F.C. FYLDE

Chairman: David Haythornthwaite
Secretary: Martin Benson   **(T)** 07545 735 154   **(E)** info@afcfylde.co.uk
Additional Committee Members:
Dai Davis and Stuart King.

Manager: Dave Challinor
Programme Editor: Chris Park   **(E)** info@afcfylde.co.uk

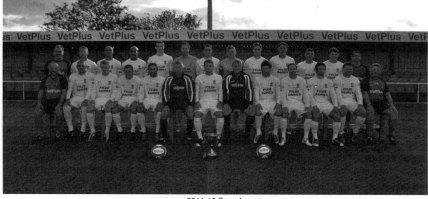

2011-12 Squad.
Back Row (L-R): Baldwin (Kit man), Stopforth, Allen, Thorpe, Betts, Whiteside, Steel, MacDonald, Doughty, Stringfellow, Waddington, Wilson, Fraser (Physio).
Front Row: Clarkson (Reserve Team Coach), Penswick, Barnes, Heywood, Kay, Steel, Fuller (Assistant Manager), Mercer (Capt), O'Hanlon, Mercer, Booth, Swarbrick, Jarvis, McNiven (1st Team Coach), Mitchell (Goalkeeping Coach).

Club Factfile

Founded: 1988   **Nickname:**
Previous Names: Wesham FC and Kirkham Town amalgamated in 1988 to form Kirkham & Wesham > 2008
Previous Leagues: West Lancashire, North West Counties 2007-09

Club Colours (change): All white (Blue and red stripes/blue/blue)

Ground: Kellamergh Park, Bryning Lane, Warton, Preston PR4 1TN   **(T)** 01772 682 593
Capacity: 1,426   **Seats:** 282   **Covered:** 282   **Clubhouse:** Yes   **Shop:** Yes

Directions: AFC Fylde is based in an area called 'The Fylde Coast' located between Blackpool and Preston. Kellamergh Park is located in WARTON. EXIT via Junction 3 M55 (signposted A585 Fleetwood/Kirkham). Up approach and turn left towards signs for Kirkham. In around 3/4 mile you will approach a new roundabout. Then follow the signs for Wrea Green and Lytham St. Annes (2nd exit) B5259. After another 500 yards you will drop down almost immediately to a small mini roundabout (go straight on) and 1/4 mile you will go over main Preston/Blackpool railway bridge and drop down almost immediately to a small mini roundabout (pub on left called Kingfisher). Carry on straight over this and up to main roundabout (another 200 yards) at junction of main Preston/Blackpool A583. Go straight over roundabout and drive on into Wrea Green Village. At 2nd mini roundabout in the centre of the village (Church on right and Primary School) take left turn into Bryning Lane, signposted on The Green (small white signpost) to Warton (2 miles). The Green will now be on your right as you exit out of the village and in around 1.8 miles you will come to the Birley Arms Pub on your left. Turn left at The Birley Arms Pub Car park and continue to drive through the car park down an access road and park in the Main Club Car Park.

Previous Grounds: Coronation Road > 2006

Record Attendance: 1,217 v New Mills - North West Counties 09/05/2009
Record Victory: Not known
Record Defeat: Not known
Record Goalscorer: Not known
Record Appearances: Not known
Additional Records:

Senior Honours:
West Lancashire League 1999-2000, 00-01, 01-02, 03-04, 04-05, 05-06, 06-07.
FA Vase 2007-08.
North West Counties League 2008-09. Northern Premier Division 1 North 2011-12.

10 YEAR RECORD

02-03		03-04		04-05		05-06		06-07		07-08		08-09		09-10		10-11		11-12	
WYkP	2	WYkP	1	WYkP	1	WYkP	1	WYkP	1	NWC2	2	NWCP	1	NP1N	13	NP1N	5	NP1N	1

ASHTON UNITED

Chairman: David Aspinall
Secretary: Andy Finnigan   **(T)** 07866 360200   **(E)** aufc2006@tiscali.co.uk
Additional Committee Members:
Jackie Tierney, John Milne, Denise Pinder, Steve Hobson, Eric Stafford, James Pinder, Andrew Evans, Michael Cummins, Michael Bennett, Tony Robinson, Jan Sutherland.
Manager: Danny Johnson
Programme Editor: Martin Crabtree   **(E)** aufc2006@tiscali.co.uk

Club Factfile

Founded: 1878   **Nickname:** Robins
Previous Names: Hurst 1878-1947
Previous Leagues: Manchester, Lancashire Combination 1912-33, 48-64, 66-68, Midland 1964-66, Cheshire County 1923-48, 68-82, North West Counties 1982-92

Club Colours (change): Red and white halves/black/red (Navy and sky stripes/navy/sky)

Ground: Hurst Cross, Surrey Street, Ashton-u-Lyne OL6 8DY   **(T)** 0161 339 4158 (Club) 330 1511 (Social)
Capacity: 4,500   **Seats:** 250   **Covered:** 750   **Clubhouse:** Yes   **Shop:** Yes

Directions: From the M62 (approx 7.5 miles) Exit at Junction 20, take A627M to Oldham exit (2.5 miles) Take A627 towards Oldham town centre At King Street Roundabout take Park Road Continue straight onto B6194 Abbey Hills Road Follow B6194 onto Lees Road Turn right at the stone cross memorial and 1st right into the ground. From the M60 (approx 2.5 miles); Exit at Junction 23, take A635 for Ashton town centre Follow by-pass to B6194 Mossley Road. At traffic lights turn left into Queens Road Continue onto B6194 Lees Road Turn left at the stone cross memorial and 1st right into the ground.

Previous Grounds: Rose Hill 1878-1912

Record Attendance: 11,000 v Halifax Town - FA Cup 1st Round 1952
Record Victory: 11-3 v Stalybridge Celtic - Manchester Intermediate Cup 1955
Record Defeat: 1-11 v Wellington Town - Cheshire League 1946-47
Record Goalscorer: Not known
Record Appearances: Micky Boyle - 462
Additional Records: Paid £9,000 to Netherfield for Andy Whittaker 1994
Received £15,000 from Rotherham United for Karl Marginson 1993
Senior Honours:
Manchester Challenge Shield 1992-93. Northern Premier League Division 1 Cup 1994-95, League Cup 2010-11.
Manchester Senior Cup x4. Manchester Premier Cup x5, Manchester Junior Cup x3.

10 YEAR RECORD

02-03	03-04	04-05	05-06	06-07	07-08	08-09	09-10	10-11	11-12
NP P 16	NP P 14	Conf N 21	NP P 15	NP P 18	NP P 10	NP P 9	NP P 12	NP P 14	NP P 12

ASHTON UNITED

No.	Date	Comp	H/A	Opponents	Att:	Result	Goalscorers	Pos
1	Aug 13	NPL P	H	Matlock Town	178	W 3 - 0	Burns 5 (pen) Amadi 80 Bennett 90	
2	16		A	Stocksbridge Park Steels	161	D 1 - 1	Burns 43 (pen)	
3	20		A	Rushall Olympic	130	L 0 - 1		10
4	24		H	Burscough	124	W 3 - 2	Amadi 52 67 Bennett 68	
5	27		H	Worksop Town	147	W 4 - 2	Bennett 8 Amadi 37 64 Burns 72	5
6	29		A	Northwich Victoria	402	L 1 - 3	Lambert 57	
7	Sept 3		A	Frickley Athletic	266	W 1 - 0	Madeley 79	9
8	7		H	Chester	528	L 0 - 2		
9	10		H	Hednesford Town	145	L 1 - 2	Wright 30	10
10	14		A	Whitby Town	202	D 2 - 2	Bathurst 75 Wright 90	
11	17	FAC 1Q	H	Runcorn Town	100	W 5 - 1	Wright 29 30 (pen) Bennett 56 Bathurst 58 Amadi 75	
12	24		A	Marine	328	L 0 - 1		12
13	28		H	Buxton	154	W 4 - 2	Dawson 46 Burns 73 Wright 81 Kosylo 85	
14	Oct 1	FAC 2Q	H	Spennymoor Town	234	L 0 - 3		
15	8		H	Stafford Rangers	153	L 1 - 5	Kosylo 90	12
16	11		A	North Ferriby United	165	L 3 - 6	Bathurst 28 43 Madeley 79	
17	15		A	Chorley	779	D 2 - 2	Wright 34 Kosylo 90	13
18	22	FAT 1Q	A	Chester	1264	L 1 - 2	Wright 72 (pen)	
19	Nov 5		H	Nantwich Town	147	D 1 - 1	Burns 35 (pen)	15
20	12		A	Chasetown	247	L 0 - 1		15
21	19		H	Bradford PA	182	L 0 - 1		18
22	23		A	Chester	2247	L 0 - 1		
23	26		H	Frickley Athletic	148	W 2 - 0	Madeley 17 68	17
24	30		H	Whitby Town	113	L 1 - 2	Amadi 53	
25	Dec 3		A	Hednesford Town	471	D 0 - 0		17
26	10		H	Kendal Town	122	W 1 - 0	Amadi 76	14
27	17		A	Mickleover Sports	120	D 1 - 1	Burns 5	16
28	26		A	FCUnited	1926	L 1 - 2	Amadi 13	16
29	Jan 2		H	Northwich Victoria	362	L 0 - 3		16
30	7		A	Burscough	111	W 3 - 2	Burns 13 (pen) 73 Kosylo 71	16
31	28		A	Matlock Town	283	W 2 - 0	Peers 6 9	15
32	Feb 18		A	Stafford Rangers	447	W 2 - 1	O'Neill 45 Burns 50	13
33	25		H	Chorley	254	W 3 - 1	Kosylo 34 Burns 75 78	13
34	29		H	Chasetown	103	W 4 - 0	Melling 19 Pears 27 Bennett 45 Burns 51(pen)	
35	March 3		A	Nantwich Town	326	D 1 - 1	Lambert 58	9
36	7		H	North Ferriby United	101	L 0 - 1		
37	10		A	Buxton	244	L 1 - 2	Burns 74 (pen)	12
38	17		H	Stocksbridge PS	120	L 1 - 2	Haigh 77 (og)	13
39	24		A	Bradford PA	395	L 0 - 4		14
40	31		H	Marine	144	L 1 - 3	Sherlock 16	15
41	Apr 4		H	Rushall Olympic	102	W 3 - 1	Roberts 42 Amadi 84 Beattie 87	
42	7		A	Worksop Town	226	D 3 - 3	Amadi 62 Burns 77 McDonald 90 (og)	14
43	9		H	FC United	816	W 1 - 0	Sanasy 82	
44	14		A	Kendal Town	133	W 3 - 1	Bennett 45 Burns 47 53	
45	21		H	Mickleover Sports	162	L 0 - 3		12

BLYTH SPARTANS

Chairman: Tony Platten
Secretary: Ian Evans   **(T)** 0790 598 4308   **(E)** generalmanager@blythspartans.
Additional Committee Members:
Kevin Scott, Colin Baxter, Steve Frake, Ms Jane Freeman, Andrew Bowron, Steve Ord,
Jeff Young.
Manager: Tommy Cassidy
Programme Editor: Glen Maxwell   **(E)** glen_maxwell@live.co.uk

BLYTH SPARTANS FIRST TEAM SQUAD 2011/2012
Back Row (L-R): Carl King (Goalkeeping Coach), Gavin Fell (Assistant Manager), Liam Atkin,
Wayne Buchanan, Neal Hooks, Matt Hunter, Max Johnson, Matt Crook, Carl Jones,
Glen Taylor, David Coulson, Tony Kennedy (Kit Manager) Susan Dale (Physiotherapist).
Front Row (L-R): Dan Groves, Michael Pearson, Dylan Purvis, Lee Mason, Chris Emms,
Steve Cuggy (Manager), Graeme Armstrong, Wayne Phillips, Richard Slaughter,
Phil Bannister, Phil Cave.

Club Factfile

Founded: 1899   **Nickname:** Spartans
Previous Names: None
Previous Leagues: Northumberland 1901-07, Northern All. 1907-13, 46-47, North Eastern 1913-39, Northern Com. 1945-46, Midland 1958-60, Northern Counties 1960-62, Northern 1962-94, Northern Premier 1994-2006

Club Colours (change): Green & white stripes/black/green (White & red/white/red)

Ground: Croft Park, Blyth, Northumberland NE24 3JE   **(T)** 01670 352 373
Capacity: 4,435   **Seats:** 563   **Covered:** 1,000   **Clubhouse:** Yes   **Shop:** Yes

Directions: From the Tyne Tunnel, take the A19 signposted MORPETH. At second roundabout take the A189 signposted ASHINGTON.
From A189 take A1061 signposted BLYTH. At 1st roundabout follow signs A1061 to BLYTH. Go straight across next two
roundabouts following TOWN CENTRE/SOUTH BEECH. At next roundabout turn left onto A193 go straight across next roundabout,
and at the next turn right into Plessey Rd and the ground is situated on your left. Team coach should the turn left into William St (3rd
left) and reverse up Bishopton St to the designated parking spot.

Previous Grounds: Not known.

Record Attendance: 10,186 v Hartlepool United - FA Cup 08/12/1956
Record Victory: 18-0 v Gateshead Town - Northern Alliance 28/12/1907
Record Defeat: 0-10 v Darlington - North Eastern League 12/12/1914
Record Goalscorer: Not known.
Record Appearances: Eddie Alder - 605 (1965-68)
Additional Records: Received £30,000 from Hull City for Les Mutrie

Senior Honours:
North Eastern League 1935-36. Northern League 1972-73, 74-75, 75-76, 79-80, 80-81, 81-82, 82-83, 83-84, 86-87, 87-88.
Northern League Division 1 1994-95. Northern Premier League Premier Division 2005-06.

10 YEAR RECORD

02-03	03-04	04-05	05-06	06-07	07-08	08-09	09-10	10-11	11-12
NP P 19	NP P 21	NP P 12	NP P 1	Conf N 7	Conf N 18	Conf N 15	Conf N 13	Conf N 9	Conf N 21

BLYTH SPARTANS

No.	Date	Comp	H/A	Opponents	Att:	Result	Goalscorers	Pos
1	Sat-13-Aug	BSN	A	Histon	428	D 2-2	Coulson 61, Armstrong 80	10
2	Tue-16-Aug	BSN	H	FC Halifax Town	736	L 2-3	Groves 49, Taylor 61	16
3	Sat-20-Aug	BSN	H	Bishops Stortford	469	W 3-1	Emms 19, Hooks 45, Atkin 46	10
4	Tue-23-Aug	BSN	A	Guiseley	476	L 0-5		16
5	Sat-27-Aug	BSN	A	Gainsborough Trinity	407	L 0-2		18
6	Mon-29-Aug	BSN	H	Harrogate Town	559	D 3-3	Coulson 2 (20, 85), Armstrong 25	19
7	Sat-03-Sep	BSN	A	Eastwood Town	420	D 0-0		17
8	Sat-10-Sep	BSN	H	Droylsden	488	L 1-3	Cave pen 68	19
9	Sat-17-Sep	BSN	H	Boston United	456	W 1-0	Cave pen 60	18
10	Tue-20-Sep	BSN	A	Stalybridge Celtic	440	L 0-2		18
11	Sat-24-Sep	BSN	A	Corby Town	543	L 0-4		20
12	Sat-08-Oct	BSN	H	Worcester City	485	L 1-2	Mason 85	20
13	Sat-22-Oct	BSN	A	Gloucester City	302	L 0-4		21
14	Sat-05-Nov	BSN	H	Colwyn Bay	451	D 2-2	Og (Lea) 7, Mole 61	22
15	Mon-07-Nov	BSN	A	Hyde FC	351	L 0-1		22
16	Tue-15-Nov	BSN	H	Vauxhall Motors	358	L 1-2	Buchanan 41	22
17	Sat-19-Nov	BSN	H	Hinckley United	364	D 3-3	Emms 16, Armstrong 55, Taylor 90	22
18	Sat-03-Dec	BSN	A	Bishops Stortford	297	D 3-3	Hooks 59, Taylor 69, Mason 78	22
19	Tue-06-Dec	BSN	H	Guiseley	301	L 1-2	Mason 66	22
20	Sat-10-Dec	BSN	A	FC Halifax Town	1059	L 0-3		22
21	Mon-26-Dec	BSN	A	Workington	590	L 0-2		22
22	Mon-02-Jan	BSN	H	Workington	641	L 0-3		22
23	Sat-07-Jan	BSN	A	Boston United	986	D 1-1	Armstrong 52	22
24	Sat-14-Jan	BSN	A	Nuneaton Town	768	D 2-2	Taylor 31, Armstrong 51	21
25	Sat-21-Jan	BSN	H	Corby Town	305	L 1-2	Harrop 59	21
26	Tue-24-Jan	BSN	H	Altrincham	356	D 1-1	Taylor 58	21
27	Sat-18-Feb	BSN	A	Altrincham	840	L 1-2	Armstrong 53	22
28	Tue-21-Feb	BSN	H	Stalybridge Celtic	339	D 1-1	Taylor 41	22
29	Sat-25-Feb	BSN	A	Worcester City	643	L 1-2	Kendrick 78	22
30	Sat-03-Mar	BSN	A	Colwyn Bay	279	W 2-0	Bannister 30, Kendrick 75	22
31	Tue-06-Mar	BSN	H	Histon	343	W 2-1	Bannister 2 (25, 57)	21
32	Sat-10-Mar	BSN	H	Eastwood Town	455	W 1-0	Utterson 6	21
33	Tue-13-Mar	BSN	A	Droylsden	170	D 3-3	Armstrong 73, Ferrell 75, Mason 90	21
34	Sat-17-Mar	BSN	H	Solihull Moors	245	D 2-2	Kendrick 20, Slaughter 87	21
35	Sat-24-Mar	BSN	A	Gloucester City	452	L 0-1		21
36	Sat-31-Mar	BSN	A	Vauxhall Motors	209	L 1-2	Dale 79	21
37	Tue-03-Apr	BSN	H	Solihull Moors	238	W 2-1	Dale 73, Mason 85	21
38	Sat-07-Apr	BSN	H	Gainsborough Trinity	392	L 2-3	Armstrong 26, Taylor 49	21 Relegated
39	Mon-09-Apr	BSN	A	Harrogate Town	425	D 0-0		21
40	Sat-14-Apr	BSN	H	Hyde FC	321	L 0-1		21
41	Sat-21-Apr	BSN	A	Hinckley United	624	W 3-1	Dale 14, Kendrick 28, Groves 37	21
42	Sat-28-Apr	BSN	H	Nuneaton Town	363	L 2-3	Phillips 4, Kendrick 33	21

CUPS

No.	Date	Comp	H/A	Opponents	Att:	Result	Goalscorers
1	Sat-01-Oct	FAC 2Q	H	Bedlington Terriers	835	W 2-1	Phillips 74, Hooks 81
2	Sat-15-Oct	FAC 3Q	A	Whitby Town	506	W 2-1	Tait 13, Emms 42
3	Sat-29-Oct	FAC 4Q	A	Droylsden	393	D 0-0	
4	Tue-01-Nov	FAC 4QR	H	Droylsden	678	W 2-1	Mole 2 (17, 75)
5	Sat-12-Nov	FAC 1	H	Gateshead	2763	L 0-2	
6	Sat-26-Nov	FAT 3Q	H	Stalybridge Celtic	324	L 1-3	Armstrong 10

BUXTON

Chairman: Tony Tomlinson
Secretary: Don Roberts   **(T)** 07967 822 448   **(E)** admin@buxtonfc.co.uk
Additional Committee Members:
Chris Brindley, Gary Taylor, Paul Jenner, David Belfield, David Hopkins, John Yates,
Mike Barton, M Shenton.
Manager: Martin McIntosh
Programme Editor: Mike Barton   **(E)** mike@buxtonfc.co.uk

Club Factfile

Founded: 1877   **Nickname:** The Bucks

Previous Names: Not known

Previous Leagues: Combination 1891-99, Manchester 1899-1932, Cheshire County 1932-40, 46-73,
Northern Premier 1973-98, Northern Counties East 1998-2006

Club Colours (change): All royal blue (All red)

Ground: The Silverlands, Buxton, Derbyshire SK17 6QH   **(T)** 01298 231 197

Capacity: 4,000   **Seats:** 490   **Covered:** 2,500   **Clubhouse:** Yes   **Shop:** Yes

Directions FROM STOCKPORT (A6): Turn left at first roundabout after dropping down the hill into the town, turn right at next roundabout, right at traffic lights (London Road pub) to Buxton Market Place. After two sets of pedestrian lights turn right at Royles shop then turn immediate left and follow road approx 500 metres to ground (opposite police station.) FROM BAKEWELL (A6): Turn left at roundabout on to Dale Road and follow road to traffic lights then as above. FROM MACCLESFIELD/CONGLETON/LEEK: Follow road to Burbage traffic lights and take right fork in the road at the Duke of York pub (Macclesfield Road.) Then at next traffic lights turn left (London Road pub) and follow as above. FROM ASHBOURNE (A515): Go straight on at first traffic lights (London Road pub) and follow directions as above.

Previous Grounds: Not known

Record Attendance: 6,000 v Barrow - FA Cup 1st Round 1961-62

Record Victory: Not known

Record Defeat: Not known

Record Goalscorer: Mark Reed - 164 (in 265 appearances 2002-07, 2009-)

Record Appearances: David Bainbridge - 642

Additional Records: Paid £5,000 to Hyde United for Gary Walker 1989

Senior Honours: Received £16,500 from Rotherham for Ally Pickering 1989

Manchester League 1931-32, Lge cup 1925-26, 26-27. Cheshire Co. League 1972-73, Lge Cup 1956-57, 57-58, 68-69.
N.C.E. League 2005-06, Presidents Cup 2004-05, 05-06. N.P.L. Division 1 2006-07, President's Cup 1981-82, 2006-07.
Derbyshire Senior Cup 1938-39, 45-46, 56-57, 59-60, 71-72, 80-81, 85-86, 86-87, 2008-09.

10 YEAR RECORD

02-03		03-04		04-05		05-06		06-07		07-08		08-09		09-10		10-11		11-12	
NCEP	4	NCEP	7	NCEP	9	NCEP	1	NP 1	1	NP P	5	NP P	14	NP P	8	NP P	6	NP P	13

BUXTON

No.	Date	Comp	H/A	Opponents	Att:	Result	Goalscorers	Pos
1	Aug 13	NPL P	H	Northwich Victoria	402	L 2 - 3	Agus 37 Lugsden 80	
2	16		A	Hednesford Town	510	L 2 - 3	Lugsden 27 56	
3	20		A	Chorley	855	L 0 - 1		20
4	23		H	Rushall Olympic	209	L 1 - 2	Maxfield 53	
5	27		H	F.C.United	904	L 0 - 4		21
6	29		A	Stocksbridge PS	223	W 1 - 0	Lugsden 3	
7	Sept 3		H	Nantwich Town	323	W 4 - 3	Lugsden 9 Weir-Daly 33 87 Taylor 45	15
8	7		A	Worksop Town	357	L 1 - 2	Weir-Daly	
9	10		A	North Ferriby United	229	W 4 - 1	Lugsden 3 Ridley 45 (pen) Stevens 85 Weir-Daley 90	17
10	14		H	Marine	152	L 0 - 4		
11	18	FAC 1Q	A	Louth Town	335	W 2 - 0	Pembleton 42 Lugsden 48	
12	24		H	Mickleover Sports	236	W 2 - 0	Reed 22 Lugsden 45	14
13	28		A	Ashton United	154	L 2 - 4	Pembleton 1 Lugsden 69	
14	Oct 1	FAC 2Q	H	Rushall Olympic	238	L 0 - 2		
15	8		A	Kendall Town	250	D 0 - 0		17
16	12		H	Chester	602	D 1 - 1	Wilde 55	
17	15		A	Marine	314	L 0 - 1		18
18	22	FAT 1Q	H	Garforth Town	188	W 4 - 2	Lugsden 18 32 Liversedge 36 Reed 74	
19	29		H	Burscough	225	D 2 - 2	Reed 43 Towey 53	19
20	Nov 1		A	Frickley Athletic	228	D 1 - 1	Reed 7	
21	5	FAT 2Q	A	Northwich Victoria	421	L 0 - 3		
22	12		H	Hednesford Town	305	L 1 - 3	Stevens 61	19
23	19		H	Chasetown	344	D 0 - 0		19
24	22		H	Worksop Town	223	L 1 - 3	Reed 7	
25	26		A	Nantwich Town	367	D 0 - 0		20
26	Dec 3		H	North Ferriby United	214	L 1 - 3	Ridley 20	20
27	17		A	Whitby Town	214	W 4 - 3	Reed 12 40 Barraclough 45 Lugsden 76	19
28	26		A	Matlock Town	693	D 1 - 1	Barraclough 3	19
29	Jan 2		H	Stocksbridge PS	303	L 1 - 4	Barraclough 10	20
30	7		A	Northwich Victoria	605	D 1 - 1	Barraclough 89	20
31	21		H	Chorley	310	L 1 - 3	Barraclough 18	20
32	28		A	Rushall Olympic	238	L 1 - 3	Wilde 66	20
33	Feb 25		A	Chester	2470	L 0 - 4		21
34	March 3		A	Burscough	186	W 2 - 1	Barraclough 68 Stevens 77	21
35	10		H	Ashton United	244	W 2 - 1	Barraclough 4 Lugsdon 73	21
36	12		A	Bradford PA	315	L 1 - 3	Reed 75	
37	17		H	Frickley Athletic	242	W 3 - 0	Reed 45 58 Barraclough 73	21
38	24		A	Chasetown	359	W 3 - 1	Istead 28 Roberts 74 Barraclough 87	20
39	28		A	Mickleover Sports	315	W 3 - 1	Barraclough 18 Reed 38 Davidson 43	
40	31		H	Bradford PA	379	L 1 - 3	Stevens 37	18
41	Apr 7		A	FC United	2279	W 2 - 1	Reed 21 Barraclough 73	16
42	9		H	Matlock Town	386	W 2 - 1	Reed 41 Towey 89	
43	11		H	Stafford Rangers	278	W 3 - 1	Lugsden 26 Reed 38 72	
44	14		A	Stafford Rangers	502	W 2 - 0	Roberts 67 Stevens 80	14
45	17		H	Kendall Town	203	W 5 - 3	REED 4 (16 pen 28 42 62 pen) Lugsden 23	
46	21		H	Whitby Town	375	L 0 - 1		13

CHORLEY

Chairman: Ken Wright
Secretary: Harold Taylor   **(T)** 07749 643 310   **(E)** harold@harold7.wanadoo.co.uk
Additional Committee Members:
B Pilkington, G Watkinson, P Hardcastle, J Gibbons, J Lee, T Garner.

Manager: Gary Flitcroft
Programme Editor: Mark Locke   **(E)**

THE NON-LEAGUE CLUB DIRECTORY

Book Holiday Inn Hotels and Save today!

Home

Clubs

Steps 1 - 4

League Tables

35 Years of Non-League Football

The Non-League Club Directory has developed into a comprehensive record of competitions within the non-League game, giving this level of football the

www.non-leagueclubdirectory.co.uk

Club Factfile

Founded: 1883   **Nickname:** Magpies

Previous Names: Not known

Previous Leagues: Lancashire Alliance 1890-94, Lancashire 1894-1903, Lancashire Combination 1903-68, 69-70,
Northern Premier 1968-69, 70-72, 82-88, Cheshire County 1970-82, Conference 1988-90

Club Colours (change): Black and white stripes/black/white (All sky blue)

Ground: Victory Park, Duke Street, Chorley, Lancs PR7 3DU   **(T)** 01257 263 406

Capacity: 4,100   **Seats:** 2,800   **Covered:** 900   **Clubhouse:** Yes   **Shop:** Yes

Directions

M61 leave at junction 6, follow A6 to Chorley, going past the Yarrow Bridge Hotel on Bolton Road. Turn left at first set of traffic lights into Pilling Lane, first right into Ashley St. Ground 2nd entrance on left.

M6 junction 27, follow Chorley, turn left at lights, A49 continue for 2 ½ miles, turn right onto B5251. Drive through Coppull and into Chorley for about 2 miles. On entering Chorley turn right into Duke Street 200 yards past Plough Hotel. Turn right into Ashby Street after Duke Street school, and first right into Ground.

Previous Grounds: Dole Lane 1883-1901, Rangletts Park 1901-05, St George's Park 1905-20

Record Attendance: 9,679 v Darwen - FA Cup 1931-32

Record Victory: Not known
Record Defeat: Not known

Record Goalscorer: Peter Watson - 371 (158-66)

Record Appearances: Not known

Additional Records: Received £30,000 from Newcastle United for David Eatock 1996

Senior Honours:

Lancashire Alliance 1892-93. Lancashire League 1896-97, 98-99. Lancashire Combination x11.
Cheshire County League 1975-76, 76-77, 81-82. Northern Premier League 1987-88.
Lancashire FA Trophy x14. Lancashire Combination League cup x3.

02-03		03-04		04-05		05-06		06-07		07-08		08-09		09-10		10-11		11-12	
NP 1	5	NP 1	18	NP 1	16	NP 1	18	NP 1	23	NP1N	14	NP1N	14	NP1N	16	NP1N	3	NP P	3

CHORLEY

No.	Date	Comp	H/A	Opponents	Att:	Result	Goalscorers	Pos
1	Aug 13	NPL P	A	North Ferriby United	293	W 2 - 1	Denham 44 Foster 48 (pen)	
2	16		H	Frickley Athletic	693	W 6 - 0	FOSTER 3 (14 30 45) Russell 18 Payne 74 McEvilly 89	
3	20		H	Buxton	855	W 1 - 0	Foster 72 (pen)	1
4	23		A	Stafford Rangers	471	W 1 - 0	Roscoe 82	
5	27		A	Chasetown	341	D 1 - 1	Jansen 90	1
6	29		H	Marine	952	L 1 - 2	Whitham 12	
7	Sept 3		A	Whitby Town	282	W 1 - 0	Foster 16	4
8	6		H	Northwich Victoria	805	D 0 - 0		
9	10		H	F.C.United	1074	W 2 - 0	McEvilly 38 (pen) Teague 47	2
10	14		A	Burscough	290	W 4 - 1	Roscoe 37 53 Whaley 48 Ince 56	
11	17	FAC 1Q	A	AFC Fylde	411	D 1 - 1	Ince 50	
12	20	FAC 1Qr	H	AFC FYlde	516	L 0 - 1		
13	24		H	Worksop Town	1004	W 4 - 1	Whitham 42 69 Whaley 51 Williams 77	2
14	28		A	Chester	3310	L 0 - 3		
15	Oct 1		H	Burscough	797	W 2 - 1	McEvilly 11 (pen) Payne 90	1
16	8		A	Matlock Town	441	L 0 - 4		3
17	11		H	Rushall Olympic	613	W 1 - 0	Foster 50	
18	15		H	Ashton United	779	D 2 - 2	Foster 8 Walwyn 86	3
19	22	FAT 1Q	A	Marine	279	L 0 - 1		
20	29		A	Mickleover Sports	211	W 4 - 3	Russell 41 Foster 46 Roscoe 49 Walwyn 75	
21	Nov 5		A	Rushall Olympic	257	L 0 - 1		3
22	12		H	Stocksbridge PS	870	D 0 - 0		3
23	19		A	Hednesford Town	577	L 0 - 2		4
24	22		A	Northwich Victoria	537	W 3 - 1	Roscoe 7 Flitcroft 29 Denham 68	
25	26		H	WhitbyTown	657	D 2 - 2	Maden 62 Foster 77	4
26	Dec 3		A	FCUnited	2075	D 0 - 0		4
27	10		H	Nantwich Town	766	W 1 - 0	Foster 37	
28	26		H	Kendal Town	1091	L 2 - 3	Foster 57 Whitham 69	4
29	Jan 2		A	Marine	575	W 4 - 2	Ince 20 Foster 53 (pen) Ross71 Denham 72	
30	7		H	North Ferriby United	1224	W 2 - 0	Denham 12 Denton 90 (og)	4
31	14		A	Frickley Athletic	260	L 1 - 2	Turner 41 (og)	4
32	21		A	Buxton	310	W 3 - 1	Denham 5 Roscoe 69 Foster 74	4
33	28		H	Stafford Rangers	1085	D 2 - 2	Walwyn 15 45	3
34	Feb 18		H	Matlock Town	798	W 1 - 0	Foster 79 (pen)	2
35	25		A	Ashton United	254	L 1 - 3	Walwyn 24	3
36	March 3		H	Mickleover Sports	754	W 1 - 0	Foster 47	4
37	17		A	Worksop Town	340	W 5 - 1	Kilheeney 10 83 WALWYN 3 (44 67 87)	3
38	24		H	Hednesford Town	945	W 5 - 1	Foster 2 Walwyn 36 Kilheeney 40 Denham 45 Cunliffe 89	3
39	31		A	Stocksbridge PS	247	W 3 - 0	Teague 4 Kilheeney 25 86	4
40	Apr 2		A	Bradford PA	502	L 0 - 1		
41	7		H	Chasetown	852	W 3 - 2	Kilheeney 22 Foster 31 84 (pen)	4
42	9		A	Kendal Town	403	W 2 - 1	Kilheeney 7 Teague 88	
43	14		A	Nantwich Town	417	L 0 - 1		3
44	17		H	Chester	2213	L 0 - 2		
45	21		H	Bradfod PA	1277	W 3 - 1	Roscoe 9 51 Foster 89	
46	28	Play-Off SF H		FC United	2754	L 0 - 2		

EASTWOOD TOWN

Chairman: Steven Lynch
Secretary: Miss S. Demetroi   **(T)** 07414 111810   **(E)**
Additional Committee Members:
Chris Young (Vice Chairman), Pat Farrell(Life V.P), Carole Smith (Life V.P)
Jane Cheatle (Treasurer), Roy Cheatle, John Farmer (Life Members).
Manager: John Ramshaw
Programme Editor: Andy Cope   **(E)**

THE NON-LEAGUE CLUB DIRECTORY

Book Holiday Inn Hotels and Save today!

Home

Clubs

Steps 1 - 4

League Tables

35 Years of Non-League Football

The Non-League Club Directory has developed into a comprehensive record of competitions within the non-League game, giving this level of football the

www.non-leagueclubdirectory.co.uk

Club Factfile

Founded: 1953   **Nickname:** The Badgers

Previous Names: None

Previous Leagues: Notts Alliance 1953-61, Central Alliance 1961-67, East Midlands 1967-71, Midland Counties 1971-82, Northern Counties East 1982-87, 2003-04, Northern Premier 1987-2003, 04-09

Club Colours (change): Black & white stripes/black/black (Green & white hoops/green/green)

Ground: Coronation Park, Eastwood, Notts NG16 3GL   **(T)** 01773 711 819

Capacity: 5,500 **Seats:** 650   **Covered:** 1,150   **Clubhouse:** Yes   **Shop:** Yes

Directions: M1 TRAVELLING SOUTH At junction 27, leave the motorway (A608) Heanor. At roundabout take 3rd exit A608. Past the Sandhills Tavern to a T- junction signposted Brinsley Heanor. Going through Brinsley will take you to Eastwood. At the lights turn left onto Nottingham Road. Look for the Fire Station on your right, then turn 1st right into Chewton Street. Ground is 150 metres on your right.
M1 TRAVELLING NORTH Exit junction 26. At roundabout take exit onto A610 Ripley. Leave the A610 at the first junction signed Ilkeston. Turn right at junction onto B6010, following the signs for Eastwood. Turn 1st left after the Man In Space pub into Chewton Street. Ground is 150 metres on your right.

Previous Grounds: Not known

Record Attendance: 2,723 v Enfield - FA Amateur Cup February 1965

Record Victory: 21-0 v Rufford Colliery - 1954-55
Record Defeat: 0-8 v Hucknall Town (A) - 2000-01

Record Goalscorer: Martin Wright - 147

Record Appearances: Arthur Rowley - 800+ with no bookings (1955-76)

Additional Records: Paid £500 to Gainsborough Trinity for Jamie Kay
Recieved £72,500 from Middlesbrough for Richard Liburd

Senior Honours:
Midland League 1975-76. Northern Premier League Premier Division 2008-09
Notts Senior Cup x10

02-03	03-04	04-05	05-06	06-07	07-08	08-09	09-10	10-11	11-12
NP 1 21	NCEP 2	NP 1 6	NP 1 7	NP 1 3	NP P 4	NP P 1	Conf N 10	Conf N 4	Conf N 22

EASTWOOD TOWN

No.	Date	Comp	H/A	Opponents	Att:	Result	Goalscorers	Pos
1	Sat-13-Aug	BSN	H	Droylsden	309	D 2-2	Armstrong 53, Burge 90	12
2	Tue-16-Aug	BSN	A	Solihull Moors	240	W 2-0	Riley 8, Morris 17	4
3	Sat-20-Aug	BSN	A	Colwyn Bay	370	L 0-2		13
4	Tue-23-Aug	BSN	H	Gloucester City	262	W 2-1	Bradley 30, Morris 75	9
5	Sat-27-Aug	BSN	H	Worcester City	311	L 0-1		12
6	Mon-29-Aug	BSN	A	Corby Town	555	L 0-5		15
7	Sat-03-Sep	BSN	H	Blyth Spartans	420	D 0-0		14
8	Sat-10-Sep	BSN	A	Stalybridge Celtic	540	L 1-2	Gregory 22	16
9	Sat-17-Sep	BSN	A	Nuneaton Town	675	L 0-4		19
10	Tue-20-Sep	BSN	H	Bishops Stortford	176	L 3-4	Bradley 2 (24, 33), Burge 90	20
11	Sat-24-Sep	BSN	H	Hyde FC	232	D 2-2	Burge 45, Bradley pen 75	19
12	Sat-08-Oct	BSN	A	FC Halifax Town	1320	L 1-2	Westcarr 64	19
13	Sat-22-Oct	BSN	H	Histon	214	L 1-2	Westcarr 75	20
14	Tue-25-Oct	BSN	H	Gainsborough Trinity	321	L 1-6	Westcarr 22	21
15	Sat-29-Oct	BSN	A	Vauxhall Motors	201	W 2-1	Sheridan 53, Westcarr 79	20
16	Sat-05-Nov	BSN	A	Altrincham	761	L 0-2		21
17	Sat-12-Nov	BSN	H	Guiseley	292	D 2-2	Bradley pen 22, Edwards 45	21
18	Sat-19-Nov	BSN	A	Harrogate Town	314	L 1-2	Christie 70	21
19	Sat-03-Dec	BSN	H	Nuneaton Town	415	L 0-5		21
20	Mon-05-Dec	BSN	A	Hyde FC	302	L 1-4	Edwards 90	21
21	Sat-17-Dec	BSN	H	Workington	209	L 0-3		21
22	Mon-26-Dec	BSN	A	Boston United	1247	L 2-4	F Green 2 (2, 12)	21
23	Sun-01-Jan	BSN	H	Boston United	596	D 2-2	F Green 11, Christie 23	21
24	Sat-07-Jan	BSN	A	Hinckley United	405	L 0-4		21
25	Sat-14-Jan	BSN	H	Colwyn Bay	238	L 0-1		22
26	Tue-24-Jan	BSN	A	Droylsden	175	D 3-3	Burge 64, Haggerty 2 (67, 76)	22
27	Sat-28-Jan	BSN	A	Gloucester City	289	L 0-2		22
28	Sat-11-Feb	BSN	A	Workington	319	L 0-3		22
29	Sat-18-Feb	BSN	H	FC Halifax Town	579	D 2-2	Green pen 48, Christie 63	21
30	Tue-21-Feb	BSN	H	Solihull Moors	184	D 1-1	Christie 48	21
31	Sat-25-Feb	BSN	A	Guiseley	484	W 2-1	F Green 46, Simmons 90	21
32	Sat-03-Mar	BSN	H	Hinckley United	284	L 0-3		21
33	Tue-06-Mar	BSN	H	Vauxhall Motors	151	L 2-4	Haggerty 12, Hanson 79	22
34	Sat-10-Mar	BSN	A	Blyth Spartans	455	L 0-1		22
35	Sat-17-Mar	BSN	H	Harrogate Town	173	L 0-1		22
36	Sat-24-Mar	BSN	A	Gainsborough Trinity	471	L 0-2		22 Relegated
37	Sat-31-Mar	BSN	H	Stalybridge Celtic	243	L 0-1		22
38	Sat-07-Apr	BSN	A	Worcester City	857	L 0-1		22
39	Mon-09-Apr	BSN	H	Corby Town	189	L 1-4	Elliott 8	22
40	Sat-14-Apr	BSN	A	Histon	310	L 0-3		22
41	Sat-21-Apr	BSN	H	Altrincham	239	L 1-6	Burgess 83	22
42	Sat-28-Apr	BSN	A	Bishops Stortford	502	L 0-4		22

CUPS

1	Sat-01-Oct	FAC 2Q	H	Evesham United	226	L 0-3	
2	Sat-26-Nov	FAT 3Q	A	Guiseley	323	L 0-7	

F.C. UNITED OF MANCHESTER

Chairman: Andy Walsh (General Manager)
Secretary: Lindsey Howard   **(T)** 0161 273 8950   **(E)** office@fc-utd.co.uk
Additional Committee Members:
Adam Brown, Paul Farrell, Alan Hargrave, Rob Nugent, Martin Morris, Chris Hammond,
Phil Sheeran, Mike Sherrard, Jules Spencer, Steve Pagnam, Alison Watt.
Manager: Karl Marginson
Programme Editor: Tony Howard   **(E)** office@fc-utd.co.uk

THE NON-LEAGUE CLUB DIRECTORY

Book Holiday Inn Hotels and Save today!

Home

Clubs

Steps 1 - 4

League Tables

35 Years of Non-League Football

The Non-League Club Directory has
developed into a comprehensive record
of competitions within the non-League
game, giving this level of football the

www.non-leagueclubdirectory.co.uk

Club Factfile

Founded: 2005   **Nickname:** F.C.

Previous Names: None
Previous Leagues: North West Counties 2005-07

Club Colours (change): Red/white/black (White with diagonal stripe/black/white)

Ground: Bury F.C., Gigg Lane, Bury B19 9HR   **(T)** 0161 273 8950 / 764 4881

Capacity: 11,840 **Seats:** NK   **Covered:** NK   **Clubhouse:** Yes   **Shop:** Yes

Directions: Exit M60 at junction 17 (s/p A56 Whitefield, Salford). At roundabout follow signs to Whitfield A56, Radcliffe (A665), Bury A56 onto the A56. After 0.3 miles go straight over double traffic lights passing McDonalds on LHS (s/p Bury A56, Radcliffe A665). At lights after 0.8 miles (just after the Bulls Head pub) bear right (s/p Bury A56). Straight on at lights after 1.0 miles (s/p Town Centre). After 1.0 miles turn right (s/p Football Ground) into Gigg Lane. Ground is on RHS after 0.1 miles. From North and East (via M66): Exit M66 at junction 2 and follow signs to Bury A58, Football Ground onto the A58 Rochdale Road. After 0.5 miles turn left at traffic lights by the Crown Hotel (s/p Football Ground) onto Heywood Street. After 0.4 miles turn right at second mini-roundabout (s/p Football Ground, Manchester, Salford B6219) into Wellington Road. At next mini-roundabout turn left into Market Street. Straight on over mini-roundabout after 0.1 miles and right at T-junction after 0.2 miles into Gigg Lane.

Previous Grounds: None

Record Attendance: 6,023 v Great Harwood Town - 22/04/2006

Record Victory: 10-2 v Castleton Gabriels - 10/12/2005
Record Defeat: 1-5 v Bradford Park Avenue - 24/03/2010

Record Goalscorer: Rory Patterson - 99 (2005-08)

Record Appearances: Simon Carden - 199 (2005-10)

Additional Records: Simon Carden scored 5 goals against Castleton Gabriels 10/12/2005

Senior Honours:
North West Counties League Division 2 2005-06, Division 1 2006-07.
Northern Premier League Division 1 North Play-off 2007-08.

02-03	03-04	04-05	05-06	06-07	07-08	08-09	09-10	10-11	11-12
			NWC2 1	NWC1 1	NP1N 2	NP P 6	NP P 13	NP P 4	NP P 6

F.C. UNITED OF MANCHESTER

No.	Date	Comp	H/A	Opponents	Att:	Result	Goalscorers	Pos
1	Aug 13	NPL P	A	Stafford Rangers	1707	W 2 - 0	Wolfendon 1 Scott 45	
2	17		H	North Ferriby United	1532	W 6 - 3	Wolfendon 26 Peat 47 (og) Deegan 56 Greaves 83 (og) Roca 86 (pen) Torpey 89	
3	20		H	Chasetown	2049	L 1 - 2	Wolfenden 1	3
4	24		A	Chester	3219	L 1 - 2	Norton 78	
5	27		A	Buxton	904	W 4 - 0	Jones 15 Norton 67 Grimshaw 87 Torpey 90	8
6	29		H	Bradford P.A.	1831	W 5 - 2	Neville 24 Jones 45 Torpey 79 (pen) Carr 81 Wolfenden 89	
7	Sept 3		H	Rushall Olympic	2445	D 0 - 0		7
8	6		A	Kendal Town	635	L 1 - 3	Wolfenden	
9	10		A	Chorley	1074	L 0 - 2		9
10	14		H	Nantwich Town	1353	L 1 - 3	Chadwick 78	
11	17	FAC 1Q	H	Woodley Sports	1109	D 1 - 1	Platt 39	
12	20	FAC 1Qr	A	Woodley Sports	328	W 4 - 1	Roca 28 (pen) Deegan 48 Jones 51 Norton 80	
13	24		A	Burscough	602	W 5 - 3	Norton 13 18 Roca 25 (pen) 56 Jones 77	9
14	28		H	Whitby Town	1408	W 3 - 0	Jacobs 16 Deegan 25 70	9
15	Oct 1	FAC 2Q	H	Lancaster City	1147	L 0 - 1		
16	8		H	Marine	1704	D 1 - 1	Wolfenden 59	9
17	11		A	Frickley United	497	W 3 - 1	Ludlam 53 (og) Wolfenden 56 Deegan 65	
18	15		H	Chester	3112	L 2 - 3	Roca 32 (pen) 37	7
19	22	FAT 1Q	A	Frickley Athletic	524	W 4 - 0	Roca 22 43 Carr 20 44	7
20	29		A	Stocksbridge PS	676	D 2 - 2	Norton 61 75	7
21	Nov 5	FAT 2Q	A	Durham City	533	D 1 - 1	Norton 44	
22	9	FAT 2Qr	H	Durham City	672	W 3 - 1*	Norton 30 Holden 93 Mulholland 120	
23	12		A	Mickleover Sports	753	W 2 - 0	Mulholland 25 27	7
24	19		A	Worksop Town	821	W 3 - 2	Platt 26 Neville 37 Shields 70 (og)	6
25	23		H	Kendal Town	1517	W 1 - 0	Norton 6	
26	27	FAT 3Q	A	Altrincham	1945	W 2 - 1	Roca 45 Norton 78	
27	29		A	Nantwich Town	752	D 1 - 1	Norton 81	
28	Dec 3		H	Chorley	2075	D 0 - 0		7
29	10	FAT 1	A	Guiseley	810	L 0 - 2		
30	17		A	Northwich Victoria	1114	L 1 - 2	Norton 90	7
31	26		H	Ashton United	1926	W 2 - 1	Norton 3 Neville 49	7
32	Jan 2		A	Bradford PA	1288	W 5 - 2	Platt 32 Armstrong 35 Norton 36 Jones 62 Wolfenden 67	7
33	7		H	Stafford Rangers	1947	L 1 - 2	Norton 75	
34	14		A	North Ferriby United	613	D 0 - 0		7
35	21		A	Chasetown	731	W 3 - 0	Norton 25 Stott 59 (pen) Wolfenden 90	7
36	28		H	Hednesford Town	1815	W 2 - 1	Wolfenden 52 Norton 81	
37	Feb 18		H	Frickley Athletic	1791	D 2 - 2	Roca 61 Platt 90	
38	25		A	Marine	1111	W 2 - 1	Norton 55 Jones 89	7
39	29		H	Matlock Town	1458	W 2 - 1	Gaughan 12 (og) Wolfenden 31	
40	March 3		A	Rushall Olympic	1056	L 0 - 1		7
41	10		H	Stocksbridge PS	1999	W 3 - 0	WOLFENDEN 3 (39 49 84)	6
42	17		A	Hednesford Town	1228	W 2 - 1	Jones 2 Neville 13	
43	24		H	Worksop Town	2863	W 3 - 1	Norton 16 Wolfenden 35 Nevill 58	5
44	28		A	Whitby Town	614	D 0 - 0		
45	31		H	Mickleover Sports	1730	W 4 - 0	Norton 21 Wolfenden 24 Jones 59 Platt 77	5
46	Apr 7		H	Buxton	2279	L 1 - 2	Wolfenden 6	
47	9		A	Ashton United	816	L 0 1		6
48	14		A	Matlock Town	1319	L 1 - 2	Yates 31 (og)	
49	17		H	Burscough	1505	D 1 - 1	Stott 44 (pen)	
50	21		H	Northwich Victoria	2542	W 4 - 1	Cottrell 24 Johnson 34 Collins 49 (og) Wolfenden 61	6
51	28	Play-Off SF	A	Chorley	2754	W 2 - 0	Norton 63 Mulholland 79	
52	May 6	Play-Off F	A	Bradford PA	1897	L 0 - 1*		

FRICKLEY ATHLETIC

Chairman: Gareth Dando
Secretary: Steve Pennock **(T)** 07985 291 074 **(E)** steve@pennocks.freeserve.co.uk
Additional Committee Members:
Gareth Dando, Phil McCroakam, Barry Johnson, Peter Bywater.

Manager: Karl Rose
Programme Editor: Gareth Dando **(E)**

Club Factfile

Founded: 1910 **Nickname:** The Blues
Previous Names: Frickley Colliery
Previous Leagues: Sheffield, Yorkshire 1922-24, Midland Counties 1924-33, 34-60, 70-76, Cheshire County 1960-70, Northern Premier 1976-80, Conference 1980-87

Club Colours (change): All blue (All yellow)

Ground: Westfield Lane, South Elmsall, Pontefract WF9 2EQ **(T)** 01977 642 460
Capacity: 2,087 **Seats:** 490 **Covered:** 700 **Clubhouse:** Yes **Shop:** Yes

Directions
From North : Leave A1 to join A639, go over flyover to junction. Turn left and immediately right, signed South Elmsall. Continue to roundabout and take 2nd exit to traffic lights and turn left onto Mill Lane (B6474). Turn right at the T-junction and continue down hill to next T-junction. Turn right and immediately left up Westfield Lane. The ground is signposted to the left after about half a mile.

From South : Exit M18 at J2 onto A1 (North). Leave A1 for A638 towards Wakefield. Continue on A638, going straight on at the first roundabout and turn left at next roundabout to traffic lights. Continue as above from traffic lights.

Previous Grounds: Not known

Record Attendance: 6,500 v Rotherham United - FA Cup 1st Round 1971
Record Victory: Not known
Record Defeat: Not known
Record Goalscorer: K Whiteley
Record Appearances: Not known
Additional Records: Received £12,500 from Boston United for Paul Shirtliff and from Northampton Town for Russ Wilcox

Senior Honours:
Hallamshire Senior Cup x10

10 YEAR RECORD

02-03		03-04		04-05		05-06		06-07		07-08		08-09		09-10		10-11		11-12	
NP P	20	NP P	22	NP P	18	NP P	2	NP P	16	NP P	14	NP P	11	NP P	15	NP P	18	NP P	19

FRICKLEY ATHLETIC

No.	Date	Comp	H/A	Opponents	Att:	Result	Goalscorers	Pos
1	Aug 13	NPL P	H	Burscough	189	W 2 - 0	Smith 37 Walsh 86 (pen)	
2	16		A	Chorley	693	L 0 - 6		
3	20		A	Northwich Victoria	343	D 2 - 2	Whitehouse 50 (pen) Longstaff 53	14
4	23		H	Matlock Town	275	L 0 - 2		
5	27		H	Nantwich Town	173	L 1 - 2	Grayson 15	17
6	29		A	Whitby Town	268	D 1 - 1	Adams 90	
7	Sept 3		H	Ashton United	266	L 0 - 1		19
8	6		A	North Ferriby United	167	W 2 - 1	Ashmore 78 86	
9	10		A	Chasetown	221	L 1 - 2	Mallon 61	18
10	13		H	Stocksbridge P.S.	220	W 2 - 0	Knox 73 Grayson 77	
11	17	FAC 1Q	A	Garforth Town	170	W 2 - 0	Cyrus 27 Ashmore 55	
12	24		H	Rushall Olympic	249	D 0 - 0		15
13	28		A	Mickleover Sports	192	W 6 - 3	Grayson 31 Knox 50 64 Ashmore 52 58 Mallon 81	
14	Oct 1	FAC 2Q	H	Harrogate Town	285	D 1 - 1	Darley 45	
15	4	FAC 2Qr	A	Harrogate Town	275	W 2 - 1	Turl 73 (og) Ludlam 90	
16	8		A	Hednesford Town	552	L 0 - 1		14
17	11		H	FC United	497	L 1 - 3	Grayson 64	
18	15	FAC 3Q	A	Gainsborough Trinity	644	L 0 - 2		17
19	22	FAT 1Q	H	FC United	524	L 0 - 4		
20	29		A	Chester	2485	D 2 - 2	Ashmore 29 (pen) Grayson 66	
21	Nov 1		H	Buxton	228	D 1 - 1	Gray 88	16
22	5		A	Burscough	106	W 3 - 1	Ryan 2 Grayson 23 Turner 81	13
23	12		H	Kendal Town	213	W 2 - 1	Ashmore 11 (pen) Knox 54	
24	19		A	Marine	359	L 1 - 2	Mallon 83	12
25	22		H	North Ferriby United	222	W 1 - 0	Ashmore 29 (pen)	
26	26		A	Ashton United	148	L 0 - 2		12
27	29		A	Stocksbridge PS	167	D 1 - 1	Grayson 74	
28	Dec 3		H	Chasetown	177	L 0 - 1		12
29	10		H	Bradford PA	208	L 1 - 2	South 87	
30	17		A	Stafford Rangers	354	L 0 - 2		17
31	26		A	Worksop Town	434	L 1 - 2	Ashmore 45	17
32	Jan 2		H	Whitby Town	273	L 1 - 2	Ryan 76	
33	7		A	Matlock Town	311	L 0 - 3		18
34	14		H	Chorley	260	W 2 - 1	Ludlam 75 Ashmore 80 (pen)	17
35	21		H	Northwich Victoria	227	D 0 - 0		16
36	28		A	Kendal Town	180	D 1 - 1	South 63	17
37	Feb 18		A	FC United	1791	D 2 - 2	Ashmore 5 (pen) 26	
38	25		H	Hednesford Town	204	D 1 - 1	South 90	16
39	March 3		H	Chester	720	L 1 - 3	Knox 64	16
40	10		H	Mickleover Sports	207	L 1 - 2	South 72	17
41	17		A	Buxton	242	L 0 - 3		19
42	24		H	Marine	213	L 0 - 1		21
43	Apr 7		A	Nantwich Town	336	D 0 - 0		21
44	9		H	Worksop Town	249	W 2 1	South 2 13	20
45	14		A	Bradford PA	398	L 0 - 3		19
46	17		A	Rushall Olympic	167	D 2 - 2	Grayson 51 Ludlam 69	
47	21		H	Stafford Rangers	341	W 4 - 3	Ludlam 22 South 25 59 Grayson 29	19

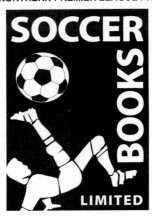

SOCCER BOOKS LIMITED

72 ST. PETERS AVENUE (Dept. NLD)
CLEETHORPES
N.E. LINCOLNSHIRE
DN35 8HU
ENGLAND

Tel. 01472 696226   Fax 01472 698546

Web site   www.soccer-books.co.uk
e-mail   info@soccer-books.co.uk

Established in 1982, Soccer Books Limited has one of the largest ranges of English-Language soccer books available. We continue to expand our stocks even further to include many more titles including German, French, Spanish and Italian-language books.

With well over 200,000 satisfied customers over the past 30 years, we supply books to virtually every country in the world but have maintained the friendliness and accessibility associated with a small family-run business. The range of titles we sell includes:

YEARBOOKS – All major yearbooks including many editions of the Sky Sports Football Yearbook (previously Rothmans), Supporters' Guides, Playfair Annuals, South and North & Central American Yearbooks, Non-League Club Directories, Almanack of World Football.

CLUB HISTORIES – Complete Statistical Records, Official Histories, Definitive Histories plus many more including photographic books.

WORLD FOOTBALL – World Cup books, European Championships History, Statistical histories for the World Cup, European Championships, South American and European Club Cup competitions and foreign-language Season Preview Magazines for dozens of countries.

BIOGRAPHIES & WHO'S WHOS – of Managers and Players plus Who's Whos etc.

ENCYCLOPEDIAS & GENERAL TITLES – Books on Stadia, Hooligan and Sociological studies, Histories and hundreds of others, including the weird and wonderful!

DVDs – Season reviews for British clubs, histories, European Cup competition finals, World Cup matches and series reviews, player profiles and a selection of almost 60 F.A. Cup Finals with many more titles becoming available all the time.

For a printed listing showing a selection of our titles, contact us using the information at the top of this page. Alternatively, our web site offers a secure ordering system for credit and debit card holders and Paypal users and lists our full range of 2,000 new books and 400 DVDs.

GRANTHAM TOWN

Chairman: Steve Boam
Secretary: Patrick Nixon   **(T)** 07747 136 033   **(E)** psnixon@hotmail.com
Additional Committee Members:
Roger Booth, Barry Palmer, Peter Railton, Darren Quinn

Manager: Wayne Hallcro and Jimmy Albans
Programme Editor: Mike Koranski   **(E)** psnixon@hotmail.com

2011-12 Squad - Back row (l-r): Phil Watt, Sam Saunders, Niall O'Rafferty, Alistair Asher, Rob Murray, Grant Brindley, Rhys Lewis, Lee Potts.
Middle Row: Tris Whitman, Tom Maddison, Jamie McGhee, Sam Purcicoe, Gio Carchedi, Matt Glass, Rob Norris, Steve Melton, Paul Grimes, Martin Ball, Joe Briers.
Front row: Nige Marshall (Physio), Dennis Rhule (Coach), Pat Nixon (Secretary), Pete Railton (Director), Steve Boam (Chairman), Darron Quinn (Director), Wayne Hallcro (Joint Manager), Becky Cope (Commercial Assistant).

Club Factfile

Founded: 1874   **Nickname:** Gingerbreads

Previous Names: Not known

Previous Leagues: Midland Amateur Alliance, Central Alliance 1911-25, 59-61, Midland Counties 1925-59, 61-72, Southern 1972-79, 85-2006, Northern Premier 1979-85

Club Colours (change): Hove black & white stripes/hove black/plain black (All neath red & black)

Ground: South Kesteven Sports Stadium, Trent Road, Gratham NG31 7XQ   **(T)** 01476 402 224

Capacity: 7,500   **Seats:** 750   **Covered:** 1,950   **Clubhouse:** Yes   **Shop:** Yes

Directions
FROM A1 NORTH Leave A1 At A607 Melton Mowbray exit. Turn left at island on slip road into Swingbridge Lane. At T junction turn left into Trent Road ground is 100yds on right.
FROM A52 NOTTINGHAM. Pass over A1 and at first island turn right into housing estate & Barrowby Gate. Through housing estate to T junction. Turn right and then immediately left into Trent road ground is 100 yards on the left.
FROM A607 MELTON MOWBRAY. Pass under A1 and take next left A1 South slip road. At island turn right into Swingbridge Road then as for A1 North above. From all directions follow brown signs for Sports Complex, which is immediately behind the stadium.

Previous Grounds: London Road

Record Attendance: 3,695 v Southport - FA Trophy 1997-98
Record Victory: 13-0 v Rufford Colliery (H) - FA Cup 15/09/1934
Record Defeat: 0-16 v Notts County Rovers (A) - Midland Amateur Alliance 22/10/1892
Record Goalscorer: Jack McCartney - 416
Record Appearances: Chris Gardner - 664
Additional Records: Received £20,000 from Nottingham Forest for Gary Crosby

Senior Honours:
Southern League Midland Division 1997-98. Lincolnshire Senior Cup x20. Lincolnshire County Senior Cup x2.
Northern Premier Division 1 South 2011-12.

10 YEAR RECORD

02-03		03-04		04-05		05-06		06-07		07-08		08-09		09-10		10-11		11-12	
SthP	16	SthP	22	SthP	13	SthP	11	NP P	22	NP 1	6	NP1S	13	NP1S	11	NP1S	5	NP1S	1

HEDNESFORD TOWN

Chairman: Stephen Price
Secretary: Terry McMahon　　**(T)** 07901 822 040　　**(E)** office@hednesfordfc.co.uk
Additional Committee Members:
Carole Price, Michael Johnson, David Smith

Manager: Robert Smith
Programme Editor: Simon Faulkner　　**(E)** office@hednesfordfc.co.uk

Club Factfile

Founded:　1880　　**Nickname:** The Pitmen
Previous Names: Hednesford 1938-74
Previous Leagues: Walsall & District, Birmingham Combination 1906-15, 45-53, West Midlands 1919-39, 53-72, 74-84,
　　Midland Counties 1972-74, Southern 1984-95, 2001-2005, 2009-11, Conference 1995-2001, 05-06, Northern Premier 2006-09

Club Colours (change): White/black/black (All red)

Ground: Keys Park, Park Road, Hednesford, Cannock WS12 2DZ　　　　**(T)** 01543 422 870
Capacity: 6,039　**Seats:** 1,010　**Covered:** 5,334　**Clubhouse:** Yes　**Shop:** Yes

Directions: Leave M6 at J11 and follow the signs for Cannock. At the next island take the third exit towards Rugeley (A460). On reaching the A5 at Churchbridge island, rejoin the A460 signposted Rugeley and follow this road over five traffic islands. At the sixth traffic island, by a Texaco petrol station, turn right past a McDonalds restaurant and follow this road to the next island which is 'Cross Keys Island'. Go over this island to the next small island and turn right. Keys Park football ground is on left.

Previous Grounds: Not known

Record Attendance: 3,169 v York City - FA Cup 3rd Round 13/01/1997
Record Victory: 12-1 v Redditch United - Birmingham Combination 1952-53
Record Defeat: 0-15 v Burton - Birmingham Combination 1952-53
Record Goalscorer: Joe O'Connor - 230 in 430 games
Record Appearances: Kevin Foster - 463
Additional Records: Paid £12,000 to Macclesfield Town for Steve Burr
Senior Honours:　Received £50,000 from Blackpool for Kevin Russell
Southern League Premier Division 1994-95. FA Trophy 2004-05.
Staffordshire Senior Cup x2. Birmingham Senior Cup 1935-36.

10 YEAR RECORD

02-03		03-04		04-05		05-06		06-07		07-08		08-09		09-10		10-11		11-12	
SthP	11	SthP	20	SthP	4	Conf N	22	NP P	7	NP P	8	NP P	8	SthP	4	SthP	2	NP P	5

HEDNESFORD TOWN

No.	Date	Comp	H/A	Opponents	Att:	Result	Goalscorers	Pos
1	Aug 13	NPL P	A	Bradford PA	442	W 1 - 0	Dunckley 3	
2	16		H	Buxton	510	W 3 - 2	Quinn 8 Clements 73 (pen) Dunckley 90	
3	20		H	Chester	1009	W 1 - 0	Osborne 88	3
4	24		A	Mickleover Sports	280	W 2 - 1	Denny 55 Monteiro 78	
5	27		A	Kendal Town	173	L 1 - 2	Osborne 85	3
6	29		H	Stafford Rangers	1086	W 5 - 4	ROBINSON 3 (44 84 90) Clements 79 (pen) Quinn 88	
7	Sept 3		H	Stocksbridge P.S.	621	D 1 - 1	Quinn 58	
8	6		A	Rushall Olympic	422	L 1 - 2	Quinn	
9	10		A	Ashton United	145	W 2 - 1	Wellecomme 9 19	
10	13		H	Matlock Town	463	D 1 - 1	Hay 6	
11	17	FAC 1Q	A	Redditch United	348	W 2 - 0	Hay 17 Clements 22	
12	24		A	North Ferriby United	226	W 2 - 1	Clements 37 Shaw 45	5
13	27		H	Burscough	451	W 4 - 0	Robinson 14 Osborne 25 Clements 36 Wellecomme 59	4
14	Oct 1	FAC 2Q	A	Carlton Town	230	W 1 - 0	Clements 81 (pen)	
15	8		H	Frickley Athletic	552	W 1 - 0	Clements 45	4
16	15	FAC 3Q	H	Corby Town	602	L 2 - 4	Clements 21 (pen) Wellecomme 45	
17	22	FAT 1Q	A	Bedworth United	192	W 1 - 0	Hay 42	
18	29		H	Whitby Town	491	W 3 - 1	Jevons 5 Bailey 76 Danks 80	4
19	Nov 5	FAT 2Q	H	Matlock Town	391	D 0 - 0		
20	9	FAT 2Qr	A	Matlock Town	279	L 1 - 2	Robinson 18	
21	12		A	Buxton	305	W 3 - 1	Campion 3 Wellecomme 36 Clements 62	4
22	19		H	Chorley	577	W 2 - 0	Hay 37 64	3
23	22		H	Rushall Olympic	614	W 4 - 1	Hay 6 Durrell 14 Clements 35 Jevons 71	
24	26		A	Stocksbridge PS	141	L 0 - 4		3
25	30		A	Matlock Town	314	W 2 - 1	Osborne 44 Clements 70 (pen)	
26	Dec 3		H	Ashton United	471	D 0 - 0		3
27	10		H	Mickleover Sports	441	W 6 - 1	Campion 31 Danks 53 Hay 55 Durrell 75 (pen) Denny 80 Haynes 90	
28	17		A	Worksop Town	270	L 0 - 1		3
29	26		H	Chasetown	1606	L 0 - 1		3
30	Jan 2		A	Stafford Rangers	1132	W 1 - 0	Robinson 37	
31	7		H	Bradford PA	529	D 1 - 1	Campion 68	3
32	14		A	Nantwich Town	493	D 2 - 2	Dunckley 64 74	3
33	21		A	Chester	3343	W 2 - 1	Clements 22 Hay 34	2
34	24		A	Marine	284	L 0 - 1		
35	28		A	FC United	1815	L 0 - 2		2
36	Feb 18		H	Marine	448	D 1 - 1	Durrell 55	4
37	25		A	Frickley Athletic	204	D 1 - 1	Jevons 43	2
38	March 3		A	Whitby Town	293	W 2 - 0	Osborne 76 Beesley 85	3
39	10		H	Northwich Victoria	511	L 0 - 2		3
40	13		A	Burscough	117	W 4 - 0	Barnett 56 (og) Denny 58 Clements 63 Wellecombe 90	
41	17		H	FcUnited	1226	L 1 - 2	Johnson 58	4
42	24		A	Chorley	945	L 1 - 5	Clements 56	3
43	31		H	Nantwich Town	425	D 0 - 0		
44	Apr 7		H	Kendal Town	374	L 2 - 3	Clements 45 Wellecombe 57	6
45	9		A	Chasetown	543	W 2 - 1	Wellecombe 45 Londell 81	5
46	13		A	Northwich Victoria	282	W 2 - 1	Clements 60 Durrell 80	
47	17		H	North Ferriby United	412	D 0 - 0		5
48	21		H	Worksop Town	582	D 0 - 0		5
49	28	Play-Off SF	A	Bradford PA	609	L 0 - 5		

Northern Premier League Action...

Action from Ilkeston's 0-0 draw with Colaville Town (stripes) in their Division One South match.

Photo: Bill Wheatcroft.

ILKESTON

Chairman: David Mantle
Secretary: Andrew Raisin   **(T)** 07813 357 393   **(E)** a.raisin@ilkestonfc.co.uk
Additional Committee Members:
David Mantle

Manager: Kevin Wilson
Programme Editor: Terry Bowles   **(E)** a.raisin@ilkestonfc.co.uk

2011-12 Squad - Back row (left to right): Joe Maguire, Dan Partridge, Josh Hill, Liam Green, Ryan Swift, Aaron Butcher, Josh Wisdom, Ryan Wlson, Tyrell Waite, Jerome Palmer.
Front row: Joe Wilcox, Will McCall, Daryll Thomas, Jimmy Davison (physio), Kevin Wilson (manager), Darren Caskey (player-coach), Adam Colton, Russell Peel, Andrew Osei-Siribour.

Club Factfile

Founded: 1945   **Nickname:** The Robins
Previous Names: Ikeston Town > 2011.
Previous Leagues: Notts & Derbyshire 1945-47, Central Alliance 1947-61, Midlands counties 1961-71, 73-82, Southern 1971-73, 95-2004, N.C.E. 1982-86, Central Midlands 1986-90, West Midlands Reg. 1990-94, N.P.L. 2004-09

Club Colours (change): Red & white/red/red (Orange with black cuffs/orange/orange)

Ground: New Manor Ground, Awsworth Road, Ilkeston, Derbyshire DE7 8JF   **(T)** 0115 944 428
Capacity: 3,029   **Seats:** 550   **Covered:** 2,000   **Clubhouse:** Yes   **Shop:** Yes

Directions: M1 Junction 26, take the A610 signed Ripley, leave at the first exit on to the A6096 signed Awsworth / Ilkeston, at the next island take the A6096 signed Ilkeston, keep on this road for about half a mile, then turn right into Awsworth Road, Signed Cotmanhay (Coaches can get down this road) the ground is about half a mile on the left hand side down this road. Car Parking available at the ground £1 per car.

Previous Grounds: Manor Ground 1945-1992

Record Attendance: Manor Ground: 9,592 v Peterborough - FAC 4thQ 1955-56. New Manor: 2,538 v Rushden & D. - FAC 1st Rnd 1999/00
Record Victory: 14-2 v Codnor M.W. - 1946-47
Record Defeat: 1-11 v Grantham Town - 1947-48. 0-10 v VS Rugby - 1985-86
Record Goalscorer: Jackie Ward - 141
Record Appearances: Terry Swincoe - 377
Additional Records: Paid £7,500 to Southport for Justin O'Reilly 1998
Received £25,000 from Peterborough United for Francis Green
Senior Honours:
Derbyshire Senior Cup 1948-49, 52-53, 55-56, 57-58, 62-63, 82-83, 92-93, 98-99, 99-00, 05-06, 06-07. Central Alliance 1951-52, 52-53, 53-54, 54-55, League Cup 1957-58. Midland Counties League 1967-68. Central Midlands League Cup 1986-87. West Midlands Div.1 1991-92, Premier 93-94, Div.1 League Cup 91-92, Premier League Cup 93-94. NPL D1S Play-offs 2011-12.

10 YEAR RECORD

02-03		03-04		04-05		05-06		06-07		07-08		08-09		09-10		10-11		11-12	
SthP	21	SthW	10	NP 1	2	NP P	16	NP P	12	NP P	17	NP P	2	Conf N	8	Conf N Exp		NP1S	3

KENDAL TOWN

Chairman: Haydon Munslow
Secretary: Craig Campbell   **(T)** 07980 660 428   **(E)** info@kendaltownfootballclub.co.uk
Additional Committee Members:
Graham O'Callaghan, Tom Roe, Steve Dixon, Meril Tummey.

Manager: Lee Ashcroft
Programme Editor: Steve Presnail   **(E)** info@kendaltownfootballclub.co.uk

KENDAL TOWN F.C.

THE NON-LEAGUE CLUB DIRECTORY

Book Holiday Inn Hotels and Save today!

Home

Clubs

Steps 1 - 4

League Tables

35 Years of Non-League Football

The Non-League Club Directory has developed into a comprehensive record of competitions within the non-League game, giving this level of football the

www.non-leagueclubdirectory.co.uk

Club Factfile

Founded: 1919   **Nickname:** Town

Previous Names: Netherfield

Previous Leagues: Westmorland, North Lancashire Combination 1945-68, Northern Premier 1968-83, North West Counties 1983-87

Club Colours (change): Black and white stripes/black/red (All red)

Ground: Cosy Seal Stadium, Parkside Road, Kendal, Cumbria LA9 7BL   **(T)** 01539 727 472

Capacity: 2,490   **Seats:** 450   **Covered:** 1000   **Clubhouse:** Yes   **Shop:** Yes

Directions: M6 junction 36, via A590/591/A6 to Kendal (South). At first traffic lights turn right, left at roundabout, right into Parkside Road. Ground on right over brow of hill.

Previous Grounds: Not known

Record Attendance: 5,184 v Grimsby Town - FA Cup 1st Round 1955

Record Victory: 11-0 v Great Harwood - 22/03/1947
Record Defeat: 0-10 v Stalybridge Celtic - 01/09/1984

Record Goalscorer: Tom Brownlee

Record Appearances: Not known

Additional Records: Received £10,250 from Manchester City for Andy Milner 1995

Senior Honours:
Westmorlands Senior Cup x12. Lancashire Senior Cup 2002-03.

02-03		03-04		04-05		05-06		06-07		07-08		08-09		09-10		10-11		11-12	
NP 1	12	NP 1	21	NP 1	5	NP 1	3	NP P	19	NP P	11	NP P	5	NP P	5	NP P	8	NP P	11

KENDAL TOWN

No.	Date	Comp	H/A	Opponents	Att:	Result	Goalscorers	Pos
1	Aug 7	NPL P	H	Worksop Town	276	W 3 - 0	Williams 31 Cotterill 33 (og) Jackson 50	
2	20		A	Matlock Town	270	L 0 - 1		15
3	23		H	Whitby Town	206	W 2 - 1	Jackson 54 Kilifin 81	
4	27		H	Hednesford Town	305	W 2 - 1	Williams 75 Joseph 88	9
5	29		A	Burscough	156	D 2 - 2	Dunn 52 Jackson 79	
6	Sept 3		A	Mickleover Sports	189	W 6 - 0	Jackson 12 42 Williams 37 Peers 48 Dunn 69 Taylor 87	8
7	6		H	F.C.United	635	W 3 - 1	Jackson Newton (Goalkeeper) Donnelly	
8	10		H	Stafford Rangers	258	L 0 - 1		7
9	14		A	Chester	2029	L 0 - 4		
10	17	FAC 1Q	H	Whitley Bay	298	W 1 - 0	Leadbetter 21	
11	20		A	Northwich Victoria	384	L 0 - 2		
12	24		A	Chasetown	278	L 1 - 2	Curtis 22	10
13	27		H	Marine	197	D 3 - 3	Wainwright 24 Jackson 26 Leadbetter 86	
14	Oct 2	FAC 2Q	A	Wakefield	98	W 4 - 1	Dunn 48 Swinglehurst 53 Jackson 60 McKevatt 82	
15	8		H	Buxton	250	D 0 - 0		11
16	15	FAC 3Q	A	Nantwich Town	468	L 1 - 2	Williams 46	
17	22	FAT 1Q	H	Nantwich Town	192	W 1 - 0	Leadbetter 7 (pen)	
18	29		H	North Ferriby United	169	L 2 - 3	Leadbetter 35 Jackson 80	14
19	Nov 5	FAT 2Q	A	Stourbridge	338	D 3 - 3	Leadbetter 16 Taylor 36 Jackson 85	
20	8	FAT 2Qr	H	Stourbridge	207	L 0 - 6		
21	12		A	Frickley Athletic	213	L 1 - 2	Gray 9	18
22	19		H	Nantwich Town	183	W 4 - 0	Wisdom 51 Walmsley 52 Connerton 60 Jackson 85	15
23	23		A	FCUnited	1517	L 0 - 1		
24	26		H	Mickleover Sports	125	D 3 - 3	Connerton 3 (36 44 74)	
25	Dec 3		A	Stafford Rangers	433	W 2 - 1	Joseph 39 Esply 81 (og)	16
26	10		A	Ashton United	122	L 0 - 1		17
27	17		H	Stocksbridge PS	146	W 4 - 2	Jackson 53 Wisdom 66 Dunn 68 75	
28	26		A	Chorley	1091	W 3 - 2	Wisdom 18 Gray 28 Ross 38 (og)	15
29	Jan 2		H	Burscough	258	L 3 - 4	McKevatt 23 40 Comozzi 38	16
30	7		A	Worksop Town	320	W 5 - 3	McKEVATT 4 (23 41 48 71) Taylor 60	
31	14		A	Whitby Town	284	D 1 - 1	Jackson 28	11
32	21		H	Matlock Town	152	W 2 - 1	Dunn 50 Winters 54	8
33	28		H	Frickley Athletic	180	D 1 - 1	Taylor 60	9
34	Feb 25		H	Bradford PA	329	D 1 - 1	Leadbetter 81 (pen)	9
35	28		A	Marine	304	D 1 - 1	Leadbetter 40	
36	March 3		A	North Ferriby United	212	L 2 - 4	Lavin 29 (og) Osman 79	11
37	6		H	Northwich Victoria	229	W 4 - 1	McKevatt 2 9 Leadbetter 16 (pen) 57	
38	10		A	Rushall Olympic	164	W 3 - 2	Jackson 21 Winters 90 Leadbetter 90 (pen)	
39	17		H	Rushall Olympic	157	L 1 - 3	Jackson 81	8
40	24		A	Nantwich Town	324	L 0 - 3		10
41	26		A	Bradford PA	303	L 1 - 4	Dunn 9	
42	31		H	Chasetown	157	L 1 - 4	Leadbetter 37	12
43	Apr 2		H	Chester	701	L 0 - 3		
44	7		A	Hednesford Town	374	W 3 - 2	Leadbetter 45 (pen) Williams 77 Wisdom 79	10
45	9		H	Chorley	403	L 1 - 2	Farrell 20	13
46	14		H	Ashton United	133	L 1 - 3	Leadbetter 17	
47	17		A	Buxton	203	L 3 - 5	Leadbetter 3 Wisdom 17 Taylor 32	11
48	21		A	Stocksbridge PS	131	W 3 - 1	McKevatt 29 Taylor 41 Wiliams 70	11

MARINE

Chairman: Paul Leary
Secretary: Richard Cross   **(T)** 07762 711 714   **(E)** info@marinefc.com
Additional Committee Members:
Brian Lawlor, Mark Prescott, Paul Eustace, Barry Godfrey, Geoff Maddock, Peter McCormack, Dave McMillan, Mark Williams, John Wildman, David Wotherspoon Geoff Kewley, Dennis Hargreaves, Roly Howard.
Manager: Kevin Lynch
Programme Editor: Dave McMillan   **(E)** info@marinefc.com

Back Row(L-R): Geoff Maddock, Richard Cross (Secretary), Paul Leary (Chairman), Peter McCormack, Maurice Broderick (Treasurer), Paul Eustace, Barry Godfrey
Middle Row(L-R): Gary Trowler (Kit Manager), Robbie Lawton, Liam Dawson, Alan Burton, Paul Lundon, John Shaw, Liam Duff, Ryan McMahon, Callum Williams, Matty Brown, Danny Grannon, Jonathan Goulding, Nick Rogan, Andy Fowler, Nick McCarthy (Sports Therapist)
Front Row (L-R): Matty Devine, Michael Ordish, Karl Noon, Shaun Dowling, Tony Sayer, Kevin Lynch (Manager), Phil Brazier (Assistant Manager), Liam Rice, Thomas Moore, Marcus Carver
Photo by kind permission of Ray Farley Photography.

Club Factfile

Founded: 1894   **Nickname:** Mariners
Previous Names: None
Previous Leagues: Liverpool Zingari, Liverpool County Combination, Lancashire Combination 1935-39, 46-69, Cheshire County 1969-79

Club Colours (change): White/black/black (Yellow/green/green)

Ground: Arriva Stadium, College Road, Crosby, Liverpool L23 3AS   **(T)** 0151 924 1743
Capacity: 3,185   **Seats:** 400   **Covered:** 1,400   **Clubhouse:** Yes   **Shop:** Yes

Directions
From the East & South: Leave the M62 at junction 6 and take the M57 to Switch Island at the end. At the end of the M57 take the A5036 (signposted Bootle & Docks). At the roundabout, at the end of the road (by Docks), turn right onto the A565 following signs for 'Crosby' and 'Marine AFC' and follow this road for 1 mile. After passing the Tesco Express on your right, turn left at the traffic lights (by Merchant Taylors' School) into College Road. The ground is half a mile on your left
From the North: Leave the M6 at junction 26 and join the M58. Travel along the M58 to Switch Island at the end. Take the A5036 (signposted Bootle & Docks) and follow directions above.

Previous Grounds: Waterloo Park 1894-1903

Record Attendance: 4,000 v Nigeria - Friendly 1949
Record Victory: 14-0 v Sandhurst - FA Cup 1st Qualifying Round 01/10/1938
Record Defeat: 2-11 v Shrewsbury Town - FA Cup 1st Round 1995
Record Goalscorer: Paul Meachin - 200
Record Appearances: Peter Smith 952
Additional Records: Paid £6,000 to Southport for Jon Penman October 1985
Received £20,000 from Crewe Alexandra for Richard Norris 1996
Senior Honours:
Northern Premier League Premier Division 1993-94, 84-95.
Lancashire Junior Cup 1978-79, Lancashire Trophy x3. Lancashire Amateur Cup x5. Lancashire Senior Cup x6.
Liverpool Non-League Cup x3. Liverpool Challenge Cup x3.

10 YEAR RECORD

02-03		03-04		04-05		05-06		06-07		07-08		08-09		09-10		10-11		11-12	
NP P	11	NP P	16	NP P	15	NP P	3	NP P	4	NP P	7	NP P	13	NP P	9	NP P	9	NP P	7

MARINE

No.	Date	Comp	H/A	Opponents	Att:	Result	Goalscorers	Pos
1	Aug 13	NPL P	H	Stocksbrisge P.S.	308	W 1 - 0	Fowler 72	
2	17		A	Nantwich `Town	323	W 2 - 1	Rey 40 Fowler 62	
3	20		A	Worksop Town	339	W 3 - 0	Cotterill 11 (og) Williams 13 (og) Shaw 35	2
4	23		H	Northwich Victoria	415	L 0 - 2		
5	27		H	Matlock Town	353	D 2 - 2	Davies 32 Lukic 75 (og)	7
6	29		A	Chorley	952	W 2 - 1	Harvey 5 56	
7	Sept 3		A	Stafford Rangers	504	L 1 - 2	Brown 30	10
8	7		H	Bradford P.A.	281	L 0 - 2		
9	10		H	Mickleover Sports	252	L 2 - 3	Harvey 33 Everett-Elliott 40 (og)	11
10	14		A	Buxton	152	W 4 - 0	Rey 19 Moore 78 Harvey 90 90	
11	17	FAC 1Q	A	**Witton Albion**	246	**L 0 - 2**		
12	24		H	Ashton United	328	W 1 - 0	Johnson 68	7
27	27		A	Kendal Town	197	D 3 - 3	Barnes 11 Rey 64 Harvey 90	
14	Oct 1		H	Worksop Town	310	W 4 - 0	Harvey 22 68 Moore 55 (pen) Gargan 79	
15	8		A	F.C.United	1704	D 1 - 1	Johnson 39	6
16	15		H	Buxton	314	W 1 - 0	Johnson 52	5
17	22	FAT 1Q	H	**Chorley**	279	**W 1 - 0**	**Brown 68**	
18	29		H	Chasetown	296	L 2 - 3	Rey 40 Moore 60 (pen)	
19	Nov 5	FAT 2Q	H	**Chasetown**	213	**W 5 - 2**	**Fowler 20 Rey 42 Lundon 53 Harvey 79 Gargan 88**	
20	12		A	North Ferriby United	243	L 0 - 2		8
21	19		H	Frickley Athletic	359	W 2 - 1	Moore 86 Harvey 90	
22	21		A	Bradford PA	288	W 1 - 0	Rey 87	
23	26	FAT 3Q	A	**Vauxhall Motors**	329	**L 2 - 3**	**Jones 37 (og) Fowler 39**	
24	Dec 3		A	Mickleover Sports	221	W 1 - 0	Harvey 75	6
25	10		A	Matlock Town	168	W 1 - 0	Brown 7	6
26	17		H	Chester	1268	L 1 - 2	Moore 3	
27	26		A	Burscough	207	W 4 - 0	Rey 5 Harvey 45 64 Brown 47	
28	Jan 2		H	Chorley	575	L 2 - 4	Harvey 42 (pen) Rey 68	
29	7		A	Stocksbridge PS	169	D 1 - 1	Brown 9	5
30	14		H	Stafford Rangers	458	L 0 - 1		5
31	21		A	Whitby Town	242	W 2 - 1	Harvey 74 Rey 78	5
32	24		H	Hednesford Town	284	W 1 - 0	Harvey 20	
33	28		A	Northwich Victoria	545	W 2 - 1	Ordish 12 Harvey 42	5
34	Feb 14		H	Nantwich Town	286	D 0 - 0		
35	18		A	Hednesford Town	448	D 1 - 1	Moore 39	5
36	25		H	FC United	1111	L 1 - 2	Goulding 27	6
37	28		H	Kendall Town	304	D 1 - 1	Rey 47	
38	March 3		A	Chasetown	303	W 1 - 0	Barnes 20	6
39	10		H	North Ferriby United	337	L 0 - 2		7
40	13		H	Whitby Town	350	L 1 - 2	Rey 53	7
41	24		A	Frickley Atheltic	213	W 1 - 0	Rogan 75	7
42	31		A	Ashton United	144	W 2 - 1	Byers 53 Fowler 60	7
43	Apr 7		H	Matlock Town	295	D 1 - 1	Rey 58	7
44	9		H	Burscough	560	D 0 - 0		7
45	14		H	Rushall Olympic	329	L 0 - 3		7
46	21		A	Chester	3686	L 0 - 4		7

MATLOCK TOWN

Chairman: Tom Wright
Secretary: Keith Brown   **(T)** 07831 311 427   **(E)** clubshop@matlocktownfc.com
Additional Committee Members:
P Bates, J Beaumont, R Blunt, S Else, Mrs C Else, P Eyre, S Greenhough, P Power,
D Reynolds, I Richardson, A Smith, J Taylor, GM Tomlinson, Mrs LH West, T Weston.
Manager: Mark Atkins
Programme Editor: Mike Tomlinson   **(E)** clubshop@matlocktownf.co.uk

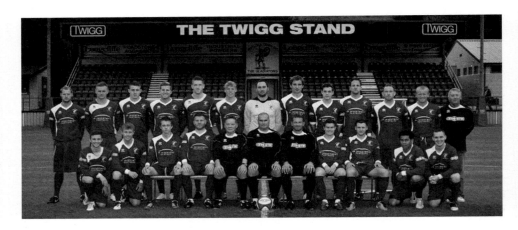

Photo courtesy of Mark Ludbrook from sportsshots.co.uk

Club Factfile

Founded: 1885   **Nickname:** The Gladiators
Previous Names: Not known
Previous Leagues: Midland Combination 1894-96, Matlock and District, Derbyshire Senior, Central Alliance 1924-25, 47-61, Central Combination 1934-35, Chesterfield & District 1946-47, Midland Counties 1961-69

Club Colours (change): All royal blue (Tangerine/black/tangerine)

Ground: Reynolds Stadium, Causeway Lane, Matlock, Derbyshire DE4 3AR   **(T)** 01629 583 866
Capacity: 5,500   **Seats:** 560   **Covered:** 1,200   **Clubhouse:** Yes   **Shop:** Yes
Directions On A615, ground is 500 yards from Town Centre and Matlock BR.

Previous Grounds: Not known

Record Attendance: 5,123 v Burton Albion - FA Trophy 1975
Record Victory: 10-0 v Lancaster City (A) - 1974
Record Defeat: 0-8 v Chorley (A) - 1971
Record Goalscorer: Peter Scott
Record Appearances: Mick Fenoughty
Additional Records: Paid £2,000 for Kenny Clark 1996
Received £10,000 from York City for Ian Helliwell
Senior Honours:
FA Trophy 1974-75. Anglo Italian Non-League Cup 1979.
Derbyshire Senior Cup x7.

10 YEAR RECORD

02-03	03-04	04-05	05-06	06-07	07-08	08-09	09-10	10-11	11-12
NP 1 8	NP 1 2	NP P 11	NP P 9	NP P 5	NP P 16	NP P 15	NP P 7	NP P 11	NP P 14

MATLOCK TOWN

No.	Date	Comp	H/A	Opponents	Att:	Result	Goalscorers	Pos
1	Aug 13	NPL P	A	Ashton United	178	L 0 - 3		
2	17		H	Chasetown	404	D 2 - 2	Holmes 2 Nightingale 70	
3	20		H	Kendal Town	270	W 1 - 0	Holmes 14 (pen)	13
4	23		A	Frickley Athletic	275	W 2 - 0	Nightingale 17 Lukic 77	
5	27		A	Marine	353	D 2 - 2	Holmes 44 57	12
6	29		H	Mickleover Sports	368	W 2 - 1	Simpson 2 (og) Nightingale 20	
7	Sept 3		A	Burscough	123	W 2 - 1	Holmes 77 Bower 84	5
8	7		H	Stafford Rangers	388	D 1 - 1	Yates	
9	10		H	Bradford PA	398	L 0 - 1		8
10	13		A	Hednesford Town	463	D 1 - 1	King 37	8
11	17	FAC1Q	H	Hucknall Town	356	W 2 - 0	Algor 52 Holmes 88	8
12	24		A	Whitby Town	321	D 1 - 1	Bettney 32	8
13	28		H	North Ferriby United	300	W 3 - 0	Holmes 26 90 King 40	8
14	Oct 1	FAC 2Q	H	Hinckley United	411	L 1 - 3	Joynes 65	
15	8		H	Chorley	441	W 4 - 0	Bettney 31 JOYNES 3 (36 48 85)	7
16	11		A	Nantwich Town	273	L 1 - 2	Holmes 90	
17	15		H	Northwich Victoria	377	L 0 - 2		8
18	22	FAT 1Q	H	Stamford	299	W 3 - 0	Hunter 38 Algar 53 Radford 73	
19	29		A	Northwich Victoria	410	D 0 - 0		8
20	Nov 2		H	Stocksbridge P.A.	254	W 4 - 0	Algar 18 70 Holmes 64 Nightingale 83	7
21	5	FAT 2Q	A	Hednesford Town	891	D 0 - 0		
22	9	FAT 2Qr	H	Hednesford Town	279	W 2 - 1	Kukic 20 Holmes 44	
23	12		H	Worksop Town	430	D 1 - 1	Harcourt 90	6
24	19		A	Chester	2605	L 0 - 4		8
25	22		A	Stafford Rangers	370	D 1 - 1	King 61	
26	26	FAT 3Q	H	Hyde United	367	L 0 - 1		
27	30		H	Hednesford Town	314	L 1 - 2	King 86	
28	Dec 3		A	Bradford PA	282	D 2 - 2	Nightingale 11 25	10
29	10		A	Stocksbridge PS	168	D 1 - 1	Nightingale 90	
30	26		H	Buxton	693	D 1 - 1	Morris 59	11
31	Jan 2		A	Mickleover Sports	420	L 1 - 3	Hunter 39	
32	7		H	Frickley Athletic	311	W 3 - 0	Holmes 12 47 Hunter 70	11
33	21		A	Kendal Town	152	L 1 - 2	Hunter 59	13
34	28		H	Ashton United	283	L 0 - 2		13
35	Feb 18		A	Chorley	798	L 0 - 1		14
36	21		A	North Ferriby United	218	D 1 - 1	Holmes 21	
37	25		H	Rushall Oympic	335	W 1 - 0	McMahon 90 (pen)	11
38	29		A	FCUnited	1458	L 1 - 2	Holmes 61	
39	March 10		H	Nantwich Town	360	W 1 - 0	McMahon 75	15
40	17		H	Burscough	242	W 3 - 1	Algar 51 McMahon 56 71	12
41	20		A	Chasetown	227	D 1 - 1	Wilkin 20	
42	24		H	Chester	1036	L 0 - 1		11
43	31		A	Worksop Town	300	L 0 - 1		13
44	Apr 7		H	Marine	295	D 1 - 1	Luckic 88	
45	9		A	Buxton	396	L 1 - 2	McMahon 68	12
46	14		H	FC United	1319	W 2 - 1	Holmes 9 King 73	
47	19		H	Whitby Town	171	L 2 - 4	McMahon 17 King 30	14
48	21		A	Rushall Olympic	268	L 0 - 1		

NANTWICH TOWN

Chairman: Jon Gold
Secretary: Janet Stubbs   **(T)** 01270 621 771   **(E)** janet.stubbs@nantwichtownfc.com
Additional Committee Members:
John Dunning, Clive Jackson (Vice-Chairman), Bob Melling (Non-Executive), Steve Talbot.
Life Vice-Presidents: Neville Clarke, Albert Pye, Peter Temmen
Manager: Jimmy Quinn
Programme Editor: Michael Chatwin   **(E)** programme@nantwichtownfc.com

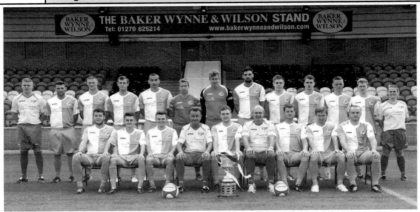

BACK ROW (left to right): Antony Swindells (physio), Kyle Wilson, JJ Bailey, Will Jones, Rod McDonald,
Paddy Chesters (goalkeeper coach), Jonny Brain, Mat Bailey, Lewis Short, Niall Maguire, Josh Lane, Zack Foster,
Michelle Pennell (head physio).
FRONT ROW (left to right): Matt Lowe, Caspar Hughes, Sean Cooke, Martin Stubbs (assistant manager), Chris Flynn,
Jimmy Quinn (manager), Darren Moss, Mark Beesley, Fraser McLachlan. Trophy: Cheshire Senior Cup.
Photo: Simon J Newbury Photography.

Club Factfile

Founded: 1884   **Nickname:** Dabbers
Previous Names: Nantwich
Previous Leagues: Shropshire & Dist. 1891-92, Combination 1892-94, 1901-10, Cheshire Junior 1894-95, Crewe & Dist. 1895-97, North Staffs & Dist. 1897-1900, Cheshire 1900-01, Manchester 1910-12, 65-68, Lancs. Com. 1912-14, Cheshire Co. 1919-38, 68-82, Crewe & Dist. 1938-39, 47-48, Crewe Am. Comb. 1946-47, Mid-Cheshire 1948-65, North West Co. 1982-2007
Club Colours (change): Green & white halves/green/green (Yellow/blue/blue)

Ground: Weaver Stadium, Waterlode, Kingsley Fields, Nantwich, CW5 5BS   **(T)** 01270 621 771
Capacity: 3,500   **Seats:** 350   **Covered:** 495   **Clubhouse:** Yes   **Shop:** Yes
Directions: M6 Jun 16 A500 towards Nantwich. Over 4 roundabouts onto A51 towards Nantwich Town Centre, through traffic lights and over railway crossing. Over next r/bout then left at next r/bout past Morrisons supermarket on right. Continue over r/bout through traffic lights. Ground on right at next set of traffic lights.
SATNAV Postcode: CW5 5UP

Previous Grounds: London Road/Jackson Avenue (1884-2007)

Record Attendance: 5,121 v Winsford United - Cheshire Senior Cup 2nd Round 1920-21
Record Victory: 20-0 v Whitchurch Alexandra (home) 1900/01 Cheshire League Division 1, 5 April 1901
Record Defeat: 2-16 v Stalybridge Celtic (away) 1932/33 Cheshire County League, 22 Oct 1932
Record Goalscorer: John Scarlett 161 goals (1992/3 to 2005/6). **Goals in a season:** Bobby Jones 60 goals (1946/7)
Record Appearances: Not known
Additional Records: Gerry Duffy scored 42 during season 1961-62
Senior Honours: Record Fee Received undisclosed fee from Crewe Alexandra for Kelvin Mellor - Feb 2008
FA Vase Winners 2005/06. Cheshire Senior Cup Winners 1932/33, 1975/76, 2007/08 & 2011/12. Cheshire County League Champions 1980/81. Mid-Cheshire League Champions 1963/64. North West Counties League Challenge Cup Winners 1994/95. Cheshire Amateur Cup Winners 1895/96 & 1963/64.

10 YEAR RECORD

02-03		03-04		04-05		05-06		06-07		07-08		08-09		09-10		10-11		11-12	
NWC1	6	NWC1	13	NWC1	16	NWC1	4	NWC1	3	NP1S	3	NP P	3	NP P	10	NP P	17	NP P	10

NANTWICH TOWN

No.	Date	Comp	H/A	Opponents	Att:	Result	Goalscorers	Pos
1	Aug 13	NPL P	A	Mickleover Sports	306	L 1 - 3	Lowe 79	
2	17		H	Marine	323	L 1 - 2	Moss 60	
3	20		H	Bradford PA	292	L 0 - 3		22
4	23		A	Chasetown	269	D 4 - 4	Carter 6 Mills 31 (pen) 65 Lennon 87	
5	27		A	Frickley Athletic	173	W 2 - 1	Foster 60 Mills 72	15
6	29		H	Chester F.C.	1561	W 4 - 1	Mills 28 53 (pen) Lennon 75 Prince 84	
7	Sept 3		A	Buxton	323	L 3 - 4	Lennon 67 Bailey 82 Maguire 87	13
8	6		H	Burscough	203	L 3 - 4	Cooke 34 67 Mills 68	
9	10		H	Whitby Town	223	W 2 - 0	Lennon 43 Mills 75	14
10	14		A	FC United	1353	W 3 - 1	Lennon 55 Cooke 62 Maguire 64	
11	20	FAC 1Q	A	**Ramsbottom United**	217	W 2 - 1	Bailey 87 Cooke 90	
12	24		H	Stocksbridge PS	316	W 1 - 0	Mills 66	11
13	27		A	Rushall Olympic	225	W 1 - 0	Adaggio 64	
14	Oct 1	FAC 2Q	A	**Northwich Victoria**	542	W 2 - 1	Moss 50 Cooke 84	
15	8		A	Worksop Town	265	L 0 - 3		10
16	11		H	Matlock Town	273	W 2 - 1	Mills 57 (pen) Lennon 78	10
17	15	FAC 3Q	H	**Kendal Town**	468	W 2 - 1	Bailey 55 Solovjovs 71	
18	22	FAT 1Q	A	**Kendal Town**	192	L 0 - 1		10
19	29	FAC 4Q	H	**Nuneaton Town**	1011	W 1 - 0	Lowe 69	
20	Nov 1		H	Northwich Victoria	561	W 3 - 2	McLachlan 5 Bailey 12 Mills 37	
21	5		A	Ashton United	147	D 1 - 1	Bailey 52	9
22	12	FAC 1	A	**MK Dons**	4110	L 0 - 6		
23	19		A	Kendal Town	183	L 1 - 4	Lennon 49	10
24	23		A	Burscough	123	L 1 - 2	Cooke 14	
25	26		H	Buxton	367	D 0 - 0		10
26	29		H	F.C.United	752	D 1 - 1	Cooke 9 (pen)	
27	Dec 3		A	Whitby Town	267	W 5 - 4	McPHERSON 3 (41 62 74) Cooke 65 84	
28	10		A	Chorley	766	L 0 - 1		10
29	26		H	Stafford Rangers	792	W 2 - 0	Mills 32 Flynn 41	9
30	Jan 2		A	Chester	3560	D 1 - 1	Lennon 51	10
31	7		H	Mickleover Sports	409	D 1 - 1	Lennon 40	8
32	14		H	Hednesford Town	493	D 2 - 2	Lennon 28 Everall 77	
33	21		A	Bradford PA	257	L 1 - 3	Sheriff 63	10
34	28		H	Chasetwon	411	D 0 - 0		11
35	Feb 14		A	Marine	286	D 0 - 0		
36	18		H	Worksop Town	420	L 0 - 1		11
37	25		H	North Ferriby United	289	W 2 - 1	Bailey 28 Cooke 41	8
38	March 3		H	Ashton United	326	D 1 - 1	Bailey 71	10
39	10		A	Matlock Town	360	L 0 - 1		13
40	17		A	Northwich Victoria	301	L 1 - 2	Everall 47	14
41	24		H	Kendal Town	324	W 3 - 0	Lennon 71 90 Everall 83	
42	27		H	Rushall Olympic	252	W 4 - 1	McPherson 34 (pen) 66 McDonald 51 Urwin 90	
43	31		A	Henesford Town	425	D 0 - 0		8
44	Apr 7		H	Frickley Athletic	336	D 0 - 0		8
45	9		A	Stafford Rangers	416	D 1 - 1	Cooke 89	
46	14		H	Chorley	417	W 1 - 0	Unwin 85	
47	17		A	Stocksbridge PS	126	W 5 - 1	Lane 4 58 Lennon 22 MacPherson 51 Everall 80	
48	21		A	FC United	2542	L 1 - 4	McPherson 22 (pen)	10

NORTH FERRIBY UNITED

Chairman: Les Hare
Secretary: Steve Tather   **(T)** 07845 378 512   **(E)** info@northferribyunitedfc.co.uk
Additional Committee Members:
Colin Wicks, Alan Sage, Steve Turtle, Richard Hodgkinson, Jim White, Phil Withers,
Chris Holbrough, Richar Watts, John Cartlich, Shaun Harris.
Manager: Billy Heath
Programme Editor: Richard Watts   **(E)** info@northferribyunitedfc.co.uk

Back l-r Chris Hall, NeilStevens, Nathan Peat, Liam King, Ryan Kendal, Jack Maldoon, Russell Fry, Louis Mobbs, Tim Taylor, Ben Hunter
Middle l-r Danny Clark, Lee Morris, Sam Belcher, Gregg Anderson, Antoni Pecora, Adam Nicklin, Paul Foot, Mark Gray, Dene Lisle, Chris Bolder
Front l-r James Williams, Steve Gardner, Martin Woodmansey (Kit Manager), Billy Heath (Manager), Mark Carroll (Coach), Sara Henderson (Physio), Gary Bradshaw, Steve Ridley. Photo: Paul Whiteley.

Club Factfile

Founded: 1934   **Nickname:** United
Previous Names: None
Previous Leagues: East Riding Church, East Riding Amateur, Yorkshire 1969-82, Northern Counties East 1982-2000

Club Colours (change): White with green trim/green/green (Yellow with green trim/yellow/yellow)

Ground: Rapid Solicitors Stadium, Church Road, North Ferriby HU14 3AA   **(T)** 01482 634 601
Capacity: 3,000   **Seats:** 250   **Covered:** 1,000   **Clubhouse:** Yes   **Shop:** Yes

Directions: Main Leeds to Hull road A63 or M62. North Ferriby is approx. 8 miles west of Hull.
Proceed through village past the Duke of Cumberland Hotel.
Turn right down Church Road. Ground mile down on left.

Previous Grounds: Not known

Record Attendance: 1,927 v Hull City - Charity game 2005
Record Victory: 9-0 v Hatfield Main - Northern Counties East 1997-98
Record Defeat: 1-7 v North Shields - Northern Counties East 1991
Record Goalscorer: Mark Tennison - 161
Record Appearances: Paul Sharp - 497 (1996-2006)
Additional Records: Andy Flounders scored 50 during season 1998-99
Senior Honours: Received £60,000 from Hull City for Dean Windass
Northern Counties East 1999-2000. Northern Premier League Division 1 2004-05.
East Riding Senior Cup x11.

10 YEAR RECORD

02-03		03-04		04-05		05-06		06-07		07-08		08-09		09-10		10-11		11-12	
NP 1	4	NP 1	17	NP 1	1	NP P	5	NP P	13	NP P	15	NP P	10	NP P	4	NP P	5	NP P	9

NORTH FERRIBY UNITED

No.	Date	Comp	H/A	Opponents	Att:	Result	Goalscorers	Pos
1	Aug 13	NPL P	H	Chorley	293	L 1 - 2	Harsley 86	
2	17		A	F.C. United	1532	L 3 - 6	Bradshaw 22 Bolder 53 Brooksby 75	
3	20		A	Burscough	119	W 2 - 1	Bolder 7 Brooksby 88	16
4	23		H	Stocksbridge P.S.	194	W 2 - 1	Bradshaw 51 Bolder 62	
5	27		H	Rushall Olympic	134	W 1 - 0	Bolder 27	10
6	29		A	Worksop Town	359	D 0 - 0		
7	Sept 3		A	Chester F.C.	2150	L 0 - 6		12
8	7		H	Frickley Athletic	167	L 1 - 2	Mulready	
9	10		H	Buxton	229	L 1 - 4	Black 58 (og)	15
10	12		A	Bradford P.A.	298	L 0 - 1		
11	17	FAC 1Q	H	**Worksop Town**	168	W 1 - 0	**Wright 48**	
12	24		H	Hednesford Town	226	L 1 - 2	Bradshaw 26	18
13	28		A	Matlock Town	300	L 0 - 3		
14	Oct 1	FAC 2Q	A	**Whitby Town**	253	L 1 - 2	**Bradshaw 38**	
15	8		A	Northwich Victoria	342	L 0 - 2		19
16	11		H	Ashton United	165	W 6 - 3	BRADSHAW 3 (4 44 89) Harsley 63 (pen) Davidson 65 69	
17	15		H	Mickleover Sports	228	W 3 - 1	Davidson 6 Bradshaw 84 Brooksby 90	16
18	22	FAT 1Q	H	**Lincoln Un ited**	122	W 3 - 1	**Clarke 64 Harsley 67 Bradshaw 83**	
19	29		A	Kendal Town	189	W 3 - 2	Davidson 12 Clarke 43 Harsley 78	13
20	Nov 5	FAT 2Q	H	**Salford City**	135	W 3 - 0	**DAVIDSON 3 (74 77 81)**	
21	12		H	Marine	243	W 2 - 0	Bradshaw 51 Bolder 54	14
22	19		A	Stafford Rangers	436	D 1 - 1	Foot 33	13
23	22		A	Frickley Athletic	288	L 0 - 1		15
24	26	FAT 3Q	A	**Corby Town**	519	D 1 - 1	**Davidson 45**	
25	29	FAT 3Qr	H	**Corby Town**	170	W 3 - 2	**Davidson 43 Brooksby 54 Fry 87**	
26	Dec 3		A	Buxton	214	W 3 - 1	Bradshaw 48 Bolder 54 Brooksby 75	14
27	10	FAT 1	H	**Chester F.C.**	510	L 1 - 6	**Harsley 58 (pen)**	
28	13		H	Bradford PA	180	W 2 - 1	Bradshaw 9 80	
29	26		A	Whitby Town	314	W 2 - 0	Brooksby 47 Fry 66	
30	Jan 2		H	Worksop Town	326	D 0 - 0		
31	7		A	Chorley	1224	L 0 - 2		
32	14		H	FC United	613	D 0 - 0		
33	21		H	Burscough	223	D 0 - 0		
34	28		A	Stocksbridge PS	427	L 0 - 7		
35	Feb 18		H	Northwich Victoria	258	L 2 - 3	Brooksby 78 Fry 89	
36	21		H	Matlock Town	218	D 1 - 1	Fry 77	
37	25		A	Nantwich Town	289	L 1 - 2	Fry 2 (pen)	
38	March 3		H	Kendal Town	212	W 4 - 2	Foot 54 Bradshaw 58 Brooksby 71 Hunter 89	
39	7		A	Ashton United	101	W 1 - 0	Morris 55	
40	10		A	Marine	337	W 2 - 0	Anderson 8 24	
41	13		H	Chasetown	175	D 1 - 1	Brooksby 71	
42	17		A	Mickleover Sports	325	L 0 - 4		
43	24		H	Stafford Rangers	271	W 3 - 1	Bradshaw 14 83 Brooksby 3	
44	27		H	Chester	459	L 0 - 3		
45	Apr 7		A	Rushall Olympic	176	D 1 - 1	Bolder 23	
46	9		H	Whitby Town	192	W 1 - 0	Brooksby 36	
47	14		A	Chasetown	227	D 2 - 2	Bradshaw 34 57	
48	17		A	Hednesford United	412	D 0 - 0		
49	21		H	Nantwich Town	172	W 3 - 1	Anderson 32 Bolder 47 Bradshaw 52	9

RUSHALL OLYMPIC

Chairman: John C Allen
Secretary: Peter Athersmith　　**(T)** 07771 361 002　　**(E)** rushallolympic@yahoo.co.uk
Additional Committee Members:
Nicholas J Allen, Brian Greenwood, Raymond Barrow, Darren Stockall, Paul Seward,
Stuart Perry, Daniel Hopley, Steve Stuart, Simon Haynes.
Manager: Neil Kitching
Programme Editor: Darren Stockall　　**(E)** rushallolympic@yahoo.co.uk

Back Row (L-R) – Gary Fitzpatrick, Josh Craddock, Louis Keenan, Decio Gomes, Dave Walker, Kyle Haynes, Mitchell Tolley
Middle Row (L-R) – Lucan Spittle, Leo Brown, Steve Palmer, Tom Burns, Chris Gemmell, Wayne Daniel, Steve Abbott, Michael Clarke,
Dave Harrison (Kit Man)
Front Row (L-R) – Andre Landell, Martyn Naylor, Paul Hayward (Goalkeeping Coach), Ian Cooper (First Team Coach),
Neil Kitching (Manager), Nick Amos (Assistant Manager), Jonny Haynes, Grant Beckett.
Juniors (L-R) Tom and Danny Kitching.
Credit for photo – Steve Walker

Club Factfile

Founded: 1951　　**Nickname:** The Pics
Previous Names: None
Previous Leagues: Walsall Amateur 1952-55, Staffordshire County (South) 1956-78, West Midlands 1978-94,
Midland Alliance 1994-2005, Southern 2005-08

Club Colours (change): Gold and black/black/black (Red with white trim/red with white trim/red)

Ground: Dales Lane off Daw End Lane, Rushall, Nr Walsall WS4 1LJ　　**(T)** 01922 641 021
Capacity: 2,500　**Seats:** 200　　**Covered:** 200　　**Clubhouse:** Yes　**Shop:** Yes

Directions: M6 J10 follow signs for Walsall stay on this dual carriage way for about four miles until you come to the Walsall Arboretum and turn left following signs for Lichfield A461. Go under the bridge and you will come to McDonald's on your right, turn right into Daw End Lane. Go over the canal bridge and turn right opposite the Royal Oak Public House and the ground is on the right.
Alternative: From the A38 to it's junction with the A5 (Muckley Corner Hotel) take the A461 to Walsall after about five miles you will reach some traffic lights in Rushall by Mcdonald's, turn left into Daw End Lane go over the canal bridge and turn right opposite The Royal Oak Public House the ground is on the right.

Previous Grounds: Rowley Place 1951-75, Aston University 1976-79

Record Attendance: 2,000 v Leeds United Ex players
Record Victory: Not known
Record Defeat: Not known
Record Goalscorer: Graham Wiggin
Record Appearances: Alan Dawson - 400+
Additional Records:

Senior Honours:
West Midlands League 1979-80. Midland Alliance 2004-05.

10 YEAR RECORD

02-03		03-04		04-05		05-06		06-07		07-08		08-09		09-10		10-11		11-12	
MidAl	2	MidAl	14	MidAl	1	SthW	10	SthM	15	SthM	5	NP1S	5	NP1S	12	NP1S	3	NP P	8

RUSHALL OLYMPIC

No.	Date	Comp	H/A	Opponents	Att:	Result	Goalscorers	Pos
1	Aug 13	NPL P	A	Chester F.C.	2326	D 1 - 1	Lewis 37 (pen)	
2	16		H	Mickleover Sports	177	D 1 - 1	Lewis 71	
3	20		H	Ashton United	130	W 1 - 0	Morris 4	8
4	23		A	Buxton	209	W 2 - 1	Edwards 72 (pen) Morris 90	
5	27		A	North Ferriby United	134	L 0 - 1		11
6	29		H	Chasetown	452	W 1 - 0	Spittle 69	
7	Sept 3		A	F.C.United	2445	D 0 - 0		11
8	6		H	Hednesford Town	422	W 2 - 1	Lewis Obeng	
9	10		H	Burscough	172	W 3 - 0	Lewis 16 28 Dacres 17	6
10	13		A	Stafford Rangers	453	D 1 - 1	Heler 80 (og)	
11	17	FAC 1Q	H	Bedworth United	168	W 1 - 0	Brown 27 (pen)	
12	24		A	Frickley Athletic	249	D 0 - 0		5
13	27		H	Nantwich Town	225	L 0 - 1		
14	Oct 1	FAC 2Q	A	Buxton	238	W 2 - 1	Bottomer 24 Tolley 39 (pen)	
15	8		H	Whitby Town	241	W 3 - 2	Lewis 9 Tolley 35 (pen) Obeng 65	8
16	11		A	Chorley	613	L 0 - 1		9
17	15	FAC 3Q	A	Barrow Town	318	W 3 - 0	Obeng 9 53 Tolley 30 (pen)	
18	22	FAT 1Q	H	Cambridge City	173	L 0 - 2		
19	29	FAC 4Q	A	Stourbridge	720	L 0 - 5		
20	Nov 2		A	Worksop Town	275	L 1 - 2	Obeng 28	
21	5		H	Chorley	257	W 1 - 0	Obeng 23	8
22	12		H	Northwich Victoria	286	L 0 - 3		10
23	19		A	Stocksbridge PS	161	L 0 - 2		9
24	22		A	Hednesford Town	614	L 1 - 4	Obeng 39	
25	26		H	Stafford Rangers	308	W 2 - 1	Obeng 32 Bottomer 52	9
26	Dec 3		A	Burscough	102	W 4 - 2	Keenon 45 Platt 64 (pen) Haynes 71 Wilkes 75	8
27	10		H	Marine	158	L 0 - 1		8
28	26		H	Bradford PA	241	D 0 - 0		10
29	Jan 2		A	Chasetown	476	W 2 - 0	Forde 55 Turner 58 (og)	
30	7		H	Chester	714	L 0 - 4		9
31	14		A	Mickleover Sports	226	D 2 - 2	Tolley 68 Wilkes 90	9
32	28		H	Buxton	238	W 3 - 1	Haynes 24 Bottomer 45 Obeng 78	8
33	Feb 18		A	Whitby Town	286	L 1 - 2	Bottomer 14	8
34	25		A	Matlock Town	335	L 0 - 1		10
35	28		H	Worksop Town	218	D 0 - 0		
36	March 3		H	FC United	1056	W 1 - 0	Melbourne 10	8
37	10		H	Kendal Town	164	L 2 - 3	Amos 9 Dacres 54	10
38	17		A	Kendal Town	157	W 3 - 1	OBENG 3 (25 44 90)	9
39	24		H	Stocksbridge PS	229	W 3 - 0	BANNISTER 3 (2 25 56)	8
40	27		A	Nantwich Town	252	L 1 - 4	Tolley 28 (pen)	
41	31		A	Northwich Victoria	244	L 0 - 2		9
42	Apr 4		A	Ashton United	102	L 1 - 2	Spittle 35	
43	7		H	North Ferriby United	178	D 1 - 1	Melbourne 29	9
44	9		A	Bradford PA	331	W 2 - 0	Kitching 17 Amos 19	
45	14		A	Marine	329	W 3 - 0	Bannister 11 (pen) Haynes 36 Melbourne 54	
46	17		H	Frickley Athletic	167	D 2 - 2	Beckett 61 Brady 74	8
47	21		H	Matlock Town	268	W 1 - 0	Brady 90	8

STAFFORD RANGERS

Chairman: Ron Woodward
Secretary: Robbie Mullin   **(T)** 07977 038 534   **(E)** info@staffordrangersfc.co.uk
Additional Committee Members:
Cliff Went, Reg Bates, Roly Tonge, Mike Hughes.

Manager: Greg Clowes
Programme Editor: Stuart Maun   **(E)** info@staffordrangersfc.co.uk

Back Row: (Left to Right) Sean Kinsella, Dean Clarke, Danny Quinn, Jermaine Johnson, Christian Dacres, Fabrice Kasiama, Ryan Dicker.
Middle Row: (Left to Right) Mick Hathaway (coach), Luke George, Karl Espley, Oliver Davies, Danny Read, Adam Alcock, Jimmy Turner, Alex Forde, Sid Kelly (kit man).
Front Row: (Left to Right) Kevin Street, Simon Everall, Greg Clowes (manager), Lee Downes, Michael Carr, Liam Walshe, Dorrian Garner (assistant manager), Courtney Pitt, Ryan Brown.

Club Factfile

Founded: 1876   **Nickname:** Rangers
Previous Names: None
Previous Leagues: Shropshire 1891-93, Birmingham 1893-96, N. Staffs. 1896-1900, Cheshire 1900-01, Birmingham Comb. 1900-12, 46-52, Cheshire County 1952-69, N.P.L. 1969-79, 83-85, Alliance 1979-83, Conf. 1985-95, 2005-11. Southern >2005.

Club Colours (change): Black & white stripes/black/black (All red)

Ground: Marston Road, Stafford ST16 3BX   **(T)** 01785 602 430
Capacity: 6,000   **Seats:** 4,264   **Covered:** 3,500   **Clubhouse:** Yes   **Shop:** Yes
Directions: M6 Junction 14. Follow signs for Uttoxeter and Stone. Straight over at 1st and 2nd (A34) islands, 3rd right sign posted Common Road and Astonfields Road Ind. Estate. The ground is straight ahead after three quarters of a mile. The route from the Motorway is highlighted by the standard football road signs.

Previous Grounds: Not known

Record Attendance: 8,536 v Rotherham United - FA Cup 3rd Round 1975
Record Victory: 14-0 v Kidsgrove Athletic - Staffordshire Senior Cup 2003
Record Defeat: 0-12 v Burton Town - Birmingham League 1930
Record Goalscorer: M. Cullerton - 176
Record Appearances: Jim Sargent
Additional Records: Paid £13,000 to VS rugby for S. Butterworth
Senior Honours: Received £100,000 from Crystal Palace for Stan Collymore
Northern Premier League 1971-72, 84-85. FA trophy 1971-72.
Staffordshire Senior Cup x7

10 YEAR RECORD

02-03		03-04		04-05		05-06		06-07		07-08		08-09		09-10		10-11		11-12	
SthP	2	SthP	3	Conf N	8	Conf N	2	Conf	20	Conf	23	Conf N	18	Conf N	16	Conf N	20	NP P	16

STAFFORD RANGERS

No.	Date	Comp	H/A	Opponents	Att:	Result	Goalscorers	Pos
1	Aug 13	NPL P	H	F.C.United	1707	L 0 - 2		
2	17		A	Worksop Town	456	D 1 - 1	Budrys 58	
3	20		A	Stocksbridge PS	172	L 0 - 1		18
4	23		H	Chorley	471	L 0 - 1		
5	27		H	Whitby Town	420	D 3 - 3	Nagington 33 Thompson 55 Sheldon 69	
6	29		A	Hednesford Town	1086	L 4 - 5	Kinsella 6 Douglas 15 Thompson 20 Budrys 81	20
7	Sept 3		H	Marine	504	W 2 - 1	Thompson 21 Kinsella 83 (pen)	
8	7		A	Matlock Town	388	D 1 - 1	Kinsella 38	
9	10		A	Kendal Town	258	W 1 - 0	Shotton 72	16
10	13		H	Rushall Olympic	453	D 1 - 1	Kinsella 82	
11	17	FAC 1Q	A	Old Wulfrunians	304	W 3 - 2	Stevenson 1 Nagington 55 Thompson 78	
12	24		H	Chester	1098	L 0 - 3		17
13	27		A	Northwich Victoria	530	W 1 - 0	Kinsella 44	
14	Oct 1	FAC 2Q	H	Stratford Town	438	L 2 - 4	Gregory 16 (og) Nagington 65	
15	8		A	Ashton United	153	W 5 - 1	Blackhurst 31 STREET 3 (43 76 89) Espley 74	13
16	11		H	Mickleover Sports	400	D 1 - 1	Kinsella 26	
17	15		A	Chasetown	419	W 1 - 0	Thompson 40	11
18	22	FAT 1Q	A	Newcastle Town	505	D 1 - 1	George 20	
19	25	FAT 1Qr	H	Newcastle Town	374	W 5 - 2	Sheldon 8 11 Thompson 15 56 Nagington 49	
20	29		H	Worksop Town	498	D 2 - 2	Blackhurst 82 Kinsella 90	11
21	Nov 5	FAT 2Q	A	Chester	1551	L 0 - 2		
22	12		A	Burscough	155	W 3 - 2	Nagington 53 Morton 87 Stevenson 90	11
23	19		H	North Ferriby United	436	D 1 - 1	Nagington 4 (pen)	11
24	22		A	Matlock Town	370	D 1 - 1	Thompson 31	
25	26		A	Rushall Olympic	308	L 1 - 2	Dicker 2	11
26	Dec 3		H	Kendal Town	433	W 1 - 2	Joseph 50 (og)	10
27	17		H	Frickley Athletic	354	W 2 - 0	Bell 20 Carr 81(pen)	
28	26		A	Nantwich Town	792	L 0 - 2		15
29	Jan 2		H	Hednesford Town	1132	L 0 - 1		15
30	7		A	FC United	1947	W 2 - 1	Heler 31 Dicker 42	14
31	14		A	Marine	458	W 1 - 0	Thompson 66	13
32	21		H	Stocksbridge PS	406	W 5 - 1	Morris 29 Sheldon 60 Thompson 66 89 Stevenson 90	9
33	28		A	Chorley	1085	D 2 - 2	Carr 36 Sheldon 52	10
34	Feb 11		A	Chester	2381	L 0 - 2		10
35	18		H	Ashton United	447	L 1 - 2	Stevenson 45	12
36	25		A	Mickleover Sports	326	L 0 - 1		
37	28		H	Northwich Victoria	475	D 1 - 1	Heler 29	12
38	March 3		A	Bradford PA	532	L 1 - 3	Morris 83	11
39	10		H	Bradford PA	452	W 3 - 1	Dicker 48 Stevenson 54 Morris 70	10
40	17		H	Chasetown	593	W 4 - 1	Carr 51 70 George 55 Morris 81	12
41	24		A	North Ferriby United	271	L 1 - 3	Blackhurst 52	11
42	31		H	Burscough	395	D 1 - 1	Kinsella 17	13
43	Apr 7		A	Whitby Town	371	L 1 - 2	Morris 62	
44	9		H	Nantwich Town	416	D 1 - 1	Nagington 86	15
45	11		A	Buxton	278	L 1 - 3	Kinsella 15	16
46	14		H	Buxton	502	L 0 - 2		
47	21		A	Frickley Athletic	341	L 3 - 4	Kinsella 42 Gray 90 (og) Stevenson 90	16

STOCKSBRIDGE PARK STEELS

Chairman: Allen Bethel
Secretary: Michael Grimmer   **(T)** 07801 626 725   **(E)** mickgrimmer@gmail.com
Additional Committee Members:
Trevor Grayson, Andrew Horsley, Wayne Cefferty, Dean Cefferty, Peter Kenney, Jack Newton, William Fieldsend, Ron Sellers, John Gosling, Philip Birkinshaw, Graham Furness, David Bradley.
Manager: Chris Willcock
Programme Editor: Philip Birkenshaw   **(E)** mickgrimmer@gmail.com

Club Factfile

Founded: 1986   **Nickname:** Steels
Previous Names: Stocksbridge Works and Oxley Park merged in 1986
Previous Leagues: Northern Counties East 1986-96

Club Colours (change): Yellow/blue/blue (Red/white/red)

Ground: Look Loacl Stadium, Bracken Moor Lane, Stocksbridge, Sheffield S36 2AN   **(T)** 0114 288 8305
Capacity: 3,500   **Seats:** 400   **Covered:** 1,500   **Clubhouse:** Yes   **Shop:** Yes

Directions: From West onto A616. Immediately you reach the Stocksbridge bypass turn Right signed (Stocksbridge West), then continue until you reach the shopping centre approx 1.5 miles. 300 yards past the centre you will see Gordons Autos on your left. Turn right directly opposite signed (Nanny Hill) and continue up the hill for Approx 500 yds, Ground is on the Left.
From M1- From North Junction 36 on to A61 Sheffield to McDonalds Roundabout. From South Junction 35a on to A616 Manchester to McDonalds Roundabout. From McDonalds roundabout on A616 Manchester for approx 6 miles then take Stocksbridge West exit, then continue until you reach the shopping centre approx 1.5 miles. 300yds past the centre you will see Gordons Autos on your Left. Turn right directly opposite signed (Nanny Hill) and continue up the hill for Approx 500yds, ground on Left.

Previous Grounds: Stonemoor 1949-51, 52-53

Record Attendance: 2,050 v Sheffield Wednesday - opening of floodlights October 1991
Record Victory: 17-1 v Oldham Town - FA Cup 2002-03
Record Defeat: 0-6 v Shildon
Record Goalscorer: Trevor Jones - 145
Record Appearances: Not known
Additional Records: Paul Jackson scored 10 v Oldham Town in the 2002-03 FA Cup - a FA Cup record
Senior Honours: Received £15,000 from Wolverhampton Wanderers for Lee Mills
Northern Counties East Division 1 1991-92, Premier Division 1993-94, League Cup 1994-95.
Sheffield Senior Cup 1951-52, 92-93, 95-96, 98-99

10 YEAR RECORD

02-03		03-04		04-05		05-06		06-07		07-08		08-09		09-10		10-11		11-12	
NP 1	17	NP 1	19	NP 1	14	NP 1	6	NP 1	6	NP1S	5	NP1S	3	NP P	11	NP P	13	NP P	18

STOCKSBRIDGE PARK STEELS

No.	Date	Comp	H/A	Opponents	Att:	Result	Goalscorers	Pos
1	Aug 13	NPL P	A	Marine	308	L 0 - 1		
2	16		H	Ashton United	161	D 1 - 1	Lloyd 9 (pen)	
3	20		H	Stafford Rangers	172	W 1 - 0	Marrison 33	12
4	23		A	North Ferriby United	194	L 1 - 2	Marrison 37 (pen)	
5	27		A	Chester	2040	L 1 - 5	Marrison 20	16
6	29		H	Buxton	223	L 0 - 1		
7	Sept 3		A	Hednesford Town	621	D 1 - 1	Muldoon 89	18
8	7		H	Whitby Town	114	L 0 - 2		
9	10		H	Northwich Victoria	174	L 3 - 4	Ward 42 76 Riorden 47	20
10	13		A	Frickley Athletic	220	L 0 - 2		
11	17	FAC 1Q	A	Armthorpe Welfare	110	D 1 - 1	Muldoon 31	
12	20	FAC 1Qr	H	Armthorpe Welfare	86	W 3 - 1	Ring 60 80 Cusworth 75	
13	24		A	Nantwich Town	316	L 0 - 1		21
14	27		H	Bradford PA	168	D 2 - 2	Cusworth 54 74	
15	Oct 1	FAC 2Q	H	Colwyn Bay	128	W 3 - 1	Adam 29 Muldoon 45 Ward 90 (pen)	
16	8		H	Burscough	110	L 0 - 2		22
17	11		A	Chasetown	210	W 3 - 1	Muldoon 23 Cusworth 47 49	
18	15	FAC 3Q	A	Droylsden	230	L 1 - 4	Cusworth 37	21
19	22	FAT 1Q	H	Ossett Town	94	D 2 - 2	Sirrup 11 Muldoon 64	
20	25	FAT 1Qr	A	Ossett Town	71	L 2 - 3	Ring 23 Muldoon 70	
21	29		H	F.C.United	676	D 2 - 2	Muldoon 3 Stirrup 73	20
22	Nov 2		A	Matlock Town	254	L 0 - 4		
23	5		A	Bradford PA	329	L 0 - 2		20
24	12		A	Chorley	870	D 0 - 0		20
25	19		H	Rushall Olympic	161	W 2 - 0	Stirrup 40 Muldoon 87	20
26	23		A	Whitby Town	224	D 3 - 3	Cusworth 6 29 Muldoon 47	
27	26		H	Hednesford Town	141	W 4 - 0	Cusworth 54 60 Muldoon 89 Ward 90	19
28	29		H	Frickley Athletic	167	D 1 - 1	Muldoon 16	
29	Dec 3		A	Northwich Victoria	421	L 0 - 2		19
30	10		H	Matlock Town	168	D 1 - 1	Lovell 24	
31	17		A	Kendal Town	146	L 2 - 4	Lovell 49 (pen) Muldoon 71	20
32	26		H	Mickleover Sports	192	D 1 - 1	Lovell 60 (pen)	20
33	Jan 2		A	Buxton	303	W 4 - 1	Cusworth 31 Telling 64 Hogan 69 86	
34	7		H	Marine	169	D 1 - 1	Harrison 90	19
35	21		A	Stafford Rangers	406	L 1 - 5	Hogan 79	19
36	28		H	North Ferriby United	427	W 7 - 0	Telling 2 Collery 5 Hogan 27 Muldoon 34, Stirrup 47, Whitehouse 71 Harrison 88	18
37	Feb 18		A	Buescough	154	D 1 - 1	Muldoon 44	18
38	25		H	Chasetown	162	W 2 - 0	Stirrup 54 75	18
39	March 10		A	FC United	1999	L 0 - 3		19
40	17		A	Ashton United	120	W 2 - 1	Muldoon 43 Haigh 57	16
41	20		H	Worksop Town	181	W 3 - 0	Stirrup 3 Telling 50 Coleman 84	16
42	24		A	Rushall Olympic	229	L 0 - 3		17
43	31		H	Chorley	247	L 0 - 3		19
44	Apr 7		H	Chester	1009	L 1 - 2	Weston 51	
45	9		A	Mickleover Sports	181	W 3 - 1	Hogan 26 50 Muldoon 83	
46	14		A	Worksop Town	225	D 1 - 1	Coleman 13	18
47	17		H	Nantwich Town	126	L 1 5	Hogan 20	
48	21		H	Kendal Town	131	L 1 - 3	Haigh 5	

WHITBY TOWN

Chairman: Anthony Graham Manser
Secretary: Peter Tyreman　　**(T)** 01947 605 153　　**(E)**
Additional Committee Members:
A J Spenceley, M Agar, J Nellist, C Bone, G Osbourne, M Osbourne, D Griffiths,
J Smith, M Green, W Robinson, K Robinson.
Manager: Darren Williams
Programme Editor: Lee West　　　　　　　　**(E)**

Club Factfile

Founded: 1926　　**Nickname:** Seasiders
Previous Names: Whitby United (pre 1950)
Previous Leagues: Northern League 1926-97

Club Colours (change): All royal blue (All white)

Ground: Turnbull Ground, Upgang Lane, Whitby, North Yorks YO21 3HZ　　**(T)** 01947 604 847
Capacity: 2,680　**Seats:** 622　**Covered:** 1,372　**Clubhouse:** Yes　**Shop:** Yes
Directions: On entering Whitby from both the A169 and A171 roads, take the first fork and follow signs for the "West Cliff". Then turn left at the Spa Shop and Garage, along Love Lane to junction of the A174. Turn right and the ground is 600 yards on the left.

Previous Grounds: Not known

Record Attendance: 4,000 v Scarborough - North Riding Cup 18/04/1965
Record Victory: 11-2 v Cargo Fleet Works - 1950
Record Defeat: 3-13 v Willington - 24/03/1928
Record Goalscorer: Paul Pitman - 382
Record Appearances: Paul Pitman - 468
Additional Records: Paid £2,500 to Newcastle Blue Star for John Grady 1990
　　　　　　　　　　　　Received £5,000 from Gateshead for Graham Robinson 1997
Senior Honours:
Rothmans National Cup 1975-76, 77-78. Northern League 1992-93. FA Vase 1996-97.
Northern Premier League Division 1 1997-98.
North Riding Senior Cup x5.

10 YEAR RECORD

02-03	03-04	04-05	05-06	06-07	07-08	08-09	09-10	10-11	11-12
NP P　10	NP P　15	NP P　4	NP P　6	NP P　11	NP P　12	NP P　19	NP P　14	NP P　16	NP P　17

WHITBY TOWN

No.	Date	Comp	H/A	Opponents	Att:	Result	Goalscorers	Pos
1	Aug 13	NPL P	A	Chasetown	351	D 1 - 1	Faichney 38	
2	17		H	Bradford P.A.	346	L 1 - 4	Faichney 14	
3	20		H	Mickleover Sports	243	D 1 - 1	Blackford 25	17
4	23		A	Kendal Town	206	L 1 - 2	Robinson 9	18
5	27		A	Stafford Rangers	420	D 3 - 3	Robinson 45 (pen) 62 Tymon 51	
6	29		H	Frickley Athletic	268	D 1 - 1	Tymon 7	
7	Sept 3		H	Chorley	282	L 0 - 1		20
8	7		A	Stocksbridge P.S.	114	W 2 - 0	Tynan McTiernan	
9	10		A	Nantwich Town	223	L 0 - 2		19
10	13		H	Ashton Uited	202	D 2 - 2	McTiernan 21 Rimmer 49 (og)	
11	17	FAC 1Q	A	Parkgate	116	W 3 - 1	Hodgson 17 McTiernan 45 Dunford 83	
12	24		H	Matlock Town	321	D 1 - 1	Hodgson 4	19
13	28		A	F.C.United	1408	L 0 - 3		
14	Oct 1	FAC 2Q	H	North Ferriby United	253	W 2 - 1	Hassan 51 Faichney 87	
15	8		A	Rushall Olympic	241	L 2 - 3	Tymon 55 Martin 75	20
16	12		H	Worksop Town	275	L 3 - 4	McTiernan 62 Tymon 79 Robinson 90 (pen)	
17	15	FAC 3Q	H	Blyth Spartans	506	L 1 - 2	Faichney 81	
18	22	FAT 1Q	A	Woodley Sports	63	L 1 - 3	Faichney 75	
19	29		A	Hednesford Town	491	L 1 - 3	Robinson 8	21
20	Nov 5		A	Mickleover Sports	173	L 0 - 5		21
21	12		H	Chester	652	L 0 - 4		21
22	19		A	Northwich Victoria	425	L 0 - 2		21
23	23		H	Stocksbridge Park Steels	224	D 3 - 3	Robinson 24 (pen) Beadle 25 Appleby 84	
24	26		A	Chorley	657	D 2 - 2	Beadle 2 Clarke 20	
25	30		A	Ashton United	113	W 2 - 1	Beadle 85 Hassan 90	21
26	Dec 3		H	Nantwich Town	267	L 4 - 5	Hughill 7 Burgess 22 Leeson 26 Beadle 79	
27	17		H	Buxton	214	L 3 - 4	Beadle 1 Clarke 17 62	
28	26		H	North Ferriby United	314	L 0 - 2		21
29	Jan 2		A	Frickley Athletic	273	W 2 - 1	Appleby 17 Tymon 90	
30	7		H	Chasetown	238	W 2 - 0	Portas 40 Appleby 48	21
31	14		H	Kendal Town	284	D 1 - 1	Beadle 44	21
32	21		H	Marine	242	L 1 - 2	Shaw 77 (og)	21
33	Feb 18		H	Rushall Olympic	286	W 2 - 1	Apleby 72 84	20
34	20		A	Bradford PA	220	L 0 - 3		20
35	25		A	Worksop Town	306	W 1 - 0	Burgess 72	20
36	March 3		H	Hednesford Town	293	L 0 - 2		20
37	10		A	Burscough	135	W 1 - 0	Clarke 44 (pen)	20
38	17		A	Marine	350	W 2 - 1	Clarke 45 85	18
39	24		H	Northwich Victoria	301	W 2 - 1	Portas 9 Smith 77	
40	28		H	FC United	614	D 0 - 0		20
41	31		A	Chester	3128	L 0 - 2		17
42	Apr 7		H	Stafford Rangers	371	W 2 - 1	Smith 19 Clarke 44 (pen)	18
43	9		A	North Ferriby United	192	L 0 - 1		
44	14		H	Burscough	352	D 3 - 3	Portas 27 Clarke 53 Burgess 67	17
45	19		A	Matlock Town	171	W 4 - 2	Clarke 8 (pen) 9 Mulligan 46 71	18
46	21		A	Buxton	375	W 1 - 0	Ports 11	17

Northern Premier League Action...

Witton's Titchiner shapes up to cross the ball under pressure from Stoke City's Murphy in a pre-season friendly.

Photo: Keith Clayton.

WITTON ALBION

Chairman: Ian Dobson
Secretary: Graham Shuttleworth **(T)** 07966 289 434 **(E)** wafc43008@o2.co.uk
Additional Committee Members:
Mark Harris, Reg Hardingham, Alison Atkins, Vijay Anthwal, Ernest Fryer,
Paul Worthington.
Manager: Brian Pritchard
Programme Editor: Jamie Thompson **(E)** jamie.thompson4@talktalk.net

2011-12 Squad.

Club Factfile

Founded: 1887 **Nickname:** The Albion
Previous Names: None
Previous Leagues: Lancashire Combination, Cheshire County > 1979, Northern Premier 1979-91, Conference 1991-94

Club Colours (change): Red & white stripes/blue/red (All yellow)

Ground: Help for Heros Stadium, Wincham Park, Chapel Street, Wincham, CW9 6DA **(T)** 01606 430 08
Capacity: 4,500 **Seats:** 650 **Covered:** 2,300 **Clubhouse:** Yes **Shop:** Yes

Directions: M6 Junction 19: Follow A556 for Northwich for three miles, through two sets of traffic lights. Turn right at the beginning of the dual carriageway onto A559. After ¾ mile turn right at traffic lights by Slow & Easy Public House, still following A559. After a further ¾ mile turn left a Black Greyhound Public House (signposted). Follow the road through the industrial estate for about ½ mile. Turn left immediately after crossing the canal bridge (signposted) **From M56 Junction 10:** Follow the A558 (Northwich Road) towards Northwich for approximately 6 miles. Turn right at the crossroads by the Black Greyhound Public House (signposted). Follow the road through the industrial estate for about ½ mile. Turn left immediately after crossing the canal bridge (signposted)

Previous Grounds: Central Ground (1910-1989)

Record Attendance: 3,940 v Kidderminster Harries - FA Trophy Semi-final 13/04/1991
Record Victory: 13-0 v Middlewich (H)
Record Defeat: 0-9 v Macclesfield Town (A) - 18/09/1965
Record Goalscorer: Frank Fidler - 175 (1947-50)
Record Appearances: Brian Pritchard - 729
Additional Records: Paid £12,500 to Hyde United for Jim McCluskie 1991
Senior Honours: Received £11,500 from Chester City for Peter Henderson
Northern Premier League Premier Division 1990-91, Division 1 North Play-offs 2011-12. Cheshire Senior Cup x7.

10 YEAR RECORD

02-03	03-04	04-05	05-06	06-07	07-08	08-09	09-10	10-11	11-12
NP P 7	NP P 5	NP 1 8	NP 1 8	NP P 2	NP P 2	NP P 20	NP1S 7	NP1N 10	NP1N 3

WORKSOP TOWN

Chairman: Jason Clark
Secretary: Keith Ilett   **(T)** 07734 144 961   **(E)** k.ilett@sky.com
Additional Committee Members:
Chris Smith, Ian Smith, Kevin Keep.

Manager: Simon Clark
Programme Editor: Steve Jarvis   **(E)** k.ilett@sky.com

Back row left to right: A Lake R Mooney C Unknown B Holden S Craven L Shiels M Ziccardi A Hawes P Bastock L Beeson S Ludlam
L Menga D Frecklington (Asst Manager) S Clark (Manager).
Front R to L. M McDonald R Clarke S Towers M Young L Mettam J Davies M Telling C Shaw C Wood C King O Warlow.

Club Factfile

Founded: 1861   **Nickname:** Tigers
Previous Names: Not known
Previous Leagues: Midland Co. 1896-98, 1900-30, 49-60, 61-68, 69-74, Sheffield Amateur 1898-99, 1931-33, Central Combination 1933-35,
Yorkshire 1935-39, Central Alliance1947-49, 60-61, Northern Premier 1968-69, 74-2004, Conference 2004-07

Club Colours (change): Yellow/navy/navy (Black & blue stripes/black/black)

Ground: Babbage Way, off Sandy Lane, Worksop S80 1TN   **(T)** 07734 144 961
Capacity: **Seats:**   **Covered:**   **Clubhouse:** Yes   **Shop:** NK

Directions
From M1 junc 31 take A57 Worksop after 7 miles carry on to by-pass at 3rd roundabout take 1st exit Sandy Lane industrial estate
Ground 1ml on left at side of Tyre Centre.

From A1 junc34 take B6045 Blyth, then take A57 Worksop at 1st set of lights go straight on pass the Hospital on the left,next set of
lights straight on, at the next set go under the bridge,the next set of lights turn right,100mts up the road 1st right then turn first left into
the ground.

Previous Grounds: Central Avenue, Sandy Lane, shared with Ilkeston Town (New Manor Ground)

Record Attendance: 8,171 v Chesterfield - FA Cup 1925 (Central Avenue)
Record Victory: 20-0 v Staveley - 01/09/1984
Record Defeat: 1-11 v Hull City Reserves - 1955-56
Record Goalscorer: Kenny Clark - 287
Record Appearances: Kenny Clark - 347
Additional Records: Paid £5,000 to Grantham Town for Kirk Jackson
Senior Honours: Received £47,000 from Sunderland for Jon Kennedy 2000
Sheffield Senior Cup 1923-24, 52-53, 54-55, 65-66, 69-70,72-73, 81-82, 84-85, 94-95, 96-97, 2002-03.
Northern Premier League President's Cup 1985-86, 96-97, Chairman's Cup 2001-02.

10 YEAR RECORD

02-03		03-04		04-05		05-06		06-07		07-08		08-09		09-10		10-11		11-12	
NP P	5	NP P	7	Conf N	17	Conf N	9	Conf N	21	NP P	9	NP P	17	NP P	18	NP P	7	NP P	15

WORKSOP TOWN

No.	Date	Comp	H/A	Opponents	Att:	Result	Goalscorers	Pos
1	Aug 13	NPL P	A	Kendal Town	276	L 0 - 3		
2	17		H	Stafford Rangers	456	D 1 - 1	Hudson 6	
3	20		H	Marine	339	L 0 - 3		19
4	22		A	Bradford P.A.	354	L 0 - 1		
5	27		A	Ashton United	147	L 2 - 4	Hudson 44 (pen) Shiels 63	20
6	29		H	North Ferriby United	359	D 0 - 0		
7	Sept 3		A	Northwich Victoria	503	L 1 - 2	Sherriff 20	21
8	7		H	Buxton	357	W 2 - 1	Cotterill 7 Hudson 69	
9	10		H	Chester	570	L 0 - 3		21
10	14		A	Mickleover Sports	211	D 1 - 1	Roberts 2	
11	17	FAC 1Q	A	North Ferriby United	168	L 0 - 1		
12	24		A	Chorley	1004	L 1 - 4	Jackson 43	20
13	28		H	Chasetown	292	W 4 - 1	Burbeary 21 52 Jackson 74 McDonald 84	
14	Oct 1		A	Marine	310	L 0 - 4		20
15	8		H	Nantwich Town	265	W 3 - 0	Burbeary 36 Taylor 47 59	
16	12		A	Whitby Town	275	W 4 - 3	Burbeary 6 Jackson 37 64 Gardner 41	20
17	15		A	Burscough	152	W 2 - 0	Burbeary 37 Hudson 40 (pen)	14
18	22	FAT 1Q	A	**Bradford PA**	269	D 1 - 1	Hudson 31	
19	26	FAT 1Qr	H	**Bradford PA**	281	W 4 - 1	Hudson 26 53 Davidson 88 Jackson 90	
20	29		A	Stafford Rangers	498	D 2 - 2	Roberts 55 90	12
21	Nov 2		H	Rushall Olympic	275	W 2 - 1	Burbeary 43 Jackson 84	
22	5	FAT 2Q	A	**Radcliffe Borough**	143	D 1 - 1	Hudson 67 (pen)	
23	9	FAT 2Qr	H	**Radcliffe Borough**	261	W 2 - 0	Duncum 13 McDonald 84	
24	12		A	Matlock Town	430	D 1 - 1	Jackson 55	13
25	19		H	FC United	821	L 2 - 3	Hudson 53 McDonald 69	14
26	23		A	Buxton	223	W 3 - 1	Hudson 34 (pen) Jackson 82 Sharry 86	
27	26	FAT 3Q	H	**Curzon Ashton**	238	W 3 - 2	McDonald 18 Shiels 58 Hudson 81 (pen)	
28	30		H	Mickleover Sports	807	W 5 - 4	JACKSON 3 (9 29 90) Burbeary 11 Wood 65	11
29	Dec 3		A	Chester	1850	L 0 - 2		11
30	10	FAT 1	H	**Tamworth**	343	W 1 - 0	Burbeary 62	
31	17		H	Hednesford Town	270	W 1 - 0	Hudson 55	9
32	26		H	Frickley Athletic	434	W 2 - 1	Warlow 58 King 90	8
33	Jan 2		A	North Ferriby United	326	D 0 - 0		9
34	7		H	Kendal Town	320	L 3 - 5	Jackson 18 Young 20 Hudson 90 (pen)	10
35	24	FAT 2	H	**Newport County**	538	L 1 - 3	McDonald 71	
36	28		H	Bradford PA	401	L 0 - 2		12
37	Feb 18		A	Nantwich Town	420	W 1 - 0	McDonald 75	12
38	25		H	Whitby Town	306	L 0 - 1		14
39	28		A	Rushall Olympic	218	D 0 - 0		
40	March 3		H	Northwich Victoria	302	L 0 - 1		13
41	10		A	Chasetown	329	W 2 - 1	Burbeary 31 Shiels 45	
42	17		H	Chorley	340	L 1 - 5	Warlow 11	
43	20		A	Stocksbridge PS	181	L 0 3		
44	24		A	FC United	2873	L 1 - 2	Warlow 40	15
45	31		H	Matlock Town	300	W 2 - 0	Beeson 18 57	14
46	Apr 4		H	Burscough	157	L 2 - 3	Warlow 6 McDonald 22	
47	7		H	Ashton United	226	D 3 - 3	Jackspn 22 48 McDonald 26	15
48	9		A	Frickley Athlletic	249	L 1 - 2	McDonald 40	
49	14		H	Stocksbridge PS	225	D 1 - 1	Shields 61	15
50	21		A	Hednesford Town	582	D 0 - 0		15

BAMBER BRIDGE

Chairman: Terry Gammans
Secretary: George Halliwell   **(T)** 07970 042 954   **(E)**
Additional Committee Members:
Phil Entwhistle, Cath Doherty.
Dave Rowland.
Manager: Neil Crowe
Programme Editor: Peter Nowell   **(E)**

THE NON-LEAGUE CLUB DIRECTORY

Book Holiday Inn Hotels and Save today!

Home

Clubs

Steps 1 - 4

League Tables

35 Years of Non-League Football

The Non-League Club Directory has developed into a comprehensive record of competitions within the non-League game, giving this level of football the

www.non-leagueclubdirectory.co.uk

Club Factfile

Founded: 1952   **Nickname:** Brig

Previous Names: None

Previous Leagues: Preston & District 1952-90, North West Counties 1990-93

Club Colours (change): White/black/black (All yellow)

Ground: The QED Stadium, Brownedge Road, Bamber Bridge PR5 6UX   **(T)** 01772 909 690

Capacity: 3,000   **Seats:** 554   **Covered:** 800   **Clubhouse:** Yes   **Shop:** Yes

Directions Junction 29, A6 (Bamber Bridge by-pass)onto London Way. First roundabout take 3rd exit Brownedge Road (East) then take first right. Ground on left at the bottom of the road.

Previous Grounds: King George V, Higher Wallton 1952-86

Record Attendance: 2,300 v Czech Republic - Pre Euro '96 friendly

Record Victory: 8-0 v Curzon Ashton - North West Counties 1994-95

Record Defeat: Not known

Record Goalscorer: Not known

Record Appearances: Not known

Additional Records: Paid £10,000 to Horwich RMI for Mark Edwards
Received £15,000 from Wigan Athletic for Tony Black 1995

Senior Honours:
ATDC Lancashire Trophy 1994-95.
Northern Premier League Premier Division 1995-96, Challenge Cup 1995-96.

02-03	03-04	04-05	05-06	06-07	07-08	08-09	09-10	10-11	11-12
NP 1 13	NP 1 10	NP P 21	NP 1 13	NP 1 13	NP1N 5	NP1N 11	NP1N 14	NP1N 7	NP1N 10

BURSCOUGH

Chairman: Gary Wright
Secretary: Stan Petheridge   **(T)** 07815 954 304   **(E)**
Additional Committee Members:
Rod Cottam (President), Dave Hughes Stuart Heaps, Roy Baldwin, Roy Proctor,
Caroline Proctor, Josanne Saint, Adam Saint, Stuart Saint.
Manager: Derek Goulding
Programme Editor: Stuart Saint   **(E)**

THE NON-LEAGUE CLUB DIRECTORY
Book Holiday Inn Hotels and Save today!

Home
Clubs
Steps 1 - 4
League Tables

35 Years of Non-League Football
The Non-League Club Directory has
developed into a comprehensive record
of competitions within the non-League
game, giving this level of football the

www.non-leagueclubdirectory.co.uk

Club Factfile

Founded: 1946   **Nickname:** Linnets

Previous Names: None

Previous Leagues: Liverpool County Combination 1946-53, Lancashire Combination 1953-70, Cheshire County 1970-82, North West Counties 1982-98, Northern Premier League 1998-2007, Conference 2007-09

Club Colours (change): All green (Sky blue/navy/sky)

Ground: Victoria Park, Bobby Langton Way, Mart Lane, Burscough L40 0SD   **(T)** 01704 893 237

Capacity: 2,500   **Seats:** 270   **Covered:** 1,000   **Clubhouse:** Yes   **Shop:** Yes

Directions
M6 to J27. Follow signs for 'Parbold' (A5209), carry on through Newburgh into Burscough passing Briars Hall Hotel on left. Turn right at second mini-roundabout into Junction Lane (signposted 'Burscough & Martin Mere') into village, over canal. Take second left into Mart Lane to ground at end.

Previous Grounds: Not known

Record Attendance: 4,798 v Wigan Athletic - FA Cup 3rd Qualifying Round 1950-51

Record Victory: 10-0 v Cromptons Rec - 1947 and v Nelson - 1948-49 both Lancashire Combination
Record Defeat: 0-9 v Earltown - Liverpool County Combination 1948-49

Record Goalscorer: Wes Bridge - 188

Record Appearances: Not known

Additional Records: Johnny Vincent scored 60 goals during the 1953-64 season
Louis Bimpson scored 7 goals in one game.

Senior Honours:
North West Counties League Division 1 1982-83. FA Trophy 2002-03. Northern Premier League Premier Division 2006-07.
Liverpool Challenge Cup x3. Liverpool Non-League Senior Cup x2.

02-03		03-04		04-05		05-06		06-07		07-08		08-09		09-10		10-11		11-12	
NP P	18	NP P	19	NP P	6	NP P	7	NP P	1	Conf N	8	Conf N	21	NP P	16	NP P	19	NP P	22

LAIRDS

CAMMELL LAIRD FC

CAMMELL LAIRD

Chairman: Frank Games
Secretary: Anthony R Wood   **(T)** 07931 761 429   **(E)** toddywood@hotmail.com
Additional Committee Members:
George Higham, John Lynch, Janet Skillen, Colin Skillen, Tony Thelwell.

Manager: Tony Sullivan
Programme Editor: Debbie Smaje   **(E)** toddywood@hotmail.com

Cammell Laird Football Club 2012/13

Club Factfile

Founded: 1907   **Nickname:** Lairds
Previous Names: Not known
Previous Leagues: West Cheshire, North West Counties

Club Colours (change): All royal blue (All yellow)

Ground: Kirklands, St Peter's Road, Rock Ferry, Birkenhead CH42 1PY   **(T)** 0151 645 3121
Capacity: 2,000   **Seats:** 150   **Covered:** Yes   **Clubhouse:** Yes   **Shop:** Yes

Directions FROM CHESTER: M53, leave at Junction 5, take third exit on to A41 and travel towards Birkenhead. At New Ferry signpost take B5136 towards New Ferry. After approx 1 mile at sign for Lairds Sports Club, turn right down Proctor Road, ground on the left.
FROM LIVERPOOL: Take the Birkenhead Tunnel then A41 signposted North Wales for approx 1 mile. At large roundabout take B5136 signposted New Ferry, Rock Ferry. Follow until 2nd set of traffic lights at Abbotsford pub. Turn left then first right into St Peters Road. Ground at bottom of road on right.

Previous Grounds: Not known

Record Attendance: 1,700 v Harwich & Parkeston - FA Vase 5th Round 1990-91
Record Victory: Not known
Record Defeat: Not known
Record Goalscorer: Not known
Record Appearances: Not known
Additional Records:

Senior Honours:
North West Counties League Division 2, League Cup and Trophy 2004-05, Division 1 2005-06.
West Cheshire League x19 (Most recently 2000-01). Cheshire Amateur Cup x11.
Wirral Senior Cup.

10 YEAR RECORD

02-03		03-04		04-05		05-06		06-07		07-08		08-09		09-10		10-11		11-12	
WCh1	3	WCh1	2	NWC2	1	NWC1	1	NP 1	2	NP1S	2	NP P	18	NP1S	16	NP1N	19	NP1N	22

CLITHEROE

Chairman: Anne Barker
Secretary: Colin Wilson   **(T)** 07949 031 039   **(E)** wilsoncfc424370@aol.com
Additional Committee Members:
Andrew Jackson, Chris Musson.

Manager: Paul Moore
Programme Editor: Chris Musson   **(E)** wilsoncfc424370@aol.com

Back Row (L-R): Kirsty McKillop, Dave Hughes, Jon Stevenson, Chris Smalley, Andy Naylor, Danny Bell, Jack Higgins, Hakan Burton, Will James, Jordan Williams, R ob Flint, Simon Nangle, Paul Moore
Front Row (L-R): Lee Pugh, Richard Mottram, Louis Edwards, James Gardner, Connor Smith, Marcus Calvert, Ross Dent, Ollie Devenney, Alex Johnson, Alex Johnson.

Club Factfile

Founded: 1877   **Nickname:** The Blues
Previous Names: None
Previous Leagues: Blackburn & District, Lancashire Combination 1903-04, 05-10, 25-82, North West Counties 1982-85

Club Colours (change): Royal Blue/royal blue/red (All red)

Ground: Shawbridge, off Pendle Road, Clitheroe, Lancashire BB7 1DZ   **(T)** 01200 444 487
Capacity: 2,400   **Seats:** 250   **Covered:** 1,400   **Clubhouse:** Yes   **Shop:**
Directions: M6 junction 31, A59 to Clitheroe (17 miles) at 5th roundabout turn left after half a mile at Pendle Road. Ground is one mile behind Bridge Inn on the right.

Previous Grounds: Not known

Record Attendance: 2,050 v Mangotsfield - FA Vase Semi-final 1995-96
Record Victory: Not known
Record Defeat: Not known
Record Goalscorer: Don Francis
Record Appearances: Lindsey Wallace - 670
Additional Records: Received £45,000 from Crystal Palace for Carlo Nash

Senior Honours:
North West Counties League 1984-85, 2003-04.
Lancashire Challenge Trophy 1984-85. East Lancashire Floodlit Trophy 1994-95.

10 YEAR RECORD

02-03		03-04		04-05		05-06		06-07		07-08		08-09		09-10		10-11		11-12	
NWC1	2	NWC1	1	NP 1	19	NP 1	16	NP 1	16	NP1N	13	NP1N	12	NP1N	8	NP1N	6	NP1N	19

CURZON ASHTON

Chairman: Harry Galloway
Secretary: Robert Hurst   **(T)** 07713 252 310   **(E)** office@curzon-ashton.co.uk
Additional Committee Members:
Harry Twamley, Ronnie Capstick, Simon Shuttleworth, Paul Price, James Newall, David Jones,
Steve Ball, Ian Seymour, Nigel Seymour, Ron Walber, Wayne Salkeld, John Clayton.
Manager: John Flanagan
Programme Editor: Ian Seymour   **(E)** office@curzon-ashton.co.uk

THE NON-LEAGUE CLUB DIRECTORY

Book Holiday Inn Hotels and Save today!

Home

Clubs

Steps 1 - 4

League Tables

35 Years of Non-League Football

The Non-League Club Directory has
developed into a comprehensive record
of competitions within the non-League
game, giving this level of football the

www.non-leagueclubdirectory.co.uk

Club Factfile

Founded: 1963   **Nickname:** Not known

Previous Names: None

Previous Leagues: Manchester Amateur, Manchester > 1978, Cheshire County 1978-82,
North West Counties 1982-87, 98-2007, Northern Premier 1987-97, Northern Counties East 1997-98,

Club Colours (change): All royal blue (All red)

Ground: Tameside Stadium, Richmond Street, Ashton-u-Lyme OL7 9HG   **(T)** 0161 330 6033

Capacity: 5,000   **Seats:** 504   **Covered:** Yes   **Clubhouse:** Yes   **Shop:** Yes

Directions: From Stockport (south) direction Leave the M60 at junc 23 (Ashton-U-Lyne). Turn left at the top of the slip road, go straight through the next set of lights, and bear right (onto Lord Sheldon Way) at the next set. Continue on this road until you come to a set of traffic lights with the Cineworld Cinema on your right. Turn left here onto Richmond St. Over the bridge, across the mini-roundabout and then first left down to the ground. From Oldham (north) direction Leave the M60 at junc 23 (Ashton-U-Lyne) and turn right at the top of the slip road signposted A635 Manchester. Turn right at the second set of traffic lights, sign posted Ashton Moss, and then follow directions as from the south.

Previous Grounds: Katherine Street > 204, Stalybridge Celtic FC 2004-06

Record Attendance: 1,826 v Stamford - FA Vase Semi-final

Record Victory: 7-0 v Ashton United
Record Defeat: 0-8 v Bamber Bridge

Record Goalscorer: Alan Sykes

Record Appearances: Alan Sykes

Additional Records:

Senior Honours:
Manchester Premier Cup x5

02-03		03-04		04-05		05-06		06-07		07-08		08-09		09-10		10-11		11-12	
NWC1	18	NWC1	7	NWC1	4	NWC1	7	NWC1	2	NP1N	4	NP1N	4	NP1N	3	NP1N	4	NP1N	2

FARSLEY A.F.C.

Chairman: John Palmer
Secretary: Joshua Greaves   **(T)** 07725 999 758   **(E)** josh@farsleyafc.com
Additional Committee Members:
J Farrell, Mrs D Farrell, Mrs M Palmer, P Palmer, S Palmer.

Manager: Neil Parsley
Programme Editor: Joshua Greaves   **(E)** josh@farsleyafc.com

Club Factfile

Founded: 2010   **Nickname:** The Villagers
Previous Names: Farsley Celtic > 2010
Previous Leagues: Northern Counties East 2010-11.

Club Colours (change): Blue/blue/white (Yellow/black/yellow)

Ground: Throstle Nest, Newlands, Pudsey, Leeds, LS28 5BE   **(T)** 0113 255 7292
Capacity: 4,000   **Seats:** 300   **Covered:** 1,500   **Clubhouse:** Yes   **Shop:** Yes

Directions: Farsley is sandwiched between Leeds and Bradford approximately 1 mile from the junction of the Leeds Outer Ring Road (A6110) and the A647 towards Bradford. At the junction, take the B6157 towards Leeds, passing the police station on the left hand side. At New Street (the junction cornered by Go Outdoors) turn left. Newlands is approximately 300 yards on the right. Throstle Nest is situated at the end of Newlands with parking available outside the ground.

Previous Grounds: Not known

Record Attendance: None
Record Victory: 8-0 v Arnold Town (H) Northern Counties East Premier 2010-11.
Record Defeat: 5-1 v Tadcaster Albion, President's Cup Final 27/04/11.
Record Goalscorer: Not known
Record Appearances: Not known
Additional Records: None

Senior Honours:
Northern Counties East Premier Division 2010-11.

				10 YEAR RECORD						
02-03	03-04	04-05	05-06	06-07	07-08	08-09	09-10	10-11	11-12	
								NCEP 1	NP1N 4	

GARFORTH TOWN

Chairman: Simon Clifford
Secretary: Joe Fella   **(T)** 07516 358 452   **(E)** wright4854@hotmail.com
Additional Committee Members:
Christopher Wright

Manager: Vernon Blair
Programme Editor: Chris Mather   **(E)** wright4854@hotmail.com

THE NON-LEAGUE CLUB DIRECTORY

Book Holiday Inn Hotels and Save today!

Home

Clubs

Steps 1 - 4

League Tables

35 Years of Non-League Football

The Non-League Club Directory has developed into a comprehensive record of competitions within the non-League game, giving this level of football the

www.non-leagueclubdirectory.co.uk

Club Factfile

Founded: 1964   **Nickname:** The Miners

Previous Names: Garforth Miners 1964-85

Previous Leagues: Leeds Sunday Combination 1964-72, West Yorkshire 1972-78, Yorkshire 1978-83, Northern Counties East 1983-2007

Club Colours (change): Yellow/blue/white (Blue and white stripes/white/blue)

Ground: Genix Healthcare Stadium, Cedar Ridge, Garforth, Leeds LS25 2PF   **(T)** 0113 287 7145

Capacity: 3,000   **Seats:**   **Covered:** 200   **Clubhouse:** Yes   **Shop:** Yes

Directions: From North: travel south on A1 and join M1. Turn off at 1st junc (47). From South: M1 to junc 47. From Leeds area: join M1 at junc 44 or 46 and turn off at junc 47. From West: M62 to junc 29, join M1 and off at junc 47. From junc 47: take turning signe 'Garforth' (A642). Approx. 200 yds turn left into housing estate opposite White House. (Cedar Ridge). Stadium at end of lane. From the South (alternative): A1, turn off on to A63 signposted 'Leeds' immediately after 'Boot & Shoe' Public House. At 1st roundabout turn right on to A656 and follow to next roundabout. Take 1st left on to A642 (Garforth) and follow from M1 junc 47.

Previous Grounds: Not known

Record Attendance: 1,385 v Tadcaster Albion - Socrates debut - Northern Counties East League record

Record Victory: Not known

Record Defeat: Not known

Record Goalscorer: Simeon Bambrook - 67

Record Appearances: Philip Matthews - 1982-93

Additional Records:

Senior Honours:
Northern Counties East Division 1 1997-98

02-03	03-04	04-05	05-06	06-07	07-08	08-09	09-10	10-11	11-12
NCEP	20	NCE1	6	NCE1	2	NCEP	10	NP1N	4	NP1N	10	NP1N	16	NP1N	20	NP1N	13	NP1N	5

GOOLE AFC

Chairman: Des O'Hearne
Secretary: Andrew Morris   **(T)** 07751 457 254   **(E)** andym236566609@aol.com
Additional Committee Members:
Craig Whincup, Graeme Wilson, Eric Lawton, Geoff Bruines, Graeme Smith, Carol Smith,
Ann Smith, Harry Harrison.
Manager: John Reed
Programme Editor: Malcolm Robinson   **(E)** malrob01@tiscali.co.uk

THE NON-LEAGUE CLUB DIRECTORY

Book Holiday Inn Hotels and Save today!

Home

Clubs

Steps 1 - 4

League Tables

35 Years of Non-League Football

The Non-League Club Directory has developed into a comprehensive record of competitions within the non-League game, giving this level of football the

www.non-leagueclubdirectory.co.uk

Club Factfile

Founded: 1997   **Nickname:** The Badgers

Previous Names: Goole Town > 1996.

Previous Leagues: Central Midlands 1997-98.
Northern Counties East 2000-04.

Club Colours (change): White with red trim/white/red (Yellow/blue/blue)

Ground: Victoria Pleasure Gardens, Marcus Road, Goole DN14 6WW   **(T)** 01405 762 794 (Match days)

Capacity: 3,000   **Seats:** 200   **Covered:** 800   **Clubhouse:** Yes   **Shop:** Yes

Directions: Leave the M62 at Junction 36 and follow signs to Goole Town Centre.
Turn right at the 2nd set of traffic lights into Boothferry Road. Turn right again after 300 yards into Carter Street.
The Victoria Pleasure Grounds is at the end of the road. 366 Metres from Goole Railway Station.

Previous Grounds:

Record Attendance: 976 v Leeds United - 1999

Record Victory: Not known
Record Defeat: Not known

Record Goalscorer: Kevin Severn (1997-2001)

Record Appearances: Phil Dobson - 187 (1999-2001)

Additional Records:

Senior Honours:
Central Midlands 1997-98.
Northern Counties East Division 1 1999-2000, Premier Division 2003-04.

02-03		03-04		04-05		05-06		06-07		07-08		08-09		09-10		10-11		11-12	
NCEP	3	NCEP	6	NCEP	1	NP 1	21	NP 1	7	NP 1	9	NP1S	18	NP1S	18	NP1S	13	NP1S	10

HARROGATE RAILWAY ATHLETIC

Chairman: TBC
Secretary: Michael Sunley   **(T)** 07970 447 823   **(E)** mail4rail@ntlworld.com
Additional Committee Members:
Chris Parkes, Bob Moffat, Andy Hope, Mark Poulter, John Gray, Ray Dodds, Billy Robson, Dave Green, Dave Bolam, Malcolm Shutt, Nigel Corner, Harry Wood, Dave Cartledge, Alec Spence.
Manager: Billy Miller
Programme Editor: TBC   **(E)**

THE NON-LEAGUE CLUB DIRECTORY

Book Holiday Inn Hotels and Save today!

Home

Clubs

Steps 1 - 4

League Tables

35 Years of Non-League Football

The Non-League Club Directory has developed into a comprehensive record of competitions within the non-League game, giving this level of football the

www.non-leagueclubdirectory.co.uk

Club Factfile

Founded: 1935   **Nickname:** The Rail

Previous Names: None
Previous Leagues: West Yorkshire, Harrogate & District, Yorkshire 1955-73, 80-82, Northern Counties East 1982-2006

Club Colours (change): Red/green/red (All blue)

Ground: Station View, Starbeck, Harrogate, North Yorkshire HG2 7JA   **(T)** 01423 883 104

Capacity: 3,500   **Seats:** 800   **Covered:** 600   **Clubhouse:** Yes   **Shop:** No

Directions: From All Areas I would suggest using the M1 A1 Link Road heading North. Once on the A1 North stay on it until Junction 47. Exit at Junction 47 and take the 1st Exit at the Roundabout A59 heading towards Knaresborough and Harrogate. At the next Roundabout take the 3rd exit A59 Knaresborough. Stay on the A59 through Knaresborough and on towards Harrogate, after approx 1 mile from Knaresborough you will enter Starbeck. Proceed through Starbeck over the Railway Crossing. Station View is the 1st Right after the Railway Crossing. The Ground is at the far end of Station View. If you are coming from Harrogate towards Knaresborough on the A59 turn left immediately prior to pelican crossing just before the Railway Crossing. The Ground is at the far end of Station View.

Previous Grounds:

Record Attendance: 3,500 v Bristol City - FA Cup 2nd Round 2002-03

Record Victory: Not known
Record Defeat: Not known

Record Goalscorer: Not known

Record Appearances: Not known

Additional Records: Received £1,000 from Guiseley for Colin Hunter

Senior Honours:
Northern Counties East Division 2 North & League cup 1983-84, Division 1 1989-99.

02-03		03-04		04-05		05-06		06-07		07-08		08-09		09-10		10-11		11-12	
NCEP	10	NCEP	12	NCEP	3	NCEP	3	NP 1	12	NP1N	12	NP1N	18	NP1N	17	NP1N	20	NP1N	21

LANCASTER CITY

Chairman: Mick Hoyle
Secretary: Barry Newsham   **(T)** 07759 530 901   **(E)** lancastercityfc@btinternet.com
Additional Committee Members:
Stuart Houghton, David Needham, Ian Sharp, Norman Wilson, Steve Ball, Eric Williams.

Manager: Tony Hesketh
Programme Editor: Barry Newsham   **(E)** lancastercityfc@btinternet.com

THE NON-LEAGUE CLUB DIRECTORY

Book Holiday Inn Hotels and Save today!

Home

Clubs

Steps 1 - 4

League Tables

35 Years of Non-League Football

The Non-League Club Directory has developed into a comprehensive record of competitions within the non-League game, giving this level of football the

www.non-leagueclubdirectory.co.uk

Club Factfile

Founded: 1905   **Nickname:** Dolly Blues

Previous Names: None

Previous Leagues: Lancashire Combination 1905-70, Northern Premier League 1970-82, 87-2004, North West Counties 1982-87, Conference 2004-07

Club Colours (change): Blue/white/blue (Yellow/blue/yellow)

Ground: Giant Axe, West Road, Lancaster LA1 5PE   **(T)** 01524 382 238

Capacity: 3,064   **Seats:** 513   **Covered:** 900   **Clubhouse:** Yes   **Shop:** Yes

Directions: From the South: Exit M6 at Junction 33. At roundabout take the second exit onto the A6, pass through Galgate and then Lancaster University on the right until the next roundabout. Take the second main exit into Lancaster and follow signs for the railway station. At the traffic lights by Waterstones Bookshop turn immediately left. Take the second right onto Station Road and follow downhill on West Road and take the first right into the ground. From the North: Exit M6 at Junction 34 and turn left onto the A683. Follow signs for railway station into City around the one way system. Move over to the right hand side lane at the police station and through traffic lights. Manoeuvre into the left-hand lane until traffic lights at Waterstones Bookshop. Follow directions as from the south.

Previous Grounds: Not known

Record Attendance: 7,500 v Carlisle United - FA Cup 1936

Record Victory: 8-0 v Leyland Motors (A) - 1983-84
Record Defeat: 0-10 v Matlock Town - Northern Premier League Division 1 1973-74

Record Goalscorer: David Barnes - 130

Record Appearances: Edgar J Parkinson - 591

Additional Records: Paid £6,000 to Droylsden for Jamie Tandy
Received £25,000 from Birmingham City for Chris Ward

Senior Honours:

Lancashire Junior Cup (ATS Challenge Trophy) 1927-28, 28-29, 30-31, 33-34, 51-52, 74-75.
Northern Premier League Division 1 1995-96.

02-03		03-04		04-05		05-06		06-07		07-08		08-09		09-10		10-11		11-12	
NP P	17	NP P	8	Conf N	13	Conf N	15	Conf N	24	NP1N	11	NP1N	7	NP1N	2	NP1N	8	NP1N	6

MOSSLEY

Chairman: Vacant
Secretary: Harry Hulmes   **(T)** 07944 856 343   **(E)** harry.hulmes@mossleyafc.com
Additional Committee Members:
Steve Burgess, Mark Griffin, John Lamer, Bob Murphy, Joanne Blackshaw,
John Cawthorne, Elaine Field, Colin Fielding, Michelle Freeman, Steve Porter, Steve Tague.
Manager: Steve Halford
Programme Editor: John Cawthorne   **(E)** harry.hulmes@btinternet.com

www.non-leagueclubdirectory.co.uk

Club Factfile

Founded: 1903   **Nickname:** Lilywhites

Previous Names: Park Villa 1903-04, Mossley Juniors

Previous Leagues: Ashton, South East Lancashire, Lancashire Combination 1918-19, Cheshire County 1919-72, Northern Premier 1972-95, North West Counties 1995-2004

Club Colours (change): White/black/black (All orange)

Ground: Seel Park, Market Street, Mossley, Lancashire OL5 0ES   **(T)** 01457 832 369

Capacity: 4,500   **Seats:** 200   **Covered:** 1,500   **Clubhouse:** Yes   **Shop:** Yes

Directions: Exit M60 Junction 23 following A635 Ashton-under-Lyne. Take 3rd exit off roundabout then 3rd exit off next roundabout (Asda) and then 3rd exit off next roundabout signed Mossley A670. At junction turn right on to Mossley Rd through traffic lights. After approx 2.5 miles drop down hill entering Mossley town centre. Passing supermarket on left turn right before next traffic lights. Continue up the hill and left into Market Street. Ground is approx 200 yards on the left.

Previous Grounds: Not known

Record Attendance: 7,000 v Stalybridge Celtic 1950

Record Victory: Not known
Record Defeat: Not known

Record Goalscorer: David Moore - 235 (1974-84)

Record Appearances: Jimmy O'Connor - 613 (1972-87)

Additional Records: Paid £2,300 to Altrincham for Phil Wilson
Received £25,000 from Everton for Eamonn O'Keefe

Senior Honours:
Northern Premier League 1978-79, 79-80, Challenge Cup 78-79, Division 1 2005-06

02-03		03-04		04-05		05-06		06-07		07-08		08-09		09-10		10-11		11-12	
NWC1	3	NWC1	2	NP 1	7	NP 1	1	NP P	20	NP1N	15	NP1N	10	NP1N	7	NP1N	15	NP1N	14

NEW MILLS

Chairman: Raymond Coverley
Secretary: Duncan Hibbert   **(T)** 07957 482 343   **(E)** duncanhibbert@newmillsafc.co.uk
Additional Committee Members:
Andrew Bowers, Patrick Kenyon, John Bradbury, Glyn Jones, Allan Jones,
Michael Bradbury.
Manager: Ally Pickering
Programme Editor: Glyn Jones   **(E)** glynjones@newmillsafc.co.uk

THE NON-LEAGUE CLUB DIRECTORY

Book Holiday Inn Hotels and Save today!

Home

Clubs

Steps 1 - 4

League Tables

35 Years of Non-League Football

The Non-League Club Directory has
developed into a comprehensive record
of competitions within the non-League
game, giving this level of football the

www.non-leagueclubdirectory.co.uk

Club Factfile

Founded: pre1890   **Nickname:** The Millers

Previous Names: New Mills St Georges until 1919

Previous Leagues: Manchester, North West Counties, Cheshire

Club Colours (change): Amber/amber/black (White/white/black).

Ground: Church Lane, New Mills, SK22 4NP   **(T)** 01663 747 435

Capacity: 1,650   **Seats:** 120   **Covered:** 400   **Clubhouse:** Yes   **Shop:**

Directions

Via Buxton: Follow the A6 By-Pass, go straight through the roundabout, under railway bridge and about 1 mile further on turn right onto Marsh Lane (Past Furness Vale primary school), this road takes you straight to the ground. Coach drivers should proceed on the A6 a couple of miles turning right opposite the Swan.

From Chesterfield, take the A619 then the A623 and after the hair pin bend at Sparrow pit, proceed down the A623 turning right onto the A6 By-Pass, Follow directions as above.

Previous Grounds: Not known

Record Attendance: Att: 4,500 v Hyde United, Manchester Junior Cup 09/09/1922

Record Victory: 20-3 v Winton United, Manchester Junior Cup 10/11/1962
Record Defeat: Not known

Record Goalscorer: In a season - Neville Holdgate - 62 1937-38

Record Appearances: Not known

Additional Records:

Senior Honours:
Manchester League Premier Division 1924, 26, 56, 63, 65, 66, 67, 68, 70, 71.
North West Counties Division Two 2007-08, Challenge Cup 2008-09, Premier Division 2010-11.

02-03		03-04		04-05		05-06		06-07		07-08		08-09		09-10		10-11		11-12	
MancP	10	MancP	14	NWC2	9	NWC2	12	NWC2		NWC2	1	NWCP	2	NWCP	2	NWCP	1	NP1S	9

OSSETT ALBION

Chairman: Steven Hanks
Secretary: Alan Nash   **(T)** 07585 952 295   **(E)** ossettalbion@sky.com
Additional Committee Members:
N Wigglesworth, P Hanks, S Chambers, L Burns, J Bowker, A Lightfoot, J Hirst, K Fletcher, J Ferguson, M Baker,
N Yarrow, P Riordan, J Butterworth, J Shaw, P Eaton, J Murgatroyd, J McGinty, A Weatherill, S Garside.
Manager: Lloyd Fellow & Paul Watson
Programme Editor: Stephen Hanks   **(E)** ossettalbion@sky.com

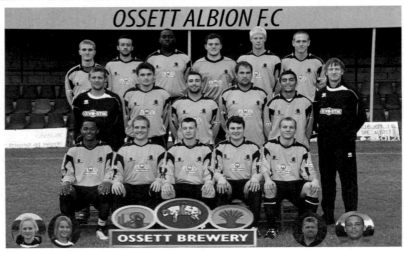

2011-12 Squad.

Club Factfile

Founded: 1944   **Nickname:** Albion
Previous Names: Not known
Previous Leagues: Heavy Woollen Area 1944-49, West Riding County Amateur 1949-50, West Yorkshire 1950-57,
Yorkshire 1957-82, Northern Counties East 1982-2004

Club Colours (change): Gold/black/black (All white)

Ground: The Warehouse Systems Stadium, Dimple Wells, Ossett, Yorkshire WF5 8JU **(T)** 01924 273 746
Capacity: 3,000   **Seats:** Yes   **Covered:** 750   **Clubhouse:** Yes   **Shop:** Yes
Directions: From M1 Junction 40: Follow Wakefield signs for 200 yards. Turn right at traffic lights (Holiday Inn on the corner). At the end of Queens Drive turn right and then 2nd left onto Southdale Road. At the end of Southdale Road turn right then immediately left onto Dimple Wells Road, the ground is facing. NOTE: There is a weight limit on Southdale Road. Coaches will need to continue on Station Road to the end, turn left, then at the end left again. Take 1st right onto Priory Road following for 200 yards turning left twice.

Previous Grounds: Fearn House

Record Attendance: 1,200 v Leeds United - Opening of floodlights 1986
Record Victory: 12-0 v British Ropes (H) - Yorkshire League Division 2 06/05/1959
Record Defeat: 2-11 v Swillington (A) - West Yorkshire League Division 1 25/04/1956
Record Goalscorer: John Balmer
Record Appearances: Peter Eaton - 800+ (22 years)
Additional Records:

Senior Honours:
Northern Counties East League Division 1 1986-87, Premier Division 1998-99, 2003-04, League Cup 1983-84, 2002-03.
West Riding County Cup x4.

10 YEAR RECORD																			
02-03		03-04		04-05		05-06		06-07		07-08		08-09		09-10		10-11		11-12	
NCEP	5	NCEP	1	NP 1	12	NP 1	14	NP 1	11	NP1N	6	NP1N	6	NP1N	21	NP1N	22	NP1N	18

OSSETT TOWN

Chairman: Graham Firth
Secretary: Ian Adamson   **(T)** 07907 090 348   **(E)** ossetttownfc@gmail.com
Additional Committee Members:
James Rogers, Ian Adamson, Steph Joy, Justin Fozzard, John Rankin, Ann Sheriffe, Jacqueline Seed.
Manager: Craig Elliott
Programme Editor: David Clegg   **(E)** ossetttownfc@gmail.com

2011-12 Squad.

Club Factfile

Founded: 1936   **Nickname:** Town
Previous Names:
Previous Leagues: Leeds 1936-39, Yorkshire 1945-82, Northern Counties East 1983-99

Club Colours (change): All red (All blue)

Ground: Ingfield, Prospect Road, Ossett, Wakefield WF5 9HA   **(T)** 01924 280 028
Capacity: 4,000   **Seats:** 360   **Covered:** 1,000   **Clubhouse:** Yes   **Shop:** Yes

Directions: From M1 Junction 40: Take A638 signposted Ossett Town Centre. Take first left off A638 onto Wakefield Road, sixth left turn into Dale Street (B6120) to traffic lights. Turn left at lights. The Ground is in front of you opposite the bus station. The entrance to the Ground is just before the Esso petrol station.

Previous Grounds:

Record Attendance: 2,600 v Manchester United - Friendly 1989
Record Victory: 10-1 v Harrogate RA (H) - Northern Counties East 27/04/1993
Record Defeat: 0-7 v Easington Colliery - FA Vase 08/10/1983
Record Goalscorer: Dave Leadbitter
Record Appearances: Steve Worsfold
Additional Records: Received £1,350 from Swansea Town for Dereck Blackburn

Senior Honours:
West Riding County Cup 1958-59, 81-82

10 YEAR RECORD

02-03	03-04	04-05	05-06	06-07	07-08	08-09	09-10	10-11	11-12
NP 1 20	NP 1 14	NP P 16	NP P 11	NP P 10	NP P 18	NP P 12	NP P 19	NP P 21	NP1N 17

PRESCOT CABLES

Chairman: Tony Zeverona
Secretary: Doug Lace **(T)** 07753 143 273 **(E)** prescotcables@hotmail.com
Additional Committee Members:
D Bellairs, G Conway, M Flaherty, P Kneale, N Parr, K Derbyshire, J Gibileru.

Manager: David Powell
Programme Editor: Paul Watkinson **(E)** prescotcables@hotmail.com

Club Factfile

Founded: 1884   **Nickname:** Tigers
Previous Names: Prescot > 1995
Previous Leagues: Liverpool County Combination, Lancashire Combination 1897-98, 1918-20, 27-33, 36-76,
Mid Cheshire 1976-78, Cheshire County 1978-82, North West Counties 1982-2003

Club Colours (change): Amber/black/black (All red)

Ground: Valerie Park, Eaton Street, Prescot L34 6HD   **(T)** 0151 430 0507
Capacity: 3,000   **Seats:** 500   **Covered:** 600   **Clubhouse:** Yes   **Shop:** Yes

Directions
From North: M6 to Junction 26, onto M58 to Junction 3. Follow A570 to junction with A580 (East Lancs Road). (Approach junction in right hand lane of the two lanes going straight on). Cross A580 and take first road on right (Bleak Hill Road). Follow this road through to Prescot (2 miles). At traffic lights turn right, straight on at large roundabout (do not follow route onto Prescot by-pass) and right at next lights. 100 yards turn right at Hope and Anchor pub into Hope Street. Club will be in sight at bottom of road. **From South:** M6 to Junction 21a (M62 junction 10). Follow M62 towards Liverpool, to junction 7. Follow A57 to Rainhill and Prescot. Through traffic lights at Fusilier pub, 100 yards turn right at Hope and Anchor pub (as above). **From East:** Follow M62 as described in 'From South' or A580 East Lancs Road to Junction with A570 (Rainford by-pass), turn left and take first right. Follow route as 'From North'.

Previous Grounds: Not known

Record Attendance: 8,122 v Ashton National - 1932
Record Victory: 18-3 v Great Harwood - 1954-55
Record Defeat: 1-12 v Morecambe - 1936-37
Record Goalscorer: Freddie Crampton
Record Appearances: Harry Grisedale
Additional Records:

Senior Honours:
Lancashire Combination 1956-57. North West Counties League 2002-03.
Liverpool Non-League Cup x4. Liverpool Challenge Cup x6.

10 YEAR RECORD									
02-03	03-04	04-05	05-06	06-07	07-08	08-09	09-10	10-11	11-12
NWC1 1	NP 1 12	NP P 5	NP P 13	NP P 14	NP P 13	NP P 22	NP1N 15	NP1N 21	NP1N 16

RADCLIFFE BOROUGH

Chairman: Vacant
Secretary: Graham Fielding   **(T)** 07407 427 028   **(E)** rbfc@hotmail.co.uk
Additional Committee Members:
David Chalmers

Manager: Benny Phillips
Programme Editor: David Chalmers   **(E)** rbfc@hotmail.co.uk

2011-12 Squad - Back Row (L-R): Reece Kelly, Steve Howson, Griff Jones, Ben Wharton, Nick Culkin, Mark Jones, Simon Kelly, James Mullineux, Daniel Thomas, Craig Flowers.
Front Row: Shaun Connor, Alastair Brown, Jordan Hadfield, Dave Sherlock, Tom Brooks, Steve Burke and Ryan Broadhead.

Club Factfile

Founded: 1949   **Nickname:** Boro
Previous Names: None
Previous Leagues: South East Lancashire, Manchester 1953-63, Lancashire Combination 1963-71, Cheshire County 1971-82, North West Counties 1982-97

Club Colours (change): Blue & black stripes/black/blue (Red and black stripes/black/white)

Ground: Stainton Park, Pilkington Road, Radcliffe, Lancashire M26 3PE   **(T)** 0161 724 8346
Capacity: 3,000   **Seats:** 350   **Covered:** 1,000   **Clubhouse:** Yes   **Shop:** Yes

Directions: M62 junction 17 – follow signs for 'Whitefield' and 'Bury'.
Take A665 to Radcliffe via by-pass to Bolton Road. Signposted to turn right into Unsworth Street opposite Turf Hotel. The Stadium is on the left approximately half a mile turning Colshaw Close East.

Previous Grounds: Not known

Record Attendance: 2,495 v York City - FA Cup 1st Round 2000-01
Record Victory: Not known
Record Defeat: Not known
Record Goalscorer: Ian Lunt - 147
Record Appearances: David Bean - 401
Additional Records: Paid £5,000 to Buxton for Gary Walker 1991
Senior Honours: Received £20,000 from Shrewsbury Town for Jody Banim 2003
North West Counties 19984-85. Northern Premier League Division 1 1996-97.

10 YEAR RECORD

02-03		03-04		04-05		05-06		06-07		07-08		08-09		09-10		10-11		11-12	
NP 1	3	NP P	20	NP P	9	NP P	18	NP P	21	NP1N	16	NP1N	16	NP1N	10	NP1N	18	NP1N	15

RAMSBOTTOM UNITED

Chairman: Harry Williams
Secretary: Malcolm Holt   **(T)** 07854 466 214   **(E)** holt9uu@btinternet.com
Additional Committee Members:
Chris Woolfall, Jack Wolfenden, Andrew Edmondson, Geoff Lay, Keith Topping,
Tony Cunningham, Eric Whalley.
Manager: Anthony Johnson
Programme Editor: Richard Isaacs   **(E)** holt9uu@btinternet.com

THE NON-LEAGUE CLUB DIRECTORY

Book Holiday Inn Hotels and Save today!

Home

Clubs

Steps 1 - 4

League Tables

35 Years of Non-League Football

The Non-League Club Directory has developed into a comprehensive record of competitions within the non-League game, giving this level of football the

www.non-leagueclubdirectory.co.uk

Club Factfile

Founded: 1966   **Nickname:** The Rams

Previous Names: None
Previous Leagues: Bury Amateur, Bolton Combination & Manchester League

Club Colours (change): Blue/blue/white (Red/black/red).

Ground: The Harry Williams Stadium, Acrebottom (off Bridge Street) BL0 0BS.   **(T)** 07854 466214

Capacity: **Seats:** Yes   **Covered:** Yes   **Clubhouse:** Yes   **Shop:** No

Directions
From South,M66(north) to junction1,take the A56 towards Ramsbottom, after 1 mile turn left at traffic lights down Bury New Road follow the road towards the centre then turn left just before the railway crossing, ground runs parallel with the railway line.

From the North leave the A56 (Edenfield by pass) at the start of the M66, follow the signs for Ramsbottom into the centre turn left down Bridge street then after 100 yards turn immediately right after the railway level crossing ground parallel with railway line.

Previous Grounds:

Record Attendance: Att: 1,653 v FC United of Manchester 07.04.2007.

Record Victory: 9-0 v Stantondale (Home, NWCFL Division Two, 9th November 1996)
Record Defeat: 0-7 v Salford City (Away, NWCFL Division One, 16th November 2002)

Record Goalscorer: Russell Brierley - 176 (1996-2003). **Record in a season:** Russell Brierley - 38 (1999-2000)

Record Appearances: Not known
Additional Records:

Senior Honours:
North West Counties Division Two 1996-97, Premier Division 2011-12.

02-03		03-04		04-05		05-06		06-07		07-08		08-09		09-10		10-11		11-12	
NWC1	15	NWC1	17	NWC1	5	NWC1	18	NWC1	8	NWC1	16	NWCP	14	NWCP	4	NWCP	2	NWCP	1

SALFORD CITY

Chairman: Darren Quick
Secretary: Andrew Giblin   **(T)** 07867 823 713   **(E)** andrewgiblin@aol.com
Additional Committee Members:
Hazel Blears, Dave Russell, Frank McCauley, Jon Barton, Jimmy Birtwistle, Derek Brent, Peter Byram, Ged Carter,
Barbara Gaskill,Terry Gaskill,Ian Jolly,Ian Malone,Paul Raven,George Russell,John Simpson,P Smith,B Taylor,D Wilson.
Manager: Darren Sheridan
Programme Editor: TBC   **(E)**

35 Years of Non-League Football

The Non-League Club Directory has developed into a comprehensive record of competitions within the non-League game, giving this level of football the

www.non-leagueclubdirectory.co.uk

Club Factfile

Founded: 1940   **Nickname:** Ammies

Previous Names: Salford Central 1940-63, Salford Amateurs 1963 until merger with Anson Villa, Salford F.C. > 1990
Previous Leagues: Manchester 1963-80, Cheshire County 1980-82, North West Counties 1982-2008

Club Colours (change): Tangerine/black/tangerine (Sky blue/navy blue/sky)

Ground: Moor Lane, Kersal, Salford, Manchester M7 3PZ   **(T)** 0161 792 6287

Capacity: 8,000   **Seats:** 260   **Covered:** 600   **Clubhouse:** Yes   **Shop:** No

Directions
M62 to Junction 17 (Prestwich, Whitefield). Take A56 Bury New Road towards Manchester.
Continue through four sets of traffic lights.
Turn right into Moor Lane. Ground 500 yards on left.
Take first left after ground (Oaklands Road), first left again into Nevile Road and follow along to main entrance.

Previous Grounds:

Record Attendance: 3,000 v Whickham - FA Vase 1980

Record Victory: Not known
Record Defeat: Not known
Record Goalscorer: Not known
Record Appearances: Not known
Additional Records:

Senior Honours:
Manchester League Premier Division 1975, 76, 77, 79. North West Counties League Cup 2006.

02-03		03-04		04-05		05-06		06-07		07-08		08-09		09-10		10-11		11-12	
NWC1	9	NWC1	15	NWC1	18	NWC1	5	NWC1	4	NWC1	2	NP1N	20	NP1N	11	NP1N	12	NP1N	13

SKELMERSDALE UNITED

Chairman: Paul Griffiths
Secretary: Bryn Jones   **(T)** 07904 911 234   **(E)** skelmersdaleunited@hotmail.com
Additional Committee Members:
Mrs L Boardman, Mr M Boardman, Mr D Bolderston, Mr A Gore, Mr T Garner, Mr N Leatherbarrow,
Mr B Jones, Mr P McGee, Mr J Sewell, Mr M Sewell, Mr D Tucker.
Manager: Tommy Lawson
Programme Editor: Neil Leatherbarrow   **(E)** skelmersdaleunited@hotmail.com

Club Factfile

Founded: 1882   **Nickname:** Skem
Previous Names: None
Previous Leagues: Liverpool County Combination, Lancashire Combination 1891-93, 1903-07, 21-24, 55-56, 76-78, Cheshire County 1968-71, 78-82, Northern Premier 1971-76, North West Counties 1983-2006

Club Colours (change): All royal blue (All red)

Ground: West Lancashire College Stadium, Selby Place, Statham Road WN8 8EF   **(T)** 01695 722 123
Capacity: 2,300   **Seats:** 240   **Covered:** 500   **Clubhouse:** Yes   **Shop:** Yes
Directions: Exit M58 J4 (signposted Skelmersdale), carry straight on at next roundabout (Hope Island) into Glenburn Road, left at next roundabout (Half Mile Island) into Neverstitch Road (signposted Stanley Industrial Estate). Immediately right at next roundabout into Staveley Road and then left into Statham Road. Ground is 500 yards on left in Selby Place.

Previous Grounds:

Record Attendance: 7,000 v Slough Town - FA Amateur Cup Semi-final 1967
Record Victory: Not known
Record Defeat: Not known
Record Goalscorer: Stuart Rudd - 230
Record Appearances: Robbie Holcroft - 422 including 398 consecutively
Additional Records: Paid £2,000 for Stuart Rudd
Senior Honours: Received £4,000 for Stuart Rudd
FA Amateur Cup 1970-71. Barassi Anglo-Italian Cup 1970-71.
Lancashire Junior Cup x2. Lancashire Non-League Cup x2.

10 YEAR RECORD

02-03		03-04		04-05		05-06		06-07		07-08		08-09		09-10		10-11		11-12	
NWC1	5	NWC1	8	NWC1	6	NWC1	2	NP 1	15	NP1N	3	NP1N	2	NP1N	5	NP1N	2	NP1N	7

TRAFFORD

Chairman: Howard Nelson
Secretary: Graham Foxall   **(T)** 07796 864 151   **(E)** davem@traffordfc.co.uk
Additional Committee Members:
D Brown, D Law, D Murray, T Walmsley, B Whitten, S Dobson, M.Brown, N.Brown,
G Cheetham, B Griffin, A Heathcote, L.Knights, H Nelson, P Thomas, J Williams.
Manager: Garry Vaughan
Programme Editor: Dave Murray   **(E)** davem@traffordfc.co.uk

THE NON-LEAGUE CLUB DIRECTORY

Book Holiday Inn Hotels and Save today!

Home
Clubs
Steps 1 - 4
League Tables

35 Years of Non-League Football

The Non-League Club Directory has
developed into a comprehensive record
of competitions within the non-League
game, giving this level of football the

www.non-leagueclubdirectory.co.uk

Club Factfile

Founded: 1990   **Nickname:** The North

Previous Names: North Trafford 1990-94

Previous Leagues: Mid Cheshire 1990-92, North West Counties 1992-97, 2003-08, Northern Premier 1997-2003

Club Colours (change): All white (All yellow)

Ground: Shawe View, Pennybridge Lane, Flixton Urmston M41 5DL   **(T)** 0161 747 1727

Capacity: 2,500   **Seats:** 292   **Covered:** 740   **Clubhouse:** Yes   **Shop:** Yes

Directions: Anti-Clockwise exit at J10 (Trafford Centre) and turn right towards Urmston B5214. Straight across two roundabouts. First lights turn right into Moorside Road, at next roundabout take second exit in to Bowfell Road. At next lights turn sharp left then immediately right in to Pennybridge Lane next to Bird In Hand Pub, parking on left 100 yards.
Or Leave M60 at J8, taking A6144 towards Lymm, Partington, Carrington. At second set of traffic lights turn right on B5158 towards Flixton. Remain on B5158 crossing railway bridge at Flixton Station and turn right at next set of traffic lights. Passing Bird in Hand Pub take immediate right in to Pennybridge Lane. Parking on left 100 yards.

Previous Grounds: Not known

Record Attendance: 803 v Flixton - Northern Premier League Division 1 1997-98

Record Victory: Not known
Record Defeat: Not known

Record Goalscorer: Garry Vaughan - 88

Record Appearances: Garry Vaughan - 293

Additional Records:

Senior Honours:
North West Counties Division 1 1996-97, 2007-08.
Manchester Challenge Trophy 2004-05. Northern Premier President's Cup 2008-09.

02-03		03-04		04-05		05-06		06-07		07-08		08-09		09-10		10-11		11-12	
NP 1	22	NWC1	16	NWC1	12	NWC1	15	NWC1	5	NWC1	1	NP1N	15	NP1N	12	NP1N	14	NP1N	12

WAKEFIELD

Chairman: Peter Matthews
Secretary: Peter Matthews   **(T)** 0794 382 9818   **(E)** peter.matthews@wakefieldfc.com
Additional Committee Members:
Alan Blackman, Pete Belvis, Daniel Brownhill.

Manager: Paul Lines
Programme Editor: Dan Brownhill   **(E)** daniel.brownhill@wakefieldfc.com

THE NON-LEAGUE CLUB DIRECTORY

Book Holiday Inn Hotels and Save today!

Home
Clubs
Steps 1 - 4
League Tables

35 Years of Non-League Football

The Non-League Club Directory has developed into a comprehensive record of competitions within the non-League game, giving this level of football the

www.non-leagueclubdirectory.co.uk

Club Factfile

Founded: 1903   **Nickname:** The Bears

Previous Names: Emley AFC 1903-2002, Wakefield & Emley AFC 2002-04, 2004-06 Wakefield - Emley AFC

Previous Leagues: Huddersfield > 1969, Yorkshire 1969-82, Northern Counties East 1982-89

Club Colours (change): Blue with yellow trim/blue/blue (Yellow with blue trim/yellow/yellow)

Ground: Wakefield Trinity Wildcats, Belle Vue, Wakefield. WF1 5EY   **(T)** 07921 156561

Capacity: **Seats:**   **Covered:**   **Clubhouse:** Yes   **Shop:** Nk

Directions
From Wakefield take A368 – Doncaster Road, Belle Vue is on the left hand side behind Superbowl.

Previous Grounds: Welfare Ground 1903-2000, Belle Vue 2000-06. Ingfield 2006-12.

Record Attendance: 5,134 v Barking - FA Amateur Cup 3rd Round 01/02/1969 at Welfare Ground

Record Victory: 12-0 v Ecclesfield Red Rose - Sheffield & Hallamshire Senior Challenge Cup 2nd Round 10/12/1996
Record Defeat: 1-7 v Altrincham - Northern Premier League Premier Division 25/04/1998

Record Goalscorer: Mick Pamment - 305

Record Appearances: Ray Dennis - 762

Additional Records: Received £60,000 from Ayr United for Michael Reynolds 1998

Senior Honours:
Yorkshire League 1975-76, 77-78, 79-80, 81-82, League Cup 1969-70, 78-79, 81-82.
Northern Counties East 1987-88, 88-89.
Sheffield & Hallamshire Senior Cup 1975-76, 79-80, 80-81, 83-84, 88-89, 90-91, 91-92, 97-98.

02-03	03-04	04-05	05-06	06-07	07-08	08-09	09-10	10-11	11-12
NP P 12	NP P 23	NP P 13	NP P 20	NP 1 21	NP1N 7	NP1N 9	NP1N 18	NP1N 16	NP1N 20

WARRINGTON TOWN

THE WIRE

Chairman: Gary Skeltenbury
Secretary: Chris Henshall   **(T)** 07969 123 786   **(E)** info@warringtontown.co.uk
Additional Committee Members:
Richard Sutton, Toby McCormac, Kevin Read, Bill Carr, David Hughes, Jeff Greenwood,
Martin Simcock, Ken Lacey.
Manager: Shaun Reid
Programme Editor: TBC   **(E)**

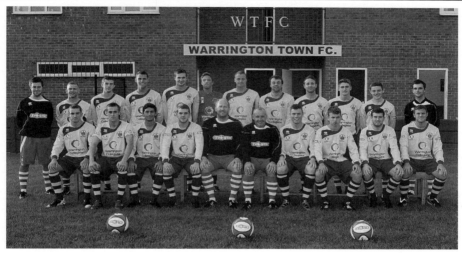

2011-12 Squad.

Club Factfile

Founded: 1948   **Nickname:** The Town
Previous Names: Stockton Heath 1949-62
Previous Leagues: Warrington & District 1949-52, Mid Cheshire 1952-78, Cheshire County 1978-82,
North West Counties 1982-90 Northern Premier 1990-97

Club Colours (change): Yellow and blue/blue/yellow (Blue & white/white/blue)

Ground: Cantilever Park, Common Lane, Latchford, Warrington WA4 2RS   **(T)** 01925 653 044
Capacity: 2,000   **Seats:** 350   **Covered:** 650   **Clubhouse:** Yes   **Shop:** Yes

Directions
From M62 Junction 9 Warrington Town Centre: Travel 1 mile south on A49, turn left at traffic lights into Loushers Lane, ground ½ mile on right hand side. From M6 North or South Junction 20: Follow A50 (Warrington signs) for 2 miles, cross Latchford Swingbridge, turn immediate left into Station Road, ground on left.

Previous Grounds:

Record Attendance: 2,600 v Halesowen Town - FA Vase Semi-final 1st leg 1985-86
Record Victory: Not known
Record Defeat: Not known
Record Goalscorer: Steve Hughes - 167
Record Appearances: Neil Whalley
Additional Records: Paid £50,000 to Preston North End for Liam Watson
Senior Honours: Received £60,000 from Preston North End for Liam Watson
North West Counties 1989-90, Division 2 2000-01, League Cup 1985-86, 87-88, 88-89

10 YEAR RECORD

02-03	03-04	04-05	05-06	06-07	07-08	08-09	09-10	10-11	11-12
NWC1 16	NWC1 5	NP 1 20	NP 1 19	NP 1 22	NP1S 13	NP1N 19	NP1N 9	NP1N 9	NP1N 11

BELPER TOWN

Chairman: Alan Benfield
Secretary: David Laughlin   **(T)** 07768 010 604   **(E)** info@belpertownfc.co.uk
Additional Committee Members:
Phil Varney, Christopher Balls, Rex Barker, Graham Boot, Steve Boxall,
Andrew Carter, Greg Ford, Graham Hulland, David Winterbotham, Vaughan Williams.
Manager: Peter Duffield
Programme Editor: David Laughlin   **(E)** info@belpertownfc.co.uk

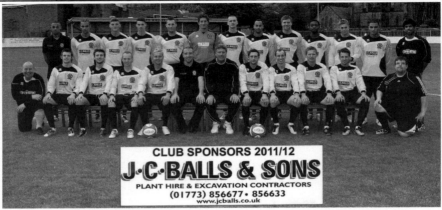

CLUB SPONSORS 2011/12
J·C·BALLS & SONS
PLANT HIRE & EXCAVATION CONTRACTORS
(01773) 856677 • 856633
www.jcballs.co.uk

2011-12 Squad - Back Row (L-R): Ollie Graham, Deon Meikle, Rob Ludlam, Ben Spargo, Matt Plant, Andy Richmond, Tommy Hannigan, Matty Thorpe, Richard Adams, Ruben Wiggins-Thomas, Liam Davis, Paris Simmons, Jinesh Lal (Physio).

Front Row: Paul Bennett (Kitman), Aaron Pride, Joaquin Ortuno, Luke Fedorenko, Lee Morris, Jon Froggatt, Tommy Taylor (Manager), Damien Magee, Andy Rushbury, Mark Camm, Jamie Smith, David Bennett (Kitman).

Club Factfile

Founded: 1883   **Nickname:** Nailers
Previous Names: Not known
Previous Leagues: Central Alliance 1957-61, Midland Counties 1961-82, Northern Counties East 1982-97

Club Colours (change): Yellow/black/black (All white)

Ground: Christchurch Meadow, Bridge Street, Belper DE56 1BA   **(T)** 01773 825 549
Capacity: 2,650   **Seats:** 500   **Covered:** 850   **Clubhouse:** Yes   **Shop:** Yes

Directions: From North: Exit M1: Exit junction 28 onto A38 towards Derby. Turn off at A610 (signposted 'Ripley/Nottingham') 4th exit at roundabout towards Ambergate. At junction with A6 (Hurt Arms Hotel) turn left to Belper. Ground on right just past first set of traffic lights. Access to the ground is by the lane next to the church.
From South: Follow A6 north from Derby towards Matlock. Follow A6 through Belper until junction with A517. Ground on left just before traffic lights at this junction. Access to the ground is by the lane next to the church.
NB. Please do not attempt to bring coaches into the ground – these can be parked outside

Previous Grounds: Acorn Ground > 1951

Record Attendance: 3,200 v Ilkeston Town - 1955
Record Victory: 15-2 v Nottingham Forest 'A' - 1956
Record Defeat: 0-12 v Goole Town - 1965
Record Goalscorer: Mick Lakin - 231
Record Appearances: Craig Smithurst - 678
Additional Records: Paid £2,000 to Ilkeston Town for Jamie Eaton 2001
Senior Honours: Received £2,000 from Hinckley United for Craig Smith
Central Alliance League 1958-59, Derbyshire Senior Cup 1958-59, 60-61, 62-63, 79-80.
Midland Counties 1979-80. Northern Counties East 1984-85.

10 YEAR RECORD

02-03		03-04		04-05		05-06		06-07		07-08		08-09		09-10		10-11		11-12	
NP 1	6	NP 1	20	NP 1	17	NP 1	9	NP 1	19	NP 1	8	NP1S	2	NP1S	6	NP1S	14	NP1S	6

BRIGG TOWN

Chairman: Kiron Brown
Secretary: Martin North   **(T)** 07891 122 242   **(E)** briggtownfc@chessmail.co.uk
Additional Committee Members:
John Martin, Bob Taylor, Jack Dunderdale, Kenny Bowers, Carl Atkinson, Dennis Hunter, Craig Tock, Robert Driscoll.
Manager: Michael Gray
Programme Editor: Michael Harker   **(E)** briggtownfc@chessmail.co.uk

THE NON-LEAGUE CLUB DIRECTORY

Book Holiday Inn Hotels and Save today!

Home

Clubs

Steps 1 - 4

League Tables

35 Years of Non-League Football

The Non-League Club Directory has developed into a comprehensive record of competitions within the non-League game, giving this level of football the

www.non-leagueclubdirectory.co.uk

Club Factfile

Founded: 1864   **Nickname:** Zebras

Previous Names: Not known

Previous Leagues: Lincolnshire 1948-76, Midland Counties 1976-82, Northern Counties East 1982-2004

Club Colours (change): Black and white stripes/black/red (All green)

Ground: The Hawthorns, Hawthorn Avenue, Brigg DN20 8PG*   **(T)** 01652 651 605

Capacity: 2,500   **Seats:** 370   **Covered:** Yes   **Clubhouse:** Yes   **Shop:** Yes

Directions: From M180 (Exit 4 - Scunthorpe East) A18 to Brigg. Leave Town via Wrawby Road, following signs for Airport and Grimsby. 100 metres after Sir John Nelthorpe Lower School, and immediately after bus stop/shelter, turn left into Recreation ground (signposted "Football Ground") and follow road into club car park.

*SAT NAV postcode DN20 8DT

Previous Grounds: Old Manor House Convent, Station Road > 1939, Brocklesby 1939-59

Record Attendance: 2,000 v Boston United - 1953

Record Victory: Not known
Record Defeat: Not known

Record Goalscorer: Not known

Record Appearances: Not known

Additional Records:

Senior Honours:

Midland Counties League 1977-78. FA Vase 1995-96, 2002-03. Northern Counties East Premier Division 2000-01.
Lincolnshire League x8, League Cup x5. Lincolnshire 'A' Senior Cup x4. Lincolnshire 'B' Senior Cup x5.

02-03		03-04		04-05		05-06		06-07		07-08		08-09		09-10		10-11		11-12	
NCEP	2	NCEP	3	NP 1	8	NP 1	8	NP 1	17	NP 1	16	NP1S	20	NP1S	15	NP1S	4	NP1S	17

CARLTON TOWN

Chairman: Michael Garton
Secretary: Paul Shelton   **(T)** 07854 586 875   **(E)** info@carltontownfc.co.uk
Additional Committee Members:
Roger Smith, Terence Fowler, Bob Sharp, Tim Harris, Simon Harris, Mark Steggles,
Jennie Shaw, Tim Bee, Brian Dennett, Alan Murphy, Ian White, Trevor Williams, Greg Last.
Manager: Les McJannet
Programme Editor: Tim Harris   **(E)** info@carltontownfc.co.uk

Photo: Keith Clayton.

Club Factfile

Founded: 1904   **Nickname:** Town
Previous Names: Sneinton
Previous Leagues: Notts Alliance, Central Midlands, Northern Counties East

Club Colours (change): Blue & yellow hoops/blue & white/blue & yellow hoops (Navy with yellow & white trim/navy & yellow/navy)

Ground: Bill Stokeld Stadium, Stoek Lane, Gedling, Nottingham NG4 2QP*   **(T)** 0115 940 3192 / 940 2531
Capacity: 1,500   **Seats:** 164   **Covered:** 100   **Clubhouse:** Yes   **Shop:** No

Directions: From M1 J26 take A610 to Nottingham Ring Road. Follow signs for Mansfield (A60) for approx 4 miles via 2 roundabouts until reaching junction with A60 at Arnold. Take right turn at Vale Hotel on to Thackerays Lane. Proceed to roundabout and take 3rd exit on to Arno Vale Road. Proceed through traffic lights to top of hill and continue straight on at next lights on to Arnold Lane. Continue past golf course, the old Gedling Colliery and church to mini roundabout. Continue straight on to the old junction with A612. (Southwell) must turn right here and at next set of lights turn left and follow the loop road to the next junction. Take left turn on to the new A612 Gedling By Pass and follow to the next set of traffic lights at Severn Trent Works. Turn left on to Stoke Lane. Entrance to Carlton Town is immediate right. **[Ground must be accessed via the new A612 between Netherfield and Burton Joyce. Football club is signposted in both directions on the approach to the ground).** *Sat Nav postcode NG4 2QW

Previous Grounds:

Record Attendance: 1,000 - Radio Trent Charity Match
Record Victory: Not known
Record Defeat: Not known
Record Goalscorer: Not known
Record Appearances: Not known
Additional Records:

Senior Honours:
Notts Alliance League Division 2 1984-85, Division 1 1992-93. Central Midlands Supreme Division 2002-03.
Northern Counties East Division 1 2005-06

10 YEAR RECORD

02-03		03-04		04-05		05-06		06-07		07-08		08-09		09-10		10-11		11-12	
CM Su	1	NCE1	9	NCE1	3	NCE1	1	NCEP	3	NP 1	10	NP1S	4	NP1S	9	NP1S	8	NP1S	2

CHASETOWN

Chairman: John Donnelly
Secretary: John Richards   **(T)** 07866 902 093   **(E)** (club) chastownfc@gmail.com
Additional Committee Members:
Brian Baker, Michael Joiner, John Franklin, Janice Brookes, John Goddard, Steve Maden, Mark Prince, Paul Mullins,
Robert Brookes, Barbara Hawkes, Dave Birt, Lawrence Hawkes, Colin Faunch, Michael Hampton, Steve Seed.
Manager: Craig Harris
Programme Editor: Pamela Mullins   **(E)** chastownfc@gmail.com

Back row l-r: Jordon Archer, Theo Robinson, Dave Bate, Mark Hands, John Richadrson, Matthew Jukes, Jack Farmer
Lee Evans, Ryan Price, Gavin Saunders, Nick Wellecomme, Greg Downes, Chris Slater, Gary Hay,
Dave Egan, Danny Smith
Front row l-r: John Birt (goalkeeping coach), Dave Reid (first team coach), Johnathan Gould, Danny Ashton, Simon Brown,
Paul Sullivan, Tyronne oconnell-Clarke, Kev Sweeney (assistant manager), Craig Harris (manager) , Andy Westwood, Matty Johnson,
Anthony Maguire, Mark Branch, Chad Degville,
Mick Andrews (sports therapist) Gary Mchale (sports therapist)

Club Factfile

Founded: 1954   **Nickname:** The Scholars
Previous Names: Chase Terrace Old Scholars 1954-72
Previous Leagues: Cannock Youth 1954-58, Lichfield & District 1958-61, Staffordshire County 1961-72,
West Midlands 1972-94, Midland Alliance 1994-2006, Southern 2006-09

Club Colours (change): Royal blue/royal blue/white (All bright red)

Ground: The Scholars, Church Street, Chasetown, Walsall WS7 8QL   **(T)** 01543 682 222
Capacity: 2,000   **Seats:** 151   **Covered:** 220   **Clubhouse:** Yes   **Shop:** Yes

Directions: From the M42 junction10 towards Tamworth or from the M6 Junction 11 or 12 towards Cannock or the A38 southbound from Derby - follow signs for A5 towards Brownhills, At the traffic lights at the Terrace Restaurant turn towards Burntwood onto the A5195. Straight over first island towards Chasetown and Hammerwich, over toll road and at second island turn left into Haney Hay Road which leads into Highfields Road signposted Chasetown, up the hill to mini island, then straight on into Church Street past the church on left and school on right. Ground is on the left at end of road. If using M6 Toll exit at junction T6 Burntwood - turn left out of Toll booths and left at second island and follow over toll road as above.

Previous Grounds: Burntwood Recreation

Record Attendance: 2,420 v Cardiff City - FA Cup 3rd Round January 2008
Record Victory: 14-1 v Hanford - Walsall Senior Cup 1991-92
Record Defeat: 1-8 v Telford United Reserves - West Midlands League
Record Goalscorer: Tony Dixon - 197
Record Appearances: Not known
Additional Records:

Senior Honours:
West Midlands League 1978, League Cup x2.
Midland Alliance 2005-06.
Walsall Senior Cup x2.

10 YEAR RECORD

02-03	03-04	04-05	05-06	06-07	07-08	08-09	09-10	10-11	11-12
MidAl 9	MidAl 7	MidAl 2	MidAl 1	SthM	SthM 7	SthM 4	NP1S 2	NP P 10	NP P 20

COALVILLE TOWN

Chairman: Glyn Rennocks
Secretary: James Jarvis   **(T)** 07791 231 860   **(E)** web@coalvilletownfc.co.uk
Additional Committee Members:
Mick Jordan, Robert Brooks, Jack Sarson, Dan Gallacher, Jon Bailiss.

Manager: Adam Stevens
Programme Editor: Dan Gallicher   **(E)** web@coalvilletownfc.co.uk

The Ravens

Club Factfile

Founded: 1994   **Nickname:** The Ravens
Previous Names: Ravenstoke Miners Ath. 1925-58. Ravenstoke FC 58-95. Coalville 95-98.
Previous Leagues: Coalville & Dist. Amateur. North Leicester. Leicestershire Senior. Midland Alliance > 2011.

Club Colours (change): Black & white stripes/white/white (Red & yellow stripes/red/red)

Ground: Owen Street Sports Ground, Owen St, Coalville LE67 3DA   **(T)** 01530 833 365
Capacity: 2,000   **Seats:** 240   **Covered:** 240   **Clubhouse:** Yes   **Shop:** Yes
Directions From the M42/A42 take the exit signposted Ashby and follow A511 to Coalville and Leicester. After approx. 3 miles and at the first roundabout take the second exit (A511). At the next roundabout take the 3rd exit into Coalville Town Centre. At the traffic lights go straight over to mini-roundabout then straight on for 50 meters before turning right into Owen Street. Ground is at the top of Owen Street on the left.

Previous Grounds: Not known

Record Attendance: 1,500.
Record Victory: Not known
Record Defeat: Not known
Record Goalscorer: Not known
Record Appearances: Nigel Simms.
Additional Records: 153 goals scored during 2010-11 season.

Senior Honours:
Leicestershire Senior Cup 1999-00. Leicestershire Senior 2001-02, 02-03. Midland Football Alliance 2010-11.

10 YEAR RECORD

02-03		03-04		04-05		05-06		06-07		07-08		08-09		09-10		10-11		11-12	
LeicS	1	MidAl	8	MidAl	3	MidAl	8	MidAl	18	MidAl	8	MidAl	3	MidAl	2	MidAl	1	NP1S	14

GRESLEY

Chairman: Barry North
Secretary: Reg Shorthouse   **(T)** 07779 049 847   **(E)** reg.shorthouse@gresleyfc.com
Additional Committee Members:
Mark Harrison, Gary Brockway, George Sutton, Mark Alflat, Robin Mansfield, Andrew Lager.

Manager: Gary Norton
Programme Editor: Robin Mansfield   **(E)** robin@gresleyfc.com

Back Row: Jordi Gough, Dean Oliver, Marc Strzyzewski, Michael Nottingam, Craig Atwood, Kyle Bryant, Marc Goodfellow.
Middle Row: Christina Cooper (physio), Matt Roome, James Jepson, Richard Hanslow, Jamie Barrett, Tom Gutteridge, Dan Douglas, Oliver Hancock, Rob Spencer, Matt Dingley (kit manager).
Front Row: Reg Shorthouse (secretary), Royce Turville, Phil Massingham, Hannah Dingley (coach), Gary Norton (joint manager), Martin Rowe (joint manager), Steve Titterton (asst. Manager), Tom Betteridge, Mickey Lyons, Barry North (chairman).
Players unavailable: Gary Hateley, Gareth Langford, Lavel White.

Club Factfile

Founded: 2009   **Nickname:**
Previous Names: Gresley Rovers
Previous Leagues: East Midlands 2009-11. Midland Football Alliance 2011-12.

Club Colours (change): Red/white/red (White/red/white)

Ground: The Moat Ground, Moat Street, Church Gresley, Derbyshire DE11 9RE   **(T)** 01283 216 315
Capacity: **Seats:** Yes   **Covered:** Yes   **Clubhouse:** Yes   **Shop:** Yes

Directions

From the South: Follow the M42 northbound to Junction 11, turn off onto the A444 toward Burton Upon Trent. Turn right onto the A514 (Castle Road) toward Gresley and follow the road up the hill to the traffic island at the top. Continue on the A514 over the island and take the second road on the left (School Street), the next left into Moat Street where the Moat Ground is located. **From the North-East:** Follow the M1 south to junction 23a, turn off on to the A42 southbound. Continue on the A42 to Ashby-de-la-Zouch then turn off onto the A511 toward Swadlincote. At Woodville turn off the A511 onto the A514 toward Church Gresley, follow the road signs to Gresley, the School Street turn off is second on the right after the Gresley island. Take the first turn on the left in School Street to take you to the ground. **From the North-West:** From Stoke-on-Trent follow the A50 toward Burton-Upon-Trent, turn on to the A511 and continue through Burton. Turn off the A511 onto the A444 toward Nuneaton. Follow the A444 until you reach the turn off for the A514. Turn left onto the A514 (Castle Road) toward Gresley and follow the road up the hill to the traffic island at the top. Continue on the A514 over the island and take the second road on the left (School Street), the next left into Moat Street where the Moat Ground is located.

Previous Grounds:

Record Attendance: 861 v Whitehawk (FA Vase Quarter Final 27th Feb 2010)
Record Victory: 9-0 v Anstey Nomads 30th August 2010 (EMCL)
Record Defeat: 1-5 v Westfields (MFA)
Record Goalscorer: Royce Turville - 61
Record Appearances: Jamie Barrett - 142
Additional Records:

Senior Honours:
East Midlands Counties League 2010-11. Midland Alliance 2011-12.

10 YEAR RECORD

02-03	03-04	04-05	05-06	06-07	07-08	08-09	09-10	10-11	11-12
							EMC 2	EMC 1	MidAl 1

HALESOWEN TOWN

Chairman: Colin Brookes
Secretary: Andrew While   **(T)** 07976 769 972   **(E)** andrew.while@blueyonder.co.uk
Additional Committee Members:
Dave Smith, Colin Brookes, John Russell, Andrew While, Sandra Checketts,
Michael Serdetschiny, Mike Burke, Sarah Titmus, John Smith, Stewart Tildesley, Gary Willetts.
Manager: Shaun Cunnington
Programme Editor: Rob Edmonds   **(E)** info@ht-fc.com

THE NON-LEAGUE CLUB DIRECTORY

Book Holiday Inn Hotels and Save today!

Home

Clubs

Steps 1 - 4

League Tables

35 Years of Non-League Football

The Non-League Club Directory has developed into a comprehensive record of competitions within the non-League game, giving this level of football the

www.non-leagueclubdirectory.co.uk

Club Factfile

Founded: 1873   **Nickname:** Yeltz

Previous Names: None
Previous Leagues: West Midlands 1892-1905, 06-11, 46-86, Birmingham Combination 1911-39

Club Colours (change): Blue/blue/blue (All green)

Ground: Old Hawne Lane, Halesowen B63 3TB   **(T)** 0121 550 9433

Capacity: 3,150   **Seats:** 525   **Covered:** 930   **Clubhouse:** Yes   **Shop:** Yes

Directions
Leave M5 at Junction 3, follow A456 Kidderminster to first island and turn right (signposted A459 Dudley).
Turn left at next island (signposted A458 Stourbridge).
At next island take third exit into Old Hawne Lane.
Ground about 400 yards on left.

Previous Grounds: Not known

Record Attendance: 5,000 v Hendon - FA Cup 1st Round Proper 1954

Record Victory: 13-1 v Coventry Amateurs - Birmingham Senior cup 1956
Record Defeat: 0-8 v Bilston - West Midlands League 07/04/1962

Record Goalscorer: Paul Joinson - 369

Record Appearances: Paul Joinson - 608

Additional Records: Paid £7,250 to Gresley Rovers for Stuart Evans
Received £40,000 from Rushden & Diamonds for Jim Rodwell

Senior Honours:
FA Vase 1984-85, 85-86 (R-up 1982-83). Southern League Midland Division 1989-90, Western Division 2001-02.
Birmingham Senior Cup 1983-84, 97-98. Staffordshire Senior Cup 1988-89.
Worcestershire Senior Cup 1951-52, 61-62, 2002-03, 04-05.

02-03		03-04		04-05		05-06		06-07		07-08		08-09		09-10		10-11		11-12	
SthP	19	SthW	4	SthP	9	SthP	8	SthP	6	SthP	3	SthP	10	SthP	8	SthP	21	Sthsw	12

HUCKNALL TOWN

Chairman: Derek Blow
Secretary: Tony Knowles   **(T)** 07535 124 295   **(E)** committee@hucknalltownfc.com
Additional Committee Members:
Brian Holmes, Liz Morley, Nigel Bramley, Andy Johnson, Geoff Gospel, Dawn Scotney,
Andy Graves, Dawn Scotney, Ivan Sanders, Brian Reece, Amanda Thornley, David Paling.
Manager: Brett Reece
Programme Editor: Amanda Thornley   **(E)** committee@hucknalltownfc.com

THE NON-LEAGUE CLUB DIRECTORY

Book Holiday Inn Hotels and Save today!

Home

Clubs

Steps 1 - 4

League Tables

35 Years of Non-League Football

The Non-League Club Directory has
developed into a comprehensive record
of competitions within the non-League
game, giving this level of football the

www.non-leagueclubdirectory.co.uk

Club Factfile

Founded: 1987   **Nickname:** The Town

Previous Names: None

Previous Leagues: Bulwell & District 1946-59, 60-65, Central Alliance 1959-60 Notts Spartan 1965-70,
Central Midlands 1989-92

Club Colours (change): Yellow/black/yellow (All white)

Ground: Watnall Road, Hucknall, Notts NG15 6EY   **(T)** 01159 30206

Capacity: 3,013   **Seats:** 500   **Covered:** 900   **Clubhouse:** Yes   **Shop:** Yes

Directions: Exit the M1 at Junction 27 and take the A608 towards Hucknall. Turn right onto the A611 to Hucknall then take the Hucknall bypass.
At the second roundabout join Watnall Road (B6009) and the ground is 100 yards on the right.

Previous Grounds: Not known

Record Attendance: 1,841 v Bishop's Stortford - FA Trophy Semi-final 2004-05

Record Victory: 12-1 v Teversal - Notts Senior Cup 1989-90
Record Defeat: Not known

Record Goalscorer: Maurice Palethorpe - 400 approx. (1980-90)

Record Appearances: Dave McCarthy - 282

Additional Records: Received £10,000 from Brentford for Stuart Nelson 2003-04

Senior Honours:
Central Midlands League 1989-90, 90-91, League Cup x3. Northern Counties East 1997-98, League Cup x3.
Northern Premier League Premier Division 2003-04.
Notts Senior Cup x5.

02-03	03-04	04-05	05-06	06-07	07-08	08-09	09-10	10-11	11-12
NP P 8	NP P 1	Conf N 10	Conf N 12	Conf N 13	Conf N 20	Conf N 22	NP P 17	NP P 20	NP1S 11

KIDSGROVE ATHLETIC

Chairman: John Rowley
Secretary: Lisa Fitzjohn   **(T)** 07960 560 391   **(E)** kidsgroveathletic@aol.com
Additional Committee Members:
David James, Ray Green.

Manager: Shaun Hollinshead
Programme Editor: Lisa Fitzjohn   **(E)** kidsgroveathletic@aol.com

THE NON-LEAGUE CLUB DIRECTORY

Book Holiday Inn Hotels and Save today!

Home

Clubs

Steps 1 - 4

League Tables

35 Years of Non-League Football

The Non-League Club Directory has developed into a comprehensive record of competitions within the non-League game, giving this level of football the

www.non-leagueclubdirectory.co.uk

Club Factfile

Founded: 1952   **Nickname:** The Grove

Previous Names: None

Previous Leagues: Buslem and Tunstall 1953-63, Staffordshire County 1963-66, Mid Cheshire 1966-90, North West Counties 1990-2002

Club Colours (change): All blue (All red)

Ground: The Seddon Stadium, Hollinwood Road, Kidsgrove, Staffs ST7 1DQ   **(T)** 01782 782 412

Capacity: 4,500   **Seats:** 1,000   **Covered:** 800   **Clubhouse:** Yes   **Shop:** Yes

Directions: Leave the M6 at Junction 16, join the A500 towards Stoke-on-Trent. Take the 2nd exit signposted Newcastle & Kidsgrove. Top of the slip road, turn left onto A34 Kidsgrove/Congleton. Straight over at roundabout. At 1st set of traffic lights (by Caudwell Arms pub) turn right onto A34. Continue to next set of lights, turn right into Cedar Avenue. Continue then take 2nd right into Lower Ash Road. Take 3rd left into Hollinwood Road, Ground on left at top.

Previous Grounds: Vickers and Goodwin 1953-60

Record Attendance: 1,903 v Tiverton Town - FA Vase Semi-final 1998

Record Victory: 23-0 v Cross Heath W.M.C. - Staffordshire Cup 1965
Record Defeat: 0-15 v Stafford Rangers - Staffordshire Senior Cup 20/11/2001

Record Goalscorer: Scott Dundas - 53 (1997-98)

Record Appearances: Not known

Additional Records: Paid £10,000 to Stevenage Borough for Steve Walters
Received £3,000 for Ryan Baker 2003-04

Senior Honours:
Mid Cheshire League x4, League Cup x3.
North West Counties Division 1 1997-98, 2001-02, Challenge Cup 1997-98.
Staffordshire Senior Cup 2010-11.

02-03	03-04	04-05	05-06	06-07	07-08	08-09	09-10	10-11	11-12
NP 1 19	NP 1 22	NP 1 10	NP 1 17	NP 1 8	NP 1 17	NP1S 15	NP1S 4	NP1S 7	NP1S 13

KING'S LYNN TOWN

Chairman: Keith Chapman
Secretary: Norman Cesar   **(T)** 01553 631 336   **(E)** office@kltown.co.uk
Additional Committee Members:
Mrs Cheryl Chapman, Jonathan Chapman.

Manager: Gary Setchell
Programme Editor: Rob Galliard   **(E)** office@kltown.co.uk

THE NON-LEAGUE CLUB DIRECTORY

Book Holiday Inn Hotels and Save today!

Home

Clubs

Steps 1 - 4

League Tables

35 Years of Non-League Football

The Non-League Club Directory has developed into a comprehensive record of competitions within the non-League game, giving this level of football the

www.non-leagueclubdirectory.co.uk

Club Factfile

Founded: 1879   **Nickname:** Linnets

Previous Names: King's Lynn > 2010

Previous Leagues: N'folk & Suffolk, Eastern Co. 1935-39, 48-54, UCL 1946-48, Midland Co. 1954-58, NPL 1980-81, Southern, Conf

Club Colours (change): Yellow with royal blue trim/royal blue/ yellow (Turquoise/black/turquoise)

Ground: The Walks Stadium, Tennyson Road, King's Lynn PE30 5PB   **(T)** 01553 760 060

Capacity: 8,200   **Seats:** 1,200   **Covered:** 5,000   **Clubhouse:** Yes   **Shop:** Yes

Directions: At the roundabout, at the junction of A47 and the A17, follow the A47, signposted King's Lynn and Norwich. Travel along the dual carriageway for approx. one and a half miles branching off left, following the signs for Town Centre, onto the Hardwick roundabout. Take the first exit, following the signs for Town Centre, travel through two sets of traffic lights until reaching a further set of traffic lights at the Southgates roundabout. Take the fourth exit onto Vancouver Avenue, and travel for approx. 300 metres, going straight across a mini roundabout, The Walks is a further 200 metres along on the left hand side, with car parking outside the ground. The changing rooms and hospitality suite are located at the rear of the main stand.

Previous Grounds:

Record Attendance: Att: 12,937 v Exeter City FAC 1st Rnd 1950-51.

Record Victory: Not known
Record Defeat: Not known

Record Goalscorer: Malcolm Lindsey 321.

Record Appearances: Mick Wright 1,152 (British Record)
Additional Records:

Senior Honours:
Southern League Division 1 East 2003-04, Premier Division 2007-08, League Cup 2004-05.

02-03		03-04		04-05		05-06		06-07		07-08		08-09		09-10		10-11		11-12	
SthE	6	SthE	1	SthP	11	SthP	3	SthP	3	SthP	1	Conf N	17	NP P	dnf	UCL P	2	UCL P	2

LEEK TOWN

Chairman: Andrew Wain
Secretary: Brain Wain   **(T)** 07967 204 470   **(E)**
Additional Committee Members:
A. Reeves, T. Reynolds, C Hermiston, P Bateman, N. Baker, D. Bates, M Howson.

Manager: Lee Casswell
Programme Editor: Tracy Reynolds   **(E)**

THE NON-LEAGUE CLUB DIRECTORY

Book Holiday Inn Hotels and Save today!

Home

Clubs

Steps 1 - 4

League Tables

35 Years of Non-League Football

The Non-League Club Directory has developed into a comprehensive record of competitions within the non-League game, giving this level of football the

www.non-leagueclubdirectory.co.uk

Club Factfile

Founded: 1946   **Nickname:** The Blues

Previous Names: None

Previous Leagues: Staffordshire Co., Manchester 1951-54, 57-73, West Midlands (B'ham) 1954-56,Cheshire Co. 1973-82, North West Counties 1982-87, N.P.L. 1987-94, 95-97, Southern 1994-95, Conference 1997-99

Club Colours (change): Blue/dark blue/blue (Amber & black/amber/black)

Ground: Harrison Park, Macclesfield Road, Leek, Cheshire ST13 8LD   **(T)** 01538 399 278

Capacity: 3,600   **Seats:** 625   **Covered:** 2,675   **Clubhouse:** Yes   **Shop:** Yes

Directions **From the South:** Leave M6 at J15, over roundabout on to the A500, go over the flyover, up the slip road, onto the A50 and follow the signs to Leek. Go straight over the roundabout (Britannia Building on the left) to large set of lights. Go straight across St. Georges Street to top of road to junction, turn left, go down the hill for about a half a mile. The Ground is on the left. **From the North:** Leave M6 at J19. Take Macclesfield signs. Follow into Macclesfield then take A523 Leek/Buxton signs. Follow these to Leek. Ground is situated on the right as you come into Leek. From West Midlands: M6 J15. A500 towards Stoke, over flyover, take A50 past Brittania Stadium. After approx 3 miles join A53 signposted Leek. On entering the town, straight ahead up St Edwards St. (Remainder as above)

Previous Grounds: Not known

Record Attendance: 5,312 v Macclesfield Town - FA Cup 1973-74

Record Victory: Not known

Record Defeat: Not known

Record Goalscorer: Dave Sutton - 144

Record Appearances: Gary Pearce - 447

Additional Records: Paid £2,000 to Sutton Town for Simon Snow
Received £30,000 from Barnsley for Tony Bullock

Senior Honours:
Northern Premier League 1996-97. Staffordshire Senior Cup 1995-96.

02-03		03-04		04-05		05-06		06-07		07-08		08-09		09-10		10-11		11-12	
NP 1	9	NP 1	8	NP P	7	NP P	12	NP P	17	NP P	19	NP1S	9	NP1S	8	NP1S	16	NP1S	5

LINCOLN UNITED

Chairman: Malcolm Chapman
Secretary: John Wilkinson   **(T)** 07773 284 017   **(E)** johnwilk@live.co.uk
Additional Committee Members:
Maurice Bull, Allen Crombie, Michelle Waters, John Bustin, Gordon Marsh.

Manager: Terry Fleming
Programme Editor: John Wilkinson   **(E)** johnwilk@live.co.uk

2011-12 Squad - Back Row (l-R): Scott Coupland, Josh Raby, Craig Leverett, Alex Troughton, Peter McDaid, Sean Wright, Stuart Reddington, Nigel Wallace, James Stokes, Jordan Hempenstall, Lee Pickering, David Coyde
Front Row: Steve Churcher(Kit Manager), George Zuerner, Liam Bull, Chris Funnell, Terry Fleming, Darren Dye, Brendan McDaid, Kallum Smith, Jack McGovern, Phil McGann

Club Factfile

Founded: 1938   **Nickname:** United
Previous Names: Lincoln Amateurs > 1954
Previous Leagues: Lincolnshire 1945-46, 60-67, Lincoln 1946-60, Yorkshire 1967-82,
Northern Counties East 1982-86, 92-95, Central Midlands 1982-92

Club Colours (change): White/white with red trim/red (Sky blue/white/sky)

Ground: Ashby Avenue, Hartsholme, Lincoln LN6 0DY   **(T)** 01522 696 400
Capacity: 2,714   **Seats:** 400   **Covered:** 1,084   **Clubhouse:** Yes   **Shop:** Yes
Directions Along Lincoln Relief Road (A46) until reaching roundabout with exit for Birchwood. Take this exit which is Skellingthorpe Road for approximately 1 mile, at 30 mph sign turn right into Ashby Avenue. Entrance to ground is 200 yards on right.

Previous Grounds: Skew Bridge 1940s, Co-op Sports Ground > 1960s, Hartsholme Cricket Club > 1982

Record Attendance: 2,000 v Crook Town - FA Amateur Cup 1st Round 1968
Record Victory: 12-0 v Pontefract Colliery - 1995
Record Defeat: 0-7 v Huddersfield Town - FA Cup 1st Round 16/11/1991
Record Goalscorer: Tony Simmons - 215
Record Appearances: Steve Carter - 447
Additional Records: Paid £1,000 to Hucknall Town for Paul Tomlinson December 2000
Senior Honours: Received £3,000 from Charlton Athletic for Dean Dye July 1991
Northern Counties East Division 1 1985-86, 92-93, Premier Division 1994-95.

10 YEAR RECORD

02-03		03-04		04-05		05-06		06-07		07-08		08-09		09-10		10-11		11-12	
NP 1	16	NP 1	4	NP P	14	NP P	19	NP P	15	NP P	20	NP1S	10	NP1S	19	NP1S	12	NP1S	18

LOUGHBOROUGH DYNAMO

Chairman: Frank Fall
Secretary: Brian Pugh   **(T)** 07775 825 321   **(E)** contact@loughboroughdynamofc.co.uk
Additional Committee Members:
Ian Beach, Greg Blood, John Cherry, Keith Hawes, Tony King, Colin Westley.

Manager: Scott Clamp
Programme Editor: Rob Smith   **(E)** contact@loughboroughdynamofc.co.uk

Club Factfile

Founded: 1955   **Nickname:** Dynamo
Previous Names: None
Previous Leagues: Loughborough Alliance 1957-66, Leicestershire & District 1966-71, East Midlands 1971-72,
Central Alliance 1972-89, Leicestershire Senior 1989-2004, Midland Alliance 2004-08

Club Colours (change): Gold/black/gold (Green and white hoops/white/green and white hoops)

Ground: Nanpantan Sports Ground, Nanpantan Road, Loughborough LE11 3YE   **(T)** 01509 237 148
Capacity: 1,500   **Seats:** 250   **Covered:** Yes   **Clubhouse:** Yes   **Shop:** No
Directions
From M1: At Junction 23 turn towards Loughborough (A512). At 1st set of traffic lights turn right on to Snells Nook Lane.. At 1st crossroads ("Priory" pub on left) turn left on to Nanpantan Rd. Turn (1st) right after 0.75 miles on to Watermead Lane. The ground is at the end of the lane. **From Leicester (A6):** Turn left at 3rd roundabout on Epinal Way (Ring Road) on to Forest Road. After 2 miles turn (5th) left on to Watermead Lane. **From Nottingham (A60):** Turn right at 1st set of traffic lights in Loughborough. Go through next 4 sets of traffic lights. Turn left at the first roundabout on to Epinal Way straight on at next roundabout and then take the third exit at following roundabout on to Forest Road. After 2 miles turn (5th) left on to Watermead Lane.

Previous Grounds: Not known

Record Attendance: Not known
Record Victory: Not known
Record Defeat: Not known
Record Goalscorer: Not known
Record Appearances: Not known
Additional Records:

Senior Honours:
Leicestershire Senior League Division 1 2001-02, Premier Division 2003-04.
Leicestershire Senior Cup 2002-03, 03-04.

10 YEAR RECORD

02-03		03-04		04-05		05-06		06-07		07-08		08-09		09-10		10-11		11-12	
LeicS	4	LeicS	1	MidAl	14	MidAl	13	MidAl	9	MidAl	2	NP1S	14	NP1S	14	NP1S	17	NP1S	8

MARKET DRAYTON TOWN

Chairman: Julian Parton
Secretary: Brian Garratt   **(T)** 07854 725 957   **(E)**
Additional Committee Members:
Nick Alsop, Clive Jones, Frank Hodgkiss, Pauline Mellor, Alex Mutch, Mark Parton,
Paul Littlehales, Mick Murphy, Tom Mellor, Ian Macintosh, Ron Ebrey, Andy Cooke.
Manager: Jimmy Mullen
Programme Editor: Stuart Holloway   **(E)**

THE NON-LEAGUE CLUB DIRECTORY

Book Holiday Inn Hotels and Save today!

Home

Clubs

Steps 1 - 4

League Tables

35 Years of Non-League Football

The Non-League Club Directory has
developed into a comprehensive record
of competitions within the non-League
game, giving this level of football the

www.non-leagueclubdirectory.co.uk

Club Factfile

Founded: 1969   **Nickname:**

Previous Names: Little Drayton Rangers > 2003
Previous Leagues: West Midlands (Regional) 1969-2006, Midland Alliance 2006-09

Club Colours (change): All red (All blue)

Ground: Greenfields Sports Ground, Greenfields Lane, Market Drayton TF9 3SL   **(T)** 01630 655 088

Capacity: **Seats:**   **Covered:**   **Clubhouse:** Yes   **Shop:** Nk

Directions
Take the A41 to Ternhill Island, turn right on A53 for Newcastle-under-Lyne. Straight on at first island (by Muller factory). At next island turn right to town centre (by Gingerbread Inn). Approx 200yds take 2nd right into Greenfields Lane. Ground 150 yards on right, car park opposite.

From Stoke-on-Trent take A53 for Shrewsbury, at Gingerbread Inn turn left for town centre then as above.

Previous Grounds: Not known

Record Attendance: 440 vs. AFC Telford, Friendly 11/07/09. 229 vs. Witton Albion, Unibond South 25/08/09

Record Victory: (League) 9-0 Home vs. Racing Club Warwick 10/03/09
Record Defeat: Not known

Record Goalscorer: Not known

Record Appearances: Not known

Additional Records:

Senior Honours:
West Midlands (Regional) League 2005-06. Midland Alliance 2008-09.

02-03		03-04		04-05		05-06		06-07		07-08		08-09		09-10		10-11		11-12	
WMP	4	WMP	7	WMP	2	WMP	1	MidAl	13	MidAl	3	MidAl	1	NP1S	13	NP1S	18	NP1S	16

MICKLEOVER SPORTS

Chairman: Stuart Clarke
Secretary: Russell Sellors **(T)** 07535 434 205 **(E)** secretary.msfc@gmail.com
Additional Committee Members:
Roger Lee, Steve Rigg, Tony Shaw, Phil Taylor, Dave Chambers, Dave Mackenzie, James Edge, Iain Wilson, Kevin Haddon, Anita Nahall, Alan Brown, Kevin Dickenson, Sharon Taylor, Cath Grant, Neil Wetherstone.
Manager: Richard Pratley
Programme Editor: Ian Wilson **(E)** secretary.msfc@gmail.com

THE NON-LEAGUE CLUB DIRECTORY

Book Holiday Inn Hotels and Save today!

Home

Clubs

Steps 1 - 4

League Tables

35 Years of Non-League Football

The Non-League Club Directory has developed into a comprehensive record of competitions within the non-League game, giving this level of football the

www.non-leagueclubdirectory.co.uk

Club Factfile

Founded: 1948 **Nickname:** Sports

Previous Names: None
Previous Leagues: Central Midlands 1993-99, Northern Counties East 1999-2009

Club Colours (change): Red and black stripes/black/red (Blue/white/blue)

Ground: Raygar Stadium, Station Road, Mickleover Derby DE3 9FB **(T)** 01332 512 826

Capacity: 1,500 **Seats:** 280 **Covered:** 500 **Clubhouse:** Yes **Shop:** Yes

Directions
M1 NORTH - J28. A38 to Derby. At Markeaton Island right A52 Ashbourne, 2nd left Radbourne Lane, 3rd Left Station Road 50 yds.

M1 SOUTH – J25. A52 to Derby. Follow signs for Ashbourne, pick up A52 at Markeaton Island (MacDonalds) then as above.

FROM STOKE A50 – Derby. A516 to A38 then as above.

Previous Grounds: Not known

Record Attendance: Not known

Record Victory: Not known
Record Defeat: Not known

Record Goalscorer: Not known

Record Appearances: Not known

Additional Records: Won 16 consecutive League matches in 2009-10 - a Northern Premier League record

Senior Honours:
Central Midlands Supreme Division 1998-99. Northern Counties East Division 1 2002-03, Premier Division 2008-09.
Northern Premier League Division 1 South 2009-10.

02-03		03-04		04-05		05-06		06-07		07-08		08-09		09-10		10-11		11-12	
NCE1	1	NCEP	13	NCEP	7	NCEP	13	NCEP	7	NCEP	14	NCEP	1	NP1S	1	NP P	15	NP P	21

NEWCASTLE TOWN

Chairman: Paul Ratcliffe
Secretary: Ray Tatton   **(T)** 07792 292 849   **(E)** rftatton@tiscali.co.uk
Additional Committee Members:
Michael Pagett, Alan Salt, Terry Donlan, Geoff Eccleston, Alistair Miller, Les Morris,
Colin Spencer, Tony Caveney.
Manager: John Diskin
Programme Editor: Ray Tatton   **(E)** rftatton@tiscali.co.uk

Club Factfile

Founded: 1964   **Nickname:** Castle
Previous Names: Parkway Hanley, Clayton Park & Parkway Clayton. Merged as NTFC 86
Previous Leagues: Newcatle & District, Staffs Co & Mid Cheshire, North West Counties

Club Colours (change): Blue/blue/white (All white)

Ground: The Aspire Stadium, Buckmaster Avenue, Clayton, ST5 3BX   **(T)** 01782 662 350
Capacity: 4,000   **Seats:** 300   **Covered:** 1,000   **Clubhouse:** Yes   **Shop:** Yes
Directions: FROM M6: Leave the M6 at Junction 15 and immediately turn left up the bank (signposted A519 Newcastle.) Go to the second roundabout and turn right into Stafford Avenue. Take the first left into Tittensor Road (signposted Newcastle Town FC.) Go to the end and the ground is below in the parkway. (Entrance through the gateway signposted Newcastle Town FC.) FROM A50 DERBY: Follow the A50 to the end and join the A500 (signposted M6 South) just past Stoke City Football Ground. Follow the A500 to the Motorway and at the roundabout turn right up the bank (A519 Newcastle.) Go to the second roundabout and turn right into Stafford Avenue. Take the first left into Tittensor Road (signposted Newcastle Town FC.) Go to the end and the ground is below in the parkway. (Entrance through the gateway signposted Newcastle Town FC.)

Previous Grounds: Not known

Record Attendance: 3,948 v Notts County - FA Cup 1996
Record Victory: Not known
Record Defeat: Not known
Record Goalscorer: Andy Bott - 149
Record Appearances: Dean Gillick - 632
Additional Records:

Senior Honours:
Mid Cheshire League 1985-86. Walsall Senior Cup 1993-94, 94-95.

10 YEAR RECORD									
02-03	03-04	04-05	05-06	06-07	07-08	08-09	09-10	10-11	11-12
NWC1 4	NWC1 6	NWC1 2	NWC1 6	NWC1 12	NWC1 3	NWCP 3	NWCP 1	NP1S 2	NP1S 15

NORTHWICH VICTORIA

Chairman: James Rushe
Secretary: Dave Thomas   **(T)** 07798 564 596   **(E)** dave.thomas@northwichvics.co.uk
Additional Committee Members:
Martin Rushe, D R Nuttall

Manager: Andy Mutch
Programme Editor: David Thomas   **(E)** david.thomas@northwichvics.co.uk

THE NON-LEAGUE CLUB DIRECTORY

Book Holiday Inn Hotels and Save today!

Home

Clubs

Steps 1 - 4

League Tables

35 Years of Non-League Football

The Non-League Club Directory has developed into a comprehensive record of competitions within the non-League game, giving this level of football the

www.non-leagueclubdirectory.co.uk

Club Factfile

Founded: 1874   **Nickname:** Vics, Greens or Trickies

Previous Names: None

Previous Leagues: The Combination 1890-92, 1894-98, Football League 1892-94, Cheshire 1898-1900, Manchester 1900-12
Lancashire 1912-19, Cheshire County 1919-68, Northern Premier 1968-79, Conference 1979-2010

Club Colours (change): Green and white hoops/white/white (Yellow/blue/blue)

Ground: Stafford Rangers FC., Marston Road, Stafford. ST16 3BX   **(T)** 07798 564596

Capacity: 6,000   **Seats:** 4,264   **Covered:** 3,500   **Clubhouse:** Yes   **Shop:** Yes

Directions: M6 Junction 14. Follow signs for Uttoxeter and Stone. Straight over at 1st and 2nd(A34) islands,3rd right signposted Common Road and Astonfields Road Ind. Estate. The ground is straight ahead after three-quarters of a mile. The route from the Motorway is highlighted by the standard football road signs.

Previous Grounds: The Drill Field. Victoria Stadium.

Record Attendance: 11,290 v Witton Albion - Cheshire League Good Friday 1949

Record Victory: 17-0 v Marple Association 1883
Record Defeat: 3-10 v Port Vale - 1931

Record Goalscorer: Peter Burns - 160 (1955-65)

Record Appearances: Ken Jones - 970 (1969-85)

Additional Records: Paid £12,000 to Hyde United for Malcolm O'Connor August 1988. Received £50,000 from Leyton Orient for Gary Fletcher June 1921 and from Chester City for Neil Morton October 1990.

Senior Honours:
FA Trophy 1983-84.
Conference North 2005-06.
Cheshire Senior Cup x15. Staffordshire Senior Cup x3.

02-03	03-04	04-05	05-06	06-07	07-08	08-09	09-10	10-11	11-12
Conf 14	Conf 22	Conf 19	Conf N 1	Conf 13	Conf 19	Conf 22	Conf N 12	NP P 12	NP P 2

RAINWORTH MINERS WELFARE

Chairman: Les Lee
Secretary: Les Lee   **(T)** 07740 576 958   **(E)** leslie.lee7@ntlworld.com
Additional Committee Members:
Eileen Wright, Mark Buttery, Robbie Blamford, Derek Bentley, Gordon Foster, Brian Martin, John Lock, Frank Bramwell, Les Bakewell.
Manager: Kevin Gee
Programme Editor: Gordon Foster   **(E)** leslie.lee7@ntlworld.com

THE NON-LEAGUE CLUB DIRECTORY

Book Holiday Inn Hotels and Save today!

Home

Clubs

Steps 1 - 4

League Tables

35 Years of Non-League Football

The Non-League Club Directory has developed into a comprehensive record of competitions within the non-League game, giving this level of football the

www.non-leagueclubdirectory.co.uk

Club Factfile

Founded: 1922   **Nickname:** The Wrens

Previous Names: Rufford Colliery

Previous Leagues: Notts Alliance 1922-03, Central Midlands League 2003-07, Northern Counties East 2007-10

Club Colours (change): All White (Red/black/black).

Ground: Welfare Ground, Kirklington Road, Rainworth, Mansfield NG21 0JY   **(T)** 01623 792 495

Capacity: 2,201   **Seats:** 221   **Covered:** 350   **Clubhouse:** Yes   **Shop:** No

Directions: From M1 (Junction 29) – take A617. At Pleasley turn right onto the new Mansfield Bypass road which is still the A617 and follow to Rainworth. At roundabout with B6020 Rainworth is off to the right, but it is better to go straight over onto the new Rainworth Bypass and then right at the next roundabout (the ground can be seen on the way along the Bypass) At mini roundabout, turn right onto Kirklington Road and go down the hill for ¼ mile – ground and car park on the right
Alternatively you can reach the new A617 Bypass from the A38 via Junction 28 on the M1.   From A614 at roundabout, take the A617 to Rainworth for 1 mile. Left at 1st roundabout into village. At mini roundabout right into Kirklington road – ¼ mile down hill as above.

Previous Grounds: Not known

Record Attendance: 5,071 v Barton Rovers FA Vase SF 2nd Leg, 1982. (A record for a Vase match outside of the final)

Record Victory: Not known
Record Defeat: Not known

Record Goalscorer: Not known

Record Appearances: Not known

Additional Records:

Senior Honours:
Notts Senior Cup Winners 1981-82

02-03		03-04		04-05		05-06		06-07		07-08		08-09		09-10		10-11		11-12	
NottS	5	CM P	3	CM Su	20	CM Su	9	CM Su	3	NCE1	4	NCE1	2	NCEP	2	NP1S	20	NP1S	19

ROMULUS

Chairman: Andrew Wilson
Secretary: Peter Lowe   **(T)** 07738 604 391   **(E)** peterwloweuk@yahoo.co.uk
Additional Committee Members:
Roger Evans, Peter Morgan, Paul Dockerill, Tom Clarke, Philip Hobson,
Keith Brown, Keith Higham, Andy Mitchell, Mark Taylor.
Manager: Richard Evans
Programme Editor: Paul Dockerill   **(E)** peterwloweuk@yahoo.co.uk

THE NON-LEAGUE CLUB DIRECTORY

Book Holiday Inn Hotels and Save today!

Home

Clubs

Steps 1 - 4

League Tables

35 Years of Non-League Football

The Non-League Club Directory has
developed into a comprehensive record
of competitions within the non-League
game, giving this level of football the

www.non-leagueclubdirectory.co.uk

Club Factfile

Founded: 1979   **Nickname:** The Roms

Previous Names: None
Previous Leagues: Midland Combination 1999-2004, Midland Alliance 2004-07, Southern 2007-2010

Club Colours (change): Red and white/red/red (Green & black/black/green)

Ground: Sutton Coldfield FC, Central Ground, Coles Lane B72 1NL   **(T)** 0121 354 2997

Capacity: 4,500   **Seats:** 200   **Covered:** 500   **Clubhouse:** Yes   **Shop:** Yes

Directions: From M42 Junc 9, take A4097 (Minworth sign). At island, follow signs to Walmley Village. At traffic lights turn right (B4148). After shops turn left at traffic lights into Wylde Green Road. Over railway bridge turn right into East View Road, which becomes Coles Lane.

Previous Grounds: Not known

Record Attendance: Not known

Record Victory: Not known
Record Defeat: Not known

Record Goalscorer: Not known

Record Appearances: Not known
Additional Records:

Senior Honours:
Midland Combination Division One 1999-00, Premier Division 2003-04, Challenge Cup 03-04.

02-03		03-04		04-05		05-06		06-07		07-08		08-09		09-10		10-11		11-12	
MCmP	5	MCmP	1	MidAl	12	MidAl	4	MidAl	2	SthM	10	SthM	11	SthM	8	NP1S	10	NP1S	20

SHEFFIELD

Chairman: Richard Tims
Secretary: Stephen Hall   **(T)** 07761 207 447   **(E)**
Additional Committee Members:
R. Dyson, J. Harrison, G. Higton, R. Tims, D. Field, A. Methley, P. Bowden, N. Hughes, D.Risely, W. Towning, M. Turnidge, L. Walshaw, C. Williamson, Mrs. D. Risely and Mrs J. Towning.
Manager: Curtis Woodhouse
Programme Editor: Stuart James   **(E)**

THE NON-LEAGUE CLUB DIRECTORY

Book Holiday Inn Hotels and Save today!

Home

Clubs

Steps 1 - 4

League Tables

35 Years of Non-League Football

The Non-League Club Directory has developed into a comprehensive record of competitions within the non-League game, giving this level of football the

www.non-leagueclubdirectory.co.uk

Club Factfile

Founded: 1857   **Nickname:** Not known

Previous Names: None

Previous Leagues: Yorkshire 1949-82

Club Colours (change): Red/black/black (All blue)

Ground: The BT Local Business Stadium, Sheffield Road, Dronfield S18 2GD   **(T)** 01246 292 622

Capacity: 1,456   **Seats:** 250   **Covered:** 500   **Clubhouse:** Yes   **Shop:** Yes

Directions — **From the South** – M1 to Junc 29, A617 into Chesterfield. At Roundabout follow A61 Sheffield. This is a dual carriageway passing over 2 roundabouts. At the 3rd roundabout take the 3rd exit signposted Dronfield. The Coach and Horses Public House is at the bottom of the hill on the right and the BT Local Business Stadium directly behind it. Entrance to the ground is by turning right at the traffic lights and immediate right into the Club Car Park. **From the East** - M18 to M1 north to Junc 33 (Sheffield). Turn towards Sheffield and take the 3rd exit from dual carriageway signposted 'Ring Road / Chesterfield'. Go straight on at traffic island so that you are travelling alongside dual carriageway for a short period. At the junction turn left onto A61 Chesterfield. This is a dual carriageway passing through numerous traffic lights and two traffic islands. Follow Chesterfield sign at all times. After passing Graves Tennis centre on your left, turn left at next traffic island (still signposted Chesterfield). At next traffic island take 2nd exit signposted Dronfield The Coach and Horses Public House is at the bottom of the hill on the right and the BT Local Business Stadium directly behind it. Entrance to the ground is by turning right at the traffic lights and immediate right into the Club Car Park.

Previous Grounds: Abbeydale Park, Dore 1956-89, Sheffield Amateur Sports Stadium, Hillsborough Park 1989-91, Don Valley Stadium 1991-97

Record Attendance: 2,000 v Barton Rovers - FA Vase Semi-final 1976-77

Record Victory: Not known

Record Defeat: Not known

Record Goalscorer: Not known

Record Appearances: Not known

Additional Records: Paid £1,000 to Arnold Town for David Wilkins. Received £1,000 from Alfreton for Mick Godber 2002. World's first ever Football Club.

Senior Honours:
FA Amateur Cup 1902-03. Northern Counties East Division 1 1988-89, 90-91, League Cup 2000-01, 04-05.
Sheffield and Hallamshire Senior Cup 1993-94, 2004-05, 05-06.

02-03		03-04		04-05		05-06		06-07		07-08		08-09		09-10		10-11		11-12	
NCEP	7	NCEP	4	NCEP	4	NCEP	4	NCEP	2	NP 1	4	NP1S	11	NP1S	5	NP1S	11	NP1S	4

STAMFORD

Chairman: TBC
Secretary: Phil Bee   **(T)** 07772 646 776   **(E)** phil.bee@queen-eleanor.lincs.sch.uk
Additional Committee Members:
Guy Walton, John Burrows, Dave Salisbury, Roger Twiddy, David Whitby,
Keith Scarber.
Manager: Graham Drury
Programme Editor: Robert Herniman   **(E)** phil.bee@queen-eleanor.lincs.sch.uk

THE NON-LEAGUE CLUB DIRECTORY

Book Holiday Inn Hotels and Save today!

Home

Clubs

Steps 1 - 4

League Tables

35 Years of Non-League Football

The Non-League Club Directory has
developed into a comprehensive record
of competitions within the non-League
game, giving this level of football the

www.non-leagueclubdirectory.co.uk

Club Factfile

Founded: 1894   **Nickname:** The Daniels

Previous Names: Stamford Town and Rutland Ironworks amalgamated in 1894 to form Rutland Ironworks > 1896

Previous Leagues: Peterborough, Northants (UCL) 1908-55, Central Alliance 1955-61, Midland counties 1961-72, United Counties 1972-98, Southern 1998-2007

Club Colours (change): All red (White/black/black)

Ground: Kettering Road, Stamford, Lincs PE9 2JS   **(T)** 01780 763 079

Capacity: 2,000   **Seats:** 250   **Covered:** 1,250   **Clubhouse:** Yes   **Shop:** Yes

Directions Travel on A1 Southbound. Leave A1 by A43 slip road.
At junction turn left. Ground is one mile on the left.

Previous Grounds: None

Record Attendance: 4,200 v Kettering Town - FA Cup 3rd Qualifying Round 1953

Record Victory: 13-0 v Peterborough Reserves - Northants League 1929-30
Record Defeat: 0-17 v Rothwell - FA Cup 1927-28

Record Goalscorer: Bert Knighton - 248

Record Appearances: Dick Kwiatkowski - 462

Additional Records:

Senior Honours:
FA Vase 1979-80. United Counties League x7. Lincolnshire Senior Cup, Senior Shield. Lincolnshire Senior 'A' Cup x3.

02-03		03-04		04-05		05-06		06-07		07-08		08-09		09-10		10-11		11-12	
SthE	3	SthE	7	SthE	21	SthE	4	SthP	8	NP P	20	NP1S	7	NP1S	10	NP1S	19	NP1S	7

SUTTON COLDFIELD TOWN

Chairman: Tom Keogh
Secretary: Bill Worship   **(T)** 07837 375 369   **(E)** billandpatworship@tiscali.co.uk
Additional Committee Members:
Bernard Bent, Ken Hawkings, Andy Taylor, Neil Murrall, John Watson, Nick Thurston.

Manager: Chris Keogh
Programme Editor: Lyn Coley   **(E)** billandpatworship@tiscali.co.uk

Club Factfile

Founded: 1897   **Nickname:** Royals
Previous Names: Sutton Coldfield F.C. 1879-1921
Previous Leagues: Central Birmingham, Walsall Senior, Staffordshire County, Birmingham Combination 1950-54, West Midlands (Regional) 1954-65, 79-82, Midlands Combination 1965-79

Club Colours (change): All blue (All yellow)

Ground: Central Ground, Coles Lane, Sutton Coldfield B72 1NL   **(T)** 0121 354 2997
Capacity: 4,500   **Seats:** 200   **Covered:** 500   **Clubhouse:** Yes   **Shop:** Yes

Directions: From M42 Junc 9, take A4097 [Minworth sign]. At island, follow signs to Walmley Village. At traffic lights turn right [B4148]. After shops turn left at traffic lights into Wylde Green Road. Over railway bridge turn right into East View Road, which becomes Coles Lane.

Previous Grounds: Meadow Plat 1879-89, Coles Lane 1890-1919

Record Attendance: 2,029 v Doncaster Rovers - FA Cup 1980-81
Record Victory: Not known
Record Defeat: Not known
Record Goalscorer: Eddie Hewitt - 288
Record Appearances: Andy Ling - 550
Additional Records: Paid £1,500 to Gloucester for Lance Morrison, to Burton Albion for Micky Clarke and to Atherstone United for Steve Farmer 1991. Received £25,000 from West Bromwich Albion for Barry Cowdrill 1979
Senior Honours: West Midlands League 1979-80. Midland Combination x2.

10 YEAR RECORD

02-03	03-04	04-05	05-06	06-07	07-08	08-09	09-10	10-11	11-12
SthW 11	SthW 8	SthW 18	SthW 7	SthM 12	SthM 4	SthM 6	SthM 6	NP1S 6	NP1S 12

Northern Premier League Action...

Ilkeston' keeper makes sure he holds on to this shot with Coalville's No.9 ready to pounce on anything spilt.

Photo: Bill Wheatcroft.

PREMIER DIVISION

		P	W	D	L	F	A	GD	Pts
1	(C) Brackley Town	42	25	10	7	92	48	44	85
2	(P) Oxford City	42	22	11	9	68	41	27	77
3	AFC Totton	42	21	11	10	81	43	38	74
4	Chesham United	42	21	10	11	76	53	23	73
5	Cambridge City	42	21	9	12	78	52	26	72
6	Stourbridge	42	20	12	10	67	45	22	72
7	Leamington	42	18	15	9	60	47	13	69
8	St. Albans City	42	17	11	14	72	77	-5	62
9	Barwell	42	17	10	15	70	61	9	61
10	Bedford Town	42	15	10	17	60	69	-9	55
11	Chippenham Town	42	14	11	17	55	53	2	53
12	Frome Town	42	12	16	14	44	49	-5	52
13	Bashley	42	13	13	16	58	74	-16	52
14	Hitchin Town	42	13	12	17	54	57	-3	51
15	Redditch United	42	14	9	19	45	50	-5	51
16	Banbury United	42	13	10	19	54	61	-7	49
17	Weymouth	42	13	9	20	54	75	-21	48
18	Arlesey Town	42	12	11	19	43	60	-17	47
19	Hemel Hempstead Town	42	10	14	18	46	66	-20	44
20	(R) Evesham United	42	12	8	22	49	71	-22	44
21	(R) Swindon Supermarine	42	11	11	20	50	86	-36	44
22	(R) Cirencester Town	42	7	9	26	40	78	-38	30

PLAY-OFFS
Semi-Finals
AFC Totton 3-2 Chesham United
Oxford City 1-0 Cambridge City

Final (@ Hednesford Town, 7/5/12)
Oxford City 4-2 AFC Totton

		1	2	3	4	5	6	7	8	9	10	11	12	13	14	15	16	17	18	19	20	21	22
1	AFC Totton		6-0	2-1	2-1	2-0	2-0	2-2	2-3	3-0	1-1	3-0	3-1	1-1	2-0	0-1	1-1	6-0	0-0	1-1	1-0	4-0	2-0
2	Arlesey Town	0-2		2-1	1-2	0-2	1-0	2-0	0-1	2-4	1-1	0-1	1-0	0-1	3-0	0-0	0-2	1-4	0-3	1-1	1-1	1-1	3-1
3	Banbury United	0-1	1-2		3-0	4-0	1-2	0-2	2-0	1-2	1-1	2-1	1-2	2-2	0-0	1-1	1-1	1-1	1-0	2-0	4-1	1-1	1-5
4	Barwell	3-2	1-1	3-1		2-3	1-1	5-4	0-3	2-0	5-3	1-1	1-1	3-1	2-3	2-1	3-1	0-2	1-1	0-1	2-2	2-0	1-0
5	Bashley	4-4	0-0	0-3	0-2		3-3	1-1	0-1	3-1	0-0	2-3	0-0	1-1	2-0	1-3	2-1	0-2	2-1	4-1	1-0	3-3	3-3
6	Bedford Town	1-2	0-2	1-0	3-2	2-2		5-2	1-2	0-4	1-0	1-1	3-1	0-1	0-1	1-3	1-2	1-2	0-1	2-2	2-2	3-0	2-1
7	Brackley Town	0-3	2-1	1-1	2-1	3-2	7-1		4-2	3-2	5-1	0-0	2-0	1-1	3-0	3-0	5-2	2-0	6-0	0-2	4-0	3-1	
8	Cambridge City	1-0	3-1	3-0	2-1	4-0	6-1	2-3		2-2	3-0	3-1	1-2	2-3	3-0	3-1	2-2	2-0	1-1	4-0	0-0	1-1	3-0
9	Chesham United	2-1	2-0	3-0	1-0	2-1	3-4	2-3	1-0		1-2	2-1	2-1	2-0	2-1	2-0	1-1	1-1	1-0	2-2	4-2	2-1	4-1
10	Chippenham Town	2-1	1-1	1-1	0-3	1-3	3-0	0-1	2-2	1-0		0-1	1-0	1-1	4-1	0-1	1-2	0-1	1-2	4-0	1-2	0-2	3-0
11	Cirencester Town	1-2	0-3	1-2	2-2	0-1	2-4	0-2	0-2	1-1	0-1		1-2	0-1	0-2	2-2	2-1	0-1	1-0	0-2	1-2	1-3	0-1
12	Evesham United	1-0	1-3	2-5	1-3	0-1	0-0	0-2	2-1	0-2	2-4	2-3		1-0	2-2	1-0	1-2	0-1	1-0	1-1	0-1	3-4	4-0
13	Frome Town	1-3	2-2	0-1	1-0	1-1	0-0	1-1	1-1	0-1	0-2	1-0	1-2		1-1	0-0	0-0	0-3	3-2	0-1	1-1	2-0	0-0
14	Hemel Hempstead Town	0-3	1-1	2-1	2-3	2-2	1-1	1-1	1-2	1-1	1-1	4-1	2-3	3-1		2-0	1-1	2-0	0-2	0-4	2-0	0-0	1-2
15	Hitchin Town	2-2	2-0	1-2	0-0	2-3	1-3	2-1	3-2	1-1	0-0	6-2	0-1	1-3	3-0		0-0	0-3	2-1	0-3	2-0	0-1	3-1
16	Leamington	2-1	1-0	3-1	3-0	1-0	0-4	0-0	4-2	3-2	0-0	2-0	1-1	1-1	3-1	1-0		1-1	1-2	1-0	4-2	2-2	4-1
17	Oxford City	2-2	3-0	0-1	2-0	3-0	1-0	1-1	0-0	2-0	2-1	0-0	2-0	2-0	1-1	0-0	2-1		1-1	3-1	1-2	7-1	2-0
18	Redditch United	0-0	0-1	1-0	2-0	2-2	2-0	2-3	2-0	1-0	1-0	0-2	3-1	0-4	1-0	1-4	1-1	1-1		3-4	0-1	0-1	2-0
19	St Albans City	3-4	2-2	1-1	1-6	2-0	1-2	1-1	3-0	1-1	1-4	4-1	4-1	2-1	2-1	4-4	2-1	3-2	2-0		2-1	2-1	2-2
20	Stourbridge	2-1	2-0	5-0	1-1	5-0	1-1	1-0	1-1	2-1	3-1	2-1	3-1	4-0	1-1	0-0	0-0	2-0	1-0	2-1		4-1	1-2
21	Swindon Supermarine	0-0	2-1	2-0	0-2	1-2	0-1	0-2	3-1	0-6	0-4	4-4	2-2	0-2	1-3	2-1	0-1	2-4	0-2	2-1	2-1		2-2
22	Weymouth	3-1	0-2	2-1	1-1	2-1	0-2	0-1	1-2	2-2	2-0	3-1	2-2	0-3	0-1	2-1	2-1	1-0	2-1	3-1	1-1	2-2	

DIVISION ONE CENTRAL

		P	W	D	L	F	A	GD	Pts
1	(C) St. Neots Town	42	29	6	7	115	36	79	93
2	Slough Town	42	26	9	7	74	42	32	87
3	(P) Bedworth United	42	23	9	10	90	57	33	78
4	Uxbridge	42	22	8	12	79	59	20	74
5	Beaconsfield SYCOB	42	20	9	13	65	55	10	69
6	Rugby Town	42	19	10	13	67	65	2	67
7	Northwood	42	19	9	14	74	62	12	66
8	Biggleswade Town	42	19	7	16	75	54	21	64
9	Ashford Town (Middx)	42	16	11	15	62	61	1	59
10	AFC Hayes	42	14	16	12	58	59	-1	58
11	Barton Rovers	42	16	8	18	64	63	1	56
12	Chalfont St. Peter	42	14	14	14	65	68	-3	56
13	Leighton Town	42	15	10	17	60	67	-7	55
14	Bedfont Town	42	15	9	18	53	64	-11	54
15	Burnham	42	13	13	16	64	67	-3	52
16	Daventry Town	42	15	5	22	52	72	-20	50
17	Chertsey Town	42	15	5	22	65	93	-28	50
18	North Greenford United	42	13	10	19	56	72	-16	49
19	Woodford United	42	12	8	22	56	70	-14	44
20	Aylesbury	42	12	8	22	50	82	-32	44
21	Fleet Town	42	8	8	26	43	83	-40	32
22	(R) Marlow	42	6	10	26	50	86	-36	28

PLAY-OFFS
Semi-Finals
Bedworth United 2-1 Uxbridge
Slough Town 1-2 Beaconsfield SYCOB

Final (@ Bedworth United, 7/5/12)
Bedworth United 3-1 Beaconsfield SYCOB

		1	2	3	4	5	6	7	8	9	10	11	12	13	14	15	16	17	18	19	20	21	22
1	AFC Hayes		1-2	3-3	1-1	1-2	0-1	2-4	1-1	2-2	2-2	0-3	1-1	2-1	0-1	2-1	2-1	1-4	2-2	1-1	0-3	2-1	1-2
2	Ashford Town (Middx)	0-0		4-1	0-2	1-1	1-2	2-2	0-2	1-1	0-0	5-4	1-2	3-1	1-0	0-0	3-2	1-0	1-2	0-2	0-0	0-2	
3	Aylesbury	2-0	2-1		0-3	1-3	2-1	2-4	0-1	3-4	2-2	1-1	2-1	2-1	2-2	0-3	0-1	1-0	0-3	2-0	0-2	0-1	1-0
4	Barton Rovers	0-2	2-4	1-1		1-1	0-1	1-0	0-2	4-2	4-0	0-1	1-0	4-1	2-2	2-1	2-1	1-0	1-1	0-3	0-1	1-2	2-1
5	Beaconsfield SYCOB	0-1	0-1	4-2	3-1		1-0	1-1	0-0	3-2	3-0	4-2	1-2	2-1	3-0	0-1	1-2	1-3	0-0	0-2	0-2	1-1	1-0
6	Bedfont Town	1-3	1-0	1-0	0-1	0-2		0-4	1-3	0-0	2-3	2-2	3-0	0-1	2-1	2-2	1-1	1-0	3-1	1-2	1-0	1-4	1-1
7	Bedworth United	2-1	2-1	3-1	4-1	4-0	2-2		3-1	1-1	0-2	1-1	3-1	3-1	4-1	3-2	2-0	1-3	4-1	5-3	0-3	1-4	2-1
8	Biggleswade Town	3-0	4-1	4-1	1-1	4-0	1-2	2-4		1-1	2-1	2-3	4-0	0-1	3-2	2-0	4-0	1-3	0-1	1-1	1-3	2-4	3-1
9	Burnham	1-1	1-1	1-0	3-4	1-2	0-0	0-0	2-4		1-3	4-2	3-0	3-1	5-1	0-0	2-0	1-2	0-2	1-1	0-3	1-3	2-1
10	Chalfont St Peter	0-1	2-1	1-1	1-0	3-0	2-3	0-3	1-1	0-1		1-2	2-2	2-2	1-1	4-3	1-2	3-3	0-2	2-1	1-5	0-1	1-1
11	Chertsey Town	1-1	1-2	3-2	1-5	0-3	0-2	1-0	3-2	0-2	0-0		1-4	0-2	5-1	2-1	2-0	2-1	0-1	3-5	0-2	5-4	0-3
12	Daventry Town	0-2	4-3	3-0	3-4	1-3	0-2	1-0	2-1	1-1	2-4		2-1	3-1	3-1	1-0	0-1	1-0	1-1	0-3	0-2	2-1	
13	Fleet Town	3-3	0-1	3-1	1-0	1-4	0-3	2-1	1-0	1-0	1-2	0-3	1-3		1-2	1-1	1-0	1-4	1-0	0-1	0-1	2-4	0-3
14	Leighton Town	1-1	2-3	0-1	1-0	0-0	2-1	0-0	1-0	3-1	1-3	3-1	1-0	3-1		2-0	1-1	5-2	1-2	0-1	1-1	4-0	4-4
15	Marlow	2-2	0-1	0-1	2-1	1-2	4-3	1-3	1-3	0-2	1-4	2-1	0-0	3-3	0-1		2-4	4-2	3-5	0-3	0-0	2-2	1-2
16	North Greenford United	1-1	1-1	3-2	0-3	1-3	5-2	2-1	0-3	2-1	1-2	1-2	2-1	2-0	1-1			2-3	4-0	0-0	2-2	0-1	2-3
17	Northwood	1-2	2-1	1-1	2-1	1-1	1-0	3-3	3-0	2-1	1-5	4-0	1-0	0-1	3-2	1-1		3-3	2-4	4-1	1-2	0-1	
18	Rugby Town	1-4	0-4	0-2	1-1	1-2	1-1	1-0	3-2	4-1	2-1	1-0	2-0	3-3	3-0	1-0	4-2	0-0		2-0	2-4	4-0	1-3
19	Slough Town	1-1	4-3	0-0	2-1	1-1	2-1	2-1	2-1	1-2	1-1	3-0	2-1	3-0	0-3	3-0	0-2	1-0	4-0		2-0	2-0	2-1
20	St Neots Town	0-1	1-1	9-2	5-3	4-2	3-0	1-2	1-2	3-3	4-1	7-0	2-0	4-1	4-0	6-0	8-0	3-0	5-1	0-1		0-0	3-0
21	Uxbridge	0-1	1-2	3-0	4-1	2-3	5-1	1-1	1-0	1-1	0-0	5-2	5-2	3-0	1-1	2-1	1-3	0-3	2-1	0-2	1-2		2-1
22	Woodford United	0-3	2-3	1-3	1-1	2-1	1-1	1-2	0-2	2-3	2-3	2-1	2-1	1-0	0-3	2-1	1-1	0-0	0-1	1-2	1-2	2-3	

DIVISION ONE SOUTH & WEST

		P	W	D	L	F	A	GD	Pts
1	(C) Bideford	40	28	8	4	77	41	36	92
2	Poole Town	40	25	6	9	78	39	39	81
3	(P) Gosport Borough	40	22	14	4	73	44	29	80
4	Sholing	40	22	8	10	71	43	28	74
5	Hungerford Town	40	21	8	11	65	44	21	71
6	North Leigh	40	21	5	14	90	63	27	68
7	Paulton Rovers	40	18	10	12	60	39	21	64
8	Thatcham Town	40	16	14	10	51	42	9	62
9	Tiverton Town	40	16	11	13	52	42	10	59
10	Cinderford Town	40	17	8	15	49	39	10	59
11	Bishops Cleeve	40	16	11	13	40	42	-2	59
12	Halesowen Town	40	15	6	19	55	56	-1	51
13	Yate Town	40	13	11	16	58	59	-1	50
14	Mangotsfield United	40	14	7	19	62	66	-4	49
15	Bridgwater Town	40	13	4	23	47	77	-30	43
16	Didcot Town	40	11	9	20	39	68	-29	42
17	Taunton Town	40	10	10	20	47	76	-29	40
18	(R) Abingdon United	40	9	10	21	35	69	-34	37
19	(R) Wimborne Town	40	8	11	21	50	77	-27	35
20	(R) Clevedon Town	40	9	6	25	51	75	-24	33
21	(R) Stourport Swifts	40	5	5	30	39	88	-49	20

PLAY-OFFS
Semi-Finals
Poole Town 2-1 Hungerford Town
Gosport Borough 1-0 Sholing

Final @ Poole Town, 7/5/12)
Poole Town 1-3 Gosport Borough

		1	2	3	4	5	6	7	8	9	10	11	12	13	14	15	16	17	18	19	20	21
1	Abingdon United		0-0	0-0	2-0	0-0	0-4	3-0	0-2	1-3	0-2	1-0	1-3	1-1	1-3	2-1	3-2	2-0	0-2	0-2	0-1	0-2
2	Bideford	1-0		2-1	4-0	4-0	3-1	2-1	2-2	2-0	1-0	2-1	3-2	0-0	2-2	3-2	1-0	1-0	1-0	1-1	3-1	2-2
3	Bishops Cleeve	0-0	0-1		0-0	0-0	2-0	0-1	1-1	0-1	1-0	2-1	2-1	1-0	0-1	2-1	0-0	1-1	1-0	1-0		
4	Bridgwater Town	1-1	2-4	1-2		0-0	2-1	3-2	0-1	0-1	0-1	1-3	1-3	3-1	1-2	0-3	2-1	1-2	1-3	2-0	4-3	2-1
5	Cinderford Town	1-2	0-1	1-2	1-1		2-1	1-0	2-2	1-0	0-1	3-0	1-2	1-2	1-2	0-1	6-0	2-0	0-1	2-3	0-3	0-0
6	Clevedon Town	3-0	1-2	0-3	1-3	0-2		0-2	1-5	3-2	0-1	3-2	0-3	0-2	1-0	0-1	3-2	4-0	1-2	0-0	1-1	4-2
7	Didcot Town	2-3	1-1	0-1	1-0	0-0	1-0		0-3	0-2	0-1	1-0	0-5	1-0	2-5	0-4	1-0	5-1	0-3	0-2	2-2	1-1
8	Gosport Borough	3-0	2-1	2-1	2-1	0-2	1-1	1-1		2-1	0-0	2-1	3-3	2-0	2-1	1-0	4-3	2-0	1-0	1-1	5-3	4-1
9	Halesowen Town	2-0	3-1	1-1	3-1	0-1	2-1	1-0	1-3		1-3	0-1	1-0	1-2	0-0	1-2	4-1	0-1	3-0	1-2	3-0	0-2
10	Hungerford Town	4-0	1-2	4-0	3-0	2-1	1-1	2-1	1-2	2-0		1-3	3-6	1-0	0-2	4-1	0-0	1-1	2-1	1-0	3-0	3-1
11	Mangotsfield United	3-2	1-3	0-0	4-1	1-3	3-2	1-1	1-1	2-3	1-0		2-3	3-2	2-1	0-0	6-2	4-0	1-2	2-2	2-1	0-2
12	North Leigh	5-0	1-2	1-2	2-3	1-2	3-0	3-3	2-1	4-2	3-1	1-3		1-3	1-2	2-3	1-0	4-2	4-0	2-0	2-1	1-4
13	Paulton Rovers	1-1	1-2	0-2	3-1	0-1	2-0	3-1	0-0	1-1	3-3	3-2	2-1		1-2	0-0	2-0	2-0	4-0	2-1	7-0	3-2
14	Poole Town	2-1	3-1	4-1	0-1	3-1	5-3	3-0	3-0	1-0	0-1	4-1	3-1	1-0		0-0	3-1	6-0	2-3	0-0	3-1	1-1
15	Sholing	6-1	3-1	3-2	1-2	1-1	3-1	4-0	1-2	2-3	3-3	2-1	0-1	0-2	3-2		2-0	2-1	2-2	3-1	1-0	1-2
16	Stourport Swifts	4-3	0-3	0-1	2-0	1-3	0-2	0-1	0-1	1-1	3-4	2-1	2-2	0-2	1-2	0-1		0-1	1-2	1-2	2-1	0-3
17	Taunton Town	1-1	2-3	3-3	6-2	0-1	1-1	1-0	2-2	3-1	1-0	1-1	3-3	1-0	1-2	0-1	4-4		1-1	0-2	2-0	2-3
18	Thatcham Town	1-0	1-2	3-1	4-0	1-2	3-2	1-1	0-0	0-0	1-1	0-0	0-1	0-0	0-0	1-1	3-0	2-0		1-1	3-2	1-0
19	Tiverton Town	0-0	0-1	2-0	2-1	1-0	2-1	0-1	3-1	4-2	1-2	5-0	1-4	1-1	0-1	1-1	0-0	1-1		1-1	3-0	
20	Wimborne Town	1-3	0-3	1-1	0-1	0-2	3-3	1-1	2-2	5-4	2-1	1-0	1-1	1-1	0-1	0-2	4-1	1-1	0-0	2-1		0-2
21	Yate Town	0-0	3-3	1-2	1-2	0-2	1-0	3-4	1-1	0-0	1-1	0-2	0-1	1-0	3-1	1-1	2-2	4-0	3-2	1-2	1-4	

LEAGUE CUP

PRELIMINARY ROUND

Stourbridge 2-1 Evesham United

Weymouth 0-1 Sholing

ROUND 1

Bishops Cleeve 0-2 Paulton Rovers

Bedford Town 3-1 St Neots Town

Cinderford Town 1-2 Clevedon Town

Abingdon United 0-1 Oxford City

AFC Hayes 1-6 Chertsey Town

AFC Totton 3-2 Gosport Borough

Aylesbury 1-2 North Leigh

Banbury United 4-0 Bedworth United

Barton Rovers 1-1, 7-6p Arlesey Town

Bideford 2-1 Tiverton Town

Bridgwater Town 3-4 Taunton Town

Daventry Town 3-1 Barwell

Fleet Town 1-5 Uxbridge

Leighton Town 4-1 Cambridge City

Marlow 0-2 Bedfont Town

North Greenford United 3-0 Burnham

Northwood 3-0 Ashford Town (Mddx)

Redditch United 1-0 Halesowen Town

Slough Town 1-2 Chesham United

Stourbridge 5-2 Stourport Swifts

Woodford United 1-2 Rugby Town

Yate Town 6-1 Mangotsfield United

Frome Town 4-1 Cirencester Town

Swindon Supermarine 2-0 Chippenham Town

Thatcham Town 1-0 Didcot Town

Bashley 2-5 Poole Town

Chalfont St Peter 1-1, 3-4p Beaconsfield SYCOB

Leamington 2-2, 3-5p Brackley Town

St Albans City 0-3 Hemel Hempstead Town

Sholing 2-3 Wimborne Town

ROUND 2

Beaconsfield SYCOB 1-0 Bedfont Town

Hitchin Town 1-2 Hemel Hempstead Town

AFC Totton 1-0 Poole Town

Bideford 4-3 Taunton Town

Clevedon Town 2-1 Paulton Rovers

Hungerford Town 1-2 Daventry Town

North Greenford United 1-1, 4-2p Chertsey Town

Northwood 3-1 Uxbridge

Wimborne Town 2-3 Thatcham Town

Yate Town 2-6 Frome Town

Swindon Supermarine 3-2 Brackley Town

Chesham United 3-1 Barton Rovers

Leighton Town 0-1 Bedford Town

Oxford City 1-0 North Leigh

Rugby Town 4-3 Stourbridge

Redditch United 0-2 Banbury United

ROUND 3

Beaconsfield SYCOB 1-3 Hemel Hempstead Tn

AFC Totton 3-0 Swindon Supermarine

Bedford Town 2-3 North Greenford United

Bideford 2-3 Clevedon Town

Chesham United 6-0 Northwood

Oxford City 2-3 Banbury United

Thatcham Town 2-1 Frome Town

Rugby Town 2-1 Daventry Town

QUARTER FINALS

AFC Totton 6-1 North Greenford United

Thatcham Town 1-4 Clevedon Town

Chesham United 2-1 Rugby Town

Hemel Hempstead Town 0-2 Banbury United

SEMI-FINALS

AFC Totton 2-3 Clevedon Town

Banbury United 0-0, 5-4p Chesham United

FINAL (2 Legs)

Clevedon Town 0-0 Banbury United

Banbury United 1-2 Clevedon Town

Southern League Premier Division Statistics 2011-12

	Games Played & Goals Scored & Conceded	Top Goalscorers League, FAC & FAT	Number of Scorers per Club	Hat Tricks Scored	Penalties Scored	Best Individual Consecutive Scoring Run	Number of Clean Sheets	Number of Games in which club failed to score	Scorers with 10+
AFC Totton	50-103/60	Sherborne 15-5-1=21	16	Charles 2, Sherborne 2 & Brown	11	Sherborne 4	18(4)	6	Sherborne 21 Gosney 20 (9 pens) & Charles 15
Arlesey Town	61-50/72	Dillon 12-4-2=18	15+1og	0	7	Dillon 3	11(4)	17(4)	Dillon 18
Banbury United	47-59/69	Green 8-0-2=10	16	0	4	Green 4	11(5)	11	Green 10
Barwell	47-82/72	Towers 24-0-2=26	17	Towers 2 & Charley	6	7 x 2	7	11	Towers 26 & Charley 15
Bashley	45-62/81	Stokoe 12-0-2=14	14	0	4	Gillespie 3	7	15	Stokoe 14 & Gamble 13
Bedford Town	44-62/72	Roberts 31-0-4=35	15+1og	Roberts 3	7	Roberts 4	9	12	Roberts 32
Brackley Town	47-98/56	Diggin 16-0-1=17	17+1og	0	10	Diggin 3	16(6)	8	Diggin 17 (4p) Sandy 17 (3p) & Louis 16 (2p)
		Sandy 16-0-1=17				Sandy 3			
Cambridge City	46-84/59	Hammond 25-1-0=26	17	Kelly 2 & Hammond	4	Hammond 3	14	6	Hammond 26, Kelly 12 & Theobald 10
Chesham United	47-87/61	Thomas Si 20-0-2=22	16+2ogs	Archer & Effiong	1	Simon Thomas 4	13	5	Thomas (Simon) 32 & Potton 13
Chippenham T	50-67/59	Griffin A 19-0-5=24	10	Gilroy & Griffin	5	Powell 4	14	12	Griffin A 24(5p) Gray 10 & Powell 10
Crencester T	45-46/84	Griffin S 6-0-0=6	19+1og	0	2	Griffin 3	7	15	0
Evesham United	48-59/81	Palmer 8-5-0=13	20+1og	Palmer	6	McPike & Eze 3	10	11	0
Frome Town	46-46/55	Hulbert 5-2-0=6	17+1og	0	5	Harris 3	14	16	0
		Balinger 5-1-0=6							
Hemel Hempst'd	48-51/73	Pearce 10-0-1=11	17	0	3	Lafyette,Pearce 3	11	16	Pearce 11
Hitchin Town	45-58/62	Frendo 23-0-4=27	14	Frendo 3	9	Frendo 4	13	17(4)	Frendo 27 (7pens)
Leamington	45-66/50	Blyth 16-2-0=18	15	Berwick & Kolodynski	7	Blyth 3	14	8	Blyth 18(5p) Kolodynski 12 & Morley 10
Oxford City	50-82/49	Basham 16-5-0=21	13	0	5	Basham 3	20(4)	11	Basham 21 & Barcelos 15
Redditch U	44-46/54	Deabill 8-0-0=8	19+1og	0	3	3 x 2	13	16(4)	0
St Albans City	47-80/86	Bakare 12-0-0=12	24+1og	0	4	Newton 4	10	6	Bakare 12
Stourbridge	52-92/58	Geddes 14-3-1=18	18+1og	0	13	Geddes 3	15	9	Geddes 18 (13pens) & Rowe 15
Swindon Super.	47-55/93	Gray 9-0-1=10	13	0	4	5 x 2	8	17(4)	Gray & Stanley 10
		Stanley 10-0-0=10							
Weymouth	53-76/94	Byerley 18-1-7=26	16	Byerley, Ford & Malcom	9	Byerley 5	7	16	Byerley 26 (7p)

AFC TOTTON

Chairman: Paul Wallace
Secretary: Alec Hayter   **(T)**   **(E)** footballsecretary@afctotton.com
Additional Committee Members:
John Tull, Charles Wood, John Heskins, Ann Dunwell, Sean McGlead.

Manager: Stephen Riley
Programme Editor: Stephen Cain   **(E)** programme@afctotton.com

Club Factfile

Founded: 1886   **Nickname:** Stags
Previous Names: Totton FC until merger with Totton Athletic in 1979
Previous Leagues: Hampshire 1982-86, Wessex 1986-2008

Club Colours (change): All blue (All yellow)

Ground: Testwood Stadium, Salisbury Road, Calmore, Totton SO40 2RW   **(T)** 02380 868 981
Capacity: 3,000   **Seats:** 500   **Covered:** 500   **Clubhouse:** Yes   **Shop:** Yes
Directions: From the M27 Junction 2. From the east take the first exit at the roundabout or from the west take the third exit at the roundabout.
Take the first left within 100 yards, signposted Totton Central.
At the T junction turn left and you will find the entrance to the ground approximately 1 mile on the left hand side, just before the
Calmore Roundabout.

Previous Grounds:

Record Attendance: 600 v Windsor & Eton - FA Cup 4th Qualifying Round 1982-83
Record Victory: Not known
Record Defeat: Not known
Record Goalscorer: Not known
Record Appearances: James Sherlington
Additional Records:

Senior Honours:
Hampshire League 1981-82, 84-85. Wessex League Premier Division 2007-08.
Southern League Division South & West 2010-11.
Hampshire Senior Cup 2010-11.

10 YEAR RECORD

02-03		03-04		04-05		05-06		06-07		07-08		08-09		09-10		10-11		11-12	
Wex	3	Wex	8	Wex1	8	Wex1	4	WexP	2	WexP	1	Sthsw	3	Sthsw	2	Sthsw	1	SthP	3

AFC TOTTON

No.	Date	Comp	H/A	Opponents	Att:	Result	Goalscorers	Pos
1	Aug 13	Sth P	A	Arlesey Town	141	W 2 - 0	Gosney 9 Osman 83	
2	16		H	Oxford City	354	W 6 - 0	Hill 21 Brown 36 43 Gosney 44 61 Sherborne 90	
3	20		H	Swindfon Supermarine	252	W 4 - 0	Gosney 73 SHERBORNE 3 (77 82 90)	1
4	23		A	Hemel Hempstead	148	W 3 - 0	CHARLES 3 (2 4 58)	1
5	27		A	Leamington	601	L 1 - 2	Davies 13	1
6	29		H	Weymouth	580	W 2 - 0	Richardson 8 Gosney 76	
7	Sept 3		H	Barwell	365	W 2 - 1	Sherborne 10 Hill 90	
8	10		A	Brackley Town	285	W 3 - 0	Gosney 8 (pen) Sherborne 55 Charles 90	1
9	13		A	St Albans City	329	W 4 - 3	Sherborne 13 Oldring 22 Gosney 38 (pen) Charles 49	
10	17	FAC 1Q	H	Fleet Town	394	W 2 - 0	Gosney 24 Sherborne 35	
11	24		H	Hitchin Town	438	L 0 - 1		1
12	Oct 1	FAC 2Q	A	Clevedon Town	140	W 2 - 1	Gosney 34 (pen) Scott 87	
13	4		H	Cirencester Town	377	W 3 - 0	Charles 2 12 Gosney 68	1
14	8		A	Evesham United	130	L 0 - 1		1
15	15	FAC 3Q	H	Weymouth	712	W 4 - 2	Sherborne 32 (pen) 79 (pen) Charles 44 Osman 57	
16	22	FAT 1Q	A	Weymouth	512	L 2 - 3	Gosney 25 (pen) Sherbourne 64	
17	25		H	Cambridge City	317	L 2 - 3	Campbell 35 Jack 66	2
18	29	FAC 4Q	H	Hanworth Villa	764	W 3 - 2	Davies 42 Campbell 45 Sherborne 81	
19	Nov 5		A	Redditch United	2041	D 0 - 0		1
20	12	FAC 1	H	Bradford PA	2315	W 8 - 1	Davies 13 90 Gosney 29 (pen) 52 Charles 32, BROWN 3(64 74 79)	
21	16		A	Frome Town	120	W 3 - 1	Osman 13 Brown 37 55	
22	19		A	Bedford Town	255	W 2 - 1	Gosney 37 (pen) 56 (pen)	1
23	Dec 3	FAC 2	H	Bristol Rovers	2236	L 1 - 6	Sherborne 70	
24	10		H	Hemel Hempstead	295	W 2 - 0	Davies 42 48	2
25	17		A	Oxford City	243	D 2 - 2	Sherborne 34 Hill 90	3
26	26		H	Bashley	577	W 2 - 0	Hill 12 Gosney 47	1
27	31		A	Chippenham Town	610	L 1 - 2	Gosney 80 (pen)	4
28	Jan 2		A	Weymouth	901	L 1 - 3	Charles 90	
29	7		H	Chesham United	579	W 3 - 0	Gosney 15 (pen) Jack 72 88	2
30	14		H	Brackley Town	654	D 2 - 2	Charles 1 Osman 72	2
31	17		H	Banbury Town	328	W 2 - 1	Charles 36 Davies 75	2
32	21		A	Barwell	174	L 2 - 3	Jack 14 Gosney 47	2
33	28		A	Cirencester Town	126	W 2 - 1	Whisken 65 Brown 82	2
34	Feb 18		H	Evesham United	406	W 3 - 1	Sherborne 7 62 Brown 90	2
35	22		A	Swindon Supermatine	110	D 0 - 0		
36	25		A	Cambridge City	352	L 0 - 1		3
37	28		H	St Albans City	353	D 1 - 1	Gosney 44	
38	March 3		H	Frome Town	540	D 1 - 1	Jack 75	2
39	10		A	Banbury United	271	W 1 - 0	Moss 45	2
40	17		H	Redditch United	460	D 0 - 0		2
41	20		H	Stourbridge	335	W 1 - 0	Moss 77	
42	24		H	Leamington	148	D 1 - 1	Moss 2	2
43	27		A	Hitchin Town	333	D 2 - 2	Osman 35 Whisken 71	
44	31		A	Chesham United	472	L 1 - 2	Osman 59	3
45	Apr 7		H	Chippenham Town	627	D 1 - 1	Bottomley 81	4
46	9		A	Bashley	463	D 4 - 4	Whisken 16 SHERBORNE 3(79 83 90)	
47	14		H	Arlesey Town	342	W 6 - 0	CHARLES 3(16 61 67) Sherborne 40 49 Coutts 58	
48	21		A	Stourbridge	728	L 1 - 2	Davies 25	3
49	28		A	Bedford Town	551	W 2 - 0	Moss 68 Davies 90	3
50	May 3	Play-Off SF	H	Chesham United	521	W 3 - 2	Davies 13 Charles 44 Moss 6	
51	7	Play-Off F	A	Oxford City	1280	L 2 - 4	Brown 50 Osman 84	

ARLESEY TOWN

Chairman: Manny Cohen
Secretary: Chris Sterry   **(T)** 07540 201 473   **(E)** chris.sterry@ntlworld.com
Additional Committee Members:
Trevor Flint, Mick Marshall, Gary King

Manager: Zema Abbey
Programme Editor: Jason Marshall   **(E)** jasonmarshall1@live.co.uk

THE NON-LEAGUE CLUB DIRECTORY

Book Holiday Inn Hotels and Save today!

Home

Clubs

Steps 1 - 4

League Tables

35 Years of Non-League Football

The Non-League Club Directory has developed into a comprehensive record of competitions within the non-League game, giving this level of football the

www.non-leagueclubdirectory.co.uk

Club Factfile

Founded: 1891   **Nickname:** The Blues

Previous Names: Not known

Previous Leagues: Biggleswade & Dist., Bedfordshire Co. (South Midlands) 1922-26, 27-28, Parthenon, London 1958-60, United Co. 1933-36, 82-92, Spartan South Mid. 1992-2000, Isthmian 2000-04, 06-08, Southern 2004-07

Club Colours (change): Light blue/dark blue/dark blue (Yellow/black/black)

Ground: Armadillo Stadium, Hitchin Road, Arlesey SG15 6RS   **(T)** 01462 734 504

Capacity: 2,920   **Seats:** 150   **Covered:** 600   **Clubhouse:** Yes   **Shop:** Yes

Directions
From the A1 exit at Baldock(J10) and follow the signs for Stotfold then Arlesey. You will enter Arlesey from the area known as Church End, this is the opposite end of Arlesey, but as there is only one main street just follow keep driving until you pass the Biggs Wall building and the ground is on your left.

Coming of the M1 at Luton and follow the signs for Hitchin, pass Hitchin Town FC on the Shefford Road and turn right into Turnpike Lane, this is Ickleford. Follow the road out of Ickleford and bear left away from the Letchworth turning, the ground is a little further on, on the right.

Previous Grounds:

Record Attendance: 2,000 v Luton Town Reserves - Bedfordshire Senior Cup 1906

Record Victory: Not known
Record Defeat: Not known

Record Goalscorer: Not known

Record Appearances: Gary Marshall

Additional Records:

Senior Honours:

South Midlands Premier Division x5. United Counties Premier Division 1984-85. FA Vase 1994-95.
Isthmian League Division 3 2000-01. Southern League Division 1 Central 2010-11.
Bedfordshire Senior Cup 1965-66, 78-79, 96-97, 2010-11.

02-03		03-04		04-05		05-06		06-07		07-08		08-09		09-10		10-11		11-12	
Isth1N	16	Isth1N	8	SthE	14	SthE	10	Isth1N	18	Isth1N	15	SthC	18	SthC	9	SthC	1	SthP	18

ARLESEY TOWN

No.	Date	Comp	H/A	Opponents	Att:	Result	Goalscorers	Pos
1	Aug 13	Sth P	H	AFC Totton	141	L 0 - 2		
2	16		A	Leamington	540	L 0 - 1		
3	20		A	Frome Town	204	D 2 - 2	Gray 29 Dillon 55	17
4	23		H	Brackley Town	113	W 2 - 0	Dillon 28 Deaney 87	
5	27		A	Stourbridge	205	L 0 - 2		18
6	29		H	Cambridge City	228	L 0 - 1		
7	Sept 3		A	Bedford Town	322	W 2 - 0	Dillon 64 (pen) 86	16
8	10		H	Swindon Supermarine	114	D 1 - 1	Mason 16	14
9	13		A	Hemel Hempstead	171	D 1 - 1	Fenemore 51	
10	17	FAC 1Q	A	**Tilbury**	**90**	**W 2 - 1**	**Sinclair 36 Deeney 86**	
11	24		H	Bashley	110	L 0 - 2		15
12	Oct 1	FAC 2Q	H	**Hampton & Richmond**	**156**	**W 6 - 2**	**Allinson 1 56 Marsh 34 Mason 44 Dillon 46 Frater 59**	
13	4		H	Barwell	115	L 1 - 2	Fenemore 81	
14	8		A	St Albans City	396	D 2 - 2	Dillon 72 Marsh 73	19
15	15	FAC 3Q	A	**Thurrock**	**73**	**D 0 - 0**		
16	18	FAC 3Qr	H	**Turrock**	**136**	**W 4 - 1**	**Allinson 11 Patrick 51 Dillon 77 (pen) 88**	
17	22	FAT 1Q	H	**AFC Sudbury**	**185**	**W 3 - 1**	**Dillon 3 90 (pen) Mason 73**	
18	29	FAC 4Q	H	**Forest Green Rovers**	**343**	**W 2 - 3**	**Dillon 85 (pen) Deeney 90**	
19	Nov 5	FAT 2Q	A	**Thamesmead Town**	**32**	**L 0 - 4**		
20	8		H	Oxford City	101	L 1 - 3	Mason 78	20
21	12	FAC 1	A	**Salisbury City**	**1298**	**L 1 - 1**	**Sinclair 41**	**20**
22	15		A	Banbury United	106	W 2 - 1	Deeney 5 Dillon 30	
23	19		H	Chippenham Town	121	D 1 - 0	Osman 17	19
24	26		A	Redditch United	225	W 1 - 1	Dillon 74 (pen)	17
25	Dec 3		H	Frome Town	108	L 0 - 1		18
26	6		A	Evesham United	59	W 3 - 1	Deaney 39 70 Mason 75	
27	13		H	Cirencester Town	101	L 0 - 2		
28	17		H	Leamington	181	L 0 - 0		18
29	26		H	Hitchin Town	526	D 0 - 2		18
30	31		A	Chesham United	375	L 0 - 3		19
31	Jan 2		A	Cambridge City	375	L 1 - 1	Goss 43	
32	7		H	Weymouth	173	W 3 - 2	Patrick 15 33 Marsh 37	19
33	10		H	Brackley Town	146	L 1 - 0	Dillon 55 (pen)	
34	21		H	Bedford Town	317	W 1 - 1	Patrick 6	19
35	28		A	Barwell	152	D 1 - 1	Dillon 31	19
36	Feb 18		H	St Albans City	246	D 1 - 1	Broughton 18	19
37	20		A	Swindon Supermarine	82	L 1 - 2	Dillon 70 (pen)	19
38	25		A	Oxford City	153	L 0 - 3		19
39	March 3		H	Banbury United	143	W 2 - 1	Cole 32 Marsh 45	19
40	10		A	Cirencester Town	61	W 3 - 0	Brown 39 Green 49 (og) Dillon 69	
41	13		H	Hemel Hempstead	120	W 3 - 0	Frater 52 Goss 67 Marsh 70	14
42	17		H	Evesham United	112	W 1 - 0	Marsh 1§7	
43	20		A	Bashley	146	D 0 - 0		14
44	24		H	Stourbridge	145	D 1 - 1	Patrick 48	14
45	31		A	Weymouth	481	W 2 - 0	Dillon 15 Marsh 53	
46	Apr 7		H	Chesham United	195	L 2 - 4	Frater 3 Marsh 40	
47	9		A	Hitchin Town	514	L 0 - 2		15
48	14		A	AFC Totton	342	L 0 - 6		18
49	21		H	Redditch United	155	L 0 - 3		
50	28		A	Chippenham Town	372	D 1 1	Abbey 83	

BANBURY UNITED

Chairman: Paul Jones
Secretary: Barry Worlsey **(T)** 07941 267 567 **(E)** bworsley@btinternet.com
Additional Committee Members:
Nigel Porter, Richard Cox, Peter Meadows.

Manager: Ady Fuller
Programme Editor: David Shadbolt **(E)** djshadbolt@tiscali.o.uk

Club Factfile

Founded: 1933 **Nickname:** Puritans
Previous Names: Banbury Spencer. Club reformed in 1965 as Banbury United
Previous Leagues: Banbury Junior 1933-34, Oxon Senior 1934-35, Birmingham Combination 1935-54,
West Midlands 1954-66, Southern 1966-90, Hellenic 1991-2000

Club Colours (change): Red with gold trim/red/red/ (White/blue/blue)

Ground: Spencer Stadium, off Station Road, Banbury OX16 5TA **(T)** 01295 263 354
Capacity: 6,500 **Seats:** 250 **Covered:** 50 **Clubhouse:** Yes **Shop:** Yes

Directions: From M40, Junction 11, head towards Banbury, over first roundabout, left at next roundabout into Concorde Avenue. Straight on at next roundabout, taking left hand lane, and turn left at traffic lights, turn first right into Station Approach. At station forecourt and car park, take narrow single track road on extreme right and follow to Stadium.(Direct SatNav to OX16 5AB).

Previous Grounds: Not known

Record Attendance: 7,160 v Oxford City - FA Cup 3rd Qualifying Round 30/10/1948
Record Victory: 12-0 v RNAS Culham - Oxon Senior Cup 1945-46
Record Defeat: 2-11 v West Bromwich Albion 'A' - Birmingham Combination 1938-39
Record Goalscorer: Dick Pike and Tony Jacques - 222 (1935-48 and 1965-76 respectively)
Record Appearances: Jody McKay - 576
Additional Records: Paid £2,000 to Oxford United for Phil Emsden
Received £20,000 from Derby County for Kevin Wilson 1979
Senior Honours:
Hellenic Premier 1999-2000. Oxford Senior Cup 1978-79, 87-88, 2003-04.

10 YEAR RECORD

02-03		03-04		04-05		05-06		06-07		07-08		08-09		09-10		10-11		11-12	
SthE	8	SthE	8	SthP	17	SthP	7	SthP	13	SthP	9	SthP	19	SthP	12	SthP	16	SthP	16

BANBURY UNITED

No.	Date	Comp	H/A	Opponents	Att:	Result	Goalscorers	Pos
1	Aug 13	Sth P	H	Hitchin Town	256	D 1 - 1	Green 54 (pen)	
2	16		A	Barwell	173	L 1 - 3	Green 7	
3	20		A	Bashley	202	W 3 - 0	Dolman 14 Woodley 38 Green 53	11
4	23		H	Redditch United	305	W 1 - 0	Stanbridge 90	
5	27		H	St Albans City	269	W 2 - 0	Green 65 Woodley 72	5
6	29		A	Oxford City	418	W 1 - 0	Green 57	
7	Sept 3		H	Hemel Hempstead	316	D 0 - 0		4
8	10		A	Evesham United	140	W 5 - 2	Walker 4 53 Williams 11 Green 13 Woodley 65	
9	13		H	Chesham United	301	L 1 - 2	Stanbridge 1	7
10	17	FAC 1Q	H	Slough Town	349	L 1 - 3	Williams 36	
11	24		A	Cambridge City	310	L 0 - 3		9
12	Oct 4		A	Stourbridge	345	L 0 - 5		
13	8		H	Weymouth	353	L 1 - 5	Walker 37	13
14	15		A	Chippenham Town	379	D 1 - 1	Bailey 19	13
15	22	FAT 1Q	A	Leighton Town	137	W 1 - 0	Green 26 (pen)	
16	29		H	Swindon Supermarine	220	D 1 - 1	Green 30	11
17	Nov 5	FAT 2Q	H	Paulton Rovers	207	W 3 - 1	Woodley 7 Green 9 Williams 39	13
18	15		H	Arlesey Town	106	L 1 - 2	Green 58	
19	19		H	Cirencester Town	100	W 2 - 1	Cole 20 Dolman 45	
20	26	FAT 3Q	H	Wealdstone	370	D 0 - 0		
21	29	FAT 3Qr	A	Wealdstone	222	L 0 - 4		
22	Dec 3		H	Bashley	179	W 4 - 0	Cole 49 Walker 61 Polk 87 Woodley 90	
23	10		A	Redditch United	172	L 0 - 1		10
24	17		H	Barwell	193	W 3 - 0	Polk 33 Shildon 38 Woodley 77	
25	26		A	Brackley Town	603	D 1 - 1	Walker 4	
26	31		H	Bedford Town	259	L 1 - 2	Johnston 30	
27	Jan 2		H	Oxford City	339	D 1 - 1	Blake 17	12
28	7		A	Frome Town	257	W 1 - 0	Blake 26 (pen)	11
29	14		H	Evesham United	198	L 1 - 2	Edmond 18	11
30	17		A	AFC Totton	328	L 1 - 2	Blake 52	
31	21		A	Hemel Hempstead	245	L 1 - 2	Johnson 86	13
32	28		H	Stourbridge	314	W 4 - 1	Edmond 5 Johnson 38 90 Blake 53	11
33	Feb 18		A	Weymouth	402	L 1 - 2	Dolman 87	16
34	25		H	Chippenham Town	201	D 1 - 1	Johnson 14	15
35	28		H	Cambridge City	168	W 2 - 0	Edmond 77 80	
36	March 3		A	Arlesey Town	143	L 1 - 2	Angus 69	12
37	10		H	AFC Totton	61	L 0 - 1		14
38	13		A	Chesham United	214	L 0 - 3		
39	17		A	Swindon Supermarine	173	L 0 - 2		17
40	20		A	Leamington	388	L 1 - 3	Johnson 31 (pen)	
41	24		A	St Albans City	482	D 1 - 1	Johnson 60 (pen)	17
42	31		H	Frome Town	225	D 2 - 2	Kinch 17 Johnson 84	17
43	Apr 7		A	Bedford Town	336	L 0 - 1		18
44	9		H	Brackley Town	483	L 0 - 2		
45	14		A	Hitchin Town	347	W 2 - 1	Blake 47 Johnson 64 (pen)	16
46	21		H	Leamington	564	D 1 - 1	Johnson 53	17
47	28		A	Cirencester Town	179	W 3 - 1	Johnson 17 41 Blake 58	16

BARWELL

Chairman: David Laing
Secretary: Mrs Shirley Brown   **(T)** 07961 905 141   **(E)** shirley.brown16@ntlworld.com
Additional Committee Members:
Mandy French, Colin Burton, Viv Coleman, Steve Brown

Manager: Jimmy Ginnelly
Programme Editor: Dave Richardson   **(E)** daverichardson@cleartherm.com

THE NON-LEAGUE CLUB DIRECTORY

Book Holiday Inn Hotels and Save today!

Home

Clubs

Steps 1 - 4

League Tables

35 Years of Non-League Football

The Non-League Club Directory has developed into a comprehensive record of competitions within the non-League game, giving this level of football the

www.non-leagueclubdirectory.co.uk

Club Factfile

Founded: 1992   **Nickname:** Canaries

Previous Names: Barwell Athletic FC and Hinckley FC amalgamated in 1992.
Previous Leagues: Midland Alliance 1992-2010, Northern Premier League 2010-11.

Club Colours (change): Yellow with green trim/green/yellow (All blue)

Ground: Kirkby Road Sports Ground, Kirkby Road, Barwell LE9 8FQ   **(T)** 01455 843 067

Capacity: 2,500   **Seats:** 256   **Covered:** 750   **Clubhouse:** Yes   **Shop:** No

Directions: **FROM M6 NORTH/M42/A5 NORTH:** From M6 North join M42 heading towards Tamworth/Lichfield, leave M42 at Junction 10(Tamworth Services) and turn right onto A5 signposted Nuneaton. Remain on A5 for approx 11 miles, straight on at traffic lights at Longshoot Motel then at next roundabout take first exit signposted A47 Earl Shilton. In about 3 miles at traffic lights go straight on and in 1 mile at roundabout take first exit signposted Barwell. In about 1.5 miles, centre of village, go straight over mini roundabout and then in 20 metres turn right into Kirkby Road. Entrance to complex is 400 metres on right opposite park. **FROM M1 SOUTH:** From M1 South Take M69)Signposted Coventry) Take Junction 2 Off M69 (Signposted Hinckley) Follow signs to Hinckley . Go straight on at traffic lights with Holywell Pub on the right. The road bears to the right at next traffic lights turn right signposted Earl Shilton/Leicester. Keep on this road past golf club on right at Hinckley United Ground on left and at large roundabout take second exit signposted Barwell. In about 1.5 miles, centre of village, go straight over mini roundabout and then in 20 metres turn right into Kirkby Road. Entrance to complex is 400 metres on right opposite park.

Previous Grounds:

Record Attendance: Not known

Record Victory: Not known
Record Defeat: Not known

Record Goalscorer: Andy Lucas

Record Appearances: Adrian Baker

Additional Records:

Senior Honours:
Midland Alliance League Cup 2005-06, Champions 2009-10.
Northern Premier Division One South 2010-11.

02-03		03-04		04-05		05-06		06-07		07-08		08-09		09-10		10-11		11-12	
MidAl	12	MidAl	18	MidAl	13	MidAl	9	MidAl	6	MidAl	10	MidAl	2	MidAl	1	NP1S	1	SthP	9

BARWELL

No.	Date	Comp	H/A	Opponents	Att:	Result	Goalscorers	Pos
1	Aug 13	Sth P	A	Chesham United	341	L 0 - 1		
2	16		H	Banbury United	173	W 3 - 1	Barlone 24 77 Towers 68	
3	20		H	St Albans City	163	L 0 - 1		14
4	23		A	Bedford Town	227	L 2 - 3	Julien 4 Pearson 86	
5	27		A	Hemel Hempstead	161	W 3 - 2	Charley 43 75 Barlone 90	15
6	29		H	Stourbridge	204	D 2 - 2	Richards 67 (pen) Charley 75	
7	Sept 3		A	AFC Totton	285	L 1 - 2	Richards 37 (pen)	
8	10		H	Oxford City	116	L 0 - 2		16
9	13		H	Brackley Town	109	W 5 - 4	Baines 44 63 Towers 45 83 Hadland 54	
10	17	FAC 1Q	H	**Stone Dominoes**	118	W 3 - 2	Charley 20 Barlone 71 Pearson 85	
11	24		A	Weymouth	421	D 1 - 1	Charley 1 (pen)	14
12	Oct 1	FAC 2Q	H	**Stourbridge**	130	L 0 - 2		
13	4		A	Arlesey	115	W 2 - 1	Rickards 29 (pen) Sanders 50	
14	8		H	Chippenham Town	152	W 5 - 3	Charley 11 80 TOWERS 3 (28 62 72)	12
15	15		H	Cirencester Town	118	D 1 - 1	Charley 20	11
16	23	FAT 1Q	A	**Evesham United**	107	D 2 - 2	Griffiths 27 Towers 85	
17	25	FAT 1Qr	H	**Evesham United**	104	W 5 - 1	Barlone 28 Julian 34 Charley 42 Towers 50 Griffiths 68	
18	29		A	Cambridge City	357	L 1 - 2	Charley 24	13
19	Nov 5	FAT 2Q	A	**Ossett Town**	71	L 2 - 4	Julian 63 75	
20	12		H	Frome Town	142	W 3 - 1	Julian 15 Towers 17 30	10
21	15		A	Redditch United	155	L 0 - 2		
22	19		A	Evesham United	91	W 3 - 1	Charley 58 Stanley 63 Barlone 66	9
23	26		A	Hitchin Town	340	D 0 - 0		
24	Dec 3		A	St Albans City	324	W 6 - 1	CHARLEY 3 (18 31 76) Barlone 60 Towers 29 (pen) 88	9
25	10		H	Bedford Town	172	D 1 - 1	Daley 80	
26	13		H	Swindon Supermarine	112	W 2 - 0	Rickards 13 Towers 52	
27	17		A	Banbury United	193	L 0 - 3		7
28	26		H	Leamington	375	W 3 - 1	Towers 22 90 Sanders 53	7
29	Jan 2		A	Stourbridge	481	D 1 - 1	Sanders 47	9
30	7		H	Bashley	162	L 2 - 3	Towers 45 85	9
31	21		H	AFC Totton	174	W 3 - 2	Baines 59 65 Towers 89	9
32	28		H	Arlesey Town	152	D 1 - 1	Barlone 65	9
33	Feb 18		A	Chippenham Town	383	W 3 - 0	TOWERS 3(17 38 58)	9
34	21		A	Brackley Town	146	L 1 - 2	Sanders 42	
35	25		A	Cirencester Town	108	D 2 - 2	West 14 Towers 90 (pen)	
36	March 3		H	Redditch United	193	D 1 - 1	Lower 88	10
37	6		A	Oxford City	116	L 0 - 2		
38	10		A	Frome Town	222	L 0 - 1		10
39	17		H	Cambridge City	158	L 0 - 2		11
40	24		H	Hemel Hempstead	115	L 2 - 3	Weale 32 Charley 67	11
41	27		H	Weymouth	127	W 1 - 0	Towers 90	
42	31		A	Bashley	194	W 2 - 0	Weale 54 West 60	9
43	Apr 7		H	Hitchin Town	150	W 2 - 1	Towers 7 Weale 80	9
44	9		A	Leamington	370	L 0 - 3		
45	14		H	Chesham United	139	W 2 - 0	Towers 19 Stanley 67	9
46	21		A	Swindon Supermarine	157	W 2 - 0	Burns 21 Towers 90	
47	28		H	Evesham Town	230	D 1 - 1	West 28	9

BASHLEY

Chairman: Richard Millbery
Secretary: Colin Bell   **(T)**   **(E)** thebellfamily24@btinternet.com
Additional Committee Members:
Ian Roberts

Manager:
Programme Editor: Richard Millbery   **(E)** rw_millbery@lineone.net

Club Factfile

Founded: 1947   **Nickname:** The Bash
Previous Names: Not known
Previous Leagues: Bournemouth 1953-83, Hampshire 1983-86, Wessex 1986-89, Southern 1989-2004, Isthmian 2004-06

Club Colours (change): Gold/black/black (White/blue/blue)

Ground: Bashley Road Ground, Bashley Road, New Milton, Hampshire BH25 5RY   **(T)** 01425 620 280
Capacity: 4,250   **Seats:** 250   **Covered:** 1,200   **Clubhouse:** Yes   **Shop:** Yes

Directions
Take the A35 from Lyndhurst towards Christchurch, turn left onto B3058 towards New Milton.
The ground is on the left hand side in Bashley village.

Previous Grounds:

Record Attendance: 3,500 v Emley - FA Vase Semi-final 1st Leg 1987-88
Record Victory: 21-1 v Co-Operative (A) - Bournemouth League 1964
Record Defeat: 2-20 v Air Speed (A) - Bournemouth League 1957
Record Goalscorer: Richard Gillespie - 134
Record Appearances: John Bone - 829
Additional Records: Paid £7,500 to Newport (IOW) for Danny Gibbons and from Dorchester Tn for David Elm. Received £15,000 from
Senior Honours: Salisbury for Craig Davis, from Eastleigh for Paul Sales and from AFC Bournemouth for Wade Elliott.
Wessex League 1986-87, 87-88, 88-89. Southern League Southern Division 1989-90, Division 1 South & West 2006-07.

10 YEAR RECORD										
02-03	03-04	04-05	05-06	06-07	07-08	08-09	09-10	10-11	11-12	
SthE 5	SthE 11	Isth1 14	Isth1 9	Sthsw 1	SthP 5	SthP 14	SthP 7	SthP 11	SthP 13	

BASHLEY

No.	Date	Comp	H/A	Opponents	Att:	Result	Goalscorers	Pos
1	Aug 13	Sth P	A	Evesham United	117	W 1 - 0	Stokoe 80	
2	16		H	Weymouth	335	D 3 - 3	Allen 21 (pen) Gamble 23 Stokoe 63	
3	20		H	Banbury United	202	L 0 - 3		12
4	23		A	Oxford City	182	L 0 - 3		
5	27		H	Redditch United	190	W 2 - 1	Lloyd 14 35	13
6	29		A	Swindon Supermarine	139	W 2 - 1	Knowles 62 Stokoe 90	
7	Sept 3		A	Hitchin Town	420	W 3 - 2	Knowles 32 Hill 36 Gamble 41	7
8	10		H	Cambridge City	227	L 0 - 1		11
9	13		H	Chippenham Town	184	D 0 - 0		
10	17	FAC 1Q	A	Hartley Wintney	100	L 0 - 1		
11	24		A	Arlesey	110	W 2 - 0	Gamble 11 75	11
12	Oct 8		H	Stourbridge	173	W 1 - 0	Green 17	9
13	15		A	Leamington	560	L 0 - 1		10
14	22	FAT 1Q	H	Worthing	184	D 2 - 2	Gamble 76 Middleton 88	
15	25	FAT 1Qr	A	Worthing	153	L 2 - 4	Stokoe 37 87	
16	29		H	St Albans City	357	W 4 - 1	Gamble 62 Allen 68 71 (pen) Stokoe 83	8
17	Nov 12		A	Brackley Town	208	L 2 - 3	Gamble 27 Stokoe 88	
18	19		A	Hemel Hempstead	227	D 2 - 2	Stokes 26 80	
19	26		H	Bedford Town	238	D 3 - 3	Oliver 26 Stokoe 43 Whitley 90	
20	Dec 3		A	Banbury United	179	L 0 - 4		11
21	10		H	Oxford City	234	L 0 - 2		11
22	17		A	Weymouth	421	L 1 - 2	Allen 69 (pen)	15
23	26		A	AFC Totton	577	L 0 - 2		16
24	31		H	Cirencester Town	242	L 2 - 3	Gillespie 9 57	17
25	Jan 2		H	Swindon Supermarine	162	D 3 - 3	Gillespie 13 26 Vokes 18	17
26	7		A	Barwell	162	W 3 - 2	Gillespie 47 Allen 78 (pen) Middleton 90	17
27	14		A	Cambridge City	436	L 0 - 4		17
28	18		A	Frome Town	213	D 1 - 1	Vokes 57	17
29	21		H	Hitchin Town	200	L 1 - 3	Penny 74	17
30	28		H	Frome Town	201	D 1 - 1	Whitley 33	17
31	31		H	Chesham United	145	W 3 - 1	Stokoe 9 Gamble 14 33	
32	Feb 7		A	Chippenham Town	222	W 3 - 1	Stokoe 44 45 Oliver 78	14
33	18		A	Stourbridge	361	L 0 - 5		14
34	25		H	Leamington	219	W 2 - 1	Gamble 72 Allen 83	12
35	March 3		A	Chesham United	377	L 1 - 2	Gamble 25	15
36	10		H	Brackley Town	259	D 1 - 1	Gillespie 41	13
37	17		A	St Albans City	407	L 0 - 2		16
38	20		H	Arlesey Town	146	D 0 - 0		
39	24		A	Redditch United	219	D 2 - 2	Allen 39 Middleton 55	16
40	31		H	Barwell	194	L 0 - 2		15
41	Apr 7		A	Cirencester Town	93	W 1 - 0	Casey 77	
42	9		H	AFC Totton	463	D 4 - 4	Gillespie 13 Middleton 43 Allen 52 Gamble 74	14
43	14		H	Evesham United	201	D 0 - 0		14
44	21		A	Bedford Town	252	D 2 - 2	Gamble 21 Stokoe 30	
45	28		H	Hemel Hempstead	194	W 2 - 0	Green 74 Middleton 82	13

BEDFORD TOWN

Chairman: David Howell
Secretary: Dave Swallow   **(T)** 07939 812 965   **(E)** david.swallow@bedfordeagles.net
Additional Committee Members:
Paul Searing, Gerry Edmunds, Mick Hooker, Tony Luff, Dave Redman,

Manager: Nick Platnauer
Programme Editor: Dave Swallow   **(E)** david.swallow@bedfordeagles.net

Back Row L to R. Josh Beech, Gareth Price, Michael Built, Jamaine Ivy, Mark Bell, Nick Beasant, Ian Brown (Captain), Dan Crowie, Greg Ling, Seb Simpson, Steve Kinniburgh, Chris Gibbons (Physio), Adam Sandy (Assistant Manager)

Front Row L to R. Ollie Wilkinson, Leigh Stevens, Callum Lewis, David Howell (Chairman), Nick Platnauer (Manager), Paul Cooper, Eugene Libertucci, Ashley Fuller

Club Factfile

Founded: 1989   **Nickname:** The Eagles
Previous Names: Original Bedford Town founded in 1908 folded in 1982
Previous Leagues: South Midlands 1989-94, Isthmian 1994-2004, Southern 2004-06, Conference 2006-07

Club Colours (change): Blue with white trim/blue/blue (White with navy trim/navy/white)

Ground: The Eyrie, Meadow Lane, Cardington, Bedford MK44 3SB   **(T)** 01234 831 558
Capacity: 3,000   **Seats:** 300   **Covered:** 1,000   **Clubhouse:** Yes   **Shop:** Yes

Directions: From A1: Take A603 from Sandy to Bedford, go through Willington and ground is a mile and a half on right, signposted Meadow Lane. From M1: Off at Junction 13, take A421, carry on A421 onto Bedford Bypass and take A603 Sandy turn off. Ground is on left.

Previous Grounds: Allen Park, Queens Park, Bedford Park Pitch 1991-93

Record Attendance: 3,000 v Peterborough United - Ground opening 06/08/1993
Record Victory: 9-0 v Ickleford and v Cardington
Record Defeat: 0-5 v Hendon
Record Goalscorer: Jason Reed
Record Appearances: Eddie Lawley
Additional Records:

Senior Honours:
Isthmian League Division 2 1998-99. Bedfordshire Senior Cup 1994-95. Southern League Play-offs 2005-06.

10 YEAR RECORD

02-03	03-04	04-05	05-06	06-07	07-08	08-09	09-10	10-11	11-12
Isth P 9	Isth P 15	SthP 5	SthP 5	Conf S 22	SthP 19	SthP 15	SthP 18	SthP 17	

BEDFORD TOWN

No.	Date	Comp	H/A	Opponents	Att:	Result	Goalscorers	Pos
1	Aug 13	Sth P	H	Frome Town	357	L 0 - 1		
2	16		A	Redditch United	294	L 0 - 2		
3	20		A	Brackley Town	205	L 1 - 7	Richardson 86	22
4	23		H	Barwell	227	W 3 - 2	Roberts 11 (pen) 79 Faulkner 56	
5	27		A	Weymouth	471	W 2 - 0	Roberts 70 (pen) 72	17
6	29		H	Hitchin Town	512	L 1 - 3	Roberts 20	
7	Sept 3		H	Arlesey Town	322	L 0 - 2		18
8	10		A	Chippenham Town	323	L 0 - 3		18
9	14		A	Leamington	406	W 4 - 0	ROBERTS 4 (13 pen 59 81 90)	
10	17	FAC 1Q	A	**East Thurrock United**	116	L 0 - 1		
11	24		H	Oxford City	259	L 1 - 2	Roberts 37	17
12	Oct 8		A	Cirencester Town	101	W 4 - 2	Roberts 26 42 Faulkner 67 86	16
13	11		H	St Albans City	270	D 2 - 2	Roberts 76 77	
14	15		A	Swindon Supermarine	124	W 1 - 0	Roberts 89 (pen)	15
15	22	FAT 1Q	A	**East Thurrock United**	141	D 1 - 1	**Price 27**	
16	25	FAT 1Qr	H	**East Thurrock United**	189	L 1 - 2	**Roberts 37**	
17	29		H	Chesham United	316	L 0 - 4		15
18	Nov 15		H	Hemel Hempstead	209	L 0 - 1		
19	19		H	AFC Totton	255	L 1 - 2	Hall 46	18
20	26		A	Bashley	238	D 3 - 3	Hall 34 Roberts 79 (pen) Thorne 80	
21	Dec 3		H	Brackley Town	273	W 5 - 2	Hatch 19 ROBERTS 3(21 56 60) Hall 71	
22	10		A	Barwell	172	D 1 - 1	Roberts 89	16
23	17		H	Redditch United	217	L 0 - 1		17
24	26		H	Cambridge City	407	L 1 - 2	Ivy 90	19
25	31		A	Banbury United	259	W 2 - 1	Damon 21 Beech 48	18
26	Jan 2		A	Hitchin Town	597	W 3 - 1	Hoyte19 Hatch 24 Thorne 37	
27	7		H	Evesham United	256	W 3 - 0	ROBERTS 3 (18 61 73)	16
28	14		H	Chippenham Town	279	W 1 - 0	Roberts 52	13
29	21		A	Arlesey Town	317	L 0 - 1		14
30	28		A	St Albans City	463	W 2 - 1	Beech 21 Roberts 80	13
31	Feb 18		H	Cirencester Town	251	D 1 - 1	Hatch 81	13
32	25		H	Swindon Supermarine	260	W 3 - 0	Beech 77 Roberts 80 (pen) 86	11
33	28		A	Stourbridge	372	D 1 - 1	Thorne 90	
34	March 3		A	Hemel Hempstead	284	D 1 - 1	Roberts 40	11
35	10		H	Stourbridge	288	D 2 - 2	Hatch 43 46	11
36	13		H	Leamingtoon	248	L 1 - 2	Roberts 16 (pen)	
37	17		A	Chesham United	336	W 4 - 3	Hatch 35 43 Roberts 40 Thomas 47	10
38	24		H	Weymouth	348	W 2 - 1	Dickson 50 (og) Hatch 86	9
39	27		A	Oxford City	178	L 0 - 1		
40	31		A	Evesham United	126	D 0 - 0		
41	Apr 7		H	Banbury United	336	W 1 - 0	Roberts 90	10
42	9		A	Cambridge City	405	L 1 - 6	Cole 15	
43	14		A	Frome Town	248	D 0 - 0		
44	21		H	Bashley	252	D 2 - 2	Hatch 66 Clarke 88	10
45	28		A	AFC Totton	551	L 0 - 2		10

BEDWORTH UNITED

Chairman: Peter Randle
Secretary: Graham Bloxham **(T)** 07748 640 613 **(E)** graham@greenbacks1.free-online.co.uk
Additional Committee Members:
Blake Timms

Manager: Steve Farmer
Programme Editor: Alan Robinson **(E)** alanrobinson8@btinternet.com

Club Factfile

Founded: 1896 **Nickname:** Greenbacks
Previous Names: Bedworth Town 1947-68
Previous Leagues: Birmingham Combination 1947-54, Birmingham/West Midlands 1954-72

Club Colours (change): All green (Gold/blue/gold)

Ground: The Oval, Coventry Road, Bedworth CV12 8NN **(T)** 02476 314 752
Capacity: 7,000 **Seats:** 300 **Covered:** 300 **Clubhouse:** Yes **Shop:** Yes

Directions: 1 1/2 miles from M6 J3, take B4113 Coventry–Bedworth Road and after third set of traffic lights (Bedworth Leisure Centre). Ground 200 yards on right opposite cemetery.
Coaches to park in Leisure Centre.

Previous Grounds: British Queen Ground 1911-39

Record Attendance: 5,127 v Nuneaton Borough - Southern League Midland Division 23/02/1982
Record Victory: Not known
Record Defeat: Not known
Record Goalscorer: Peter Spacey - 1949-69
Record Appearances: Peter Spacey - 1949-69
Additional Records: Paid £1,750 to Hinckley Town for Colin Taylor 1991-92
Senior Honours: Received £30,000 from Plymouth Argyle for Richard Landon
Birmingham Combination x2. Birmingham Senior Cup x3. Midland Floodlit Cup 1981-82, 92-93. Southern Division 1 Central Play-offs 2011-12.

10 YEAR RECORD

02-03		03-04		04-05		05-06		06-07		07-08		08-09		09-10		10-11		11-12	
SthW	18	SthW	19	SthW	15	SthW	16	SthM	16	SthM	15	SthM	14	SthM	16	SthC	15	SthC	3

BIDEFORD

Chairman: Roy Portch
Secretary: Kevin Tyrrell **(T)** 07929 078 613 **(E)** k.tyrrell@talktalk.net
Additional Committee Members:
Darren Hollyoak

Manager: Sean Joyce
Programme Editor: Ian Knight **(E)** ianknight160@btinternet.com

THE NON-LEAGUE CLUB DIRECTORY

Book Holiday Inn Hotels and Save today!

Home

Clubs

Steps 1 - 4

League Tables

35 Years of Non-League Football

The Non-League Club Directory has developed into a comprehensive record of competitions within the non-League game, giving this level of football the

www.non-leagueclubdirectory.co.uk

Club Factfile

Founded: 1949 **Nickname:** The Robins

Previous Names: Bideford Town

Previous Leagues: Devon & Exeter 1947-49, Western 1949-72, 75-2010, Southern 1972-75

Club Colours (change): All red (All blue)

Ground: The Sports Ground, Kingsley Road, Bideford EX39 2LH **(T)** 01237 474 974

Capacity: 6,000 **Seats:** 375 **Covered:** 1,000 **Clubhouse:** Yes **Shop:**

Directions: Exit M5 at J.27. A361 to Barnstaple. Turn left onto A39 to Bideford.
9 miles turn left into town.
Ground on right hand side as entering town centre.

Previous Grounds:

Record Attendance: 6,000 v Gloucester City - FA Cup 4th Qualifying Round

Record Victory: Not known
Record Defeat: Not known

Record Goalscorer: Tommy Robinson - 259

Record Appearances: Derek May - 527

Additional Records:

Senior Honours:

Western League 1963-64, 70-71, 71-72, 81-82, 82-83, 2001-02, 03-04, 04-05, 05-06, 09-10, Division 1 1951-52, Division 3 1949-50.
Southern Division 1 South & West 2011-12.
Devon Senior Cup 1979-80

02-03		03-04		04-05		05-06		06-07		07-08		08-09		09-10		10-11		11-12	
WestP	3	WestP	1	WestP	1	WestP	1	WestP	4	WestP	6	WestP	6	WestP	1	Sthsw	10	Sthsw	1

CAMBRIDGE CITY

Chairman: Kevin Satchell
Secretary: Andy Dewey   **(T)**   **(E)** andy@cambridgecityfc.com
Additional Committee Members:
Terry Dunn, Ken Ledran, Roger de Ste Croix, Gill Wordingham, Rick Winter, Andy Harnwell
Andrew Dunn, Rab Crangle
Manager: Gary Roberts
Programme Editor: Chris Farrington   **(E)** ccfc.editor@googlemail.com

Back Row left to right.. Charlie Death, Christian Lester, Dave Theobald, Craig Hammond, Zac Barrett, Enol Ordonez, Lee Chaffey,
Jack Dekanski, Victor Torres, Joey Abbs.
Front Row left to right…..Joe Miller (Therapist),Tom Pepper, Pat Bexfield, Neil Midgley, Gary Roberts (Manager), Adrian Cambridge,
Robbie Nightingale, Lee Clift, David Prada, Brian Chapman (Kit Man).
Missing… Jordan Patrick, Ben Seymour-Shove, Mitchell Bryant, Luke Allen, James Brighton.

Club Factfile

Founded: 1908   **Nickname:** Lilywhites
Previous Names: Cambridge Town 1908-51
Previous Leagues: Bury & District 1908-13, 19-20, Anglian 1908-10, Southern Olympian 1911-14,
Southern Amateur 1913-35, Spartan 1935-50, Athenian 1950-58, Southern 1958-2004

Club Colours (change): White/black/black (All light blue)

Ground: City Ground, Milton Road, Cambridge CB4 1UY   **(T)** 01223 357 973
Capacity: 2,722   **Seats:** 526   **Covered:** 220   **Clubhouse:** Yes   **Shop:** Yes

Directions: Take Junction 13 on M11 and head for City Centre. At mini roundabout turn left then straight on at traffic lights. The road then runs parallel with the river. On reaching traffic lights controlling entry to one way system, get into middle lane up beside Staples Office Furniture and follow lane behind Staples where it becomes nearside lane. Stay in this lane until road straightens then take first left. Ground is behind Westbrook Centre.

Previous Grounds: Not known

Record Attendance: 12,058 v Leytonstone - FA Amateur Cup 1st Round 1949-50
Record Victory: Not known
Record Defeat: Not known
Record Goalscorer: Gary Grogan
Record Appearances: Mal Keenan
Additional Records: Paid £8,000 to Rushden & Diamonds for Paul Coe
Received £100,000 from Millwall for Neil Harris 1998
Senior Honours:
Southern League 1962-63, Southern Division 1985-86.
Suffolk Senior Cup 1909-10. East Anglian x9.

10 YEAR RECORD

02-03		03-04		04-05		05-06		06-07		07-08		08-09		09-10		10-11		11-12	
SthP	18	SthP	8	Conf S	2	Conf S	7	Conf S	13	Conf S	14	SthP	4	SthP	6	SthP	4	SthP	5

CAMBRIDGE CITY

No.	Date	Comp	H/A	Opponents	Att:	Result	Goalscorers	Pos
1	Aug 13	Sth P	A	Weymouth	667	W 2 - 1	Midgley 63 Hammond 77	
2	16		H	St Albans City	305	W 4 - 0	Nicell 19 Robins 38 42 Hammond 85	
3	20		H	Stourbridge	325	D 0 - 0		3
4	23		A	Chesham United	252	L 0 - 1		
5	27		H	Frome Town	269	L 2 - 3	Burke 45 (pen) Hammond 74	10
6	29		A	Arlesey Town	228	W 1 - 0	Clift 89	
7	Sept 3		H	Chippenham Town	290	W 3 - 0	Theobald 18 Burke 61 Hammond 82	5
8	10		A	Bashley	227	W 1 - 0	Clift 80	3
9	12		A	Hitchin Town	412	L 2 - 3	Hammond 43 75 (pen)	
10	17	FAC 1Q	H	Malden & Tiptree	266	D 2 - 2	Hammond 7 Theobald 90	
11	20	FAC 1Qr	A	Malden & Tiptree	98	L 1 - 2	Kelly 32	
12	24		H	Banbury United	310	W 3 - 0	KELLY 3 (26 45 71)	4
13	Oct 4		H	Hemel Hempstead	327	W 3 - 0	KELLY 3 (14 28 84)	
14	8		A	Redditch United	271	L 0 - 2		5
15	22	FAT 1Q	A	Rushall Olympic	173	W 2 - 0	Gould 60 Abbs 85	
16	25		A	AFC Totton	317	W 3 - 2	Gould 22 Hammond 44 51	
17	28		H	Barwell	357	W 2 - 1	Theobald 68 Clift 69	1
18	Nov 5	FAT 2Q	H	Redbridge	291	L 1 - 2	Gould 59	
19	12		A	Leamington	631	L 2 - 4	Hammond 3 15	5
20	15		H	Brackley Town	256	L 2 - 3	Deen 25 Hudson 27	
21	19		A	Swindon Supermarine	133	L 1 - 3	Abbs 61	6
22	26		H	Evesham United	306	L 1 - 2	Yamfam 35	
23	Dec 6		A	Stourbridge	404	D 1 - 1	Abbs 16	
24	10		H	Chesham United	319	D 2 - 2	Yamfam 14 Hammond 86	7
25	17		A	St Albans City	362	L 0 - 3		9
26	26		A	Bedford Town	407	W 2 - 1	Hammond 60 Clift 62	9
27	31		H	Oxford City	450	W 2 - 0	Cambridge 71 Hammond 74	8
28	Jan 2		H	Arlesey Town	375	W 3 - 1	Kelly 22 Theobald 68 Yamfam 88	
29	7		A	Cirencester Town	113	W 2 - 0	Gould 19 Theobald 34	
30	14		H	Bashley	438	W 4 - 0	HAMMOND 3 (10 pen 19 29) Gould 32	3
31	21		A	Chippenham Town	447	D 2 - 2	Kelly 38 Yamfam 65	3
32	28		A	Hemel Hempstead	342	W 2 - 1	Clift 7 Hammond 79	3
33	Feb 18		H	Redditch United	301	D 1 - 1	Clift 68	3
34	21		H	Hitchin Town	281	W 3 - 1	Kelly 53 70 Midgeley 74	
35	25		H	AFC Totton	352	W 1 - 0	Theobald 48	2
36	28		A	Banbury United	168	L 0 - 2		
37	March 3		A	Bracknell Town	348	L 2 - 4	Theobald 30 Hammond 90	3
38	10		H	Leamington	442	D 2 - 2	Clift 39 Bryant 45	4
39	17		A	Barwell	158	W 2 - 0	Hammond 2 39	3
40	24		A	Frome town	244	D 1 - 1	Hammond 24	5
41	31		H	Cirencester Town	306	W3 - 1	Theobald 28 Marriott 31 Hammond 62	
42	Apr 7		A	Oxford Clty	367	D 0 - 0		5
43	9		H	Bedford Town	405	W 6 - 1	Bryant 10 52 Marriott 48 66 Hammond 59 81	
44	14		H	Weymouth	395	W 3 - 0	Theobald 52 Marriott 72 Prada 84	
45	21		A	Evesham United	123	L 1 - 2	Hammond 36 (pen)	4
46	28		H	Swindon Supermarine	505	D 1 - 1	Theobald 70	5
47	May 3	Play-Off SF	A	Oxford City	564	L 0 - 1		

CHESHAM UNITED

Chairman: Brian McCarthy
Secretary: Brian McCarthy   (T)   (E) brian.mccarthy@cheshamunited.co.uk
Additional Committee Members:
Mike Dragisic, Mike Warrick, Giles Stevenson, Simon Newbury, Len Vockins,
Martin Woolnough, Neil Calder, Alan Lagdon.
Manager: Andy Leese
Programme Editor: Steve Doman   (E) programme@cheshamunited.co.uk

2011-12 Squad.

Club Factfile

Founded: 1917   **Nickname:** The Generals
Previous Names: Not known
Previous Leagues: Spartan 1917-47, Corinthian 1947-63, Athenian 1963-73, Isthmian 1973-2004

Club Colours (change): All claret (Yellow/black/yellow)

Ground: The Meadow, Amy Lane, Amersham Road, Chesham HP5 1NE   (T) 01494 783 964
Capacity: 5,000   **Seats:** 284   **Covered:** 2,500   **Clubhouse:** Yes   **Shop:** Yes
Directions: From M25 Junction 20 take A41 (Aylesbury), leave A41 at turn-off for Chesham (A416), pass through Ashley Green into Chesham. Follow signs to Amersham, still on A416 pass two petrol stations opposite each other and at next roundabout take third exit into ground.
From M1 Junction 8 follow signs for Hemel Hempstead then joining the A41 for Aylesbury, then as above.

Previous Grounds: Not known

Record Attendance: 5,000 v Cambridge United - FA Cup 3rd Round 05/12/1979
Record Victory: Not known
Record Defeat: Not known
Record Goalscorer: John Willis
Record Appearances: Martin Baguley - 600+
Additional Records: Received £22,000 from Oldham Athletic for Fitz Hall

Senior Honours:
Isthmian League 1992-93, Division 1 1986-87, 97-97. Berks & Bucks Senior Cup x12.

10 YEAR RECORD

02-03		03-04		04-05		05-06		06-07		07-08		08-09		09-10		10-11		11-12	
Isth P	21	Isth1N	4	SthP	12	SthP	22	Sthsw	15	SthM	6	SthM	5	SthM	4	SthP	6	SthP	4

CHESHAM UNITED

No.	Date	Comp	H/A	Opponents	Att:	Result	Goalscorers	Pos
1	Aug 13	Sth P	H	Barwell	341	W 1 - 0	Archer 46	
2	16		A	Brackley Town	203	L 2 - 3	Thomas 38 84	
3	20		A	Chippenham Town	322	L 0 - 1		15
4	23		H	Cambridge City	252	W 1 - 0	Talbot 23	
5	27		H	Swindon Supermarine	203	W 2 - 1	Alford 53 (og) Wilson 80	
6	29		A	Cirencester Town	105	D 1 - 1	Thomas 3	
7	Sept 3		A	Stourbridge	446	L 1 - 2	Archer 48	11
8	10		H	Weymouth	313	W 4 - 1	Wadkins 29 Thomas 43 87 Talbot 81	9
9	12		A	Banbury United	301	W 2 - 1	Archer 33 Lambert 61	
10	17	FAC 1Q	H	**Staines Lammas**	237	W 3 - 2	Whatford 6 (og) Potton 25 30	
11	24		H	Evesham United	304	W 2 - 1	Thomas 22 Kyriacou 86	5
12	Oct 1	FAC 2Q	A	**Dunstable Town**	229	L 1 - 2	Bruce 89 (og)	
13	4		H	Hitchin Town	315	W 2 - 0	Watters 46 Talbot 72	
14	8		A	Hemel Hempstead	406	D 1 - 1	Thomas 75	4
15	15		H	Redditch United	316	W 1 - 0	Potton 35	
16	22	FAT 1Q	H	**Horsham**	303	W 5 - 0	Watson 18 ARCHER 3(43 74 89) Thomas 59	
17	29		A	Bedford Town	316	W 4 - 0	Wales 7 70 Potton 61 Wadkins 89	4
18	Nov 5	FAT 2Q	H	**Tiverton Town**	323	D 2 - 2	Archer 10 Thomas 52 (pen)	
19	8	FAT 2Qr	A	**Tiverton Town**	208	L 0 - 1		
20	12		H	Cirencester Town	340	W 2 - 1	Archer 13 Wadkins 87	3
21	19		H	Leamington	445	D 1 - 1	Batchelor 32 (og)	5
22	26		A	Frome Town	206	W 1 - 0	Thomas 49	4
23	Dec 3		H	Chippenhamm Town	369	L 1 - 2	Potton 21	5
24	10		A	Cambridge City	319	D 2 - 2	Wadkins 80 Talbot 88	
25	13		H	Oxford City	206	D 1 - 1	Willmott 90	5
26	17		H	Brackley Town	342	L 2 - 3	Potton 40 Thomas 87	5
27	26		A	St Albans City	606	D 1 - 1	Bartley 54	5
28	31		H	Arlesey Town	375	W 2 - 0	Thomas 32 Wales 39	2
29	Jan 7		A	AFC Totton	579	L 0 - 3		5
30	21		H	Stourbridge	100	W 4 - 0	Potton 7 Wales 45 Archer 67 Wilson 87	4
31	28		A	Hitchin Town	466	D 1 - 1	Moran 87	5
32	31		A	Bashley	145	L 1 - 3	Thomas 78	
33	Feb 18		H	Hemel Hempstead	390	W 2 - 1	Wadkins 10 Watters 75	
34	25		A	Redditch United	182	D 1 - 1	Potton 90	5
35	March 3		H	Bashley	377	W 2 - 1	Wales 49 S.Thomas 68	5
36	10		A	Oxford City	283	L 0 - 2		5
37	13		H	Banbury United	214	W 3 - 0	EFFIONG 3 (18 40 79)	
38	17		H	Bedford Town	336	L 3 - 4	Potton 24 76 S Thomas 89	6
39	20		A	Evesham United	93	W 2 - 0	Effiong 20 Potton 68	
40	24		A	Swindon Supermarine	148	W 6 - 0	Effiong 21 44 Potton 55 Scott Thomas7 Watters 90, S Thomas 90	3
41	31		H	AFC Totton	472	W 2 - 1	S Thomas 18 Wales 36	4
42	Apr 2		A	Weymouth	455	D 2 - 2	Effiong 12 S Thomas 42	
43	7		A	Arlesey Town	195	W 4 - 2	Wales 1 27 S.Thomas 28 Wadkins 90	2
44	9		H	St Albans City	501	D 2 - 2	S.Thomas 25 75	
45	14		A	Barwell	139	L 0 - 2		5
46	19		H	Frome Town	439	W 2 - 0	Potton 12 Watters 30	2
47	28		A	Leamington	601	L 2 - 3	Watters 21 S.Thomas 83	4
48	May 3	Play-Off SF A		**AFC Totton**	521	L 2 - 3	Watters 53 S. Thomas56	

CHIPPENHAM TOWN

Chairman: John Applegate
Secretary: Angela Townsley   **(T)** 07909 634 875   **(E)** angelatownsley_chiptownfc@talktalk.net
Additional Committee Members:
Leila Garraway, Barry Stephens, Doug Webb, Richard Chappell, Barry Lane, Avril Mays, Hazel Ralph, Robin Townsley.
Manager: Nathan Rudge
Programme Editor: Will Hulbert & Chris Blake   **(E)** angelatownsley_chiptownfc@talktalk.net

CHIPPENHAM TOWN F.C.

BACK ROW: Matty Bown, Pete Hussey, Mani Randhawa, Ashley Williams, Scott Lye, Dave Gilroy, Alex Kite, Alan Griffin, Josh Dempsey, Toby Osman, Lee Phillips, James Guthrie, Luke Ballinger, Scott Garraway. Coach Goal/K Coach Physio
FRONT ROW: Dean Griffiths, Iain Harvey, Shaun Lamb, Scott Rogers, Nathan Rudge, Richard Fey, Steve Casey, Brandon Barnes, Josh Egan, Tom Seery.
Player Manager Assist Manager

2012-2013 SEASON

Club Factfile

Founded: 1873   **Nickname:** The Bluebirds
Previous Names: Not known
Previous Leagues: Hellenic, Wiltshire Senior, Wiltshire Premier, Western

Club Colours (change): All blue (All white)

Ground: Hardenhuish Park, Bristol Road, Chippenham SN14 6LR   **(T)** 01249 650 400
Capacity: 3,000   **Seats:** 300   **Covered:** 1,000   **Clubhouse:** Yes   **Shop:** Yes

Directions: Exit 17 from M4. Follow A350 towards Chippenham for three miles to first roundabout, take second exit (A350); follow road to third roundabout (junction with A420). Turn left and follow signs to town centre. Ground is 1km on left hand side adjacent to pedestrian controlled traffic lights. Car/Coach park next to traffic lights.

Previous Grounds:

Record Attendance: 4,800 v Chippenham United - Western League 1951
Record Victory: 9-0 v Dawlish Town (H) - Western League
Record Defeat: 0-10 v Tiverton Town (A) - Western League
Record Goalscorer: Dave Ferris
Record Appearances: Ian Monnery
Additional Records:

Senior Honours:
Western League 1951-52. Les Phillips Cup 1999-2000. Wiltshire Senior Cup. Wiltshire Senior Shield x4.

10 YEAR RECORD									
02-03	03-04	04-05	05-06	06-07	07-08	08-09	09-10	10-11	11-12
SthP 5	SthP 21	SthP 2	SthP 4	SthP 7	SthP 4	SthP 8	SthP 3	SthP 7	SthP 11

CHIPPENHAM TOWN

No.	Date	Comp	H/A	Opponents	Att:	Result	Goalscorers	Pos
1	Aug 13	Sth P	A	Stourbridge	216	L 1 - 3	Gilroy 13	
2	16		H	Evesham United	353	W 1 - 0	Jack 40	
3	20		H	Chesham United	322	W 1 - 0	Casey 1	9
4	23		A	Weymouth	468	L 0 - 2		
5	27		H	Brackley Town	251	L 0 - 1		16
6	29		A	Frome Town	605	W 2 - 0	Pitcher 6 Griffin 80	
7	Sept 2		A	Cambridge City	290	L 0 - 3		13
8	10		H	Bedford Town	323	W 3 - 0	GILROY 3 (66 87 90)	
9	13		A	Bashley	184	D 0 - 0		
10	17	FAC 1Q	H	Wells City	273	W 3 - 0	Gilroy 35 37 Steam 71	
11	24		H	Hemel Hempstead	322	W 4 - 1	Griffin 25 Gilroy 29 Guthrie 75 Pitcher 83	12
12	Oct 1		A	Cirencester Town	185	W 1 - 0	Gilroy 49	7
13	4		H	Leamington	328	L 1 - 2	Griffin 70	
14	8		A	Barwell	152	L 3 - 5	Osman 12 Griffin 36 (pen) 82	
15	15		H	Banbury United	379	D 1 - 1	Lye 41	9
16	22	FAT 1Q	A	**Poole Town**	316	D 1 - 1	**Griffin 43**	
17	25	FAT 1Qr	H	**Poole Town**	244	W 2 - 1	**Griffin 67 (pen) 71 (pen)**	
18	29		A	Hitchin Town	345	D 0 - 0		10
19	Nov 5	FAT 2Q	H	**Mangotsfield Town**	361	D 1 - 1	**Knighton 61**	
20	7	FAT 2Qr	A	**Mangotsfield Town**	250	W 2 - 0	**Wilson 22 Osman 67**	
21	12		H	Redditch United	343	W 2 - 0	Griffin 63 Kite 74	8
22	19		A	Arlesey Town	121	D 1 - 1	Osman 17	8
23	22		H	StAlbans City	287	W 4 - 0	Osman 13 Steam 20 Powell 70 88	
24	26	FAT 3Q	H	**Eastleigh**	421	D 1 - 1	**Osman 43**	
25	29	FAT 3Qr	A	**Bury Town**	214	D 1 - 1*	**Griffin 11 Chippenham Town won 8-7 on penalties**	
26	Dec 3		A	Chesham United	369	W 2 - 0	Powell 14 55	6
27	10	FAT 1	A	**Weymouth**	568	L 1 - 2	**Griffin 88**	
28	17		A	Evesham United	101	W 4 - 2	GRIFFIN 3 (24 52 57) Powell 48	6
29	26		A	Swindon Supermarine	311	W 4 - 0	Powell 6 50 Steam 60 Guthrie 89	6
30	21		H	AFC Totton	610	W 2 - 1	Powell 84 90	5
31	Jan 2		H	Frome Town	657	D 1 - 1	Powell 90	4
32	7		A	Oxford City	194	L 1 - 2	Griffin 58 (pen)	8
33	14		A	Bedford Town	279	L 0 - 1		8
34	21		H	Cambridge City	447	D 2 - 2	Griffin 45 Gilroy 90	7
35	28		A	Leamington	470	D 0 - 0		7
36	Feb 7		H	Bashley	222	L 1 - 3	Lye 55	7
37	14		H	Weymouth	305	W 3 - 0	Griffin 58 63 Gilroy 68	
38	18		H	Barwell	383	L 0 - 3		6
39	25		A	Banbury United	201	D 1 - 1	Griffin 63	7
40	March 3		H	Cirencester Town	393	L 0 - 1		8
41	10		A	Redditch United	180	L 0 - 1		8
42	17		H	Hitchin Town	363	L 0 - 1		9
43	20		A	Hemel Hempstead	120	D 1 - 1	Rudge 79	
44	24		A	Brackley Town	272	L 1 - 5	Griffin 87 (pen)	10
45	31		H	Oxford City	370	L 0 - 1		
46	Apr 2		A	AFC Totton	627	D 1 - 1	Griffin 54	11
47	9		H	Swindon Supermarine	316	L 0 - 2		
48	14		H	Stourbridge	393	L 1 - 2	Griffin 90	13
49	21		A	St Albans City	457	W 4 1	Stearn 2 45 Griffin 15 67	11
50	28		H	Arlesey Town	372	D 1 - 1	Stearn 53	11

FROME TOWN

Chairman: Jeremy Alderman
Secretary: Ian Pearce   **(T)** 07811 511 222   **(E)** ian@frometownfc.co.uk
Additional Committee Members:
Ivan Carver, Raymond Pearce, Gary Collinson, Neil Clark, Gary Collison, Jon Curle, Brian Stevens.
Manager: Darren Perrin
Programme Editor: Andrew Meaden   **(E)** programmes@amprintcopy.co.uk

2011-12 Squad - Back row: LR - Derek Graham (Assistant Manager), Shaun Baker (Kit Manager), Darren White, Twaine Plummer, Alex Lapham, Kyle Tooze, Ed Quelch, Tom Drewitt, Darren Chitty, Ryan Bennett, Ben Thomson, Mike Perrott, Dean Flockton, Mike Reaney, Sam Babatunde, Matt Peters, Reynold Turnock, Lloyd Chamberlain (GK Coach), Mike Kilgour (Coach).
Front Row: Ricky Hulbert, Josh Brigham, Luke Ballinger, Richard Hudson (Treasurer), Gary Collinson (Community Development), Jeremy Alderman (Chairman), Terry Wolff (Vice-Chairman), Ian Pearce (Club Secretary), Jamie Cheeseman, Dean Evans, Simeon Allison, Kris Miller.

Club Factfile

Founded: 1904   **Nickname:** The Robins
Previous Names: None
Previous Leagues: Wiltshire Premier 1904, Somerset Senior 1906-19, Western 1919, 63-2009

Club Colours (change): All red (All yellow)

Ground: Aldersmith Stadium, Badgers Hill, Berkley Road, Frome BA11 2EH   **(T)** 01373 464 087
Capacity: 2,000   **Seats:** 150   **Covered:** 200   **Clubhouse:** Yes   **Shop:** Yes

Directions: From Bath, take A36 and then A361. At third roundabout, follow A361 and at fourth roundabout take A3098. Take first right and ground is one mile on left hand side. From south follow A36 (Warminster) and take A3098 to Frome. At T Junction turn right and take second exit at roundabout. Ground is first right and follow road for one mile on left hand side.

Previous Grounds:

Record Attendance: 8,000 v Leyton Orient - FA Cup 1st Round 1958
Record Victory: Not Known
Record Defeat: Not Known
Record Goalscorer: Not Known
Record Appearances: Not Known
Additional Records:

Senior Honours:
Somerset County League 1906-07, 08-09, 10-11.
Western League Division 1 1919-20, 2001-02, Premier Division 1962-63, 78-79.
Somerset Senior Cup 1932-33, 33-34, 50-51 Somerset Premier Cup 1966-67, 68-69 (shared), 82-83, 2008-09.

10 YEAR RECORD

02-03		03-04		04-05		05-06		06-07		07-08		08-09		09-10		10-11		11-12	
WestP	11	WestP	3	WestP	3	WestP	7	WestP	3	WestP	4	WestP	2	Sthsw	6	Sthsw	4	SthP	12

FROME TOWN

No.	Date	Comp	H/A	Opponents	Att:	Result	Goalscorers	Pos
1	Aug 13	Sth P	A	Bedford Town	357	W 1 - 0	Tooze 34	
2	17		H	Swindon Supermarine	331	W 2 - 0	Brigham 70 (pen) Evans 82	
3	20		H	Arlesey Town	204	D 2 - 2	Hulbert 23 80	5
4	23		A	Evesham United	110	L 0 - 1		
5	27		A	Cambridge City	268	W 3 - 2	Smith 16 Miller 43 Tooze 75	6
6	29		H	Chippenham Town	605	L 0 - 2		
7	Sept 3		H	Brackley Town	253	D 1 - 1	Brigham 68	10
8	10		A	Cirencester Town	149	W 1 - 0	Smith 46	8
9	13		A	Oxford City	120	L 0 - 2		
10	**17**	**FAC 1Q**	**A**	**Hallen**	**91**	**D 2 - 2**	**Hulbert 55 Ballinger 58**	
11	24		H	Redditch United	220	W 3 - 2	Ballinger 34 Hulbert 67 Smith 87	10
12	**Oct 1**	**FAC 2Q**	**H**	**Basingstoke Town**	**300**	**D 0 - 0**		
13	**4**	**FAC 2Qr**	**A**	**Basingstoke Town**	**450**	**L 0 - 3**		
14	8		A	Hitchin Town	542	W 3 - 1	Brigham 10 (pen) 85 (pen) Bennison 23	8
15	15		A	St Albans City	303	L 1 - 2	Ballinger 90	8
16	**22**	**FAT 1Q**	**H**	**Thatcham Town**	**199**	**L 0 - 1**		
17	29		H	Hemel Hempstead	225	D 1 - 1	Bennett 90	9
18	Nov 12		A	Barwell	142	L 1 - 3	Ballinger 44	11
19	28		H	AFC Totton	120	L 1 - 3	Hulbert ?	
20	19		A	Stourbridge	678	L 0 - 4		13
21	26		H	Chesham United	206	L 0 - 1		13
22	Dec 3		A	Arlesey Town	108	W 1 - 0	Harris 41	
23	10		H	Evesham United	166	L 1 - 2	Harris 30	14
24	17		A	Swindon Supermarine	131	W 2 - 0	Harris 10 51	13
25	26		H	Weymouth	535	D 0 - 0		12
26	31		A	Leamington	638	D 1 - 1	Smith 40	12
27	Jan 2		A	Chippenham Town	657	D 1 - 1	Smith 25	
28	7		H	Banbury United	257	L 0 - 1		14
29	14		H	Cirencester Town	226	W 1 - 0	Evans 45	
30	18		H	Bashley	213	D 1 - 1	Evans 40	11
31	21		A	Brackley Town	210	D 1 - 1	Reaney 90	11
32	28		A	Bashley	201	D 1 - 1	Parrott 43 (pen)	12
33	Feb 18		H	Hitchin Town	186	D 0 - 0		12
34	25		H	St Albans City	236	L 0 - 1		16
35	March 3		A	AFC Totton	540	D 1 - 1	Ballinger 19	16
36	10		H	Barwell	222	W 1 - 0	Thmpson 87	12
37	17		A	Hemel Hempstead	179	L 1 - 3	Smith 1	15
38	20		A	Redditch United	149	W 4 - 0	Perrow 24 Ballinger 72 Brigham 80 (pen) Hulbert 83	
39	24		H	Cambridge City	244	D 1 - 1	Evans 18	12
40	31		A	Banbury United	225	D 2 - 2	Smith 7 Matthews 45	
41	Apr 7		H	Leamington	314	D 0 - 0		13
42	9		A	Weymouth	721	W 3 - 0	Evans 66 Gerring 83 (og) Matthews 89	
43	14		H	Bedford Town	248	D 0 - 0		12
44	21		A	Chesham United	439	L 0 - 2		13
45	24		H	Oxford City	146	L 0 - 3		
46	28		H	Stourbridge	504	D 1 - 1	Cooper 74	12

Southern League Action...

Chippenham midfielder, Ross Stearn, finds Evesham's Josh Quaynor barring his progress during Town's 4-2 League win.

Photo: Jonathan Holloway.

GOSPORT BOROUGH

Chairman: Mark Hook
Secretary: Brian Cosgrave   **(T)** 01329 235961   **(E)** brian.cosgrave@hotmail.co.uk
Additional Committee Members:
Mick Marsh, John Simpson, Paul Hook.

Manager: Alex Pike
Programme Editor: Jeremy Fox   **(E)** programme@gosportboroughfc.co.uk

THE NON-LEAGUE CLUB DIRECTORY

Book Holiday Inn Hotels and Save today!

Home

Clubs

Steps 1 - 4

League Tables

35 Years of Non-League Football

The Non-League Club Directory has developed into a comprehensive record of competitions within the non-League game, giving this level of football the

www.non-leagueclubdirectory.co.uk

Club Factfile

Founded: 1944   **Nickname:** The 'Boro'

Previous Names: Gosport Borough Athletic

Previous Leagues: Portsmouth 1944-45, Hampshire 1945-78, Southern 1978-92, Wessex 1992-2007

Club Colours (change): Yellow/navy/navy (Navy/yellow/yellow)

Ground: Privett Park, Privett Road, Gosport, Hampshire PO12 0SX   **(T)** 023 9250 1042 (Match days only)

Capacity: 4,500   **Seats:** 450   **Covered:** 600   **Clubhouse:** Yes   **Shop:** Yes

Directions: Exit M27 at J11. Take A32 Fareham to Gosport road.
After 3 miles take the 3rd exit at Brockhurst r/a, into Military Road.
At next r/a take 1st exit into Privett Road. Ground is approx. 400 yards on left.

Previous Grounds:

Record Attendance: 4,770 v Pegasus - FA Amateur Cup 1951

Record Victory: 14-0 v Cunliffe Owen - Hampshire League 1945-46
Record Defeat: 0-9 v Gloucester City - Southern Premier Division 1989-90 and v Lymington & N.M. - Wessex Lge 99-2000

Record Goalscorer: Ritchie Coulbert - 192

Record Appearances: Tony Mahoney - 765

Additional Records:

Senior Honours:
Hampshire League 1945-46, 76-77, 77-78. Hampshire Senior Cup 1987-88. Wessex League Cup 1992-93.
Wessex League 2006-07. Southern Division 1 South & West Play-offs 2011-12.

02-03		03-04		04-05		05-06		06-07		07-08		08-09		09-10		10-11		11-12	
Wex	2	Wex	3	Wex1	4	Wex1	5	WexP	1	Sthsw	11	Sthsw	12	Sthsw	8	Sthsw	13	Sthsw	3

HEMEL HEMPSTEAD TOWN

Chairman: David Boggins
Secretary: Dean Chance **(T)** 07858 990 550 **(E)** dean.chance@ntlworld.com
Additional Committee Members:
John Adams, Diane Kintas, Tony Conway

Manager: Stuart Maynard & Dean Brennan
Programme Editor: Tony Conway **(E)** tonyconway@yahoo.com

THE NON-LEAGUE CLUB DIRECTORY

Book Holiday Inn Hotels and Save today!

| Home |
| Clubs |
| Steps 1 - 4 |
| League Tables |

35 Years of Non-League Football

The Non-League Club Directory has developed into a comprehensive record of competitions within the non-League game, giving this level of football the

www.non-leagueclubdirectory.co.uk

Club Factfile

Founded: 1885 **Nickname:** The Tudors

Previous Names: Hemel Hempstead FC
Previous Leagues: Spartan 1922-52, Delphian 1952-63, Athenian 1963-77, Isthmian 1977-2004

Club Colours (change): Red with white trim/red/red (All green)

Ground: Vauxhall Road, Adeyfield Road, Hemel Hempstead HP2 4HW **(T)** 01442 259 777

Capacity: 3,152 **Seats:** 300 **Covered:** 900 **Clubhouse:** Yes **Shop:** Yes

Directions
Leave M1 at Junction 8 - follow dual carriageway over two roundabouts.
Get into outside lane and after 100 yards turn right.
Follow road to mini-roundabout turn left, next large roundabout take third exit into ground car park.

Previous Grounds: Crabtree Lane

Record Attendance: 3,500 v Tooting & Mitcham - Amateur Cup 1962 (Crabtree Lane)

Record Victory: Not known
Record Defeat: Not known

Record Goalscorer: Dai Price

Record Appearances: John Wallace - 1012
Additional Records:

Senior Honours:
Isthmian League Division 3 1998-99. Herts Senior Cup x7. Herts Charity Cup x6.

02-03		03-04		04-05		05-06		06-07		07-08		08-09		09-10		10-11		11-12	
Isth1N	3	Isth1N	6	SthP	19	SthW	4	SthP	5	SthP	7	SthP	5	SthP	20	SthP	15	SthP	19

HEMEL HEMPSTEAD TOWN

No.	Date	Comp	H/A	Opponents	Att:	Result	Goalscorers	Pos
1	Aug 13	Sth P	H	Leamington	296	D 1 - 1	Blake 64	
2	15		A	Hitchin Town	359	L 0 - 3		
3	20		A	Redditch United	267	L 0 - 1		19
4	23		H	AFC Totton	148	L 0 - 3		
5	27		H	Barwell	181	L 2 - 3	Pearce 18 Toomey 30	21
6	29		A	St Albans City	596	L 1 - 2	Toomey 6	
7	Sept 3		A	Banbury United	316	D 0 - 0		22
8	10		H	Stourbridge	201	W 2 - 0	May 18 McEntegart 64	19
9	13		H	Arlesey Town	171	D 1 - 1	Toomey 3	
10	17	FAC 1Q	H	Brentwood Town	245	D 0 - 0		
11	20	FAC 1Qr	A	Brentwood Town	104	D 0 - 0	Hemel Hempstead won 4-2 on penalties	
12	24		A	Chippenham Town	322	L 1 - 4	Arlick 53	22
13	Oct 1	FAC 2Q	A	Lowestoft Town	669	L 0 - 3		
14	4		A	Cambridge City	327	L 0 - 3		
15	8		H	Chesham United	406	D 1 - 1	Smith 53	21
16	22	FAT 1Q	H	Croydon Athletic	214	D 1 - 1	Blake 11	
17	26	FAT 1Qr	A	Croydon Athletic	96	W 2 - 0	Lafayette 39 Pearce 85 (pen)	
18	29		A	Frome Town	225	D 1 - 1	Lafayette 90	22
19	Nov 5	FAT 2Q	H	Brackley Town	210	L 2 - 3	Lafayette 20 May 79	
20	12		H	Weymouth	316	L 1 - 2	Stowen 68	
21	15		A	Bedford Town	209	W 1 - 0	Gorman 82	
22	19		H	Bashley	227	D 2 - 2	Wright 36 54	20
23	26		A	Cirencester Town	101	D 0 - 0		21
24	Dec 3		H	Redditch United	211	L 0 - 2		21
25	10		A	AFC Totton	295	L 0 - 2		21
26	17		H	Hitchin Town	236	W 2 - 0	Pearce 56 (pen) Batchelor 45	21
27	26		A	Oxford City	191	D 1 - 1	Stowen 64	20
28	31		H	Brackley Town	262	D 1 - 1	Scowen 31	20
29	Jan 2		H	St Albans City	488	L 0 - 4		21
30	7		A	Swindon Supermarine	101	W 3 - 1	Remy 42 Smith 70 Pearce 75	20
31	21		H	Banbury United	245	W 2 - 1	Smith 16 Morgan 87	20
32	24		A	Stourbridge	338	D 1 - 1	Pearce 2	
33	28		H	Cambridge City	342	L 1 - 2	Pearce 44	20
34	Feb 18		A	Chesham United	390	L 1 - 2	Pearce 59 (pen)	20
35	26		A	Evesham United	113	D 2 - 2	Schmidt 2 Lafayette 79	
36	March 3		H	Bedford Town	284	D 1 - 1	Pearce 49	21
37	6		H	Evesham United	135	L 2 - 3	Pearce 14 22	
38	10		A	Weymouth	669	W 1 - 0	Howarth 84	21
39	13		A	Arlesey Town	120	L 0 - 3		
40	17		H	Frome Town	179	W 3 - 1	May 40 44 Shariff 61	21
41	20		H	Chippenham Town	120	D 1 - 1	Shariff 44	
42	24		A	Barwell	115	W 3 - 2	May 45 Lafayette 58 70	20
43	31		H	Swindon Supermarine	243	D 0 - 0		
44	Apr 7		A	Brackley Town	275	L 0 - 3		21
45	14		A	Leamington	373	L 1 - 3	Shariff 61	21
46	21		H	Cirencester Town	250	W 4 - 1	Pearce 5 McEntegart 24 Blake 33 Lafayette 46	
47	23		H	Oxford City	212	W 2 - 0	Lafayette 42 76	
48	28		A	Bashley	194	L 0 - 2		19

HITCHIN TOWN

Chairman: Terry Barratt
Secretary: Roy Izzard **(T)** 07803 202 498 **(E)** roy.izzard@hitchintownfc.co.uk
Additional Committee Members:
Eileen Bone, Neil Jensen

Manager: Carl Williams
Programme Editor: Neil Jensen **(E)** neil.jensen@db.com

Club Factfile

Founded: 1865 **Nickname:** Canaries
Previous Names: Re-formed in 1928
Previous Leagues: Spartan 1928-39, Herts & Middlesex 1939-45, Athenian 1945-63, Isthmian 1964-2004

Club Colours (change): Yellow/green/green (Green/yellow/yellow)

Ground: Top Field, Fishponds Road, Hitchin SG5 1NU **(T)** 01462 459 028 (match days only)
Capacity: 5,000 **Seats:** 500 **Covered:** 1,250 **Clubhouse:** Yes **Shop:** Yes

Directions
From East A1 to J8 onto A602 to Hitchin.
At Three Moorhens Pub roundabout, take third exit (A600) towards Bedford, over next roundabout and lights, turn right at next roundabout, turnstiles on left, parking 50 yards on.

Previous Grounds: Not known

Record Attendance: 7,878 v Wycombe Wanderers - FA Amateur Cup 3rd Round 08/02/1956
Record Victory: 13-0 v Cowley and v RAF Uxbridge - both Spartan League 1929-30
Record Defeat: 0-10 v Kingstonian (A) and v Slough Town (A) - 1965-66 and 1979-80 respectively
Record Goalscorer: Paul Giggle - 214 (1968-86)
Record Appearances: Paul Giggle - 769 (1968-86)
Additional Records: Paid £2,000 to Potton United for Ray Seeking
Received £30,000 from Cambridge United for Zema Abbey, January 2000
Senior Honours:
AFA Senior Cup 1931-32. London Senior Cup 1969-70. Isthmian League Division 1 1992-93.
Herts Senior Cup x19 (a record)

10 YEAR RECORD

02-03	03-04	04-05	05-06	06-07	07-08	08-09	09-10	10-11	11-12
Isth P 14	Isth P 20	SthP 18	SthP 14	SthP 11	SthP 18	SthP 20	SthC 2	SthC 2	SthP 14

HITCHIN TOWN

No.	Date	Comp	H/A	Opponents	Att:	Result	Goalscorers	Pos
1	Aug 13	Sth P	A	Banbury United	256	D 1 - 1	Burke 90	
2	15		H	Hemel Hempstead	359	W 3 - 0	Burke 20 Frendo 56 (pen) 79	
3	20		H	Evesham United	295	L 0 - 1		10
4	23		A	St Albans City	452	D 4 - 4	Frendo 5 75 Anderson 9 45	
5	27		H	Cirencester Town	312	W 6 - 2	Lewis 12 35 FRENDO 3 (51 57 61 pen) Edgeley 80	9
6	29		A	Bedford Town	512	W 3 - 1	Cole 2 Burke 38 Frendo 89	
7	Sept 3		H	Bashley	420	L 2 - 3	Burke 19 Frendo 55	9
8	10		A	Leamington	510	L 0 - 1		13
9	12		H	Cambridge City	412	W 3 - 2	Frendo 27 Lee 51 Leach 85 (pen)	
10	17	FAC 1Q	A	Waltham Forest	70	L 0 - 2		
11	24		A	AFC Totton	473	W 1 - 0	Lewis 78	7
12	Oct 4		A	Chesham United	315	L 0 - 2		
13	8		H	Frome Town	542	L 1 - 3	Frendo 8	11
14	15		A	Brackley Town	242	L 0 - 3		14
15	22	FAT 1Q	A	Eastbourne Town	181	W 3 - 1	FRENDO 3 (12 33 (pen) 43)	
16	29		H	Chippenham Town	345	D 0 - 0		12
17	Nov 5	FAT 2Q	H	Lowestoft Town	282	L 1 - 3	Frendo 12	
18	12		A	Swindon Supermarine	131	L 1 - 2	Anderson 90	14
19	19		A	Oxford City	241	D 0 - 0		14
20	26		H	Barwell	340	D 0 - 0		14
21	Dec 4		A	Evesham United	119	L 0 - 1		17
22	10		H	St Albans City	418	L 0 - 3		16
23	12		H	Weymouth	202	W 3 - 1	Essiong 8 Donnelly 25 40	16
24	17		A	Hemel Hempstead	238	L 0 - 2		13
25	19		H	Stourbridge	251	W 2 - 0	Stewart 60 Frendo 79 (pen)	
26	26		A	Arlesey Town	526	D 0 - 0		13
27	Jan 2		H	Bedford Town	597	L 1 - 3	Frendo 14	15
28	7		A	Redditch United	266	W 4 - 1	Donnelly 12 FRENDO 3(14 45(pen) 83)	13
29	14		H	Leamington	444	D 0 - 0		15
30	21		A	Bashley	200	W 3 - 1	Burke 27 Frendo 45 90(pen)	12
31	28		H	Chesham United	466	D 1 - 1	Frendo 70	14
32	Feb 18		A	Frome Town	188	D 0 - 0		15
33	21		A	Cambridge City	281	L 1 - 3	Essiong 38	
34	25		H	Brackley Town	344	W 2 - 0	Frendo 28 Essiong 52	13
35	March 3		A	Stourbridge	339	D 0 - 0		13
36	10		H	Swindon Supermarine	364	L 0 - 1		15
37	17		A	Chippenham Town	363	W 1 - 0	Frendo 64	12
38	24		A	Cirencester Town	99	D 2 - 2	Burke 26 Donnelly 30	13
39	27		H	AFC Totton	333	D 2 - 2	Burke 2 Lewis 17	
40	31		H	Redditch United	457	W 2 - 1	Lewis 33 Medson 41	
41	Apr 7		A	Barwell	150	L 1 - 2	Frendo 45	12
42	9		H	Arlesey Town	514	W 2 - 0	Donnelly 39 Frendo 72 (pen)	
43	14		H	Banbury United	347	L 1 - 2	Leach 76 (pen)	11
44	21		A	Weymouth	674	L 1 - 2	Gregson 48	12
45	28		H	Oxford City	387	L 0 - 3		14

KETTERING TOWN

Chairman: Imraan Ladak
Secretary: Mike Cobb-Pernak   **(T)**
Additional Committee Members:

(E) info@ketteringtownfc.co.uk

Manager: John Beck
Programme Editor: Bob Brown   **(E)** info@ketteringtownfc.co.uk

THE NON-LEAGUE CLUB DIRECTORY

Book Holiday Inn Hotels and Save today!

Home

Clubs

Steps 1 - 4

League Tables

35 Years of Non-League Football

The Non-League Club Directory has developed into a comprehensive record of competitions within the non-League game, giving this level of football the

www.non-leagueclubdirectory.co.uk

Club Factfile

Founded: 1872   **Nickname:** The Poppies

Previous Names: Kettering > 1924

Previous Leagues: Midland 1892-1900, also had a team in United Counties 1896-99, Southern 1900-30, 1950-79, 2001-02, Birmingham 1930-50, Alliance/Conference 1979-2001, 02-03, Isthmian 2003-04

Club Colours (change): Red & black/black/red (Blue & white hoops with blue sleeves/white/blue)

Ground: Nene Park, Irthlingborough, Northants NN9 5QF   **(T)** 01536 483 028

Capacity: 6,635   **Seats:** Yes   **Covered:** All   **Clubhouse:** Yes   **Shop:** Yes

Directions: Leave the M1 at junction 15 (Direction Northampton) and follow the A45 for approximately 15 miles. At the Wilby Road roundabout take the 3rd exit and continue on the A45 for a further 6 miles. Turn left at the roundabout with the A6 (Direction Kettering). Nene Park is on your right approximately half a mile along the A6.

Previous Grounds: North Park, Green Lane, Rockingham Road > 2011.

Record Attendance: 11,536 v Peterborough - FA Cup 1st Round replay 1958-59

Record Victory: 16-0 v Higham YMCI - FA Cup 1909
Record Defeat: 0-13 v Mardy - Southern League Division Two 1911-12

Record Goalscorer: Roy Clayton - 171 (1972-81)

Record Appearances: Roger Ashby

Additional Records: Paid £25,000 to Macclesfield for Carl Alford 1994. Recieved £150,000 from Newcastle United for Andy Hunt

Senior Honours:
Southern League 1927-28, 56-57, 72-73, 2001-02. Conference North 2007-08.

02-03		03-04		04-05		05-06		06-07		07-08		08-09		09-10		10-11		11-12	
Conf	22	Isth P	9	Conf N	4	Conf N	6	Conf N	2	Conf N	1	Conf	8	Conf	6	Conf	14	Conf	24

KETTERING TOWN

No.	Date	Comp	H/A	Opponents	Att:	Result	Goalscorers	Pos
								- 3 points Feb
1	Sat-13-Aug	BSP	H	Newport County	2047	W 3-2	Marna 2 (51, pen 90), Cunnington 60	4
2	Tue-16-Aug	BSP	A	Stockport County	3429	L 0-1		11
3	Sat-20-Aug	BSP	A	Gateshead	661	D 1-1	McKenzie 63	12
4	Tue-23-Aug	BSP	H	York City	1595	L 1-5	McKenzie 43	17
5	Sat-27-Aug	BSP	A	Mansfield Town	2051	L 1-3		19
6	Mon-29-Aug	BSP	H	Cambridge United	2000	D 0-0		20
7	Sat-03-Sep	BSP	H	Fleetwood Town	1209	L 2-3	Marna 2 (74, 82)	22
8	Sat-10-Sep	BSP	A	Lincoln City	2269	W 2-0	Marna 63, Ashikodi pen 82	18
9	Sat-17-Sep	BSP	H	Tamworth	1955	L 0-2		19
10	Tue-20-Sep	BSP	A	Grimsby Town	2470	L 1-2	Ashikodi 28	20
11	Sat-24-Sep	BSP	A	Bath City	734	W 1-0	Sangare 2	18
12	Tue-27-Sep	BSP	H	Hayes & Yeading United	1119	L 3-5	Ashikodi 44, Cunnington 57, Sangare 90	20
13	Sat-01-Oct	BSP	H	Kidderminster Harriers	1301	L 0-1		21
14	Sat-08-Oct	BSP	A	Alfreton Town	851	D 1-1	Cunnington pen 72	20
15	Tue-11-Oct	BSP	H	Braintree Town	1115	W 2-1	Cunnington 55, Verma 71	20
16	Sat-15-Oct	BSP	A	Forest Green Rovers	823	W 1-0	Cunnington 52	16
17	Tue-18-Oct	BSP	A	Newport County	1249	L 1-3	Ashikodi 45	19
18	Sat-22-Oct	BSP	H	Ebbsfleet United	1402	D 2-2	Bridges 13, Dawkin 50	17
19	Sat-05-Nov	BSP	H	Southport	1368	L 2-3	Hughes-Mason 58, Ashikodi 77	19
20	Fri-18-Nov	BSP	A	Tamworth	1197	D 2-2	Ashikodi 2, Marna 16	17
21	Sat-26-Nov	BSP	H	Grimsby Town	1354	L 1-2	Bridges 90	19
22	Tue-29-Nov	BSP	A	Fleetwood Town	1221	L 0-3		19
23	Sat-03-Dec	BSP	A	York City	2899	L 0-7		20
24	Tue-06-Dec	BSP	H	Darlington	924	D 0-0		20
25	Sat-17-Dec	BSP	H	Bath City	1096	D 1-1	Jones 84	20
26	Mon-26-Dec	BSP	A	Luton Town	7164	L 0-5		20
27	Sun-01-Jan	BSP	H	Luton Town	3247	L 0-5		22
28	Sat-07-Jan	BSP	A	AFC Telford	2035	L 1-3	Marna 5	22
29	Sat-21-Jan	BSP	A	Wrexham	4066	L 1-4	Sangare 67	22
30	Tue-24-Jan	BSP	H	Gateshead	804	W 2-1	Mills 57, Verma 85	21
31	Sat-28-Jan	BSP	H	Lincoln City	1417	W 1-0	Verma pen 36	20
32	Sat-18-Feb	BSP	A	Barrow	1090	L 0-3		22
33	Tue-21-Feb	BSP	H	Forest Green Rovers	830	L 1-3	Mills 90	22
34	Sat-25-Feb	BSP	A	Braintree Town	730	L 1-2	Sangare 60	22
35	Sat-03-Mar	BSP	H	Wrexham	1377	L 0-1		23
36	Sat-10-Mar	BSP	A	Hayes & Yeading United	253	L 0-1		23
37	Tue-13-Mar	BSP	A	Southport	753	D 0-0		23
38	Sat-17-Mar	BSP	H	Alfreton Town	1093	L 0-2		23
39	Tue-20-Mar	BSP	H	Tamworth	939	W 2-1	Wyke 50, Joyce 60	23
40	Sat-24-Mar	BSP	A	Ebbsfleet United	957	L 0-1		23
41	Sat-31-Mar	BSP	H	Stockport County	1281	L 1-3	Westwood 76	23
42	Sat-07-Apr	BSP	H	Mansfield Town	1818	L 0-3		23 Relegated
43	Mon-09-Apr	BSP	A	Cambridge United	2578	L 0-3		23
44	Sat-14-Apr	BSP	A	Kidderminster Harriers	1967	L 1-4	Ford 19	23
45	Sat-21-Apr	BSP	H	Barrow	896	D 1-1	Bridges 45	24
46	Sat-28-Apr	BSP	A	Darlington	1792	L 1-3	Wyke pen 59	24

CUPS

No.	Date	Comp	H/A	Opponents	Att:	Result	Goalscorers	
1	Sat-29-Oct	FAC 4Q	H	Southend Manor	987	W 3-1	McKenzie 7, Marna 2 (47, 59)	
2	Sat-12-Nov	FAC 1	A	Sutton United	1532	L 0-1		
3	Sat-10-Dec	FAT 1	A	Gateshead	402	L 2-3	Dawkin 10, Davis pen 58	

LEAMINGTON

Chairman: Jim Scott
Secretary: Richard Edy   **(T)**   **(E)** matchsecretary@leamingtonfc.co.
Additional Committee Members:
Nic Sproul, Russell Davis, Graham Moody, Kevin Watson, Roger Austin.

Manager: Paul Holleran
Programme Editor: Sally Ellis   **(E)** programme@leamingtonfc.co.uk

Back Row L to R: Andy Jenkins (kitman) James Mace, Craig Owen, Joe Magunda, Michael Quirke, Liam Daly, Kevin Sawyer,
Matty Dodd, Richard Batchelor, Mark Davidson (Community Director).
Front Row L to R: Alex Taylor, Dean Perrow, Lee Chilton, James Husband, Liam O'Neill (Coach) Jamie Hood,
Paul Holleran (manager), Michael Tuohy, Sam Adkins, Stephan Morley, Tom Berwick.

Club Factfile

Founded: 1892   **Nickname:** The Brakes
Previous Names: Leamington Town 1892-1937, Lockheed Borg & Beck 1944-46 , Lockheed Leamington 1946-73, AP Leamington 1973-88
Previous Leagues: Birmingham Combination, Birmingham & District, West Midlands Regional, Midland Counties, Southern, Midland Combination, Midland Alliance

Club Colours (change): Gold with black trim/black with gold trim/gold with black trim (All royal blue)

Ground: New Windmill Ground, Harbury Lane, Whitmarsh, Leamington CV33 9QB   **(T)** 01926 430 406
Capacity: 5,000   **Seats:** 120   **Covered:** 720   **Clubhouse:** Yes   **Shop:** Yes

Directions
From West and North – M40 Southbound – Exit J14 and take A452 towards Leamington. Ahead at 1st island. Next island take 2nd exit A452 (Europa Way). Next island take 4th exit (Harbury Lane) signposted Harbury and Bishops Tachbrook. Next island take 3rd exit (Harbury Lane). At traffic lights continue straight ahead Harbury Lane. Ground is 1.5 miles on left.
From South – M40 northbound – Exit J13. Turn right onto A452 towards Leamington. At 1st island take 3rd exit A452 (Europa Way) and follow as above (Europa Way onwards).

Previous Grounds: Old Windmill Ground

Record Attendance: 1,380 v Retford United - 17/02/2007
Record Victory: Not known
Record Defeat: Not known
Record Goalscorer: Josh Blake - 166
Record Appearances: Josh Blake - 314
Additional Records:

Senior Honours:
Birmingham & District 1961-62. West Midlands Regional 1962-63. Midland Counties 1964-65.
Southern League 1982-83, Division 1 Midlands 2008-09.
Midland Combination Division 2 2000-01, Premier Division 2004-05. Midland Alliance 2006-07, League cup 2005-06.

10 YEAR RECORD

02-03		03-04		04-05		05-06		06-07		07-08		08-09		09-10		10-11		11-12	
MCmP	3	MCmP	2	MCmP	1	MidAl	5	MidAl	1	SthM	2	SthM	1	SthP	10	SthP	5	SthP	7

LEAMINGTON

No.	Date	Comp	H/A	Opponents	Att:	Result	Goalscorers	Pos
1	Aug 13	Sth P	A	Hemel Hempstead	296	D 1 - 1	Tuohy 88	
2	16		H	Arlesey Town	540	W 1 - 0	Husband 7	
3	20		H	Weymouth	579	W 4 - 1	BERWICK 3 (16 17 90) Morley 86	4
4	23		A	Stourbridge	467	D 0 - 0		
5	27		H	AFC Totton	601	W 2 - 1	Blyth 59 (pen) 67	3
6	29		A	Redditch United	523	D 1 - 1	Husband 28	
7	Sept 3		A	Oxford City	366	L 1 - 2	Morley 78	8
8	10		H	Hitchin Town	510	W 1 - 0	Kolodynski 78	6
9	13		H	Bedford Town	406	L 0 - 4		
10	17	FAC 1Q	H	Boldmere St Michaels	422	W 5 - 0	Batchelor 23 Blyth 54 Kolodynski 83 86 Adkins 90	
11	24		A	Swindon Supermarine	207	W 1 - 0	Blyth 90	6
12	Oct 1	FAC 2Q	A	Daventry Town	551	L 1 - 2	Blyth (pen) 89	
13	4		A	Chippenham Town	328	W 2 - 1	Kolodynski 10 Owen 49	
14	8		H	Brackley Town	612	D 0 - 0		6
15	15		H	Bashley	560	W 1 - 0	Blyth 29 (pen)	3
16	22	FAT 1Q	A	Romulus	154	L 0 - 1		
17	29		A	Cirencester Town	237	L 1 - 2	Hood 79	6
18	Nov 12		H	Cambridge City	631	W 4 - 2	Kolodynski 6 Hood 36 Blyth 47 69	6
19	15		A	Evesham United	172	W 2 - 1	Kolodynski 25 Mace 54	
20	19		A	Chesham United	445	D 1 - 1	Blyth 62	4
21	26		H	St Albans City	511	W 1 - 0	Blyth 80 (pen)	1
22	Dec 3		A	Weymouth	622	L 1 - 2	Blyth 87 (pen)	
23	10		H	Stourbridge	511	W 4 - 2	Taylor 23 80 Husband 49 Tuohy 78	
24	17		A	Arlesey Town	181	W 2 - 0	Morley 36 Batchelor 58	1
25	26		A	Barwell	375	L 1 - 3	Morley 74	3
26	31		H	Frome Town	638	D 1 - 1	Blyth 51	3
27	Jan 2		H	Redditch United	603	L 1 - 2	Blyth 38	
28	7		A	St Albans City	480	L 1 - 2	Kolodynski 86	6
29	14		A	Hitchin Town	444	D 0 - 0		5
30	21		H	Oxford City	552	D 1 - 1	Morley 65	6
31	28		H	Chippenham Town	470	D 0 - 0		6
32	Feb 18		A	Brackley Town	407	L 0 - 3		8
33	25		A	Bashley	219	L 1 - 2	Blyth 69	8
34	March 3		H	Evesham United	434	D 1 - 1	Daly 29	9
35	10		A	Cambridge City	442	D 2 - 2	Morley 31 (pen) Taylor 84	9
36	13		A	Bedford Town	248	W 2 - 1	Blyth 6 Kolodynski 17	
37	17		H	Cirencester Town	447	W 2 - 0	Hood 67 Taylor 73	7
38	20		H	Banbury United	388	W 3 - 1	Daly 3 Blyth 33 89	
39	24		A	AFC Totton	467	D 1 - 1	Chiltern 57	7
40	27		H	Swindon Supermarine	315	D 2 - 2	Chilton 19 Morley 39	
41	Apr 7		A	Frome Town	314	D 0 - 0		7
42	9		H	Barwell	370	W 3 - 0	Taylor 13 Kolodynski 52 Morley 62	
43	14		H	Hemel Hempstead	373	W 3 - 1	Morley 30 (pen) Steele 43 Blyth 84	7
44	21		A	Banbury United	564	D 1 - 1	Steele 38	7
45	28		H	Chesham United	601	W 3 - 2	KOLODYNSKI 3(21 54 55)	7

REDDITCH UNITED

Chairman: Chris Swan
Secretary: Ian Milne　　　**(T)** 07903 319680　　　**(E)** ian.milne94@googlemail.com
Additional Committee Members:
Sallie Swan, Jeff Watson.

Manager: Simon Redhead
Programme Editor: Sallie Swan & Craig Swan　**(E)** programmeeditor.reds@yahoo.com

Club Factfile

Founded: 1891　　　**Nickname:** The Reds
Previous Names: Redditch Town
Previous Leagues: Birmingham combination 1905-21, 29-39, 46-53, West Midlands 1921-29, 53-72,
Southern 1972-79, 81-2004, Alliance 1979-80. Conference 2004-11.

Club Colours (change): Red/black/black (White/blue/blue)

Ground: Valley Stadium, Bromsgrove Road, Redditch B97 4RN　　　**(T)** 01527 67450
Capacity: 5,000　**Seats:** 400　**Covered:** 2,000　**Clubhouse:** Yes　**Shop:** Yes

Directions: M42 J2, at island first exit onto the A441 for 2 miles, next island first exit onto Birmingham Road A441 for 1.2 miles then at island third exit onto Middlehouse Lane B4184 for 0.3 miles. At traffic lights (next to the fire station) turn left onto Birmingham Road for 0.2 miles then turn right into Clive Road for 0.3 miles. At island take first exit onto Hewell Road for 0.2 miles then at 'T' junction right onto Windsor Street for 0.1 miles. At traffic lights (next to bus station) continue straight ahead onto Bromsgrove Road for 0.3 miles and at the brow of the hill, turn right into the ground's entrance.

Previous Grounds: HDA Sports Ground, Millsborough Road

Record Attendance: 5,500 v Bromsgrove Rovers - Wets Midlands League 1954-55
Record Victory: Not known
Record Defeat: Not known
Record Goalscorer: Not known
Record Appearances: Not known
Additional Records: Paid £3,000 to Halesowen Town for Paul Joinson
Received £40,000 from Aston Villa for David Farrell
Senior Honours:
Worcestershire Senior Cup 1893-94, 29-30, 74-75, 76-76, 2007-08.
Birmingham Senior Cup 1924-25, 31-32, 38-39, 76-77, 2004-05.
Southern League Division 1 North 1975-76, Western Division 2003-04. Staffordshire Senior Cup 1990-91.

10 YEAR RECORD

02-03		03-04		04-05		05-06		06-07		07-08		08-09		09-10		10-11		11-12	
SthW	7	SthW	1	Conf N	9	Conf N	20	Conf N	19	Conf N	13	Conf N	14	Conf N	19	Conf N	21	SthP	15

REDDITCH UNITED

No.	Date	Comp	H/A	Opponents	Att:	Result	Goalscorers	Pos
1	Aug 13	Sth P	A	Oxford City	208	D 1 - 1	Brown 82	
2	16		H	Bedford Town	294	W 2 - 0	Jones 77 Blenkinsopp 90	
3	20		H	Hemel Hempstead	267	W 1 - 0	Brown 26	7
4	23		A	Banbury United	305	L 0 - 1		
5	27		A	Bashley	190	L 1 - 2	Blenkinsopp 71	11
6	29		H	Leamington	523	D 1 - 1	Howell 68	
7	Sept 3		H	Cirencester Town	100	L 0 - 2		14
8	10		A	St Albans City	355	L 0 - 2		15
9	13		H	Swindon Supermarine	201	L 0 - 1		
10	17	FAC 1Q	H	**Hednesford Town**	**348**	L 0 - 2		
11	24		A	Frome Town	220	L 2 - 3	Robinson 19 Deards 15	16
12	Oct 1		A	Brackley Town	193	L 0 - 2		
13	8		H	Cambridge City	271	W 2 - 0	McKenzie 10 (pen) Hines 44	17
14	15		A	Chesham United	316	L 0 - 1		
15	22	FAT 1Q	A	**Stourbridge**	**291**	L 1 - 2	Deards 26	
16	Nov 5		H	AFC Totton	204	D 0 - 0		17
17	12		A	Chippenham Town	343	L 0 - 2		18
18	15		H	Barwell	155	W 2 - 0	Deabill 67 69	
19	19		A	Weymouth	493	W 3 - 2	Deards 27 Deabill 45 Halsall 60	16
20	26		H	Arlesey Town	225	L 0 - 1		16
21	Dec 3		A	Hemel Hempstead	211	W 2 - 0	Jones 15 Berwick 75	
22	10		H	Banbury United	172	W 1 - 0	Berwick 83	13
23	17		A	Bedford Town	217	W 1 - 0	Osbourne 30	12
24	26		H	Stourbridge	416	L 0 - 1		14
25	31		A	Evesham United	213	L 0 - 1		15
26	Jan 2		A	Leamington	603	W 2 - 1	Ford 73 Osbourne 90	
27	7		H	Hitchin Town	266	L 1 - 4	Halsall 37	15
28	21		A	Cirencester Town	123	L 0 - 1		16
29	28		H	Brackley Town	221	L 2 - 3	Jones 70 Adams 76 (pen)	18
30	31		H	St Albans City	84	L 3 - 4	Deabill 28 45 Jones 31	
31	Feb 18		A	Cambridge City	301	D 1 - 1	Russell 17	18
32	25		H	Chesham United	182	D 1 - 1	Halsall 39	
33	March 3		A	Barwell	193	D 1 - 1	Benbow 66	18
34	7		A	Swindon Supermarine	107	W 2 - 0	Osbourne 52 Benbow 58	
35	10		H	Chippenham Town	180	W 1 - 0	Deabill 15	17
36	17		A	AFC Totton	460	D 0 - 0		18
37	20		H	Frome Town	149	L 0 - 4		
38	24		H	Bashley	219	D 2 - 2	S Hendrie 46 Benbow 79	
39	31		A	Hitchin Town	457	L 1 - 2	Deabill 65	
40	Apr 7		H	Evesham United	380	W 3 - 1	Clark 19 (og) Lee Hendrie 32 Grimes 61	
41	9		A	Stourbridge	488	L 0 - 1		
42	10		H	Oxford City	251	D 1 - 1	Deabill 15	
43	21		A	Arlesey Town	155	W 3 - 0	S.Hendrie 49 L.Hendrie 60 89	15
44	28		H	Weymouth	371	W 2 - 0	S Hendrie 11 Osbourne 81 (pen)	15

ST ALBANS CITY

Chairman: Ian Ridley
Secretary: Steve Eames **(T)** 01727 848914 **(E)**
Additional Committee Members:
Nick Archer, Garath Davies, Kate Gosnold

Manager: David Howell
Programme Editor: Nick Archer **(E)** nick.archer@gsp-stalbans.co.uk

Club Factfile

Founded: 1908 **Nickname:** The Saints
Previous Names:
Previous Leagues: Herts County 1908-10, Spartan 1908-20, Athenian 1920-23, Isthmian 1923-2004, Conference 2004-11.

Club Colours (change): Yellow/blue/yellow (All white)

Ground: Clarence Park, York Road, St. Albans, Herts AL1 4PL **(T)** 01727 848 914
Capacity: 5,007 **Seats:** 667 **Covered:** 1,900 **Clubhouse:** Yes **Shop:** Yes

Directions: From the M25 (Clockwise) Exit M25 at junction 21A(A405). Follow signs to St. Albans from slip road. At Noke Hotel roundabout (Shell garage will be straight ahead), bear right on A405 and stay on A405 until London Colney roundabout (traffic light controlled). Turn left onto A1081. Follow road for approx 1 mile until mini roundabout (Great Northern pub on left). Turn right into Alma Road. At traffic lights turn right into Victoria Street and continue to junction with Crown pub. Go straight across into Clarence Road, ground is first on left about 50 yards past junction or take the next turning on the left into York Road, ground entrance is at the end of the road on the left. From the M25 (Counter-clockwise) Exit M25 at junction 22 (A1081). Follow signs to St. Albans from slip road. At London Colney roundabout (traffic light controlled) exit onto A1081. Follow road for approx 1 mile until mini roundabout (Great Northern pub on left). Turn right into Alma Road. At traffic lights turn right into Victoria Street and continue to junction with Crown pub. Go straight across into Clarence Road, ground is first on left about 50 yards past junction or take the next turning on the left into York Road, ground entrance is at the end of the road on the left.

Previous Grounds: None

Record Attendance: 9,757 v Ferryhill Athletic - FA Amateur Cup 1926
Record Victory: 14-0 v Aylesbury United (H) - Spartan League 19/10/1912
Record Defeat: 0-11 v Wimbledon (H) - Isthmian League 1946
Record Goalscorer: Billy Minter - 356 (Top scorer for 12 consecutive season from 1920-32)
Record Appearances: Phil Wood - 900 (1962-85)
Additional Records: Paid £6,000 to Yeovil Town for Paul Turner August 1957
Received £92,759 from Southend United for Dean Austin 1990
Senior Honours:
Athenian League 1920-21, 21-22. Isthmian League 1923-24, 26-27, 27-28.
London Senior Cup 1970-71.

10 YEAR RECORD

02-03		03-04		04-05		05-06		06-07		07-08		08-09		09-10		10-11		11-12	
Isth P	4	Isth P	19	Conf S	14	Conf S	2	Conf	24	Conf S	19	Conf S	12	Conf S	13	Conf S	22	SthP	8

ST ALBANS CITY

No.	Date	Comp	H/A	Opponents	Att:	Result	Goalscorers	Pos
1	Aug 13	Sth P	H	Cirencester Town	384	W 4 - 1	Hawarth 12 Sol Shields 27 Sean Shields 37 Furlong 75	
2	16		A	Cambridge City	305	L 0 - 4		
3	21		A	Barwell	163	W 1 - 0	Sol Shields 56	10
4	23		H	Hitchin Town	452	D 4 - 4	Pooley 10 Sean Shields 65 Ijaha 67 Bakare 90 (pen)	
5	27		A	Banbury United	269	L 0 - 2		12
6	29		H	Hemel Hempstead	596	W 2 - 1	Hart 12 Walker 23	
7	Sept 3		A	Swindon Supermarine	149	L 1 - 2	Sean Shields 32	12
8	10		H	Redditch United	355	W 2 - 0	Hart 1 Walker 61	10
9	13		H	AFC Totton	329	L 3 - 4	Jinadu 3 48 Bakare 80	
10	17	FAC 1Q	H	Berkhamsted	351	D 0 - 0		
11	20	FAC 1Qr	A	Berkhamsted	306	W 3 - 0	Haworth 22 Moran 49 Walker 64	
12	24		A	Stourbridge	320	L 1 - 2	Haworth 10	13
13	Oct 1	FAC 2Q	A	East Thurrock United	101	D 3 - 3	Jinadu 10 Matthews 15 (pen) Haworth 44	
14	4	FAC 2Qr	H	East Thurrock United	250	L 1 - 3	Watts 81	
15	8		H	Arlesey Town	396	D 2 - 2	Haworth 18 Walker 30	14
16	11		A	Bedford Town	270	D 2 - 2	Bakare 10 Watts 45	
17	15		H	Frome Town	303	W 2 - 1	Bakare 44 45	12
18	22	FAT 1Q	H	Ashford Town (Middx)	275	L 1 - 3	Moran 17	
19	29		A	Bashley	233	L 1 - 4	Furlong 32	14
20	Nov 5		A	Oxford City	241	L 1 - 3	Sol Shields 87	14
21	12		H	Evesham United	288	W 4 - 1	Furlong 14 18 Hyde 20 (og) Shariff 45	
22	19		H	Brackley Town	377	D 1 - 1	Sean Shields 2	11
23	22		A	Chippenham Town	287	L 0 - 4		
24	26		A	Leamington	511	L 0 - 1		12
25	Dec 3		H	Barwell	324	L 1 - 6	Watts 39 (pen)	14
26	10		A	Hitchin Town	418	W 3 - 0	Furlong 20 Gray 43 45	12
27	17		H	Cambridge City	362	W 3 - 0	Martin 40 59 Cutchey 64	11
28	26		H	Chesham United	606	D 1 - 1	Hart 40	11
29	31		A	Weymouth	720	L 1 - 3	Furlong 48	13
30	Jan 2		A	Hemel Hempstead	488	W 4 - 0	Bakare 15 Clarke 17 Hyde 79 (pen) Lansiquot 90	
31	7		H	Leamington	480	W 2 - 1	Blake 8 78	10
32	21		H	SWindon Supermarine	446	W 2 - 1	Gray 6 Bakare 90 (pen)	10
33	28		H	Bedford Town	463	L 1 - 2	Gray 74	10
34	31		A	Redditch United	84	W 4 - 3	Bakare 6 Ngakam 41 Ijaha 73 Henry 88	
35	Feb 18		A	Arlesey Town	248	D 1 - 1	Newton 90	10
36	25		A	Frome Town	236	W 1 - 0	Martin 5	9
37	28		A	AFC Totton	353	D 1 - 1	Hart 45	
38	March 3		H	Oxford City	414	W 3 - 2	Bakare 63 70 Ngakam 90	7
39	10		A	Evesham United	154	D 1 - 1	Ngakam 76	7
40	17		H	Bashley	407	W 2 - 0	Bakare 73 Martin 83	
41	24		H	Banbury Town	482	D 1 - 1	Newton 69	8
42	27		H	Stourbridge	366	W 2 - 1	Diarra 10 Newton 63	
43	Apr 7		H	Weymouth	539	D 2 - 2	Newton 47 Sean Shields 68	8
44	9		A	Chesham United	501	D 2 - 2	Newton 49 Bakare 77	
45	14		A	Cirencester Town	101	W 2 - 0	Henry 22 32	8
46	21		H	Chippenham Town	457	L 1 - 4	Henry 8	8
47	28		A	Brackley Town	535	L 0 - 6		8

STOURBRIDGE

Chairman: Andy Pountney
Secretary: Clive Eades   **(T)** 07958 275 986   **(E)** clive.eades2@capita.co.uk
Additional Committee Members:
Ian Pilkington, Andy Bullingham, Neil Smith, Steve Hyde

Manager: Gary Hackett
Programme Editor: Nigel Gregg   **(E)** ng004f7624@blueyonder.co.uk

2011-12 Squad.
Back Row (L to R): Sean Geddes, Aaron Griffiths, James Dyson, Aaron Drake, Leon Broadhurst, Craig Slater, Nathan Bennett, Lewis Solly, Sam Smith, Linden Dovey, Jamie Oliver, Josh Craddock, Paul McCone, Ashley Edwards, Will Worthington.
Front Row: Paul Lloyd, David Plinston, Sam Rock, Steve Johnson (GK coach), Richard Drewett (physio), Jon Ford (Asst Manager), Ian Pilkington (Chairman), Gary Hackett (Manager), Mark Clifton (Coach), Ben Billingham, Ryan Rowe, Ryan Mahon, Drew Canavan.
Photo courtesy of Andrew Roper.

Club Factfile

Founded: 1876   **Nickname:** The Glassboys
Previous Names: Not known
Previous Leagues: West Midlands (Birmingham League) 1892-1939, 54-71, Birmingham Combination 1945-53, Southern 1971-2000
Club Colours (change): Red and white stripes/red/red (Yellow with green trim/green/yellow)

Ground: War Memorial Athletic Ground, High Street, Amblecote DY8 4HN   **(T)** 01384 394 040 / 444 075
Capacity: 2,000   **Seats:** 250   **Covered:** 750   **Clubhouse:** Yes   **Shop:** Yes

Directions
From Stourbridge Ring-Road follow signs A491 to Wolverhampton.
The ground is on the left within 300 yards immediately beyond the third traffic lights and opposite the Royal Oak public house.

Previous Grounds: Not known

Record Attendance: 5,726 v Cardiff City - Welsh Cup Final 1st Leg 1974
Record Victory: Not known
Record Defeat: Not known
Record Goalscorer: Ron Page - 269
Record Appearances: Ron Page - 427
Additional Records: Received £20,000 from Lincoln City for Tony Cunningham 1979

Senior Honours:
Southern League Division 1 North 1973-74, Midland Division 90-91, League Cup 92-93. Midland Alliance 2001-02, 02-03.
Worcestershire Junior Cup 1927-28. Hereford Senior Cup 1954-55. Birmingham Senior Cup x3.
Worcestershire Senior Cup x9

10 YEAR RECORD

02-03		03-04		04-05		05-06		06-07		07-08		08-09		09-10		10-11		11-12	
MidAl	1	MidAl	9	MidAl	8	MidAl	2	SthM	7	SthM	3	SthP	16	SthP	9	SthP	8	SthP	6

STOURBRIDGE

No.	Date	Comp	H/A	Opponents	Att:	Result	Goalscorers	Pos
1	Aug 13	Sth P	H	Chippenham Town	216	W 3 - 1	Rowe 45 Craddock 60 Geddes 82 (pen)	
2	16		A	Cirencester Town	120	W 2 - 1	Rowe 77 Dovey 87	
3	20		A	Cambridge City	325	D 0 - 0		6
4	23		H	Leamington	467	D 0 - 0		
5	27		H	Arlesey Town	205	W 2 - 0	Bennett 20 Rowe 72	4
6	29		A	Barwell	204	D 2 - 2	Geddes 45 90	
7	Sept 3		H	Chesham United	446	W 2 - 1	Rowe 75 Dovey 86	3
8	10		A	Hemel Hempstead	201	L 0 - 2		7
9	13		A	Evesham United	150	W 1 - 0	Rowe 33	
10	17	FAC 1Q	A	**Bewdley Town**	301	W 2 - 1	**Broadhurst 68 Drake 75**	
11	24		H	St Albans City	320	W 2 - 1	Rowe 61 68	3
12	Oct 1	FAC 2Q	A	**Barwell**	130	W 2 - 0	**Rowe 8 Geddes 48 (pen)**	
13	4		H	Banbury United	345	W 5 - 0	DRAKE 3 (21 52 56) Canavan 61 Rock 85	
14	8		A	Bashley	273	L 0 - 1		3
15	15	FAC 3Q	H	**Evesham United**	518	W 5 - 0	**Rowe 25 Drake 42 Geddes 49 (pen) Craddock 75 Dyson 89**	
16	22	FAT 1Q	H	**Redditch United**	291	W 2 - 1	**Smith 45 Billingham 57**	
17	29	FAC 4Q	H	**Rushall Olympic**	720	W 5 - 0		
18	Nov 5	FAT 2Q	H	**Kendal Town**	338	D 3 - 3	**Canavan 23 Billingham 28 Geddes 45 (pen)**	
19	8	FAT 2Qr	A	**Kendal Town**	207	W 6 - 0	**Evans 41 Rowe 45 54 Newton 59 (og) Canavan 68 McCone 78**	
20	15	FAC 1	A	**Plymouth Argyle**	6173	D 3 - 3	**Drake 37 Rowe 53 Geddes 82 (pen)**	
21	19		H	Frome Town	678	W 4 - 0	Rock 12 Geddes 22 (pen) Evans 32 Griffin 64	7
22	22	FAC 1r	H	**Plymouth Argyle**	2519	W 2 - 0	**McCone 52 Evans 73**	
23	26	FAT 3Q	H	**Chester**	1481	L 0 - 2		
24	Dec 3	FAC 2	H	**Stevenage Town**	3,200	L 0 - 3		
25	6		H	Cambridge City	404	D 1 - 1	Geddes 36 (pen)	
26	10		A	Leamington	511	L 2 - 4	Drake 64 Broadhurst 66	9
27	17		H	Cirencester Town	374	W 2 - 1	Rowe 21 Griffin 80	8
28	19		A	Hitchin Town	251	L 0 - 2		8
29	26		A	Redditch United	418	W 1 - 0	Billingham 61	
30	31		H	Swindon Supermarine	464	W 4 - 1	Griffin 22 Canavan 40 41 Drake 47	7
31	Jan 2		H	Barwell	481	D 1 - 1	Rowe 68	8
32	7		A	Brackley Town	278	W 2 - 0	Geddes 89 (pen) Rowe 90	7
33	21		A	Chesham United	100	L 2 - 4	Broadhurst 35 Bennett 45	8
34	24		H	Hemel Hempstead	338	D 1 - 1	Bennett 36	
35	28		A	Banbury United	314	L 1 - 4	Rock 25	8
36	31		H	Weymouth	287	L 1 - 2	Drake 9	
37	Feb 18		H	Bashley	361	W 5 - 0	Broadhurst 21 Billingham 58 Griffin 62 Rock 74 Dovey 85	7
38	21		A	Oxford City	175	W 2 - 1	Geddes 36 (pen) 66 (pen)	
39	25		A	Weymouth	508	D 1 - 1	Geddes 90	6
40	28		H	Bedford Town	372	D 1 - 1	Geddes 75 (pen)	6
41	March 3		H	Hitchin Town	339	D 0 - 0		6
42	10		A	Bedford Town	288	D 2 - 2	McCone 34 Broadhurst 66	6
43	13		H	Evesham United	314	W 3 - 1	Broadhurst 52 Bennett 75 Geddes 81 (pen)	
44	17		H	Oxford City	421	W 2 - 0	Broadhurst 13 Billingham 90	5
45	20		A	AFC Totton	335	L 0 - 1		
46	24		A	Arlesey Town	145	D 1 - 1	Geddes 90 (pen)	6
47	27		A	St Albans City	366	L 1 - 2	Bennett 54	
48	31		H	Brackley Town	623	W 1 - 0	Kemp 48 (og)	6
49	Apr 7		A	Swindon Supermarine	178	L 1 - 2	Broadhurst 83	6
50	9		H	Redditch United	488	W 1 - 0	Bennett 76	
51	14		A	Chippenham Town	393	W 2 - 1	Oliver 48 Geddes 57	6
52	21		H	AFC Totton	728	W 2 - 1	McCone 45 Palmer 63	
53	28		A	Frome Town	504	D 1 - 1	Geddes 41 (pen)	6

Southern League Action...

Banbury Utd keeper catches the ball in front of Redditch forward Jimmy Deabrill at the Valley Stadium.

Photo: Jonathan Holloway.

ST. NEOTS TOWN

Chairman: Mike Kearns
Secretary: Peter Naylor   **(T)** 07702 400 205   **(E)** secretary@stneotsfc.com
Additional Committee Members:
Lee Kearns, Marian Izzard, Louise Sales.

Manager: Iain Parr
Programme Editor: Mark Davies   **(E)** mark@blueprwandesign.co.uk

Club Factfile

Founded: 1879   **Nickname:** Saints
Previous Names: St. Neots & District > 1951.
Previous Leagues: S Midlands, Cent. Alliance, UCL, Eastern Co., Hunts, United Counties > 2011.

Club Colours (change): All dark blue (All red)

Ground: Hunts Post Community Stadium, Cambridge Road, St Neots, PE19 6SN   **(T)** 01480 470 012
Capacity: 3,000   **Seats:** 250   **Covered:** 850   **Clubhouse:** Yes   **Shop:** No
Directions From St Neots town centre, take the B1428 Cambridge Road, after going under the railway bridge, turn left at the first roundabout into Dramsell Rise. Follow the road up the hill to Kester Way and the ground. If approaching from Cambridge on the A428, turn right at the first roundabout as you approach St Neots onto the Cambridge Road. At the second roundabout, turn right into Dramsell Rise and follow as above. If travelling via the A1, follow signs for the A428 Cambridge. Go straight over roundabout with Tescos on left hand side, then turn left at next roundabout. Follow final instructions above as if approaching from Cambridge.

Previous Grounds: Not known

Record Attendance: Att: 2,000 v Wisbech 1966
Record Victory: Not known
Record Defeat: Not known
Record Goalscorer: Not known
Record Appearances: Not known
Additional Records:

Senior Honours:
United Counties League 1967-68, 2010-11. Division One 1994-95.Southern League Division 1 Central 2011-12.
Huntingdonshire Senior Cup x35 2009-10 the most recent. Huntingdonshire Premier Cup 2001-02.

10 YEAR RECORD

02-03	03-04	04-05	05-06	06-07	07-08	08-09	09-10	10-11	11-12
UCL P 13	UCL P 4	UCL P 14	UCL P 4	UCL P 17	UCL P 8	UCL P 17	UCL P 2	UCL P 1	SthC 1

WEYMOUTH

Chairman: Amanda Rolls
Secretary: Nigel Biddlecombe **(T)** 07880 508 240 **(E)** biddie@weymoff.com
Additional Committee Members:
Mark Coleman, Tony McDonnell, Alan Pepperell, Ralph Ricardo, Steve Taylor,
Shuan Hennessy, Tony Greaves.
Manager: Brendan King
Programme Editor: Nigel Biddlecombe **(E)** biddie@weymoff.com

2011-12 Squad.
Back row (L-R): Carl Mutch (reserve team coach), Alex Halloran (now Portland), Joe Toghill, Mitch Conning, Scott Dixon,
Lewis Tasker, Tom Manley, Nick Jordan, Jamie Beasley, Sam Poole, T-J Lang, Rob Wolleaston, Rex Buttle (reserve team physio).
Front Row: Stephen Reed, Ollie Tribe, Emma Tonkin, Ben Gerring, Brendon King (manager), Mattie Groves (asst. manager),
Warren Byerley, Ritchy Marshallsay, Ryan McKechnie, Kyle Bassett.

Club Factfile

Founded: 1890 **Nickname:** The Terras
Previous Names: None
Previous Leagues: Dorset, Western 1907-23, 28-49, Southern 1923-28, 49-79, 89-2005,
Alliance/Conference 1979-89, 2005-10

Club Colours (change): Claret with sky blue sleeves/claret/claret (All yellow)

Ground: Bob Lucas Stadium, Radipole Lane, Weymouth DT4 9XJ **(T)** 01305 785 558
Capacity: 6,600 **Seats:** 800 **Covered:** Yes **Clubhouse:** Yes **Shop:** Yes
Directions Approach Weymouth from Dorchester on the A354.
Turn right at first roundabout onto Weymouth Way, continue to the next roundabout then turn right (signposted Football Ground).
At the next roundabout take third exit into the ground.

Previous Grounds: Recreation Ground > 1987.

Record Attendance: 4,995 v Manchester United - Ground opening 21/10/97
Record Victory: Not known
Record Defeat: Not known
Record Goalscorer: W 'Farmer' Haynes - 275
Record Appearances: Tony Hobsons - 1,076
Additional Records: Paid £15,000 to Northwich Victoria for Shaun Teale
Received £100,000 from Tottenham Hotspur for Peter Guthrie 1988
Senior Honours:
Southern League 1964-65, 65-66. Conference South 2005-06.
Dorset Senior Cup x27

10 YEAR RECORD

02-03		03-04		04-05		05-06		06-07		07-08		08-09		09-10		10-11		11-12	
SthP	17	SthP	2	Conf S	7	Conf S	1	Conf	11	Conf	18	Conf	23	Conf S	22	SthP	18	SthP	17

WEYMOUTH

No.	Date	Comp	H/A	Opponents	Att:	Result	Goalscorers	Pos
1	Aug 13	Sth P	H	Cambridge City	667	L 1 - 2	Byerley 23	
2	16		A	Bashley	335	D 3 - 3	Marshallsay 10 Byerley 14 Wolleston 30	
3	20		A	Leamington	579	L 1 - 4	Reed 20	18
4	23		H	Chippenham Town	468	W 2 - 0	Wolleston 62 Byerley 86	
5	27		H	Bedford Town	471	L 0 - 2		19
6	29		A	AFC Totton	580	L 0 - 2		
7	Sept 3		H	Evesham United	446	D 2 - 2	Byerley 34 (pen) Marshallsay 37	19
8	10		A	Chesham United	313	L 1 - 4	Stephenson 7	21
9	13		A	Cirencester Town	121	W 1 - 0	Byerley 87	
10	17	FAC 1Q	H	Taunton Town	369	D 0 - 0		
11	24		H	Barwell	421	D 1 - 1	Groves 89	16
12	Oct 1	FAC 2Q	H	Hungerford Town	404	D 3 - 3	Malsom 11 Duff 47 Groves 72	
13	4	FAC 2Qr	A	Hungerford Town	214	W 3 - 1	Byerley12 Groves 21 86	
14	8		A	Banbury Town	353	W 5 - 1	Duff 20 42 Malson 45 Byerley 81 90	15
15	15	FAC 3Q	A	AFC Totton	712	L 2 - 4	Beasley 71 Poole 73	
16	22	FAT 1Q	H	AFC Totton	512	W 3 - 2	Byerley 3 12 Malsom 7	
17	25		H	Oxford City	622	W 1 - 0	Reed 10	
18	29		H	Brackley	542	L 0 - 1		16
19	Nov 5	FAT 2Q	A	Thatcham	249	D 1 - 1	Beasley 90 (pen)	
20	8	FAT 2Qr	H	Thatcham	367	W 6 - 1	Malsom 2 18 Beesley 28 BYERLEY 3 (37 82 pen 87)	
21	11		A	Hemel Hempstead	316	W 2 - 1	Byerley 51(pen) Groves 67	15
22	15		H	Swindon Supermarine	368	D 2 - 2	Malsom 28 Byerley 46	
23	19		H	Redditch United	493	L 2 - 3	Byerley 85 (pen) Duff 90	15
24	26	FAT 3Q	H	Havant & Waterlooville	421	D 0 - 0		
25	29	FAT 3Qr	A	Havant & Waterlooville	238	W 2 - 0	Groves 53 Byerley 61	
26	Dec 3		H	Leamington	622	W 2 - 1	Byerley 90 (pen) 90	15
27	10	FAT 1	H	Chippenham Town	568	W 2 - 1	Duff 37 Byerley 53 (pen)	
28	12		A	Hitchin Town	202	L 1 - 3	Byerley 90	15
29	17		H	Bashley	421	W 2 - 1	Byerley 63 Groves 76	14
30	26		A	Frome Town	535	D 0 - 0		15
31	31		H	St Albans City	720	W 3 - 1	Reed 9 Poole 24 Coutts 68	14
32	Jan 2		H	AFC Totton	901	W 3 - 1	MALSOM 3(2 54 88)	
33	7		A	Arlesey Town	173	L 1 - 3	Duff 87	12
34	14	FAT 2	H	Alfreton Town	739	L 0 - 6		
35	22		A	Evesham United	187	L 0 - 4		15
36	28		A	Oxford City	260	L 0 - 2		
37	31		A	Stourbridge	287	W 2 - 1	Byerley 57(pen) 85	
38	Feb 15		A	Chippenham Town	305	L 0 - 3		
39	18		H	Banbury United	402	W 2 - 1	Ford 77 90	11
40	25		H	Stourbriddge	508	D 1 - 1	Tribe 28	14
41	March 3		A	Swindon Supermarine	233	D 2 - 2	Byerley 19 Paul 44	14
42	10		H	Hemel Hempsead	669	L 0 - 1		16
43	13		H	Cirencester Town	451	W 3 - 1	FORD 3 (16 48 84)	
44	17		A	Brackley Town	257	L 1 - 3	Byerley 85	13
45	24		A	Bedford Town	348	L 1 - 2	Napper 34	15
46	27		A	Barwell	127	L 0 - 1		
47	31		H	Arlesey Town	481	L 0 - 2		
48	Apr 2		H	Chesham United	455	D 2 - 2	Tribe 2 Lambert 84 (og)	
49	7		A	St Albans City	539	D 2 - 2	Ford 81 Duff 88	18
50	9		H	Frome Town	721	L 0 - 3		
51	14		A	Cambridge City	395	L 0 - 3		16
52	21		H	Hitchin Town	674	W 2 - 1	Duff 69 (pen) Ford 72	17
53	28		A	Redditch United	371	L 0 - 2		

AFC HAYES

Chairman: Barry Stone
Secretary: Barry Crump (T) (E) afchayesfootballsec@hotmail.co.uk
Additional Committee Members:
Roger Galloway, Mrs Cinta Green, Keith Gavin, Dave Swan.

Manager: Ian Crane
Programme Editor: Dave Swan (E) daveswan03@hotmail.com

2011-12 Squad.

Club Factfile

Founded: 1974 **Nickname:** The Brook
Previous Names: Brook House > 2008.
Previous Leagues: Spartan South Midlands, Isthmian

Club Colours (change): Blue and white stripes/blue/blue (Red/white/red)

Ground: Farm Park, Kingshill Avenue, Hayes UB4 8DD (T) 020 8845 0110
Capacity: 2,000 **Seats:** 150 **Covered:** 200 **Clubhouse:** Yes **Shop:** No
Directions: From the A40 McDonalds Target roundabout take A312 south towards Hayes.
At White Hart roundabout take third exit into Yeading Lane.
Turn right at first traffic lights into Kingshill Avenue.
Ground approx one miles on the right-hand side.

Previous Grounds:

Record Attendance: Not known
Record Victory: Not known
Record Defeat: Not known
Record Goalscorer: Not known
Record Appearances: Not known
Additional Records:

Senior Honours:
Spartan South Midlands Premier South 1997-98, Premier Cup 1999-2000, Challenge Trophy 2003-04.
Isthmian Associate Members Trophy 2005-06.
Middlesex Senior Cup 2008-09.

10 YEAR RECORD

02-03		03-04		04-05		05-06		06-07		07-08		08-09		09-10		10-11		11-12	
Isth P	7	Isth P	8	Conf S	12	Conf S	20	Conf S	20	Sthsw	14	Sthsw	9	Sthsw	21	SthC	19	SthC	10

ASHFORD TOWN (MIDDLESEX)

Chairman: Dave Baker
Secretary: Geoff Knock **(T)** 07928 101 876 **(E)** football.secretary@atmfc.co.uk
Additional Committee Members:
Alan Constable, Gareth Coates,

Manager: Paul Burgess
Programme Editor: Phil Marshall **(E)** club.manager@atmfc.co.uk

Club Factfile

Founded: 1964 **Nickname:** Ash Trees
Previous Names:
Previous Leagues: Hounslow & District 1964-68, Surrey Intermediate 1968-82, Surrey Premier 1982-90,
Combined Counties 1990-2000, Isthmian 2000-04, 06-10, Southern 2004-06

Club Colours (change): Tangerine and white stripes/black/tangerine (Blue/white/blue)

Ground: Robert Parker Stadium, Stanwell, Staines TW19 7BH **(T)** 01784 245 908
Capacity: 2,550 **Seats:** 250 **Covered:** 250 **Clubhouse:** Yes **Shop:** No

Directions: M25 junction 13, A30 towards London,
third left at footbridge after Ashford Hospital crossroads,
ground sign posted after 1/4 mile on the right down Short Lane,
two miles from Ashford (BR) and Hatton Cross tube station.

Previous Grounds: Clockhouse Lane Rec

Record Attendance: 992 v AFC Wimbledon - Isthmian League Premier Division 26/09/2006
Record Victory: Not known
Record Defeat: Not known
Record Goalscorer: Andy Smith
Record Appearances: Alan Constable - 650
Additional Records: Received £10,000 from Wycombe Wanderers for Dannie Bulman 1997

Senior Honours:
Surrey Premier League 1982-90. Combined Counties League 1994-95, 95-96, 96-97, 97-98.
Middlesex Charity Cup 2000-01. Middlesex Premier Cup 2006-07. Isthmian League Cup 2006-07.

10 YEAR RECORD

02-03	03-04	04-05	05-06	06-07	07-08	08-09	09-10	10-11	11-12
Isth1S 17	Isth1S 12	SthW 6	SthW 2	Isth P 17	Isth P 6	Isth P 10	Isth P 20	SthC 16	SthC 9

AYLESBURY

Chairman: Danny Martone
Secretary: Ian Brown   **(T)** 07947 338 462   **(E)** brownzola@aol.com
Additional Committee Members:
Steve Macdonald, Russell Whiting, Maria Butler, Warren Sheward

Manager: Craig Faulconbridge
Programme Editor: Russell Williams   **(E)** cmartone040@btinternet.com

Club Factfile

Founded: 1897   **Nickname:** The Moles
Previous Names: Haywood United > 2004, Haywood FC 2004-05, Aylesbury Vale 2005-09
Previous Leagues: Spartan South Midlands

Club Colours (change): Red with black trim/black/black (Yellow with blue trim/yellow/yellow)

Ground: Haywood Way, Aylesbury, Bucks. HP19 9WZ   **(T)** 01296 421 101
Capacity: **Seats:** Yes   **Covered:** Yes   **Clubhouse:** Yes   **Shop:** No

Directions
When entering Aylesbury from all major routes, join the ring road and follow signposts for A41 Bicester and Waddesdon. leave the ring road at the roundabout by the Texaco Garage and Perry dealership. From the Texaco Garage cross straight over four roundabouts. At the fifth roundabout with the Cotton Wheel Pub on the right hand side, turn right into Jackson Road. Take the second left into Haywood Way, club is at the bottom of the road. If entering Aylesbury from Bicester (A41), turn left into Jackson Road by the Cotton Wheel Pub, and then second left into Haywood Way.

Previous Grounds:

Record Attendance: Not known
Record Victory: Not known
Record Defeat: Not known
Record Goalscorer: Not known
Record Appearances: Not known
Additional Records: Not known

Senior Honours:
Spartan South Midlands League Division 1 2003-04, Premier Division 2009-10.

10 YEAR RECORD									
02-03	03-04	04-05	05-06	06-07	07-08	08-09	09-10	10-11	11-12
SSM1 9	SSM1 1	SSM P 3	SSM P 5	SSM P 5	SSM P 9	SSM P 15	SSM P 1	SthC 8	SthC 20

BARTON ROVERS

Chairman: Chris Larkin
Secretary: Vacant   **(T)**   **(E)**
Additional Committee Members:
Darren Whiley, Derek Tripney

Manager: Dan Kennoy
Programme Editor: W Fleckney & D Thornton   **(E)**

THE NON-LEAGUE CLUB DIRECTORY

Book Holiday Inn Hotels and Save today!

Home

Clubs

Steps 1 - 4

League Tables

35 Years of Non-League Football

The Non-League Club Directory has
developed into a comprehensive record
of competitions within the non-League
game, giving this level of football the

www.non-leagueclubdirectory.co.uk

Club Factfile

Founded: 1898   **Nickname:** Rovers

Previous Names: Not known

Previous Leagues: Luton & district 1947-54, South Midlands 1954-79, Isthmian 1979-2004

Club Colours (change): Royal blue with white trim/royal blue/royal blue with white bands (Yellow with black trim/black/yellow with white band)

Ground: Sharpenhoe Road, Barton-le-Clay, Bedford MK45 4SD   **(T)** 01582 707 772

Capacity: 4,000   **Seats:** 160   **Covered:** 1,120   **Clubhouse:** Yes   **Shop:** Yes

Directions
Leave M1 at J12 head towards Harlington.
Follow signs through Sharpenhoe Village to Barton.
At T-junction in village turn right, continue 500 yards and turn right into ground on concrete roadway adjacent to playing fields.

Previous Grounds:

Record Attendance: 1,900 v Nuneaton Borough - FA Cup 4th Qualifying Round 1976

Record Victory: Not known
Record Defeat: Not known

Record Goalscorer: Richard Camp - 152 (1989-98)

Record Appearances: Tony McNally - 598 (1988-2005)

Additional Records: Paid £1,000 to Hitchin Town for B. Baldry 1980
Received £1,000 from Bishop's Stortford for B. Baldry 1981

Senior Honours:

South Midlands League x8. Bedfordshire Senior Cup x7. Bedfordshire Premier Cup 1995-96.

02-03	03-04	04-05	05-06	06-07	07-08	08-09	09-10	10-11	11-12
Isth1N 19	Isth1N 18	SthE 8	SthE 19	SthM 20	SthM 11	SthM 17	SthM 21	SthC 12	SthC 11

BEACONSFIELD SYCOB

Chairman: Fred Deanus (Chief Exec.)
Secretary: Robin Woolman   **(T)**   **(E)** robin.woolman@btinternet.com
Additional Committee Members:
Paul Hughes, Paul Witney, Tony Blay

Manager: Byron Walton
Programme Editor: **(E)**

2011-12 Squad.

Club Factfile

Founded: 1994   **Nickname:** The Rams
Previous Names: Slough YCOB and Beaconsfield United merged in 1994
Previous Leagues: Spartan South Midlands 1004-2004, 07-08, Southern 2004-07

Club Colours (change): Red and white quarters/black/red and white (Yellow with blue trim/blue with yellow trim/blue)

Ground: Holloways Park, Windsor Road, Beaconsfield, Bucks HP9 2SE   **(T)** 01494 676 868
Capacity: **Seats:**   **Covered:**   **Clubhouse:** Yes   **Shop:**
Directions: Leave Junction 2 of M40, take A355 towards Slough, 50 yards off roundabout turn left and at next roundabout turn complete right, coming back towards A355 to continue across A355, then turn right and 150 yards on left is sign to club. Go through gate and clubhouse is 200 yards on right.

Previous Grounds:

Record Attendance: Not known
Record Victory: Not known
Record Defeat: Not known
Record Goalscorer: Allan Arthur
Record Appearances: Allan Arthur
Additional Records:

Senior Honours:
Spartan South Midlands 2000-01, 03-04, 07-08. Berks and Bucks Senior Trophy 2003-04

10 YEAR RECORD

02-03		03-04		04-05		05-06		06-07		07-08		08-09		09-10		10-11		11-12	
SSM P	2	SSM P	1	SthE	14	SthW	13	Sthsw	22	SSM P	1	Sthsw	4	SthM	19	SthC	22	SthC	5

BIGGLESWADE TOWN

Chairman: Maurice Dorrington
Secretary: Andy McDonnell   **(T)** 07879 802 105   **(E)** andy.mcdonnell@ntlworld.com
Additional Committee Members:
Brian Doggett, Mike Draxler, Mick Jarvis.

Manager: Chris Nunn
Programme Editor: David Simpson   **(E)** simpson_david@hotmail.co.uk

Club Factfile

Founded: 1874   **Nickname:** The Waders
Previous Names:
Previous Leagues: Biggleswade & District, Bedford & District, Spartan South Midlands 1951-55, 80-2009, Eastern Counties 1955-63, United Counties 1963-80

Club Colours (change): Green and white stripes/green/green (Sky blue and white stripes/black/sky blue)

Ground: The Carlsberg Stadium, Langford Road, Biggleswade SG18 9JJ   **(T)**
Capacity: **Seats:**   **Covered:**   **Clubhouse:** Yes   **Shop:**

Directions: From the south – up the A1, past the first roundabout (Homebase) signposted Biggleswade. At next roundabout (Sainsburys) turn right onto A6001. As you approach the Town Centre, go straight over the mini roundabout following signs for Langford (Teal Road). At traffic lights, turn right (still heading towards Langford). Continue along Hitchin Street over two mini roundabouts and as you pass under the A1, the ground entrance is 200 yards on the right. From the north – exit A1 at the Sainsburys roundabout and follow instructions as above.

Previous Grounds: Fairfield

Record Attendance: 2,000
Record Victory: Not known
Record Defeat: Not known
Record Goalscorer: Not known
Record Appearances: Not known
Additional Records:

Senior Honours:
Spartan South Midlands Premier Division 2008-09. Bedfordshire Premier Cup 2009.

10 YEAR RECORD

02-03	03-04	04-05	05-06	06-07	07-08	08-09	09-10	10-11	11-12
SSM P 11	SSM P 15	SSM P 10	SSM P 15	SSM P 18	SSM P 3	SSM P 1	SthM 12	SthC 4	SthC 8

BURNHAM

Chairman: Bob Breen
Secretary: Alan King   **(T)**   **(E)** burnhamfcsec@aol.com
Additional Committee Members:
Michael Boxall, Rod Saunders

Manager: Martin Stone
Programme Editor: Gareth Stoneman   **(E)**

THE NON-LEAGUE
CLUB DIRECTORY

Book Holiday Inn Hotels and Save today!

| Home |
| Clubs |
| Steps 1 - 4 |
| League Tables |

35 Years of Non-League Football

The Non-League Club Directory has
developed into a comprehensive record
of competitions within the non-League
game, giving this level of football the

www.non-leagueclubdirectory.co.uk

Club Factfile

Founded: 1878   **Nickname:** The Blues

Previous Names: Burnham & Hillingdon 1985-87
Previous Leagues: Hellenic 1971-77, 95-99, Athenian 1977-84, London Spartan 1984-85, Southern 1985-95

Club Colours (change): Blue and white quarters/blue/blue (Red and black quarters/black/red)

Ground: The Gore, Wymers Wood Road, Burnham, Slough SL1 8JG   **(T)** 01628 668 654

Capacity: 2,500   **Seats:**   **Covered:**   **Clubhouse:** Yes   **Shop:** Yes

Directions: Approx. 2 miles from M4 junction 7 and 5 miles from M40 junction 2. From M40 take A355 to A4 signposted Maidenhead. From M4 take A4 towards Maidenhead until you reach roundabout with Sainsbury Superstore on left. Turn right into Lent Rise Road and travel approx 11/2 miles over 2 double roundabouts. 100 yards after second double roundabout fork right into Wymers Wood Road. Ground entrance on right.

Previous Grounds: Baldwin Meadow until 1920s

Record Attendance: 2,380 v Halesowen Town - FA Vase 02/04/1983

Record Victory: 18-0 v High Duty Alloys - 1970-71
Record Defeat: 1-10 v Ernest Turner Sports - 1963-64

Record Goalscorer: Fraser Hughes - 65 (1969-70)

Record Appearances: Not known
Additional Records:

Senior Honours:
Hellenic League 1975-76, 98-99, League Cup 1975-76, 98-99, Division 1 Cup 1971-72.

02-03	03-04	04-05	05-06	06-07	07-08	08-09	09-10	10-11	11-12
SthE 13	SthE 17	SthW 9	SthW 4	Sthsw 3	Sthsw 10	Sthsw 17	SthM 3	SthC 14	SthC 15

CHALFONT ST PETER

Chairman: Dennis Mair
Secretary: John Carroll   **(T)** 07950 981 008   **(E)** jc.chalfontfc@fsmail.net
Additional Committee Members:
Charlotte Mair

Manager: Danny Edwards
Programme Editor: Ian Doorbar   **(E)** doors8jz@hotmail.com

Club Factfile

Founded: 1926   **Nickname:** Saints
Previous Names: Not known
Previous Leagues: G W Comb. Parthernon. London. Spartan. L Spartan. Athenian. Isthmian, Spartan South Midlands 2006-11.

Club Colours (change): Red/green/red. (Yellow/blue/blue).

Ground: Mill Meadow, Gravel Hill, Amersham Road, Chalfont St Peter SL9 9QX   **(T)** 01753 885 797
Capacity: 4,500   **Seats:** 220   **Covered:** 120   **Clubhouse:** Yes   **Shop:** Yes

Directions
Follow A413 (Amersham Road).
The ground is adjacent to the Chalfont Community Centre off Gravel Hill which is part of the A413.
Players and officials can park inside the ground.
The A413 is the Denham to Aylesbury road.

Previous Grounds:

Record Attendance: Att: 2,550 v Watford benefit match 1985   **App:** Colin Davies
Record Victory: Not known
Record Defeat: Not known
Record Goalscorer: Not known
Record Appearances: Not known
Additional Records:

Senior Honours:
Isthmian Lge Div 2 87-88, Berks & Bucks Intermediate Cup 52-53.
Spartan South Midlands Premier Division 2010-11.

10 YEAR RECORD

02-03		03-04		04-05		05-06		06-07		07-08		08-09		09-10		10-11		11-12	
Isth2	15	Isth2	14	Isth2	11	Isth2	8	SSM P	6	SSM P	2	SSM P	3	SSM P	2	SSM P	1	SthC	12

CHERTSEY TOWN

Chairman: Steve Powers
Secretary: Chris Gay   **(T)** 07713 473 313   **(E)** chrisegay@googlemail.com
Additional Committee Members:
Sue Powers, Wendy Blaby.

Manager: David Johnston
Programme Editor: Chris Gay   **(E)** chrisegay@googlemail.com

2011-12 Team - Photo: Alan Coomes.

Club Factfile

Founded: 1890   **Nickname:** Curfews
Previous Names: None
Previous Leagues: Metropolitan. Spartan. Athenian. Isthmian, Combined Counties 2006-11.

Club Colours (change): White with blue trim/white/white (All navy)

Ground: Alwyns Lane, Chertsey, Surrey KT16 9DW   **(T)** 01932 561 774
Capacity: 3,000   **Seats:** 240   **Covered:** 760   **Clubhouse:** Yes   **Shop:** Yes

Directions: Leave M25 at junction 11, East on St. Peters Way (A317). Left at roundabout in Chertsey Road (A317). Left into Eastworth Road (A317). Straight on into Chilsey Green Road (A320), 3rd exit on roundabout (towards Staines) (A320). 1st right after car showrooms into St. Ann's Road (B375). Right at Coach & Horses in Grove Road (residential). Alwyns Lane is very narrow and not suitable for large motor coaches.

Previous Grounds:

Record Attendance: Att: 2150 v Aldershot Town, Isthmian Div.2 04/12/93. **Goals:** Alan Brown (54) 1962-63.
Record Victory: Not known
Record Defeat: Not known
Record Goalscorer: Not known
Record Appearances: Not known
Additional Records:
Senior Honours:
Surrey Senior Champions 1959, 61, 62. Isthmian League Cup 1994.

10 YEAR RECORD

02-03		03-04		04-05		05-06		06-07		07-08		08-09		09-10		10-11		11-12	
Isth1S	24	Isth2	4	Isth2	6	Isth2	6	CCP	8	CCP	8	CCP	3	CCP	2	CCP	2	SthC	17

DAVENTRY TOWN

Chairman: Iain Humphrey
Secretary: Matt Hogsden **(T)** 07854 468 925 **(E)** dtfcsec@hotmail.co.uk
Additional Committee Members:
Mike Tebbitt, Harvey Potter, Sally Simpkin

Manager: Mark Kinsella
Programme Editor: Harvey Potter **(E)** h.potter@shebanguk.net

Photo: Keith Clayton.

Club Factfile

Founded: 1886 **Nickname:** The Town
Previous Names: Not known
Previous Leagues: Northampton Town (pre-1987), Central Northways Comb 1987-89, United Counties 1989-2010.

Club Colours (change): Purple/white/white (Yellow/white/white)

Ground: Communications Park, Browns Road, Daventry, Northants NN11 4NS **(T)** 01327 311 239
Capacity: 2,000 **Seats:** 250 **Covered:** 250 **Clubhouse:** Yes **Shop:**
Directions: From Northampton or J.16 of the M1, follow A45 westbound into Daventry, crossing the A5 on the way.
At first roundabout bear left along A45 Daventry Bypass.
At next roundabout go straight over onto Browns Road.
The Club is at the top of this road on the left.

Previous Grounds:

Record Attendance: 850 v Utrecht (Holland) - 1989
Record Victory: Not known
Record Defeat: Not known
Record Goalscorer: Not known
Record Appearances: Not known
Additional Records:

Senior Honours:
United Counties League Division 1 1989-90, 90-91, 2000-01, 2007-08, Premier Division 2009-10.

10 YEAR RECORD

02-03	03-04	04-05	05-06	06-07	07-08		08-09		09-10		10-11		11-12	
UCL P	UCL P	UCL P	UCL P	UCL P	UCL 1	1	UCL P	7	UCL P	1	SthC	2	SthC	16

FLEET TOWN

Chairman: Steve Cantle
Secretary: Richard Whittington **(T)**   **(E)**
Additional Committee Members:
Steve Cantle, John Goodyear.

Manager: Craig Davis
Programme Editor: Matt Thorne   **(E)** thornematthew@hotmail.com

Club Factfile

Founded: 1890   **Nickname:** The Blues
Previous Names: Fleet FC 1890-1963
Previous Leagues: Hampshire 1961-77, Athenian, Combined Counties, Chiltonian, Wessex 1989-95, 2000-02, Southern 1995-2000, 02-04, 07-08, Isthmian 2004-07, 2008-11.

Club Colours (change): All blue (Yellow & black/black/yellow & black)

Ground: Calthorpe Park, Crookham Road, Fleet, Hants GU51 5FA   **(T)** 01252 623 804
Capacity: 2,000   **Seats:** 250   **Covered:** 250   **Clubhouse:** Yes   **Shop:** Yes
Directions: Leave the M3 at junction 4A. Follow signs to Fleet via A3013.
At 5th roundabout (a T-junction) turn left over railway bridge.
Carry on past Oatsheaf Pub on the right, ground is a further 1/4 mile on the right.

Previous Grounds: Watsons Meadow > 1923.

Record Attendance: 1,336 v AFC Wimbledon, Isthmian League 08/01/2005
Record Victory: 15-0 v Petersfield , Wessex League 26/12/1994
Record Defeat: 0-7 v Bashley, Southern League 12/04/2004
Record Goalscorer: Mark Frampton - 428
Record Appearances: Mark Frampton - 250
Additional Records: Paid £3,000 to Aldershot for Mark Russell

Senior Honours:
Wessex League 1994-95.

10 YEAR RECORD

02-03	03-04	04-05	05-06	06-07	07-08	08-09	09-10	10-11	11-12
SthE 20	SthE 22	Isth1 19	Isth1 14	Isth1S 5	Sthsw 2	Isth1S 3	Isth1S 6	Isth1S 13	SthC 21

GODALMING TOWN

Chairman: Kevin Young
Secretary: Glenn Moulton   **(T)**   **(E)** secretary@godalmingtownfc.co.uk
Additional Committee Members:
Ian Curtis, Chris Terry, Glenn Moulton

Manager: Neil Baker & Jon Underwood
Programme Editor: Nick Mitchell   **(E)** njm91@hotmail.co.uk

THE NON-LEAGUE CLUB DIRECTORY

Book Holiday Inn Hotels and Save today!

Home
Clubs
Steps 1 - 4
League Tables

35 Years of Non-League Football

The Non-League Club Directory has developed into a comprehensive record of competitions within the non-League game, giving this level of football the

www.non-leagueclubdirectory.co.uk

Club Factfile

Founded: 1950   **Nickname:** The G's

Previous Names: Godalming & Farncombe United, Godalming & Guildford
Previous Leagues: Combined Counties, Southern 2006-08

Club Colours (change): Yellow/green/yellow

Ground: Wey Court, Mead Row, Guildford, Surrey GU7 3JE   **(T)** 01483 417 520

Capacity: 3,000   **Seats:** 200   **Covered:** 400   **Clubhouse:** Yes   **Shop:** Yes

Directions: A3100 from Guildford, pass the Manor Inn on the left and then the petrol station on the right. Wey Court is 50 yards further along the road on the right hand side.
A3100 from Godalming, pass the Three Lions pub on the left and then turn left into Wey Court immediately after the Leathern Bottle pub.
Parking: Please note that the club car park is for players and officials only. Spectators are asked to use the public car park next door to the ground.

Previous Grounds:

Record Attendance: 1,305 v AFC Wimbledon - 2002

Record Victory: Not Known
Record Defeat: Not Known

Record Goalscorer: Not Known

Record Appearances: Not Known
Additional Records:

Senior Honours:
Combined Counties League Premier Division 1983-84, 2005-06.

02-03		03-04		04-05		05-06		06-07		07-08		08-09		09-10		10-11		11-12	
CC	7	CCP	11	CCP	4	CCP	1	Isth1S	22	Sthsw	12	Isth1S	9	Isth1S	4	Isth1S	17	Isth1S	5

GUILDFORD CITY

Chairman: Chris Pegman
Secretary: Matt Howell **(T)** 07912 689 953 **(E)** barry.underwood@guildfordcityfc.co.uk
Additional Committee Members:

Manager: Kevin Rayner
Programme Editor: Jack Underwood **(E)** jack.underwood@guildfordcityfc.co.uk

Guildford City's Austen Gachera shapes up to control the ball on his chest during his side's league match against Badshot Lea. Photo: Eric Marsh.

Club Factfile

Founded: 1996 **Nickname:** The City
Previous Names: AFC Guildford 1996-2005. Guildford United 05-06.
Previous Leagues: Surrey Senior.

Club Colours (change): Red & white stripes/black/black

Ground: Spectrum Leisure Centre, Parkway, Guildford GU1 1UP **(T)** 01483 443 322
Capacity: 1100 **Seats:** 269 **Covered:** Yes **Clubhouse:** Yes **Shop:** Yes
Directions From Guildford main line station, take no.100 shuttle bus to Spectrum. From London Road Station walk via Stoke Park. From A3, exit at Guildford – follow signs to leisure centre.

Previous Grounds:

Record Attendance: Att: 211 v Godalming & Guildford, 2004
Record Victory:
Record Defeat:
Record Goalscorer:
Record Appearances:
Additional Records: Combined Counties Division 1 Champions 2003-04, Premier Division 2010-11.

Senior Honours:
Combined Counties Division One 2003-04, Premier Division 2010-11, 11-12

10 YEAR RECORD									
02-03	03-04	04-05	05-06	06-07	07-08	08-09	09-10	10-11	11-12
SuCS 9	CC1 1	CCP 12	CCP 17	CCP 21	CCP 2	CCP 20	CCP 7	CCP 1	CCP 1

LEIGHTON TOWN

Chairman: Richard Graham
Secretary: Ken Slater   **(T)** 07854 900 168   **(E)** secretary@leightontownfc.co.uk
Additional Committee Members:
Roy Parker, Vicky Janes,

Manager: Craig Wells
Programme Editor: Andrew Parker   **(E)** andrewparker-leightontownfc@virginmedia.com

Leighton Town's Ben Gallent takes the ball around the defender
to give himself space to shoot - a shot that resulted in a goal.

Club Factfile

Founded: 1885   **Nickname:** Reds
Previous Names: Leighton United 1922-63
Previous Leagues: Leighton & District, South Midlands 1922-24, 26-29, 46-54, 55-56, 76-92, Spartan 1922-53, 67-74,
United Counties 1974-76, Isthmian

Club Colours (change): Red and white stripes/red/red (Yellow/black/yellow)

Ground: Lake Street, Leighton Buzzard, Beds LU7 1RX   **(T)** 01525 373 311
Capacity: 2,800   **Seats:** 155   **Covered:** 300   **Clubhouse:** Yes   **Shop:** No
Directions: Ground is situated just south of Town Centre on the A4146 Leighton Buzzard to Hemel Hemstead Road.
Entrance to car park and ground is opposite Morrisons Supermarket Petrol Station.
1/2 mile south of town centre.

Previous Grounds: Wayside

Record Attendance: 1,522 v Aldershot Town - Isthmian League Division 3 30/01/1993
Record Victory: v Met Railway (H) - Spartan League 1925-26
Record Defeat: 0-12 v Headington United (A) - Spartan League 18/10/1947
Record Goalscorer: Not known
Record Appearances: Not known
Additional Records:

Senior Honours:
South Midlands League 1966-67, 91-92. Isthmian League Division 2 2003-04.
Bedfordshire Senior Cup 1926-27, 67-68, 69-70, 92-93.

10 YEAR RECORD

02-03		03-04		04-05		05-06		06-07		07-08		08-09		09-10		10-11		11-12	
Isth2	6	Isth2	1	SthE	10	SthW	8	SthM	18	SthM	9	SthM	8	SthM	10	SthC	7	SthC	13

NORTH GREENFORD UNITED

Chairman: John Bivens
Secretary: Mrs Barbara Bivens   **(T)** 07915 661 580   **(E)** barbarabivens@talktalk.net
Additional Committee Members:
John Chorley, Tony Tuohy, Lorraine Chorley, Pat Hillier.

Manager: Jon-Barrie Bates
Programme Editor: Pat Hillier   **(E)** agneshillier@aol.com

THE NON-LEAGUE CLUB DIRECTORY

Book Holiday Inn Hotels and Save today!

Home
Clubs
Steps 1 - 4
League Tables

35 Years of Non-League Football

The Non-League Club Directory has developed into a comprehensive record of competitions within the non-League game, giving this level of football the

www.non-leagueclubdirectory.co.uk

Club Factfile

Founded: 1944   **Nickname:** Blues

Previous Names: None
Previous Leagues: London Spartan, Combined Counties 2002-10

Club Colours (change): Royal blue & white/royal blue & white/royal blue (Yellow with red trim/yellow & red/yellow)

Ground: Berkeley Fields, Berkley Avenue, Greenford UB6 0NX   **(T)** 0208 422 8923

Capacity: 2,000   **Seats:** 150   **Covered:** 100   **Clubhouse:** Yes   **Shop:** No

Directions: A40 going towards London. At the Greenford Flyover come down the slip road, keep in the left hand lane, turn left onto the Greenford Road (A4127). At the third set of traffic lights, turn right into Berkeley Av. Go to the bottom of the road. There is a large car park. We are on the right hand side.

Previous Grounds:

Record Attendance: 985 v AFC Wimbledon

Record Victory: Not known
Record Defeat: Not known

Record Goalscorer: John Hill - 98

Record Appearances: Not known

Additional Records:

Senior Honours:
Combined Counties League Premier Division 2009-10

02-03		03-04		04-05		05-06		06-07		07-08		08-09		09-10		10-11		11-12	
CC	10	CCP	14	CCP	2	CCP	13	CCP	5	CCP	6	CCP	2	CCP	1	SthC	20	SthC	18

NORTHWOOD

Chairman: Ian Barry
Secretary: Alan Evans   **(T)** 07960 744 349   **(E)** alan.evansnfc@btopenworld.com
Additional Committee Members:
Ken Green, Pete Barry, Allan Green, Shamira Hamirani, Tino Nannavecchia

Manager: Gary Meakin
Programme Editor: Ken Green   **(E)** ken.green01@ntlworld.com

www.non-leagueclubdirectory.co.uk

Club Factfile

Founded: 1899   **Nickname:** Woods

Previous Names: Northwood Town

Previous Leagues: Harrow & Wembley 1932-69, Middlesex 1969-78, Hellenic 1979-84, London Spartan 1984-93, Isthmian 1993-2005, 2007-10, Southern 2005-07

Club Colours (change): All red (All yellow)

Ground: Northwood Park, Chestnut Avenue, Northwood, Middlesex HA6 1HR   **(T)** 01923 827 148

Capacity: 3,075   **Seats:** 308   **Covered:** 932   **Clubhouse:** Yes   **Shop:** No

Directions: M25 Junction 18, take A404 through Rickmansworth to Northwood. After passing under grey railway bridge, take first right into Chestnut Avenue. Ground is in grounds of Northwood Park, entrance is 400 metres on left. (Ground is 20 minutes from J.18).

Previous Grounds:

Record Attendance: 1,642 v Chlesea - Friendly July 1997

Record Victory: 15-0 v Dateline (H) - Middlesex Intermediate Cup 1973
Record Defeat: 0-8 v Bedfont - Middlesex League 1975

Record Goalscorer: Not known

Record Appearances: Chris Gell - 493+

Additional Records: Lawrence Yaku scored 61 goals during season 1999-2000

Senior Honours:
Isthmian League Division 1 North 2002-03, Charity Shield 2002.
Middlesex Premier Cup 1994-95.

02-03		03-04		04-05		05-06		06-07		07-08		08-09		09-10		10-11		11-12	
Isth1N	1	Isth P	21	Isth P	17	SthP	19	SthP	22	Isth1N	10	Isth1N	6	Isth1N	10	SthC	20	SthC	7

ROYSTON TOWN

Chairman: Steve Jackson
Secretary: Terry McKinnell **(T)** 07772 086 709 **(E)** terry.mckinnell@talktalk.net
Additional Committee Members:
David Baulk, Steve Endacott

Manager: Paul Attfield
Programme Editor: Kelly Taylor **(E)**

THE NON-LEAGUE CLUB DIRECTORY

Book Holiday Inn Hotels and Save today!

Home

Clubs

Steps 1 - 4

League Tables

35 Years of Non-League Football

The Non-League Club Directory has developed into a comprehensive record of competitions within the non-League game, giving this level of football the

www.non-leagueclubdirectory.co.uk

Club Factfile

Founded: 1872 **Nickname:** Crows

Previous Names: None
Previous Leagues: Cambridgeshire & Herts Co. Isthmian

Club Colours (change): White/black/black (Red/white/red).

Ground: Garden Walk, Royston, Herts, SG8 7HP **(T)** 01763 241 204

Capacity: **Seats:** Yes **Covered:** Yes **Clubhouse:** Yes **Shop:**

Directions: From A505 (Town Bypass) take A10 towards town centre (signposted London).
Go straight on at next roundabout.
Garden Walk is on the left after the 3rd set of pedestrian lights (opposite Catholic Church).
Entrance to ground is approx 75 metres on left.

Previous Grounds:

Record Attendance: Att: 876 v Aldershot Town, 1993-94.

Record Victory:
Record Defeat:
Record Goalscorer:
Record Appearances:
Additional Records:

Senior Honours:
Herts County Champions 1976-77. South Midlands Div.1 1978-79, 2008-09, Premier Division 2011-12.

02-03	03-04	04-05	05-06	06-07	07-08	08-09	09-10	10-11	11-12
SSM P 16	SSM P 13	SSM P 16	SSM P 18	SSM P 20	SSM1 5	SSM1 1	SSM P 4	SSM P 3	SSM P 1

RUGBY TOWN

Chairman: Brian Melvin
Secretary: Doug Wilkins   **(T)** 07976 284 614   **(E)** dougwilkins44@hotmail.com
Additional Committee Members:
Mike Yeats, Les Leeson, Danny Lorden, Lisa Melvin, Darren Knapp, Jim Melvin.

Manager: Martin Sockett
Programme Editor: Neil Melvin   **(E)** neilmelvin@melbros.com

2011-12 Squad.

Club Factfile

Founded: 1956   **Nickname:** The Valley
Previous Names: Valley Sports 1956-71, Valley Sport Rugby 1971-73, VS Rugby 1973-2000, Rugby United 2000-05
Previous Leagues: Rugby & District 1956-62, Coventry & Partnership, North Warwickshire 1963-69, United Counties 1969-75
      West Midlands 1975-83

Club Colours (change): Sky blue/white/sky blue (All orange)

Ground: Butlin Road, Rugby, Warwicks CV21 3SD   **(T)** 01788 844 806
Capacity: 6,000   **Seats:** 750   **Covered:** 1,000   **Clubhouse:** Yes   **Shop:** Yes

Directions: From M6 J.1 North and South, take A426 signed Rugby at third island turn left into Boughton Road.
Continue along Boughton Road after passing under viaduct turn right at traffic lights, B5414 up the hill take second left at mini island
into Butlin Road.

Previous Grounds:

Record Attendance: 3,961 v Northampton Town - FA Cup 1984
Record Victory: 10-0 v Ilkeston Town - FA Trophy 04/09/1985
Record Defeat: 1-11 v Ilkeston Town (A) - 18/04/1998
Record Goalscorer: Danny Conway - 124
Record Appearances: Danny Conway - 374
Additional Records: Paid £3,500 for R Smith, I Crawley and G Bradder
Senior Honours: Received £15,000 from Northampton Town for Terry Angus
FA Vase 1982-83. Southern League Midland Division 1986-87. Midland Combination Division 1 2001-02.
Birmingham Senior Cup 1988-89, 91-92

10 YEAR RECORD

02-03		03-04		04-05	05-06		06-07		07-08		08-09		09-10		10-11		11-12	
MCmP	6	MCmP	3		SthP	15	SthP	17	SthP	15	SthP	17	SthP	22	SthC	6	SthC	6

SLOUGH TOWN

Chairman: Steve Easterbrook
Secretary: Kath Lathey   **(T)** 07792 126 124   **(E)** gensec@sloughtownfc.net
Additional Committee Members:
Roy Merryweather, Glen Riley, Alan Harding,
Mike Lightfoot, Gary Thomas, Chris Sliski, Kevin Merryweather
Manager: Steve Bateman
Programme Editor: Glen Riley   **(E)** programme@sloughtownfc.net

THE NON-LEAGUE CLUB DIRECTORY

Book Holiday Inn Hotels and Save today!

Home

Clubs

Steps 1 - 4

League Tables

35 Years of Non-League Football

The Non-League Club Directory has
developed into a comprehensive record
of competitions within the non-League
game, giving this level of football the

www.non-leagueclubdirectory.co.uk

Club Factfile

Founded: 1890   **Nickname:** The Rebels

Previous Names: Not known

Previous Leagues: Southern Alliance 1892-93, Berks & Bucks 1901-05, Gt Western Suburban 1909-19, Spartan 1920-39, Herts & Middx 1940-45, Corinthian 1946-63, Athenian 1963-73, Isthmian 1973-90, 94-95, Conf. 1990-94

Club Colours (change): Amber/navy blue/amber (Red and navy shirts/black/red)

Ground: Sharing with Beaconsfield SYCOB, Holloways Park, Slough Rd HP9 2SG   **(T)** 01494 676 868

Capacity: 3,500   **Seats:** 200   **Covered:** Yes   **Clubhouse:** Yes   **Shop:** Yes

Directions: Leave M40 at Junction 2, take A355 towards Slough, only 50 yards off the roundabout on the A355 is slip road on right with sign giving Club name. Turn right through gate and clubhouse is 200 metres on the right. The ground is 'signposted' from both sides of the carriageway (A355).

Previous Grounds:

Record Attendance: 8,000 v Liverpool - Schoolboys 1976

Record Victory: 17-0 v Railway Clearing House - 1921-22

Record Defeat: 1-11 v Chesham Town - 1909-10

Record Goalscorer: Tony Norris - 84 (1925-26)

Record Appearances: Terry Reardon - 458 (1964-81)

Additional Records: Paid £18,000 to Farnborough Town for Colin Fielder
Received £22,000 from Wycombe Wanderers for Steve Thompson

Senior Honours:
Isthmian League 1980-81, 89-90. Athenian League x3. Berks & Bucks Senior Cup x10.

02-03		03-04		04-05		05-06		06-07		07-08		08-09		09-10		10-11		11-12	
Isth1S	4	Isth1S	4	Isth P	13	Isth P	17	Isth P	22	Sthsw	21	Sthsw	16	SthM	5	SthC	5	SthC	2

THATCHAM TOWN

Chairman: Eric Bailey
Secretary: Alan Lovegrove   **(T)** 07817 723 846   **(E)** mail@alanlovegrove.wanadoo.co.uk
Additional Committee Members:
David Tait, Sylvia Bailey, Peter Woodage.

Manager: Neville Roach
Programme Editor: Andy Morris   **(E)** acmorris@madasafish.com

2011-12 Squad.
Back Row (L-R): Richard Fox (Physio), Callum Willmoth, Sean Cook, Mark James, Paul Strudley, Gareth Thomas (Captain),
Steve Howe, Sam Flegg, Marc Green, Tom Melledew.
Front Row: Sam Hamilton, Paul Taplin, Scott Rees, James Clark, Gary Ackling (Manager), Eric Bailey (Chairman),
Will Bratt (Player/Coach), Mark Hughes, Matt Pedder, Robbie Sadler.

Club Factfile

Founded: 1895   **Nickname:** The Kingfishers
Previous Names: Not known
Previous Leagues: Hellenic 1974-82, Athenian 1982-84, London Spartan 1984-86, Wessex 1986-2006

Club Colours (change): Blue and white stripes/blue/blue (Red/black/black)

Ground: Waterside Park, Crookham Hill, Thatcham, Berks RG19 4PA   **(T)** 01635 862 016
Capacity: 3,000   **Seats:** 300   **Covered:** 300   **Clubhouse:** Yes   **Shop:** Yes

Directions: A4 Thatcham at Sony roundabout turn into Pipers Way.
At next roundabout turn left, crossing over the railway line.
Entrance to Waterside Park 300 metres on left-hand side.

Previous Grounds: Station Road 1946-52, Lancaster Close 1952-92

Record Attendance: 1,400 v Aldershot - FA Vase
Record Victory: Not known
Record Defeat: Not known
Record Goalscorer: Not known
Record Appearances: Not known
Additional Records:

Senior Honours:
Hellenic League 1974-75. Wessex League 1995-96.

10 YEAR RECORD

02-03		03-04		04-05		05-06		06-07		07-08		08-09		09-10		10-11		11-12	
Wex	9	Wex	10	Wex1	3	Wex1	2	Sthsw	6	Sthsw	15	Sthsw	6	Sthsw	12	Sthsw	5	Sthsw	8

UXBRIDGE

Chairman: Alan Holloway
Secretary: Roger Stevens   **(T)** 01895 236 879   **(E)** sec@uxbridgefc.co.uk
Additional Committee Members:
Mick Burrell, Averill Hinde, D Gill, D Marshall, C Rycraft, D Tucker, R Turton.

Manager: Tony Choules
Programme Editor: Zoe Nealon   **(E)** program.editor@uxbridgefc.co.uk

Back Row: Karis Baker (Ass't Physio), Gary Mills (Chief Scout), Patrick Lynott, Gavin Brown, Max Howell, Damian Panter, Mark Dennison, John Peacock
Matthew Elston-Bull, Nicke Kabamba, Tyrone Rowe-McKenzie, Jake Jenkins, Stuart Farrell, Daniel Julienne, Scott Everley (Ass't Physio), Stuart Everley (Club Physio)
Front Row: Danny Tilbury, Shaun Lucien, Andrew Capewell, Mark Smith, Paul Mill (1st Team Ass't Manager) Tony Choules (Club Manager)
Wayne Carter (Captain) Kevin Warner, Matt Woods, Chris Moore

Club Factfile

Founded: 1871   **Nickname:** The Reds
Previous Names: Uxbridge Town 1923-45
Previous Leagues: Southern 1894-99, Gt Western Suburban 1906-19, 20-23, Athenian 1919-20, 24-37, 63-82, Spartan 1937-38, London 1938-46, Gt Western Comb. 1939-45, Corinthian 1946-63, Isthmian

Club Colours (change): Red/white/red (Sky blue/navy/navy)

Ground: Honeycroft Road, West Drayton, Middlesex UB7 8HX   **(T)** 01895 443 557
Capacity: 3,770   **Seats:** 339   **Covered:** 760   **Clubhouse:** Yes   **Shop:**

Directions
M4 to Junction 4 (Heathrow),
take A408 towards Uxbridge for 1 mile,
turn left into Horton Road.
Ground 1/2 mile on right.

Previous Grounds: RAF Stadium 1923-48, Cleveland Road 1948-78

Record Attendance: 1,000 v Arsenal - Opening of the floodlights 1981
Record Victory: Not known
Record Defeat: Not known
Record Goalscorer: Phil Duff - 153
Record Appearances: Roger Nicholls - 1,054
Additional Records:
Senior Honours:
Middlesex Senior Cup 1893-94, 95-96, 1950-51, 2000-01. London Challenge Cup 1993-94, 96-97, 98-99.

10 YEAR RECORD

02-03		03-04		04-05		05-06		06-07		07-08		08-09		09-10		10-11		11-12	
Isth1N	5	Isth1N	13	SthE	4	SthE	14	Sthsw	8	Sthsw	5	Sthsw	13	Sthsw	15	SthC	13	SthC	4

WOODFORD UNITED

Chairman: Andrew Worrall
Secretary: David Allen   **(T)** 07889 847 428   **(E)** allend@wufc.biz
Additional Committee Members:
Yvonne Worrall, R Adams, D Grogan.

Manager: Phil Mason
Programme Editor: Richard Usher   **(E)** richard-usher@sky.com

Club Factfile

Founded: 1946   **Nickname:** Reds
Previous Names: Not known
Previous Leagues: Central Northants Combination 1946-70, United Counties 1971-2006

Club Colours (change): All red (Yellow/black/yellow)

Ground: Byfield Road, Woodford Halse, Daventry, Northants NN11 3QR   **(T)** 01327 263 734
Capacity: 3,000   **Seats:** 252   **Covered:** 252   **Clubhouse:** Yes   **Shop:** No

Directions
From M1 J18, M40 J11,
take A361 Banbury to Daventry road.
Exit A361 in Byfield, follow signs for Woodford Halse.
Ground on left 200 yards past industrial estate.

Previous Grounds:

Record Attendance: 1,500 v Stockport County
Record Victory: Not known
Record Defeat: Not known
Record Goalscorer: Not known
Record Appearances: Not known
Additional Records:

Senior Honours:
United Counties League Division 2 1973-74, Premier Division 2005-06.

10 YEAR RECORD

02-03	03-04	04-05	05-06	06-07	07-08	08-09	09-10	10-11	11-12
UCL P 14	UCL P 12	UCL P 7	UCL P 1	SthM 8	SthM 19	SthM 20	SthM 7	SthC 9	SthC 19

ABINGDON UNITED

Chairman: Mrs Deborah Blackmore
Secretary: John Blackmore　　**(T)** 07747 615 691　　**(E)** john.blackmore2@ntlworld.com
Additional Committee Members:
Alf White, Pat Evans, Shirley Evans, Bill Fletcher, Doreen White, Chris Jane, Derek Turner, Robin Yuill.

Manager: Richie Bourne
Programme Editor: Bill Fletcher　　　　**(E)** billfletcher@ntlworld.com

THE NON-LEAGUE CLUB DIRECTORY

Book Holiday Inn Hotels and Save today!

| Home |
| Clubs |
| Steps 1 - 4 |
| League Tables |

35 Years of Non-League Football

The Non-League Club Directory has developed into a comprehensive record of competitions within the non-League game, giving this level of football the

www.non-leagueclubdirectory.co.uk

Club Factfile

Founded: 1946　　**Nickname:** The U's

Previous Names: Not known
Previous Leagues: North Berkshire 1949-58, Hellenic 1958-2006

Club Colours (change): All yellow (White/red/white)

Ground: The North Court, Northcourt Road, Abingdon OX14 1PL　　　　**(T)** 01235 203 203

Capacity: 2,000　**Seats:** 158　**Covered:** 258　**Clubhouse:** Yes　**Shop:**

Directions
From the north – Leave A34 at Abingdon north turning. Ground on right at first set of traffic lights.
From the south – Enter Town Centre, leave north on A4183 (Oxford Road).
Ground on left after one mile.

Previous Grounds:

Record Attendance: 1,500 v Oxford United - Friendly 1994

Record Victory: Not known
Record Defeat: Not known

Record Goalscorer: Not known

Record Appearances: Not known
Additional Records:

Senior Honours:
Hellenic League Division 1 1981-82, League Cup 1965-66. Berks & Bucks Senior Trophy x2.

02-03	03-04	04-05	05-06	06-07	07-08	08-09	09-10	10-11	11-12
Hel P　8	Hel P　11	Hel P　5	Hel P　3	Hel P　18	Sthsw　16	Sthsw　15	Sthsw　14	Sthsw　16	Sthsw　18

BISHOP'S CLEEVE

Chairman: David Walker
Secretary: Nigel Green   **(T)** 07919 518 880   **(E)** negreen@tiscali.co.uk
Additional Committee Members:
Dave Lewis, Hanif Tai, Bob Weaver, Hilary Green, John Pickup.

Manager: Alex Sykes
Programme Editor: **(E)**

Back Row L-R; Sam Avery, Ryan Clarke, Louie Barnfather, Iain Sercombe, James Nortei, Alex Hoyle, Sam O'Neil
Middle Row L-R; Alice Wood (Physio), Jon Crowford, Mike Davis, Stuart Midwinter, Jake Lee, Mike Tambling, Lamin Sankoh, Dean Ackland (Coach)
Front Row L-R; Will Gayton, Lee Davis, Matt Rose (Asst. Manager), Michael Jackson (Capt), Alex Sykes (Manager), Adam Mace, Carl Brown

Club Factfile

Founded: 1892   **Nickname:** Villagers
Previous Names:
Previous Leagues: Cheltenham, North Gloucestershire, Hellenic 1983-2006

Club Colours (change): Blue & white/blue/blue (Yellow & white/yellow/yellow)

Ground: Kayte Lane, Bishop's Cleeve, Cheltenham GL52 3PD   **(T)** 01242 676 166
Capacity: 1,500   **Seats:** 50   **Covered:** 50   **Clubhouse:** Yes   **Shop:** Yes

Directions: From Cheltenham take A435 towards Evesham.
Pass racecourse, take right at traffic lights then first left into Kayte Lane.
Ground 1/2 mile on left.

Previous Grounds: Stoke Road and ground shared with Moreton Town, Wollen Sports, Highworth Town and Forest Green Rovers

Record Attendance: 1,300 v Cheltenham Town - July 2006
Record Victory: Not known
Record Defeat: Not known
Record Goalscorer: Kevin Slack
Record Appearances: John Skeen
Additional Records:

Senior Honours:
Hellenic League Division 1 1986-87, Premier League Cup 1988.
Gloucestershire Junior Cup North. Gloucestershire Senior Amateur Cup North x3.

10 YEAR RECORD

02-03	03-04	04-05	05-06	06-07	07-08	08-09	09-10	10-11	11-12
Hel P 9	Hel P 3	Hel P 3	Hel P 2	SthM 13	SthM 12	Sthsw 18	Sthsw 11	Sthsw 15	Sthsw 11

BRIDGWATER TOWN 1984

Chairman: Alan Hurford
Secretary: Roger Palmer   **(T)** 07587 775 227   **(E)** palmer449@btinternet.com
Additional Committee Members:
Keith Setter, Jennie Parker.

Manager: Kevin Milsom
Programme Editor: Roger Palmer   **(E)** palmer449@btinternet.com

THE NON-LEAGUE CLUB DIRECTORY

Book Holiday Inn Hotels and Save today!

Home

Clubs

Steps 1 - 4

League Tables

35 Years of Non-League Football

The Non-League Club Directory has developed into a comprehensive record of competitions within the non-League game, giving this level of football the

www.non-leagueclubdirectory.co.uk

Club Factfile

Founded: 1984   **Nickname:** The Robins

Previous Names: Bridgwater Town
Previous Leagues: Somerset Senior, Western

Club Colours (change): Red/white/white (White/yellow/yellow)

Ground: Fairfax Park, College Way, Bath Road, Bridgwater, Somerset TA6 4TZ   **(T)** 01278 446 899

Capacity: 2,500 **Seats:** 128 **Covered:** 500 **Clubhouse:** Yes **Shop:** Yes

Directions
Southbound from Bristol M5 J.23- enter town on A39 from Glastonbury. Ground is between Bridgwater College and Rugby Ground by railway bridge.
Northbound from Taunton – M5 J.24- enter town on A38, follow signs for Glastonbury (A39). Ground is between Bridgwater College and Rugby Ground as you pass over railway bridge.

Previous Grounds:

Record Attendance: 1,112 v Taunton Town - 26/02/1997

Record Victory: Not Known
Record Defeat: Not Known

Record Goalscorer: Not Known

Record Appearances: Not Known
Additional Records:

Senior Honours:
Somerset Senior League x3. Somerset Senior Cup 1993-94, 95-96. Western League Division 1 1995-96.

02-03	03-04	04-05	05-06	06-07	07-08	08-09	09-10	10-11	11-12
WestP 6	WestP 6	WestP 6	WestP 11	WestP 2	Sthsw 6	Sthsw 7	Sthsw 3	Sthsw 18	Sthsw 15

CINDERFORD TOWN

Chairman: Ashley Saunders
Secretary: Robert Maskell   **(T)** 07835 511 774   **(E)** maskellbilly@yahoo.co.uk
Additional Committee Members:
Stuart Tait, Ray Reed, Mike James, Alan Jones, Robert Knight, Ken McNally, Beryl Reed,
Barry Turner, Chris Warren.
Manager: Steve Peters
Programme Editor: Liam Maskell   **(E)** liammaskell@googlemail.com

THE NON-LEAGUE CLUB DIRECTORY

Book Holiday Inn Hotels and Save today!

Home

Clubs

Steps 1 - 4

League Tables

35 Years of Non-League Football

The Non-League Club Directory has
developed into a comprehensive record
of competitions within the non-League
game, giving this level of football the

www.non-leagueclubdirectory.co.uk

Club Factfile

Founded: 1922   **Nickname:** The Foresters

Previous Names: Not known

Previous Leagues: Gloucestershire Northern Senior 1922-39, 60-62, Western 1946-59, Warwickshire Combination 1963-64, West Midlands 1965-69, Gloucestershire Co. 1970-73, 85-89, Midland Comb. 1974-84, Hellenic 1990-95

Club Colours (change): All white (All yellow)

Ground: The Causeway, Hildene, Cinderford, Gloucestershire GL14 2QH   **(T)** 01594 827 147 / 822 039

Capacity: 3,500   **Seats:** 250   **Covered:** 1,000   **Clubhouse:** Yes   **Shop:** Yes

Directions: Take A40 west out of Gloucester, then A48 for 8 miles. Turn right at Elton Garage onto A4151 (Forest of Dean). Continue through Littledean, climb steep hill, turn right at crossroads (football ground), then second left into Latimer Road. Or if coming from Severn Bridge take A48 Chepstow through Lydney, Newnham then left at Elton Garage – then as above.

Previous Grounds: Mousel Lane, Royal Oak

Record Attendance: 4,850 v Minehead - Western League 1955-56

Record Victory: 13-0 v Cam Mills - 1938-39
Record Defeat: 0-10 v Sutton Coldfield - 1978-79

Record Goalscorer: Not known

Record Appearances: Russel Bowles - 528

Additional Records:

Senior Honours:

Western League Division 2 1956-57. Midland Combination 1981-82. Hellenic Premier Division 1994-95, League Cup 94-95.
Gloucestershire Senior Amateur Cup North x6. Gloucestershire Junior Cup North 1980-81.
Gloucestershire Senior Cup 2000-01.

02-03		03-04		04-05		05-06		06-07		07-08		08-09		09-10		10-11		11-12	
SthW	15	SthW	20	SthW	16	SthW	15	SthM	9	SthM	16	SthM	11	Sthsw	16	Sthsw	12	Sthsw	10

CIRENCESTER TOWN

Chairman: Stephen Abbley
Secretary: Scott Griffin   **(T)** 01285 654543   **(E)** scott.griffin@cirentownfc.plus.com
Additional Committee Members:
Alan Sykes, Alan Lloyd, James French

Manager: Brian Hughes
Programme Editor: Scott Griffin   **(E)** scott.griffin@cirentownfc.plus.com

CIRENCESTER TOWN
FOOTBALL CLUB

Club Factfile

Founded: 1889   **Nickname:** Centurions
Previous Names:
Previous Leagues: Hellenic

Club Colours (change): Red and black stripes/black/red (All orange)

Ground: The Corinium Stadium, Kingshill Lane, Cirencester GL7 1HS   **(T)** 01285 654 543
Capacity: 4,500   **Seats:** 550   **Covered:** 1,250   **Clubhouse:** Yes   **Shop:** Yes

Directions: Leave bypass at Burford Road roundabout.
Aim for Stow, turn right at traffic lights, then right again at next junction, first left into Kingshill Lane.
Ground 500 yards on right.

Previous Grounds: Smithfield Stadium

Record Attendance: 2,600 v Fareham Town - 1969
Record Victory: Not known
Record Defeat: Not known
Record Goalscorer: Not known
Record Appearances: Not known
Additional Records: Paid £4,000 to Gloucester City for Lee Smith

Senior Honours:
Hellenic League Premier Division 1995-96.
Gloucestershire Senior Amateur Cup 1989-90. Gloucestershire County Cup 1995-96.

10 YEAR RECORD

02-03		03-04		04-05		05-06		06-07		07-08		08-09		09-10		10-11		11-12	
SthW	14	SthW	3	SthP	7	SthP	18	SthP	21	SthP	21	Sthsw	14	Sthsw	5	SthP	13	SthP	22

CLEVEDON TOWN

Chairman: Steve Spicer
Secretary: Brian Rose   **(T)** 07768 100 632   **(E)** brian.rose@blueyonder.co.uk
Additional Committee Members:

Manager: Micky Bell
Programme Editor: Dave Wright   **(E)** smallwavedave@hotmail.com

Back row (left to right) John Roberts (Kit Manager), Jack McKenna, Curtis Jack, Cameron Ricketts, Steve Kingdon, Lee Matthews, Ben Murray, Aaron Robbins, Jordan Walker, Jonny Moss, Adie Adams, Jenny Moore (Physio).
Front row (left to right) Bawan Hussain, Jack Flurry, Alex Russell, Paul McLoughlin (Coach), Steve Spicer (Chairman), Micky Bell (Manager), Matt Fisher, Adam Mahdi, Reeko Best.

Club Factfile

Founded: 1880   **Nickname:** Seasiders
Previous Names: Clevedon FC and Ashtonians merged in 1974
Previous Leagues: Weston & District, Somerset Senior, Bristol Charity, Bristol & District, Bristol Suburban, Western 1974-93

Club Colours (change): Royal blue & white stripes/royal/royal

Ground: Hand Stadium, Davis Lane, Clevedon BS21 6TG   **(T)** 01275 871 600
Capacity: 3,500   **Seats:** 300   **Covered:** 1,600   **Clubhouse:** Yes   **Shop:** Yes

Directions:
Exit J20 from M5, at bottom of slip road, turn left at roundabout into Central Way.
At next roundabout turn left to Kenn Road.
Stay on Kenn Road out of town, cross river, take 1st left into Davis Lane, over motorway.
Ground 200m on right.

Previous Grounds: Dial Hill until early 1890s, Teignmouth Road > 1991

Record Attendance: 2,300 v Billingham Synthonia - FA Amateur Cup 1952-53
Record Victory: 18-0 v Dawlish Town (H) - Western League Premier Division 24/04/1993
Record Defeat: 3-13 v Yate YMCA (A) - Bristol Combination 1967-68
Record Goalscorer: Not known
Record Appearances: Not known
Additional Records:

Senior Honours:
Somerset Senior Cup 1901-02, 04-05, 28-29, 2000-01, 01-02. Somerset Premier Cup x4.
Southern League Western Division 1992-93, 2005-06, Midland Division 1998-99.

10 YEAR RECORD

02-03		03-04		04-05		05-06		06-07		07-08		08-09		09-10		10-11		11-12	
SthW	13	SthW	11	SthW	4	SthW	1	SthP	18	SthP	11	SthP	18	SthP	21	Sthsw	20	Sthsw	20

DIDCOT TOWN

Chairman: John Bailey
Secretary: Pat Horsman   **(T)** 07882 154 612   **(E)** didcot@fernring.co.uk
Additional Committee Members:
Mr R Neal, Mr M Roberts, Mr P Haywood, Mr P Cox, Mr S Clare, Mr J Lambourne,
Mr P Leach, Mr M Mottershead, Ms J Chalk, Mr P Chalk, Mr D Warwick.
Manager: Dave Mudge
Programme Editor: Steve Clare   **(E)** stclare@tiscali.co.uk

THE NON-LEAGUE CLUB DIRECTORY

Book Holiday Inn Hotels and Save today!

Home

Clubs

Steps 1 - 4

League Tables

35 Years of Non-League Football

The Non-League Club Directory has
developed into a comprehensive record
of competitions within the non-League
game, giving this level of football the

www.non-leagueclubdirectory.co.uk

Club Factfile

Founded: 1907   **Nickname:** Railwaymen

Previous Names: Not known
Previous Leagues: Metropolitan 1957-63, Hellenic 1963-2006

Club Colours (change): Red with white sleeves/white/red & white (Gold/black/black)

Ground: NPower Loop Meadow Stadium, Bowmont Water, Didcot OX11 7GA   **(T)** 01235 813 138

Capacity: 5,000   **Seats:** 250   **Covered:** 200   **Clubhouse:** Yes   **Shop:** Yes

Directions
From A34 take A4130 towards Didcot.
At first roundabout take first exit, at next roundabout take third exit, then straight across next two roundabouts.
At fifth roundabout turn right into Avon Way.
Follow Avon Way for 1/2 mile till you get to a mini roundabout.
Straight across it, ground is on the left after 100 yards, in Bowmont Water.

Previous Grounds:

Record Attendance: 1,512 v Jarrow roofing - FA Vase Semi-final 2005

Record Victory: Not known
Record Defeat: Not known

Record Goalscorer: Ian Concanon

Record Appearances: Not known
Additional Records:

Senior Honours:
Hellenic League Premier Division 1953-54, 2005-06, Division 1 1976-77, 87-88, League Cup x6.
FA Vase 2004-05. Berks & Bucks Senior Trophy 2001-02, 02-03, 05-06.

02-03		03-04		04-05		05-06		06-07		07-08		08-09		09-10		10-11		11-12	
Hel P	5	Hel P	5	Hel P	2	Hel P	1	Sthsw	10	Sthsw	3	Sthsw	5	SthP	15	SthP	19	Sthsw	16

EVESHAM UNITED

Chairman: Jim Cockerton
Secretary: Mike Peplow   **(T)** 07889 011 539   **(E)** rwestmacot@aol.com
Additional Committee Members:
Steve Lane, Roger Westmacott.

Manager: Matt Clarke
Programme Editor: Mike Peplow   **(E)** rwestmacot@aol.com

Club Factfile

Founded: 1945   **Nickname:** The Robins
Previous Names: Not known
Previous Leagues: Worcester, Birmingham Combination, Midland Combination 1951-55, 65-92,
West Midlands (Regional) 1955-62

Club Colours (change): Red and white stripes/white/red (Blue and white stripes/blue/blue)

Ground: Worcester City FC, St George's Lane, Worcester WR1 1QT   **(T)** 01905 23003
Capacity: 2,000   **Seats:** 350   **Covered:** 600   **Clubhouse:** Yes   **Shop:** Yes
Directions: Leave M5 at Junction 6 (Worcester North), follow signs for Worcester along the A449. Follow the dual carrigeway until you come to roundabout, take second turning towards Worcester. Stay on this road for about one mile (Ombersley Road) until you reach T-junction and traffic lights. Turn right at lights. St George's Lane is third turning on left between tool hire shop and 'In Toto Kitchen' showrooms. Ground is 500 yards on left.

Previous Grounds: The Crown Meadow > 1968, Common Reed 1968-2006

Record Attendance: 2,338 v West Bromwich Albion - Friendly 18/07/1992
Record Victory: 11-3 v West Heath United
Record Defeat: 1-8 v Ilkeston Town
Record Goalscorer: Sid Brain
Record Appearances: Rob Candy
Additional Records: Paid £1,500 to Hayes for Colin Day 1992
Senior Honours: Received £5,000 from Cheltenham Town for Simon Brain
Midland Combination Premier Division 1991-92, Division 1 1965-66, 67-68, 68-69.
Southern League Division 1 Midlands 2007-08.
Worcestershire Senior Urn x2

10 YEAR RECORD

02-03		03-04		04-05		05-06		06-07		07-08		08-09		09-10		10-11		11-12	
SthW	12	SthW	14	SthW	3	SthP	20	SthM	5	SthM	1	SthP	9	SthP	16	SthP	12	SthP	20

HUNGERFORD TOWN

Chairman: Steve Skipworth
Secretary: Ken Holmes   **(T)** 07932 890 336   **(E)** kensven@tiscali.co.uk
Additional Committee Members:
Ron Tarry, Ray Brown, John Sopp, Mick Butler, Norman Matthews, Jim Goslin, Simon Liddiard, Terry Wild, Garth Franklin.
Manager: Bobby Wilkinson
Programme Editor: John Smyth   **(E)** john.smyth@saxon-brands.com

2011-12 Squad.

Club Factfile

Founded: 1886   **Nickname:** The Crusaders
Previous Names: None
Previous Leagues: Newbury & District, Swindon & District, Hellenic 1958-78, 2003-09, Isthmian 1978-2003

Club Colours (change): All white

Ground: Bulpitt Lane, Hungerford RG17 0AY   **(T)** 01488 682 939
Capacity: 2,500   **Seats:** 170   **Covered:** 400   **Clubhouse:** Yes   **Shop:** Yes

Directions: From M4 Junction, take A338 to Hungerford. First Roundabout turn right on to A4, next roundabout first left, 100 yards roundabout 1st left up High Street, go over three roundabouts, at fourth roundabout turn first left signposted 'Football Club'. Take second left into Bulpitt Lane, go over crossroads, ground on left.

Previous Grounds: None

Record Attendance: 1,684 v Sudbury Town - FA Vase Semi-final 1988-89
Record Victory: Not known
Record Defeat: Not known
Record Goalscorer: Ian Farr - 268
Record Appearances: Dean Bailey and Tim North - 400+
Additional Records: Paid £4,000 to Yeovil Town for Joe Scott
     Received £3,800 from Barnstaple Town for Joe Scott
Senior Honours:
Hellenic Division 1 1970-71, Premier Division 2008-09, League Cup 2006-07, 07-08.
Berks & Bucks Senior Cup 1981-82.
Isthmian representatives in Anglo Italian Cup 1981.

10 YEAR RECORD

02-03		03-04		04-05		05-06		06-07		07-08		08-09		09-10		10-11		11-12	
Isth2	5	Hel P	6	Hel P	17	Hel P	16	Hel P	3	Hel P	3	Hel P	1	Sthsw	17	Sthsw	7	Sthsw	5

MANGOTSFIELD UNITED

Chairman: Mike Richardson
Secretary: David Jones **(T)** 07903 655 723 **(E)** davidj693@hotmail.co.uk
Additional Committee Members:
Bob Jenkins, Peter Crowley, Martin Preedy.

Manager: Richard Thompson
Programme Editor: Bob Smale **(E)** bob_smale@yahoo.co.uk

Back Row: John House, (Matchday assistant), Matt Thorne, Sam Teale, Ryan Bath, Danny Greaves, Clayton Fortune,
Josh Klein-Davies, Doug Pringle (Physio).
Middle Row: Marcus Duharty, Charlie Rich, Kyle Thomas, Tom Parrinello, Lyham Douglas, Kyle Tooze, Joe Turley, Todd Winter.
Front Row: Michael Whittington, Neil Arndale (Capt), Lee Barlass (Assistant Manager), Richard Thompson (Manager),
Bob Jenkins (Vice Chairman), Lee Jefferies (Assistant Manager), Nick Dunn.

Club Factfile

Founded: 1950 **Nickname:** The Field
Previous Names: None
Previous Leagues: Bristol & District 1950-67. Avon Premier Combination 1967-72. Western 1972-2000.

Club Colours (change): Sky blue/maroon/sky blue (Yellow/black/yellow)

Ground: Cossham Street, Mangotsfield, Bristol BS16 9EN **(T)** 0117 956 0119
Capacity: 2,500 **Seats:** 300 **Covered:** 800 **Clubhouse:** Yes **Shop:** Yes

Directions
Exit the M32 at Junction 1 and follow the A4174 towards Downend following signs to Mangotsfield.
Turn left into Cossham Street, the ground is approx 300 yards on the right.

Previous Grounds: None

Record Attendance: 1,253 v Bath City - F.A. Cup 1974
Record Victory: 17-0 v Hanham Sports (H) - 1953 Bristol & District League
Record Defeat: 3-13 v Bristol City United - Bristol & District League Division 1
Record Goalscorer: John Hill
Record Appearances: John Hill - 600+
Additional Records: In the last 10 matches of the 2003/04 season, the club went 738 minutes (just over 8 games) without scoring
Senior Honours: and then finished the campaign with 13 goals in the last two, which included a 9-0 away win.
Gloucestershire Senior Cup 1968-69, 75-76, 2002-03. Somerset Premier Cup 1987-88. Western League 1990-91.
Southern League Division One West 2004-05. Gloucestershire F.A. Trophy x6.

10 YEAR RECORD

02-03		03-04		04-05		05-06		06-07		07-08		08-09		09-10		10-11		11-12	
SthW	6	SthW	13	SthW	1	SthP	10	SthP	9	SthP	14	SthP	22	Sthsw	9	Sthsw	3	Sthsw	14

MERTHYR TOWN

Chairman: John Strand
Secretary: Jamie Mack   **(T)** 07823 776 422   **(E)** merthysec@gmail.com
Additional Committee Members:

Manager: Garry Shephard
Programme Editor: Malcolm Johnson   **(E)** malc.johnson@talk21.com

Photo: Peter Harman.

Club Factfile

Founded: 2010   **Nickname:** Martyrs
Previous Names: None
Previous Leagues: Western League 2010-12.

Club Colours (change): White/black/black & white (All red)

Ground: Penydarren Park, Park Terrace, Merthyr Tydfil CF47 8RF   **(T)** 07980 363 675
Capacity: **Seats:** Yes   **Covered:** Yes   **Clubhouse:** Yes   **Shop:**

Directions: Leave the M4 at Junction 32 and join the A470 to Merthyr Tydfil. After approx 22 miles at the fourth roundabout take 3rd exit. At next roundabout go straight on and go straight on through two sets of traffic lights. At third set turn left (ground signposted Merthyr Tydfil FC from here). After 50 yards take first right, then first right just after Catholic Church into Park Terrace. The ground is at the end of the road approx. 200 yards on.

Previous Grounds: None

Record Attendance:
Record Victory:
Record Defeat:
Record Goalscorer:
Record Appearances:
Additional Records:

Senior Honours:
Western League Division One 2010-11, Premier Division 2011-12.

10 YEAR RECORD									
02-03	03-04	04-05	05-06	06-07	07-08	08-09	09-10	10-11	11-12
								West1 1	WestP 1

NORTH LEIGH

Chairman: Peter King
Secretary: Keith Huxley   **(T)** 01993 851 497   **(E)** keith.huxley08@tiscali.co.uk
Additional Committee Members:
Jon Twiss, Barry Norton

Manager: Mark Gee
Programme Editor: Mike Burnell   **(E)** michael.burnell1@ntlworld.com

Club Factfile

Founded: 1908   **Nickname:** The Millers
Previous Names: Not known
Previous Leagues: Witney & District, Hellenic 1990-2008

Club Colours (change): Yellow/black/yellow (All sky blue)

Ground: Eynsham Hall Park, North Leigh, Witney, Oxon OX29 6SL   **(T)** 07583 399 577
Capacity: 2,000   **Seats:** 100   **Covered:** 200   **Clubhouse:** Yes   **Shop:** No
Directions: Ground is situated off A4095 Witney to Woodstock road, three miles east of Witney. Entrance 300 yards east of main park entrance.

Previous Grounds:

Record Attendance: 426 v Newport County - FA Cup 3rd Qualifying Round 16/10/2004
Record Victory: Not known
Record Defeat: Not known
Record Goalscorer: P Coles
Record Appearances: P King
Additional Records:

Senior Honours:
Hellenic Premier Division 2001-02, 02-03, 07-08. Oxon Charity Cup x2.

10 YEAR RECORD

02-03	03-04	04-05	05-06	06-07	07-08	08-09	09-10	10-11	11-12
Hel P 1	Hel P 8	Hel P 7	Hel P 4	Hel P 2	Hel P 1	Sthsw 8	Sthsw 10	Sthsw 6	Sthsw 6

PAULTON ROVERS

Chairman: David Bissex
Secretary: Andrew Harris   **(T)** 07760 377 302   **(E)** ahbr23112@blueyonder.co.uk
Additional Committee Members:
Tim Pow, David Bissex, Les Rogers, Tony Walsh

Manager: Nick Bunyard
Programme Editor: Peter Lord   **(E)** lord_p7@sky.com

Action from Dan Cleverley's (Paulton's skipper) testimonial match against Bristol Rovers which took place on 1st August 2012.

Club Factfile

Founded: 1881   **Nickname:** The Robins or Rovers
Previous Names: Not known
Previous Leagues: Wiltshire Premier, Somerset Senior, Western

Club Colours (change): All maroon

Ground: Athletic Ground, Winterfield Road, Paulton, Bristol BS39 7RF   **(T)** 01761 412 907
Capacity: 5,000   **Seats:** 253   **Covered:** 2,500   **Clubhouse:** Yes   **Shop:** Yes

Directions: From A39 at Farrington Gurney, follow A362 marked Radstock for two miles.
Turn left at roundabout, take B3355 to Paulton and ground is on the right.

Previous Grounds: Chapel Field, Cricket Ground, Recreation Ground

Record Attendance: 2,000 v Crewe Alexandra - FA Cup 1906-07
Record Victory: Not known
Record Defeat: Not known
Record Goalscorer: Graham Colbourne
Record Appearances: Steve Tovey
Additional Records:

Senior Honours:
Somerset Senior Cup x12

10 YEAR RECORD

02-03		03-04		04-05		05-06		06-07		07-08		08-09		09-10		10-11		11-12	
WestP	5	WestP	2	SthW	8	SthW	17	Sthsw	2	Sthsw	7	Sthsw	10	Sthsw	7	Sthsw	11	Sthsw	7

POOLE TOWN

Chairman: Clive Robbins
Secretary: Bill Reid　　**(T)** 01794　517 991　**(E)** secretary@pooletownfc.co.uk
Additional Committee Members:
Chris Reeves, Mark Bumford, Nick Spetch, Rob Bayston, Peter Hough, Rod Taylor.

Manager: Tommy Killick
Programme Editor: Ian Claxton　　　　**(E)** ian.claxton@btinternet.com

2011-12 Squad Back row : Steve Smith, Tom Jeffes, Dave Sturgess, Scott Joyce, Michael Walker, Dan Cann, Jake Smeeton
Middle row: Tom Killick (Manager), James Woods (Assistant Manager), Gavin Reeves (Coach), Tom Price, Sam Clarke, Steve
Richardson, Carl Preston, Aaron Skelton, Nic Jones (GK), Nick Hutchings (GK), Mick Hubbard, Will Spetch, Glenn Howes,
Lamin Dibba, Kevin Gill, Dick Thomas (Physio) Ian Claxton (Programme Editor), Paul Ayley (Kitman)
Front Row: (Board of Directors) Doug Huggins (Treasurer), Rob Bayston, Peter Hough, Clive Robbins (Chairman), Chris Reeves (Vice
Chairman) Mark Bumford (Commercial) Bill Reid (Club Secretary)

Club Factfile

Founded: 1880　　**Nickname:** The Dolphins
Previous Names: Poole Rovers 1884, Poole Hornets 1886 - amalgamated on 20.09.1890 to form Town. Know as Poole & St. Mary's 1919-20.
Previous Leagues: Dorset 1896-1903, 04-05, 10-11. Hampshire 1903-04, 05-10, 11-23, 34-35, 96-2004. Western 1923-26, 30-34, 35-57. Southern 1926-30, 57-96. Wessex 2004-11.

Club Colours (change): Red & white halves/red/white

Ground: Tatnam Ground, Oakdale School, School Lane, Poole BH15 3JR　　**(T)** 07771 604 289 (Match days)
Capacity: 2,000　**Seats:** 154　　**Covered:** 200　　**Clubhouse:** Yes　**Shop:** Yes

Directions: Follow the A35 into Poole and at the roundabout by the fire station take the second exit into Holes Bay Road (A350). At next roundabout take 1st exit onto Broadstone Way (A349) and turn right at Wessex Gate East traffic lights into Willis Way. Turn right into Fleets Way and continue until you see Poole Motor Cycles. Turn left into Palmer Road opposite Poole Motor Cycles and take first right into School Lane which will take you into the Club/School car park. The ground is on the right hand side. Nearest Railway Station: Poole (3/4 mile)

Previous Grounds: Ye Old Farm Ground. Wimborne Road Rec > 1933. Poole Stadium 1933-94. Hamworthy Utd FC 1994-96. Holt Utd 1996.

Record Attendance: Att: 10,224 v Queens Park Rangers, FA Cup 1st Rnd Replay, 1946 (at Poole Stadium).
Record Victory: 11-0 v Horndean (A) Hampshire League 11/02/1998.
Record Defeat: 1-8 v East Cowes VA (A) Hampshire League 01/05/2001.
Record Goalscorer: Not known
Record Appearances: Not known
Additional Records: Got to 3rd Round of FA Cup in 1926 v Everton. Transfer fee paid £5,000 for Nicky Dent 1990.
Senior Honours: Transfer fee received £70,000 for Charlie Austin from Swindon Town 2009.
Western League 1956-57. Dorset Senior Cup (12).
Wessex League Champions 2008-09, 09-10, 10-11.

10 YEAR RECORD

02-03	03-04	04-05	05-06	06-07	07-08	08-09	09-10	10-11	11-12
HantP 4	HantP 3	Wex2 2	Wex1 8	WexP 4	WexP 4	WexP 1	WexP 1	WexP 1	Sthsw 2

SHOLING

Chairman: Sean Whelan
Secretary: Colin Chamberlain   **(T)** 07770 452 660   **(E)** secretary.sholingfc@gmail.com
Additional Committee Members:
Dave Diaper, Trevor Lewis, Dave Bennett, Malcolm Stokes, Caroline Hookway

Manager: David Diaper
Programme Editor: Mrs Chris Lewis   **(E)** chrislewis@tiscali.co.uk

Club Factfile

Founded: 1916   **Nickname:** The Boatmen
Previous Names: Woolston Works, Thornycrofts (Woolston) 1918-52, Vospers 1960-2003, VT FC 2003-10
Previous Leagues: Hampshire 1991-2004, Wessex 2004-09

Club Colours (change): Red & white stripes/black/red

Ground: VT Group Sportsground, Portsmouth Road, Sholing, SO19 9PW   **(T)** 02380 403 829
Capacity: **Seats:** Yes   **Covered:** Yes   **Clubhouse:** Yes   **Shop:**

Directions: Leave the M27 at J8 and follow the signs towards Hamble. As you drive up dual carriageway (remain in the L/H lane), you come to Windover roundabout. Take the second exit towards Hamble. Take the R/H lane and carry on straight across the small roundabout. After 200 yards bear right across a second small roundabout (2nd exit). After about 100 yards turn right into Portsmouth Road. Follow straight on for about half mile. VT ground is on right opposite a lorry entrance.

Previous Grounds:

Record Attendance: 150
Record Victory: Not known
Record Defeat: Not known
Record Goalscorer: George Diaper - 100+
Record Appearances: Not known
Additional Records:

Senior Honours:
Hampshire Premier Division 2000-01, 03-04

10 YEAR RECORD									
02-03	03-04	04-05	05-06	06-07	07-08	08-09	09-10	10-11	11-12
	HantP 1	Wex1 12	Wex1 13	WexP 3	WexP 2	WexP 2	Sthsw 4	Sthsw 2	Sthsw 4

SHORTWOOD UNITED

Chairman: Peter Webb
Secretary: Mark Webb   **(T)** 07792 323784   **(E)**
Additional Committee Members:
Paul Benneyworth, Jim Cunneen

Manager: John Evans
Programme Editor: Paul Benneyworth   **(E)** prbrab@btinternet.com

THE NON-LEAGUE CLUB DIRECTORY

Book Holiday Inn Hotels and Save today!

Home
Clubs
Steps 1 - 4
League Tables

35 Years of Non-League Football

The Non-League Club Directory has developed into a comprehensive record of competitions within the non-League game, giving this level of football the

www.non-leagueclubdirectory.co.uk

Club Factfile

Founded: 1900   **Nickname:** The Wood

Previous Names: None.

Previous Leagues: Gloucestershire County.

Club Colours (change): Red & white/white/black.

Ground: Meadowbank, Shortwood, Nailsworth GL6 0SJ   **(T)** 01453 833 936

Capacity: 2,000   **Seats:** 50   **Covered:** 150   **Clubhouse:** Yes   **Shop:** No

Directions
When entering Nailsworth from Stroud turn right at mini roundabout, when coming from Cirencester go straight over roundabout, and when from Bath turn left at mini roundabout.
Proceed up Spring Hill 30 yards turn left at Raffles Wine Warehouse, straight through town turn left at Brittannia Pub carry on for 1 mile until you come to Shortwood village you will see sign post on fork in the road keep to the left follow on for quarter of a mile ground opposite church.

Previous Grounds:

Record Attendance: Att: 1,000 v Forest Green Rovers, FA Vase 5th Rnd 1982.

Record Victory:
Record Defeat:

Record Goalscorer: Peter Grant.

Record Appearances: Peter Grant.

Additional Records: Gloucestershire Lge Champions 1981-82.

Senior Honours:
Hellenic League Champions 1984-85, 91-92.
Gloucestershire Senior Cup (x 2).

02-03	03-04	04-05	05-06	06-07	07-08	08-09	09-10	10-11	11-12
Hel P 13	Hel P 19	Hel P 15	Hel P 15	Hel P 8	Hel P 5	Hel P 2	Hel P 2	Hel P 6	Hel P 2

SWINDON SUPERMARINE

Chairman: Jez Webb
Secretary: Judi Moore   **(T)** 07785 970 954   **(E)** judimoore6@aol.com
Additional Committee Members:
Marcus Cook, Dave Rideout, Steve Nichols, Roy Heather, Freda Heather, Steve Wheeler.

Manager: Dave Webb
Programme Editor: Keith Yeomans   **(E)** supermarinefc@aol.com

Club Factfile

Founded: 1992   **Nickname:** Marine
Previous Names: Club formed after the amalgamation of Swindon Athletic and Supermarine
Previous Leagues: Wiltshire, Hellenic1992-2001.

Club Colours (change): All blue & white trim (All red & white trim)

Ground: The Webbs Stadium, South Marston, Swindon SN3 4BZ   **(T)** 01793 828 778
Capacity: 3,000   **Seats:** 300   **Covered:** 300   **Clubhouse:** Yes   **Shop:** Yes

Directions: From M5 Junction 11a, take the A417 to Cirencester, then A419 Swindon. At the A361 junction by Honda Factory take road to Highworth. After one mile Club is on 4th roundabout.

From M4 Junction 15, take A419 towards Swindon Cirencester, take A361, then as above .

From A420 Swindon take A419 to Cirencester, near Honda factory take A361, then as above.

Previous Grounds: Supermarine: Vickers Airfield > Mid 1960s

Record Attendance: 1,550 v Aston Villa
Record Victory: Not known
Record Defeat: Not known
Record Goalscorer: Damon York - 136 (1990-98)
Record Appearances: Damon York - 314 (1990-98)
Additional Records: Paid £1,000 to Hungerford Town for Lee Hartson

Senior Honours:
Hellenic League Premier Division 1997-98, 2000-01, Challenge Cup 97-97, 99-2000.

10 YEAR RECORD

02-03		03-04		04-05		05-06		06-07		07-08		08-09		09-10		10-11		11-12	
SthW	19	SthW	17	SthW	19	SthW	5	Sthsw	4	SthP	12	SthP	13	SthP	14	SthP	10	SthP	21

TAUNTON TOWN

Chairman: Kevin Sturmey
Secretary: Martin Dongworth   **(T)** 07791 948 686   **(E)** secretary@tauntontown.com
Additional Committee Members:
Andy Power, Harold Needs, Brian Pollard, Gordon Nelson.

Manager: Leigh Robinson
Programme Editor: Martin Dongworth   **(E)** secretary@tauntontown.com

Club Factfile

Founded: 1947   **Nickname:** The Peacocks
Previous Names: None
Previous Leagues: Western 1954-77, 83-2002, Southern 1977-83

Club Colours (change): Sky blue/claret/sky blue

Ground: Wordsworth Drive, Taunton, Somerset TA1 2HG   **(T)** 01823 278 191
Capacity: 2,500   **Seats:** 300   **Covered:** 1,000   **Clubhouse:** Yes   **Shop:** Yes

Directions: From M5 Junction 25 follow signs to Town Centre.
Proceed along Toneway then bear left at roundabout into Chritchard Way.
At traffic lights proceed into Wordsworth Drive and the ground is on the left.

Previous Grounds: None

Record Attendance: 3,284 v Tiverton Town - FA Vase Semi-final 1999
Record Victory: 12-0 v Dawlish Town (A) - FA Cup Preliminary Round 28/08/1993
Record Defeat: 0-8 v Cheltenham Town (A) - FA Cup 2nd Qualifying Round 28/09/1991
Record Goalscorer: Tony Payne
Record Appearances: Tony Payne
Additional Records: Reg Oram scored 67 in one season

Senior Honours:
Western League 1968-69, 89-90, 95-96, 98-99, 99-2000, 2000-01. FA Vase 2000-01.
Somerset Premier Cup 2002-03, 05-06.

10 YEAR RECORD

02-03		03-04		04-05		05-06		06-07		07-08		08-09		09-10		10-11		11-12	
SthW	10	SthW	15	SthW	17	SthW	18	Sthsw	5	Sthsw	18	Sthsw	20	Sthsw	19	Sthsw	9	Sthsw	17

TIVERTON TOWN

Chairman: Matthew Conridge
Secretary: Ramsey Findlay **(T)** 07761 261 990 **(E)** ramsayfindlay@hotmail.co.uk
Additional Committee Members:
Dave Graham, John Clarkson, Dave Wright, Mike Bargery, Kimm Smith
John Fournier - Commercial Manager - 07980 543 634
Manager: Mark Saunders
Programme Editor: Alan Reidy **(E)** alanreidy@tiscali.co.uk

Back Row: Joe Bushin, Lewis Tasker, Russell Jee, Paul Kendall, Chris Wright, Tom Gardner, Jules Emati-Emati, Rob Pengelly, Mark Saunders (Player-manager)
Front: Michael Nardiello, Kevin Hill, Harry Nodwell, Andy Taylor, Josh Concanen, Alex Faux, Adam Faux, Josh Searle

Club Factfile

Founded: 1913 **Nickname:** Tivvy
Previous Names: None
Previous Leagues: Devon and Exeter, Western

Club Colours (change): All yellow

Ground: Ladysmead, Bolham Road, Tiverton, Devon EX16 6SG **(T)** 01884 252 397
Capacity: 3,500 **Seats:** 520 **Covered:** 2,300 **Clubhouse:** Yes **Shop:** Yes

Directions: M5 Junction 27, follow A361 to Tiverton's second exit at roundabout, turning left.
Continue for about 400 yards, crossing roundabout until reaching mini-roundabout.
Carry on straight across. Ground is 200 yards on right.

Previous Grounds: None

Record Attendance: 3,000 v Leyton Orient - FA Cup 1st Round Proper 1994-95
Record Victory: 10-0 v Exmouth Town, Devon St Lukes Cup 16/02/1994
Record Defeat: 2-6 v Stafford Rangers (A) - Southern League 2001-02 & Heavitree United, Les Philips Cup 29/11/1997
Record Goalscorer: Phil Everett
Record Appearances: Not known
Additional Records:

Senior Honours:
FA Vase 1997-98, 98-99. Western League x5. Southern League Cup 2006-07.
Devon Senior Cup 1955-56, 65-66. East Devon Senior Cup x7.

10 YEAR RECORD

02-03		03-04		04-05		05-06		06-07		07-08		08-09		09-10		10-11		11-12	
SthP	4	SthP	15	SthP	8	SthP	12	SthP	15	SthP	17	SthP	12	SthP	19	SthP	20	Sthsw	9

WIMBORNE TOWN

Chairman: Ken Stewart
Secretary: Peter Barham   **(T)** 07956 833 316   **(E)** barhamp@tiscali.co.uk
Additional Committee Members:
Paul Miller

Manager: Steve Cuss
Programme Editor: Ken Fergus   **(E)** kenfergus@sky.com

Club Factfile

Founded: 1878   **Nickname:** Magpies
Previous Names: Not known
Previous Leagues: Dorset, Dorset Combination, Western 1981-86, Wessex 1986-2010

Club Colours (change): Black and white stripes/black/black

Ground: The Cuthbury, Cowgrove Road, Wimborne, Dorset, BH21 4EL   **(T)** 01202 884 821
Capacity: 3,250   **Seats:** 275   **Covered:** 425   **Clubhouse:** Yes   **Shop:** Yes

Directions
On the Wimborne To Blandford Road (B3082), turn left into Cowgrove Road just past Victoria Hospital.
Postcode for Sat nav is BH21 4EL.

Previous Grounds:

Record Attendance: 3,250 v Bamber Bridge
Record Victory: Not known
Record Defeat: Not known
Record Goalscorer: Jason Lovell
Record Appearances: James Sturgess
Additional Records:

Senior Honours:
FA Vase 1991-92. Wessex League 1991-92, 93-94, 99-2000.
Dorset Senior Amateur Cup 1936-37, 63-64.

10 YEAR RECORD

02-03		03-04		04-05		05-06		06-07		07-08		08-09		09-10		10-11		11-12	
Wex	4	Wex	2	Wex1	7	Wex1	12	WexP	6	WexP	3	WexP	4	WexP	2	Sthsw	19	Sthsw	19

WINCHESTER CITY

Chairman:
Secretary: Bernadette   **(T)** 07884 225 611   **(E)** bernie.21@hotmail.com
Additional Committee Members:
Scott Balaam

Manager: Guy Butters
Programme Editor: Steve Woodgate   **(E)**

THE NON-LEAGUE CLUB DIRECTORY

Book Holiday Inn Hotels and Save today!

Home
Clubs
Steps 1 - 4
League Tables

35 Years of Non-League Football

The Non-League Club Directory has developed into a comprehensive record of competitions within the non-League game, giving this level of football the

www.non-leagueclubdirectory.co.uk

Club Factfile

Founded: 1884   **Nickname:** The Capitals

Previous Names: None

Previous Leagues: Hampshire 1898-71, 73-03. Southern 1971-73, 2006-09. Wessex 2003-06.

Club Colours (change): Red/black/red (All white)

Ground: The City Ground, Hillier Way, Winchester SO23 7SR   **(T)** 01962 810 200

Capacity: 2,500   **Seats:** 200   **Covered:** 275   **Clubhouse:** Yes   **Shop:** Yes

Directions
From Junction 9 on the M3 take the A33/A34 for one mile then follow A33 for a further mile.
Take the first left into Kings Worthy and follow the road for about three miles.
When you enter the 30mph zone take the second left, first right, then left into Hillier Way, Ground is on the right.

Previous Grounds:

Record Attendance: 1,818 v Bideford, FA Vase Semi-final.

Record Victory:
Record Defeat:
Record Goalscorer: Andy Forbes.
Record Appearances: Ian Mancey.
Additional Records:

Senior Honours:
Hants Senior Cup 1932, 2005. Southampton Senior Cup 2000-01.
Hampshire Premier Division 2002-03. Wessex Division One 2003-04, 05-06, Premier Division 2011-12.
FA Vase 2004.

02-03		03-04		04-05		05-06		06-07		07-08		08-09		09-10		10-11		11-12	
HantP	1	Wex	1	Wex1	2	Wex1	1	SthW	13	SthW	17	SthW	22	WexP	11	WexP	3	WexP	1

YATE TOWN

Chairman: Peter Jackson
Secretary: Terry Tansley **(T)** 07875 272 126 **(E)** admin@yatetownfc.com
Additional Committee Members:
R. Berry, P. Crowley, R. Hawkins, B. Neal, W. Perks, C. Pick, J. Powell, M. Powell, R. Pullin, M. Robinson, C. Roddan, D. Smith, I. Summers
Manager: Rovert Cousins
Programme Editor: Terry Tansley **(E)** admin@yatetownfc.com

2011-12 Squad - Back L-R: NICK POPADOPOLOUS (Team Physio), NEIKELL PLUMMER, SCOTT THOMAS, TOM KINGTON, SAM WILLIAMS, TYRONE MINGS, JOE WHITE, MARK BADMAN.
Middle L-R: JAKE COX, JOE McCLENNAN, TOM WARREN, JOSH DEMPSEY, SAMDUGGAN, ROBIN NICHOLLS, RUSS CHURCH, KARL TROTTER (Fitness coach).
Front L-R: EDD VAHID (Capt), ROBIN COUSINS (Player-Manager), MICHAEL MEAKER (Player Coach), ADIE ADAMS.

Club Factfile

Founded: 1946 **Nickname:** The Bluebells
Previous Names: Yate YMCA 1946-70
Previous Leagues: Bristol Premier Combination > 1968, Gloucestershire County 1968-83, Hellenic 1983-89, 2000-03, Southern 1989-2000

Club Colours (change): White/blue navy/white (All yellow)

Ground: Lodge Road, Yate, Bristol BS37 7LE **(T)** 01454 228 103
Capacity: 2,000 **Seats:** 236 **Covered:** 400 **Clubhouse:** Yes **Shop:** Yes

Directions: From East: leave M4 J18, enter Yate on A432 via Chipping Sodbury bypass. Turn right at first small roundabout (Link Road), straight over next roundabout into Goose Green Way, over more roundabouts and 2 major sets of traffic lights. Turn right at third set of lights (by The Fox), then immediately left into Lodge Road. Ground 200m on right. From North: M5 (South) exit J14, B4509/B4060 into Chipping Sodbury. Turn right into Chipping Sodbury High Street, down Bowling Hill and right at first roundabout into Goose Green Way – then as above. From South: Leave M5 at J15, then join M5. Leave M4 at J19, take second exit onto M32. Leave M32 at J1, at roundabout take first exit onto A4174. Continue on A4174 over traffic lights, then at roundabout take first exit onto A432. Enter Yate on A432, at traffic lights turn left into Stover Road (B4059), then at roundabout take second exit – still on B4059. Left at traffic lights (Fox PH) and immediately left into Lodge Road.

Previous Grounds:

Record Attendance: 2,000 v Bristol Rovers v Bristol Rovers Past XI - Vaughan Jones testimonial 1990
Record Victory: 13-3 v Clevedon - Bristol Premier Combination 1967-68
Record Defeat: Not known
Record Goalscorer: Kevin Thaws
Record Appearances: Gary Hewlett
Additional Records: Paid £2,000 to Chippenham Town for Matt Rawlings 2003
Senior Honours: Received £15,000 from Bristol Rovers for Mike Davis
Hellenic League 1987-88, 88-89. Gloucestershire Senior Cup 2004-05, 05-06.

10 YEAR RECORD

02-03		03-04		04-05		05-06		06-07		07-08		08-09		09-10		10-11		11-12	
Hel P	2	SthW	16	SthW	2	SthP	6	SthP	14	SthP	10	SthP	21	Sthsw	13	Sthsw	14	Sthsw	13

A click away from memory lane!

Over 35 years of publishing the Non-League Club Directory has filled a room full of information and photographs covering the game we know and love.

What we intend, over time, is to create a website that shares with you everything we have accumulated, which we hope will bring back some fond memories of season's gone by.

Log on to **www.non-leagueclubdirectory.co.uk** today and see how many faces from teams gone by you recognise

Ryman
football league

PREMIER DIVISION

		P	W	D	L	F	A	GD	Pts
1	(C) Billericay Town	42	24	13	5	82	38	44	85
2	(P) AFC Hornchurch	42	26	4	12	68	35	33	82
3	Lowestoft Town	42	25	7	10	80	53	27	82
4	Wealdstone	42	20	15	7	76	39	37	75
5	Bury Town	42	22	9	11	85	55	30	75
6	Lewes	42	21	10	11	55	47	8	73
7	Hendon	42	21	9	12	69	44	25	72
8	Canvey Island	42	22	5	15	66	55	11	71
9	Cray Wanderers	42	20	8	14	74	55	19	68
10	East Thurrock United	42	18	8	16	70	65	5	62
11	Kingstonian	42	18	7	17	58	64	-6	61
12	Metropolitan Police	42	18	6	18	63	46	17	60
13	Wingate & Finchley	42	16	11	15	63	79	-16	59
14	Concord Rangers	42	16	9	17	72	66	6	57
15	Margate	42	15	9	18	66	65	1	54
16	Carshalton Athletic	42	14	10	18	48	55	-7	52
17	Harrow Borough	42	13	8	21	53	70	-17	47
18	Hastings United	42	13	8	21	43	61	-18	47
19	(R) Leatherhead	42	11	8	23	46	62	-16	41
20	(R) Aveley	42	5	12	25	41	88	-47	27
21	(R) Tooting & Mitcham United	42	7	6	29	47	116	-69	27
22	(R) Horsham	42	3	6	33	38	105	-67	15

PLAY-OFFS
Semi-Finals
AFC Hornchurch 3-1 Bury Town
Lowestoft Town 2-1 Wealdstone

Final (@: AFC Hornchurch, 6/5/12)
AFC Hornchurch 2-1 Lowestoft Town

		1	2	3	4	5	6	7	8	9	10	11	12	13	14	15	16	17	18	19	20	21	22
1	AFC Hornchurch		2-1	0-0	0-1	1-2	1-1	2-0	1-2	1-0	0-0	0-1	0-1	0-2	3-0	2-1	1-0	3-0	3-0	1-0	6-0	1-1	1-0
2	Aveley	2-3		0-6	1-2	2-4	1-1	3-3	1-1	0-3	3-2	0-1	1-7	2-1	0-0	1-1	0-0	0-1	1-3	0-2	1-3	0-3	1-2
3	Billericay Town	0-1	2-1		4-4	4-2	1-1	0-0	3-1	1-0	3-0	2-0	2-1	2-2	6-0	2-1	1-0	1-4	1-1	2-1	5-1	0-0	2-0
4	Bury Town	2-1	1-0	1-1		2-0	2-0	2-0	1-1	5-2	2-2	5-0	0-1	3-0	1-1	2-1	2-1	2-3	2-1	0-1	4-2	1-1	2-2
5	Canvey Island	4-1	0-3	0-2	0-1		1-2	0-2	1-2	1-0	1-0	1-2	3-1	1-0	0-2	3-1	1-2	3-2	5-0	2-2	2-0	3-1	2-3
6	Carshalton Athletic	1-2	0-0	0-1	2-1	0-1		0-2	2-3	0-1	0-1	2-0	0-3	2-1	0-1	1-1	1-2	1-4	2-1	2-1	3-0	0-0	3-0
7	Concord Rangers	1-2	3-0	0-0	4-2	1-2	0-0		1-1	4-5	1-0	2-2	2-0	5-0	2-3	2-1	2-3	3-2	1-1	0-3	3-4	1-2	1-1
8	Cray Wanderers	2-5	2-2	2-3	2-0	0-0	1-0	2-4		3-0	1-2	1-0	0-0	3-1	0-0	1-2	0-1	0-2	2-4	2-1	4-1	2-1	3-2
9	East Thurrock United	0-1	4-1	1-2	2-1	2-1	1-1	4-1	1-2		0-3	0-2	0-0	1-0	0-1	3-0	1-0	1-3	3-0	4-2	1-0	3-3	1-2
10	Harrow Borough	1-0	1-1	1-1	2-1	3-4	1-2	0-3	0-4	3-1		1-1	4-2	1-0	1-3	2-0	0-1	2-4	0-2	2-1	1-1	0-0	1-3
11	Hastings United	1-3	2-1	0-0	0-1	1-1	0-2	1-1	0-2	1-2	3-1		0-2	5-0	1-0	0-0	1-1	2-0	2-2	0-2	2-0	0-2	0-1
12	Hendon	2-0	1-1	1-2	3-4	1-0	1-1	1-0	1-0	1-1	3-2	2-1		1-1	2-1	1-2	2-2	1-0	0-3	1-3	5-0	1-1	1-1
13	Horsham	0-3	1-3	0-5	1-3	1-2	1-3	0-3	1-5	1-5	1-3	1-2	0-3		1-3	1-4	0-1	1-2	1-2	2-2	2-0	1-1	1-2
14	Kingstonian	0-2	2-0	0-2	1-1	1-2	2-3	0-1	4-2	2-5	1-0	1-1	1-0	3-4		0-3	1-0	2-0	2-1	2-1	2-1	0-3	2-2
15	Leatherhead	0-1	2-0	0-2	0-5	0-1	1-1	1-3	1-4	2-1	2-0	2-0	0-1	2-1	0-2		0-1	1-2	2-0	1-1	2-4	1-1	2-2
16	Lewes	0-4	4-1	2-1	1-1	1-2	1-0	1-0	0-0	2-2	4-2	2-1	3-2	1-1	1-1	1-0		2-2	2-0	1-1	3-1	1-0	0-0
17	Lowestoft Town	2-1	1-0	1-0	2-1	1-1	3-2	5-0	2-1	1-1	1-2	1-3	2-0	1-0	3-2	2-2	3-1		2-1	2-2	2-2	2-1	2-0
18	Margate	0-2	3-0	2-2	2-3	1-1	0-1	1-0	1-3	5-0	1-0	4-1	0-2	2-1	2-1	0-0	5-1	1-4		1-3	1-2	0-2	5-0
19	Metropolitan Police	0-2	0-0	0-1	0-1	3-1	5-0	3-0	1-0	1-2	1-0	4-0	0-1	4-1	2-1	2-1	0-0	0-2	1-3		3-0	1-2	2-0
20	Tooting & Mitcham United	1-2	1-2	4-2	1-1	0-1	4-3	0-6	0-4	0-1	1-1	1-3	1-2	0-3	2-2	1-4	1-4	2-2	2-1	1-1		0-6	1-1
21	Wealdstone	2-1	5-2	1-1	3-1	1-2	1-1	3-1	1-1	2-2	4-0	2-1	0-2	3-0	4-1	1-0	0-0	1-1	0-0	1-1	1-0		2-4
22	Wingate & Finchley	1-2	2-2	1-4	3-2	0-2	2-1	3-1	0-2	3-3	2-2	3-1	0-5	3-2	0-2	1-0	1-2	2-1	2-2	2-1	4-2	0-5	

DIVISION ONE NORTH

		P	W	D	L	F	A	GD	Pts
1	(C) Leiston	42	28	7	7	99	41	58	91
2	(P) Enfield Town	42	27	9	6	96	46	50	90
3	Tilbury	42	23	11	8	82	62	20	80
4	Needham Market	42	23	8	11	104	56	48	77
5	Grays Athletic (-3)	42	24	8	10	80	47	33	77
6	Redbridge	42	21	10	11	80	59	21	73
7	Harlow Town	42	21	8	13	70	49	21	71
8	AFC Sudbury	42	20	9	13	65	57	8	69
9	Brentwood Town	42	18	8	16	58	42	16	62
10	Thamesmead Town	42	17	7	18	68	71	-3	58
11	Maldon & Tiptree	42	16	10	16	62	66	-4	58
12	Potters Bar Town	42	16	9	17	67	76	-9	57
13	Romford	42	15	12	15	64	73	-9	57
14	Waltham Abbey	42	15	10	17	79	76	3	55
15	Chatham Town	42	16	6	20	54	63	-9	54
16	Heybridge Swifts	42	15	7	20	59	64	-5	52
17	Waltham Forest	42	12	7	23	59	95	-36	43
18	Cheshunt	42	9	12	21	42	83	-41	39
19	Soham Town Rangers	42	7	13	22	55	93	-38	34
20	Ilford	42	8	6	28	47	85	-38	30
21	Ware	42	8	6	28	40	78	-38	30
22	(R) Great Wakering Rovers	42	6	11	25	43	91	-48	29

PLAY-OFFS
Semi-Finals
Enfield Town 2-2 Grays Athletic (enfield Town won 3-1 on penalties)
Tilbury 3-4 Needham Market

Final (@ Enfield Town, 6/5/12)
Enfield Town 1-0 Needham Market

		1	2	3	4	5	6	7	8	9	10	11	12	13	14	15	16	17	18	19	20	21	22
1	AFC Sudbury		1-0	1-0	1-4	0-1	1-2	1-2	2-2	1-2	1-4	1-0	2-3	3-2	1-0	1-1	2-2	4-1	0-2	2-2	1-0	1-2	3-1
2	Brentwood Town	1-2		3-0	1-2	1-2	1-2	5-0	0-1	2-0	1-3	0-1	1-1	1-1	1-0	0-1	4-2	2-1	1-1	1-2	2-0	5-1	1-0
3	Chatham Town	0-3	0-1		4-0	2-3	0-2	1-0	2-1	3-2	2-0	0-2	1-1	0-2	2-2	1-1	0-3	4-2	1-2	3-0	2-1	3-1	5-2
4	Cheshunt	1-4	0-5	1-0		0-5	0-1	2-0	2-0	1-4	2-2	0-2	0-0	1-8	2-1	1-2	3-1	0-0	1-1	1-5	0-1	2-1	0-0
5	Enfield Town	3-3	1-0	3-0	1-1		2-1	2-1	0-3	3-1	5-0	1-0	4-0	2-2	4-2	3-0	1-0	3-0	5-0	3-4	1-1	4-3	2-1
6	Grays Athletic	4-0	2-0	1-1	0-0	0-3		3-2	1-1	2-0	3-2	1-0	0-1	4-2	3-1	0-2	1-2	4-1	1-2	1-3	2-0	0-0	4-0
7	Great Wakering Rovers	1-3	0-2	2-3	2-2	1-1	0-1		1-1	0-0	0-0	0-4	1-1	0-1	0-3	2-3	2-0	1-1	2-1	1-2	0-2	2-2	4-2
8	Harlow Town	0-1	1-0	3-0	5-3	1-1	1-1	3-1		1-1	2-0	0-3	1-2	0-0	1-1	2-1	1-0	3-1	3-2	3-0	1-1	2-3	4-0
9	Heybridge Swifts	1-2	4-0	0-1	1-3	0-1	1-1	3-1	1-3		3-2	2-1	1-0	1-1	0-3	0-3	0-1	2-2	0-1	0-2	2-3	1-0	1-0
10	Ilford	0-0	0-1	0-1	3-2	1-1	0-5	1-2	1-2	2-1		2-3	0-2	1-2	1-0	1-2	2-3	2-2	1-0	2-2	3-2	0-1	1-2
11	Leiston	1-1	2-1	4-0	2-1	2-2	2-0	1-4	3-1	3-0		4-1	3-0	6-0	1-1	4-2	2-0	2-2	3-0	2-1	6-0	1-1	
12	Maldon & Tiptree	2-3	1-2	0-1	2-1	2-0	1-3	3-2	0-1	2-2	2-3	3-1		1-2	0-3	3-1	0-0	2-1	1-0	0-0	2-5	3-0	2-0
13	Needham Market	2-1	1-2	0-1	7-0	0-1	2-1	7-0	3-1	3-4	4-2	0-5	4-1		7-0	2-0	3-3	2-3	4-0	4-1	3-1	3-0	4-0
14	Potters Bar Town	5-1	1-1	2-1	1-1	0-0	1-3	1-1	2-0	2-1	3-1	1-3	4-3	2-3		1-5	1-0	3-3	0-3	3-2	2-3	0-0	2-1
15	Redbridge	2-2	2-2	0-4	1-0	3-5	2-3	2-1	2-1	3-1	1-2	2-2	1-1	3-2	0-2		3-0	3-2	1-1	3-0	1-1	4-1	2-1
16	Romford	1-0	0-0	1-1	1-2	0-5	2-2	1-0	2-1	2-0	2-0	0-1	3-2	1-1	0-4	1-0		3-3	0-1	1-1	2-2	2-0	3-2
17	Soham Town Rangers	3-1	0-3	1-0	1-1	0-4	3-2	3-3	1-3	1-1	1-1	2-0	2-1	0-1	2-2	1-1	1-0		1-3	0-1	1-3	2-3	1-4
18	Thamesmead Town	2-1	0-1	2-0	1-2	2-0	1-5	4-0	0-3	0-4	1-0	0-1	1-2	2-4	5-0	1-4	2-2	4-0		3-4	4-4	4-3	1-2
19	Tilbury	0-1	2-0	1-1	2-1	2-1	2-1	3-1	2-1	1-3	4-1	3-1	1-1	1-1	1-0	1-1	4-1	4-2	0-0		3-2	3-3	2-1
20	Waltham Abbey	0-3	1-1	1-0	2-2	0-1	7-0	1-3	1-2	2-1	3-3	1-1	0-4	3-0	1-1	4-5	5-2	2-3	2-2		0-1	3-2	
21	Waltham Forest	0-1	0-2	3-1	2-1	1-2	1-2	1-2	2-0	0-2	4-3	0-5	3-2	3-1	1-4	2-7	3-4	0-0	2-0	2-5	2-3		1-1
22	Ware	0-2	0-0	2-2	1-0	2-3	1-2	0-2	1-0	0-1	2-1	0-1	1-3	0-2	1-3	0-1	1-0	1-1	1-2	0-2	1-3	2-0	

DIVISION ONE SOUTH

		P	W	D	L	F	A	GD	Pts
1	(C) Whitehawk (-3)	40	29	6	5	81	26	55	90
2	(P) Bognor Regis Town	40	26	10	4	105	38	67	88
3	Dulwich Hamlet	40	26	8	6	74	26	48	86
4	Folkestone Invicta	40	23	7	10	82	52	30	76
5	Godalming Town	40	22	7	11	77	53	24	73
6	Maidstone United	40	20	7	13	68	50	18	67
7	Worthing	40	18	10	12	69	45	24	64
8	Hythe Town	40	17	8	15	62	62	0	59
9	Merstham	40	17	8	15	63	69	-6	59
10	Ramsgate	40	16	7	17	60	73	-13	55
11	Walton & Hersham	40	14	8	18	54	51	3	50
12	Chipstead (-6)	40	16	8	16	59	58	1	50
13	Corinthian Casuals	40	12	12	16	49	63	-14	48
14	Eastbourne Town	40	11	13	16	49	63	-14	46
15	Walton Casuals	40	12	6	22	51	74	-23	42
16	Crawley Down	40	12	5	23	65	81	-16	41
17	Faversham Town	40	10	10	20	43	67	-24	40
18	Whitstable Town	40	12	4	24	45	85	-40	40
19	Sittingbourne	40	6	12	22	35	75	-40	30
20	Burgess Hill Town (-3)	40	9	6	25	38	89	-51	30
21	(R) Whyteleafe	40	6	10	24	38	67	-29	28

Croydon Athletic's record expunged.

PLAY-OFFS
Semi-Finals
Bognor Regis Town 4-4 Godalming Town (Bognor Regis Town won 5-3 on penalties)
Dulwich Hamlet 2-1 Folkestone Invicta

Final (@ Bognor Regis Town, 6/5/12)
Bognor Regis Town 1-0 Dulwich Hamlet

		1	2	3	4	5	6	7	8	9	10	11	12	13	14	15	16	17	18	19	20	21
1	Bognor Regis Town		5-0	2-1	2-1	5-1	2-2	4-0	2-0	1-1	6-0	3-0	2-0	2-0	2-2	4-2	1-1	6-1	1-0	2-2	4-1	1-0
2	Burgess Hill Town	0-4		1-3	0-1	0-5	1-0	3-3	1-2	2-2	0-4	0-2	2-3	4-2	1-2	3-0	1-0	1-1	0-2	3-2	0-4	2-2
3	Chipstead	1-3	5-1		1-1	1-0	1-2	2-3	1-1	1-4	1-2	1-1	0-1	1-0	1-2	2-0	2-0	1-0	1-1	4-1	1-0	1-0
4	Corinthian-Casuals	3-1	5-2	1-1		2-3	1-1	1-1	1-1	3-1	0-3	1-1	0-1	0-1	3-2	0-2	0-2	2-1	0-3	2-3	2-2	3-3
5	Crawley Down	3-3	5-0	1-3	0-0		0-4	1-2	3-1	0-1	0-4	2-3	1-5	4-1	1-2	5-1	3-5	6-1	0-3	3-0	1-1	2-0
6	Dulwich Hamlet	0-0	2-0	3-0	3-0	1-1		2-0	3-1	5-2	0-1	1-0	0-0	3-1	1-0	2-0	0-0	3-1	0-2	4-1	2-0	3-1
7	Eastbourne Town	1-0	0-1	3-1	0-1	3-1	1-3		3-0	0-0	0-3	1-2	1-3	1-1	1-1	0-1	1-3	0-0	2-3	1-0	0-1	2-2
8	Faversham Town	0-2	1-1	1-2	1-3	2-0	0-3	1-1		1-4	0-1	2-1	2-2	3-2	4-0	1-2	1-0	1-2	0-2	0-0		0-1
9	Folkestone Invicta	2-2	1-0	2-0	4-2	4-1	1-3	1-1	0-0		2-2	8-0	3-2	0-4	2-3	4-1	2-1	1-0	2-0	4-1	0-1	3-1
10	Godalming Town	2-4	7-0	1-0	4-0	5-2	2-2	4-2	0-1	2-1		3-0	1-1	0-4	2-0	0-0	1-2	0-2	2-1	4-1	0-2	1-0
11	Hythe Town	2-3	2-3	1-1	1-1	3-1	1-0	3-2	3-0	0-2	1-2		1-0	3-1	3-2	1-1	2-3	2-2	0-1	4-0	4-0	3-1
12	Maidstone United	2-4	1-0	3-0	2-1	2-0	2-0	1-1	1-3	0-3	4-1	2-0		1-1	4-1	1-0	2-0	0-1	0-3	4-0	2-0	0-0
13	Merstham	0-4	2-1	1-1	2-1	4-2	0-3	3-0	2-1	0-4	1-0	1-1	2-4		4-2	1-1	1-0	1-0	2-3	3-2	1-1	2-1
14	Ramsgate	1-4	3-2	1-4	0-1	1-0	0-1	0-0	3-2	3-2	2-2	2-0	1-0	4-2		3-2	0-3	1-3	0-3	1-2	1-2	4-3
15	Sittingbourne	0-0	0-0	2-2	0-2	2-1	0-1	1-2	2-2	2-0	1-3	1-2	0-3	1-2	1-1		0-0	1-1	2-0	0-1	0-0	0-2
16	Walton & Hersham	0-0	1-0	1-4	0-1	4-1	0-3	1-1	2-3	5-0	1-2	0-3	1-4	1-1	1-2	4-0		4-1	0-1	5-0	2-1	0-1
17	Walton Casuals	0-5	0-2	1-3	0-1	1-3	0-2	4-2	0-0	2-4	1-1	1-0	3-2	2-0	3-1	5-1	2-0		0-2	2-3	3-2	0-1
18	Whitehawk	3-0	2-0	4-0	3-0	1-0	1-1	1-0	4-0	0-1	1-1	1-0	2-2	2-1	2-1	4-3	3-1	2-0		3-0	3-0	1-1
19	Whitstable Town	2-5	0-1	3-2	2-2	0-0	1-2	0-2	1-1	2-4	2-0	0-2	0-0	1-2	1-0	2-0	0-5		2-1		2-3	
20	Whyteleafe	0-4	2-0	0-2	3-0	0-1	0-2	2-3	1-1	1-2	1-0	0-1	3-2	2-3	2-2	0-1	0-3	0-3	2-0			0-2
21	Worthing	1-0	2-1	2-0	0-0	0-1	1-0	1-1	3-0	0-1	4-0	5-0	5-1	5-1	2-0	4-1	0-0	5-3	1-1	1-2	2-2	

LEAGUE CUP

ROUND 1

Dulwich Hamlet 2-2, 4-2p Godalming Town

Great Wakering Rovers 2-2, 2-4p Maldon & Tiptree

ROUND 2

Billericay Town 2-1 Grays Athletic

Bury Town 1-0 Harlow Town

Canvey Island 1-1, 4-2p Aveley

Chatham Town 4-1 Ilford

Cheshunt 3-1 AFC Hornchurch

Concord Rangers 3-3, 1-3p Needham Market

Corinthian- Casuals 1-1, 5-4p Hythe Town

Crawley Down 0-4 Lewes

Cray Wanderers 0-4 Ramsgate

Dulwich Hamlet 4-1 Burgess Hill

East Thurrock United 2-3 Redbridge

(Redbridge withdrawn for fielding an eligible player)

Enfield Town 3-0 Waltham Forest

Faversham Town 0-3 Eastbourne Town

Folkestone Invicta 5-0 Horsham

Harrow Borough 2-1 Hendon

Heybridge Swifts 0-1 AFC Sudbury

Leatherhead 2-2, 4-3p Wealdstone

Leiston 3-0 Waltham Abbey

Lowestoft Town 2-2, 3-1 Tilbury

Maldon & Tiptree 4-1 Romford

Margate 3-1 Kingstonian

Maidstone United 6-0 Merstham

Sittingbourne 0-2 Hastings United

Soham Town Rangers 0-3 Brentwood Town

Thamesmead Town 1-0 Wingate & Finchley

Tooting & Mitcham 3-1 Croydon Athletic

Walton Casuals 0-5 Bognor Regis Town

Ware 1-0 Potters Bar Town

Whitehawk 0-2 Metropolitan Police

Whitstable Town 0-0, 3-5p Chipstead

Whyteleafe 0-2 Walton & Hersham

Worthing 1-3 Carshalton Athletic

ROUND 3

Bury Town 3-2 Chatham Town

Canvey Island 5-1 Ware

Corinthian Casuals 2-0 Eastbourne Town

Dulwich Hamlet 2-1 Walton & Hersham

East Thurrock United 2-0 Thamesmead Town

Enfield Town 0-2 AFC Sudbury

Harrow Borough 1-2 Cheshunt

Hastings United 2-1 Tooting & Mitcham United

Leatherhead 2-0 Bognor Regis Town

Leiston 1-0 Billericay Town

Lewes 3-1 Folkestone Invicta

Maidstone United 2-2, 4-2p Carshalton Athletic

Maldon & Tiptree 0-1 Lowestoft Town

Metropolitan Police 3-2 Margate

Needham Market 3-0 Brentwood Town

Ramsgate 2-1 Chipstead

ROUND 4

Bury Town 2-1 Corinthian Casuals

Canvey Island 2-0 Cheshunt

East Thurrock United 5-1 Ramsgate

Leiston 0-1 Hastings United

Maidstone United 3-0 Leatherhead

Lowestoft Town 1-0 Dulwich Hamlet

Metropolitan Police 1-2 Lewes

Needham Market 2-2, 3-4p AFC Sudbury

QUARTER FINAL

East Thurrock United 3-0 Maidstone United

Hastings United 0-2 Bury Town

Lewes 1-1, 5-4p AFC Sudbury

Lowestoft Town 3-2 Canvey Island

SEMI FINALS

Bury Town 2-0 Lowestoft Town

East Thurrock United 1-0 Lewes

FINAL

Bury Town 1-0 East Thurrock United

Isthmian League Premier Division Statistics 2011-12

	Games Played & Goals Scored & Conceded	Top Goalscorers League, FAC & FAT	Number of Scorers per Club	Hat Tricks Scored	Penalties Scored	Best Individual Consecutive Scoring Run	Number of Clean Sheets	Number of Games in which club failed to score	Scorers with 10+
AFC Hornchurch	52-85/47	Tuohy 28-0-3-31	18	Tuohy 1	1	Tuohy 5	22(4)	10	Tuohy 31 and Smith 20
Aveley	45-43/90	Francis 7-0-0-7	19	0	3	Knight 2	6	18	0
Billericay Town	48-92/42	May 14-0-0-14	18+3ogs	1	5	Knight 4	21(2x4)	9	May14 and Swaine 14
Bury Town	48-95/62	Smith Lee 14-0-0-14	13	Clark, Sands & Smith 3	3	Smith 4	13(4)	5	Smith 14 (1p), Sands 12 & S.Reed 12, Clark 11 and Cunningham 10 (1p)
Canvey Island	47-79/63	King 11-0-6-17	12+2ogs	1	2	King 4	11	9	King 17, Curran 11 and Heale 10
Carshalton Athletic	51-66/65	Vines 18-2-7-27	17	Vines 2	3	Vines 3	13	17	Vines 27 (2pens)
Concord Rangers	46-80/74	Stokes =28	18+1og	Stokes 2 & H.Elmes 3	6	Stokes 6	13	9	Stokes 28 (3pens) and H.Elmes 17 (1Pen)
Cray Wanderers	45-83/59	Whitnell 20-5-1-26	15	Whitnell 2, Clark,Bremner 4	1	Whitnell 4(2)	13	7	Whitnell 26 (1p) Clark 13 & Bremner 13
Eat Thurrock United	55-98/85	Higgins 31-4-3-38	17+2ogs	Higgins 4	10	Higgins 5	11	9	Higgins 38 (5p), Newby 15 (4p) & Ruel 13
Harrow Borough	46-58/76	Bates 10-1-1-12	22+1og	0	2	4 x 2	9	16	Bates 12
Hastings United	45-44/67	Attwood 10-1-0-11	19+1og	0	1	4 x 2	9	18	Attwood 11
Hendon	47-78/55	Ngoyi 13-3-0-16	17+1og	Rankin 1	6	Ngoyi & Rankin 3	20	6	Ngoyi 16 (1p), Rankin 12 & Charles 11
Horsham	47-48/119	Nwachukwu 8-3-0-11	19+1og	Nwachukwu 1	5	4 x 2	2	14	Nwachukwu 11 (4 pens)
Kingstonian	44-58/68	Traynor 15-0-0-15	18+2ogs	0	5	Traynor 3	12	12(4)	Traynor 15
Leatherhead	49-63/67	Hutchings 14-3-1-18	16+1og	0	6	Hutchings 5	9	15	Hutchings 18 & Andrws 10
Lewes	45-60/55	Booth 12-0-2-14	15+2ogs	0	5	Booth 3	14	8	Booth 14 & Malcolm 10
Lowestoft Town	51-99/68	Henderson 13-0-0-13	20+1og	0	12	Guentchev 4	11	5	Henderson 13, Francis 12 (5 pens), Frew 12
Margate	49-82/73	Appiah 22-9-3-34	13+1og	Appiah 3	6	Appiah 5	10	11	Guentchev 12 & Nolan 10
Met Police	49-65/51	Palmer 14-1-0-15	18+1og	0	2	T.Smith 6	14	11	Appiah 34 & Bradbrook 12
Tooting & Mitcham U	44-47/122	Stimson 7-0-0-7	22	0	3	Stimson 4	0	18(6)	Palmer 15 & Smith Tyrone 11 (2pens)
Wealdstone	56-100/48	Jolly 32-0-13-45	15-2ogs	Jolly 3	2	Jolly 5	22	9	Stimson 7
Wingate & Finchley	44-64/84	Smith Leon 23-0-0-23	14-3ogs	Karagul 1	0	Smith Leon 4	3	13((4)	Jolly 45 (1p) & Fitzgerald 10 (2p)
									Smith Leon 23 & Laird 11

Non-League Action...

Max Porter (Newport County) and York's Jon Challinor vie for the ball during the FA Trophy final.

Photo: Graham Brown.

BOGNOR REGIS TOWN

Chairman: Dominic Reynolds
Secretary: Simon Cook   **(T)** 07527 455 167   **(E)** sajcook2@aol.com
Additional Committee Members:
Roger Nash, Jack Pearce

Manager: Jamie Howell & Darin Kilpatrick
Programme Editor: Rob Garforth   **(E)** rjgarforth@hotmail.com

Action from Bognor's pre-season friendly against AFC Wimbledon.

Club Factfile

Founded: 1883   **Nickname:** The Rocks
Previous Names: None
Previous Leagues: West Sussex 1896-1926, Brighton & Hove District 1926-27, Sussex County 1927-72, Southern League 1972-81, Isthmian 1982-2004, Conference 2004-09

Club Colours (change): White with green trim/green/white (Gold/black/gold)

Ground: Nyewood Lane, Bognor Regis PO21 2TY   **(T)** 01243 822 325
Capacity: 4,100   **Seats:** 350   **Covered:** 2,600   **Clubhouse:** Yes   **Shop:** Yes
Directions West along sea front from pier past Aldwick shopping centre then turn right into Nyewood Lane.

Previous Grounds:

Record Attendance: 3,642 v Swnsea City - FA Cup 1st Round replay 1984
Record Victory: 24-0 v Littlehampton - West Sussex League 1913-14
Record Defeat: 0-19 v Shoreham - West Sussex League 1906-07
Record Goalscorer: Kevin Clements - 206
Record Appearances: Mick Pullen - 967 (20 seasons)
Additional Records: Paid £2,000 for Guy Rutherford 1995-96. Received £10,500 from Brighton & Hove for John Crumplin and
Senior Honours: Geoff Cooper, and from Crystal Palace for Simon Rodger.
Sussex Professional Cup 1973-74. Sussex Senior Cup x9.
Isthmian League Division 1 South Play-offs 2011-12.

10 YEAR RECORD

02-03		03-04		04-05		05-06		06-07		07-08		08-09		09-10		10-11		11-12	
Isth1S	2	Isth P	10	Conf S	9	Conf S	12	Conf S	12	Conf S	18	Conf S	21	Isth P	22	Isth1S	2	Isth1S	2

BURY TOWN

Chairman: Russell Ward
Secretary: Mrs Wendy Turner **(T)** 07795 661 959 **(E)** wturner@burytownfc.freeserve.co.uk
Additional Committee Members:
Chris Ward

Manager: Richard Wilkins
Programme Editor: Christopher Ward **(E)** cpward@burytownfc.co.uk

Club Factfile

Founded: 1872 **Nickname:** The Blues
Previous Names: Bury St Edmunds 1895-1902, Bury United 1902-06
Previous Leagues: Norfolk & Suffolk Border, Essex & Suffolk Border, Eastern Counties 1935-64, 76-87, 97-2006, Metropolitan 1964-71, Southern 1971-76, 87-97

Club Colours (change): All blue (orange/black/orange)

Ground: Ram Meadow, Cotton Lane, Bury St Edmunds IP33 1XP **(T)** 01284 754 721
Capacity: 3,500 **Seats:** 300 **Covered:** 1,500 **Clubhouse:** Yes **Shop:** Yes
Directions Follow signs to Town Centre from A14. At second roundabout take first left into Northgate Street then left into Mustow Street at T junction at lights and left again into Cotton Lane. Ground is 350 yards on the right.

Previous Grounds:

Record Attendance: 2,500 v Enfield - FA Cup 1986
Record Victory: Not known
Record Defeat: Not known
Record Goalscorer: Doug Tooley
Record Appearances: Doug Tooley
Additional Records: Paid £1,500 to Chelmsford City for Mel Springett
Received £5,500 from Ipswich Town for Simon Milton
Senior Honours:
Eastern Counties League 1963-64.
Suffolk Premier Cup x9.
Southern League Division One Central 2010/11

10 YEAR RECORD

02-03		03-04		04-05		05-06		06-07		07-08		08-09		09-10		10-11		11-12	
ECP	9	ECP	9	ECP	2	ECP	2	Isth1N	17	Isth1N	7	SthC	7	SthC	1	Isth P	3	Isth P	5

BURY TOWN

No.	Date	Comp	H/A	Opponents	Att:	Result	Goalscorers	Pos
1	Aug 20	Isth P	A	Horsham	264	W 3 - 1	Short 10 Smith 12 Essandoh 81	
2	23		H	Hendon	410	L 0 - 1		
3	27		H	Hastings United	359	W 5 - 0	Leabon 10 Smith 33 S.Reed 69 Short 78 Nurse 86	2
4	29		A	Billericay Town	339	D 4 - 4	L.Reed 7 45 Leabon 59 S.Reed 80	
5	Sept 3		A	Wealdstone	501	L 1 - 3	S.Reed 40	
6	10		H	Met Police	411	L 0 - 1		12
7	13		A	Canvey Island	302	W 1 - 0	Cunningham 45	
8	17	FAC 1Q	H	Gorleston	450	W 3 - 0	L Reed 20 83 Hipperson 77	
9	24		H	Aveley	422	W 1 - 0	Bullard 45	9
10	27		H	Concord Rangers	346	W 2 - 0	Watts (og) 59 Cunningham 61	8
11	Oct 1	FAC 2Q	A	Redbridge	120	L 0 - 1		
12	4		A	AFC Hornchurch	197	W 1 - 0	Cunningham 20	
13	8		H	Leathehead	386	W 2 - 1	Cunningham 13 53	7
14	22	FAT 1Q	A	Aveley	102	W 1 - 0	L.Reed 79	
15	29		A	Harrow Borough	176	L 1 - 2	Leabon 1	
16	Nov 1		A	Carshalton Athletic	122	L 1 - 2	Leabon 65	8
17	5	FAT 2Q	H	Hythe Town	302	W 3 - 2	Cunningham 14 S.Reed 37 51	
18	12		A	Lewes	730	D 1 - 1	Leabon 44	8
19	19		H	East Thurrock	384	W 5 - 2	L.Reed 8 Sands 12 43 Nunn 25 Clark 36	8
20	22		H	Kingstonian	376	D 1 - 1	Leabon 3	8
21	26	FAT 3Q	A	Farnborough	312	D 2 - 2	B.Clarke 3 11	
22	29	FAT 3Qr	H	Farnborough		L 0 - 2		
23	Dec 3		H	Tooting & Mitcham U	357	W 4 - 2	Bullard 63 B.Clark 74 90 S.Reed 81	
24	10		A	Cray Wanderers	125	L 0 - 2		8
25	17		H	Canvey Island	385	W 2 - 0	Cunningham 9 Nurse 37	8
26	20		A	Wingate & Finchley	103	L 2 - 3	Cunningham 48 Smith 59	
27	26		A	Lowestoft Town	1066	L 1 - 2	S.Reed 22	8
28	31		A	Hendon	172	W 4 - 3	Cunningham 30 (pen). Hipperson 38. Leabon 52 , Clark 90	
29	Jan 2		H	Billericay Town	560	D 1 - 1	S.Reed 19	7
30	7		H	Carshalton Athletc	432	W 2 - 0	L.Reed 23 Cunningham 63	7
31	14		A	Concord Rangers	173	L 2 - 4	Smith 28 L.Reed 85	7
32	21		H	AFC Hornchurch	456	W 2 - 1	S.Reed 23 Sands 90	6
33	28		A	Leatherhead	315	W 5 - 0	Sands 41 SMITH 3 (43 63 79) Nunn 54	5
34	Feb 18		H	Harrow Borough	362	D 2 - 2	Nunn 62 Smth 78	6
35	25		A	Margate	345	W 3 - 2	Smith 7 Sands 41 64	6
36	28		H	Margate	342	W 2 - 1	Smith 59 Nunn 65	
37	March 3		H	Lewes	402	W 2 - 1	S.Read 36 Bullard 47	4
38	11		A	Kingstonian	411	D 1 - 1	L.Smith 78 (pen)	
39	17		H	Horsham	360	W 3 - 0	L.Smith 14 L.Reed 32 Leabon 39	4
40	20		A	East Thurrock	158	L 1 - 2	S.Reed 90	4
41	25		A	Hastings United	421	W 1 - 0	Clark 75	4
42	31		H	Wealdstone	413	D 1 - 1	Massey 90 (og)	
43	Apr 2		H	Wingate & Finchley	310	D 2 - 2	Sands 37 L.Smith 44	4
44	7		A	Met Police	127	W 1 - 0	Sands 8	
45	9		H	Lowestoft Town	868	L 2 - 3	S.Reed 2 Nunn 29	
46	14		A	Aveley	149	W 2 - 1	Clark 7 Sands 71	4
47	21		H	Cray Wanderers	478	D 1 - 1	L.Smith 36	
48	28		A	Tooting & Mitcham	191	W 7 - 1	SANDS 3 (18 21 60) CLARK 3 (33 34 72pen) Leabon 80	5
49	May 2	Play-Off SF	A	AFC Hornchurch	646	L 1 3	Clark 63	

CANVEY ISLAND

Chairman: George Frost
Secretary: Gary Sutton   **(T)** 0779 002 5828   **(E)** gary.sutton@sky.com
Additional Committee Members:
Chris Sutton, Steve Chaplin

Manager: Steve Tilson
Programme Editor: Glen Eckett   **(E)** gleneckett@another.com

THE NON-LEAGUE CLUB DIRECTORY

Book Holiday Inn Hotels and Save today!

Home

Clubs

Steps 1 - 4

League Tables

35 Years of Non-League Football

The Non-League Club Directory has developed into a comprehensive record of competitions within the non-League game, giving this level of football the

www.non-leagueclubdirectory.co.uk

Club Factfile

Founded: 1926   **Nickname:** The Gulls

Previous Names:

Previous Leagues: Southend & District, Thurrock & Thames Combination, Parthenon, Metropolitan, Greater London 1964-71, Essex Senior 1971-95, Isthmian 1995-2004, Conference 2004-06

Club Colours (change): Yellow and sky blue/sky blue/yellow (White with sky blue trim/white with sky blue trim/sky blue)

Ground: The Prospects Stadium, Park Lane, Canvey Island, Essex SS8 7PX   **(T)** 01268 682 991

Capacity: 4,100   **Seats:** 500   **Covered:** 827   **Clubhouse:** Yes   **Shop:** Yes

Directions
A130 from A13 or A127 at Sadlers Farm roundabout.
One mile through Town Centre, first right past old bus garage.

Previous Grounds:

Record Attendance: 3,553 v Aldershot Town - Isthmian League 2002-03

Record Victory: Not Known
Record Defeat: Not Known

Record Goalscorer: Andy Jones

Record Appearances: Steve Ward

Additional Records: Paid £5,000 to Northwich Victoria for Chris Duffy
Received £4,500 from Farnborough Town for Brian Horne

Senior Honours:
Isthmian Division 1 1993-94, Premier Division 2003-04.
FA Trophy 2000-01. Essex Senior Cup 1998-99, 2000-01, 2001-02.

02-03		03-04		04-05		05-06		06-07		07-08		08-09		09-10		10-11		11-12	
Isth P	2	Isth P	1	Conf N	18	Conf N	4	Isth1N	6	Isth1N	5	Isth P	12	Isth P	16	Isth P	6	Isth P	8

CANVEY ISLAND

No.	Date	Comp	H/A	Opponents	Att:	Result	Goalscorers	Pos
1	Aug 20	Isth P	H	Carshalton Athletic	402	L 1 - 2	Dobinson 18	
2	23		A	AFC Hornchurch	270	W 2 - 1	D.Heale 32 King 63	
3	27		A	Kingstonian	318	W 2 - 1	Rhodes 37 King 73	7
4	29		H	East Thurrock	409	W 1 - 0	King 78	
5	Sept 3		H	Harrow Borough	402	W 1 - 0	King 65	3
6	10		A	Wingate & Finchley	171	W 2 - 0	Gordon 30 Curran 89	3
7	13		H	Bury Town	302	L 0 - 1		
8	17	FAC 1Q	H	**Stansted**	259	W 4 - 1	**D.HEALE 3 (28 65 90) Gordon 69**	
9	24		A	Leatherhead	306	W 1 - 0	D.Heale 60	2
10	27		H	Aveley	304	L 0 - 3		
11	Oct 1	FAC 2Q	H	**Bishop's Stortford**	316	L 0 - 1		7
12	4		A	Lowestoft Town	633	D 1 - 1	King 18	
13	8		H	Lewes	371	L 1 - 2	Rhodes 74	8
14	15		H	Tooting & Mitcham U	487	W 2 - 0	Heale10 Curran 70	8
15	22	FAT 1Q	H	**Hendon**	262	W 4 - 0	**KING 3 (24 46 89) Hallett 86**	
16	29		A	Billericay Town	601	L 2 - 4	King 16 Hallett 74	9
17	Nov 5	FAT 2Q	A	**Grays Athletic**	344	W 3 - 2	Heale 35 King 67 88	
18	8		A	Cray Wanderers	175	D 0 - 0		
19	12		A	Hendon	198	L 0 - 1		9
20	19		A	Wealdstone	434	W 2 - 1	Curran 57 King 74 (pen)	9
21	22		H	Hastings United	283	L 1 - 2	Manning (og) 35	
22	26	FAT 3Q	A	**Hampton & Richmond**	289	L 2 - 4	**King 73 Rhodes 74**	
23	Dec 3		A	Margate	358	D 1 - 1	Heale 7	9
24	10		H	Horsham	334	W 1 - 0	Heale 90	9
25	17		A	Bury Town	385	L 0 - 2		
26	26		H	Concord Rangers	763	L 0 - 2		9
27	31		H	AFC Hornchurch	428	W 4 - 1	Dobbinson 66 Hallett 75 Curran 90 Woods-Garness 90	
28	Jan 2		A	East Thurrock United	276	L 1 - 2	Rhodes 61	10
29	7		H	Cray Wanderers	322	L 1 - 2	Rhodes 26	12
30	14		A	Aveley	223	W 4 - 2	Easterford 20 Woods-Garness 45 Curran 90 Hallett 90	11
31	21		H	Lowestoft Town	371	W 3 - 2	Rhodes 13 Woods-Garness 43 Curran 45	10
32	28		A	Lewes	607	W 2 - 1	Rhodes 51 Woods-Garness 73	8
33	31		H	Metropolitan Police	262	D 2 - 2	Curran 13 Hallett 69	
34	Feb 18		H	Billericay Town	506	L 0 - 2		9
35	25		A	Tooting & Mitcham U	252	W 1 - 0	Easterford 61	8
36	March 3		H	Hendon	323	W 3 - 1	KIng 54 Woods-Garness 66 90	7
37	7		A	Metropolitan Police	133	L 1 - 3	Woods-Garness	
38	10		A	Hastings United	382	D 1 - 1	Woods-Garness 39	7
39	17		A	Carshalton Athletic	162	W 1 - 0	Mason 43	8
40	25		H	Kingstonian	356	L 0 - 2		11
41	27		H	Wealdstone	262	W 3 - 1	Curran 25 70 King 32 (pen)	8
42	31		A	Harrow Borough	183	W 4 - 3	Hallett 22 60 King 84 (pen) Sheehan 86	9
43	Apr 7		H	Wingate & Finchley	343	L 2 - 3	Curran 48 Mason 53	
44	9		A	Concord Rangers	672	W 2 - 1	Dumas 3 Heale 48	
45	14		H	Leaherhead	301	W 3 - 1	Dumas 41 Nnamani 61(og) Gordon 73	8
46	21		A	Horsham	189	W 2 - 1	Curran 70 Hallett 75	8
47	28		H	Margate	342	W 5 - 0	Dobinson 3 73 King 17 Hallett 34 Sheehan 89	

CARSHALTON ATHLETIC

Chairman: Alan Walker
Secretary: John Kistner   **(T)** 07720 438425   **(E)** john.kistner@carshaltonathletic.co.uk
Additional Committee Members:
James Barrett, Paul williams

Manager: Paul Dipre
Programme Editor: Chris Blanchard   **(E)** chrisblanchard@carshaltonathletic.co.uk

2011-12 Squad along with the club's Junior teams.

Club Factfile

Founded: 1905   **Nickname:** Robins
Previous Names: None
Previous Leagues: Southern Suburban > 1911, Surrey Senior 1922-23, London 1923-46, Corinthian 1946-56, Athenian 1956-73, Isthmian 1973-2004, Conference 2004-06

Club Colours (change): All red (All purple)

Ground: War Memorial Sports Ground, Colston Avenue, Carshalton SM5 2PW   **(T)** 0208 642 2551
Capacity: 8,000   **Seats:** 240   **Covered:** 4,500   **Clubhouse:** Yes   **Shop:** Yes
Directions: Turn right out of Carshalton Station exit,
turn right again,
and then left into Colston Avenue.

Previous Grounds:

Record Attendance: 7,800 v Wimbledon - London Senior Cup
Record Victory: 13-0 v Worthing - Isthmian League Cup 28/01/1991
Record Defeat: 0-11 v Southall - Athenian League March 1963
Record Goalscorer: Jimmy Bolton - 242
Record Appearances: Jon Warden - 504
Additional Records: Paid £15,000 to Enfield for Curtis Warmington
     Received £30,000 from Crystal Palace for Ian Cox
Senior Honours:
Isthmian League Division 1 South 2002-03.
Surrey Senior Shield 1975-76. London Challenge Cup 1991-92. Surrey Senior Cup x3.

10 YEAR RECORD

02-03	03-04	04-05	05-06	06-07	07-08	08-09	09-10	10-11	11-12
Isth1S 1	Isth P 7	Conf S 19	Conf S 21	Isth P 13	Isth P 18	Isth P 4	Isth P 17	Isth P 13	Isth P 16

CARSHALTON ATHLETIC

No.	Date	Comp	H/A	Opponents	Att:	Result	Goalscorers	Pos
1	Aug 20	Isth P	A	Canvey Island	402	W 2 - 1	McDonald 25 Vines 75	
2	23		H	Wealdstone	155	D 0 - 0		
3	27		H	Hendon	174	L 0 - 3		13
4	29		A	Cray Athletic	177	L 0 - 1		
5	Sept 3		A	Hastings United	431	W 2 - 0	McDonald 16 49	11
6	10		H	Billericay Town	134	L 0 - 1		13
7	13		A	Horsham	185	W 3 - 1	Davis 18 Hearn 55 Hamici 83	
8	17	FAC 1Q	H	**Faversham**	160	W 3 - 0	Vines 30 34 Joseph 49	
9	24		H	Lowestoft Town	212	L 1 - 4	Davis 59	13
10	28		A	Metropolitan Police	178	L 0 - 5		
11	Oct 1	FAC 2Q	A	**Dover Athletic**	639	L 0 - 3		
12	8		A	Margate	340	W 1 - 0	Vines 69	13
13	15		H	Harrow Borough	294	L 0 - 1		14
14	22	FAT 1Q	H	**Bideford**	200	W 3 - 1	Onochie 65 Vines 83 88	
15	29		A	Concord Rangers	130	D 0 - 0		15
16	Nov 1		H	Bury Town	122	W 2 - 1	Nolan 27 Vines 84	
17	5	FAT 2Q	H	**Cirencester Town**	225	W 3 - 1	Lodge 7 (pen) Hamici 53 Vines 70	
18	13		A	Kingstonian	486	W 3 - 2	Vines (2) Hamici	
19	19		H	Leatherhead	364	D 1 - 1	Lodge 37	12
20	22		A	Carshalton Athletic	219	D 1 - 1	Roberts 41	
21	26	FAT 3Q	A	**Maldon & Tiptree**	72	W 1 - 0	Ray 63	
22	Dec 3		H	Wingate & Finchley	192	W 3 - 0	McDonald 65 Ayres 77 Nolan 88	12
23	10	FAT 1	H	**Bishop's Stortford**	243	W 5 - 0	Vines 14 Nolan 39 Pigden 43 Davis 67 Crook 76	
24	13		H	Lewes	150	L 1 - 2	Ray 67	
25	17		H	Horsham	189	W 2 - 1	Crook 50 McDonald 59	10
26	20		H	East Thurrock United	137	L 0 - 1		
27	26		A	Tooting & Mitcham United	491	L 3 - 4	Vines 37 Ayres 51 68	11
28	31		A	Wealdstone	463	D 1 - 1	Fitzgerald 34 (pen)	
29	Jan 2		H	Cray Wanderers	208	L 2 - 3	Crook 39 Hamici 58	13
30	7		A	Bury Town	432	L 0 - 2		13
31	9		A	Aveley	162	D 1 - 1	Finn 70	14
32	14	FAT 2	A	**Lincoln City**	1743	D 0 - 0		
33	18	FAT 2r	H	**Lincoln City**	488	W 3 - 1	VINES 3 (38 pen 41 56)	
34	21		A	East Thurrock United	161	D 1 - 1	Vines 17	
35	28		H	Margate	290	W 2 - 1	Vines 89 Davis 90	
36	Feb 7	FAT 3	A	**Newport County**	975	L 0 - 4		
37	18		H	Concord Rangers	216	L 0 - 2		15
38	25		A	Harrow Borough	145	W 2 - 1	Hamici 39 69	14
39	28		A	Leatherhead	295	W 1 - 0	Pigden 45	
40	March 3		H	Kingstonian	383	L 0 - 1		14
41	10		A	Lewes	574	L 0 - 1		14
42	13		H	AFC Hornchurch	138	L 1 - 2	Vines 90	
43	17		H	Canvey Island	162	L 0 - 1		16
44	24		A	Hendon	183	D 1 - 1	Sogbanmu 17	18
45	31		H	Hastings United	203	W 2 - 0	Vines 69 78	16
46	Apr 2		H	Metropolitan Police	164	W 2 - 1	Vines 22 90 (pen)	
47	6		A	Billericay Town	876	D 1 - 1	Ayres 74	
48	9		H	Tooting & Mitcham U	281	W 3 - 0	VINES 3 (17 55 64)	
49	14		A	Lowestoft Town	601	L 2 - 3	Vines 18 Ayres 51	
50	21		H	Aveley	490	D 0 - 0		16
51	28		A	Wingate & Finchley	112	L 1 - 2	Vines 65	

CONCORD RANGERS

Chairman: Antony Smith
Secretary: Chris Crerie   **(T)** 0790 952 8818   **(E)** concordrangers@btinternet.com
Additional Committee Members:
Jack Smith junior, Ron Heyfron

Manager: Danny Cowley
Programme Editor: Phil Crowe   **(E)** phil@hopesun.co.uk

Back Row: Harry Elmes Nicky Cowley Lee White Dan Scopes James Dudley Danny Cowley Nick Skelton Richard Halle James Elmes
Front Row: Adam Wickenden Michael Begg Seb Dunbar Michael Noone Tom Bruno Billy Coyne Tyler Campbell David Adepide Tony Stokes
Connor French Gary Ewers

2011-12 Squad.

Club Factfile

Founded: 1967   **Nickname:** Beach Boys
Previous Names:
Previous Leagues: Southend & District, Southend Alliance, Essex Intermediate 1988-91, Essex Senior 1991-2008

Club Colours (change): Yellow/blue/blue (Blue/white/white)

Ground: Aspect Arena, Thames Road, Canvey Island, Essex SS8 0HH   **(T)** 01268 515 750
Capacity: 1,500   **Seats:** Yes   **Covered:** Yes   **Clubhouse:** Yes   **Shop:**

Directions
A130 onto Canvey Island.
Turn right into Thorney Bay Road.
Then right again into Thames Road.

Previous Grounds: Waterside

Record Attendance: 1,500 v Lee Chapel North - FA Sunday Cup 1989-90
Record Victory: Not Known
Record Defeat: Not Known
Record Goalscorer: Not Known
Record Appearances: Not Known
Additional Records:

Senior Honours:
Essex Intermediate League Division 2 1990-91. Essex Senior League 1997-98, 2003-04, 07-08

10 YEAR RECORD									
02-03	03-04	04-05	05-06	06-07	07-08	08-09	09-10	10-11	11-12
ESen 2	ESen 1	ESen 9	ESen 7	ESen 7	ESen 1	Isth1N 5	Isth1N 2	Isth P 8	Isth P 14

CONCORD RANGERS

No.	Date	Comp	H/A	Opponents	Att:	Result	Goalscorers	Pos
1	Aug 20	Isth P	A	Hendon	164	L 0 - 1		
2	23		H	Cray Wanderers	131	D 1 - 1	Charles 52	
3	27		H	Tooting & Mitcham	162	L 3 - 4	Campbell 6 59 H.Elmes 72	20
4	29		A	Aveley	113	D 3 - 3	Noone 75 (pen) Cowley 84 Sabola 90	
5	Sept 3		A	Lowestoft Town	701	L 0 - 5		21
6	10		H	Hastings United	196	D 2 - 2	Asante 38 Noone 42 (pen)	
7	13		A	Billericay Town	282	D 0 - 0		
8	17	FAC 1Q	A	AFC Hornchurch	280	W 3 - 1	Asante 20 H.Elmes 52 Marshall 80	
9	24		H	Metropolitan Police	142	L 0 - 3		21
10	27		A	Bury Town	346	L 0 - 2		
11	Oct 1	FAC 2Q	A	Wroxham	220	D 2 - 2	King 90 Asante 90	
12	4	FAC 2Qr	H	Wroxham	235	L 1 - 2	Stokes 54	
13	8		A	Horsham	548	W 3 - 0	Stokes 1 21 H.Elmes 67	20
14	22	FAT 1Q	H	Harlow Town	190	L 2 - 3	H.Elmes 6 Stokes 14	
15	25		H	Margate	147	D 1 - 1	Stokes 3 (pen)	
16	29		H	Carshalton Athletic	130	D 0 - 0		19
17	Nov 1		H	Kingstonian	134	L 2 - 3	Stokes 89 Beckford 90	
18	5		A	Wingate & Yeading	94	L 1 - 3	Stokes 25	
19	12		H	AFC Hornchurch	162	L 1 - 2	Stokes 35 (pen)	19
20	19		H	Harrow Borough	132	W 1 - 0	Stokes 89	
21	Dec 3		H	Wealdstone	152	L 1 - 2	Stokes 28	19
22	10		A	Lewes	649	W 2 - 1	Stanley 39 Stokes 62	
23	17		H	Billericay Town	290	D 0 - 0		18
24	26		A	Canvey Island	763	W 2 - 0	J.Elmes 25 H Elmes 40	17
25	31		A	Cray Wanderers	205	W 4 - 2	H.Elmes 43 STOKES 3 (26 55 71)	
26	Jan 2		H	Aveley	162	W 3 - 0	H.ELMES 3 (20 25 44)	
27	7		A	Margate	393	L 0 - 1		17
28	10		A	East Thurrock United	182	L 1 - 4	Miller 8	
29	14		H	Bury Town	173	W 4 - 2	King 23 Stanley 41 58 H.Elmes 44	15
30	21		A	Kingstonian	273	W 1 - 0	Stokes 78	14
31	28		H	Horsham	172	W 5 - 0	STOKES 3 (14 60 81) Stanley 45 Hann 84	
32	Feb 15		A	Leatherhead	204	W 3 - 1	H.Elmes 50 Miller 76 Okojie 81	
33	18		A	Carshalton Athletic	216	W 2 - 0	H.Elmes 17 Stanley 65	13
34	25		H	Leatherhead	131	W 2 - 1	Stanley 69 Stokes 83	12
35	March 3		A	AFC Hornchurch	328	L 0 - 2		12
36	6		A	Harrow Borough	78	W 3 - 0	Cowley 36 H.Elmes 67 Stokes 90	
37	10		H	Wingate & Finchley	126	D 1 - 1	Stokes 43 (pen)	11
38	17		H	Hendon	132	W 2 - 0	Stokes 34 71	11
39	24		A	Tooting & Mitcham	182	W 6 - 0	H.Elmes 4 56 Harris 10 Stokes11 62 Miller 87	10
40	31		H	Lowestoft Town	247	W 3 - 2	H.Elmes 74 81(pen) Stanley 87	9
41	Apr 7		A	Hastings United	335	D 1 - 1	Stokes 56	
42	9		H	Canvey Island	672	L 1 - 2	Easterford 9 (og)	
43	14		A	Met Police	115	L 0 - 3		12
44	17		H	East Thurrock United	124	L 4 - 5	King 15 Stokes 39 45 Stanley 89	
45	21		H	Lewes	252	L 2 - 3	Robinson 29 Beckford 73	12
46	27		A	Wealdstone	770	L 1 - 3	King 11	14

CRAY WANDERERS

Chairman: Gary Hillman
Secretary: Kerry Phillips   **(T)** 07718 353 583   **(E)** kerryphillips@hotmail.com
Additional Committee Members:
Martin Hodson, Jerry Dowlen

Manager: Ian Jenkins
Programme Editor: Jerry Dowlen   **(E)** jerry.dowlen@btopenworld.net

Cray in action during a 3-1 win at Margate (April 2012).

Club Factfile

Founded: 1860   **Nickname:** Wanderers or Wands
Previous Names: Cray Old Boys (immediately after WW1); Sidcup & Footscray (start of WW2).
Previous Leagues: Kent 1894-1903, 1906-07, 1909-1914, 1934-38, 1978-2004; West Kent & South Suburban Leagues (before WW1); London 1920-1934, 1951-1959; Kent Amateur 1938-1939, 1946-1951; South London Alliance 1943-1946; Aetolian 1959-1964; Greater London 1964-1966; Metropolitan 1966-1971; Met. London 1971-1975; London Spartan 1975-1978.
Club Colours (change): Amber/black/black (Pale blue/white/pale blue)

Ground: Bromley FC, Hayes Lane, Bromley, Kent BR2 9EF   **(T)** 020 8460 5291
Capacity: 5,000   **Seats:** 1,300   **Covered:** 2,500   **Clubhouse:** Yes   **Shop:** Yes

Directions — **From M25:** Leaving the motorway at junction 4, follow the A21 to Bromley and London, for approximately 4 miles and then fork left onto the A232 signposted Croydon/Sutton. At the second set of traffic lights, turn right into Baston Road (B265), following it for about two miles as it becomes Hayes Street and then Hayes Lane. Cray Wanderers FC is on the right hand side of the road just after the mini roundabout. There is ample room for coaches to drive down the driveway, turn round and park.

Previous Grounds: Star Lane (1860s), Derry Downs (until 1898), Fordcroft (1898-1936), Twysdens (1936-1939), St Mary Cray Rec (1940s),
Previous Grounds: Cont. Northfield Farm (1950-51), Tothills (aka Fordcroft, 1951-1955), Grassmeade (1955-1973), Oxford Road (1973-1998).

Record Attendance: (Grassmeade) 2,160vLeytonstone – FA Am.C 3rd Rd, 1968-69; (Oxford R) 1,523vStamford – FAV QF 79-80; (Hayes L) 1,082vAFC Wim. – 04-05
Record Victory: 15-0 v Sevenoaks - 1894-95.
Record Defeat: 2-15 (H) and 0-14 (A) v Callenders Athletic - Kent Amateur League, 1947-48.
Record Goalscorer: Ken Collishaw 274 (1954-1965)
Record Appearances: John Dorey - 500 (1961-72).
Additional Records: Unbeaten for 28 Ryman League games in 2007-2008.

Senior Honours:
Kent League 1901-02, 80-81, 2002-03, 03-04 (League Cup 83-84, 2002-03); London League 1956-57, 57-58 (League Cup 54-55); Aetolian League 1962-63 (League Cup 63 -64); Greater London League 1965-66 (League Cup 64-65, 65-66); Met. Lge Cup 1970-71; Met. London League & League Cup 1974-75; London Spartan League 1976-77, 77 -78. Kent Amateur Cup 1930-31, 62-63, 63-64, 64-65. Kent Senior Trophy 1992-93, 2003-04.

10 YEAR RECORD

02-03		03-04		04-05		05-06		06-07		07-08		08-09		09-10		10-11		11-12	
Kent P	1	Kent P	1	Isth1	6	Isth1	11	Isth1S	12	Isth1S	3	Isth1S	2	Isth P	15	Isth P	9	Isth P	9

CRAY WANDERERS

No.	Date	Comp	H/A	Opponents	Att:	Result	Goalscorers	Pos
1	Aug 21	Isth P	H	AFC Hornchurch	173	L 2 - 5	Bremner 14 85	
2	23		A	Concord Rangers	131	D 1 - 1	Whitnell 42	
3	27		A	Leatherhead	264	W 4 - 1	Whitnell 46 BREMNER 3 (62 68 84)	9
4	29		H	Carshalton Athletic	177	W 1 - 0	Clark 45	
5	Sept 3		H	East Thurrock	187	W 3 - 0	Whitnell 6 Clark 25 Bremner 90	4
6	10		A	Harrow Borough	171	W 4 - 0	Whitnell 45 Saunders 46 Clark 64 Long 77	4
7	13		H	Wingate & Finchley	148	W 3 - 2	Saunders 13 Bentley 49 Whitnell 90	
8	17	FAC 1Q	A	**Hastings United**	301	W 3 - 0	WHITNELL 3 (23 85 87)	
9	24		A	Lewes	721	L 0 - 1		5
10	28		A	Tooting & Mitcham U	283	W 4 - 0	CLARK 3 (21 71 80) Willy 31	
11	Oct 2	FAC 2Q	H	**Erith Town**	183	W 4 - 0	Whitnell 25 Perkins 33 36 Sterling 50	4
12	4		H	Wealdstone	164	W 2 - 1	Perkins 11 Clark 73	
13	8		A	Kingstonian	353	L 2 - 4	Clark 6 Saunders 28	5
14	15	FAC 3Q	H	**Dartford**	69	L 1 - 2	Whitnell 47	
15	22	FAT 1Q	A	**Lewes**	536	L 1 - 2	Whitnell 65	
16	29		A	Metropolitan Police	130	L 0 - 1		7
17	Nov 5		H	Aveley	156	D 2 - 2	Long 79 Willy 89	
18	8		H	Canvey Island	175	D 0 - 0		
19	12		A	Hastings United	487	W 2 - 0	Perkins 33 Clark 90	5
20	19		A	Lowestoft Town	663	L 1 - 2	Whitnell 50	6
21	26		H?	Hendon	190	D 0 - 0		
22	29		H	Billericay Town	172	L 2 - 1	Bremner 9 Clark 17	
23	Dec 3		A	Horsham	184	W 5 - 0	Willy 16 Bremner 61 Phillips 66 82 Dolby 87	7
24	10		H	Bury Town	125	W 2 - 0	Bremner 34 Whitnell 58	
25	17		A	Wingate & Finchley	85	W 2 - 4	Young 21 Whitnell 60	
26	27		H	Margate	369	L 2 - 4	Clark 3 Perkins 45	6
27	31		H	Concord Rangers	205	L 2 - 4	Whitnell 20 Bremner 85	
28	Jan 2		A	Carshalton Athletic	208	W 3 - 2	Whitnell 7 71 Bremner 89	6
29	7		A	Canvey Island	322	W 2 - 1	Whitnell 27 Clark 44	5
30	21		A	Wealdstone	445	D 1 - 1	Whitnell 58	5
31	28		H	Kingstonian	254	D 0 - 0		7
32	Feb 14		H	Tooting & Mitcham U	184	W 4 - 1	WHITNELL 3 (5 41 65) Clark 90	
33	18		H	Met. Police	162	W 2 - 1	Bentley 47 Perkins 52	4
34	25		A	Billericay Town	488	L 1 - 3	Saunders 35	5
35	March 3		H	Hastings United	143	W 1 - 0	Saunders 18	5
36	10		A	Aveley	159	D 1 - 1	Bremner 48	6
37	17		A	AFC Hornchurch	287	W 2 - 1	Bremner 69 Vines 88	
38	25		H	Leatherhead	268	L 1 - 2	Darvill 85	
39	31		A	East Thurrock United	165	W 2 - 1	Whitnell 24 (pen) 70	5
40	Apr 7		H	Harrow Borough	180	L 1 - 2	Whitnell 28	5
41	9		A	Margate	257	W 3 - 1	Long 33 Darvill 67 Whitnell 79 (pen)	
42	14		H	Lewes	229	L 0 - 1		8
43	21		A	Bury Town	478	D 1 - 1	Perkins 37	9
44	24		H	Lowestoft Town	188	L 0 - 2		
45	28		H	Horsham	177	W 3 - 1	Power 6 10 Dolby 85	9

EAST THURROCK UNITED

Chairman: Brian Mansbridge
Secretary: Neil Speight   **(T)** 0788 531 3435   **(E)** speight.n@sky.com
Additional Committee Members:
Mick Stephens, Ian Simes

Manager: John Coventry
Programme Editor: Neil Speight   **(E)** speight.n@sky.com

Back (from left): Payan Patel (Physio), Kris Newby, Sam Higgins, Steve Sheehan, Spencer Harrison, Richard Wray, Jamie Riley, Simon Peddie, Lewis Bentley, Ross Parmenter, Kye Ruel, Neil Gray (GK coach). Front: Sam Collins, Ryan Sammons, John Coventry (Manager) Reiss Gilbey (Capt), Jay Devereux (Assistant manager), Matt Hall, Tom Stephen.

Club Factfile

Founded: 1969   **Nickname:** Rocks
Previous Names: Corringham Social > 1969 (Sunday side)
Previous Leagues: South Essex Combination, Greater London, Metropolitan 1972-75, London Spartan 1975-79, Essex Senior 1979-92, Isthmian 1992-2004, Southern 2004-05

Club Colours (change): Amber with black trim/black/black (Black & white stripes/black/black)

Ground: Rookery Hill, Corringham, Essex SS17 9LB   **(T)** 01375 644 166
Capacity: 4,000 **Seats:** 160 **Covered:** 1,000 **Clubhouse:** Yes **Shop:** No

Directions
From A13 London-Southend road,
take A1014 at Stanford-le-Hope for two and half miles,
Ground is on the left.

Previous Grounds: Billet, Stanford-le-Hope 1970-73, 74-76, Grays Athletic 1973-74, Tilbury FC 1977-82, New Thames Club 1982-84

Record Attendance: 1,215 v Woking FA Cup 2003
Record Victory: 7-0 v Coggeshall (H) - Essex Senior League 1984
Record Defeat: 0-9 v Eton Manor (A) - Essex Senior League 1982
Record Goalscorer: Graham Stewart - 102
Record Appearances: Glen Case - 600+
Additional Records: £22,000 from Leyton Orient for Greg Berry 1990

Senior Honours:
Isthmian League Division Three 1999-2000, Division One North 2010-11. East Anglian Cup 2002-03.

10 YEAR RECORD

02-03	03-04	04-05	05-06	06-07	07-08	08-09	09-10	10-11	11-12
Isth1N 17	Isth1N 12	SthE 2	Isth P 12	Isth P 16	Isth P 20	Isth1N 2	Isth1N 5	Isth1N 1	Isth P 10

EAST THURROCK UNITED

No.	Date	Comp	H/A	Opponents	Att:	Result	Goalscorers	Pos
1	Aug 20	Isth P	A	Tooting & Mitcham	215	W 1 - 0	Kalipha 81	
2	23		H	Hastings Unitred	139	L 0 - 2		
3	27		H	Wealdstone	193	D 3 - 3	Richmond 19 75 Ruel 65	12
4	29		A	Canvey Island	409	L 0 - 1		
5	Sept 3		A	Cray Wanderers	187	L 0 - 3		18
6	10		H	Horsham	135	W 1 - 0	Richmond 70	
7	13		A	Hendon	151	D 1 - 1	Ruel 32	17
8	17	FAC 1Q	H	Bedford Town		W 1 - 0	Elbi 64	
9	24		H	Billericay Town	249	L 1 - 2	Newby 6 (pen)	16
10	27		H	Lowestoft Town	148	L 1 - 3	Collins 3	
11	Oct 1	FAC 2Q	H	St Albans City	181	D 3 - 3	Newby 8 Elbi 46 Ruel 52	
12	4	FAC 2Qr	A	StAlbans City	250	W 3 - 1	Elbi 51 55 Newby 63	
13	8		H	AFC Hormchurch	255	L 0 - 1		19
14	11		A	Leatherhead	260	L 1 - 2	Higgins 73	19
15	15	FAC 3Q	H	North Greenford	123	D 3 - 3	Ruel 53 Cohen 61 Higgins 77	
16	18	FAC 3Qr	A	North Greenford	102	W 3 - 0	Higgins 45 73 Gilbey 55	
17	22	FAT 1Q	H	Bedford Town	141	D 1 - 1	Higgins 52	
18	25	FAT 1Qr	A	Bedford Town	189	W 2 - 1	Newby 58 Collins 65	
19	29	FAC 4Q	A	Eastbourne Borough	603	W 2 - 1	Higgins 57 Newby 73 (pen)	
20	Nov 5	FAT 2Q	A	Faversham Town	137	W 4 - 2	Newby 42 75 Elbi 48 Ladapo 90 (pen)	
21	12	FAC 1	H	Macclesfield Town	1207	L 0 - 3		
22	19		A	Bury Town	384	L 2 - 5	Higgins 14 Ruel 31	22
23	22		H	Lewes	132	W 1 - 0	Newby 89 (pen)	20
24	26	FAT 3Q	A	Redbridge	108	W 2 - 1	Newby11 Elbi 52	
25	29		A	Margate	219	L 0 - 5		
26	Dec 3		H	Kingstonian	194	L 0 - 1		20
27	10	FAT 1	H	Welling United	224	W 2 - 1	Hall 4 Higgins 33	
28	17		H	Hendon	109	D 0 - 0		21
29	20		A	Carshalton Athletic	137	W 1 - 0	Higgins 35	
30	27		A	Aveley	247	W 3 - 0	HIGGINS 3 (5 716)	19
31	31		A	Hastings United	426	W 2 - 1	Newby 60 Whitehead 66 (og)	
32	Jan 2		H	Canvey Island	276	W 2 - 1	Newby 44 (pen) Higgins45	16
33	7		H	Leatherhead	189	W 3 - 0	Higgins 55 57 Newby 70	14
34	10		H	Concord Rangers	182	W 4 - 1	Higgins 22 90 Ruel 57 60	13
35	14	FAT 2	H	Hampton & Richmond B	231	D 1 - 1	Higgins 80	
36	21		A	Carshalton Athletic	161	D 1 - 1	Higgins 61	13
37	28		A	AFC Hornchurch	357	L 0 - 1		16
38	31	FAT 2r	A	Hampton & Richmond B	184	L 1 - 4	Newby 65	
39	Feb 18		H	Margate	176	W 3 - 0	Collins 40 Cohen 42 Newby 70 (pen)	
40	25		A	Lewes	444	D 2 - 2	Cohen 53 Hall 72	16
41	March 3		H	Met Police	161	W 4 - 2	HIGGINS 3(7 57pen 90) Gorbell 68	15
42	6		A	Wingate & Finchley	55	D 3 - 3	H.Cook 6 Higgins 21 27	
43	10		A	Harrow Borough	142	L 1 - 3	Ruel 18	16
44	13		A	Lowestoft Town	541	D 1 - 1	Higgins 34 (pen)	
45	17		H	Tooting & Mitcham U	202	W 1 - 0	Collins 82	14
46	20		H	Bury Town	158	W 2 - 1	Higgins 58 (pen) Bullard (og) 67	
47	24		A	Wealdstone	448	D 2 - 2	Keith 23 Higgins 44	13
48	31		H	Cray Wanderers	165	L 1 - 2	Higgins 7	14
49	Apr 2		A	Harrow Borough	121	L 0 - 3		
50	7		H	Horsham	187	W 5 - 1	Ruel 45 Higgins 45 70 Hall 57 Newby 90	
51	9		H	Aveley	152	W 4 - 1	Harrison 27 Higgins 48 (pen) Ruel 56 Wood 62	12
52	14		A	Billericay Town	648	L 0 - 1		
53	17		A	Concord Rangers	124	W 5 - 4	HIGGINS 3 (11 32 34) Ruel 3 Gilbey 19	
54	21		H	Wingate & Finchley	148	L 1 - 2	Higgins 55 (pen)	13
55	24		A	Met Police	132	W 2 - 1	Ruel 1 Collins 79	
56	28		A	Kingstonian	307	W 5 - 2	HIGGINS 3(17 34 83) Wood 48 Ruel 65	10

Non-League Action...

Mark Stephenson of West Auckland Town shields the ball during their FA Vase Quarter Final with Bournemouth Poppies.

Photo: Graham Brown.

ENFIELD TOWN

Chairman: Paul Millington
Secretary: Peter Coath   **(T)** 0794 937 8931   **(E)** peter.coath@virginmedia.com
Additional Committee Members:
Keith Wortley, Ciaron Glennon, Dave Farenden

Manager: Steve Newing
Programme Editor: Ciaron Glennon   **(E)** ciaron.glennon@btopenworld.com

Back row: Michael Ewang, Joe O'Brien, Dave Kendall, Jordan Lockie, Liam Hope, Phil Kane, Mark Kirby, Dean Pennant, Gary Burrell, Mitch Hahn, Leon Osei, Danny Barber, Joe Stevens, Adam Wallace.
Front row: Jeyasiva Sivapathasundaram, Tyler Campbell, Neil Johnston, Bryan Hammatt, Noel Imber, Jason Dale (assistant manager), Steve Newing (manager), Peter Hammatt (coach), James Chalk, Craig McKay, Walid Matata, Lee Allen, Michael Bardle.
The trophy is the Supporters Direct Cup. Enfield Town beat Wrexham 3-1 to win it.

Club Factfile

Founded: 2001   **Nickname:** ET's or Towners
Previous Names: Broke away from Enfield F.C. in 2001
Previous Leagues: Essex Senior League

Club Colours (change): White/blue/blue (Red & yellow hoops/red/red & yellow hoops)

Ground: Quenn Elizabeth Stadium, Donkey Lane, Enfield EN1 4BT   **(T)** 020 8363 7398
Capacity: **Seats:** Yes   **Covered:** Yes   **Clubhouse:**   **Shop:**

Directions: Turn off A10 at Carterhanger Lane,
then turn immediately into Donkey Lane.

Previous Grounds: Brimsdown Rovers FC 2001-2010

Record Attendance: 562 v Enfield - Middlesex Charity Cup 2002-03
Record Victory: 7-0 v Ilford (A) - 29/04/2003
Record Defeat: Not known
Record Goalscorer: Dan Clarke - 68
Record Appearances: Stuart Snowden - 147
Additional Records:

Senior Honours:
Essex Senior League 2002-03, 04-05. Isthmian League Division 1 North Play-offs 2011-12.

10 YEAR RECORD

02-03	03-04	04-05	05-06	06-07	07-08	08-09	09-10	10-11	11-12
ESen 1	ESen 4	ESen 1	SthE 3	Isth1N 3	Isth1N 12	Isth1N 12	Isth1N 4	Isth1N 6	Isth1N 2

HAMPTON & RICHMOND BOROUGH

Chairman: Steve McPherson
Secretary: Nick Hornsey **(T)** 07768 861 446 **(E)** secretary@hamptonfc.net
Additional Committee Members:
Rob Overfield, David Rees.

HRBFC

Manager: Mark Harper
Programme Editor: William Downing **(E)** hamptonwdjw@gmail.com

Back Row Mo Harkin, Malvin Kamara, Joe Benjamin, Max Hustwick, Paul Johnson, Rodney Chiweshe, Billy Jeffreys, Lloyd Anderson,
Dean Inman, Joe Turner, Elliot Bent, Charlie Moone, James Simmonds, Richard Johnson (Physio)
Front Row Neil Jenkins, Karle Carder, Gary Holloway, Nigel Edgecombe (Coach), Paul Barry (Coach), Mark Harper (Manager),
Andy Smith (Assistant Manager), Anson Cousins, Tom Hickey, Alan Bray
Not pictures JJ Bates, Darren Powell

Club Factfile

Founded: 1921   **Nickname:** Beavers or Borough
Previous Names: Hampton > 1999
Previous Leagues: Kingston & District, South West Middlesex, Surrey Senior 1959-64, Spartan 1964-71, Athenian 1971-73, Isthmian 1973-2007

Club Colours (change): Red with blue flash/blue/red (Sky blue/white/sky blue)

Ground: Beveree Stadium, Beaver Close, Station Road, Hampton TW12 2BX   **(T)** 0208 8979 2456
Capacity: 3,000 **Seats:** 300 **Covered:** 800 **Clubhouse:** Yes **Shop:** Yes

Directions
From M25; Exit M25 at Junction 10 (M3 Richmond). Exit M3 at Junction 1 and take 4th exit (Kempton Park, Kingston).
After approximately 3 miles turn left in to High Street, Hampton. Immediately turn left on to Station Road.
The entrance to the ground is 200 yards on the right hand side.

Previous Grounds:

Record Attendance: 2,520 v AFC Wimbledon - 11/10/2005
Record Victory: 11-1 v Eastbourne United - Isthmian League Division 2 South 1991-92
Record Defeat: 0-13 v Hounslow Town - Middlesex Senior Cup 1962-63
Record Goalscorer: Peter Allen - 176 (1964-73)
Record Appearances: Tim Hollands - 750 (1977-95)
Additional Records: Paid £3,000 to Chesham United for Matt Flitter June 2000
Senior Honours: Received £40,000 from Queens Park Rangers for Leroy Phillips
Isthmian League Premier Division 2006-07.
Spartan League x4. London Senior Cup x2.

10 YEAR RECORD

02-03	03-04	04-05	05-06	06-07	07-08	08-09	09-10	10-11	11-12
Isth P 24	Isth1S 5	Isth P 6	Isth P 5	Isth P 1	Conf S 3	Conf S 2	Conf S 14	Conf S 18	Conf S 21

HAMPTON & RICHMOND BOROUGH

No.	Date	Comp	H/A	Opponents	Att:	Result	Goalscorers	Pos
1	Sat-13-Aug	BSS	H	Bromley	539	L 1-2	Moone 73	15
2	Tue-16-Aug	BSS	A	Woking	1467	L 1-2	Erskine 72	18
3	Sat-20-Aug	BSS	A	Dartford	937	L 1-2	Erskine 32	21
4	Sat-27-Aug	BSS	H	Farnborough	420	D 1-1	Tarpey 19	19
5	Mon-29-Aug	BSS	A	Basingstoke Town	415	D 2-2	Moone 44, Erskine 60	21
6	Sat-03-Sep	BSS	A	Salisbury City	803	L 2-4	Moone pen 2, Ruby 69	22
7	Sat-10-Sep	BSS	H	Chelmsford City	489	L 0-4		22
8	Tue-13-Sep	BSS	H	Dorchester Town	260	L 0-2		22
9	Sat-17-Sep	BSS	A	Eastleigh	463	D 1-1	Collier 51	22
10	Sat-24-Sep	BSS	H	Weston-Super-Mare	391	W 3-1	J Simmonds 2 (pen 28, 54), Tarpey 50	21
11	Sat-08-Oct	BSS	A	Tonbridge Angels	523	L 0-1		22
12	Sat-15-Oct	BSS	H	Boreham Wood	401	L 0-1		22
13	Sat-22-Oct	BSS	H	Havant & Waterlooville	475	D 3-3	Collier 50, J Simmonds 58, Tarpey 90	22
14	Sat-29-Oct	BSS	A	Welling United	572	L 1-2	Drmola 53	22
15	Sat-05-Nov	BSS	H	Eastbourne Borough	441	W 3-1	Ledgister 2 (47, 89), Tarpey 57	21
16	Sat-12-Nov	BSS	A	Dorchester Town	447	L 0-1		21
17	Tue-15-Nov	BSS	A	Maidenhead United	227	W 2-0	Tarpey 65, Collier 81	19
18	Sat-19-Nov	BSS	H	Thurrock	590	L 0-2		20
19	Tue-22-Nov	BSS	A	Bromley	298	W 2-1	Ledgister 3, Og (Taylor) 17	19
20	Sat-17-Dec	BSS	A	Truro City	250	D 3-3	Ledgister 35, Huggins 40, Tarpey 72	20
21	Mon-26-Dec	BSS	H	Staines Town	629	L 1-2	O'Donnell 47	20
22	Sun-01-Jan	BSS	A	Staines Town	592	W 4-1	Beadle 8, Tarpey pen 56, Ruby 59, Inman 67	20
23	Sat-07-Jan	BSS	H	Tonbridge Angels	524	D 1-1	Carder-Andrews 39	19
24	Tue-10-Jan	BSS	A	Sutton United	529	D 2-2	J Simmonds 56, Moone 72	19
25	Sat-21-Jan	BSS	H	Dartford	656	L 1-3	J Simmonds 8	20
26	Sat-28-Jan	BSS	A	Havant & Waterlooville	645	D 2-2	Tarpey 2, Alabi 67	20
27	Sat-18-Feb	BSS	H	Eastleigh	371	L 0-4		21
28	Sat-25-Feb	BSS	H	Woking	1069	D 1-1	Huggins 43	21
29	Sat-03-Mar	BSS	A	Chelmsford City	821	L 0-1		21
30	Sat-10-Mar	BSS	H	Truro City	369	W 4-3	Moone 3 (14, 52, 64), Jones 90	21
31	Tue-13-Mar	BSS	H	Dover Athletic	369	D 2-2	Jones 17, Inman 27	21
32	Sat-17-Mar	BSS	H	Maidenhead United	296	D 0-0		21
33	Sat-24-Mar	BSS	A	Weston-Super-Mare	249	W 2-1	Tarpey 45, Jones 53	21
34	Tue-27-Mar	BSS	A	Dover Athletic	525	W 1-0	Tarpey 32	20
35	Sat-31-Mar	BSS	H	Sutton United	669	D 0-0		19
36	Mon-02-Apr	BSS	A	Boreham Wood	251	L 1-2	J Simmonds pen 51	19
37	Sat-07-Apr	BSS	A	Farnborough	593	W 2-0	Inman 31, J Simmonds 42	18
38	Sat-14-Apr	BSS	A	Eastbourne Borough	633	L 0-2		20
39	Tue-17-Apr	BSS	H	Salisbury City	469	L 1-2	Inman 85	20
40	Sat-21-Apr	BSS	H	Welling United	519	L 0-2		21
41	Tue-24-Apr	BSS	H	Basingstoke Town	569	L 0-2		21
42	Sat-28-Apr	BSS	A	Thurrock	246	W 2-0	Jeffreys 40, Moone 50	21 Relegated

CUPS

No.	Date	Comp	H/A	Opponents	Att:	Result	Goalscorers
1	Sat-01-Oct	FAC 2Q	A	Arlesey Town	156	L 2-6	Tarpey 22, Erskine 80
2	Sat-26-Nov	FAT 3Q	H	Canvey Island	289	W 4-2	Tarpey 3 (4, 48, 90), Collier 60
3	Sat-10-Dec	FAT 1	H	Hayes & Yeading United	242	W 2-0	Tarpey 2 (54, 66)
4	Sat-14-Jan	FAT 2	A	East Thurrock United	231	D 1-1	Og (Stephen) 11
5	Tue-31-Jan	FAT 2R	H	East Thurrock United	184	W 4-1	Tarpey 3 (54, 57, 90+1), Og (Wood) 90+4
6	Tue-14-Feb	FAT 3Q	A	Northwich Victoria	237	L 1-4	Tarpey 57

HARROW BOROUGH

Chairman: Peter Rogers
Secretary: Peter Rogers   **(T)** 0795 618 5685   **(E)** peter@harrowboro.co.uk
Additional Committee Members:
Stuart Hobbs

Manager: Dave Anderson
Programme Editor: Peter Rogers   **(E)** peter@harroboro.co.uk

Club Factfile

Founded: 1933   **Nickname:** Boro
Previous Names: Roxonian 1933-38, Harrow Town 1938-66
Previous Leagues: Harrow & District 1933-34, Spartan 1934-40, 45-58, West Middlesex Combination 1940-41, Middlesex Senior 1941-45, Delphian 1956-63, Athenian 1963-75

Club Colours (change): Red with white trim/red/red (Blue with white trim/blue/blue)

Ground: Earlsmead, Carlyon Avenue, South Harrow HA2 8SS   **(T)** 0844 561 1347
Capacity: 3,070   **Seats:** 350   **Covered:** 1,000   **Clubhouse:** Yes   **Shop:** Yes

Directions
From the M25 junction 16, take the M40 East towards Uxbridge and London. Continue onto A40, passing Northolt Aerodrome on the left hand side. At the Target Roundabout junction (A312) turn left towards Northolt.
Just after passing Northolt Underground Station on the left hand side, turn left at the next set of traffic lights, onto Eastcote Lane, becoming Field End Road.
At next roundabout, turn right onto Eastcote Lane. At a small parade of shops, take the turning on the right into Carlyon Avenue. Earlsmead is the second turning on the right.

Previous Grounds:

Record Attendance: 3,000 v Wealdstone - FA Cup 1st Qualifying Road 1946
Record Victory: 13-0 v Handley Page (A) - 18/10/1941
Record Defeat: 0-8 on five occasions
Record Goalscorer: Dave Pearce - 153
Record Appearances: Les Currell - 582, Colin Payne - 557, Steve Emmanuel - 522
Additional Records:

Senior Honours:
Isthmian League 1983-84.
Middlesex Senior Cup 1982-83, 92-93. Middlesex Premier Cup 1981-82.
Middlesex Senior Charity Cup 1979-80, 92-93, 2005-06, 06-07

10 YEAR RECORD

02-03	03-04	04-05	05-06	06-07	07-08	08-09	09-10	10-11	11-12
Isth P 18	Isth P 17	Isth P 16	Isth P 16	Isth P 19	Isth P 16	Isth P 14	Isth P 14	Isth P 5	Isth P 17

HARROW BOROUGH

No.	Date	Comp	H/A	Opponents	Att:	Result	Goalscorers	Pos
1	Aug 20	Isth P	A	Metropiltan Police	84	L 0 - 1		
2	23		H	Billericay Town	160	D 1 - 1	Fenton 45	
3	27		H	Aveley	128	D 1 - 1	Bates 53	18
4	29		A	Hendon	262	L 2 - 3	Jones 68 (pen) Lawrence 90	
5	Sept 3		A	Canvey Island	402	L 0 - 1		20
6	10		H	Cray Wanderers	171	L 0 - 4		21
7	13		A	Lowestoft Town	546	W 2 - 1	Ofori-Acheampong 74 Bates 84	
8	17	FAC 1Q	H	Marlow	113	W 2 - 0	Jones 40 (pen) 70	
9	24		H	Hastings United	202	D 1 - 1	Bates 76	19
10	27		A	Horsham	145	W 3 - 1	Delgado 26 65 Bates 30	
11	Oct 1	FAC 2Q	A	Dartford	803	L 0 - 5		
12	4		H	Tooting & Mitcham U	155	D 1 - 1	Delgado 34	14
13	11		A	Wingate & Finchley	137	D 2 - 2	Bates 10 Leech 25	
14	15		A	Carshalton Athletic	204	W 1 - 0	Rowe 24	12
15	22	FAT 1Q	A	Dulwich Hamlet	294	W 2 - 0	Delgado 20 Bates 59	
16	25		H	Kingstonian	177	L 1 - 3	Habu 75	
17	29		H	Bury Town	176	W 2 - 1	Bates 20 73	12
18	Nov 5	FAT 2Q	H	AFC Hornchurch	123	D 1 - 1	Rowe 56	
19	12		H	Leatherhead	201	W 2 - 0	Delgado 23 Savage 81	12
20	19		A	Concord Rangers	132	L 0 - 1		13
21	26		H	Margate	205	L 0 - 2		16
22	Dec 3		H	Lewes	179	L 0 - 1		16
23	17		H	Lowestoft Town	186	L 2 - 4	Leech 68 Thomas 72	16
24	27		A	Wealdstone	876	L 0 - 4		16
25	31		A	Billericay Town	429	L 0 - 3		
26	Jan 2		H	Hendon	208	W 4 - 2	Buckle 4 87 Walters 86 Barima 90	17
27	8		A	Kingstonian	265	L 0 - 1		
28	10		A	AFC Hornchurch	232	D 0 - 0		
29	14		H	Horsham	188	W 2 - 0	Huckle 27 Toney 50	16
30	21		A	Tooting & Mitcham U	252	W 3 - 1	Leech 22 Toney 59 Buckle 64	16
31	28		H	Wingate & Finchley	171	L 1 - 3	Walters 75	17
32	Feb 18		A	Bury Town	362	D 2 - 2	Bates 38 Barima 84	17
33	25		H	Carshalton Athletic	145	L 1 - 2	Wolleaston 17	
34	March 3		A	Leatherhead	275	L 0 - 2		18
35	6		H	Concord Rangers	78	L 0 - 3		
36	10		H	East Thurrock United	142	W 3 - 1	Leech 1 63 Wray 88 (og)	18
37	13		A	Margate	192	L 0 - 1		
38	17		H	Met Police	121	W 2 - 1	Buckle 26 Akinola 90	17
39	24		A	Aveley	129	L 2 - 3	Buckle 42 Sa 56	18
40	31		H	Canvey Island	183	L 3 - 4	Ferguson 14 69 Buckle 55	19
41	Apr 2		A	East Thurrock United	121	W 3 - 0	Watson 28 Akinola 34 78	
42	7		A	Cray Wanderers	180	W 2 - 1	Toney 49 Buckle 76	17
43	11		H	Wealdstone	617	D 0 - 0		17
44	14		A	Hastings United	335	L 1 - 3	Bates 72	17
45	21		H	AFC Hornchurch	203	W 1 - 0	Bates 62	17
46	28		A	Lewes	1038	L 2 - 4	Bates 2 Leech 73	17

HASTINGS UNITED

Chairman: David Walters
Secretary: Tony Cosens   **(T)** 0771 265 4288   **(E)** richardcosens@btinternet.com
Additional Committee Members:
Sean Adams, Sean Logan-Walker

Manager: Sean Ray
Programme Editor: Simon Rudkins   **(E)**

THE NON-LEAGUE CLUB DIRECTORY

Book Holiday Inn Hotels and Save today!

Home

Clubs

Steps 1 - 4

League Tables

35 Years of Non-League Football

The Non-League Club Directory has developed into a comprehensive record of competitions within the non-League game, giving this level of football the

www.non-leagueclubdirectory.co.uk

Club Factfile

Founded: 1894   **Nickname:** The Us

Previous Names: Hastings and St Leonards Amateurs, Hastings Town > 2002

Previous Leagues: South Eastern 1904-05, Southern 1905-10, Sussex County 1921-27, 52-85, Southern Amateur 1927-46, Corinthian 1946-48

Club Colours (change): Claret/white/white (Light blue/claret/claret)

Ground: The Pilot Field, Elphinstone Road, Hastings TN34 2AX   **(T)** 01424 444 635

Capacity: 4,050   **Seats:** 800   **Covered:** 1,750   **Clubhouse:** Yes   **Shop:** Yes

Directions
From A1 turn left at third roundabout into St Helens Road.
Then left after one mile into St Helens Park Road leading into Downs Road.
Turn left at T-junction at the end of the road. Ground is 200 yards on the right.

Previous Grounds: Bulverhythe Recreation > 1976

Record Attendance: 4,888 v Nottingham Forest - Friendly 23/06/1996

Record Victory: Not Known
Record Defeat: Not Known

Record Goalscorer: Terry White scored 33 during 1999-2000

Record Appearances: Not Known

Additional Records: Paid £8,000 to Ashford Town for Nicky Dent
Received £30,000 from Nottingham Forest for Paul Smith

Senior Honours:
Southern League Division 1 1991-92, 2001-01, League Cup 1994-95.

02-03		03-04		04-05		05-06		06-07		07-08		08-09		09-10		10-11		11-12	
SthP	20	SthE	18	Isth1	11	Isth1	12	Isth1S	4	Isth P	14	Isth P	17	Isth P	7	Isth P	18	Isth P	18

HASTINGS TOWN

No.	Date	Comp	H/A	Opponents	Att:	Result	Goalscorers	Pos
1	Aug 20	Isth P	H	Wingate & Finchley	297	L 0 - 1		
2	23		A	East Thurrock United	139	W 2 - 0	Hall 22 Pogue 90	
3	27		A	Bury Town	359	L 0 - 5		
4	29		H	Margate	348	D 2 - 2	Billings 32 Jirbandey 47	
5	Sept 3		H	Carshalton Athletic	431	L 0 - 2		19
6	10		A	Concord Rangers	196	D 2 - 2	Hopkinson 31 Hall 34	
7	13		H	Kingstonian	263	W 1 - 0	Foreman 43	17
8	17	FAC 1Q	H	Cray Wanderers	301	L 0 - 3		
9	24		A	Harrow Borough	202	D 1 - 1	Sutton 70	15
10	27		H	Leatherhead	248	D 0 - 0		
11	Oct 4		A	Billericay Town	273	L 0 - 2		14
12	8		H	Hendon	319	L 0 - 2		18
13	15		A	Wealdstone	400	L 1 - 2	Attwood 76	
14	22	FAT 1Q	A	Bedfont Town	79	D 1 - 1	Attwood 89	
15	25	FAT 1Qr	H	Bedfont Town	165	L 0 - 2		
16	29		H	Horsham	325	W 5 - 0	Pogue 6 77 Carey 67 (pen) Crellin 80 Attwood 81	16
17	31		A	Aveley	186	W 1 - 0	Carey 73	
18	Nov 12		H	Cray Wanderers	487	L 0 - 2		15
19	19		H	AFC Hornchurch	399	L 1 - 3	Attwood 86	16
20	22		A	Canvey Island	283	W 2 - 1	Sheehan (og) 55 Thomson 89	
21	26		A	Tooting & Mitcham U	227	W 2 - 1	Carey 13 Attwood 30	12
22	Dec 3		A	Metropolitan Police	152	L 0 - 4		15
23	17		A	Kingstonian	307	D 1 - 1	Davison 48	15
24	26		H	Lewes	689	L 0 - 1		15
25	31		H	East Thurrock United	426	L 1 - 2	Attwood 9	
26	Jan 2		A	Margate	471	L 1 - 4	Attwood 60	
27	7		H	Aveley	324	W 2 - 1	Coney 28 Pogue 48	16
28	14		A	Leatherhead	331	L 0 - 2		18
29	21		H	Billericay Town	368	D 0 - 0		18
30	28		A	Hendon	132	L 1 - 2	Carey 31	18
31	Feb 18		A	Horsham	201	W 2 - 1	Tuna 30 Ellis 44	
32	28		H	Lowestoft Town	321	W 2 - 0	Manning 2 31	
33	March 3		A	Cray Wanderers	143	L 0 - 1		17
34	6		A	AFC Hornchurch	209	W 1 - 0	Ray 71	
35	10		H	Canvey Island	382	D 1 - 1	Attwood 72	17
36	13		H	Tooting & Mitcham U	323	W 2 - 0	Goldberg 10 Attwood 23	
37	17		A	Wingate & Finchley	111	L 1 - 3	Goldberg 50	18
38	24		H	Bury Town	421	L 0 - 1		
39	31		A	Carshalton Athletic	203	L 0 - 2		17
40	Apr 2		H	Wealdstone	338	L 0 - 2		17
41	7		H	Concord Rangers	335	D 1 - 1	Jirbandy 54	
42	9		A	Lewes	692	L 1 - 2	Manning 83	
43	14		H	Harrow Borough	335	W 3 - 1	Attwood 49 69 Goldberg 75	18
44	21		A	Lowestoft Town	741	W 3 - 1	Jirbander 20 Goldberg 53 Camara 76	
45	28		H	Met Police	564	L 0 - 2		18

HENDON

Chairman: Simon Lawrence
Secretary: Graham Etchell   **(T)** 07973 698 552   **(E)** hendonfc@freenetname.co.uk
Additional Committee Members:
Steve Rogers, David Balheimer

Manager: Gary McCann
Programme Editor: Graham Etchell   **(E)** hendonfc@freenetname.co.uk

Team April 2011 - Back Row: Parker, Hudson, Reading, Vargas, Cousins, C.Maclaren.
Front Row: Aite-Ouakrim, Burgess, Busby, Munnelley, Morgan. Photo: Andrew Aleksiejczuk.

Club Factfile

Founded: 1908   **Nickname:** Dons or Greens
Previous Names: Christ Church Hampstead > 1908, Hampstead Town > 1933, Golders Green > 1946
Previous Leagues: Finchley & District 1908-11, Middlesex 1910-11, London 1911-14, Athenian 1914-63

Club Colours (change): All green & white (All tangerine)

Ground: Wembley FC, Vale Farm, Watford Road, Wembley HA0 3HG   **(T)** 020 8908 3553
Capacity: 2,450   **Seats:** 350   **Covered:** 950   **Clubhouse:** Yes   **Shop:**

Directions: 400 yards from Sudbury Town underground station.
Or 10 minutes walk from North Wembley BR.

Previous Grounds: Claremont Road

Record Attendance: 9,000 v Northampton Town - FA Cup 1st Round 1952
Record Victory: 13-1 v Wingate - Middlesex County Cup 02/02/1957
Record Defeat: 2-11 v Walthamstowe Avenue, Athenian League 09/11/1935
Record Goalscorer: Freddie Evans - 176 (1929-35)
Record Appearances: Bill Fisher - 787 - (1940-64)
Additional Records: Received £30,000 from Luton Town for Iain Dowie

Senior Honours:
FA Amateur Cup 1959-60, 64-65, 71-72. Isthmian League 1964-65, 72-73. European Amateur Champions 1972-73.
Athenian League x3. London Senior Cup 1963-64, 68-69. Middlesex Senior Cup x14

10 YEAR RECORD

02-03		03-04		04-05		05-06		06-07		07-08		08-09		09-10		10-11		11-12	
Isth P	3	Isth P	4	Isth P	11	Isth P	19	Isth P	14	Isth P	7	Isth P	16	Isth P	10	Isth P	15	Isth P	7

HENDON

No.	Date	Comp	H/A	Opponents	Att:	Result	Goalscorers	Pos
1	Aug 20	Isth P	H	Concord Rangers	164	W 1 - 0	Busby 48 (pen)	
2	23		A	Bury Town	410	W 1 - 0	Busby 70	
3	27		A	Carshalton Athletic	174	W 3 - 0	McCluskey 10 Ngoyi 18 Godfrey 48	1
4	29		H	Harrow Borough	262	W 3 - 2	Diedhiou 43 McCluskey 50 Rankin 81	
5	Sept 4		H	Lewes	293	D 2 - 2	Godfrey 27 Ngoyi 65	1
6	10		A	Margate	37	W 2 - 0	Busby 71(pen) Smelt 78 (og)	1
7	13		H	East Thurrock United	151	D 1 - 1	Ngoyi 51	
8	17	FAC 1Q	A	AFC Hayes		W 3 - 0	Busby 2 (pen) 90 Ngoyi 16	
9	24		A	Kingstonian	312	L 0 - 1		3
10	26		A	Wealdstone	506	W 2 - 0	Charles 79 Ngoyi 80	
11	Oct 1	FAC 2Q	A	Oxhey Jets	376	W 2 - 1	Charles 45 Ngoyi 59	
12	8		A	Hastings United	319	W 2 - 0	Peacock 74 Charles 77	3
13	15	FAC 3Q	A	Malden & Tiptree	159	W 3 - 1	McCluskey 61 Ngoyi 65 Godfrey 90	
14	22	FAT 1Q	A	Canvey Island	262	L 0 - 4		
15	25		H	Metropolitan Police	138	L 1 - 3	Busby 14 (pen)	5
16	29	FAC 4Q	A	Luton Town	2329	L 1 - 5	McCluskey 5	
17	Nov 2		H	Horsham	174	D 1 - 1	Diedhiou 24	
18	6		H	Leatherhead	202	L 1 - 2	Charles 42	
19	12		H	Canvey Island	198	W 1 - 0	Rankin 48	6
20	15		A	Lowestoft Town	504	L 0 - 2		
21	19		H	Billericay Town	240	L 1 - 2	Rankin 90	7
22	26		A	Cray Wanderers	190	D 0 - 0		
23	29		A	AFC Hornchurch	187	W 1 - 0	Godfrey 23	
24	Dec 3		H	Aveley	141	D 1 - 0	Charles 83	6
25	10		A	Tooting & Mitcham	180	W 3 - 0	Charles 37 Ngoyi 72 Federico 79	5
26	17		A	East Thurrock Unitted	109	D 0 - 1		7
27	26		H	Wingate & Finchley	183	D 1 - 1	Ngoyi 68	7
28	31		H	Bury Town	172	L 3 - 4	Ngoyi 44 45 Charles 90	
29	Jan 2		A	Harrow Borough	208	L 2 - 4	Ngoyi 20 Charles 45	8
30	7		A	Metropolitan Police	156	W 1 - 0	Currie 11	8
31	21		A	Horsham	207	W 3 - 0	Wharton 38 Ngoyi 73 Charles 75	7
32	24		H	Wealdstone	401	D 1 - 1	Ngoyi 45	
33	28		H	Hastings United	132	W 2 - 1	Charles 14 M.Lewis 17	4
34	Feb 13		A	Billericay Town	301	L 1 - 2	Rankin 90	
35	18		A	Leatherhead	322	W 1 - 0	Rankin 87	5
36	25		H	Lowestoft	210	W 1 - 0	Rankin 82	4
37	March 3		A	Canvey Island	323	L 1 - 3	McCluskey 38	6
38	10		H	AFC Hornchurch	209	W 2 - 0	Charles 45 Rankin 90	5
39	17		A	Concord Rangers	1342	L 0 - 2		6
40	24		H	Carshalton Athletic	183	D 1 - 1	Busby 28 (pen)	6
41	27		H	Cray Wanderers	175	W 1 - 0	McCluskey 51	6
42	31		A	Lewes	648	L 2 - 3	Aite-Ouakrim 15 Cousins 90	7
43	Apr 7		H	Margate	186	L 0 - 3		
44	9		A	Wingate & Finchley	240	W 5 - 0	Rankin 6 C. McLaren 20 Diedhiou 29 33 McCluskey 89	6
45	14		H	Kingstonian	224	W 2 - 1	McCluskey 8 Mazzone 81	
46	21		H	Tooting & Mitcham United	184	W 5 - 0	Shulton 9 13 Rankin 68 Ngoyi 90 McCluskey 90	7
47	28		A	Aveley	155	W 7 - 1	Ngoyi 6 (pen) Shulton 50 (pen) RANKIN 3(54 58 61) Charles 67 Godfrey 90	7

KINGSTONIAN

Chairman: John Fenwick
Secretary: Gerry Petit   **(T)** 0785 937 7778   **(E)** gandjpetit149@tiscali.co.uk
Additional Committee Members:
Ali Kazemi, Clinton Arthur

Manager: Alan Dowson
Programme Editor: Robert Wooldridge   **(E)** floiing@aol.com

Back row: James Street, Allan Tait, Kieran Murphy, Byron Napper, Aaron Goode, Dominic Sterling, Gary MacDonald, Tom Hutchinson, Simon Huckle, Mark Francis
Middle row: Mark Hams, Mat Somner, Bashiru Alimi, Karl Murray, Rob Tolfrey, Alan Dowson, Jake Whincup, Craig Mullen, Saheed Sankoh, Matt Pattison, Martin Tyler, Gerry Petit
Front row: Paul Ferrie, Goma Lambu, Charles Ofosu-Hene, Dean Lodge, Stuart Duff, Andre McCollin, Wade Small, Mark Nwokeji, Sam Clayton, Alan Smith

Club Factfile

Founded: 1885   **Nickname:** The K's
Previous Names: Kingston & Suburban YMCA 1885-87, Saxons 1887-90, Kingston Wanderers 1893-1904, Old Kingstonians 1908-19
Previous Leagues: Kingston & District, West Surrey, Southern Suburban, Athenian 1919-29, Isthmian 1929-98, Conference 1998-2001

Club Colours (change): Red and white hoops/black/red & white (Yellow with blue piping/blue/blue)

Ground: Kingsmeadow Stadium, Kingston Road, Kingston KT1 3PB   **(T)** 0208 330 6869
Capacity: 4,262   **Seats:** 1,080   **Covered:** 2,538   **Clubhouse:** Yes   **Shop:** Yes

Directions: Take Cambridge Road from Town Centre (A2043) to Malden Road.
From A3 turn off at New Malden and turn left onto A2043.
Ground is 1 mile on the left which is half a mile from Norbiton BR.

Previous Grounds: Several > 1921, Richmond Road 1921-89

Record Attendance: 4,582 v Chelsea - Freindly
Record Victory: 15-1 v Delft - 1951
Record Defeat: 0-11 v Ilford - Isthmian League 13/02/1937
Record Goalscorer: Johnnie Wing - 295 (1948-62)
Record Appearances: Micky Preston - 555 (1967-85)
Additional Records: Paid £18,000 to Rushden & Diamonds for David Leworthy 1997
Received £150,000 from West Ham United for Gavin Holligan 1999
Senior Honours:
FA Amateur Cup 1932-33. Isthmian League 1933-34, 36-37, 97-98, Division 1 South 2008-09.
FAT Trophy 1998-99, 99-2000. Athenian League x2. London Senior Cup x3. Surrey Senior Cup x3.

10 YEAR RECORD

02-03	03-04	04-05	05-06	06-07	07-08	08-09	09-10	10-11	11-12
Isth P 11	Isth P 18	Isth P 22	Isth1 7	Isth1S 13	Isth1S 7	Isth1S 1	Isth P 5	Isth P 7	Isth P 11

KINGSTONIAN

No.	Date	Comp	H/A	Opponents	Att:	Result	Goalscorers	Pos
1	Aug 20	Isth P	A	Kingstonian	190	D 0 - 0		
2	22		H	Horsham	320	L 3 - 4	Hutchinson 37 60 Huckle 73	
3	27		H	Canvey Island	318	L 1 - 2	Traynor 12	16
4	29		A	Tooting & Mitcham U	414	W 4 - 1	Traynor 16 23 (pen) Tait 74 MacDonald 79	
5	Sept 3		A	Billericay Town	429	L 0 - 6		17
6	10		H	Wealdstone	393	L 0 - 3		19
7	13		A	Hastings United	263	L 0 - 1		
8	17	FAC 1Q	A	Poole Town	320	L 0 - 3		
9	24		H	Hendon	312	W 1 - 0	Traynor 78 (pen)	17
10	26		H	Lewes	326	W 1 - 0	Traynor 30	
11	Oct 8		H	Cray Wanderers	353	W 4 - 2	Huckle 10 MacDonald 57 Chaaban 57 Tait 78	11
12	15		A	AFC Hornchurch	281	L 0 - 3		13
13	23	FAT 1Q	H	Godalming Town	258	L 0 - 1		
14	25		A	Harrow Borough	177	W 3 - 1	Hutchinson 10 Chaaban 58 Rowe 79 (og)	
15	29		H	Wingate & Finchley	187	D 2 - 2	Clayton 68 Bird 70	13
16	Nov 1		A	Concord Rangers	134	W 3 - 2	Clayton 23 McCrae 25 57	
17	8		A	Metropolitan Police	412	L 1 - 2	Traynor 38 (pen)	
18	13		H	Carshalton Athletic	486	L 2 - 3	MacDonald (2)	
19	19		A	Margate	364	L 1 - 2	Tolfrey 45 (pen)	14
20	22		A	Bury Town	376	D 1 - 1	Byatt 13	
21	26		A	Horsham	291	W 3 - 1	Clayton 7 (pen) 89 McDonald 61	
22	Dec 3		A	East Thurrock	194	W 1 - 0	Clayton 62	10
23	11		H	Leatherhead	412	L 0 - 3		
24	17		H	Hastings United	307	D 1 - 1	Hutchinson 89	11
25	Jan 2		H	Tooting & Mitcham U	407	W 2 - 1	Fletcher 15 (og) Duff 82	
26	8		H	Harrow Borough	265	W 1 - 0	McDonald 90	
27	14		A	Lewes	711	D 1 - 1	Duff 81	12
28	21		H	Concord Rangers	273	L 0 - 1		12
29	28		A	Cray Wanderers	254	D 0 - 0		12
30	30		H	Lowestoft Town	294	W 2 - 0	Woods 30 Traynor 90	
31	Feb 18		A	Wingate & Finchley	171	W 2 - 0	Alimi 30 Goode 43	11
32	20		H	Margate	278	W 2 - 1	Clayton 63 Woods 84	
33	25		H	AFC Hornchurch	299	L 0 - 2		10
34	March 3		A	Carshalton Athletic	383	W 1 - 0	Goode 56	8
35	11		H	Bury Town	411	D 1 - 1	Beadle 80	
36	17		H	Aveley	236	W 2 - 0	Traynor 22 42	9
37	24		A	Canvey Island	356	W 2 - 0	Traynor 25 Gayle 80	8
38	27		A	Lowestoft Town	523	L 2 - 3	Traynor 38 Sankoh 55	10
39	31		H	Billericay Town	383	L 0 - 2		11
40	Apr 7		A	Wealdstone	527	L 1 - 4	Traynor 53 (pen)	
41	9		H	Met Police	273	W 2 - 1	Tait 9 86	10
42	14		A	Hendon	224	L 1 - 2	Sankoh 7	
43	21		A	Leatherhead	470	W 2 - 0	Traynor 73 Woods 85	11
44	28		H	East Thurrock United	307	L 2 - 5	Traynor 16 70	11

Non-League Action...

FA Vase Final - Mark Hudson (West Auckland) holds off man of the match Andrew Bulford fo Dunston UTS.

Photo: Graham Brown.

LEISTON

Chairman: Andrew Crisp
Secretary: David Rees   **(T)** 07977 782 559   **(E)** gagrees@aol.com
Additional Committee Members:

Manager: Mark Morsley
Programme Editor: David Rees   **(E)** gagrees@aol.com

THE NON-LEAGUE CLUB DIRECTORY

Book Holiday Inn Hotels and Save today!

| Home |
| Clubs |
| Steps 1 - 4 |
| League Tables |

35 Years of Non-League Football

The Non-League Club Directory has developed into a comprehensive record of competitions within the non-League game, giving this level of football the

www.non-leagueclubdirectory.co.uk

Club Factfile

Founded: 1880   **Nickname:** The Blues

Previous Names: None

Previous Leagues: Suffolk & Ipswich, Eastern Counties > 2011.

Club Colours (change): Blue/white/red (All red)

Ground: LTAA, Victory Road, Leiston IP16 4DQ   **(T)** 01728 830 308

Capacity: 2,500   **Seats:** 124   **Covered:** 500   **Clubhouse:**   **Shop:**

Directions: Take junction 28 off the M25, take the A12/A1023 exit to Chelmsford/Romford/Brentwood, keep left at the fork, follow signs for Chelmsford/A12 (E) and merge onto A12, at the roundabout, take the 3rd exit onto the A14 ramp, merge onto A14, at junction 58, exit toward A12, keep left at the fork, follow signs for Lowestoft/Woodbridge/A12 (N) and merge onto A12, go through 7 roundabouts, turn right onto A1094, turn left onto Snape Rd/B1069, continue to follow B1069, turn left onto Victory Rd, ground will be on the left.

Previous Grounds:

Record Attendance: Att: 271 v AFC Sudbury, 13.11.04.

Record Victory: Not known
Record Defeat: Not known

Record Goalscorer: Lee McGlone - 60 (League).

Record Appearances: Tim Sparkes - 154 (League).

Additional Records:

Senior Honours:
Eastern Counties League Premier Division 2010-11. Isthmian League Division 1 North 2011-12.

02-03		03-04		04-05		05-06		06-07		07-08		08-09		09-10		10-11		11-12	
EC1	7	EC1	3	ECP	10	ECP	9	ECP	5	ECP	9	ECP	7	ECP	3	ECP	1	Isth1N	1

LEWES

Chairman: Terry Parris
Secretary: Kevin Brook   **(T)** 07785 074 081   **(E)** clubsecretary@lewesfc.com
Additional Committee Members:
Stuart Fuller, Lee Cobb

Manager: Simon Wormull
Programme Editor: James Boyes   **(E)** james-boyes@lineone.net

Back row - Ray Bugg (kit manager), Steve Brinkhurst, Jay Conroy, Steve Robinson, Pawel Szelemej, Kieron Thorp, Chris Breach, Lewis Hamilton, Callum Dunne, Lee Cooper, Sam Piper (assistant kit man).
Front row - Karl Beckford, Charlie Leach, Arron Hopkinson, Nathan Crabb, Simon Wormull (manager),
Nick Brown (1st team coach & U18 manager), Layton Schaaf, Max Howell, Jack Walder, Dan Bolwell.

Club Factfile

Founded: 1885   **Nickname:** Rooks
Previous Names: None
Previous Leagues: Mid Sussex 1886-1920, Sussex County 1920-65, Athenian 1965-77, Isthmian 1977-2004, Conference 2004-11.

Club Colours (change): Red and black stripes/white/white (Light blue & white/black/blue)

Ground: The Dripping Pan, Mountfield Road, Lewes, East Sussex BN7 2XD   **(T)** 01273 470 820
Capacity: 3,000   **Seats:** 400   **Covered:** 1,400   **Clubhouse:** Yes   **Shop:** Yes

Directions: After leaving the M23, follow the A23 to Brighton. On the outskirts of Brighton join the A27 eastbound. Stay on the A27 for about 5 miles. At the roundabout take first exit into Lewes. Follow this road until you reach traffic lights outside Lewes Prison. Turn right at the lights and follow the road down the hill until you reach a mini roundabout outside the Swan public house. Turn left at roundabout into Southover High Street and continue over next mini roundabout outside the Kings Head public house. At the next roundabout go straight over into Mountfield Road. The Dripping Pan is on your right.

Previous Grounds:

Record Attendance: 2,500 v Newhaven - Sussex County League 26/12/1947
Record Victory: Not known
Record Defeat: Not known
Record Goalscorer: 'Pip' Parris - 350
Record Appearances: Terry Parris - 662
Additional Records: Paid £2,000 for Matt Allen
     Received £2,500 from Brighton & Hove Albion for Grant Horscroft
Senior Honours: Mid Sussex League 1910-11, 13-14. Sussex County League 1964-65.
Sussex Senior Cup 1964-65, 70-71, 84-85, 2000-01, 05-06. Athenian League Division 2 1967-68, Division 1 1969-70.
Isthmian League Division 2 2001-02, Division 1 South 2003-04. Conference South 2007-08

10 YEAR RECORD

02-03	03-04	04-05	05-06	06-07	07-08	08-09	09-10	10-11	11-12
Isth1S 3	Isth1S 1	Conf S 4	Conf S 4	Conf 9	Conf S 1	Conf 24	Conf S 19	Conf S 21	Isth P 6

LEWES

No.	Date	Comp	H/A	Opponents	Att:	Result	Goalscorers	Pos
1	Aug 20	Isth P	A	Lowestoft Town	762	L 1 - 3	Crane 6 (og)	
2	23		H	Met Police	502	W 1 - 0	Booth 42	
3	27		H	Billericay Town	483	W 2 - 1	Malcolm 15 30	4
4	29		A	Horsham	435	W 1 - 0	Booth 23	
5	Sept 4		A	Hendon	293	D 2 - 2	Malcolm 2 56	6
6	10		H	Aveley	601	W 4 - 1	Booth 11 Ciardini 22 Nanetti 39 Malcolm 88	5
7	14		A	Tooting & Mitcham U	273	D 2 - 2	Ciardini 70 Lee 72	
8	17	FAC 1Q	A	Chertsey Town	280	L 1 - 4	Somner 29	
9	24		H	Cray Wanderers	721	W 1 - 0	Booth 37 (pen)	4
10	26		A	Kingstonian	326	L 0 - 1		
11	Oct 1		H	Wealdstone	749	W 1 - 0	Ciardini 17 (pen)	3
12	8		A	Canvey Island	371	W 2 - 1	Nicholas 4 Malcolm 20	4
13	22	FAT 1Q	H	Cray Wanderers	536	W 2 - 1	Booth 47 78	
14	29		H	AFC Hornchurch	642	L 0 - 4		6
15	Nov 1		H	Margate	394	W 2 - 0	Sterling 18 Nicholas 79	3
16	5	FAT 2Q	A	Harlow Town	183	L 2 - 3	Draycott 26 46	
17	12		H	Bury Town	730	D 1 - 1	Draycott 20	7
18	19		H	Wingate & Finchley	573	D 0 - 0		5
19	22		A	East Thurrock United	132	L 0 - 1		
20	26		A	Leatherhead	363	W 1 - 0	Malcolm 74	5
21	Dec 3		A	Harrow Borough	179	W 1 - 0	Harding 7	
22	10		H	Concord Rangers	649	L 1 - 2	King 45 (og)	
23	13		A	Carshalton Athletic	150	W 2 - 1	Malcolm 3 Stavrinou 34	5
24	17		H	Tooting & Mitcham	559	W 3 - 1	Nanatti 45 Malcolm 63 Stavinou 68	
25	26		A	Hastings United	689	W 1 - 0	Malcolm 86	3
26	31		A	Metropolitan Police	365	D 0 - 0		
27	Jan 2		H	Horsham	1007	D 1 - 1	Harding 36	4
28	7		A	Wealdstone	476	L 0 - 1		4
29	14		H	Kingstonian	711	D 1 - 1	Booth 17	4
30	21		A	Margate	454	L 1 - 5	Booth 64 (pen)	4
31	28		H	Canvey Island	607	L 1 - 2	Booth 24	6
32	Feb 18		A	AFC Hornchurch	298	L 0 - 1		7
33	25		H	East Thurrock United	444	D 2 - 2	Booth 4 Medlock 84	7
34	March 3		A	Bury Town	402	L 1 - 2	Harding 52	9
35	10		H	Carshalton Athletic	574	W 1 - 0	Crabb 2	8
36	13		A	Wingate & Finchley	111	W 2 - 1	Booth 60 Draycott 75	7
37	17		H	Lowestoft Town	680	D 2 - 2	Crabb 7 13	
38	21		H	Leatherhead	347	W 1 - 0		
39	24		A	Billericay Town	651	L 0 - 1		7
40	31		H	Hendon	648	W 3 - 2	Breach 47 Crabb 49 Booth 51	7
41	Apr 7		A	Aveley	189	D 0 - 0		6
42	9		H	Hastings United	692	W 2 - 1	Crabb 12 Howell 41	
43	14		A	Cray Wanderers	229	W 1 - 0	Draycott 22	
44	21		A	Concord Rangers	252	W 3 - 2	Crabb 4 48 Harding 90 (pen)	5
45	28		H	Harrow Borough	1038	W 4 - 2	Booth 26 66 Breach 35 Crabb 50	6

LOWESTOFT TOWN

Chairman: Gary Keyzor
Secretary: Terry Lynes   **(T)** 0793 087 2947   **(E)** terrylynes@fsmail.net
Additional Committee Members:
Steven End, Joe Annis

Manager: Micky Chapman and Ady Gallagher
Programme Editor: Terry Lynes   **(E)** terrylynes@fsmail.net

THE NON-LEAGUE CLUB DIRECTORY

Book Holiday Inn Hotels and Save today!

Home
Clubs
Steps 1 - 4
League Tables

35 Years of Non-League Football

The Non-League Club Directory has developed into a comprehensive record of competitions within the non-League game, giving this level of football the

www.non-leagueclubdirectory.co.uk

Club Factfile

Founded: 1880   **Nickname:** The Trawler Boys or Blues

Previous Names: Original club merged with Kirkley in 1887 to form Lowestoft and became Lowestoft Town in 1890

Previous Leagues: North Suffolk 1897-35, Eastern Counties 1935-2009

Club Colours (change): All royal blue (All white)

Ground: Crown Meadow, Love Road, Lowestoft NR32 2PA   **(T)** 01502 573 818

Capacity: 3,000   **Seats:** 466   **Covered:** 500   **Clubhouse:** Yes   **Shop:** Yes

Directions: Just off A12.
Ten minutes from Lowestoft BR.

Previous Grounds:

Record Attendance: 5,000 v Watford - FA Cup 1st Round 1967

Record Victory: Not Known
Record Defeat: Not Known

Record Goalscorer: Not Known

Record Appearances: Not Known

Additional Records:

Senior Honours:
Eastern Counties League 1935-36 (shared), 37-38, 62-63, 64-65, 65-66, 66-67, 67-68, 69-70, 70-71, 77-78, 2005-06, 08-09.
Isthmian League Division 1 North 2009-10.
Suffolk Senior Cup 1902-03, 22-23, 25-26, 31-32, 35-36, 46-47, 47-48, 48-49, 55-56.

02-03		03-04		04-05		05-06		06-07		07-08		08-09		09-10		10-11		11-12	
ECP	4	ECP	8	ECP	4	ECP	1	ECP	3	ECP	11	ECP	1	Isth1N	1	Isth P	4	Isth P	3

LOWESTOFT TOWN

No.	Date	Comp	H/A	Opponents	Att:	Result	Goalscorers	Pos
1	Aug 20	Isth P	H	Lewes	762	W 3 - 1	Cave-Brown 27 Guentchev 46 Henderson 90	
2	23		A	Wingate & Finchley	111	L 1 - 2	Frew 75	
3	27		A	Margate	506	W 4 - 1	Frew 34 Henderson 50 Guentchev 67 Forshaw 83	3
4	29		H	AFC Hornchurch	727	W 2 - 1	Nolan 64 Guentchev 90	
5	Sept 3		H	Concord Rangers	701	W 5 - 0	Guentchev 16 69 Frew 37 39 Nolan 56	1
6	10		A	Leatherhead	372	W 2 - 1	Guentchev 25 Ainsley 62	2
7	13		H	Harrow Borough	546	L 1 - 2	Frew 7	
8	17	FAC 1Q	A	Heybridge Swifts	240	W 2 - 1	Guentchev 62 Nolan 70	
9	24		A	Carshalton Athletic	212	W 4 - 1	Nolan 26 Roberts 47 (og) Francis 50 62	1
10	27		A	East Thurrock United	148	W 3 - 1	Guentchev 26 Crane 34 Forbes 46	
11	Oct 1	FAC 2Q	H	Hemel Hempstead	669	W 3 - 0	Francis 10 (pen) Nolan 16 38	1
12	4		H	Canvey Island	633	D 1 - 1	Halliday 31	
13	8		A	Wealdstone	626	D 0 - 0		2
14	15	FAC 3Q	H	Chelmsford City	1065	L 2 - 5	Francis 16 Cockrill 85 (pen)	
15	22	FAT 1Q	A	Brentwood Town	197	W 3 - 2	O'Rowe 47 (og) Nolan 77 Cockrill 82	
16	29		A	Tooting & Mitcham United	259	L 1 - 2	Forbes 69	4
17	Nov 5	FAT 2Q	A	Hitchin Town	282	W 3 - 1	Nolan 19 Mitchell 76 Francis 87 (pen)	
18	8		H	Horsham	457	W 1 - 0	Forbes 57	
19	12		A	Aveley	182	W 1 - 0	Mitchell 22	3
20	15		H	Hendon	504	W 2 - 0	Cockrill Nolan	
21	19		H	Cray Wanderers	663	W 2 - 1	Cockrill 25 (pen) 81 (pen)	1
22	26	FAT 3Q	A	Harlow Town		W 2 - 1	Forshaw 71 83	
23	29		H	Metropolitan Police	474	D 2 - 2	Fisk 60 Nolan 90	
24	Dec 3		H	Billericay Town	812	W 1 - 0	Smith 63	2
25	10	FAT 1	A	Salisbury City	494	L 1 - 4	Frew 10	
26	17		A	Harrow Borough	186	W 4 - 2	Guentchev 28 Smith 36 Frew 40 Francis 60	2
27	26		H	Bury Town	1056	W 2 - 1	Cockrill 54 (pen) Mitchell 84	2
28	31		H	Wingate & Finchley	721	W 2 - 0	Mitchell 8 Guentchev 56	
29	Jan 2		A	AFC Hornchurch	450	L 0 - 3		2
30	7		A	Horsham	241	W 2 - 1	Francis 8 (pen) 78 (pen)	1
31	21		A	Canvey Island	371	L 2 - 3	Guentchev 35 Henderson 66	3
32	28		H	Wealdstone	855	W 2 - 1	Henderson 50 Francis 60 (pen)	3
33	30		A	Kingstonian	294	L 0 - 2		
34	Feb 18		H	Tooting & Mitcham United	626	D 2 - 2	Eagle 7 Henderson 85	3
35	25		A	Hendon	210	L 0 - 1		3
36	28		A	Hastings United	321	L 0 - 2		
37	March 3		H	Aveley	605	W 1 - 0	Francis 88	3
38	10		A	Met Police	141	W 2 - 0	Henderson 65 74	3
39	13		H	East Thurrock United	541	D 1 - 1	Sinclair 58	
40	17		A	Lewes	680	D 2 - 2	Sinclair 43 (pen) Stone 90	3
41	24		H	Margate	642	W 2 - 1	Goughran 45 Francis78	3
42	27		H	Kingstonian	523	W 3 - 2	Henderson 12 Fisk 21 Sinclair 75 (pen)	3
43	31		A	Concord Rangers	247	L 2 - 3	Mitchell 14 Henderson 47	3
44	Apr 7		H	Leatherhead	619	D 2 - 2	Henderson 34 82	
45	9		A	Bury Town	868	W 3 - 2	Sinclair 24 Gaughran 52 Guentchev 90	3
46	14		H	Carshalton Athletic	601	W 3 - 2	Eagle 2 19 Frew 20	3
47	21		H	Hastings United	741	L 1 - 3	Henderson 47	
48	24		A	Cray Wanderers	188	W 2 - 0	Francis 43 Frew 85	
49	28		A	Billericay Town	1145	W 4 1	Frew 10 75 Guentchev28 Cockrill 58	2
50	May 2	Play-Off SF	H	Wealdstone	1158	W 2 - 1	Henderson 21 Sinclair 90 (pen)	
51	7	Play-Off F	A	AFC Hornchurch	1411	L 1 - 2*	Sinclair 104 (pen)	

MARGATE

Chairman: Keith Piper
Secretary: Ken Tomlinson   **(T)** 0771 003 3566   **(E)** ken.tomlinson@margate-fc.com
Additional Committee Members:
Steve Wells, Peter Cove

Manager: Chris Kinnear
Programme Editor: Don Walker   **(E)** don.walker@margate-fc.com

2011-12 Squad - Back Row (l-r): Kevin Rayne, Kwesi Appiah, Dean Hill, Tom Bradbrook, Curtis Robinson, Richard Avery, Jack Smelt,
Wayne Wilson, Craig Cloke, Dean Pooley, Laurence Ball, Mark Corneille, Jake Leberl (Coach), Paul Wilson (Physio)
Front Row (l-r): Liam Coleman, Dan Stubbs, Adam Burchell, Cliff Egan (CEO), Richard Piper (Director), Chris Kinnear (Manager),
Keith Piper (Director), Colin Page (Director), Dean Grant, Matt Bodkin, Ashley Groombridge

Club Factfile

Founded: 1896   **Nickname:** The Gate
Previous Names: None
Previous Leagues: Kent 1911-23, 24-28, 29-33, 37-38, 46-59. Southern 1933-37, 59-2001, Conference 2001-04

Club Colours (change): Royal blue & white hoops/royal blue/white

Ground: Hartsdown Park, Hartsdown Road, Margate, Kent CT9 5QZ   **(T)** 01843 221 769
Capacity: 3,000   **Seats:** 350   **Covered:** 1,750   **Clubhouse:** Yes   **Shop:** Yes

Directions: From M25 continue onto M26 merge onto M20, at junction 7, exit onto Sittingbourne Rd/A249 toward
Sheerness/Canterbury/Ramsgate, continue to follow A249, take the ramp onto M2, continue onto A299 (signs for
Margate/Ramsgate) keep right at the fork, at the roundabout, take the 2nd exit onto Canterbury Rd (Birchington)/A28 continue to
follow A28, turn right onto The Square/A28 continue to follow A28, turn right onto George V Ave/B2052, turn right onto Hartsdown
Rd/B2052, ground will be on the left.

Previous Grounds:

Record Attendance: 14,500 v Tottenham Hotspur - FA Cup 3rd Round 1973
Record Victory: 8-0 v Tunbridge Wells (H) - 1966-67, v Chatham Town (H) - 1987-88 and v Stalybridge Celtic (H) - 2001-02
Record Defeat: 0-11 v AFC Bournemouth (A) - FA Cup 20/11/1971
Record Goalscorer: Jack Palethorpe scored 66 during 1929-30
Record Appearances: Bob Harrop
Additional Records: Paid £5,000 to Dover Athletic for Steve Cuggy

Senior Honours:
Southern League Premier Division 1935-36, 2000-01, Division 1 1962-63, Division 1 South 1977-78.

10 YEAR RECORD

02-03		03-04		04-05		05-06		06-07		07-08		08-09		09-10		10-11		11-12	
Conf	10	Conf	16	Conf S	21	Isth P	14	Isth P	6	Isth P	9	Isth P	19	Isth P	19	Isth P	16	Isth P	15

MARGATE

No.	Date	Comp	H/A	Opponents	Att:	Result	Goalscorers	Pos
1	Aug 20	Isth P	A	Wealdstone	448	D 1 - 1	Appiah 7	
2	23		H	Aveley	335	W 3 - 0	Avery 38 Cloke 45 Bradbrook 87	
3	27		H	Lowestoft Town	506	L 1 - 4	Bodkin 24	12
4	29		A	Hastings United	348	D 2 - 2	Appiah 21 71 (pen)	
5	Sept 3		A	Horsham	289	W 2 - 1	Bradbrook 11 77	8
6	10		H	Hendon	370	L 0 - 2		11
7	14		A	Met Police	138	W 3 - 1	Bradbrook 14 4 Appiah 54	
8	17	FAC 1Q	H	Tooting & Mitcham U	340	W 3 - 0	Appiah 16 (pen) 60 Bradbrook 75	
9	24		H	Tooting & Mitcham U	373	L 1 - 2	Avery 63	12
10	27		H	AFC Hornchurch	254	L 0 - 2		
11	Oct 1	FAC 2Q	H	Thamesmead	267	D 0 - 0		
12	4	FAC 2Qr	A	Thamesmead	142	W 6 - 1	APPIAH 5 (35 60 65 82 90) Cloke 60	
13	8		H	Carshalton Athl;etic	340	L 0 - 1		15
14	15	FAC 3Q	H	Bromley	515	L 2 - 3	Appiah 1 20	
15	22	FAT 1Q	A	Chipstead	120	W 3 - 1	Bradbrook 10 Appiah 14 77	
16	25		A	Concord Rangers	147	D 1 - 1	Appiah 44	17
17	Nov 1		A	Lewes	394	L 0 - 2		17
18	5	FAT 2Q	H	Wealdstone	304	D 1 - 1	Avery 45	
19	8	FAT 2Qr	A	Wealdstone	228	L 1 - 2	Appiah 50 (pen)	
20	12		H	Wingate & Finchley	289	W 5 - 0	APPIAH 4 (6 pen 58 65 86) Stubbs 23	17
21	19		H	Kingstonian	364	W 2 - 1	MacDonald 7 (og) Appiah 90	15
22	26		A	Harrow Borough	205	W 2 - 0	Appiah 58 88 (pen)	14
23	29		H	East Thurrock United	219	W 5 - 0	Cornielle 18 Cloke 23 86 Appiah 28 43	
24	Dec 3		H	Canvey Island	358	D 1 - 1	Pooley 72	11
25	10		A	Billericay Town	388	D 1 - 1	Avery 79	
26	17		H	Met Police	308	L 1 - 3	Burchell 83	12
27	27		A	Cray Wanderers	369	W 4 - 2	Robinson 11 Appiah 12 51 Stubbs 75	11
28	31		A	Aveley	188	W 3 - 1	Bradbrook 8 Appiah 57 Cloke 90	
29	Jan 2		H	Hastings United	471	W 4 - 1	APPIAH 3(2 8 63) Bradbrook 72	9
30	7		H	Concord Rangers	393	W 1 - 0	Appiah 74	9
31	21		H	Lewes	454	W 5 - 1	Bodkin 58 76 Stubbs 60 Avery 67 Appiah 86	8
32	28		A	Carshalton Athletic	290	L 1 - 2	Cloke 10	9
33	31		A	Leatherhead	204	L 0 - 2		
34	Feb 18		A	East Thurrock United	176	L 0 - 3		12
35	20		A	Kingstonian	278	L 1 - 2		
36	25		H	Bury Town	345	L 2 - 3	Cloke 29 (pen) Avery 43	13
37	28		A	Bury Town	342	L 1 - 2	Robinson 55	
38	March 3		A	Wingate & Finchley	105	D 2 - 2	Bradbrook 1 Stubbs 89	13
39	10		H	Leatherhead	354	D 0 - 0		13
40	13		H	Harrow Borough	192	W 1 - 0	Murphy 86	
41	24		A	Lowestoft Town	642	L 1 - 2	Murphy 6	14
42	27		A	AFC Hornchurch	220	L 0 - 3		13
43	31		H	Horsham	243	W 2 - 1	Hill 34 Bradbrook 60	
44	Apr 7		A	Hendon	186	W 3 - 0	Murphy 8 68 Bradbrook 90	
45	9		H	Cray Wanderers	257	L 1 - 3	Beales 35	13
46	14		A	Tooting & Mitcham U	155	D 1 - 1	Bodkin 30	15
47	21		H	Billericay Town	536	D 2 - 2	Stubbs 6 (pen) 50	
48	24		H	Wealdstone	246	L 0 - 2		
49	27		A	Canvey Island	342	L 0 - 5		15

METROPOLITAN POLICE

Chairman: Des Flanders
Secretary: Tony Brooking   **(T)** 0796 133 4523   **(E)** tony.brooking@met.police.uk
Additional Committee Members:
Peter Allen, Graham Fulcher

Manager: Jim Cooper
Programme Editor: Richard Peirce   **(E)** mpfc@talktalk.net

Club Factfile

Founded: 1919   **Nickname:** The Blues
Previous Names: None
Previous Leagues: Spartan 1928-60, Metropolitan 1960-71, Southern 1971-78

Club Colours (change): All blue (All red)

Ground: Imber Court, Ember Lane, East Molesey, Surrey KT8 0BT   **(T)** 0208 398 7358
Capacity: 3,000   **Seats:** 297   **Covered:** 1,800   **Clubhouse:** Yes   **Shop:** No

Directions: From London A3 take A309 towards Scilly Isles roundabout then right into Hampton Court Way.
Left at first roundabout into Imber Court Road. Ground is in 300 yards.

Previous Grounds:

Record Attendance: 4,500 v Kingstonian - FA Cup 1934
Record Victory: 10-1 v Tilbury - 1995
Record Defeat: 1-11 v Wimbledon - 1956
Record Goalscorer: Mario Russo
Record Appearances: Pat Robert
Additional Records:

Senior Honours:
Spartan League x7.
Middlesex Senior Cup 1927-28, Surrey Senior Cup 1932-33. London Senior Cup 2009-10.
Isthmian League Division One South 2010-11.

10 YEAR RECORD

02-03	03-04	04-05	05-06	06-07	07-08	08-09	09-10	10-11	11-12
Isth1S 23	Isth1S 20	Isth1 5	Isth1 4	Isth1S 6	Isth1S 4	Isth1S 4	Isth1S 10	Isth1S 1	Isth P 12

METROPOLITAN POLICE

No.	Date	Comp	H/A	Opponents	Att:	Result	Goalscorers	Pos
1	Aug 20	Isth P	H	Harrow Borough	84	W 1 - 0	T.Smith 78 (pen)	
2	23		A	Lewes	503	L 0 - 1		
3	31		H	Leatherhead	265	W 2 - 1	Palmer 16 Finn 76	
4	Sept 3		H	AFC Hornchurch	171	L 0 - 2		12
5	6		A	Wingate & Finchley	75	L 1 - 2	Wilson-Dennis 78	
6	10		A	Bury Town	411	W 1 - 0	Finn 34	10
7	14		H	Margate	138	L 1 - 3	Palmer 18	
8	17	FAC 1Q	A	Beckenham Town	120	L 2 - 4	Palmer 35 Wilson-Dennis 85	
9	24		A	Concord Rangers	142	W 3 - 0	Gwyther 1 Palmer 66 70	
10	28		H	Carshalton Athletic	178	W 5 - 0	T.Smith 15 Wilson-Dennis 43 O'Flaharty 60 Sutherland 80 858	
11	Oct 3		A	Aveley	155	W 2 - 0	Palmer 15 O'Flaherty 38	
12	8		H	Billericay Town	132	L 0 - 1		9
13	15		A	Horsham	194	D 2 - 2	Palmer 52 Jeffrey 80	9
14	22	FAT 1Q	A	Folkestone Invicta	202	L 0 - 1		
15	25		A	Hendon	138	W 3 - 1	T. Smith 26 Reynolds 29 Wilson-Dennis 87	
16	29		H	Cray Wanderers	130	W 1 - 0	T.Smith 59 (pen)	3
17	Nov 8		H	Kingstonian	412	W 2 - 1	T.Smith 40 Palmer 80	
18	19		H	Tooting & Mitcham U	163	W 3 - 0	Reynolds 21 T.Smith 23 Bourne 56	4
19	29		A	Lowestoft Town	474	D 2 - 2	T.Smith 15 72	
20	Dec 3		H	Hastings United	152	W 4 - 0	Wilson-Denis 38 68 Lovatt 40 T.Smith 74	4
21	17		A	Margate	308	W 3 - 1	Palmer 23 E.Smith 55 65	5
22	31		H	Lewes	365	D 0 - 0		
23	Jan 2		A	Leatherhead	407	D 1 - 1	Browne 39	5
24	7		H	Hendon	156	L 0 - 1		6
25	21		H	Aveley	136	D 0 - 0		9
26	28		A	Billericay Town	533	L 1 - 2	Macleod 47	10
27	31		A	Canvey Island	262	D 2 - 2	Sutherland 43 E.Smith 58	
28	Feb 18		A	Cray Wanderers	162	L 1 - 2	James 79	10
29	25		H	Horsham	1277	W 4 - 0	Palmer 37 James 46 Macleod 82 Bourne 86	9
30	March 3		A	East Thurrock United	161	L 2 - 4	T.Smith 25 Lovatt 28	11
31	7		H	Canvey Island	133	W 3 - 1	T.Smith 59 Palmer 75 E Smith 89	
32	10		H	Lowestoft Town	141	L 0 - 2		9
33	12		A	Wealdstone	428	L 0 - 1		
34	14		A	Tooting & Mitcham U	185	W 1 - 0	Moon 84	
35	17		A	Harrow Borough	121	L 1 - 2	E.Smith 73	10
36	24		H	Wingate & Finchley	91	W 2 - 1	E.Smith 70 Palmer77	
37	31		A	AFC Hornchurch	265	L 0 - 1		11
38	Apr 2		A	Carshalton Athletic	164	L 1 - 2	Hurrell 39	
39	7		H	Bury Town	127	L 0 - 1		12
40	9		A	Kingstonian	273	L 1 - 2	Goode 74 (og)	
41	14		H	Concord Rangers	115	W 3 - 0	Gallagher 14 90 Palmer 21	11
42	21		H	Wealdstone	322	L 1 - 2	Hurrell 28	11
43	24		H	East Thurrock United	132	L 1 - 2	Palmer 30	
44	28		A	Hastings United	584	W 2 0	Moon 64 Palmer 72	

THURROCK

Chairman: Tommy South
Secretary: Mark Southgate **(T)** 07979 525 117 **(E)** mark.southgate@purcom.com
Additional Committee Members:
Mike Pink, Tony Flood, Tony Perkins

Manager: Mark Stimson
Programme Editor: Mark Kettlety **(E)** sundayonly1@aol.com

THURROCK FC 2011 - 2012

Club Factfile

Founded: 1985 **Nickname:** Fleet
Previous Names: Purfleet > 2003
Previous Leagues: Essex Senior 1985-89, Isthmian 1989-2004

Club Colours (change): Yellow/green/green (All purple)

Ground: South Way, Ship Lane, Grays, Essex RM19 1YN **(T)** 01708 865 492
Capacity: 4,500 **Seats:** 300 **Covered:** 1,000 **Clubhouse:** Yes **Shop:** Yes

Directions: Approaching the ground from the North - along the M25 in a clockwise direction. Leave the motorway at junction 30. At the roundabout take the second exit and stay in the left hand lane. This leads to a large roundabout controlled by traffic lights. The fifth exit is Ship Lane and the ground is approximately 50 yards on the right hand side. Approaching the ground from the South - anti-clockwise on the M25. When going through the Dartford Tunnel take the left hand bore. On coming out of the tunnel take the first exit - junction 31. This leads to a large roundabout controlled by traffic lights. Take the third exit which is Ship Lane. The ground is situated approximately 50 yards on the right hand side.

Previous Grounds:

Record Attendance: 2,572 v West Ham United - Friendly 1998
Record Victory: 10-0 v Stansted (H) - Essex Senior Lge 1986-87 and v East Ham United (A) - Essex Senior Lge 1987-88
Record Defeat: 0-6 v St Leonards Stamco (A) - FA Trophy 1996-97 and v Sutton United (H) - Isthmian League 1997-98
Record Goalscorer: George Georgiou - 106
Record Appearances: Jimmy McFarlane - 632
Additional Records:

Senior Honours:
Isthmian League Division 2 1991-92.
Essex Senior Cup 2003-04, 05-06.

10 YEAR RECORD

02-03	03-04	04-05	05-06	06-07	07-08	08-09	09-10	10-11	11-12
Isth P 8	Isth P 3	Conf S 3	Conf S 10	Conf S 18	Conf S 12	Conf S 20	Conf S 10	Conf S 20	Conf S 22

THURROCK

No.	Date	Comp	H/A	Opponents	Att:	Result	Goalscorers	Pos
1	Sat-13-Aug	BSS	A	Salisbury City	738	D 1-1	Boylan pen 76	13
2	Tue-16-Aug	BSS	H	Dover Athletic	443	L 0-4		16
3	Sat-20-Aug	BSS	H	Weston-Super-Mare	156	L 0-3		20
4	Tue-23-Aug	BSS	A	Maidenhead United	221	L 0-4		21
5	Sat-27-Aug	BSS	A	Boreham Wood	162	L 1-2	Osborn 4	22
6	Mon-29-Aug	BSS	H	Welling United	397	L 1-4	Cracknell 12	22
7	Sat-03-Sep	BSS	A	Staines Town	276	W 3-2	Cracknell 2 (28, 48), Poole 90	21
8	Sat-10-Sep	BSS	H	Tonbridge Angels	358	D 0-0		21
9	Sat-17-Sep	BSS	A	Havant & Waterlooville	607	L 0-3		21
10	Tue-20-Sep	BSS	H	Eastbourne Borough	284	L 1-4	Boylan 43	21
11	Sat-24-Sep	BSS	H	Truro City	201	D 1-1	Bowditch 85	22
12	Sat-08-Oct	BSS	A	Farnborough	504	W 2-0	Boylan 58, Terry 63	21
13	Sat-22-Oct	BSS	A	Dover Athletic	793	L 1-3	Osborn 88	21
14	Tue-25-Oct	BSS	H	Dartford	642	L 0-3		21
15	Sat-29-Oct	BSS	H	Eastleigh	196	L 1-3	Broughton 64	21
16	Sat-05-Nov	BSS	A	Tonbridge Angels	478	L 2-3	Bowditch 6, Poole 55	22
17	Sat-19-Nov	BSS	A	Hampton & Richmond Boro'	590	W 2-0	Boylan 2 (28, 73)	21
18	Sat-03-Dec	BSS	H	Staines Town	219	L 1-2	Guy 53	22
19	Sat-10-Dec	BSS	A	Eastleigh	317	L 2-3	Ashton 82, Guy pen 90	22
20	Sat-17-Dec	BSS	H	Woking	380	D 1-1	Guy 26	22
21	Mon-26-Dec	BSS	A	Chelmsford City	1064	L 0-1		22
22	Sun-01-Jan	BSS	H	Chelmsford City	729	L 0-2		22
23	Sat-07-Jan	BSS	A	Dorchester Town	493	L 0-3		22
24	Tue-10-Jan	BSS	H	Salisbury City	186	D 1-1	Cutler 86	22
25	Sat-14-Jan	BSS	A	Sutton United	517	D 1-1	Hunt 47	22
26	Sat-21-Jan	BSS	H	Havant & Waterlooville	194	D 0-0		22
27	Sat-28-Jan	BSS	A	Dartford	1206	L 0-6		22
28	Tue-14-Feb	BSS	H	Bromley	218	D 1-1	Knight 57	22
29	Sat-18-Feb	BSS	H	Maidenhead United	156	D 1-1	A Deen 45	22
30	Tue-21-Feb	BSS	H	Farnborough	218	L 0-1		22
31	Sat-25-Feb	BSS	A	Basingstoke Town	391	L 1-3	A Deen 81	22
32	Sat-03-Mar	BSS	H	Sutton United	299	L 0-1		22
33	Sat-10-Mar	BSS	A	Weston-Super-Mare	208	D 2-2	Boylan 2 (78, 90)	22
34	Sat-17-Mar	BSS	H	Dorchester Town	176	W 2-0	Nesbitt 14, Boylan pen 59	22
35	Sat-24-Mar	BSS	A	Truro City	492	L 0-3		22
36	Tue-27-Mar	BSS	A	Eastbourne Borough	557	L 1-2	Knight 57	22
37	Sat-31-Mar	BSS	A	Woking	1754	L 1-5	Boylan 64	22
38	Fri-06-Apr	BSS	H	Boreham Wood	214	W 1-0	Boylan 54	22
39	Mon-09-Apr	BSS	A	Welling United	511	L 0-1		Relegated 22
40	Sat-14-Apr	BSS	H	Basingstoke Town	211	L 1-2	Boylan 90	22
41	Sat-21-Apr	BSS	A	Bromley	688	D 0-0		22
42	Sat-28-Apr	BSS	H	Hampton & Richmond Boro'	246	L 0-2		22

CUPS

1	Sat-01-Oct	FAC 2Q	A	VCD Athletic	104	D 2-2	Boylan 42, Bowditch 75
2	Mon-03-Oct	FAC 2QR	H	VCD Athletic	87	W 1-0	Boylan 23
3	Sat-15-Oct	FAC 3Q	H	Arlesey Town	73	D 0-0	
4	Tue-18-Oct	FAC 3QR	A	Arlesey Town	136	L 1-4	Terry 12
5	Sat-26-Nov	FAT 3Q	H	AFC Hornchurch	211	L 0-5	

WEALDSTONE

Chairman: Howard Krais
Secretary: Paul Fruin **(T)** 0779 003 8095 **(E)** paul@pfruin.orangehome.co.uk
Additional Committee Members:
Alan Couch, Nick Dugard, Peter Worby

Manager: Gordon Bartlett
Programme Editor: Mark Hyde **(E)** mik@markhyde.plus.com or mark@markhyde.co.uk

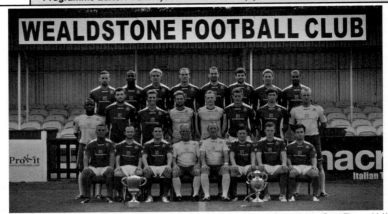

2011-12 Squad - Back Row (L-R): Peter Dean, James Hammond, Danny Spendlove, Kieron Knight, Scott Fitzgerald, Wes Parker, David Hicks, Alex Dyer. **Middle Row:** Micky Johnson (Coach), Darren Locke, Jake Parsons, Jonathan North, Sam Beagle, Alan Massey, Sean Cronin, Mark Gill (Coach). **Front Row:** Kurtney Brooks, Richard Jolly, Lee Chappell, Gordon Bartlett (Manager), Leo Morris (Assistant Manager), Dean Wallace, Jordan Lumsden, Tom O'Regan. **Not Pictured:** Nikki Ahamed, Denzil Conteh, Eddie Adjei & Scott McCubbin

Club Factfile

Founded: 1899 **Nickname:** The Stones
Previous Names:
Previous Leagues: Willesden & District 1899-1906, 08-13, London 1911-22, Middlesex 1913-22, Spartan 1922-28, Athenian 1928-64, Isthmian 1964-71, 95-2006, Southern 1971-79, 81-82, 88-95, Conference 1979-81, 82-88

Club Colours (change): All blue with white trim (Yellow with blue trim/blue/yellow)

Ground: St. Georges Stadium, Grosvenor Vale, Ruislip, Middlesex HA4 6JQ **(T)** 01895 637 487
Capacity: 2,300 **Seats:** 300 **Covered:** 450 **Clubhouse:** Yes **Shop:**

Directions
From the M1: Follow Signs for Heathrow Airport on the M25. Come off at Junction 16 onto the A40, come off at The Polish War Memorial junction A4180 sign posted to Ruislip, continue on West End Road, right into Grosvenor Vale after approx 1.5 miles, the ground is at the end of the road.
From the M25: Follow Take Junction 16 Off M25 onto A40. Then come off at The Polish War Memorial junction A4180 sign posted to Ruislip, continue on West End Road, right into Grosvenor Vale after approx 1.5 miles, the ground is at the end of the road.
From the M4: Junction 4B, take the M25 towards Watford, come off Junction 16 and join A40, come off at The Polish War Memorial junction A4180 sign posted to Ruislip, continue on West End Road, right into Grosvenor Vale after approx 1.5 miles, the ground is at the end of the road.

Previous Grounds: Lower Mead Stadium, Watford FC, Yeading FC, Northwood FC

Record Attendance: 13,504 v Leytonstone - FA Amateur Cup 4th Round replay 05/03/1949 (at Lower Mead Stadium)
Record Victory: 22-0 v The 12th London Regiment (The Rangers) - FA Amateur Cup 13/10/1923
Record Defeat: 0-14 v Edgware Town (A) - London Senior Cup 09/12/1944
Record Goalscorer: George Duck - 251
Record Appearances: Charlie Townsend - 514
Additional Records: Paid £15,000 to Barnet for David Gipp
Received £70,000 from Leeds United for Jermaine Beckford
Senior Honours:
Athenian League 1951-52. Southern League Division 1 South 1973-74, Southern Division 1981-82. Conference 1984-85. Isthmian League Division 3 1996-97. FA Amateur Cup 1965-66. London Senior Cup 1961-62. FA Trophy 1984-85. Middlesex Senior Cup x11

10 YEAR RECORD

02-03	03-04	04-05	05-06	06-07	07-08	08-09	09-10	10-11	11-12
Isth1N 9	Isth1N 7	Isth P 18	Isth P 18	SthP 19	Isth P 13	Isth P 7	Isth P 6	Isth P 12	Isth P 4

WEALDSTONE

No.	Date	Comp	H/A	Opponents	Att:	Result	Goalscorers	Pos
1	Aug 20	Isth P	H	Margate	448	D 1 - 1	O'Regan 68	
2	23		A	Carshalton Athletic	155	D 0 - 0		
3	27		A	East Thurrock	193	D 3 - 3	Jolly 54 85 (pen) Dyer 81	15
4	29		H	Wingate & Finchley	431	L 2 - 4	Jolly 71 Brooks 74	
5	Sept 3		H	Bury Town	501	W 3 - 1	Knight 62 66 Dyer 76	13
6	10		A	Kingstonian	393	W 3 - 0	Parker 24 Hicks 53 Jolly 56	9
7	12		H	Leatherhead	376	W 1 - 0	Massey 32	
8	17	FAC 1Q	H	Beaconsfield	350	L 0 - 2		
9	24		A	AFC Hornchurch	287	D 1 - 1	Jolly 70	10
10	26		H	Hendon	506	L 0 - 2		
11	Oct 1		A	Lewes	749	L 0 - 1		11
12	4		A	Cray Wanderers	164	L 1 - 2	Jolly 79	
13	8		H	Lowestoft Town	626	D 0 - 0		11
14	15		H	Hastings United	400	W 2 - 1	Jolly 39 41	11
15	22	FAT 1Q	H	Tooting & Mitcham U		W 3 - 0	Parker 26 Fitzgerald 38 (pen) Jolly 62	
16	29		A	Aveley	172	W 3 - 0	Jolly 10 71 Hicks 66	10
17	Nov 5	FAT 2Q	A	Margate	304	D 1 - 1	Fitzgerald 57	
18	8	FAT 2Qr	H	Margate	228	W 2 - 1	Jolly 23 Dyer 77	
19	12		A	Billericay Town	474	D 0 - 0		11
20	19		H	Canvey Island	434	L 1 - 2	Parker 18	11
21	26	FAT 3Q	A	Banbury United	370	D 0 - 0		
22	29	FAT 3Qr	H	Banbury United	222	W 4 - 0	O'Leary 19 JOLLY 3 (21 48 79)	
23	Dec 3		A	Concord Rangers	152	W 2 - 1	Assombalonga 13 Jolly 82	13
24	10	FAT 1	H	Uxbridge	373	W 5 - 0	JOLLY 3(39 42 82) Assombalonga 63 68	
25	17		A	Leatherhead	352	D 1 - 1	Jolly 4	13
26	26		H	Harrow Borough	876	W 4 - 0	Leech 20 (og) Jolly 31 90 Assombalonga 78	10
27	31		H	Carshalton Athletic	463	D 1 - 1	Fitzgerald 34 (pen)	
28	Jan 2		A	Wingate & Finchley	267	W 5 - 0	Fitzgerald 22 Assombalonga 45 50 Jolly 75 78	11
29	7		H	Lewes	476	W 1 - 0	Fitzgerald 7	
30	10		A	Horsham	192	D 1 - 1	Dean 39	10
31	14	FAT 2	H	Barrow	722	W 2 - 1	Jolly 52 Assombalonga 59	
32	21		H	Cray Wanderers	445	D 1 - 1	Parker 60	11
33	24		A	Hendon	401	D 1 - 1	Hicks 52	
34	28		A	Lowestoft Town	855	L 1 - 2	Assombalonga 21	11
35	30		H	Tooting & Mitcham United	408	W 2 - 0	Assombalonga 20 Jolly 90	
36	Feb 14	FAT 3	A	Dartford	770	D 2 - 2	Jolly 45 O'Leary 80	
37	18		H	Aveley	430	W 5 - 2	Jolly 5 81 Chappell 32 Mulley 67 (og) Fitzgerald 78	8
38	21	FAT 3r	H	Dartford	670	W 1 0	Chappel	
39	25	FAT QF	A	Cambridge United	2034	W 2 - 1	Jolly 4 68	10
40	March 3		H	Billericay Town	617	D 1 - 1	Jolly 3	
41	10	FAT SF 1	A	Newport County	2209	L 1 - 3	Jolly 49	12
42	12		H	Horsham	402	W 3 - 0	Jolly 26 65 Parker 28	
43	17	FAT SF 2	H	Newport County	2092	D 0 - 0		
44	19		H	Met Police	428	W 1 - 0	Jolly 55	12
45	24		H	East Thurrock U	448	D 2 - 2	Jolly 54 Dyer 82	12
46	27		A	Canvey Island	262	L 1 3	Smith	
47	31		A	Bury Town	413	D 1 - 1	O'Leary 8	8
48	Apr 2		A	Hastings United	338	W 2 - 0	Jolly 78 86	
49	7		H	Kingstonian	527	W 4 - 1	Chappell 38 Jolly 56 Dean 75 Smith 87	
50	11		A	Harrow Borough	617	D 0 - 0		6
51	14		H	AFC Hornchurch	538	W 2 - 1	Fitzgerald 59 Pett 40	
52	17		A	Tooting & Mitcham United	255	W 6 - 0	JOLLY 3 (1 16 35) Chappell 50 Parker 53 Smith 55	
53	21		A	Met Police	322	W 2 - 1	Dyer 35 Jolly 54	
54	24		A	Margate	246	W 2 - 0	Parker 15 Fitzgerald 45	
55	28		H	Concord Rangers	770	W 3 - 1	Dyer 1 Jolly 50 Fitzgerald 77	4
56	May 2	Play-Off SF	A	Lowestoft Town	1158	L 1 - 2	Fitzgerald 63	

Non-League Action...

FA Trophy Final - York's Matty Blair takes on three Newport County defenders.

Photo: Graham Brown.

WHITEHAWK

Chairman: Peter McDonnell
Secretary: John Rosenblatt **(T)** 07724 519 370 **(E)** johnrosenblatt@whitehawkfc.com
Additional Committee Members:
Fed Moore, Kevin Keehan, Keith Fowler

Manager: Darren Freeman
Programme Editor: Nathan Jones **(E)** nathanjones1275@yahoo.co.uk

THE NON-LEAGUE CLUB DIRECTORY

Book Holiday Inn Hotels and Save today!

Home

Clubs

Steps 1 - 4

League Tables

35 Years of Non-League Football

The Non-League Club Directory has developed into a comprehensive record of competitions within the non-League game, giving this level of football the

www.non-leagueclubdirectory.co.uk

Club Factfile

Founded: 1945 **Nickname:** Hawks

Previous Names: Whitehawk & Manor Farm Old Boys untill 1958

Previous Leagues: Brighton & Hove District, Sussex County > 2010

Club Colours (change): All red (All blue)

Ground: Enclosed Ground, East Brighton Park, Wilson Avenue, Brighton BN2 5TS **(T)** 01273 609 736

Capacity: 3,000 **Seats:** Yes **Covered:** 500 **Clubhouse:** Yes **Shop:** No

Directions: From N (London) on M23/A23 – after passing Brighton boundary sign & twin pillars join A27 (sp Lewes); immediately after passing Sussex University (on L) leave A27 via slip rd at sp B2123, Falmer, Rottingdean; at roundabout at top of slip rd turn R onto B2123 (sp Falmer, Rottingdean); in 2m at traffic lights in Woodingdean turn R by Downs Hotel into Warren Road; in about 1m at traffic lights turn L into Wilson Ave, crossing racecourse; in 1¼m turn L at foot of hill (last turning before traffic lights) into East Brighton Park; follow lane for the ground.

Previous Grounds:

Record Attendance: 2,100 v Bognor Regis Town - FA Cup 1988-89

Record Victory: Not known
Record Defeat: Not known

Record Goalscorer: Billy Ford

Record Appearances: Ken Powell - 1,103

Additional Records:

Senior Honours:

Sussex County League Division 1 1961-62, 63-64, 83-84, 2009-10. Division 2 1967-68, 80-81. Isthmian League Division 1 South 2011-12. Sussex Senior Cup 1950-51, 61-62 Sussex RUR Charity Cup x3.

02-03	03-04	04-05	05-06	06-07	07-08	08-09	09-10	10-11	11-12
SxC1 2	SxC1 8	SxC1 3	SxC1 3	SxC1 2	SxC1 2	SxC1 13	SxC1 1	Isth1S 3	Isth1S 1

WINGATE & FINCHLEY

Chairman: Aron Sharpe
Secretary: David Thrilling **(T)** 0797 700 7746 **(E)** secretary@wingatefinchley.com
Additional Committee Members:
Ricky Deller, Paul Lerman

Manager: David Norman
Programme Editor: Paul Lerman **(E)** paul@wingatefinchley.com

2011-12 Squad - Back Row (L-R): Ewa Trochym, David Norman, Lewis Jones, Gary Burrell, Ahmet Rifat, Bobby Smith, Gavin King, David Laird,
Ajet Shehu, Ola Williams, Joe O'Brien, Dean Smith, Andrew Zeller.
Front Row: Marc Weatherstone, Murat Karagul, Josh Cooper, Jordan Fowler, Daniel Nielsen, Leon Smith, Paul Wright, Angus McLachlan, Marc Henry.

Club Factfile

Founded: 1991 **Nickname:** Blues
Previous Names: Wingate (founded 1946) and Finchley (founded late 1800s) merged in 1991
Previous Leagues: South Midlands 1991-95, Isthmian 1995-2004, Southern 2004-2006

Club Colours (change): Royal blue with navy piping/royal blue with navy piping/navy (White with gold piping/black/black)

Ground: Harry Abraham Stadium, Summers Lane, Finchley N12 0PD **(T)** 020 8446 2217
Capacity: 8,500 **Seats:** 500 **Covered:** 500 **Clubhouse:** Yes **Shop:** No

Directions
The simplest way to get to The Harry Abrahams Stadium is to get on to the A406 North Circular Road.
If coming from the West (eg via M1), go past Henlys Corner (taking the left fork after the traffic lights) and then drive for about 1 mile. The exit to take is the one immediately after a BP garage. Take the slip road and then turn right at the lights onto the A1000.
If coming from the East (eg via A10, M11) take the A1000 turn off. At the end of the slip road turn left at the lights. Go straight over the next set of lights. Then after 100m pass through another set of lights, then at the next set of lights turn right into Summers Lane. The Abrahams Stadium is a few hundred metres down on the right hand side.

Previous Grounds:

Record Attendance: 528 v Brentwood Town (Division One North Play-Off) 2010/11
Record Victory: 9-1 v Winslow (South Midlands League) 23/11/1991
Record Defeat: 0-9 v Edgware - Isthmian Division 2 15/01/2000
Record Goalscorer: Marc Morris 650 (including with Wingate FC) FA Record for one Club
Record Appearances: Marc Morris 720 (including with Wingate FC) FA Record for one Club
Additional Records:

Senior Honours:
Isthmian League Cup 2010-11.
London Senior Cup 2010-11.

10 YEAR RECORD

02-03	03-04	04-05	05-06	06-07	07-08	08-09	09-10	10-11	11-12
Isth1N 18	Isth1N 11	SthE 12	SthE 12	Isth1N 9	Isth1N 18	Isth1N 7	Isth1N 3	Isth1N 3	Isth P 13

WINGATE & FINCHLEY

No.	Date	Comp	H/A	Opponents	Att:	Result	Goalscorers	Pos
1	Aug 20	Isth P	A	Hastings United	297	W 1 - 0	L.Smith 31	
2	23		H	Lowestoft Town	111	W 2 - 1	L.Smith 9 Karagul 25	
3	29		A	Wealdstone	431	W 4 - 2	L.Smith 6 17 Laird 44 Weatherstone 50	
4	Sept 3		A	Tooting & Mitcham U	253	D 1 - 1	Weatherstone 22	5
5	6		H	Met Police	75	W 2 - 1	Jones 13 73	
6	10		H	Canvey Island	171	L 0 - 2		6
7	13		A	Cray Wanderers	148	L 2 - 3	LSmith 8 44	
8	17	FAC 1Q	H	Redbridge	120	L 0 - 3		
9	24		H	Horsham	285	W 3 - 2	L.Smith 7 34 Weatherstone 43	6
10	27		H	Billericay Town	128	L 1 - 4	L.Smith 12	
11	Oct 1		A	AFC Hornchurch	221	L 0 - 1		9
12	11		H	Harrow Borough	137	D 2 - 2	Megicks 15 Weatherstone 57	
13	15		H	Aveley	125	D 2 - 2	L.Smith 22 Hogan 80 (og)	
14	22	FAT 1Q	H	AFC Hornchurch	162	L 1 - 2	Henry 10	
15	29		A	Kingstonian	187	D 2 - 2	Rifat 9 Burke 27	11
16	Nov 5		H	Concord Rangers	94	W 3 - 1	L.Smith 5 Rifat 11 67	9
17	12		A	Margate	289	L 0 - 5		10
18	19		A	Lewes	573	D 0 - 0		10
19	Dec 3		A	Carshalton Athletic	192	L 0 - 3		14
20	17		H	Cray Wanderers	85	L 0 - 2		14
21	20		H	Bury Town	103	W 3 - 2	KARAGUL 3 (10 18 28)	
22	26		A	Hendon	183	D 1 - 1	Mitchell 8	13
23	31		A	Lowestoft	721	L 0 - 2		
24	Jan 2		H	Wealdstone	267	L 0 - 5		14
25	7		H	AFC Hornchurch	150	L 1 - 2	Weatherstone 39	
26	14		A	Billericay Town	419	L 0 - 2		17
27	21		H	Leatherhead	112	W 1 - 0	L.Smith 9	17
28	28		A	Harrow Borough	171	W 3 - 1	L.Smith 7 Douti 18 Douglas 90	15
29	Feb 18		H	Kingstonian	171	L 0 - 2		16
30	21		A	Leatherhead	171	D 2 - 2	Laird 11 L.Smith 28	
31	25		A	Aveley	128	W 2 - 1	Olafunbosom 38 (og) L.Smith78	15
32	March 3		H	Margate	105	D 2 - 2	L.Smith 2 Douti 39	16
33	6		H	East Thurrock United	55	L 3 - 3	Laird 42 88 L.Smith 78	
34	10		A	Concord Rangers	126	D 1 - 1	Wiliams74	15
35	13		H	Lewes	95	L 1 - 2	L.Smith27	
36	17		H	Hastings United	111	W 3 - 1	Fisher 7 L.Smith 57 Laird 75	15
37	24		A	Met Police	91	L 0 - 2		15
38	31		H	Tooting & Mitcham	122	W 4 - 2	Karagul 6 L.Smith 40 Burke 60 76	15
39	Apr 2		A	Bury Town	310	D 2 - 2	Laird 22 90	
40	7		A	Canvey Island	343	W 3 - 2	Laird 11 78 L.Smith 46	
41	9		H	Hendon	240	L 0 - 5		
42	14		A	Horsham	124	W 2 - 1	Laird 47 61	15
43	21		A	East Thurrock United	148	W 2 - 1	Wood 4 (og) L.Smith 27	13
44	28		H	Carshalton Athletic	112	W 2 - 1	Burke 29 L.Smith 88	14

AFC SUDBURY

Chairman: Philip Turner
Secretary: Davis Webb   **(T)** 07885 327 510   **(E)** dave-afc@supanet.com
Additional Committee Members:
Mark Peaman, Danny Crosbie

Manager: Chris Tracey
Programme Editor: Darren Theobald   **(E)** theobaldd@hotmail.co.uk

Club Factfile

Founded: 1999   **Nickname:** Yellows
Previous Names: Sudbury Town (1874) and Sudbury Wanderers (1958) merged in 1999
Previous Leagues: Eastern Counties 1999-2006, Isthmian 2006-08, Southern 2008-10

Club Colours (change): Yellow/blue/yellow (All red)

Ground: The Mel Group Stadium, Kingsmarsh Brundon Lane, Sudbury CO10 7HN   **(T)** 01787 376 213
Capacity: 2,500   **Seats:** 200   **Covered:** 1,500   **Clubhouse:** Yes   **Shop:** Yes

Directions: Follow Halstead/Chelmsford road from Sudbury centre for a mile.
First right after bridge at foot of steep hill and first right again after left hand bend.

Previous Grounds:

Record Attendance: 1,800
Record Victory: Not known
Record Defeat: Not known
Record Goalscorer: Gary Bennett - 172
Record Appearances: Paul Betson - 376
Additional Records:

Senior Honours:
Eastern Counties League 2000-01, 01-02, 02-03, 03-04, 04-05.
Suffolk Premier Cup 2002, 2003, 2004.

10 YEAR RECORD

02-03		03-04		04-05		05-06		06-07		07-08		08-09		09-10		10-11		11-12	
ECP	1	ECP	1	ECP	1	ECP	3	Isth1N	5	Isth1N	2	SthM		SthM	14	Isth1N	7	Isth1N	8

AVELEY

Chairman: Graham Gennings
Secretary: Craig Johnston   **(T)** 0794 643 8540   **(E)** craigjohnston@aveleyfc.freeserve.co.uk
Additional Committee Members:
Terry King, Colin Munford, Alan Suttling

Manager: Justin Gardner
Programme Editor: Craig Johnston   **(E)** craigjohnston@aveleyfc.freeserve.co.uk

Standing L to R Jessica Fox, Carey Eastwood, Marc Sontag, Jordan Cox, Ronnie Worster, Jay Leader (c), David McCartney, Alfred Kamara, Paul Burnett, Ricky Edwards, Sheldon Sellears, Tom Querry, Kevin Head.

Sitting L to R Ellis Sands, Jack Stevenson, Charlie Stevenson, Gary Nesbit, Justin Gardner, Victor Renner, Billy Holland, Junior Appiah, Shane Oakley.

Club Factfile

Founded: 1927   **Nickname:** The Millers
Previous Names: None
Previous Leagues: Thurrock Combination 1946-49, London 1949-57, Delphian 1957-63, Athenian 1963-73, Isthmian 1973-2004, Southern 2004-06
Club Colours (change): All blue (All red)

Ground: Mill Field, Mill Road, Aveley, Essex RM15 4SJ   **(T)** 01708 865 940
Capacity: 4,000   **Seats:** 400   **Covered:** 400   **Clubhouse:** Yes   **Shop:** No

Directions: London - Southend A1306, turn into Sandy Lane at Aveley.

Previous Grounds:

Record Attendance: 3,741 v Slough Town - FA Amateur Cup 27/02/1971
Record Victory: 11-1 v Histon - 24/08/1963
Record Defeat: 0-8 v Orient, Essex Thameside Trophy
Record Goalscorer: Jotty Wilks - 214
Record Appearances: Ken Riley - 422
Additional Records:

Senior Honours:
Athenian League 1970-71. Isthmian League Division 1 North 2008-09.
Thameside Trophy 1980, 2005, 2007.

10 YEAR RECORD

02-03	03-04	04-05	05-06	06-07	07-08	08-09	09-10	10-11	11-12
Isth1N 6	Isth1N 14	SthE 17	SthE 20	Isth1N 15	Isth1N 11	Isth1N 1	Isth P 3	Isth P 19	Isth P 20

BRENTWOOD TOWN

Chairman: Brian Hallett
Secretary: Ray Stevens   **(T)** 0776 800 6370   **(E)** r.w.stevens@btinternet.com
Additional Committee Members:
Ken Hobbs

Manager: Steve Witherspoon
Programme Editor: Ken Hobbs   **(E)** khobbs1057@aol.com

THE NON-LEAGUE CLUB DIRECTORY

Book Holiday Inn Hotels and Save today!

Home

Clubs

Steps 1 - 4

League Tables

35 Years of Non-League Football

The Non-League Club Directory has developed into a comprehensive record of competitions within the non-League game, giving this level of football the

www.non-leagueclubdirectory.co.uk

Club Factfile

Founded: 1954   **Nickname:** Blues

Previous Names: Manor Athletic, Brentwood Athletic, Brentwood F.C.

Previous Leagues: Romford & District, South Essex Combination, London & Essex Border, Olympian, Essex Senior

Club Colours (change): Sky blue/white/white (All claret)

Ground: The Arena, Brentwood Centre, Doddinghurst Road, Brentwood CM15 9NN   **(T)** 01708 800 6370

Capacity: 1,000   **Seats:** 50   **Covered:** 250   **Clubhouse:** Yes   **Shop:** No

Directions: From High Street (Wilson's Corner) turn north into Ongar Road.
Then at third mini roundabout turn right into Doddinghurst Road.

Previous Grounds: King George's Playing Fields (Hartswood), Larkins Playing Fields 1957-93

Record Attendance: 472 v West Ham United - 27/07/2004

Record Victory: Not known
Record Defeat: Not known

Record Goalscorer: Not known

Record Appearances: Not known

Additional Records:

Senior Honours:
Essex Senior League 2000-01, 2006-07, League Cup 1975-76, 78-79, 90-91, 2006-07.
Essex Olympian League Cup 1967-68.

02-03		03-04		04-05		05-06		06-07		07-08		08-09		09-10		10-11		11-12	
ESen	11	ESen	14	ESen	14	ESen	8	ESen	1	Isth1N	6	Isth1N	3	Isth1N	12	Isth1N	5	Isth1N	9

CHATHAM TOWN

Chairman: Jeff Talbot
Secretary: Henry Longhurst   **(T)** 0796 746 5554   **(E)** h.longhurst@sky.com
Additional Committee Members:
Mike Green

Manager: Kevin Watson
Programme Editor: Rachel Willett   **(E)** rachel.willett1987@yahoo.co.uk

Club Factfile

Founded: 1882   **Nickname:** Chats
Previous Names: Chatham FC 1882-1974, Medway FC 1974-79
Previous Leagues: Southern 1894-1900, 1920-21, 27-29, 83-88, 2001-, Kent 1894-96, 1901-1905, 29-59, 68-83, 88-2001, Aetolian 1959-64, Metropolitan 1964-68

Club Colours (change): Red & black stripes/black/black (Blue & black stripes/blue/blue)

Ground: Maidstone Road Sports Ground, Maidstone Road, Chatham ME4 6LR   **(T)** 01634 812 194
Capacity: 2,000   **Seats:** 600   **Covered:** 600   **Clubhouse:** Yes   **Shop:** Yes
Directions: M2, A229 Chatham turn-off,
follow signs to Chatham,
ground is one and half miles on the right opposite garage.
One mile from Chatham BR.

Previous Grounds: Great Lines, Chatham 1882-90

Record Attendance: 5,000 v Gillingham - 1980
Record Victory: Not known
Record Defeat: Not known
Record Goalscorer: Not known
Record Appearances: Not known
Additional Records: Received Transfer fee of £500

Senior Honours:
Kent League 1894-95, 1903-04, 04-05, 71-72, 73-74, 75-76, 76-77, 79-80, 2000-01.
Kent Senior Cup 1888-89, 1904-05, 10-11, 18-19. Kent Senior Shield 1919-20.

10 YEAR RECORD

02-03		03-04		04-05		05-06		06-07		07-08		08-09		09-10		10-11		11-12	
SthE	15	SthE	13	SthE	11	SthE	17	Isth1S	16	Isth1S	18	Isth1N	10	Isth1S	17	Isth1S	21	Isth1N	15

CHESHUNT

Chairman: Dean Williamson
Secretary: Alex Kalinic   **(T)** 0775 483 1800   **(E)** alex@cheshuntfc.com
Additional Committee Members:

Manager: Tony Faulkner
Programme Editor: Alex Kalinic   **(E)** alex@cheshuntfc.com

Club Factfile

Founded: 1946   **Nickname:** Ambers
Previous Names:
Previous Leagues: London 1947-51, 56-59, Delphian 1952-55, Aetolian 1960-62, Spartan 1963-64, 88-93, Athenian 1965-76, Isthmian 1977-87, 94-2005, Southern 2006-08

Club Colours (change): Amber/black/black (Sky blue/white/sky blue)

Ground: Cheshunt Stadium, Theobalds Lane, Cheshunt, Herts EN8 8RU   **(T)** 01992 633 500
Capacity: 3,500   **Seats:** 424   **Covered:** 600   **Clubhouse:** Yes   **Shop:** No

Directions:
M25, junction 25 take A10 north towards Hertford.
Third exit at roundabout towards Waltham Cross A121.
First exit at roundabout towards Cheshunt B176.
Under railway bridge then left onto Theobalds Lane.
Ground is 800 yard on the right.

Previous Grounds: Not known

Record Attendance: 5,000
Record Victory: v Bromley - FA Amateur Cup 2nd Round 28/01/1950
Record Defeat: 0-10 v Etonn Manor - London League 17/04/1956
Record Goalscorer: Eddie Sedgwick - 148 (1967-72, 1980)
Record Appearances: John Poole - 526 (1970-76, 79-83)
Additional Records: Received £10,000 from Peterborough United for Lloyd Opara

Senior Honours:
London League Premier Division 1950, Division 1 1948, 49. Athenian League Premier Division 1976, Division 1 1968.
Spartan League 1963. Isthmian League Division 2 2003.
London Charity Cup 1974. East Anglian Cup 1975. Herts Charity Cup 2006, 2008.

10 YEAR RECORD

02-03		03-04		04-05		05-06		06-07		07-08		08-09		09-10		10-11		11-12	
Isth2	1	Isth1N	3	Isth P	19	SthP	16	SthP	16	SthP	22	Isth1N	14	Isth1N	15	Isth1N	18	Isth1N	18

GRAYS ATHLETIC

Chairman: Keith Burns
Secretary: Val Pepperell   **(T)** 07931 731 358   **(E)** graysathleticfc@hotmail.co.uk
Additional Committee Members:
Chris Jones, Steve Pepperell

Manager: Hakan Hayrettin
Programme Editor: Chris Jones   **(E)** cmjones007@hotmail.com

THE NON-LEAGUE CLUB DIRECTORY

Book Holiday Inn Hotels and Save today!

| Home |
| Clubs |
| Steps 1 - 4 |
| League Tables |

35 Years of Non-League Football

The Non-League Club Directory has developed into a comprehensive record of competitions within the non-League game, giving this level of football the

www.non-leagueclubdirectory.co.uk

Club Factfile

Founded: 1890   **Nickname:** The Blues

Previous Names: Not known

Previous Leagues: Athenian 1912-14, 58-83, London 1914-24, 26-39, Kent 1924-26, Corinthian 1945-58, Isthmian 1958-2004, Conference 2004-10

Club Colours (change): All royal blue (All white)

Ground: Rush Green Sports & Leisure Centre, Rush Green Road, Romford RM7 0LU **(T)**

Capacity: **Seats:**   **Covered:**   **Clubhouse:** Yes   **Shop:** No

Directions
At junction 8, exit onto M25 toward Dartford, Continue onto A282, Partial toll road.
At junction 31, take the A1090/A1306 exit to Thurrock (Lakeside)/Purfleet/W Thurrock/A126 Toll road.
At the roundabout, take the 3rd exit onto Arterial Road Purfleet/A1306
Continue to follow A1306. Go through 3 roundabouts
At the roundabout, take the 3rd exit onto Rainham Rd/A125.
At the roundabout, take the 1st exit onto Dagenham Rd/A1112
Continue to follow A1112
At the roundabout, take the 2nd exit onto Rainham Rd S/A1112
At the roundabout, take the 2nd exit onto Wood Ln/A124
Continue to follow A124. Destination will be on the left

Previous Grounds: Recreation Ground Bridge Road. Rookery Hill (East Thurrock Utd).

Record Attendance: 9,500 v Chelmsford City - FA Cup 4th Qualifying Round 1959

Record Victory: 12-0 v Tooting & Mitcham United - London League 24/02/1923
Record Defeat: 0-12 v Enfield (A) - Athenian League 20/04/1963

Record Goalscorer: Harry Brand - 269 (1944-52)

Record Appearances: Phil Sammons - 673 (1982-97)

Additional Records:

Senior Honours:
Conference South 2004-05. FA Trophy 2004-05, 05-06.
Essex Senior Cup x8

02-03	03-04	04-05	05-06	06-07	07-08	08-09	09-10	10-11	11-12
Isth P 19	Isth P 6	Conf S 1	Conf 3	Conf 19	Conf 10	Conf 19	Conf 23	Isth1N 10	Isth1N 5

HARLOW TOWN

Chairman: John Barnett
Secretary: John McClelland   **(T)** 0781 639 1892   **(E)** maccahtfc@hotmail.com
Additional Committee Members:
Ray Dyer, David Square, Steve Clark

Manager: Danny Chapman
Programme Editor: Mark Kettley   **(E)** sundayonly1@aol.com

2011-12 Squad.

Club Factfile

Founded: 1879   **Nickname:** Hawks
Previous Names: None
Previous Leagues: East Hertfordshire > 1932, Spartan 1932-39, 46-54, London 1954-61, Delphian 1961-63, Athenian 1963-73, Isthmian 1973-92, Inactive 1992-93, Southern 2004-06

Club Colours (change): All red (White/black/black)

Ground: Barrows Farm Std, off Elizabeth Way, The Pinnacles, Harlow CM19 5BE   **(T)** 01279 443 196
Capacity: 3,500   **Seats:** 500   **Covered:** 500   **Clubhouse:** Yes   **Shop:** Yes

Directions

Barrows Farm is situated on the western side of town just off of the Roydon Road (A1169) on the Pinnacles Industrial Estate.
If coming into Harlow from the M11 (North or South) exit at Junction 7 and follow the A414 until the first roundabout where you turn left onto the A1169. Follow the A1169 signed for Roydon until you see the ground ahead of you at the Roydon Road roundabout. Go straight over the roundabout and the entrance to the ground is on the left.
If coming into town from the west on the A414 turn right at the first roundabout (the old ground was straight ahead) signed Roydon A1169. Follow the A1169 for approx 1 mile and the entrance to the ground is on the right.

Previous Grounds: Marigolds 1919-22, Green Man Field 1922-60

Record Attendance: 9,723 v Leicester City - FA Cup 3rd Round replay 08/01/1980
Record Victory: 14-0 v Bishop's Stortford - 11/04/1925
Record Defeat: 0-11 v Ware (A) - Spartan Division 1 East 06/03/1948
Record Goalscorer: Dick Marshall scored 64 during 1928-29
Record Appearances: Norman Gladwin - 639 (1949-70)
Additional Records:

Senior Honours:
Athenian League Division 1 1971-72. Isthmian League Division 1 1978-79, Division 2 North 1988-89.
Essex Senior cup 1978-79

10 YEAR RECORD

02-03		03-04		04-05		05-06		06-07		07-08		08-09		09-10		10-11		11-12	
Isth1N	10	Isth1N	10	SthE	15	SthE	9	Isth1N	2	Isth P	15	Isth P	20	Isth1N	22	Isth1N	4	Isth1N	7

HEYBRIDGE SWIFTS

Chairman: Nick Bowyer
Secretary: Jill Hedgecock   **(T)** 07522 158487   **(E)** blackwater1@sky.com
Additional Committee Members:
Michael Gibson

Manager: Mark Hawkes
Programme Editor: Jill Hedgecock   **(E)** blackwater1@sky.com

Club Factfile

Founded: 1880   **Nickname:** Swifts
Previous Names:
Previous Leagues: Essex & Suffolk Border, North Essex, South Essex, Essex Senior 1971-84

Club Colours (change): Black and white stripes/black/black (Yellow/white/white)

Ground: Scraley Road, Heybridge, Maldon, Essex CM9 8JA   **(T)** 01621 852 978
Capacity: 3,000   **Seats:** 550   **Covered:** 1,200   **Clubhouse:** Yes   **Shop:** Yes

Directions: Leave Maldon on the main road to Colchester,
pass through Heybridge then turn right at sign to Tolleshunt Major (Scraley Road).
The ground is on the right.

Previous Grounds:

Record Attendance: 2,477 v Woking - FA Trophy 1997
Record Victory: Not known
Record Defeat: Not known
Record Goalscorer: Julian Lamb - 115 (post War)
Record Appearances: Hec Askew - 500+. John Pollard - 496
Additional Records: Paid £1,000 for Dave Rainford and for Lee Kersey
Senior Honours: Received £35,000 from Southend United for Simon Royce
Isthmian League Division 2 North 1989-90, Essex Senior League x3.
Essex Junior Cup 1931-32. East Anglian Cup 1993-94, 94-95.

10 YEAR RECORD

02-03		03-04		04-05		05-06		06-07		07-08		08-09		09-10		10-11		11-12	
Isth P	20	Isth P	16	Isth P	7	Isth P	2	Isth P	12	Isth P	12	Isth P	21	Isth1N	6	Isth1N	9	Isth1N	16

ILFORD

Chairman: Roger Chilvers
Secretary: Marion Chilvers   **(T)** 07710 285571   **(E)** rogerchilvers@aol.com
Additional Committee Members:
Colin Walton

Manager: Kevin Lucas
Programme Editor: Len Llewellyn   **(E)** exseniorlenl@aol.com

THE NON-LEAGUE CLUB DIRECTORY

Book Holiday Inn Hotels and Save today!

Home

Clubs

Steps 1 - 4

League Tables

35 Years of Non-League Football

The Non-League Club Directory has developed into a comprehensive record of competitions within the non-League game, giving this level of football the

www.non-leagueclubdirectory.co.uk

Club Factfile

Founded: 1987   **Nickname:** The Foxes

Previous Names: Reformed as Ilford in 1987 after the original club merged with Leytonstone in 1980.

Previous Leagues: Spartan 1987-94, Essex Senior 1996-2004, Isthmian 2004-05, Southern 2005-06

Club Colours (change): Blue and white hoops/blue/blue (All red)

Ground: Cricklefield Stadium, 486 High Road, Ilford, Essex IG1 1UE   **(T)** 020 8514 8352

Capacity: 3,500   **Seats:** 216   **Covered:** Yes   **Clubhouse:** Yes   **Shop:** No

Directions: Taking the A127, from the east travel towards London before coming to the traffic light controlled junction at Barley Lane, Goodmayes (B177) . Turn Left by taking the slip road and follow Barley Lane to its junction with the traffic light controlled High Road, Goodmayes (A118) (it is the first set of traffic control lights for traffic rather than pedestrians on that road). Turn Right and follow the road past Seven Kings station (which should be on your right) and on towards Ilford. The entrance to the ground is some 400 yards past the station with the Ilford Swimming Baths on the left being the point at which both coaches and those in cars or on foot should turn left into the car parks. Both on Saturday and after 6pm. during the week, the public car park is free of charge.

Previous Grounds:

Record Attendance: Not known

Record Victory: Not known
Record Defeat: Not known

Record Goalscorer: Not known

Record Appearances: Not known

Additional Records:

Senior Honours:
Isthmian League Division Two 2004-05.

02-03		03-04		04-05		05-06		06-07		07-08		08-09		09-10		10-11		11-12	
ESen	3	ESen	2	Isth2	1	SthE	21	Isth1N	21	Isth1N	21	Isth1N	17	Isth1N	20	Isth1N	20	Isth1N	20

MALDON & TIPTREE

Chairman: Ed Garty
Secretary: Phil Robinson   **(T)** 0775 906 6636   **(E)** robbophil@hotmail.com
Additional Committee Members:
Peter Bond

Manager: Terry Spillane
Programme Editor: Richard Buckby   **(E)** buckby1996@hotmail.co.uk

THE NON-LEAGUE CLUB DIRECTORY

Book Holiday Inn Hotels and Save today!

Home

Clubs

Steps 1 - 4

League Tables

35 Years of Non-League Football

The Non-League Club Directory has developed into a comprehensive record of competitions within the non-League game, giving this level of football the

www.non-leagueclubdirectory.co.uk

Club Factfile

Founded: 2010   **Nickname:** The Hoops

Previous Names: Maldon Town (1975) and Tiptree United (1933) merged in 2010 to form today's club
Previous Leagues: None

Club Colours (change): Blue and red stripes/blue/blue (All orange)

Ground: Wallace Binder Ground, Park Drive, Maldon CM9 6XX   **(T)** 01621 853 762

Capacity: 2,800 **Seats:** 155 **Covered:** 300 **Clubhouse:** Yes **Shop:**

Directions
From M25 junction 28 travel north on A12 until A414 to Maldon.
Turn right at Safeways roundabout, then over next two roundabouts.
Ground is on the right.

Previous Grounds:

Record Attendance: Not known

Record Victory: Not known
Record Defeat: Not known

Record Goalscorer: Not known

Record Appearances: Not known
Additional Records:

Senior Honours:
None

02-03	03-04	04-05	05-06	06-07	07-08	08-09	09-10	10-11	11-12
								Isth1N 8	Isth1N 11

NEEDHAM MARKET

Chairman: David Bugg
Secretary: Mark Easlea   **(T)** 0779 545 6502   **(E)** m.easlea@sky.com
Additional Committee Members:
Paul Collier, Wendy Hall

Manager: Danny Laws
Programme Editor: Mark Easlea   **(E)** m.easlea@sky.com

THE NON-LEAGUE CLUB DIRECTORY

Book Holiday Inn Hotels and Save today!

Home

Clubs

Steps 1 - 4

League Tables

35 Years of Non-League Football

The Non-League Club Directory has developed into a comprehensive record of competitions within the non-League game, giving this level of football the

www.non-leagueclubdirectory.co.uk

Club Factfile

Founded: 1919   **Nickname:** The Marketmen

Previous Names: None
Previous Leagues: Suffolk & Ipswich Senior, Eastern Counties

Club Colours (change): All red (Yellow/black/black)

Ground: Bloomfields, Quinton Road, Needham Market IP6 8DA   **(T)** 01449 721 000

Capacity: 1,000   **Seats:** 250   **Covered:** 250   **Clubhouse:** Yes   **Shop:** Yes
Directions: Quinton Road is off Barretts Lane which in turn is off Needham Market High Street.

Previous Grounds:

Record Attendance: 750 v Ipswich Town - Suffolk Premier Cup 2007

Record Victory: Not known
Record Defeat: Not known

Record Goalscorer: Alvin King

Record Appearances: Not known

Additional Records:

Senior Honours:
Suffolk Senior Cup 1989-90, 2004-05. Suffolk & Ipswich Senior League 1995-96. East Anglian Cup 2006-07.
Eastern Counties Premier Division 2009-10.

02-03		03-04		04-05		05-06		06-07		07-08		08-09		09-10		10-11		11-12	
EC1	11	EC1	14	EC1	2	ECP	6	ECP	4	ECP	2	ECP	3	ECP	1	Isth1N	2	Isth1N	4

POTTERS BAR TOWN

Chairman: Peter Waller
Secretary: Alan Evans   **(T)** 0783 363 2965   **(E)** potters_bar_sec@hotmail.co.uk
Additional Committee Members:
Dave Quinlan

Manager: Adam Lee
Programme Editor: Jeff Barnes   **(E)** jeff@jeffbarnes.co.uk

Photo: Alan Coomes.

Club Factfile

Founded: 1960   **Nickname:** Grace or Scholars
Previous Names: None
Previous Leagues: Barnet & District 1960-65, North London Combination 1965-68, Herts Senior County 1968-91, Spartan South Midlands 1991-2005, Southern 2005-06

Club Colours (change): Maroon/white/white (All yellow)

Ground: The South Mimms Travel Stad., Parkfield, Watkins Rise, Pot.Bar EN6 1QN   **(T)** 01707 654 833
Capacity: 2,000   **Seats:** 150   **Covered:** 250   **Clubhouse:** Yes   **Shop:** Yes

Directions: M25 junction 24 enter Potters Bar along Southgate Road (A111) turn right into High Street at first lights (A1000) then left into The Walk after half a mile. Ground is 200 yards on the right - opposite Potters Bar Cricket Club.

Previous Grounds:

Record Attendance: 268 v Wealdstone - FA Cup 1998 (4,000 watched a charity match in 1997)
Record Victory: Not known
Record Defeat: Not known
Record Goalscorer: Not known
Record Appearances: Not known
Additional Records:

Senior Honours:
Spartan South Midlands League Premier 1996-97, 2004-05.

10 YEAR RECORD

02-03	03-04	04-05	05-06	06-07	07-08	08-09	09-10	10-11	11-12
SSM P 3	SSM P 4	SSM P 1	SthE 15	Isth1N 14	Isth1N 17	Isth1N 19	Isth1N 14	Isth1N 13	Isth1N 12

REDBRIDGE

Chairman: Jim Chapman
Secretary: Bob Holloway   **(T)** 0789 069 9907   **(E)** r.holloway338@btinternet.com
Additional Committee Members:
Len Cordell, Adam Dennehy

Manager: Steve Portway and Del Robinson
Programme Editor: Adam Silver   **(E)** adammichaelsilver@hotmail.com

Redbridge players are unable to hide their delight as Ryan Murray scores against Conference side Ebbsfleet United in the FA Cup last season.

Club Factfile

Founded: 1958   **Nickname:** Motormen
Previous Names: Ford United 1958-2004
Previous Leagues: Aetolian 1959-64, Greater London 1964-71, Metropolitan 1971-74, Essex Senior 1974-97, Isthmian 1997-2004, Conference 2004-05

Club Colours (change): Red with black trim/black/black (White and red/red/red)

Ground: Oakside Stadium, Station Road, Barkingside, Ilford IG6 1NB   **(T)** 020 8550 3611
Capacity: 3,000   **Seats:** 316   **Covered:** 1,000   **Clubhouse:** Yes   **Shop:** Yes

Directions: A12 from London, turn left off Eastern Avenue into Horns Road, Barkingside (Greengate). Right into Craven Gardens, right again into Carlton Drive and left into Station Road. Go over bridge and ground is on the right. Adjacent to Barkingside Underground Station (Central Line).

Previous Grounds: Ford Sports & Social Club > 2000

Record Attendance: 58,000 v Bishop Auckland
Record Victory: Not known
Record Defeat: Not known
Record Goalscorer: Jeff Wood - 196
Record Appearances: Roger Bird
Additional Records:

Senior Honours:
Aetolian League 1959-60, 61-62. Greater London League 1970-71. Essex Senior League 1991-92, 96-97.
Isthmian League Division 3 1998-99, Division 1 2001-02,

10 YEAR RECORD

02-03	03-04	04-05	05-06	06-07	07-08	08-09	09-10	10-11	11-12
Isth P 15	Isth P 13	Conf S 22	Isth P 22	Isth1N 16	Isth1N 3	Isth1N 8	Isth1N 18	Isth1N 16	Isth1N 6

ROMFORD

Chairman: Steve Gardener
Secretary: Colin Ewenson   **(T)** 0797 371 7074   **(E)** ewenson@aol.com
Additional Committee Members:

Manager: Paul Martin
Programme Editor: Keith Preston   **(E)** prestonruf@aol.com

THE NON-LEAGUE CLUB DIRECTORY

Book Holiday Inn Hotels and Save today!

- Home
- Clubs
- Steps 1 - 4
- League Tables

35 Years of Non-League Football

The Non-League Club Directory has developed into a comprehensive record of competitions within the non-League game, giving this level of football the

www.non-leagueclubdirectory.co.uk

Club Factfile

Founded: 1876   **Nickname:** Boro

Previous Names: Original club founded in 1876 folded during WW1, Reformed in 1929 folded again in 1978 and reformed in 1992

Previous Leagues: Athenian 1931-39, Isthmian 1945-59, 97-2002, Southern 1959-78, Essex Senior 1992-96, 2002-09

Club Colours (change): Blue and yellow stripes/blue/blue (Red and black/black/black)

Ground: Thurrock FC, South Way, Ship Lane, Aveley RM19 1YN   **(T)** 01708 865492

Capacity: 4,500   **Seats:** 300   **Covered:** 1,000   **Clubhouse:** Yes   **Shop:**

Directions: Approaching the ground from the North - along the M25 in a clockwise direction. Leave the motorway at junction 30. At the roundabout take the second exit and stay in the left hand lane. This leads to a large roundabout controlled by traffic lights. The fifth exit is Ship Lane and the ground is approximately 50 yards on the right hand side. Approaching the ground from the South - anti-clockwise on the M25. When going through the Dartford Tunnel take the left hand bore. On coming out of the tunnel take the first exit - junction 31. This leads to a large roundabout controlled by traffic lights. Take the third exit which is Ship Lane. The ground is situated approximately 50 yards on the right hand side.

Previous Grounds: The Mill Field (Aveley FC).

Record Attendance: 820 v Leatherhead - Isthmian Division 2

Record Victory: Not known
Record Defeat: Not known

Record Goalscorer: Danny Benstock

Record Appearances: S Horne - 234

Additional Records:

Senior Honours:
Essex Senior League 1995-96, 2008-09. Isthmian League Division 2 1996-97.

02-03		03-04		04-05		05-06		06-07		07-08		08-09		09-10		10-11		11-12	
ESen	5	ESen	5	ESen	5	ESen	12	ESen	2	ESen	5	ESen	1	Isth1N	13	Isth1N	12	Isth1N	13

SOHAM TOWN RANGERS

Chairman: Colin Murfit
Secretary: Mark Bailey   **(T)** 07903 289938   **(E)** strfc1@fsmail.net
Additional Committee Members:
Desmond Camp

Manager: Steve Falloni
Programme Editor: Fred Parker   **(E)** fred@fredparker.plus.com

Club Factfile

Founded: 1947   **Nickname:** Town or Rangers
Previous Names: Soham Town and Soham Rangers merged in 1947
Previous Leagues: Peterborough & District, Eastern Counties 1963-2008, Southern 2008-11.

Club Colours (change): All green with white trim (All blue)

Ground: Julius Martin Lane, Soham, Ely, Cambridgeshire CB7 5EQ   **(T)** 01353 720 732
Capacity: 2,000   **Seats:** 250   **Covered:** 1,000   **Clubhouse:** Yes   **Shop:** Yes

Directions: Take the turning off the A14 for Soham/Ely. Join the A142 following signs for Ely/Soham. On approaching Soham at the Q8 Petrol Station, continue down the Soham by-pass for approx. 1.5 miles. Turn left after the Bypass Motel, continue bearing left across the Common into Bushel Lane, at end of road, turn right into Hall Street. Julius Martin Lane is 2nd left.

Previous Grounds:

Record Attendance: 3,000 v Pegasus - FA Amateur Cup 1963
Record Victory: Not known
Record Defeat: Not known
Record Goalscorer: Not known
Record Appearances: Not known
Additional Records:

Senior Honours:
Eastern Counties League Premier Division 2007-08

10 YEAR RECORD										
02-03	03-04	04-05	05-06	06-07	07-08	08-09	09-10	10-11	11-12	
ECP 3	ECP 5	ECP 7	ECP 10	ECP	ECP 1	SthC 15	SthC 11	SthC 17	Isth1N 19	

THAMESMEAD TOWN

Chairman: Terry Hill
Secretary: David Joy   **(T)** 0799 061 2495   **(E)** davejoyo@yahoo.co.uk
Additional Committee Members:
Keith McMahon

Manager: Keith McMahon
Programme Editor: Albert Panting   **(E)** gianpaulo.panting@btinternet.com

THE NON-LEAGUE CLUB DIRECTORY

Book Holiday Inn Hotels and Save today!

Home

Clubs

Steps 1 - 4

League Tables

35 Years of Non-League Football

The Non-League Club Directory has developed into a comprehensive record of competitions within the non-League game, giving this level of football the

www.non-leagueclubdirectory.co.uk

Club Factfile

Founded: 1970   **Nickname:** The Mead

Previous Names: None

Previous Leagues: Spartan 1987-91, Kent 1991-2008

Club Colours (change): All green (All light blue)

Ground: Bayliss Avenue, Thamesmead, London SE28 8NJ   **(T)** 020 8311 4211

Capacity: 400   **Seats:** 161   **Covered:** 125   **Clubhouse:** Yes   **Shop:**

Directions
From the A2 take the A2018 exit toward Dartford/Wilmington, at the roundabout, take the 1st exit onto Shepherd's Ln/A2018.
At the roundabout, take the 1st exit onto Rochester Way. Slight right at Swan Ln, continue onto Station Rd.
At the roundabout, take the 1st exit onto Crayford Rd/A207, continue to follow A207, slight right to stay on A207, turn left at London Rd/A2000 continue to follow A2000, turn right at Perry St/A2000.
At the roundabout, take the 2nd exit onto Northend Rd/A206, continue to follow A206. Go through 1 roundabout.
At the roundabout, take the 2nd exit onto Bronze Age Way/A2016, continue to follow A2016. Go through 1 roundabout.
At the roundabout, take the 2nd exit onto Eastern Way/A2016. Take the ramp. At the roundabout, take the 3rd exit onto Carlyle Rd/A2041.
At the roundabout, take the 3rd exit onto Crossway. Turn right at Bayliss Ave, take the 1st left onto Chadwick Way. Ground will be on the left.

Previous Grounds:

Record Attendance: 400 v Wimbledon - Ground opening 1988

Record Victory: 9-0 v Kent Police - Kent League 19/04/1994
Record Defeat: Not known

Record Goalscorer: Delroy D'Oyley

Record Appearances: Not known
Additional Records:

Senior Honours:
Kent Senior Trophy 2004-05. Kent Premier 2007-08

02-03	03-04	04-05	05-06	06-07	07-08	08-09	09-10	10-11	11-12
Kent P 3	Kent P 2	Kent P 8	Kent P 3	Kent P 4	Kent P 1	Isth1N 18	Isth1N 7	Isth1N 17	Isth1N 10

TILBURY

Chairman: Robin Nash
Secretary: Anthony Mercer   **(T)** 07718 881 593   **(E)** amercer67@googlemail.com
Additional Committee Members:
Linda Vaughan, George Hammond

Manager: Paul Vaughan
Programme Editor: Mark Kettlety   **(E)** sundayonly1@aol.com

Club Factfile

Founded: 1900   **Nickname:** The Dockers
Previous Names:
Previous Leagues: Grays & District/South Essex, Kent 1927-31, London, South Essex Combination (Wartime), Corinthian 1950-57, Delphian 1962-63, Athenian 1963-73, Isthmian 1973-2004, Essex Senior 2004-05

Club Colours (change): Black & white stripes/black/red (Red/red/white)

Ground: Chadfields, St Chads Road, Tilbury, Essex RM18 8NL   **(T)** 01375 843 093
Capacity: 4,000   **Seats:** 350   **Covered:** 1,000   **Clubhouse:** Yes   **Shop:** No
Directions: A13 Southend bound go left at Chadwell St Mary's turning, then right after 400 metres and right again at roundabout (signed Tilbury). Right into St Chads Road after five miles, first right into Chadfields for ground.

Previous Grounds:

Record Attendance: 5,500 v Gorleston - FA Cup 1949
Record Victory: Not known
Record Defeat: Not known
Record Goalscorer: Ross Livermore - 282 in 305 games
Record Appearances: Nicky Smith - 424 (1975-85)
Additional Records: Received £2,000 from Grays Athletic for Tony Macklin 1990 and from Dartford for Steve Connor 1985

Senior Honours:
Athenian League 1968-69. Isthmian League Division 1 1975-76.
Essex Senior Cup x4.

10 YEAR RECORD

02-03	03-04	04-05	05-06	06-07	07-08	08-09	09-10	10-11	11-12
Isth1N 20	Isth1N 22	SthE 22	ESen 3	Isth1N 19	Isth1N 20	Isth1N 11	Isth1N 11	Isth1N 19	Isth1N 3

WALTHAM ABBEY

Chairman: Joe Collins
Secretary: Dave Marrion   **(T)** 07813 148488   **(E)** walthamabbeyfc@btconnect.com
Additional Committee Members:
Dave Marrion

Manager: Paul Wickenden
Programme Editor: **(E)**

Club Factfile

Founded: 1944   **Nickname:** Abbotts
Previous Names: Abbey Sports amalgamated with Beechfield Sports in 1974 to form Beechfields. Club then renamed to Waltham Abbey in 1976
Previous Leagues: Spartan, Essex & Herts Border, Essex Senior

Club Colours (change): Green and white hoops/white/green (All blue)

Ground: Capershotts, Sewardstone Road, Waltham Abbey, Essex EN9 1LU   **(T)** 01992 711 287
Capacity: 2,000   **Seats:** 300   **Covered:** 500   **Clubhouse:** Yes   **Shop:** No

Directions
Exit M25 at junction 26 and take 2nd left at roundabout into Honey Lane (A121).
At the Sewardstone roundabout, take third right into Sewarstone Road which takes you over the M25.
Ground is first right before cemetery.

Previous Grounds:

Record Attendance: Not known
Record Victory: Not known
Record Defeat: Not known
Record Goalscorer: Not known
Record Appearances: Not known
Additional Records:

Senior Honours:
London Spartan League Division 1 1977-78, Senior Division 1978-79.
London Senior Cup 1999. Essex Senior Cup 2004-05.

10 YEAR RECORD

02-03	03-04	04-05	05-06	06-07	07-08	08-09	09-10	10-11	11-12
ESen 10	ESen 6	ESen 3	ESen 2	Isth1N 10	Isth1N 14	Isth1N 4	Isth1N 21	Isth1N 11	Isth1N 14

WALTHAM FOREST

Chairman: Isaac Johnson
Secretary: Tony Brazier **(T)** 0771 564 0171 **(E)** bjmapbr@ntlworld.com
Additional Committee Members:
Andrzej Perkins

Manager: Olawale Ojelabi
Programme Editor: Andrzej Perkins **(E)** forestgimp@hotmail.co.uk

2011-12 Squad.

Club Factfile

Founded: 1995 **Nickname:** The Stags
Previous Names: Leyton Pennant formed when Leyton and Walthamstow Pennant merged in 1995. Changed to Waltham Forest in 2003.
Previous Leagues: Isthmian 2003-04, Southern 2004-06

Club Colours (change): White/blue/blue (Orange/black/orange)

Ground: Ilford FC, Cricklefield Stadium, 486 High Road, Ilford, Essex IG1 1UE **(T)** 0208 514 8352
Capacity: 3,500 **Seats:** 216 **Covered:** Yes **Clubhouse:** Yes **Shop:**

Directions: Taking the A127, from the east travel towards London before coming to the traffic light controlled junction at Barley Lane, Goodmayes (B177) . Turn Left by taking the slip road and follow Barley Lane to its junction with the traffic light controlled High Road, Goodmayes (A118) (it is the first set of traffic control lights for traffic rather than pedestrians on that road). Turn Right and follow the road past Seven Kings station (which should be on your right) and on towards Ilford. The entrance to the ground is some 400 yards past the station with the Ilford Swimming Baths on the left being the point at which both coaches and those in cars or on foot should turn left into the car parks. Both on Saturday and after 6pm. during the week, the public car park is free of charge.

Previous Grounds: Wadham Lodge

Record Attendance: Not known
Record Victory: Not known
Record Defeat: Not known
Record Goalscorer: Not known
Record Appearances: Not known
Additional Records:

Senior Honours:
None

10 YEAR RECORD

02-03	03-04	04-05	05-06	06-07	07-08	08-09	09-10	10-11	11-12
Isth1N 22	Isth1N 16	SthE 9	SthE 8	Isth1N 8	Isth1N 19	Isth1N 20	Isth1N 16	Isth1N 21	Isth1N 17

WARE

Chairman: Mike Varney
Secretary: Sean Mynott   **(T)** 07812 097924   **(E)** seanmynott@aol.com
Additional Committee Members:
Aiden Mynott

Manager: Kristian Munt
Programme Editor: Mark Kettlety   **(E)** sundayonly1@aol.com

WARE FOOTBALL CLUB

Club Factfile

Founded: 1892   **Nickname:** Blues
Previous Names:
Previous Leagues: East Herts, North Middlesex 1907-08, Herts County 1908-25, Spartan 1925-55, Delphian 1955-63, Athenian 1963-75

Club Colours (change): Blue with white piping/blue/blue (Amber/black/amber)

Ground: Wodson Park, Wadesmill Road, Ware, Herts SG12 0UQ   **(T)** 01920 462 064
Capacity: 3,300   **Seats:** 500   **Covered:** 312   **Clubhouse:** Yes   **Shop:** Yes
Directions: A10 off junction A602 and B1001 turn right at roundabout after 300 yards and follow Ware sign, past Rank factory. Turn left at main road onto A1170 (Wadesmill Road) Stadium is on the right after 3/4 mile.

Previous Grounds: Highfields, Canons Park, London Road, Presdales Lower Park 1921-26

Record Attendance: 3,800 v Hendon - FA Amateur Cup 1956-57
Record Victory: 10-1 v Wood Green Town
Record Defeat: 0-11 v Barnet
Record Goalscorer: George Dearman scored 98 goals during 1926-27
Record Appearances: Gary Riddle - 654
Additional Records:

Senior Honours:
Isthmian League Division 2 2005-06.
East Anglian Cup 1973-74. Herts Senior Cup x5.

10 YEAR RECORD

02-03	03-04	04-05	05-06	06-07	07-08	08-09	09-10	10-11	11-12
Isth2 8	Isth2 8	Isth2 10	Isth2 1	Isth1N 7	Isth1N 4	Isth1N 9	Isth1N 19	Isth1N 14	Isth1N 21

WITHAM TOWN

Chairman: Tony Last
Secretary: Alison Barker   **(T)** 01376 324 324   **(E)** Bakerboy@aol.com
Additional Committee Members:
George Vale, Jamie Baker

Manager: Garry Kimble
Programme Editor: Steve Parker   **(E)** steveparker007@ntlworld.com

THE NON-LEAGUE CLUB DIRECTORY

Book Holiday Inn Hotels and Save today!

- Home
- Clubs
- Steps 1 - 4
- League Tables

35 Years of Non-League Football

The Non-League Club Directory has developed into a comprehensive record of competitions within the non-League game, giving this level of football the

www.non-leagueclubdirectory.co.uk

Club Factfile

Founded: 1947   **Nickname:** Town

Previous Names: None.
Previous Leagues: Mid. Essex. Essex & Suff. B. Essex Senior 1971-87. Isthmian 1987-2009

Club Colours (change): White/blue/green (All yellow).

Ground: Spicer McColl Stadium, Spa Road, Witham CM8 1UN   **(T)** 01376 511 198

Capacity: 2,500   **Seats:** 157   **Covered:** 780   **Clubhouse:** Yes   **Shop:** No

Directions: From M25: At junction 28, take the A12/A1023 exit to Chelmsford/Romford/Brentwood.
At the roundabout, take the 1st exit onto the A12 ramp to Chelmsford/Harwich/A120.
Merge onto A12. At junction 21, exit onto Hatfield Rd/B1389 toward Witham.
Go through 2 roundabouts. Turn left onto Spinks Lane. Turn right onto Highfields Road.
Turn left ground will be on the right.

Previous Grounds:

Record Attendance: Att: 800 v Billericay Town, Essex Senior Lge, May 1976.

Record Victory: Not known
Record Defeat: Not known

Record Goalscorer: Colin Mitchell.

Record Appearances: Keith Dent.

Additional Records:

Senior Honours:
Essex Senior League 1970-71, 85-86, 2011-12.

02-03	03-04	04-05	05-06	06-07	07-08	08-09	09-10	10-11	11-12
Isth2	7	Isth2	6	Isth2	5	Isth2	2	Isth1N	20	Isth1N	20	Isth1N	21	ESen	2	ESen	3	ESen	1

WROXHAM

Chairman: Martin Roberts
Secretary: Chris Green   **(T)** 07508 219 072   **(E)** secretary@wroxhamfc.com
Additional Committee Members:
James Hernandez, Sean Douce.

Manager: David Batch
Programme Editor: Chris Green   **(E)** secretary@wroxhamfc.com

Club Factfile

Founded: 1892   **Nickname:** Yachtsmen
Previous Names: None
Previous Leagues: East Norfolk. Norwich City. East Anglian. Norwich & Dist. Anglian Comb.

Club Colours (change): Blue/white/blue (White/blue/white)

Ground: Trafford Park, Skinners Lane, Wroxham NR12 8SJ   **(T)** 01603 783 538
Capacity: 2,500   **Seats:** 50   **Covered:** 250   **Clubhouse:** Yes   **Shop:** No

Directions: From Norwich, turn left at former Castle Pub and keep left to ground.
Under two miles from Wroxham & Hoveton BR. Buses 722,724 and 717.

Previous Grounds:

Record Attendance: Att: 1,011 v Wisbech Town, Eastern Co. Lge, 16.03.93.
Record Victory: Not known
Record Defeat: Not known
Record Goalscorer: Matthew Metcalf.
Record Appearances: Stu Larter.
Additional Records:

Senior Honours:
Anglian County League 1981-82, 82-83, 83-84, 84-85, 86-87.
Eastern Counties League Division One 1988-89, Prem 91-92, 92-93, 93-94, 96-97, 97-98, 98-99, 2006-07, 11-12.
Norfolk Senior Cup 1992-93, 95-96, 97-98, 99-00, 03-04.

10 YEAR RECORD

02-03		03-04		04-05		05-06		06-07		07-08		08-09		09-10		10-11		11-12	
ECP	2	ECP	3	ECP	5	ECP	8	ECP	1	ECP	3	ECP	5	ECP	8	ECP	3	ECP	1

BURGESS HILL TOWN

Chairman: Kevin Newell
Secretary: Tim Spencer   **(T)** 0781 264 2498   **(E)** timspencer57@hotmail.com
Additional Committee Members:
Allan Turpin, Richard Strange

Manager: Ian Chapman
Programme Editor: Dave Bradbury   **(E)** bradders723@hotmail.co.uk

Club Factfile

Founded: 1882   **Nickname:** Hillians
Previous Names: None
Previous Leagues: Mid Sussex, Sussex County > 2003, Southern 2003-04

Club Colours (change): Green & black stripes/black/black (Yellow & black/black/black)

Ground: Leylands Park, Maple Drive, Burgess Hill, West Sussex RH15 8DL   **(T)** 01444 254 832
Capacity: 2,250   **Seats:** 307   **Covered:** Yes   **Clubhouse:** Yes   **Shop:** Yes

Directions: Turn east from A273 London Road into Leylands Road,
take 4th left sign posted Leyland Park.
Nearest station is Wivelsfield.

Previous Grounds: None

Record Attendance: 2,005 v AFC Wimbledon - Isthmian League Division 1 2004-05
Record Victory: Not known
Record Defeat: Not known
Record Goalscorer: Ashley Carr - 208
Record Appearances: Paul Williams - 499
Additional Records:

Senior Honours:
Sussex County League x6 (Most recently 2001-02, 02-03).
Sussex Senior Cup 1883-84, 84-85, 85-86.

10 YEAR RECORD

02-03		03-04		04-05		05-06		06-07		07-08		08-09		09-10		10-11		11-12	
SxC1	1	SthE	9	Isth1	10	Isth1	19	Isth1S	14	Isth1S	12	Isth1S	19	Isth1S	7	Isth1S	7	Isth1S	20

CHIPSTEAD

Chairman: Geoff Corner
Secretary: Heather Armstrong   **(T)** 07525 443 802   **(E)** heather.chipsteadfc@virginmedia.com
Additional Committee Members:
Terry Tiernan, Barry Jolly

Manager: Mark Tompkins
Programme Editor: Mark Budd   **(E)** mgbudd70@yahoo.co.uk

Club Factfile

Founded: 1906   **Nickname:** Chips
Previous Names:
Previous Leagues: Surrey Intermediate 1962-82, Surrey Premier 1982-86, Combined Counties 1986-2007

Club Colours (change): Green and white hoops/green/black (All red)

Ground: High Road, Chipstead, Surrey CR5 3SF   **(T)** 01737 553 250
Capacity: 2,000   **Seats:** 150   **Covered:** 200   **Clubhouse:** Yes   **Shop:** No

Directions: From the Brighton Road north bound,
go left into Church Lane and left into Hogcross Lane.
High Road is on the right.

Previous Grounds:

Record Attendance: 1,170
Record Victory: Not known
Record Defeat: Not known
Record Goalscorer: Mick Nolan - 124
Record Appearances: Not known
Additional Records:

Senior Honours:
Combined Counties Premier 1989-90, 2006-07.

10 YEAR RECORD

02-03		03-04		04-05		05-06		06-07		07-08		08-09		09-10		10-11		11-12	
CC	16	CCP	8	CCP	8	CCP	14	CCP	1	Isth1S	15	Isth1S	21	Isth1S	19	Isth1S	10	Isth1S	12

CORINTHIAN CASUALS

Chairman: Brian Vandervilt
Secretary: Brian Vandervilt **(T)** 0773 637 7498 **(E)** chairman@corinthian-casuals.com
Additional Committee Members:
Rob Cavallini, Vincent Huggett

Manager: Kim Harris
Programme Editor: Rob Cavallini **(E)** rob_cavallini@hotmail.com

Back Row L-R: Sam Labinjo, David Ocquaye, Adam Cheadle, Dave Hodges, Jordan Cheadle, Aaron Gough, Danny Bracken, Adam Peck, Danny Dudley, Francois Gabbidon, Joe Hicks, Steve Goddard, Joel Thompson.
Front Row L- R: Olakunle Akinwande, Matt Ellis, Midi Nsugba, Tom Jelley, Jason Turley, Ben Ewing, Jamie Byatt, Joe Davies, Rob Stevenson, Daniel Green.

Club Factfile

Founded: 1939 **Nickname:** Casuals
Previous Names: Casuals and Corinthians merged in 1939
Previous Leagues: Isthmian 1939-84, Spartan 1984-96, Combined Counties 1996-97

Club Colours (change): Chocolate and pink halves/chocolate/chocolate (All blue)

Ground: King George's Field, Queen Mary Close, Hook Rise South, KT6 7NA **(T)** 0208 397 3368
Capacity: 2,000 **Seats:** 161 **Covered:** 700 **Clubhouse:** Yes **Shop:** Yes

Directions:
A3 to Tolworth (Charrington Bowl) roundabout.
Hook Rise is the slip road immediately past the Toby Jug Pub.
Left under railway bridge after 1/4 mile and ground is on the right.
1/2 mile from Tolworth BR.

Previous Grounds: Kennington Oval, shared with Kingstonian and Dulwich Hamlet

Record Attendance: Not known
Record Victory: Not known
Record Defeat: Not known
Record Goalscorer: Cliff West - 219
Record Appearances: Simon Shergold - 526
Additional Records:

Senior Honours:
London Spartan League Senior Division 1985-86.
Surrey Senior Cup 2010-11.

10 YEAR RECORD

02-03	03-04	04-05	05-06	06-07	07-08	08-09	09-10	10-11	11-12
Isth1S 21	Isth1S 23	Isth1 13	Isth1 23	Isth1S 22	Isth1S 20	Isth1S 20	Isth1S 13	Isth1S 20	Isth1S 13

CRAWLEY DOWN GATWICK

Chairman: Brian Suckling
Secretary: Jane Suckling   **(T)** 07712 814 113   **(E)** b.suckling@btinternet.com
Additional Committee Members:
Michael Martin, Howard Griggs

Manager: John Maggs
Programme Editor: Michael Martin   **(E)** martinmd@btinternet.com

THE NON-LEAGUE CLUB DIRECTORY

Book Holiday Inn Hotels and Save today!

Home
Clubs
Steps 1 - 4
League Tables

35 Years of Non-League Football

The Non-League Club Directory has developed into a comprehensive record of competitions within the non-League game, giving this level of football the

www.non-leagueclubdirectory.co.uk

Club Factfile

Founded: 1993   **Nickname:** The Anvils

Previous Names: Crawley Down United > 1993. Crawley Down Village > 1999. Crawley Down > 2012.
Previous Leagues: Mid Sussex, Sussex County > 2011.

Club Colours (change): All Red (All white)

Ground: The Haven Sportsfield, Hophurst Lane, Crawley Down RH10 4LJ   **(T)** 01342 717 140

Capacity: 1,000   **Seats:**   **Covered:** 50   **Clubhouse:**   **Shop:**

Directions
From the North: Turn off the M23 at Junction 10 signposted East Grinstead At the roundabout at the Copthorne Hotel, take the 2nd exit, signed A264 East Grinstead. At the next roundabout (Duke's Head) take the 3rd exit, B2028 south, toward Turners Hill After approx. 1 mile turn left into Sandy Lane. (just after entering the 30mph zone and a telephone box in the layby on the right). At the end of Sandy Lane (war memorial on the right), turn left signed Felbridge.After a couple of bends the Haven Centre is on your left. **From the East:** Travel through East Grinstead on the A22 until the Junction with the A264 at the Felbridge Traffic lights. Turn left (Sign posted Crawley) and after 100 Meters take the Left Fork towards Crawley Down. Approx 1.5 Miles Haven Centre on Right. **From the South:** Travel North through Turners Hill on the B2028 after approx 2 Miles take the 2nd turning on your right (Vicarage Road). This is a Right fork and is sited just after passing over a small bridge. Follow Vicarage Road for approx 1/2 Mile past Junction with Sandy Lane and The Haven Centre is 200 Meters on your left.

Previous Grounds:

Record Attendance: 404 v East Grinstead Town 96

Record Victory: Not known
Record Defeat: Not known

Record Goalscorer: Not known

Record Appearances: Not known
Additional Records:

Senior Honours:
Sussex County Division One 2010-11.

02-03	03-04	04-05	05-06	06-07	07-08	08-09	09-10	10-11	11-12
SxC2	15	SxC2	11	SxC2	10	SxC2	5	SxC2	16	SxC2	6	SxC2	3	SxC1	8	SxC1	1	Isth1S	16

DULWICH HAMLET

Chairman: Jack Payne
Secretary: Martin Eede **(T)** 0795 739 5948 **(E)** eede.martin@gmail.com
Additional Committee Members:
John Lawrence, Paul Griffin

Manager: Gavin Rose
Programme Editor: John Lawrence **(E)** john_lawrence@hotmail.co.uk

Back Row: Erhun Aksel Öztümer, Ellis Green, Dominic Weston, Suliaman Bangura, Ethan Pinnock, Vernon Francis, James Tedder, Phil Wilson, Carl Wilson-Denis, Josh Turner, Luke Hickie, Lewis Gonsalves, Kalvin Morath-Gibbs.
Front Row: Laura McPherson (Physiotherapist), Frankie Sawyer, Dean Carpenter, Kevin James (Coach), Gavin Rose (Manager), Junior Kadi (Assistant Manager), Ahmed Deen, Peter Adeniyi, Nyren Clunis, Corinna Kehaya (Physiotherapist).

Club Factfile

Founded: 1889 **Nickname:** Hamlet
Previous Names: None
Previous Leagues: Camberwell 1894-97, Southern Suburban 1897-1900, 01-07, Dulwich 1900-01, Spartan 1907-08

Club Colours (change): Navy blue and pink/navy blue/navy blue (White/black/black)

Ground: Champion Hill Stadium, Dog Kennell Hill, Edgar Kail Way SE22 8BD **(T)** 0207 274 8707
Capacity: 3,000 **Seats:** 500 **Covered:** 1,000 **Clubhouse:** Yes **Shop:** Yes

Directions:
East Dulwich station, 200 yards.
Denmark Hill station, 10 minutes walk.
Herne Hill station then bus 37 stops near ground.
Buses 40 & 176 from Elephant & Castle, 185 from Victoria.

Previous Grounds: Woodwarde Rd 1893-95, College Farm 95-96, Sunray Ave 1896-02, Freeman's Gd, Champ Hill 02-12, Champ Hill (old grd)12-92

Record Attendance: 1,835 v Southport - FA Cup 1998-99
Record Victory: Not known
Record Defeat: Not known
Record Goalscorer: Edgar Kail - 427 (1919-33)
Record Appearances: Reg Merritt - 576 (1950-66)
Additional Records: Received £35,000 from Charlton Athletic for Chris Dickson 2007

Senior Honours:
FA Amateur Cup 1919-20, 31-32, 33-34, 36-37.
Isthmian League Premier Division x4, Division 1 1977-78. London Senior Cup x5. Surrey Senior Cup x16.
London Challenge Cup 1998-99.

10 YEAR RECORD

02-03		03-04		04-05		05-06		06-07		07-08		08-09		09-10		10-11		11-12	
Isth1S	4	Isth1S	7	Isth1	15	Isth1	13	Isth1S	8	Isth1S	6	Isth1S	12	Isth1S	12	Isth1S	5	Isth1S	3

EASTBOURNE TOWN

Chairman: David Jenkins
Secretary: Mark Potter   **(T)** 0772 084 6857   **(E)** markpotter@eastbournera.fsnet.co.uk
Additional Committee Members:
Robert Hylands

Manager: Danny Bloor
Programme Editor: Mark Potter   **(E)** markpotter@eastbournera.fsnet.co.uk

THE NON-LEAGUE CLUB DIRECTORY

Book Holiday Inn Hotels and Save today!

Home
Clubs
Steps 1 - 4
League Tables

35 Years of Non-League Football

The Non-League Club Directory has developed into a comprehensive record of competitions within the non-League game, giving this level of football the

www.non-leagueclubdirectory.co.uk

Club Factfile

Founded: 1881   **Nickname:** Town

Previous Names: None

Previous Leagues: Southern Amateur 1907-46, Corinthian 1960-63, Athenian 1963-76, Sussex County 1976-2007

Club Colours (change): Navy & yellow/navy/navy (Red/gold/red)

Ground: The Saffrons, Compton Place Road, Eastbourne BN21 1EA   **(T)** 01323 723 734

Capacity: 3,000   **Seats:** 200   **Covered:** Yes   **Clubhouse:** Yes   **Shop:** No

Directions: Turn South West off the A22 into Grove Road.

Previous Grounds:

Record Attendance: 7,378 v Hastings United - 1953

Record Victory: Not known
Record Defeat: Not known

Record Goalscorer: Not known

Record Appearances: Not known

Additional Records:

Senior Honours:
Sussex County League 1976-77, Sussex Senior Cup x12.
Sussex RUR Charity Cup x3. AFA Senior Cup x2.

02-03		03-04		04-05		05-06		06-07		07-08		08-09		09-10		10-11		11-12	
SxC2	2	SxC1	5	SxC1	10	SxC1	5	SxC1	1	Isth1S	19	Isth1S	13	Isth1S	22	Isth1S	18	Isth1S	14

FAVERSHAM TOWN

Chairman: Ray Leader
Secretary: Mrs Wendy Walker   **(T)** 0778 963 8367   **(E)** wendy-walker@hotmail.co.uk
Additional Committee Members:
Mark Downs

Manager: Ray Turner
Programme Editor: Mark Downs   **(E)** lilywhite.editor@googlemail. com

Club Factfile

Founded: 1884   **Nickname:** Lillywhites
Previous Names: Faversham Invicta, Faversham Services, Faversham Railway and Faversham Rangers pre War.
Previous Leagues: Metropolitan, Athenian, Kent

Club Colours (change): White/black/black (All yellow)

Ground: Salters Lane, Faversham Kent ME13 8ND   **(T)** 01795 591 900
Capacity: 2,000   **Seats:** 200   **Covered:** 1,800   **Clubhouse:** Yes   **Shop:**
Directions: From the M25 continue onto M26 9.9 miles. Continue onto M20 8.1 miles. Exit onto Slip Road (M20 J7) 0.2 miles. Bear left 0.1 miles. Continue onto Sittingbourne Road A249 0.9 miles. Bear right onto Detling Hill A249 4.6 miles. Bear left 0.1 miles. Continue onto Slip Road (M2 J5) 0.4 miles. Continue onto M2 10.5 miles. Exit onto Slip Road (M2 J6) 0.1 miles. Turn left onto Ashford Road A251 0.5 miles. Turn right onto Canterbury Road A2 0.2 miles. Turn right onto Westwood Place 0.1 miles.

Previous Grounds:

Record Attendance: Not Known
Record Victory: Not Known
Record Defeat: Not Known
Record Goalscorer: Not Known
Record Appearances: Not Known
Additional Records:

Senior Honours:
Kent League 1969-70, 70-71, 89-90, 2009-10.

10 YEAR RECORD

02-03	03-04	04-05	05-06	06-07	07-08	08-09	09-10	10-11	11-12
Kent P 16				Kent P 12	Kent P 13	Kent P 4	Kent P 1	Isth1S 8	Isth1S 17

FOLKESTONE INVICTA

Chairman: Mark Jenner
Secretary: Richard Murrill   **(T)** 07810 864228   **(E)** richardmurrill@gmail.com
Additional Committee Members:
Elaine Orsbourne, Andy Bowden, Phil Orris

Manager: Neil Cugley
Programme Editor: Richard Murrill   **(E)** richardmurrill@gmail.com

2-11-12 Squad - Back Row (L-R): Mick Dix (Asst. Manager), Luke Webb, Adam Slegg, Neil Cugley (Manager)
Middle Row: Neil Pilcher (Football Secretary), Brian Merryman (Director), Willy Webb (Kit Manager), Liam Dickson, Frankie Chappell, Liam Friend, Tyson Dennigan, Jack Delo, Josh Vincent, Pete Williams, Niall Jackson, Jo Denby (Physio), Alex Bartlett (Physio), Dave Williams (Physio)
Front Row: Paul Jones, James Everitt, Olly Bartrum, Micheal Everitt, Roland Edge, Simon Austin, Darren Smith

Club Factfile

Founded: 1936   **Nickname:** The Seasiders
Previous Names:
Previous Leagues: Kent 1990-98, Southern 1998-2004

Club Colours (change): Black & amber stripes/black with amber trim/black (White & sky stripes/sky/sky)

Ground: The Buzzlines Stadium, The New Pavilion, Cheriton Road CT19 5JU   **(T)** 01303 257 461
Capacity: 6,500   **Seats:** 900   **Covered:** 3,500   **Clubhouse:** Yes   **Shop:** Yes
Directions: On the A20 behind Morrisons Supermarket, midway between Folkestone Central and West BR stations

Previous Grounds: South Road Hythe > 1991, County League matches on council pitches

Record Attendance: 7,881 v Margate - Kent Senior Cup 1958
Record Victory: 13-0 v Faversham Town - Kent League Division 1
Record Defeat: 1-7 v Crockenhill - Kent League Division 1
Record Goalscorer: Not Known
Record Appearances: Not Known
Additional Records:

Senior Honours:
None

10 YEAR RECORD

02-03		03-04		04-05		05-06		06-07		07-08		08-09		09-10		10-11		11-12	
SthP	22	SthE	5	Isth P	13	Isth P	13	Isth P	18	Isth P	21	Isth1S	11	Isth1S	2	Isth P	22	Isth1S	4

HERNE BAY

Chairman: Trevor Kennett
Secretary: John Bathurst **(T)** 07788 718 745 **(E)** johnbhbfc@aol.com
Additional Committee Members:
Ray Kelly, Tony Day

Manager: Simon Halsey
Programme Editor: John Bathurst **(E)** johnbhbfc@aol.com

Club Factfile

Founded: 1886 **Nickname:** The Bay
Previous Names: None.
Previous Leagues: East Kent. Faversham & Dist. Cantebury & Dist. Kent Am. Athenian.

Club Colours (change): Blue & white strips/blue/blue (Yellow/black/black)

Ground: Safety Net Stadium, Winch's Field, Stanley Gardens, Herne Bay CT6 5SG **(T)** 01227 374 156
Capacity: 3,000 **Seats:** 200 **Covered:** 1,500 **Clubhouse:** Yes **Shop:** Yes

Directions
From M25 exit onto Sittingbourne Rd/A249 toward Sheerness.
Continue to follow A249. At the roundabout, take the 1st exit onto the M2 ramp to Canterbury/Dover/Ramsgate.
Merge onto M2. Continue onto Thanet Way/A299.
Continue to follow A299. Take the A291 exit toward Canterbury/Herne Bay.
At the roundabout, take the 2nd exit onto A291. At the roundabout, take the 1st exit onto Canterbury Rd/B2205.
Turn left onto Spenser Rd. Take the 1st left onto Stanley Gardens.
Take the 1st left to stay on Stanley Gardens.

Previous Grounds: Mitchell's Athletic Ground. Herne Bay Memorial Park.

Record Attendance: 2,303 v Margate, FA Cup 4th Qual. 1970-71.
Record Victory: 19-3 v Hythe Wanderers - Feb 1900.
Record Defeat: 0-11 v 7th Dragon Guards - Oct 1907.
Record Goalscorer:
Record Appearances:
Additional Records: Most League Victories in a Season: 34 - 1996-97.

Senior Honours:
Kent League 1991-92, 93-94, 96-97, 97-98, 2011-12, Premier Cup 1996-97, 2009-10, 2010-11.
Kent Senior Trophy 1978-79, 1996-97.

10 YEAR RECORD

02-03	03-04	04-05	05-06	06-07	07-08	08-09	09-10	10-11	11-12
Kent P 11	Kent P 10	Kent P 2	Kent P 7	Kent P 9	Kent P 6	Kent P 6	Kent P 2	Kent P 2	Kent P 1

HORSHAM

Chairman: Kevin Borrett
Secretary: Annie Raby   **(T)** 07800 922 442   **(E)** ivan.raby@btinternet.com
Additional Committee Members:
Adam Hammond, Tim Hewlett

Manager: Simon Colbran
Programme Editor: Adam Hammond   **(E)** adam@horshampress.co.uk

THE NON-LEAGUE CLUB DIRECTORY

Book Holiday Inn Hotels and Save today!

Home

Clubs

Steps 1 - 4

League Tables

35 Years of Non-League Football

The Non-League Club Directory has developed into a comprehensive record of competitions within the non-League game, giving this level of football the

www.non-leagueclubdirectory.co.uk

Club Factfile

Founded: 1881   **Nickname:** Hornets

Previous Names:

Previous Leagues: West Susses Senior, Sussex County 1926-51, Metropolitan 1951-57, Corinthian 1957-63, Athenian 1963-73

Club Colours (change): Amber and green/green/amber (White/black/white)

Ground: Horsham YMCA, Gorings Mead, Horsham RH13 5BP   **(T)** 01403 266 888

Capacity: 1,575   **Seats:** 150   **Covered:** 200   **Clubhouse:** Yes   **Shop:**

Directions From the east, take A281 (Brighton Road, and the ground is on the left and sign posted opposite Gorings Mead.

Previous Grounds: Horsham Park, Hurst Park, Springfield Park

Record Attendance: 8,000 v Swindon - FA Cup 1st Round Novmber 1966

Record Victory: 16-1 v Southwick - Sussex County League 1945-46
Record Defeat: 1-11 v Worthing - Sussex Senior Cup 1913-14

Record Goalscorer: Mick Browning

Record Appearances: Mark Stepney

Additional Records:

Senior Honours:
Athenian League Division 1 1972-73. Sussex Senior Cup x7

02-03		03-04		04-05		05-06		06-07		07-08		08-09		09-10		10-11		11-12	
Isth1S	8	Isth1S	15	Isth1	3	Isth1	2	Isth1S	9	Isth P	11	Isth P	13	Isth P	11	Isth P	17	Isth P	22

HYTHE TOWN

Chairman: Paul Markland
Secretary: Martin Giles   **(T)** 07908 763 101   **(E)** martinrgiles@sky.com
Additional Committee Members:
Richard Giles, David Skeel

Manager: Scott Porter
Programme Editor: Martin Whybrow   **(E)** martinw@ibspublishing.com

THE NON-LEAGUE CLUB DIRECTORY

Book Holiday Inn Hotels and Save today!

Home

Clubs

Steps 1 - 4

League Tables

35 Years of Non-League Football

The Non-League Club Directory has
developed into a comprehensive record
of competitions within the non-League
game, giving this level of football the

www.non-leagueclubdirectory.co.uk

Club Factfile

Founded: 1910   **Nickname:** Town

Previous Names: Hythe Town > 1988. Hythe Town 1988 Ltd > 92. Hythe United 95- 01.
Previous Leagues: Southern, Kent League > 2011.

Club Colours (change): All red (All blue)

Ground: Reachfields Stadium, Fort Road, Hythe CT21 6JS   **(T)** 01303 264 932

Capacity: 3,000   **Seats:**   **Covered:**   **Clubhouse:** Yes   **Shop:** No

Directions
The Reachfields Stadium is easily accessible from the M20 motorway. Leave the M20 at junction 11, then at the roundabout take the
3rd exit onto the B2068, signposted Hastings, Hythe. At the next roundabout take the 2nd exit onto Ashford Road, A20.
Continue forward onto Ashford Road, A20. Entering Newingreen, at the T-junction turn left onto Hythe Road, A261, signposted
Hythe. Continue forward down London Road, A261. Entering Hythe, continue forward at the traffic lights onto Scanlons Bridge Road,
A2008.
Turn right at the next set of lights onto Dymchurch Road, A259. Either take the 1st left down Fort Road and turn right at the end of
Fort Road for the car-park, or after a few hundred yards turn left onto the Reachfields estate. Follow the road round and the stadium
will be on your right.

Previous Grounds:

Record Attendance: Att: 2,147 v Yeading, FA Vase Semi-Final, 1990.

Record Victory: Not known
Record Defeat: Not known

Record Goalscorer: Not known

Record Appearances: Not known
Additional Records:

Senior Honours:
Kent League 1988-89, Premier Division 2010-11.
Kent Senior Trophy 1990-91.

02-03		03-04		04-05		05-06		06-07		07-08		08-09		09-10		10-11		11-12	
Kent P	8	Kent P	6	Kent P	6	Kent P	12	Kent P	6	Kent P	4	Kent P	2	Kent P	3	Kent P	1	Isth1S	8

LEATHERHEAD

Chairman: Peter Ashdown
Secretary: Jean Grant   **(T)** 07966 710 089   **(E)** jeanlisagrant@blackberry.orange.co.uk
Additional Committee Members:
Richard Wilkinson, John Loveridge

Manager: Richard Brady
Programme Editor: Neil Grant   **(E)** neilgrant66@msn.com

THE NON-LEAGUE CLUB DIRECTORY

Book Holiday Inn Hotels and Save today!

Home
Clubs
Steps 1 - 4
League Tables

35 Years of Non-League Football

The Non-League Club Directory has developed into a comprehensive record of competitions within the non-League game, giving this level of football the

www.non-leagueclubdirectory.co.uk

Club Factfile

Founded: 1946   **Nickname:** The Tanners

Previous Names:

Previous Leagues: Surrey Senior 1946-50, Metropolitan 1950-51, Delphian 1951-58, Corinthian 1958-63, Athenian 1963-72

Club Colours (change): Green/white/green (All red)

Ground: Fetcham Grove, Guildford Road, Leatherhead, Surrey KT22 9AS   **(T)** 01372 360 151

Capacity: 3,400   **Seats:** 200   **Covered:** 45   **Clubhouse:** Yes   **Shop:** Yes

Directions: M25 junction 9 to Leatherhead, follow signs to Leisure Centre, ground adjacent.
Half a mile from Leatherhead BR.

Previous Grounds:

Record Attendance: 5,500 v Wimbledon - 1976

Record Victory: 13-1 v Leyland Motors - Surrey Senior League 1946-47
Record Defeat: 1-11 v Sutton United

Record Goalscorer: Steve Lunn scored 46 goals during 1996-97

Record Appearances: P Caswell - 200

Additional Records: Paid £1,500 to Croydon for B Salkeld
Received £1,500 from Croydon for B Salkeld
Senior Honours:
Athenian League 1963-64.
Surrey Senior Cup 1968-69. Isthmian League cup 1977-78.

02-03	03-04	04-05	05-06	06-07	07-08	08-09	09-10	10-11	11-12
Isth1S 14	Isth1S 13	Isth1 7	Isth1 10	Isth1S 11	Isth1S 17	Isth1S 15	Isth1S 5	Isth1S 4	Isth P 19

MAIDSTONE UNITED

Chairman: (Chief Exec.) Bill Williams
Secretary: Darren Lovell　　**(T)** 0777 374 5577　　**(E)** dlovell@maidstoneunited.co.uk
Additional Committee Members:
Ian Tucker, Julian Thorne

Manager: Jay Saunders
Programme Editor: Ian Tucker　　　　**(E)** mufcprogramme@btopenworld.com

THE NON-LEAGUE CLUB DIRECTORY

Book Holiday Inn Hotels and Save today!

| Home |
| Clubs |
| Steps 1 - 4 |
| League Tables |

35 Years of Non-League Football

The Non-League Club Directory has developed into a comprehensive record of competitions within the non-League game, giving this level of football the

www.non-leagueclubdirectory.co.uk

Club Factfile

Founded: 1992　　**Nickname:** The Stones

Previous Names: None
Previous Leagues: Kent County, Kent

Club Colours (change): Amber/black/black (Sky/white/white)

Ground: The Gallagher Stadium, James Whatman Way, Maidstone, Kent ME14 1LQ　**(T)** 01622 753817

Capacity:　　**Seats:** Yes　　**Covered:** Yes　　**Clubhouse:** Yes　　**Shop:** Yes

Directions: M20 (junction 6) and M2 (junction 3).
Follow signs to Maidstone on the A229.
At the White Rabbit roundabout, take the third exit on to James Whatman Way.

Previous Grounds: London Road 1992-2001, Central Park (Sittingbourne) 2001-02 11-12, The Homelands 2002-11.

Record Attendance: 1,589 v Gillingham - Friendly

Record Victory: 12-1 v Aylesford - Kent League 1993-94
Record Defeat: 2-8 v Scott Sports - 1995-96

Record Goalscorer: Richard Sinden - 98

Record Appearances: Aaron Lacy - 187
Additional Records: Paid £2,000 for Steve Jones - 2000

Senior Honours:
Kent League 2001-02, 05-06, League cup 05-06. Isthmian Division 1 South 2006-07.
Kent Senior Trophy 2002-03.

02-03		03-04		04-05		05-06		06-07		07-08		08-09		09-10		10-11		11-12	
Kent P	2	Kent P	4	Kent P	4	Kent P	1	Isth1S	1	Isth P	17	Isth P	15	Isth P	18	Isth P	20	Isth1S	6

MERSTHAM

Chairman: Ted Hickman
Secretary: Richard Baxter   **(T)** 0772 029 0027   **(E)** richardbaxter01@hotmail.com
Additional Committee Members:
Kevin Austen, Mr R Richardson

Manager: Hayden Bird
Programme Editor: Kevin Austen   **(E)** ka@merstham.co.uk

Club Factfile

Founded: 1905   **Nickname:** Moatsiders
Previous Names:
Previous Leagues: Redhill & District, Surrey Senior 1964-78, London Spartan 1978-84, Combined Counties 1984-2008

Club Colours (change): Amber & black/black/amber (All blue)

Ground: Moatside Stadium, Weldon Way, Merstham, Surrey RH1 3QB   **(T)** 01737 644 046
Capacity: 2,500   **Seats:** 174   **Covered:** 100   **Clubhouse:** Yes   **Shop:** No
Directions: Leave Merstham village (A23) by School Hill,
take 5th right (Weldon Way).
Clubhouse and car park on the right.
Ten minutes walk from Merstham BR.

Previous Grounds:

Record Attendance: 1,587 v AFC Wimbledon - Combined Counties League 09/11/2002
Record Victory: Not Known
Record Defeat: Not Known
Record Goalscorer: Not Known
Record Appearances: Not Known
Additional Records:
Senior Honours:
Combined Counties League Premier Division 2007-08.

10 YEAR RECORD

02-03		03-04		04-05		05-06		06-07		07-08		08-09		09-10		10-11		11-12	
CC	17	CCP	12	CCP	16	CCP	2	CCP	2	CCP	1	Isth1S	8	Isth1S	16	Isth1S	19	Isth1S	9

RAMSGATE

Chairman: Richard Lawson
Secretary: Martin Able   **(T)** 0795 899 3959   **(E)** secretary@ramsgate-fc.co.uk
Additional Committee Members:
Edward Lucas, John Vahid

Manager: Tim Dixon
Programme Editor: Steve Redford   **(E)** media@ramsgate.fc.co.uk

2011-12 Squad - (Back Row L-R): Liam Quinn, Ryan Harker, Aaron Beech, Luke Wheatley, Gareth Cornhill, Mitchell Sherwood, James Brown, Pascal Ebigbo.
(Middle Row L-R): Simon Pettit, Warren Schulz, Ben Laslett, Mark Lovell, Brett Mills, Daren Hawkes, Joseph Afusi, Joe Taylor, Ollie Gray, Darren Beale.
(Front Row L-R): Ada Hubbard, Iona McCarvill, Paul Jefcoate, Richard Lawson, Jim Ward, Tim Dixon, Jan Whittaker, Edward Lucas.
(Not Pictured): James Gregory and Steve O'Brien.

Club Factfile

Founded: 1945   **Nickname:** Rams
Previous Names: Ramsgate Athletic > 1972
Previous Leagues: Kent 1949-59, 1976-2005, Southern 1959-76

Club Colours (change): All red (Yellow/black/black)

Ground: Southwood Stadium, Prices Avenue, Ramsgate, Kent CT11 0AN   **(T)** 01843 591 662
Capacity: 5,000   **Seats:** 400   **Covered:** 600   **Clubhouse:** Yes   **Shop:** Yes

Directions
Approach Ramsgate via A299 (Canterbury/London) or A256 (Dover/Folkestone) to Lord of Manor roundabout.
Follow the signpost to Ramsgate along Canterbury Road East, counting via 2nd exit of the 1st roundabout.
At the 2nd roundabout, continue towards Ramsgate on London Road (2nd exit).
Take the 3rd turning on the left, into St Mildred's Avenue, then 1st left into Queen Bertha Road.
After the right hand bend, take left into Southwood Road, and 1st left into Prices Ave. The stadium is at the end of Prices Avenue.

Previous Grounds:

Record Attendance: 5,200 v Margate - 1956-57
Record Victory: 11-0 & 12-1 v Canterbury City - Kent League 2000-01
Record Defeat: Not Known
Record Goalscorer: Mick Willimson
Record Appearances: Not Known
Additional Records:

Senior Honours:
Kent League Division 1 1949-50, 55-56, 56-57, Premier League 1998-99, 2004-05, Kent League Cup x6.
Isthmian League Division 1 2005-06, League Cup 2007-08.
Kent Senior Cup 1963-64, Kent Senior Trophy x3.

10 YEAR RECORD

02-03		03-04		04-05		05-06		06-07		07-08		08-09		09-10		10-11		11-12	
Kent P	5	Kent P	9	Kent P	1	Isth1	1	Isth P	8	Isth P	5	Isth P	22	Isth1S	14	Isth1S	9	Isth1S	10

SITTINGBOURNE

Chairman: Andy Spice
Secretary: John Pltts **(T)** 0750 513 4135 **(E)** johncp49@hotmail.com
Additional Committee Members:
Peter Pitts

Manager: Jim Ward and Danny Ward
Programme Editor: John Pitts **(E)** johncp49@hotmail.com

THE NON-LEAGUE CLUB DIRECTORY

Book Holiday Inn Hotels and Save today!

Home

Clubs

Steps 1 - 4

League Tables

35 Years of Non-League Football

The Non-League Club Directory has developed into a comprehensive record of competitions within the non-League game, giving this level of football the

www.non-leagueclubdirectory.co.uk

Club Factfile

Founded: 1886 **Nickname:** Brickies

Previous Names: Sittingbourne United 1881-86

Previous Leagues: Kent 1894-1905, 1909-27, 30-39, 45-59, 68-91, South Eastern 1905-09, Southern 1927-30, 59-67

Club Colours (change): Red with black stripes/black/black (All blue)

Ground: Bourne Park, Central Park Stadium, Eurolink, Sittingbourne ME10 3SB **(T)** 01795 435 077

Capacity: 3,000 **Seats:** 300 **Covered:** 600 **Clubhouse:** Yes **Shop:** Yes

Directions: Through Sittingbourne on the main A2,
club sign posted clearly and regularly from both east and west.
One mile from Sittingbourne BR station.

Previous Grounds: Sittingbourne Rec. Ground 1881-90, Gore Court Cricket Grd 1890-92, The Bull Ground 1892-1990

Record Attendance: 5,951 v Tottenham Hotspur - Friendly 26/01/1993

Record Victory: 15-0 v Orpington, Kent League 1922-23)
Record Defeat: 0-10 v Wimbledon, SL Cup 1965-66)

Record Goalscorer: Not Known

Record Appearances: Not Known

Additional Records: Paid £20,000 to Ashford Town for Lee McRobert 1993
Received £210,000 from Millwall for Neil Emblem and Michael Harle 1993

Senior Honours:
Southern League Southern Division 1992-93, 95-96. Kent League x7, League cup x4.
Kent Senior Cup 1901-02, 28-29, 29-30, 57-58.

02-03	03-04	04-05	05-06	06-07	07-08	08-09	09-10	10-11	11-12
SthE 12	SthE 10	SthE 19	SthE 18	Isth1S 10	Isth1S 9	Isth1S 6	Isth1S 9	Isth1S 11	Isth1S 19

THREE BRIDGES

Chairman: Alan Bell
Secretary: Martin Clarke   **(T)** 07885 662 940   **(E)** m-clarke@blueyonder.co.uk
Additional Committee Members:
Ken Towning, John Jackson

Manager: Paul Falli
Programme Editor: Alf Blackler   **(E)** alfblackler@gmail.com

THE NON-LEAGUE CLUB DIRECTORY

Book Holiday Inn Hotels and Save today!

Home

Clubs

Steps 1 - 4

League Tables

35 Years of Non-League Football

The Non-League Club Directory has developed into a comprehensive record of competitions within the non-League game, giving this level of football the

www.non-leagueclubdirectory.co.uk

Club Factfile

Founded: 1901   **Nickname:** Bridges

Previous Names: Three Bridges Worth 1936-52, Three Bridges Utd 53-64
Previous Leagues: Mid Sussex, E Grinstead, Redhill & Dist 36-52

Club Colours (change): Amber & black stripes/black/black. (Blue & white stripes /blue/blue)

Ground: Jubilee Field, Three Bridges Rd, Crawley, RH10 1LQ   **(T)** 01293 442 000

Capacity: 3,500   **Seats:** 120   **Covered:** 600   **Clubhouse:** Yes   **Shop:**

Directions: Leave the M23 at Junction 10 heading towards Crawley on the A2011 (Crawley Avenue). At the roundabout take the first left heading towards Three Bridges Train Station (Hazelwick Avenue). Pass Tesco on your left and head straight over the roundabout (second exit). As you approach the traffic lights remain in the right hand side lane. After turning right in to Haslett Avenue at these lights move immediately in to the right turn lane at the next set of lights. Turn right at these lights in to Three Bridges Road. Follow the road round to the left then turn left after one hundred yards in to Jubilee Walk (directly opposite the Plough Pub). Follow the road to the end and turn right (still Jubilee Walk) and head straight on where Three Bridges Jubilee Field Stadium is at the far end.

Previous Grounds:

Record Attendance: 2,000 v Horsham 1948

Record Victory: Not known
Record Defeat: Not known

Record Goalscorer: Not known

Record Appearances: John Malthouse
Additional Records:

Senior Honours:
Sussex RUR Cup 1982-83. Sussex County League Division One 2011-12.

02-03		03-04		04-05		05-06		06-07		07-08		08-09		09-10		10-11		11-12	
SxC1	14	SxC1	4	SxC1	7	SxC1	15	SxC1	12	SxC1	6	SxC1	5	SxC1	7	SxC1	5	SxC1	1

TOOTING & MITCHAM UNITED

Chairman: Anthony Richard Hill
Secretary: Gary Harding   **(T)** 07720 635074   **(E)** gary.harding@tmcsc.co.uk
Additional Committee Members:
Karen Muir, Nigel Wood, Lyn Catchpole

Manager: Roberto Forzoni
Programme Editor: Karen Muir   **(E)** karen@muir54.fsnet.co.uk

THE NON-LEAGUE CLUB DIRECTORY

Book Holiday Inn Hotels and Save today!

Home

Clubs

Steps 1 - 4

League Tables

35 Years of Non-League Football

The Non-League Club Directory has developed into a comprehensive record of competitions within the non-League game, giving this level of football the

www.non-leagueclubdirectory.co.uk

Club Factfile

Founded: 1932   **Nickname:** The Terrors

Previous Names: Tooting Town (Founded in 1887) and Mitcham Wanderers (1912) merged in 1932 to form Tooting & Mitcham FC.
Previous Leagues: London 1932-37, Athenian 1937-56

Club Colours (change): Black and white stripes/black/black (blue/white/blue)

Ground: Imperial Fields, Bishopsford Road, Morden, Surrey SM4 6BF   **(T)** 020 8685 6193

Capacity: 3,50   **Seats:** 600   **Covered:** 1,200   **Clubhouse:** Yes   **Shop:** Yes

Directions: M25 junction 8, take the A217 northbound, this goes through Tadworth and Cheam. It's dual carriageway most of the way, although long stretches have a 40mph speed limit. This leads to a major roundabout with lights (Rose Hill). Take the third exit (Mitcham A217), this is Bishopsford Road and the ground is a mile further on. Go through two sets of lights, the road dips, and the entrance is on the right opposite a petrol station.
From the South: M25 junction 7, M23 then A23 northbound. Turn left onto the A237 after passing under a railway bridge at Coulsdon South station. Through Hackbridge and Beddington, then turn left onto the A239. Turn left again at lights by Mitcham Cricket Green into the A217, the ground is 800 yards on the left.

Previous Grounds: Sandy Lane, Mitcham

Record Attendance: 17,500 v Queens Park Rangers - FA Cup 2nd Round 1956-57 (At Sandy Lane)

Record Victory: 11-0 v Welton Rovers - FA Amateur Cup 1962-63
Record Defeat: 1-8 v Kingstonian - Surrey Senior Cup 1966-67

Record Goalscorer: Alan Ives - 92

Record Appearances: Danny Godwin - 470

Additional Records: Paid £9,000 to Enfield for David Flint
                                   Received £10,000 from Luton Town for Herbie Smith
Senior Honours:
Athenian League 1949-50, 54-55. Isthmian League 1975-76, 59-60, Division 2 2000-01. Full Members Cup 1992-93. London Senior Cup 1942-43, 48-49, 58-59, 59-60, 2006-07, 07-08. Surrey Senior cup 1937-38, 43-44, 44-45, 52-53, 59-60, 75-76, 76-77, 77-78, 2007-07. Surrey Senior Shield 1951-52, 60-61, 61-62, 65-66. South Thames Cup 1969-70.

02-03	03-04	04-05	05-06	06-07	07-08	08-09	09-10	10-11	11-12
Isth1S 11	Isth1S 11	Isth1 8	Isth1 6	Isth1S 2	Isth1S 2	Isth P 9	Isth P 12	Isth P 14	Isth P 21

WALTON & HERSHAM

Chairman: Alan Smith
Secretary: Michael Groom **(T)** 0771 023 0694 **(E)** mhgroom@aol.com
Additional Committee Members:
Mervyn Rees, John Crawford, Mark Massingham

Manager: Chuck Martini
Programme Editor: Mark Massingham **(E)** mark@waltonfc.freeserve.co.uk

THE NON-LEAGUE CLUB DIRECTORY

Book Holiday Inn Hotels and Save today!

Home
Clubs
Steps 1 - 4
League Tables

35 Years of Non-League Football

The Non-League Club Directory has developed into a comprehensive record of competitions within the non-league game, giving this level of football the

www.non-leagueclubdirectory.co.uk

Club Factfile

Founded: 1945 **Nickname:** Swans

Previous Names: Walton FC (Founded in 1895) amalgamated with Hersham FC in 1945.
Previous Leagues: Surrey Senior, Corinthian 1945-50, Athenian 1950-71

Club Colours (change): All red (Yellow/blue/yellow)

Ground: Sports Ground, Stompond Lane, Walton-on-Thames KT12 1HF **(T)** 01932 245 263

Capacity: 5,000 **Seats:** 400 **Covered:** 2,500 **Clubhouse:** Yes **Shop:** Yes

Directions: From Walton Bridge go over and along New Zealand Avenue, down one way street and up A244 Hersham Road. Ground is second on the right.

Previous Grounds:

Record Attendance: 10,000 v Crook Town - FA Amateur Cup 6th Round 1951-52

Record Victory: 10-0 v Clevedon - FA Amateur Cup 1960
Record Defeat: 3-11 v Kingstonian - Surrey Shield 1958

Record Goalscorer: Reg Sentance - 220 (During 11 seasons)

Record Appearances: Terry Keen - 449 (During 11 seasons)

Additional Records: Paid £6,000. Received £150,000 from Bristol Rovers for Nathan Ellington 1999.

Senior Honours:
Athenian League 1968-69.
FA Amateur Cup 1972-73. Barassi Cup 1973-74.
Surrey Senior Cup x6. London Senior Cup.

02-03		03-04		04-05		05-06		06-07		07-08		08-09		09-10		10-11		11-12	
Isth1S	7	Isth1S	9	Isth1	2	Isth P	9	Isth P	19	Isth1S	10	Isth1S	14	Isth1S	8	Isth1S	6	Isth1S	11

WALTON CASUALS

Chairman: Tony Gale
Secretary: Gus Schofield   **(T)** 0782 469 6705   **(E)** g.schofield1@ntlworld.com
Additional Committee Members:
David Symonds

Manager: Mike Sullivan
Programme Editor: David Symons   **(E)** dave.symonds@jti.com

Back L to R – Dick Errington (Physio), Mark Norman(Fitness Coach), AJ Morrison, Jon Boswell, Jahmahl King, Sean Bradley, Gareth Williams, Kieran Campbell, Brendan Sebuliba, Ashley Thompson, Robb Sheridan, Matt Druce, Steve Honey(Goalkeeping Coach), Kwaku Agyeman (Fitness Coach).
Front L-R – Michael Corbett, James Hamsher, Marlon Wallen, Sol Patterson-Bohner, Craig Lewington, Martin Beard (Head Coach), Mick Sullivan (Manager), Peter Thomas (Assistant Manager), Hassan Nyang, Byron Brown, Sam Robinson, Matt Robinson.

Club Factfile

Founded: 1948   **Nickname:** The Stags
Previous Names:
Previous Leagues: Surrey Intermediate, Surrey Senior, Suburban, Surrey Premier, Combined Counties

Club Colours (change): Tangerine/black/black

Ground: The Waterside Stadium, Waterside Drive, Walton KT12 2JP   **(T)** 01932 787 749
Capacity: 2,000   **Seats:** 153   **Covered:** 403   **Clubhouse:** Yes   **Shop:** Yes
Directions: Left off Terrace Road at first major roundabout out of Walton centre.
Ground is next to The Xcel Leisure Centre.

Previous Grounds:

Record Attendance: 1,748 v AFC Wimbledon - Combined Counties League 12/04/2004
Record Victory: Not Known
Record Defeat: Not Known
Record Goalscorer: Greg Ball - 77
Record Appearances: Craig Carley - 234
Additional Records:

Senior Honours:
Combined Counties League Premier Division 2004-05, League Cup 1999-2000.

10 YEAR RECORD

02-03		03-04		04-05		05-06		06-07		07-08		08-09		09-10		10-11		11-12	
CC	18	CCP	7	CCP	1	Isth1	15	Isth1S	17	Isth1S	16	Isth1S	17	Isth1S	21	Isth1S	12	Isth1S	15

WHITSTABLE TOWN

Chairman: Gary Johnson
Secretary: Gary Johnson   **(T)** 07957 424 810   **(E)** secretary@whitstabletownfc.co.uk
Additional Committee Members:
Philip Gurr, Andy Short

Manager: Justin Luchford
Programme Editor: Andy Short   **(E)** programme@whitstabletownfc.co.uk

2011-12 Squad - Photo courtesy Per LaLeng

Club Factfile

Founded: 1886   **Nickname:** Oystermen or Natives
Previous Names:
Previous Leagues: East Kent 1897-1909, Kent 1909-59, Aetolian 1959-60, Kent Amateur 1960-62, 63-64, South East Anglian 1962-63, Greater London 1964-67, Kent 1967-2007

Club Colours (change): Red & white/white/red (Yellow/blue/yellow)

Ground: The D & J Tyres Belmont Grd, Belmont Rd, Belmont, Whitstable CT5 1QP   **(T)** 01227 266 012
Capacity: 2,000   **Seats:** 500   **Covered:** 1,000   **Clubhouse:** Yes   **Shop:** Yes
Directions: From Thanet Way (A299) turn left at Tesco roundabout and Millstrood Road.
Ground at bottom of road,
400 yards from Whitstable BR station.

Previous Grounds:

Record Attendance: 2,500 v Gravesend & Northfleet - FA Cup 19/10/1987
Record Victory: Not known
Record Defeat: Not known
Record Goalscorer: Barry Godfrey
Record Appearances: Frank Cox - 429 (1950-60)
Additional Records:

Senior Honours:
Kent Amateur Cup 1928-29.
Kent League 2006-07, League Trophy 2006-07.

10 YEAR RECORD

02-03		03-04		04-05		05-06		06-07		07-08		08-09		09-10		10-11		11-12	
Kent P	6	Kent P	5	Kent P	3	Kent P	5	Kent P	10	Isth1S	14	Isth1S	16	Isth1S	18	Isth1S	15	Isth1S	18

WORTHING

Chairman: Dave Agnew & Mrs Deborah McKail
Secretary: Gareth Nicholas **(T)** 01903 239 575 **(E)** garethbnicholas@hotmail.co.uk
Additional Committee Members:
Paul Long, Monty Hollis

Manager: Chris White
Programme Editor: Alistar McKail **(E)** al@worthingfc.com

THE NON-LEAGUE CLUB DIRECTORY

Book Holiday Inn Hotels and Save today!

Home

Clubs

Steps 1 - 4

League Tables

35 Years of Non-League Football

The Non-League Club Directory has developed into a comprehensive record of competitions within the non-League game, giving this level of football the

www.non-leagueclubdirectory.co.uk

Club Factfile

Founded: 1886 **Nickname:** Rebels

Previous Names:

Previous Leagues: West Sussex 1896-1904, 1905-14, 19-20, Brighton Hove & District 1919-20, Sussex County 1920-40, Corinthian 1948-63, Athenian 1963-77

Club Colours (change): All red (All yellow)

Ground: Woodside Road, Worthing, West Sussex BN14 7HQ **(T)** 01903 239 575

Capacity: 3,650 **Seats:** 500 **Covered:** 1,500 **Clubhouse:** Yes **Shop:**

Directions
A24 or A27 to Grove Lodge roundabout.
A24 (Town Centre exit) and right into South Farm Road.
Over five roundabouts take last on right (Pavilion Road) before level crossing.
Woodside Road on right, ground on left. 1/2 mile from BR.

Previous Grounds:

Record Attendance: 3,600 v Wimbledon - FA Cup 14/11/1936

Record Victory: 25-0 v Littlehampton (H) - Sussex League 1911-12
Record Defeat: 0-14 v Southwick (A) - Sussex County League 1946-47

Record Goalscorer: Mick Edmonds - 276

Record Appearances: Mark Knee - 414

Additional Records: Received £7,500 from Woking for Tim Read 1990

Senior Honours:

Sussex League 1920-21, 21-22, 26-27, 28-29, 30-31, 33-34, 38-39. Sussex League West 1945-46.
Isthmian League Division 2 1981-82, 92-93, Division 1 1982-83.
Sussex Senior Cup x21.

02-03		03-04		04-05		05-06		06-07		07-08		08-09		09-10		10-11		11-12	
Isth1S	12	Isth1S	2	Isth P	10	Isth P	8	Isth P	20	Isth1S	5	Isth1S	5	Isth1S	3	Isth1S	14	Isth1S	7

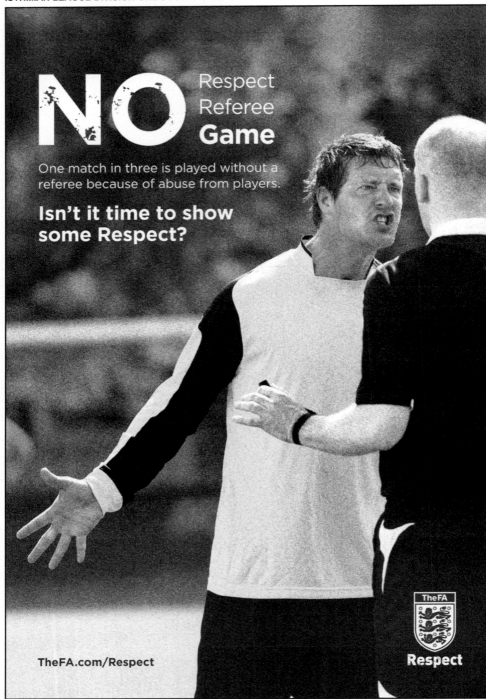

COMBINED COUNTIES LEAGUE

Sponsored by: Cherry Red Records
Founded: 1978
Recent Champions:
2007: Chipstead
2008: Merstham
2009: Bedfont Green
2010: North Greenford United
2011: Guilford City
combinedcountiesleague.co.uk

PREMIER DIVISION	P	W	D	L	F	A	Pts
1 (P) Guildford City	42	30	7	5	125	51	97
2 Windsor	42	29	9	4	124	44	96
3 Hanworth Villa (-3)	42	26	6	10	118	55	81
4 Egham Town	42	25	5	12	102	64	80
5 Molesey	42	24	4	14	103	61	76
6 Camberley Town	42	22	4	16	107	68	70
7 Horley Town	42	20	6	16	79	62	66
8 South Park	42	19	7	16	83	61	64
9 Raynes Park Vale	42	18	7	17	72	96	61
10 Wembley	42	16	12	14	66	64	60
11 Cove	42	16	7	19	84	109	55
12 Farnham Town	42	13	11	18	66	77	50
13 Ash United	42	14	7	21	75	82	49
14 Epsom & Ewell (-6)	42	15	9	18	71	77	48
15 Sandhurst Town	42	15	3	24	64	106	48
16 Croydon	42	13	8	21	62	80	47
17 Badshot Lea	42	13	8	21	66	91	47
18 Dorking	42	13	8	21	55	103	47
19 Colliers Wood United	42	12	9	21	64	90	45
20 Chessington & Hook United	42	13	4	25	60	102	43
21 (R) Mole Valley SCR	42	11	4	27	57	99	37
22 (R) Banstead Athletic	42	9	7	26	54	115	34

EL RECORDS PREMIER CHALLENGE CUP

ROUND 1
Badshot Lea 4-1 Frimley Green
Bookham 1-2 Raynes Park Vale
Camberley Town 2-2 Farnham Town
(Farnham Town won 3-2 after penalties)
Croydon 0-1 Ash United
Knaphill 2-3 Epsom & Ewell
Westfield 1-1 CB Hounslow United
(CB Hounslow United won 3-2 after penalties)
Windsor 3-1 Chessington & Hook United
Worcester Park 4-2 Molesey

ROUND 2
Badshot Lea 3-1 Mole Valley SCR
Banstead Athletic 2-0 Hartley Wintney
Cobham 3-2 Horley Town
Colliers Wood United 2-2 Cove
(Colliers Wood United won 5-4 after penalties)
Dorking 5-3 Farnham Town
Egham Town 5-1 Eversley
Farleigh Rovers 3-2 Sheerwater
Feltham 0-5 CB Hounslow United
Guernsey 4-1 Ash United
Guildford City 2-1 Hanworth Villa
Raynes Park Vale 4-0 Bedfont Sports
South Park 2-2 Sandhurst Town
(Sandhurst Town won 4-3 after penalties)
Staines Lammas 3-2 Warlingham
Wembley 0-0 South Kilburn
(Wembley won 5-4 after penalties)
Windsor 1-2 Spelthorne Sports
Worcester Park 4-1 Epsom & Ewell

ROUND 3
Badshot Lea 8-1 Sandhurst Town
Banstead Athletic 4-3 Worcester Park
Cobham 3-2 CB Hounslow United
Colliers Wood United 2-1 Dorking (AET)
Egham Town 2-5 Guernsey
Guildford City 2-2 Wembley
(Guildford City won 5-3 after penalties)
Raynes Park Vale 3-0 Farleigh Rovers
Spelthorne Sports 0-1 Staines Lammas

ROUND 4
Cobham 2-3 Banstead Athletic
Guildford City 3-2 Badshot Lea
Raynes Park Vale 1-2 Colliers Wood United
Staines Lammas 0-2 Guernsey

SEMI FINAL
Colliers Wood United 3-2 Banstead Athletic (AET)
Guernsey 4-2 Guildford City

FINAL
at Farnborough FC Att. 667
Colliers Wood United 0-2 Guernsey (AET)

PREMIER DIVISION	1	2	3	4	5	6	7	8	9	10	11	12	13	14	15	16	17	18	19	20	21	22
1 Ash United		1-1	1-1	0-3	3-2	0-2	2-2	3-1	3-0	1-2	1-4	2-2	0-4	4-1	5-2	2-2	1-0	2-3	6-1	5-0	2-2	1-1
2 Badshot Lea	2-0		5-0	3-2	0-2	1-0	3-2	0-1	4-3	3-1	2-2	3-3	1-6	0-7	1-3	0-3	1-1	1-1	3-2	1-1	0-0	2-3
3 Banstead Athletic	3-2	2-1		3-4	1-3	4-2	1-2	3-2	0-2	1-3	0-1	3-4	0-2	1-3	0-1	2-1	1-3	2-2	2-2	1-3	0-1	1-3
4 Camberley Town	4-1	2-3	0-0		1-1	7-1	0-4	0-2	9-0	1-0	4-0	6-0	1-2	3-0	0-1	4-0	1-2	3-1	4-1	0-2	2-1	1-3
5 Chessington & Hook Utd	1-2	2-1	4-3	2-8		0-2	3-4	3-1	1-1	3-8	5-5	0-1	1-4	0-5	1-0	0-2	0-2	1-4	1-3	0-3	1-3	2-1
6 Colliers Wood United	2-1	1-1	1-2	3-4	2-0		1-1	4-2	1-2	2-2	2-2	2-5	4-2	1-4	1-6	1-2	4-3	1-2	2-3	1-1	0-0	0-2
7 Cove	3-2	1-4	11-2	5-5	0-3	2-0		1-2	3-2	1-7	1-2	3-0	4-3	6-1	4-1	0-2	4-4	4-3	1-7	1-1	1-1	1-7
8 Croydon	1-2	5-1	4-0	4-1	1-3	0-1	1-1		3-1	2-3	2-2	1-1	1-1	1-1	2-1	3-0	0-4	4-1	0-2	2-3	1-5	0-0
9 Dorking	2-3	6-4	0-3	1-5	2-2	2-3	2-0	0-1		2-1	1-1	3-2	0-5	1-1	0-2	2-1	1-6	2-2	2-0	0-3	0-0	1-1
10 Egham Town	3-2	4-2	4-0	3-1	3-0	3-3	3-1	4-0	4-3		0-2	1-1	1-1	3-1	2-1	4-2	3-0	0-1	2-1	3-2	1-2	1-3
11 Epsom & Ewell	0-2	0-2	2-0	0-1	0-1	3-1	2-3	2-1	5-0	1-4		1-4	2-3	2-2	0-2	3-1	0-6	1-2	2-3	3-1	1-0	2-2
12 Farnham Town	0-3	5-1	2-0	1-2	4-2	3-3	0-2	6-0	0-1	2-2	0-0		0-3	2-1	4-1	0-2	1-3	1-1	1-1	1-1	1-1	1-1
13 Guildford City	4-1	2-0	4-1	1-1	4-0	2-0	5-0	2-1	3-2	1-3	1-1	3-1		2-1	6-0	1-1	2-5	4-2	4-1	4-1	1-2	2-2
14 Hanworth Villa	5-3	2-1	3-0	3-0	1-0	3-1	0-2	4-0	7-0	2-0	0-3	4-1	1-2		3-2	3-0	0-2	3-1	4-1	1-0	3-0	2-2
15 Horley Town	0-1	W-L	1-1	1-0	4-1	2-0	1-1	2-1	0-2	1-2	3-1	2-2	3-5	0-0		3-1	3-0	1-0	2-2	1-3	1-1	1-2
16 Mole Valley SCR	2-1	3-0	4-2	2-4	2-3	0-1	0-3	1-3	5-0	0-4	2-4	0-2	2-6	0-4	0-4		0-2	3-6	0-1	0-6	2-2	2-3
17 Molesey	4-2	0-3	4-0	4-0	4-0	0-2	3-1	2-2	5-0	3-1	1-0	0-3	1-6	2-3	0-1			1-3	3-0	3-3	3-3	3-4
18 Raynes Park Vale	2-0	3-2	2-2	1-7	0-4	2-2	3-1	0-3	2-0	2-1	3-2	1-0	0-1	1-5	2-5	3-3	0-4		3-1	1-1	2-4	0-3
19 Sandhurst Town	2-0	3-2	1-3	2-3	3-0	3-1	1-3	1-1	0-1	0-2	3-1	0-2	1-5	1-8	2-1	2-0	1-4	1-0		1-7	1-3	3-4
20 South Park	1-0	2-0	1-2	2-1	0-1	1-2	1-1	5-0	1-3	2-1	2-1	1-4	4-0	2-1	0-2	0-3	0-1	4-0			1-3	0-1
21 Wembley	1-0	0-1	2-2	0-2	1-0	4-1	1-2	1-0	1-1	1-2	4-1	1-2	3-3	1-5	2-1	2-1	0-2	2-4	1-2	1-3		1-4
22 Windsor	4-2	4-0	11-0	2-0	3-0	2-0	7-0	2-0	0-1	4-1	1-0	2-0	2-1	3-3	4-2	0-1	4-3	10-0	5-0	1-1	1-2	

COMBINED COUNTIES - STEP 5/6

DIVISION ONE		P	W	D	L	F	A	Pts
1	(P) Guernsey	34	31	1	2	138	22	94
2	(P) Bedfont Sports	34	25	5	4	84	34	80
3	(P) Hartley Wintney	34	24	7	3	101	42	79
4	Warlingham	34	19	7	8	73	50	64
5	Eversley & California	34	18	6	10	81	54	60
6	Staines Lammas	34	18	4	12	70	53	58
7	Spelthorne Sports	34	16	7	11	75	52	55
8	Westfield	34	16	4	14	64	65	52
9	Worcester Park	34	14	7	13	83	75	49
10	Frimley Green	34	11	7	16	55	82	40
11	Cobham	34	11	6	17	51	70	39
12	Knaphill	34	11	5	18	58	81	38
13	Feltham	34	11	1	22	47	68	34
14	South Kilburn	34	8	9	17	38	62	33
15	CB Hounslow United	34	10	2	22	50	82	32
16	Farleigh Rovers	34	8	6	20	50	84	30
17	Bookham	34	4	6	24	32	97	18
18	Sheerwater	34	3	6	25	49	126	15

RESERVE DIVISION		P	W	D	L	F	A	Pts
1	Farnham Town	28	23	4	1	99	22	73
2	Eversley	27	21	4	2	70	27	67
3	Warlingham	28	20	4	4	94	36	64
4	Worcester Park	28	14	7	7	59	34	49
5	Westfield	28	13	7	8	74	43	46
6	Raynes Park Vale	28	13	6	9	63	44	45
7	CB Hounslow United	27	11	4	12	41	51	37
8	Bedfont Sports	28	10	4	14	63	67	34
9	Sandhurst Town	28	9	5	14	54	57	32
10	Knaphill	28	6	8	14	37	75	26
11	Staines Lammas	28	6	7	15	50	71	25
12	Frimley Green	28	7	4	17	48	82	25
13	Farleigh Rovers	28	6	6	16	29	56	24
14	Bookham	28	6	5	17	32	88	23
15	Sheerwater	28	3	7	18	36	96	16

LEMON RECORDS DIV. ONE CHALLENGE CUP

ROUND 1
CB Hounslow United 1-3 South Kilburn
Eversley 2-1 Worcester Park
ROUND 2
Bedfont Sports 1-2 Westfield
Bookham 0-2 Staines Lammas
South Kilburn 1-2 Frimley Green
Eversley 1-3 Hartley Wintney
Farleigh Rovers 5-2 Sheerwater (AET)
Feltham 2-2 Cobham
(Cobham won 5-3 on penalties)
Knaphill 0-3 Warlingham
Spelthorne Sports 0-1 Guernsey
ROUND 3
Cobham 3-2 Guernsey
Farleigh Rovers 1-3 Staines Lammas
Warlingham 2-1 Frimley Green
Westfield 1-0 Hartley Wintney
SEMI-FINAL
Warlingham 1-0 Cobham
Staines Lammas 0-1 Westfield
FINAL
At Windsor FC Att.180
Warlingham 4-2 Westfield

RESERVE CHALLENGE CUP

ROUND 1
Bedfont Sports 4-3 Sheerwater
Bookham 4-0 Knaphill
CB Hounslow United 1-3 Westfield
Eversley 7-2 Worcester Park
Farleigh Rovers 1-4 Farnham Town
Frimley Green wo Staines Lammas
Warlingham 6-0 Sandhurst Town
ROUND 2
Raynes Park Vale 0-3 Farnham Town
Bedfont Sports 3-2 Frimley Green (AET)
Westfield 1-2 Eversley
Warlingham 8-1 Bookham
SEMI-FINAL
Bedfont Sports 3-1 Farnham Town
Warlingham 0-0 Eversley
(Eversley won 5-3 after penalties)
FINAL
At Bedfont (Town) FC
Bedfont Sports 5-1 Eversley

DIVISION ONE	1	2	3	4	5	6	7	8	9	10	11	12	13	14	15	16	17	18
1 Bedfont Sports		2-1	6-2	2-0	1-0	6-1	6-1	4-0	1-3	0-0	3-0	7-1	3-0	2-1	1-1	1-0	2-1	1-0
2 Bookham	0-3		1-1	1-4	1-2	1-1	2-1	1-3	2-3	0-3	0-4	3-1	2-1	2-1	0-6	1-2	0-2	1-1
3 CB Hounslow United	1-3	3-1		2-0	2-3	1-3	1-3	1-2	0-4	1-3	2-1	5-0	2-0	1-4	1-4	1-3	3-4	0-3
4 Cobham	1-3	0-0	0-4		1-1	1-1	1-0	0-1	0-4	2-4	0-2	5-1	3-1	0-4	4-0	0-4	4-0	2-6
5 Eversley	2-2	4-2	8-0	2-0		3-1	2-0	3-0	1-2	3-1	1-2	3-2	2-2	2-2	1-3	1-2	2-1	2-5
6 Farleigh Rovers	0-2	3-1	1-3	1-3	1-0		3-1	5-1	1-5	0-3	1-4	5-1	1-2	1-2	1-2	0-6	0-1	1-1
7 Feltham	1-0	3-1	0-2	2-0	1-2	1-2		0-4	1-3	1-3	2-0	4-2	2-3	4-2	2-3	1-5	0-2	3-2
8 Frimley Green	0-1	4-0	1-0	2-2	1-2	2-2	1-3		0-5	1-0	5-2	3-3	3-1	0-4	0-3	0-0	1-5	3-3
9 Guernsey	7-1	7-0	2-0	6-1	2-3	4-0	2-0	5-0		4-0	5-0	9-0	2-1	2-0	5-0	3-0	4-2	5-0
10 Hartley Wintney	2-2	3-1	4-0	2-3	4-0	5-2	2-1	9-1	2-2		3-3	3-1	0-0	3-3	2-1	2-2	5-1	3-2
11 Knaphill	1-3	4-0	2-0	0-6	0-2	2-2	3-2	3-2	0-8	2-3		4-2	1-1	1-3	2-2	2-2	1-2	4-0
12 Sheerwater	0-5	2-2	1-2	1-1	0-8	4-3	0-1	3-5	1-4	0-4	0-2		2-2	1-8	0-4	1-2	3-3	1-0
13 South Kilburn	1-4	1-1	2-0	2-2	1-1	2-3	0-3	1-2	0-3	0-3	1-0	2-1		1-1	1-1	2-0	1-0	2-4
14 Spelthorne Sports	1-1	3-1	2-4	3-1	4-2	4-0	1-0	2-2	2-1	2-3	2-0	3-3	1-0		0-1	1-1	1-2	2-0
15 Staines Lammas	0-1	6-3	2-1	3-0	1-4	1-0	2-0	2-1	1-3	0-1	7-3	0-3	2-1	2-1		1-2	0-2	2-2
16 Warlingham	4-1	2-0	3-2	1-2	3-3	3-1	2-0	0-0	1-5	0-4	2-1	3-2	3-0	3-1	2-1		2-3	2-2
17 Westfield	0-1	8-0	2-2	1-2	0-5	2-2	2-1	1-0	0-5	1-6	3-1	4-1	3-1	2-3	1-0	1-3		1-2
18 Worcester Park	1-3	3-0	4-0	3-0	2-3	4-1	2-2	6-4	1-4	2-4	4-1	7-5	1-2	3-1	2-6	4-3	1-1	

PREMIER DIVISION

ASH UNITED
Founded: 1911   Nickname: Green Army

Secretary: Paul Blair   **(T)** 07837 832 323   **(E)** sec@ashunited.co.uk
Chairman: Kevin Josey   **Manager:** Paul Bonner   **Prog Ed:** Kevin Josey
Ground: Shawfields Stadium, Youngs Drive off Shawfield Road, Ash, GU12 6RE.   **(T)** 01252 320 385 / 345 757
Capacity: 2500   **Seats:** 152   **Covered:** 160   **Midweek Matchday:** Tuesday   **Clubhouse:** Yes   **Shop:** No

Colours(change): All green.
Previous Names: None
Previous Leagues: Surrey Intermediate
Records: **Att:** 914 v AFC Wimbledon Combined Co 2002-03. **Goals:** Shaun Mitchell (216). **Apps:** Paul Bonner (582).
Senior Honours: Aldershot Senior Cup 1998-99, 01-02.

10 YEAR RECORD

02-03		03-04		04-05		05-06		06-07		07-08		08-09		09-10		10-11		11-12	
CC	9	CCP	9	CCP	13	CCP	3	CCP	4	CCP	15	CCP	9	CCP	11	CCP	18	CCP	13

BADSHOT LEA
Founded: 1907   Nickname: Baggies

Secretary: Mrs Nicky Staszkiewicz   **(T)** 07921 466 858   **(E)** nstaszkiewicz@ashgatepublishing.com
Chairman: Mark Broad   **Manager:** Mark Anderson   **Prog Ed:** Peter Collison
Ground: Godalming Town FC, Weycourt, Meadow, Farncombe, GU7 3JE   **(T)** 01483 417 520
Capacity: 2,500   **Seats:** 230   **Covered:** 100   **Midweek Matchday:** Tuesday   **Clubhouse:** Yes   **Shop:** Yes

Colours(change): Claret & blue/blue/claret & blue
Previous Names:
Previous Leagues: Surrey Intermediate. Hellenic > 2008.
Records: **Att:** 276 v Bisley, 16.04.07.
Senior Honours:

10 YEAR RECORD

02-03		03-04		04-05		05-06		06-07		07-08		08-09		09-10		10-11		11-12	
		Hel1E	14	Hel1E	7	Hel1E	12	Hel1E	3	Hel P	11	CCP	7	CCP	10	CCP	6	CCP	17

BEDFONT SPORTS
Founded: 1962   Nickname: The Eagles

Secretary: David Sturt   **(T)** 07712 824 112   **(E)** dave.sturt2@blueyonder.co.uk
Chairman: David Reader   **Manager:** Gavin Bamford   **Prog Ed:** Terry Reader
Ground: Bedfont Sports Club, Hatton Road, Bedfont TW14 8JA   **(T)** 0208 831 9067
Capacity: 3,000   **Seats:** Yes   **Covered:** 200   **Midweek Matchday:** Tuesday   **Clubhouse:**   **Shop:**

Colours(change): Red/black/black
Previous Names: Bedfont Sunday became Bedfont Sports in 2002 - Bedfont Eagles (1978) merged with the club shortly afterwards.
Previous Leagues: Middlesex County > 2009
Records:
Senior Honours: Middlesex County Premier Cup 2009-10.

10 YEAR RECORD

02-03	03-04	04-05	05-06	06-07	07-08	08-09	09-10		10-11		11-12	
							CC1	9	CC1	4	CC1	2

CAMBERLEY TOWN
Founded: 1895   Nickname: Reds or Town

Secretary: Ben Clifford   **(T)** 07876 552 210   **(E)** benjaminclifford@sky.com
Chairman: Christopher Goff   **Manager:** Ronnie Wilson   **Prog Ed:** Andy Vaughan
Ground: Krooner Park, Krooner Road, Camberley, Surrey GU15 2QW   **(T)** 01276 65392
Capacity: 1,976   **Seats:** 196   **Covered:** 300   **Midweek Matchday:** Tuesday   **Clubhouse:** Yes   **Shop:** Yes

Colours(change): Red and white stripes/blue/red
Previous Names: None
Previous Leagues: Surrey Senior Lge. Spartan Lge. Athenian Lge. Isthmian Lge.
Records: **Att:** 2066 v Aldershot Town, Isthmian Div.2 25/08/90. **Apps:** Brian Ives.
Senior Honours:

10 YEAR RECORD

02-03		03-04		04-05		05-06		06-07		07-08		08-09		09-10		10-11		11-12	
Isth2	16	Isth2	10	Isth2	12	Isth2	14	CCP	7	CCP	3	CCP	5	CCP	3	CCP	4	CCP	6

CHESSINGTON & HOOK UNITED — Founded: 1921 — Nickname: Chessey

Secretary: Chris Blackie **(T)** 07748 877 704 **(E)** kandcblackie@googlemail.com

Chairman: Graham Ellis **Manager:** Glyn Stevens **Prog Ed:** Eric Wicks

Ground: Chalky Lane, Chessington, Surrey KT9 2NF **(T)** 01372 602 263

Capacity: 3000 **Seats:** 167 **Covered:** 600 **Midweek Matchday:** Tuesday **Clubhouse:** Yes **Shop:** No

Colours(change): All blue
Previous Names: Chessington United.
Previous Leagues: Surrey Senior. Surrey County Premier.
Records:
Senior Honours:

10 YEAR RECORD

02-03	03-04	04-05	05-06	06-07	07-08	08-09	09-10	10-11	11-12
CC 14	CCP 10	CCP 3	CCP 8	CCP 11	CCP 11	CCP 19	CCP 6	CCP 12	CCP 20

COLLIERS WOOD UNITED — Founded: 1874 — Nickname: The Woods

Secretary: Tony Hurrell **(T)** 07956 983 947 **(E)** collierswoodutd@btconnect.com

Chairman: Tony Eldridge **Manager:** Mark Douglas **Prog Ed:** Chris Clapham

Ground: Wibandune Sports Gd, Lincoln Green, Wimbledon SW20 0AA **(T)** 0208 942 8062

Capacity: 2000 **Seats:** 102 **Covered:** 100 **Midweek Matchday:** Wednesday **Clubhouse:** Yes **Shop:** Yes

Colours(change): Blue & black stripes/black/black
Previous Names: Vandyke Colliers United
Previous Leagues: Surrey County Senior Lge.
Records: **Att:** 151 v Guildford City 06/08/2010. **Win:** 9-1 v Bedfont 05/03/2008.
Senior Honours:

10 YEAR RECORD

02-03	03-04	04-05	05-06	06-07	07-08	08-09	09-10	10-11	11-12
SuCS 2	CC1 2	CCP 14	CCP 4	CCP 13	CCP 7	CCP 14	CCP 19	CCP 11	CCP 19

COVE — Founded: 1897 — Nickname:

Secretary: Graham Brown **(T)** 07713 250 093 **(E)** covefc1897@aol.com

Chairman: Phil Wentworth **Manager:** Dean Thomas **Prog Ed:** Graham Brown

Ground: Oak Farm Fields, 7 Squirrels Lane, Farnborough GU14 8PB **(T)** 01252 543 615

Capacity: 2500 **Seats:** 110 **Covered:** 100 **Midweek Matchday:** Tuesday **Clubhouse:** Yes **Shop:** No

Colours(change): Yellow/black/yellow
Previous Names: None
Previous Leagues: Isthmian League. Hampshire.
Records: **Att:** 1798 v Aldershot Town, Isthmian Div.3 01/05/93.
Senior Honours: Aldershot Senior Cup (x5)

10 YEAR RECORD

02-03	03-04	04-05	05-06	06-07	07-08	08-09	09-10	10-11	11-12
CC 23	CCP 24	CCP 20	CCP 16	CCP 18	CCP 4	CCP 6	CCP 12	CCP 9	CCP 11

CROYDON — Founded: 1953 — Nickname: The Trams

Secretary: Antonio Di Natale **(T)** 07758 815 040 **(E)** croydonfc@footballfans.co.uk

Chairman: Dickson Gill **Manager:** John Fowler **Prog Ed:** Simon Hawkins

Ground: Croydon Sports Arena, Albert Road, South Norwood SE25 4QL **(T)** 0208 654 8555

Capacity: 8,000 **Seats:** 500 **Covered:** 1,000 **Midweek Matchday:** Tuesday **Clubhouse:** Yes **Shop:** Yes

Colours(change): All sky blue
Previous Names: Croydon Amateurs > 1974.
Previous Leagues: Surrey Senior. Spartan. Athenian. Isthmian > 2006. Kent 2006-09.
Records: **Att:** 1,450 v Wycombe Wders, FA Cup 4th Qual. 1975. **Goalscorer:** Alec Jackson - 111. **Apps:** Alec Jackson - 452 (1977-88).
Senior Honours:

10 YEAR RECORD

02-03	03-04	04-05	05-06	06-07	07-08	08-09	09-10	10-11	11-12
Isth1S 18	Isth1S 21	Isth1 22	Isth2 10	Kent P 3	Kent P 12	Kent P 9	CCP 16	CCP 20	CCP 16

DORKING
Founded: 1880 Nickname: The Chicks

Secretary: Ray Collins **(T)** 07795 231816 **(E)** ray.collins@hotmail.co.uk
Chairman: Jack Collins **Manager:** Glynn Stephens **Prog Ed:** Bryan Bletso
Ground: Meadowbank, Mill Lane, Dorking Surrey RH4 1DX **(T)** 01306 884 112
Capacity: 3500 **Seats:** 200 **Covered:** 800 **Midweek Matchday:** Tuesday **Clubhouse:** Yes **Shop:** Yes

Colours(change): Green & white hoops/green & white/green
Previous Names: Guildford & Dorking (when club merged 1974). Dorking Town 77-82
Previous Leagues: Corinthian, Athenian, Isthmian > 2006.
Records: **Att:** 4500 v Folkstone Town FAC 1955 & v Plymouth Argyle FAC 1993. **Goals:** Andy Bushell. **Apps:** Steve Lunn.
Senior Honours:

10 YEAR RECORD

02-03		03-04		04-05		05-06		06-07		07-08		08-09		09-10		10-11		11-12	
Isth2	14	Isth2	2	Isth1	21	Isth2	9	CCP	16	CCP	22	CC1	3	CCP	22	CCP	19	CCP	18

EGHAM TOWN
Founded: 1877 Nickname: Sarnies

Secretary: Daniel Bennett **(T)** 07932 612 424 **(E)** sales@beautiful-bathrooms.co.uk
Chairman: Patrick Bennett **Manager:** J Hamsher **Prog Ed:** Paul Bennett
Ground: Runnymead Stadium, Tempest Road, Egham TW20 8XD **(T)** 01784 435 226 or 01784 437055
Capacity: 5500 **Seats:** 262 **Covered:** 3300 **Midweek Matchday:** Tuesday **Clubhouse:** Yes **Shop:** No

Colours(change): All red
Previous Names: Runnymead Rovers 1877-1905. Egham F.C. 05-63.
Previous Leagues: Spartan Lge. Athenian Lge. Isthmian Lge. Southern Lge.
Records: **Att:** 1400 v Wycombe Wanderers, FAC 2nd Qual. 1972-73. **Goals:** Mark Butler (153). **Apps:** Dave Jones (850+).
Senior Honours:

10 YEAR RECORD

02-03		03-04		04-05		05-06		06-07		07-08		08-09		09-10		10-11		11-12	
Isth1S	10	Isth1S	22	SthW	22	Isth2	5	CCP	10	CCP	12	CCP	13	CCP	4	CCP	13	CCP	4

EPSOM & EWELL
Founded: 1918 Nickname: E's

Secretary: Peter Beddoe **(T)** 07767 078 132 **(E)** p.beddoe1@ntlworld.com
Chairman: Tony Jeffcoate **Manager:** Lyndon Buckwell **Prog Ed:** Richard Lambert
Ground: Chipstead FC, High Road, Chipstead, Surrey CR5 3SF **(T)** 01737 553250
Capacity: 2,000 **Seats:** 150 **Covered:** 200 **Midweek Matchday:** Tuesday **Clubhouse:** Yes **Shop:** No

Colours(change): Royal blue & white hoops/royal blue/royal blue & white hoops
Previous Names: Epsom T (previously Epsom FC) merged with Ewell & Stoneleigh in 1960
Previous Leagues: Corinthian Lge. Athenian Lge. Surrey Senior Lge. Isthmian Lge.
Records: **Att:** 5000 v Kingstonian, FAC 2Q 15/10/49. **Goals:** Tommy Tuite - 391. **Apps:** Graham Morris - 658.
Senior Honours:

10 YEAR RECORD

02-03		03-04		04-05		05-06		06-07		07-08		08-09		09-10		10-11		11-12	
Isth1S	9	Isth1S	24	Isth2	14	Isth2	15	CCP	17	CCP	10	CCP	4	CCP	5	CCP	10	CCP	14

FARNHAM TOWN
Founded: 1906 Nickname: The Town

Secretary: Ross Moore **(T)** 07810 698 272 **(E)** rossjm@btinternet.com
Chairman: Ray Bridger **Manager:** Paul Tanner **Prog Ed:** Ross Moore
Ground: Memorial Ground, West Street, Farnham GU9 7DY **(T)** 01252 715 305
Capacity: 1,500 **Seats:** 50 **Covered:** **Midweek Matchday:** Tuesday **Clubhouse:** **Shop:**

Colours(change): Claret & sky blue/white, claret & sky blue/sky blue
Previous Names:
Previous Leagues: Spartan 1973-75, London Spartan 1975-80, Combined Co. 1980-92, 93-2006, Isthmian 1992-93 (resigned pre-season).
Records:
Senior Honours: Combined Counties League 1990-91, 91-92, Division 1 2006-07.

10 YEAR RECORD

02-03		03-04		04-05		05-06		06-07		07-08		08-09		09-10		10-11		11-12	
CC	22	CCP	22	CCP	21	CCP	21	CC1	1	CC1	5	CC1	8	CC1	11	CC1	2	CCP	12

GUERNSEY

Founded: 2011   **Nickname:** Green Lions

Secretary: Mark Le Tissier   **(T)** 07781 119 169   **(E)** mark.letissier@guernseyfc.com

Chairman: Steve Dewsnip   **Manager:** Tony Vance   **Prog Ed:** Andy Richards

Ground: Footes Lane Stadium, St Peter Port, Guernsey GY1 2UL   **(T)** 01481 747 279

Capacity: 5,000   **Seats:** Yes   **Covered:** Yes   **Midweek Matchday:** Wednesday   **Clubhouse:** Yes   **Shop:**

Colours(change): Green & white/white/green
Previous Names: None
Previous Leagues: None
Records:
Senior Honours: Combined Counties League Division 2011-12.

10 YEAR RECORD

02-03	03-04	04-05	05-06	06-07	07-08	08-09	09-10	10-11	11-12
									CC1 1

HANWORTH VILLA

Founded: 1976   **Nickname:** The Vilans

Secretary: Dave Brown   **(T)** 07971 650 297   **(E)** david.h.brown@btconnect.com

Chairman: Gary Brunning   **Manager:** Bobby Dawson   **Prog Ed:** Gary Brunning

Ground: Rectory Meadows, Park Road, Hanworth TW13 6PN   **(T)** 020 8831 9391

Capacity: 600   **Seats:** 100   **Covered:** Yes   **Midweek Matchday:** Tuesday   **Clubhouse:**   **Shop:**

Colours(change): Red & white/black/black
Previous Names:
Previous Leagues: Hounslow & District Lge. West Middlesex Lge. Middlesex County League.
Records:
Senior Honours: West Middlesex Div. 1 & Div. 2 Champions. Middlesex County Champions 2002-03, 04-05.

10 YEAR RECORD

02-03	03-04	04-05	05-06	06-07	07-08	08-09	09-10	10-11	11-12
MidCo 1	MidCo 4	MidCo 1	CC1 7	CC1 6	CC1 2	CC1 2	CCP 17	CCP 5	CCP 3

HARTLEY WINTNEY

Founded: 1897   **Nickname:** The Row

Secretary: Luke Mullen   **(T)** 07860 729 608   **(E)** mulley@ntlworld.com

Chairman: Luke Mullen   **Manager:** Dave Tuttle   **Prog Ed:** Luke Mullen

Ground: Memorial Playing Fields, Green Lane, Hartley Wintney RG27 8DL   **(T)** 01252 843 586

Capacity: 2,000   **Seats:** 113   **Covered:** Yes   **Midweek Matchday:** Tuesday   **Clubhouse:**   **Shop:**

Colours(change): Orange & black/black/orange
Previous Names:
Previous Leagues:
Records: 1,392 v AFC Wimbledon , 25/01/02.
Senior Honours: Combined Counties League 1982-83.

10 YEAR RECORD

02-03	03-04	04-05	05-06	06-07	07-08	08-09	09-10	10-11	11-12
CC 11	CCP 15	CCP 23	CC1 5	CC1 16	CC1 3	CCP 21	CC1 5	CC1 7	CC1 3

HORLEY TOWN

Founded: 1896   **Nickname:** The Clarets

Secretary: Mrs Nicky Maybury   **(T)** 07753 216 403   **(E)** maybury@hotmail.com

Chairman: Mark Sale   **Manager:** Ali Rennie   **Prog Ed:** Philippa Burbidge

Ground: The New Defence, Court Lodge Road, Horley RH6 8SP   **(T)** 01293 822 000

Capacity: 1800   **Seats:** 101   **Covered:** Yes   **Midweek Matchday:** Tuesday   **Clubhouse:** Yes   **Shop:** Yes

Colours(change): Sky blue/claret/claret
Previous Names: Horley >1975
Previous Leagues: Surrey Senior, London Spartan, Athenian, Surrey County Senior, Crawley & District
Records: Att: 1,500 v AFC Wimbledon, 2003-04. **Goalscorer:** Alan Gates. **Win:** 12-1 v Egham. **Defeat:** 2-8 v Redhill 1956/57.
Senior Honours:

10 YEAR RECORD

02-03	03-04	04-05	05-06	06-07	07-08	08-09	09-10	10-11	11-12
SuCS 3	CCP 17	CCP 7	CCP 5	CC1 2	CCP 5	CCP 12	CCP 14	CCP 16	CCP 7

MOLESEY
Founded: 1953 Nickname: The Moles

Secretary: Tracy Teague **(T)** 07939 387 277 **(E)** teaguetracy90@yahoo.co.uk
Chairman: Tracy Teague **Manager:** Steve Webb **Prog Ed:**
Ground: 412 Walton Road, West Molesey KT8 2JG. **(T)** 020 8979 4283 (Clubhouse)
Capacity: 4,000 **Seats:** 160 **Covered:** Yes **Midweek Matchday:** Tuesday **Clubhouse:** Yes **Shop:** Yes

Colours(change): White/black/black.
Previous Names: None.
Previous Leagues: Surrey Senior. Spartan. Athethian. Isthmian.
Records:
Senior Honours: **Record Att:** 1,255 v Sutton United, Surrey Senior Cup sem-final 1966. **Goalscorer:** Michael Rose (139). **Apps:** Frank Hanley (453).

10 YEAR RECORD

02-03	03-04	04-05	05-06	06-07	07-08	08-09	09-10	10-11	11-12
Isth1S 22	Isth1S 19	Isth1 16	Isth1 17	Isth1S 15	Isth1S 22	CCP 11	CCP 8	CCP 3	CCP 5

RAYNES PARK VALE
Founded: 1995 Nickname: The Vale

Secretary: Paul Armour **(T)** 07980 914 211 **(E)** paul.armour2@btinternet.com
Chairman: Fred Stevens **Manager:** Lee Dobinson **Prog Ed:** Syd Toulson
Ground: Prince George's Playing Field, Raynes Park SW20 9NB **(T)** Jon Morris
Capacity: 1500 **Seats:** 120 **Covered:** 100 **Midweek Matchday:** Tuesday **Clubhouse:** Yes **Shop:** No

Colours(change): Blue/blue/red
Previous Names: Raynes Park > 1995 until merger with Malden Vale.
Previous Leagues: Surrey County Premier Lge. Isthmian.
Records: **Att:** 1871 v AFC Wimbledon (At Carshalton Athletic).
Senior Honours:

10 YEAR RECORD

02-03	03-04	04-05	05-06	06-07	07-08	08-09	09-10	10-11	11-12
CC 8	CCP 16	CCP 9	CCP 9	CCP 15	CCP 19	CCP 8	CCP 18	CCP 15	CCP 9

SANDHURST TOWN
Founded: 1910 Nickname: Fizzers

Secretary: John Muir **(T)** 07834 271 705 **(E)** secretarystfc@hotmail.co.uk
Chairman: Tony Dean **Manager:** Salvatore Difrima **Prog Ed:** John Muir
Ground: Bottom Meadow, Memorial Ground, Yorktown Rd, GU47 9BJ **(T)** 01252 878 768
Capacity: 1000 **Seats:** 102 **Covered:** 100 **Midweek Matchday:** Tuesday **Clubhouse:** Yes **Shop:** No

Colours(change): Red/black/black.
Previous Names: None
Previous Leagues: Reading & District. East Berkshire. Aldershot Senior. Chiltonian.
Records: **Att:** 2,449 v AFC Wimbledon, Combined Counties 17.08.2002.
Senior Honours: Aldershot FA Senior Invitation Challenge Cup 2000-01, 05-06. Combined Counties Premier Challenge Cup 2010-11.

10 YEAR RECORD

02-03	03-04	04-05	05-06	06-07	07-08	08-09	09-10	10-11	11-12
CC 6	CCP 5	CCP 5	CCP 7	CCP 12	CCP 16	CCP 16	CCP 9	CCP 7	CCP 15

SOUTH PARK
Founded: 1897 Nickname:

Secretary: Nick Thatcher **(T)** 07817 613 674 **(E)** spfcsecretary@hotmail.co.uk
Chairman: Colin Puplett **Manager:** Joe McElligott **Prog Ed:** Nick Thatcher
Ground: King George's Field, Whitehall Lane, South Park RH2 8LG **(T)** 01737 245 963
Capacity: 700 **Seats:** 100 **Covered:** Yes **Midweek Matchday:** Wednesday **Clubhouse:** **Shop:**

Colours(change): All red
Previous Names: South Park & Reigate Town 2001-03.
Previous Leagues: Crawley & District > 2006.
Records: **Att:** 230 v Warlingham 10/08/2007.
Senior Honours:

10 YEAR RECORD

02-03	03-04	04-05	05-06	06-07	07-08	08-09	09-10	10-11	11-12
				CC1 7	CC1 12	CC1 14	CC1 6	CC1 3	CCP 8

WEMBLEY
Founded: 1946   Nickname: The Lions

Secretary: Mrs Jean Gumm   **(T)** 07834 900 690   **(E)** wembleyfc@aol.com

Chairman: Brian Gumm   **Manager:** Ian Bates   **Prog Ed:** Richard Markiewicz

Ground: Vale Farm, Watford Road, Sudbury, Wembley HA0 3HG.   **(T)** 0208 904 8169

Capacity: 2450   **Seats:** 350   **Covered:** 950   **Midweek Matchday:** Tuesday   **Clubhouse:** Yes   **Shop:** No

Colours(change): Red & white/red/red
Previous Names: None
Previous Leagues: Middlesex Lge. Spartan. Delphian. Corinthian. Athenian. Isthmian.
Records: Att: 2654 v Wealdstone, FA Amateur Cup 1952-53. **Goals:** Bill Handraham (105). **Apps:** Spud Murphy (505).
Senior Honours:

10 YEAR RECORD

02-03	03-04	04-05	05-06	06-07	07-08	08-09	09-10	10-11	11-12
Isth1N 23	Isth2 11	Isth2 13	Isth2 11	CCP 3	CCP 14	CCP 17	CCP 15	CCP 14	CCP 10

WINDSOR
Founded: 1892   Nickname: The Royalists

Secretary: Steve Rowland   **(T)** 07887 770 630   **(E)** secretary@windsorfc.net

Chairman: Kevin Stott   **Manager:** Keith Scott   **Prog Ed:** Hayden Wheeler

Ground: Stag Meadow, St Leonards Road, Windsor, Berks SL4 3DR   **(T)** 01753 860 656

Capacity: 3,085   **Seats:** 302   **Covered:** 650   **Midweek Matchday:** Tuesday   **Clubhouse:** Yes   **Shop:** Yes

Colours(change): Red & green/red & green/red
Previous Names: Windsor & Eton 1892-2011.
Previous Leagues: W.Berks, Gt Western, Suburban, Athenian 22-29,63-81, Spartan 29-32, Gt W.Comb. Corinthian 45-50, Met 50-60, Delphian 60-63, Isth 63-06, Sth06-11
Records: 8,500 - Charity Match
Senior Honours: Athenian League 1979-80, 80-81. Isthmian League Division 1 1983-84. Southern League Division 1 South & West 2009-10. Berks & Bucks Senior Cup x11.

10 YEAR RECORD

02-03	03-04	04-05	05-06	06-07	07-08	08-09	09-10	10-11	11-12
Isth1S 13	Isth1S 3	Isth P 15	Isth P 21	Sthsw 14	Sthsw 8	Sthsw 2	Sthsw 1	SthP Exp	CCP 2

Farnham Town F.C.   Photo: Alan Coomes.

AFC CROYDON ATHLETIC
Founded: 1947   Nickname: The Rams

Secretary: Peter Smith   **(T)**
Chairman: Paul Smith   **Manager:** Anthony Williams
Ground: Croydon Sports Arena, Albert Road, South Norwood, London SE25 4QL
Colours(change): All maroon

(E) secretary@afccroydonathletic.co.uk
Prog Ed: Peter Smith
(T) 020 8654 8555   **Capacity:** 8,000

ADDITIONAL INFORMATION: Record Att: 1,372 v AFC Wimbledon 2004-05
Previous Names: Norwood FC and Wandsworth FC amalgamated in 1986 to form Wandsworth & Norwood > 1990.
Croydon Athletic 1990-2011.
Honours: London Spartan League 1994-95. Isthmian League Division 3 2001-02, Division 1 South 2009-10.

BANSTEAD ATHLETIC
Founded: 1944   Nickname: A's

Secretary: Terry Molloy   **(T)** 07958 436 483
Chairman: Terry Molloy   **Manager:** Andrew Tucker
Ground: Merland Rise, Tadworth, Surrey KT20 5JG
Colours(change): Amber & black/black/black

(E) terrymolloy@leyfield.eclipse.co.uk
Prog Ed: Bob Lockyar
(T) 01737 350 982   **Capacity:** 3500

ADDITIONAL INFORMATION:
Previous Leagues: London Spartan League. Athenian League. Isthmian > 2006.
Honours: London Spartan LC 1965-67. Athenian LC 190-82.
Record Att: 1400 v Leytonstone, FA Amateur Cup 1953. **Goals:** Harry Clark. **Apps:** Dennis Wall.

CB HOUNSLOW UNITED
Founded: 1989   Nickname:

Secretary: Stephen Hosmer   **(T)** 07900 604 936
Chairman: Frank James   **Manager:** Neil Cummings
Ground: Osterley S.C., Tentelow Lane, Norwood Green UB2 4LW
Colours(change): All dark blue

(E) stephen.hosmer@btinternet.com
Prog Ed: Stephen Hosmer
(T) 0208 574 7055   **Capacity:** 1000+

ADDITIONAL INFORMATION:
Previous League: Middlesex County.

COBHAM
Founded: 1892   Nickname: Hammers

Secretary: Ken Reed   **(T)** 07850 211 165
Chairman: Peter Knight   **Manager:** Kevin Petters
Ground: The Reg Madgwick Stadium, Leg O'Mutton Field, Anvil Lane, Cobham KT11 1AA
Colours(change): Red & black/black/black

(E) cobhamfootballclub@hotmail.com
Prog Ed: Peter Knight
(T) 01932 866 386   **Capacity:** 2000

ADDITIONAL INFORMATION: Att: 2000 - Charity game 1975.
Honours: Combined Counties League Cup 2001-02.

EPSOM ATHLETIC
Founded: 1997   Nickname:

Secretary: Simon Stevens   **(T)** 07814 809 119
Chairman: Paul Burstow   **Manager:** Luke Reynolds
Ground: Chessington & Hook Utd Fc, Chalky Lane, Chessington, Surrey KT9 2NF
Colours(change): All navy blue with white trim

(E) epsomathletic@hotmail.co.uk
Prog Ed: Simon Stevens
(T) 01372 745 777   **Capacity:** 3,000

ADDITIONAL INFORMATION:
Previous League: Surrey Elite > 2012.
Honours: Surrey Elite 2011-12.

EVERSLEY & CALIFORNIA
Founded: 1910   Nickname: Wild Boars

Secretary: Martin McMahon   **(T)** 07834 363 053
Chairman: David Bland   **Manager:** Ian Savage
Ground: ESA Sports Complex, Fox Lane, Eversley RG27 0NS
Colours(change): Yellow & royal blue stripes/royal blue/royal blue

(E) mljmcmahon@hotmail.com
Prog Ed: Paul Latham
(T) 0118 973 2400   **Capacity:** 300+

ADDITIONAL INFORMATION:
Previous League: Surrey Elite Intermediate.
Honours: Surrey Elite Intermediate 2008-09.

FARLEIGH ROVERS
Founded: 1922   Nickname: The Foxes

Secretary: Peter Collard   **(T)** 07545 444 820
Chairman: Mark Whittaker   **Manager:** Wilson Frimpong
Ground: Parsonage Field, Harrow Road, Warlingham CR6 9EX
Colours(change): Black & red stripes/black/black

(E) peter.collard@aquatots.com
Prog Ed: Peter Collard
(T) 01883 626 483   **Capacity:** 500

ADDITIONAL INFORMATION:
Previous League: Surrey County Premier.
Honours: Surrey County Premier 1982-83.

FELTHAM

Founded: 1946   Nickname: The Blues

Secretary: Scott Savoy   **(T)** 07539 219 924   **(E)** ssavoyffc@msn.com
Chairman: Brian Barry   **Manager:** Wayne Tisson   **Prog Ed:** Scott Savoy
Ground: Bedfont FC, The Orchard, Hatton Road, Bedfont TW14 9QT   **(T)** 020 8890 7264   **Capacity:** 1200
Colours(change): Blue & white/blue/blue

ADDITIONAL INFORMATION:
Record Att: 1,938 v Hampton - Middx Senior Cup 1972-73. **Goalscorer:** Paul Clarke - 135. **Apps:** Colin Ryder - 363.
Honours: Isthmian Division 2 1980-81.

FRIMLEY GREEN

Founded: 1919   Nickname: The Green

Secretary: Mark O'Grady   **(T)** 07812 026 390   **(E)** mogradyuk@yahoo.co.uk
Chairman: Mark O'Grady   **Manager:** Paul Miles   **Prog Ed:** Mark O'Grady
Ground: Frimley Green Rec. Ground, Frimley Green, Camberley GU16 6JY   **(T)** 01252 835 089   **Capacity:** 2000
Colours(change): All blue

ADDITIONAL INFORMATION:
Previous League: Surrey County Premier.
Record Att: 1,152 v AFC Wimbledon 2002-03. **Win:** 6-1 v Farnham Town 21/12/02. **Defeat:** 1-7 v Walton Casuals 2002/03.

KNAPHILL

Founded: 1924   Nickname: The Knappers

Secretary: Bryan Freeman   **(T)** 07876 162 904   **(E)** knaphillfc.honsecretary@gmail.com
Chairman: David Freeman   **Manager:** Phil Ellery   **Prog Ed:** David Freeman
Ground: Brookwood Country Park, Redding Way, Knaphill GU21 2AY   **(T)** 01483 475 150   **Capacity:** 750
Colours(change): Red/black/red

ADDITIONAL INFORMATION: **Att:** 134 v Westfield 26/12/2007. **Goalscorer:** Matt Baker - 24.
Honours: Woking & District League 1978-79. Surrey Intermediate League Division One 2005-06, Premier 06-07.

MOLE VALLEY SCR

Founded: 1978   Nickname: Commoners

Secretary: Darren Salmon   **(T)** 07596 537 933   **(E)** scr1112@live.co.uk
Chairman: Alan Salmon   **Manager:** Darren Salmon   **Prog Ed:** Gary Brigden
Ground: Cobham FC, Leg of Mutton Field, Anvil Lane, Downside Bridge Road KT11 1AA   **(T)** 01932 866 386   **Capacity:** 500
Colours(change): All blue

ADDITIONAL INFORMATION:
Previous Names: Inrad FC. Centre 21 FC . SCR Plough, SCR Grapes, SRC Litten Tree, SCR Kingfisher.
Previous Leagues: South Eastern Combination.

SHEERWATER

Founded: 1958   Nickname: Sheers

Secretary: Trevor Wenden   **(T)** 07791 612 008   **(E)** trevor.wenden2@ntlworld.com
Chairman: **Manager:** John Cook   **Prog Ed:** Trevor Wenden
Ground: Sheerwater Recreation Ground, Blackmore Crescent, Woking GU21 5QJ   **(T)** 07791 612 008   **Capacity:** 1,000
Colours(change): All royal blue

ADDITIONAL INFORMATION:
Previous League: Surrey County Premier.

SOUTH KILBURN

Founded: 2005   Nickname: SK

Secretary: Mrs Amanda Jennings   **(T)** 07595 256 309   **(E)** jenningsmandy@ymail.com
Chairman: Dennis Woolcock   **Manager:** Mick Jennings   **Prog Ed:** Francis Webb
Ground: Vale Farm, Watford Road, North Wembley HA0 3HE   **(T)** 0208 908 6545   **Capacity:**
Colours(change): White & black/black/black

ADDITIONAL INFORMATION: **Att:** 65 v Rayners Lane 25/08/2008.

SPELTHORNE SPORTS

Founded: 1922   Nickname: Spelly

Secretary: Chris Devlin   **(T)** 07956 321 558   **(E)** secretary.spelthornesportsfc@hotmail.co.uk
Chairman: Ian Croxford   **Manager:** Steve Flatman   **Prog Ed:** Chris Devlin
Ground: Spelthorne Sports Club, 296 Staines Rd West, Ashford Common, TW15 1RY   **(T)** 01932 783 625   **Capacity:**
Colours(change): Blue & white stripes/blue/white

ADDITIONAL INFORMATION: **Previous League:** Surrey Elite Intermediate.
Honours: Surrey Elite Intermediate League 2010-11.

STAINES LAMMAS
Founded: 1926   Nickname:

Secretary: Bob Parry **(T)** 07771 947 757 **(E)** bobandtracey1@btopenworld.com
Chairman: Greg Clarke **Manager:** Nathan Wharf **Prog Ed:** Clive Robertson
Ground: Ashford Tn (Mx) FC, The Robert Parker Stadium, Short Lane, Stanwell TW19 7BH **(T)** 01784 245 908 **Capacity:** 2550
Colours(change): All blue

ADDITIONAL INFORMATION:
Record Att: 107 v Hanworth Villa, January 2006. **Goalscorer:** Jay Coombs - 270+ **Win:** 19-1 v Cranleigh (Surrey Senior Lge) 19/03/03.
Honours: Combined Counties Division 1 2007-08, 08-09.

WARLINGHAM
Founded: 1896   Nickname: The Wars

Secretary: Les Badcock **(T)** 07890 589 030 **(E)** lesbadcock@hotmail.com
Chairman: Steve Rolfe **Manager:** Trevor Giles **Prog Ed:** Steve Rolfe
Ground: Whyteleafe FC, Church Road, Whyteleafe, Surrey CR3 0AR **(T)** 020 8660 5491 **Capacity:** 5,000
Colours(change): Black & white stripes/black/black

ADDITIONAL INFORMATION:
Previous League: Surrey South Eastern Combination.
Honours: Combined Counties League Division 1 2005-06.

WESTFIELD
Founded: 1953   Nickname: The Field

Secretary: Michael Lawrence **(T)** 07780 684 416 **(E)** michaelgeorgelawrence@hotmail.com
Chairman: Stephen Perkins **Manager:** John Comer **Prog Ed:** Pat Kelly
Ground: Woking Park, off Elmbridge Lane, Kingfield, Woking GU22 9BA **(T)** 01483 771 106 **Capacity:** 1000
Colours(change): Yellow/black/black

ADDITIONAL INFORMATION:
Previous League: Surrey Senior.
Honours: Surrey Senior 1972-73, 73-74.

WORCESTER PARK
Founded: 1921   Nickname: The Skinners

Secretary: Kristina Maitre **(T)** 07557 784733 **(E)** kristinajayne@hotmail.co.uk
Chairman: Sam Glass **Manager:** Dave Perry **Prog Ed:** Darren Talbot
Ground: Skinners Field, Green Lane, Worcester Park, Surrey KT4 8AJ **(T)** 0208 337 4995 **Capacity:**
Colours(change): All blue

ADDITIONAL INFORMATION:
Previous League: Surrey County Premier.
Honours: Surrey County Premier/Senior League 1999-2000, 2000-01. Combined Counties Division One 2010-11.

Warlingham FC.   Photo: Alan Coomes

GROUND DIRECTIONS

ASH UNITED - Youngs Drive GU12 6RE - 01252 320 385
FROM M3: Get off the M3 at J4, onto the A331: Take 3rd Exit off to Woking. Up to the roundabout turn left into Shawfields Road, follow road for about 500 yards, Football Ground is on the left, take next turning on your left into Youngs Drive where club is 50yards on. FROM M25: Get onto the A3 heading to Guildford/Portsmouth. Keep on this until you reach the A31(Hog's Back). Then go onto the A31 until you reach the exit for the A331 to Aldershot. Follow the signs for Aldershot, which will be the 1st exit off the A331.When you reach the roundabout take the exit for Woking, which will be the 3rd exit off. Up to the roundabout turn left into Shawfields Road, then as above.

BADSHOT LEA - Godalming Town FC, Weycourt, Meadow, Farncombe, GU7 3JE - 01483 417 520
A3100 from Guildford, pass the Manor Inn on the left and then the petrol station on the right. Wey Court is 50 yards further along the road on the right hand side.
A3100 from Godalming, pass the Three Lions pub on the left and then turn left into Wey Court immediately after the Leathern Bottle pub.

BEDFONT SPORTS - Bedfont Sports Club TW14 9QT
From Junction 13, M25 – Staines. At Crooked Billet roundabout turn right onto the A30 Signposted C. London, Hounslow. At Clockhouse Roundabout take the 2nd exit onto the A315 Signposted Bedfont. Turn left onto Hatton Road. Arrive on Hatton Road, Bedfont Sports Club.

CAMBERLEY TOWN - Krooner Park GU15 2QW - 01276 65392
Exit M3 Motorway at Junction 4. At the end of the slip road take the right hand land signposted A331, immediately take the left hand lane signposted Frimley and Hospital (Red H Symbol) and this will lead you up onto the A325. Continue to the roundabout and turn left onto the B3411 (Frimley Road) Continue past Focus DIY store on Left and stay on B3411 for approx 1.5 miles. At the next Mini roundabout turn left into Wilton Road, proceed through industrial estate (past the Peugeot garage) and the entrance to the ground is right at the end.

CHESSINGTON & HOOK UNITED - Chalky Lane KT9 2NF - 01372 745 777
Chalky Lane is off A243 (Opposite Chessington World of Adventures) which leads to Junction 9 on M25 or Hook Junction on the A3.

COLLIERS WOOD UTD - Wibbandune Sports Ground SW20 0AA - 0208 942 8062
On A3 Southbound 1 mile from Robin Hood Gate.

COVE - Squirrel Lane GU14 8PB - 01252 543 615
From M3 junction 4, follow signs for A325, then follow signs for Cove FC.

CROYDON - Croydon Sports Arena, Albert Road, South Norwood SE25 4QL - 0208 654 8555
From M25: Exit at either Junction 6 and then take the A22 to Purley Cross and then join the A23 London Road and then directions below from Purley, or exit at Junction 7 and take the A23 London Road all the way. From Streatham and Norbury: Take the A23 London Road to the roundabout at Thornton Heath, continue down the A23 Thornton Road. Then take the 1st on the Right past the No Entry road (Fairlands Avenue), Silverleigh Road, 50 yards, at the fork, keep left (signposted Croydon Athletic FC) into Trafford Road, then Mayfield Road (which is a continuation of Trafford Road) Go to the end of Mayfield Road, then left at the last house. Follow the lane, passed allotments, past an open car park space and continue along the lane to our club car park.

DORKING - Meadowbank Stadium RH4 1DX - 01306 884 112
Dorking Football Club's Meadowbank ground is very close to the town centre and only a ten minute walk from any of the three railway stations that serve the town.
Deepdene and Dorking West are on the (First Great Western Link) Reading to Gatwick Airport line. Dorking is on the (South West Trains) Horsham to London Waterloo line.
Follow the signs for the town centre from all stations. Meadowbank is on Mill Lane which is well signposted from the High Street.

EGHAM TOWN - Runnymead Stadium TW20 8HX - 01784 435 226
From M25 - J13 - Take the A30, heading south. The road runs parallel with the M25 briefly, and sweeps round a sharp left hand bend, under the M25. Stay right, down to the r'about in front of you just the other side of the M25. Go round the r'about and back under the M25.This road is called The Causeway. Carry on down this road, over the small r'about at Sainsbury's and at the bigger r'about turn right (signposted B3376 - Thorpe, Chertsey, Woking). Proceed down Thorpe Rd, over a level crossing, to a mini r'about, go over, and on the left, after the green turn into Pond Road. Left into Wards Place then first right and you will see the entrance to the football ground.

EPSOM & EWELL - Chipstead FC, High Road, Chipstead, Surrey CR5 3SF - 01737 553250
From the Brighton Road north bound, go left into Church Lane and left into Hogcross Lane. High Road is on the right.

FARNHAM TOWN - Memorial Ground, West St. GU9 7DY - 01252 715 305
Follow A31 to Coxbridge roundabout (passing traffic lights at Hickleys corner. Farnham station to left.) At next roundabout take 3rd exit to Farnham town centre. At the mini roundabout take 2nd exit. The ground is to the left.

GUERNSEY - Footes Lane Stadium, St Peter Port, Guernsey GY1 2UL - 01481 747 279
The ground is located centrally in the island, is easily accessible with parking for several hundred cars in the immediate vicinity and on a regular bus route stopping immediately outside the stadium. It is approximately three miles north easterly from Guernsey Airport and one mile west from St Peter Port, the island's capital.

HANWORTH VILLA - Rectory Meadows, Park Road TW13 6PN - 0208 831 9391
From M25 and M3 once on the M3 towards London. This becomes the A316, take the A314 (Hounslow Rd) exit signposted Feltham & Hounslow. Turn left onto Hounslow Rd, at the second mini round about (Esso garage on the corner) turn left into Park Rd. Continue down Park Road past the Hanworth Naval Club on the right and Procter's Builders Merchants on the left. Follow the road around the 90 degree bend and continue to the end of the road past the Hanworth Village Hall. Once past the two houses next to the village hall turn left into Rectory Meadows.

HARTLEY WINTNEY - Memorial Playing Fields RG27 8DL - 01252 843 586
On entering Hartley Wintney via the A30 take the turn at the mini roundabout signposted A323 Fleet. Take the 1st right turn, Green Lane, which has St John's Church on the corner. Continue down Green Lane for about 800 metres and turn right into car park, which has a shared access with Greenfields School. Turn left at St John's Church if coming down the A323 from Fleet.

HORLEY TOWN - The New Defence RH6 8RS - 07545 697 234
From centre of town go North up Victoria where it meets the A23, straight across to Vicarage Lane, 2nd left into Court Lodge Road follow it through estate and we are behind adult education centre.

MOLESEY - 412 Walton Road West KT8 0JG - 0208 979 4283
Take A3 towards Cobham/London & exit at Esher-Sandown turn. 1st exit at roundabout to A244 through Esher to Marquis of Granby Pub. 1st exit A309 at next roundabout. 1st exit at end of road turn right, follow until mini roundabout left into Walton Road after 1 mile ground on left.

RAYNES PARK VALE - Prince Georges Fields SW20 9NB - 0208 540 8843
Exit Raynes Park station into Grand Drive cross Bushey Road at the traffic lights continue up Grand Drive for 400 yards entrance on the left follow drive to clubhouse. From the A3. Onto Bushey Road towards South Wimbledon. Grand Drive on the right, ground in Grand Drive on the left hand side.

SANDHURST TOWN - Bottom Meadow GU47 9BJ - 01252 878 768
Situated on A321 approx 5 miles from Junction 4 on M3, or approx 8 miles from junction 10 on the M4 Park in Council Offices car park and walk down tarmac footpath beside the stream to ground.

SOUTH PARK - King George's Field RH2 8LG - 01737 245 963
From junction 8 of the M25, take A217 and follow signs to Gatwick. Follow through the one way system via Reigate town centre and continue on until traffic lights and crossroads by The Angel public house, turn right at these lights, into Prices Lane, and continue on road. After a sharp right bend into Sandcross Lane past Reigate Garden Centre. Take next left after school into Whitehall Lane.

WEMBLEY - Vale Farm, Watford Road HA0 3AG - 0208 904 8169
From Sudbury Town Station 400 yards along Watford Road.

WINDSOR - Stag Meadow, St Leonards Road, Windsor, Berks SL4 3DR - 01753 860 656
Exit M4 at Junction 6, follow dual carriageway (signposted Windsor) to large roundabout at end, take third exit into Imperial Road, turn left at T-junction into St Leonards Road. Ground approx ½ mile on right opposite Stag & Hounds public house.

Bedfont Sports F.C. Photo: Eric Marsh

Frimley Green F.C. Photo: Eric Marsh

DIVISION ONE

AFC CROYDON ATHLETIC - Croydon Sports Arena, Albert Road, South Norwood, London SE25 4QL
See Croydon.

BANSTEAD ATHLETIC - Merland Rise KT20 5JG - 01737 350 982
From M25 junction 8 follow signs to Banstead Sports Centre.

CB HOUNSLOW UNITED - Osterley Sports Club UB2 4LW - 0208 574 7055
From the A4 (Great West Road). Turn left at Master Robert, Church Rd. Turn left at Heston Road. Follow for 1 mile. Turn right at Norwood Green (Tentelow Lane). Club is 1 mile on the Right.

COBHAM - Leg of Mutton Field - 07787 383 407
From Cobham High Street, turn right into Downside Bridge Road and turn right into Leg of Mutton Field.

EPSOM ATHLETIC - Chessington & Hook United FC, Chalky Lane KT9 2NF - 01372 745 777
Chalky Lane is off A243 (Opposite Chessington World of Adventures) which leads to Junction 9 on M25 or Hook Junction on the A3.

EVERSLEY & CALIFORNIA - ESA Sports Complex, Fox Lane, Eversley RG27 0NS - 0118 973 2400
Leave the M3 at junction 4a signposted Fleet/Farnborough. At the roundabout take the 2nd exit towards Yateley. At the roundabout take the 2nd exit towards Yateley. At the roundabout take the 2nd exit towards Yateley. At the roundabout take the 1st exit and proceed through Yateley on the Reading Road. At the roundabout take the 2nd exit and follow the road for about 1 mile. Turn right down the first turning for Fox Lane and then follow the road round to the right where the ground will be signposted.

FARLEIGH ROVERS - Parsonage Field, Harrow Road CR6 9EX - 01883 626 483
From M25 junction 6 left at lights up Godstone Hill (Caterham bypass) to roundabout. Take fourth turning off of roundabout. Up Succombs Hill then right into Westhall Rd. Right at the green then second left into Farleigh Rd. Left at mini round about continue still on Farleigh Rd. Right at the Harrow Pub. This is Harrow Road. Right at the end of the houses and the ground is behind the houses.

FELTHAM - Bedfont FC, Beveree TW14 9QT - 0208 890 7264
Hatton Road runs alongside the A30 at Heathrow. Ground is opposite the Duke of Wellington Public House.

FRIMLEY GREEN - Frimley Green Recreation Ground GU16 6SY - 01252 835 089
Exit M3 at junction 4 and follow the signs to Frimley High Street. At the mini roundabout in front of the White Hart public house turn into Church Lane. At the top of the hill by the Church the road bends right and becomes Frimley Green Road. Follow the road for approx of a mile, go over the mini roundabout which is the entrance to Johnson's Wax factory, and the Recreation Ground is the second turning on the left, just past Henley Drive, which is on your right.

KNAPHILL - Brookwood Country Park GU21 2AY - 01483 475 150
From A3: A322 from Guildford through towards Worplesdon. At Fox Corner rounabaout, take 2bd exit onto Bagshot Road, A322 signposted Bagshot. Pat West Hill Golf Club, at traffice lights turn right onto Brookwood Lye Road, A324 signposted Woking. Turn left into Hermitage Road on A324, up to roundabout, take 1st exit onto Redding Way, then 1st left entering driveway towards car park and ground.
From M3: Take A322 towards Bisley on Guildford Road, continue forwards onto Bagshot Road A322. At traffic lights, left into Brookwood Lye Road at traffic lights - A324 Woking. At Hermitage Road roundabout, 1st exit onto Redding ay, then 1st turning on left entering driveway towards car park and ground.
From M25: Towards Woking Town Centre on A320 Chertsey Road, signposted town centre. At roundabout take 2nd exit onto Victoria Way signposted Guildford. Keep to the right and at Traffic lights turn right into Lockfield Drive A324 signpost Aldershot. At next roundabout take 2nd exit signposted Knaphill. At Robin Hood roundabout 1st exit Amstell Way marked A324 Aldershot. Up to roundabout, 2nd exit into Hermitage Road, past Woking Crematorium. Then Min-roundabout and continue forward and enter Hermitage Roundabout 2nd exit in Redding Way. Take 1st left entering driveway towards car park and ground.

MOLE VALLEY SCR - Cobham FC, Leg of Mutton Field - 07787 383 407
From Cobham High Street, turn right into Downside Bridge Road and turn right into Leg of Mutton Field.

SHEERWATER - Sheerwater Recreation Ground GU21 5QJ - 01932 348 192
From M25(J11) take the A320 towards Woking, At Six Cross roundabout take the exit to Monument Road. At the lights turn left into Eve Road for Sheerwater Estate. First left is Blackmore Crescent, Entrance is Quarter of a mile on left.

SOUTH KILBURN - Vale Farm, Watford Road HA0 3HE - 0208 908 6545
Leave A40 onto A404, Watford Road, continue along Watford Road, you will see the sign for Vale Farm Sports Ground on right.

SPELTHORNE SPORTS - 296 Staines Rd West, Ashford Common, TW15 1RY - 01932 783 625
From M25 (J13) take the A30 exit to London (W)/Hounslow/Staines. At the roundabout, take the 1st exit onto Staines Bypass/A30 heading to London(W)/Hounslow/Staines/Kingston/A308. Turn left onto Staines Bypass/A308 Continue to follow A308. Go through 1 roundabout. Make a U-turn at Chertsey Rd. Ground will be on the left.

STAINES LAMMAS - Ashford T (Mx), The Robert Parker Std, Short Lane, Stanwell TW19 7BH - 01784 245908
M25 junction 13, A30 towards London, third left at footbridge after Ashford Hospital crossroads, ground sign posted after 1/4 mile on the right down Short Lane, two miles from Ashford (BR) and Hatton Cross tube station.

WARLINGHAM - Whyteleafe FC, Church Road, Whyteleafe, Surrey CR3 0AR - 020 8660 5491
FROM THE M25 AND THE SOUTH: From Junction 6 of the M26 head north along the A22 (signposted to London, Croydon and Caterham). At Wapses Lodge Roundabout, the Ann Summers building is clearly visible opposite, take the third exit. Take the first left adjacent to Whyteleafe South railway station and cross the level crossing. Fork right after 200 yards into Church Road. The ground is a quarter of a mile down the road on the right. FROM THE NORTH: From Purley Cross (where the A23 crosses the A22), head south signposted to Eastbourne and the M25. Pass 'My Old China' (Chinese restaurant) on your right and continue under a railway bridge. Follow the A22 through Kenley and into Whyteleafe. At the first roundabout (with Whyteleafe Tavern opposite), turn right and cross a level crossing adjacent to Whyteleafe Station. Take first left into Church Road keeping St Luke Church to your right. The ground is a quarter of a mile up the road on the left.

WESTFIELD - Woking Park, off Elmbridge Lane GU22 7AA - 01483 771 106
Follow signs to Woking Leisure Centre on the A247.

WORCESTER PARK - Skinners Field, Green Lane KT4 8AJ - 0208 337 4995
From M25, come off at A3 turn off and head towards London, then come off at Worcester Park turn off, stay on this road until you pass station on your left and go under bridge, then take first left which is Green Lane, ground is 500 yards on the left.

Action from Ash United versus Camberley Town from the Combined Counties Premier Division.

Combined Counties Division One action between Frimley Green and eventual champions Guernsey.

More action from Ash United, this time playing host to Sandhurst Town.

Photos: Eric Marsh.

N⊗N LEAGUE DAY

What is Non-League Day?

- A celebration of the semi-professional and amateur game.

- A chance for fans of bigger clubs to experience football at a level they may be otherwise unfamiliar with.

- A chance to shine a light on the hundreds of clubs in this country who are almost exclusively volunteer run, and do so much good for the local community.

- And much, much more.

So on the 13th of October 2012, why not give **your** local club the support it needs, and deserves.

SAT 13TH OCTOBER

For more information:

www.nonleagueday.co.uk

EAST MIDLAND COUNTIES LEAGUE

Sponsored by: No sponsor

Founded: 2008

Recent Champions:
2009: Kirby Muxloe SC
2010: Dunkirk
2011: Gresley
emc-fl.com

		P	W	D	L	F	A	Pts
1	(P) Heanor Town	36	28	4	4	121	48	88
2	Borrowash Victoria	36	26	3	7	81	30	81
3	Oadby Town	36	24	6	6	95	33	78
4	St Andrews	36	21	5	10	78	60	68
5	Barrow Town	36	20	5	11	89	56	65
6	Holbrook Sports	36	18	9	9	68	56	63
7	Thurnby Nirvana	36	18	5	13	82	64	59
8	Blackwell Miners Welfare	36	17	4	15	73	61	55
9	Anstey Nomads	36	14	9	13	66	60	51
10	Bardon Hill	36	15	6	15	68	71	51
11	Holwell Sports	36	14	4	18	67	74	46
12	Blaby & Whetstone Athletic	36	12	10	14	48	60	46
13	Gedling Miners Welfare	36	12	2	22	55	94	38
14	Graham St Prims	36	10	6	20	49	85	36
15	Greenwood Meadows	36	10	5	21	38	73	35
16	Radcliffe Olympic	36	10	4	22	58	84	34
17	Radford	36	9	4	23	41	80	31
18	Ibstock United (-1)	36	7	6	23	33	77	26
19	Ellistown (-4)	36	5	7	24	57	101	18

LEAGUE CUP

ROUND 1
Greenwood Meadows 3-3 Gedling Miners Welfare
Gedling Miners Welfare AW Greenwood Meadows
Holbrook Sports 3-2 Thurnby Nirvana
Radcliffe Olympic 2-1 Anstey Nomads

ROUND 2
Bardon Hill 7-2 Ibstock United
Blaby & Whetstone Athletic 3-4 Graham St Prims
Borrowash Victoria 3-1 Greenwood Meadows
Ellistown AW Barrow Town
Heanor Town 4-0 Holwell Sports
Oadby Town 2-3 Holbrook Sports
Radford FC 1-2 Blackwell Miners Welfare
St Andrews 0-2 Radcliffe Olympic

QUARTER FINALS
Graham St Prims 1-2 Borrowash Victoria
Barrow Town 4-3 Holbrook Sports
Heanor Town 2-1 Blackwell Miners Welfare
Bardon Hill 1-2 Radcliffe Olympic

SEMI-FINALS
Borrowash Victoria 2-1 Barrow Town
Heanor Town 0-1 Radcliffe Olympic

FINAL
Borrowash Victoria 1-0 Radcliffe Olympic

		1	2	3	4	5	6	7	8	9	10	11	12	13	14	15	16	17	18	19
1	Anstey Nomads		1-1	1-2	0-1	3-2	0-7	4-1	4-1	1-1	0-2	1-5	1-2	2-0	4-0	0-1	3-0	2-0	1-2	3-2
2	Bardon Hill	1-1		2-4	3-3	2-1	3-1	3-1	2-1	2-0	0-2	1-4	1-1	1-1	4-2	0-2	4-3	3-0	0-4	2-4
3	Barrow Town	2-2	1-2		3-1	2-4	1-1	5-0	0-1	2-1	7-0	1-3	4-0	3-1	2-3	0-2	4-2	4-0	0-0	2-1
4	Blaby & Whetstone Athletic	3-3	1-1	1-2		0-3	1-1	2-1	2-1	0-1	4-1	1-3	0-0	1-1	2-2	0-5	2-1	2-1	3-1	1-2
5	Blackwell Miners Welfare	2-0	1-4	3-3	0-0		0-3	4-3	4-3	2-1	4-0	1-3	1-2	5-1	1-0	0-4	5-3	3-1	2-3	0-2
6	Borrowash Victoria	4-0	3-1	2-0	0-1	2-1		1-0	5-0	2-3	2-0	1-2	1-0	3-1	3-0	2-0	4-3	2-0	4-2	2-3
7	Ellistown	1-1	0-1	3-4	1-2	1-3	0-5		3-3	6-1	1-0	4-5	2-3	2-3	2-1	0-2	0-4	3-1	0-4	3-3
8	Gedling Miners Welfare	0-3	1-2	2-0	3-3	0-6	1-2	5-3		5-2	0-4	0-8	0-2	2-3	2-1	1-6	1-2	1-0	4-6	2-1
9	Graham Street Prims	1-1	0-7	3-6	4-2	0-1	0-5	5-1	0-3		1-2	0-1	0-3	0-3	0-0	1-3	0-4	1-2	3-4	3-1
10	Greenwood Meadows	0-4	2-1	4-2	0-0	0-3	0-1	1-1	1-3	0-1		0-5	2-1	0-1	0-2	0-0	0-2	1-1	1-3	3-3
11	Heanor Town	2-3	4-3	3-6	4-0	1-0	3-1	7-2	2-0	1-1	6-1		5-1	4-1	2-1	4-3	1-1	4-1	0-0	9-0
12	Holbrook Sports	3-2	2-1	1-0	0-2	2-2	1-1	5-5	4-2	2-2	3-2	2-3		3-1	0-1	3-2	2-0	1-1	2-3	2-0
13	Holwell Sports	0-4	4-1	0-4	4-2	1-2	0-2	1-1	2-0	3-4	0-3	1-3	1-3		3-0	0-5	5-1	7-0	7-0	2-4
14	Ibstock United	2-2	0-1	0-3	1-0	4-2	0-1	2-1	0-1	1-3	0-1	0-4	0-3	3-3		1-1	1-3	2-1	0-2	0-2
15	Oadby Town	4-2	7-2	1-1	2-0	1-0	1-0	1-0	1-2	5-0	2-1	1-2	2-2	5-0	1-1		6-0	1-0	3-1	2-4
16	Radcliffe Olympic	0-2	0-1	1-3	2-0	2-1	0-1	0-0	3-1	2-3	1-3	1-2	0-1	0-3	5-0	1-5		3-3	2-3	2-2
17	Radford	2-1	2-1	0-1	0-3	2-0	1-2	2-1	1-2	0-2	4-1	3-2	3-3	1-0	2-1	1-4	3-4		0-1	0-3
18	St Andrews	2-2	5-3	1-4	2-0	1-1	0-2	0-3	2-1	1-0	1-0	2-2	3-1	0-2	6-0	0-3	4-0	5-0		3-2
19	Thurnby Nirvana	1-2	2-1	4-1	1-2	1-3	1-2	7-1	4-0	1-1	3-0	3-2	0-2	0-1	4-1	1-1	5-0	3-2	2-1	

ANSTEY NOMADS
Founded: 1947   Nickname:

Secretary: Chris Hillebrandt **(T)** 0794 685 6430 **(E)** chille1055@hotmail.com
Chairman: Tony Ford **Manager:** Andy Miller **Prog Ed:** Gareth Hussey
Ground: Cropston Road, Anstey, Leicester LE7 7BP **(T)** 0116 236 4868 **Capacity:**
Colours(change): Red & white stripes/black/red (All blue)

ADDITIONAL INFORMATION:
Previous League: Leicestershire Senior. Central Alliance. East Midlands Regional.
Honours: Leicestershire Senior League 1951-52, 53-54, 81-82, 82-83, 2008-09. Leicestershire Senior Cup 1994-95.
Record Attendance: 4,500 v Hayes, 2nd Round FA Amateur Cup.

AYLESTONE PARK
Founded: 1968   Nickname:

Secretary: Mrs Frances Hargrave **(T)** 07563 713 700 **(E)** beaumonttownfc@hotmail.co.uk
Chairman: Bob Stretton **Manager:** Wayne Batson **Prog Ed:** Jonny Hood
Ground: Mary Linwood Recreation Ground, Saffron Lane, Leicester LE6 6TG **(T)** 0116 278 5485 **Capacity:**
Colours(change): Red/black/red (All blue)

ADDITIONAL INFORMATION:
Previous Name: Aylestone Park Old Boys > 2007.
Previous Leagues: Leicestershire Senior 1992-2012.

BARDON HILL
Founded: Nickname:

Secretary: Adrian Bishop **(T)** 07999 879 841 **(E)** ade_bish@hotmail.co.uk
Chairman: **Manager:** Rob Middleton & Don Gethfield **Prog Ed:** Adrian Bishop
Ground: Bardon Close, Coalville, Leicester LE67 4BS **(T)** 01530 815 569 **Capacity:**
Colours(change): Royal blue/royal blue/white (All red)

ADDITIONAL INFORMATION:
Previous League: Leics Senior. **Previous Name:** Bardon Hill Sports

BARROW TOWN
Founded: Late 1800s   Nickname:

Secretary: Andy Dermott **(T)** 07875 291 365 **(E)** secretary@barrowtown.net
Chairman: Michael Bland **Manager:** John Folwell & Adam Beazeley **Prog Ed:** Andy Dermott
Ground: Riverside Park, Bridge Street, Quorn, Leicestershire LE12 8EN **(T)** 07999 879 841 **Capacity:**
Colours(change): Royal blue/royal blue/white (All red)

ADDITIONAL INFORMATION:
Previous League: Leicestershire Senior

BASFORD UNITED
Founded: 1900   Nickname:

Secretary: Chris Munroe **(T)** 07803 890 446 **(E)** chrismunroe@me.com
Chairman: **Manager:** Darren Saunders **Prog Ed:** Chris Munroe
Ground: Greenwich Avenue, off Bagnall Road, Basford, Nottingham NG6 0LD **(T)** 07803 890 446 **Capacity:**
Colours(change): Yellow/black/black (All navy)

ADDITIONAL INFORMATION:
Honours: Notts Alliance Division One 1997-98. Central Midlands Southern 2011-12.

BLABY & WHETSTONE ATHLETIC
Founded: Nickname:

Secretary: Sue Warner **(T)** 07757 513 333 **(E)** suewarner2@aol.com
Chairman: Mark Jenkins **Manager:** Steve Orme **Prog Ed:** Roger Morris
Ground: Warwick Road, Whetstome, Leicester LE8 6LW **(T)** 0116 275 1182 **Capacity:**
Colours(change): All navy blue (Yellow & blue/yellow/yellow)

ADDITIONAL INFORMATION:
Previous Lge: Leicestershire Senior > 2011.

BORROWASH VICTORIA
Founded: Nickname:

Secretary: Ian Collins **(T)** 07733 055 212 **(E)** chunkyvics@ntlworld.com
Chairman: Frazer Watson **Manager:** Mark Wilson **Prog Ed:** Adrian Randle
Ground: Watkinsons Construction Bowl, Borrowash Rd, Spondon, Derby DE21 7PH **(T)** 01332 669 688 **Capacity:**
Colours(change): Red & white stripes/black/black (All blue)

ADDITIONAL INFORMATION:
Previous League: Central Midlands

ELLISTOWN

Founded: 1993   Nickname:

Secretary: Sue Matthews   **(T)** 07881 723 033   **(E)** suematthews7@hotmail.com
Chairman: Andy Roach   **Manager:** Andy Noble   **Prog Ed:** Jordan Watret
Ground: Terrace Road, Terrace Road, Ellistown, Leicestershire LE67 1GD   **(T)** 01530 230 159   **Capacity:**
Colours(change): Yellow & blue/blue/yellow (Grey/black/black)

ADDITIONAL INFORMATION:
Previous League: Leicestershire Senior
Club formed after the merger of Bagworth and Ellis Colliery.

GEDLING MINERS WELFARE

Founded: Nickname:

Secretary: Norman Hay   **(T)** 07748 138 732   **(E)** norman.hay@virginmedia.com
Chairman: Vic Hulme   **Manager:** Andy Muldon   **Prog Ed:** Ian Williams
Ground: Plains Social Club, Plains Road, Mapperley, Nottingham NG3 5RH   **(T)** 0115 926 6300   **Capacity:**
Colours(change): Yellow/blue/yellow (All red)

ADDITIONAL INFORMATION:
Previous League: Central Midlands

GRAHAM ST. PRIMS

Founded: 1904   Nickname: Prims

Secretary: Peter Davis   **(T)** 07969 160 574   **(E)** j.davis16@sky.com
Chairman: John Lindsay (Vice)   **Manager:** Mark Webster   **Prog Ed:** Edward Davis
Ground: Asterdale Sports Centre, Borrowash Road, Spondon, Derbyshire DE21 7PH   **(T)** 07969 160 574   **Capacity:**
Colours(change): Red/black/black (All royal blue)

ADDITIONAL INFORMATION:
Previous League: Central Midlands

GREENWOOD MEADOWS

Founded: 1987   Nickname:

Secretary: Christine Burton   **(T)** 0771 253 0706   **(E)** christineburton@live.co.uk
Chairman: Mark Burton   **Manager:** Nev Silcock   **Prog Ed:** Martin Asher
Ground: Lenton Lane Ground, Lenton Lane, Nr Clifton Bridge, Nottingham NG7 2SA   **(T)** 07712 530 706   **Capacity:**
Colours(change): Green/black/green (Yellow/green/yellow)

ADDITIONAL INFORMATION:
Previous League: Central Midlands

HOLBROOK SPORTS

Founded: 1931   Nickname:

Secretary: Paul Romney   **(T)** 07833 228230   **(E)**
Chairman: Howard Williams   **Manager:** Leigh Grant   **Prog Ed:** Phil Alcock
Ground: JJN Ground, Shaw Lane, Holbrook, Derbyshire DE56 0TG   **(T)** 01332 880 259   **Capacity:**
Colours(change): All blue (Black & yellow/black/black)

ADDITIONAL INFORMATION:
Previous Names: Holbrook, Holbrook Miners Welfare
Previous League: Central Midlands

HOLWELL SPORTS

Founded: Nickname:

Secretary: Martin Rooney   **(T)** 07957 618046   **(E)** holwellsportsguy@btinternet.com
Chairman: Paul Teare   **Manager:** Simon Daws   **Prog Ed:** Martin Rooney
Ground: Welby Road, Asfordby Hill, Melton Mowbray, Leicestershire LE14 3RD   **(T)** 07523 427 450   **Capacity:**
Colours(change): Green & gold/green/green & gold (All sky blue)

ADDITIONAL INFORMATION:
Previous League: Leicestershire Senior

IBSTOCK UNITED

Founded: Nickname:

Secretary: Chris Pallett   **(T)** 07817 772 119   **(E)** chris_iufc@hotmail.co.uk
Chairman: **Manager:** Neil Scott   **Prog Ed:** Chris Pallett
Ground: The Welfare Ground, Leicester Road, Ibstock, Leicestershire LE67 6HN   **(T)** 01530 260656   **Capacity:**
Colours(change): Red & white/red/red (Blue & white/blue/blue)

ADDITIONAL INFORMATION:
Previous Name: Ibstock Welfare
Previous League: Leicestershire Senior

LUTTERWORTH ATHLETIC

Founded: 1993   Nickname:

Secretary: Mick English   **(T)** 07545 432 200
Chairman: Mick English   **Manager:** Lee English
Ground: Hall Park, Hall Lane, Bitteswell, Lutterworth LE17 4LN
Colours(change): Green & white/white/white (All red)

(E) mike622@btinternet.com
Prog Ed: Ed Robinson
(T) 07545 432 200   **Capacity:**

ADDITIONAL INFORMATION:
Previous League: Leicestershire Senior > 2012.

RADCLIFFE OLYMPIC

Founded: 1876   Nickname:

Secretary: Michael Bradley   **(T)** 07825 285024
Chairman: John Bower   **Manager:** Kevin Waddley
Ground: The Rec. Grd, Wharfe Lane, Radcliffe on Trent, Nottingham NG12 2AN
Colours(change): Blue & red/blue & red/blue (Red & black/red & black/black)

(E) knacks@hotmail.com
Prog Ed: Brendan Richardson
(T) 07825 285 024   **Capacity:**

ADDITIONAL INFORMATION:
Previous Leagues: Notts Alliance, Central Midlands

RADFORD

Founded: 1964   Nickname:

Secretary: John Holt   **(T)** 07508 384 276
Chairman: Bob Thomas   **Manager:** Iain McCulloch and Alf Stacey
Ground: Selhurst Street, Off Radford Road, Nottingham NG7 5EH
Colours(change): All claret (All sky blue)

(E) vote4holt@hotmail.co.uk
Prog Ed: John Holt
(T) 0115 942 3250   **Capacity:**

ADDITIONAL INFORMATION:
Previous League: Central Midlands

ST. ANDREWS

Founded: Nickname:

Secretary: Les Botting   **(T)** 07793 500 937
Chairman: Bill Wells   **Manager:** Clem Dublin
Ground: Canal Street, Aylestone, Leicester LE2 8LX
Colours(change): Black & white/black/black (All blue)

(E) standrewsfc@btconnect.com
Prog Ed: Darren Creed
(T) 0116 283 9298   **Capacity:**

ADDITIONAL INFORMATION:
Previous League: Leicestershire Senior

THURNBY NIRVANA

Founded: 2008   Nickname:

Secretary: Zak Hajat   **(T)** 07811 843 136
Chairman: Pat Darby   **Manager:** Damion Qualiey
Ground: Dakyn Road, Thurnby Lodge, Leicester LE5 2ED
Colours(change): All green (Red & black/black/black)

(E) nirvanafc@hotmail.com
Prog Ed: Chris Tonge
(T) 0116 243 3308   **Capacity:**

ADDITIONAL INFORMATION:
Previous Name: Thurnby Rangers and Leicester Nirvana merged to form today's club in 2008.
Previous League: Leicestershire Senior

Josh Royce scores the only goal of the game for Heanor Town against Blackwell Miners Welfare - a goal that secured the East Midlands League title.

Photo: Gordon Whittington.

EASTERN COUNTIES LEAGUE

Sponsored by: Ridgeons
Founded: 1935
Recent Champions:
2007: Wroxham
2008: Soham Town Rangers
2009: Lowestoft Town
2010: Needham Market
2011: Leiston

ridgeonsleague.co.uk

LEAGUE CUP

PRELIMINARY ROUND
Cambridge University Press 4-1 Long Melford
FC Clacton 3-1 Woodbridge Town
Haverhill Rovers 1-0 CRC
Ipswich Wanderers 3-7 Hadleigh United
March Town United 2-4 Ely City
Walsham-le-Willows 4-2 Great Yarmouth Town
ROUND 1
Dereham Town 1-0 Ely City
Diss Town 1-2 Gorleston
Downham Town 1-4 Wisbech Town
FC Clacton 3-0 Wivenhoe Town
Godmanchester Rovers 4-0 Halstead Town
Hadleigh United 2-1 Brantham Athletic
Haverhill Rovers 3-1 Cambridge University Press
Mildenhall Town 5-0 Swaffham Town
Newmarket Town 0-2 Team Bury
Norwich United 1-1 Walsham-le-Willows
(Walsham win on penalties)
Stanway Rovers 2-0 Brightlingsea Regent
Stowmarket Town 0-3 Kirkley & Pakefield
Thetford Town 1-2 Fakenham Town
Whitton United 1-3 Felixstowe & Walton United
Wroxham WO Debenham LC
ROUND 2
Cornard United 0-2 Felixstowe & Walton United
Dereham Town 2-0 Fakenham Town
Godmanchester Rovers 1-2 Stanway Rovers
Hadleigh United 1-6 Haverhill Rovers
Mildenhall Town 0-1 Kirkley & Pakefield
Norwich United 1-0 Wisbech Town
Team Bury 2-3 FC Clacton
Wroxham 2-0 Gorleston
QUARTER FINALS
Felixstowe & Walton United 0-3 Stanway Rovers
Kirkley & Pakefield 1-3 Dereham Town
Norwich United 3-2 FC Clacton
Wroxham 2-1 Haverhill Rovers
SEMI-FINALS
Dereham Town 1-3 Stanway Rovers
Wroxham 0-2 Norwich United
FINAL
Norwich United 1-2 Stanway Rovers

PREMIER DIVISION

	P	W	D	L	F	A	Pts
1 (P) Wroxham	40	28	6	6	94	34	90
2 Ely City	40	25	7	8	81	60	82
3 Brantham Athletic	40	23	7	10	86	49	76
4 Wisbech Town	40	23	6	11	84	55	75
5 Stanway Rovers	40	21	7	12	86	57	70
6 Woodbridge Town	40	19	8	13	86	61	65
7 Mildenhall Town	40	19	7	14	76	60	64
8 CRC	40	18	9	13	79	62	63
9 Norwich United	40	18	9	13	57	50	63
10 Dereham Town	40	19	4	17	72	65	61
11 Hadleigh United	40	18	6	16	76	72	60
12 Gorleston	40	16	9	15	63	69	57
13 Kirkley & Pakefield	40	14	10	16	66	60	52
14 Haverhill Rovers	40	15	7	18	70	73	52
15 FC Clacton	40	16	4	20	69	78	52
16 Diss Town	40	14	8	18	37	48	50
17 Walsham-le-Willows	40	12	9	19	68	73	45
18 Felixstowe & Walton United	40	12	8	20	64	67	44
19 Wivenhoe Town	40	11	6	23	44	71	39
20 (R) Newmarket Town	40	3	7	30	36	117	16
21 (R) Great Yarmouth Town	40	2	4	34	32	145	10

PREMIER DIVISION	1	2	3	4	5	6	7	8	9	10	11	12	13	14	15	16	17	18	19	20	21
1 Brantham Athletic		2-0	2-2	1-0	2-2	2-1	3-1	2-2	5-0	0-6	3-1	2-1	4-0	8-1	1-2	4-2	0-3	2-2	0-3	1-0	1-0
2 CRC	1-0		3-1	0-2	3-3	0-2	2-0	0-2	2-0	3-3	2-3	5-4	1-3	3-0	2-2	1-1	3-0	3-3	6-0	1-2	1-0
3 Dereham Town	3-4	1-5		2-0	3-1	4-1	3-1	2-0	4-1	2-0	2-1	1-4	5-0	1-0	1-4	2-1	1-2	2-0	0-4	0-3	
4 Diss Town	1-0	1-0	2-0		0-0	1-0	0-0	1-2	4-2	0-1	1-0	2-1	1-3	1-3	0-0	0-3	3-2	0-2	2-1	1-1	0-1
5 Ely City	1-0	4-3	1-1	2-0		1-0	3-0	4-2	2-0	1-1	4-3	3-3	1-0	2-1	2-1	2-4	1-0	3-1	1-0	3-1	1-2
6 FC Clacton	1-1	3-1	2-0	1-0	0-2		0-2	0-2	5-0	2-3	2-0	1-1	2-4	2-1	0-1	1-0	0-6	1-5	4-1	2-4	1-0
7 Felixstowe & WaltonUnited	1-2	1-3	2-1	1-4	0-2	0-4		6-0	2-0	1-2	1-1	1-1	2-4	2-0	0-0	3-1	4-1	0-2	2-0	1-1	1-3
8 Gorleston	0-0	1-1	3-0	2-1	1-2	6-5	0-4		5-1	2-3	2-1	2-1	0-1	3-1	2-0	1-1	0-4	2-2	1-1	1-2	2-3
9 Great Yarmouth Town	4-3	0-2	1-2	1-1	2-4	2-8	1-7	2-2		1-3	0-3	0-4	0-4	3-1	0-5	0-4	1-3	0-1	2-2	1-8	0-7
10 Hadleigh United	0-3	0-6	4-1	2-0	1-3	2-3	1-0	3-0	2-1		3-1	3-1	2-4	3-0	1-3	3-0	1-2	3-1	1-6	1-6	0-2
11 Haverhill Rovers	0-3	5-3	0-3	2-0	5-1	5-2	3-1	2-2	3-0	0-0		2-2	1-0	6-1	0-3	3-2	3-0	0-5	0-2	1-4	1-2
12 Kirkley & Pakefield	1-0	0-2	1-1	1-0	1-2	1-2	2-1	1-3	2-0	5-2	3-0		0-3	0-0	1-1	1-3	4-3	4-2	3-0	1-1	0-1
13 Mildenhall Town	0-1	1-1	1-3	2-1	2-5	1-2	1-0	1-1	4-1	1-1	0-2	3-0		1-1	5-4	2-1	9-0	0-0	2-1	1-3	
14 Newmarket Town	0-6	0-0	0-3	0-0	0-3	1-3	4-1	0-1	6-1	1-3	0-0	0-2	1-1		2-3	0-2	1-4	2-5	1-3	4-5	0-4
15 Norwich United	0-4	1-1	2-1	0-1	2-0	3-1	1-3	2-0	2-0	1-1	2-2	1-1	1-0	3-0		1-2	2-1	0-3	3-2	2-1	0-1
16 Stanway Rovers	3-1	1-2	3-0	1-1	1-3	5-1	2-6	2-1	6-1	2-0	1-4	2-0	3-0	3-1	0-1		1-1	3-1	2-1	0-2	2-2
17 Walsham-le-Willows	0-5	1-2	1-1	2-2	0-2	2-2	1-1	0-2	5-0	0-0	2-1	0-3	2-2	0-3	1-1		1-2	3-1	3-1	3-2	
18 Wisbech Town	0-1	1-3	0-3	0-1	2-1	1-1	0-0	3-1	2-0	4-1	1-2	2-1	4-0	4-0	3-1	5-2		3-0	0-0	1-2	
19 Wivenhoe Town	1-3	1-0	0-3	0-2	4-1	2-0	0-4	2-0	2-0	2-1	1-1	1-6	1-4	4-0	2-0	0-2	1-1	0-1		0-0	0-2
20 Woodbridge Town	2-3	1-2	2-0	1-0	6-0	0-2	3-1	1-2	2-2	1-6	5-2	0-1	1-0	5-0	4-2	1-1	1-5	1-4	3-2		0-0
21 Wroxham	1-1	6-0	2-1	5-0	2-2	3-1	3-3	1-2	6-1	3-2	2-0	0-0	2-4	7-0	1-0	2-0	2-1	2-1	1-0	3-0	

EASTERN COUNTIES - STEP 5/6

DIVISION ONE	P	W	D	L	F	A	Pts
1 (P) Godmanchester Rovers	30	24	4	2	94	26	76
2 (P) Thetford Town	30	25	1	4	86	24	76
3 Whitton United	30	20	6	4	67	29	66
4 March Town United	30	16	4	10	58	30	52
5 Brightlingsea Regent	30	17	1	12	55	47	52
6 Halstead Town	30	15	5	10	65	46	50
7 Debenham LC	30	15	3	12	54	48	48
8 Cambridge University Press (-1)	30	12	6	12	46	42	41
9 Long Melford	30	12	2	16	46	60	38
10 Team Bury	30	11	3	16	46	45	36
11 Fakenham Town	30	10	6	14	44	48	36
12 Ipswich Wanderers	30	11	2	17	47	78	35
13 Swaffham Town	30	10	2	18	45	75	32
14 Downham Town	30	6	6	18	32	66	24
15 Stowmarket Town	30	5	3	22	42	76	18
16 Cornard United	30	2	4	24	23	110	10

DIVISION ONE LEAGUE CUP

PRELIMINARY ROUND
Cornard United 2-2 Brightlingsea Regent
(Cornard win on penalties)

ROUND 1
Cornard United 0-4 Whitton United
Cambridge University Press 7-1 Downham Town
Debenham LC 1-0 Halstead Town
Fakenham Town 0-5 Godmanchester Rovers
Ipswich Wanderers 1-5 Stowmarket Town
Long Melford 2-2 Team Bury
(Team Bury win on penalties)
Swaffham Town 0-5 Thetford Town

QUARTER FINALS
Debenham LC 2-3 Godmanchester Rovers
Stowmarket Town 1-2 Whitton United
Team Bury 3-4 Cambridge University Press
Thetford Town 0-1 March Town United

SEMI-FINALS
Godmanchester Rovers 2-0 March Town United
Whitton United 2-1 Cambridge University Press

FINAL
Godmanchester Rovers 1-0 Whitton United

DIVISION ONE	1	2	3	4	5	6	7	8	9	10	11	12	13	14	15	16
1 Brightlingsea Regent		0-1	2-0	2-3	6-1	1-0	3-2	3-0	2-1	0-1	1-3	2-1	3-2	4-0	0-1	2-1
2 Cambridge University Press	2-1		2-1	0-3	3-3	1-1	1-2	1-3	2-3	2-3	1-0	4-1	2-3	4-1	1-3	0-1
3 Cornard United	2-4	0-5		2-4	2-0	1-3	1-7	3-3	3-0	0-4	0-2	0-3	2-3	0-4	0-5	0-8
4 Debenham LC	2-3	0-2	1-1		1-1	0-2	0-5	3-2	2-3	2-0	2-1	2-1	3-1	3-1	1-5	0-1
5 Downham Town	1-2	0-2	2-0	1-2		0-1	1-1	2-0	6-2	3-2	0-7	2-1	2-2	0-1	1-2	0-2
6 Fakenham Town	1-0	2-2	6-1	0-3	1-2		0-0	0-1	6-2	3-0	3-2	1-1	5-0	2-1	0-4	0-2
7 Godmanchester Rovers	2-0	2-0	10-0	1-0	2-0	2-0		3-3	3-0	5-1	0-3	3-1	7-1	5-3	2-0	5-0
8 Halstead Town	4-0	2-0	4-0	3-2	6-0	2-1	1-2		1-1	4-1	1-1	1-2	4-1	2-1	1-3	1-1
9 Ipswich Wanderers	2-1	0-2	1-1	2-4	6-2	1-0	0-3	0-5		2-0	0-4	1-0	3-2	0-2	1-4	2-1
10 Long Melford	1-3	2-2	3-1	1-2	2-0	1-1	1-3	1-0	3-2		2-0	3-2	2-1	2-0	1-3	1-2
11 March Town United	1-2	1-1	4-0	1-0	2-0	2-0	0-1	3-1	4-1	1-0		2-1	1-3	2-0	2-0	2-2
12 Stowmarket Town	4-0	0-1	2-0	1-4	1-1	5-0	1-4	3-4	0-4	3-4	1-1		0-2	0-4	1-4	2-4
13 Swaffham Town	1-2	1-0	1-1	1-4	1-0	2-1	1-6	0-3	2-4	4-3	1-5	5-2		0-2	1-2	1-2
14 Team Bury	0-3	0-1	4-0	1-1	3-0	3-3	1-2	1-2	5-1	1-0	2-0	3-1	0-1		1-1	0-2
15 Thetford Town	4-0	2-0	10-0	1-0	2-0	4-1	1-2	5-0	5-2	3-1	3-1	5-1	1-0	1-0		2-0
16 Whitton United	3-3	1-1	3-1	2-0	1-1	2-0	2-2	2-1	3-0	5-0	1-0	5-0	3-1	2-1	3-0	

BRANTHAM ATHLETIC
Founded: 1887 Nickname:

Secretary: Barry Felgate **(T)** 07890 130583 **(E)** branthamathfc@hotmail.co.uk
Chairman: Peter Crowhurst **Manager:** Tony Hall **Prog Ed:** Barry Felgate
Ground: Brantham Leisure Centre, New Village, Brantham CO11 1RZ. **(T)** 01206 392 506
Capacity: 1,200 **Seats:** 200 **Covered:** 200 **Midweek Matchday:** Tuesday **Clubhouse:** Yes **Shop:**

Colours(change):	All blue. (Red and black/black/black)
Previous Names:	Brantham & Stutton United 1996-98.
Previous Leagues:	Eastern Counties. Suffolk & Ipswich.
Records:	Att: 1,700 v VS Rugby, FA Vase 5R 1982-83.
Senior Honours:	Suffolk & Ipswich Senior League Champions 2007-08.

10 YEAR RECORD

02-03	03-04	04-05	05-06	06-07	07-08	08-09	09-10	10-11	11-12
		S&I 1 2	S&I S 14	S&I S 4	S&I S 1	EC1 8	EC1 3	ECP 13	ECP 3

CRC
Founded: Nickname:

Secretary: Julie Ankers **(T)** 07782 120 354 **(E)** julieankers@cambridge-united.co.uk
Chairman: Robert Smith **Manager:** Mark Bonner **Prog Ed:**
Ground: Cambridge Utd FC, R Costings Abbey Stad, Newmarket Road CB5 8LN **(T)** 07782 120 354
Capacity: 9,217 **Seats:** 200 **Covered:** Yes **Midweek Matchday:** Wednesday **Clubhouse:** Yes **Shop:** Yes

Colours(change):	Amber/black/black (All white)
Previous Names:	None.
Previous Leagues:	None
Records:	
Senior Honours:	

10 YEAR RECORD

02-03	03-04	04-05	05-06	06-07	07-08	08-09	09-10	10-11	11-12
				ECP 17	ECP 13	ECP 2	ECP 2	ECP 11	ECP 8

DEREHAM TOWN
Founded: 1884 Nickname: Magpies

Secretary: Nigel Link **(T)** 07885 144039 **(E)** patnige1954@fsmail.net
Chairman: Mike Baldry **Manager:** Matt Henman **Prog Ed:** Barnes Print
Ground: Aldiss Park, Norwich Road, Dereham, Norfolk NR20 3PX **(T)** 01362 690 460
Capacity: 3,000 **Seats:** 50 **Covered:** 500 **Midweek Matchday:** Tuesday **Clubhouse:** Yes **Shop:** Yes

Colours(change):	White & black/black/black. (Green & white/green/green)
Previous Names:	Dereham and Dereham Hobbies.
Previous Leagues:	Norwich District. Dereham & District. Norfolk & Suffolk. Anglian Comb.
Records:	Att: 3000 v Norwich City, Friendly, 07/2001.
Senior Honours:	Anglian Combination Division 1 Champions 1989-90. Premier Division 97-98. Norfolk Senior Cup 2005-06, 06-07.

10 YEAR RECORD

02-03	03-04	04-05	05-06	06-07	07-08	08-09	09-10	10-11	11-12
ECP 19	ECP 18	ECP 15	ECP 12	ECP 6	ECP 4	ECP 4	ECP 10	ECP 2	ECP 10

DISS TOWN
Founded: 1888 Nickname: Tangerines

Secretary: Steve Flatman **(T)** 07855 531 341 **(E)** pam@dissfc.wanadoo.co.uk
Chairman: Richard Upson **Manager:** Robert Taylor **Prog Ed:** Gary Enderby
Ground: Brewers Green Lane, Diss, Norfolk IP22 4QP **(T)** 01379 651 223
Capacity: **Seats:** **Covered:** **Midweek Matchday:** Tuesday **Clubhouse:** Yes **Shop:**

Colours(change):	Tangerine/navy/tangerine (Sky blue/navy/sky blue)
Previous Names:	
Previous Leagues:	Anglian Combination
Records:	1,731 v Atherton LR, FA Vase Semi Final, 19.03.94.
Senior Honours:	Eastern Counties Division One 1991-92. FA Vase winners 1993-94.

10 YEAR RECORD

02-03	03-04	04-05	05-06	06-07	07-08	08-09	09-10	10-11	11-12
ECP 5	ECP 4	ECP 12	ECP 11	ECP 20	EC1 4	EC1 9	EC1 5	EC1 3	ECP 16

ELY CITY

Founded: 1885 Nickname: Robins

Secretary: Derek Oakey **(T)** 07720 542 882 **(E)** derek.oakey@tesco.net
Chairman: Robert Button **Manager:** Alan Alsop **Prog Ed:** Barnes Print
Ground: Unwin Sports Ground, Downham Road, Ely CB6 2SH **(T)** 01353 662 035
Capacity: 1,500 **Seats:** 150 **Covered:** 350 **Midweek Matchday:** Tuesday **Clubhouse:** Yes **Shop:** Yes

Colours(change): All red. (All blue).
Previous Names: None.
Previous Leagues: Peterborough. Central Alliance.
Records: **Att:** 260 v Soham, Eastern Counties Div.1, 12.04.93.
Senior Honours: Cambridgeshire Senior Cup 1947-48. Eastern Counties Division 1 1996-97.

10 YEAR RECORD

02-03		03-04		04-05		05-06		06-07		07-08		08-09		09-10		10-11		11-12	
ECP	23	EC1	10	EC1	9	EC1	7	EC1	4	EC1	2	ECP	14	ECP	9	ECP	15	ECP	2

FC CLACTON

Founded: 1892 Nickname: The Seasiders

Secretary: Barry Leatherdale **(T)** 07545 998 242 **(E)** secretary@fcclacton.com
Chairman: David Ballard **Manager:** Andy Taylor **Prog Ed:** Martin Oswick
Ground: Rush Green Bowl, Rush Green Rd, Clacton-on-Sea CO16 7BQ **(T)** 07792 352 187
Capacity: 3,000 **Seats:** 200 **Covered:** Yes **Midweek Matchday:** Tuesday **Clubhouse:** Yes **Shop:** Yes

Colours(change): White & royal blue/royal blue/royal blue. (Yellow/black/black).
Previous Names: Clacton Town > 2007
Previous Leagues: Eastern Counties. Essex County. Southern League.
Records: **Att:** 3,505 v Romford, FA Cup 1952 at Old Road.
Senior Honours: Eastern Counties Division 1 1994-95, 98-99.

10 YEAR RECORD

02-03		03-04		04-05		05-06		06-07		07-08		08-09		09-10		10-11		11-12	
ECP	11	ECP	6	ECP	8	ECP	22	ECP	21	EC1	10	EC1	7	EC1	2	ECP	16	ECP	15

FELIXSTOWE & WALTON UNITED

Founded: 2000 Nickname: Seasiders

Secretary: Andy Wilding **(T)** 07785 386 072 **(E)** andy@globexfm.co.uk
Chairman: Andy Wilding **Manager:** Steve Buckle **Prog Ed:** Adam Whalley
Ground: Goldstar Ground, Dellwood Avenue, Felixstowe IP11 9HT **(T)** 01394 282 917
Capacity: 2,000 **Seats:** 200 **Covered:** 200 **Midweek Matchday:** Tuesday **Clubhouse:** Yes **Shop:** Yes

Colours(change): Red & white stripes/white/red. (Yellow & blue/yellow/yellow).
Previous Names: Felixstowe Port & Town and Walton United merged in July 2000.
Previous Leagues: None
Records:
Senior Honours:

10 YEAR RECORD

02-03		03-04		04-05		05-06		06-07		07-08		08-09		09-10		10-11		11-12	
EC1	16	EC1	15	EC1	17	EC1	2	ECP	13	ECP	8	ECP	12	ECP	7	ECP	18	ECP	18

GODMANCHESTER ROVERS

Founded: 1911 Nickname: Goody/Rovers

Secretary: Roger Carpenter **(T)** 07552 277 133 **(E)** rogercc1@virginmedia.com
Chairman: Keith Gabb **Manager:** David Hurst **Prog Ed:** Sue Hurst
Ground: Bearscroft Lane, Godmanchester, Huntingdon, Cambs PE29 2LQ **(T)** 07774 830507
Capacity: **Seats:** **Covered:** **Midweek Matchday:** Wednesday **Clubhouse:** Yes **Shop:**

Colours(change): Blue & white stripes/blue/blue (Red & white stripes/red/red)
Previous Names:
Previous Leagues:
Records: **Att:** 138 v Cambridge City Reserves, Dec. 2003.
Senior Honours: Eastern Counties League Division One 2011-12.

10 YEAR RECORD

02-03		03-04		04-05		05-06		06-07		07-08		08-09		09-10		10-11		11-12	
EC1	12	EC1	7	EC1	20	EC1	14	EC1	17	EC1	16	EC1	10	EC1	12	EC1	9	EC1	1

GORLESTON

Founded: 1887 **Nickname:**

Secretary: Ann Santon **(T)** 07597 926 329 **(E)** santonmicks@aol.com

Chairman: Alan Gordon **Manager:** Richard Daniels **Prog Ed:** Colin Bray

Ground: Emerald Park, Woodfarm Lane, Gorleston, Norfolk NR31 9AQ **(T)** 01493 602 802

Capacity: **Seats:** Yes **Covered:** Yes **Midweek Matchday:** Tuesday **Clubhouse:** Yes **Shop:**

Colours(change): All green (Red/black/black)
Previous Names:
Previous Leagues: Anglian Combination
Records: **Record Att:** 4,473 v Orient, FA Cup 1st Round, 29.11.51.
Senior Honours: Norfolk & Suff. Lge (x 7). Norfolk Senior Cup (x 15). Anglian Comb 1968-69. Eastern Counties 1952-53, 72-73, 79-80, 80-81.
Division One 1995-96, 2010-11.

10 YEAR RECORD

02-03		03-04		04-05		05-06		06-07		07-08		08-09		09-10		10-11		11-12	
ECP	15	ECP	20	ECP	21	EC1	18	EC1	14	EC1	8	EC1	6	EC1	4	EC1	1	ECP	12

HADLEIGH UNITED

Founded: 1892 **Nickname:** Brettsiders

Secretary: Louise Hay **(T)** 07962 274 986 **(E)** louise.hay1@yahoo.co.uk

Chairman: Rolf Beggerow **Manager:** Stuart Crawford **Prog Ed:** Chris Towell

Ground: Millfield, Tinkers Lane, Duke St, Hadleigh IP7 5NF **(T)** 01473 822 165

Capacity: 3,000 **Seats:** 250 **Covered:** 500 **Midweek Matchday:** Tuesday **Clubhouse:** Yes **Shop:**

Colours(change): White/blue/blue (All blue)
Previous Names: None
Previous Leagues: Suffolk & Ipswich
Records: **Att:** 518 v Halstead Town, FA Vase replay, 17.01.95.
Senior Honours: Suffolk & Ipswich League Champions 1953-54, 56-57, 73-74, 76-77, 78-79.
Suffolk Senior Cup 1968-69, 71-72, 82-83, 2003-04. Eastern Counties League Champions 1993-94.

10 YEAR RECORD

02-03		03-04		04-05		05-06		06-07		07-08		08-09		09-10		10-11		11-12	
EC1	4	EC1	18	EC1	16	EC1	21	EC1	9	EC1	5	EC1	2	ECP	18	ECP	9	ECP	11

HAVERHILL ROVERS

Founded: 1886 **Nickname:** Rovers

Secretary: Gary Brown **(T)** 07894 553 267 **(E)** gabrown306@hotmail.com

Chairman: Michael Tokley **Manager:** Peter Betts **Prog Ed:** Gary Brown

Ground: The New Croft, Chalkstone Way, Haverhill, Suffolk CB9 0BW **(T)** 01440 702 137

Capacity: 3,000 **Seats:** 200 **Covered:** 200 **Midweek Matchday:** Tuesday **Clubhouse:** Yes **Shop:**

Colours(change): All red. (All green).
Previous Names: None.
Previous Leagues: East Anglian. Essex & Suffolk Border.
Records:
Senior Honours: Essex & Suffolk Border League Champions 1947-48, 62-63, 63-64.
Eastern Counties League Cup 1964-65, League Champions 78-79. Suffolk Senior Cup 1995-96.

10 YEAR RECORD

02-03		03-04		04-05		05-06		06-07		07-08		08-09		09-10		10-11		11-12	
EC1	10	EC1	11	EC1	5	EC1	8	EC1	2	ECP	10	ECP	21	ECP	12	ECP	8	ECP	14

KIRKLEY & PAKEFIELD

Founded: 1886 **Nickname:** The Kirks

Secretary: Barrie Atkins **(T)** 07970 659 001 **(E)** atkins_2006@tiscali.co.uk

Chairman: Robert Jenkerson **Manager:** Paul Tong **Prog Ed:** Jak Ruby

Ground: K. & P. Community Sports & S. Club, Walmer Rd, Lowestoft NR33 7LE **(T)** 01502 513 549

Capacity: 2,000 **Seats:** 150 **Covered:** 150 **Midweek Matchday:** Wednesday **Clubhouse:** Yes **Shop:** Yes

Colours(change): Royal blue & maroon/royal/royal. (All yellow).
Previous Names: Kirkley. Kirkley & Waveney 1929-33. Merged with Pakefield in 2007.
Previous Leagues: Norfolk & Suffolk. Anglian Combination.
Records: **Att:** 1,125 v Lowestoft Town. **Goalscorer:** Barry Dale - 241. **Apps:** Barry Dale - 495.
Senior Honours: Suffolk Senior Cup 1900-01, 01-02, 24-25, 00-01, 01-02. Anglian Combination League 2001-02, 02-03.

10 YEAR RECORD

02-03		03-04		04-05		05-06		06-07		07-08		08-09		09-10		10-11		11-12	
AngP	1	EC1	5	EC1	3	ECP	14	ECP	7	ECP	6	ECP	6	ECP	4	ECP	12	ECP	13

MILDENHALL TOWN

Founded: 1898   **Nickname:** The Hall

Secretary: Brian Hensby   **(T)** 07932 043 261   **(E)** bhensby@talktalk.net

Chairman: Martin Tuck   **Manager:** Christian Appleford   **Prog Ed:** Frank Marshall

Ground: Recreation Way, Mildenhall, Suffolk IP28 7HG   **(T)** 01638 713 449

Capacity: 2,00   **Seats:** 50   **Covered:** 200   **Midweek Matchday:** Tuesday   **Clubhouse:** Yes   **Shop:** Yes

Colours(change): Amber/black/black. (Red & white/white/red).
Previous Names: None
Previous Leagues: Bury & District. Cambridgeshire. Cambridgeshire Premier.
Records: **Att:** 450 v Derby County, Friendly, July 2001.
Senior Honours:

10 YEAR RECORD

02-03		03-04		04-05		05-06		06-07		07-08		08-09		09-10		10-11		11-12	
ECP	10	ECP	12	ECP	6	ECP	5	ECP	2	ECP	5	ECP	11	ECP	6	ECP	5	ECP	7

NORWICH UNITED

Founded: 1903   **Nickname:** Planters

Secretary: Keith Cutmore   **(T)** 07788 437 515   **(E)** secretary.nufc@hotmail.co.uk

Chairman: John Hilditch   **Manager:** Paul Chick   **Prog Ed:** Barnes Print

Ground: Plantation Park, Blofield, Norwich NR13 4PL   **(T)** 01603 716 963

Capacity: 3,000   **Seats:** 100   **Covered:** 1,000   **Midweek Matchday:** Tuesday   **Clubhouse:** Yes   **Shop:** Yes

Colours(change): Yellow & blue/blue/blue. (All red)
Previous Names: Poringland & District > 1987
Previous Leagues: Norwich & District. Anglian Combination
Records: **Att:** 401 v Wroxham, Eastern Co. Lge, 1991-92. **Goalscorer:** M. Money. **Apps:** Tim Sayer.
Senior Honours: Anglian Combination Senior Cup 1983-84. Eastern Counties League Division One 1990-91, 01-02.

10 YEAR RECORD

02-03		03-04		04-05		05-06		06-07		07-08		08-09		09-10		10-11		11-12	
ECP	16	ECP	11	ECP	14	ECP	20	ECP	16	ECP	15	ECP	19	ECP	15	ECP	6	ECP	9

STANWAY ROVERS

Founded: 1956   **Nickname:** Rovers

Secretary: Paul Rogers   **(T)** 07986 615 481   **(E)** paul.rogers2@ntlworld.com

Chairman: Roy Brett   **Manager:** Steve Pitt   **Prog Ed:**

Ground: Hawthorns, New Farm Road, Stanway, Colchester CO3 0PG   **(T)** 01206 578 187

Capacity: 1,500   **Seats:** 100   **Covered:** 250   **Midweek Matchday:** Wednesday   **Clubhouse:** Yes   **Shop:** Yes

Colours(change): Amber & black/black/black. (Claret & sky/sky/claret).
Previous Names: None.
Previous Leagues: Colchester & East Essex. Essex & Suffolk Border.
Records: **Att:** 210 v Harwich & P, Eastern Co. Lge Div.1, 2004.
Senior Honours: Eastern Counties League Division 1 Champions 2005-06, League Cup 2008-09.

10 YEAR RECORD

02-03		03-04		04-05		05-06		06-07		07-08		08-09		09-10		10-11		11-12	
EC1	5	EC1	4	EC1	6	EC1	1	ECP	14	ECP	7	ECP	9	ECP	5	ECP	7	ECP	5

THETFORD TOWN

Founded: 1883   **Nickname:**

Secretary: Bob Richards   **(T)** 07795 255 160   **(E)** bobrich60@talktalk.net

Chairman: Mick Bailey   **Manager:** Mark Scott   **Prog Ed:** Barnes Print

Ground: Recreation Ground, Mundford Road, Thetford, Norfolk IP24 1NB   **(T)** 01842 766 120

Capacity: **Seats:**   **Covered:**   **Midweek Matchday:** Tuesday   **Clubhouse:** Yes   **Shop:**

Colours(change): Claret/blue/blue (Blue & claret/claret/claret)
Previous Names:
Previous Leagues: Founder member of Eastern Counties League
Records: **Att:** 394 v Diss Town, Norfolk Senior Cup, 1991.
Senior Honours: Norfolk Senior Cup 1947-48, 90-91. Norfolk & Suffolk League 1954-55.

10 YEAR RECORD

02-03		03-04		04-05		05-06		06-07		07-08		08-09		09-10		10-11		11-12	
EC1	17	EC1	19	EC1	19	EC1	22	EC1	11	EC1	13	EC1	16	EC1	11	EC1	5	EC1	2

WALSHAM-LE-WILLOWS

Founded: 1888   Nickname:

Secretary: Gordon Ross   **(T)** 07742 111 892   **(E)** gordonaross@aol.com
Chairman: Mike Powles   **Manager:** Paul Smith   **Prog Ed:** Barnes Print
Ground: The Meadow, Summer Road, Walsham-le-Willows IP31 3AH   **(T)** 01359 259 298
Capacity: **Seats:** 100   **Covered:** 100   **Midweek Matchday:** Wednesday   **Clubhouse:** Yes   **Shop:**

Colours(change): White with red stripe/red/red (Light blue & white/black/blue)
Previous Names: None
Previous Leagues: Bury & District. Suffolk & Ipswich.
Records:
Senior Honours: Suffolk & Ipswich Senior League Champions 2001-02, 02-03. Suffolk Senior Cup 2005-06.
Eastern Counties League Division 1 Champions 2006-07.

10 YEAR RECORD

02-03		03-04		04-05		05-06		06-07		07-08		08-09		09-10		10-11		11-12	
S&I S	1	S&I S	2	EC1	4	EC1	5	EC1	1	ECP	16	ECP	10	ECP	13	ECP	17	ECP	17

WISBECH TOWN

Founded: 1920   Nickname: Fenmen

Secretary: Colin Gant   **(T)** 07803 021 699   **(E)** colin@gant5366.freeserve.co.uk
Chairman: Barry Carter   **Manager:** Steve Appleby   **Prog Ed:** Spencer Larham
Ground: The Fenland Stadium, Lynn Road, Wisbech PE14 7AM   **(T)** 01945 581 511
Capacity: **Seats:** 118   **Covered:** Yes   **Midweek Matchday:** Tuesday   **Clubhouse:**   **Shop:**

Colours(change): All red. (Yellow/green/yellow).
Previous Names: None
Previous Leagues: East Midlands. Peterborough. United Co. Eastern Co. Midland. Southern.
Records: **Att:** 8,044 v Peterborough Utd, Midland Lge 25/08/1957 **Goalscorer:** Bert Titmarsh - 246 (1931-37) **Apps:** Jamie Brighty - 731
Senior Honours: United Counties League Champions 1946-47, 47-48. Southern League Division 1 1961-62.
Eastern Counties League 1971-72, 76-77, 90-91, League Cup 2010-11. East Anglian Cup 1987-88.

10 YEAR RECORD

02-03		03-04		04-05		05-06		06-07		07-08		08-09		09-10		10-11		11-12	
ECP	6	ECP	14	ECP	16	ECP	4	ECP	11	ECP	12	ECP	16	ECP	11	ECP	4	ECP	4

WIVENHOE TOWN

Founded: 1925   Nickname: The Dragons

Secretary: Lorraine Rogers   **(T)** 07531 134 001   **(E)** lorraine.rogers@btopenworld.com
Chairman: Mo Osman   **Manager:** Mo Osman   **Prog Ed:** Richard Charnock
Ground: Broad Lane, Elmstead Road, Wivenhoe CO7 7HA   **(T)** 01206 827 144
Capacity: 2876   **Seats:** 161   **Covered:** 1300   **Midweek Matchday:** Tuesday   **Clubhouse:** Yes   **Shop:** Yes

Colours(change): All blue (Yellow with blue sleevs/yellow/yellow)
Previous Names: Wivenhoe Rangers.
Previous Leagues: Brightlingsea & District, Colchester & East Essex. Essex & Suffolk Border, Essex Senior, Isthmian
Records: **Att:** 1,912 v Runcorn, FA Trophy, 1st Round, Feb. 1990. **Goalscorer:** (258 in 350 games). **Apps:** Keith Bain (538).
Senior Honours: Isthmian Division 2 North 1987-88. Division 1 1989-90. Essex Senior Trophy 1987-88.

10 YEAR RECORD

02-03		03-04		04-05		05-06		06-07		07-08		08-09		09-10		10-11		11-12	
Isth1N	21	Isth1N	17	SthE	5	SthE	6	Isth1N	11	Isth1N	22	ECP	17	ECP	20	ECP	20	ECP	19

WOODBRIDGE TOWN

Founded: 1885   Nickname: The Woodpeckers

Secretary: Allan Kitchen   **(T)** 07951 217 060   **(E)** allan.kitchen@btinternet.com
Chairman: John Beecroft   **Manager:** Mark Scopes   **Prog Ed:** Richard Scott
Ground: Notcutts Park, Fynn Road, Woodbridge IP12 4LS   **(T)** 01394 385 308
Capacity: 3,000   **Seats:** 50   **Covered:** 200   **Midweek Matchday:** Wednesday   **Clubhouse:** Yes   **Shop:** No

Colours(change): Black & white stripes/black/black. (All red).
Previous Names: None.
Previous Leagues: Ipswich & District. Suffolk & Ipswich.
Records: **Att:** 3,000 v Arsenal, for the opening of the floodlights, 02.10.90.
Senior Honours: Suffolk Senior Cup 1885, 77-78, 92-93, 93-94.
Ipswich & District Senior Champions 1912-13. Suffolk & Ipswich Senior 1988-89.

10 YEAR RECORD

02-03		03-04		04-05		05-06		06-07		07-08		08-09		09-10		10-11		11-12	
ECP	20	ECP	17	ECP	17	ECP	16	ECP	9	ECP	17	ECP	18	ECP	19	ECP	10	ECP	6

DIVISION ONE

BRIGHTLINGSEA REGENT

Founded: Pre 1908   Nickname: The Tics

Secretary: Tom Rothery   **(T)** 07805 094 697   **(E)** t.rothery@sky.com
Chairman: Terry Doherty   **Manager:** James Webster   **Prog Ed:**
Ground: North Road, Brightlingsea, Essex CO7 0PL   **(T)** 01206 304 199   **Capacity:**
Colours(change): Red & black stripes/red/red

ADDITIONAL INFORMATION:
Previous Lge: Essex & Suffolk Border > 2011.
Honours: Essex & Suffolk Border League 2010-11.

CAMBRIDGE UNIVERSITY PRESS

Founded: 1893   Nickname:

Secretary: Gary Crick   **(T)** 07728 344 088   **(E)** gary@cupfc.net
Chairman: Nigel Atkinson   **Manager:** Graham Daniels   **Prog Ed:**
Ground: The Glassworld Stadium, Bridge Road, Impington, Cambridge CB24 9PH   **(T)** 01223 237 373   **Capacity:** 3,250
Colours(change): Sky blue/navy blue/sky blue (Yellow/black/yellow)

ADDITIONAL INFORMATION:
Honours: Cambridgeshire Senior Cup 1913-14. Cambridgeshire Premier League 1934-35.

CORNARD UNITED

Founded: 1964   Nickname: Ards

Secretary: Chris Symes   **(T)** 07811 096 832   **(E)** chrissymes@hotmail.com
Chairman: Wayne Pannell   **Manager:** Chris Symes   **Prog Ed:** Chris Symes
Ground: Blackhouse Lane, Great Cornard, Sudbury, Suffolk CO10 0NL   **(T)** 07811 096 832   **Capacity:**
Colours(change): Blue & white/blue/blue (Gold & black/black/black)

ADDITIONAL INFORMATION:
Record Att: 400 v Colchester United 1997. **Goalscorer:** Andy Smiles. **Apps:** Keith Featherstone.
Honours: Essex & Suffolk Border League Champions 1988-89. Eastern Counties Div. 1 1989-90. Suffolk Senior Cup 89-90.

DEBENHAM LC

Founded: 1991   Nickname: The Hornets

Secretary: Dan Snell   **(T)** 07840 246 837   **(E)** snelly1992@hotmail.co.uk
Chairman: Stephen Anderson   **Manager:** Dale Vince   **Prog Ed:** Martyn Clarke
Ground: Debenham Leisure Centre, Gracechurch Street, Debenham IP14 6BL   **(T)** 01728 861 101   **Capacity:** 1,000
Colours(change): Yellow/black/yellow. (All navy blue).

ADDITIONAL INFORMATION: Record Att: 400. **Goalscorer:** Lee Briggs. **Apps:** Steve Nelson.
Previous Name: Debenham Angels > 2005.
Previous League: Suffolk & Ipswich > 2005.

DOWNHAM TOWN

Founded: 1881   Nickname: Town

Secretary: George Dickson   **(T)** 07834 329 781   **(E)** george.dickson@britishsugar.com
Chairman: Sandra Calvert   **Manager:** Garth Good   **Prog Ed:** Barnes Print
Ground: Memorial Field, Lynn Road, Downham Market PE38 9QE   **(T)** 01366 388 424   **Capacity:**
Colours(change): All red (All blue)

ADDITIONAL INFORMATION:
Record Att: 325 v Wells Town, Norfolk Senior Cup, 1998-99. **Honours:** Peterborough Senior Cup 1962, 63, 67, 72, 87.
Peterborough League 1963, 74, 79, 87, 88. Norfolk Senior Cup 1964, 66.

FAKENHAM TOWN

Founded: 1884   Nickname: Ghosts

Secretary: Andrew Mitchell   **(T)** 07540 778 379   **(E)** andrewmitchell@fakenhamtownfc.co.uk
Chairman: Geoffrey Saunders   **Manager:** Wayne Anderson   **Prog Ed:** Barnes Print
Ground: Clipbush Park, Clipbush Lane, Fakenham, Norfolk NR21 8SW   **(T)** 07540 778 379   **Capacity:**
Colours(change): Amber & black stripes/black/amber (Blue & white stripes/blue/blue)

ADDITIONAL INFORMATION:
Record Att: 1,100 v Watford, official opening of new ground.
Honours: Norfolk Senior Cup 1970-71, 72-73, 73-74, 91-92, 93-94, 94-95.

GREAT YARMOUTH TOWN

Founded: 1897   Nickname:

Secretary: Len Beresford   **(T)** 07873 861 983   **(E)** sandysauce@hotmail.com
Chairman: Colin Jones   **Manager:** Mike Derbyshire   **Prog Ed:** Superjako
Ground: The Wellesley, Sandown Road, Great Yarmouth NR30 1EY   **(T)** 01493 656 099   **Capacity:** 3,600
Colours(change): Yellow & black stripes/black/yellow (All claret)

ADDITIONAL INFORMATION: Att: 8,944 v Crystal Palace FA Cup R1 52-53. **Goalscorer:** Gordon South - 298 (1927-47). **Apps:** Mark Vincent -
Eastern Counties League Champions 1968-69, Division 1 2009-10. Norfolk Senior Cup (x 12)

HALSTEAD TOWN
Founded: 1879 · Nickname: The Town

Secretary: Steve Webber **(T)** 07848 822 802 · **(E)** halsteadtownfc@aol.com
Chairman: Jimmy Holder **Manager:** Jimmy Holder · **Prog Ed:** Barnes Print
Ground: Rosemary Lane, Broton Industrial Estate, Halstead, Essex CO9 1HR · **(T)** 01787 472 082 · **Capacity:**
Colours(change): Black & white/black/black (All blue)

ADDITIONAL INFORMATION:
Record Att: 4,000 v Walthamstowe Avenue, Essex Senior Cup 1949.
Honours: Eastern Counties Champions 1994-95, 95-96. Div.1 2002-03. Essex Senior Trophy 1994-95, 96-97.

IPSWICH WANDERERS
Founded: 1983 · Nickname: Wanderers

Secretary: Paul Crickmore **(T)** 07577 745 778 · **(E)** iwfc@hotmail.co.uk
Chairman: Terry Fenwick **Manager:** Glenn Read · **Prog Ed:** Roger Wosahlo
Ground: SEH Sports Centre, Humber Doucy Lane, Ipswich IP4 3NR · **(T)** 01473 728 581 · **Capacity:**
Colours(change): Blue & white/blue/white (All orange)

ADDITIONAL INFORMATION:
Record Att: 335 v Woodbridge, Eastern Counties League 1993-94.
Honours: Eastern Counties Div.1 Champions 1997-98, 04-05.

LONG MELFORD
Founded: 1868 · Nickname: The Villagers

Secretary: Richard Powell **(T)** 07897 751 298 · **(E)** richard.j.powell@hotmail.co.uk
Chairman: Colin Woodhouse **Manager:** Robbie Benson · **Prog Ed:** Andy Cussans
Ground: Stoneylands Stadium, New Road, Long Melford, Suffolk CO10 9JY · **(T)** 01787 312 187 · **Capacity:**
Colours(change): Black & white stripes/black/black (All red)

ADDITIONAL INFORMATION:
Honours: Essex & Suffolk Border Champions x5. Suffolk Senior Cup x8.

MARCH TOWN UNITED
Founded: 1885 · Nickname: Hares

Secretary: Raymond Bennett **(T)** 07944 721 312 · **(E)** r.bennett639@btinternet.com
Chairman: Phil White **Manager:** Paul Crosbie · **Prog Ed:** Gary Wesley
Ground: GER Sports Ground, Robin Goodfellow Lane, March, Cambs PE15 8HS · **(T)** 01354 653 073 · **Capacity:**
Colours(change): Amber & black/black/black (All blue)

ADDITIONAL INFORMATION:
Record Att: 7,500 v King's Lynn, FA Cup 1956.
Honours: United Counties League 1953-54. Eastern Counties 1987-88.

NEWMARKET TOWN
Founded: 1877 · Nickname: The Jockeys

Secretary: Elaine Jeakins **(T)** 07801 815 682 · **(E)** elaine.jeakins@ntlworld.com
Chairman: John Olive **Manager:** Kevin Grainger · **Prog Ed:** Elaine Jeakins
Ground: Town Ground, Cricket Field Road, Off Cheveley Rd, Newmarket CB8 8BT · **(T)** 01638 663 637 · **Capacity:** 2,750
Colours(change): Yellow/blue/yellow (Blue/blue/yellow)

ADDITIONAL INFORMATION: **Att:** 2,701 v Abbey United (now Cambridge Utd) FA Cup, 01.10.49.
Suffolk Senior Cup 1934-35, 93-94. Suffolk Premier Cup 1993-94, 94-95, 96-97.
Eastern Counties League Division 1 2008-09.

SAFFRON WALDEN TOWN
Founded: 1872 · Nickname: The Bloods

Secretary: Brian Wilson **(T)** 07747 500 659 · **(E)** secretary@swtfc.com
Chairman: Cliff Treadwell **Manager:** Colin Wallington & Nick Smith · **Prog Ed:** Jim Duvall
Ground: 1 Catons Lane, Saffron Walden, Essex CB10 2DU · **(T)** 01799 520 980 · **Capacity:**
Colours(change): Red & black stripes/black/black & red (Blue & white hoops/white/blue & white)

ADDITIONAL INFORMATION:
Record Goalscorer: Alec Ramsey - 192. **Apps:** Les Page - 538. **Honours:** Essex Senior League 1973-74, 99-00.
Eastern Counties 1982-83. Essex Senior Challenge Trophy 1982-83, 83-84, 84-85.
Previous Lge: Eastern Counties > 2011. Folded in 2011 reformed for 2012-13 season.

STOWMARKET TOWN
Founded: 1883 · Nickname:

Secretary: TBC **(T)** 07747 774030 (Chairman) · **(E)** dofadult@stowmarkettownfc.co.uk
Chairman: Neil Sharp **Manager:** Shane Austin · **Prog Ed:** Alex Moss
Ground: Greens Meadow, Bury Road, Stowmarket, Suffolk IP14 1JQ · **(T)** 01449 612 533 · **Capacity:**
Colours(change): Gold & black/black/black (All red)

ADDITIONAL INFORMATION:
Previous League: Essex & Suffolk Border. **Record Att:** 1,200 v Ipswich Town, friendly, July 1994.
Honours: Suffolk Senior Cup x10

SWAFFHAM TOWN
Founded: 1892 **Nickname:** Pedlars

Secretary: Ray Ewart **(T)** 07990 526 744 **(E)** rayewart@aol.com
Chairman: Wayne Hardy **Manager:** Paul Hunt **Prog Ed:** Barnes Print
Ground: Shoemakers Lane, Swaffham, Norfolk PE37 7NT **(T)** 01760 722 700 **Capacity:**
Colours(change): Black & white stripes/black/black (All red)

ADDITIONAL INFORMATION:
Record Att: 250 v Downham Town, Eastern Counties League Cup, 03.09.91.
Honours: Eastern Counties Division 1 2000-01.

TEAM BURY
Founded: 2005 **Nickname:**

Secretary: Ross Wilding **(T)** 07971 199 810 **(E)** ross.wilding@wsc.ac.uk
Chairman: Alan Collen **Manager:** Ross Wilding **Prog Ed:** Ross Wilding
Ground: Bury Town FC, Ram Meadow, Cotton Lane, Bury St Edmunds IP33 1XP **(T)** 01284 754 721 **Capacity:**
Colours(change): All blue (All red)

ADDITIONAL INFORMATION:

WHITTON UNITED
Founded: 1926 **Nickname:**

Secretary: Phil Pemberton **(T)** 07429 116 538 **(E)** pemby64@hotmail.com
Chairman: Ruel Fox **Manager:** Paul Bugg **Prog Ed:** Phil Pemberton
Ground: King George V Playing Fields, Old Norwich Road, Ipswich IP1 6LE **(T)** 01473 464 030 **Capacity:**
Colours(change): All green (Yellow/black/black)

ADDITIONAL INFORMATION:
Record Att: 528 v Ipswich Town, 29.11.95.
Honours: Suffolk & Ipswich League 1946-47, 47-48, 65-66, 67-68, 91-92, 92-93. Suffolk Senior Cup 1958-59, 62-63, 92-93.

GROUND DIRECTIONS

BRANTHAM ATHLETIC - Brantham Leisure Centre CO11 1RZ - 01206 392 506
Turn off the A12 heading towards East Bergholt, stay on the B1070 through East Bergholt and go straight across the roundabout with the A137. Turn left immediately at the T-junction and follow this road around the sharp curve to the right and turn right immediately before the Village Hall. Follow this road around the sharp left hand turn and the Social Club and the car park are on the right.

CRC - The Trade Recruitment Stadium CB5 8LN - 01223 566 500
Exit the A14 at the fourth junction (situated east of Cambridge), up the slip road to the roundabout (sign posted Stow-Cum-Quy). Turn right onto the A1303, and return westwards towards Cambridge. Go straight over the first roundabout, passing Marshall Airport to the left. Go straight over two sets of traffic lights to a roundabout. The Ground's floodlights can be seen from here and McDonald's is on the right.

DEREHAM TOWN - Aldiss Park, Norwich Road NR20 3PX - 01362 690 460
Take the A47 towards Swaffham & Dereham. Do not take first slip road into Dereham. Carry on along the by-pass and take the second slip road, onto the B1110, sign posted B1147 to Bawdeswell, Swanton Morley and the Dereham Windmill. Follow the slip road round and Aldiss Park is 500 yards on your right.

DISS TOWN - Brewers Green Lane IP22 4QP - 01379 651 223
Off B1066 Diss -Thetford road near Roydon school. One and a half miles from Diss (BR).

ELY CITY - Unwin Sports Ground CB6 2SH - 01353 662 035
Follow signs for Kings Lynn/Downham Market as you approach Ely. Don't go into the city centre. After the Little Chef roundabout (junction of A10/A142) continue for approx half a mile until the next roundabout. Turn left for Little Downham (the B1411). There is also a sign for a Golf Course. The Golf Course is part of a Sports Complex which includes the football club. After turning left at the roundabout take another left after only about 50 metres into the Sports Complex entrance. The football club is at the end of the drive past the rugby club and tennis courts.

FC CLACTON - Rush Green Bowl CO16 7BQ - 01255 432 590
Leave the A12 at junction 29, then at roundabout take the 1st exit, then merge onto the A120 (sign posted Clacton, Harwich). Branch left, then merge onto the A133 (sign posted Clacton). Continue along the A133 following signs to Clacton until St Johns Roundabout (tiled Welcome to Clacton sign) take the 4th exit onto St Johns Rd - B1027 (sign posted St Osyth) Entering Clacton On Sea B1027 (fire station on left). B1027 At second mini-roundabout turn left onto Cloes Lane (Budgens on right). Continue down Cloes Lane for about 1/2 mile, passing St.Clares School on your right, at traffic lights, turn right onto Rush Green Rd. Rush Green Bowl will then appear on the right after 1/4 mile.

FELIXSTOWE & WALTON - Town Ground, Dellwood Ave IP11 9HT - 01394 282 917
The A12 meets the A14 (Felixstowe to M1/M6 trunk road) at Copdock interchange, just to the South of Ipswich. For Felixstowe take the A14 heading east over the Orwell Bridge. Follow the A14, for approx. 14 miles until you come to a large roundabout with a large water tower on your right, take the 1st exit off the roundabout, which is straight on. Take the first exit at the next roundabout, straight ahead again. At the next roundabout take the fourth exit onto Beatrice Avenue, take the first left into Dellwood Avenue. The ground is 100 yards down on the left behind tall wooden fencing.

GODMANCHESTER ROVERS - Bearscroft Lane PE29 2LQ - 07774 830 507
From A14 turn off for Godmanchester. Take A1198 towards Wood Green Animal Shelter, Bearscroft Lane is half mile from A14 on the left.

GORLESTON - Emerald Park, Woodfarm Lane NR31 9AQ - 01493 602 802
On Magdalen Estate follow signs to Crematorium, turn left and follow road to ground.

HADLEIGH UNITED - Millfield, Tinkers Lane IP7 5NG - 01473 822 165
On reaching Hadleigh High Street turn into Duke Street (right next to Library), continue on for approximately 150 metres and take left turn into narrow lane immediately after going over small bridge, continue to end of the lane where you will find the entrance to club car park.

HAVERHILL ROVERS - The New Croft, Chalkstone Way CB9 0LD - 01440 702 137
Take the A143 in to Haverhill and, at the roundabout by Tesco, turn left and then right in the one in front of the store. Carry on over the next roundabout past Aldi on the left and past the Sports Centre, Cricket Club and garage on the left. Just after the Workspace Office Solutions building take a right towards the town centre (towards Parking (South). The drive way into Hamlet Croft is a small turning on the left just after Croft Lane (look for the sign for Tudor Close).

KIRKLEY & PAKEFIELD - K & P Community & Sports Club, Walmer Road, NR33 7LE - 01502 513 549.
From A12 to Lowestoft town centre and go over roundabout at Teamways Garage and past Teamways Pub. Take next left into Walmer Road.

MILDENHALL TOWN - Recreation Way, Mildenhall, Suffolk IP28 7HG - 01638 713449 (club)
Next to swimming pool and car park a quarter of a mile from town centre.

NORWICH UNITED - Plantation Park, Blofield, Norwich, Norfolk NR13 4PL - 01603 716963
Off the A47.

STANWAY ROVERS - `Hawthorns', New Farm Road CO3 0PG - 01206 578 187
Leave A12 at Jct 26 to A1124. Turn right(from London)or left from Ipswich onto Essex Yeomanry Way. A1124 towards Colchester 1st right into Villa Rd,then left into Chaple Rd, and left into New Farm Rd. Ground 400 yds on left.Nearest BR station is Colchester North.

THETFORD TOWN - Recreation Ground, Munford Road IP24 1NB - 01842 766 120
Off bypass (A11) at A143 junction - ground 800 yards next to sports ground.

WALSHAM LE WILLOWS - Walsham Sports Club, Summer Road IP31 3AH 01359 259 298
From Bury - Diss road (A143) turn off down Summer Lane in Walsham-le-Willows and ground is on the right.

WISBECH TOWN - The Tom Wood's Fenland Stadium, Lynn Road, Wisbech PE14 7AN
The Tom Wood's Bear Fenland Stadium is on the B198 Lynn Road, just on the northern outskirts of Wisbech.

WIVENHOE TOWN - Broad Lane, Elmstead Road CO7 7HA - 01206 825 380
The ground is situated off the B1027 to the north of Wivenhoe.

WOODBRIDGE TOWN - Notcutts Park, Seckford Hall Road IP12 4DA - 01394 385 308
From Lowestoft turn left into Woodbridge at last roundabout (or first roundabout from Ipswich). Take first turning left and first left again. Drive to ground at end of road on left.

DIVISION ONE

BRIGHTLINGSEA REGENT - North Road, Brightlingsea, Essex CO7 0PL - 01206 304 199
Take exit 28 off M25, take slip road left for A12 toward Brentwood / Chelmsford / Romford, turn left onto slip road, merge onto A12, take slip road left for A120, take slip road left for A133, at roundabout, take 2nd exit, turn left onto B1029 / Great Bentley Road, turn right onto B1027 / Tenpenny Hill, and then immediately turn left onto B1029 / Brightlingsea Road, turn left to stay on B1029 / Ladysmith Avenue, bear left onto Spring Road, turn left onto North Road.

CAMBRIDGE UNI. PRESS - The Glassworld Stadium, Bridge Road, Impington, Cambridge CB24 9PH - 01223 237 373 - Take exit 14 M11, take slip road left for A14 (E) toward Ely / Newmarket, take slip road left, at roundabout, take 1st exit onto B1049 / Cambridge Road, ground 1/2 mile.

CORNARD UNITED - Blackhouse Lane CO10 0NL - 07811 096 382
Left off roundabout on A134 coming from Ipswich/Colchester into Sudbury, follow signs for Country Park - ground is immediately opposite along Blackhouse Lane.

DEBENHAM LC - Debenham Leisure Centre IP14 6BL - 01728 861 101
Approach Ipswich along the A14. Turn left at junction 51 onto the A140 signposted towards Norwich. After approx 4 miles turn right towards Mickfield and follow the road into Debenham turning left into Gracechurch Street. Debenham Leisure Centre is approx 1 mile on the right hand side.

DOWNHAM TOWN - Memorial Field, Lynn Road   PE38 9QE - 01366 388 424
One and a quarter miles from Downham Market (BR) - continue to town clock, turn left and ground is three quarters of a mile down Lynn Road.

FAKENHAM TOWN - Clipbush Pk, Clipbush Lane NR21 8SW - 01328 855 859
Corner of A148 & Clipbush Lane.

GREAT YARMOUTH TOWN - The Wellesley, Sandown Road NR30 1EY - 01493 656 099
Just off Marine Parade 200 yards north of the Britannia Pier. Half a mile from the BR station.

HALSTEAD TOWN - Rosemary Lane CO9 1HR - 01787 472 082
From A1311 Chelmsford to Braintree road follow signs to Halstead.

IPSWICH WANDERERS - SEH Sports Centre IP4 3NR 01473 728 581

LONG MELFORD - Stoneylands Stadium CO10 9JY - 01787 312 187
Turn down St Catherine Road off Hall St (Bury-Sudbury road) and then turn left into New Road.

MARCH TOWN UNITED - GER Sports Ground PE15 8HS - 01354 653 073
5 mins from town centre, 10 mins from BR station.

NEWMARKET TOWN - Town Ground, Cricket Field Road CB8 8BG - 01638 663 637 (club).
Four hundred yards from Newmarket BR.Turn right into Green Road and right at cross roads into new Cheveley Rd. Ground is at top on left.

SAFFRON WALDEN TOWN - Catons Lane CB10 2DU - 01799 522 789
Into Castle Street off Saffron-W High St. Then left at T jct and 1st left by Victory Pub.

STOWMARKET TOWN - Greens Meadow, Bury Road IP14 1JQ - 01449 612 533
About 800 yards from Stowmarket station (BR).Turn right at lights and head out of town over roundabout into Bury Road, Ground is on the right.

SWAFFHAM TOWN - Shoemakers Lane PE37 7NT - 01760 722 700

TEAM BURY - Ram Meadow, Cotton Lane IP33 1XP - 01284 754 721

WHITTON UNITED - King George V Playing Fields IP1 6LE - 01473 464 030
Turn off A14, junction A1156 approx 3 miles west of A12/A14 junction.

ESSEX SENIOR LEAGUE

Sponsored by: No sponsor
Founded: 1971
Recent Champions:
2007: Brentwood Town
2008: Concord Rangers
2009: Romford
2010: Witham Town
2011: Enfield 1893
essexseniorfootballleague.moonfruit.com

		P	W	D	L	F	A	Pts
1	(P) Witham Town	34	25	7	2	117	24	82
2	Southend Manor	34	23	6	5	72	32	75
3	Takeley	34	21	5	8	68	40	68
4	Burnham Ramblers	34	19	7	8	75	42	64
5	Barking	34	19	3	12	81	53	60
6	Sawbridgeworth Town	34	16	8	10	69	54	56
7	Enfield	34	15	9	10	52	36	54
8	Barkingside	34	16	6	12	56	45	54
9	Bethnal Green United	34	15	6	13	53	53	51
10	Sporting Bengal United (-3)	34	13	8	13	49	62	44
11	Hullbridge Sports	34	11	10	13	63	65	43
12	Haringey & Waltham Development (-1)	34	9	9	16	58	69	35
13	London APSA	34	8	6	20	46	87	30
14	Eton Manor (-9)	34	10	6	18	43	85	27
15	Bowers & Pitsea (-1)	34	6	9	19	47	77	26
16	Stansted (-3)	34	7	8	19	50	82	26
17	Clapton (-3)	34	6	8	20	35	78	23
18	Basildon United	34	3	7	24	42	92	16

GORDON BRASTED TROPHY

ROUND 1

Hullbridge Sports 2-1 Sawbridgeworth Town
Sporting Bengal United 4-3 Eton Manor

ROUND 2

Basildon United 1-3 Hullbridge Sports
Bethnal Green United 3-1 Enfield 1893
Bowers & Pitsea 0-3 Southend Manor
Clapton 1-2 Barkingside
Haringey & Waltham Development 0-3 Burnham Ramblers
Sporting Bengal United 1-2 Takeley
Stansted 1-2 London APSA
Witham Town 3-1 Barking

QUARTER FINALS

Barkingside 1-4 Southend Manor
Hullbridge Sports 1-2 Burnham Ramblers
London APSA 1-0 Sporting Bengal United
Witham Town 1-0 Bethnal Green United

SEMI-FINALS

London APSA 2-3 Southend Manor
Witham Town 2-0 Burnham Ramblers

FINAL

Southend Manor 0-3 Witham Town

		1	2	3	4	5	6	7	8	9	10	11	12	13	14	15	16	17	18
1	Barking		2-1	2-1	4-0	2-1	0-1	2-2	2-4	3-4	2-3	4-2	3-1	4-0	0-3	4-0	1-3	3-4	0-2
2	Barkingside	0-3		3-1	1-1	0-1	1-3	0-1	0-1	6-1	3-0	2-0	5-3	4-1	1-1	0-1	2-2	1-2	1-1
3	Basildon United	0-4	1-3		1-1	2-4	2-2	2-4	1-1	2-3	2-2	1-4	2-3	1-3	0-4	2-3	0-5	1-3	0-3
4	Bethnal Green United	3-2	0-1	3-2		4-2	1-2	2-1	1-1	1-3	2-1	1-3	3-0	1-2	2-3	2-1	3-2	0-2	0-1
5	Bowers & Pitsea	0-3	1-0	2-5	0-3		1-1	3-0	2-1	1-1	3-5	1-4	1-2	2-2	0-2	2-3	3-1	0-2	1-1
6	Burnham Ramblers	2-2	1-1	2-0	2-3	5-0		2-1	0-1	5-0	2-0	2-4	5-0	2-0	4-1	1-2	4-1	4-1	1-3
7	Clapton	0-2	0-1	3-2	1-2	2-1	1-2		1-2	1-1	0-0	0-3	1-2	3-6	1-1	0-1	1-2	2-1	0-7
8	Enfield 1893	4-0	0-2	2-3	2-0	0-1	1-1	1-1		5-0	3-3	1-1	1-0	0-1	0-0	5-1	0-2	0-1
9	Eton Manor	0-2	1-1	2-1	0-3	3-2	3-2	2-1	0-3		3-1	0-2	4-1	0-1	0-1	2-1	0-2	0-5	1-10
10	Haringey & Waltham Development	0-4	1-2	2-0	2-2	3-3	1-2	0-1	1-1	3-1		2-2	2-3	3-1	2-4	3-0	2-4	0-2	0-2
11	Hullbridge Sports	1-1	0-2	2-2	2-0	2-2	2-3	1-1	2-3	2-2	5-1		0-2	0-3	3-5	2-1	3-1	0-2	1-1
12	London APSA	2-3	0-1	1-1	3-1	2-2	1-1	1-1	1-1	5-1	1-2	0-2		2-4	1-4	1-2	3-0	1-2	1-6
13	Sawbridgeworth Town	0-1	2-1	0-0	3-1	4-2	2-2	5-1	2-3	1-1	2-1	2-0	6-1		1-1	1-1	6-1	1-1	1-3
14	Southend Manor	3-0	0-1	4-0	0-2	0-0	4-3	4-1	1-0	3-0	0-2	4-2	2-0	3-2		3-0	2-0	2-0	0-1
15	Sporting Bengal United	3-6	5-2	A-A	1-2	4-1	1-4	1-0	0-3	1-0	1-5	4-4	0-0	1-1	0-2		2-1	0-2	1-1
16	Stansted	1-5	0-2	1-2	2-2	1-1	2-1	1-1	0-1	2-2	2-2	2-2	4-2	0-1	1-2	1-1		1-3	0-6
17	Takeley	0-4	1-4	2-1	0-0	3-1	0-0	4-1	0-0	3-1	2-1	3-0	5-0	2-1	0-0	2-5	6-2		1-2
18	Witham Town	2-1	7-1	9-1	0-1	2-1	0-1	11-0	5-0	2-1	2-2	4-0	9-0	5-1	2-2	2-2	3-1		1-0

LEAGUE CUP

ROUND 1 (2 LEGS)

Bethnal Green United 0-0 Eton Manor

Eton Manor HW Bethnal Green United

Enfield 1893 2-3 Haringey & Waltham Development

Haringey & Waltham Development 0-0 Enfield 1893

ROUND 2

London APSA 1-3 Takeley

Takeley 3-1 London APSA

Haringey & Waltham Development 0-2 Witham Town

Witham Town 4-1 Haringey & Waltham Development

Stansted 2-0 Sawbridgeworth Town

Sawbridgeworth Town HW Stansted

Burnham Ramblers 1-2 Hullbridge Sports

Hullbridge Sports 0-3 Burnham Ramblers

Barking 1-2 Southend Manor

Southend Manor 3-5 Barking

Clapton 0-0 Basildon United

Basildon United 3-1 Clapton

Barkingside 3-2 Sporting Bengal United

Sporting Bengal United 1-1 Barkingside

Eton Manor 0-1 Bowers & Pitsea

Bowers & Pitsea 5-3 Eton Manor

QUARTER FINALS (2 LEGS)

Bowers & Pitsea 0-2 Takeley

Takeley 2-1 Bowers & Pitsea

Sawbridgeworth Town 1-0 Barking

Barking 4-0 Sawbridgeworth Town

Burnham Ramblers 2-2 Basildon United

Basildon United 0-3 Burnham Ramblers

Witham Town 3-1 Barkingside

Barkingside 2-4 Witham Town

SEMI-FINALS (2 LEGS)

Burnham Ramblers 4-1 Takeley

Takeley 4-4 Burnham Ramblers

Witham Town 2-1 Barking

Barking 2-3 Witham Town

FINAL

Burnham Ramblers 1-2 Witham Town

BARKING

Founded: 1880   Nickname: The Blues

Secretary: Peter Ball   **(T)** 07790 594 530   **(E)** secretary@barking-fc.co.uk

Chairman: Rob O'Brien   **Manager:** Alan Dickens   **Prog Ed:** Ashley Hanson

Ground: Mayesbrook Park, Lodge Avenue, Dagenham RM8 2JR   **(T)** 0776 458 7112

Capacity: 2,500 **Seats:** 200 **Covered:** 600 **Midweek Matchday:** Tuesday   **Clubhouse:** Yes **Shop:** Yes

Colours(change): Royal blue/blue/blue. (All yellow).

Previous Names: Barking Rov. Barking Woodville. Barking Working Lads Institute, Barking Institute. Barking T. Barking & East Ham U.

Previous Leagues: South Essex, London, Athenian. Isthmian. Southern.

Records: **Att:** 1,972 v Aldershot, FA Cup 2nd Rnd, 1978. **Goalscorer:** Neville Fox - 241 (65-73). **Apps:** Bob Makin - 566.

Senior Honours: Essex Senior Cup 1893-94, 95-96, 1919-20, 45-46, 62-63, 69-70, 89-90. London Senior Cup 1911-12, 20-21, 26-27, 78-79.

10 YEAR RECORD

02-03		03-04		04-05		05-06		06-07		07-08		08-09		09-10		10-11		11-12	
Isth1N	12	Isth1N	23	SthE	6	SthE	5	ESen	6	ESen	9	ESen	12	ESen	8	ESen	6	ESen	7

BARKINGSIDE

Founded: 1898   Nickname:

Secretary: Jimmy Flanagan   **(T)** 07956 894 194   **(E)** confclothing@aol.com

Chairman: Jimmy Flanagan   **Manager:** Matt Frew   **Prog Ed:** Jimmy Flanagan

Ground: Oakside Stadium, Station Road, Barkingside IG6 1NB   **(T)** 0208 550 3611

Capacity: 3,000 **Seats:** 350 **Covered:** 850 **Midweek Matchday:** Monday   **Clubhouse:** Yes **Shop:** No

Colours(change): Sky blue & navy/navy blue/navy blue. (All orange)

Previous Names: None

Previous Leagues: London. Greater London. Met London. Spartan, South Midlands.

Records: **Att:** 957 v Arsenal Reserves, London League, 1957.

Senior Honours: London Senior Cup 1996-97. Spartan South Midlands League Premier Division 1998-99. Essex Senior Cup 2008-09.

10 YEAR RECORD

02-03		03-04		04-05		05-06		06-07		07-08		08-09		09-10		10-11		11-12	
ESen	9	ESen	11	ESen	4	ESen	4	ESen	3	ESen	3	ESen	5	ESen	9	ESen	15	ESen	8

BASILDON UNITED

Founded: 1963   Nickname:

Secretary: Richard Mann   **(T)** 0796 435 6642   **(E)** rm006e7184@blueyonder.co.uk

Chairman: Paul Smith   **Manager:** John Higley   **Prog Ed:** Richard Mann

Ground: The Stadium, Gardiners Close, Basildon SS14 3AW   **(T)** 01268 520 268

Capacity: 2,000 **Seats:** 400   **Covered:** 1,000   **Midweek Matchday:** Wednesday   **Clubhouse:** Yes   **Shop:** No

Colours(change): Gold/black/black. (All red).
Previous Names: Armada Sports.
Previous Leagues: Grays & Thurrock. Greater London. Essex Senior. Athenian. Isthmian.
Records: Att: 4,000 v West Ham, ground opening 11.08.70.
Senior Honours: Isthmian League Division 2 Champions 1983-84.

10 YEAR RECORD

02-03		03-04		04-05		05-06		06-07		07-08		08-09		09-10		10-11		11-12	
ESen	13	ESen	7	ESen	7	ESen	11	ESen	10	ESen	16	ESen	8	ESen	12	ESen	12	ESen	18

BETHNAL GREEN UNITED

Founded: 2000   Nickname:

Secretary: Akhtar Imran Ahmed   **(T)** 07590 568 422   **(E)** akhtarx@hotmail.com

Chairman: Mohammed Nural Hoque   **Manager:** Anton Stephenson   **Prog Ed:** Akhtar Imran Ahmed

Ground: Mile End Stadium, Rhodeswell Rd, Poplar E14 7TW   **(T)** 020 8980 1885

Capacity: **Seats:** Yes   **Covered:** Yes   **Midweek Matchday:** Wednesday   **Clubhouse:**   **Shop:**

Colours(change): Green & white/green & white/green. (All red)
Previous Names: None.
Previous Leagues: Middlesex 2000-09.
Records:
Senior Honours:

10 YEAR RECORD

02-03	03-04		04-05		05-06	06-07	07-08		08-09		09-10		10-11		11-12	
	Midx1	2	MidxP	7			MidxP	8	MidxP	1	ESen	5	ESen	4	ESen	9

BOWERS & PITSEA

Founded: 1946   Nickname:

Secretary: Lee Stevens   **(T)** 07910 626 727   **(E)** lee-stevens@sky.com

Chairman: Barry Hubbard   **Manager:** John Doyle   **Prog Ed:** Lee Stevens

Ground: Len Salmon Stadium, Crown Avenue, Pitsea, Basildon SS13 2BE   **(T)** 01268 581 977

Capacity: 2,000 **Seats:** 200   **Covered:** 1,000   **Midweek Matchday:** Wednesday   **Clubhouse:** Yes   **Shop:** Yes

Colours(change): All claret. (All sky blue).
Previous Names: Bowers United > 2004.
Previous Leagues: Thurrock & Thameside Combination. Olympian.
Records: Att: 1,800 v Billericay Town, FA Vase.
Senior Honours:

10 YEAR RECORD

02-03		03-04		04-05		05-06		06-07		07-08		08-09		09-10		10-11		11-12	
ESen	7	ESen	8	ESen	10	ESen	15	ESen	4	ESen	7	ESen	11	ESen	17	ESen	14	ESen	15

BURNHAM RAMBLERS

Founded: 1900   Nickname: Ramblers

Secretary: Shaun Pugh   **(T)** 0752 509 9914   **(E)** secretarybrfc@sapugh.gotadsl.co.uk

Chairman: William Hannan   **Manager:** Keith Wilson   **Prog Ed:** Martin Leno

Ground: Leslie Fields Stadium, Springfield Road CM0 8TE   **(T)** 01621 783 484

Capacity: 2,000 **Seats:** 156   **Covered:** 300   **Midweek Matchday:** Tuesday   **Clubhouse:** Yes   **Shop:** No

Colours(change): Navy & sky blue stripes/navy/sky blue (All red).
Previous Names: None
Previous Leagues: North Essex. Mid-Essex. Olympian. South East Essex.
Records: Att: 1,500 v Arsenal, opening of stand.
Senior Honours:

10 YEAR RECORD

02-03		03-04		04-05		05-06		06-07		07-08		08-09		09-10		10-11		11-12	
ESen	8	ESen	12	ESen	2	ESen	5	ESen	5	ESen	8	ESen	7	ESen	3	ESen	7	ESen	4

CLAPTON
Founded: 1878   Nickname: Tons

Secretary: Shirley Doyle   **(T)** 0798 358 8883   **(E)** shirley.10@hotmail.co.uk
Chairman: Vince McBean (Cheif Exe)   **Manager:** Chris Wood   **Prog Ed:** Dennis Wright
Ground: The Old Spotted Dog, Upton Lane, Forest Gate E7 9NU   **(T)** 0794 400 9386
Capacity: 2,000   **Seats:** 100   **Covered:** 180   **Midweek Matchday:** Tuesday   **Clubhouse:** Yes   **Shop:** No

Colours(change): Red & white stripes/black/red (Black & red stripes/red/red)
Previous Names: None
Previous Leagues: Southern (founder member). London. Isthmian (founder member).
Records: **Att:** 12,000 v Tottenham Hotspur, FA Cup, 1898-99. First English club to play on the continent, beating a Belgian XI in 1890.
Senior Honours: Isthmian League Champions 1910-11, 22-23, Division 2 1982-83. Essex Senior Cup (x 4).

10 YEAR RECORD

02-03		03-04		04-05		05-06		06-07		07-08		08-09		09-10		10-11		11-12	
Isth2	9	Isth2	15	Isth2	16	Isth2	16	ESen	14	ESen	11	ESen	16	ESen	16	ESen	17	ESen	17

ENFIELD 1893 FC
Founded: 1893   Nickname:

Secretary: Mark Wiggs   **(T)** 0795 764 7820   **(E)** enfieldfc@ntlworld.com
Chairman: Steve Whittington   **Manager:** Gordon Boateng   **Prog Ed:** Mark Kettlety
Ground: Goldsdown Road, Enfield, Middlesex EN3 7RP   **(T)** 01438 210 073
Capacity: 500   **Seats:** 300   **Covered:** Yes   **Midweek Matchday:** Wednesday   **Clubhouse:** Yes   **Shop:**

Colours(change): White/blue/white. (Yellow/blue/yellow).
Previous Names: Enfield Spartans > 1900. Enfield > 2007.
Previous Leagues: Tottenham & District, North Middlesex, London, Athenian, Isthmian, Alliance, Southern
Records: **Att:** 10,000 v Spurs, floodlight opening at Southbury Rd., 10.10.62. **Goals:** Tommy Lawrence - 191 (1959-64). **Apps:** Andy Pape - 643 (85-92 93-99)
Senior Honours: FA Trophy 1981-82, 87-88. Alliance League 1982-83, 85-86. FA Amateur Cup 1966-67, 69-70. Essex Senior League 2010-11.

10 YEAR RECORD

02-03		03-04		04-05		05-06		06-07		07-08		08-09		09-10		10-11		11-12	
Isth P	23	Isth1N	24	Isth2	2	SthE	16	Isth1N	13	ESen	2	ESen	2	ESen	4	ESen	1	ESen	7

ETON MANOR
Founded: 1901   Nickname: The Manor

Secretary: Enrique Nespereira   **(T)** 07740 457 686   **(E)**
Chairman: Reg Curtis   **Manager:** Luke Giddings   **Prog Ed:** Reg Curtis
Ground: Waltham Abbey FC, Capershotts, Sewardstone Road, Waltham Abbey EN9 1LU   **(T)** 01992 711 287
Capacity: 2,500   **Seats:** 200   **Covered:** 600   **Midweek Matchday:** Monday   **Clubhouse:** Yes   **Shop:**

Colours(change): Sky blue & navy. (Black & white/black/black).
Previous Names: Wildernes Leyton.
Previous Leagues: London. Greater London. Metropolitan.
Records: **Att:** 600 v Leyton Orient, opening of floodlights. **Goalscorer:** Dave Sams.
Senior Honours:

10 YEAR RECORD

02-03		03-04		04-05		05-06		06-07		07-08		08-09		09-10		10-11		11-12	
ESen	16	ESen	9	ESen	12	ESen	13	ESen	11	ESen	4	ESen	6	ESen	15	ESen	8	ESen	14

GREAT WAKERING ROVERS
Founded: 1919   Nickname: Rovers

Secretary: Daniel Ellis   **(T)** 07828 048 671   **(E)** danielellis@hotmail.co.uk
Chairman: Roy Ketteridge   **Manager:** Dan Trenkel   **Prog Ed:** Dan Ellis
Ground: Burroughs Park, Little Wakering Hall Lane, Gt Wakering SS3 0HH   **(T)** 01702 217 812
Capacity: 2,500   **Seats:** 150   **Covered:** 300   **Midweek Matchday:**   **Clubhouse:** Yes   **Shop:** No

Colours(change): Green and white stripes/white/green
Previous Names: Not known
Previous Leagues: Southend & Dist. 1919-81, Southend All. 1981-89, Essex Inter 1989-92, Essex Sen 1992-99, Isth. 1999-2004, Sthn 2004-05
Records: 1,150 v Southend United - Friendly 19/07/2006
Senior Honours: Essex Senior League 1994-95. Isthmian League Division 3.

10 YEAR RECORD

02-03		03-04		04-05		05-06		06-07		07-08		08-09		09-10		10-11		11-12	
Isth1N	14	Isth1N	21	SthE	20	SthE	13	Isth1N	12	Isth1N	13	Isth1N	13	Isth1N	9	Isth1N	15	Isth1N	22

HARINGEY & WALTHAM DEVELOPMENT Founded: Nickname:

Secretary: Lindsay Boyaram　　**(T)** 0743 212 1547　　**(E)**

Chairman: Burk Gravis　　**Manager:**　　**Prog Ed:**

Ground: Haringey Boro' FC, Coles Park, White Hart Lane N17 7JP　　**(T)** TBA

Capacity:　　**Seats:**　　**Covered:**　　**Midweek Matchday:** Wednesday　　**Clubhouse:** Yes　　**Shop:** No

Colours(change): All red (Royal blue/black/black)
Previous Names: Mauritius Sports merged with Walthamstow Avenue & Pennant 2007. Mauritius Sports Association 2007-11.
Previous Leagues: London Intermediate.
Records:
Senior Honours:

10 YEAR RECORD

02-03	03-04	04-05	05-06	06-07	07-08	08-09	09-10	10-11	11-12
LonInt 8					ESen 13	ESen 15	ESen 18	ESen 11	ESen 12

HULLBRIDGE SPORTS　　Founded: 1945　　Nickname:

Secretary: Mrs Beryl Petre　　**(T)** 01702 230 630　　**(E)** beryl@petre1942.fsnet.co.uk

Chairman: Andrew Burgess　　**Manager:** Enrico Tiritera　　**Prog Ed:** Beryl Petre

Ground: Lower Road, Hullbridge, Hockley Essex SS5 6BJ　　**(T)** 01702 230 420

Capacity: 1,500　**Seats:** 60　**Covered:** 60　　**Midweek Matchday:** Tuesday　　**Clubhouse:** Yes　　**Shop:** No

Colours(change): Royal blue & white stripes/royal/royal. (All pink black).
Previous Names: None
Previous Leagues: Southend & District. Southend Alliance.
Records: Att: 800 v Blackburn Rovers, FA Youth Cup 1999-00.
Senior Honours:

10 YEAR RECORD

02-03	03-04	04-05	05-06	06-07	07-08	08-09	09-10	10-11	11-12
ESen 15	ESen 16	ESen 15	ESen 14	ESen 12	ESen 14	ESen 9	ESen 11	ESen 9	ESen 11

LONDON APSA　　Founded: 1993　　Nickname:

Secretary: Zabir Bashir　　**(T)** 07956 660 699　　**(E)** zabirbashir23@hotmail.com

Chairman: Zulfi Ali　　**Manager:** Zakir Hussain　　**Prog Ed:**

Ground: Mill Road, Averley, South Ockendon, Essex RM15 4TR　　**(T)**

Capacity: 4,000　**Seats:** 400　**Covered:** 400　　**Midweek Matchday:** Thursday　　**Clubhouse:**　　**Shop:**

Colours(change): All blue (Green & white/green & white/green)
Previous Names: Ahle Sunnah
Previous Leagues: Asian League.
Records:
Senior Honours:

10 YEAR RECORD

02-03	03-04	04-05	05-06	06-07	07-08	08-09	09-10	10-11	11-12
	ESen 15	ESen 13	ESen 9	ESen 13	ESen 17	ESen 14	ESen 13	ESen 10	ESen 13

LONDON BARI　　Founded: 1995　　Nickname:

Secretary: Ricky Eaton　　**(T)** 07534 913 087　　**(E)**

Chairman:　　**Manager:**　　**Prog Ed:**

Ground: The Old Spotted Dog, Upton Lane, Forest Gate E7 9NU　　**(T)**

Capacity: 2,000　**Seats:** 100　**Covered:** 180　　**Midweek Matchday:**　　**Clubhouse:** Yes　　**Shop:**

Colours(change): Yellow/black/black
Previous Names: Bari FC.
Previous Leagues: South Essex 1995-98. Asian League. Essex Sunday Corinthian League > 2012.
Records:
Senior Honours:

10 YEAR RECORD

02-03	03-04	04-05	05-06	06-07	07-08	08-09	09-10	10-11	11-12
									EsxSC 1

SAWBRIDGEWORTH TOWN
Founded: 1890 **Nickname:** Robins

Secretary: Mrs Leslie Atkins **(T)** 07762 553 924 **(E)** sawbosec@hotmail.com

Chairman: Steve Day **Manager:** Pete Wickham **Prog Ed:** Steve Tozer

Ground: Crofters End, West Road, Sawbridgeworth CM21 0DE **(T)** 01279 722 039

Capacity: 2,500 **Seats:** 175 **Covered:** 300 **Midweek Matchday:** Tuesday **Clubhouse:** Yes **Shop:** No

Colours(change): Red & black/black/black. (Green/green/white).
Previous Names: Sawbridgeworth > 1976.
Previous Leagues: Stortford. Spartan. Herts County. Essex Olympian.
Records: **Att:** 610 v Bishops Stortford.
Senior Honours:

10 YEAR RECORD

02-03		03-04		04-05		05-06		06-07		07-08		08-09		09-10		10-11		11-12	
ESen	6	ESen	3	ESen	8	ESen	6	ESen	8	ESen	12	ESen	13	ESen	10	ESen	16	ESen	6

SOUTHEND MANOR
Founded: 1955 **Nickname:** The Manor

Secretary: John Bastin **(T)** 0778 097 7728 **(E)** john.bastin1@gmail.com

Chairman: Robert Westley **Manager:** Russell Faulker **Prog Ed:** Bob Westley

Ground: The Arena, Southchurch Pk, Lifstan Way, Southend SS1 2TH **(T)** 01702 615 577

Capacity: 2,000 **Seats:** 500 **Covered:** 700 **Midweek Matchday:** Tuesday **Clubhouse:** Yes **Shop:** No

Colours(change): Yellow/black/yellow. (White/red/red).
Previous Names: None
Previous Leagues: Southend Borough Combination. Southend & District Alliance.
Records: **Att:** 1,521 v Southend United, opening floodlights, 22.07.91.
Senior Honours: Essex Senior League Champions 1990-91. Essex Senior Trophy 92-93.

10 YEAR RECORD

02-03		03-04		04-05		05-06		06-07		07-08		08-09		09-10		10-11		11-12	
ESen	4	ESen	10	ESen	6	ESen	10	ESen	9	ESen	6	ESen	4	ESen	7	ESen	5	ESen	2

SPORTING BENGAL UNITED
Founded: 1996 **Nickname:** Bengal Tigers

Secretary: Khayrul Alam **(T)** 0207 392 2126 **(E)** bfauk@btconnect.com

Chairman: Aroz Miah **Manager:** Mamun Chowdhury **Prog Ed:** Nasyar Miah

Ground: Mile End Stadium, Rhodeswell Rd, Off Burdett Rd E14 4TW **(T)** 020 8980 1885

Capacity: **Seats:** Yes **Covered:** **Midweek Matchday:** Wednesday **Clubhouse:** **Shop:**

Colours(change): All royal blue (All yellow).
Previous Names: None.
Previous Leagues: Asian League. London Intermediate, Kent 2003-11.
Records: **Att:** 4,235 v Touring Phalco Mohammedan S.C.
Senior Honours:

10 YEAR RECORD

02-03		03-04		04-05		05-06		06-07		07-08		08-09		09-10		10-11		11-12	
02-03		Kent P	17	Kent P	14	Kent P	15	Kent P	17	Kent P	17	Kent P	17	Kent P	15	Kent P	15	ESen	10

STANSTED
Founded: 1902 **Nickname:** Blues

Secretary: Terry Shoebridge **(T)** 0774 304 4824 **(E)** terry.sue.shoebridge@btinternet.com

Chairman: Terry Shoebridge **Manager:** Dave Roach **Prog Ed:** Andy Taylor

Ground: Hargrave Park, Cambridge Road, Stansted CM24 8DL **(T)** 01279 812 897

Capacity: 2,000 **Seats:** 200 **Covered:** 400 **Midweek Matchday:** Tuesday **Clubhouse:** Yes **Shop:** No

Colours(change): All royal blue (All red).
Previous Names: None.
Previous Leagues: Spartan. London. Herts County.
Records: **Att:** 828 v Whickham, FA Vase, 1983-84.
Senior Honours:

10 YEAR RECORD

02-03		03-04		04-05		05-06		06-07		07-08		08-09		09-10		10-11		11-12	
ESen	14	ESen	13	ESen	11	ESen	16	ESen	16	ESen	10	ESen	10	ESen	1	ESen	2	ESen	16

TAKELEY

Founded: 1903

Nickname:

Secretary: Michael Rabey   **(T)** 0783 184 5466   **(E)** mcrab@btinternet.com

Chairman: Pat Curran   **Manager:** Don Watters   **Prog Ed:** David Edwards

Ground: Station Road, Takeley, Bishop's Stortford CM22 6SQ   **(T)** 01279 870 404

Capacity: **Seats:**   **Covered:**   **Midweek Matchday:** Tuesday   **Clubhouse:**   **Shop:**

Colours(change): All royal blue with white trim. (All red with white trim).
Previous Names: None.
Previous Leagues: Essex Intermediate/Olympian.
Records:
Senior Honours: Essex Olympian League 2001-02.

10 YEAR RECORD

02-03		03-04		04-05		05-06		06-07		07-08		08-09		09-10		10-11		11-12	
EssxO	2	EssxO	6	EssxO	8	EssxO	9	EssxO	3	EssxO	2	ESen	3	ESen	6	ESen	13	ESen	3

A click away from memory lane!

Over 35 years of publishing the Non-League Club Directory has filled a room full of information and photographs covering the game we know and love.

What we intend, over time, is to create a website that shares with you everything we have accumulated, which we hope will bring back some fond memories of season's gone by.

Log on to **www.non-leagueclubdirectory.co.uk** today
and see how many faces from teams gone by you recognise

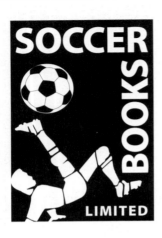

SOCCER BOOKS LIMITED

72 ST. PETERS AVENUE (Dept. NLD)
CLEETHORPES
N.E. LINCOLNSHIRE
DN35 8HU
ENGLAND

Tel. 01472 696226   Fax 01472 698546

Web site   www.soccer-books.co.uk
e-mail   info@soccer-books.co.uk

Established in 1982, Soccer Books Limited has one of the largest ranges of English-Language soccer books available. We continue to expand our stocks even further to include many more titles including German, French, Spanish and Italian-language books.

With well over 200,000 satisfied customers over the past 30 years, we supply books to virtually every country in the world but have maintained the friendliness and accessibility associated with a small family-run business. The range of titles we sell includes:

YEARBOOKS – All major yearbooks including many editions of the Sky Sports Football Yearbook (previously Rothmans), Supporters' Guides, Playfair Annuals, South and North & Central American Yearbooks, Non-League Club Directories, Almanack of World Football.

CLUB HISTORIES – Complete Statistical Records, Official Histories, Definitive Histories plus many more including photographic books.

WORLD FOOTBALL – World Cup books, European Championships History, Statistical histories for the World Cup, European Championships, South American and European Club Cup competitions and foreign-language Season Preview Magazines for dozens of countries.

BIOGRAPHIES & WHO'S WHOS – of Managers and Players plus Who's Whos etc.

ENCYCLOPEDIAS & GENERAL TITLES – Books on Stadia, Hooligan and Sociological studies, Histories and hundreds of others, including the weird and wonderful!

DVDs – Season reviews for British clubs, histories, European Cup competition finals, World Cup matches and series reviews, player profiles and a selection of almost 60 F.A. Cup Finals with many more titles becoming available all the time.

For a printed listing showing a selection of our titles, contact us using the information at the top of this page. Alternatively, our web site offers a secure ordering system for credit and debit card holders and Paypal users and lists our full range of 2,000 new books and 400 DVDs.

HELLENIC LEAGUE

Sponsored by: Uhlsport
Founded: 1953
Recent Champions:
2007: Slimbridge
2008: North Leigh
2009: Hungerford Town
2010: Almondsbury Town
2011: Wantage Town
hellenicleague.co.uk

LEAGUE CHALLENGE CUP

ROUND 1
Abingdon Town 2-1 Didcot Town Reserves
Ascot United 1-1 Malmesbury Victoria Pens
Bracknell Town 4-1 Hook Norton
Chalfont Wasps 0-1 Fairford Town
Chinnor 0-5 Cheltenham Saracens
Cirencester Town 'Dev' 2-6 Oxford City Nomads
Cricklade Town 1-2 Letcombe
Easington Sports 5-5 Old Woodstock Town
(Easington Sports won on penalties)
Finchampstead HW Bicester Town
Headington Amateurs 4-2 Henley Town
Lambourn Sports 4-4 Highmoor Ibis
(Lambourn Sports won on penalties)
Lydney Town 2-1 Hungerford Town Reserves
Milton United 1-2 Shrivenham
New College Swindon 5-0 Maidenhead United Reserves
Newbury 2-0 Brimscombe & Thrupp
Purton 0-1 Carterton
Rayners Lane 3-2 Clanfield
Reading Town 1-2 Abingdon United Reserves
Thame United 1-0 Penn & Tylers Green
Thatcham Town Reserves 2-3 Witney Town
Trowbridge Town 2-3 Woodley Town
Tytherington Rocks 2-2 Wootton Bassett Town
(Wootton Bassett won on penalties)
Wokingham & Emmbrook 4-1 Winterbourne United
ROUND 2
Abingdon Town 0-2 Shortwood United
Abingdon United Reserves 2-5 Flackwell Heath
Fairford Town 3-1 Cheltenham Saracens
Headington Amateurs 5-2 Kidlington
Holyport 2-3 Binfield
Lydney Town 5-1 Bracknell Town
Rayners Lane 4-3 Finchampstead
Shrivenham 0-1 Slimbridge
Wantage Town 1-1 Letcombe
(Wantage Town won on penalties)
Wootton Bassett Town 4-3 Carterton
Ardley United 3-0 Thame United
Oxford City Nomads 5-0 Easington Sports
New College Swindon 0-3 Wokingham & Emmbrook
Lambourn Sports 1-7 Highworth Town
Witney Town 2-1 Malmesbury Victoria
Woodley Town 2-2 Newbury
(Woodley Town won on penalties)
ROUND 3
Lydney Town 2-1 Slimbridge
Rayners Lane HW Wantage Town
Wokingham & Emmbrook 2-0 Flackwell Heath
Wootton Bassett Town 0-1 Headington Amateurs
Fairford Town 1-3 Binfield
Highworth Town 3-2 Ardley United
Witney Town 0-3 Oxford City Nomads
Woodley Town 1-2 Shortwood United

PREMIER DIVISION

		P	W	D	L	F	A	Pts
1	Oxford City Nomads	40	30	4	6	120	48	94
2	(P) Shortwood United	40	29	6	5	97	32	93
3	Ardley United	40	26	6	8	112	64	84
4	Flackwell Heath	40	23	6	11	90	54	75
5	Slimbridge	40	21	11	8	79	49	74
6	Highworth Town (-3)	40	23	5	12	79	46	71
7	Reading Town	40	20	10	10	81	50	70
8	Binfield	40	21	4	15	86	64	67
9	Thame United	40	17	9	14	72	64	60
10	Wokingham & Emmbrook	40	17	4	19	60	56	55
11	Abingdon Town	40	16	5	19	63	74	53
12	Wantage Town	40	13	12	15	66	67	51
13	Holyport	40	13	6	21	59	70	45
14	Ascot United	40	11	11	18	71	82	44
15	Cheltenham Saracens (-1)	40	13	6	21	65	83	44
16	Shrivenham	40	12	8	20	63	88	44
17	(R) Henley Town	40	12	7	21	60	81	43
18	Kidlington	40	9	6	25	48	103	33
19	Witney Town	40	8	5	27	40	94	29
20	(R) Fairford Town	40	8	5	27	47	109	29
21	(R) Bracknell Town	40	8	4	28	42	122	28

PREMIER DIVISION

PREMIER DIVISION	1	2	3	4	5	6	7	8	9	10	11	12	13	14	15	16	17	18	19	20	21
1 Abingdon Town		1-4	0-2	1-0	3-2	5-0	2-0	1-1	4-0	4-2	3-0	1-0	1-0	0-4	1-4	1-2	1-1	1-1	1-0	1-3	1-3
2 Ardley United	2-1		0-2	0-1	7-1	2-1	1-2	2-0	5-1	4-1	1-5	2-1	4-3	2-2	3-0	6-0	2-2	3-1	4-0	3-1	5-3
3 Ascot United	5-2	1-1		1-2	3-4	1-1	6-1	0-5	3-2	1-2	6-3	4-0	2-3	1-2	0-2	3-2	2-2	1-1	1-5	3-1	1-1
4 Binfield	2-3	0-3	3-0		5-0	1-3	4-1	2-2	1-2	0-2	2-2	2-0	0-2	1-5	4-2	6-1	0-1	1-1	4-1	2-0	2-1
5 Bracknell Town	1-1	1-9	2-1	1-4		3-1	4-1	1-8	0-2	3-1	0-3	0-1	1-2	2-3	1-4	0-3	0-6	2-0	0-2	1-1	0-3
6 Cheltenham Saracens	1-3	1-1	3-1	0-2	1-1		7-1	1-2	3-0	1-4	0-3	1-2	2-4	2-1	0-1	1-1	1-2	0-2	0-5	3-0	1-0
7 Fairford Town	2-3	2-3	1-3	1-5	2-1	3-2		0-2	1-3	1-2	1-0	0-2	2-1	1-1	0-4	4-2	1-1	0-3	3-4	0-1	1-0
8 Flackwell Heath	4-1	5-0	1-0	4-1	3-1	5-3	5-0		2-0	0-1	0-1	3-0	0-2	2-1	1-1	3-1	2-2	2-1	2-1	2-2	3-2
9 Henley Town	3-1	3-4	2-1	0-1	0-2	3-5	1-1	2-0		0-3	4-3	1-2	0-1	1-2	0-1	1-2	1-1	2-2	2-0	2-0	
10 Highworth Town	2-1	0-2	2-2	5-0	0-0	5-0	2-0	0-1	0-4		1-0	7-0	2-2	0-2	2-1	1-2	2-2	1-2	1-2	6-0	2-0
11 Holyport	0-1	1-3	4-2	1-2	1-3	1-0	3-2	1-2	1-2	0-1		2-1	0-2	0-3	1-2	2-1	0-1	3-1	2-2	1-3	1-2
12 Kidlington	2-4	3-4	2-2	0-6	4-0	1-5	0-3	1-3	2-4	3-2		1-1	2-0	0-2	2-2	1-1	1-3	2-2	3-1	2-3	
13 Oxford City Nomads	3-0	7-1	4-1	5-2	10-0	2-0	6-1	1-5	4-1	1-0	5-0	9-3		1-1	2-0	4-1	0-0	4-2	3-1	4-0	2-1
14 Reading Town	2-0	1-4	3-1	3-1	5-3	0-0	4-1	3-1	0-2	1-0	1-2		1-2		1-2	1-1	3-3	1-1	4-1	1-2	
15 Shortwood United	2-1	4-2	4-0	3-0	5-0	4-1	4-0	3-1	2-0	1-1	1-1	7-0	3-1	2-1		2-0	1-0	3-0	1-1	3-0	2-0
16 Shrivenham	2-1	1-1	2-2	0-6	3-0	2-2	6-1	5-2	2-2	0-3	2-2	2-0	2-5	1-3	1-2		0-1	1-2	1-1	2-0	3-2
17 Slimbridge	5-2	1-4	0-0	1-4	5-1	4-2	1-0	1-0	4-1	2-1	0-0	3-0	2-3	1-2	1-4	4-2		2-0	2-0	1-2	4-2
18 Thame United	2-0	1-4	2-2	0-3	1-0	1-2	4-1	3-0	4-3	1-3	1-1	1-1	3-4	0-1	2-2	3-1	3-2		1-1	3-1	3-2
19 Wantage Town	2-2	1-0	0-1	3-0	4-0	3-3	3-3	2-2	3-1	1-4	2-1	2-1	1-3	1-0	0-1	2-0	0-4	0-1		2-1	1-3
20 Witney Town	0-3	1-3	3-1	2-2	3-0	1-2	0-4	2-3	2-3	0-1	1-4	1-1	0-4	0-4	3-0	1-2	1-2	0-6	2-2		0-2
21 Wokingham & Emmbrook	3-0	1-1	2-2	1-2	1-0	0-1	3-0	2-1	3-1	0-1	2-0	1-0	1-2	1-1	1-2	1-2	0-2	2-1	0-1		

HELLENIC LEAGUE - STEP 5/6

DIVISION ONE WEST	P	W	D	L	F	A	Pts
1 Tytherington Rocks	32	26	2	4	104	41	80
2 Old Woodstock Town	32	19	5	8	77	34	62
3 Winterbourne United	32	18	4	10	77	50	58
4 Brimscombe & Thrupp	32	18	3	11	64	48	57
5 Wootton Bassett Town	32	15	7	10	69	47	52
6 Easington Sports	32	14	8	10	56	50	50
7 Purton	32	14	6	12	63	53	48
8 Clanfield	32	12	8	12	43	53	44
9 Hook Norton	32	12	7	13	58	64	43
10 Cricklade Town	32	11	8	13	62	67	41
11 New College Swindon	32	12	4	16	60	71	40
12 (R) Cirencester Town 'Dev'	32	11	6	15	50	55	39
13 Lydney Town	32	10	9	13	47	52	39
14 Headington Amateurs	32	11	5	16	62	73	38
15 Carterton	32	9	8	15	55	73	35
16 Malmesbury Victoria	32	6	8	18	35	61	26
17 (R) Trowbridge Town	32	2	6	24	26	116	12

DIVISION ONE EAST	P	W	D	L	F	A	Pts
1 (P) Newbury	30	20	4	6	86	39	64
2 (P) Highmoor Ibis	30	20	3	7	72	39	63
3 Rayners Lane	30	17	5	8	86	44	56
4 Chalfont Wasps	30	16	5	9	68	52	53
5 Woodley Town	30	16	4	10	49	46	52
6 Thatcham Town Reserves	30	16	3	11	58	47	51
7 Finchampstead	30	14	3	13	61	57	45
8 Lambourn Sports (-3)	30	13	7	10	54	53	43
9 Maidenhead United Reserves	30	12	6	12	67	60	42
10 Chinnor	30	11	9	10	44	49	42
11 Abingdon United Reserves	30	11	4	15	52	75	37
12 Penn & Tylers Green	30	10	6	14	53	65	36
13 Letcombe	30	8	4	18	52	90	28
14 Milton United	30	6	5	19	48	67	23
15 Hungerford Town Reserves	30	5	7	18	52	75	22
16 Didcot Town Reserves	30	4	7	19	35	79	19

LEAGUE CHALLENGE CUP continued...

QUARTER FINALS
Binfield 3-1 Rayners Lane
Headington Amateurs 3-1 Lydney Town
Shortwood United 0-4 Oxford City Nomads
Wokingham & Emmbrook 1-1 Highworth Town
(Highworth Town won on penalties)

SEMI-FINALS
Binfield 6-0 Headington Amateurs
Highworth Town 5-0 Oxford City Nomads

FINAL
Highworth Town 6-0 Binfield

FLOODLITE CUP

ROUND 1
Cirencester Town 'Dev' 2-5 Cheltenham Saracens
Fairford Town 3-0 Clanfield
Henley Town 0-5 Rayners Lane
Kidlington 5-2 Thame United
Milton United 1-2 Wootton Bassett Town
Oxford City Nomads 5-2 Wokingham & Emmbrook
Thatcham Town Reserves 5-2 Highworth Town

ROUND 2
Binfield 4-0 Hook Norton
Highmoor Ibis 4-1 Shrivenham
Ascot United 1-3 Holyport
Carterton 0-5 Shortwood United
Wantage Town 1-1 Hungerford Town Reserves
(Wantage Town won on penalties)
Lydney Town 1-0 Malmesbury Victoria
Didcot Town 0-6 Kidlington
Rayners Lane 2-0 Bracknell Town
Slimbridge 0-1 Fairford Town
Reading Town 3-0 Wootton Bassett Town
Ardley United 1-3 Flackwell Heath
Maidenhead United 2-1 New College Swindon
Abingdon Town 2-2 Thatcham Town Reserves
(Thatcham Town Res. won on penalties)
Cheltenham Saracens 4-2 Newbury
Oxford City Nomads 7-0 Abingdon United
Witney Town 3-2 Winterbourne United

ROUND 3
Flackwell Heath 4-1 Kidlington
Cheltenham Saracens 1-4 Shortwood United
Lydney Town 1-2 Highmoor Ibis
Holyport 0-0 Maidenhead United
(Maidenhead United won on penalties)
Binfield 1-0 Reading Town
Witney Town 0-3 Rayners Lane
Fairford Town 2-3 Wantage Town
Oxford City Nomads H/W Thatcham Town Reserves

QUARTER FINALS
Binfield 3-2 Flackwell Heath
Highmoor Ibis 2-2 Shortwood United
(Shortwood United won on penalties)
Maidenhead United 4-0 Rayners Lane
Wantage Town 0-3 Oxford City Nomads

SEMI-FINALS
Maidenhead United 0-4 Shortwood United
Oxford City Nomads 0-1 Binfield

FINAL
Binfield 2-0 Shortwood United

SUPPLEMENTARY CUP

ROUND 1
Clanfield 3-1 Bracknell Town
Thame United 0-2 Chalfont Wasps
Trowbridge Town 0-4 Milton United
Tytherington Rocks 1-0 Carterton
Thatcham Town Reserves 3-1 Old Woodstock Town
Ascot United 4-1 Lambourn Sports

ROUND 2
Chinnor 3-1 Winterbourne United
Cricklade Town 3-2 Purton
Holyport 2-0 Abingdon Town
Letcombe 2-1 Hook Norton
Cirencester Town 'Dev' 0-3 Reading Town
Finchampstead 1-2 Abingdon United Reserves
Hungerford Town Reserves 5-1 Shrivenham
Brimscombe & Thrupp 1-1 Chalfont Wasps
(Brimscombe & Thrupp won on penalties)
Clanfield 0-0 Didcot Town Reserves
(Clanfield won on penalties)
Easington Sports 0-1 Cheltenham Saracens
Tytherington Rocks 2-0 Penn & Tylers Green
Henley Town 1-2 Malmesbury Victoria
New College Swindon 0-5 Newbury
Milton United 3-4 Kidlington
Highmoor Ibis 3-0 Thatcham Town Reserves
Maidenhead United Reserves 4-1 Ascot United

ROUND 3
Abingdon United Reserves 0-4 Holyport
Brimscombe & Thrupp 2-4 Reading Town
Cheltenham Saracens 4-2 Letcombe
Cricklade Town 2-2 Malmesbury Victoria
(Malmesbury Victoria won on penalties)
Chinnor 2-1 Maidenhead United Reserves
Clanfield 3-1 Tytherington Rocks
Highmoor Ibis 2-0 Hungerford Town Reserves
Newbury 8-0 Kidlington

QUARTER FINALS
Malmesbury Victoria 1-2 Reading Town
Highmoor Ibis 3-0 Clanfield
Cheltenham Saracens 5-2 Newbury
Holyport 1-0 Chinnor

SEMI-FINALS
Holyport 0-1 Highmoor Ibis
Cheltenham Saracens 1-2 Reading Town

FINAL
Highmoor Ibis 3-4 Reading Town

CHAIRMAN'S RESERVE DIVISION ONE CUP

FINAL
Binfield Reserves 1-1 Gloucester City Reserves
(Gloucester City won on penalties)

PRESIDENT'S RESERVE DIVISION TWO CUP

FINAL
Penn & Tylers Green Reserves 5-0 Henley Town Reserves

DIVISION ONE WEST

	1	2	3	4	5	6	7	8	9	10	11	12	13	14	15	16	17
1 Brimscombe & Thrupp		5-1	2-1	0-1	1-3	3-0	3-4	1-2	6-2	2-1	2-1	1-3	3-2	4-0	2-1	2-1	0-1
2 Carterton	1-3		3-1	0-2	2-2	0-1	2-2	3-2	2-2	5-1	1-2	2-2	2-1	2-0	0-2	1-3	2-2
3 Cirencester Town 'Dev'	2-0	2-4		0-1	1-3	1-1	2-2	2-6	1-0	4-0	1-3	4-2	1-0	1-1	2-2	1-3	1-0
4 Clanfield	4-0	2-2	1-1		1-0	0-1	1-0	1-1	2-2	0-2	2-2	2-3	2-3	3-0	1-1	1-1	0-2
5 Cricklade Town	0-3	5-0	1-3	8-0		2-4	2-1	2-2	2-2	1-1	3-1	0-2	0-5	6-3	3-6	0-0	1-2
6 Easington Sports	1-3	2-1	3-1	0-1	3-3		2-1	0-6	3-0	2-1	2-3	0-0	6-2	5-0	0-2	3-2	1-1
7 Headington Amateurs	1-2	2-0	0-2	2-3	5-3	3-1		6-0	2-0	0-0	3-6	1-3	1-1	3-1	1-2	2-4	5-4
8 Hook Norton	2-1	2-5	2-1	2-1	5-0	1-1	2-0		2-1	0-0	3-4	2-3	2-1	3-0	0-1	2-1	1-1
9 Lydney Town	2-2	1-1	2-4	1-2	0-0	2-0	3-0	5-0		0-0	4-0	3-1	0-1	2-1	2-3	2-1	0-2
10 Malmesbury Victoria	0-1	1-0	0-3	0-0	1-1	1-3	2-4	3-2	1-1		1-3	1-4	5-1	0-1	1-4	3-0	
11 New College Swindon	1-3	0-5	2-0	1-2	0-3	1-4	1-2	2-2	2-0	3-0		2-2	1-3	2-2	0-3	2-3	0-2
12 Old Woodstock Town	5-0	4-1	2-0	1-3	5-0	1-1	2-3	5-0	2-0	3-0	4-1		1-3	9-0	0-1	3-0	0-0
13 Purton	2-5	4-1	2-0	3-1	1-2	3-1	6-0	1-1	1-1	0-0	0-4	0-2		1-1	0-4	6-2	2-3
14 Trowbridge Town	1-1	1-3	0-4	1-0	1-3	1-2	1-1	2-1	0-2	0-6	0-4	0-1	1-1		2-3	1-5	1-13
15 Tytherington Rocks	1-0	7-0	3-1	6-1	3-1	1-0	5-4	3-2	7-0	6-0	5-0	2-1	1-3	10-1		2-6	4-0
16 Winterbourne United	0-2	5-1	2-2	4-1	0-1	2-2	3-1	6-0	1-2	1-0	2-1	1-0	2-1	4-1	3-5		3-0
17 Wootton Bassett Town	1-1	2-2	2-0	3-1	3-1	1-1	4-0	1-0	0-3	4-2	2-5	0-1	1-2	6-1	5-1	1-2	

DIVISION ONE EAST

	1	2	3	4	5	6	7	8	9	10	11	12	13	14	15	16
1 Abingdon United Reserves		3-5	0-4	2-0	2-2	2-1	3-2	0-1	3-2	3-3	2-4	3-1	2-2	0-6	0-5	0-1
2 Chalfont Wasps	0-2		1-1	3-2	2-0	0-1	3-0	3-2	4-1	2-1	4-3	0-4	3-0	3-3	2-1	5-0
3 Chinnor	0-0	0-3		2-2	2-1	1-2	2-1	0-0	2-0	2-1	1-1	1-4	3-2	1-0	2-0	0-1
4 Didcot Town Reserves	0-7	2-0	2-2		1-1	1-2	2-2	2-2	3-2	2-3	1-3	1-5	0-0	2-4	0-5	0-2
5 Finchampstead	3-1	2-4	3-1	3-0		0-3	2-2	1-5	4-3	6-1	3-1	2-1	3-2	5-2	0-3	1-2
6 Highmoor Ibis	4-2	3-1	2-1	4-0	3-0		0-1	2-2	3-3	3-2	4-0	3-2	2-1	0-1	2-1	2-1
7 Hungerford Town Reserves	3-4	1-3	4-1	1-1	1-2	6-6		0-2	4-0	0-1	3-3	0-6	0-1	2-4	3-2	2-2
8 Lambourn Sports	2-0	3-2	2-2	5-2	1-4	0-3	3-0		2-1	0-0	3-2	1-2	1-1	2-1	3-1	0-3
9 Letcombe	1-2	3-4	4-1	2-1	1-0	0-4	6-5	3-2		1-1	1-5	1-3	2-1	0-4	2-3	2-3
10 Maidenhead United Rreserves	4-1	2-2	2-3	2-3	2-1	2-1	5-2	4-2	3-4		2-1	0-1	3-1	0-3	5-0	7-1
11 Milton United	0-2	2-4	0-2	4-1	1-0	0-2	2-2	2-3	0-0	1-0		2-2	2-4	1-5	0-2	1-3
12 Newbury	8-0	5-3	5-0	3-1	2-0	4-1	1-0	2-2	5-2	3-2	2-0		2-3	2-3	4-0	3-1
13 Penn & Tylers Green	1-3	3-1	0-3	1-0	4-8	3-2	1-2	2-2	2-2	3-3	3-2	1-3		1-2	0-0	3-2
14 Rayners Lane	3-1	1-1	0-0	5-2	2-0	1-3	4-2	5-0	11-0	1-5	2-1	2-2	3-1		0-2	1-2
15 Thatcham Town Reserves	4-2	1-0	3-3	0-1	2-3	2-1	2-1	2-0	1-2	2-2	4-2	2-0	3-1	0-6		1-2
16 Woodley Town	3-0	0-0	3-1	2-0	0-1	0-2	1-0	1-2	4-1	5-1	1-0	1-1	1-4	2-1	0-4	

DIVISION TWO WEST

		P	W	D	L	F	A	Pts
1	Gloucester City 'Dev'	26	23	2	1	93	24	71
2	Brimscombe & Thrupp Res.	26	17	7	2	56	19	58
3	Fairford Town Reserves	26	16	3	7	71	42	51
4	Wootton Bassett Town Res.	26	15	3	8	45	35	48
5	Easington Sports Reserves	26	13	5	8	60	29	44
6	Highworth Town Reserves	26	12	5	9	63	39	41
7	Shrivenham Reserves	26	12	3	11	56	45	39
8	Old Woodstock Town Res.	26	9	3	14	43	59	30
9	Wantage Town Reserves (-3)	26	9	4	13	40	57	28
10	Kidlington Reserves	26	8	3	15	43	61	27
11	Cheltenham Saracens Res.	26	7	3	16	34	61	24
12	Cricklade Town Reserves	26	5	4	17	32	90	19
13	Hook Norton Reserves	26	4	6	16	24	54	18
14	Witney Town Reserves	26	4	5	17	31	76	17

DIVISION TWO EAST

		P	W	D	L	F	A	Pts
1	Binfield Reserves	26	19	5	2	94	30	62
2	Rayners Lane Reserves	26	18	2	6	77	30	56
3	Thame United Reserves	26	17	3	6	93	36	54
4	Newbury Reserves	26	18	0	8	61	36	54
5	Chalfont Wasps Reserves	26	13	4	9	68	44	43
6	Reading Town Reserves	26	14	1	11	68	52	43
7	Ascot United Reserves	26	11	8	7	55	40	41
8	Chinnor Reserves	26	12	4	10	42	36	40
9	Penn & Tylers Green Res. (-3)	26	12	4	10	57	44	37
10	Finchampstead Reserves	26	9	3	14	46	67	30
11	Henley Town Reserves	26	6	3	17	40	89	21
12	Flackwell Heath Reserves	26	5	1	20	44	82	16
13	Milton United Reserves	26	3	4	19	22	112	13

ABINGDON TOWN
Founded: 1870   Nickname: The Abbots

Secretary: Wendy Larman   **(T)** 01235 763 985   **(E)** thomas.larman@btinternet.com
Chairman: Tom Larman   **Manager:** Shaun Smith   **Prog Ed:** Kenny More
Ground: Culham Road, Abingdon OX14 3HP   **(T)** 01235 521 684
Capacity: 3,000 **Seats:** 271 **Covered:** 1,771 **Midweek Matchday:** Tuesday   **Clubhouse:** Yes **Shop:** Yes

Colours(change): All yellow and green
Previous Names: Abingdon FC (merged with St Michaels in 1899) > 1928.
Previous Leagues: Reading Senior, Reading & District, Oxfordshire Senior, North Berkshire, Spartan, Isthmian
Records: Att: 4,000 v Swindon Town, Maurice Owen Benefit, 1950.
Senior Honours: Berks & Bucks Senior Cup 58-59. Spartan Lge 88-89. Isthmian Lge Div.2 South 90-91.

10 YEAR RECORD

02-03		03-04		04-05		05-06		06-07		07-08		08-09		09-10		10-11		11-12	
Isth2	4	Isth2	9	Isth2	7	Hel P	18	Hel P	18	Hel P	19	Hel P	19	Hel P	12	Hel P	14	Hel P	11

ARDLEY UNITED
Founded: 1945   Nickname:

Secretary: Norman Stacey   **(T)** 07711 009198   **(E)** ardley.house@virgin.net
Chairman: Norman Stacey   **Manager:** Kevin Brock   **Prog Ed:** Peter Sawyer
Ground: The Playing Fields, Oxford Road, Ardley OX27 7NZ   **(T)** 07711 009 198
Capacity: 1,000 **Seats:** 100 **Covered:** 200 **Midweek Matchday:** Tuesday   **Clubhouse:** Yes **Shop:** No

Colours(change): All sky blue.
Previous Names: None
Previous Leagues: Oxford Senior.
Records: Att: 278 v Kidlington, 29.08.05.
Senior Honours: Hellenic League Division One 1996-97, 97-98.

10 YEAR RECORD

02-03		03-04		04-05		05-06		06-07		07-08		08-09		09-10		10-11		11-12	
Hel1W	5	Hel1W	5	Hel P	18	Hel P	10	Hel P	4	Hel P	13	Hel P	5	Hel P	7	Hel P	3	Hel P	3

ASCOT UNITED
Founded: 1965   Nickname: Yellaman

Secretary: Mark Gittoes   **(T)** 07798 701995   **(E)** mark.gittoes@ascotunited.net
Chairman: Mike Harrison   **Manager:** Jeff Lamb   **Prog Ed:** Ian Watson
Ground: Ascot Racecourse, Car Park 10, Winkfield Rd, Ascot SL5 7RA   **(T)** 01344 291 107
Capacity: **Seats:** **Covered:** **Midweek Matchday:** Tuesday   **Clubhouse:** Yes **Shop:**

Colours(change): Yellow/blue/yellow
Previous Names: None.
Previous Leagues: Reading Senior.
Records: Att: 1,149 - 19/08/2011.
Senior Honours:

10 YEAR RECORD

02-03		03-04		04-05		05-06		06-07		07-08		08-09		09-10		10-11		11-12	
ReadS	6	ReadS	6	ReadS	3	ReadS	4	ReadS	1	Hel1E	4	Hel1E	2	Hel P	15	Hel P	12	Hel P	14

BINFIELD
Founded: 1892   Nickname: Moles

Secretary: Rob Challis   **(T)** 07515 336989   **(E)** robchallis@binfieldfc.com
Chairman: Bob Bacon   **Manager:** Mark Tallentire   **Prog Ed:** Colin Byers
Ground: Stubbs Lane off Hill Farm Lane, Binfield RG42 5NR   **(T)** 01344 860 822
Capacity: **Seats:** **Covered:** **Midweek Matchday:** Monday   **Clubhouse:** Yes **Shop:**

Colours(change): All red.
Previous Names: None.
Previous Leagues: Ascot & District. Great Western Combination. Reading & Dist. Chiltonian.
Records: Att: 1000+ Great Western Combination.
Senior Honours: Hellenic League Division 1 East 2008-09.

10 YEAR RECORD

02-03		03-04		04-05		05-06		06-07		07-08		08-09		09-10		10-11		11-12	
Hel1E	8	Hel1E	5	Hel1E	5	Hel1E	8	Hel1E	11	Hel1E	9	Hel1E	1	Hel P	8	Hel P	2	Hel P	8

CHELTENHAM SARACENS

Founded: 1964   Nickname: Sara's

Secretary: Denise Pates   **(T)** 07958 382 221   **(E)** denisepates@gmail.com

Chairman: Mark Griffiths   **Manager:** Gerry Oldham   **Prog Ed:** Bob Attwood

Ground: Petersfield Park, Tewkesbury Road GL51 9DY   **(T)** 01242 584 134

Capacity: **Seats:**   **Covered:**   **Midweek Matchday:** Wednesday   **Clubhouse:** Yes   **Shop:**

Colours(change): All navy blue
Previous Names:
Previous Leagues:
Records: **Att:** 327 v Harrow Hill 31/08/2003.
Senior Honours: Glouscestershire Senior Cup 1991-92. Hellenic League Division 1 1999-2000.

10 YEAR RECORD

02-03		03-04		04-05		05-06		06-07		07-08		08-09		09-10		10-11		11-12	
Hel1W	9	Hel1W	13	Hel1W	6	Hel1E	8	Hel1W	6	Hel1W	5	Hel1W	12	Hel1W	4	Hel1W	3	Hel P	15

FLACKWELL HEATH

Founded: 1907   Nickname: Heath

Secretary: Geoff Turner   **(T)** 07734 465 790   **(E)** euro5cups@hotmail.com

Chairman: Geoff Turner   **Manager:** James Pritchard   **Prog Ed:** Geoff Turner

Ground: Wilks Park, Magpie Lane, Heath End Rd, Flackwell Hth HP10 9EA.   **(T)** 01628 523 892

Capacity: 2,000 **Seats:** 150 **Covered:** Yes **Midweek Matchday:** Tuesday   **Clubhouse:** Yes **Shop:** No

Colours(change): All red.
Previous Names: None.
Previous Leagues: Great Western Combination. Hellenic. Isthmian.
Records: **Att:** 1,500 v Oxford United, charity match, 1966. **Goalscorer:** Tony Wood. **Apps:** Lee Elliott.
Senior Honours:

10 YEAR RECORD

02-03		03-04		04-05		05-06		06-07		07-08		08-09		09-10		10-11		11-12	
Isth2	3	Isth2	5	Isth2	9	Isth2	4	Isth1N	22	Hel P	9	Hel P	16	Hel P	4	Hel P	8	Hel P	4

HIGHMOOR-IBIS

Founded: 2001   Nickname: Mighty Moor

Secretary: Chris Gallimore   **(T)** 01189 588 518   **(E)** chris.gallimore@sjpp.co.uk

Chairman: Phillip Mullin   **Manager:** Paul Hamilton   **Prog Ed:** Martin Law

Ground: Palmer Park Stadium, Wokingham Road, Reading RG6 1LF   **(T)** 01189 375 080

Capacity: **Seats:**   **Covered:**   **Midweek Matchday:** Monday   **Clubhouse:**   **Shop:**

Colours(change): All blue
Previous Names: Highmoor and Ibis merged to form today's club in 2001.
Previous Leagues: Reading > 2011.
Records:
Senior Honours: Reading League Senior Division 2003-04, 10-11.

10 YEAR RECORD

02-03		03-04		04-05		05-06		06-07		07-08		08-09		09-10		10-11		11-12	
ReadS	4	ReadS	1	ReadS	4	ReadS	3	ReadS	2	ReadS	6	ReadS	2	ReadS	4	ReadS	1	Hel1E	2

HIGHWORTH TOWN

Founded: 1893   Nickname: Worthians

Secretary: Fraser Haines   **(T)** 07939 032 451   **(E)** fraserhaines@btinternet.com

Chairman: Rohan Haines   **Manager:** John Fisher   **Prog Ed:** Mike Markham

Ground: Elm Recreation Ground, Highworth SN6 7DD   **(T)** 01793 766 263

Capacity: 2,000 **Seats:** 150 **Covered:** 250 **Midweek Matchday:** Tuesday   **Clubhouse:** Yes **Shop:** No

Colours(change): Red/black/red.
Previous Names: None.
Previous Leagues: Swindon & District. Wiltshire.
Records: **Att:** 2,000 v QPR, opening of floodlights. **Goalscorer:** Kevin Higgs. **Apps:** Rod Haines.
Senior Honours: Hellenic League Champions 2004-05.

10 YEAR RECORD

02-03		03-04		04-05		05-06		06-07		07-08		08-09		09-10		10-11		11-12	
Hel P	4	Hel P	9	Hel P	1	Hel P	12	Hel P	15	Hel P	6	Hel P	6	Hel P	9	Hel P	4	Hel P	6

HOLYPORT

Founded: 1934   Nickname: The Villagers

Secretary: Graham Broom   **(T)** 07702 369 708   **(E)** grahambroom@btinternet.com

Chairman: Tony Andrews   **Manager:** Derek Sweetman   **Prog Ed:** Richard Tyrell

Ground: Summerleaze Village SL6 8SP   **(T)** 07702 369 708 / 07879 041 359

Capacity: **Seats:**   **Covered:**   **Midweek Matchday:** Tuesday   **Clubhouse:**   **Shop:**

Colours(change): Claret/green/claret
Previous Names:
Previous Leagues:
Records: Att: 218 v Eton Wick, 2006.
Senior Honours: Norfolkian Senior Cup 1999-2000. Hellenic League Division One East 2010-11.

10 YEAR RECORD

02-03	03-04	04-05	05-06	06-07	07-08	08-09	09-10	10-11	11-12
Hel1E 15	Hel1E 17	Hel1E 15	Hel1E 14	Hel1E 9	Hel1E 7	Hel1E 5	Hel1E 3	Hel1E 1	Hel P 13

KIDLINGTON

Founded: 1909   Nickname:

Secretary: David Platt   **(T)** 07956 531 185   **(E)** dplatt45@hotmail.co.uk

Chairman: Gary Johnson   **Manager:** Paul Berry   **Prog Ed:** Donna Conelly

Ground: Yarnton Road, Kidlington, Oxford OX5 1AT   **(T)** 01865 841 526

Capacity: **Seats:** Yes   **Covered:** Yes   **Midweek Matchday:** Tuesday   **Clubhouse:** Yes   **Shop:** No

Colours(change): All green
Previous Names: None.
Previous Leagues: Oxford Senior.
Records: Att: 2,500 v Showbiz XI, 1973.
Senior Honours:

10 YEAR RECORD

02-03	03-04	04-05	05-06	06-07	07-08	08-09	09-10	10-11	11-12
Hel1W 7	Hel1W 12	Hel1W 3	Hel P 20	Hel P 9	Hel P 15	Hel P 9	Hel P 11	Hel P 7	Hel P 18

MARLOW

Founded: 1870   Nickname: The Blues

Secretary: Paul Burdell   **(T)** 07961 145 949   **(E)** marlow.fc@virgin.net

Chairman: Terry Staines   **Manager:** Mark Bartley   **Prog Ed:** Terry Staines

Ground: Alfred Davies Memorial Ground, Oak tree Road, Marlow SL7 3ED   **(T)** 01628 483 970

Capacity: 3,000 **Seats:** 250 **Covered:** 600   **Midweek Matchday:** Tuesday   **Clubhouse:** Yes   **Shop:**

Colours(change): All royal blue
Previous Names: Great Marlow
Previous Leagues: Reading & District, Spartan 1908-10, 28-65, Gt Western Suburban, Athenian 1965-84, Isthmian 1984-2004. Southern 2004-12
Records: 3,000 v Oxford United - FA Cup 1st Round 1994
Senior Honours: Isthmian League Division 1 1987-88, League Cup 92-93.
Berks & Bucks Senior Cup x11

10 YEAR RECORD

02-03	03-04	04-05	05-06	06-07	07-08	08-09	09-10	10-11	11-12
Isth1N 11	Isth1S 16	SthW 13	SthW 6	Sthsw 7	Sthsw 9	SthM 9	SthM 15	SthC 11	SthC 22

NEWBURY

Founded: 1887   Nickname:

Secretary: Knut Riemann   **(T)** 07855 031 000   **(E)** kriemann@yahoo.com

Chairman: Ian Passey   **Manager:** Steve Melledew   **Prog Ed:** Martin Strafford

Ground: Faraday Road, Newbury RG14 2AD   **(T)** 01635 41031

Capacity: **Seats:**   **Covered:**   **Midweek Matchday:**   **Clubhouse:**   **Shop:**

Colours(change): Amber & black/black/amber & black
Previous Names: Old London Apprentice > 2005. O L A Newbury 2005-2007.
Previous Leagues: Reading Senior > 2008.
Records: Att: 246 v Kintbury Rangers 27/12/2008.
Senior Honours: Hellenic League 1978-79, 80-81, Division One East 2011-12. Athenian League 1982-83.

10 YEAR RECORD

02-03	03-04	04-05	05-06	06-07	07-08	08-09	09-10	10-11	11-12
Read4 2	Read3 2	Read2 1	Read1 4	Read1 1	ReadS 2	Hel1E 3	Hel1E 16	Hel1E 3	Hel1E 1

OXFORD CITY NOMADS

Founded: 1936   Nickname: The Nomads

Secretary: Colin Taylor   **(T)** 07817 885 396   **(E)** ctoxford@btinternet.com

Chairman: Richard Lawrence   **Manager:** Chris Fontaine   **Prog Ed:** Colin Taylor

Ground: Court Place Farm Stadium, Marsh Lane, Marston OX3 0NQ   **(T)** 01865 744 493

Capacity: 3,000 **Seats:** 300 **Covered:** 400 **Midweek Matchday:** Wednesday   **Clubhouse:** Yes **Shop:** Yes

Colours(change):	Blue & white hoops/blue/blue.
Previous Names:	Quarry Nomads > 2005.
Previous Leagues:	Chiltonian.
Records:	**Att:** 334 v Headington Amateurs, 25.08.03.
Senior Honours:	Hellenic League Premier Division 2011-12.

10 YEAR RECORD

02-03		03-04		04-05		05-06		06-07		07-08		08-09		09-10		10-11		11-12	
Hel1E	1	Hel1W	7	Hel1W	15	Hel1E	11	Hel1E	12	Hel1W	9	Hel1W	3	Hel P	10	Hel P	17	Hel P	1

READING TOWN

Founded: 1966   Nickname: Town

Secretary: Richard Grey   **(T)** 07762 494 324   **(E)** richardigrey@aol.com

Chairman: Roland Ford   **Manager:** Michael Butcher   **Prog Ed:** Richard Wickson

Ground: Reading Town Sports Ground, Scours Lane, Reading RG30 6AY   **(T)** 0118 945 3555

Capacity: 2000 **Seats:** 120 **Covered:** 200 **Midweek Matchday:** Tuesday   **Clubhouse:** Yes **Shop:** No

Colours(change):	Red/black/black
Previous Names:	Lower Burghfield, XI Utd, Vincents Utd, Reading Garage, ITS Reading T.
Previous Leagues:	Chiltonian Lge. Combined Counties.
Records:	**Att:** 1067 v AFC Wimbledon, Combined Counties 03.05.03.
Senior Honours:	

10 YEAR RECORD

02-03		03-04		04-05		05-06		06-07		07-08		08-09		09-10		10-11		11-12	
CC	15	CCP	3	CCP	19	CCP	10	CCP	9	CCP	13	Hel P	8	Hel P	3	Hel P	13	Hel P	7

SHRIVENHAM

Founded: 1900   Nickname: Shrivy

Secretary: Andy Timbrell   **(T)** 07999 133 439   **(E)** timbrell.andrew63@btopenworld.com

Chairman: Neil Sutton   **Manager:** Michael McNally   **Prog Ed:** Matt Hirst

Ground: The Recreation Ground, Shrivenham SN6 8BJ   **(T)** 07767 371 414

Capacity: **Seats:** **Covered:** **Midweek Matchday:** Tuesday   **Clubhouse:** Yes **Shop:**

Colours(change):	Blue & white hoops/blue/blue.
Previous Names:	None.
Previous Leagues:	North Berkshire.
Records:	**Att:** 800 v Aston Villa, 21.05.2000.
Senior Honours:	Hellenic Division One West 2004-05.

10 YEAR RECORD

02-03		03-04		04-05		05-06		06-07		07-08		08-09		09-10		10-11		11-12	
Hel1W	12	Hel1W	3	Hel1W	1	Hel P	8	Hel P	10	Hel P	8	Hel P	18	Hel P	16	Hel P	20	Hel P	16

SLIMBRIDGE

Founded: 1899   Nickname: The Swans

Secretary: Colin Gay   **(T)** 07702 070 229   **(E)** colin1956bcfc@o2.co.uk

Chairman: John Mack   **Manager:** Leon Sterling   **Prog Ed:** Tim Blake

Ground: Wisloe Road, Cambridge, Glos GL2 7AF   **(T)** 07835 927 226

Capacity: **Seats:** Yes **Covered:** Yes **Midweek Matchday:** Tuesday   **Clubhouse:** Yes **Shop:** Yes

Colours(change):	Blue/blue/white.
Previous Names:	None
Previous Leagues:	Stroud & District. Gloucester Northern. Gloucestershire County.
Records:	Since 2002-03. **Att:** 525 v Shortwood United, Hellenic Prem. 24.08.03. **Goals:** Julian Freeman - 79 (from 122 apps.).
Senior Honours:	Gloucester Northern League 2007-08. Gloucestershire County League 2008-09.

10 YEAR RECORD

02-03		03-04		04-05		05-06		06-07		07-08		08-09		09-10		10-11		11-12	
Hel1W	1	Hel P	4	Hel P	4	Hel P	5	Hel P	1	GlN1	1	GlCo	1	Hel1W	1	Hel P	5	Hel P	5

THAME UNITED
Founded: 1883   Nickname: United

Secretary: Jake Collinge   **(T)** 07753 502 955   **(E)** jake@jcpc.org.uk
Chairman: Jake Collinge   **Manager:** Mark West   **Prog Ed:** Jake Collinge
Ground: The ASM Stadium, Meadow View Pk, Tythrop Wa, Thame, Oxon, OX9 3RN   **(T)** 01844 214 401
Capacity: 2,500 **Seats:** Yes   **Covered:** Yes   **Midweek Matchday:** Tuesday   **Clubhouse:** Yes   **Shop:**

Colours(change): Red & black/black/black.
Previous Names: Thame F.C.
Previous Leagues: Oxon Senior. Hellenic. South Midlands. Isthmian. Southern.
Records: **Att:** 1,035 v Aldershot, Isthmian Div.2, 04.04.94. **Goalscorer:** Not known. **Apps:** Steve Mayhew.
Senior Honours: Isthmian Division 2 1994-95.

10 YEAR RECORD
02-03	03-04	04-05	05-06	06-07	07-08	08-09	09-10	10-11	11-12
Isth1N 8	Isth1N 15	SthW 11	SthW 22	Hel P 20	Hel1E 10	Hel1E 9	Hel1E 1	Hel P 10	Hel P 9

WANTAGE TOWN
Founded: 1892   Nickname: Alfredians

Secretary: John Culley   **(T)** 07522 418 760   **(E)** john_clly@yahoo.co.uk
Chairman: Tony Woodward   **Manager:** Andy Wallbridge   **Prog Ed:** Tony Woodward
Ground: Alfredian Park, Manor Road, Wantage OX12 8DW   **(T)** 01235 764 781
Capacity: 1,500 **Seats:** 50   **Covered:** 300   **Midweek Matchday:** Tuesday   **Clubhouse:** Yes   **Shop:** No

Colours(change): Green & white hoops/white/green.
Previous Names: None.
Previous Leagues: Swindon & District. North Berkshire. Reading & District.
Records: **Att:** 550 v Oxford United, July 2003.
Senior Honours:

10 YEAR RECORD
02-03	03-04	04-05	05-06	06-07	07-08	08-09	09-10	10-11	11-12
Hel P 21	Hel1E 1	Hel P 10	Hel P 9	Hel P 11	Hel P 12	Hel P 11	Hel P 5	Hel P 1	Hel P 12

WITNEY TOWN
Founded: 2001   Nickname: The Blanketmen

Secretary: Lisa Brooks   **(T)**   **(E)** secretary@witneytownfc.com
Chairman: Tom Amer   **Manager:** Justin Merritt   **Prog Ed:** Rich Wickson
Ground: Marriot Stadium, Downs Road, Witney OX29 7WT   **(T)** 01993 848 558 (Office)
Capacity: 3,500 **Seats:** 280   **Covered:** 2,000   **Midweek Matchday:** Tuesday   **Clubhouse:** Yes   **Shop:** Yes

Colours(change): Yellow/black/yellow.
Previous Names: Witney United > 2001-11.
Previous Leagues: None.
Records: **Att:** 628 v Oxford United, 26.02.08
Senior Honours:

10 YEAR RECORD
02-03	03-04	04-05	05-06	06-07	07-08	08-09	09-10	10-11	11-12
Hel1W 15	Hel1W 4	Hel P 11	Hel P 6	Hel P 6	Hel P 4	Hel P 3	Hel P 6	Hel P 18	Hel P 19

WOKINGHAM & EMMBROOK
Founded: 2004   Nickname: Satsumas

Secretary: Sally Blee   **(T)** 07714 732 790   **(E)** sally.blee@tesco.net
Chairman: Paul Rance   **Manager:** Roger Herridge   **Prog Ed:** Clive McNelly
Ground: Bracknell Town FC, Larges Lane, Bracknell RG12 9AN   **(T)** 01344 412 305
Capacity: 2,500 **Seats:** 190   **Covered:** 400   **Midweek Matchday:** Tuesday   **Clubhouse:** Yes   **Shop:**

Colours(change): Orange/black/black.
Previous Names: Club formed when Wokingham Town and Emmbrook Sports merged.
Previous Leagues: Isthmian (Wokingham). Reading (Emmbrook Sports).
Records: **Att:** 305 v Binfield, 25.03.2005.
Senior Honours:

10 YEAR RECORD
02-03	03-04	04-05	05-06	06-07	07-08	08-09	09-10	10-11	11-12
		Hel1E 11	Hel1E 3	Hel1E 8	Hel1E 12	Hel1E 4	Hel1E 2	Hel P 11	Hel P 10

DIVISION ONE EAST & WEST

AFC HINKSEY
Founded: 2005 Nickname:

Secretary: Stuart Parsons (T) 07975 723123
Chairman: Daniel English **Manager:** Gavin Preston
Ground: The Pheonix Club Barton Village Rd, Barton, Oxford, OX3 9LA
Colours(change): Purple/black/black

(E) afchinksey@rocketmail.com
Prog Ed: Stuart Parsons
(T) 07975 723123 **Capacity:**

ADDITIONAL INFORMATION:
Previous League: Oxfordshire Senior > 2012.
Honours: Oxfordshire Senior League 2011-12.

BRACKNELL TOWN
Founded: 1896 Nickname: The Robins

Secretary: Darrell Freeland (T) 07712 473142
Chairman: Ian Nugent **Manager:** Stephen Nebbett
Ground: Larges Lane Bracknell RG12 9AN
Colours(change): Red and white hoops/red/red

(E) darrell_freeland@hotmail.com
Prog Ed: Rob Scully
(T) 01344 412 305 **Capacity:** 2,500

ADDITIONAL INFORMATION: Att: 2,500 v Newquay - FA Amateur Cup 1971. **Goalscorer:** Justin Day. **Apps:** James Woodcock.

CHALFONT WASPS
Founded: 1922 Nickname: The Stingers

Secretary: Bob Cakeboard (T) 07895 094 579
Chairman: Steve Waddington **Manager:** Dave Fisher
Ground: Crossleys Bowstridge, Lane Chalfont, St Giles HP8 4QN
Colours(change): Yellow and black stripes/black/black

(E) robert.cakeboard@btinternet.com
Prog Ed: Al Yeomans
(T) 01494 875 050 **Capacity:**

ADDITIONAL INFORMATION:
Record Att: 82 v Didcot Town 17/12/2005.
Honours: Hellenic League Division 1 East 2007-08.

CHINNOR
Founded: 1884 Nickname:

Secretary: Richard Carr (T) 07786 115 089
Chairman: Jim Marshall **Manager:** David Ridgley
Ground: Station Road, Chinnor, Oxon OX39 4PV
Colours(change): All royal blue

(E) richard.carr@eu.sony.com
Prog Ed: Craig Williams
(T) 01844 352 579 **Capacity:**

ADDITIONAL INFORMATION:
Previous League: Oxfordshire Senior.
Record Att: 306 v Oxford Quarry Nomads, 29.08.2005.

DIDCOT TOWN RESERVES
Founded: 1907 Nickname: Railwaymen

Secretary: Pat Horsman (T) 07882 154 612
Chairman: John Bailey **Manager:** Paul Noble
Ground: NPower Loop Meadow Stadium, Bowmont Water, Didcot OX11 7GA
Colours(change): Red & white/white/red & white

(E) didcot@fernring.co.uk
Prog Ed: Steve Clare
(T) 01235 813 138 **Capacity:** 5,000

ADDITIONAL INFORMATION:
Previous League: Hellenic Reserves.

EASINGTON SPORTS
Founded: 1946 Nickname: The Clan

Secretary: Angela Clives (T) 07815 325 905
Chairman: Neil Clarke **Manager:** Phil Lines
Ground: Addison Road, Banbury OX16 9DH
Colours(change): Red & white/black/black, red & white

(E) aclives@btinternet.com
Prog Ed: James Collier
(T) 01295 257 006 **Capacity:**

ADDITIONAL INFORMATION:
Record Att: 258 v Hook Norton.
Hnours: Oxfordshire Senior League 1957-58, 58-59. Division 1 1965-66. Oxfordshire Senior Ben Turner Trophy 1970-71.

FINCHAMPSTEAD
Founded: 1952 Nickname: Finches

Secretary: Nick Markman (T) 07793 866 324
Chairman: Richard Laugharne **Manager:** John Laugharne
Ground: Memorial Park The Village, Finchampstead RG40 4JR
Colours(change): Sky blue & white/sky/sky

(E) njm826@btinternet.com
Prog Ed: Nick Markman
(T) 0118 9732 890 **Capacity:**

ADDITIONAL INFORMATION:
Record Att: 425 v Sandhurst, 1958-59.
Honours: Chiltonian League 1987-88. Reading Senior Challenge Cup 1986-87. Hellenic League Division 1 East 2001-02.

HEADINGTON AMATEURS

Founded: 1949   Nickname: A's

Secretary: Donald Light   **(T)** 07764 943 778   **(E)** donald.light@ntlworld.com
Chairman: Donald Light   **Manager:** Luke Cuff   **Prog Ed:** Donald Light
Ground: The Pavillion, Barton Recreation Ground, Oxford OX3 9LA   **(T)** 01865 762 974   **Capacity:**
Colours(change): All red

ADDITIONAL INFORMATION:
Record Att: 250 v Newport AFC, 1991. **Goalscorer:** Tony Penge. **Apps:** Kent Drackett.
Honours: Oxfordshire Senior League 1972-73, 73-74, 75-76, 76-77, Division 1 1968-69. Hellenic League Division One West 2010-11.

HENLEY TOWN

Founded: Nickname: Lillywhites

Secretary: Geoff Biggs   **(T)** 07710 795 190   **(E)** cavaman@gmail.com
Chairman: Jack Hollidge   **Manager:** Mark Coles   **Prog Ed:** Geoff Biggs
Ground: The Triangle Ground, Mill Lane, Henley RG9 4HB   **(T)** 07758 376 369   **Capacity:**
Colours(change): White/black/black

ADDITIONAL INFORMATION: Att: 2000+ v Reading, 1922. **Goalscorer:** M. Turner.
Hellenic League Div.1 1963-64, 67-68, Div.1 East 2000-01. Chiltonian League Division 1 1987-88. Premier 1999-00.

MAIDENHEAD UNITED RESERVES

Founded: 1870   Nickname: Magpies

Secretary: Ken Chandler   **(T)** 07726 351 286   **(E)** kenneth.chandler@btinternet.com
Chairman: Peter Griffin   **Manager:** Sam Lock   **Prog Ed:** Graham Alfred
Ground: York Road, Maidenhead, Berkshire SL6 1SF   **(T)** 01628 636 314   **Capacity:** 4,500
Colours(change): Black & white stripe/black/red

ADDITIONAL INFORMATION: Previous League: Hellenic Reserves.

MILTON UNITED

Founded: 1909   Nickname: Miltonians

Secretary: Debbie Taylor   **(T)**   **(E)** milton.united.fc@hotmail.co.uk
Chairman: Andy Burchette   **Manager:** Steve McMahon   **Prog Ed:** Craig Selby
Ground: Potash Lane, Milton Heights, OX13 6AG   **(T)** 01235 832 999   **Capacity:**
Colours(change): Claret & sky/claret & sky/claret

ADDITIONAL INFORMATION:
Record Att: 608 Carterton v Didcot Town, League Cup Final, 07.05.05. **Goalscorer:** Nigel Mott.
Honours: Hellenic League 1990-91.

PENN & TYLERS GREEN

Founded: 1905   Nickname:

Secretary: Andrea Latta   **(T)** 07904 538 868   **(E)** hsvlatta1955@yahoo.co.uk
Chairman: Tony Hurst   **Manager:** Giovanni Sepede   **Prog Ed:** James Keating
Ground: French School Meadows, Elm Road, Penn, Bucks HP10 8LF   **(T)** 01494 815 346   **Capacity:**
Colours(change): Blue & white stripes/blue/blue

ADDITIONAL INFORMATION:
Previous League: Chiltonian (Founder member).
Record Att: 125 v Chalfont Wasps, August 2000.

RAYNERS LANE

Founded: Nickname: The Lane

Secretary: Tony Pratt   **(T)** 01895 233 853   **(E)** richard.mitchell@tesco.net
Chairman: Martin Noblett   **Manager:** Dean Gardner   **Prog Ed:** Richard Mitchell
Ground: Tithe Farm Social Club, Rayners Lane, South Harrow HA2 0XH   **(T)** 0208 868 8724   **Capacity:**
Colours(change): Yellow/green/yellow

ADDITIONAL INFORMATION:
Record Att: 550 v Wealdstone 1983.
Honours: Hellenic League Division 1 1982-83.

THATCHAM TOWN RESERVES

Founded: 1895   Nickname: Kingfishers

Secretary: Alan Lovegrove   **(T)** 07817 723 846   **(E)** mail@alanlovegrove.wanadoo.co.uk
Chairman: Eric Bailey   **Manager:** Andy Allum   **Prog Ed:** Duncan Groves
Ground: Waterside Park, Crookham Hill, Thatcham RG19 4PA   **(T)** 01635 862 016   **Capacity:** 3,000
Colours(change): Blue & white/blue/blue

ADDITIONAL INFORMATION: Previous Lge: Hellenic Reserves.

Division One West

WOODLEY TOWN
Founded: 1904   Nickname: Town

Secretary: John Mailer   **(T)** 07883 341 628   **(E)** john_mailer@hotmail.co.uk
Chairman: Mark Rozzier   **Manager:** Cyril Fairchild   **Prog Ed:** Mark Beaven
Ground: East Park Farm, Park Lane, Charvil, Berks RG10 9TR   **(T)** 07703 474 555   **Capacity:**
Colours(change): All navy blue

ADDITIONAL INFORMATION:
Previous League: Reading.
Honours: Reading Football League Senior Division 2008-09. Berkshire Trophy Centre Senior Cup 2008-09.

BRIMSCOMBE & THRUPP
Founded: Nickname: Lilywhites

Secretary: John Mutton   **(T)** 01453 757 880   **(E)** johncolin123@gmail.com
Chairman: Clive Baker   **Manager:** Phil Baker   **Prog Ed:** Clive Baker
Ground: 'The Meadow', London Road, Brimscombe Stroud, Gloucestershire GL5 2SH   **(T)** 07833 231 464   **Capacity:**
Colours(change): White/blue/blue.

ADDITIONAL INFORMATION: Previous League: Gloucestershire County > 2011.
Honours: Gloucestershire County League 2010-11.

CARTERTON
Founded: 1918   Nickname:

Secretary: Ann Callen   **(T)** 07734 350 408   **(E)** ann.callen@virgin.net
Chairman: TBA   **Manager:** Martin Wilkinson   **Prog Ed:** TBA
Ground: Kilkenny Lane, Carterton, Oxfordshire OX18 1DY.   **(T)** 01993 842 410   **Capacity:** 1,500
Colours(change): Red/green/red.

ADDITIONAL INFORMATION: Record Att: 650 v Swindon Town, July 2001. **Goalscorer:** Phil Rodney.

CLANFIELD
Founded: 1890   Nickname: Robins

Secretary: John Osborne   **(T)** 01993 771 631   **(E)** johnosborne6@sky.com
Chairman: John Osborne   **Manager:** Chris Hurley   **Prog Ed:** Trevor Cuss
Ground: Radcot Road, Clanfield OX18 2ST   **(T)** 01367 810 314   **Capacity:**
Colours(change): All red

ADDITIONAL INFORMATION:
Record Att: 197 v Kidlington August 2002.
Honours: Hellenic League Division 1 1969-70.

CRICKLADE TOWN
Founded: 1897   Nickname: Crick

Secretary: Rebecca Ross   **(T)** 07970 066 581   **(E)** alisdair.ross@venuesevent.com
Chairman: Alisdair Ross   **Manager:** Graham Jackson   **Prog Ed:** Kevin Midgley
Ground: Cricklade Leisure Centre, Stones Lane, Cricklade SN6 6JW   **(T)** 01793 750 011   **Capacity:**
Colours(change): Green/black/black

ADDITIONAL INFORMATION:
Record Att: 170 v Trowbridge Town 2003-04.
Honours: Wiltshire League 2000-01.

FAIRFORD TOWN
Founded: 1891   Nickname: Town

Secretary: William Beach   **(T)** 07919 940 909   **(E)** wbeach007@btinternet.com
Chairman: Mike Tanner   **Manager:** Paul Braithwaite   **Prog Ed:** Andrew Meadon
Ground: Cinder Lane, London Road, Fairford GL7 4AX   **(T)** 01285 712 071   **Capacity:** 2,000
Colours(change): All red.

ADDITIONAL INFORMATION: Att: 1,525 v Coventry City, friendly, July 2000. **Goalscorer:** Pat Toomey.

HOOK NORTON
Founded: 1898   Nickname: Hooky

Secretary: Garnet Thomas   **(T)** 07866 035 642   **(E)** thomasz@tiscali.co.uk
Chairman: Garnet Thomas   **Manager:** Mark Boyland   **Prog Ed:** Mark Willis
Ground: The Bourne, Hook Norton OX15 5PB   **(T)** 01608 737 132   **Capacity:**
Colours(change): Royal blue/royal blue/white

ADDITIONAL INFORMATION:
Record Att: 244 v Banbury United, 12/12/98.
Honours: Oxfordshire Senior League 1999-00, 00-01. Hellenic League Division 1 West 2001-02.

LAMBOURN SPORTS

Founded: 1946   Nickname:

Secretary: Martyn Benson   **(T)** 07838 001 906   **(E)** martyn.benson@live.com
Chairman: Jason Williams   **Manager:** Robert Clark   **Prog Ed:** Chris Dams
Ground: Bockhampton Road Lambourn, Hungerford, Berkshire RG17 8PS   **(T)** 01488 72212   **Capacity:**
Colours(change): Red/white/black

ADDITIONAL INFORMATION: Previous League: North Berkshire > 2011.
Honours: North Berkshire League Division One 2010-11.

LETCOMBE

Founded: 1910   Nickname: Brooksiders

Secretary: Des Williams   **(T)** 07765 144 985   **(E)** deswilliams45@btinternet.com
Chairman: Dennis Stock   **Manager:** Alan Gifford   **Prog Ed:** Russell Stock
Ground: Bassett Road, Letcombe Regis OX12 9JU   **(T)** 07765 144 985   **Capacity:**
Colours(change): All purple

ADDITIONAL INFORMATION:
Record Att: 203 v Old Woodstock Town, 29/08/04.
Honours: North Berkshire League Division One 1989-90. Chiltonian League Division One 1990-91.

LYDNEY TOWN

Founded: 1911   Nickname: The Town

Secretary: Roger Sansom   **(T)** 07887 842 125   **(E)** rsansom@glatfelter.com
Chairman: Peter Elliott   **Manager:** Mark Lee   **Prog Ed:** Roger Sansom
Ground: Lydney Recreation Ground, Swan Road, Lydney GL15 5RU   **(T)** 01594 844 523   **Capacity:**
Colours(change): Black & white stripes/black/black & white

ADDITIONAL INFORMATION:
Record Att: 375 v Ellwood, 05.11.05.
Honours: Gloucestershire County League 2005-06. Hellenic League Division 1 West 2006-07.

MALMESBURY VICTORIA

Founded: Nickname: The Vics

Secretary: Julie Exton   **(T)** 07595 725 263   **(E)** jmexton@aol.com
Chairman: Phil Exton   **Manager:** Simon Winstone   **Prog Ed:** Andrew Meadon
Ground: Flying Monk Ground, Gloucester Road, SN16 0AJ   **(T)** 01666 822 141   **Capacity:**
Colours(change): Black & white/black/red

ADDITIONAL INFORMATION:
Record Att: 261 v Cirencester United, 25.08.02.
Honours: Wiltshire League 1999-00. Wiltshire Senior Cup 01-02.

NEW COLLEGE SWINDON

Founded: Nickname: College

Secretary: Rob Hopkins   **(T)** 07739 914 888   **(E)** rob.hopkins@newcollege.ac.uk
Chairman: Paul Bodin   **Manager:** Mark Teasdale   **Prog Ed:** Rob Hopkins
Ground: Sumpermarine RFC Sports & Social, Supermarine Rd, South Marston SN3 4BZ   **(T)** 01793 824 828   **Capacity:**
Colours(change): All royal blue

ADDITIONAL INFORMATION: Previous League: Wiltshire > 2011.
Previous Name: New College Academy > 2012.

NORTH LEIGH RESERVES

Founded: 1908   Nickname: The Millers

Secretary: Keith Huxley   **(T)** 07775 818 066   **(E)** keith.huxley08@tiscali.co.uk
Chairman: Peter King   **Manager:** Paul Lewis   **Prog Ed:** Barry Norton
Ground: Eynsham Hall Park Sports Ground OX29 6PN.   **(T)** 07775 818 066   **Capacity:** 2,000
Colours(change): Yellow/black/yellow

ADDITIONAL INFORMATION:
Previous Leagues: Hellenic Reserves.

OLD WOODSTOCK TOWN

Founded: 1998   Nickname:

Secretary: Ian Whelan   **(T)** 07714 267224   **(E)** i.whelan@ntlworld.com
Chairman: Ted Saxton   **Manager:** Eddie Nix   **Prog Ed:** Louise Jordon
Ground: New Road, Woodstock OX20 1PD   **(T)** 07748 152 243   **Capacity:**
Colours(change): Royal blue & red/royal/royal.

ADDITIONAL INFORMATION:
Previous Names: Woodstock Town (1911) and Old Woodstock (1920) merged in 1998 to form today's club.
Record Att: 258 v Kidlington, 27.08.01.
Honours: Oxfordshire Senior League 1998-99.

PURTON

Founded: 1923 Nickname: The Reds

Secretary: Alan Eastwood
Chairman: Alan Eastwood
Ground: The Red House, Purton SN5 4DY
Colours(change): All red

(T) 07950 889 177
Manager: Chris Pethick

(E) alan.eastwood830@ntlworld.com
Prog Ed: Alan Eastwood
(T) 01793 770 262 (MD) Capacity:

ADDITIONAL INFORMATION:
Honours: Wiltshire League 1945-46, 46-47, 47-48. Wiltshire County League 1985-86. Hellenic League Division 1 1995-96, Division 1 West 2003-04. Wiltshire Senior Cup 1938-39, 48-49, 50-51, 54-55, 87-88, 88-89, 94-95.

TYTHERINGTON ROCKS

Founded: 1896 Nickname: The Rocks

Secretary: Graham Shipp
Chairman: Ted Travell
Ground: Hardwicke Playing Field, Tytherington Glos GL12 8UJ
Colours(change): Amber & black/black/black

(T) 07811 318 424
Manager: Gary Powell

(E) tramar1618@btinternet.com
Prog Ed: Mark Brown
(T) 07837 555 776 Capacity:

ADDITIONAL INFORMATION:
Previous League: Gloucestershire County.
Record Att: 424 v Winterbourne United, 26/08/2007.

WOOTTON BASSETT TOWN

Founded: 1882 Nickname:

Secretary: Ian Thomas
Chairman: Andy Walduck
Ground: Gerard Buxton Sport Ground, Rylands Way SN4 8AW
Colours(change): Blue & yellow/blue/yellow.

(T) 07714 718 122
Manager: Dave Turner

(E) ian.thomas@wbtfc.co.uk
Prog Ed: Mark Smedley
(T) 01793 853 880 Capacity: 2,000

ADDITIONAL INFORMATION: Record Att: 2,103 v Swindon Town, July 1991. Goalscorer: Brian 'Tony' Ewing. Apps: Steve Thomas.
Previous Leagues: Wiltshire.

GROUND DIRECTIONS

ABINGDON TOWN - Culham Road OX14 3HP - 01235 521 684

From Town Centre follow signs for Culham, go over bridge, ground is 300 yards on right.

ARDLEY UNITED - The Playing Fields OX27 7NZ - 07711 009 198

From M40 Junction 10 take B430 towards Middleton Stoney the ground is on the right hand side after mile. From Oxford take B430 through Weston-on-the-Green & Middleton Stoney then on the left hand side after passing Church in village.

ASCOT UNITED - Ascot Racecourse SL5 7RA - 07798 701 995

From Ascot High Street, with Ascot Racecourse on the left, follow the A329 to the mini-roundabout, at the end of the High Street, turn left on Winkfield Rd, go through road underpass and take the first right (signposted Car Park 7&8). Follow the track past the Ascot United welcome sign, through gates into the large car park and the ground is approx. 600m further on.

BINFIELD - Hill Farm Lane RG42 5NR - 01344 860 822

From M4 Junction 10 take A329 signposted Wokingham & Binfield, at roundabout take 1st exit. Go through 1st set of traffic lights, turn left at 2nd set opposite Travel Lodge. Follow road through village over two mini-roundabouts, at 'T' junction with church in front of you turn right. Take left filter road after 150 yards into Stubbs Lane. Ground is on left at end of short lane.

CHELTENHAM SARACENS - PETERSFIELD PARK GL51 9DY - 01242 584 134

Follow directions into Cheltenham following signs for railway station. At Station roundabout take Gloucester Road, in a Northerly direction for approx 2 miles. Turn left at lights past Tesco entrance onto Tewkesbury Rd, follow road past 'The Range' store over railway bridge. Take 1st left and then 1st left again, then left into service road into car park.

FLACKWELL HEATH - Wilks Park, Magpie Lane HP10 9EA - 01628 523 892
Junction 4 of M40 Follow signs A404 (High Wycombe) Turn right at traffic lights halfway down Marlow Hill, signposted Flackwell Heath. Ground three (3) miles on left.

HIGHMOOR - IBIS - Palmer Park Stadium, Wokingham Road, Reading RG6 1LF - 01189 375 080

From A4 (Also indicated as London Road Reading) At the Kings Road/A 329 Junction turn into the A329 the Palmer Park ground is approx. 300 metres on the left.

HIGHWORTH TOWN - Elm Recreation Ground SN6 7DD - 01793 766 263
Enter Town on A361, turn into The Green by Veterinary Surgery, Ground and Car Park 100 yards on left.

HOLYPORT - Summerleaze Village SL6 8SP - 07702 369 708
From the A4 Maidenhead take the B4447 towards Cookham after   mile turn right into Ray Mill Road West, at the T-junction turn left into Blackamoor Lane. As road bends sharply you will see the entrance to the ground on left, signposted Holyport FC. Please observe speed limit down track to the ground.

KIDLINGTON - Yarnton Road OX5 1AT - 01865 841 526
From Kidlington Roundabout take A4260 into Kidlington. After 3rd set of traffic lights take 2nd left into Yarnton Road. Ground 300 yards on left, just past Morton Avenue.

NEWBURY   - Faraday Road RG14 2AD - 01635 41031
Leave M4 at junction 13 taking Newbury road. Take A4 towards Thatcham, then take 1st right by 'Topp Tiles' into Faraday Road, ground is at end of road.

OXFORD CITY NOMADS - Court Place Farm Stadium OX3 0NQ - 01865 744 493
From South: From Newbury travel along the A34 towards Oxford turn onto Ring Road heading towards London (East). Follow Ring Road over 5 roundabouts to the Green Road roundabout signposted London, M40 East. Go straight over towards Banbury. A fly-over is visible, turn left onto the slip road and follow road to Court Place Farm Stadium on left. From North: At the North Oxford roundabout, travel towards London M40 on the Eastern by-pass, turn off at the flyover, the ground is visible to the left as you go over bridge.

READING TOWN - Scours Lane   RG30 6AY - 0118 945 3555
Leave M4 at junction 12 and take A4 towards Reading. Turn left at 1st lights go through Tilehurst Centre turn right into Norcot Road then left into Oxford Road and 1st right into Scours Lane.

SHORTWOOD UNITED - Meadowbank GL6 0SJ - 01453 833 936
12 miles west of Cirencester head for Cirencester, proceed up Spring Hill for 30 yards turn left through the Car Park, then left at Britannia Inn. Proceed up hill for approx mile to Shortwood. Ground is on the left hand side opposite the Church.

SHRIVENHAM - The Recreation Ground SN6 8BJ - 07767 371 414
Shrivenham village is signposted off A420 Oxford to Swindon road, six miles east of Swindon, four miles west of Faringdon. Drive through village turn into Highworth Road, ground is on right, car park on left.

SLIMBRIDGE - Wisloe Road GL2 7AF - 07835 927 226
From the A38 take the A4135 to Dursley. Ground is 100 yards on the left.

THAME UNITED - The ASM Stadium, Meadow View Park, Tythrop Wa, Thame, Oxon, OX9 3RN
01844 214 401. From the west: At the Oxford Road roundabout on the edge of Thame take the first left (sign posted Aylesbury) and follow the by-pass. At the next roundabout take the third exit on to Tythrop Way. The ground is 200 yards on the left.
From the east: Leave the M40 at Junction 6 and follow the signposts to Thame. On arriving in Thame, take the first right on to Wenman Road (B4012). Stay on the B4012 as it by-passes Thame, going straight over two roundabouts. The ground is on the right, directly off the by-pass, approximately half a mile after you pass Chinnor Rugby Club.

WANTAGE TOWN - Alfredian Park, Manor Road OX12 8DW - 01235 764 781
Proceed to Market Square. Take road at southeast corner (Newbury Street signposted to Hungerford). Continue for approximately a quarter of a mile take right turning into the ground. Clearly marked 'Wantage Town FC'.

WOKINGHAM & EMMB' - Bracknell Town FC RG12 9AN - 01344 412 305
Leave M4 at J10, take A329M signposted Wokingham & Bracknell. Follow road for 5 miles, over roundabout, pass Southern industrial estate (Waitrose etc.) on right to a 2nd r'about with traffic lights; take 2nd exit and follow signposts for M3. At next r'about take 1st exit. At next r'about take 3rd exit, Church Road dual carriageway. This brings you to another r'about with Bracknell & Wokingham college on right and Old Manor PH on left, take 5th exit for Ascot - A329. Go down hill on dual carriageway, London Road to next r'about take 4th exit back up the dual carriageway, London Road, Larges Lane last left turn before reaching r'about again. Ground 200 yards on right.

WITNEY UNITED - Polythene UK Stadium OX29 7WT - 01993 848 558
From West: A40 towards Oxford. At Minster Lovell roundabout, take the 1st exit to Minster Lovell. Two miles turn right into Downs Road (signposted for Witney Lakes Golf Club), ground half a mile on right. From Witney town centre: go west on Welch Way, at roundabout take 3rd exit into Curbridge Road. Take 3rd exit at roundabout into Deer Park Road, Left at traffic lights into Range Road, then left ground 400 yards on right.

DIVISION 1 EAST

AFC HINKSEY - The Pheonix Club Barton Village Rd, Barton, Oxford, OX3 9LA
A40 from London take last exit at Headington Roundabout. A40 from Witney take first exit. Take first left after leaving roundabout into North Way. Follow North Way to end where road merges to become Barton Village Road. Ground at bottom of hill on left.

BRACKNELL TOWN - Larges Lane RG12 9AN - 01344 412 305
Leave M4 at J10, take A329M signposted Wokingham & Bracknell. Follow road for 5 miles, over roundabout, pass Southern industrial estate (Waitrose etc.) on right to a 2nd r'about with traffic lights; take 2nd exit and follow signposts for M3. At next r'about take 1st exit. At next r'about take 3rd exit, Church Road dual carriageway. This brings you to another r'about with Bracknell & Wokingham college on right and Old Manor PH on left, take 5th exit for Ascot - A329. Go down hill on dual carriageway, London Road to next r'about take 4th exit back up the dual carriageway, London Road, Larges Lane last left turn before reaching r'about again. Ground 200 yards on right.

CHALFONT WASPS - Crossleys Bowstridge Lane HP8 4QN - 01494 875 050
A413 to Chalfont St Giles, follow signposts for village centre. Bowstridge Lane is 400 yards on left immediately after the shops. Crossleys is 400 yards along Bowstridge Lane on the right. Ground is directly ahead.

CHINNOR - Station Road OX39 4PV - 01844 352 579
Leave M40 at junction 6 and follow B4009 sign posted Princes Risborough. After 3 miles enter Chinnor and turn left at Crown PH roundabout. Ground is 400 yards on right.

DIDCOT TOWN RESERVES - Npower Loop Meadow Stad' OX11 7GA - 01235 813 138
From A34 take A4130 towards Didcot, at first roundabout take first exit, at next roundabout take third exit, then straight across next two roundabouts, at 5th roundabout turn right into Avon Way, ground is on the left. Also footpath direct from Didcot Railway Station.

EASINGTON SPORTS - Addison Road OX16 9DH - 01295 257 006
From North/South M40- Leave M40 at J11, follow A422 to Banbury, 2nd r'about take A4260 to Adderbury. Go through three sets of traffic lights, at top of hill at T-junc' turn left. Take 3rd right into Addison Rd. From South West A361 – Entering Banbury take 1st right turning into Springfield Av after 'The Easington' PH. Follow road, take T-junc' right into Grange Rd, 1st right into Addison Rd. Ground on left at end of road.

FINCHAMPSTEAD - Memorial Park, The Village RG40 4JR - 0118 973 2890
A321 from Wokingham, then fork right onto B3016. At the Greyhound Public House turn right onto the B3348. The ground is 200 yards on the right.

HEADINGTON AM' - Barton Recreation Ground OX3 9LA - 01865 760 489
A40 from London take last exit at Headington Roundabout. A40 from Witney take first exit. Take first left after leaving roundabout into North Way. Follow North Way to end where road merges to become Barton Village Road. Ground at bottom of hill on left.

HENLEY TOWN - The Triangle Ground RG9 4HB - 01491 411 083
From Henley Town Centre take the A4155 towards Reading. Mill Lane is approximately one mile from the Town Centre on the left immediately before the Jet Garage. From M4 Junction 11 head towards Reading on the A33 inner distribution road then follow A4155 signed to Henley, turn right into Mill Lane after the Jet Garage. Ground & Car Park on the left over the Railway Bridge.

MAIDENHEAD UNITED RESERVES - York Road, Maidenhead, Berkshire SL6 1SF 01628 636 314
The Ground is in the town centre. 200 yards from the station and two minutes walk from the High Street.
Access from M4 Junctions 7 or 8/9.

MILTON UNITED - Potash Lane OX13 6AG - 01235 832 999
Exit A34 at Milton, 10 miles south of Oxford & 12 miles north of junction 13 of M4. Take A4130 towards Wantage approximately 200 metres turn 1st left then right into Milton Hill. Ground 400 metres on the left.

PENN & TYLERS GREEN - French School Meadows HP10 8LF - 01494 815 346
From West - 'M40 to High Wycombe leave at J4. Follow A404 to Amersham, via Wycombe. Stay on A404 up the hill past railway station approx. 3 miles at Hazlemere Crossroads turn right onto the B474 signposted to Penn and Beaconsfield. Continue for approx. one mile go past three new houses on left, turn into Elm Road, the ground is on the left. From East -Leave M40 at Junction 2 and take the road signed Beaconsfield. From Beaconsfield follow the road through Penn towards Hazlemere, pass the pond on green and entrance to ground is on the right had side of road before the hill.

RAYNERS LANE - Tithe Farm Social Club HA2 0XH - 0208 868 8724
From A40 Polish War Memorial turn left into A4180 (West End Road), approx. 500 metres turn right into Station Approach, at traffic lights turn right into Victoria Road. At next roundabout continue straight on to traffic lights at junction with Alexandra Avenue (Matrix Bar & Restaurant on left). Continue straight on over traffic lights and take second turning on left into Rayners Lane. Ground is approximately half a mile on the left.

THATCHAM TOWN RESERVES - Waterside Park, Crookham Hill, Thatcham RG19 4PA - 01635 862 016
A4 Thatcham at Sony roundabout turn into Pipers Way. At next roundabout turn left, crossing over the railway line.
Entrance to Waterside Park 300 metres on left-hand side.

WOODLEY TOWN - East Park Farm, Park Lane RG10 9TR - 07703 474 555
Take A4, Bath Road & exit onto A3032 at @Wee Waif' roundabout to Twyford & Charvil. Take right exit at mini-roundabout into Park Lane then 2nd exit at mini-roundabout on Park Lane then left turn into East Park Farm. After-match Hospitality is at the Earley Home Guard Club.

DIVISION 1 WEST
BRIMSCOMBE & THRUPP - 'The Meadow', London Road, Brimscombe Stroud, Gloucestershire GL5 2SH - 07833 231 464
9 miles north of Cirencester on A419. 2 miles south of Stroud on A419.

CARTERTON - Kilkenny Lane OX18 1DY - 01993 842 410
Leave A40 follow B4477 for Carterton continue along Monahan Way turning right at roundabout, at traffic lights turn right onto Upavon Way. At next set of lights turn right onto B4020 to Burford. Take 2nd right into Swinbrook Road carry onto Kilkenny Lane, a single-track road). Ground & car park 200 metres on left hand side.

CLANFIELD - Radcot Road OX18 2ST - 01367 810 314
Situated on A4095 at southern end of village, 8 miles west of Witney and 4 miles east of Faringdon.

CRICKLADE TOWN - Cricklade Leisure Centre SN6 6JW - 01793 750 011
Cricklade is eight miles North of Swindon signposted off the A419. Leisure Centre is signposted off the B4040 Malmesbury Road.

FAIRFORD TOWN - Cinder Lane London Road GL7 4AX - 01285 712 071
Take A417 from Lechlade, turn left down Cinder Lane 150 yards after 40 mph sign. From Cirencester take Lechlade Road, turn right down Cinder Lane 400 yards after passing the Railway Inn.

HOOK NORTON - The Bourne OX15 5PB - 01608 737 132
From Oxford – A44 to junction with A361 turn right, take 1st left to a 'T' junction, turn right & enter village, after 30 MPH turn left then 1st right into 'The Bourne', take 1st left into ground.

LAMBOURN SPORTS - Bockhampton Road Lambourn, Hungerford, Berkshire RG17 8PS - 01488 72212
Follow signs to Lambourn Village Church, head to village centre and into Station Road, turn left into Bockhampton Road, ground is on left.

LETCOMBE - Bassett Road OX12 9JU - 07765 144 985
Take the B4507 from Wantage (Sign posted White Horse). Turn left after half a mile to Letcombe Regis. Ground on Far side of Village, on the right hand side of road.

LYDNEY TOWN - Lydney Recreation Ground GL15 5RU - 01594 844 523
From Gloucester – take Lydney road off A48 down Highfield Hill and into the town centre. Take 1st left into Swan Road after 2nd set of pelican lights. From Chepstow – at by-pass roundabout take Lydney road. Go over railway crossing then take 2nd right into Swan Road.

MALMESBURY VICTORIA - Flying Monk Ground SN16 0AJ
Off A429 signpost Cirencester take B4014 to Tetbury. First left signpost Town Centre Ground on right directly after Somerfield supermarket, narrow right turning into ground behind supermarket.

NEW COLLEGE SWINDON - Supermarine RFC Sports & Social Supermarine Road South Marston SN3 4BZ - 01793 824 828
From M5 Junction 11a, take the A417 to Cirencester, then A419 Swindon. At the A361 junction by Honda Factory take road to Highworth. After one mile Club is on 4th roundabout.
From M4 Junction 15, take A419 towards Swindon Cirencester, take A361, then as above .
From A420 Swindon take A419 to Cirencester, near Honda factory take A361, then as above.

NORTH LEIGH RESERVES - Eynsham Hall Park Sports Ground OX29 6PN - 07775 818 066
Ground situated on A4095 Witney to Woodstock road, three miles east of Witney. Entrance 300 yards east of main park entrance.

OLD WOODSTOCK TOWN - New Road, Woodstock OX20 1PD - 07748 152 243
A44 from Oxford, turn right opposite The Crown into Hensington Road. After half a mile road bends to right, take 1st turning right into New Road. Ground on left.

OLD WOODSTOCK TOWN - Eynsham Hall Park OX29 6PN - 07748 152 243
Ground situated on the A4095 Witney to Woodstock road, some 3 miles East of Witney. The entrance is 300 yards east of the main Eynsham Hall Park entrance. (North Leigh FC)

PURTON - THE RED HOUSE SN5 4DY - 01793 770 262 MD
Red House is near Village Hall Square; Purton is well signposted from all directions, situated on the B4041 Wootton Bassett to Cricklade Road, NW of Swindon.

TYTHERINGTON ROCKS - Hardwicke Playing Field GL12 8UJ - 07837 555 776
From M5 Junction 14 take A38 for Bristol. Tytherington turn-off is approximately three (3) miles. Enter village, ground is signposted.

WINTERBOURNE UNITED - Oakland Park, Alomondsbury, Bristol BS32 4AG - 07976 255 666
From M4 (West) leave at junction 20 to M5 (Sth West). Leave immediately at junction 16 (A38 Thornbury), turn right onto A38, then first left 100 yards from junction, in front of Motorway Police HQ, Ground next door. Signposted from A38 'Gloucestershire FA HQ'.

WOOTTON BASSETT - Gerard Buxton Sports Ground   SN4 8AW - 01793 853 880
Leave M4 at junction 16 and proceed towards Wootton Bassett Town Centre. Take 1st left after BP Petrol Station in Longleaze. Take 3rd turning on right into Rylands Way. Ground 150 metres on right hand side. Approaching from Calne or Devizes Area - proceed through Wootton Bassett Town Centre, take first right after Shell Garage into Longleaze then follow previous instructions.

Bly Spartans - Champions of the Kent Invicta League.

Photo: Alan Coomes.

Hollands and Blair.

Photo: Alan Coomes.

KENT INVICTA LEAGUE

Sponsored by: No sponsor
Founded: 2011

		P	W	D	L	F	A	Pts
1	(P) Bly Spartans	30	17	9	4	75	33	60
2	Phoenix Sports	30	17	7	6	60	30	58
3	Hollands & Blair	30	17	4	9	66	30	55
4	Bridon Ropes	30	16	7	7	57	38	55
5	Ashford United	30	15	7	8	65	44	52
6	Sutton Athletic	30	14	6	10	49	42	48
7	Bearsted	30	11	11	8	40	34	44
8	Lewisham Borough	30	13	4	13	48	42	43
9	Woodstock Park	30	12	4	14	54	59	40
10	Seven Acre & Sidcup	30	10	9	11	47	51	39
11	Rusthall	30	10	3	17	39	58	33
12	Lydd Town	30	9	5	16	51	64	32
13	Erith & Dartford	30	9	5	16	38	65	32
14	Crockenhill	30	9	4	17	43	83	31
15	Meridian	30	7	6	17	51	85	27
16	Orpington	30	6	5	19	42	67	23

CHALLENGE TROPHY

ROUND 1

Rusthall 0-1 Lewisham Borough

Bearsted 1-0 Bridon Ropes

Hollands & Blair 5-1 Meridian

Erith & Dartford Town 8-2 Crockenhill

Phoenix Sports 2-1 Sutton Athletic

Ashford United 5-0 Lydd Town

Seven Acre Sports 3-1 Woodstock Park

Orpington 0-5 Bly Spartans

ROUND 2

Seven Acre & Sidcup 0-3 Hollands & Blair

Bearsted 0-2 Erith & Dartford Town

Bly Spartans 3-0 Lewisham Borough

Phoenix Sports 5-3 Ashford United

SEMI-FINALS

Bly Spartans 0-0 Hollands & Blair

(Bly win 4-3 on penalties)

Phoenix Sports 3-2 Erith & Dartford Tn

FINAL

Phoenix Sports 2-2 Bly Spartans

(1-1 at 90 min. Bly win 4-2 on penalties)

		1	2	3	4	5	6	7	8	9	10	11	12	13	14	15	16
1	Ashford United		1-1	1-3	2-3	1-3	4-0	2-2	1-0	4-0	3-3	3-0	1-2	4-3	2-1	1-0	3-0
2	Bearsted	0-0		0-1	1-0	4-0	1-0	3-0	0-0	1-1	2-1	3-0	1-1	2-1	1-1	1-1	3-3
3	Bly Spartans	4-5	1-0		3-3	1-2	1-5	1-1	3-1	5-1	5-0	6-0	0-0	1-1	1-1	0-0	5-2
4	Bridon Ropes	4-3	2-1	1-1	1	1-1	4-0	1-0	0-1	2-1	3-0	0-0	0-4	0-0	0-5	2-0	2-1
5	Crockenhill	2-5	2-1	0-4	0-0		1-1	0-1	3-2	2-6	0-4	2-1	2-2	3-2	1-2	1-0	1-3
6	Erith & Dartford Town	2-2	0-1	0-4	2-1	2-1		0-7	0-1	1-2	5-2	1-8	0-4	1-0	0-0	0-3	6-1
7	Hollands & Blair	1-0	0-1	1-2	1-3	5-0	3-2		1-0	3-2	7-0	3-0	2-0	2-0	3-0	5-1	4-0
8	Lewisham Borough	1-2	1-1	0-3	0-2	4-1	2-0	1-1		1-2	4-2	2-0	1-2	1-0	0-0	7-1	1-5
9	Lydd Town	0-1	4-2	1-1	1-3	3-4	0-2	1-0	2-4		2-2	3-2	3-3	0-2	4-1	3-0	1-1
10	Meridian	0-5	6-2	0-8	1-2	0-5	5-2	1-1	0-4	2-1		1-1	0-3	5-0	1-2	1-2	1-1
11	Orpington	1-4	1-2	4-2	1-1	0-0	0-2	0-5	4-0	3-0	1-4		2-1	3-0	2-2	1-2	0-3
12	Phoenix Sports	3-0	2-1	1-2	4-1	2-1	1-1	2-0	2-0	1-2	5-2	1-1		2-0	1-3	1-0	3-0
13	Rusthall	0-3	1-0	2-4	1-1	2-0	0-2	1-0	3-2	2-1	4-2	4-3	0-2		3-1	2-4	0-1
14	Seven Acre & Sidcup	1-1	1-1	0-2	1-1	2-0	0-3	2-3	0-4	3-0	2-2	3-2	1-3	3-0		1-2	2-5
15	Sutton Athletic	1-1	1-1	0-1	0-3	6-2	0-0	4-3	0-1	2-1	2-0	5-1	1-1	3-0	5-0		2-1
16	Woodstock Park	3-0	1-2	0-0	2-0	6-3	3-1	0-1	1-2	4-3	1-3	1-0	2-1	2-5	1-3	0-1	

ASHFORD UNITED

Founded: 1930 Nickname: The Nuts & Bolts

Secretary: Elaine Orsbourne **(T)** 01233 646 713 **(E)** orsbournes@ntlworld.com
Chairman: Ernie Warren **Manager:** Paul Chambers **Prog Ed:** Annmarie Kelly
Ground: The Homelands, Ashford Road TN26 1NJ **(T)** **Capacity:**
Colours(change): Green & white/green/green & white (Yellow & green/yellow/yellow & green)

ADDITIONAL INFORMATION:

BEARSTED

Founded: 1895 Nickname:

Secretary: Roy Benton **(T)** 07849 809 875 **(E)** benton951@aol.com
Chairman: **Manager:** Tony Cornwell **Prog Ed:** Duncan Andrews
Ground: Otham Sports Club, Honey Lane, Otham, Maidstone ME15 8RG **(T)** 07860 360 280 **Capacity:**
Colours(change): White/blue/blue (All yellow)

ADDITIONAL INFORMATION:
Previous League: Kent County > 2011.

BRIDON ROPES

Founded: 1935 Nickname:

Secretary: Richard Clements **(T)** 0208 244 1167 **(E)** rich.clements@live.co.uk
Chairman: **Manager:** **Prog Ed:** Reggie Boatswain
Ground: Meridian Sports & Social Club, Charlton Park Lane, Charlton, London SE7 8QS **(T)** 0208 8561923 **Capacity:**
Colours(change): Blue & white/blue/blue (All red)

ADDITIONAL INFORMATION:
Previous Lge: Kent County > 2011.

CROCKENHILL

Founded: 1946 Nickname:

Secretary: Steve Cullen **(T)** 07702 886 966 **(E)** steve@crockenhillfc.co.uk
Chairman: Keith Jarvis **Manager:** **Prog Ed:** Alan Curnick
Ground: Wested Meadow Ground, Eynesford Road, Crockenhill, Kent BR8 8EJ **(T)** 01322 666067 **Capacity:**
Colours(change): Red & white stripes/black/black (Yellow & black stripes/yellow/yellow)

ADDITIONAL INFORMATION:
Previous Lge: Kent County > 2011.

ELTHAM PALACE

Founded: 1961 Nickname:

Secretary: Liam Kelly **(T)** 07825 997 598 **(E)** elthampalace@gmail.com
Chairman: **Manager:** **Prog Ed:** Liam Kelly
Ground: Green Court Sports Club, Green Court Rd, Crockenhill, Kent BR8 8HF **(T)** **Capacity:**
Colours(change): Yellow/blue/yellow (All white)

ADDITIONAL INFORMATION:

HOLLANDS & BLAIR

Founded: 1970 Nickname:

Secretary: Laurence Plummer **(T)** 07540 841 799 **(E)** laurence.plummer@btinternet.com
Chairman: **Manager:** **Prog Ed:** Laurence Plummer
Ground: Star Meadow Sports Club, Darland Avenue, Gillingham, Kent ME7 3AN **(T)** 01634 573839 **Capacity:**
Colours(change): All red (Yellow & blue)

ADDITIONAL INFORMATION:
Previous Lge: Kent County > 2011.
Honours: Kent County 2010-11.

KENT FOOTBALL UNITED

Founded: Nickname:

Secretary: Roy MacNeil **(T)** 07968 661 929 **(E)** roymacneil@tiscali.co.uk
Chairman: **Manager:** **Prog Ed:** Bradley Ambridge
Ground: Oakwood (VCD Ath. FC) Old Road, Crayford, Kent DA1 4DN **(T)** 07501 684 838 **Capacity:**
Colours(change): Blue & white/blue/blue (Yellow & black/black/black)

ADDITIONAL INFORMATION:

LEWISHAM BOROUGH
Founded: 2003   Nickname: -

Secretary: Ray Simpson & Juliet Walker   **(T)** 07958 946 236   **(E)** grancan_jamaica@yahoo.co.uk
Chairman: **Manager:**   **Prog Ed:** Ray Simpson & Juliet Walker
Ground: Ladywell Arena, Silvermere Road, Catford, London SE6 4QX   **(T)**   **Capacity:**
Colours(change): All royal blue (All yellow)

ADDITIONAL INFORMATION:
Previous Lge: Kent county > 2011.

LYDD TOWN
Founded: 1885   Nickname:

Secretary: Bruce Marchant   **(T)** 01303 275 403   **(E)** brucemarchant@hotmail.com
Chairman: **Manager:**   **Prog Ed:** Dave Johncock
Ground: The Lindsey Field, Dengemarsh Road, Lydd, Kent TN29 9JH   **(T)** 01797 321 904   **Capacity:**
Colours(change): Green & red/green/red (Blue & white stripes/blue/blue)

ADDITIONAL INFORMATION:
Previous Lge: Kent County > 2011.

MERIDIAN
Founded: 1995   Nickname:

Secretary: Dwinder Tamma   **(T)** 07977 274 179   **(E)** dtamna@meridianfc.co.uk
Chairman: **Manager:**   **Prog Ed:** Dwinder Tamma
Ground: Meridian Sports & Social Club, 110 Charlton Park Lane, London SE7 8QS   **(T)** 0208 856 1923   **Capacity:**
Colours(change): All sky blue (All red)

ADDITIONAL INFORMATION:
Previous Lge: Kent County > 2011.

ORPINGTON
Founded: 1939   Nickname:

Secretary: Paul Wade   **(T)** 01689 889 619   **(E)** paul.wade@virgin.net
Chairman: **Manager:**   **Prog Ed:** Phil Alder
Ground: Green Court Road, Crockenhill, Kent BR8 8HJ   **(T)** 07940 355 595   **Capacity:**
Colours(change): Amber/black/amber (All blue)

ADDITIONAL INFORMATION:
Previous Lge: Kent County > 2011.

PHOENIX SPORTS
Founded: 1935   Nickname:

Secretary: Alf Levy   **(T)** 07795 182 927   **(E)** alf_levy@sky.com
Chairman: **Manager:**   **Prog Ed:** Paul Pettet
Ground: Phoenix Sports Ground, Mayplace Road East, Barnehurst, Kent DA7 6JT   **(T)** 01322 526 159   **Capacity:**
Colours(change): Green/black/black (Red & white/red/red)

ADDITIONAL INFORMATION:
Previous Lge: Kent County > 2011.

RUSTHALL
Founded: 1890   Nickname:

Secretary: Alan Hawkins   **(T)** 01892 532 212   **(E)** hawkins48@btinternet.com
Chairman: **Manager:**   **Prog Ed:** Alan Hawkins
Ground: Jockey Farm, Nellington Road, Rusthall, Tunbridge Wells, Kent TN4 8SH   **(T)** 07865 396 299   **Capacity:**
Colours(change): Green & white stripes/green/green (Blue & black/black/black)

ADDITIONAL INFORMATION:
Previous Lge: Kent County > 2011.

SEVEN ACRE & SIDCUP
Founded: 1900   Nickname:

Secretary: Lee Hill   **(T)** 07834 583 395   **(E)** lhsasfc@gmail.com
Chairman: **Manager:**   **Prog Ed:** Lee Hill
Ground: Sidcup & District Conservative Club, Oxford Road, Sidcup, Kent, DA14 6LW.   **(T)** 020 8300 2987   **Capacity:**
Colours(change): Red & black/black/black (Green/black/black)

ADDITIONAL INFORMATION:
Previous Lge: Kent County > 2011.

SUTTON ATHLETIC

Founded: 1898   Nickname:

Secretary: Peter Johnson   **(T)** 07802 984 838   **(E)** pwjohnson.ltd@btinternet.com
Chairman: **Manager:**   **Prog Ed:** John Ball
Ground: The Pavillion Lower Road, Sports Ground, Lower Road, Hextable, Kent BR8 7RZ   **(T)** 07788 446 495   **Capacity:**
Colours(change): All green & white/green/green (Black & white/black/white)

ADDITIONAL INFORMATION:
Previous League: Kent County > 2011.
Previous Names: Sutton United > 2012.

WOODSTOCK PARK

Founded: 1970   Nickname:

Secretary: David Brown   **(T)** 07795 465 384   **(E)** secretary@woodstockparkfc.co.uk
Chairman: **Manager:**   **Prog Ed:**
Ground: W.E.Manin Ltd. Stadium, Woodstock Park, Broadoak Road, Sittingbourne ME9 8HL   **(T)** 01795 410777   **Capacity:**
Colours(change): All navy blue (All red)

ADDITIONAL INFORMATION:
Previous Lge: Kent County > 2011.

Bridon Ropes F.C.   Photo: Alan Coomes.

Lewisham Borough (Community) F.C.   Photo: Alan Coomes.

KENT LEAGUE

Sponsored by: Hurlimann
Founded: 1966
Recent Champions:
2007: Whitstable Town
2008: Thamesmead Town
2009: VCD Athletic
2010: Faversham Town
2011: Hythe Town
kentleague.com

PREMIER DIVISION	P	W	D	L	F	A	Pts
1 (P) Herne Bay	30	21	5	4	73	31	68
2 Erith & Belvedere (-3)	30	19	4	7	77	47	58
3 VCD Athletic	30	18	4	8	54	26	58
4 Erith Town	30	17	6	7	56	38	57
5 Tunbridge Wells	30	17	4	9	66	40	55
6 Beckenham Town	30	14	11	5	72	36	53
7 Corinthian	30	13	6	11	54	40	45
8 Woodstock Sports	30	14	2	14	55	58	44
9 Canterbury City	30	12	5	13	53	59	41
10 Fisher	30	10	6	14	51	62	36
11 Cray Valley PM	30	9	7	14	34	50	34
12 Lordswood	30	8	8	14	43	57	32
13 Holmesdale	30	7	4	19	43	73	25
14 Sevenoaks Town	30	5	8	17	29	55	23
15 Deal Town	30	5	8	17	26	70	23
16 Greenwich Borough	30	5	4	21	29	73	19

LEAGUE CUP

ROUND 1 (2 LEGS)
Herne Bay 3-0 Deal Town
Deal Town 0-3 Herne Bay
Tunbridge Wells 1-3 VCD Athletic
VCD Athletic 0-1 Tunbridge Wells
Woodstock Sports 3-1 Greenwich Borough
Greenwich Borough 1-2 Woodstock Sports
Corinthian 1-1 Holmesdale
Holmesdale 3-4 Corinthian
Fisher 6-6 Canterbury City
Canterbury City 2-5 Fisher
Sevenoaks Town 0-2 Erith & Belvedere
Erith & Belvedere 3-0 Sevenoaks Town
Cray Valley 2-6 Beckenham Town
Beckenham Town 0-1 Cray Valley
Lordswood 1-0 Erith Town
Erith Town 3-0 Lordswood

ROUND 2 (2 LEGS)
Woodstock Sports 0-1 Erith Town
Erith Town 3-5 Woodstock Sports
Herne Bay 3-1 Erith & Belvedere
Erith & Belvedere 0-4 Herne Bay
Beckenham Town 2-1 VCD Athletic
VCD Athletic 2-0 Beckenham Town
Corinthian 2-0 Fisher
Fisher 0-0 Corinthian

SEMI-FINALS (2 LEGS)
VCD Athletic 1-0 Herne Bay
Herne Bay 1-2 VCD Athletic
Woodstock Sports 0-4 Corinthian
Corinthian 1-0 Woodstock Sports

FINAL
VCD Athletic 2-0 Corinthian

PREMIER DIVISION	1	2	3	4	5	6	7	8	9	10	11	12	13	14	15	16
1 Beckenham Town		3-1	1-1	4-1	7-0	2-2	3-0	2-2	4-0	2-4	5-0	4-0	1-1	3-0	0-0	3-1
2 Canterbury City	0-0		0-2	1-1	3-2	1-5	1-3	2-4	5-0	2-3	1-1	1-0	3-1	1-6	3-1	2-1
3 Corinthian	1-0	2-1		0-1	10-0	2-2	1-3	1-2	3-1	1-1	3-1	3-3	1-0	1-0	1-2	1-2
4 Cray Valley PM	1-1	1-4	2-1		1-0	4-2	2-1	1-2	0-0	0-3	3-2	1-2	0-2	2-3	1-1	1-2
5 Deal Town	0-0	1-0	0-4	0-0		2-2	3-1	1-1	2-0	0-4	1-4	0-2	2-2	1-1	1-3	0-1
6 Erith & Belvedere	4-3	2-3	5-2	4-0	3-1		1-2	3-1	2-0	3-2	2-1	2-3	1-0	1-1	1-2	2-1
7 Erith Town	4-2	2-2	1-1	0-4	2-1	4-1		3-0	0-0	2-2	4-3	2-0	1-0	1-3	2-1	3-1
8 Fisher	0-4	0-2	1-1	0-0	4-0	0-2	1-1		2-3	1-5	5-1	2-2	4-0	1-3	1-2	2-1
9 Greenwich Borough	0-2	1-2	1-3	1-0	4-2	0-4	1-2	2-6		0-2	1-5	3-3	0-3	2-5	0-1	3-0
10 Herne Bay	1-1	2-1	2-0	3-0	2-1	1-2	1-0	3-0	5-0		4-2	3-1	1-0	2-3	0-0	3-1
11 Holmesdale	2-4	2-3	1-2	1-2	1-1	2-5	0-6	3-1	0-1	1-4		0-1	2-1	2-2	1-0	0-3
12 Lordswood	2-4	1-2	1-0	1-2	1-1	3-1	0-1	0-1	3-2	3-4	1-1		2-2	0-1	1-1	4-4
13 Sevenoaks Town	1-1	3-3	0-2	1-1	0-1	2-3	1-1	0-5	1-0	1-1	1-1	0-2		2-3	0-5	3-1
14 Tunbridge Wells	1-3	3-1	1-3	2-0	5-0	0-1	0-3	6-1	1-1	0-2	4-1	4-0	2-0		0-2	4-0
15 VCD Athletic	3-0	2-1	3-1	1-0	0-1	1-2	0-1	4-0	3-1	2-1	3-0	2-0	4-0	1-2		2-1
16 Woodstock Sports	3-3	4-1	2-0	5-2	2-1	1-7	2-0	4-1	2-1	1-2	0-1	3-2	1-2	2-0	3-2	

KENT LEAGUE - STEP 5

DIVISION ONE		P	W	D	L	F	A	Pts
1	Herne Bay Reserves	16	12	2	2	50	23	38
2	Faversham Town Reserves	16	12	1	3	49	12	37
3	Whitstable Town Reserves	16	11	1	4	46	16	34
4	Maidstone United Reserves	16	7	5	4	45	24	26
5	Erith Town Reserves	16	7	3	6	27	21	24
6	Chatham Town Reserves	16	6	2	8	28	38	20
7	Margate Reserves	16	3	2	11	26	57	11
8	Erith & Belvedere Reserves	16	3	0	13	18	51	9
9	Deal Town Reserves	16	2	2	12	14	61	8

DIVISION TWO		P	W	D	L	F	A	Pts
1	Phoenix Sports Reserves	14	11	1	2	45	14	34
2	VCD Athletic Reserves	14	11	1	2	40	15	34
3	Ramsgate Reserves	14	7	2	5	26	21	23
4	Holmesdale Reserves	14	6	2	6	23	17	20
5	Welling United Reserves	14	6	2	6	28	23	20
6	Folkestone Invicta Reserves	14	3	4	7	13	23	13
7	Lordswood Reserves	14	3	2	9	9	36	11
8	Woodstock Sports Reserves	14	1	2	11	10	45	5

Cray Valley Paper Mills. Photo: Alan Coomes.

Cray Valley 'keeper, Jack Carthy, punches clear from Erith Town's Lee Craig. Photo: Alan Coomes.

BECKENHAM TOWN
Founded: 1887   Nickname: Reds

Secretary: Peter Palmer   **(T)** 07774 728 758   **(E)** peterpalmer3@sky.com

Chairman: Peter Palmer   **Manager:** Jason Huntley   **Prog Ed:** Sam Percival

Ground: Eden Park Avenue, Beckenham Kent BR3 3JL   **(T)** 07774 728 758

Capacity: 4,000 **Seats:** 120 **Covered:** 120 **Midweek Matchday:** Tuesday   **Clubhouse:** Yes **Shop:** Yes

Colours(change): All red (All blue).
Previous Names: Stanhope Rovers.
Previous Leagues: South East London Amateur. Metropolitan. London Spartan.
Records: **Att:** 720 v Berkhamsted, FA Cup 1994-95. **Goalscorer:** Ricky Bennett. **Apps:** Lee Fabian - 985.
Senior Honours:

10 YEAR RECORD

02-03	03-04	04-05	05-06	06-07	07-08	08-09	09-10	10-11	11-12
Kent P 10	Kent P 12	Kent P 10	Kent P 2	Kent P 11	Kent P 3	Kent P 15	Kent P 4	Kent P 10	Kent P 6

CANTERBURY CITY
Founded: 1904   Nickname:

Secretary: Stuart McCluskey (Acting)   **(T)** 07826421127   **(E)** stuccfc@sky.com

Chairman: Tim Clarke   **Manager:** Simon Austin   **Prog Ed:** John Fabre

Ground: Herne Bay FC, Winch's Field, Standley Gardens, Heren Bay CT6 5SG   **(T)**

Capacity: 3,000 **Seats:** 200 **Covered:** 1,500 **Midweek Matchday:** Tuesday   **Clubhouse:** Yes **Shop:** Yes

Colours(change): All burgundy (All green)
Previous Names:
Previous Leagues: Kent 1947-59, 94-01, Metropolitan 1959-60, Southern 1960-61, 94, Kent County 2007-11.
Records:
Senior Honours: Kent County League Division One East 2007-08, 08-09.

10 YEAR RECORD

02-03	03-04	04-05	05-06	06-07	07-08	08-09	09-10	10-11	11-12
					KC1E 1	KC1E 1	KC P 5	KC P 2	Kent P 9

CORINTHIAN
Founded: 1972   Nickname:

Secretary: Sue Billings   **(T)** 07734 855 554   **(E)** corinthians@billingsgroup.com

Chairman: R J Billings   **Manager:** Tony Stitford   **Prog Ed:**

Ground: Gay Dawn Farm, Valley Road, Longfield DA3 8LY   **(T)** 01474 573 118

Capacity: **Seats:** **Covered:** **Midweek Matchday:** Tuesday   **Clubhouse:** Yes **Shop:**

Colours(change): Green & white hoops/white (Yellow/green/green)
Previous Names: Welling United Reserves > 2009.
Previous Leagues: Southern 1985-91.
Records:
Senior Honours:

10 YEAR RECORD

02-03	03-04	04-05	05-06	06-07	07-08	08-09	09-10	10-11	11-12
						Kent 2 6	Kent P 14	Kent P 12	Kent P 7

CRAY VALLEY PAPER MILLS
Founded: Nickname:

Secretary: Dave Wilson   **(T)** 07715 961 886   **(E)** wilson433@ntlworld.com

Chairman: Mac MacAnallen   **Manager:** Steve Chapman   **Prog Ed:** Dave Wilson

Ground: Badgers Sports, Middle Park Avenue, Eltham SE9 5HT   **(T)**

Capacity: **Seats:** **Covered:** **Midweek Matchday:** Tuesday   **Clubhouse:** **Shop:**

Colours(change): Green/black/black (Sky blue/white/white).
Previous Names:
Previous Leagues: Spartan 1991-97, Spartan South Midlands 1997-98, London Intermediate 1998-01, Kent County 2001-11.
Records:
Senior Honours: Kent County League Premier Division 2004-05.

10 YEAR RECORD

02-03	03-04	04-05	05-06	06-07	07-08	08-09	09-10	10-11	11-12
		KC P 1		KC P 7	KC P 9	KC P 5	KC P 6	KC P 3	Kent P 11

Erith & Belvedere. Photo: Alan Coomes.

Fisher FC. Photo: Alan Coomes.

Erith Town. Photo: Alan Coomes.

DEAL TOWN
Founded: 1908   Nickname: Town

Secretary: Paul Rivers   **(T)** 07507 231 730   **(E)** candpadams@btinternet.com

Chairman: David Melody   **Manager:** Derek Hares   **Prog Ed:** Colin Adams

Ground: Charles Sports Ground, St Leonards Road, Deal. CT14 9BB   **(T)** 01304 375 623

Capacity: 2,500 **Seats:** 180 **Covered:** 180 **Midweek Matchday:** Tuesday   **Clubhouse:** Yes **Shop:** Yes

Colours(change): Black & white/black. (Claret & blue/blue/claret).
Previous Names: Deal Cinque Ports FC > 1920
Previous Leagues: Thanet. East Kent. Kent. Aetolian. Southern. Greater London.
Records: **Att:** 2,495 v Newcastle Town, FA Vase S-F, 26.03.2000.
Senior Honours:

10 YEAR RECORD

02-03		03-04		04-05		05-06		06-07		07-08		08-09		09-10		10-11		11-12	
Kent P	4	Kent P	16	Kent P	13	Kent P	9	Kent P	8	Kent P	9	Kent P	12	Kent P	9	Kent P	11	Kent P	15

ERITH & BELVEDERE
Founded: 1922   Nickname: Deres

Secretary: Simon Kidby   **(T)** 07590 258 325   **(E)** simonkidby@googlemail.com

Chairman: John McFadden   **Manager:** Micky Collins   **Prog Ed:** Martin Tarrant/Brian Spurrell

Ground: Welling FC, Park View Rd, Welling, DA16 1SY   **(T)** 020 8304 0333

Capacity: 4,000 **Seats:** 1,070 **Covered:** 1,000 **Midweek Matchday:** Tuesday   **Clubhouse:** Yes **Shop:** Yes

Colours(change): Blue & white quarters/blue/blue. (Red & white quarters/red/red)
Previous Names: Belvedere & District FC (Formed 1918 restructured 1922)
Previous Leagues: Kent. London. Corinthian. Athenian. Southern.
Records: **Att:** 5,573 v Crook C.W., FA Am. Cup 1949. **Goalscorer:** Colin Johnson - 284 (61-71). **Apps:** Dennis Crawford - 504 (56-71).
Senior Honours:

10 YEAR RECORD

02-03		03-04		04-05		05-06		06-07		07-08		08-09		09-10		10-11		11-12	
SthE	18	SthE	21	SthE	21	Kent P	4	Kent P	7	Kent P	7	Kent P	8	Kent P	12	Kent P	5	Kent P	2

ERITH TOWN
Founded: 1959   Nickname: The Dockers

Secretary: Jim Davie   **(T)** 07831 131 278   **(E)** jamesdavie@ntlworld.com

Chairman: Albert Putman   **Manager:** Tony Russell   **Prog Ed:** Ian Birrell

Ground: Erith Sports Stadium, Avenue Road, Erith DA8 3AT   **(T)** 01322 350 271

Capacity: 1,450 **Seats:** 1,006 **Covered:** 1,066 **Midweek Matchday:** Monday   **Clubhouse:** Yes **Shop:** No

Colours(change): Red & black/black/black. (Yellow & black/white/white).
Previous Names: Woolwich Town 1959-89 and 1990-97.
Previous Leagues: London Metropolitan Sunday. London Spartan.
Records: **Att:** 325 v Charlton Athletic, friendly. **Goalscorer:** Dean Bowey.
Senior Honours:

10 YEAR RECORD

02-03		03-04		04-05		05-06		06-07		07-08		08-09		09-10		10-11		11-12	
Kent P	15	Kent P	7	Kent P	15	Kent P	14	Kent P	14	Kent P	5	Kent P	7	Kent P	12	Kent P	8	Kent P	4

FISHER
Founded: 1908   Nickname: The Fish

Secretary: Dan York   **(T)** 07719 632 635   **(E)** dan@fisherfc.co.uk

Chairman: Ben Westmancott   **Manager:** Steve Firkins   **Prog Ed:** Jevon Hall

Ground: Dulwich Hamlet FC, Edgar Kail Way, East Dulwich SE22 8BD   **(T)**

Capacity: 3,000 **Seats:** 500 **Covered:** 1,000 **Midweek Matchday:** Monday   **Clubhouse:** Yes **Shop:** Yes

Colours(change): Black & white/white/black. (Blue/black/red).
Previous Names: Fisher Athletic. Reformed as Fisher F.C. in 2009.
Previous Leagues: Parthenon, Kent Amateur, London Spartan, Southern, Isthmian, Conference.
Records: **Att:** 4,283 v Barnet Conference 04/05/1991. **Goalscorer:** Paul Shinners - 205. **Apps:** Dennis Sharp - 720.
Senior Honours: Southern League Southern Division 1982-83, Premier 86-87, Eastern 2004-05. Kent Senior Cup 1983-84. Isthmian League Cup 2005-06.

10 YEAR RECORD

02-03		03-04		04-05		05-06		06-07		07-08		08-09		09-10		10-11		11-12	
SthE	14	SthE	14	SthE	1	Isth P	3	Conf S	10	Conf S	4	Conf S	22	Kent P	13	Kent P	16	Kent P	10

Sevenoaks Town. Photo: Alan Coomes.

Tunbridge Wells. Photo: Roger Turner.

GREENWICH BOROUGH
Founded: 1928 **Nickname:** Boro

Secretary: Gerry Fox **(T)** 07427 454 102 **(E)** gerrycox@btinternet.com
Chairman: Devon Hanson **Manager:** **Prog Ed:** Gerry Fox
Ground: Holmesdale FC, 68 Oakley Road, Bromley, Kent BR2 8HQ **(T)**
Capacity: **Seats:** **Covered:** **Midweek Matchday:** Tuesday **Clubhouse:** Yes **Shop:** No

Colours(change): Red & black stripes/black/black. (Blue & black stripes/black or white/black or white).
Previous Names: Woolwich Borough Council Athletic FC.
Previous Leagues: South London Alliance. Kent Amateur. London Spartan.
Records: Att: 2,000 v Charlton Athletic, turning on of floodlights, 1978.
Senior Honours: Kent League 86-87, 87-88.

10 YEAR RECORD

02-03		03-04		04-05		05-06		06-07		07-08		08-09		09-10		10-11		11-12	
Kent P	14	Kent P	8	Kent P	9	Kent P	13	Kent P	5	Kent P	8	Kent P	3	Kent P	5	Kent P	4	Kent P	16

HOLMESDALE
Founded: 1956 **Nickname:**

Secretary: Ross Mitchell **(T)** 07875 730 862 **(E)** secretary@holmesdalefc.co.uk
Chairman: Mark Harris **Manager:** Fabio Rossi **Prog Ed:** Mark Harris
Ground: Holmesdale Sp.& Soc.Club, 68 Oakley Rd, Bromley BR2 8HQ **(T)** 020 8462 4440
Capacity: **Seats:** **Covered:** **Midweek Matchday:** Wednesday **Clubhouse:** Yes **Shop:** Yes

Colours(change): Green & yellow/green. (All blue).
Previous Names: None.
Previous Leagues: Thornton Heath & Dist. Surrey Inter. Surrey South Eastern. Kent County.
Records: Goals: M Barnett - 410 (in 429 apps).
Senior Honours:

10 YEAR RECORD

02-03		03-04		04-05		05-06		06-07		07-08		08-09		09-10		10-11		11-12	
KC1W	4	KC1W	4	KC1W	8	KC1W	1	KC P	1	Kent P	15	Kent P	5	Kent P	10	Kent P	14	Kent P	13

LORDSWOOD
Founded: 1968 **Nickname:** Lords

Secretary: Steve Lewis **(T)** 07968 429 941 **(E)** slew1953@hotmail.co.uk
Chairman: Ron Constantine **Manager:** Jason Lillis **Prog Ed:** John O'Halloran
Ground: Martyn Grove, Northdane Way, Walderslade, ME5 8YE **(T)** 01634 669 138
Capacity: 600 **Seats:** 123 **Covered:** 123 **Midweek Matchday:** Tuesday **Clubhouse:** Yes **Shop:** No

Colours(change): Orange & black/black. (All white).
Previous Names: None.
Previous Leagues: Rochester & Dist. Kent County.
Records:
Senior Honours:

10 YEAR RECORD

02-03		03-04		04-05		05-06		06-07		07-08		08-09		09-10		10-11		11-12	
Kent P	13	Kent P	13	Kent P	16	Kent P	8	Kent P	13	Kent P	16	Kent P	16	Kent P	16	Kent P	13	Kent P	12

ROCHESTER UNITED
Founded: 1982 **Nickname:**

Secretary: Tony Wheeler **(T)** 07775 735 543 **(E)** tony.wheelerrufc@yahoo.co.uk
Chairman: David Archer **Manager:** Glen Barlow **Prog Ed:**
Ground: Bly Spartans Sports Ground, Rede Court Road, Strood, Kent ME2 3TU **(T)** 01634 710577
Capacity: **Seats:** **Covered:** **Midweek Matchday:** Tuesday **Clubhouse:** **Shop:**

Colours(change): All maroon (All white)
Previous Names: Templars. Bly Spartans.
Previous Leagues: Kent County > 2011. Founder Members of Kent Invicta 2011-12.
Records:
Senior Honours: Kent County League Division One West 2007-08. Kent Invicta League 2011-12.

10 YEAR RECORD

02-03		03-04		04-05		05-06		06-07		07-08		08-09		09-10		10-11		11-12	
KC1W		KC1W	2	KC1W	3	KC1W	10	KC1W	2	KC1W	1	KC P	10	KC P	12	KC P	15	K_Iv	1

SEVENOAKS TOWN
Founded: 1883 Nickname: Town

Secretary: Eddie Diplock **(T)** 01732 454 280 **(E)** suesmart53@hotmail.co.uk
Chairman: Tony Smart **Manager:** Simon Jones **Prog Ed:** Ian Murphy
Ground: Greatness Park, Seal Road, Sevenoaks TN14 5BL **(T)** 01732 741 987
Capacity: 2,000 **Seats:** 110 **Covered:** 200 **Midweek Matchday:** Tuesday **Clubhouse:** **Shop:**

Colours(change): Blue stripes/navy. (Green & white/white).
Previous Names: None.
Previous Leagues: Sevenoaks League. Kent Amateur/County.
Records:
Senior Honours:

10 YEAR RECORD

02-03	03-04	04-05	05-06	06-07	07-08	08-09	09-10	10-11	11-12
KC P 1	Kent P 11	Kent P 11	Kent P 16	Kent P 10	Kent P 11	Kent P 14	Kent P 6	Kent P 7	Kent P 14

TUNBRIDGE WELLS
Founded: 1886 Nickname: The Wells

Secretary: Phill Allcorn **(T)** 07900 243 508 **(E)** secretary@twfcexec.com
Chairman: Joe Crocker **Manager:** Martin Larkin **Prog Ed:** Joe Crocker
Ground: Culverden Stadium, Culverden Down, Tunbridge Wells TN4 9SG **(T)** 01892 520 517
Capacity: 3,750 **Seats:** 250 **Covered:** 1,000 **Midweek Matchday:** Tuesday **Clubhouse:** Yes **Shop:** No

Colours(change): All red (Blue & black/blueblue)
Previous Names: None.
Previous Leagues: Isthminan. London Spartan.
Records: Att: 967 v Maidstone United, FA Cup 1969. **Goalscorer:** John Wingate - 151. **Apps:** Tony Atkins - 410.
Senior Honours:

10 YEAR RECORD

02-03	03-04	04-05	05-06	06-07	07-08	08-09	09-10	10-11	11-12
Kent P 12	Kent P 14	Kent P 7	Kent P 10	Kent P 15	Kent P 10	Kent P 10	Kent P 7	Kent P 6	Kent P 5

VICKERS CRAYFORD DARTFORD ATHLETIC
Founded: 1916 Nickname: The Vickers

Secretary: Debbie Rump **(T)** **(E)** vcddebbie@virginmedia.com
Chairman: Gary Rump **Manager:** Ricky Bennett **Prog Ed:** Brian Norris
Ground: VCD Athletic Club, Old Road, Crayford DA1 4DN **(T)** 01322 524 262
Capacity: **Seats:** Yes **Covered:** Yes **Midweek Matchday:** Wednesday **Clubhouse:** Yes **Shop:** No

Colours(change): Green & white/white (Blue/black/black)
Previous Names: Vickers (Erith). Vickers (Crayford).
Previous Leagues: Dartford & District. Kent County. Isthmian
Records:
Senior Honours:

10 YEAR RECORD

02-03	03-04	04-05	05-06	06-07	07-08	08-09	09-10	10-11	11-12
Kent P 7	Kent P 3	Kent P 5	Kent P 6	Kent P 2	Kent P 2	Kent P 1	Isth1N 8	Kent P 3	Kent P 3

WHYTELEAFE
Founded: 1946 Nickname: Leafe

Secretary: Chris Layton **(T)** 0771 845 7875 **(E)** chris@theleafe.co.uk
Chairman: Mark Coote **Manager:** Steve Griffin **Prog Ed:** Chris Layton
Ground: 15 Church Road, Whyteleafe, Surrey CR3 0AR **(T)** 0208 660 5491
Capacity: 5,000 **Seats:** 400 **Covered:** 600 **Midweek Matchday:** **Clubhouse:** Yes **Shop:** Yes

Colours(change): Green/white/white (All maroon)
Previous Names: Not known
Previous Leagues: Caterham & Ed, Croydon, Thornton Heath & Dist, Surrey Interm. (East) 1954-58, Surrey Sen 58-75, Spartan 75-81, Athenian 81-84, Isthmian 84-2012
Records: 2,210 v Chester City - FA Cup 1999-2000
Senior Honours: Surrey Senior Cup 1968-69.

10 YEAR RECORD

02-03	03-04	04-05	05-06	06-07	07-08	08-09	09-10	10-11	11-12
Isth1S 5	Isth1S 17	Isth1 9	Isth1 18	Isth1S 20	Isth1S 11	Isth1S 18	Isth1S 15	Isth1S 16	Isth1S 21

WOODSTOCK SPORTS

Founded: 1927   Nickname:

Secretary: Colin Page   **(T)** 07970 549 355   **(E)** c_page@blueyonder.co.uk

Chairman: Ron Welling   **Manager:** Ben Taylor   **Prog Ed:** Mike Wood

Ground: The WE Mannin Stadium, Woodstock Park, Broadoak Rd, Sittingbourne ME9 8AG   **(T)** 07970 549 355

Capacity: 3,000   **Seats:** 200   **Covered:** 1,500   **Midweek Matchday:** Wednesday   **Clubhouse:** Yes   **Shop:** Yes

Colours(change): Blue & white/black. (All red).

Previous Names: Amalgamated with Teynham & Lynsted in 1998, Norton Sports 1998-2011.

Previous Leagues: Kent County.

Records:

Senior Honours:

10 YEAR RECORD

02-03	03-04	04-05	05-06	06-07	07-08	08-09	09-10	10-11	11-12
		KC1E 1		KC P 3	KC P 1	Kent P 11	Kent P 11	Kent P 9	Kent P 8

Kent League Champions 2011-12 - Herne Bay. Photo: Roger Turner.

MIDLAND COMBINATION

Sponsored by: Athium Limited

Founded: 1927

Recent Champions:
2007: Coventry Sphinx. 2008: Coleshill Town. 2009: Loughborough University
2010: Heath Hayes. 2011: Heather St. Johns

midcomb.com

PREMIER DIVISION	P	W	D	L	F	A	Pts
1 (P) Continental Star	32	21	7	4	72	39	70
2 Southam United	32	21	3	8	87	48	66
3 Coventry Copsewood	32	18	6	8	58	30	60
4 Bolehall Swifts	32	17	7	8	73	44	58
5 Castle Vale	32	17	6	9	56	34	57
6 Brocton	32	17	4	11	67	45	55
7 Bloxwich United	32	16	6	10	68	62	54
8 Earlswood Town	32	12	6	14	52	54	42
9 Bartley Green	32	11	6	15	39	53	39
10 Pilkington XXX	32	11	5	16	41	68	38
11 Nuneaton Griff	32	9	10	13	56	64	37
12 (R) Cadbury Athletic	32	9	8	15	46	56	35
13 Racing Club Warwick	32	10	5	17	46	57	35
14 Walsall Wood	32	9	6	17	45	50	33
15 Pelsall Villa	32	9	5	18	33	58	32
16 Pershore Town	32	8	7	17	43	72	31
17 Castle Vale JKS	32	6	5	21	57	105	23

DIVISION ONE	P	W	D	L	F	A	Pts
1 (P) Blackwood	34	24	2	8	72	46	74
2 (P) Littleton	34	22	2	10	82	52	68
3 (P) Bromsgrove Sporting	34	19	8	7	94	44	65
4 (P) Lichfield City	34	19	6	9	72	44	63
5 Alvis	34	18	6	10	67	46	60
6 Shirley Town	34	18	3	13	67	46	57
7 Knowle	34	14	14	6	56	35	56
8 Archdale '73	34	15	7	12	81	62	52
9 Hampton	34	15	6	13	57	71	51
10 West Midlands Police	34	14	6	14	75	80	48
11 Stretton Eagles	34	13	8	13	68	61	47
12 Feckenham	34	12	7	15	62	62	43
13 Fairfield Villa	34	11	9	14	67	65	42
14 Coton Green	34	7	10	17	39	74	31
15 FC Glades Sporting	34	7	9	18	42	74	30
16 Northfield Town	34	8	5	21	39	73	29
17 Droitwich Spa	34	6	4	24	38	76	22
18 Phoenix United	34	6	4	24	34	101	22

PREMIER DIVISION	1	2	3	4	5	6	7	8	9	10	11	12	13	14	15	16	17
1 Bartley Green		1-2	1-5	0-2	1-1	0-2	2-2	0-3	3-1	3-0	2-0	1-0	4-3	1-1	1-4	1-0	1-4
2 Bloxwich United	1-1		1-2	2-1	1-0	1-2	4-3	3-2	0-2	1-1	2-7	1-0	1-0	9-3	1-1	4-3	1-0
3 Bolehall Swifts	0-3	3-1		0-1	4-0	1-0	11-2	2-2	1-0	4-1	1-1	5-1	3-2	1-1	2-0	2-4	0-2
4 Brocton	4-1	1-2	1-1		1-0	3-1	3-2	2-3	1-3	1-0	5-0	6-0	5-0	6-0	1-2	1-3	1-3
5 Cadbury Athletic	2-1	2-4	5-1	3-2		0-0	6-0	0-1	1-0	2-3	1-1	1-1	2-1	2-1	1-2	1-4	0-0
6 Castle Vale	1-0	3-1	2-2	3-1	2-0		3-1	1-2	2-0	4-1	1-0	1-1	4-1	1-0	6-0	1-4	0-0
7 Castle Vale JKS	2-0	0-0	1-4	2-4	3-1	2-1		0-5	2-4	5-2	2-3	2-2	3-4	1-2	0-7	2-3	1-3
8 Continental Star	5-1	3-1	3-2	0-0	0-0	4-2	4-2		1-1	3-0	2-2	1-0	2-1	2-0	3-1	2-4	2-1
9 Coventry Copsewood	2-0	1-2	1-0	4-0	5-1	2-0	2-1	5-0		3-0	1-1	1-0	3-3	2-0	2-0	0-1	1-0
10 Earlswood Town	0-0	2-2	2-1	0-3	3-0	0-0	1-1	1-3	1-3		1-3	3-0	5-0	6-0	0-1	2-3	3-0
11 Nuneaton Griff	0-2	4-4	2-2	1-1	0-5	1-0	3-5	3-4	1-0	1-2		1-2	4-1	3-3	3-0	2-0	2-2
12 Pelsall Villa	3-0	0-2	1-1	0-2	0-2	2-1	4-2	0-4	2-2	3-2	3-1		0-1	0-1	0-2	1-5	1-0
13 Pershore Town	0-0	4-3	0-2	1-2	4-2	0-1	5-3	0-0	1-1	1-1	0-0	1-0		0-1	2-1	2-2	3-2
14 Pilkington XXX	0-4	2-4	0-2	5-1	4-0	1-1	2-1	3-2	0-2	0-3	2-1	1-3	2-1		1-1	1-4	2-0
15 Racing Club Warwick	0-1	2-1	1-3	0-1	2-2	0-2	0-3	1-1	3-1	2-3	1-3	0-1	5-1	2-1		2-3	0-0
16 Southam United	2-1	3-2	1-2	2-2	3-2	1-3	9-0	0-1	1-1	1-2	2-1	3-1	5-0	2-0	4-2		4-2
17 Walsall Wood	1-2	3-4	1-3	1-2	1-1	2-5	1-1	0-2	1-2	0-1	5-1	2-1	3-0	0-1	3-1	2-1	

CUP FINALS

THE LES JAMES CHALLENGE CUP

Feckenham FC 3 v 0 Racing Club Warwick FC

CHALLENGE BOWL UNDER 21'S

Lougbborough Dynamo FC 1 v 2 Redditch United FC

CHALLENGE TROPHY

Quorn FC 2 - 3 Chasetown FC

CHALLENGE URN

Coleshill Town FC Res 3 AET 4 Walsall Wood FC Res

CHALLENGE VASE

Chelmsley Town FC 4 - 3 Polesworth FC

PRESIDENTS CUP

Archdale "73" FC 1 v 2 Littleton FC

DIVISION ONE	1	2	3	4	5	6	7	8	9	10	11	12	13	14	15	16	17	18
1 Alvis		0-1	3-1	2-2	0-0	4-1	3-0	4-1	2-1	4-0	1-2	3-2	3-0	4-2	2-0	0-3	2-2	3-2
2 Archdale '73	2-4		2-1	1-0	5-2	1-2	4-4	2-0	1-5	3-2	2-2	1-1	5-3	4-0	7-0	0-3	2-2	5-0
3 Blackwood	1-0	3-2		2-1	6-0	2-0	3-1	1-1	1-1	3-2	0-2	0-2	3-1	3-1	4-1	2-1	2-1	2-0
4 Bromsgrove Sporting	2-2	5-1	5-0		3-1	3-2	4-1	5-0	1-2	5-2	1-1	1-0	2-1	4-1	5-2	3-2	4-1	1-1
5 Coton Green	0-4	2-2	2-3	0-0		1-0	2-2	2-4	1-2	0-3	1-0	1-3	0-1	2-0	1-0	2-2	0-4	3-3
6 Droitwich Spa	1-3	2-1	1-4	0-1	1-0		2-1	1-1	1-3	5-0	1-3	1-5	0-3	0-4	2-1	1-4	1-2	1-1
7 Fairfield Villa	2-0	2-2	3-1	1-1	1-1	2-1		1-1	3-1	1-2	0-0	5-3	1-2	6-0	4-3	0-1	2-3	3-2
8 FC Glades Sporting	1-0	2-1	1-2	1-1	1-1	1-1	4-2		1-2	0-1	0-2	2-2	1-4	3-1	4-0	0-2	1-1	1-7
9 Feckenham	3-4	0-0	1-2	1-3	1-1	3-0	1-3	1-3		4-0	0-2	1-5	0-2	5-2	1-1	2-1	4-0	3-3
10 Hampton	0-3	0-5	1-4	2-1	1-1	6-4	2-3	3-1	0-2		1-1	2-2	1-4	3-3	1-0	3-2	2-1	3-1
11 Knowle	0-1	2-0	1-2	3-2	4-0	2-0	4-4	1-1	2-2	0-0		1-1	1-3	1-2	1-1	3-0	1-1	1-1
12 Lichfield City	2-1	0-4	1-1	2-1	3-0	1-0	3-1	4-1	2-0	1-2	0-0		0-3	1-2	3-0	6-0	1-2	3-2
13 Littleton	4-0	1-4	1-2	2-2	1-2	1-0	2-1	3-0	4-3	3-1	1-1	3-2		1-0	8-1	0-2	4-2	3-1
14 Northfield Town	1-2	0-3	0-1	0-4	4-3	1-1	2-1	1-1	2-0	1-1	1-3	0-2	1-2		2-0	0-4	0-1	1-3
15 Phoenix United	1-0	2-1	0-6	2-11	1-2	2-0	0-3	5-1	0-0	1-2	4-3	1-2	3-2	0-2		0-6	0-4	0-4
16 Shirley Town	0-0	5-2	0-2	2-3	5-2	2-1	1-0	2-0	4-2	1-2	0-2	0-1	4-0	1-0	0-0		3-0	4-0
17 Stretton Eagles	3-3	1-4	6-1	2-1	3-1	3-2	2-2	3-0	1-2	0-1	0-1	2-4	2-4	0-0	3-0	5-0		2-3
18 West Midlands Police	3-0	4-1	2-1	1-6	1-2	4-2	2-1	5-3	4-3	1-5	1-3	0-2	1-5	3-2	4-2	2-0	3-3	

MIDLAND COMBINATION DIVISION ONE CONSTITUTION 2012-13

ALVIS	ALVIS SPORTS & SOCIAL CLUB, GREEN LANE, COVENTRY CV3 6EG	NONE
ARCHDALE '73	County Sports Ground, Claines Lane, Worcester WR3 7SS	07736 309670
ASTON	Coleshill Town FC Pack Meadow, Packington Lane, Coleshill, B46 3JQ	07412 008047
CADBURY ATHLETIC	Alvechurch FC Lye Meadow, Redditch Road, Alvechurch, Worcestershire, B48 7RS	07725 868328
CHELMSLEY TOWN	The Pavilion, Coleshill Road, Marston Green, Birmingham B37 7HW	0121 779 5400
COTON GREEN	Red Lion Ground, Armitage Lane, Brereton, Rugeley WS15 1ED	01889 585526
DROITWICH SPA	Droitwich Spa Leisure Centre, Briar Mill, Droitwich WR9 0RZ	01905 771212
FAIRFIELD VILLA	Recreation Ground, Stourbridge Road, Fairfield, Bromsgrove B61 9LZ	01527 877049
FC GLADES SPORTING	The Glades, Lugtrout Lane, Solihull B91 2RX	None
FECKENHAM	Studley Sports & Social Club, Eldorado Close, Studley B80 7HP	01527 852671
GREENHILL	Dudley Sports FC, Dudley S&S, Hillcrest Avenue, Brierley Hill DY5 3QH	01384 826420
HAMPTON	Field Lane Sports Ground, Lugtrout Lane, Solihull B91 2RT	None
KNOWLE	Hampton Road, Knowle, Solihull B93 0NX	01564 779807
NORTHFIELD TOWN	Shenley Lane Community Centre, Shenley Lane, Selly Oak, Birmingham B29 4HZ	0121 475 3870
PHOENIX UNITED	Pavilion Sports Ground, Thimblemill Road, Smethwick, Warley B66 6NR	0121 429 2459
SHIRLEY TOWN	Tilehouse Lane, Whitlocks End, Solihull B90 1PN	None
STRETTON EAGLES	Shobnall Sports & Social Club, Shobnall Road, Burton-on-Trent DE14 2BB	01283 567991
WEST MIDLANDS POLICE	Tally Ho! Traing Centre, Pershore Road, Edgbaston, Birmingham B5 7RD	0121 626 8228

MIDLAND COMBINATION - STEP 6/7

DIVISION TWO

		P	W	D	L	F	A	Pts
1	(P) Greenhill	26	18	6	2	59	22	60
2	(P) Aston	26	17	4	5	66	28	55
3	(P) Chelmsley Town	26	16	7	3	64	31	55
4	Henley Forest	26	16	4	6	73	40	52
5	Barton United	26	13	8	5	59	37	47
6	Perrywood	26	11	3	12	58	60	36
7	FC Stratford	26	10	5	11	53	57	35
8	Polesworth	26	10	1	15	42	52	31
9	Enville Athletic	26	7	5	14	36	56	26
10	Coventry Spartans	26	5	9	12	33	59	24
11	Leamington Hibernian	26	6	5	15	30	59	23
12	Clements '83 (-3)	26	6	7	13	40	51	22
13	Inkberrow	26	5	7	14	34	49	22
14	Burntwood Town	26	4	5	17	31	77	17

Young Warriors - record expunged

RESERVE DIVISION ONE

		P	W	D	L	F	A	Pts
1	Chasetown Reserves	22	16	6	0	72	13	54
2	Quorn Reserves	22	11	7	4	57	29	40
3	Oadby Town Reserves	22	10	6	6	42	37	36
4	Gresley Reserves	22	10	5	7	51	43	35
5	Rugby Town Reserves	22	10	4	8	48	43	34
6	Boldmere St Michael Res. (-1)	22	9	6	7	40	34	32
7	Coalville Town Reserves	22	9	4	9	42	37	31
8	Stratford Town Reserves	22	8	5	9	38	55	29
9	Banbury United Reserves	22	6	10	6	30	29	28
10	Barwell Reserves	22	7	6	9	33	34	27
11	Highgate United Reserves	22	1	6	15	16	59	9
12	(R) Brocton Reserves	22	2	1	19	23	79	7

RESERVE DIVISION TWO

		P	W	D	L	F	A	Pts
1	Coleshill Town Reserves	26	19	3	4	91	27	60
2	(P) Lichfield City Reserves	26	17	5	4	57	31	56
3	Continental Star Reserves	26	16	2	8	50	40	50
4	Earlswood Town Reserves	26	15	4	7	63	41	49
5	Bromsgrove Sporting Reserves	26	12	4	10	60	44	40
6	Racing Club Warwick Reserves	26	12	3	11	39	47	39
7	Walsall Wood Reserves	26	11	4	11	43	40	37
8	Tipton Town Reserves	26	11	3	12	65	62	36
9	Shirley Town Reserves	26	8	6	12	32	44	30
10	Knowle Reserves	26	8	6	12	36	63	30
11	Droitwich Spa Reserves	26	8	3	15	34	42	27
12	Cadbury Athletic Reserves	26	7	3	16	41	63	24
13	Northfield Town Reserves	26	4	7	15	31	56	19
14	Coton Green Reserves	26	4	7	15	35	77	19

DIVISION TWO

	DIVISION TWO	1	2	3	4	5	6	7	8	9	10	11	12	13	14
1	Aston		6-1	3-1	3-3	3-0	3-3	2-0	3-2	0-1	3-2	3-0	3-0	5-2	2-1
2	Barton United	2-2		3-0	2-2	1-0	9-0	0-0	3-0	3-1	0-3	1-0	2-1	2-0	5-1
3	Burntwood Town	0-2	1-3		1-3	2-1	1-1	0-0	3-3	1-3	0-4	3-2	1-2	2-1	0-2
4	Chelmsley Town	1-0	2-1	9-1		1-0	2-0	3-0	6-0	1-1	2-0	2-0	3-0	3-2	0-2
5	Clements '83	0-2	1-2	3-0	3-3		2-0	0-3	1-3	1-1	1-1	2-2	3-0	0-1	2-0
6	Coventry Spartans	1-5	2-2	3-3	0-1	5-1		2-1	0-1	0-3	1-1	1-3	1-1	2-1	4-1
7	Enville Athletic	1-5	2-2	3-2	1-2	1-1	2-0		2-1	1-3	1-5	1-2	3-1	2-3	1-2
8	FC Stratford	0-2	2-2	5-2	2-3	5-0	7-1	5-3		0-4	1-1	2-0	2-1	2-3	2-1
9	Greenhill	1-1	2-1	4-0	3-1	3-3	1-1	2-1	1-2		3-1	2-0	0-0	2-1	4-1
10	Henley Forest	3-1	1-3	7-2	3-2	4-3	3-2	6-1	6-0	0-4		1-0	4-2	2-1	1-0
11	Inkberrow	0-3	2-2	2-2	0-0	2-2	1-1	1-2	2-0	1-2	2-2		1-3	3-5	1-2
12	Leamington Hibernian	1-4	2-2	3-0	2-2	1-3	0-0	1-2	1-0	1-3	1-7	0-3		1-6	1-2
13	Perrywood	1-0	3-2	4-1	3-3	4-3	4-0	2-2	2-2	0-2	2-4	2-4	1-2		4-2
14	Polesworth	1-0	1-3	1-2	1-4	1-4	0-2	3-0	4-4	0-3	2-1	3-0	1-2	7-0	

MIDLAND COMBINATION DIVISION TWO CONSTITUTION 2012-13

ALCESTER TOWN	Stratford Road, Oversley Green, Alcester, Warwickshire, B49 6LN	07970 148893
BARNT GREEN SPARTAK	TSA Sports Ground, Eckersall Road, Kings Norton, Birmingham, B38 8SR	07806 298217
BARTON UNITED	Holland SC, Efflinch Lane, Barton-under-Needwood, Burton-upon-Trent DE13 8ET	01283 713972
BURNTWOOD TOWN	Memorial Ground, Rugeley Road, Burntwood WS7 9BE	07946 269153
CLEMENTS '83	Sedgemere Sports & Social, Sedgemere Road, Yardley, Birmingham B26 2AX	0121 783 0888
COVENTRY SPARTANS	Westwood Heath Sports Ground, Westwood Heath Road, Westwood Heath, Coventry CV4 8GP	None
COVENTRY SPIRES	Westwood Heath Sports Grd, Westwood Heath Rd, Westwood Heath, Coventry, CV4 8GP	07841 923904
ENVILLE ATHLETIC	Enville Athletic Club, Hall Drive, Enville, Stourbridge DY7 5HB	01384 872368
FC STRATFORD	Knights Lane, Tiddington, Stratford-upon-Avon CV37 7BZ	None
HENLEY FOREST	Henley-in-Arden Sports/S Grnd, Stratford Road, Henley-in-Arden B95 6AD	01564 792022
INKBERROW	Sands Road, Inkberrow, Worcester WR7 4HJ	None
KENILWORTH TOWN KH	Gypsy Lane, Kenilworth, Warwickshire, CV8 1FA	07946 144831
LEAMINGTON HIBERNIAN	Ajax Park, Hampton Road, Warwick CV35 8HA	01926 495786
PERRYWOOD	Neel Park, Droitwich Road, Perdiswell, Worcester WR3 7SN	07808 768222
POLESWORTH	North Warks Sports & Social, Hermitage Hill, Polesworth, Tamworth B78 1HS	01827 892482
RUGELEY RANGERS	Brereton Social FC, Armitage Lane, , Staffordshire, WS15 1ED	07805 988182
YOUNG WARRIORS	Coventry Sphinx FC, Sphinx Drive, Siddeley Avenue, Coventry CV3 1WA	024 7645 1361

ATHERSTONE TOWN
Founded: 2004   Nickname: The Adders

Secretary: Graham Read   **(T)** 01908 211166   **(E)** grahamgdr777@aol.com
Chairman: Robert Weale   **Manager:** Mark Grainger   **Prog Ed:** Graham Read
Ground: Sheepy Road, Atherston, Warwickshire CV9 3AD   **(T)** 01827 717 829   **Capacity:**
Colours(change): Red and white stripes/black/red

ADDITIONAL INFORMATION:
Previous Leagues: Midland Combination 2004-06. Midland Alliance 2006-08, 11-12. Southern 2008-11.
Honours: Midland Combination Division 1 2004-05, Premier Division 2005-06. Midland Alliance 2007-08.

BLACKWOOD
Founded: 1964   Nickname:

Secretary: Terry Moyens   **(T)** 07811378 652   **(E)** terrymoyens@blueyonder.co.uk
Chairman: Malcom Hudson   **Manager:** Jim Brogan   **Prog Ed:**
Ground: The Coppice, Tythe Barn Lane, Shirley, Solihull, West Midlands, B90 1PH   **(T)**   **Capacity:**
Colours(change): Blue & black stripes/black/black

ADDITIONAL INFORMATION:
Honours: Midland Combination Division Three 2009-10, Division Two 2010-11, Division One 2011-12.

BLOXWICH UNITED
Founded: 2006   Nickname:

Secretary: Ian Mason   **(T)** 07771 717 349   **(E)** i.mason@blueyonder.co.uk
Chairman: Dennis Holford   **Manager:**   **Prog Ed:**
Ground: Red Lion Ground, Somerfield Road, Bloxwich, Walsall WS3 2EJ   **(T)** 01922 405 835   **Capacity:**
Colours(change): All red

ADDITIONAL INFORMATION: Previous League: West Midlands > 2011.

BOLEHILL SWIFTS
Founded: 1953   Nickname:

Secretary: Philip Crowley   **(T)** 07702 786 722   **(E)** bolehallswifts.philcrowley@hotmail.co.uk
Chairman: Les Fitzpatrick   **Manager:** Daren Fulford   **Prog Ed:**
Ground: Rene Road, Bolehall, Tamworth, Staffordshire B77 3NN   **(T)**   **Capacity:**
Colours(change): All yellow.

ADDITIONAL INFORMATION:
Honours: Midland Combination Division 2 1984-85.

BROCTON
Founded: 1937   Nickname:

Secretary: Terry Homer   **(T)** 07791 841 774   **(E)** terryhomer@yahoo.co.uk
Chairman: Brian Townsend   **Manager:** John Berks   **Prog Ed:**
Ground: Silkmore Lane Sports Grd, Silkmore Lane, Stafford, Staffordshire ST17 4JH   **(T)**   **Capacity:**
Colours(change): Green & white/white/green & white

ADDITIONAL INFORMATION:

BROMSGROVE SPORTING
Founded: 2009   Nickname: The Rouslers

Secretary: Geoff Bayley   **(T)** 07837 105 368   **(E)** geoffreybayley@tiscali.co.uk
Chairman: John Teece   **Manager:** Keith Draper   **Prog Ed:**
Ground: The Victoria Ground, Birmingham Road, Bromsgrove, Worcs, B61 0DR   **(T)** 01527 876949   **Capacity:** 4,893
Colours(change): Red & white stripes/blue/blue

ADDITIONAL INFORMATION:

CASTLE VALE JKS
Founded: 1998   Nickname:

Secretary: Barry Lee   **(T)** 07957 422 145   **(E)** pneumaticsys@aol.com
Chairman: Duval Palgrave   **Manager:**   **Prog Ed:**
Ground: Vale Stadium, Farnborough Road, Castle Vale, Birmingham B35 7DA   **(T)**   **Capacity:**
Colours(change): Yellow & blue/blue/yellow & blue

ADDITIONAL INFORMATION:
Honours: Midland Combination Division 1 2008-09.

COVENTRY COPSEWOOD
Founded: 1923 Nickname:

Secretary: David Wilson   **(T)** 07807 969 327   **(E)** copsewoodfc@btopenworld.com
Chairman: TBA   **Manager:** Darren Dickson   **Prog Ed:**
Ground: Copsewood Sports & Social Club, Allard Way, Binley, Coventry CV3 1JP   **(T)**   **Capacity:**
Colours(change): All blue

ADDITIONAL INFORMATION:
Previous Names: G.P.T. Coventry > 2000, Coventry Marconi > 2005.
Honours: Midland Combination Challenge Cup 2006-07.

EARLSWOOD TOWN
Founded: 1968 Nickname:

Secretary: Clive Faulkner   **(T)** 07866 122 254   **(E)** faulkner-c1@sky.com
Chairman: Graham Ashford   **Manager:**   **Prog Ed:**
Ground: Studley FC, Abbeyfields Drive, Studley, B80 7BE   **(T)**   **Capacity:**
Colours(change): All red.

ADDITIONAL INFORMATION:
Honours: Midland Combination League Division One 2010-11.

LICHFIELD CITY
Founded: 1970 Nickname:

Secretary: Michael Tyler   **(T)** 07756 521 301   **(E)** tylermick1954@hotmail.co.uk
Chairman: Darren Leaver   **Manager:** Russell Dodd   **Prog Ed:**
Ground: Brownsfield Park, Brownsfield Road, Lichfield, Staffs, WS13 6AY   **(T)**   **Capacity:**
Colours(change): All blue

ADDITIONAL INFORMATION:

LITTLETON
Founded: 1890 Nickname:

Secretary: Mrs M Brighton   **(T)** 01386 832 906   **(E)** mbrighton1@hotmail.co.uk
Chairman: Colin Emms   **Manager:** Andy Robbins   **Prog Ed:**
Ground: 5 Acres, Pebworth Road, North Littleton, Evesham, Worcs, WR11 8QL   **(T)**   **Capacity:**
Colours(change): Red/white/red

ADDITIONAL INFORMATION:

NUNEATON GRIFF
Founded: 1972 Nickname:

Secretary: Peter Kemp   **(T)** 07931 297 935   **(E)** nuneatongriff@talktalk.net
Chairman: John Gore   **Manager:**   **Prog Ed:**
Ground: The Pingles Stadium, Avenue Road, Nuneaton, Warwickshire CV11 4LX   **(T)**   **Capacity:**
Colours(change): Blue & white/blue/blue

ADDITIONAL INFORMATION:
Honours: Midland Combination Premier Division 1999-2000, 00-01.

PELSALL VILLA
Founded: 1898 Nickname:

Secretary: Shaun Mason   **(T)** 07779 111 023   **(E)** shaunmason1967@yahoo.co.uk
Chairman: Shaun Mason   **Manager:** Mark Bentley   **Prog Ed:**
Ground: The Bush Ground, Walsall Road, Walsall, West Midlands WS3 4BP   **(T)**   **Capacity:**
Colours(change): Red & black stripes/black/black

ADDITIONAL INFORMATION:

PERSHORE TOWN
Founded: 1988 Nickname:

Secretary: Jane Conway   **(T)** 07841 377 788   **(E)** jane.chamberlain@homecall.co.uk
Chairman: Damien Rourke   **Manager:**   **Prog Ed:**
Ground: King George V Playing Field, King George's Way, Pershore WR10 1AA   **(T)**   **Capacity:**
Colours(change): Blue & white stripes/blue/blue

ADDITIONAL INFORMATION:
Previous League: Midland Alliance (Founder members).
Honours: Midland Combination Division 2 1989-90, Premier 1993-94.

PILKINGTON XXX

Founded: 2002   Nickname:

Secretary: Ms Kim Holland   **(T)** 07432 784 340   **(E)** pilkingtonxxx@gmail.com
Chairman: Saul Gray   **Manager:** Graeme Dunkley   **Prog Ed:**
Ground: TSA Sports Ground, Eckersall Road, Kings Norton, Birmingham B38 8SR   **(T)**   **Capacity:**
Colours(change): All red

ADDITIONAL INFORMATION:
Previous Name: Burman Hi-Ton > 2002.
Honours: Midland Combination Division 2 2001-02.

RACING CLUB WARWICK

Founded: 1919   Nickname: Racers

Secretary: Pat Murphy   **(T)** 07926 188 553   **(E)** pja.murphy@hotmail.co.uk
Chairman: Bob Dhillon   **Manager:** Mark O'Callaghan   **Prog Ed:**
Ground: Townsend Meadow, Hampton Road, Warwick, Warwickshire CV34 6JP   **(T)** 01926 495 786   **Capacity:**
Colours(change): Amber/black/black

ADDITIONAL INFORMATION:
Record Att: 1,280 v Leamington FC, Midland All.26/12/2005. **Goalscorer:** Steve Edgington - 200. **Apps:** Steve Cooper - 600+
Honours: Midland Combination Premier Division 1987-88.

SOUTHAM UNITED

Founded: 1905   Nickname:

Secretary: Charles Hill   **(T)** 07802 949 781   **(E)** charles@southamunitedfc.com
Chairman: Charles Hill   **Manager:** Barry Shearsby (Caretaker)   **Prog Ed:**
Ground: Banbury Road, Southam, Warwickshire CV47 2BJ   **(T)**   **Capacity:**
Colours(change): Yellow/royal blue/royal blue

ADDITIONAL INFORMATION:
Honours: Midland Combination Division 3 1980-81.

STAFFORD TOWN

Founded: 1976   Nickname:

Secretary: David Howard   **(T)** 07789 110 923   **(E)** staffordtown@hotmail.co.uk
Chairman: Gordon Evans   **Manager:** Adam Cunningham   **Prog Ed:**
Ground: Evans Park, Riverway, Stafford ST16 3TH   **(T)**   **Capacity:**
Colours(change): All red

ADDITIONAL INFORMATION:
Previous Leagues: Midland Combination 1977-84. Staffordshire 1984-93. West Midlands (Regional) 1993-2012.
Previous Names: Stafford > 1981.

WALSALL WOOD

Founded: 1907   Nickname:

Secretary: Ivor Osborne   **(T)** 07583 175 664   **(E)** ivorjosborne@talktalk.net
Chairman: Andy Roper   **Manager:** Mark Swann   **Prog Ed:**
Ground: Oak Park, Lichfield Road, Walsall Wood, Walsall WS9 9NP   **(T)**   **Capacity:**
Colours(change): All red

ADDITIONAL INFORMATION:
Previous League: West Midlands (Regional).
Honours: Worcestershire/Midland Combination 1951-52.

GROUND DIRECTIONS

ATHERSTONE TOWN - Sheepy Road, Atherston, Warwickshire CV9 3AD - 01827 717 829

Take M42 towards Atherstone. Exit at Junction 10. Travel southbound on A5 towards Nuneaton for approximately 4 miles. At third roundabout take first exit to Holly Lane Industrial Estate. Over railway bridge (Aldi HQ on left). At the next roundabout turn right onto Rowlands Way. Ground is 300 yards on the right. Car park and street parking in Rowlands Way.

BLACKWOOD - Ground: Hampton Sports Club, Field Lane , Solihull , West Midlands , B91 2RT

From M42 North or South: Exit motorway at junction 5 (signposted Solihull). Take 1st Exit left (A41). Continue on A41 until you reach 1st set of traffic lights and turn right into Hampton Lane, after approx 1/2 mile turn left into Field Lane, ground is approx 3/4 mile on the right hand side.

BLOXWICH UNITED - Ground: Red Lion Ground, Somerfield Road, Bloxwich, Walsall, West Midlands, WS3 2EJ

From junction 10 of M6 take A454 (Wolverhampton Road) towards Walsall, on to Blue Lane West. At traffic lights turn left onto Green Lane (A34). Keep straight on for approximately 1½ miles. At roundabout, go straight over onto A34. Ground is approximately ½ mile up on right hand side.

BOLEHILL SWIFTS - Rene Road, Bolehall, Tamworth, Staffordshire B77 3NN

Exit M42 at Junction 10, take A5 towards Tamworth, exit A5 at 2nd exit (Glascote & Amington Industrial Estate). Turn right onto Marlborough Way, at next island turn left (B5000), turn right into Argyle Street (opposite chip shop). At T-junction, turn left into Amington Road, drive over the canal bridge, and turn 2nd right into Leedham Avenue. Take right fork into Rene Road. Club is situated 150 yards on right immediately after school.

BROCTON - Ground: Silkmore Lane Sports Ground, Silkmore Lane , Stafford , Staffordshire , ST17 4JH

From M6 J13 take A449 towards Stafford for 1.5 miles until reaching traffic lights by Esso petrol station. Turn right at lights into Rickescote Road, follow road round over railway bridge to mini island, at island bear left into Silkmore Lane. At next mini island take 4th exit for entrance to ground. From Lichfield/Rugeley. After passing Staffs Police HQ at Baswick go downhill past BMW garage and pub to large island, take 1st exit into Silkmore Lane, at next mini island take 2nd exit into ground entrance. Do not turn into Lancaster Road or Silkmore Crescent as directed by Sat Navs.

BROMSGROVE SPORTING - Ground: The Victoria Ground, Birmingham Road, Bromsgrove, Worcs, B61 0DR

From M5 J4 take A38 to Bromsgrove, after island at M42 J1, take 1st right at Traffic Lights (signposted Bromsgrove North). Ground is 1000 metres on right (opposite Tesco Garage). From M42 J1, follow above directions from islands.

CASTLE VALE JKS - Ground: Vale Stadium, Farnborough Road, Castle Vale , Birmingham , West Midlands , B35 7DA

From M6 Junction 5 turn right at the island onto the A452 to island with Spitfire sculpture, turn right into Tangmere Drive, then right into Farnborough Road. Ground is on the right hand side after approximately 1/2 mile.

COVENTRY COPSEWOOD - Ground: Copsewood Sports & Social Club, Allard Way, Binley , Coventry , West Midlands , CV3 1HQ

M6 South: Leave at junction 2 and follow A4600 signs for City Centre. Go over 3 roundabouts and past 1 set of traffic lights, on reaching the 2nd set of traffic lights with Coventry Oak pub on left, turn left down Hipswell Highway. Follow road for 1 mile and reach another set of lights (Fire Station is on left and Mill Pool pub is on right). Go over lights and the ground is 300 yards on the left. From M40: Follow A46 signs to Coventry and Leicester, stay on this road until very end, you then reach a roundabout with a flyover, go round the roundabout following M69 signs. This road takes you past Asda and you reach a set of traffic lights with a roundabout. Take 2nd left turn off the roundabout, again following M69 signs, This is Allard Way and takes you past Matalan on left, Go under railway bridge and ground is 400 yards on the right. A45 from Birmingham Direction: Follow A45 until reaching a slip road signposted A46, this slip road has the Festival Pub on left side of it. It is after a roundabout with big Peugeot car showroom on left. Go down slip road and take 2nd exit. , this is another slip road leading to A46, signposted B4114 Coventry. Follow road until reaching roundabout with a flyover, and then follow as M40 directions above.

EARLSWOOD TOWN - Ground: Studley FC, Abbeyfields Drive, Studley, B80 7BE

Leave M42 at junction 3 (Redditch A435) and turn towards Redditch. Follow dual carriageway to the end. Stay on A435 and go straight on at island. Pass 'The Boot' public house and after 550 yards turn left into Abbeyfields Drive. The ground is on the right.

LICHFIELD CITY - Ground: Brownsfield Park, Brownsfield Road , Lichfield , Staffordshire , WS13 6AY

From M42 J10, follow A5 towards Brownhills, or J9 and follow A446 to Lichfield, then follow signs for A38 Lichfield/Derby. From Swinfen Roundabout take 3rd exit for A38 north and then take next off A38 onto A5192 (Cappers Lane). Follow A5192 through 2 islands onto Eastern Avenue. The Ground is on the right at the top of the hill next to Norgreen factory. From M6 J12, follow A5 towards Lichfield then A38 to Lichfield Derby, then follow instructions as above.

LITTLETON - Ground: Five Acres, Pebworth Road, North Littleton , Evesham , Worcestershire , WR11 8QL

Get on A46 and aim for Bidford-on-Avon, leave A46 at Bidford roundabout and follow signs for B439 (Bidford 0.5 miles). Come to roundabout in Bidford and take exit B4085 (Cleeve Prior), over a very narrow bridge controlled by traffic lights, straight over crossroads following sign to Honeybourne Broadway. Straight on for approx. 3 miles signpost right turn for the Littletons at crossroads, the ground is 1.25 miles on the right.

NUNEATON GRIFF - Ground: The Pingles Stadium, Avenue Road , Nuneaton , Warwickshire , CV11 4LX

From M5, M42 & M6: Take M6 south to junction 3 and leave by turning left onto A444 (Nuneaton). Stay on A444 through Bermuda Park, McDonalds and George Eliot Hospital roundabouts until reaching large roundabout with footbridge over road. Carry straight on (2nd exit) and downhill, taking right hand lane. At bottom of hill you reach Coton Arches Island, take 2nd exit (A4252 Avenue Road) and travel 1/2 mile to Cedar Tree Pub traffic lights, turn left into Stadium car park service road. It is unsuitable for coaches to turn around in. From A5: Travel south following signs for Nuneaton. After passing through Atherstone travel for 2 1/2 miles until junction with A444. At this junction (Royal Red Gate Pub) turn right at staggered junction and continue on A444 through Caldecote and Weddington into Nuneaton. Join one-way system at Graziers Arms by turning left and immediately take right hand lane for 300 yards and follow A4254 for Coventry. At Third Island turn left on to dual carriageway (Coton Road) for 1/2 mile and turn left at Coton Arches island on to A4252 (Avenue Road) then as above.

PELSALL VILLA - Ground: The Bush Ground, Walsall Road , Walsall , West Midlands , WS3 4BP

Leave M6 at junction 7 sign-posted A34 Birmingham. Take A34 towards Walsall to 1st Island, turn right (marked Ring Road) across 3 islands. At large island at the bottom of the hill, take last exit marked Lichfield. Up hill and across next island to traffic lights, continue to next set of lights and turn left (B4154 Pelsall). Go over Railway Bridge to Old Bush Public House, the ground is next to the public house signposted Pelsall Cricket Club. From Birmingham East: Follow A452 from Spitfire Island then follow signs towards Brownhills. At the traffic lights at the Shire Oak P.H, turn left onto A461 (Walsall) and pass the entrance to Walsall Wood FC. At the traffic lights in Shelfield (The Spring Cottage PH) turn right (signposted Pelsall). At the next set of traffic lights turn left, the Bush is approx 400 yards on left. From: Coventry: Take A45 to Stonebridge Island, turn right onto A452 but then keep to the right following A446 (signposted Lichfield). Follow the A446 to Bassett's Pole Island. Take the 3rd exit onto A38 (Lichfield). Leave the A38 at sliproad for the A5 and take the 2nd exit at the island. Follow the A5 over next 2 islands and at Muckley Corner turn left (inside lane) to join A461. Go straight on at the traffic lights and follow directions as above.

PERSHORE TOWN - Ground: King George V Playing Field, King George's Way , Pershore , Worcestershire , WR10 1AA

M5 Junction 7, take B4080 (formerly A44) to Pershore. On entering the town turn left at 2nd set of traffic lights (signposted Leisure Centre). The ground is 300 yards on the left hand side.

PILKINGTON XXX - Ground: Triplex Sports, Eckersall Road, Kings Norton , Birmingham , West Midlands , B38 8SR

From Cotteridge A441 through and past Kings Norton Station, 150 yards turn right across dual carriageway at petrol station, approximately 300 yards there is a sharp bend, turn right. Ground is on right.

RACING CLUB WARWICK - Ground: Hampton Road , Warwick , Warwickshire , CV34 6JP

M40 Junction 15, signposted Warwick. At roundabout with traffic lights take A429 to Warwick. Follow this road for 1/2 mile and you will come to houses on your left. Take the 2nd turn on the left into Shakespeare Avenue. Follow to T-junction. Turn right into Hampton Road. Entrance to ground is 50 yards on left.

SOUTHAM UNITED - Ground: Banbury Road , Southam , Warwickshire , CV47 2BJ

From Birmingham: M40 Junction 12, exit to A4451 to Southam. Approximately 6 1/2 miles to an island in Southam, turn right, at 2nd island turn right again, ground is 100 yards on right. From Coventry: take A423 Banbury Road; the ground is approximately 12 1/2 miles from Coventry.

STAFFORD TOWN - Evans Park, Riverway, Stafford ST16 3TH

From M6 junction 13, take A449 towards Stafford for 1½ miles until reaching traffic lights by an Esso petrol station. Turn right at the lights into Rickerscote Road, follow the road round over railway bridge to a mini island. At the island bear left into Silkmore Lane, after approximately 600 yards take the 2nd exit at the mini island and carry on until a large island, take the 2nd exit towards Stafford town centre (A34 Lichfield Road). Go over the railway bridge with Alstrom factory on the left hand side. Straight on at 1st set of traffic lights, then bear left at next set of lights (A518 Uttoxeter) and follow road round with B&Q and Argos on your left hand side. At the roundabout (with KFC and Pizza Hut in front of you) take the 2nd exit (A518 Uttoxeter) and follow to traffic lights. Go straight over lights into Riverway, the ground entrance is approximately 80 yards on the right hand side. Follow the driveway behind the cricket pavilion to the stadium entrance.

WALSALL WOOD - Ground: Oak Park, Lichfield Road, Walsall Wood , Walsall , West Midlands , WS9 9NP

From North using M6 motorway: M6 south to junction 12. Take A5 until big island just outside Brownhills (next island after the Turn pub on left). Take A452 Chester Road North through Brownhills High Street to traffic lights at Shire Oak (pub at junction on right hand side). Turn right on to A461 for Walsall, go to next set of traffic lights, cross over and turn right immediately on to Oak Park Leisure Centre car park (rear of Kentucky Fried Chicken). Proceed diagonally over car park and follow road round to ground entrance. From South using M5/M6 motorways: M5 North past junction 1 on to M6 north. Leave at junction 9 (Wednesbury turn off). Take A4148 to Walsall. Proceed for about 2 miles over several islands until going down a hill alongside the Arboretum. At big island at bottom, turn right onto A461 for Lichfield. Take A461 for about 4 miles and go through Walsall Wood (after Barons Court Hotel on right), up the hill after village, Oak Park is on the left opposite Fitness First, turn left and go diagonally across Oak Park Leisure Centre car park, Follow road round to the ground entrance. M5/M6 alternative M5 North and bear left after junction 1 (West Bromwich) onto M6 south. Go to next junction (Junction 7 Great Barr) and follow signs for A34 Birmingham Road to junction with Queslett Road (A4041). Turn left at the junction (traffic lights) and take A4041 past Asda and over several islands to A452 Chester Road. Turn left at this island and travel for about 4 miles to Shire Oak crossroads (traffic lights with Shire Oak pub opposite). Turn left at the lights onto A461 for Walsall. Go to next lights and cross over, Oak Park is immediately on the right opposite Fitness First. Turn right onto car park and go diagonally across, following road round to the ground entrance.

DIVISION ONE

ALVIS - Ground: Alvis Sports & Social Club, Green Lane, Coventry, West Midlands, CV3 6EA

From roundabout on A45, Kenpas Highway/Stonebridge Highway, take B4113 into St Martins Road. After turn right into Green Lane South after the school. The ground is on the left hand side.

ARCHDALE '73 - Ground: County Sports Ground, Claines Lane , Worcester , Worcestershire , WR3 7SS

M5 to Junction 6, take A449 (link road) signposted Kidderminster, down to the bottom, at island turn sharp left into Claines Lane, continue past church on right, ground is on the left (about 1/2 mile).

ASTON - Ground: Pack Meadow, Packington Lane, Coleshill, Warwickshire, B46 3JQ

Exit M6 at Junction 4, take A446 signposted Lichfield, turn right across dual carriageway onto B4117 to Coleshill. After scholl on right, turn right into Packington Lane, ground is 0.5 miles of the left.

CADBURY ATHLETIC - Ground: Lye Meadow, Redditch Road , Alvechurch , Worcestershire , B48 7RS

M42 Junction 2, Follow signs for Redditch, taking dual carriageway. At 1st island turn right (Signposted Alvechurch), ground approximately 1km on right. Car Park entrance before ground.

CHELMSLEY TOWN - Ground: Shenley Lane Community Ass., 472 Shenley Lane, Selly Oak, Birmingham, West Midlands, B29 4HZ

From Birmingham City Centre: Take the A38 (Bristol Road) towards Bromsgrove, travel through the districts of Bournbrook and Selly Oak. Once through Selly Oak, the road changes to a dual carriageway, following this until just before the end, where the Royal Orthopaedic Hospital is situated on the left. Turn right across the carriageway at the hospital and proceed down Whitehill Lane. At the bottom turn right across the dual carriageway and 1st right again into the ground. A-Z ref 2A 104. From the M42: From the M6 North join the M42 and head towards Worcester, follow the M42 until the junction A441 Redditch/Birmingham is reached. Leave the motorway and head towards Birmingham. As you head towards Birmingham you will go up a hill, at the top of the hill you will come to a mini roundabout. At this island turn left into Longbridge Lane. Follow this all the way to the end, at the end you will come to a dual carriageway, turn right on to this. The dual carriageway is the main A38 heading towards Birmingham. Follow this road until the end when you will come into Northfield centre. As you go through Northfield you will come to a junction controlled by traffic lights, turn left into Bell Lane. As you go down the hill you will join a dual carriageway, at the bottom of the hill, turn across the carriageway and the ground is facing you. From the M5: Leave the motorway at junction 4 (A38). Follow signs for Birmingham, this is a dual carriageway. After 3 miles you will come to an island, the Rover car plant at Longbridge is directly in front of you. Turn left, still on the A38. Follow this road until the end when you will come into Northfield centre. As you go through Northfield you will come to a junction controlled by traffic lights, turn left into Bell Lane. As you go down the hill you will join a dual carriageway, at the bottom of the hill, turn across the carriageway and the ground is facing you.

COTON GREEN - Ground: New Mill Lane, Fazeley , Tamworth , Staffordshire , B78 3RX

From M42 junction 9, take A446 exit towards The Belfry, at the next island turn right towards Tamworth and Drayton Manor Park (A4091), continue for approximately 4 miles, past entrance to Drayton Mark Park on your left, continue over the canal with 'Debbies Boat Hire' on your right and 'Fazeley Marina' on your left. As you enter Fazeley you need to turn right immediately after the start of the 30mph speed limit, into New Mill Lane (there is a right filter lane). Once in New Mill Lane, follow lane past houses, turn right at the bottom and follow into car park.

DROITWICH SPA - Ground: Droitwich Spa Leisure Centre, Briar Mill , Droitwich , Worcestershire , WR9 0RZ

M5 junction 5, take A38 to Droitwich, At traffic lights by Chateau Impney, go onto dual carriageway, at roundabout take 1st exit (Kidderminster Road), pass Homebase and take next right into Salwarpe Road. Go straight over at next roundabout, next right into Briarmill Road and ground is behind the all weather complex.

FAIRFIELD VILLA - Ground: Recreation Ground, Stourbridge Road, Fairfield , Bromsgrove , Worcestershire , B61 9LZ

From M42 Junction 1: Take A38 North to junction 4 M5 and then take A491 towards Stourbridge, travel 2 miles to next roundabout, then left onto B4091 up into Fairfield Village. Go past Swan Public House and approximately 200 yards on your left you will see a school warning sign and telephone booth. Turn left here, up drive to ground. From M5 Junction 4: See above From A38 South to M5 junction 4: see above.

FC GLADES SPORTING - Ground: The Glades, Lugtrout Lane , Solihull , West Midlands , B91 2RX

From M42 North or South: Exit motorway at junction 5 (signposted Solihull). Take 1st Exit left (A41). Continue on A41 until you reach 1st set of traffic lights and turn right into Hampton Lane, take the 2nd left (after approx 2 miles) into Lugtrout Lane. Continue on Lugtrout Lane past houses on either side. Entrance to the ground will be on your left (opposite cricket ground).

FECKENHAM - Ground: Studley Sports & Social Club, Eldorado Close , Studley , Warwickshire , B80 7HP

Leave M42 at junction 3 then, at roundabout, take the 3rd exit onto the A435, signposted Redditch / Evesham. At the next roundabout take the 2nd exit staying on the A435, at the next roundabout, take the 2nd exit onto the B4092, signposted Astwood Bank, then take the 3rd turning on the right into Eldorado Close. Leave the M5 south at junction 4. At the roundabout take the 2nd exit onto the A38, signposted Bromsgrove. Travel for approximately 3 miles then turn onto the A448, signposted Redditch, the A448 will then merge with the A4189. At the next roundabout take the 3rd turning staying on the A4189. At the next roundabout take the 2nd turning still on the A4189, at the next roundabout take the 3rd turning onto the A435 signposted Evesham. At the next roundabout take the 2nd exit, staying on the A435. At the next roundabout take the 2nd exit onto the B4092, signposted Astwood Bank, then take the 3rd turning on the right into Eldorado Close.

GREENHILL - Ground: Dudley Sports & Social Club, Hillcrest Avenue, Brierley Hill, West Midlands, DY5 3QH

The ground is situated in Brierley Hill, just off A461. It can be approached from Stourbridge off the ring road to Amblecote, turning right at the 3rd set of traffic lights or from Dudley passing through Brierley Hill Town Centre. A-Z Ref 4H, page 67.

HAMPTON - Ground: Hampton Sports Club, Field Lane , Solihull , West Midlands , B91 2RT

From M42 North or South: Exit motorway at junction 5 (signposted Solihull). Take 1st Exit left (A41). Continue on A41 until you reach 1st set of traffic lights and turn right into Hampton Lane, after approx 1/2 mile turn left into Field Lane, ground is approx 3/4 mile on the right hand side.

KNOWLE - Ground: Hampton Road, Knowle , Solihull , West Midlands , B93 0NX

Directions: M42 Junction 5, A4140 to Knowle, turn left at Toby Carvery into Hampton Road. Ground is 200 yards on right.

NORTHFIELD TOWN - Ground: Shenley Lane Community Association, Shenley Lane, Selly Oak , Birmingham , West Mids , B29 4HZ

From Birmingham City Centre: Take the A38 (Bristol Road) towards Bromsgrove, travel through the districts of Bournbrook and Selly Oak. Once through Selly Oak, the road changes to a dual carriageway, following this until just before the end, where the Royal Orthopaedic Hospital is situated on the left. Turn right across the carriageway at the hospital and proceed down Whitehill Lane. At the bottom turn right across the dual carriageway and 1st right again into the ground. A-Z ref 2A 104. From the M42: From the M6 North join the M42 and head towards Worcester, follow the M42 until the junction A441Redditch/Birmingham is reached. Leave the motorway and head towards Birmingham. As you head towards Birmingham you will go up a hill, at the top of the hill you will come to a mini roundabout. At this island turn left into Longbridge Lane. Follow this all the way to the end, at the end you will come to a dual carriageway, turn right on to this. The dual carriageway is the main A38 heading towards Birmingham. Follow this road until the end when you will come into Northfield centre. As you go through Northfield you will come to a junction controlled by traffic lights, turn left into Bell Lane. As you go down the hill you will join a dual carriageway, at the bottom of the hill, turn across the carriageway and the ground is facing you. From the M5: Leave the motorway at junction 4 (A38). Follow signs for Birmingham, this is a dual carriageway. After 3 miles you will come to an island, the Rover car plant at Longbridge is directly in front of you. Turn left, still on the A38. Follow this road until the end when you will come into Northfield centre. As you go through Northfield you will come to a junction controlled by traffic lights, turn left into Bell Lane. As you go down the hill you will join a dual carriageway, at the bottom of the hill, turn across the carriageway and the ground is facing you.

PHOENIX UNITED - Ground: The Pavilions, Malthouse Lane, Earlswood , Solihull , West Midlands , B94 5DX

From M42 (Junction 3) A435 Evesham to Birmingham Road, at Motorway Island take minor exit to Foreshaw Heath. Follow for 3/4 mile. Turn right into Poolhead Lane. After passing Earlswood Trading Estate (on right) turn first left into Small Lane (no road sign) just before the road crosses the motorway. The ground 1/2 mile on right hand side. From A34 Heading away from Birmingham, leave Shirley. Turn right into Blackford Road (B4102) signposted Earlswood/Redditch. Follow this road for 4 miles. After passing the crossroads at Earlswood (Reservoir Public House) turn next right into Springbrook Lane. Go to the end of Springbrook Lane, Turn left into Malthouse Lane. Ground approximately 1/4 mile on left.

SHIRLEY TOWN - Ground: Tilehouse Lane, Shirley , Solihull , West Midlands , B90 1PH

Directions: Tanworth Lane after 150yds, turn right into Dickens Heath Road (Chiswick Green Inn on Left). Follow road to island, take 3rd exit and then after 100 yards go right into Tythe Barn Lane. Follow road then approx 3/4 miles at T junction turn right into Tilehouse Lane. Ground 200 yds on Right (opposite Whitlock's End Station car park). From West & M42: Leave @ J3 onto A435 to Birmingham. After 1 1/2 miles (Beckets Island) take 4th Exit (signposted Earlswood) entering Station Road. After 3/4 miles bear right over railway bridge entering Norton Lane. After 1/4 miles turn left into Lowbrook Road. After 1/4 mile at crossroads turn left into Tilehouse lane. After 1 mile approx ground is on right hand side (opposite Whitlock's End Station Car Park).

STRETTON EAGLES - Ground: Shobnall Sports Gound, Shobnall Road , Burton-upon-Trent , Staffordshire , DE14 2BB

Take A38 to Burton on Trent, leave at A5121 and take the 3rd exit towards Burton. At the lights take left hand lane for Burton, go straight through in 200 metres (You will see Bannatynes Leisure on your right). At the roundabout go straight on (A5234 Abbots Bromley). Stay on this road across 3 mini islands, you will then pass the recycling centre before reaching another island. Turn left into Shobnall Road and follow for 400 metres before turning right into Shobnall Leisure Centre. The ground is 200 yards on the right of the driveway.

WEST MIDLANDS POLICE - Ground: Tally Ho Training Centre, Pershore Road, Edgbaston , Birmingham , West Midlands , B5 7RD

Directions: From M5: Exit at junction 3, take A456 Hagley Road to 'Five Ways', turn right on to Islington Row, turn right at traffic lights at Bristol Road. Turn left at next set of traffic lights into Priory Road, then right into Pershore Road. Tally Ho! is on your left. From M6: Exit at junction 6; take Aston Expressway (A38) through Queensway underpasses emerging in Bristol Street/Bristol Road. Turn left at traffic lights at junction with Priory Road. Turn right at next set of traffic lights. Pershore Road and Tally Ho! is on your left (A-Z Reference 3G Page 89).

MIDLAND FOOTBALL ALLIANCE

Sponsored by: Aspire

Founded: 1994

Recent Champions:
2007: Leamington. 2008: Atherstone Town. 2009: Market Drayton Town.
2010: Barwell. 2011: Coalville Town

midland footballalliance.co.uk

		P	W	D	L	F	A	Pts
1	(P) Gresley	42	27	8	7	96	56	89
2	Westfields	42	27	6	9	93	49	87
3	Coventry Sphinx	42	26	7	9	74	44	85
4	Tividale	42	21	9	12	81	56	72
5	Loughborough University	42	20	9	13	94	56	69
6	Rocester	42	20	7	15	77	58	67
7	Causeway United	42	17	15	10	74	56	66
8	Stratford Town (-1)	42	19	8	15	79	55	64
9	Tipton Town	42	18	10	14	73	63	64
10	Bridgnorth Town	42	17	11	14	59	56	62
11	Kirby Muxloe	42	16	12	14	75	68	60
12	Boldmere St Michaels	42	14	12	16	58	61	54
13	Alvechurch	42	14	9	19	58	67	51
14	Heath Hayes	42	14	9	19	76	90	51
15	Ellesmere Rangers	42	13	11	18	49	65	50
16	Coleshill Town	42	14	8	20	55	73	50
17	Studley (-6)	42	16	6	20	78	82	48
18	Dunkirk	42	14	6	22	59	87	48
19	Heather St Johns	42	13	8	21	56	73	47
20	Highgate United	42	12	8	22	60	77	44
21	(R) Atherstone Town	42	11	9	22	48	78	42
22	(R) Willenhall Town	42	3	4	35	43	145	13

LEAGUE CUP

FINAL
Loughborough 2-0 Tipton Town

		1	2	3	4	5	6	7	8	9	10	11	12	13	14	15	16	17	18	19	20	21	22
1	Alvechurch		0-0	1-2	1-3	0-0	1-4	1-2	1-1	2-1	0-2	2-0	0-1	2-0	1-0	0-4	0-1	2-0	3-3	1-1	2-3	1-1	4-1
2	Atherstone Town	1-2		0-0	2-3	0-3	2-2	0-3	0-3	3-2	0-1	1-1	2-4	2-0	1-1	1-1	1-0	0-3	2-3	2-1	0-1	3-1	1-0
3	Boldmere St Michaels	1-1	0-0		5-1	1-0	2-2	0-2	1-1	1-1	2-1	1-0	2-0	1-0	0-3	0-2	2-0	1-2	5-1	2-2	0-2	2-1	3-0
4	Bridgnorth Town	0-1	3-0	2-0		1-1	1-1	0-2	0-2	2-1	2-2	4-2	1-0	1-0	0-1	3-0	1-1	0-1	1-1	3-1	1-0	0-2	4-0
5	Causeway United	2-3	1-2	3-0	1-1		1-1	1-1	3-1	0-0	2-3	3-0	2-1	2-0	2-2	2-0	0-2	1-1	2-2	2-2	1-0	2-1	9-1
6	Coleshill Town	1-0	2-1	2-0	0-1	1-3		1-0	3-0	0-2	1-3	2-3	1-1	2-2	3-2	0-2	1-2	0-3	2-0	1-2	0-3	0-1	4-1
7	Coventry Sphinx	1-0	2-0	2-1	1-1	0-1	1-0		1-3	1-2	4-4	2-0	3-3	6-2	2-1	2-1	0-1	3-1	1-0	1-0	0-2	0-0	2-0
8	Dunkirk	1-3	1-3	1-0	4-3	0-1	0-1	2-4		1-0	1-3	3-2	3-0	0-6	1-1	1-1	1-0	3-2	1-3	3-5	1-1	0-1	4-2
9	Ellesmere Rangers	0-2	3-1	0-0	1-2	1-2	0-0	0-1	1-0		3-0	1-1	1-1	1-1	0-0	1-0	3-0	1-4	1-3	1-4	1-1	0-0	3-2
10	Gresley	2-4	1-1	1-2	1-1	2-2	2-0	2-1	2-0	3-2		7-0	2-0	2-0	3-3	2-0	1-0	2-0	2-1	4-0	3-2	3-2	4-2
11	Heath Hayes	4-0	4-0	1-1	4-0	2-1	3-5	1-4	4-1	1-1	1-4		3-3	2-1	2-0	0-4	3-1	2-2	2-1	2-0	1-3	1-3	7-0
12	Heather St Johns	1-0	1-3	3-2	2-2	1-2	1-2	0-2	3-4	1-2	0-2	0-1		2-0	3-0	0-2	2-1	1-2	0-1	0-2	0-3	0-3	4-3
13	Highgate United	2-0	3-1	0-4	0-1	1-2	3-1	2-1	2-1	2-1	0-1	1-4	2-2		1-1	2-1	2-3	1-2	2-2	0-0	4-1	2-3	2-0
14	Kirby Muxloe	2-2	3-1	5-2	1-2	4-2	2-1	4-0	3-1	0-2	1-1	1-3	2-0	1-2		0-0	3-2	2-2	2-1	1-3	2-0	1-3	4-1
15	Loughborough University	1-0	2-0	1-3	0-0	2-1	2-0	0-1	8-0	7-1	2-5	1-1	3-0	4-2	6-1		4-2	0-0	2-1	1-2	1-2	4-1	4-0
16	Rocester	2-2	3-1	3-1	2-2	3-3	5-0	1-3	3-0	0-3	2-0	5-2	1-1	2-0	3-1	2-2		2-1	3-1	1-2	2-0	3-1	7-1
17	Stratford Town	4-1	1-2	2-1	1-2	2-2	3-1	1-1	0-2	0-2	2-2	3-0	0-1	4-2	3-1	2-3	2-0		6-1	1-1	3-0	0-2	3-0
18	Studley	3-1	1-4	4-0	1-2	4-2	2-1	1-1	0-2	4-1	4-2	8-1	0-1	1-1	2-1	2-3	2-0	2-4		1-3	2-4	0-3	1-0
19	Tipton Town	2-0	2-2	1-2	1-0	2-2	1-0	0-2	4-2	0-1	0-2	1-1	3-3	2-1	1-2	3-2	0-1	0-1	0-5		3-1	1-1	4-1
20	Tividale	1-0	3-0	2-2	0-1	3-3	1-2	3-1	7-1	2-4	3-1	0-0	0-1	2-2	3-1	5-0	1-5	0-3	3-1	1-0		1-1	4-0
21	Westfields	1-2	4-1	2-1	2-1	1-1	6-0	3-2	4-1	2-0	5-1	2-1	3-1	5-2	2-1	2-0	1-4	1-0	1-0	3-1	1-2		6-3
22	Willenhall Town	4-6	3-1	1-1	1-0	3-2	1-2	0-1	1-1	0-2	0-3	2-2	2-4	1-4	1-5	2-4	1-1	0-5	1-2	0-6	1-4	0-5	

ALVECHURCH
Founded: 1929   Nickname: The Church

Secretary: Stephen Denny   **(T)** 07710 012 733   **(E)** alvechurch@btinternet.com

Chairman: Peter Eacock   **Manager:**   **Prog Ed:**

Ground: Lye Meadow, Redditch Road, Alvechurch B48 7RS   **(T)** 0121 445 2929

Capacity: 3,000   **Seats:** 100   **Covered:** 300   **Midweek Matchday:** Tuesday   **Clubhouse:** Yes   **Shop:** No

Colours(change): Gold/black/black. (All blue).
Previous Names: Alvechurch FC >1992. Re-formed in 1994.
Previous Leagues: Midland Combination
Records:
Senior Honours: Since 1994: Midland Combination Premier 2002-03. Worcestershire Senior Urn 03-04, 04-05.

10 YEAR RECORD

02-03		03-04		04-05		05-06		06-07		07-08		08-09		09-10		10-11		11-12	
MCmP	1	MidAl	19	MidAl	15	MidAl	14	MidAl	10	MidAl	14	MidAl	10	MidAl	7	MidAl	20	MidAl	13

BOLDMERE ST. MICHAELS
Founded: 1883   Nickname: The Mikes

Secretary: Rob Paterson   **(T)** 07528 177 046   **(E)** robb4paterson@btinternet.com

Chairman: Keith Fielding   **Manager:**   **Prog Ed:**

Ground: Trevor Brown Memorial Gd, Church Rd, Boldmere B73 5RY   **(T)** 0121 373 4435

Capacity: 2,500   **Seats:** 230   **Covered:** 400   **Midweek Matchday:** Tuesday   **Clubhouse:** Yes   **Shop:** No

Colours(change): Black & white stripes/black/black. (All yellow & blue)
Previous Names: None.
Previous Leagues: West Midlands (Regional). Midland Combination.
Records:
Senior Honours: AFA Senior Cup 1947-48. Midland Combination Premier 1985-86, 88-89, 89-90.

10 YEAR RECORD

02-03		03-04		04-05		05-06		06-07		07-08		08-09		09-10		10-11		11-12	
MidAl	14	MidAl	15	MidAl	10	MidAl	10	MidAl	7	MidAl	4	MidAl	4	MidAl	6	MidAl	3	MidAl	12

BRIDGNORTH TOWN
Founded: 1946   Nickname:

Secretary: Zoe Griffiths   **(T)** 07702 562 127   **(E)** zoebtfc@aol.com

Chairman: Zoe Griffiths   **Manager:**   **Prog Ed:**

Ground: Crown Meadow, Innage Lane, Bridgnorth WV16 4HL   **(T)** 01746 763 001

Capacity: **Seats:**   **Covered:**   **Midweek Matchday:** Tuesday   **Clubhouse:**   **Shop:** Yes

Colours(change): Royal blue/navy blue/navy blue. (All red).
Previous Names: None.
Previous Leagues: Worcestershire Combination/Midland Combination. Southern. West Mids.
Records:
Senior Honours: Midland Combination 1979-80, 82-83. West Midlands (Regional) 07-08.

10 YEAR RECORD

02-03		03-04		04-05		05-06		06-07		07-08		08-09		09-10		10-11		11-12	
MidAl	16	MidAl	10	MidAl	22	MCmP	5	WMP	7	WMP	1	MidAl	12	MidAl	20	MidAl	15	MidAl	10

CAUSEWAY UNITED
Founded: 1957   Nickname:

Secretary: Frank Webb   **(T)** 07977 599 847   **(E)**

Chairman: Edward Russell   **Manager:**   **Prog Ed:**

Ground: Stourbridge FC, Amblecote, Stourbridge DY8 4HN   **(T)** 01384 394 040

Capacity: **Seats:**   **Covered:**   **Midweek Matchday:** Tuesday   **Clubhouse:** Yes   **Shop:**

Colours(change): All blue. (All white).
Previous Names: None.
Previous Leagues: West Midlands (Regional).
Records: **Att:** 150. **Apps:** Malcolm Power - 300+
Senior Honours:

10 YEAR RECORD

02-03		03-04		04-05		05-06		06-07		07-08		08-09		09-10		10-11		11-12	
MidAl	11	Isth P	17	MidAl	16	MidAl	19	MidAl	17	MidAl	6	MidAl	9	MidAl	12	MidAl	10	MidAl	7

COLESHILL TOWN
Founded: 1894   Nickname:

Secretary: David Brown   **(T)** 07799 075 828   **(E)** dave.brown@skanska.co.uk

Chairman: Paul Billing   **Manager:**   **Prog Ed:** As secretary

Ground: Pack Meadow, Packington Lane, Coleshill B46 3JQ   **(T)** 01675 463 259

Capacity: **Seats:** **Covered:** **Midweek Matchday:** Tuesday   **Clubhouse:** Yes **Shop:**

Colours(change): White/blue/red (Red/red/green)
Previous Names: None.
Previous Leagues: Midland Combination.
Records:
Senior Honours: Midland Combination Division Two 1969-70. Premier 07-08.

10 YEAR RECORD

02-03	03-04	04-05	05-06	06-07	07-08	08-09	09-10	10-11	11-12
MCmP 14	MCmP 18	MCmP 9	MCmP 11	MCmP 4	MCmP 1	MidAl 11	MidAl 8	MidAl 12	MidAl 16

CONTINENTAL STAR
Founded: 1973   Nickname:

Secretary: Keith John   **(T)** 07956 429 046   **(E)** keith.john6@hotmail.co.uk

Chairman: Keith John   **Manager:**   **Prog Ed:**

Ground: Rushall Olympic FC, Dales Lane, Rushall, Walsall, West Midlands WS4 1LJ   **(T)** 01922 641 021

Capacity: **Seats:** **Covered:** **Midweek Matchday:**   **Clubhouse:** **Shop:**

Colours(change): Yellow/blue/blue (Red/black/white)
Previous Names: Handsworth Continental Star 2001-02.
Previous Leagues: Midland Combination 1993-2012.
Records:
Senior Honours: Midland Combination Division 2 1995-96, Premier Division 2011-12.

10 YEAR RECORD

02-03	03-04	04-05	05-06	06-07	07-08	08-09	09-10	10-11	11-12
MCmP 13	MCmP 19	MCmP 20	MCmP 22	MCmP 19	MCmP 18	MCmP 17	MCmP 14	MCmP 11	MCmP 1

COVENTRY SPHINX
Founded: 1946   Nickname: Sphinx

Secretary: Jackie McGowan   **(T)** 07843 477 799   **(E)** jackie.mcgowan@coventrysphinx.co.uk

Chairman: Dannie Cahill   **Manager:**   **Prog Ed:**

Ground: Sphinx Spts & Social Club, Sphinx Drive, Coventry CV3 1WA   **(T)** 02476 451 361

Capacity: **Seats:** **Covered:** Yes **Midweek Matchday:** Tuesday   **Clubhouse:** Yes **Shop:**

Colours(change): Sky blue & white stripes/navy/navy or sky blue (Yellow & black stripes/black & yellow/yellow).
Previous Names: Sphinx > 1995.
Previous Leagues: Midland Combination.
Records:
Senior Honours: Midland Combination Premier 2006-07.

10 YEAR RECORD

02-03	03-04	04-05	05-06	06-07	07-08	08-09	09-10	10-11	11-12
MCmP 7	MCmP 4	MCmP 2	MCmP 2	MCmP 1	MidAl 19	MidAl 7	MidAl 9	MidAl 16	MidAl 3

DUNKIRK
Founded: 1946   Nickname: The Boatmen

Secretary: Steve Throssell   **(T)** 07903 322 446   **(E)** philipallen1982@hotmail.co.uk

Chairman: David Johnson   **Manager:**   **Prog Ed:**

Ground: Ron Steel Spts Grd, Lenton Lane, Clifton Bridge, Nottingham NG7 2SA   **(T)** 0115 985 0803

Capacity: 1,500 **Seats:** 150 **Covered:** 150 **Midweek Matchday:** Tuesday   **Clubhouse:** Yes **Shop:**

Colours(change): Red/black/black (All yellow)
Previous Names: None
Previous Leagues: Notts Amateur 1946-75, Notts Alliance 1975-95, Central Midlands 1995-2008, East Midlands Counties > 2010
Records:
Senior Honours: Notts Amateur League 1973-75. Central Midlands League Supreme Division 2004-05. East Midlands Counties 2009-10

10 YEAR RECORD

02-03	03-04	04-05	05-06	06-07	07-08	08-09	09-10	10-11	11-12
CM Su 12	CM Su 6	CM Su 1	CM Su 8	CM Su 6	CM Su 4	EMC 5	EMC 1	MidAl 8	MidAl 18

ELLESMERE RANGERS
Founded: 1969 Nickname:

Secretary: John Edge **(T)** 07947 864 357 **(E)** john.edge2@homecall.co.uk

Chairman: Neil Williams **Manager:** **Prog Ed:**

Ground: Beech Grove, Ellesmere, Shropshire SY12 0BT **(T)** 07947 864 357

Capacity: **Seats:** **Covered:** **Midweek Matchday:** Tuesday **Clubhouse:** **Shop:**

Colours(change): Sky blue/navy/navy (Yellow/black/yellow)
Previous Names:
Previous Leagues: West Midlands
Records:
Senior Honours: West Midlands League Premier Division 2009-10.

10 YEAR RECORD

02-03	03-04	04-05	05-06	06-07	07-08	08-09	09-10	10-11	11-12
		WM2 4	WM1	WMP 12	WMP 7	WMP 4	WMP 1	MidAl 13	MidAl 15

GORNAL ATHLETIC
Founded: 1945 Nickname:

Secretary: Kevin Williams **(T)** 07762 585 149 **(E)** gornalathleticfc1@hotmail.co.uk

Chairman: TBC **Manager:** **Prog Ed:**

Ground: Garden Walk Stadium, Garden Walk, Lower Gornal, Dudley DY3 2NR **(T)** 01384 358 398

Capacity: **Seats:** **Covered:** **Midweek Matchday:** **Clubhouse:** **Shop:**

Colours(change): Yellow & green/green/green (All royal blue)
Previous Names: Lower Gornal Athletic 1945-72.
Previous Leagues: Worcestershire Combination 1951-63. West Midlands (Regional) 1963-2012.
Records:
Senior Honours: West Midlands (Regional) Division One South 2003-04, Premier Division 2011-12.

10 YEAR RECORD

02-03	03-04	04-05	05-06	06-07	07-08	08-09	09-10	10-11	11-12
WMP 22	WM1S 1	WMP 10	WMP 2	WMP 4	WMP 16	WMP 15	WMP 17	WMP 2	WMP 1

HEATH HAYES
Founded: 1964 Nickname:

Secretary: Kathlyn Davies **(T)** 07969 203 063 **(E)** kathlyndavies@aol.com

Chairman: Craig Brotherton **Manager:** **Prog Ed:**

Ground: Coppice Colliery Grd, Newlands Lane, Heath Hayes, Cannock, WS12 3HH **(T)** 07969 203 063

Capacity: **Seats:** **Covered:** **Midweek Matchday:** Tuesday **Clubhouse:** **Shop:**

Colours(change): Blue & white stripes/blue/white (Yellow/black/yellow)
Previous Names:
Previous Leagues: Staffordshire County, West Midlands, Midland Combination 2006-10.
Records:
Senior Honours: Staffordshire County League Division 1 1977-78. West Midlands League Division 1 North 1998-99. Midland Combination Premier Division 2009-10.

10 YEAR RECORD

02-03	03-04	04-05	05-06	06-07	07-08	08-09	09-10	10-11	11-12
WMP 12	WMP 6	WMP 6	WMP 13	MCmP 8	MCmP 10	MCmP 10	MCmP 1	MidAl 11	MidAl 14

HEATHER ST. JOHN'S
Founded: 1949 Nickname:

Secretary: Adrian Rock **(T)** 07952 633 331 **(E)** adrianrock@hotmail.co.uk

Chairman: Paul Harrison **Manager:** **Prog Ed:**

Ground: St John's Park, Ravenstone Rd, Heather LE67 2QJ. **(T)** 01530 263 986

Capacity: **Seats:** **Covered:** **Midweek Matchday:** **Clubhouse:** **Shop:**

Colours(change): All royal blue (All red)
Previous Names: Heather Athletic 1949-2007.
Previous Leagues: Midland Combination > 2011.
Records:
Senior Honours: Midland Combination 2010-11.

10 YEAR RECORD

02-03	03-04	04-05	05-06	06-07	07-08	08-09	09-10	10-11	11-12
	MCm2 5	MCm1 13	MCm1 12	MCm1 6	MCmP 7	MCmP 5	MCmP 2	MCmP 1	MidAl 19

HIGHGATE UNITED
Founded: 1948   Nickname: Red or Gate

Secretary: Paul Davis   **(T)** 07527 941 993   **(E)** jimmymerry777@gmail.com

Chairman: Gary Bishop   **Manager:** Mark Burge   **Prog Ed:**

Ground: The Coppice, Tythe Barn Lane, Shirley Solihull B90 1PH   **(T)** 0121 744 4194

Capacity: **Seats:**   **Covered:**   **Midweek Matchday:** Tuesday   **Clubhouse:**   **Shop:**

Colours(change): All red (White/black/black)
Previous Names: None.
Previous Leagues: Worcestershire/Midland Combination.
Records: Not known
Senior Honours: Midland Combination Premier 1972-73, 73-74, 74-75.

10 YEAR RECORD

02-03	03-04	04-05	05-06	06-07	07-08	08-09	09-10	10-11	11-12
MCmP 9	MCmP 12	MCmP 18	MCmP 14	MCmP 3	MCmP 2	MidAl 13	MidAl 18	MidAl 18	MidAl 20

KIRKBY MUXLOE
Founded: 1910   Nickname:

Secretary: Philip Moloney   **(T)** 07775 992 778   **(E)** pmoloney1@hotmail.com

Chairman: Les Warren   **Manager:**   **Prog Ed:**

Ground: Kirby Muxloe Sports Club, Ratby Lane LE9 2AQ   **(T)** 0116 239 3201

Capacity: **Seats:**   **Covered:**   **Midweek Matchday:** Tuesday   **Clubhouse:** Yes   **Shop:**

Colours(change): Royal blue & navy/royal blue/royal blue (All orange)
Previous Names:
Previous Leagues: Leicester Mutual. Leicester City. Leicestershire Senior. East Midlands Co.
Records:
Senior Honours: Leicestershire Co. Cup 2006-07. Leicestershire Senior Champions 07-08.
East Midlands Counties Champions 2008-09.

10 YEAR RECORD

02-03	03-04	04-05	05-06	06-07	07-08	08-09	09-10	10-11	11-12
LeicS 7	LeicS 2	LeicS 4	LeicS 8	LeicS 2	LeicS 1	EMC 1	MidAl 10	MidAl 9	MidAl 11

LOUGHBOROUGH UNIVERSITY
Founded: 1920   Nickname:

Secretary: Margaret Folwell   **(T)** 01509 226 127 (Office Hrs)   **(E)** secretary@loughboroughfootball.co.uk

Chairman: Stuart McLaren   **Manager:**   **Prog Ed:**

Ground: Loughborough Uni Stadium, Holywell Sports Complex, Holywell Park LE11 3TU   **(T)** 01509 228 774

Capacity: **Seats:**   **Covered:**   **Midweek Matchday:**   **Clubhouse:**   **Shop:**

Colours(change): Purple/purple/white. (White/white/purple).
Previous Names: None
Previous Leagues: Leicestershire Senior. Midland Combination.
Records:
Senior Honours: Midland Combination 2008-09.

10 YEAR RECORD

02-03	03-04	04-05	05-06	06-07	07-08	08-09	09-10	10-11	11-12
					MCmP 4	MCmP 1	MidAl 13	MidAl 4	MidAl 5

ROCESTER
Founded: 1876   Nickname: Romans

Secretary: Barry Smith   **(T)** 07770 762 825   **(E)** rocesterfc@btinternet.com

Chairman: Mark Deaville   **Manager:**   **Prog Ed:** Barry Smith

Ground: Hillsfield, Mill Street, Rocester, Uttoxeter ST14 5JX   **(T)** 01889 591 301

Capacity: 4,000   **Seats:** 230   **Covered:** 500   **Midweek Matchday:** Tuesday   **Clubhouse:** Yes   **Shop:** Yes

Colours(change): Amber & black stripes/black/black. (All royal blue).
Previous Names: None.
Previous Leagues: Staffs Sen. (Founder Member). W.Mids (Reg). Mid.All (FM) Southern. NPL
Records: **Apps:** Peter Swanwick 1962-82.
Senior Honours: Staffordshire Senior 1985-86, 86-87. West Mids (Regional) Div.1 87-88. Midland Alliance 1998-99, 2003-04.

10 YEAR RECORD

02-03	03-04	04-05	05-06	06-07	07-08	08-09	09-10	10-11	11-12
SthW 21	MidAl 1	NPL 1 22	MidAl 22	MidAl 12	MidAl 5	MidAl 20	MidAl 16	MidAl 14	MidAl 6

STOURPORT SWIFTS

Founded: 1882   Nickname: Swifts

Secretary: Laura McDonald   **(T)** 07793 768 793   **(E)** Lmacca65@hotmail.com

Chairman: Chris Reynolds   **Manager:**   **Prog Ed:**

Ground: Walshes Meadow, Harold Davis Drive, Stourport on Severn DY13 0AA   **(T)** 01299 825 188

Capacity: 2,000 **Seats:** 250   **Covered:** 150   **Midweek Matchday:**   **Clubhouse:** Yes   **Shop:** Yes

Colours(change):   Gold & blackj/black/black (All blue)
Previous Names: Not known
Previous Leagues: Kidderminster/Worcestershire/West Midlands (Regional) > 1998, Midland Alliance 1998-2001
Records: 2,000
Senior Honours: Midland Alliance 2000-01

10 YEAR RECORD

02-03	03-04	04-05	05-06	06-07	07-08	08-09	09-10	10-11	11-12
SthW 16	SthW 18	SthW 14	SthW 20	SthM 22	SthM 17	SthM 16	SthM 17	Sthsw 17	Sthsw 21

STRATFORD TOWN

Founded: 1944   Nickname: The Town

Secretary: Brian Rose   **(T)** 07833 776 834   **(E)** brian_rose@nfumutual.co.uk

Chairman: Craig Hughes   **Manager:**   **Prog Ed:**

Ground: Knights Lane, Tiddington, Stratford Upon Avon CV37 7BZ   **(T)** 01789 269 336

Capacity: **Seats:** Yes   **Covered:** Yes   **Midweek Matchday:** Tuesday   **Clubhouse:** Yes   **Shop:** Yes

Colours(change):   All royal blue. (Tangerine/black/tangerine)
Previous Names: Stratford Town Amateurs 1964-70.
Previous Leagues: Worcestershire/Midland Comb. Birmingham & Dist. W.Mid (Reg). Hellenic.
Records: **Att:** 1,078 v Aston Villa, Birmingham Senior Cup, Oct. 1996.
Senior Honours: Worcestershire/Midland Combination 1956-57, 86-87.
   Birmingham Senior Cup 1962-63. Midland Alliance League Cup 2002-03, 03-04, 10-11.

10 YEAR RECORD

02-03	03-04	04-05	05-06	06-07	07-08	08-09	09-10	10-11	11-12
MidAl 3	MidAl 3	MidAl 11	MidAl 15	MidAl 4	MidAl 7	MidAl 6	MidAl 3	MidAl 5	MidAl 8

STUDLEY

Founded: 1987   Nickname: Bees

Secretary: Bob Fletcher   **(T)** 07745 310 077   **(E)** bobtheat@hotmail.co.uk

Chairman: Barry Cromwell   **Manager:**   **Prog Ed:**

Ground: The Beehive, Abbeyfields Drive, Studley B80 7BE   **(T)** 01527 853 817

Capacity: 1,500 **Seats:** 200   **Covered:** Yes   **Midweek Matchday:** Tuesday   **Clubhouse:** Yes   **Shop:** Yes

Colours(change):   Sky blue/navy/sky blue. (All yellow)
Previous Names: Studley BKL > 2002.
Previous Leagues: Redditch & Sth Warwicks Sunday Combination. Midland Combination.
Records: **Att:** 810 v Leamington 2003-04. **Goalscorer:** Brian Powell. **Apps:** Lee Adams - 523.
Senior Honours: Midland Combination Div.1 1991-92. Worcestershire FA Senior Urn 00-01,01-02, 02-03.

10 YEAR RECORD

02-03	03-04	04-05	05-06	06-07	07-08	08-09	09-10	10-11	11-12
MidAl 7	MidAl 5	MidAl 18	MidAl 16	MidAl 20	MidAl 13	MidAl 14	MidAl 11	MidAl 7	MidAl 17

TIPTON TOWN

Founded: 1948   Nickname:

Secretary: Keith Birch   **(T)** 07765 141 410   **(E)** birchkeith@yahoo.co.uk

Chairman: John Cross   **Manager:**   **Prog Ed:**

Ground: Tipton Sports Academy, Wednesbury Oak Road, Tipton DY4 0BS   **(T)** 0121 502 5534

Capacity: 1,000 **Seats:** 200   **Covered:** 400   **Midweek Matchday:** Wednesday   **Clubhouse:** Yes   **Shop:** No

Colours(change):   Black & white stripes/black/red. (All blue).
Previous Names: None.
Previous Leagues: West Midlands (Regional).
Records: **Att:** 1,100 v Wolves, 01.08.88.
Senior Honours: Wednesbury Senior Cup 1975-76, 76-77, 80-81, 95-96. West Midlands (Regional) Div.1 83-84. Prem 04-05.

10 YEAR RECORD

02-03	03-04	04-05	05-06	06-07	07-08	08-09	09-10	10-11	11-12
WestP 3	WestP 2	WestP 1	MidAl 11	MidAl 5	MidAl 9	MidAl 5	MidAl 4	MidAl 2	MidAl 9

TIVIDALE

Founded: 1954 Nickname:

Secretary: Leon Murray | **(T)** 07939 234 813 | **(E)** loentivi@hotmail.com
Chairman: Chris Dudley | **Manager:** Leon Murray | **Prog Ed:**
Ground: The Beeches, Packwood Road, Tividale, West Mids B69 1UL | **(T)** 01384 211 743
Capacity: **Seats:** **Covered:** **Midweek Matchday:** | **Clubhouse:** **Shop:**

Colours(change): Yellow/navy/yellow (All royal blue)
Previous Names: None
Previous Leagues: West Midlands (Regional) 1966- 2011.
Records: Not known
Senior Honours: West Midlands (Regional) League Division One 1972-73, Premier Division 2010-11.

10 YEAR RECORD

02-03	03-04	04-05	05-06	06-07	07-08	08-09	09-10	10-11	11-12
WMP 5	WMP 8	WMP 16	WMP 8	WMP 2	WMP 11	WMP 13	WMP 7	WMP 1	MidAl 4

WESTFIELDS

Founded: 1966 Nickname: The Fields

Secretary: Andrew Morris | **(T)** 07860 410 548 | **(E)** andrew@andrew-morris.co.uk
Chairman: John Morgan | **Manager:** | **Prog Ed:**
Ground: Allpay Park, Widemarsh Common, Hereford HR4 9NA | **(T)** 07860 410 548
Capacity: 2,000 **Seats:** 150 **Covered:** 150 **Midweek Matchday:** Tuesday | **Clubhouse:** Yes **Shop:** Yes

Colours(change): All Maroon & sky blue/sky blue/sky blue (All white)
Previous Names: None.
Previous Leagues: Herefordshire Sunday. Worcester & Dist. West Midlands (Regional).
Records: Att: 518 v Rushden & Daimonds, FA Cup, 1996. **Goalscorer:** Paul Burton. **Apps:** Jon Pugh.
Senior Honours: Hereford Senior Cup 1985-86, 88-89, 91-92, 95-96, 01-02, 02-03, 04-05, 05-06, 07-08.
West Midlands (Regional) Premier 2002-03.

10 YEAR RECORD

02-03	03-04	04-05	05-06	06-07	07-08	08-09	09-10	10-11	11-12
WestP 1	MidAl 13	MidAl 6	MidAl 20	MidAl 16	MidAl 11	MidAl 17	MidAl 5	MidAl 6	MidAl 2

GROUND DIRECTIONS

ALVECHURCH - Lye Meadow, Redditch Rd., Alvechurch, B48 7RS - 0121-445 2929
M42 Junction 2. Take A441 towards Redditch. At first roundabout turn right onto
A4120 signposted Alvechurch. Ground approx 1km on right. Car park entrance on right before
ground.

BOLDMERE ST. MICHAELS - The Trevor Brown Memorial Ground, Church Road, Boldmere, Sutton Coldfield B73 5RY - 0121-384 7531
A38(M) from M6 junction 6 and A5127 from Birmingham to Yenton Traffic Lights. Left on A452
Chester Road, then 6th.right into Church Road.
From M6 junction 5 A452 Brownhills to Yenton Traffic Lights. Straight on then 6th right into Church
Road.

BRIDGNORTH TOWN - Crown Meadow, Innage Lane, Bridgnorth, WV16 4HL - 01746-763001
From the A458 follow town centre signs. At 'T' junction turn right and then first left into Victoria Road.
At crossroads of Woodberry Down Pub turn right. Follow road down and around right hand bend.
When the road straightens out, the ground is 250 yards on the right.

CAUSEWAY UNITED - War Memorial Athletic Ground, High Street, Amblecote, Stourbridge, West Midlands, DY8 4HN - 01384-394040
From Stourbridge Ring Road take A491 towards Wolverhampton. Ground is on left within 300 yards
immediately after 1st set of traffic lights and opposite the Royal Oak public house.

COLESHILL TOWN - Pack Meadow, Packington Lane, Coleshill, B46 3JQ - 01675 463 259
From M6 Junction 4 take A446 signposted Lichfield. Straight over 1st roundabout then immediately
turn right across dual carriageway onto B4117 signposted Coleshill. After school on right, turn right
into Packington Lane. Ground is ½ mile on left.

CONTINENTAL STAR - Rushall Olympic F.C. Dales Lane, Rushall, Walsall, West Midls, WS4 1LJ
01922 641 021
From M6 Junction 7 head North on Birmingham Road/A34 towards Chapel Lane. At the roundabout take the 2nd exit onto Broadway N/A4148. At the roundabout take the 1st exit onto Birmingham Road. At the roundabout take the 2nd exit onto Springhill Road. At the roundabout take the 1st exit onto Ablewell Street. Turn left onto Town Hill. Keep right at the fork. Turn right onto Upper Rushall Street. Continue onto Lower Rushall Street. Continue onto Lichfield Street/A461. Go through 1 roundabout. Turn right onto Daw End Lane/B4154. Continue to follow B4154. Turn right into Rushall Olympic Football Club.

COVENTRY SPHINX - Sphinx Drive, Off Siddeley Avenue, Coventry, CV3 1WA - 02476 451 361
From M6. Leave M6 at Junction 3 and take A444 towards Coventry. Continue to Binley Road (6 roundabouts) and turn left on A428 Binley Road towards Binley. Pass a row of shops on left and Bulls Head public house on right. After the Bulls Head, turn 1st right into Biggin Hall Crescent. Then take the 5th left turn into Siddeley Avenue. Take 1st left into Sphinx Drive and the ground is at the end. From M42 & A45. Follow A45 towards Coventry and take A4114 Coventry at Coventry Hill Hotel. At roundabout take 2nd exit to next roundabout and take 3rd exit onto Holyhead Road. After approx 2.5 miles you will come to Coventry Ring Road where you turn left and then get over to your right onto the ring road. Continue on Ring Road and leave at Junction 3 signposted M69 and Football Stadium. Follow signs for A428 Binley until you see Bulls Head public house on your right. Then follow the above instructions.

DUNKIRK - The Ron Steel Sports Ground, Lenton Lane, Clifton Bridge, Nottingham, NG7 2SA
0115 985 0803
From M1 Junction 24 take A453 towards Nottingham, through Clifton and join A52 onto Clifton Bridge. Get in middle lane down the slip road onto the island under the flyover signposted Industrial Estate. Take immediate 1st left and 1st left again onto Lenton Lane. Follow the road past Greenwood Meadows and the ground is 200 yards on the right.

ELLESMERE RANGERS - Beech Grove, Ellesmere, Shropshire, SY12 0BT - 07947 864 357
Approaching Ellesmere from Whitchurch and Shrewsbury, go past the lake on your right and follow signs for A495 Oswestry. When you get to the Lakelands School, turn right into the houses, left at the crossroads then 1st right down the lane to the ground. There will be signs for the ground on the main road.

GORNAL ATHLETIC - Garden Walk, Lower Gornal, Dudley, West Midlands, DY3 2NR
01384 358 398
From Dudley take Himley Road (B4176) to Gornal. Right turn into Central Drive. First left into Bank Road. Beear right at top. Garden Walk.

HEATH HAYES - Coppice Colliery Ground, Newlands Lane, Heath Hayes, Cannock, Staffordshire, WS12 3HH - 07969 203 063
From M6 Junction 11 take the A4601 towards Cannock and at the 1st island turn right onto the A460 signposted Rugeley/Cannock Business Parks. At the double island (A5) go straight on still on A460 and over two islands. At the 3rd island, turn right onto A5190 signposted Lichfield. Pass Texaco garage on the right and take the next right turn into Newlands Lane. Entrance to the ground is 50 yards down the lane on the left under the barrier.

HEATHER ST. JOHN'S - St. John's Park, Ravenstone Road, Heather, Leicestershire, LE67 2QJ - 01530 263 986
Exit M42 at Junction 11. Take the road towards Measham, pass the Car Auctions and go over the traffic lights. At 2nd mini island take 2nd exit onto Leicester Road. After approximately 3 miles you will enter Heather. At T junction turn left. At mini island take 2nd exit onto Ravenstone Road and go up the hill. Ground is 200 metres on the left.

HIGHGATE UNITED - The Coppice, Tythe Barn Lane, Shirley, Solihull, B90 1PH - 0121 744 4194
From M42 Junction 4 take A34 towards Birmingham. Go to far end of Shirley Village and turn left into Haslucks Green Road. Take the left hand fork by the Colebrook pub and go past Shirley Station and the Drawbridge pub. At 'T' junction turn left and go over railway bridge. Turn left into Tythe Barn Lane and the ground is the 2nd entrance on the right approx 200 yards down the lane.

KIRBY MUXLOE - Kirby Muxloe Sports Club, Ratby Lane, Kirby Muxloe, Leics, LE9 2AQ
0116 239 3201
Leave M1 at Junction 21a and follow signs to Kirby Muxloe. Road goes round and back over

Motorway and down hill to a roundabout. Go straight on to mini roundabout and straight on to Ratby Lane. Entrance is next to last house on the right.

LOUGHBOROUGH UNIVERSITY - Loughborough University Stadium, Holywell Sports Complex, Holywell Park, Loughborough, Leics, LE11 3TU - 01509 228 774

From M42/A42 exit at Junction 13 and take the A512 towards Loughborough. After crossing Junction 23 of the M1 travel approx 3/4 mile to first traffic island. Turn right into University (LE11 3QF Red Building is on your right). Keep straight on at both small islands. Bear left into large spectator car park, entrance on left hand side. Please note that there is limited parking at Stadium for Officials/ Team Coach/Cars.

ROCESTR - Hillsfield, Mill Street, Rocester, Uttoxeter, Staffordshire ST14 5JX - 01889 591 301

From Uttoxeter take the B5030, signposted Ashbourne/Alton Towers After 3 miles turn right opposite the JCB factory over humpback bridge into Rocester village. Turn right at mini island into Mill Street, ground is 500 yards on the left immediately past the JCB Academy.

STOURPORT SWIFTS - Walshes Meadow, Harold Davies Drive, Stourport on Severn, Worcs, DY13 0AA - 01299 825 188

Follw the one way system through Stourport Town Centre signposted 'Sports Centre'. Go over the river bridge and turn first left into Harold Davies Drive. Ground is at the rear of the Sports Centre.

STRATFORD TOWN - The DCS Stadium, Knights Lane, Tiddington, Stratford-u-Avon, CV37 7BZ 01789 269 336

From Town Centre follow signs for Banbury (A422) and Oxford (A3400). Cross Clopton Bridge and turn immediately left onto B4086 towards Wellesbourne. After approx 1 mile you enter the village of Tiddington. Turn 1st right into Knights Lane. Ground is approx 800 yards on right (100 yards after school).

STUDLEY - The Beehive, Abbeyfields Drive, Studley, Warks. B80 7BE - 01527 853 817

Leave M42 at junction 3 (Redditch A435) and turn towards Redditch. Follow dual carriageway to the end. Stay on A435 and go straight on at island. Pass 'The Boot' public house and after 550 yards turn left into Abbeyfields Drive. The ground is on the right.

TIPTON TOWN - Tipton Sports Academy, Wednesbury Oak Road, Tipton, West Mids, DY4 0BS 0121 502 5534

From M6 junction 9 take A461 through Wednesbury Town Centre to Ockerhill Island. Follow signs taking a full right turn towards Bilston (A4098). In ½ mile turn left at traffic lights (A4037). Ground 100 yards on left. Use 2nd Entrance.

From M5 junction 2 take A4123 for about 3 miles until you reach Burnt Tree Island. Take second exit towards Wolverhampton and continue to next set of traffic lights. Turn right A4037 and continue for 3 miles. Pass ASDA supermarket and ground is 100 yards on the right. Use 1st Entrance.

TIVIDALE - The Beeches, Packwood Road, Tividale, Oldbury, West Midlands, B69 1UL 01384 211 743

From M5 Junction 2 Take A4123 towards Dudley. After approx 1.5 miles and after foot bridge, take left up Trafalgar Road. Take 2nd right into Elm Terrace and then 1st left into Birch Crescent. Take 1st right into Packwood Road and ground is at end of road.

WESTFIELDS - 'Allpay park', Widemarsh Common, Grandstand Road., Hereford, HR4 9NA 07860 410 548

On reaching the outskirts of Hereford from Worcester, continue along A4103, over roundabout signposted Holmer and Leisure Centre. Proceed for 1 mile to large roundabout by the "Starting Gate Inn" and turn left towards Hereford. Proceed for ½ mile, past Hereford Leisure Centre and at mini roundabout, turn right. Proceed 150 yards and bear left around the Common, in front of Cricket Pavilion and immediately turn right into the driveway for allpay.park.

NORTH WEST COUNTIES LEAGUE

Sponsored by: Vodkat

Founded: 1982

Recent Champions:
2007: FC United of Manchester. 2008: Trafford. 2009: AFC Fylde
2010: Newcastle Town. 2011: New Mills

nwcfl.co.uk

PREMIER DIVISION	P	W	D	L	F	A	Pts
1 (P) Ramsbottom United	42	31	3	8	108	43	96
2 Runcorn Town	42	29	5	8	111	49	92
3 Bootle (-1)	42	24	13	5	87	43	84
4 Barnoldswick Town	42	26	5	11	73	38	83
5 Runcorn Linnets	42	22	10	10	70	62	76
6 Glossop North End	42	22	7	13	76	42	73
7 Winsford United	42	21	6	15	88	69	69
8 Colne	42	19	4	19	68	60	61
9 AFC Blackpool	42	17	10	15	67	64	61
10 Flixton	42	18	5	19	69	68	59
11 Congleton Town	42	18	5	19	56	64	59
12 Silsden	42	16	9	17	59	59	57
13 Alsager Town	42	16	9	17	63	65	57
14 Ashton Athletic	42	15	6	21	70	80	51
15 Padiham	42	14	9	19	51	65	51
16 Squires Gate	42	14	8	20	74	89	50
17 Bacup Borough (-3)	42	15	7	20	59	77	49
18 Maine Road (-4)	42	13	9	20	58	69	44
19 AFC Liverpool (-3)	42	13	6	23	60	73	42
20 Stone Dominoes	42	10	6	26	39	92	36
21 St Helens Town	42	6	8	28	50	105	26
22 (R) Atherton Laburnum Rovers	42	5	6	31	36	116	21

LEAGUE CHALLENGE CUP

BACUP BOROUGH 5-0 MAIN ROAD

Bacup Borough: Paul Horridge, Gareth Wager, Kingsley Williams (Aaron Walters 56), Otis Gorman, Adam Turner, Davey Luker (captain), Adrian Bellamy, Jamil Adam (Martin Cosgrove 86), Adam Dale (Matthew Wrigley 46), Lee Oldham, Daniel Cocks. Subs not used: Matthew Hampson, Matthew Kemp.

Goals: Jamil Adam (31), Joseph Armstrong o.g. (45), Adrian Bellamy (65pen), Jamil Adam (67), Adrian Bellamy (88)

Maine Road: Greg Hall, Andrew Thorpe, James Rothel (Matt Struminskyj 68), Alex Jay (captain) (Matthew Huntley 47), Josh Gittings, Neil Chappell (Andrew Kilheeney 38), Liam Beckford, Robert Brocklehurst, Tom Bentham, Joseph Armstrong, Eddie Moran. Subs not used: Rory Breslin, Ryan Livesey.

Attendance: 398

PREMIER DIVISION	1	2	3	4	5	6	7	8	9	10	11	12	13	14	15	16	17	18	19	20	21	22
1 AFC Blackpool		1-3	1-0	1-0	4-3	2-1	0-0	1-0	1-0	1-2	3-2	1-3	1-1	2-0	0-3	2-3	1-2	2-1	2-0	2-2	0-1	2-5
2 AFC Liverpool	3-2		2-3	0-1	1-2	1-0	0-1	2-3	1-1	0-2	2-1	0-1	0-2	1-1	2-1	0-3	0-1	3-2	2-2	6-0	7-0
3 Alsager Town	1-0	1-2		3-2	5-0	2-2	1-2	2-4	0-2	1-2	2-1	1-0	2-2	2-0	0-5	0-0	0-3	0-2	2-1	3-2	0-2	1-2
4 Ashton Athletic	1-1	3-2	1-3		4-0	2-3	0-0	1-0	3-4	2-1	0-1	0-4	2-0	1-3	1-4	1-2	1-5	0-2	2-1	4-0	3-1	2-2
5 Atherton Laburnum Rovers	2-2	0-2	3-2	0-3		1-2	0-2	1-3	2-5	0-2	0-3	2-1	2-3	1-1	1-3	0-2	0-5	1-0	3-2	0-0	1-1	1-4
6 Bacup Borough	0-2	3-2	3-3	1-4	2-0		1-3	2-1	L-W	3-4	1-1	3-0	2-0	1-0	0-1	1-6	2-1	2-4	3-2	1-1	3-6
7 Barnoldswick Town	2-0	3-1	1-0	3-1	4-0	1-2		1-1	2-0	2-0	2-1	2-1	3-1	0-2	3-0	1-1	0-1	1-2	4-0	3-0	1-0
8 Bootle	0-2	3-0	2-2	3-3	3-0	2-1	2-3		2-0	1-1	3-1	2-1	3-1	1-0	2-2	1-1	0-0	4-0	3-0	5-1	0-0	1-1
9 Colne	1-1	1-2	0-2	4-2	6-0	1-0	0-0	0-2		1-3	3-2	0-3	0-2	0-1	0-1	2-1	3-4	1-0	3-0	1-2	0-1	1-6
10 Congleton Town	0-3	1-0	2-1	1-2	1-0	1-2	0-0	2-3	1-3		0-3	0-1	0-1	2-1	0-2	1-2	2-2	1-0	3-0	1-0	1-1	1-2
11 Flixton	1-2	2-1	0-1	2-2	6-1	0-1	2-0	0-1	2-1	0-2		1-5	2-0	2-0	0-3	0-2	2-0	2-1	2-3	1-0	1-0	2-1
12 Glossop North End	2-0	0-0	1-1	2-1	3-1	0-1	2-1	0-1	1-1	4-1	7-1		1-1	0-0	1-4	5-0	0-1	1-3	2-0	3-0	4-0	1-0
13 Maine Road	2-2	3-0	0-0	0-0	3-1	3-2	1-2	2-3	0-3	2-1	0-3	1-0		3-0	0-2	1-2	0-2	0-2	3-3	2-1	0-1	1-4
14 Padiham	2-2	2-1	1-1	1-2	2-1	3-1	1-0	1-4	1-5	2-0	1-1	0-1	2-1		1-2	3-0	2-4	0-4	2-1	3-1	0-1	0-3
15 Ramsbottom United	3-2	3-1	0-1	5-3	4-0	3-2	3-2	1-1	0-2	3-0	2-2	3-1	3-1	2-3		4-2	1-2	3-0	4-0	5-0	5-0	5-2
16 Runcorn Linnets	3-3	3-0	3-2	1-0	2-0	2-1	1-0	1-1	2-1	2-0	2-1	1-1	2-2	0-0	1-2		2-1	1-0	3-2	1-0	1-1	1-5
17 Runcorn Town	1-2	1-0	2-0	4-1	6-0	7-0	1-2	1-1	1-0	3-2	6-2	2-3	4-1	2-2	1-3	3-2		3-0	0-1	4-2	4-1	3-0
18 Silsden	0-1	3-4	2-2	1-0	2-2	1-1	0-4	1-1	0-2	3-3	0-1	1-0	1-0	1-0	2-1	4-4	1-2		3-0	1-1	3-0	1-0
19 Squires Gate	2-1	2-2	2-0	4-3	2-2	2-2	1-4	1-3	1-2	5-1	3-2	0-1	3-3	3-2	1-0	0-1	2-2	2-2		6-1	3-0	1-1
20 St Helens Town	3-2	3-1	0-3	2-3	3-0	0-0	4-2	1-2	2-5	1-3	0-5	2-5	0-3	1-1	3-2	0-1	1-2	1-1	3-5		1-1	1-4
21 Stone Dominoes	1-5	4-0	0-3	0-2	2-1	1-0	1-2	2-3	0-2	1-2	1-4	1-3	0-5	0-3	0-2	5-8	1-3	1-3	3-1	2-1		0-1
22 Winsford United	2-2	1-1	3-4	3-1	3-1	0-1	1-2	0-6	3-1	0-2	3-0	1-1	3-1	1-2	0-2	0-1	2-1	5-4	5-0	1-0	1-0	

DIVISION ONE	P	W	D	L	F	A	Pts
1 (P) Wigan Robin Park	34	25	6	3	90	36	81
2 (P) Norton United	34	24	8	2	110	43	80
3 Abbey Hey	34	22	3	9	82	44	69
4 Atherton Collieries	34	15	7	12	69	52	52
5 Rochdale Town	34	14	10	10	72	57	52
6 Chadderton	34	13	10	11	53	51	49
7 Eccleshall	34	14	5	15	52	64	47
8 Cheadle Town (-3)	34	13	9	12	60	61	45
9 Holker Old Boys	34	12	9	13	53	64	45
10 Irlam	34	13	5	16	68	75	44
11 Formby	34	13	4	17	72	69	43
12 Daisy Hill	34	12	5	17	59	67	41
13 AFC Darwen	34	10	8	16	62	77	38
14 Oldham Boro	34	9	10	15	52	56	37
15 Nelson	34	9	5	20	40	83	32
16 Northwich Villa	34	7	10	17	51	86	31
17 Leek CSOB (-7)	34	10	7	17	50	70	30
18 Ashton Town	34	6	9	19	49	89	27

RESERVE DIVISION	P	W	D	L	F	A	Pts
1 Wigan Robin Park Reserves	24	17	4	3	79	30	55
2 New Mills Reserves	24	17	2	5	52	40	53
3 Ashton Athletic Reserves	24	15	5	4	69	36	50
4 Padiham Reserves (-1)	24	14	4	6	59	31	45
5 Glossop North End Reserves	24	14	2	8	67	39	44
6 Barnoldswick Town Reserves	24	13	2	9	52	41	41
7 Irlam Reserves	24	11	3	10	54	48	36
8 Silsden Reserves	24	8	7	9	40	48	31
9 Ashton Town Reserves	24	7	4	13	40	62	25
10 AFC Darwen Reserves	24	6	5	13	38	62	23
11 Cheadle Town Reserves (-1)	24	4	5	15	39	60	16
12 Daisy Hill Reserves	24	3	3	18	28	76	12
13 Nelson Reserves (-1)	24	2	4	18	23	67	9

DIVISION ONE	1	2	3	4	5	6	7	8	9	10	11	12	13	14	15	16	17	18
1 Abbey Hey		6-1	2-2	1-0	5-1	4-1	4-0	3-1	4-0	1-3	3-0	1-0	5-1	4-3	0-4	1-0	1-1	1-2
2 AFC Darwen	1-2		0-4	1-1	1-1	0-3	1-2	5-2	4-1	3-0	6-1	2-4	2-1	2-2	0-5	1-3	0-0	2-3
3 Ashton Town	1-2	5-0		1-1	1-2	0-0	2-6	1-2	0-2	1-1	3-4	3-3	2-1	1-3	0-6	2-3	1-4	0-4
4 Atherton Collieries	2-1	3-1	2-3		1-2	4-1	1-1	2-2	2-1	5-0	2-1	2-1	5-0	5-1	3-0	3-2	0-3	0-1
5 Chadderton	0-0	1-2	3-0	3-0		2-1	2-1	1-1	2-3	1-0	2-1	3-1	1-1	0-0	3-3	0-0	3-4	1-2
6 Cheadle Town	3-1	2-4	2-2	2-2	1-2		1-3	1-2	3-6	0-0	2-2	4-3	2-3	3-0	1-1	1-2	2-1	1-3
7 Daisy Hill	3-5	2-2	3-1	1-1	2-1	1-2		0-2	1-0	1-0	1-3	0-2	2-2	3-2	2-3	2-1	4-2	0-2
8 Eccleshall	3-4	3-0	4-1	0-4	2-5	0-5	3-2		1-0	1-2	5-3	2-1	2-1	1-2	0-1	1-4	1-2	2-2
9 Formby	0-1	2-3	2-2	3-0	4-1	0-1	1-3	4-1		4-3	2-5	3-4	3-0	0-1	1-0	2-0	1-2	2-3
10 Holker Old Boys	0-1	0-7	1-1	2-1	1-1	3-3	2-2	1-2			2-1	4-2	2-0	2-1	1-2	2-1	2-1	2-2
11 Irlam	0-4	1-3	1-0	3-2	2-1	1-3	4-0	0-0	2-1	1-3		5-0	3-2	0-6	2-3	4-2	1-1	1-4
12 Leek CSOB	0-3	2-0	3-0	0-0	1-0	2-3	2-1	0-0	2-2	0-3	1-1		0-1	2-2	3-3	3-2	0-1	0-4
13 Nelson	0-3	1-0	3-2	4-3	2-3	0-1	1-0	1-2	2-2	2-1	1-9	1-0		3-0	1-3	0-5	0-3	0-3
14 Northwich Villa	1-3	2-2	2-2	1-5	2-2	1-1	1-4	2-0	0-6	2-4	0-3	0-4	1-1		1-2	1-4	2-2	3-2
15 Norton United	3-2	5-1	5-1	3-2	3-0	5-0	3-1	2-0	7-4	6-3	3-0	6-1	5-0	6-1		0-0	2-2	5-2
16 Oldham Boro	2-1	2-2	1-3	0-1	0-0	0-2	3-2	1-3	1-2	0-0	2-1	1-2	1-1	2-2	1-1		2-5	0-1
17 Rochdale Town	4-3	2-2	0-1	2-3	2-3	0-1	3-2	0-1	3-2	2-2	1-1	4-1	5-2	3-0	3-3	3-3		1-4
18 Wigan Robin Park	1-0	3-1	11-0	4-1	1-0	1-1	2-1	1-0	4-4	4-0	4-1	3-0	2-1	2-3	1-1	1-1	1-0	

AFC BLACKPOOL

Founded: 1947   Nickname: Mechs

Secretary: William Singleton   **(T)** 01253 761 721   **(E)**
Chairman: Henry Baldwin   **Manager:** Stuart Parker   **Prog Ed:** David Tebbett
Ground: Mechanics Ground, Jepson Way, Common Edge Road, Blackpool, FY4 5DY   **(T)** 01253 761 721
Capacity: 2,000 **Seats:** 250 **Covered:** 1,700 **Midweek Matchday:** Tuesday   **Clubhouse:** Yes   **Shop:** Yes

Colours(change): Tangerine/white/tangerine (White/tangerine/tangerine)
Previous Names: Blackpool Mechanics. **Previous Ground:** Stanley Park 1947-49.
Previous Leagues: Fylde, Blackpool & Fylde Combination, West Lancashire, Lancashire Combination 1962-68.
Records: Att: 4,300 v FC United of Manchester, 18/02/2006 at Blackpool FC.
Senior Honours: Lancashire County FA Shield 1957/58, 1960/61. West Lancashire League 1960/61, 61/62.
North West Counties League Division Three 1985/86, Division One 2010-11.

10 YEAR RECORD

02-03	03-04	04-05	05-06	06-07	07-08	08-09	09-10	10-11	11-12
NWC2 14	NWC2 14	NWC2 10	NWC2 9	NWC1 13	NWC1 9	NWC1 15	NWC1 15	NWC1 1	NWCP 9

AFC LIVERPOOL

Founded: 2008   Nickname: Reds

Secretary: Pat Cushion   **(T)** 0151 430 0507   **(E)** clubsec@afcliverpool.org.uk
Chairman: Chris Stirrup   **Manager:** Paul Moore   **Prog Ed:** Steven Horton
Ground: Prescot Cables FC, Valerie Pk, Eaton Street, Prescot, Merseyside, L34 6ND   **(T)** 0151 430 0507
Capacity: 3,000 **Seats:** 500 **Covered:** 600 **Midweek Matchday:** Wednesday   **Clubhouse:** Yes   **Shop:** Yes

Colours(change): All red (Yellow/black/yellow)
Previous Names: None
Previous Leagues: None
Records: Att: 604 v Wigan Robin Park 06/09/2008.
Senior Honours: North West Counties Trophy 2008-09, 09-10.

10 YEAR RECORD

02-03	03-04	04-05	05-06	06-07	07-08	08-09	09-10	10-11	11-12
						NWC1 4	NWC1 5	NWC1 4	NWCP 19

ALSAGER TOWN

Founded: 1968   Nickname: The Bullets

Secretary: Chris Robinson   **(T)** 01270 882 336   **(E)**
Chairman: Terry Greer   **Manager:** Andy Turner   **Prog Ed:** John Shenton
Ground: The LAW Training Stadium, Woodland Court, Alsager ST7 2DP   **(T)** 07888 750532
Capacity: 3,000 **Seats:** 250 **Covered:** 1,000 **Midweek Matchday:** Tuesday   **Clubhouse:** Yes   **Shop:** Yes

Colours(change): White & black/black/black. (All red).
Previous Names: Alsager FC (Merger of Alsager Institute & Alsager Utd) in 1965.
Previous Leagues: Crewe. Mid Cheshire. Northern Premier.
Records: Att: 606 v Whitley Bay - 14.11.2009. **Goalscorer:** Gareth Rowe. **Apps:** Wayne Brotherton.
Senior Honours: Leek Cup 2002

10 YEAR RECORD

02-03	03-04	04-05	05-06	06-07	07-08	08-09	09-10	10-11	11-12
NWC1 11	NWC1 9	NWC1 7	NWC1 3	NP1S 16	NP1S 14	NWCP 7	NWCP 18	NWCP 20	NWCP 13

ASHTON ATHLETIC

Founded: 1968   Nickname:

Secretary: Alan Greenhalgh   **(T)** 01942 716 360   **(E)**
Chairman: Jimmy Whyte   **Manager:** Ian Street   **Prog Ed:** Alan Greenhalgh
Ground: Brockstedes Park, Downall Green, Ashton in Markerfield WN4 0NR   **(T)** 01942 716 360
Capacity: 600 **Seats:** 100 **Covered:** 300 **Midweek Matchday:** Tuesday   **Clubhouse:** Yes   **Shop:** No

Colours(change): All yellow. (All blue).
Previous Names: None.
Previous Leagues: Lancashire Combination, Manchester Amateur League
Records: Att: 165 v Runcorn Linnets 2006-07. **Apps:** Steve Rothwell - 50+
Senior Honours: Atherton Charity Cup 2006-07, 07-08, 08-09.

10 YEAR RECORD

02-03	03-04	04-05	05-06	06-07	07-08	08-09	09-10	10-11	11-12
Manc 5	Manc 10	Manc 10	Manc 4	NWC2 16	NWC2 3	NWCP 6	NWCP 21	NWCP 22	NWCP 14

BACUP BOROUGH
Founded: 1878   Nickname: The Boro

Secretary: Wendy Ennis   **(T)** 01706 878 655   **(E)**
Chairman: Frank Manning   **Manager:** Brent Peters   **Prog Ed:** Michael Carr
Ground: Brian Boys Stadium, Cowtoot Lane, Blackthorn, Bacup, OL13 8EE   **(T)** 01706 878 655
Capacity: 3,000   **Seats:** 500   **Covered:** 1,000   **Midweek Matchday:** Wednesday   **Clubhouse:** Yes   **Shop:** No

Colours(change): White/black/black. (Tangerine/claret/tangerine).
Previous Names: Bacup FC
Previous Leagues: Lancashire Combination 1903-82
Records: **Att:** 4,980 v Nelson 1947 **Goalscorer:** Jimmy Clarke
Senior Honours: North West Counties League Division Two 2002-03, Challenge Cup 2003-04.

10 YEAR RECORD

02-03	03-04	04-05	05-06	06-07	07-08	08-09	09-10	10-11	11-12
NWC2 1	NWC1 14	NWC1 9	NWC1 17	NWC1 15	NWC1 18	NWCP 8	NWCP 12	NWCP 11	NWCP 17

BARNOLDSWICK TOWN
Founded: 1972   Nickname:

Secretary: Lynn James   **(T)**   **(E)**
Chairman: Ian James   **Manager:** B. Hall, S. Airdrie & K. Richardson   **Prog Ed:** Peter Naylor
Ground: Silentnight Stadium, West Close Road, Barnoldswick, Colne, BB18 5LJ   **(T)** 01282 815 817
Capacity: **Seats:**   **Covered:**   **Midweek Matchday:** Tuesday   **Clubhouse:** Yes   **Shop:**

Colours(change): Yellow & Royal Blue/royal blue/royal blue socks (All red)
Previous Names: Today's club formed after the merger of Barnoldswick United and Barnoldswick Park Rovers in 2003
Previous Leagues: Craven, East Lancashire, West Lancashire.
Records:
Senior Honours: West Lancashire Division 1 1998-99

10 YEAR RECORD

02-03	03-04	04-05	05-06	06-07	07-08	08-09	09-10	10-11	11-12
WLaP 9	WLaP 12	WLaP 15	WLaP 15	WLaP 13	WLaP 10	WLaP 6	NWC1 2	NWCP 7	NWCP 4

BOOTLE
Founded: 1954   Nickname:

Secretary: Joe Doran   **(T)** 0151 531 0665   **(E)**
Chairman: Frank Doran   **Manager:** Neil Prince   **Prog Ed:** Dave Miley Junior
Ground: Delta Taxi Stadium, Vestey Rd, Off Bridle Road, Bootle L30 1NY   **(T)** 0151 525 4796
Capacity: **Seats:**   **Covered:**   **Midweek Matchday:** Tuesday   **Clubhouse:** Yes   **Shop:**

Colours(change): All blue. (Yellow/black/black).
Previous Names: Langton Dock 1953 - 1970.
Previous Leagues: Liverpool Shipping. Lancs Comb. Cheshire. Liverpool County Comb.
Records: **Att:** 1,078 v Everton Reserves, Liverpool Senior Cup Feb 2010.
Senior Honours: Liverpool County Champions 1964-65, 65-66, 67-68, 68-69, 69-70, 70-71, 71-72, 72-73, 73-74.
North West Counties Div.1 Champions 2008-09

10 YEAR RECORD

02-03	03-04	04-05	05-06	06-07	07-08	08-09	09-10	10-11	11-12
Liv 5	Liv 17	Liv 12	Liv 3	NWC2 10	NWC2 6	NWC1 1	NWCP 3	NWCP 6	NWCP 3

COLNE
Founded: 1996   Nickname:

Secretary: Edward Lambert   **(T)** 01282 862 545   **(E)**
Chairman: David Blacklock   **Manager:** Nigel Coates   **Prog Ed:** Ray Davies
Ground: The XLCR Stadium, Harrison Drive, Colne, Lancashire. BB8 9SL   **(T)** 01282 862 545
Capacity: 1,800   **Seats:** 160   **Covered:** 1,000   **Midweek Matchday:** Tuesday   **Clubhouse:** Yes   **Shop:** Yes

Colours(change): All Red. (All sky blue).
Previous Names: None
Previous Leagues: None
Records: **Att:** 1,742 v AFC Sudbury F.A. Vase SF 2004 **Goalscorer:** Geoff Payton **App:** Richard Walton
Senior Honours: BEP Cup Winners 1996-97 North West Counties League Division Two 2003-04.

10 YEAR RECORD

02-03	03-04	04-05	05-06	06-07	07-08	08-09	09-10	10-11	11-12
NWC2 10	NWC2 1	NWC1 10	NWC1 9	NWC1 11	NWC1 5	NWCP 18	NWCP 8	NWCP 5	NWCP 8

CONGLETON TOWN
Founded: 1901   Nickname: Bears

Secretary: Ken Mead   **(T)** 01260 278 152   **(E)**

Chairman: Peter Evans   **Manager:** Jim Vince   **Prog Ed:** Paul Brindley

Ground: Ivy Gardens, Booth Street, Crescent Road, Congleton, Cheshire CW12 4DG   **(T)** 01260 274 460
Capacity: 5,000 **Seats:** 250 **Covered:** 1,200 **Midweek Matchday:** Tuesday   **Clubhouse:** Yes **Shop:** Yes

Colours(change): Black & white stripes/black/black. (All yellow).
Previous Names: Congleton Hornets
Previous Leagues: Crew & District, North Staffs, Macclesfield, Cheshire , Mid Cheshire, NW Co, NPL
Records: **Att:** 6,800 v Macclesfield, Cheshire Lge1953-54 **Goalscorer:** Mick Bidde 150+ **App:** Ray Clack 600+ Graham Harrison 600+
Senior Honours: Cheshire Senior Cup 1920-21, 37-38.

10 YEAR RECORD

02-03	03-04	04-05	05-06	06-07	07-08	08-09	09-10	10-11	11-12
NWC1 8	NWC1 11	NWC1 19	NWC1 12	NWC1 10	NWC1 9	NWCP 4	NWCP 5	NWCP 8	NWCP 11

GLOSSOP NORTH END
Founded: 1886   Nickname: Hillmen

Secretary: Stewart Taylor   **(T)**   **(E)**

Chairman: David Atkinson   **Manager:** Paul Colgan   **Prog Ed:** Stewart Taylor

Ground: Surrey Street, Glossop, Derbys SK13 7AJ   **(T)** 01457 855 469
Capacity: 2,374 **Seats:** 209 **Covered:** 509 **Midweek Matchday:** Wednesday   **Clubhouse:** Yes **Shop:** Yes

Colours(change): Black & white/black/black (All blue).
Previous Names: Glossop North End1886-1896 and Glossop FC 1898-1992. Reformed in 1992.
Previous Leagues: The Football League. Cheshire County. Manchester. Lancashire Comb.
Records: **Att:** 10,736 v Preston North End F.A. Cup 1913-1914
Senior Honours: Manchester League 1927-28. Derbyshire Senior Cup 2000-01.

10 YEAR RECORD

02-03	03-04	04-05	05-06	06-07	07-08	08-09	09-10	10-11	11-12
NWC1 20	NWC1 18	NWC1 13	NWC1 16	NWC1 9	NWC1 7	NWCP 5	NWCP 7	NWCP 14	NWCP 6

MAINE ROAD
Founded: 1955   Nickname: Blues

Secretary: Derek Barber   **(T)** 0161 431 8243   **(E)**

Chairman: Ron Meredith   **Manager:** Ian Walker   **Prog Ed:** Derek Barber

Ground: Brantingham Road, Chorlton-cum-Hardy M21 0TT   **(T)** 0161 861 0344
Capacity: 2,000 **Seats:** 200 **Covered:** 700 **Midweek Matchday:** Monday   **Clubhouse:** Yes **Shop:** No

Colours(change): All sky blue. (Red & black stripes/black/black).
Previous Names:
Previous Leagues: Rusholme Sunday 55-66, Manchester Amateur Sunday 66-72 & Manchester 72-87
Records: **Att:** 3,125 v FC United Manchester, NWC Div.1, 04.11.06, at Stalybridge Celtic.
Senior Honours: Manchester Premier League 1982-83, 83-84, 84-85, 85-86. North West Counties Division Two 1989-90, Challenge Cup 07-08.

10 YEAR RECORD

02-03	03-04	04-05	05-06	06-07	07-08	08-09	09-10	10-11	11-12
NWC2 3	NWC2 2	NWC1 8	NWC1 10	NWC1 6	NWC1 4	NWCP 13	NWCP 6	NWCP 13	NWCP 18

NORTON UNITED
Founded: 1989   Nickname:

Secretary: Dennis Vickers   **(T)** 01782 838 290   **(E)**

Chairman: Stephen Beaumont   **Manager:** Scott Dundas   **Prog Ed:** Dennis Vickers

Ground: Norton CC & MWI Community Drive, Smallthorne, Stoke-on-Trent ST6 1QF   **(T)** 01782 838 290
Capacity: **Seats:** **Covered:** **Midweek Matchday:** Tuesday   **Clubhouse:** **Shop:**

Colours(change): Red & black/black/black (All yellow)
Previous Names:
Previous Leagues:
Records: **Att:** 1,382 v FC United of Manchester 09/04/2006.
Senior Honours: Midland League 1996-97, 98-99, 2000-01. Staffordshire Senior Vase 1998-99, 2003-04.

10 YEAR RECORD

02-03	03-04	04-05	05-06	06-07	07-08	08-09	09-10	10-11	11-12
NWC2 9	NWC2 15	NWC2 5	NWC2 8	NWC2 17	NWC2 8	NWC1 12	NWC1 3	NWC1 7	NWC1 2

PADIHAM

Founded: 1878 | Nickname: Caldersiders

Secretary: Alan Smith | **(T)** 0777 571 7698 | **(E)**
Chairman: Frank Heys | **Manager:** Steve Wilkes | **Prog Ed:** Alan Smith
Ground: Arbories Memories Sports Ground, Well Street, Padiham BB12 8LE | **(T)** 01282 773 742
Capacity: 1,688 **Seats:** 159 **Covered:** Yes **Midweek Matchday:** Wednesday **Clubhouse:** Yes **Shop:**

Colours(change): Royal blue/white/royal blue. (Red/white/black).
Previous Names: None
Previous Leagues: Lancashire Combination. East Lancashire Amateur. North East Lancashire. West Lancashire.
Records: **Att:** 9,000 v Burnley, Dec.1884 (at Calderside Ground).
Senior Honours:

10 YEAR RECORD

02-03		03-04		04-05		05-06		06-07		07-08		08-09		09-10		10-11		11-12	
NWC2	4	NWC2	12	NWC2	4	NWC2	5	NWC2	3	NWC2	12	NWC1	2	NWCP	10	NWCP	4	NWCP	15

RUNCORN LINNETS

Founded: 2006 | Nickname: Linnets

Secretary: Lynn Johnston | **(T)** 01606 43008 | **(E)**
Chairman: Derek Greenwood | **Manager:** Paul McNally | **Prog Ed:** Mark Buckley
Ground: Millbank Linnets Stadium, Murdishaw Ave, Runcorn, Cheshire WA7 6HP | **(T)** 07050 801733 (Clubline)
Capacity: **Seats:** **Covered:** **Midweek Matchday:** Tuesday **Clubhouse:** Yes **Shop:**

Colours(change): Yellow & green hoops/green/yellow & green. (Blue & white/white/blue)
Previous Names: None
Previous Leagues: None.
Records: 1,037 v Witton Albion, pre season friendly July 2010
Senior Honours:

10 YEAR RECORD

02-03	03-04	04-05	05-06	06-07		07-08		08-09		09-10		10-11		11-12	
				NWC2	2	NWC1	12	NWCP	11	NWCP	11	NWCP	12	NWCP	5

RUNCORN TOWN

Founded: 1968 | Nickname:

Secretary: Martin Fallon | **(T)** 01928 590 508 | **(E)**
Chairman: Tony Riley | **Manager:** Simon Burton | **Prog Ed:** Alan Bennett
Ground: Pavilions Sports Complex, Sandy Lane, Weston Point, Runcorn WA7 4EX | **(T)** 01928 590 508
Capacity: **Seats:** Yes **Covered:** Yes **Midweek Matchday:** Monday **Clubhouse:** **Shop:**

Colours(change): Sky & navy/navy/navy (Yellow & black/black/yellow)
Previous Names: Mond Rangers 1967-2005 (Amalgamated with ICI Weston 1974-75).
Previous Leagues: Runcorn Sunday 1967-73, Warrington & District 1973-84, West Cheshire 1984-10.
Records: **Att:** 547 v Runcorn Linnets, NWCL Premier Dec. 2011.
Senior Honours: West Cheshire League Division Two 2006-07. Runcorn Senior Cup 2004-05, 05-06, 07-08.

10 YEAR RECORD

02-03	03-04	04-05		05-06		06-07		07-08		08-09		09-10		10-11		11-12	
WCh2	WCh2	WCh2	2	WCh1	15	WCh2	1	WCh1	3	WCh1	4	WCh1	3	NWC1	2	NWCP	2

SILSDEN

Founded: 1904 | Nickname:

Secretary: John Barclay | **(T)** 01535 656213 | **(E)**
Chairman: Sean McNulty | **Manager:** Chris Reape | **Prog Ed:** Peter Hanson
Ground: Keighley Road, Keighley Road, Silsden, BD20 0EH | **(T)**
Capacity: **Seats:** Yes **Covered:** Yes **Midweek Matchday:** Wednesday **Clubhouse:** Yes **Shop:**

Colours(change): Red/black/red (All yellow).
Previous Names: Reformed in 1980.
Previous Leagues: Craven & District. West Riding County Amateur.
Records: **Att:**1,564 v FC United of Manchester- March 2007
Senior Honours:

10 YEAR RECORD

02-03	03-04	04-05		05-06		06-07		07-08		08-09		09-10		10-11		11-12	
		NWC2	2	NWC1	14	NWC1	14	NWC1	11	NWCP	9	NWCP	14	NWCP	16	NWCP	12

SQUIRES GATE

Founded: 1948   Nickname:

Secretary: John Maguire   **(T)** 01253 348 512   **(E)**

Chairman: Stuart Hopwood   **Manager:** Russ McKenna   **Prog Ed:** Steve Mclellan & Albert Cooper

Ground: School Road, Marton, Blackpool, Lancs FY4 5DS   **(T)** 01253 798 583

Capacity: 1,000   **Seats:** 100   **Covered:** Yes   **Midweek Matchday:** Tuesday   **Clubhouse:** Yes   **Shop:** No

Colours(change): All blue. (Red/black/black)
Previous Names: Squires Gate British Legion FC >1953.
Previous Leagues: Blackpool & District Amateur 1958-61. West Lancashire 1961-91.
Records: **Att:** 600 v Everton, friendly 1995.
Senior Honours:

10 YEAR RECORD

02-03	03-04	04-05	05-06	06-07	07-08	08-09	09-10	10-11	11-12
NWC1 12	NWC1 20	NWC1 17	NWC1 13	NWC1 18	NWC1 6	NWCP 10	NWCP 13	NWCP 9	NWCP 16

ST HELENS TOWN

Founded: 1946   Nickname: Town

Secretary: Jeff Voller   **(T)** 0151 222 2963   **(E)**

Chairman: John McKiernan   **Manager:** Ian Granite   **Prog Ed:** Jeff Voller

Ground: Ashton Town FC, Edge Green St, Ashton-in-Makerfield WN4 8SL   **(T)** 01942 701 483

Capacity: **Seats:**   **Covered:**   **Midweek Matchday:** Tuesday   **Clubhouse:**   **Shop:**

Colours(change): Red & white/red/red & white. (Sky blue/navy/navy).
Previous Names: St Helen's Town formed in 1903 folded in 1923.
Previous Leagues: Liverpool Co Comb 1946-49 Lancs Comb 49-75, Chesh Co. 75-82
Records: **Att:** 4,000 v Manchester City 1950. **Goalscorer:** S. Pennington. **App:** Alan Wellens
Senior Honours: Lancashire Combination 1971-72 . FA Vase 1986-87.

10 YEAR RECORD

02-03	03-04	04-05	05-06	06-07	07-08	08-09	09-10	10-11	11-12
NWC1 7	NWC1 19	NWC1 3	NWC1 8	NWC1 19	NWC1 14	NWCP 16	NWCP 9	NWCP 17	NWCP 21

STOCKPORT SPORTS

Founded: 1970   Nickname: The Saxons

Secretary: Russell Hoyte   **(T)** 07920 232 074   **(E)** secretary@stockportsportsfc.com

Chairman: John Hindley   **Manager:** Peter Withe   **Prog Ed:** Richard Smales

Ground: Stockport Sports Village, Lambeth Grove, Woodley SK6 1QX   **(T)** 07920 232 074

Capacity: 2,300   **Seats:** 300   **Covered:** Yes   **Midweek Matchday:**   **Clubhouse:** Yes   **Shop:** Nk

Colours(change): Blue/blue/white (Red/red/white)
Previous Names: Woodley Athletic. Woodley Sports > 2012.
Previous Leagues: Lancashire and Cheshire, Manchester, North West Counties
Records: 1,500 v Stockport County
Senior Honours: North West Counties League Division 2 1999-2000.
Cheshire Senior Cup 2003-04.

10 YEAR RECORD

02-03	03-04	04-05	05-06	06-07	07-08	08-09	09-10	10-11	11-12
NWC1 17	NWC1 4	NP 1 11	NP 1 4	NP 1 10	NP1N 17	NP1N 13	NP1N 19	NP1N 11	NP1N 8

STONE DOMINOES

Founded: 1987   Nickname: The Doms

Secretary: Mark Sutton   **(T)** 07733 098 929   **(E)** mark.sutton16@btinternet.com

Chairman: Jon Busfield   **Manager:** Dean Sibson   **Prog Ed:** Sue Wild

Ground: Springbank Park, Yarnfield Lane, Yarnfield, Stone, Staffs ST15 0NF   **(T)** 01785 761 891

Capacity: 1,000   **Seats:** 250   **Covered:** yes   **Midweek Matchday:** Tuesday   **Clubhouse:** Yes   **Shop:**

Colours(change): Red/black/Black (All white).
Previous Names:
Previous Leagues: Midland League
Records: **Att:** 887 v FC United of Manchester 24/03/07 (at Newcastle Town).
Senior Honours: Midland League 1999-00. North West Counties League Division One 2009-10.

10 YEAR RECORD

02-03	03-04	04-05	05-06	06-07	07-08	08-09	09-10	10-11	11-12
NWC2 2	NWC1 10	NWC1 11	NWC1 21	NWC1 22	NWC2 10	NWC1 3	NWC1 1	NWCP 19	NWCP 20

WIGAN ROBIN PARK

Founded: 2005   Nickname:

Secretary: Taffy Roberts   **(T)** 01942 404 950   **(E)**

Chairman: Steve Halliwell   **Manager:** John Neafcy   **Prog Ed:** Andrew Vaughan

Ground: Robin Park Arena, Loire Drive, Robin Park, Wigan, WN5 0UH   **(T)** 01942 404 950

Capacity: **Seats:**   **Covered:**   **Midweek Matchday:** Tuesday   **Clubhouse:**   **Shop:**

Colours(change): Red & white/black & red/black & red (Yellow/green/yellow)
Previous Names:
Previous Leagues: Manchester 2005-08.
Records: **Att:** 298 v AFC Liverpool 31/03/09.
Senior Honours: Manchester Premier 2007-08. North West Counties Division One 2011-12.
Gilgryst Cup 2007-08.

10 YEAR RECORD

02-03	03-04	04-05	05-06	06-07	07-08	08-09	09-10	10-11	11-12
			Manc1 8	Manc1 2	MancP 1	NWC1 5	NWC1 12	NWC1 8	NWC1 1

WINSFORD UNITED

Founded: 1883   Nickname: Blues

Secretary: Robert Astles   **(T)** 01606 558 447   **(E)**

Chairman: Mark Loveless   **Manager:** lloyd Morrison   **Prog Ed:** Robert Astles

Ground: The Barton Stadium, Kingsway, Winsford, Cheshire CW7 3AE   **(T)** 01606 558 447

Capacity: 6,000   **Seats:** 250   **Covered:** 5,000   **Midweek Matchday:** Tuesday   **Clubhouse:** Yes   **Shop:** Yes

Colours(change): All royal blue. (All white).
Previous Names:
Previous Leagues: The Combination 1902-04. Cheshire County 1919-40, 47-82. N.P.L. 1987-01
Records: **Att:** 8,000 v Witton Albion, 1947.   **Goalscorer:** Graham Smith 66   **Apps:** Edward Harrop 400
Senior Honours: Cheshire League 1920-21, 76-77. Cheshire Senior Cup 1958-59, 79-80, 92-93.
North West Counties League Division Two 2006-07.

10 YEAR RECORD

02-03	03-04	04-05	05-06	06-07	07-08	08-09	09-10	10-11	11-12
NWC1 22	NWC2 8	NWC2 3	NWC2 4	NWC2 1	NWC1 10	NWCP 19	NWCP 19	NWCP 3	NWCP 7

DIVISION ONE

ABBEY HEY

Founded: 1902 — Nickname:

Secretary: Tony McAllister **(T)** 0161 231 7147 **(E)**
Chairman: James Whittaker **Manager:** Barry Walker **Prog Ed:** Gordon Lester
Ground: The Abbey Stadium, Goredale Avenue, Gorton, Manchester M18 7HD **(T)** 0161 231 7147 **Capacity:**
Colours(change): Red/black/red (All blue)

ADDITIONAL INFORMATION: Previous Lge: Manchester Amateur, South East Lancashire, Manchester.
Record Att: 985 v FC United of Manchester, March 2006.
Honours: Manchester League 1981-82, 88-89, 88-89, 91-92, 93-94, 94-95.

AFC DARWEN

Founded: 2009 (reformed)Nickname:

Secretary: Derek Slater **(T)** 07989 744 584 **(E)**
Chairman: Kenny Langford **Manager:** Kenny Langford **Prog Ed:** Steve Hart
Ground: Anchor Ground, Anchor Road, Darwen, Lancs, BB3 0BB. **(T)** 01254 776 193 **Capacity:**
Colours(change): All red (All navy)

ADDITIONAL INFORMATION:
Original club founded in 1875.
Record Att: 14,000 v Blackburn Rovers 1882.
Honours: Lancashire League 1902. North West Counties League Cup 1983. North West Alliance Cup 1996.

ASHTON TOWN

Founded: 1962 — Nickname:

Secretary: Steve Barrett **(T)** 01942 701 483 **(E)**
Chairman: Mark Hayes **Manager:** John Brownrigg **Prog Ed:** Ian Promfrett
Ground: The AM Property Group Std, Edge Green St, Ashton-in-Makerfield, Wigan, WN4 8SL **(T)** 01942 701483 **Capacity:**
Colours(change): Red/black/black (White/red/red)

ADDITIONAL INFORMATION:
Record Att: 1,865 v FC United of Manchester 2007.
Honours: Warrington League Guardian Cup.

ATHERTON COLLIERIES

Founded: 1916 — Nickname: The Colts

Secretary: Emil Anderson **(T)** **(E)**
Chairman: Paul Gregory **Manager:** Steve Pilling **Prog Ed:** Emil Anderson
Ground: Alder Street, Atherton, Greater Manchester. M46 9EY. **(T)** 07968 548 056 **Capacity:**
Colours(change): Black & white stripes/black/black (All orange)

ADDITIONAL INFORMATION:
Record Att: 3,300 in Lancashire Combination 1920's.
Honours: North West Counties League Division 3 1986-87.

ATHERTON L.R.

Founded: 1956 — Nickname: The Panthers

Secretary: Natalie Waldie **(T)** 01942 883 950 **(E)**
Chairman: Jane Wilcock **Manager:** **Prog Ed:** Jeff Gorse
Ground: Crilly Park, Spa Road, Atherton, Manchester M46 9JX **(T)** 01942 883 950 **Capacity:** 3,000
Colours(change): Royal blue & yellow/royal blue/yellow. (All white).

ADDITIONAL INFORMATION: Att: 2,300 v Aldershot Town F.A. Vase Q-Final replay 93-94. **Goalscorer:** Shaun Parker **App:** Jim Evans
North West Counties League 1992-93, 93-94. Champions Trophy 1992-93, 93-94.

CHADDERTON

Founded: 1947 — Nickname: Chaddy

Secretary: David Shepherd **(T)** 0161 624 9733 **(E)**
Chairman: Bob Sopel **Manager:** Paul Buckley **Prog Ed:** Bob Sopel
Ground: Andrew Street, Chadderton, Oldham, Greater Manchester. OL9 0JT **(T)** 0161 624 9733 **Capacity:**
Colours(change): Red/black/red (Orange/black/black)

ADDITIONAL INFORMATION:
Record Att: 2,352 v FC United of Manchester 2006.
Honours: Gilgryst Cup 1969-70. Umbro International Cup 1999-00.

CHEADLE TOWN

Founded: 1961 — Nickname:

Secretary: Brian Lindon **(T)** 0161 428 2510 **(E)**
Chairman: Chris Davies **Manager:** Steve Brokenbrow **Prog Ed:** Stuart Crawford
Ground: Park Road Stadium, Cheadle, Cheshire, SK8 2AN **(T)** 0161 428 2510 **Capacity:**
Colours(change): Green/green/white (White/black/black).

ADDITIONAL INFORMATION:
Record Att: 3,377 v FC United of Manchester (At Stockport County). **Goalscorer:** Peter Tilley. **Apps:** John McArdle.
Honours: Manchester Division One 1979-80.

DAISY HILL
Founded: 1894   Nickname:

Secretary: Robert Naylor   **(T)** 01942 818 544   **(E)**
Chairman: Graham Follows   **Manager:** Craig Thomas   **Prog Ed:** Robert Naylor
Ground: New Sirs, St James Street, Westhoughton, Bolton, BL5 2EB   **(T)** 01942 818 544   **Capacity:**
Colours(change): All royal blue (All red)

ADDITIONAL INFORMATION:
Reformed in 1952.
Record Att: 2,000 v Horwich RMI, Westhoughton Charity Cup Final 1979-80. **Goalscorer & Apps:** Alan Roscoe 300gls, 450app
Honours: Bolton Combination Premier Division 1962-63, 72-73, 75-76, 77-78.

ECCLESHALL
Founded: 1971   Nickname:

Secretary: Stephen Wright   **(T)** 01785 851 351 (MD)   **(E)**
Chairman: Andy Mapperson   **Manager:** Keiron Hammett   **Prog Ed:** Richard Marsh
Ground: Pershall Park, Chester Road, Eccleshall, ST21 6NE   **(T)** 01785 851 351 (MD)   **Capacity:**
Colours(change): Blue & black stripes/black/black (All red)

ADDITIONAL INFORMATION:
Record Att: 2,011 v FC United of Manchester November 2005.
Honours: Midland League 1990, 2002-03.

FORMBY
Founded: 1919   Nickname: Squirrels

Secretary: Adrian Cook   **(T)**   **(E)**
Chairman: Hugh McAuley   **Manager:** Jim Shirley   **Prog Ed:** Adrian Cork
Ground: Altcar Road, Formby, Merseyside L37 4DL   **(T)** 01704 833 615   **Capacity:** 2,000
Colours(change): Yellow/blue/blue (All navy)

ADDITIONAL INFORMATION:
Previous Lge: Liverpool Co. Comb, 1919-68, Lancs Comb. 68-71, Cheshire Co. 71-82.
Record Att: At Brows Lane - 2,500 v Oldham Ath. FA Cup 1973. At Altar Road - 603 v Southport Liverpool Senior Cup 2003-04.

HOLKER OLD BOYS
Founded: 1936   Nickname: Cobs

Secretary: John Adams   **(T)** 01229 828 176   **(E)**
Chairman: Dick John   **Manager:** Dave Smith   **Prog Ed:** Dick John
Ground: Rakesmoor, Rakesmoor Lane, Hawcoat, Barrow-in-Furness, LA14 4QB   **(T)** 01229 828 176   **Capacity:**
Colours(change): Green & white/green/green & white (All blue)

ADDITIONAL INFORMATION:
Record Att: 2,303 v FC United of Manchester FA Cup at Craven Park 2005-06. **Goalscorer:** Dave Conlin.
Honours: West Lancashire League 1986-87.

IRLAM
Founded: 1969   Nickname:

Secretary: Warren Dodd   **(T)** 07718 756402/07969 946277   **(E)**
Chairman: Ron Parker   **Manager:** Nick Parker   **Prog Ed:** Warren Dodd
Ground: Silver Street, Irlam, Manchester M44 6HR   **(T)** 07718756402~07969946277 **Capacity:**
Colours(change): Blue & white/blue/blue (All red)

ADDITIONAL INFORMATION:
Previous Name: Mitchell Shackleton. **Previous League:** Manchester Amateur. Manchester.
Record Att: 1,600 v Hallam FA Vase.

LEEK C.S.O.B.
Founded: 1945   Nickname:

Secretary: Stan Lockett   **(T)** 01538 383734   **(E)**
Chairman: Chris McMullen   **Manager:** Brett Barlow   **Prog Ed:** Stan Lockett
Ground: Leek Town FC, Harrison Park, Macclesfield Road, Leek, Staffs. ST13 8LD   **(T)** 01538 383 734   **Capacity:**
Colours(change): Red & white stripes/red/red & white hoops (Blue/blue/blue & white hoops)

ADDITIONAL INFORMATION:
Record Att: 2,590 v FC United of Manchester August 2005.
Honours: Midland League 1995-96.

NELSON
Founded: 1883   Nickname: Blues

Secretary: Rauf Abdul Khan   **(T)**   **(E)**
Chairman: Fayyaz Ahmed   **Manager:** Paul Paynter   **Prog Ed:** Alan Maidment
Ground: Little Wembley, Lomeshaye Way, Nelson, Lancs BB9 7BN.   **(T)** 01282 613 820   **Capacity:** 1500
Colours(change): All royal blue. (Sky blue & white stripes/white/white).

ADDITIONAL INFORMATION: Att: 14,143 v Bradford Park Avenue, Div.3 North, 10.04.26.
Honours: Football League Division Three North 1922-23. **Previous Lge:** Lancashire 1889-98,1900-01. Football Lge 1898-1900.
Lancashire Combination 1901-16,46-82. NWC 1982-88. West Lancashire 1988-92.

NORTHWICH VILLA
Founded: 2005   Nickname:

Secretary: Ken Stevenson   **(T)**   **(E)**
Chairman: Robert Millington   **Manager:** Wale Ajet   **Prog Ed:** Noel McCourt
Ground: Valley Road, Flixton Manchester M41 8RQ   **(T)** 0161 748 2903   **Capacity:**
Colours(change): Green & white hoops/white/white (Yellow/blue/blue).

ADDITIONAL INFORMATION: Record Att: 146 v Northwich Victoria.
Previous Lge: Cheshire 2005-11.
Honours: Cheshire League Division One 2008-09, Division One Cup 2009-10.

OLDHAM BORO
Founded: 1964   Nickname:

Secretary: Billy O'Neill   **(T)**   **(E)**
Chairman: Mark Kilgannon   **Manager:** Tony Mills   **Prog Ed:**
Ground: Atherton Collieries FC, Alder Street, Atherton M46 9EY   **(T)**   **Capacity:**
Colours(change): Blue/black/white (Cream/royal blue/royal blue)

ADDITIONAL INFORMATION:
Record Att: 1,767 v FC United of Manchester 2006.
Honours: North West Counties Division Two 1997-98.

ROCHDALE TOWN
Founded: 1924   Nickname:

Secretary: Deborah Hibbert   **(T)** 01706 527103   **(E)**
Chairman: Mark Canning   **Manager:** Mark Canning   **Prog Ed:** Chris Morgan
Ground: Mayfield Sports Centre, Keswick Street, Castleton, Rochdale. OL11 3AG   **(T)** 01706 527 103   **Capacity:**
Colours(change): Black & white stripes/black/black (Blue/white/blue).

ADDITIONAL INFORMATION:
Record Att: 2,473 v FC United of Manchester (at Radcliffe Borough).
Honours: Manchester Division One 1986-87.

WEST DIDSBURY & CHORLTON
Founded: 1908   Nickname:

Secretary: Rob Turley   **(T)** 07891 298441   **(E)**
Chairman: Glyn Meacher   **Manager:** Andy Nelson   **Prog Ed:** John Churchman
Ground: The Recreation Ground, End of Brookburn Road, Chorlton, Manchester M21 8FF   **(T)** 07891 298 441   **Capacity:**
Colours(change): White/black/black (Claret & sky blue or sky blue/Sky blue/sky blue)

ADDITIONAL INFORMATION:
Previous Leagues: Manchester Alliance pre 1920. Lancashire & Cheshire Amateur 1920-2006. Manchester 2006-2012.

GROUND DIRECTIONS

AFC BLACKPOOL - Mechanics Ground, Jepson Way, Common Edge Road, Blackpool, Lancashire FY4 5DY. 01253 761721
M6 to M55, exit at junction 4. At roundabout turn left along A583 to traffic lights, turn right into Whitehill Road, to traffic lights (2 miles). Go straight across the main road into Jepson Way, ground at top.

AFC LIVERPOOL - Valerie Park, Eaton Street, Prescot, Merseyside, L34 6ND. 0151 430 0507
From North: M6 to Junction 26, onto M58 to Junction 3. Follow A570 to junction with A580 (East Lancs Road). (Approach junction in right hand lane of the two lanes going straight on). Cross A580 and take first road on right (Bleak Hill Road). Follow this road through to Prescot (2 miles). At traffic lights turn right, straight on at large roundabout (do not follow route onto Prescot by-pass) and right at next lights. 100 yards turn right at Hope and Anchor pub on Hope Street. Club will be in sight at bottom of road. From South: M6 to Junction 21a (M62 junction 10). Follow M62 towards Liverpool, to junction 7. Follow A57 to Rainhill and Prescot. Through traffic lights at Fusilier pub, 100 yards turn right at Hope and Anchor pub (as above). From East: Follow M62 as described in 'From South' or A580 East Lancs Road to Junction with A570 (Rainford by-pass), turn left and take first right. Follow route as 'From North'

ALSAGER TOWN - The Town Ground, Woodland Court, Alsager, Staffs, ST7 2DP 01270 882336
M6 to Junction16, A500 towards Stoke, leave A500 at 2nd exit (A34 to Congleton) at 2nd set of traffic lights on A34 turn left for Alsager, turn right opposite Caradon/Twyfords Factory (500 Yards), into Moorhouse Ave, West Grove mile on right. No available parking within the ground.

ASHTON ATHLETIC - Brocstedes Park, Downall Green, Ashton in Makerfield. WN4 0NR. 01942 716360
M6 northbound to junction 25, follow the slip road to the island and turn right A49, proceed for approx 0.50 mile turning right into Soughers Lane. At the T junction turn right into Downall Green Road and go over the motorway bridge passing a church on your right. Turn 2nd right into Booths Brow Road and turn 2nd right again into Brocstedes Road which is a narrow street. After 200 yards turn right down a shale road into the car park and ground.
From The North: M6 southbound to junction 24, proceed on to the slip road keeping in the right hand lane, turn right go over the motorway bridge and immediately re-enter the M6 Northbound for approximately 100 yards. Leave at junction 25,Follow the slip road to the island and turn right A49, proceed for approx 0.50 mile turning right into Soughers Lane. At the T junction turn right into Downall Green Road and go over the motorway bridge passing a church on your right. Turn 2nd right into Booths Brow Road and turn 2nd right again into Brocstedes Road which is a narrow street. After 200 yards turn right down a shale road into the car park and ground.

BACUP BOROUGH - Brian Boys Stadium, Cowtoot Lane, Blackthorn, Bacup, Lancashire. OL13 8EE. 01706 878655
From M62, take M66 onto A681, through Rawtenstall to Bacup Town Centre, turn left onto the A671 towards Burnley, after approx. 300 yards right immediately before the Irwell Inn climbing Cooper Street, turn right into Blackthorn Lane, then first left into Cowtoot Lane to ground.

BARNOLDSWICK TOWN - Silentnight Stadium, West Close Road, Barnoldswick, Colne, BB18 5EW. 01282 815817
ravelling from Blackburn to Colne on M65 to end, straight on at roundabout onto Vivary Way onto North Valley Road. Through two sets of traffic

lights to roundabout, turn left to Barnoldswick. Straight on till you come to roundabout in Kelbrook turn left to Barnoldswick.On entering Barnoldswick straight ahead at traffic lights, straight ahead at mini roundabout. Travel through built up area past Fosters Arms pub on left set back. Take first right onto Greenberfield Lane, travel 50 yards take middle single track (signposted) travel to bottom of track and bare right to car park at rear of ground.

Travelling from Barrow on A59 from Gisburn towards Skipton turn right at Barnoldswick signpost. Travel approx 2 miles taking 1st left onto Greenberfield Lane, travel 50 yards take middle single track (signposted) travel to bottom of track bare right to car park at rear of ground. If using a SatNav use postcode BB18 5LJ.

BOOTLE - Delta Taxi Stadium, Vestey Road, off Bridle Road, Bootle, L30 4UN. 0151 525 4796 or 07852 742790

At Liverpool end of M57and M58 follow signs for Liverpool (A59 (S)), for 1 1/2 miles. At Aintree racecourse on left and Aintree Train Station on right ,turn right at lights into Park Lane. Turn left at second set of lights into Bridle Road. After 200 yards turn left at lights into Vestey Estate , ground 200 yards.

COLNE - The XLCR Stadium, Harrison Drive, Colne, Lancashire. BB8 9SL. 01282 862545

Follow M65 to end of motorway. Turn left and follow signs for Skipton and Keighley, continue to roundabout, take 1st left up Harrison Drive, across small roundabout, follow road to ground.

CONGLETON TOWN - Booth Street, off Crescent Road, Congleton, Cheshire, CW12 4DG. 01260 274460

On approach to Congleton from M6, past Waggon & Horses Pub, at 1st roundabout 2nd exit, past fire station, 2nd right into Booth Street. Ground at top of road.

GLOSSOP NORTH END - Surrey Street, Glossop, Derbyshire. SK13 7AJ. 01457 855469

A57 to Glossop, turn left at traffic lights (near Tesco sign), Glossopbrook Road. Follow road to top of hill. Ground on right.

MAINE ROAD - Brantingham Road, Chorlton-cum-Hardy, Manchester. M21 0TT. 0161 861 0344

M60 to junction 7, A56 towards Manchester. At traffic island follow signs for Manchester United, Lancs CC, turn right at next set of traffic lights signposted A5145 (Chorlton-cum-Hardy/Stockport), through next set of traffic lights. Take left fork at Y junction (traffic lights) onto A6010 (Wilbraham Road) to Chorlton. Through traffic lights (ignore pedestrian lights) for approx 1 mile. Left at next traffic lights into Withington Road, first left into Brantingham Road. Ground 300 yards on left. From North: M60 clockwise to junction 5 onto A5103 towards Manchester Centre for approx 2 miles, turn left at traffic lights (Wilbraham Road) A6010, then right at 2nd set of lights (Withington Road), first left into Brantingham Road. Ground 300 yards on left.

NORTON UNITED - Norton CC & MWI - Community Drive, Smallthorne, Stoke-on-Trent ST6 1QF. 01782 838290

M6 to junction 16, A500 to Burslem/Tunstall, turn off bear right at traffic island to Burslem, through lights to Smallthorne, take 3rd exit on mini-roundabout, turn right by pedestrian crossing into Community Drive, ground 200 metres on left.

PADIHAM - Arbories Memorial Sports Ground, Well Street, Padiham, Lancashire, BB12 8LE. 01282 773742

M65 to Junction 8, then follow A6068 signposted Clitheroe and Padiham. At traffic lights at bottom of hill turn right into Dean Range/Blackburn Road towards Padiham. At next junction turn into Holland Street opposite church, then into Well St at the side of Hare & Hounds Pub to ground.

RUNCORN LINNETS - Millbank Linnets Stadium, Murdishaw Ave, Runcorn, Cheshire. WA7 6HP. 07050 801733 (Clubline)

orth East - M56 junction 12 take A557 Widnes/Northwich. At Roundabout take 1st Exit onto A557 heading Frodsham A56, go through 1 rounda-bout. Turn left at Chester Rd/A56, turn left at Chester Rd/A533. At the r'about, take the 2nd exit onto Murdishaw Ave. Destination on the Right. Head West on M56 towards Exit 11. At junction 11, take the A56 exit to Preston Brook/Daresbury. At the roundabout take the 1st exit onto Chester Rd/A56 heading to Preston Brook/Daresbury. Continue to follow Chester Rd, go through 2 roundabouts.At the roundabout take the 2nd exit onto Murdishaw Ave. Destination on the Right.

RUNCORN TOWN - Pavilions Sports Complex, Sandy Lane, Weston Point, Runcorn, Cheshire WA7 4EX. 01928 590 508

M56 J12. Head towards Liverpool. Come off at 4th exit (Runcorn Docks), turn left at the top of slip road, left at T-Junction, then left into Pavilions. M62 J7. Head towards Runcorn. When crossing Runcorn Bridge, stay in the right hand lane. Follow road around and come off at second exit (Runcorn Docks). Turn right at the top of slip road, left at T-Junction, then left into Pavilions.

SILSDEN - Keighley Road, Silsden, BD20 0EH

A629 Skipton to Keighley road, take A6034, ground in on the left after the golf driving range.

SQUIRES GATE - School Road, Marton, Blackpool, FY4 5DS. 01253 798583

From M55: At the end of the M55 (J4), continue along dual carriageway (A5230), and bear left at major roundabout, staying on A5230. At second traffic lights, turn left onto B5261. After passing Shovels pub on left, turn left at lights, and first car park is on left after approx 50 yards. Parking is also available down the lane leading to the Club, on your left, after another 40 yards. If both these are full, parking is also available on the Shovels car park, or on the car park adjacent to the playing fields (turn right at the lights after passing the pub).

ST HELENS TOWN - Ashton Town FC, Edge Green Street, Ashton-in-Makerfield, Wigan, Greater Manchester. 01942 701483

M6 to Junction 23, A49 to Ashton-in-Makerfield. Turn right at the traffic lights onto the A58 towards Bolton. After approx. three quarters of a mile, turn right into Golbourne Road. After 200 yards turn right into Edge Green Street. Ground at bottom of street.(Ashton Town FC)

STOCKPORT SPORTS - Lambeth Grove, Woodley, Stockport, Cheshire SK6 1QX

Take exit 25 toward BREDBURY. At the roundabout, take the 2nd exit onto Ashton Rd (A560). Turn slight left - Continue on A560. Turn right at Lower Bents Lane. Continue on School Brow (B6104). Turn slight left at Stockport Rd (B6104). Turn right at Green Lane.

STONE DOMINOES - Motiva Park, Yarnfield Lane, Yarnfield, Stone, Staffs, ST15 0NF. 01785 761891

From M6 junction 15, straight on at first roundabout following A500 to Stoke, come to first slip road)before flyover) and turn right at roundabout heading to Stone A34 (5 miles), straight on at next roundabout (Trentham Gardens on your right), through village of Tittensor (take care: cameras - 40mph), at next roundabout straight on (pub in the middle, Darlaston Inn) still on A34, 2 more roundabouts *BP garage on left) get in right hand lane and turn right into Yarnfield Lane (pub on corner called the Wayfarer) football ground is about 1 mile on left before village of Yarnfield.

WIGAN ROBIN PARK - Robin Park Arena, Loire Drive, Robin Park, Wigan, WN5 0UH. 01942 404 950

M6 J25 take road into Wigan and follow signs for the DW Stadium (Wigan Athletic) Ground is next to stadium, behind Wickes DIY store on the retail park.

WINSFORD UNITED - The Barton Stadium, Kingsway, Winsford, Cheshire. CW7 3AE. 01606 558447

From M6 junction 18, follow A54 through Middlewich for approx 3 miles, bear right at roundabout at Winsford Railway Station, follow road for approx 1 mile, turn right into Kingsway, ground is on the right.

NORTH WEST COUNTIES LEAGUE - STEP 5/6
DIVISION ONE

ABBEY HEY - The Abbey Stadium, Goredale Avenue, Gorton, Manchester M18 7HD. 0161 231 7147
M60 to junction 24, take A57 to Manchester City Centre for approx 1 mile, at first set of major traffic lights (MacDonalds on right) pass through for approx 300yards, turn left immediatley before overhead railway bridge (A.H.F.C. sign) into Woodland Avenue. Take first right, pass under railway bridge, turn first left into Goredale Avenue.

AFC DARWEN - Anchor Ground, Anchor Road, Darwen, Lancs, BB3 0BB. 07989-744584
Leave M65 at Junction 4. At traffic lights turn left onto A666 (signposted Darwen). After approx ? mile turn left between Anchor Car Sales and the Anchor Pub. Bare right and ground 200 yards on left.

ASHTON TOWN - Edge Green Street, Ashton-in-Makerfield, Wigan, Greater Manchester. WN4 8SL. 01942 701483
M6 to Junction 23, A49 to Ashton-in-Makerfield. Turn right at the traffic lights onto the A58 towards Bolton. After approx. three quarters of a mile, turn right into Golbourne Road. After 200 yards turn right into Edge Green Street. Ground at bottom of street.

ATHERTON COLLIERIES - Alder Street, Atherton, Greater Manchester. M46 9EY. 07968 548056
M61 to junction 5, follow sign for Westhoughton, turn left onto A6, turn right onto A579 (Newbrook Road/Bolton Road) into Atherton. At first set of traffic lights turn left into High Street, then second left into Alder Street to ground.

ATHERTON L.R. - Crilly Park, Spa Road, Atherton, Greater Manchester. M46 9XG. 01942 883950
M61 to Junction 5, follow signs for Westhoughton, turn left onto A6, turn right at first lights into Newbrook Road, then turn right into Upton Road, passing Atherton Central Station. Turn left into Springfield Road and left again into Hillside Road into Spa Road and ground.

CHADDERTON - Andrew Street, Chadderton, Oldham, Greater Manchester OL9 0JT. 0161 624 9733
M62 to junction 20, following A627(M) towards Manchester. Motorway becomes a dual carriageway, turn left at first major traffic lights (A699) Middleton Road, then second left into Burnley Street, Andrew Street at the end.

CHEADLE TOWN - Park Road Stadium, Cheadle, Cheshire, SK8 2AN. 0161 428 2510
M60 to junction 2 (formerly M63 junction 11), follow A560 to Cheadle. Go through first main set of traffic lights and then first left after shops into Park Road. Ground at end of road.

DAISY HILL - New Sirs, St James Street, Westhoughton, Bolton, BL5 2EB. 01942 818 544.
M61 to junction 5, A58 (Snydale Way/Park Road) for one and a half mile, left into Leigh Road (B5235) for 1 mile to Daisy Hill. Turn right into village 200 yards after mini roundabout, then left between church and school into St James Street. Ground 250 yards on left.

ECCLESHALL - Pershall Park, Chester Road, Eccleshall, ST21 6NE. 01785-851351 (Match Days Only)
M6 to junction 14 then A5013 to Eccleshall, right at mini-roundabout and then left at next mini-roundabout into High Street B5026, ground 1 mile on right.
M6 to junction 15, then A519 to Eccleshall right at mini-roundabout to High Street B5026, ground 1 mile on right.

FORMBY - Altcar Road, Formby, Merseyside, L37 8DL. 01704 833615
A565 Liverpool to Southport Road. At traffic lights opposite Tesco's superstore, turn right into Altcar Road. The ground is located 350 yards on the right, past Tesco.

HOLKER OLD BOYS - Rakesmoor, Rakesmoor Lane, Hawcoat, Barrow-in-Furness, Cumbria. LA14 4QB. 01229 828176
M6 to junction 36. Take the A590 all the way to Barrow-in-Furness. At the borough boundary continue along the A590. After 1? miles you will pass the Kimberley Clark paper mill on your right. Immediately after passing the paper mill turn left into Bank Lane, signposted "Barrow Golf Club" on the left hand side of the A590 and "Hawcoat yard on the right hand side of the A590. Follow this road to the T- junction at the top of the hill outside the Golf Club. Turn left here into Rakesmoor Lane the ground is 200 yds. down the road on the right. *Please be advised that Rakesmoor Lane beyond the ground is a single-track road and as such is unsuitable for coaches. It is not possible to turn a coach into the ground when approaching from that direction.*

IRLAM - Irlam Football Club, Silver Street, Irlam, Manchester M44 6HR. 07718 756402/07969 946277
From Peel Green Roundabout (M60 Junction 11), take A57 to Irlam, and then B5320 into Lower Irlam. After passing Morsons Project, turn right into Silver Street, at Nags Head Pub. The ground is situated at the bottom of Silver Street on the right hand side.

LEEK C.S.O.B. - Harrison Park, Macclesfield Road, Leek, Staffs. ST13 8LD (Leek Town FC). 01538 383 734.
M6 to junction 17 - A534 to Congleton - follow signs for Leek (A54) - carry on A54 until junction with A523 - turn right onto A523 - this is road direct to Leek and ground (8 miles) - ground on right just into Leek (Macclesfield Road).

NELSON - Victoria Park, Lomeshaye Way, Nelson, Lancs BB9 7BN. 01282 613 820
M65 to Junction 13. Take first left (A6068 Fence), 2nd left (B6249 Nelson), the 2nd right, signposted Lomeshaye Village, to ground.

NORTHWICH VILLA - Valley Road, Flixton, Manchester M41 8RQ - 0161 748 2903
Leave M60 junction 10, take the B5214, signposted Urmston, at the second roundabout take third exit, take right only lane on the exit in Davyhulme Road, follow this road to Valley Road, just after the left hand bend after 1 1/2 miles. The ground is at the other end of the road.

OLDHAM BORO - Whitebank Road, Oldham, Greater Manchester OL8 3JH. 0161 624 2689
M60 to Junction 18, join the new M60 motorway to junction 22, Hollinwood, turn left at next set of lights onto Hollins Road (A6104), follow road until you see fire station on right, turn right at fire station, follow road down to next left Whitebank Road. Ground is on your left.

ROCHDALE TOWN - Mayfield Sports Centre, Keswick Street, Castleton, Rochdale. OL11 3AG. 01706 527 103
M62 to junction 20, follow A627M towards Rochdale. Keep right on A627M turn right at traffic lights at BMW Garage go to next roundabout, take 2nd exit into Queensway towards Castleton and through the Industrial Estate. Turn Right at traffic lights into Manchester Road, A664. Go past Castleton Rail station and turn left at Fairwell Inn, into Keswick St, go through new housing estate to ground --- Rochdale Town FC ground is next to Castlehawk Golf Club.

WEST DIDSBURY & CHORLTON - The Recreation Ground, End of Brookburn Road, Chorlton, Manchester M21 8FF - 07891 298441
From the M60 take junction 5 onto Princess Road towards city centre. Turn left at Christie Fields offices/Premier Inn onto Barlow Moor Road and continue past Chorlton Park to Chorlton bus station. Turn left into Beech Road, then 2nd left into Reynard Road and continue past the Chorltonville sign passing over 5 speed ramps as far as Brookburn Primary School. Turn left into Brookburn Road and continue to the end of the cul de sac, through the gateway and down the tarmac access which leads into the ground. From Stretford follow Edge Lane and turn right into St Clements Road at church. Continue through Chorlton Green and pass graveyard on left and then Bowling Green PH. Go past school and turn immediately right and continue to end of Brookburn Road as above. There is car parking within the grounds of the club, but restricted access for coaches.

NORTHERN COUNTIES EAST LEAGUE

Sponsored by: Baris
Founded: 1982
Recent Champions:
2007: Retford United
2008: Winterton Rangers
2009: Mickleover Sports
2010: Bridlington Town
2011: Farsley
ncel.org.uk

LEAGUE CUP

ROUND 1
AFC Emley 4-2 Hemsworth Miners Welfare
Albion Sports 5-4 Grimsby Borough
Handsworth 2-0 Pontefract Collieries
Rossington Main 7-4 Glasshoughton Welfare
Shirebrook Town 3-0 Dinnington Town
Teversal 3-1 Hallam
Worksop Parramore 3-2 (aet) Yorkshire Amateur
Worsbrough Bridge Athletic 3-2 Appleby Frodingham

ROUND 2
Albion Sports 0-5 Barton Town Old Boys
Arnold Town 1-2 (aet) Winterton Rangers
Askern Villa 0-1 AFC Emley
Bottesford Town 2-1 Scarborough Athletic
Bridlington Town 0-1 Hall Road Rangers
Moorlands Railway 0-0 (aet) 6-7p Selby Town
Liversedge 0-1 Staveley Miners Welfare
Long Eaton United 4-3 (aet) Handsworth
Louth Town 0-2 Parkgate
Nostell Miners Welfare 5-2 Armthorpe Welfare
Pickering Town 5-0 Brighouse Town
(Brighouse Town reinstated after Pickering played an ineligible player)
Shirebrook Town 3-0 Maltby Main
Tadcaster Albion 1-3 Retford United
Teversal 4-0 Eccleshill United
Worksop Parramore 1-2 (aet) Thackley
Worsbrough Bridge Athletic 3-2 Rossington Main

ROUND 3
AFC Emley 0-2 Brighouse Town
Nostell Miners Welfare 4-0 Selby Town
Parkgate 6-4 Hall Road Rangers
Shirebrook Town 3-1 Long Eaton United
Teversal 1-3 Staveley Miners Welfare
Thackley 5-1 Retford United
Winterton Rangers 2-0 Bottesford Town
Worsbrough Bridge Athletic 2-4 (aet) Barton Town Old Boys

QUARTER FINALS
Barton Town Old Boys 2-1 Staveley Miners Welfare
Brighouse Town 0-2 Shirebrook Town
Thackley 4-1 Nostell Miners Welfare
Winterton Rangers 2-1 Parkgate

SEMI-FINALS
Barton Town Old Boys 1-3 Thackley
Shirebrook Town 2-2 (aet) 4-2p Winterton Rangers

FINAL (@ Parkgate, 7/5/11) Att: 272
Shirebrook Town 1-3 Thackley

PREMIER DIVISION

		P	W	D	L	F	A	Pts
1	Retford United	38	25	10	3	97	42	85
2	Bridlington Town	38	26	6	6	114	54	84
3	Scarborough Athletic	38	23	5	10	96	50	74
4	Brighouse Town	38	23	4	11	94	60	73
5	Staveley Miners Welfare	38	22	5	11	66	52	71
6	Winterton Rangers	38	21	5	12	71	49	68
7	Parkgate	38	20	7	11	99	72	67
8	Tadcaster Albion	38	20	7	11	68	50	67
9	Arnold Town	38	18	9	11	71	61	63
10	Thackley	38	18	8	12	71	59	62
11	Barton Town Old Boys	38	16	5	17	74	77	53
12	Pickering Town	38	15	6	17	74	75	51
13	Armthorpe Welfare	38	15	5	18	72	73	50
14	Liversedge	38	12	5	21	62	80	41
15	Long Eaton United	38	9	7	22	40	65	34
16	Hall Road Rangers (-3)	38	11	4	23	57	86	34
17	Nostell Miners Welfare	38	8	8	22	60	98	32
18	Maltby Main	38	7	8	23	39	82	29
19	Lincoln Moorlands Railway	38	6	7	25	40	96	25
20	(R) Selby Town	38	3	3	32	26	110	12

PREMIER DIVISION

		1	2	3	4	5	6	7	8	9	10	11	12	13	14	15	16	17	18	19	20
1	Armthorpe Welfare		2-0	1-2	2-4	1-0	1-3	3-3	5-2	1-0	7-1	6-1	3-0	3-1	0-1	1-4	4-0	3-1	1-2	1-2	0-3
2	Arnold Town	2-1		2-0	2-4	1-3	2-2	1-1	4-2	1-1	1-0	0-1	4-3	3-1	1-2	3-0	3-4	3-2	0-1	1-0	3-2
3	Barton Town Old Boys	3-0	4-2		2-3	5-0	2-3	3-1	1-3	2-1	3-2	2-2	1-1	1-0	0-2	2-1	2-1	1-3	1-3	1-2	1-1
4	Bridlington Town	2-1	2-2	4-0		4-1	4-0	9-0	1-0	2-1	3-0	6-0	2-5	3-2	2-2	3-1	7-0	5-2	1-2	0-0	3-1
5	Brighouse Town	3-4	5-3	5-1	2-3		2-0	5-0	4-2	1-1	2-0	2-2	3-2	4-2	4-0	2-1	6-0	0-1	2-2	2-0	0-3
6	Hall Road Rangers	2-2	1-2	0-3	2-4	0-1		0-1	2-5	2-3	4-0	2-1	1-2	3-0	1-2	3-4	3-1	1-1	4-2	0-2	2-4
7	Lincoln Moorlands Railway	0-2	1-1	2-2	0-3	4-5	2-1		2-2	0-1	2-2	3-1	3-4	1-2	0-3	0-4	3-1	1-2	0-1	1-1	0-1
8	Liversedge	0-1	0-1	4-1	2-4	2-5	4-0	2-1		2-1	1-1	2-0	0-1	1-3	0-4	2-3	4-0	0-3	1-1	2-0	1-2
9	Long Eaton United	1-3	0-1	3-1	1-3	1-2	1-2	1-2	2-0		2-1	2-2	0-0	1-3	0-1	0-5	2-0	0-1	0-1	1-3	1-1
10	Maltby Main	4-1	1-1	3-3	3-2	0-2	0-2	1-0	0-3	0-1		1-3	3-1	1-1	3-4	0-6	2-0	1-2	1-1	0-1	0-6
11	Nostell Miners Welfare	1-1	2-2	1-2	1-3	2-3	1-3	3-1	1-2	2-2	0-1		1-2	7-3	3-4	0-1	1-4	0-3	2-3	0-0
12	Parkgate	5-3	1-2	8-1	1-3	1-7	4-2	6-0	4-1	3-1	2-0	4-2		6-1	0-2	1-1	4-0	2-2	3-3	0-2	3-2
13	Pickering Town	4-1	2-0	2-1	3-1	1-5	5-2	5-0	2-2	2-0	0-1	5-0	1-2		1-1	0-4	3-0	1-2	1-1	3-3	2-1
14	Retford United	3-1	1-1	1-0	2-2	1-2	7-0	5-0	4-2	2-1	1-0	10-1	1-1	3-3		1-1	4-0	3-0	2-2	3-0	3-2
15	Scarborough Athletic	6-0	1-2	3-4	1-2	2-0	2-1	3-1	3-3	1-3	3-0	2-2	4-2	3-1	2-2		2-0	1-2	2-1	2-0	3-2
16	Selby Town	3-1	0-4	0-1	2-2	1-2	0-1	0-1	1-2	1-2	2-2	0-4	0-5	1-4	1-2	2-5		0-2	0-1	0-4	2-1
17	Staveley Miners Welfare	2-2	1-3	0-6	2-1	0-0	2-0	3-0	2-0	4-0	1-0	2-1	4-1	0-1	1-1	0-3	3-1		0-1	3-1	2-1
18	Tadcaster Albion	0-2	0-3	1-5	1-4	1-0	4-0	2-0	3-0	3-0	4-1	6-1	3-3	2-1	0-3	0-1	3-0	3-1		0-2	3-0
19	Thackley	1-1	3-3	5-4	2-2	4-1	2-1	4-3	4-0	1-1	1-1	1-2	3-4	3-2	2-0	0-5	5-0	1-2	2-1		1-2
20	Winterton Rangers	1-0	4-1	1-0	3-1	2-1	1-1	1-0	3-1	3-1	3-2	1-3	0-2	2-0	2-4	2-0	1-1	2-1	2-0	2-0	

NORTHERN COUNTIES EAST LEAGUE - STEP 5/6

DIVISION ONE	P	W	D	L	F	A	Pts
1 Handsworth	38	27	1	10	89	40	82
2 (P) Glasshoughton Welfare	38	24	7	7	102	57	79
3 (P) Worksop Parramore	38	24	5	9	95	52	77
4 Albion Sports	38	24	4	10	106	70	76
5 Pontefract Collieries	38	23	3	12	86	49	72
6 Eccleshill United (+2)	38	20	4	14	83	57	66
7 Rossington Main	38	19	7	12	85	57	64
8 Hemsworth Miners Welfare	38	18	6	14	73	66	60
9 Dinnington Town	38	18	6	14	68	67	60
10 AFC Emley (-1)	38	17	7	14	83	69	57
11 Worsbrough Bridge Athletic	38	16	9	13	74	65	57
12 Louth Town	38	16	7	15	61	64	55
13 Shirebrook Town	38	14	9	15	75	75	51
14 Hallam	38	15	6	17	66	74	51
15 Teversal	38	15	6	17	72	84	51
16 Bottesford Town	38	9	6	23	52	83	33
17 Askern Villa	38	10	3	25	54	87	33
18 Grimsby Borough	38	7	5	26	53	109	26
19 Yorkshire Amateur (-3)	38	7	7	24	53	112	25
20 Appleby Frodingham	38	2	2	34	39	132	8

PRESIDENT'S CUP

ROUND 1
Barton Town Old Boys 2-1 Glasshoughton Welfare
Pontefract Collieries 1-0 Nostell Miners Welfare
Handsworth 1-0 AFC Emley
Lincoln Moorlands Railway 4-1(aet) Louth Town
Pickering Town 2-3 Bridlington Town
Staveley Miners Welfare 2-1 Thackley
Tadcaster Albion 6-0 Yorkshire Amateur
Winterton Rangers 4-2 (aet) Parkgate

QUARTER FINALS
Barton Town Old Boys 3-1 Bridlington Town
Handsworth 0-1 Pontefract Collieries
(Pontefract Collieries removed from competition for fielding
ineligible player - Handsworth reinstated)
Tadcaster Albion 4-3 Staveley Miners Welfare
Winterton Rangers 1-0 Lincoln Moorlands Railway

SEMI-FINALS
Barton Town Old Boys 1-0 Tadcaster Albion
Handsworth 2-1 Winterton Rangers

FINAL (@ Winterton Rangers, 2/5/11) Att: 240
Barton Town Old Boys 3-4 (aet) Handsworth

WILKINSON SWORD SHIELD

ROUND 1
Grimsby Borough 4-0 Yorkshire Amateur
Hallam 4-0 Appleby Frodingham
Louth Town 5-1 Worksop Parramore
Rossington Main 2-3 Albion Sports

ROUND 2
AFC Emley 3-3 (aet) 4-3p Handsworth
Albion Sports 5-3 Eccleshill United
Askern Villa 2-2 (aet) 4-5p Louth Town
Mark Fairburn 46
Dinnington Town 2-1 Hemsworth Miners Welfare
Glasshoughton Welfare 2-0 Pontefract Collieries
Grimsby Borough 3-1 Worsbrough Bridge Athletic
Hallam 2-3 Teversal
Shirebrook Town 4-1 Bottesford Town

QUARTER FINALS
Albion Sports 4-0 Glasshoughton Welfare
Louth Town 2-1 AFC Emley
Shirebrook Town 1-0 Dinnington Town
Teversal 1-2 Grimsby Borough

SEMI-FINALS
Grimsby Borough 5-2 Albion Sports
Louth Town 2-3 Shirebrook Town

FINAL (@ Parkgate, 1/5/11) Att: 192
Grimsby Borough 3-1 (aet) Shirebrook Town

DIVISION ONE	1	2	3	4	5	6	7	8	9	10	11	12	13	14	15	16	17	18	19	20
1 AFC Emley		4-5	2-1	3-1	2-1	1-3	1-1	2-3	4-1	2-4	1-4	3-2	4-1	1-2	1-4	4-4	2-1	0-2	3-1	6-1
2 Albion Sports	2-1		4-2	3-2	2-0	2-5	3-2	1-3	7-1	3-0	3-2	2-1	3-0	1-3	3-1	5-0	4-3	2-0	2-3	5-0
3 Appleby Frodingham	0-4	2-1		1-2	3-2	3-4	1-3	3-4	0-4	1-4	0-5	1-3	1-2	0-5	1-3	1-7	2-8	2-3	0-6	2-3
4 Askern Villa	1-3	1-3	3-0		0-2	4-0	2-1	1-2	2-0	2-0	0-1	1-0	1-2	1-5	0-1	0-2	1-5	2-2	3-2	5-1
5 Bottesford Town	0-4	3-1	2-1	1-3		3-1	1-2	1-2	1-2	2-2	1-2	1-3	0-1	2-1	0-4	3-0	2-3	0-4	1-2	5-1
6 Dinnington Town	0-3	1-6	2-0	2-0	3-1		0-2	5-3	3-2	0-1	1-2	2-2	0-1	1-5	1-0	1-2	0-0	1-0	2-3	0-0
7 Eccleshill United	0-0	3-5	3-1	6-1	0-1	2-3		0-1	3-1	3-1	2-5	3-0	2-1	4-1	1-0	3-3	4-2	0-2	6-0	1-0
8 Glasshoughton Welfare	4-3	4-0	2-1	3-1	5-0	2-1	2-0		9-1	1-2	3-1	3-0	7-4	2-3	0-4	2-2	1-1	0-3	5-1	3-0
9 Grimsby Borough	0-3	3-3	3-0	7-1	2-2	1-1	3-6	1-2		1-2	0-4	2-2	1-2	2-5	2-3	2-1	0-4	1-2	1-0	2-0
10 Hallam	0-4	4-6	3-0	1-1	2-4	1-3	1-1	2-1	4-2		0-2	2-4	2-1	1-3	3-2	2-2	1-0	1-3	1-1	1-1
11 Handsworth	3-0	6-0	4-0	3-0	3-0	2-1	2-1	3-0	1-0	1-0		3-1	0-1	1-2	0-1	5-3	0-2	2-5	2-1	4-0
12 Hemsworth Miners Welfare	3-1	0-0	2-1	4-3	4-1	2-1	1-4	0-2	3-0	2-0	2-1		2-3	1-1	2-1	1-0	0-1	1-5	3-4	5-0
13 Louth Town	2-3	1-0	3-1	3-1	3-3	0-2	0-4	1-1	5-0	1-0	0-2	1-2		2-0	1-2	3-2	3-0	2-5	1-1	2-2
14 Pontefract Collieries	3-1	1-0	5-1	1-0	3-0	0-2	2-0	2-2	5-0	1-4	2-3	1-2	1-2		1-1	3-2	1-2	0-3	1-0	3-0
15 Rossington Main	0-0	2-2	2-2	1-0	3-1	3-5	3-0	1-1	3-0	1-5	1-2	4-4	2-2	0-1		4-0	6-2	5-1	2-3	2-0
16 Shirebrook Town	2-2	1-3	3-0	2-2	2-1	1-1	0-1	4-7	2-0	0-2	2-1	2-0	1-0	3-1	0-2		1-4	0-1	2-2	8-1
17 Teversal	0-2	1-7	2-1	2-1	2-2	2-3	0-4	1-1	3-1	3-2	2-2	3-5	3-2	1-5	0-5	0-1		0-1	2-2	3-2
18 Worksop Parramore	4-0	1-2	6-1	3-2	3-0	1-2	5-3	2-2	3-3	7-1	0-2	1-0	1-1	0-3	1-4	2-2	2-0		2-3	6-1
19 Worsbrough Bridge Athletic	2-2	1-1	2-2	4-1	1-1	1-2	1-2	2-1	1-0	1-0	1-3	1-1	1-0	1-0	4-0	4-0	2-3	0-1		7-1
20 Yorkshire Amateur	1-1	2-4	6-0	4-2	1-1	3-3	1-0	0-5	5-1	1-4	0-1	1-3	1-1	0-4	5-2	1-3	3-1	1-2	2-4	

PREMIER DIVISION

ARMTHORPE WELFARE
Founded: 1926 Nickname: Wellie

Secretary: Craig Trewick (T) (E) armthorpe.welfare@hotmail.co.uk
Chairman: Stephen Taylor **Manager:** Des Bennett **Prog Ed:** Martin Turner
Ground: Welfare Ground, Church Street, Armthorpe, Doncaster DN3 3AG (T) 07775 797 013 (Match days only)
Capacity: 2,500 **Seats:** 250 **Covered:** 400 **Midweek Matchday:** Tuesday **Clubhouse:** No **Shop:** No

Colours(change): All royal blue (All red)
Previous Names:
Previous Leagues: Doncaster Senior
Records: **Att:** 2,000 v Doncaster R Charity Match 1985-86. **Goalscorer:** Martin Johnson. **App:** Gary Leighton. **Win:** 10-0. **Defeat:** 1-7
Senior Honours: West Riding Challenge Cup 1981-82, 82-83. Northern Counties East Division 1 Central 1984-85.

10 YEAR RECORD

02-03		03-04		04-05		05-06		06-07		07-08		08-09		09-10		10-11		11-12	
NCEP	18	NCEP	14	NCEP	18	NCEP	10	NCEP	13	NCEP	9	NCEP	15	NCEP	3	NCEP	13	NCEP	13

ARNOLD TOWN
Founded: 1989 Nickname: Eagles

Secretary: Albert Graves (T) (E) mail@arnoldfc.com
Chairman: Roy Francis **Manager:** Gary Hayward **Prog Ed:** Mick Gretton
Ground: Eagle Valley, Oxton Road, Arnold, Nottingham NG5 8PS (T) 0115 965 6000
Capacity: **Seats:** **Covered:** **Midweek Matchday:** Tuesday **Clubhouse:** **Shop:**

Colours(change): All maroon. (Yellow/blue/yellow)
Previous Names: Arnold F.C. (founded 1928 as Arnold St. Marys) merged with Arnold Kingswell (1962) in '1989.
Previous Leagues: Central Midland 89-93
Records: **Att:** 3,390 v Bristol Rovers FAC 1-Dec 1967 **Goalscorer:** Peter Fletcher - 100. **App:** Pete Davey - 346. **Win:** 10-1 **Defeat:** 0-7
Senior Honours: Northern Counties East 1985-86. Central Midlands 92-93. Northern Counties Div.1 93-94.

10 YEAR RECORD

02-03		03-04		04-05		05-06		06-07		07-08		08-09		09-10		10-11		11-12	
NCEP	15	NCEP	18	NCEP	16	NCEP	5	NCEP	15	NCEP	10	NCEP	6	NCEP	8	NCEP	18	NCEP	9

BARTON TOWN OLD BOYS
Founded: 1995 Nickname: Swans

Secretary: Peter Mitchell (T) 01652 635 838 (E) bartontown@gmail.com
Chairman: Vacant **Manager:** Dave Anderson **Prog Ed:** Phil Hastings
Ground: The Euronics Ground, Marsh Lane, Barton-on-Humber (T) 01652 661 871
Capacity: 3,000 **Seats:** 240 **Covered:** 540 **Midweek Matchday:** Tuesday **Clubhouse:** Yes **Shop:** No

Colours(change): Sky blue & white stripes/black/sky blue (Red & black stripes/white/red)
Previous Names:
Previous Leagues: Lincolnshire 1995-00, Humber (Founder member) 2000-01, Central Midlands 2001-07.
Records:
Senior Honours: Lincolnshire League 1996-97. Central Midlands League Supreme Division 2005-06.

10 YEAR RECORD

02-03		03-04		04-05		05-06		06-07		07-08		08-09		09-10		10-11		11-12	
CM Su	13	CM Su	7	CM Su	4	CM Su	1	CM Su	2	NCE1	9	NCE1	5	NCE1	6	NCE1	2	NCEP	11

BRIDLINGTON TOWN
Founded: 1918 Nickname: Seasiders

Secretary: Gavin Branton (T) (E) gavinbranton@yahoo.co.uk
Chairman: Peter Smurthwaite **Manager:** Mitch Cook **Prog Ed:** Dom Taylor & Joe Gillot
Ground: Neil Hudgell Law Stadium, Queensgate, Bridlington YO16 7LN (T) 01262 606 879
Capacity: 3,000 **Seats:** 500 **Covered:** 500 **Midweek Matchday:** Tuesday **Clubhouse:** Yes **Shop:** Yes

Colours(change): All red (All white).
Previous Names: Original Bridlington Town folded in 1994. Greyhound FC changed to Bridlington Town.
Previous Leagues: Yorkshire 1924-39, 59-82, NCEL 1982-90, 99-2003, Northern Premier 1990-94, 2003-08
Records: **Att:** 1,006 v FC Utd of Manchester, NPLD1N, 03.11.07. **Goalscorer:** Neil Grimson - 200+ (1987-97). **Apps:** Neil Grimson - 200+ (1987-97).
Senior Honours: FA Vase 1992-93. Northern Counties East 2002-03, 2009-10, Division 1 1992-93.
ERCFA Senior Cup 1921,22,23,31,53,57,61,65,67,70,72,89,93,05

10 YEAR RECORD

02-03		03-04		04-05		05-06		06-07		07-08		08-09		09-10		10-11		11-12	
NCEP	1	NP 1	11	NP P	20	NP 1	11	NP 1	24	NP1N	18	NCEP	4	NCEP	1	NCEP	3	NCEP	2

BRIGHOUSE TOWN

Founded: 1963   Nickname: Town

Secretary: Malcolm Taylor   **(T)**   **(E)** malctay@blueyonder.co.uk

Chairman: Chris Lister   **Manager:** Paul Quinn   **Prog Ed:** Malcolm Taylor

Ground: Dual Seal Stadium, St Giles Rd, Hove Edge, Brighouse, HD6 2PL.   **(T)** 01484 380 088

Capacity: 1,000 **Seats:** 100 **Covered:** 200 **Midweek Matchday:** Tuesday   **Clubhouse:** Yes **Shop:** No

Colours(change): Orange/black/orange. (Yellow/green/yellow).
Previous Names:
Previous Leagues: Huddersfield Works. 1963-75. West Riding County Amateur 1975-08.
Records:
Senior Honours: West Riding County Amateur League: Prem Div - 1990/91 1994/95 1995/96 2000/01 2001/02, Prem Cup - 1993/94, 95/96 98/99, 00/01; Div 1 - 1988/89

10 YEAR RECORD

02-03	03-04	04-05	05-06	06-07	07-08	08-09	09-10	10-11	11-12
WRCP 2	WRCP 3	WRCP 4	WRCP 3	WRCP 3	WRCP 8	NCE1 15	NCE1 2	NCEP 16	NCEP 4

GLASSHOUGHTON WELFARE

Founded: 1964   Nickname: Welfare or

Secretary: Frank MacLachlan   **(T)** 07710 586 447   **(E)** frank.maclachlan@btinternet.com

Chairman: Phil Riding   **Manager:** Graham Hodder   **Prog Ed:** Nigel Lea

Ground: Glasshoughton Centre, Leeds Road, Glasshoughton, Castleford WF10 4PF   **(T)** 01977 511 234

Capacity: 2,000 **Seats:** **Covered:** **Midweek Matchday:** Tuesday   **Clubhouse:** Yes **Shop:**

Colours(change): Royal blue & white/royal blue/royal blue (All yellow)
Previous Names:
Previous Leagues:
Records: **Att:** 300 v Bradford City 1990. **Win:** 8-1. **Defeat:** 0-8.
Senior Honours: West Riding County Cup 1993-94.

10 YEAR RECORD

02-03	03-04	04-05	05-06	06-07	07-08	08-09	09-10	10-11	11-12
NCEP 12	NCEP 17	NCEP 11	NCEP 16	NCEP 16	NCEP 20	NCE1 19	NCE1 13	NCE1 7	NCE1 2

HALL ROAD RANGERS

Founded: 1959   Nickname: Rangers

Secretary: Alan Chaplin   **(T)**   **(E)** hallroadrangers@hotmail.com

Chairman: Mark Gregory   **Manager:** Jamie Barnwell & Martin Thacker   **Prog Ed:** Alex Blackburne

Ground: Dene Park, Dene Close, Beverley Road, Dunswell HU6 0AA   **(T)** 01482 850 101

Capacity: 1,200 **Seats:** 250 **Covered:** 750 **Midweek Matchday:** Wednesday   **Clubhouse:** Yes **Shop:** Yes

Colours(change): Blue & white/blue/blue. (Red & black/black/black)
Previous Names:
Previous Leagues: East Riding County, Yorkshire 1968-82.
Records: **App:** 1,200 v Manchester City Aug 93 **Goalscorer:** G James **App:** G James
Senior Honours: East Riding Senior Cup 1972-73, 93-94. N.C.E. Division Two 1990-91.

10 YEAR RECORD

02-03	03-04	04-05	05-06	06-07	07-08	08-09	09-10	10-11	11-12
NCE1 9	NCE1 14	NCE1 11	NCE1 14	NCE1 10	NCE1 2	NCEP 16	NCEP 11	NCEP 14	NCEP 16

HEANOR TOWN

Founded: 1883   Nickname: The Lions

Secretary: Keith Costello   **(T)** 07792 691 843   **(E)** ukinfo@jmcengineering.com

Chairman: John McCulloch   **Manager:** Craig Hopkins/Glenn Kirkwood   **Prog Ed:** Stan Wilton

Ground: The Town Ground, Mayfield Avenue, Heanor DE75 7EN   **(T)** 01773 713 742

Capacity: 2,700 **Seats:** 100 **Covered:** 1,000 **Midweek Matchday:** Wednesday   **Clubhouse:** Yes **Shop:**

Colours(change): All white (Orange/black/black)
Previous Names:
Previous Leagues: Midland 1961-72. Central Midlands 1986-2008. East Midlands Counties 2008-12.
Records:
Senior Honours: East Midlands Counties 2011-12.

10 YEAR RECORD

02-03	03-04	04-05	05-06	06-07	07-08	08-09	09-10	10-11	11-12
CM Su 11	CM Su 3	CM Su 19	CM Su 6	CM Su 14	CM Su 11	EMC 12	EMC 7	EMC 3	EMC 1

LINCOLN MOORLANDS RAILWAY
Founded: 1989 Nickname: The Moors

Secretary: Graham Peck **(T)** **(E)** graham@peckgraham.orangehome.co.uk
Chairman: Alan Hobbs **Manager:** Matt Carmichael **Prog Ed:** Graham Peck
Ground: Moorland Sports Ground, Newark Road, Lincoln LN6 8RT **(T)** 01522 874 111
Capacity: 200 **Seats:** 200 **Covered:** 100 **Midweek Matchday:** Wednesday **Clubhouse:** Yes **Shop:** No

Colours(change): Claret & blue/claret/claret & blue. (Yellow/royal blue/yellow).
Previous Names:
Previous Leagues: Central Midlands.
Records:
Senior Honours: Central Midlands Supreme 1999-00. Lincolnshire Senior Cup 2006-07.

10 YEAR RECORD

02-03	03-04	04-05	05-06	06-07	07-08	08-09	09-10	10-11	11-12
NCE1 7	NCE1 8	NCE1 4	NCE1 7	NCE1 5	NCEP 19	NCEP 18	NCEP 17	NCEP 6	NCEP 19

LIVERSEDGE
Founded: 1910 Nickname: Sedge

Secretary: Bryan Oakes **(T)** 01274 683 327 **(E)** bryan@bryanoakes.orangehome.co.uk
Chairman: Steve Newton **Manager:** Eric Gilchrist **Prog Ed:** Alan Dearden
Ground: Clayborn Ground, Quaker Lane, Hightown Road, Cleckheaton WF15 8DF **(T)** 01274 862 108
Capacity: 2,000 **Seats:** 250 **Covered:** 750 **Midweek Matchday:** Tuesday **Clubhouse:** Yes **Shop:** Yes

Colours(change): Sky blue/navy/sky blue. (All red).
Previous Names:
Previous Leagues: Spen Valley, West Riding Co. Amateur 1922-72, Yorkshire 1972-82
Records: **Att:** 986 v Thackley **Goalscorer:** Denis Charlesworth **App:** Barry Palmer
Senior Honours: Northern Counties East League Cup 2005-06.

10 YEAR RECORD

02-03	03-04	04-05	05-06	06-07	07-08	08-09	09-10	10-11	11-12
NCEP 9	NCEP 9	NCEP 6	NCEP 2	NCEP 12	NCEP 4	NCEP 14	NCEP 9	NCEP 17	NCEP 14

LONG EATON UNITED
Founded: 1956 Nickname: Blues

Secretary: Jim Fairley **(T)** **(E)** jim@longeatonutd.co.uk
Chairman: Jim Fairley **Manager:** Mick Galloway **Prog Ed:** Ritchie Woods
Ground: Grange Park, Station Rd, Long Eaton, Derbys NG10 2EG **(T)** 0115 973 5700
Capacity: 1,500 **Seats:** 150 **Covered:** 500 **Midweek Matchday:** Tuesday **Clubhouse:** Yes **Shop:** No

Colours(change): All blue. (All red).
Previous Names:
Previous Leagues: Central Alliance 1956-61, Mid Co Football Lge 1961-82, NCE 1982-89, Central Midlands 1989-2002
Records: **Att:** 2,019 v Burton Albion FA Cup 1973
Senior Honours: Derbyshire Senior Cup 1964-65, 75-76. Northern Counties East Div1S 1984-85. League Cup 2008-09.

10 YEAR RECORD

02-03	03-04	04-05	05-06	06-07	07-08	08-09	09-10	10-11	11-12
NCE1 3	NCE1 2	NCEP 12	NCEP 19	NCEP 11	NCEP 12	NCEP 2	NCEP 10	NCEP 12	NCEP 15

MALTBY MAIN
Founded: 1916 Nickname: Miners

Secretary: John Mills **(T)** 01709 813 609 **(E)** john_mills_@hotmail.co.uk
Chairman: Graham McCormick **Manager:** Chris Dunn **Prog Ed:** Nick Dunhill
Ground: Muglet Lane, Maltby, Rotherham S66 7JQ. **(T)** 07795 693 683
Capacity: 2,000 **Seats:** 150 **Covered:** 300 **Midweek Matchday:** Wednesday **Clubhouse:** No **Shop:** No

Colours(change): Red/black/red (Yellow/white/yellow)
Previous Names: Maltby Miners Welfare 1970-96
Previous Leagues: Sheffield Co Senior. Yorkshire League 1973-84
Records: **Att:** 1,500 v Sheffield Weds (friendly) 1991-2
Senior Honours: Sheffield & Hallamshire Senior Cup1977-78

10 YEAR RECORD

02-03	03-04	04-05	05-06	06-07	07-08	08-09	09-10	10-11	11-12
NCE1 15	NCE1 3	NCEP 19	NCEP 18	NCEP 10	NCEP 18	NCEP 12	NCEP 16	NCEP 11	NCEP 18

NOSTELL MINERS WELFARE

Founded: 1928   Nickname: The Welfare

Secretary: Granville Marshall   **(T)** 01924 864 462   **(E)** nostellmwfc@hotmail.com

Chairman: Granville Marshall   **Manager:** Alan Colquhoun   **Prog Ed:** Malcolm Lamb

Ground: The Welfare Grd, Crofton Co. Centre, Middle Lane, New Crofton WF4 1LB   **(T)** 01924 866 010

Capacity: 1500   **Seats:** 100   **Covered:** 200   **Midweek Matchday:** Tuesday   **Clubhouse:** Yes   **Shop:** No

Colours(change): Yellow/black/black. (All blue).
Previous Names:
Previous Leagues: Wakefield 1950-66, 69-82, West Yorkshire 1966-68, 82-2006
Records:
Senior Honours: West Yorkshire Premier Division 2004-05

10 YEAR RECORD

02-03		03-04		04-05		05-06		06-07		07-08		08-09		09-10		10-11		11-12	
WYkP	3	WYkP	5	WYkP	1	WYkP	3	NCE1	4	NCE1	5	NCEP	13	NCEP	18	NCEP	9	NCEP	17

PARKGATE

Founded: 1969   Nickname: The Steelmen

Secretary: Bruce Bickerdike   **(T)**   **(E)** secretary@parkgatefc.co.uk

Chairman: Albert Dudill   **Manager:** Doug Shelley   **Prog Ed:** Dave Platts

Ground: Roundwood Sports Complex, Green Lane, Rawmarsh, S62 6LA   **(T)** 01709 826 600

Capacity: 1,000   **Seats:** 300   **Covered:** 300   **Midweek Matchday:** Tuesday   **Clubhouse:** Yes   **Shop:** No

Colours(change): All Red & White. (All green & white).
Previous Names: BSC Parkgate (1982-86) RES Parkgate (pre 1994)
Previous Leagues: BIR County Senior. Yorkshire 1974-82.
Records: **Att:** v Worksop 1982
Senior Honours: N.C.E. Division One 2006-07. Wilkinson Sword Trophy 2006-07.

10 YEAR RECORD

02-03		03-04		04-05		05-06		06-07		07-08		08-09		09-10		10-11		11-12	
NCE1	8	NCE1	10	NCE1	12	NCE1	6	NCE1	1	NCEP	8	NCEP	11	NCEP	14	NCEP	2	NCEP	7

PICKERING TOWN

Founded: 1888   Nickname: Pikes

Secretary: Keith Usher   **(T)** 01751 473 317   **(E)** usherso8@btinternet.com

Chairman: Keith Usher   **Manager:** Jimmy Reid   **Prog Ed:** Alasdair Dinnewell

Ground: Recreation Club, off Mill Lane, Malton Road, Pickering YO18 7DB   **(T)** 01751 473 317

Capacity: 2,000   **Seats:** 200   **Covered:** 500   **Midweek Matchday:** Tuesday   **Clubhouse:** Yes   **Shop:** No

Colours(change): All blue. (All yellow).
Previous Names:
Previous Leagues: Beckett, York & District, Scarborough & District, Yorkshire 1972-1982
Records: **Att:** 1,412 v Notts County (friendly) in August 1991
Senior Honours: N.C.E. Div 2 1987-88. North Riding Cup 1990-91. Wilkinson Sword Trophy 2000-01

10 YEAR RECORD

02-03		03-04		04-05		05-06		06-07		07-08		08-09		09-10		10-11		11-12	
NCEP	13	NCEP	5	NCEP	5	NCEP	6	NCEP	9	NCEP	3	NCEP	9	NCEP	7	NCEP	7	NCEP	12

RETFORD UNITED

Founded: 1987   Nickname: The Badgers

Secretary: Annie Knight   **(T)**   **(E)** retfordunited@sky.com

Chairman: Daniel Keeton   **Manager:** Richard Sennett & Mark Turner   **Prog Ed:** Jon Knight

Ground: Cannon Park, Leverton Road, Retford, Notts DN22 6QF   **(T)** 01777 710 300

Capacity: 2,000   **Seats:** 150   **Covered:** 200   **Midweek Matchday:** Tuesday   **Clubhouse:** Yes   **Shop:** Yes

Colours(change): Black and white stripes/black/black (All yellow)
Previous Names:
Previous Leagues: Gainsborough & Dist, Nottinghamshire Alliance > 2001, Central Midlands 2001-04, Northern Counties East 2004-07
Records: 1,527 v Doncaster Rovers - Friendly July 2006
Senior Honours: Notts All. Div.1 2000-01. Central Mids Div.1 01-02, Supreme Division 03-04, Lge Cup 01-02, 03-04, Floodlit Cup 03-04. N.C.E. Prem. Division 06-07, 11-12, N.P.L. Div.1S 07-08, 08-09. Notts Sen. Cup 08-09.

10 YEAR RECORD

02-03		03-04		04-05		05-06		06-07		07-08		08-09		09-10		10-11		11-12	
CM Su	4	CM Su	1	NCE1	8	NCE1	2	NCEP	1	NP1S	1	NP1S	1	NP P	6	NP P	22	NCEP	1

SCARBOROUGH ATHLETIC
Founded: 2007   Nickname: The Seadogs

Secretary: John Clarke   **(T)**   **(E)** john.clarke@scarboroughathletic.com

Chairman: David Holland   **Manager:** Rudy Funk   **Prog Ed:** Aaron Best

Ground: Bridlington FC, Queensgate, Bridlington, East Yorks YO16 7LN   **(T)** 07545 878 467

Capacity: 3000   **Seats:** 500   **Covered:** 1,200   **Midweek Matchday:** Tuesday   **Clubhouse:** Yes   **Shop:** No

Colours(change): All Red (All yellow).
Previous Names: Formed after Scarborough F.C. folded in 2007.
Previous Leagues: N/A
Records: **Att:** 791 v Leeds Carnegie N.C.E. Div.1 - 25.04.09.
Senior Honours: Northern Counties East Division One 2008-09.

10 YEAR RECORD

02-03	03-04	04-05	05-06	06-07	07-08	08-09	09-10	10-11	11-12
					NCE1 5	NCE1 1	NCEP 5	NCEP 10	NCEP 3

STAVELEY MINERS WELFARE
Founded: 1989   Nickname: The Welfare

Secretary: Ele Reaney   **(T)** 01246 471 441   **(E)** staveleyed@hotmail.co.uk

Chairman: Terry Damms   **Manager:** Billy Fox   **Prog Ed:** Ele Reaney

Ground: Inkersall Road, Staveley, Chesterfield, S43 3JL   **(T)** 01246 471 441

Capacity: 5,000   **Seats:** 220   **Covered:** 400   **Midweek Matchday:** Wednesday   **Clubhouse:** Yes   **Shop:** Yes

Colours(change): Blue & white/blue/blue (All orange)
Previous Names:
Previous Leagues: Chesterfield & District Amateur 1989-91. County Senior 1991-93.
Records: 910 v Chesterfield, Friendly, 20/07/2011. **Goalscorer:** Ryan Damms - 102. **Apps:** Shane Turner.
Senior Honours: County Senior League Division 3 1991-92, Division 2 1992-93. N.C.E. Division One 2010-11.

10 YEAR RECORD

02-03	03-04	04-05	05-06	06-07	07-08	08-09	09-10	10-11	11-12
NCE1 17	NCE1 16	NCE1 9	NCE1 10	NCE1 6	NCE1 8	NCE1 4	NCE1 4	NCE1 1	NCEP 5

TADCASTER ALBION
Founded: 1892   Nickname: The Brewers

Secretary: Howard Clarke   **(T)**   **(E)** sandra.clarke1@tiscali.co.uk

Chairman: Rob Northfield   **Manager:** Paul Marshall   **Prog Ed:** Kevin Axtell

Ground: 2inspire Park, Ings Lane, Tadcaster LS24 9AY   **(T)** 07518 820 730 or 07949 452 054

Capacity: 1,500   **Seats:** 150   **Covered:** 400   **Midweek Matchday:** Tuesday   **Clubhouse:** Yes   **Shop:** No

Colours(change): All yellow (All red)
Previous Names: None
Previous Leagues: York, Harrogate, Yorkshire 1973-82.
Records: **Att:** 1,200 v Winterton FA Vase 4th Round 1996-7
Senior Honours: Northern Counties East Division 1 2009-10.

10 YEAR RECORD

02-03	03-04	04-05	05-06	06-07	07-08	08-09	09-10	10-11	11-12
NCE1 16	NCE1 18	NCE1 6	NCE1 3	NCE1 7	NCE1 12	NCE1 17	NCE1 1	NCEP 4	NCEP 8

THACKLEY
Founded: 1930   Nickname: Dennyboys

Secretary: Mick Lodge   **(T)**   **(E)** mick.lodge@btinternet.com

Chairman: Mike Smith   **Manager:** Vince Brockie   **Prog Ed:** John McCreery

Ground: Dennyfield, Ainsbury Avenue, Thackley, Bradford BD10 0TL   **(T)** 01274 615 571

Capacity: 3000   **Seats:** 300   **Covered:** 600   **Midweek Matchday:** Tuesday   **Clubhouse:** Yes   **Shop:** Yes

Colours(change): Red/white/red. (White/black/white).
Previous Names: Thackley Wesleyians 1930-39
Previous Leagues: Bradford Am, W. Riding Co. Am., West Yorks, Yorks 1967-82
Records: **Att:** 1,500 v Leeds United 1983
Senior Honours: W. Riding County Cup 1963-64, 66-67, 73-74, 74-75. Bradford & District Senior Cup (x13).

10 YEAR RECORD

02-03	03-04	04-05	05-06	06-07	07-08	08-09	09-10	10-11	11-12
NCEP 6	NCEP 11	NCEP 8	NCEP 9	NCEP 18	NCEP 16	NCEP 7	NCEP 4	NCEP 8	NCEP 10

WINTERTON RANGERS

Founded: 1930   Nickname: Rangers

Secretary: Mark Fowler   **(T)** 07775 907 606   **(E)** mark-fowler-68@hotmail.co.uk

Chairman: David Crowder   **Manager:** Lee Danysz   **Prog Ed:** Brian Crowder

Ground: West Street, Winterton, Scunthorpe DN15 9QF.   **(T)** 01724 732 628

Capacity: 3,000   **Seats:** 245   **Covered:** 200   **Midweek Matchday:** Wednesday   **Clubhouse:** Yes   **Shop:** No

Colours(change): All royal blue. (All red).
Previous Names:
Previous Leagues: Scunthorpe & District. 1945-65. Lincolnshire 1965-70. Yorkshire 1970-82.
Records: **Att:** 1,200 v Sheffield United, flood lights switch on, October 1978.
Senior Honours: NCE Premier 2007-08.

10 YEAR RECORD

02-03	03-04	04-05	05-06	06-07	07-08	08-09	09-10	10-11	11-12
NCE1 10	NCE1 11	NCE1 10	NCE1 5	NCE1 2	NCEP 1	NCEP 5	NCEP 6	NCEP 5	NCEP 6

WORKSOP PARRAMORE

Founded: 1936   Nickname: None

Secretary: Max Ross   **(T)**   **(E)** max@pandmleisure.co.uk

Chairman: Pete Whitehead   **Manager:** Darren Bland   **Prog Ed:** Paul Hill

Ground: The Windsor Foodservice Stadium, Sandy Land, Worksop S80 1TJ   **(T)** 01909 479 955

Capacity: 2,500   **Seats:** 200   **Covered:** 750   **Midweek Matchday:** Tuesday   **Clubhouse:** Yes   **Shop:**

Colours(change): Sky blue/black/sky blue (All orange).
Previous Names: Parramore Sports > 2010. Sheffield Parramore 2010-2011.
Previous Leagues: Sheffield & Hallam County Senior > 2008. Central Midlands > 2011.
Records:
Senior Honours: Central Midland League Supreme Division 2010-11.

10 YEAR RECORD

02-03	03-04	04-05	05-06	06-07	07-08	08-09	09-10	10-11	11-12
SHS1 6	SHS1 11	SHS1 12	SHS1 6	SHS1 13	SHS1 5	CM P 4	CM Su 8	CM Su 1	NCE1 3

DIVISION ONE

A.F.C. EMLEY

Founded: 2005   Nickname: Pewits

Secretary: John Whitehead   **(T)**   **(E)** afcemley@tiscali.co.uk

Chairman: John Whitehead   **Manager:** Darren Hepworth   **Prog Ed:** Rob Dixon

Ground: The Welfare Ground, Off Upper Lane, Emley, nr Huddersfield, HD8 9RE.   **(T)** 01924 849 392   **Capacity:** 2,000

Colours(change): Claret & sky blue/sky blue/claret (Sky blue/claret/sky blue)

ADDITIONAL INFORMATION:
Previous League: West Yorkshire 2005-06.

ALBION SPORTS

Founded: 1974   Nickname: Lions

Secretary: Jaj Singh   **(T)**   **(E)** info@albionsports.co.uk

Chairman: Kultar Singh   **Manager:** Kulwinder Singh Sandhu   **Prog Ed:** Jaj Singh

Ground: Cemetery Road, off Halifax Road, Bradford BD6 2NG   **(T)**   **Capacity:** 3,500

Colours(change): Yellow/royal blue/royal blue (All red)

ADDITIONAL INFORMATION:
Previous Lge: West Riding County Amateur > 2011.

APPLEBY FRODINGHAM

Founded: 1990   Nickname: The Steelmen

Secretary: Steve Lumley-Holmes   **(T)**   **(E)** lumleyholmes@btinternet.com

Chairman: Steve Lumley-Holmes   **Manager:** Simon Shorthose/John Simpson   **Prog Ed:** Dick Drury

Ground: Brumby Hall Sports Ground, Ashby Road, Scunthorpe, DN16 1AA   **(T)** 01724 402134 / 843024   **Capacity:** 1,100

Colours(change): Black & red/black/black (Blue & white/blue/blue)

ADDITIONAL INFORMATION:
Previous League: Central Midlands.
Honours: Lincolnshire League: 1962-63, 76-77, 77-98, 93-94; Lincolnshire Challenge Cup: 1962-63, 75-76, 76-77, 77-78, 92-93

ASKERN VILLA

Founded: 1924   Nickname: Welly or Villa

Secretary: Dave Hall   **(T)** 07799 752 890   **(E)** davidhallgfx@btinternet.com
Chairman: Austen White   **Manager:** Brian Johnston   **Prog Ed:** Dave Hall
Ground: Welfare Sports Ground, Manor Way, Doncaster Road, Askern, DN6 0AJ   **(T)**   **Capacity:** 2,000
Colours(change): Black & white/black/black & white (All red)

ADDITIONAL INFORMATION:
Previous League: Central Midlands.
Honours: Central Midlands League 2007-08.

ATHERSLEY RECREATION

Founded: 1979   Nickname: Penguins

Secretary: Peter Goodlad   **(T)**   **(E)** petegoodlad@yahoo.co.uk
Chairman: Terence Hunt   **Manager:** Peter Goodlad   **Prog Ed:** Jamie Wallman
Ground: Sheerien Park, Ollerton Road, Athersley North, Barnsley, S71 3DP   **(T)** 07910 121 070   **Capacity:** 2,000
Colours(change): Black & white/black & white/black & white (Navy & sky quarters/navy/sky)

ADDITIONAL INFORMATION:
Previous League: Sheffield & Hallamshire County Senior 1997-2012.
Honours: Sheffield & Hallamshire County Senior Division Two 1997-98, Premier Division 1999-2000, 03-04, 04-05, 06-07, 08-09, 11-12

BOTTESFORD TOWN

Founded: 1974   Nickname: The Poachers

Secretary: Tony Reeve   **(T)**   **(E)** anthony.reeve3@ntlworld.com
Chairman: Tony Reeve   **Manager:** John Corbett   **Prog Ed:** Liz Gray
Ground: Birch Park, Ontario Road, Bottesford, Scunthorpe, DN17 2TQ   **(T)** 01724 871 883   **Capacity:** 1,000
Colours(change): All blue & yellow (Red & black/black & red/black & red)

ADDITIONAL INFORMATION:
Previous Leagues: Lincolnshire 1974-2000. Central Midlands 2000-07.
Honours: Lincolnshire League 1989-90, 90-91, 91-92. Central Midlands League Supreme Division 2006-07.

CLEETHORPES TOWN

Founded: 1998   Nickname: None

Secretary: Jevon Southam   **(T)**   **(E)** jevon.southam@yahoo.com
Chairman: David Patterson   **Manager:** Andy Liddle   **Prog Ed:** Bradley King
Ground: The Bradley Football Development Centre Bradley Road, Grimsby, DN37 0AG   **(T)**   **Capacity:** 1,000
Colours(change): Blue & black stripes/black/blue & black (Red & black stripes/red/red & black)

ADDITIONAL INFORMATION:
Previous Leagues: Lincolnshire.
Honours: Lincolnshire League 2011-12.

CLIPSTONE WELFARE

Founded: 1928   Nickname: None

Secretary: Neil Hardwick   **(T)**   **(E)** clipstone.welfare.fc@gmail.com
Chairman: Neil Hardwick (Acting)   **Manager:** Lee Tryner   **Prog Ed:** Stacey Strouther
Ground: The Lido Ground, Clipstone Road East, Clipstone Village, Mansfield, NG21 9AB.   **(T)** 01623 423 730   **Capacity:** 500
Colours(change): White & black/black/black (All yellow)

ADDITIONAL INFORMATION:
Honours: Central Midlands League 1993-94, 96-97.

DINNINGTON TOWN

Founded: 2000   Nickname: Dinno

Secretary: Chris Dearns   **(T)** 07802 542 335   **(E)** chris.dearns@gmail.com
Chairman: Vacant   **Manager:** Steve Toyne & Mark Ramsden   **Prog Ed:** Wayne Rutledge
Ground: Phoenix Park, 131 Laughton Road, Dinnington, Nr Sheffield S25 2PP   **(T)** 07854 722 465   **Capacity:** 2000
Colours(change): Yellow & black/black/black. (All white).

ADDITIONAL INFORMATION:
Previous Leagues: Central Midlands 2000-2006.
Honours: Northern Counties East Division One 2007-08, League Cup 2009-10.

ECCLESHILL UNITED

Founded: 1948   Nickname: The Eagles

Secretary: Adrian Benson   **(T)**   **(E)**
Chairman: Adrian Benson   **Manager:** Ian Banks   **Prog Ed:** Paul Everett
Ground: The Rapid Solicitors Stadium, Kingsway, Wrose, Bradford, BD2 1PN   **(T)** 01274 615 739   **Capacity:** 2,225
Colours(change): Blue & white/blue/blue (White & red/red/red).

ADDITIONAL INFORMATION:
Record Att: 715 v Bradford City 1996-97. **Win:** 10-1. **Defeat:** 0-6.
Honours: Bradford Senior Cup 1985-86. Northern Counties East Division 1 1996-97.

GRIMSBY BOROUGH
Founded: 2003   Nickname: The Wilderness Boys

Secretary: Nigel Fanthorpe   **(T)**   **(E)** nigelfanthorpe@hotmail.co.uk
Chairman: Kenneth Vincent   **Manager:** Steve Newby & Nigel Fanthorpe   **Prog Ed:** Brian Sylvester
Ground: The Bradley Football Development Centre, Bradley Road, Grimsby, DN37 0AG   **(T)** 07890 318 054   **Capacity:** 1,500
Colours(change): Royal blue/royal blue/white (Yellow/white/blue)

ADDITIONAL INFORMATION:
Previous League: Central Midlands 2004-08.

HALLAM (SECOND OLDEST CLUB IN THE WORLD)
Founded: 1860   Nickname: Countrymen

Secretary: Mark Radford   **(T)** 0114 249 7287   **(E)** markradford34@yahoo.com
Chairman: David Slater   **Manager:** Julian Watts   **Prog Ed:** Russ Taylor
Ground: Sandygate Road, Crosspool, Sheffield S10 5SE   **(T)** 0114 230 9484   **Capacity:** 1,000
Colours(change): All blue (All yellow).

ADDITIONAL INFORMATION: **Att:** 2,000 v Hendon F.A. Amateur Cup. **Goalscorer:** A Stainrod 46. **App:** P. Ellis 500+. **Win:** 7-0 x2. **Defeat:** 0-7.
Honours: Northern Counties East League Cup 2003-04.
Previous League: Yorkshire 1952-82.

HEMSWORTH MINERS WELFARE
Founded: 1981   Nickname: Wells

Secretary: Phillip Crapper   **(T)** 01977 614 723   **(E)** acracknell@naue.co.uk
Chairman: Tony Benson   **Manager:** Wayne Benn   **Prog Ed:** Anthony Crapper
Ground: Fitzwilliam Stadium, Wakefield Road, Fitzwilliam, Pontefract, WF9 5AJ   **(T)** 01977 614 997   **Capacity:** 2,000
Colours(change): Royal blue/royal blue/white (White/white/royal blue)

ADDITIONAL INFORMATION:
Previous League: West Riding County Amateur 1995-2008.

KNARESBOROUGH TOWN
Founded: 1902   Nickname: None

Secretary: Clare Rudzinski   **(T)**   **(E)** clarerudzinski@btinternet.com
Chairman: Terry Hewlett   **Manager:** Brian Davey   **Prog Ed:** Paul Howard
Ground: Manse Lane, Knaresborough, HG5 8LF   **(T)** 01423 548 896   **Capacity:** 1,000
Colours(change): Red/black/red (Yellow & black stripes/black/black)

ADDITIONAL INFORMATION:
Previous Leagues: West Yorkshire 1971. Harrogate & District 1971-93. West Yorkshire 1993-2012.
Honours: West Yorkshire League Premier Division 2008-09.

LOUTH TOWN
Founded: 2007   Nickname: The White Wolves

Secretary: Richard Hill   **(T)**   **(E)** louthtownfc@gmail.com
Chairman: Stephen Clark   **Manager:** Daryl Clare   **Prog Ed:** Vacant
Ground: The Park Avenue Stadium, Park Avenue, Louth, LN11 8BY   **(T)** 01507 601 123   **Capacity:** 1,500
Colours(change): White/black/black (All blue)

ADDITIONAL INFORMATION:
Previous League: Central Midlands 2007-10.
Honours: Central Midlands League Premier Division 2008-09, Supreme Division 2009-10.

PONTEFRACT COLLIERIES
Founded: 1958   Nickname: Colls

Secretary: Rod Naylor   **(T)**   **(E)** info@pontecolls.co.uk
Chairman: Guy Nottingham   **Manager:** Brendan Ormsby   **Prog Ed:** Eddie Fogden
Ground: The Beechnut Lane Stadium, Skinner Lane, Pontefract, WF8 4QE   **(T)** 01977 600 818   **Capacity:** 1,200
Colours(change): All blue (All claret)

ADDITIONAL INFORMATION:
Previous League: Yorkshire 1979-82.
Honours: Northern Counties East League Division 1 1983-84, 95-96.

ROSSINGTON MAIN
Founded: 1919   Nickname: The Colliery

Secretary: Gerald Parsons   **(T)**   **(E)** g-parsons2@sky.com
Chairman: Carl Stokes   **Manager:** Steve Lodge   **Prog Ed:** Vacant
Ground: Welfare Ground, Oxford Street, Rossington, Doncaster, DN11 0TE   **(T)** 01302 865 524 (MD)   **Capacity:** 2,000
Colours(change): All blue (All red)

ADDITIONAL INFORMATION:
Record Att: 1,200 v Leeds United 06/08/1991. **Goalscorer:** Mark Illam. **Apps:** Darren Phipps.
Honours: Central Midlands League Premier Division 1984-85, League Cup 1983-84, 84-85.

SELBY TOWN
Founded: 1919   Nickname: The Robins

Secretary: Thomas Arkley   **(T)** 07830 218 657   **(E)** toonarkley@yahoo.co.uk
Chairman: Ralph Pearse   **Manager:** Phil Jones   **Prog Ed:** Thomas Arkley
Ground: The Rigid Group Stadium, Richard Street, Scott Road, Selby YO8 0DB   **(T)** 01757 210 900   **Capacity:** 5,000
Colours(change): All red (Black & white stripes/white/black).

ADDITIONAL INFORMATION: Att: 7,000 v Bradford PA FA Cup1st Round 1953-54
Honours: Yorkshire League 1934-35, 35-36, 52-53, 53-54. Northern Counties East Division One 1995-96.

SHIREBROOK TOWN
Founded: 1985   Nickname: None

Secretary: Aimee Radford   **(T)** 01623 742 535   **(E)** aimeeradford@yahoo.co.uk
Chairman: Gary Meredith   **Manager:** Gary Castledine   **Prog Ed:** Paul Harrison
Ground: Shirebrook Spts and So C, Langwith Rd, Shirebrook, Mansfield, NG20 8TF   **(T)** 01623 742 535   **Capacity:** 2,000
Colours(change): Red & black/black/red (All white)

ADDITIONAL INFORMATION:
Record Goalscorer: Craig Charlesworth - 345.
Honours: Central Midlands League Supreme Division 2000-01, 01-02, Northern Counties East Division One 2003-04.

TEVERSAL
Founded: 1918   Nickname: Tevie Boys

Secretary: Kevin Newton   **(T)** 07711 358 060   **(E)** enquiries@teversalfc.co.uk
Chairman: Peter Cockerill   **Manager:** Jamie Hudson   **Prog Ed:** Kevin Newton
Ground: Teversal Grange Spts and So.Centre, Carnarvon St, Teversal, NG17 3HJ   **(T)** 07711 358 060   **Capacity:**
Colours(change): Red/black/black (All royal blue)

ADDITIONAL INFORMATION:
Previous Name: Teversal Grange. **Previous League:** Central Midlands.
Honours: Central Midlands League 2004-05.

WORSBROUGH BRIDGE ATHLETIC
Founded: 1923   Nickname: Briggers

Secretary: Charlie Wyatt   **(T)** 01226 284 452   **(E)** crw@wyatts.adsl24.co.uk
Chairman: John Cooper   **Manager:** Chris Hilton   **Prog Ed:** Charlie Wyatt
Ground: Park Road, Worsbrough Bridge, Barnsley, S70 5LJ   **(T)** 01226 284 452   **Capacity:** 2,000
Colours(change): Red & white/black/black (All blue)

ADDITIONAL INFORMATION:
Record Att: 1,603 v Blyth Spatans, FA Amateur Cup 1971.
Honours: County Senior League Division One 1965-66, 69-70.

YORKSHIRE AMATEUR
Founded: 1918   Nickname: Ammers

Secretary: Bill Ellis   **(T)**   **(E)** william.ellis5@virginmedia.com
Chairman: Jeni French   **Manager:** Wayne Noteman   **Prog Ed:** Jeni French
Ground: Bracken Edge, Roxholme Road, Leeds, LS8 4DZ (Sat. Nav. LS7 4JG)   **(T)** 0113 289 2886   **Capacity:** 1,550
Colours(change): White/navy/red (All red)

ADDITIONAL INFORMATION:
Record Att: 4,000 v Wimbledon, FA Amateur Cup Quarter Final 1932.
Honours: Yorkshire League: 1931-32, Div 2 - 1958-59, Div 3 - 1977-78. Leeds & District Senior Cup.

GROUND DIRECTIONS

ARMTHORPE WELFARE - Welfare Ground, Church Street, Armthorpe, Doncaster, DN3 3AG. Tel: (01302) 842795 - Match days only
From the north, turn left at main roundabout in the centre of Doncaster and straight across at next roundabout on to Wheatley Hall Road. Turn right on to Wentworth Road, go to top of hill towards the Hospital on to Armthorpe Road. From the south, take the M18 to J4 on to the A630. At 2nd roundabout, turn left and proceed to next roundabout, then turn right. Ground 400 yards on left behind Netto.

ARNOLD TOWN - Eagle Valley, Oxton Road, Arnold, Nottingham, NG5 8PS. Tel: 0115 965 6000.
From South: From Nottingham, take the A60 Mansfield road. At the first traffic island half a mile north of Arnold, join the A614 towards Doncaster. After 200 yards, go through traffic lights and, after 300 yards, take the next right turn. The ground entrance is 200 yards on the right.
From North: A614 towards Nottingham. As you approach the first set of traffic lights, turn left 300 yards before the lights. The ground entrance is 200 yards on the right.
From M1: Leave at Junction 27. Head towards Hucknall/Nottingham. After one mile, turn right at the first set of traffic lights. One mile, turn first left at island and stay on this road for two miles until junction with A60. Turn right and, at the next island, turn left onto the A614 towards Doncaster. After 200 yards, go through traffic lights and, after 300 yards, take the next right turn. The ground entrance is 200 yards on the right.

BARTON TOWN OLD BOYS - The Euronics Ground, Marsh Lane, Barton-on-Humber. Tel: (01652) 635838
Approaching from the South on A15, Barton is the last exit before the Humber Bridge. Follow the A1077 into the town. Turn right at the mini roundabout at the bottom of the hill into Holydyke. Take second left onto George Street and then into King Street. Marsh Lane is opposite the junction of King Street and High Street. The ground is at the end of Marsh Lane, on the right, immediately after the cricket ground.

BRIDLINGTON TOWN - Queensgate Stadium, Queensgate, Bridlington, East Yorkshire, YO16 7LN. Tel: (01262) 606879
From South (Hull, Beeford, Barmston): Approach Bridlington on the A165, passing golf course on right and Broadacres Pub, Kingsmead Estate on left. Straight through traffic lights to roundabout by B&Q. Turn right. At traffic lights turn left and over the railway bridge. At roundabout bear left and carry on heading north up Quay Road. After traffic lights turn right into Queensgate. Ground is 800 yards up the road on the right.
From South and West (Driffield, Hull, York): Approach Bridlington on A614. (This was formally the A166). Straight on at traffic lights (Hospital on right) and follow the road round the bend. At roundabout straight across to mini roundabout and bear right (second exit). Follow road around to right and to traffic lights. Straight on. At next traffic lights (just after Kwikfit) turn left into Queensgate. Ground is 800 yards up the road on the right.
From North (Scarborough): Approach Bridlington (Esso garage on right) at roundabout turn left then at mini roundabout second exit. Follow road around to right and to traffic lights. Straight on. At next traffic lights (just after Kwikfit) turn left into Queensgate. Ground is 800 yards up the road on the right.

BRIGHOUSE TOWN - Dual Seal Stadium, St Giles Road, Hove Edge, Brighouse, West Yorkshire, HD6 2PL.
M1 to M62 travel westwards to J26 then come off motorway and go on to A58 Halifax to third set of traffic lights at Hipperholme. At lights, turn left onto A644 to Brighouse. Travel approx. one mile passing the Dusty Miller pub, take next left and, within 30-40 metres, turn left on to Spouthouse Lane. Follow this road for approximately 1/4 of a mile until road swings left at this point. Turn right in to car park. Be careful of oncoming traffic on bend.

GLASSHOUGHTON WELFARE - The Glasshoughton Centre, Leeds Rd, Glasshoughton, Castleford, WF10 4PF. Tel: (01977) 511234
Leave the M62 J32, signposted Castleford/Pontefract (A639). At the bottom of the slip road take the A656, taking carer to pick up the middle lane for Castleford. After approx. 1/4 mile, bear left at the first roundabout and, after a further 1/4 mile, left at the next roundabout on to Leeds Road. Ground is then 200 yards on the right.

HALL ROAD RANGERS - Dene Park, Dene Close, Beverley Road, Dunswell, nr Hull, HU6 0AA. Tel: (01482) 850101
M62 to A63, turn left before Humber Bridge onto A164 to Beverley, after approx. 5 miles turn right onto A1079. In 2 miles, turn left at large roundabout to ground 20 yards on right.

HEANOR TOWN - Mayfield Avenue, Heanor DE75 7EN - 01773 713 742
From M1: J26, take A610 Ripley Road to end of dual carriageway then take A608 to Heanor via Langley Mill. At traffic lights at top of long hill take left lane signed Ilkeston. First right into Mundy Street, second left onto Godfrey Street. Ground on left where road forks. From A608 Derby: Enter town and see Tesco on left. Turn right at roundabout to the Market Place. Turn right at end of square and at crossroads right again onto Mundy Street. Then left into Godfrey Street and ground on left where road forks.

LINCOLN MOORLANDS RAILWAY - Lincoln Moorlands Railway Sports Ground, Newark Road, Lincoln, LN6 8RT. Tel: (01522) 874111
From North: A1 to Markham Moor. Take A57 until Lincoln by-pass. At Carholme Roundabout take 3rd. exit towards Lincoln South. Travel 1.7 miles to Skellingthorpe Roundabout and take 2nd. Exit towards Lincoln South. Travel 1.6 miles to Doddington Roundabout and take 1st. exit B1190 towards Lincoln South. Travel 2.1 miles until T-Junction. Turn left onto A1434 and travel 0.4 mile. Entrance to ground is on left immediately after Chancery Close.
From Newark: A46 to Lincoln by-pass. At roundabout take last exit onto A1434 towards Lincoln. Travel for 3.1 miles, entrance to ground on left immediately after Chancery Close signposted 'Moorlands Railway Club'.

LIVERSEDGE - Clayborn Ground, Quaker Lane, Hightown Road, Cleckheaton, WF15 8DF. Tel: (01274) 682108
M62 J26, A638 into Cleckheaton, right at lights on corner of Memorial Park, through next lights and under railway bridge, first left (Hightown Rd) and Quaker Lane is approx 1/4 mile on left and leads to ground. From M1 J40, A638 thru Dewsbury and Heckmondwike to Cleckheaton, left at Memorial Park lights then as above. Buses 218 & 220 (Leeds - Huddersfield) pass top of Quaker Lane.

LONG EATON UNITED - Grange Park, Station Road, Long Eaton, NG10 2EG. Tel: (0115) 973 5700
M1 Junc 25, take A52 towards Nottingham, to island by Bardills Garden Centre, right onto B6003. Approx 2 miles to end of road to T-junction. At traffic lights, turn right A453 and take 2nd left into Station Road. Entrance on left down un-named road opposite disused car park next to Grange School.

MALTBY MAIN - Muglet Lane, Maltby, Rotherham, S66 7JQ. Tel: (07795) 693683
Exit M18 at Junc 1 with A631. Two miles into Maltby, right at Queens Hotel corner on to B6427 Muglet Lane. Ground 3/4 mile on left.

NOSTELL MINERS WELFARE - The Welfare Ground, Crofton Community Centre, Middle Lane, New Crofton, Wakefield, WF4 1LB. Tel: (01924) 866010
M1 J39, head towards Wakefield (A638), Denby Dale road. Leave Wakefield on the A638 (Doncaster Rd), towards Wakefield Trinity Ground. Continue on this road for another 2 miles, you will pass the Red Beck Motel on your right. Go under the bridge and turn right opposite the Public house 'Crofton Arms'. Follow road through Crofton village (1 1/4 miles). Turn left at 'Slipper' public house, then right onto Middle Lane, follow road round to reach Crofton Community Centre.

PARKGATE - Roundwood Sports Complex, Green Lane, Rawmarsh, Rotherham, S62 6LA. Tel: (01709) 826600
From Rotherham A633 to Rawmarsh. From Doncaster A630 to Conisbrough, then A6023 through Swinton to Rawmarsh. Grd at Green Lane - right from Rotherham, left from Conisbrough at the Crown Inn. Ground 800yds on right.

PICKERING TOWN - Recreation Club, off Mill Lane, Malton Rd, Pickering, YO18 7DB. Tel: (01751) 473317
A169 from Malton. On entering Pickering, take 1st left past Police Station and BP garage into Mill Lane, ground 200 yds on right.

RETFORD - Cannon Park, Leverton Road, Retford, Notts DN22 6QF. Tel: (01777) 869 468 / 710 300
Leave the A1 at Ranby and follow the A620 towards Retford. Go past Ranby prison and go straight on at the next 2 mini roundabouts. At the 3rd roundabout take the 3rd exit signposted Gainsborough. Passing Morrisons on the left, go through the traffic lights and move into the right hand lane. Turn right at the traffic lights. Turn left at the traffic lights by the Broken Wheel Public House into Leverton Road. Go past the Masons Arms Public House and go over 2 hump backed bridges. The ground is signposted and is on the left.

SCARBOROUGH ATHLETIC - Queensgate Stadium, Bridlington, East Yorkshire, YO16 7LN. Tel: (01262) 606879
From South (Hull, Beeford, Barmston): Approach Bridlington on the A165, passing golf course on right and Broadacres Pub, Kingsmead Estate on left. Straight through traffic lights to roundabout by B&Q. Turn right. At traffic lights turn left and over the railway bridge. At roundabout bear left and carry on heading north up Quay Road. After traffic lights turn right into Queensgate. Ground is 800 yards up the road on the right.
From South and West (Driffield, Hull, York): Approach Bridlington on A614. (This was formally the A166). Straight on at traffic lights (Hospital on right) and follow the road round the bend. At roundabout straight across to mini roundabout and bear right (second exit). Follow road around to right and to traffic lights. Straight on. At next traffic lights (just after Kwikfit) turn left into Queensgate. Ground is 800 yards up the road on the right.
From North (Scarborough): Approach Bridlington (Esso garage on right) at roundabout turn left then at mini roundabout second exit. Follow road around to right and to traffic lights. Straight on. At next traffic lights (just after Kwikfit) turn left into Queensgate. Ground is 800 yards up the road on the right.

STAVELEY MINERS WELFARE - Inkersall Road, Staveley, Chesterfield, S43 3JL. Tel: (01246) 471441
M1 J30 follow A619 Chesterfield. Staveley is 3 miles from J30. Turn left at GK Garage in Staveley town centre into Inkersall Road. Ground is 200 yards on right at side of Speedwell Rooms.

TADCASTER ALBION - 2inspire Park, Ings Lane, Tadcaster, LS24 9AY
From West Riding and South Yorks - Turn right off A659 at John Smith's Brewery Clock. From East Riding - Turn left off A659 after passing over river bridge and pelican crossing (New Street).

THACKLEY - Dennyfield, Ainsbury Avenue, Thackley, Bradford, BD10 0TL. Tel: (01274) 615571
On main Leeds/Keighley A657 road, turn off at Thackley corner which is 2 miles from Shipley traffic lights and 1 mile from Greengates lights. Ainsbury Avenue bears to the right 200yds down the hill. Ground is 200yds along Ainsbury Avenue on the right.

WINTERTON RANGERS - West Street, Winterton, Scunthorpe, DN15 9QF. Tel: (01724) 732628
From Scunthorpe - Take A1077 Barton-on-Humber for 5 miles. On entering Winterton take 3rd right (Eastgate), 3rd left (Northlands Rd) and 1st Right (West St). Ground 200 yards on left.

WORKSOP PARRAMORE - The Windsor Foodservice Stadium, Sandy Land, Worksop S80 1TJ. Tel: 01909 479 955

From either the A1 or M1 J31, take the A57 towards Worksop. After approximately 7 miles, look out for the A60/Sandy Lane turnoff at the roundabout. Continue over two mini-roundabouts for ¾mile then turn left into the retail park and left again into the stadium car park.

DIVISION ONE

A.F.C. EMLEY - The Welfare Ground, Off Upper Lane, Emley, nr Huddersfield, HD8 9RE. Tel: 01924 849392 or 07702 712287

From M1 J38: Travel on road signposted to Huddersfield through the village of Bretton to the first roundabout. Take first exit off this roundabout signposted Denby Dale. After approximately one mile turn right at road signposted Emley. After 2 miles enter the village of Emley. Entrance to ground is opposite a white bollard in centre of road. (Narrow entrance).
From M1 J39: Travel on road signposted toward Denby Dale. Travel for approximately 3 miles up hill to first roundabout. Take 2nd exit and follow directions as above.

ALBION SPORTS - Cemetery Road, off Halifax Road, Bradford BD6 2NG. Tel: 01274 604 568

M62 to J26. Join M606. Leave at second junction. At roundabout take second exit (A6036 signposted Halifax) and pass Odsal Stadium on left hand side. At next roundabout, take third exit (A6036 Halifax, Horsfall Stadium is signposted). After approximately 1 mile, turn left down Cemetery Road immediately before Kings Head Public House. Ground is 150 yards on the left.

APPLEBY FRODINGHAM - Brumby Hall Sports Ground, Ashby Road, Scunthorpe, DN16 1AA. Tel: 01724 402134 or 01724 843024

From M18, take J5 on to the M180. From M180, take J3 onto the M181 (Scunthorpe West). At the roundabout, turn right onto A18. Straight on at the mini roundabout (McDonalds). At the next large roundabout, take the third exit (A18) up the hill to the next roundabout, turn left and the entrance to the ground is 100 metres on the left.

ASKERN VILLA - Askern Villa Sports Ground, Manor Way, Doncaster Road, Askern, DN6 0AJ. Tel: (01302) 700597

Via A1 - Leave the A1 at Junction A639. Follow Signs Askern/Campsall. At T-Junction turn right towards Sutton. Take left turn at Anne Arms Public House. Take second right on to Manor Way. Car park in grounds of Askern Miners Welfare; Via M62 - Exit Junction 34 follow signs for Doncaster (A19) for about 6 miles take 1st right after "The Askern" Public House. Clubhouse on the left.

ATHERSLEY RECREATION - Sheerien Park, Ollerton Road, Athersley North, Barnsley, S71 3DP. Tel: 07910 121070

From North: M1 J38. Go down slip road, round roundabout and back under motorway. Take first left onto Haigh Lane, go to top of the hill and, at T-junction, turn right. At next T-junction, turn left onto Shaw Lane and go to bottom of hill. At T-junction of A61, turn right to Barnsley, go through first set of traffic lights and take first left onto Newstead Road. Follow to second roundabout and turn right onto Ollerton Road. Follow to second turn on left - do not take it but go past and entrance is between houses 123-125 Ollerton Road. Follow drive into ground.

BOTTESFORD TOWN - Birch Park, Ontario Road, Bottesford, Scunthorpe, DN17 2TQ. Tel: (01724) 871883

Exit M180 via M181-Scunthorpe. At circle (Berkeley Hotel), turn right into Scotter Road. At circle (Asda) straight ahead, 2nd left into South Park road then on to Sunningdale Road, turn right into Goodwood Road, Birch Park at end (right turn). Please note that Goodwood Road is not suitable for large vehicles. Instead, take 2nd right off Sunningdale Road which is Quebec Road, then 2nd right which is Ontario Road down to the bottom and ground is on the left.

CLEETHORPES TOWN - The Bradley Football Development Centre, Bradley Road, Grimsby, DN37 0AG

Head East along the M180/A180. Exit at the Great Coates Interchange. Travel back over motorway to first Roundabout. Take first exit and follow for two miles to Trawl Pub Roundabout. Take second exit, follow for two miles to Bradley Roundabout. Take second exit on to Bradley Road. The ground is approximately 500 yards on the left.

CLIPSTONE WELFARE - The Lido Ground, Clipstone Road East, Clipstone Village, Mansfield, NG21 9AB. Tel: 01623 423730

From M1 J29, take exit signposted A617 Mansfield. At next roundabout, take third exit continuing on the A617. Keep going straight on until you get to the Mansfield ring road with Riley's snooker hall on your right and a miner's statue on your left. Follow the road round underneath a pedestrian bridge and take the next left onto the A6191 (Ratcliffe Gate). After around half a mile, turn left onto the B6030 (Carter Lane). Follow the B6030 for about 3 miles, go straight on at a roundabout and the ground will be on your left.

DINNINGTON TOWN - Phoenix Park, Dinnington Resource Centre, 131 Laughton Road, Dinnington S25 2PP. Tel: (01909) 518555

From M1 J31, follow A57 Worksop Road for 1 mile. At first traffic lights, turn left onto B6463 Todwick Road then Monks Bridge Road for 2 miles. At petrol station roundabout, take third exit signposted Dinnington and travel half-a-mile, then take first left at Morrell Tyres. Cross mini-roundabout at The Squirrel pub and travel on Laughton Road for 300 yards. Ground is on the left.

ECCLESHILL UNITED - The Smith Butler Stadium, Kingsway, Wrose, Bradford, BD2 1PN. Tel: (01274) 615739

M62 J26 onto M606, right onto Bradford Ring Road A6177, left on to A650 for Bradford at 2nd roundabout. A650 Bradford Inner Ring Road onto Canal Rd, branch right at Staples (Dixons Car showrooms on right), fork left after 30mph sign to junction with Wrose Road, across junction - continuation of Kings Rd, first left onto Kingsway. Ground is 200 yards on the left.

GRIMSBY BOROUGH - Grimsby Community Stadium, Bradley Road, Grimsby, DN37 0AG

Head South East on the A180 to the Great Coates turn off come back over the A180 and follow for 1/2 mile to the roundabout, take first exit follow over one mini roundabout and through one set of traffic lights until you come to the Trawl Pub roundabout, take the second exit onto Littlecoates road and follow over one mini roundabout to the second roundabout and take the second exit onto Bradley Road. The ground is approx 800 yards on your left with car and coach parking facilities.

HALLAM - Sandygate, Sandygate Road, Crosspool, Sheffield, S10 5SE. Tel: (0114) 230 9484

A57 Sheffield to Glossop Rd, left at Crosspool shopping area signed Lodge Moor on to Sandygate Rd. Ground half mile on left opposite Plough Inn. 51 bus from Crucible Theatre.

HEMSWORTH MINERS WELFARE - Fitzwilliam Stadium, Wakefield Road, Fitzwilliam, Pontefract, WF9 5AJ. Tel: (01977) 614997

From East/West: M62 to J32 towards Pontefract then follow A628 towards Hemsworth. At Ackworth roundabout (Stoneacre Suzuki Garage), take a right on to the A638 Wakefield Road. Travel half a mile to next roundabout then take first exit. Travel one mile to crossroads and turn left into Fitzwilliam. Pass a row of shops on your right and turn left after the bus shelter before an iron bridge. To ground.
From North: A1 South to M62 then follow above directions.
From South: A1(M) North to A638 Wakefield Road. Travel to Ackworth Roundabout (Stoneacre Suzuki Garage) and go straight across and follow the A638 to the next roundabout. Take first exit then to crossroads. Turn left into Fitzwilliam and pass row of shops on your right. Turn left after bus shelter before iron bridge and carry on to the ground. Alternative: M1 to J32 then take M18 to A1(M).

KNARESBOROUGH TOWN - Manse Lane, Manse Lane, Knaresborough, HG5 8LF. Tel: 01423 548896

From West/South Leeds Area: A658 or A61 towards Harrogate. Join A658 southern bypass towards York. At roundabout with B6164, turn left to Knaresborough. Turn left at second roundabout and travel over river bridge. Manse Lane is first on right alongside garage; From East Leeds Area: A58 or A1 to Wetherby. Join B6164 to Knaresborough then as above. From East on A59 from A1: Turn right at first roundabout. Manse Lane is first turn left after speed restriction signs.

LOUTH TOWN - The Park Avenue Stadium, Park Avenue, Louth, LN11 8BY. Tel: 07891 965531

Enter Louth from the A16 onto North Home Road. Go 1/2 mile and follow the road as it bends to the right to become Newbridge Hill. At the junction, turn right onto Ramsgate. At the mini roundabout next to Morrisons, turn left onto Eastgate. Go 1/2 mile down Eastgate and turn right into Park Avenue just past the fire station.

PONTEFRACT COLLIERIES - Skinner Lane, Pontefract, WF8 4QE. Tel: (01977) 600818

M62 jct32 (Xscape) towards Pontefract. Left at lights after roundabout for park entrance and retail park. Traffic through town should follow racecourse signs through lights to roundabout and back to lights.

ROSSINGTON MAIN - Welfare Ground, Oxford Street, Rossington, Doncaster, DN11 0TE. Tel: (01302) 865524 (Matchdays only)

Enter Rossington and go over the railway crossings. Passing the Welfare Club, Oxford Street is the next road on the right. The ground is at the bottom of Oxford Street.

SELBY TOWN - The Selby Times Stadium, Richard St, Scott Rd, Selby, YO8 4BN. Tel: (01757) 210900

From Leeds, left at main traffic lights in Selby down Scott Rd, then 1st left into Richard St. From Doncaster, go straight across main traffic lights into Scott Rd then 1st left. From York, right at main traffic lights into Scott Rd and 1st left.

SHIREBROOK TOWN - Shirebrook Staff Sports and Social Club, Langwith Road, Shirebrook, Mansfield, Notts, NG20 8TF. Tel: (01623) 742535

Depart M1 at Junction 29, at roundabout take A617 towards Mansfield (for 3.5 miles), at next roundabout take 2nd Exit B6407 Common Lane towards Shirebrook (or 1.8 miles), go straight on at next roundabout (for 300 yards), at staggered crossroads turn right onto Main Street (for 1.1 miles), at T Junction turn right (for 100 yards), take the first road on the left (Langwith Road). The ground is 400 yards on the right.

TEVERSAL - Teversal Grange Sports and Social Centre, Carnarvon Street, Teversal, Sutton-in-Ashfield, NG17 3HJ. Tel: (07773) 922539

From North: Travel South on the M1 to junction 29 take the A6175 to Heath and Holmewood. Travel through Holmewood, and at the roundabout take the B6039 to Hardstaff and Tibshelf. At the T-junction in Tibshelf (pub on your left) turn left onto B6014 travelling over the motorway into Teversal. Follow the road round passing the Carnarvon Arms pub and under a bridge, take 2nd left onto Coppywood Close, travel to the top and following the road round with the ground at the top.
From South: From the M1 junction 28, take the A38 to Mansfield. Travel through a number of sets of traffic lights and after passing the Kings Mill Reservoir you will come to a major junction (King & Miller Pub and McDonalds on your left). Travel straight on taking the A6075 towards Mansfield Woodhouse, at the next set of traffic lights turn left onto the B6014 to Stanton Hill. You will come to a roundabout with a Kwik Save on your left, continue on the B6014 towards Tibshelf. Take the second right onto Coppywood Close, travel to the top and following the road round with the ground at the top.

WORSBOROUGH BRIDGE ATHLETIC - Park Road, Worsbrough Bridge, Barnsley, S70 5LJ. Tel: (01226) 284452

On the A61, Barnsley-Sheffield road two miles south of Barnsley, 2 miles from M1 J36 opposite Blackburns Bridge.

YORKSHIRE AMATEUR - Bracken Edge, Roxholme Road, Leeds, LS8 4DZ. Tel: (0113) 262 4093

From South - M1 to Leeds, then A58 to Wetherby Road to Fforde Green Hotel, left at lights and proceed to Sycamore Avenue (on right). From East - A1 to Boot & Shoe Inn then to Shaftesbury Hotel, turn right into Harehills Lane, then to Sycamore Avenue.

NORTHERN LEAGUE

Sponsored by: Skilltrainingltd
Founded: 1889
Recent Champions:
2007: Whitley Bay
2008: Durham City
2009: Newcastle Benfield
2010: Spennymoor Town
2011: Spennymoor Town
northernleague.org

LEAGUE CUP

ROUND 1
Penrith 3-4 (aet) Guisborough Town
West Auckland Town 4-2 Whitley Bay
Newton Aycliffe 1-3 Team Northumbria
Stokesley Sports Club 1-2 Northallerton Town
South Shields 0-1 Esh Winning
Birtley Town 1-1 (aet) 3-1p Thornaby
Easington Colliery 0-2 Whitehaven
Ashington 0-1 Chester-Le-Street
Dunston UTS 4-0 Tow Law Town
Jarrow Roofing 3-3 (aet) 2-4p West Allotment Celtic
Seaham Red Star 1-2 (aet) Crook Town
Brandon United 1-2 North Shields

ROUND 2
West Allotment Celtic 0-6 Hebburn Town
Alnwick Town 3-2 Chester-Le-Street
Billingham Town 1-4 Norton & Stockton Ancients
Horden C.W. 0-5 West Auckland Town
Marske United 1-2 Gillford Park
Sunderland RCA 4-3 Bishop Auckland
Whickham 0-1 Billingham Synthonia
Whitehaven 1-6 Dunston UTS
Crook Town 2-4 Bedlington Terriers
Esh Winning 5-8 (aet) Team Northumbria
Guisborough Town 3-0 Birtley Town
Morpeth Town 1-2 Spennymoor Town
Newcastle Benfield 3-0 Ryton & Crawcrook Albion
North Shields 2-2 (aet) 4-3p Darlington RA
Washington 0-1 Shildon
Consett 5-2 Northallerton Town

ROUND 3
Team Northumbria 5-0 Hebburn Town
Billingham Synthonia 6-1 Alnwick Town
Norton & Stockton Ancients 1-2 Consett
Bedlington Terriers 1-0 Gillford Park
Dunston UTS 0-1 (aet) Sunderland RCA
Guisborough Town 0-1 Spennymoor Town
Newcastle Benfield 1-2 North Shields
Shildon 0-1 West Auckland Town

QUARTER FINALS
Team Northumbria 3-1 Billingham Synthonia
Consett 1-2 West Auckland Town
Bedlington Terriers 2-0 North Shields
Spennymoor Town 4-0 Sunderland RCA

SEMI-FINALS
West Auckland Town 3-2 Bedlington Terriers
Team Northumbria 3-3 (aet) 4-2p Spennymoor Town

FINAL
Team Northumbria 4-1 West Auckland Town

DIVISION ONE

		P	W	D	L	F	A	Pts
1	Spennymoor Town	42	30	7	5	86	31	97
2	West Auckland Town	42	29	8	5	117	58	95
3	Dunston UTS	42	27	9	6	85	34	90
4	Sunderland RCA	42	27	7	8	106	54	88
5	Ashington	42	23	8	11	91	58	77
6	Whitley Bay	42	23	7	12	90	54	76
7	Bedlington Terriers	42	20	10	12	97	49	70
8	Bishop Auckland	42	20	9	13	87	69	69
9	Newton Aycliffe	42	18	11	13	70	52	65
10	Shildon	42	18	5	19	83	63	59
11	Billingham Synthonia	42	18	5	19	74	77	59
12	Newcastle Benfield	42	16	7	19	73	65	55
13	South Shields	42	15	6	21	81	92	51
14	Norton & Stockton Ancients	42	14	8	20	54	60	50
15	Consett	42	13	11	18	71	78	50
16	Guisborough Town	42	13	11	18	67	97	50
17	Billingham Town	42	15	4	23	72	95	49
18	Marske United	42	11	11	20	61	89	44
19	Penrith	42	11	7	24	59	97	40
20	(R) Jarrow Roofing	42	12	4	26	65	114	40
21	(R) Tow Law Town	42	9	1	32	44	102	28
22	(R) Stokesley Sports Club	42	0	4	38	31	176	4

DIVISION ONE	1	2	3	4	5	6	7	8	9	10	11	12	13	14	15	16	17	18	19	20	21	22
1 Ashington		1-4	2-1	3-0	7-1	3-1	2-0	2-0	5-1	1-1	0-1	2-2	3-1	6-1	2-0	2-2	4-1	3-0	0-4	2-1	3-1	1-3
2 Bedlington Terriers	2-4		1-2	2-0	0-1	0-2	0-0	1-2	2-1	3-0	5-0	1-1	2-1	4-1	2-1	4-2	0-2	15-0	1-2	5-2	3-1	4-0
3 Billingham Synthonia	0-2	2-2		3-1	2-1	1-2	1-2	0-0	4-1	2-2	2-0	0-0	1-2	3-1	0-3	2-3	1-3	4-0	0-1	5-4	1-3	3-1
4 Billingham Town	2-3	0-7	2-1		1-1	0-1	0-2	3-3	4-5	3-1	5-2	0-5	2-1	2-1	0-1	3-2	0-1	2-2	2-4	3-2	1-2	0-2
5 Bishop Auckland	1-0	2-3	2-3	5-0		3-2	1-2	2-0	1-3	2-2	3-2	1-1	2-0	5-3	2-0	2-1	0-1	3-1	0-0	3-0	1-1	1-3
6 Consett	1-2	0-0	1-5	2-0	1-1		2-2	4-2	5-1	0-4	0-2	2-2	0-0	0-0	1-5	4-3	1-0	8-1	3-4	4-1	0-3	0-4
7 Dunston UTS	2-0	1-1	2-1	3-0	1-2	2-0		2-2	1-0	5-1	1-0	0-0	1-0	5-1	2-4	3-0	0-0	5-0	2-1	5-0	1-3	1-1
8 Guisborough Town	2-2	1-1	3-3	0-2	1-2	1-4	0-1		3-1	1-1	1-4	0-1	1-1	2-1	2-1	6-0	0-7	3-1	0-7	3-0	0-7	0-4
9 Jarrow Roofing BoldonCA	1-1	0-2	1-2	1-7	2-4	2-1	0-3	3-3		0-3	0-2	0-3	0-2	2-1	0-3	3-2	4-2	4-2	0-3	0-1	2-2	1-4
10 Marske United	1-2	2-2	0-2	1-2	2-2	2-2	2-6	1-3	4-0		2-1	3-1	0-2	0-3	2-1	2-5	1-1	5-0	0-2	2-1	1-4	0-0
11 Newcastle Benfield	2-1	1-1	0-2	5-2	1-3	4-2	1-2	2-3	2-3	3-0		1-1	2-3	1-2	2-1	4-0	1-2	1-0	1-2	5-0	1-3	1-1
12 Newton Aycliffe	1-1	1-0	2-1	3-2	2-1	2-1	0-1	4-2	5-3	2-0	1-0		3-1	1-2	2-4	1-4	0-1	6-1	0-2	1-1	1-2	2-1
13 Norton & Stockton Anc	1-1	1-2	1-0	0-1	1-3	0-1	2-3	3-1	2-2	3-0	1-0	1-1		2-0	2-1	0-3	2-2	3-0	0-3	2-0	2-2	1-3
14 Penrith	2-2	2-2	3-4	3-0	1-5	0-0	0-4	1-0	4-1	5-2	0-5	1-0	0-3		1-4	0-1	0-3	4-0	0-1	2-1	4-4	2-4
15 Shildon	2-3	1-0	1-1	1-2	2-2	2-2	0-1	2-1	3-4	5-1	2-2	1-4	2-0	0-2		1-0	1-2	11-0	2-3	3-1	1-2	1-1
16 South Shields	0-1	0-0	5-1	1-5	2-1	2-0	0-1	3-4	2-1	3-4	1-1	2-4	1-0	1-2		0-3	5-2	2-3	3-1	3-4	3-2	
17 Spennymoor Town	2-1	2-1	2-0	2-1	1-1	1-0	1-1	3-1	2-0	1-1	1-0	2-0	5-0	3-0	5-0		5-1	2-0	3-0	1-1	2-0	
18 Stokesley SC	0-7	1-5	0-5	1-3	2-3	2-7	0-3	1-2	2-3	1-3	1-2	0-3	0-0	2-2	0-2	1-1	0-3		1-6	1-2	0-3	2-7
19 Sunderland Ryhope C A	5-1	3-1	2-0	2-2	3-2	2-2	2-1	7-0	2-3	2-2	3-1	0-0	4-1	1-1	2-2	1-2	1-4	2-1		3-0	2-3	4-3
20 Tow Law Town	1-2	0-3	2-1	1-4	2-6	4-1	0-3	0-1	2-3	0-1	1-0	1-2	0-2	2-0	1-3	2-1	1-3	3-2	2-1		0-2	0-1
21 West Auckland Town	2-1	2-1	9-1	2-1	3-1	2-0	1-1	7-3	4-2	0-0	0-3	1-2	2-1	5-1	2-1	5-5	1-3	3-0	2-1	3-0		6-1
22 Whitley Bay	2-0	1-2	4-0	5-2	3-1	1-0	2-2	2-2	1-0	4-0	1-1	1-0	1-0	2-1	0-1	3-1	0-1	6-0	2-3	2-0	1-2	

DIVISION TWO

	P	W	D	L	F	A	Pts
1 (P) Team Northumbria	42	28	5	9	112	49	89
2 (P) Gillford Park (-3)	42	27	8	7	125	62	86
3 (P) Hebburn Town	42	26	4	12	110	73	82
4 Morpeth Town	42	22	10	10	78	54	76
5 Darlington RA	42	22	7	13	84	68	73
6 Birtley Town	42	21	9	12	100	77	72
7 West Allotment Celtic	42	21	8	13	90	72	71
8 North Shields	42	19	11	12	77	51	68
9 Northallerton Town	42	19	11	12	99	74	68
10 Crook Town	42	18	13	11	99	69	67
11 Esh Winning	42	20	6	16	95	74	66
12 Chester-le-Street Town	42	16	8	18	70	63	56
13 Whitehaven	42	15	9	18	71	79	54
14 Washington	42	16	5	21	69	97	53
15 Whickham	42	13	10	19	76	82	49
16 Alnwick Town	42	13	10	19	56	86	49
17 Brandon United	42	13	7	22	70	94	46
18 Ryton & Crawcrook Albion	42	13	5	24	68	117	44
19 Thornaby	42	11	8	23	78	110	41
20 Seaham Red Star	42	8	7	27	61	113	31
21 Horden Colliery Welfare	42	8	6	28	44	92	30
22 Easington Colliery (-3)	42	6	7	29	60	136	22

J.R. CLEATOR CUP
(League champions v League Cup winners)

Spennymoor Town 1-1 (aet) 5-4p Newcastle Benfield

ERNSET ARMSTRONG MEMORIAL CUP

ROUND 1

Northallerton Town 3-2 Washington
Birtley Town 1-0 Esh Winning
Chester-Le-Street 3-2 (aet) Morpeth Town
Horden C.W. 1-0 Whitehaven
Brandon United 1-0 (aet) Alnwick Town
Easington Colliery 1-3 Hebburn Town

ROUND 2

West Allotment Celtic 1-1 (aet) 3-4p Birtley Town
Team Northumbria 6-0 Ryton & Crawcrook Albion
Chester-Le-Street 2-5 Whickham
Northallerton Town 3-1 Crook Town
Brandon United 1-2 (aet) Thornaby
Seaham Red Star 2-3 Gillford Park
Darlington RA 2-1 (aet) Horden C.W.
Hebburn Town 2-3 North Shields

QUARTER FINALS

Birtley Town 1-2 Team Northumbria
North Shields 1-2 Northallerton Town
Gillford Park 2-1 Thornaby
Darlington RA 4-2 Whickham

SEMI-FINALS

Darlington RA 1-2 Northallerton Town
Gillford Park 3-3 (aet) 2-4p Team Northumbria

FINAL

Northallerton Town 3-2 Team Northumbria

DIVISION TWO

	1	2	3	4	5	6	7	8	9	10	11	12	13	14	15	16	17	18	19	20	21	22
1 Alnwick Town		1-3	0-2	2-1	1-5	0-3	2-1	0-1	1-3	0-5	3-0	0-3	1-1	1-1	1-2	5-2	0-7	1-0	3-2	1-0	3-1	2-1
2 Birtley Town	1-1		2-1	2-0	2-3	1-3	4-1	3-2	2-2	2-2	1-0	4-2	1-1	3-0	1-1	6-1	1-4	3-4	5-1	2-5	1-0	4-0
3 Brandon United	2-1	0-3		0-2	1-1	2-0	4-1	1-6	0-1	6-3	4-1	0-3	1-2	5-5	3-0	2-3	2-2	2-3	4-1	5-1	1-1	0-2
4 Chester-le-Street Town	4-3	1-2	1-0		0-1	0-2	2-0	2-2	1-2	4-0	1-0	1-0	1-1	1-1	4-0	5-2	0-2	2-4	3-1	0-2	0-3	1-2
5 Crook Town	1-1	4-0	1-1	0-0		0-2	7-1	1-4	3-3	1-5	2-1	1-1	0-1	1-1	6-0	1-3	2-3	4-1	5-1	2-2	1-1	3-0
6 Darlington Railway Athletic	4-0	3-1	0-2	2-1	3-1		2-3	5-0	5-1	0-6	2-1	1-1	1-1	1-0	2-1	3-1	4-2	3-2	1-2	1-0	2-2	2-2
7 Easington Colliery	0-1	1-4	6-0	0-3	0-2	2-3		0-3	0-4	2-5	4-2	2-2	0-3	1-3	0-3	1-0	2-4	3-5	1-4	1-3	2-3	2-2
8 Esh Winning	0-1	1-1	2-3	3-0	5-5	3-0	5-3		2-5	2-3	2-1	0-2	0-2	2-1	3-4	4-1	4-1	7-1	1-2	1-0	3-3	3-0
9 Gillford Park	3-1	4-4	5-1	2-1	4-0	2-2	1-1	3-0		1-2	11-1	1-2	3-0	4-4	4-3	5-1	1-2	7-2	2-0	0-1	3-0	4-1
10 Hebburn Town	4-1	1-2	3-0	1-4	1-4	4-4	3-1	1-3	1-2		5-2	2-1	0-2	2-2	8-2	6-3	0-0	4-3	3-1	3-1	4-0	0-5
11 Horden Colliery Welfare	1-2	2-1	0-1	3-4	0-1	3-1	0-1	1-1	0-1	1-4		1-0	0-0	1-1	1-2	1-3	1-2	0-2	1-3	1-2	1-0	
12 Morpeth Town	3-3	0-3	3-1	3-2	3-0	2-0	1-0	2-0	1-1	2-1	2-0		2-1	0-1	2-1	2-0	2-2	1-1	5-1	4-2	2-1	3-0
13 North Shields	1-1	2-2	2-2	0-1	2-4	5-2	2-2	3-0	2-3	0-2	4-0	1-2		2-0	5-1	3-1	0-1	1-0	2-4	2-1	1-1	2-0
14 Northallerton Town	3-0	2-3	4-1	0-0	3-0	2-1	6-1	3-3	1-4	2-1	3-1	4-3	2-2		3-1	2-3	4-5	3-0	3-2	0-1	3-0	2-0
15 Ryton & Crawcrook Albion	1-1	1-3	0-4	1-4	1-6	0-4	3-3	2-1	1-3	1-2	2-2	2-2	2-5	4-1		5-4	2-4	1-1	2-1	1-0	1-3	1-3
16 Seaham Red Star	4-2	3-4	0-0	0-0	0-5	2-4	0-1	1-3	2-5	0-1	2-2	2-2	0-2	0-2	2-3		1-0	2-1	6-0	3-3	1-6	0-1
17 Team Northumbria	2-1	4-1	2-0	5-1	2-2	2-0	14-0	0-1	2-3	0-2	5-0	2-0	0-1	2-1	0-2	2-0		4-0	4-2	0-0	3-1	2-0
18 Thornaby	3-4	2-2	4-2	2-2	2-2	1-2	7-1	2-0	2-5	1-2	1-2	4-4	0-6	1-6	4-3	2-0	0-2		2-1	2-2	0-1	1-2
19 Washington	0-0	0-2	3-2	1-0	1-3	1-1	2-2	1-6	3-2	1-2	1-0	1-0	2-1	2-5	3-2	4-0	0-4	3-1		1-1	3-1	2-2
20 West Allotment Celtic	3-2	3-2	3-1	3-1	2-2	3-2	8-4	1-2	2-3	2-1	3-0	3-0	2-3	3-3	5-1	5-0	1-5	2-1	3-0		0-2	2-4
21 Whickham	1-1	6-5	6-1	1-1	3-1	5-2	2-2	0-3	2-1	0-3	0-1	1-2	1-4	1-2	3-3	1-2	2-2	1-3	5-0			0-3
22 Whitehaven	1-1	2-2	5-0	2-8	1-5	0-0	2-1	3-1	0-2	2-3	1-2	1-2	2-1	5-2	1-2	0-0	4-1	2-1	2-3	1-1	4-4	

ASHINGTON
Founded: 1883   Nickname: The Colliers

Secretary: Brian Robson   **(T)** 07843 661 686   **(E)** brian.robson@piramal.com

Chairman: Ian Lavery   **Manager:**   **Prog Ed:**

Ground: Woodhorn Lane, Ashington NE63 9HF   **(T)** 01670 811 991

Capacity: **Seats:**   **Covered:**   **Midweek Matchday:** Tuesday   **Clubhouse:** Yes   **Shop:** Yes

Colours(change): Black & White stripes/black/black.
Previous Names:
Previous Leagues: Northern Alliance, Football League, N. Eastern, Midland, Northern Counties, Wearside, N.P.L.
Records: **Att:** 13,199 v Rochdale FA Cup 2nd round 1950
Senior Honours: Northern League Div.2 Champions 2000-01, 03-04.

10 YEAR RECORD

02-03	03-04	04-05	05-06	06-07	07-08	08-09	09-10	10-11	11-12
NL 2 5	NL 2 1	NL 1 10	NL 1 16	NL 1 19	NL 1 17	NL 1 16	NL 1 6	NL 1 8	NL 1 5

BEDLINGTON TERRIERS COMM.
Founded: 1949   Nickname: Terriers

Secretary: David Collop   **(T)** 07853 052 450   **(E)** davidcollop@hotmail.com

Chairman: Ronan Liddane   **Manager:**   **Prog Ed:** David Collop

Ground: Welfare Park, Park Road, Bedlington, NE22 5DP   **(T)** 07514 412 137

Capacity: 3,000   **Seats:** 300   **Covered:** 500   **Midweek Matchday:** Wednesday   **Clubhouse:** Yes   **Shop:**

Colours(change): Red with white trim/red/red.
Previous Names: Bedlington Mechanics 1949-53   Bedlington United 1961-65
Previous Leagues: Northern Alliance
Records: **Att:** 2,400 v Colchester United FA Cup 1st round   **Goalscorer:** John Milner
Senior Honours: Northern Lge Div 1: 97-98, 98-99, 99-00, 2000-01, 01-02. Northumberland Senior Cup 1996-97, 97-98, 2001-02,03-04.

10 YEAR RECORD

02-03	03-04	04-05	05-06	06-07	07-08	08-09	09-10	10-11	11-12
NL 1 2	NL 1 3	NL 1 3	NL 1 2	NL 1 20	NL 1 15	NL 1 14	NL 1 7	NL 1 9	NL 1 7

BILLINGHAM SYNTHONIA
Founded: 1923   Nickname: Synners

Secretary: Graham Craggs   **(T)** 07702 530 335   **(E)** graham.craggs@gb.abb.com

Chairman: Stuart Coleby   **Manager:**   **Prog Ed:** Graeme Goodman

Ground: The Stadium, Central Ave, Billingham, Cleveland TS23 1LR   **(T)** 01642 532 348

Capacity: 1,970   **Seats:** 370   **Covered:** 370   **Midweek Matchday:** Wednesday   **Clubhouse:** Yes   **Shop:** Yes

Colours(change): Green & white quarters/white/white
Previous Names: Billingham Synthonia Recreation
Previous Leagues: Teesside 1923-the war
Records: **Att:** 4,200 v Bishop Auckland 1958   **Goalscorer:** Tony Hetherington   **App:** Andy Harbron
Senior Honours: Northern Lge 1956-57, 88-89, 89-90, 95-96. Div.2 86-87.

10 YEAR RECORD

02-03	03-04	04-05	05-06	06-07	07-08	08-09	09-10	10-11	11-12
NL 1 4	NL 1 9	NL 1 2	NL 1 7	NL 1 14	NL 1 9	NL 1 15	NL 1 12	NL 1 12	NL 1 11

BILLINGHAM TOWN
Founded: 1967   Nickname: Billy Town

Secretary: Glenn Youngman   **(T)** 07984 258 608   **(E)** CFS_IFA@hotmail.com

Chairman: Richard Bloomfield   **Manager:**   **Prog Ed:** Peter Martin

Ground: Bedford Terrace, Billingham, Cleveland TS23 4AE   **(T)** 01642 560 043

Capacity: 3,000   **Seats:** 176   **Covered:** 600   **Midweek Matchday:** Tuesday   **Clubhouse:** Yes   **Shop:** No

Colours(change): All blue
Previous Names: Billingham Social Club
Previous Leagues: Stockton & District 1968-74   Teesside 1974-82
Records: **Att:** 1,500 v Man City FA Youth Cup 1985   **Goalscorer:** Paul Rowntree 396   **App:** Paul Rowntree 505
Senior Honours: Durham Cup 1976-77, 77-78, 2003-04.

10 YEAR RECORD

02-03	03-04	04-05	05-06	06-07	07-08	08-09	09-10	10-11	11-12
NL 1 3	NL 1 5	NL 1 7	NL 1 4	NL 1 2	NL 1 10	NL 1 17	NL 1 19	NL 1 15	NL 1 17

BISHOP AUCKLAND

Founded: 1886 **Nickname:**

Secretary: Tony Duffy **(T)** 07974 286 812 **(E)** pauline@paulineduffy.wanadoo.co.uk

Chairman: Terry Jackson **Manager:** **Prog Ed:** David Ellison

Ground: Heritage Park, Bishop Auckland, Co. Durham DL14 9AE **(T)** 01388 604 605

Capacity: **Seats:** **Covered:** **Midweek Matchday:** Wednesday **Clubhouse:** Yes **Shop:** No

Colours(change): Light & dark blue/blue/blue
Previous Names: Auckland Town 1889-1893
Previous Leagues: Northern Alliance 1890-91, Northern League 1893-1988, Northern Premier 1988-2006
Records: **Att:** 17,000 v Coventry City FA Cup 2nd round 1952 **App:** Bob Hardisty
Senior Honours: Post War: Nth Lge 1949-50, 50-51, 51-52, 53-54, 54-55, 55-56, 66-67, 84-85, 85-86 (18th Nth Lge title).

10 YEAR RECORD

02-03		03-04		04-05		05-06		06-07		07-08		08-09		09-10		10-11		11-12	
NP 1	15	NP 1	13	NP P	19	NP 1	22	NL 1	16	NL 1	20	NL 1	18	NL 1	13	NL 1	14	NL 1	8

CELTIC NATION

Founded: 2005 **Nickname:**

Secretary: Michael Linden **(T)** 07717 103 666 **(E)** linden146@btinternet.com

Chairman: Stephen Skinner **Manager:** **Prog Ed:** Brian Hall

Ground: Gillford Park Railway Club, Off Pettrill Bank Rd, Carlisle, Cumbria CA1 3AF **(T)** 07970 461 749

Capacity: **Seats:** Yes **Covered:** Yes **Midweek Matchday:** **Clubhouse:** **Shop:**

Colours(change): Green & white/white/green & white
Previous Names: Gillford Park Spartans > 2005. Gillford Park 2005-12.
Previous Leagues: Northern Alliance 2005-09.
Records:
Senior Honours: Northern Alliance Division 1 2006-07, Premier Division 2008-09, Challenge Cup 2008-09.

10 YEAR RECORD

02-03	03-04	04-05	05-06		06-07		07-08		08-09		09-10		10-11		11-12	
			NAI 2	2	NAI 1	1	NAI P	3	NAI P	2	NL 2	11	NL 2	11	NL 2	2

CONSETT

Founded: 1899 **Nickname:** Steelman

Secretary: David Pyke **(T)** 07889 419 268 **(E)** david_pyke@hotmail .co.uk

Chairman: Frank Bell **Manager:** **Prog Ed:** Gary Welford

Ground: Belle Vue Park, Ashdale Road, Consett, DH8 6LZ **(T)** 01207 503 788

Capacity: 4,000 **Seats:** 400 **Covered:** 1000 **Midweek Matchday:** Wednesday **Clubhouse:** Yes **Shop:** No

Colours(change): All Red
Previous Names: None
Previous Leagues: N.All 1919-26, 35-37, N.E.C. 26-35, 37-58, 62-64, Midland 58-60, N.Co. 60-62, Wearside 64-70
Records: **Att:** 7000 v Sunderland Reserves, first match at Belle Vue 1950
Senior Honours: Norh Eastern Lg 39-40 Div 2 26-27, Northern Counties Lg 61-62, Northern Leageu Div.2 1988-89, 05-06.

10 YEAR RECORD

02-03		03-04		04-05		05-06		06-07		07-08		08-09		09-10		10-11		11-12	
NL 1	20	NL 2	3	NL 1	19	NL 2	1	NL 1	4	NL 1	2	NL 1	2	NL 1	10	NL 1	2	NL 1	15

DARLINGTON 1883

Founded: 1883 **Nickname:** The Quakers

Secretary: Colin Galloway **(T)** 0755 741 6012 **(E)** cgalloway@darlington-fc.net

Chairman: Dennis Pinnegar **Manager:** Martin Gray **Prog Ed:** Kevin Luft

Ground: Bishop Auckland FC, Heritage Park, Bishop Auckland, Co. Durham DL14 9AE **(T)** 01388 604 605

Capacity: **Seats:** **Covered:** **Midweek Matchday:** **Clubhouse:** Yes **Shop:** Yes

Colours(change): White & black hoops/white/white
Previous Names: Darlington FC 1883-2012
Previous Leagues: Northern League 1883-1908, North Eastern 1908-21, Football League 1921-89, 91-2010, Conference 1989-90, 10-12.
Records: **Record Att:** 21,023 v Bolton Wanderers - League Cup 3rd Round 14/11/1960
Senior Honours: Northern League 1895-96, 99-1900. North Eastern League 1912-13, 20-21. Football League Division 3 1924-25, Division 4 1990-91, Division 3 North Cup 1933-34. Durham Senior Cup 1919-20. FA Trophy 2010-11.

10 YEAR RECORD

02-03		03-04		04-05		05-06		06-07		07-08		08-09		09-10		10-11		11-12	
FL 3	14	FL 3	18	FL 2	8	FL 2	8	FL 2	11	FL 2	6	FL 2	12	FL 2	24	Conf	7	Conf	22

DUNSTON UTS

Founded: 1975   Nickname: The Fed

Secretary: Bill Montague   **(T)** 07981 194 756   **(E)** w.montague@sky.com

Chairman: Malcolm James   **Manager:**   **Prog Ed:** Bill Montague

Ground: UTS Stadium, Wellington Rd, Dunston, Gateshead NE11 9LJ   **(T)** 0191 493 2935

Capacity: 2,000 **Seats:** 120 **Covered:** 400 **Midweek Matchday:** Tuesday   **Clubhouse:** Yes **Shop:** No

Colours(change): All Blue with white trim/blue/blue
Previous Names: Dunston Federation Brewery > 2007. Dunston Federation > 2009.
Previous Leagues: Northern Amateur & Wearside league
Records: **Att:** 1,550 v Sunderland Shipowners Cup Final 01.04.88 **Goalscorer:** Paul King **App:** Paul Dixon
Senior Honours: Wearside League 1988-89, 89-90. Northern League Div.2 92-93. Div.1 2003-04, 04-05.

10 YEAR RECORD

02-03		03-04		04-05		05-06		06-07		07-08		08-09		09-10		10-11		11-12	
NL 1	8	NL 1	1	NL 1	1	NL 1	3	NL 1	7	NL 1	6	NL 1	6	NL 1	4	NL 1	7	NL 1	3

DURHAM CITY

Founded: 1949   Nickname: City

Secretary: Kevin Walters   **(T)** 07852 575 593   **(E)** kevin@jeck.co.uk

Chairman: Austin Carney   **Manager:**   **Prog Ed:** Luke Donkin

Ground: The Durham UTS Arena, New Ferens Park, Belmont Ind.Est. DH1 1GG   **(T)** 0191 386 9616

Capacity: 2,700 **Seats:** 270 **Covered:** 750 **Midweek Matchday:**   **Clubhouse:** Yes **Shop:** No

Colours(change): Yellow & blue sleeves/blue/blue & yellow
Previous Names: Original club founded in 1918 disbanded in 1938 and reformed in 1949
Previous Leagues: Victory 1918-19, North Eastern 1919-21, 28-38, Football League 1921-28, Wearside 1938-39, 50-51, Northern 1951-2008. NPL 2008-12.
Records: 2,750 v Whitley Bay - FA Vase Semi-final 2001-02
Senior Honours: Northern League 1994-95, 2007-08. Northern Premier League Division 1 North 2008-09, Chairman's Cup 2008-09.

10 YEAR RECORD

02-03		03-04		04-05		05-06		06-07		07-08		08-09		09-10		10-11		11-12	
NL 1	5	NL 1	2	NL 1	6	NL 1	11	NL 1	8	NL 1	1	NP1N	1	NP P	20	NP1N	17	NP1N	9

GUISBOROUGH TOWN

Founded: 1973   Nickname: Priorymen

Secretary: Keith Smeltzer   **(T)** 07811 850 388   **(E)** keithsmeltzer@hotmail.co.uk

Chairman: Dr. Stephen Hill   **Manager:**   **Prog Ed:** Keith Smeltzer

Ground: King George V Ground, Howlbeck Road, Guisborough TS14 6LE   **(T)** 01287 636 925

Capacity: **Seats:** **Covered:** **Midweek Matchday:**   **Clubhouse:** **Shop:**

Colours(change): Red & white stripes/black/red
Previous Names:
Previous Leagues: Northern Counties East 1982-85.
Records: **Att:** 3,112 v Hungerford FA Vase Semi-final. **Goalscorer:** Mark Davis 341. **Apps:** Mark Davis 587.
Senior Honours: Northern Alliance 1979-80. Northern League Cup 1987-88. Nth Riding Sen Cup 1989-90, 90-91, 91-92, 92-93, 94-95

10 YEAR RECORD

02-03		03-04		04-05		05-06		06-07		07-08		08-09		09-10		10-11		11-12	
NL 1	7	NL 1	14	NL 1	21	NL 1	19	NL 2	9	NL 2	12	NL 2	7	NL 2	5	NL 2	2	NL 1	16

HEBBURN TOWN

Founded: 1912   Nickname: Hornets

Secretary: Tom Derrick   **(T)** 07981 456 653   **(E)** tomderrick39@hotmail.com

Chairman: Bill Laffey   **Manager:**   **Prog Ed:** Richard Bainbridge

Ground: Hebburn Sports & Social, Victoria Rd West, Hebburn, Tyne&Wear NE31 1UN   **(T)** 0191 483 5101

Capacity: **Seats:** Yes **Covered:** Yes **Midweek Matchday:** Tuesday   **Clubhouse:** Yes **Shop:**

Colours(change): Royal blue with white V/royal blue/royal blue
Previous Names: Reyrolles, Hebburn Reyrolles > 1988, Hebburn 1988-2000.
Previous Leagues: Wearside 1960-89.
Records: **Att:** 503 v Darwen FA Cup Prelim replay 07/09/1991, **Win:** 10-1. **Defeat:** 3-10.
Senior Honours: Tyneside League 1938-39, Northern Combination 1943-44, Wearside League 1966-67,

10 YEAR RECORD

02-03		03-04		04-05		05-06		06-07		07-08		08-09		09-10		10-11		11-12	
NL 2	12	NL 2	8	NL 2	18	NL 2	15	NL 2	10	NL 2	15	NL 2	10	NL 2	16	NL 2	10	NL 2	3

MARSKE UNITED

Founded: 1956   Nickname: The Seasiders

Secretary: Les Holtby   **(T)** 07804 150 880   **(E)** admin@marskeunitedfc.com

Chairman: Peter Collins   **Manager:**   **Prog Ed:** Moss Holtby

Ground: GER Stad., Mount Pleasant Avenue, Marske by the Sea, Redcar TS11 7BW   **(T)** 01642 471 091

Capacity: **Seats:**   **Covered:**   **Midweek Matchday:**   **Clubhouse:**   **Shop:**

Colours(change): Yellow/blue/blue
Previous Names: None
Previous Leagues: Wearside 1985-97.
Records: **Defeat:** 3-9. **Goalscorer:** Chris Morgan 169. **Apps:** Mike Kinnair 583.
Senior Honours: Teeside League 1980-81, 84-85. Wearside League 1995-96. North Riding Senior Cup 1994-95.
North Riding County Cup 1980-81, 85-86.

10 YEAR RECORD

02-03		03-04		04-05		05-06		06-07		07-08		08-09		09-10		10-11		11-12	
NL 1	16	NL 1	20	NL 2	15	NL 2	10	NL 2	5	NL 2	8	NL 2	5	NL 2	4	NL 2	3	NL 1	18

NEWCASTLE BENFIELD

Founded: 1988   Nickname: The Lions

Secretary: Mark Hedley   **(T)** 07973 699 506   **(E)** markhedley3@msn.com

Chairman: Jimmy Rowe   **Manager:**   **Prog Ed:** Jim Clark

Ground: Sam Smiths Park, Benfield Road, Walkergate NE6 4NU   **(T)** 0191 265 9357

Capacity: 2,000 **Seats:** 150 **Covered:** 250 **Midweek Matchday:** Wednesday   **Clubhouse:** Yes **Shop:** No

Colours(change): Blue & white hoops/blue/blue
Previous Names: Heaton Corner House. Newcastle Benfield Saints.
Previous Leagues: Northern Alliance 1988-2003
Records:
Senior Honours: Northern Alliance Div 2 Champions 1989-90, Div 1 1994-95, 2002-03.
Northern League Cup 2006-07. Northern League Champions 2008-09.

10 YEAR RECORD

02-03		03-04		04-05		05-06		06-07		07-08		08-09		09-10		10-11		11-12	
NAI P	1	NL 2	2	NL 1	4	NL 1	9	NL 1	5	NL 1	4	NL 1	1	NL 1	5	NL 1	4	NL 1	12

NEWTON AYCLIFFE

Founded: 1965   Nickname: Aycliffe

Secretary: Stephen Cunliffe   **(T)** 07872 985 501   **(E)** stecunliffe@aol.com

Chairman: Gary Farley   **Manager:**   **Prog Ed:** Paul McGeary

Ground: Moore Lane Park, Moore Lane, Newton Aycliffe, Co. Durham DL5 5AG   **(T)** 01325 312 768

Capacity: **Seats:** Yes **Covered:** Yes **Midweek Matchday:**   **Clubhouse:** Yes **Shop:**

Colours(change): All blue
Previous Names: None
Previous Leagues: Wearside 1984-94, 2008-09. Durham Alliance > 2008.
Records: **Att:** 520 v Teeside Athletic (Sunderland Shipowners Final) 2008-09.
Senior Honours: Darlington & District Division 'A' 2004-05. Durham Alliance League 2007-08. Wearside League 2008-09.
Northern League Division Two 2010-11.

10 YEAR RECORD

02-03		03-04		04-05		05-06	06-07	07-08		08-09		09-10		10-11		11-12	
DaD'A'		DaD'A'		DaD'A'	1			DuAl	1	Wear	1	NL 2	9	NL 2	1	NL 1	9

NORTON & STOCKTON ANCIENTS

Founded: 1959   Nickname: Ancients

Secretary: Michael Mulligan   **(T)** 07850 622 544   **(E)** m.mulligan@nasafc.co.uk

Chairman: Michael Mulligan   **Manager:**   **Prog Ed:** Kevin McGrother

Ground: Norton (Teesside) Sports Complex, Station Rd, Norton TS20 1PE   **(T)** 01642 530 203

Capacity: 2,000 **Seats:** 200 **Covered:** yes **Midweek Matchday:** Wednesday   **Clubhouse:** **Shop:**

Colours(change): Amber, gold & black/black, gold & black/black
Previous Names: Norton & Stockton Cricket Club Trust
Previous Leagues: Teesside (pre-1982)
Records: **Att:** 1,430 v Middlesbrough, Friendly1988.
Senior Honours: Northern League Cup 1982-83.

10 YEAR RECORD

02-03		03-04		04-05		05-06		06-07		07-08		08-09		09-10		10-11		11-12	
NL 2	18	NL 2	18	NL 2	6	NL 2	7	NL 2	6	NL 2	10	NL 2	2	NL 1	8	NL 1	10	NL 1	14

PENRITH

Founded: 1894 Nickname: Blues

Secretary: Ian White **(T)** 07960 958 367 **(E)** ianwhite77@hotmail.com
Chairman: Mark Forster **Manager:** **Prog Ed:** Brian Kirkbride
Ground: The Stadium, Frenchfield Park, Frenchfield, Penrith CA11 8UA **(T)** 01768 895 990
Capacity: 4,000 **Seats:** 200 **Covered:** 1,000 **Midweek Matchday:** Tuesday **Clubhouse:** Yes **Shop:** No

Colours(change): Blue/white/blue.
Previous Names: Penrith FC. Penrith Town.
Previous Leagues: Carlisle & Dist. Northern 1942-82. NWC 1982-87, 90-97. NPL 1987-90.
Records: 2,100 v Chester 1981
Senior Honours: Northern League Division 2 Champions 2002-03, 07-08.

10 YEAR RECORD

02-03		03-04		04-05		05-06		06-07		07-08		08-09		09-10		10-11		11-12	
NL 2	1	NL 1	21	NL 2	8	NL 2	4	NL 2	7	NL 2	1	NL 1	7	NL 1	14	NL 1	17	NL 1	19

SHILDON

Founded: 1890 Nickname: Railwaymen

Secretary: Gareth Howe **(T)** 07976 822 453 **(E)** gareth.howe3@btopenworld.com
Chairman: Brian Burn **Manager:** **Prog Ed:** Gareth Howe
Ground: Dean Street, Shildon, Co. Durham DL4 1HA **(T)** 01388 773 877
Capacity: 4,000 **Seats:** 480 **Covered:** 1000 **Midweek Matchday:** Wednesday **Clubhouse:** Yes **Shop:** No

Colours(change): All red
Previous Names: Shildon Athletic > 1923.
Previous Leagues: Auckland & Dist 1892-86, Wear Valley 1896-97, Northern 1903-07, North Eastern 1907-32
Records: **Att:** 11,000 v Ferryhill Athletic, Durham Senior Cup 1922 **Goalscorer:** Jack Downing 61 (1936-7) **App:** Bryan Dale
Senior Honours: Durham Amateur Cup 1901-02, 02-03, Durham Challenge Cup 1907-08, 25-26, 71-72,
Northern League Champions 1933-34, 34-35, 35-36,36-37, 39-40, Div 2 2001-02.

10 YEAR RECORD

02-03		03-04		04-05		05-06		06-07		07-08		08-09		09-10		10-11		11-12	
NL 1	6	NL 1	4	NL 1	11	NL 1	18	NL 1	9	NL 1	5	NL 1	8	NL 1	2	NL 1	5	NL 1	10

SOUTH SHIELDS

Founded: 1974 Nickname: Mariners

Secretary: Philip Reay **(T)** 07847 173 235 **(E)** philip@sheels.fsnet.co.uk
Chairman: Gary Crutwell **Manager:** **Prog Ed:** Philip Reay
Ground: Mariners Club, Filtrona Park, Shaftesbury Ave, Jarrow NE32 3UP **(T)** 0191 427 9839
Capacity: 2,500 **Seats:** 150 **Covered:** 400 **Midweek Matchday:** Tuesday **Clubhouse:** Yes **Shop:** Yes

Colours(change): Claret & blue/white/sky blue
Previous Names: South Shields Mariners.
Previous Leagues: Northern Alliance 1974-76, Wearside 1976-95.
Records: **Att:** 1,500 v Spennymoor, Durham Challenge Cup Final 1994-95.
Senior Honours: Northern Alliance 1974-75, 75-76, Wearside League 1976-77, 92-93, 94-95.
Monkwearmouth Charity Cup 1986-87.

10 YEAR RECORD

02-03		03-04		04-05		05-06		06-07		07-08		08-09		09-10		10-11		11-12	
NL 2	8	NL 2	12	NL 2	13	NL 2	18	NL 2	4	NL 2	2	NL 1	19	NL 1	11	NL 1	11	NL 1	13

SPENNYMOOR TOWN

Founded: 1890 Nickname: Moors

Secretary: David Leitch **(T)** 07530 453 880 **(E)** leitchy1969@btinternet.com
Chairman: Bradley Groves **Manager:** **Prog Ed:** Mike Rowcroft
Ground: Brewery Field, Durham Road, Spennymoor DL16 6JN **(T)**
Capacity: 7,500 **Seats:** 300 **Covered:** 2,000 **Midweek Matchday:** Wednesday **Clubhouse:** Yes **Shop:** Yes

Colours(change): Black & white stripes/white/black
Previous Names: Amalgamation of Evenwood Town & Spennymoor Utd in 2005-06.
Previous Leagues: None
Records:
Senior Honours: Northern League Division Two 2006-07, Division One 2009-10, 2010-11, 2011-12.

10 YEAR RECORD

02-03		03-04		04-05		05-06		06-07		07-08		08-09		09-10		10-11		11-12	
						NL 2	8	NL 2	1	NL 1	12	NL 1	4	NL 1	1	NL 1	1	NL 1	1

SUNDERLAND RYHOPE C.A.
Founded: 1961   Nickname:

Secretary: Rob Jones   **(T)** 07932 951 842   **(E)** Robert-jones10@live.co.uk
Chairman: Graham Defty   **Manager:**   **Prog Ed:** Colin Wilson
Ground: Meadow Park, Beachbrooke, Stockton Rd, Ryhope, Sunderland SR2 0NZ   **(T)** 0191 523 6555
Capacity: 2,000 **Seats:** 150   **Covered:** 200   **Midweek Matchday:** Wednesday   **Clubhouse:**   **Shop:**

Colours(change): Red & white halves/black/red
Previous Names: Ryhope Community Ass. FC
Previous Leagues: S.C. Vaux: Tyne & Wear, NorthEastern Am a Ryhope CA N Alliance.>82
Records: Not Known
Senior Honours: Northern Alliance League Cup 1981.

10 YEAR RECORD

02-03	03-04	04-05	05-06	06-07	07-08	08-09	09-10	10-11	11-12
NL 2 11	NL 2 9	NL 2 16	NL 2 17	NL 2 19	NL 2 4	NL 2 4	NL 2 2	NL 1 13	NL 1 4

TEAM NORTHUMBRIA
Founded: 1999   Nickname:

Secretary: James Hartley   **(T)** 07970 478 723   **(E)** JAMES.HARTLEY@northumbria.ac.uk
Chairman: Colin Stromsoy   **Manager:** 07970 478 723   **Prog Ed:** James Hartley
Ground: Coach Lane, Benton, Newcastle upon Tyne, NE7 7XA   **(T)** 0191 215 6575
Capacity: **Seats:**   **Covered:**   **Midweek Matchday:**   **Clubhouse:**   **Shop:**

Colours(change): All red
Previous Names: Northumbria University > 2003.
Previous Leagues: Northern Alliance 1999-2006.
Records:
Senior Honours: Northern Alliance Premier 2005-06. Northern League Division Two 2011-12.

10 YEAR RECORD

02-03	03-04	04-05	05-06	06-07	07-08	08-09	09-10	10-11	11-12
NAI 1 2	NAI P 2	NAI P 3	NAI P 1	NL 2 11	NL 2 19	NL 2 12	NL 2 14	NL 2 5	NL 2 1

WEST AUCKLAND TOWN
Founded: 1893   Nickname: West

Secretary: Allen Bayles   **(T)** 07894 329 005   **(E)** allenbayles@hotmail.co.uk
Chairman: Jim Palfreyman   **Manager:**   **Prog Ed:** Michael Bainbridge
Ground: Darlington Road, West Auckland, Co. Durham DL14 9HU   **(T)** 07800 796 630
Capacity: 3,000 **Seats:** 250   **Covered:** 250   **Midweek Matchday:** Tuesday   **Clubhouse:** Yes   **Shop:** No

Colours(change): Yellow/black/yellow
Previous Names: Auckland St Helens. St Helens. West Auckland.
Previous Leagues: Auck&D.,Wear Val,Sth D'ham All.Mid D'ham, Nth Lge 1919-20.Palantine 20-24.Sth D'ham 27-28.Gaunless Val 33-34
Records: Att: 6,000 v Dulwich Hamlet FA Amateur Cup 1958-59
Senior Honours: Sir Thomas Lipton Trophy 1909, 1911, Northern League 1959-60, 60-61. Div 2 1990-91. League Cup 1958-59, 62-63, Durham Challenge Cup 1964-65

10 YEAR RECORD

02-03	03-04	04-05	05-06	06-07	07-08	08-09	09-10	10-11	11-12
NL 1 13	NL 1 13	NL 1 17	NL 1 5	NL 1 6	NL 1 16	NL 1 20	NL 1 16	NL 1 6	NL 1 2

WHITLEY BAY
Founded: 1897   Nickname: The Bay

Secretary: Derek Breakwell   **(T)** 07889 888 187   **(E)** dbreakwell@hotmail.co.uk
Chairman: Paul McIlduff   **Manager:**   **Prog Ed:** Julian Tyley
Ground: Hillheads Park, Rink Way, Whitley Bay, NE25 8HR   **(T)** 0191 291 3637
Capacity: 4,500 **Seats:** 450   **Covered:** 650   **Midweek Matchday:** Tuesday   **Clubhouse:** Yes   **Shop:** Yes

Colours(change): Blue & white stripes/blue/blue
Previous Names: Whitley Bay Athletic 1950-58
Previous Leagues: Tyneside 1909-10, Northern All. 1950-55, N. Eastern 1955-58, Northern 1958-88 N.P.L. 1988-00
Records: 7,301 v Hendon, FA Amateur Cup 1965.
Senior Honours: Northern Alliance 1952-53, 53-54. Northern League 1964-65, 65-66, 06-07. NPL Div 1 1990-91, FA Vase 2001-02, 08-09, 09-10, 10-11.

10 YEAR RECORD

02-03	03-04	04-05	05-06	06-07	07-08	08-09	09-10	10-11	11-12
NL 1 10	NL 1 10	NL 1 5	NL 1 10	NL 1 1	NL 1 3	NL 1 3	NL 1 3	NL 1 3	NL 1 6

DIVISION TWO

ALNWICK TOWN
Founded: 1879   Nickname:

Secretary: Cyril Cox   **(T)** 07570 834 789   **(E)** uk2usa@hotmail.com
Chairman: Tommy McKie   **Manager:**   **Prog Ed:** Michael Cook
Ground: St. Jame's Park, Weavers Way, Alnwick, Northumberland NE66 1BG   **(T)** 01665 603 612   **Capacity:**
Colours(change): Black & white stripes/black/black
ADDITIONAL INFORMATION: Previous Names: Alnwick Utd Services 1879-1900, Alnwick Utd Juniors 1900-1936.
Previous Lge: Northern Alliance 1935-82, 2007-11. Northern League 1982-2007.
Honours: Nothern Alliance title 9 times.

BIRTLEY TOWN
Founded: 1993   Nickname: The Hoops

Secretary: Trevor Armstrong   **(T)** 07958 540 389   **(E)** trevellen1@sky.com
Chairman: John Heslington   **Manager:**   **Prog Ed:** Andrew Walker
Ground: Birtley Sports Complex, Durham Road, Birtley DH3 2TB   **(T)** 07958 540 389   **Capacity:**
Colours(change): Green & white hoops/green/green
ADDITIONAL INFORMATION:
Previous League: Wearside 1993-2007.
Honours: Wearside League 2002-03, 06-07, Division 2 1994-95, League Cup 1998, 2002, 2006.

BRANDON UNITED
Founded: 1968   Nickname: United

Secretary: Barry Ross   **(T)** 07717 673 090   **(E)** barryross430@btinternet.com
Chairman: David Bussey   **Manager:**   **Prog Ed:** Dean Johnson
Ground: Welfare Park, Rear Commercial Street, Brandon DH7 8PR   **(T)** 07949 076 218   **Capacity:**
Colours(change): All red
ADDITIONAL INFORMATION: Previous League: Wearside 1981-83. **Record Att:** 2,500 F.A. Sunday Cup Seim-final.
Record: Goalscorer: Tommy Holden. **Apps:** Derek Charlton 1977-86. **Honours:** F.A. Sunday Cup 1975-76.
Northern Alliance Division 2 1977-78, 78-79. Northern League 2002-03, Division 2 1984-85, 99-2000.

CHESTER-LE-STREET TOWN
Founded: 1972   Nickname: Cestrians

Secretary: Lenny Lauchlan   **(T)** 07825 413 237   **(E)** l.w.lauchlan@durham.ac.uk
Chairman: Joe Burlison   **Manager:**   **Prog Ed:** Keith Greener
Ground: Moor Park, Chester Moor, Chester-le-Street, Co.Durham DH2 3RW   **(T)** 07972 419 275   **Capacity:**
Colours(change): Blue & white hoops/white/white with blue trim
ADDITIONAL INFORMATION: Previous Name: Garden Farm 1972-78. **Previous League:** Wearside 1977-83.
Record Att: 893 v Fleetwood FA Vase 1985   **App:** Colin Wake 361.
Honours: Washington League 1975-6 Wearside League1980-81, Northern League Div 2 1983-84, 97-98.

CROOK TOWN
Founded: 1889   Nickname: Black & ambers

Secretary: Ian Todd   **(T)** 07941 459 755   **(E)** iantodd147@gmail.com
Chairman: Kieron Bennett   **Manager:**   **Prog Ed:** Ian Todd
Ground: The Sir Tom Cowie Millfield, West Road, Crook, Co.Durham DL15 9PW   **(T)** 01388 762 959   **Capacity:**
Colours(change): Amber/black/amber
ADDITIONAL INFORMATION: Previous Name: Crook C.W. **Previous League:** Durham Central 1941-45.
Honours: FA Amateur Cup 1900-01, 53-54, 58-59, 61-62, 63-64. Northern League x5, League Cup x3.
Durham Challenge Cup x4. Durham Benefit Bowl x6. Ernest Armstrong Memorial Trophy 1997.

DARLINGTON R.A.
Founded: 1993   Nickname:

Secretary: Alan Hamilton   **(T)** 07872 324 808   **(E)** nobbydarlo@ntlworld.com
Chairman: Doug Hawman   **Manager:**   **Prog Ed:** Alan Hamilton
Ground: Brinkburn Road, Darlington, Co. Durham DL3 9LF   **(T)** 01325 468 125   **Capacity:**
Colours(change): All red
ADDITIONAL INFORMATION:
Previous League: Darlington & District 1993-99.
Honours: Auckland & District League 2000-01. Wearside League 2004-05.

ESH WINNING
Founded: 1885   Nickname: Stags

Secretary: David Thompson OBE   **(T)** 07901 002 468   **(E)** thompsondr@sky.com
Chairman: Charles Ryan   **Manager:**   **Prog Ed:** David Thompson OBE
Ground: West Terrace, Waterhouse, Durham DH7 9NQ   **(T)** 0191 373 3872   **Capacity:** 3,500
Colours(change): Yellow/green/yellow
ADDITIONAL INFORMATION:
Record Att: 5,000 v Newcastle Utd Res. 1910 & Bishop Auckland 1921 **Goalscorer:** Alan Dodsworth 250+ **App:** Neil McLeary - 194.
Honours: Northern League Champions 1912-13.

HORDEN C.W.

Founded: 1908   Nickname: Colliers

Secretary: John Stubbs   **(T)** 07726 694 672   **(E)** johnstubbsuk@btinternet.com
Chairman: Norman Stephens   **Manager:**   **Prog Ed:** John Stubbs
Ground: Welfare Park, Seventh Street, Horden, Peterlee, Co. Durham SR8 4LX   **(T)** 07726 694 672   **Capacity:**
Colours(change): Red/black/black

ADDITIONAL INFORMATION: Previous Name: Horden Athletic. **Previous League:** North Eastern 1962-64.
Record Att: 8,000 FA Cup 1937. **Honours:** Wearside League 1911-12, 12-13, 13-14, 33-34, 64-65, 67-68, 69-70, 70-71, 71-72, 72-73.
Northern League Division 2 2008-09.

JARROW ROOFING BOLDON C.A.

Founded: 1987   Nickname: Roofing

Secretary: Bryn Griffiths   **(T)** 07889 279 647   **(E)** bgriffiths94@btinternet.com
Chairman: Richard McLoughlin   **Manager:**   **Prog Ed:** Ashley Scott
Ground: Boldon CA Sports Ground, New Road, Boldon Colliery NE35 9DZ   **(T)** 07930 803 387   **Capacity:** 3,500
Colours(change): All blue and yellow

ADDITIONAL INFORMATION: Att: 500 v South Shields **Goalscorer:** Mick Hales **App:** Paul Chow

MORPETH TOWN

Founded: 1909   Nickname: Highwaymen

Secretary: David McMeekan   **(T)** 07425 135 301   **(E)** drmcmeekan@yahoo.co.uk
Chairman: Jim Smith   **Manager:**   **Prog Ed:** David McMeekan
Ground: Craik Park, Morpeth Common, Morpeth, Northumberland, NE61 2YX   **(T)** 07425 135 301   **Capacity:**
Colours(change): Amber & black/black/black

ADDITIONAL INFORMATION:
Previous League: Northern Alliance > 1994.
Honours: Northern Alliance 1983-84, 93-94, Northern League Division 2 1995-96. Northumberland Senior Cup 2006-07.

NORTH SHIELDS

Founded: 1992   Nickname: Robins

Secretary: Kevin Larkham   **(T)** 07976 569 006   **(E)** kevin7691@live.com
Chairman: Alan Matthews   **Manager:**   **Prog Ed:** Mark Scott
Ground: Daren Persson Staduim, Ralph Gardner Park, West Percy Rd, Chirton, North Shields **(T)** 07759 766 732   **Capacity:**
Colours(change): All red

ADDITIONAL INFORMATION:
Previous Names: Preston Colliery > 1928, North Shields Athletic 1995-99. **Previous League:** Wearside.
Honours: FA Amateur Cup 1968-69, N.C.E. Prem Div 91-92, Lge Cup 90-91. Wearside League 1998-99, 01-02, 03-04.

NORTHALLERTON TOWN

Founded: 1994   Nickname: Town

Secretary: Lesley Clark   **(T)** 07891 595 267   **(E)** lesleyclark05@yahoo.co.uk
Chairman: Les Hood   **Manager:**   **Prog Ed:** Ricky Butler
Ground: RGPS Stadium, Ainderby Road, Northallerton DL7 8HA   **(T)** 01609 778 337   **Capacity:**
Colours(change): Black & white stripes/black/black

ADDITIONAL INFORMATION: Previous Name: Northallerton FC 1994. **Previous League:** Harrogate & District.
Record Att: 695 v Farnborough Town FA Trophy 3rd Round 20/02/1993.
Honours: Northern League Division 2 1996-97, League Cup 1993-94.

RYHOPE COLLIERY WELFARE

Founded: Nickname:

Secretary: Dougie Benison   **(T)** 07515 066 344   **(E)** dougie.benison@btinternet.com
Chairman: Ronnie Crosby   **Manager:**   **Prog Ed:** Ronnie Crosby
Ground: Ryhope Recreation Park, Ryhope Street, Ryhope, Sunderland SR2 0AS   **(T)**   **Capacity:**
Colours(change): Red & white stripes/black/red

ADDITIONAL INFORMATION:
Previous League: Wearside > 2012.
Honours: Wearside League 2010-11, 11-12.

RYTON & CRAWCROOK ALBION

Founded: 1970   Nickname:

Secretary: Ken Rodger   **(T)** 07872 839 368   **(E)** kenneth@krodger.fsnet.co.uk
Chairman: Richard Hands   **Manager:**   **Prog Ed:** Chris Holt
Ground: Kingsley Park, Stannerford Road, Crawcrook NE40 3SN   **(T)** 0191 413 4448   **Capacity:** 2,000
Colours(change): Blue & black stripes/black/blue

ADDITIONAL INFORMATION: Att: 1,100 v Newcastle United 1998
Northern Alliance Division 1 Champions 1996-97.

SEAHAM RED STAR
Founded: 1973   Nickname: The Star

Secretary: Kevin Turns   **(T)** 0770 107 6848   **(E)** seahamredstarfc@aol.co.uk
Chairman: John McBeth   **Manager:**   **Prog Ed:** Sue Potts
Ground: Seaham Town Park, Stockton Road, Seaham. Co.Durham SR7 0HY   **(T)**   **Capacity:**
Colours(change): Red & white stripes/red/red

ADDITIONAL INFORMATION: Previous Name: Seaham Colliery Welfare Red Star 1978-87. **Previous League:** Wearside 1979-83.
Record Att: 1,500 v Guisborough. **App:** Michael Whitfield.
Honours: Durham Challenge Cup 1979-80, Wearside League & League Cup 1981-82, Norhtern League Cup 1992-93.

STOKESLEY SPORTS CLUB
Founded: 1920   Nickname:

Secretary: Peter Grainge   **(T)** 07712 883 874   **(E)** peterssc@hotmail.co.uk
Chairman: Robert Robertson   **Manager:**   **Prog Ed:** Tim Allison
Ground: Stokesley Sports Club, Broughton Road, Stokesley TS9 5JQ   **(T)** 01642 710 051   **Capacity:**
Colours(change): Black & red/black/black

ADDITIONAL INFORMATION:
Stokesley & District League 1975-76. Northern League Division Two 2009-10.

THORNABY
Founded: 1980   Nickname:

Secretary: Trevor Wing   **(T)** 07860 780 446   **(E)** trevor.wing10@btinternet.com
Chairman: Laurence Lyons   **Manager:**   **Prog Ed:** Trevor Wing
Ground: Teesdale Park, Acklam Road, Thornaby, Stockton on Tees TS17 7JU   **(T)** 01642 672 896   **Capacity:**
Colours(change): All blue

ADDITIONAL INFORMATION: Previous Names: Stockton Cricket Club 1965-1980, Stockton 1980-99 and Thornaby-on-Tees 1999-2000
Previous League: Wearside 1981-85. **Records Att:** 3,000 v Middlesborough friendly Aug 1986   **App:** Michael Watson
Honours: North Riding County Cup, 1985-86, Northern Lge Div 2 1987-88, 91-92

TOW LAW TOWN
Founded: 1890   Nickname: Lawyers

Secretary: Steve Moralee   **(T)** 07810 238 731   **(E)** stephen.moralee@btinternet.com
Chairman: Sandra Gordon   **Manager:**   **Prog Ed:** John Dixon
Ground: Ironworks Ground, Tow Law, Bishop Auckland DL13 4EQ   **(T)** 01388 730 443   **Capacity:** 6,000
Colours(change): Black & white stripes/black/black

ADDITIONAL INFORMATION: 5,500 v Mansfield Town FA Cup 1967.
Northern League Champions 1923-24, 24-25, 94-95. League Cup 73-74.

WASHINGTON
Founded: 1949   Nickname: Mechanics

Secretary: Barry Spendley   **(T)** 07810 536 964   **(E)** Derek.Armstrong1@ntlworld.com
Chairman: Derek Armstrong   **Manager:**   **Prog Ed:** Bob Goodwin
Ground: Nissan Sports Complex, Washington Road Sunderland SR5 3NS   **(T)** 07810 530 964   **Capacity:**
Colours(change): All red

ADDITIONAL INFORMATION:
Previous Names: Washington Mechanics, Washington Ikeda Hoover. **Previous League:** Wearside.
Record Att: 3,800 v Bradford Park Avenue FA Cup 1970.
Honours: Washington Amateur: 1956-57,57-58, 58-59,59-60,61-62,62-63, League Cup: 1955-56, 58-59, 60-61, 64-65.

WEST ALLOTMENT CELTIC
Founded: 1928   Nickname:

Secretary: Ted Ilderton   **(T)** 07795 246 245   **(E)** tedilderton@o2.co.uk
Chairman: Roland Mather   **Manager:**   **Prog Ed:** Andrew Cook
Ground: Whitley Park, Whitley Road, Benton NE12 9FA   **(T)** 0191 270 0885   **Capacity:**
Colours(change): Green & white hoops/green/green & white.

ADDITIONAL INFORMATION: Att: 510 v Cray Wanderers FA Vase 2004
Northern Am. 1956-57, 57-58, 58-59, 59-60, 81-82, 82-83, Div 2: 38-39.
Northern Alliance: 1986-87, 90-91, 91-92, 97-98, 98-99, 99-2000, 01-02, 03-04. Northern League Div 2 2004-05

WHICKHAM
Founded: 1944   Nickname:

Secretary: Les Dixon   **(T)** 07974 308 162   **(E)** Whickhamfcsecretary@hotmail.co.uk
Chairman: Brian McCartney   **Manager:**   **Prog Ed:** Mick Tucker
Ground: Glebe Sports Club, Rectory Lane, Whickham NE16 4NA   **(T)** 0191 4200 186   **Capacity:**
Colours(change): Black & white stripes/black/black

ADDITIONAL INFORMATION: Record Att: 3,165 v Windsor & Eton FA Vase SF 1981.
Honours: FA Vase 1980-81, Wearside Lge 77-78, 87-88, Sunderland Shipowners Cup 77-78, 80-81,
Northern Comb 69-70, 72-73, 73-74 Lge Cup 60-61, 73-74

WHITEHAVEN

Founded: 1994   **Nickname:**

Secretary: David Rushforth   **(T)** 07876 612 277   **(E)** secretary@whitehavenafc.co.uk
Chairman: S Hocking   **Manager:**   **Prog Ed:** D J Moors
Ground: Focus Scaffolding Sports Complex, Coach Road, Whitehaven, CA28 9DB   **(T)** 01946 692 211   **Capacity:**
Colours(change): Yellow/blue/yellow

ADDITIONAL INFORMATION: Record Att: 207 v Workington Reds, Cumberland County Cup 13/12/2007.
Honours: Wearside League Division 2 1994-95, Wearside League 2005-06. Monkwearmouth Charity Cup 2006-07.

GROUND DIRECTIONS

ALNWICK TOWN - M1, at exit 32, take slip road left for M18 toward The North / Doncaster / Hull, at exit 2, take slip road left for A1(M) toward the North, keep straight onto A1 / Doncaster by Pass, keep straight onto A1(M), take slip road for A1(M) / Aberford by Pass, road name changes to A1 / Leeming Lane, keep straight onto A1(M), keep left onto A1, take slip road left for A1068 toward Alnwick / Alnmouth, at roundabout, take 1st exit onto Willowburn Avenue, turn left, and then immediately turn left onto St James Estate, ground is on the right.

ASHINGTON - Leave the A1 at the junction with the A19 north of Newcastle. Go along the A19 eastwards untio the next roundabout . Here take the second left (A189) signposted to Bedlington and Ashington. Continue along A189 until reach Woodhorn roundabout, turn left onto A197. Turn left at first roundabout. Just before the hospital car park entrance, turn right. Ground is on left.

BEDLINGTON TERRIERS - Take the A1068 from the south, and when in the town turn right onto the A193. Turn left at the Northumberland Arms on Front Street in Bedlington town centre. Continue along this road for approx .5 mile, then turn right into Park Road. The ground is 100 yards on right.

BILLINGHAM SYNTHONIA - Leave A19 onto A1027 sign posted towards Billingham. Continue straight ahead over a couple of roundabouts, and you will be on Central Avenue. The ground is on left opposite an empty office block.

BILLINGHAM TOWN - Leave A19 on A1027 signed Billingham. Turn left at third roundabout, into Cowpen Lane. Go over a railway bridge, then first left into Warwick Crescent, then first left again into Bedford Terrace (follow one-way signs) to the ground.

BIRTLEY TOWN - Leave A1(M) at Angel of the North and follow signs to Birtley (A167). Continue along main road through town. Go past Komatsu factory on right and then after approx 200 yards turn right into an unmarked side road. Ground is directly in front of you.

BISHOP AUCKLAND - NORTH: From junction 60 of the A1 follow the A689 to Bishop Auckland. Go straight across the next 2 roundabouts. At the 3rd roundabout turn left onto the A688 and straight across the next 2 roundabouts. At the following roundabout turn left at Aldi and then go straight across at the next roundabout. The stadium is 200 yards on your right. **SOUTH:** From junction 58 from the A1, take the A68 towards Bishop Auckland. At the West Auckland by-pass, turn right at the roundabout. Go straight across at the next roundabout and the stadium is located 500 yards on your left.

BRANDON UNITED - Leave A1 on A690, go through Durham and continue on A690. Once at 'Langley Moor' (you go under a railway bridge), turn right at the "Lord Boyne" pub. After 100 yards take the next left. Go up the road for approx half a mile, and turn right at the newsagents. Take the next left, and Brandon's ground is up a small track.

CELTIC NATION - Take junction 42 off the M6 and then the A6 into Carlisle. After 1.75 miles take left turn into Petterill Bank Road (junction is at traffic lights). After half a mile turn right onto track immediately before railway bridge. This leads you to the ground.

CHESTER LE STREET - Leave A1M at junction 63 and take the A167 towards Chester Le Street and Durtham. Keep going along this road for a couple of miles. You will go under a railway bridge, and as the road begins to climb, you will see the Chester Moor pub on your left. Turn into the pub and the ground is accessed along a track at the rear of the pub car park.

CONSETT - Take the A692 from the east into Consett. On the edge of the town, the A692 takes a left at a roundabout. Continue along the A692 for approx 100 yards, before turning right into Leadgate Road. Go along here for approx .25 mile, and turn right into Ashdale Road. There is a road sign for the Leisure Centre pointing into Ashdale Road. The ground is approx 200 yards along Ashdale Road on your right.

CROOK TOWN - Leave the A1 at Junction 62, and take the A690 towards Durham. Keep on this road through Durham, Meadowfield, Willington and Helmington Row. When you arrive in Crook town centre keep going straight ahead, as the A690 becomes the A689. The ground is situated on this road on your right, approximately 300 yards from the town centre.

DARLINGTON 1883 - SEE BISHOP AUCKLAND ABOVE

DARLINGTON RAILWAY ATHLETIC - Leave A1(M) at junction 58 and follow the A68 into Darlington. Continue along the road until you see the Brown Trout public house on your right. Turn left at this point into Brinkburn Road, and the ground is 100 yards along on the left.

DUNSTON U.T.S. - From south take Dunston/Whickham exit off A1M. Turn right at top of slip road into Dunston Road and head down the bank. As the road veers left, the road becomes Wellington Road, and the ground is situated on your left.

DURHAM CITY - Leave the A1M at J62 (signed Durham City) At the top of the slip road turn left. After about 1/2 mile bear left (signed Belmont + Dragonville). At the top of the slip road turn left.
At traffic lights turn left then take the 2nd left, the stadium is on your right.

ESH WINNING - Leave the A1 at Junction 62, and take the A690 towards Durham. Keep on this road through Durham. Once you start to head down a bank on the A690, you will come to a roundabout. Take the right turn onto the B6302, which will be signposted towards Ushaw Moor. Keep on this road though Ushaw Moor (there is a staggered crossroads to negotiate), and carry on the B6302 into Esh Winning. Keep on going as the ground is not in Esh Winning, but the next village along, Waterhouses. When the road takes a sharp left you will see a track continuing straight ahead. The ground is along this track.

GUISBOROUGH TOWN - Turn off the A19 into the A174, then come off at the second junction, turning right onto the A172. Follow this round until roundabout with A1043, take left exit to join the A1043. Take right at next roundabout to join the A171. At second roundabout turn right into Middlesbrough Road (will be signposted towards Guisborough) then take left turning at traffic lights into Park Lane. Take first left into Howlbeck Road, and the ground is at the end of the road.

HEBBURN TOWN - Leave A1M on A194(M) (junction 65) and follow signs for Tyne Tunnel. Continue until fourth roundabout and turn left on to B1306 (Hebburn, Mill Lane). Right at traffic lights into Victoria Road. Ground 200 yards long this road on the left.

HORDEN C.W. - Take A19 to Peterlee turn off (B1320). Follow main road into Peterlee then through on the same road, following signs to Horden (B1320). At T-junction, turn left into Sunderland Road, at lights, (A1086) and then right into South Terrace. Ground is at bottom of South Terrace.

JARROW ROOFING - From south take A19 and follow signs for Tyne Tunnel. Turn right at junction marked Boldon Colliery (Testo Roundabout) on to the A184. Turn left at the next r'about, into the B1293, and head towards Asda. At second r'about, turn right at end of retail park. At the r'about at the entrance to Asda, take the "10 to" exit, and you will pass a large brick building on you right, known as The Shack. Turn right into the car park after this building, and at the far end of the car park there is a small lane that leads off left. Roofers ground is at the end of this track.

MARSKE UNITED - Leave A19 and join Parkway (A174) to Marske until Quarry Lane r'about. Take exit (A1085) into Marske. Take the next right after you pass under a railway, into Meadow Rd. Take the next left into Southfield Rd and the entrance is on your left shortly before a T-junc.

MORPETH TOWN - From south. Turn off the A1 onto A197, sign posted Morpeth. Turn left at sign pointing Belsay (B6524). Take right turn just before bridge under the A1. Ground is signposted and up a small track on the right.

NEWCASTLE BENFIELD - Take the A1058 from either the Tyne Tunnel or central Newcastle. Turn off this road at the junction with Benfield Road. Turn south at this junction, and the Crosslings building will be on your left. Ground is around 400 metres on left, by taking the first turning after passing railway bridge. The ground is 100 yards along this road.

NEWTON AYCLIFFE - From North, leave the A1 at junction 60, and travel west along the A689 towards Bishop Auckland. At the roundabout, turn left to join A167. Travel along here for a couple of miles, and at first traffic lights and turn right onto B6443 (Central Avenue). At first roundabout (Tesco's) turn left into Shafto Way then 3rd left into Moore Lane.

NORTHALLERTON TOWN - Leave A1 at Leeming Bar (A684) and follow signs to Northallerton. Approaching the town take the left turn B1333, signed Romanby. Ground is on left after 50 yards in Romanby.

NORTH SHIELDS - Continue north on the A19 after Tyne Tunnel. Take right exit at roundabout onto the A1058. At next roundabout take third exit at Billy Mill, signed to North Shields. At roundabout with A193, turn right, then take second left into Silkey's Lane. Ground is 100 yards on left.

NORTON & STOCKTON ANCIENTS - Leave A19 at Stockton/Norton turn off (A1027) and follow signs to Norton. At the roundabout at the top of the bank take a right turn onto the B1274. Take the next right into Station Road. Ground entrance is on left of road in a large sports complex, the entrance to which is just before the railway crossing. The ground a 200 yards along this track.

PENRITH - Turn off M6 at junction 40 then onto dual carriageway to Appleby and Scotch Corner. Take the A686 (signposted Alston), for approximately half a mile. Then take a right turn (opposite Carleton Road), and follow the track running parallel with the A66. Turn left into the sports complex and follow the road to the far end.

RYHOPE COLLIERY WELFARE - Ryhope Recreation Park, Ryhope Street, Ryhope, Sunderland SR2 0AS

RYTON & CRAWCROOK ALBION - Leave the A1 at the south side of the River Tyne (A694). At the roundabout take the A695 (sign posted Blaydon). At Blaydon take the B6317 through Ryton to reach Crawcrook. Turn right at the traffic lights (sign posted Ryton/Clara Vale). Kingsley Park is situated approximately 500 meters on the right.

SEAHAM RED STAR - Leave A19 on B1404 slip road. Follow signs to Seaham/Ryhope. Turn right at traffic lights on to the B1285. Then left at Red Star social club approximately 200 yards after the traffic lights. There is a car park at the next roundabout behind their social club The ground is a short walk at the top of the park.

SHILDON - Leave A1M at junction 58. Follow A68 signed Bishop Auckland, turn right at roundabout onto A6072. At Shildon turn right at second roundabout (onto B6282) , then left into Byerley Rd (still the B6282). Right at Timothy Hackworth pub into Main St., then at the top of the bank, left into Dean Street.

SOUTH SHIELDS - From A1 M take A194 (M) to South Shields. Follow signs for town centre. Turn left at traffic lights (TESCO supermarket) into Shaftesbury Avenue. Ground is at the far end of the road

SPENNYMOOR TOWN - Turn off A1M at J61. Onto A688 towards Spennymoor, turn right at small roundabout & straight on at Thinford roundabout (Still continuing on the A688). Straight over mini roundabout, and take fourth exit from large roundabout (B6288). Continue for approx. 2 mile and take left into Durham Road. Ground is on Wood Vue, approx 300 yards on right just off Durham Rd.

STOKESLEY SPORTS CLUB - Turn off A19 onto A174 (Teesport/Redcar). Take third exit onto A172 (Whitby/Stokesley). Turn right and keep on A172 to Stokesley. In Stokesley bear left at first roundabout, still keeping on the A172. At next roundabout go straight across into Broughton Road (Second exit - B1257). Ground is 100 yards on left-hand side.

SUNDERLAND R.C.A. - From the A19, leave at the junction with the A690, but on that roundabout take the B1286 through Doxford Park. Continue along this road for some time (there are number of roundabouts), but there are signposts to Ryhope along this road. You will eventually come to a T-junction at the end of the B1286, and turn right onto the A1018. After 200 yards you will come to another roundabout, here take a right turn. Then take the next right into a new housing estate. There is a board at the entrance pointing you to Meadow Park, the home of R.C.A. The ground is at the far end of the estate.

TEAM NORTHUMBRIA - Take the A1058 from either the A19 or central Newcastle. Turn off this road at the junction with Benfield Road. Turn north at large Crosslings warehouse into Red Hall Drive, this then becomes Coach Lane. The ground is on the right just past Newcastle University halls of residence.

THORNABY - Turn off A19 onto A1130 and head towards Thornaby. Continue along Acklam Road for about half a mile. Ground is signposted from the main road - on the right up a track between houses after half a mile.

TOW LAW TOWN - Leave the A1 at junction 58 and turn on to A68. Follow signs for Tow Law/Corbridge. Ground is at far end of Tow Law on the left side. The ground is situated on Ironworks Road, which is the first left after a sharp left hand bend on the A68 in Tow Law.

WASHINGTON - Leave the A19 on slip road marked "Nissan Offices" as you pass Sunderland travelling north. This is the A1290. Continue to follow "Nissan Offices" signs. Left at traffic lights, then right at roundabout into complex. Ground is at far end of the plant.

WEST ALLOTMENT CELTIC - Continue on the A19 north after Tyne Tunnel until A191 exit. Take left exit marked Gosforth & Newcastle. A191 for three miles. The ground, The Blue Flames Sports Ground is on left.

WEST AUCKLAND TOWN - Leave A1 at junction 58 on to the A68. Follow signs to W. Auckland/Corbridge. On entering village, ground is behind factory on left side. Ground is up a track on the left side of road next to Oakley Grange Farm.

WHICKHAM - From A1M take the A692 junction, and travel in the direction signed to Consett. At top of the back the road forks left towards Consett, but you should take the right fork along the B6317 to Whickham. Follow this road for 1.5 miles, left turn into Rectory Lane (B6316). Take first right into Holme Avenue, and then first left. The ground is at top of lane. More car parking can be found further along Rectory Lane, take the next right. Walk past the cricket pitch to access the football club.

WHITEHAVEN - From the south, on A595, take the turning into Whitehaven at the top of Inkermann Terrace at traffic lights (A5094). Pass the Chase Hotel on left until reach set of traffic lights next to a garage. Turn left into Coach Lane and travel on until see an access to the left indicating a cycleway. Turn in and follow the path until meet the gates to the ground. From the north, it is easier to travel further down the A595, and follow instructions as above. This way you avoid the town centre.

WHITLEY BAY - Leave the A19 on the A191, and turn eastwards towards Whitely Bay. Continue along New York Road (A191) which then becomes Rake Lane (A191). Pass hospital on right & then into Shields Rd. and Hillheads Rd (both A191). Ground is to the right, floodlights can be seen from miles away! It is next to an ice rink.

SOUTH WEST PENINSULA LEAGUE

Sponsored by: Carlsberg

Founded: 2007

Recent Champions:

2008: Bodmin Town. 2009: Bodmin Town

2010: Buckland Athletic. 2011: Buckland Athletic

swpleague.co.uk

PREMIER DIVISION	P	W	D	L	F	A	Pts
1 Bodmin Town	38	36	0	2	145	34	108
2 (P) Buckland Athletic	38	28	5	5	123	56	89
3 Falmouth Town	38	24	6	8	122	58	78
4 Saltash United	38	24	5	9	113	59	77
5 Launceston	38	22	6	10	78	47	72
6 Plymouth Parkway	38	22	4	12	94	53	70
7 Liskeard Athletic	38	21	5	12	74	57	68
8 AFC St Austell	38	19	5	14	79	64	62
9 Camelford	38	18	3	17	63	64	57
10 Tavistock	38	15	8	15	79	75	53
11 Elburton Villa	38	16	5	17	66	71	53
12 Torpoint Athletic	38	16	3	19	49	74	51
13 Witheridge	38	15	4	19	59	69	49
14 Dartmouth (+2)	38	13	7	18	57	73	48
15 Cullompton Rangers	38	11	6	21	65	79	39
16 Bovey Tracey	38	10	7	21	47	86	37
17 Penzance	38	8	3	27	40	110	27
18 St Blazey	38	8	2	28	41	100	26
19 Ivybridge Town	38	7	4	27	53	118	25
20 Royal Marines (-2)	38	2	2	34	26	126	6

THROGMORTON CUP

2008
WINNERS : BODMIN TOWN
FINALISTS : TAVISTOCK

2009
WINNERS : BODMIN TOWN
FINALISTS : IVYBRIDGE TOWN

2010
WINNERS : BUCKLAND ATHLETIC
FINALISTS : BODMIN TOWN

2011
WINNERS : PLYMOUTH PARKWAY
FINALISTS : ST BLAZEY

2012
WINNERS : BODMIN TOWN
FINALISTS : BUCKLAND ATHLETIC

PREMIER DIVISION	1	2	3	4	5	6	7	8	9	10	11	12	13	14	15	16	17	18	19	20
1 AFC St Austell		1-4	4-0	1-3	2-0	1-0	3-0	1-0	0-2	3-1	0-0	2-0	5-0	4-1	6-1	1-0	1-2	2-6	0-5	2-3
2 Bodmin Town	4-1		2-0	7-0	4-1	4-1	1-0	5-0	1-0	5-1	3-1	3-1	1-0	3-0	7-1	4-1	6-1	5-0	5-0	4-1
3 Bovey Tracey	4-4	0-3		0-6	0-3	0-0	2-3	0-1	0-8	1-2	2-1	1-4	1-0	1-3	1-0	0-3	3-3	0-0	0-2	1-2
4 Buckland Athletic	2-0	2-5	2-2		4-0	3-1	1-1	3-2	3-2	7-1	3-0	6-0	3-1	5-3	3-0	3-3	2-1	5-0	2-0	2-0
5 Camelford	1-0	1-5	2-0	0-3		3-0	3-1	1-0	2-3	4-2	1-1	3-0	2-3	4-1	1-4	0-1	2-0	2-1	0-2	1-3
6 Cullompton Rangers	1-2	1-4	3-6	1-1	1-3		1-2	1-2	0-0	2-3	0-4	3-1	8-0	1-2	2-1	3-3	1-0	3-3	0-1	0-1
7 Dartmouth	3-2	0-4	2-1	2-4	1-2	1-2		1-4	4-1	1-2	0-1	1-1	0-0	0-3	4-0	2-6	3-2	2-1	1-2	1-1
8 Elburton Villa	1-4	2-3	0-3	4-0	3-4	1-2	0-3		3-1	3-0	5-4	2-4	3-0	2-1	3-2	1-4	3-3	2-2	2-1	1-0
9 Falmouth Town	2-2	1-5	2-2	3-3	2-1	4-1	6-2	1-1		5-0	4-3	4-2	9-2	2-1	7-0	0-2	5-0	2-1	3-0	4-0
10 Ivybridge Town	2-3	3-4	2-6	2-6	1-1	0-6	0-0	2-1	3-7		2-3	1-2	9-2	0-3	1-0	1-3	3-4	2-6	1-2	0-3
11 Launceston	3-0	2-1	3-0	1-3	2-1	3-1	2-0	1-1	0-2	4-0		0-0	3-1	1-3	1-0	2-2	3-1	1-0	2-2	2-1
12 Liskeard Athletic	2-0	1-3	1-2	3-2	1-0	3-2	2-1	3-0	0-0	3-1	1-3		3-0	3-0	6-0	0-4	4-0	1-1	2-1	2-1
13 Penzance	0-5	0-6	6-0	1-4	0-2	4-2	4-0	0-0	0-4	1-0	1-2	0-6		0-2	0-0	0-7	1-3	1-0	1-2	0-1
14 Plymouth Parkway	5-2	1-2	0-1	0-2	1-1	2-2	1-1	5-0	3-0	1-1	2-1	3-0	4-1		6-0	4-5	4-0	1-0	1-2	2-1
15 Royal Marines	1-4	0-4	0-3	1-8	0-3	2-4	0-1	0-3	0-5	1-2	0-6	2-3	0-2	0-1		0-3	2-1	2-5	0-5	0-0
16 Saltash United	2-3	2-3	4-0	1-5	3-2	2-4	2-2	2-0	2-0	7-1	1-4	3-1	2-1	3-4	3-2		4-0	1-1	7-1	3-0
17 St Blazey	2-5	0-4	1-0	1-3	3-2	1-2	0-3	0-1	1-8	2-0	0-2	1-2	0-2	0-4	3-2	0-1		0-4	2-1	0-2
18 Tavistock	0-0	4-3	1-2	2-3	5-0	4-1	2-4	2-1	2-3	1-1	2-1	1-1	4-3	2-6	3-1	0-5	2-1		4-1	3-2
19 Torpoint Athletic	1-1	1-3	1-0	0-4	1-2	1-0	1-3	1-5	3-5	1-0	0-2	0-3	2-0	0-5	1-0	1-5	1-0	1-2		1-1
20 Witheridge	0-2	0-4	2-2	4-2	0-2	1-2	3-1	1-3	3-5	4-0	1-3	0-2	5-2	0-5	5-1	3-1	2-1	2-1	0-1	

DIVISION ONE	P	W	D	L	F	A	Pts
1 (P) Liverton United	32	26	2	4	99	30	80
2 Stoke Gabriel	32	22	5	5	109	57	71
3 Galmpton United	32	20	5	7	83	53	65
4 Crediton United	32	19	4	9	81	58	61
5 Exmouth Town	32	18	5	9	77	40	59
6 Alphington	32	18	4	10	73	53	58
7 Teignmouth	32	16	6	10	81	60	54
8 Okehampton Argyle	32	13	10	9	62	55	49
9 Newton Abbot Spurs	32	13	8	11	67	63	47
10 Totnes & Dartington SC	32	13	5	14	67	68	44
11 Budleigh Salterton	32	11	7	14	56	75	40
12 Appledore	32	11	3	18	48	53	36
13 Exeter Civil Service	32	10	6	16	46	63	36
14 Sidmouth Town	32	11	1	20	47	75	34
15 University of Exeter	32	7	8	17	54	71	29
16 Axminster Town	32	2	1	29	33	124	7
17 Ottery St Mary	32	1	2	29	28	113	5

DIVISION ONE WEST	P	W	D	L	F	A	Pts
1 (P) Newquay	32	28	3	1	127	33	87
2 Helston Athletic	32	22	7	3	89	39	73
3 Penryn Athletic	32	22	4	6	94	34	70
4 Godolphin Atlantic	32	18	8	6	64	29	62
5 Vospers Oak Villa	32	17	10	5	90	37	61
6 Callington Town	32	17	3	12	66	54	54
7 Truro City Reserves	32	15	6	11	70	54	51
8 Plymstock United (+2)	32	13	4	15	56	59	45
9 St Dennis	32	12	6	14	65	66	42
10 Dobwalls	32	13	3	16	64	66	42
11 Wadebridge Town	32	11	8	13	71	61	41
12 Porthleven	32	13	2	17	55	82	41
13 Hayle	32	10	6	16	55	64	36
14 Foxhole Stars	32	8	7	17	50	75	31
15 Holsworthy	32	8	2	22	46	58	26
16 Perranporth (-2)	32	2	3	27	19	149	7
17 Mousehole	32	2	0	30	26	147	6

DIVISION ONE EAST	1	2	3	4	5	6	7	8	9	10	11	12	13	14	15	16	17
1 Alphington		5-2	4-1	5-2	1-3	1-1	0-4	3-2	0-1	1-2	2-3	3-0	1-2	1-0	4-1	2-1	3-0
2 Appledore	1-1		2-1	0-3	1-3	1-1	0-1	0-3	0-1	0-1	1-0	2-1	1-2	2-3	2-3	5-0	2-1
3 Axminster Town	2-4	0-3		1-2	0-8	0-3	0-5	0-4	1-4	0-6	1-5	2-4	1-4	0-2	4-2	1-5	1-2
4 Budleigh Salterton	1-1	2-1	5-2		1-2	5-2	0-5	2-4	1-4	1-0	0-3	4-1	2-1	2-4	1-0	1-1	3-2
5 Crediton United	2-6	1-4	7-0	3-1		2-1	2-1	3-5	4-7	4-0	2-2	4-2	2-1	1-2	3-3	2-1	1-1
6 Exeter Civil Service	1-2	1-0	3-1	1-1	0-1		0-2	1-2	1-4	1-1	2-2	1-0	3-1	1-4	1-5	1-2	2-1
7 Exmouth Town	1-2	3-1	5-0	2-2	0-3	2-0		3-1	0-1	2-4	4-1	4-0	2-1	2-1	1-3	2-4	1-1
8 Galmpton United	0-2	2-0	5-1	3-2	3-1	2-3	1-0		2-1	2-2	4-2	8-3	3-1	1-3	3-3	3-2	3-1
9 Liverton United	2-1	2-0	4-0	5-0	4-1	3-0	2-0	2-0		4-0	1-0	5-0	7-0	5-1	2-2	3-3	3-1
10 Newton Abbot Spurs	3-2	2-1	2-2	2-2	1-2	2-2	2-6	2-2	1-3		5-2	1-0	3-1	1-6	0-1	3-3	1-1
11 Okehampton Argyle	1-2	2-2	2-0	1-1	1-1	2-1	1-1	1-2	0-4	2-1		5-0	3-2	1-0	1-3	4-3	3-3
12 Ottery St Mary	0-4	0-4	1-3	1-3	0-3	2-3	0-6	0-4	1-3	0-4	3-3		1-2	2-9	1-3	1-3	1-1
13 Sidmouth Town	3-4	0-2	5-1	2-2	2-3	2-1	0-1	1-3	0-3	0-4	0-1	1-0		2-5	1-3	2-1	2-1
14 Stoke Gabriel	4-0	3-1	4-3	3-1	5-1	3-3	4-0	4-2	3-2	3-3	5-1	2-3			5-5	3-3	5-2
15 Teignmouth	3-1	2-1	6-0	9-2	0-1	2-0	1-3	1-1	0-5	2-4	1-2	3-1	1-2	2-2		5-0	4-2
16 Totnes & Dartington SC	1-2	2-1	3-2	2-0	1-0	1-4	1-3	2-2	2-1	1-3	0-3	3-1	6-1	1-3	3-0		2-4
17 University of Exeter	3-3	1-3	3-2	0-1	1-5	2-3	2-2	1-3	4-1	4-2	0-0	4-0	2-0	2-3	1-2	0-4	

DIVISION ONE WEST	1	2	3	4	5	6	7	8	9	10	11	12	13	14	15	16	17
1 Callington Town		4-1	2-0	2-3	2-2	4-3	1-0	4-1	0-2	1-3	6-1	3-2	2-3	1-0	1-5	3-2	2-0
2 Dobwalls	1-3		3-0	0-1	3-1	0-7	1-1	7-0	1-3	0-3	6-0	0-3	7-2	4-2	0-1	0-4	3-2
3 Foxhole Stars	3-3	1-0		0-4	2-1	0-4	2-2	7-1	0-4	2-2	7-1	3-4	3-1	0-2	4-2	0-4	0-0
4 Godolphin Atlantic	0-2	0-0	2-2		2-0	3-1	2-0	2-1	2-3	2-1	8-0	1-1	3-1	2-0	1-1	1-2	0-0
5 Hayle	0-1	0-1	3-1	0-1		0-4	2-1	1-2	0-5	0-2	5-0	5-1	2-2	1-4	3-1	1-1	2-3
6 Helston Athletic	1-0	5-4	2-0	2-1	1-1		1-0	5-2	1-3	1-1	4-0	5-1	2-1	1-1	1-1	4-1	2-2
7 Holsworthy	2-4	0-1	4-2	1-2	1-2	1-2		2-0	1-4	1-0	5-0	1-0	2-3	0-4	0-1	2-3	0-2
8 Mousehole	0-5	2-4	2-3	0-3	0-4	0-2	0-4		1-6	0-7	3-1	1-4	0-2	2-4	0-5	0-6	1-5
9 Newquay	5-0	6-1	1-0	1-1	6-0	2-2	2-1	7-0		1-0	12-1	2-1	5-1	2-2	3-1	1-3	3-2
10 Penryn Athletic	3-0	2-0	7-1	3-2	4-1	2-3	1-0	3-1	3-6		6-0	2-0	5-0	5-3	0-0	1-3	3-1
11 Perranporth	0-4	1-3	2-2	1-3	0-6	0-5	1-5	4-3	1-4	0-7		0-2	0-5	1-2	0-5	0-2	1-6
12 Plymstock United	1-0	2-1	0-1	2-0	3-1	1-4	3-1	6-0	0-1	2-3	0-0		3-0	3-2	2-3	0-0	2-2
13 Porthleven	3-0	0-4	1-0	1-7	3-1	1-2	3-2	4-1	1-9	1-4	0-1	1-4		3-2	2-3	1-3	3-1
14 St Dennis	3-2	2-0	1-0	1-1	4-4	2-4	2-4	5-0	0-5	1-2	2-2	5-0	0-3		2-1	1-1	3-2
15 Truro City Reserves	3-0	0-3	2-1	0-2	1-3	2-2	0-3	6-0	5-0	3-2	2-0	2-1			1-1	3-3	
16 Vospers Oak Villa	0-0	5-2	6-1	0-0	0-0	3-3	3-1	8-0	2-3	1-3	10-0	4-0	1-1	6-1	3-3		1-0
17 Wadebridge Town	1-4	3-3	2-2	0-2	1-3	1-3	2-0	9-1	2-7	0-0	6-0	4-1	1-2	2-1	3-2	3-1	

BODMIN TOWN
Founded: 1896   Nickname:

Secretary: Nick Giles   **(T)**   **(E)** nickgiles@live.co.uk
Chairman: **Manager:** Darren Gilbert   **Prog Ed:**
Ground: Priory Park, Bodmin, Cornwall PL31 2AE   **(T)** 01208 78165   **Capacity:**
Colours(change): Yellow & black (All white)

ADDITIONAL INFORMATION:
Previous League: South Western.
Honours: South Western League 1990-91, 93-94, 2005-06. South West Peninsula Premier Division 2007-08, 08-09, 11-12.

BOVEY TRACEY
Founded: 1950   Nickname: Moorlanders

Secretary: Steve Cooney   **(T)**   **(E)** steve.cooney@hotmail.co.uk
Chairman: Peter Horrell   **Manager:** Roger Bonaparte   **Prog Ed:**
Ground: Western Counties Roofing (Mill Marsh Pk), Ashburton Rd, Bovey TQ13 9FF   **(T)** 01626 833 896   **Capacity:**
Colours(change): All red (All green)

ADDITIONAL INFORMATION:
Previous League: South Devon.
Honours: Herald Cup 1960-61. South Devon League Premier Division 2007-08.

CAMELFORD
Founded: 1893   Nickname: Camels

Secretary: Hilary Kent   **(T)**   **(E)** hilarykent@camelfordfc.fsnet.co.uk
Chairman: Mark Tapley   **Manager:** Reg Hambly   **Prog Ed:**
Ground: Trefew Park, PL32 9TS   **(T)**   **Capacity:**
Colours(change): White & blue (Blue & white)

ADDITIONAL INFORMATION:
Honours: South West Peninsula Division One West 2010-11.

CULLOMPTON RANGERS
Founded: 1945   Nickname: The Cully

Secretary: Alan Slark   **(T)**   **(E)** alanslark1@tiscali.co.uk
Chairman: Brian Barnden   **Manager:** Dane Bunney   **Prog Ed:**
Ground: Speeds Meadow, Cullompton EX15 1DW   **(T)** 01884 33090   **Capacity:**
Colours(change): Red & black (Yellow & blue)

ADDITIONAL INFORMATION:
Previous League: Devon County 1992-2007.

ELBURTON VILLA
Founded: 1982   Nickname: The Villa

Secretary: Nick Pope   **(T)**   **(E)** pope.n@sky.com
Chairman: Dave Winters   **Manager:** Simon Westlake & Mark Bowden   **Prog Ed:**
Ground: Haye Road, Elburton, Plymouth PL9 8HS   **(T)** 01752 480 025   **Capacity:**
Colours(change): Red & white stripes/black (Blue & white)

ADDITIONAL INFORMATION:
Previous League: Devon County 1992-2007.

FALMOUTH TOWN
Founded: 1950   Nickname: The Ambers

Secretary: Stephen Rose   **(T)**   **(E)** stephendrose@aol.com
Chairman: Steve Kimberley   **Manager:** Alan Carey   **Prog Ed:**
Ground: Bickland Park, Bickland Water Road, Falmouth TR11 4PB   **(T)** 01326 375 156   **Capacity:**
Colours(change): Amber & black (All blue)

ADDITIONAL INFORMATION:
Honours: South Western League 1961-62, 65-66, 67-68, 70-71, 71-72, 72-73, 73-74, 85-86, 86-87, 88-89, 89-90, 91-92, 96-97, 99 -2000. Western League 1974-75, 75-76, 76-77, 77-78. Cornwall Combination 1983-84.

IVYBRIDGE TOWN
Founded: 1925   Nickname: The Ivys

Secretary: Paul Cocks   **(T)**   **(E)** secretary@ivybridgefc.com
Chairman: Dave Graddon   **Manager:** Graeme Kirkup & Nicky Marker   **Prog Ed:**
Ground: Erme Valley, Ermington Road, Ivybridge PL21 9ES   **(T)** 01752 896 686   **Capacity:**
Colours(change): Green & black (Blue & white)

ADDITIONAL INFORMATION:
Previous League: Devon County.
Honours: Devon County League 2005-06.

LAUNCESTON
Founded: 1891   Nickname: The Clarets

Secretary: Keith Ellacott   **(T)**   **(E)** launcestonfc@aol.com
Chairman: Alan Bradley   **Manager:** Leigh Cooper   **Prog Ed:**
Ground: Pennygillam Ind. Est., Launceston PL15 7ED   **(T)** 01566 773 279   **Capacity:**
Colours(change): All claret (Sky blue & black)

ADDITIONAL INFORMATION:
Previous League: South Western.
Honours: South Western League 1995-96.

LISKEARD ATHLETIC
Founded: 1946   Nickname: The Blues

Secretary: Brian Olver   **(T)**   **(E)** brianolver25@yahoo.com
Chairman: Roger Williams   **Manager:** Martin Burgess   **Prog Ed:**
Ground: Lux Park Sport Association, Coldstyle Rd, Lux Park, Liskeard PL14 2HZ   **(T)** 01566 773 279   **Capacity:**
Colours(change): All blue (All yellow)

ADDITIONAL INFORMATION:
Previous League: South Western 1995-2007.
Honours: South Western League 1976-77, 78-79. Western League Premier Division 1987-88.

LIVERTON UNITED
Founded: 1902   Nickname: The Lilly's

Secretary: Susan Stephens   **(T)**   **(E)** sstephens3@sky.com
Chairman: Chris Stephens   **Manager:** Tony Bowker & Alan Hext   **Prog Ed:**
Ground: Halford TQ12 6JF   **(T)**   **Capacity:**
Colours(change): All blue (All orange)

ADDITIONAL INFORMATION:
Honours: South West Peninsula Division One East 2010-11, 11-12.

NEWQUAY
Founded: 1890   Nickname: The Peppermints

Secretary: Bob Steggies   **(T)**   **(E)** bob@steggies.com
Chairman: Roger Williams   **Manager:** Glyn Hooper   **Prog Ed:**
Ground: Mount Wise TR7 2BU   **(T)** 01637 872 935   **Capacity:**
Colours(change): Red & white (Blue & white)

ADDITIONAL INFORMATION:
Honours: South West Peninsula Division One West 2011-12.

PENZANCE
Founded: 1888   Nickname: The Magpies

Secretary: John Mead   **(T)**   **(E)** wjamead@googlemail.com
Chairman: John Richards   **Manager:** Robin Watt & Steve Flack   **Prog Ed:**
Ground: Penlee Park, Alexandra Place, Penzance TR18 4NE   **(T)** 01736 361 964   **Capacity:**
Colours(change): White & black (Sky & navy blue)

ADDITIONAL INFORMATION:
Honours: South Western League 1955-56, 56-57, 74-75. South West Peninsula Division One West 2008-09. Cornwall Charity Cup 2008-09.

PLYMOUTH PARKWAY AFC
Founded: 1988   Nickname: The Parkway

Secretary: Genny Turner   **(T)**   **(E)** genny.woolwell@btinternet.com
Chairman: Mark Young   **Manager:** Wayne Hillson   **Prog Ed:**
Ground: Bolitho Park, St Peters Road, Manadon, Plymouth PL5 3JH   **(T)**   **Capacity:**
Colours(change): Yellow & blue (Grey & white)

ADDITIONAL INFORMATION:
Previous Name: Ex-Air Flyers Plymouth.
Previous League: South Western 1998-2007.
Honours: Throgmorton Cup 2010-11.

SALTASH UNITED
Founded: 1945   Nickname: The Ashes

Secretary: Luke Ranford   **(T)** 07830 299 555   **(E)** luke.ranford@googlemail.com
Chairman: Kevin Doddridge   **Manager:** Kevin Hendy & Stuart Dudley   **Prog Ed:**
Ground: Kimberley Stadium, Callington Road, Saltash PL12 6DX   **(T)** 01752 845 746   **Capacity:**
Colours(change): Red & white stripes/black (Blue & black)

ADDITIONAL INFORMATION:
Previous League: South Western 2006-07.
Honours: South Western League 1953-54, 75-76. Western League Division 1 1976-77, Premier 1984-85, 86-87, 88-89.

ST. AUSTELL

Founded: 1890   Nickname: The Lily Whites

Secretary: Peter Beard   **(T)** 01726 64138   **(E)**
Chairman: James Hutchings   **Manager:** Dan Nancarrow   **Prog Ed:**
Ground: Poltair Park, Trevarthian Road, St Austell PL25 4LR   **(T)** 01726 66099   **Capacity:**
Colours(change): All white (Yellow & blue)

ADDITIONAL INFORMATION:
Previous League: South Western 1951-2007.

ST. BLAZEY

Founded: 1896   Nickname: The Green & Blacks

Secretary: Martin Richards (Acting)   **(T)**   **(E)** marty.rich60@talktalk.net
Chairman: Martin Richards   **Manager:** Bobby Oaten   **Prog Ed:**
Ground: Blaise Park, Station Road, St Blazey PL24 2ND   **(T)** 01725 814 110   **Capacity:**
Colours(change): Green & black (Blue & white)

ADDITIONAL INFORMATION:
Previous League: South Western 1951-2007.
Honours: South Western Lge 1954-55, 57-58, 62-63, 63-64, 80-81, 82-83, 98-99, 2000-01, 01-02, 02-03, 03-04, 04-05, 06-07.

TAVISTOCK

Founded: 1888   Nickname: The Lambs

Secretary: Phil Lowe   **(T)** 01822 613 715   **(E)**
Chairman: Russell Bartlett   **Manager:** Ian Southcott   **Prog Ed:**
Ground: Langsford Park, Red & Black Club, Crowndale Road, Tavistock PL19 8DD   **(T)** 01822 614 447   **Capacity:**
Colours(change): Red & black (All blue)

ADDITIONAL INFORMATION:
Previous League: South Western 1968-2007.

TORPOINT ATHLETIC

Founded: 1887   Nickname: The Point

Secretary: Robbie Morris   **(T)**   **(E)** robbietafc81@live.co.uk
Chairman: Paul Whitworth   **Manager:** Darren Edwards   **Prog Ed:**
Ground: The Mill, Mill Lane, Carbeile Road, Torpoint PL11 2RE   **(T)** 01752 812 889   **Capacity:**
Colours(change): Yellow & black (All white)

ADDITIONAL INFORMATION:
Previous League: South Western 1962-2007.
Honours: South Western League 1964-65, 66-67.

WITHERIDGE

Founded: 1920   Nickname: The Withy

Secretary: Chris Cole   **(T)**   **(E)** chris.cole@witheridgeafc.co.uk
Chairman: Andre Pike   **Manager:** Mike Taylor   **Prog Ed:**
Ground: Edge Down Park, Fore Street, Witheridge EX16 8AH   **(T)** 01884 861 511   **Capacity:**
Colours(change): All blue (All claret)

ADDITIONAL INFORMATION:
Previous League: Devon County 2006-07.

DIVISION ONE EAST CONSTITUTION 2012-13

ALPHINGTON .... The Chronicles, Church Road, Alphington, Exeter EX2 8SW.................................01392 279556
APPLEDORE.. Marshford, Churchill Way, Appledore EX39 1PA.....................................01237 475015
AXMINSTER TOWN..Ottery St Mary AFC, EX11 1EL..
BUDLEIGH SALTERTON..............................Greenway Lane, Budleigh Salterton EX9 6SG...............................01395 443850
CREDITON UNITED .... Lords Meadow, Commercial Road, Crediton EX17 1ER..............01363 774671
EXETER CIVIL SERVICE ....Foxhayes, Exwick, Exeter EX4 2BQ..
EXMOUTH TOWN...............................King George V Ground, Southern Road, Exmouth EX8 3EE.................01395 263348
GALMPTON UNITED & TORBAY GENTSWar Memorial Playing Field, Greenway Road, Galmpton, Brixham TQ5 0LP......
NEWTON ABBOT SPURS ....Recreation Ground, Marsh Road, Newton Abbot TQ12 2AR..........01626 365343
OKEHAMPTON ARGYLE.........................Simmons Park, Mill Road, Okehampton EX20 1PR.................01837 53997
PLYMSTOCK UNITED ....Dean Cross, Dean Cross Road, Plymstock PL9 7AZ................01752 406776
SIDMOUTH TOWN ....Manstone Recreation Ground, Manstone Lane, Sidmouth EX10 9TF.........01395 577087
STOKE GABRIEL............... G J Churchward Mem. Ground, Broadley Lane, Stoke Gabriel, Totnes TQ9 6RR..........01803 782223
TEIGNMOUTH ....Coombe Valley, Coombe Lane, Teignmouth TQ14 9EX....................01626 776688
TOTNES & DARTINGTON SC..................... Foxhole Sports Ground, Dartington TQ9 6EB.........................01803 868032
UNIVERSITY OF EXETER .... University Sports Ground, Topsham Road, Topsham EX3 0LY 01392 879542

DIVISION ONE WEST CONSTITUTION 2012-13

CALLINGTON TOWNGinsters Marshfield Parc, Callington Community College, Launceston Rd, Callington PL17 7DR.....01579 382647
DOBWALLS..Lantoom Park, Duloe Road, Dobwalls PL14 4LU..........................07721 689 380
FOXHOLE STARS................................Goverseth Park, Goverseth Terrace, Foxhole PL26 7UP.................01726 824615
GODOLPHIN ATLANTIC.....................................Godolphin Way, Newquay TR7 3BU ....
HAYLE .... Trevassack Park, Viaduct Hill, Hayle TR27 5HT...........................01736 757157
HELSTON ATHLETIC................................. Kellaway Parc, Clodgy Lane, Helston TR13 8PJ...................01326 573742
HOLSWORTHY.................................Upcott Field, North Road, Holsworthy EX22 6HF.....................01409 254295
MOUSEHOLE.................................. Trungle Parc, Paul, Penzance TR19 6UG...............................01736 731518
PENRYN ATHLETIC................................. Kernick, Kernick Road, Penryn TR10 9EW.......................01326 375182
PERRANPORTH .... Ponsmere Valley, Budnick Estate, Perranporth TR6 0DB.............01872 575000
PORTHLEVEN ....Gala Parc, Mill Lane, Porthleven TR13 9LQ.........................01326 569 655
ST DENNIS ....Boscawen Park, St Dennis PL26 8DW....................................01726 822635
STICKER.. Burngullow Park PL26 7EN...01726 71003
TRURO CITY RESERVES...Treyew Road, Truro TR1 2TH..........................01872 225400
VOSPERS OAK VILLA...................Weston Mill, Ferndale Road, Weston Mill, Plymouth PL2 2EL............01752 363352
WADEBRIDGE TOWN .... Bodieve Park, Bodieve Road, Wadebridge PL27 6EA...............01208 812537

GROUND DIRECTIONS - PREMIER DIVISION

BODMIN TOWN - Priory Park, Bodmin, Cornwall PL31 2AE. Tel: 01208 781 65.
Situated in Priory Park through main car park. Use football car park on Saturdays.

BOVEY TRACEY - Western Counties Roofing (Mill Marsh Park), Ashburton Road, Bovey Tracey TQ13 9FF. Tel: 01626 832 780.
Coming off the A38 East or Westbound at Drumbridges take the Bovey Tracey turn-off, straight through the lights at Heathfield. Next roundabout take 2nd exit, next roundabout take 3rd exit, then left, 35 yards, follow road to bottom of drive then enter through gate.

CAMELFORD - Trefrew Park PL32 9TS.
From the South drive into Camelford up Victoria Road for 300 yards, turn left into Oakwood Rise. Follow road around for approximately 300 yards. Entrance is on the right up the lane. From the North as you enter Camelford turn right into Oakwood Rise then as above.

CULLOMPTON RANGERS - Speeds Meadow, Cullompton EX15 1DW. Tel: 01884 33090.
Leave M5 at junction 28, left at Town Centre, at Meadow Lane turn left past Sports Centre, at end of road turn right, then in 100 yards turn left into ground at end of lane.

ELBURTON VILLA - Haye Road, Elburton, Plymouth PL9 8NS. Tel: 01752 480 025.
From Plymouth City Centre take A379 Kingsbridge Road. At third roundabout turn left into Haye Road (signposted Saltram House). Ground 50 yards on left.

FALMOUTH TOWN - Bickland Park, Bickland Water Road, Falmouth TR11 4PB. Tel: 01326 375 156.
Take Penryn by-pass from Asda roundabout. Leave by-pass at Hillhead roundabout, take first right and follow industrial estate signs. Ground 1/2 mile on the left.

IVYBRIDGE TOWN - Erme Valley, Ermington Road, Ivybridge. Tel: 01752 896 686.
From Plymouth - leave A38 at Ivybridge and follow signs towards Ermington. Ground is immediately next to South Devon Tennis Centre. From Exeter - leave A38 at Ivybridge. Ground is in front of you at the end of the slip road.

LAUNCESTON - Pennygillam, Pennygillam Ind. Est., Launceston PL15 7ED. Tel: 01566 773 279.
Leave A30 onto Pennygillam roundabout, turn into Pennygillam Industrial Estate. Ground is 400 yards on the left.

LISKEARD ATHLETIC - Lux Park Sport Association, Coldstyle Road, Lux Park, Liskeard PL14 2HZ. Tel: 01579 342 665.
From the Parade (middle of town) turn left at the monument, then first right following signs for Leisure Centre at Lux Park.

LIVERTON UNITED - Halford TQ12 6JF

At the Trago / Drumbridges exit of the A38 take signs for Old Liverton. Quarter of a mile after the Star Inn turn left then next left into ground.

PENZANCE - Penlee Park, Alexandra Place, Penzance TR18 4NE. Tel: 01736 361 964.

Follow road along harbour and promenade. Turn right at mini r'about into Alexandra Rd. Take either 1st (Mennaye Rd) 2nd (Alexandra Place) right.

NEWQUAY AFC - Mount Wise TR7 2BU

From link road turn right onto Mount Wise, just past traffic lights turn Right into Clevedon Road.

PENZANCE - Penlee Park TR18 4NE. Tel: 01736 361 964.

Go along Promenade and at the end turn right at mini-roundabout into Alexandra Road. Take either 1st or 2nd right turnings (Mennaye Rd or Alexander Place). Ground at end of both Roads.

PLYMOUTH PARKWAY - Bolitho Park, St Peters Road, Manadon, Plymouth PL5 3OZ.

From Cornwall/Exeter exit at the Manadon/Tavistock junction off the Plymouth Parkway (A38), off roundabout into St Peters Road. Entrance is one mile on the right.

SALTASH UNITED - Ground: Kimberley Stadium, Callington Road, Saltash PL12 6DX. Tel: 01752 845 746.

At the top of Town Centre fork right at mini-roundabout. Ground is situated 400m ahead on the left-hand side next to Leisure Centre and Police Station.

ST AUSTELL - Poltair Park, Trevarthian Road, St Austell PL25 4LR Tel: 07966 130 158

Near Poltair School and St Austell Brewery (5 minutes from St Austell Rail Station).

ST BLAZEY - Blaise Park, Station Road, St Blazey PL24 2ND. Tel: 01725 814 110.

A390 from Lostwithiel to St Austell. At village of St Blazey turn left at traffic lights by Church/Cornish Arms pub into Station Road. Ground is 200 yards on the left.

TAVISTOCK - Langsford Park, Red & Black Club, Crowndale Road, Tavistock PL19 8DD. Tel: 01822 614 447.

From Launceston/Okehampton, stay on A386 trhough town signposted Plymouth, past Drake's statue. Over canal turn right, signposted football ground/recycle centre. Ground is 100 metres past Tavistock college. From Plymouth, stay on A386 pass Morrisons and Texaco garage, over River Tavy, turn left signposted football ground/ recycle centre. Then as above.

TORPOINT ATHLETIC - The Mill, Mill Lane, Carbeile Road, Torpoint PL11 2NA. Tel: 01752 812 889.

Take turning at Carbeile Inn onto Carbeille Road and first turning on the right into Mill Lane.

WITHERIDGE - Edge Down Park, Fore Street, Witheridge EX16 8AH. Tel: 01884 861 511.

B3137 Tiverton to Witheridge, on entering the village football pitch is on the right-hand side before the Fire Station and School.

SPARTAN SOUTH MIDLANDS LEAGUE

Sponsored by: Molten
Founded: 1998
Recent Champions:
2007: Edgware Town
2008: Beaconsfield SYCOB
2009: Biggleswade Town
2010: Aylesbury United
2011: Chalfont St Peter
ssmfl.org

PREMIER DIVISION	P	W	D	L	F	A	Pts
1 (P) Royston Town	42	34	2	6	125	44	104
2 Dunstable Town	42	31	6	5	132	51	99
3 AFC Dunstable	42	29	5	8	103	43	92
4 Aylesbury United	42	25	5	12	96	58	80
5 Haringey Borough	42	24	7	11	103	68	79
6 Tring Athletic	42	22	9	11	75	54	75
7 Berkhamsted	42	20	6	16	87	71	66
8 Colney Heath	42	20	6	16	79	70	66
9 Stotfold	42	17	10	15	60	63	61
10 Hillingdon Borough	42	16	11	15	63	53	59
11 Leverstock Green	42	18	3	21	59	65	57
12 St Margaretsbury	42	16	7	19	83	88	55
13 (R) Broxbourne Borough	42	15	9	18	69	75	54
14 London Tigers	42	15	6	21	57	74	51
15 Hadley	42	13	9	20	63	76	48
16 Hertford Town	42	14	6	22	70	107	48
17 Oxhey Jets	42	12	9	21	69	88	45
18 Harefield United	42	11	7	24	51	92	40
19 Biggleswade United	42	10	8	24	59	89	38
20 Holmer Green	42	9	8	25	66	106	35
21 Hanwell Town	42	8	7	27	57	112	31
22 Hatfield Town	42	8	4	30	50	129	28

PREMIER DIVISION CUP

ROUND 1
Hanwell Town 2-3 Colney Heath
Holmer Green 0-3 London Tigers
Oxhey Jets 4-1 Berkhamsted
Royston Town 4-1 Haringey Borough
Aylesbury United 3-2 Broxbourne Borough
AFC Dunstable 3-1 Leverstock Green
ROUND 2
Colney Heath 4-3 Oxhey Jets
Aylesbury United 0-3 St Margaretsbury
Harefield United 2-0 London Tigers
Hatfield Town 1-2 Stotfold
Royston Town 4-0 Hillingdon Borough
AFC Dunstable 1-2 Hertford Town
Tring Athletic 2-1 Hadley
Dunstable Town 5-2 Biggleswade United
QUARTER FINALS
Tring Athletic 2-0 Colney Heath
Royston Town 2-0 Hertford Town
Dunstable Town 3-1 Stotfold
St Margaretsbury 2-0 Harefield United
SEMI-FINALS
St Margaretsbury 4-2 Dunstable Town
Royston Town 1-0 Tring Athletic
FINAL
St Margaretsbury 0-2 Royston Town

CHALLENGE TROPHY

ROUND 1
London Colney 0-0 Tokyngton Manor
(London Colney won on penalties)
Kentish Town HW MK City
MK Wanderers 2-4 Bedford
Stony Stratford Town 2-4 Bletchley Town
Harefield United 2-1 Kings Langley
Mursley United 2-4 Haringey Borough
Wodson Park 1-3 Ampthill Town
Hale Leys Utd 0-1 Colney Heath
Berkhamsted 9-2 London Lions
Aylesbury United 4-1 Tring Corinthians
Chesham Utd Reserves 3-2 Cockfosters
Risborough Rangers 3-2 St Margaretsbury
Buckingham Athletic 2-3 Langford
Hatfield Town 4-2 Aston Clinton
The 61 FC (Luton) 2-6 Holmer Green

PREMIER DIVISION	1	2	3	4	5	6	7	8	9	10	11	12	13	14	15	16	17	18	19	20	21	22
1 AFC Dunstable		1-0	5-0	3-0	3-0	1-0	1-0	3-2	7-1	1-0	1-1	6-2	4-1	3-1	6-2	0-1	2-1	2-0	2-1	0-2	3-3	3-1
2 Aylesbury United	1-2		3-2	2-2	3-1	1-3	2-2	1-2	6-0	1-2	0-1	3-2	5-3	3-2	1-3	0-1	1-0	3-0	3-2	1-1	2-0	1-2
3 Berkhamsted	3-1	0-3		3-1	3-2	0-0	0-3	1-2	1-1	3-2	1-1	2-0	5-0	2-2	3-4	3-1	3-2	1-2	0-4	1-2	2-0	1-2
4 Biggleswade United	0-2	1-2	2-1		0-2	2-4	4-4	2-1	3-0	2-0	1-2	2-2	1-3	0-0	2-2	1-2	0-2	4-2	1-6	1-2	1-2	0-2
5 Broxbourne Borough	0-0	1-2	0-1	2-0		2-1	2-1	1-1	2-2	2-3	3-2	4-1	3-4	0-1	1-2	0-2	2-0	1-1	1-3	3-3	4-2	1-2
6 Colney Heath	3-2	1-0	1-3	3-1	3-1		2-3	2-3	2-1	0-2	2-3	2-1	6-2	2-2	3-6	2-1	1-1	3-2	1-2	1-0	0-2	0-1
7 Dunstable Town	1-0	3-3	4-0	5-1	3-0	1-2		1-0	3-1	5-0	3-2	6-2	5-1	0-1	5-2	3-2	4-0	6-0	3-1	7-0	2-1	1-1
8 Hadley	1-6	0-2	2-1	1-0	0-0	0-1	0-0		2-2	2-2	3-3	0-0	1-3	3-0	2-1	0-1	2-4	0-2	2-1	1-2	1-2	2-2
9 Hanwell Town	0-6	1-4	1-1	4-2	0-4	1-2	3-6	4-1		4-2	0-3	1-2	1-2	0-3	1-2	1-3	2-0	1-3	1-5	2-2	0-1	1-0
10 Harefield United	1-4	3-0	0-3	0-5	1-0	1-0	1-4	0-4	3-1		1-3	4-1	0-3	0-0	3-3	2-1	1-2	3-3	1-6	1-1	0-1	0-2
11 Haringey Borough	1-2	2-2	4-3	0-1	4-0	1-1	1-3	3-2	4-1	2-2		4-0	1-2	6-2	6-1	1-4	3-0	4-0	1-4	3-2	3-1	1-4
12 Hatfield Town	0-6	0-1	1-6	0-0	2-3	1-4	2-7	2-1	3-5	2-1	0-6		2-4	0-3	2-0	1-0	0-2	1-3	0-6	1-2	1-1	1-5
13 Hertford Town	0-1	3-2	2-1	3-3	3-3	0-4	0-5	1-5	1-2	0-1	0-2	4-2		0-3	4-1	0-0	2-1	2-2	1-2	2-2	1-5	1-3
14 Hillingdon Borough	0-2	0-4	3-1	3-1	5-0	3-0	1-2	2-0	2-0	5-0	0-1	0-2	5-1		2-2	1-1	1-2	0-0	0-1	2-0	0-1	0-4
15 Holmer Green	2-2	1-4	0-3	2-3	1-2	1-3	3-5	2-2	2-2	1-0	2-3	4-2	2-1	1-2		2-2	4-3	1-3	1-2	1-3	1-0	1-2
16 Leverstock Green	0-2	3-1	1-3	2-1	2-0	1-2	0-2	0-3	3-4	1-0	3-4	1-0	0-5	3-1	3-0		0-2	3-0	0-2	4-1	1-0	2-3
17 London Tigers	0-1	2-3	0-4	0-3	1-3	3-3	2-2	3-0	0-0	3-1	0-1	1-0	1-4	1-1	2-0	1-0		3-2	0-2	3-4	2-0	1-3
18 Oxhey Jets	4-0	2-1	0-2	1-2	1-2	3-2	2-4	1-2	4-1	0-2	2-2	6-4	2-2	3-3	1-0	1-0	1-2		0-1	0-1	2-2	2-3
19 Royston Town	2-1	1-0	2-4	7-0	2-2	4-0	2-5	3-1	2-1	4-2	4-2	5-1	6-0	1-0	4-0	3-0	4-1	4-0		4-0	4-2	3-2
20 St Margaretsbury	2-4	2-5	2-3	2-1	2-2	2-5	1-2	6-2	4-2	3-2	1-2	1-2	3-1	0-1	2-0	2-1	1-2	5-2	2-2		2-2	0-2
21 Stotfold	3-2	3-6	2-2	2-1	1-4	2-1	0-1	0-3	1-0	3-0	2-1	0-3	1-1	0-0	2-0	0-0	1-0	2-0	2-1	2-1		1-2
22 Tring Athletic	0-0	0-2	1-6	1-1	1-3	1-1	2-0	3-2	3-1	1-1	2-3	3-1	4-0	0-0	0-0	2-1	2-0	3-3	0-3	1-0	1-0	

DIVISION ONE

		P	W	D	L	F	A	Pts
1	(P) London Colney	42	33	3	6	94	31	102
2	(P) Ampthill Town	42	26	9	7	95	43	87
3	Hoddesdon Town	42	26	4	12	121	60	82
4	Kings Langley	42	25	5	12	114	77	80
5	Harpenden Town	42	21	14	7	89	57	77
6	Crawley Green	42	22	8	12	96	68	74
7	London Lions	42	22	8	12	91	77	74
8	Cranfield United	42	22	3	17	119	74	69
9	Cockfosters	42	19	11	12	87	67	68
10	Langford	42	19	9	14	107	88	66
11	Tokyngton Manor (-1)	42	19	6	17	92	80	62
12	Bedford	42	18	8	16	88	87	62
13	St Albans City Reserves	42	18	7	17	92	68	61
14	Chesham United Reserves	42	17	7	18	78	72	58
15	New Bradwell St Peter	42	14	10	18	64	79	52
16	Wodson Park	42	15	7	20	62	77	52
17	Welwyn Garden City	42	13	6	23	62	100	45
18	Buckingham Athletic	42	9	8	25	55	83	35
19	Kentish Town	42	9	5	28	44	129	32
20	Amersham Town	42	7	6	29	65	121	27
21	Stony Stratford Town	42	8	2	32	52	135	26
22	Sun Postal Sports	42	5	4	33	55	149	19

DIVISION ONE CUP

ROUND 1
Cockfosters 5-0 Amersham Town
Langford 4-3 Hoddesdon Town
Kings Langley 3-2 Sun Postal Sports
Stony Stratford Town 0-5 Bedford
Tokyngton Manor 1-2 Cranfield United
Wodson Park 1-0 New Bradwell St Peter

ROUND 2
Chesham Utd Reserves 3-3 Bedford
(Bedford won on penalties)
Kings Langley 5-2 St Albans City Reserves
Cockfosters 3-2 Welwyn Garden City
London Lions 0-7 Crawley Green
Langford 1-2 London Colney
Cranfield United 2-3 Harpenden Town
Kentish Town 1-2 Ampthill Town
Wodson Park 0-1 Buckingham Athletic

QUARTER FINALS
Bedford 1-4 Crawley Green
Ampthill Town 4-2 Buckingham Athletic
Cockfosters 0-4 Harpenden Town
London Colney 1-2 Kings Langley

SEMI-FINALS
Kings Langley 3-0 Ampthill Town
Harpenden Town 3-3 Crawley Green
(Crawley Green won on penalties)

FINAL
Crawley Green 2-1 Kings Langley

CHALLENGE TROPHY continued...

Broxbourne Borough 6-0 Old Bradwell United
Royston Town 5-3 Totternhoe
Stotfold 2-2 St Albans City Reserves
London Tigers 0-1 Hillingdon Borough
Hadley 2-1 Winslow United
Caddington 0-5 Crawley Green
Hoddesdon Town 4-1 Sun Postal Sports
Pitstone & Ivinghoe 0-1 Welwyn Garden City
Dunstable Town 3-0 Kent Athletic
Tring Athletic 3-2 New Bradwell St Peter
Amersham Town 5-5 Oxhey Jets
(Amersham Town won on penalties)

ROUND 2
Broxbourne Borough 4-2 Amersham Town
Hoddesdon Town 2-5 Cranfield United
Biggleswade United 1-0 Bedford
Welwyn Garden City 0-1 Harpenden Town
Hanwell Town 4-4 Hillingdon Borough
(Hillingdon Borough won on penalties)
Harefield United 0-4 Haringey Borough
Leverstock Green 3-1 Hatfield Town
Tring Athletic 3-2 Ampthill Town
Aylesbury United 1-3 Risborough Rangers
Berkhamsted 2-1 Kentish Town
Chesham Utd Reserves 3-0 Langford
Crawley Green 2-3 Holmer Green
Royston Town 2-3 Bletchley Town
Hertford Town 1-2 Hadley
Dunstable Town 2-1 Stotfold
London Colney 0-2 Colney Heath

ROUND 3
Cranfield United 2-6 Broxbourne Borough
Harpenden Town 3-5 Chesham Utd Reserves
Tring Athletic 1-0 Holmer Green
Hillingdon Borough 6-1 Colney Heath
Risborough Rangers 2-3 Leverstock Green
Berkhamsted 2-6 Haringey Borough
Dunstable Town 2-3 Bletchley Town
Hadley 1-2 Biggleswade United

QUARTER FINALS
Biggleswade United 1-6 Haringey Borough
Tring Athletic 4-0 Bletchley Town
Chesham Utd Reserves 1-2 Leverstock Green
Hillingdon Borough 2-1 Broxbourne Borough

SEMI-FINALS
Hillingdon Borough 1-0 Tring Athletic
Haringey Borough 2-1 Leverstock Green

FINAL
Hillingdon Borough 0-1 Haringey Borough

DIVISION ONE

		1	2	3	4	5	6	7	8	9	10	11	12	13	14	15	16	17	18	19	20	21	22
1	Amersham Town		1-4	1-2	2-1	2-1	1-4	2-5	1-2	1-4	5-3	1-2	3-8	3-2	1-5	2-2	2-3	3-3	1-3	5-0	1-1	0-0	0-6
2	Ampthill Town	3-2		2-1	3-1	1-0	2-1	0-0	0-0	2-1	3-3	4-1	0-0	4-4	1-1	1-1	1-1	7-0	4-1	2-1	2-0	3-0	
3	Bedford	3-0	1-3		7-1	1-4	1-1	1-4	4-1	4-0	2-3	1-2	1-3	1-2	1-2	2-1	4-3	3-3	2-1	2-2	1-5	6-3	2-1
4	Buckingham Athletic	3-0	1-2	1-1		0-3	1-1	1-2	0-1	1-1	2-3	3-0	1-4	2-2	1-0	1-0	1-3	1-1	1-2	0-1	0-2	2-0	4-0
5	Chesham United Reserves	2-2	2-4	0-2	0-1		1-2	3-1	1-4	4-1	4-2	2-2	2-2	1-1	0-2	1-3	3-1	3-2	3-0	3-0	2-3	3-1	3-0
6	Cockfosters	3-2	1-2	1-1	2-0	2-0		1-3	2-2	0-0	2-0	6-0	2-0	3-6	0-2	1-5	3-3	0-4	5-2	5-1	2-5	0-2	7-3
7	Cranfield United	2-0	2-1	0-2	3-4	1-4	2-1		0-1	2-2	4-1	8-1	3-0	4-3	1-3	1-3	1-3	7-0	6-0	4-0	3-1	1-1	1-1
8	Crawley Green	5-1	1-0	0-0	3-2	2-3	1-2	2-5		2-2	0-2	7-2	2-2	3-1	2-3	2-2	2-2	4-1	2-3	2-5	1-0	3-0	
9	Harpenden Town	3-0	1-1	7-0	3-3	1-1	0-2	1-0	0-3		2-1	3-1	2-2	2-2	1-0	1-1	1-0	4-2	3-1	5-4	3-1	6-1	6-0
10	Hoddesdon Town	4-1	3-0	7-1	6-1	2-0	2-0	2-3	5-0	2-1		1-1	6-0	3-2	0-2	3-1	1-2	6-0	0-1	3-1	7-1	2-1	
11	Kentish Town	0-2	0-2	0-3	4-1	1-2	0-6	1-9	4-3		2-4		2-0	0-5	0-3	0-4	0-4	4-0	1-0	0-3	1-1	1-1	0-4
12	Kings Langley	2-0	0-2	2-1	2-0	3-1	2-2	4-3	2-1	1-5	2-1	5-0		1-2	4-0	2-1	3-0	7-2	6-4	2-3	4-0	3-0	
13	Langford	3-1	3-1	3-2	4-2	4-0	1-1	3-2	2-2	0-2	1-4	7-1	7-2		0-3	5-2	2-0	3-1	7-0	2-0	3-3	2-4	1-2
14	London Colney	5-1	1-0	1-2	2-1	2-0	5-0	3-1	1-0	1-1	1-0	3-0	4-1	3-1		1-2	1-0	4-0	4-0	2-0	3-2	1-1	
15	London Lions	1-0	1-6	3-3	2-1	4-3	0-0	3-2	3-2	0-0	1-2	4-1	0-4	3-1	1-3		1-1	3-2	3-1	4-0	2-1	0-2	3-0
16	New Bradwell St Peter	2-1	1-0	4-3	0-3	1-1	0-2	3-2	1-4	3-2	1-6	2-2	1-2	1-6		1-0	3-7	3-0	5-1	1-0	1-2		
17	St Albans City Reserves	4-4	3-2	5-0	1-1	0-2	3-4	3-1	2-0	1-2	0-5	1-2	5-3	2-3	1-0	4-0	0-1		3-1	11-0	1-0	1-0	5-1
18	Stony Stratford Town	5-3	0-4	3-4	0-0	1-3	0-2	2-4	2-5	0-1	1-4	2-0	3-2	2-3	1-4	2-3	1-1	1-4		3-2	1-3	2-3	1-0
19	Sun Postal Sports	3-5	0-2	1-3	3-2	2-0	0-2	1-8	1-8	2-5	1-6	2-2	1-5	2-3	1-4	2-4	1-2	1-1	2-0		2-2	3-4	2-3
20	Tokyngton Manor	1-0	2-3	2-2	4-2	3-2	1-1	0-4	1-6	5-0	1-4	3-0	2-5	4-1	1-2	1-1	4-2	0-2	5-0	6-2		1-2	3-2
21	Welwyn Garden City	3-0	0-6	0-7	2-1	2-4	1-5	2-3	0-1	2-2	2-2	3-0	0-1	3-3	1-2	2-1	2-2	1-0	0-3	4-0	0-2		3-1
22	Wodson Park	3-2	1-0	3-0	1-0	1-1	0-0	3-2	1-2	0-2	1-1	2-0	3-3	1-2	0-2	3-3	1-5	0-1	5-1	1-0	2-0	1-2	

SPARTAN SOUTH MIDLANDS LEAGUE - STEP 5/6/7

	DIVISION TWO	P	W	D	L	F	A	Pts
1	Aston Clinton	26	20	4	2	87	28	64
2	Risborough Rangers	26	19	2	5	80	26	59
3	Totternhoe	26	15	5	6	57	41	50
4	Mursley United	26	15	3	8	46	34	48
5	The 61 FC (Luton)	26	14	4	8	52	40	46
6	Kent Athletic	26	14	1	11	40	41	43
7	(P) Winslow United	26	11	8	7	59	43	41
8	Bletchley Town	26	8	7	11	56	59	31
9	Pitstone & Ivinghoe	26	8	5	13	41	56	29
10	Old Bradwell United	26	7	7	12	38	55	28
11	Hale Leys United	26	7	3	16	43	77	24
12	Caddington	26	6	3	17	52	75	21
13	Tring Corinthians	26	4	4	18	41	74	16
14	MK Wanderers	26	4	4	18	43	86	16

DIVISION TWO	1	2	3	4	5	6	7	8	9	10	11	12	13	14
1 Aston Clinton		3-0	2-0	7-0	6-0	2-2	3-0	4-0	5-1	1-2	1-1	3-0	3-1	4-3
2 Bletchley Town	0-4		2-3	3-1	0-4	3-2	6-0	7-0	2-2	0-5	4-1	1-3	2-2	3-3
3 Caddington	0-4	2-2		6-0	1-2	2-3	1-5	2-5	5-7	3-2	0-2	2-2	1-2	4-5
4 Hale Leys United	0-4	1-4	1-5		2-1	5-2	1-2	4-2	1-2	1-6	1-1	3-4	2-1	0-1
5 Kent Athletic	2-5	3-1	4-2	3-2		1-0	2-1	1-0	0-0	1-3	1-2	0-2	2-0	0-2
6 MK Wanderers	2-5	2-1	5-3	2-4	1-5		0-4	1-1	4-1	0-3	1-2	0-3	4-5	2-2
7 Mursley United	1-1	2-1	4-3	2-1	0-1	3-1		0-1	3-0	0-0	1-2	2-0	2-1	0-0
8 Old Bradwell United	2-3	2-3	1-1	2-2	2-0	6-3	0-1		2-1	1-1	2-2	2-4	2-1	2-1
9 Pitstone & Ivinghoe	0-3	2-0	4-0	2-0	0-2	3-3	0-1	3-1		0-2	1-3	3-1	2-0	2-4
10 Risborough Rangers	5-3	1-2	4-0	4-0	4-1	7-0	1-2	3-0	5-0		4-2	3-0	4-2	3-2
11 The 61 FC (Luton)	1-2	4-2	3-1	2-3	0-1	3-0	3-1	3-1	3-2	0-3		0-2	3-4	4-2
12 Totternhoe	2-2	3-3	1-2	1-1	3-1	4-2	3-2	3-0	3-0	1-0	0-1		2-0	3-2
13 Tring Corinthians	2-4	3-3	2-3	2-4	0-2	3-1	1-5	1-1	3-3	1-4	0-4	2-3		1-4
14 Winslow United	1-3	1-1	1-0	6-3	2-0	5-0	1-2	0-0	0-0	3-1	0-0	4-4	4-1	

	RESERVE DIVISION ONE	P	W	D	L	F	A	Pts
1	Kings Langley Reserves	30	19	5	6	80	43	62
2	Hadley Reserves	30	18	4	8	66	45	58
3	Royston Town Reserves (-1)	30	17	7	6	79	41	57
4	AFC Dunstable Reserves	30	17	4	9	86	63	55
5	The 61 FC (Luton) Reserves	30	15	6	9	60	43	51
6	Cockfosters Reserves	30	15	5	10	72	64	50
7	Hoddesdon Town Reserves	30	14	5	11	85	56	47
8	Oxhey Jets Reserves	30	14	4	12	70	62	46
9	St Margaretsbury Reserves (-3)	30	14	5	11	66	63	44
10	Stotfold Reserves	30	12	5	13	75	62	41
11	London Colney Reserves	30	11	7	12	54	52	40
12	Risborough Rangers Reserves	30	10	8	12	43	54	38
13	Holmer Green Reserves	30	9	4	17	48	71	31
14	Langford Reserves	30	7	3	20	45	90	24
15	Hatfield Town Reserves	30	3	6	21	39	94	15
16	Wodson Park Reserves	30	1	10	19	28	93	13

	RESERVE DIVISION TWO	P	W	D	L	F	A	Pts
1	Kent Athletic Reserves	26	22	2	2	95	33	68
2	London Lions Reserves	26	20	1	5	84	29	61
3	Ampthill Town Reserves	26	20	1	5	75	36	61
4	Crawley Green Reserves	26	17	2	7	64	40	53
5	Harpenden Town Reserves	26	11	7	8	60	51	40
6	Totternhoe Reserves	26	11	5	10	65	63	38
7	Buckingham Athletic Reserves	26	11	5	10	43	46	38
8	Bletchley Town Reserves	26	10	3	13	49	62	33
9	Winslow United Reserves	26	9	5	12	48	51	32
10	New Bradwell St Peter Reserves	26	9	4	13	55	69	31
11	Welwyn Garden City Reserves	26	7	2	17	51	87	23
12	Old Bradwell United Reserves	26	7	3	16	42	72	21
13	Stony Stratford Town Reserves	26	2	5	19	29	82	11
14	Sun Postal Sports Reserves	26	2	3	21	37	76	9

AFC DUNSTABLE
Founded: 1981   Nickname: Od's

Secretary: Craig Renfrew   **(T)** 07976 192 530   **(E)** renfrewcraig@aol.com
Chairman: Simon Bullard   **Manager:** Alex Butler   **Prog Ed:** Craig Renfrew
Ground: Dunstable Town FC, Creasey Pk, Creasey Pk Dr, Brewers Hill Rd, LU6 1BB   **(T)**
Capacity: 3,500   **Seats:** 350   **Covered:** 1,000   **Midweek Matchday:**   **Clubhouse:** Yes   **Shop:** Yes

Colours(change): Blue/blue/white (Red & white stripes/red/red)
Previous Names: Old Dunstablians 1981- 2004.
Previous Leagues:
Records:
Senior Honours: Spartan South Midlands Division Two 2003-04, 06-07.

10 YEAR RECORD

02-03		03-04		04-05		05-06		06-07		07-08		08-09		09-10		10-11		11-12	
SSM2	2	SSM2	1	SSM2	6	SSM2	2	SSM2	1	SSM2	4	SSM2	3	SSM1	5	SSM1	2	SSM P	3

AMPTHILL TOWN
Founded: 1881   Nickname:

Secretary: Eric Turner   **(T)** 07866 336 421   **(E)** ericturner789@btinternet.com
Chairman: Bernie Stuttard   **Manager:** Steve Roach   **Prog Ed:** Eric Turner
Ground: Ampthill Park, Woburn Street, Ampthill MK45 2HX   **(T)** 01525 404440
Capacity: **Seats:** Yes   **Covered:** Yes   **Midweek Matchday:**   **Clubhouse:** Yes   **Shop:**

Colours(change): Yellow/blue/blue (Blue/yellow/blue)
Previous Names: None
Previous Leagues: United Counties 1965.
Records:
Senior Honours:

10 YEAR RECORD

02-03		03-04		04-05		05-06		06-07		07-08		08-09		09-10		10-11		11-12	
SSM1	18	SSM1	18	SSM1	17	SSM1	16	SSM1	4	SSM1	7	SSM1	15	SSM1	13	SSM1	16	SSM1	2

AYLESBURY UNITED
Founded: 1897   Nickname: The Ducks

Secretary: Steve Baker   **(T)** 07768 353 265   **(E)** stevepb42@hotmail.com
Chairman: Graham Read   **Manager:** Tony Joyce   **Prog Ed:** Steve Baker
Ground: Leighton Town FC, Lake Street, Leighton Buzzard, Beds LU7 1RX   **(T)** 01525 373311
Capacity: 2,800   **Seats:** 155   **Covered:** 300   **Midweek Matchday:**   **Clubhouse:** Yes   **Shop:** No

Colours(change): Green/white/white (Orange/black/black)
Previous Names: None
Previous Leagues: Post War: Spartan >1951, Delphian 51-63, Athenian 63-76, Southern 76-88, 2004-10, Conf. 88-89, Isthmian 89-2004
Records: Att: 6,000 v England 1988. **Goalscorer:** Cliff Hercules - 301. **Apps:** Cliff Hercules 651+18.
Senior Honours: Southern League 1987-88. Berks & Bucks Senior Cup x4. Isthmian Cup 1994-95.

10 YEAR RECORD

02-03		03-04		04-05		05-06		06-07		07-08		08-09		09-10		10-11		11-12	
Isth P	17	Isth P	24	SthP	10	SthP	21	SthM	6	SthM	8	SthM	10	SthM	22	SSM P	6	SSM P	4

BERKHAMSTED
Founded: 2009   Nickname: Comrades

Secretary: Grant Hastie   **(T)** 01799 584053   **(E)** gshastie@hotmail.com
Chairman: Steve Davis   **Manager:** Mick Vipond   **Prog Ed:** Grant Hastie
Ground: Broadwater, Lower Kings Road, Berkhamsted HP4 2AL   **(T)** 01442 865977
Capacity: 2,500   **Seats:** 170   **Covered:** 350   **Midweek Matchday:**   **Clubhouse:** Yes   **Shop:** Yes

Colours(change): Yellow/blue/blue (White/black/black)
Previous Names:
Previous Leagues:
Records:
Senior Honours: Spartan South Midlands League Division 1 2009-10, 10-11.

10 YEAR RECORD

02-03	03-04	04-05	05-06	06-07	07-08	08-09	09-10		10-11		11-12	
							SSM1	1	SSM1	1	SSM P	7

BIGGLESWADE UNITED
Founded: 1929 · Nickname:

Secretary: Tracey James   **(T)** 07714 661 827   **(E)** tracey.james58@btinternet.com

Chairman: Steve Rowland   **Manager:** Phil Childs   **Prog Ed:** Tracey James

Ground: Second Meadow, Fairfield Rd, Biggleswade, Beds SG18 0BS   **(T)** 01767 600 408

Capacity: 2,000   **Seats:** 30   **Covered:** 130   **Midweek Matchday:** Wednesday   **Clubhouse:** Yes   **Shop:** No

Colours(change): Red/navy/red (Yellow/royal blue/yellow)
Previous Names: None
Previous Leagues: Beds & District and Midland. Herts County.
Records: Att: 250 v Biggleswade Town
Senior Honours: Spartan South Midlands Division One 1996-97, Premier Division 2008-09. Hunts FA Premier Cup 1998-99. Beds Senior Trophy 2003-04. Beds Senior Cup 2001-02.

10 YEAR RECORD

02-03	03-04	04-05	05-06	06-07	07-08	08-09	09-10	10-11	11-12
SSM1 8	SSM1 8	SSM1 3	SSM P 9	SSM P 14	SSM P 18	SSM P 1	SSM P 20	SSM P 20	SSM P 19

COLNEY HEATH
Founded: 1907   Nickname: Magpies

Secretary: Martin Marlborough   **(T)** 07960 155 463   **(E)** m.marlborough@stalbans.gov.uk

Chairman: Martin Marlborough   **Manager:** Glen Parry   **Prog Ed:** Martin Marlborough

Ground: The Recreation Ground, High St, Colney Heath, St Albans AL4 0NS   **(T)** 01727 826 188

Capacity: **Seats:**   **Covered:**   **Midweek Matchday:**   **Clubhouse:** Yes   **Shop:**

Colours(change): Black & white stripes/black/black & white (All tangerine or All royal blue)
Previous Names:
Previous Leagues: Herts Senior County League 1953-2000
Records:
Senior Honours: Herts County League Div 2 Champions 1953-54 Div 1 A 55-56, Prem 58-99, 99-00, Div 1 88-89, Spartan South Midlands Div 1 2005-06 , SSML Cup 05-06

10 YEAR RECORD

02-03	03-04	04-05	05-06	06-07	07-08	08-09	09-10	10-11	11-12
SSM1 5	SSM1 6	SSM1 5	SSM1 1	SSM P 16	SSM P 15	SSM P 12	SSM P 5	SSM P 5	SSM P 8

DUNSTABLE TOWN
Founded: 1998   Nickname: The Blues

Secretary: Paul Harris   **(T)** 07798 716 263   **(E)** hpaulharris@aol.com

Chairman: Roger Dance   **Manager:** Darren Croft & Paul Reeve   **Prog Ed:** Paul Harris

Ground: Creasey Park Stadium, Brewers Hill Rd, Dunstable LU6 1BB   **(T)** 07798 716 263

Capacity: 3,500   **Seats:** 350   **Covered:** 1000   **Midweek Matchday:** Tuesday   **Clubhouse:** Yes   **Shop:** Yes

Colours(change): All blue (All red)
Previous Names:
Previous Leagues: Spartan South Midlands 1998-2000. Isthmian 2003. Southern 2004-09.
Records:
Senior Honours: Spartan Sth. Midlands Div.1 1999-00. Premier 02-03. Bedfordshire Senior Cup 03-04, 08-09.

10 YEAR RECORD

02-03	03-04	04-05	05-06	06-07	07-08	08-09	09-10	10-11	11-12
SSM P 1	Isth1N 5	SthP 20	SthW 21	SthM 11	SthM 13	SthM 21	SSM P 7	SSM P 7	SSM P 2

HADLEY
Founded: 1882   Nickname:

Secretary: Bob Henderson   **(T)** 07748 267 295   **(E)** gensecretary@hadleyfc.com

Chairman: Guy Slee   **Prog Ed:** Guy Slee

Manager: Franco Sidoli

Ground: Potters Bar Town FC, Watkins Rise (off The Walk), Potters Bar EN6 1QB   **(T)** 01707 654 833

Capacity: 2,000   **Seats:** 150   **Covered:** 250   **Midweek Matchday:**   **Clubhouse:** Yes   **Shop:** Yes

Colours(change): Red/black/black (Black & white stripes/white/white)
Previous Names:
Previous Leagues: Barnet & Dist. 1922-57, Nth Suburban 57-70, Mid Herts 70-77, Herts Sen. 77-85, 99-2007, Sth Olym. 85-99, W Herts 2007-08.
Records:
Senior Honours: Hertfordshire Senior County League Division 3 1977-78, Division 1 2001-02, Premier 2003-04, 04-05. West Hertfordshire League 2007-08. Aubrey Cup 2005-06.

10 YEAR RECORD

02-03	03-04	04-05	05-06	06-07	07-08	08-09	09-10	10-11	11-12
HertP 8	HertP 1	HertP 1	HertP 3	HertP 2	WHert 1	SSM2 2	SSM1 2	SSM P 14	SSM P 15

HANWELL TOWN
Founded: 1948 Nickname: Magpies

Secretary: Clive Cooke **(T)** 07791 314 689 **(E)** clivecooke2@sky.com
Chairman: Bob Fisher **Manager:** Ray Duffy **Prog Ed:** Bob Fisher
Ground: Reynolds Field, Preivale Lane, Perivale, Greenford, UB6 8TL **(T)** 0208 997 1801
Capacity: 1,250 **Seats:** 175 **Covered:** 600 **Midweek Matchday:** Tuesday **Clubhouse:** Yes **Shop:** No
Colours(change): Black & white stripes/black/black & white (Sky blue/navy blue/sky blue)
Previous Names:
Previous Leagues: Dauntless. Wembley & Dist. Middlesex. London Spartan. Southern.
Records: **Att:** 600 v Spurs **Goalscorer:** Keith Rowlands. **App:** Phil Player 617 (20 seasons)
Senior Honours: London Spartan Senior Div. 83-84. London Senior Cup 1991-92, 92-93.

10 YEAR RECORD

02-03		03-04		04-05		05-06		06-07		07-08		08-09		09-10		10-11		11-12	
SSM P	8	SSM P	6	SSM P	2	SSM P	3	SthS	21	SSM P	9	SSM P	7	SSM P	13	SSM P	15	SSM P	21

HAREFIELD UNITED
Founded: 1868 Nickname: Hares

Secretary: Glenn Bellis **(T)** 07973 563 282 **(E)** glennbellis@btconnect.com
Chairman: Keith Ronald **Manager:** Phil Granville **Prog Ed:** Keith Ronald
Ground: Preston Park, Breakespeare Road North, Harefield, UB9 6NE **(T)** 01895 824 287
Capacity: 1,200 **Seats:** 150 **Covered:** Yes **Midweek Matchday:** Tuesday **Clubhouse:** Yes **Shop:** No
Colours(change): Red/black/black. (Yellow/red/red)
Previous Names:
Previous Leagues: Uxbridge & District, Great Western Comb, Panthernon, Middlesex, Athenian & Isthmian.
Records: **Att:** 430 v Bashley FA Vase
Senior Honours: Middlesex Premier Cup 1985-86

10 YEAR RECORD

02-03		03-04		04-05		05-06		06-07		07-08		08-09		09-10		10-11		11-12	
SSM P	4	SSM P	5	SSM P	5	SSM P	4	SSM P	2	SSM P	5	SSM P	2	SSM P	6	SSM P	21	SSM P	18

HARINGEY BOROUGH
Founded: 1907 Nickname: Borough

Secretary: John Bacon **(T)** 07979 050 190 **(E)** clubsecretary@haringeyboroughfc.com
Chairman: Aki Achillea **Manager:** Tom Loizu **Prog Ed:** John Bacon
Ground: Coles Park, White Hart Lane, Tottenham, London N17 7JP **(T)** 0208 889 1415 (Matchday)
Capacity: 2,500 **Seats:** 280 **Covered:** yes **Midweek Matchday:** **Clubhouse:** Yes **Shop:** No
Colours(change): Yellow/green/yellow (Green/yellow/green)
Previous Names: Tufnell Park 1907
Previous Leagues: London, Isthmian, Spartan, Delphian, Athenian
Records: **Att:** 400
Senior Honours: London Senior Cup 1912-13, 90-91, Athenian League 1913-14

10 YEAR RECORD

02-03		03-04		04-05		05-06		06-07		07-08		08-09		09-10		10-11		11-12	
SSM P	15	SSM P	18	SSM P	18	SSM P	19	SSM P	21	SSM1	2	SSM P	18	SSM P	15	SSM P	8	SSM P	5

HATFIELD TOWN
Founded: 1886 Nickname: Blueboys

Secretary: Joanne Maloney **(T)** 07725 071 014 **(E)** secretary@hatfieldtownfc.co.uk
Chairman: Chris Maloney **Manager:** Mike Hollister **Prog Ed:** Tom Bailey
Ground: Gosling Sport Park, Stanborough Rd, Welwyn Garden City, Herts AL8 6XE **(T)** 01707 384 300
Capacity: 1,500 **Seats:** 40 **Covered:** 120 **Midweek Matchday:** **Clubhouse:** Yes **Shop:** Yes
Colours(change): All royal blue. (Orange/white/white).
Previous Names: Hatfield FC > 1906. Hatfield Utd > 1922. Hatfield Utd Ath. > 1948
Previous Leagues: Mid. Hertfordshire. Herts County. Parthenon. London. Metropolitan.
Records:
Senior Honours: Herts Senior Champions 2007-08

10 YEAR RECORD

02-03		03-04		04-05		05-06		06-07		07-08		08-09		09-10		10-11		11-12	
Hert1	1	HertP	7	HertP	3	HertP	2	HertP	5	HertP	1	SSM1	3	SSM P	12	SSM P	11	SSM P	22

HERTFORD TOWN

Founded: 1908   Nickname: The Blues

Secretary: Michael Persighetti   **(T)** 07530 056 401   **(E)** m.persighetti@ntlworld.com

Chairman: Peter Sinclair   **Manager:** Marvin Samuel   **Prog Ed:** Daniel Sinclair

Ground: Hertingfordbury Park, West Street, Hertford, SG13 8EZ   **(T)** 01992 583 716

Capacity: 6,500   **Seats:** 200   **Covered:** 1,500   **Midweek Matchday:** Tuesday   **Clubhouse:** Yes   **Shop:** Yes

Colours(change): All blue (Yellow/black/yellow)
Previous Names:
Previous Leagues: Herts Co. Spartan. Delphian 59-63. Athenian 63-72. Eastern Co 72-73.
Records: **Att:** 5,000 v Kingstonian FA Am Cup 2nd Round 55-56   **App:** Robbie Burns
Senior Honours: Herts Senior Cup 66-67 East Anglian Cup 62-63, 69-70

10 YEAR RECORD

02-03	03-04	04-05	05-06	06-07	07-08	08-09	09-10	10-11	11-12
Isth1N 24	Isth2 3	Isth2 4	Isth2 13	SSM P 3	SSM P 4	SSM P 10	SSM P 16	SSM P 9	SSM P 16

HILLINGDON BOROUGH

Founded: 19190   Nickname: Boro

Secretary: Graham Smith   **(T)** 01895 673 181   **(E)** jackieandgraham@talktalk.net

Chairman: Mick Harris   **Manager:** Jesse Smith   **Prog Ed:** Oliver Chalk

Ground: Middlesex Stadium, Breakspear Rd, Ruislip HA4 7SB   **(T)** 01895 639 544

Capacity: 1,500   **Seats:** 150   **Covered:** 150   **Midweek Matchday:**   **Clubhouse:** Yes   **Shop:**

Colours(change): White/royal blue/royal (All purple or Navy blue/yellow/navy blue)
Previous Names: Yiewsley. Bromley Park Rangers.
Previous Leagues: Southern 1964-84, 2006-08. South Midlands 1990-2006. Isthmian 2008-09.
Records:
Senior Honours: South Midlands Cup 1996-97.

10 YEAR RECORD

02-03	03-04	04-05	05-06	06-07	07-08	08-09	09-10	10-11	11-12
SSM P 12	SSM P 12	SSM P 6	SSM P 2	SthW 16	SthW 13	Isth1N 22	SSM P 18	SSM P 16	SSM P 10

HOLMER GREEN

Founded: 1908   Nickname:

Secretary: John Ostinelli   **(T)** 07900 081 814   **(E)** j.ostinelli@sky.com

Chairman: Frank Francies   **Manager:** Chris Allen   **Prog Ed:** John Anderson

Ground: Airedale Park, Watchet Lane, Holmer Green, Bucks HP15 6UF   **(T)** 01494 711 485

Capacity: 1,000   **Seats:** 25   **Covered:** yes   **Midweek Matchday:** Tuesday   **Clubhouse:** Yes   **Shop:**

Colours(change): Green & white stripes/green/green (All red)
Previous Names:
Previous Leagues: Chesham 1908-38, Wycombe Combination 1984-95, Chiltonian 1995-98.
Records:
Senior Honours: Spartan South Midlands Senior 1995-96, 98-99, Division 1 2009-10.

10 YEAR RECORD

02-03	03-04	04-05	05-06	06-07	07-08	08-09	09-10	10-11	11-12
SSM P 19	SSM P 19	SSM P 13	SSM P 7	SSM P 19	SSM P 20	SSM P 20	SSM1 1	SSM P 17	SSM P 20

LEVERSTOCK GREEN

Founded: 1895   Nickname: The Green

Secretary: Brian Barter   **(T)** 07982 072 783   **(E)** b.barter@btopenworld.com

Chairman: Kate Binns   **Manager:** Steven Benitez   **Prog Ed:** Brian Barter

Ground: Pancake Lane, Leverstock Green, Hemel Hempstead, Herts HP2 4NQ   **(T)** 01442 246 280

Capacity: 1,500   **Seats:** 50   **Covered:** 100   **Midweek Matchday:** Tuesday   **Clubhouse:** Yes   **Shop:** No

Colours(change): White/green/green. (Yellow/blue/blue or Green & yellow/green/green)
Previous Names: None
Previous Leagues: West Herts (pre 1950) & Herts County 50-91
Records: **Att:** 1,000   **App:** Jonnie Wallace
Senior Honours: South Midlands Senior Division 1996-97.

10 YEAR RECORD

02-03	03-04	04-05	05-06	06-07	07-08	08-09	09-10	10-11	11-12
SSM1 4	SSM P 9	SSM P 14	SSM P 6	SSM P 5	SSM P 7	SSM P 6	SSM P 10	SSM P 4	SSM P 11

LONDON COLNEY

Founded: 1907 Nickname: Blueboys

Secretary: Dave Brock **(T)** 07508 035835 **(E)** davebrock42@hotmail.com

Chairman: Tony Clafton **Manager:** Ryan Thompson **Prog Ed:** Tony Clafton

Ground: Cotlandswick Playing Fields, London Colney, Herts AL2 1DW **(T)** 01727 822132

Capacity: **Seats:** **Covered:** **Midweek Matchday:** **Clubhouse:** **Shop:**

Colours(change): All royal blue (Red & black or black & white stripes/black/black)
Previous Names:
Previous Leagues: Herts Senior 1955-93.
Records: 300 v St Albans City Hertfordshire Senior Cup 1998-99.
Senior Honours: Herts Senior League 1956-57, 59-60, 86-87, 88-89. 89-90.
South Midlands Senior Division 1994-95. Spartan South Midlands Premier Division 2001-02, Division One 2011-12.

10 YEAR RECORD

02-03		03-04		04-05		05-06		06-07		07-08		08-09		09-10		10-11		11-12	
SSM P	6	SSM P	7	SSM P	11	SSM P	14	SSM P	10	SSM P	22	SSM1	9	SSM1	3	SSM1	5	SSM1	1

LONDON TIGERS

Founded: 2006 Nickname: Tigers

Secretary: Jawar Ali **(T)** 07791 270 634 **(E)** info@londontigers.org

Chairman: Mesba Ahmed **Manager:** Goergij Minashvili **Prog Ed:** Sulthana Begum

Ground: Avenue Park, Western Avenue, Perivale, Greenford UB6 8GA **(T)** 020 7289 3395 (10am-6pm)

Capacity: **Seats:** **Covered:** **Midweek Matchday:** **Clubhouse:** **Shop:**

Colours(change): Orange/black/black (Yellow/blue/blue)
Previous Names: Kingsbury Town and London Tigers merged in 2006. Kingsbury London Tigers 2006-11.
Previous Leagues: None
Records:
Senior Honours:

10 YEAR RECORD

02-03	03-04	04-05	05-06	06-07		07-08		08-09		09-10		10-11		11-12	
				SSM P	13	SSM P	14	SSM P	5	SSM P	8	SSM P	12	SSM P	14

OXHEY JETS

Founded: Nickname: Jets

Secretary: David Fuller **(T)** 07786 627 659 **(E)** d.g.fuller@ntlworld.com

Chairman: Phil Andrews **Manager:** Benny Higham **Prog Ed:** John Elliott

Ground: Boundary Stadium, Altham Way, South Oxhey, Watford WD19 6FW **(T)** 020 8421 6277

Capacity: 1,000 **Seats:** 100 **Covered:** 100 **Midweek Matchday:** Wednesday **Clubhouse:** Yes **Shop:** No

Colours(change): All royal blue (White/black/black)
Previous Names:
Previous Leagues: Herts Senior County
Records: **Att:** 257 v Barnet Herts Senior Cup 05-06 **App:** Ian Holdon
Senior Honours: Herts Senior County Premier 2000-01, 01-02, 02-03. SSML Div 1 Champions 2004-2005,
Herts Senior Centenary Trophy 2004-2005

10 YEAR RECORD

02-03		03-04		04-05		05-06		06-07		07-08		08-09		09-10		10-11		11-12	
HertP	1	HertP	2	SSM1	1	SSM P	13	SSM P	7	SSM P	19	SSM P	13	SSM P	11	SSM P	19	SSM P	17

ST MARGARETSBURY

Founded: 1894 Nickname: Athletic

Secretary: Richard Palette **(T)** 07721 679 681 **(E)** richardpalette@aol.com

Chairman: Gary Stock **Manager:** Lee Judges **Prog Ed:** Gary Stock

Ground: Recreation Ground, Station Road, St Margarets SG12 8EW **(T)** 01920 870 473

Capacity: 1,000 **Seats:** 60 **Covered:** 60 **Midweek Matchday:** Tuesday **Clubhouse:** Yes **Shop:** No

Colours(change): Red & black stripes/black/black (Yellow & blue stripes/blue/yellow)
Previous Names: Stanstead Abbots > 1962
Previous Leagues: East Herts, Hertford & District, Waltham & District, 47-48 Herts Co. 48-92
Records: **Att:** 450 v Stafford Rangers FA Cup 2001-02
Senior Honours: Spartan Lg 95-96 Herts Senior Centenary Trophy 92-93, Herts Charity Shield 97-98

10 YEAR RECORD

02-03		03-04		04-05		05-06		06-07		07-08		08-09		09-10		10-11		11-12	
SSM P	5	SSM P	3	SSM P	7	SSM P	12	SSM P	15	SSM P	11	SSM P	14	SSM P	14	SSM P	18	SSM P	12

STOTFOLD
Founded: 1946   Nickname: The Eagles

Secretary: Julie Longhurst   **(T)** 07752 430 493   **(E)** julie.longhurst@btinternet.com
Chairman: Phil Pateman   **Manager:** Steve Young   **Prog Ed:** Phil Pateman
Ground: Roker Park, The Green, Stotfold, Hitchin, Herts SG5 4AN   **(T)** 01462 730 765
Capacity: 5,000 **Seats:** 300 **Covered:** 300 **Midweek Matchday:** Tuesday   **Clubhouse:** Yes **Shop:**

Colours(change): Amber/black/black. (All burgundy).
Previous Names:
Previous Leagues: Biggleswade & Dist, Norths Herts & South Midlands, United Counties > 2010
Records: Att:1,000 **Goalscorer:** Roy Boon **Apps:** Roy Boon & Dave Chellew
Senior Honours: S. Midlands League 1980-81. Bedfordshire Senior Cup 1964-65, 93-94. Bedfordshire Premier Cup 1981-82, 98-99. United Counties League 2007-08.

10 YEAR RECORD
02-03	03-04	04-05	05-06	06-07	07-08	08-09	09-10	10-11	11-12
UCL P 17	UCL P 10	UCL P 9	UCL P 11	UCL P 19	UCL P 1	UCL P 2	UCL P 7	SSM P 13	SSM P 9

TRING ATHLETIC
Founded: 1958   Nickname: Athletic

Secretary: Bob Winter   **(T)** 07979 816 528   **(E)** robert.winter2007@ntlworld.com
Chairman: Mick Eldridge   **Manager:** Julian Robinson   **Prog Ed:** Barry Simmons
Ground: Grass Roots Stadium, Pendley Sports Centre, Cow Lane, Tring HP23 5NT   **(T)** 01442 891 144
Capacity: 1,233 **Seats:** 150 **Covered:** 100+ **Midweek Matchday:** Tuesday   **Clubhouse:** Yes **Shop:** Yes

Colours(change): Red/black/black (Yellow/green/green)
Previous Names: None
Previous Leagues: West Herts 58-88
Records: **Goalscorer:** Andy Humphreys - 209 **App:** Mark Boniface - 642
Senior Honours: Spartan South Midlands Senior Division 1999-00

10 YEAR RECORD
02-03	03-04	04-05	05-06	06-07	07-08	08-09	09-10	10-11	11-12
SSM1 3	SSM1 4	SSM P 4	SSM P 10	SSM P 11	SSM P 10	SSM P 8	SSM P 3	SSM P 2	SSM P 6

DIVISION ONE

AMERSHAM TOWN
Founded: Nickname:

Secretary: Michael Gahagan   **(T)** 07979 081827   **(E)** amgahagan@btinternet.com
Chairman: Lawrence Lipka   **Manager:** Chris Martin   **Prog Ed:** Michael Gahagan
Ground: Spratleys Meadow, School Lane, Amersham, Bucks HP7 0EL   **(T)** No telephone   **Capacity:**
Colours(change): Black & white stripes/black/black (All yellow)

ADDITIONAL INFORMATION:

BEDFORD
Founded: 1957   Nickname:

Secretary: Paolo Riccio   **(T)** 07868 370 464   **(E)** paolo.riccio@ntlworld.com
Chairman: Lui La Mura   **Manager:** Luigi Rocco   **Prog Ed:** Paul Warne
Ground: McMullen Park, Meadow Lane, Cardington, Bedford, MK44 3SB   **(T)** 07831 594 444 or 07868 **Capacity:**
Colours(change): Purple/purple/white (Black & white stripes/black/black)

ADDITIONAL INFORMATION:
Previous League: United Counties 1970-80.
Record Att: (at Fairhill) 1,500 v Bedford Town-South Mids Div 1 1992 **Apps:** Simon Fordham - 418

BUCKINGHAM ATHELTIC
Founded: Nickname:

Secretary: Colin Howkins   **(T)** 07751 659 769   **(E)** colin@thehowkins.co.uk
Chairman: Stephen Orme   **Manager:** Damien Wiffin   **Prog Ed:** Colin Howkins
Ground: Stratford Fields, Stratford Road, Buckingham MK18 1NY   **(T)** 01280 816945 (MD)   **Capacity:**
Colours(change): Sky blue/navy blue/navy blue (Yellow/black/yellow)

ADDITIONAL INFORMATION:

CHESHAM UNITED RESERVES

Founded: Nickname:

Secretary: Alan Lagden   **(T)** 01494 782 022   **(E)** alan.lagden@sky.com
Chairman: Brian McCarthy   **Manager:** Paul Burgess   **Prog Ed:** Alan Calder
Ground: The Meadow, Amy Lane, Chesham, Bucks HP5 1NE   **(T)** 01494 783 964   **Capacity:**
Colours(change): All claret (Yellow/black/yellow)

ADDITIONAL INFORMATION:

COCKFOSTERS

Founded: 1921   Nickname: Fosters

Secretary: Graham Bint   **(T)** 07729 709926   **(E)** graham.bint@ntlworld.com
Chairman: Roy Syrett   **Manager:** Mick Roche   **Prog Ed:** Alan Simmons
Ground: Cockfosters Sports Ground, Chalk Lane, Cockfosters, Herts EN4 9JG   **(T)** 020 8449 5833   **Capacity:**
Colours(change): All red (White/blue/white)

ADDITIONAL INFORMATION:
Record Att: 408 v Saffron Walden.
Honours: London Interim Cup 1970-71, 89. Herts Sen Co Lge 78-79, 80-81. Aubrey Cup 78-79, 84-85. Herts Interm Cup 78-79

CODICOTE

Founded: 1913   Nickname:

Secretary: Ian Moody   **(T)** 07980 920 674   **(E)** codicote.fc@hotmail.co.uk
Chairman: James Bundy   **Manager:** Liam Errington   **Prog Ed:** James Bundy
Ground: Gosling Sports Park, Stanborough Road, Welwyn Garden City Herts AL8 6XR   **(T)** 01707 331 056   **Capacity:**
Colours(change): Red/white/white (White/black/black)

ADDITIONAL INFORMATION:
Previous Leagues: Hertfordshire County 1913-27, 1993-2012. North Hertfordshire 1927-93.
Honours: North Herts League Division One 1929-30, 1974-75, Division Two 1968-69, Premier Division 1977-78.
Herts Senior County League 2011-12.

CRANFIELD UNITED

Founded: Nickname:

Secretary: Larry Corkrey   **(T)** 07854 936405   **(E)** larrycor@btinternet.com
Chairman: Tony Beal   **Manager:** Lee Bearman   **Prog Ed:** Larry Corkrey
Ground: Crawley Road, Cranfield, Beds MK43 0AA   **(T)** 01234 751444   **Capacity:**
Colours(change): Red & white stripes/white/white (Navy blue/white/white)

ADDITIONAL INFORMATION:

CRAWLEY GREEN

Founded: 1988   Nickname:

Secretary: Eddie Downey   **(T)** 07956 107477   **(E)** eddied@thamesideltd.co.uk
Chairman: Alan Clark   **Manager:** Mark Smith   **Prog Ed:** Alan Clark
Ground: Barton Rovers FC, Sharpenhoe Road, Barton Le Cay, Beds MK45 4SD   **(T)** 01582 882 398   **Capacity:**
Colours(change): All maroon (Sky blue/navy/sky blue)

ADDITIONAL INFORMATION:

HARPENDEN TOWN

Founded: 1891   Nickname: Town

Secretary: Les Crabtree   **(T)** 07968 120032   **(E)** les-crabtree@lineone.net
Chairman: Les Crabtree   **Manager:** Bob Fowler   **Prog Ed:** Dennis Gibbs
Ground: Rothamstead Park, Amenbury Lane, Harpenden AL5 2EF   **(T)** 07968 120032   **Capacity:**
Colours(change): Yellow/royal blue/royal blue (Red/red/black)

ADDITIONAL INFORMATION:
Previous Name: Harpenden FC 1891-1908. **Previous League:** Hertfordshire County.
Honours: South Midlands League x2. Hertfordshire Junior Cup x5.

HODDESDON TOWN

Founded: Formed: 1879 Nickname: Lilywhites

Secretary: Jane Sinden   **(T)** 01767 631 297 & fax   **(E)** janedsinden@fsmail.net
Chairman: Roger Merton   **Manager:** Andy Crawford   **Prog Ed:** Jane Sinden
Ground: The Stewart Edwards Stadium, Lowfield, Park View Hoddesdon EN11 8PX   **(T)** 01992 463 133   **Capacity:**
Colours(change): White/black/black (All blue)

ADDITIONAL INFORMATION:
HONOURS (FA Comps & League): FA Vase 1974-75 (1st Winners).
Spartan League Champions 1970-71, Division 1 1935-36, Division 2 'B' 1927-28

KENTISH TOWN
Founded: 1994 **Nickname:** Townies

Secretary: Kevin Young **(T)** 07828 288 238 **(E)** kevin.young63@virginmedia.com
Chairman: Catherine Dye **Manager:** John Creith **Prog Ed:** Franco Zanre
Ground: Middlesex Stadium (Hillingdon B. FC), Breakspear Rd, Ruislip, Middlesex HA4 7SB **(T)** 01895 639 544 **Capacity:**
Colours(change): Sky & navy/navy/navy (Red & black/black/black)

ADDITIONAL INFORMATION:

KINGS LANGLEY
Founded: **Nickname:**

Secretary: Andy Mackness **(T)** 07976 692801 **(E)** andymackness@yahoo.co.uk
Chairman: Derry Edgar **Manager:** Ritchie Hanlon & Paul Hughes **Prog Ed:** Roy Mitchard
Ground: Gaywood Park, Hempstead Road, Kings Langley Herts WD4 8BS **(T)** 07976 692801 **Capacity:**
Colours(change): Black & white stripes/black/black (Red & white stripes/blue/red)

ADDITIONAL INFORMATION:

LANGFORD
Founded: 1908 **Nickname:** Reds

Secretary: Chris Gordon **(T)** 07876 501 357 **(E)** chrisg5@ntlworld.com
Chairman: Ian Chessum **Manager:** Wesley Byrne **Prog Ed:** Ian Chessum
Ground: Forde Park, Langford Road, Henlow, Beds SG16 6AG **(T)** 01462 816 106 **Capacity:** 2,000
Colours(change): All red. (All blue).

ADDITIONAL INFORMATION: Att: 450 v QPR 75th Anniversary 1985

LONDON LIONS
Founded: **Nickname:**

Secretary: Basil Wein **(T)** 07970 661990 **(E)** basilw@londonlions.com
Chairman: David Pollock **Manager:** Tony Gold **Prog Ed:** Dan Jacobs
Ground: Rowley Lane Sports Ground, Rowley Lane, Arkley, Barnet, Herts EN5 3HW **(T)** 020 84441 6051 **Capacity:**
Colours(change): All blue (All red or yellow/black/black)

ADDITIONAL INFORMATION:

NEW BRADWELL ST PETER
Founded: 1902 **Nickname:** Peters

Secretary: Ian Rollins **(T)** 07912 076473 **(E)** honsecretary@newbradwellstpeter.co.uk
Chairman: Scott Booden **Manager:** Simon Jay **Prog Ed:** TBA
Ground: Recreation Ground, Bradwell Road, Bradville, Milton Keynes MK13 7AD **(T)** 01908 313835 **Capacity:**
Colours(change): All maroon (Yellow/blue/blue)

ADDITIONAL INFORMATION:
Honours: South Midlands Division 1 1976-77, 83-84, Senior Division 1997-98. Berks & Berks Senior Trophy 1999-2000.

SOUTHALL
Founded: 1871 **Nickname:**

Secretary: Aman Jaswal **(T)** 07957 168 370 **(E)** apnayouth@gmail.com
Chairman: Channa Singh **Manager:** Colin Brown **Prog Ed:** Jugfesh Singh Dhillon
Ground: Hanwell Town FC, Perivale Lane, Perivale, Greenford, Middlesex UB6 8TL **(T)** 020 8998 1701 **Capacity:**
Colours(change): Red & white/black/black (Light blue & white stripes/blue/dark blue)

ADDITIONAL INFORMATION:
Previous Names: Southall Athletic.

STONY STRATFORD TOWN
Founded: 1898 **Nickname:**

Secretary: Steve Sartain **(T)** 07901 664000 **(E)** steve.sartain456@btinternet.com
Chairman: Philip Smith **Manager:** James Cain **Prog Ed:** Terry Springer
Ground: Ostlers Lane, Stony Stratford, Milton Keynes MK11 1AR **(T)** 07914 012 709 **Capacity:**
Colours(change): Sky blue & navy/navy/navy (Yellow/black/black, yellow or white)

ADDITIONAL INFORMATION:
Previous League: Northampton Combination.
Record Att: 476 v Aston Villa U21 1996.

SUN POSTAL SPORTS
Founded:　　Nickname:

Secretary: Maurice Tibbles　**(T)** 07895 066075　**(E)** sunpostalsports@btconnect.com
Chairman: Jim Kempster　**Manager:** Mark Faulkner　**Prog Ed:** TBA
Ground: Sun Postal Sports Club, Mountwood Avenue, Watford, Herts WD17 3BM　**(T)** 01923 227 453　**Capacity:**
Colours(change): Yellow/blue/blue (Orange/black/orange)

ADDITIONAL INFORMATION:
Previous Names: Sun Postal Sports 2003. Sun Sports 2005.
Previous League: Hertfordshire Senior County > 2003.

WELWYN GARDEN CITY
Founded: 1921　Nickname: Citizens

Secretary: Karen Browne　**(T)** 07876 232 670　**(E)** kazzie.browne@gmail.com
Chairman: Ray Fiveash　**Manager:** Scott O'Donoghue　**Prog Ed:** Karen Browne
Ground: Herns Way, Welwyn Garden City, Herts AL7 1TA　**(T)** 01707 329 358　**Capacity:**
Colours(change): All claret (Orange/black/orange)

ADDITIONAL INFORMATION:
Previous League: Metropolitan & Greater London.
Honours: South Midlands League 1973-74, Division 1 1981-82.

WINSLOW UNITED
Founded: 1891　Nickname:

Secretary: David Ward　**(T)** 07944 258 838　**(E)**
Chairman: Colin O'Dell　**Manager:** Kit Bamber　**Prog Ed:** Richard Warner
Ground: The Recreation Ground, Elmfields Gate, Winslow, Bucks MK18 3JG　**(T)** 01296 713 057　**Capacity:**
Colours(change): Yellow/blue/yellow (All orange)

ADDITIONAL INFORMATION:

WODSON PARK
Founded:　　Nickname:

Secretary: Lucy Bailey　**(T)** 07909 904 454　**(E)** lucy.bailey@wodsonmail.co.uk
Chairman: Lee Cook　**Manager:** Simon Riddle　**Prog Ed:** Lucy Bailey
Ground: Ware FC, Wadesmill Road, Herts SG12 0UQ　**(T)** 07909 904 454　**Capacity:**
Colours(change): Sky & navy blue stripes/navy blue/navy blue (Black & red stripes/navy/navy)

ADDITIONAL INFORMATION:

SPARTAN SOUTH MIDLANDS DIVISION TWO CONSTITUTION 2012-13

ASTON CLINTON .... Aston Clinton Park, London Road, Aston Clinton, Bucks. HP22 5HL...........................01296 631818

AYLESBURY RESERVES..............The Affinity Stadium, Haywood Way, Aylesbury, Bucks HP19 9WZ.............................01296 421101

BROXBOURNE BOROUGH V&E............. V & E Club, Goffs Lane, Cheshunt, Herts EN7 5QN...01992 624281

CADDINGTON ....Caddington Recreation Club, Manor Road, Caddington, Luton, Beds LU1 4HH....................01582 450151

HALE LEYS UNITED ....Ostlers Field, Brook End, Weston Turville, Aylesbury, Bucks HP22 5RN.........................01296 612556

KENT ATHLETIC...Tenby Drive, Luton, LU4 9BN 01582 582723

MK WANDERERS.................Kents Hill Pavilion, Frithwood Crescent, Kents Hill, Milton Keynes MK7 6HQ....................07887 570 819

MURSLEY UNITED................................. The Playing Field, Station Road, Mursley MK17 0SA.. No telephone

OLD BRADWELL UNITED.................. Abbey Road, Bradwell Village, Milton Keynes, MK13 9AR....................................01908 312355

PITSTONE AND IVINGHOE ....Pitstone Recreation Ground, Vicarage Road, Pitstone LU7 9EY..........01296 661271 (match days)

RISBOROUGH RANGERS.......... " Windors" Horsenden Lane, Princes Risborough, Bucks HP27 9NE....................07866 178822

THE 61 FC (LUTON).................................Kingsway Ground, Beverley Road, Luton LU4 8EU 07749 531492

TOTTERNHOE............................. Recreation Ground, Dunstable Road, Totternhoe, Beds LU6 1QP..............................01582 606738

TRING CORINTHIANS .... Tring Corinthians FC, Icknield Way, Tring, Herts HP23 5HJ................................07886 528214

WOLVERTON TOWN....................The New Park, Field Lane, Greenleys, Milton Keynes MK12 6AZ.............................07724 137 422

GROUND DIRECTIONS - PREMIER & DIVISION ONE

AFC DUNSTABLE - Creasey Park Stadium, Creasey Park Drive, Brewers Hill Road, Dunstable, Beds LU6 1BB Tel 01582 667555
From the South: When travelling north on the A5, go straight across the lights in the centre of Dunstable. Turn left at the next main set of lights into Brewers Hill Road. You will immediately pass the Fire Station on your left. Carry on until you hit the first roundabout. Go over the roundabout and take the immediate right into Creasey Park Drive. *From North:* When travelling south on the A5, go through the chalk cutting and over the first set of traffic lights. At the next set of lights turn right into Brewers Hill Road. Go over the roundabout and take the immediate right into Creasey Park Drive. Public Transport: Creasey Park is well served by buses. Arriva and Centrebus services from Luton, Houghton Regis Leighton Buzzard and Aylesbury all stop at the bottom of Brewers Hill Road. Some 24 services stop directly opposite Creasey Park Drive in Weatherby.

AMERSHAM TOWN - Spratleys Meadow, School Lane, Amersham, Bucks HP7 No telephone
From London, take the A413 towards Aylesbury. At the first roundabout in Amersham where the A413 turns left, keep straight on. Then carry on straight over the next four roundabouts to Amersham Old Town. At the western end of the Old Town turn right into right into Mill Lane. At the top of Mill Lane turn left into School Lane. Ground is 100 yards on the left.

AMPTHILL TOWN - Ampthill Park, Woburn Street, Ampthill Tel: 01525 404440.
From the South, leave M1 at junction 12 Toddington. Turn right as signposted until you meet the junction with the Ampthill bypass. Go straight across until you meet a mini-roundabout at the town centre. Turn left into Woburn Street. The ground is about half a mile on the right, just past a lay-by. From the North, leave the M1 at J13 and turn left. At first set of traffic lights, turn right onto A507 Ridgmont bypass. Continue until you see the right-hand turning signposted for Ampthill. Ground is about a mile on the left, opposite the rugby ground.

AYLESBURY UNITED - Leighton Town FC, Lake Street, Leighton Buzzard, Beds LU7 1RX Tel 01525 373311
From Aylesbury: Take the A418 towards Leighton Buzzard and at the bypass turn right onto the A505. Go straight over the first two roundabouts; then turn left at the third onto the A4146. Stay on the A4146 at the next two roundabouts (second exit, first exit), then carry straight on at the next mini-roundabout. The entrance to the ground is about 50 yards after this mini-roundabout on the left. Car parking is on your left as you turn. Travel from the Midlands using the M1: Leave the M1 at junction 15 and take the A508 towards Milton Keynes. After 9 miles you will reach the A5 roundabout. Take the first exit and travel about 8 miles to the roundabout at the end of the dual carriageway. Take the second exit and follow the A5 towards Dunstable. After about 3 miles you will arrive at another roundabout (Flying Fox pub is on your left) take the third exit towards Heath & Reach and Leighton Buzzard. Follow this road for about 4 miles until you arrive at a large roundabout in Leighton Buzzard then take the first exit. At the next roundabout take the second exit, you will then go through 2 sets of lights. The ground and car park is on the right, immediately after the lights and opposite a petrol station.
From the South: Take the M1 to junction 8 (Hemel Hempstead) and head towards the town centre. As you go down the hill into Hemel you will reach a multi-directional roundabout. Turn right and follow the signs for Leighton Buzzard (A4146). Leighton Buzzard is about 16 miles northwest of Hemel Hempstead along this road.

BEDFORD FC - McMullen Park, Meadow Lane, Cardington, Bedford, MK44 3SB. Tel: 01234 831024
From the M1 Junction 13: take the A421 on to the Bedford Bypass, take the third exit onto the A603, the ground is 250 yards on the left. From the A1 at Sandy: take A603 to Bedford. The ground is on the right just before you reach the Bedford Bypass.

BERKHAMSTED - Broadwater, Lower Kings Road, Berkhamsted HP4 2AL Tel 01442 865977
Exit A41 onto A416. Go straight over the town centre traffic lights in Lower Kings Road. Go over the canal bridge and take first left into Broadwater. Follow the road to the left, going parallel to the canal. The ground is on the right hand side, sandwiched between the canal and the railway.

BIGGLESWADE UNITED - Second Meadow, Fairfield Road, Biggleswade SG18 0BS Tel 01767 316270
From A1 take second roundabout (Sainsbury's NOT Homebase). Cross the river bridge and then take second left into Sun Street then take first left into Fairfield Road and travel to the very end and into lane. From A1 north, take first roundabout (Sainsbury's) and follow previous instructions.

BUCKINGHAM ATHLETIC - Stratford Fields, Stratford Road, Buckingham MK18 1NY Tel: 01280 816945 (match days & opening hours only)
From Oxford, Aylesbury or Bletchley: take the Buckingham ring road to the roundabout where the A422 from Stony Stratford/Deanshanger meet - turn left, towards town centre. The ground is situated on the left behind fir trees at the bottom of the hill where 30mph begins (opposite a recently-built block of luxury apartments). From Milton Keynes: Up A5 then (A422) to Buckingham - straight across roundabout towards the town centre - ground location as above. From M1: come off at junction 13 and follow A421 straight through, turning right where it meets the Buckingham ring road – then follow as above, turning left at the next-but-one roundabout.

CHESHAM UNITED RESERVES - The Meadow, Amy Lane, Chesham, Bucks HP5 1NE Tel 01494 783964
Take J20 off the M25 to the A41 Aylesbury/Hemel follow this road for about 7 miles, your turn off is after the Service Station, the turn off is for Berkhamsted/Chesham, take the right hand lane in the slip road to the A416 to Chesham. Follow this road through Ashley Green (being careful of the speed trap) past the college on your left, when you get to the bottom of the hill take a left turn at the mini roundabout. Follow the road for about 1.5 miles, go straight over the next two roundabouts, then get in to the left lane to take the first exit from the next roundabout, you will pass a pub called the Red Lion on your right shortly after this. Follow the road to a mini roundabout; take the right exit going past two petrol stations either side of the road. Ground is on the third exit off the next roundabout. See club website for other routes.

COCKFOSTERS - Cockfosters Sports Ground, Chalk Lane, Cockfosters, Herts EN4 9JG Tel: 020 8449 5833
Leaving the M25 motorway at junction 24 (Potters Bar), take the A111 signposted to Cockfosters. The ground is situated approximately 2 miles from the motorway on the right immediately before Cockfosters Underground Station. VEHICLE DRIVERS PLEASE BE AWARE THAT THE YELLOW LINES & PARKING RESTRICTIONS IN CHALK LANE ARE STRICTLY ENFORCED UP TO 6.30PM INCLUDING SATURDAYS

CODICOTE - Gosling Sports Park, Stanborough Road, Welwyn Garden City Herts AL8 6XR Tel 01707 331056
From A1 (M), take A414 towards Hertford/Welwyn Garden City. At the roundabout take the first exit onto the A6129, leading to Stanborough/ Wheathampstead. At the next roundabout take the second exit onto the A6129 Stanborough Road. At the next roundabout take the third exit into Gosling Sports Park.

COLNEY HEATH - The Recreation Ground, High Street, Colney Heath, St Albans, Herts AL4 0NS Tel 01727 826188
From the A1, leave at junction 3 and follow A414 St. Albans. At long roundabout take the left into the village and ground is just past the school on left after 400 yards.
From the M25, leave at junction 22 and follow B556 Colney Heath. On entering the village turn left at Queens Head PH (roundabout) and follow High Street for ½ mile. The ground is on the right just before the school.
From M1 going south; leave at junction 7. At Park Street roundabout follow A414 Hatfield. Continue on A414 past London Colney. Enter Colney Heath coming round the long roundabout and into village. The ground is past the school on the left after 400 yards.

CRANFIELD UNITED - Crawley Road, Cranfield, Beds MK43 0AA Tel: 01234 751444.
upon entering the village, take the North Crawley/Newport Pagnell road. The ground is on the left hand side just before leaving the speed limit zone.

CRAWLEY GREEN - Barton Rovers FC, Sharpenhoe Road, Barton Le Cay, Beds MK45 4SD Tel 01582 882398
From M1 J12, turn right from South turn left from North, onto the A5120. After approximately 1.5 miles, take the second turning on the right signposted Harlington and Barton. Follow the road through Sharpenhoe to Barton. At mini-roundabout turn right and after about 400 yards, turn right into the ground. Ground entrance is in Luton Road.

DUNSTABLE TOWN - Creasey Park Drive, Brewers Hill Road, Dunstable, Beds LU6 1BB Tel 01582 667555
From the south: When travelling on the A5, go straight across the lights in the centre of Dunstable. Turn left at the next main set of lights into Brewers Hill Road. You will immediately pass the Fire Station on your left. Carry on until you hit the first roundabout, Go over the roundabout and take the immediate right into Creasey Park Drive. From the north: When travelling south on the A5, go through the chalk cutting and over the first set of traffic lights. At the next set of lights, turn right into Brewers Hill Road. Then proceed as above. From the East: Turn right at the traffic lights in the centre of Dunstable. Turn left at the next main set of traffic lights into Brewers Hill Road. Then proceed as above. From the east: When coming into Dunstable, go straight across the first roundabout you come to. Then turn left at the double mini-roundabout into Drovers Way. Follow this road for about 1/2 mile as it bears to the right and becomes Brewers Hill Road. Go over two mini-roundabouts and just before you hit the larger roundabout, turn left into Creasey Park Drive.
Public Transport: Creasey Park is well served by buses. Arriva and Centrebus services from Luton, Houghton Regis, Leighton Buzzard and Aylesbury all stop at the bottom of Brewers Hill Road. Some 24 services stop directly opposite Creasey Park Drive in Weatherby.

HADLEY - Potters Bar Town FC, Parkfield Stadium, Watkins Rise (off The Walk), Potters Bar EN6 1QB Tel 01707 654833
From M25, exit at junction 24 towards Potters Bar along Southgate Road A111. Turn right at first set of traffic lights into High Street A1000. After the petrol station on the left and pedestrian crossing, take the first left into The Walk. After 200 yards, turn right into Watkins Rise. The ground is at the end on the right. Nearest BR Station: Potters Bar. PLEASE NOTE: do not park in the Mayfair Lodge Home car park opposite the ground. Offenders will be clamped.

HANWELL TOWN - Reynolds Field, Perivale Lane, Greenford, Middlesex UB6 8TL Tel 020 8998 1701
From West, junction 16 M25 and follow A40 (M) towards London. Go over the Greenford flyover and get into the nearside lane signposted Ealing & Perivale. Exit and turn right across the A40. The ground is immediately on the left. Turn left into Perivale Lane and the entrance is 200 yards on the left. Nearest railway station is Perivale (London Underground – Central Line).

HAREFIELD UNITED - Preston Park, Breakspear Road North, Harefield, Middlesex, UB9 6NE Tel: 01895 823474.
From the M25 at Junction 16 turn left. At the roundabout turn right towards Denham and at the next roundabout turn left then right at the end of the road. Turn left by the Pub and follow the road over the canal and into the village. Go straight across the roundabout into Breakspear Road and the ground is approximately 800 metres on the right.

HARINGEY BOROUGH - Coles Park, White Hart Lane, Tottenham, London N17 7JP Tel: 020 8889 1415
At junction 25 of the M25 or from the A406 (North Circular Road) turn south onto the A10 (Great Cambridge Road) towards Central London. At the junction of the A10 and White Hart Lane turn right (use slip road at traffic lights) into White Hart Lane and the ground is about 500 yards on the left, some 150 yards after a petrol station. PUBLIC TRANSPORT: Bus W3 from Finsbury Park station to Northumberland Park station via Alexandra Palace station and Wood Green underground station passes ground. In other direction W3 can be boarded at White Hart Lane station).

HARPENDEN TOWN - Rothamstead Park, Amenbury Lane, Harpenden AL5 2EF Tel: 07968 120032
Approaching Harpenden from St. Albans, turn left into Leyton Road at mini-roundabout by the Silver Cup and Fire Station. Coming from Luton, go through the town and as you leave (just past The George) turn right into Leyton Road. Turn left in Amenbury Lane and then left into car park after 300 yards. Entrance to the Club is up the pathway, diagonally across the car park in the far corner from the entrance. This is a pay-and-display car park up to 6.30pm.

HATFIELD TOWN - Gosling Sports Park, Stanborough Road, Welwyn Garden City, Herts AL8 6XE Tel 01707 384300
From A1 (M) junction 4, take A414 towards Hertford/Welwyn Garden City. At the roundabout take the 1st exit onto the A6129, heading to Stanborough/Wheathampstead. At the next roundabout take the 2nd exit onto the A6129 Stanborough Road. At the next roundabout take the 3rd exit into Gosling Sports Park.

HERTFORD TOWN - Hertingfordbury Park, West Street, Hertford, Herts SG13 8EZ Tel 01992 583716
From the A1 follow the A414 to Hertford until you see Gates Ford Dealership on the right. At next roundabout double back and immediately past Gates (now on your left) turn left into West Street. This is a narrow road and when it bears left, turn right and go down the hill and over a bridge to the ground. From the A10 follow the A414 until you see Gates.

HILLINGDON BOROUGH - Middlesex Stadium, Breakspear Road, Ruislip, Middlesex HA4 7SB Tel 01895 639544
From M40/A40 eastbound, leave the A40 at the Swakeleys roundabout, exit is sign-posted Ickenham & Ruislip and take the B467. At the second mini-roundabout turn left into Breakspear Road South. After approx 1 mile, turn right into Breakspear Road by the Breakspear Arms PH. The ground is a further 1/2 mile on the left-hand side.

HODDESDON TOWN - Stewart Edwards Stadium, Lowfield, Park View, Hoddesdon, Herts, EN11 8PU Tel: 01992 463133
For SatNav users, please key in EN11 8PX, which will take you to Park Road, directly opposite the ground
From the A10, take Hoddesdon turnoff (A1170). Follow the slip road to the roundabout at the bottom of the hill and then turn right into Amwell Street. Take the first right, at the church, into Pauls Lane. Follow the road round to left which becomes Taveners Way. At the mini-roundabout opposite the Iceland store, turn right into Brocket Road. At T junction turn left into Park View and the ground is 200 yards on the right.

HOLMER GREEN - Airedale Park, Watchet Lane, Holmer Green, Bucks HP15 6UF Tel 01494 711485
From Amersham on A404 High Wycombe Road. After approx 2 miles turn right into Sheepcote Dell Road. Continue until end of road at Bat & Ball pub. Turn right, then immediately left. Continue approx 1/2 mile until double mini-roundabouts. Turn left in front of the Mandarin Duck restaurant into Airedale Park 150 yards on the right

KENTISH TOWN - Hillingdon Borough FC, Middlesex Stadium, Breakspear Road, Ruislip, Middlesex HA4 7SB Tel 01895 639544
See above for directions..

KINGS LANGLEY - Gaywood Park, Hempstead Road, Kings Langley Herts WD4 8BS Tel: 07976 692801
From M25 leave at junction 20. Take A4251 to Kings Langley. Go through the village. The ground is approximately 1/2 mile on the right.

LANGFORD - Forde Park, Langford Road, Henlow, Beds SG16 6AG Tel: 01462 816106.
From West along A57 to Henlow then north on A6001. Ground at north end of Henlow
From North and East, leave A1 at Langford water tower then into Langford. Turn left at Boot Restaurant. Follow A6001 round to the left. Club is 1/2 mile away.

LEVERSTOCK GREEN - Pancake Lane, Leverstock Green, Hemel Hempstead, Herts Tel: 01442 246280.
From M1 at Junction 8, Follow A414 to second roundabout turn left along Leverstock Green Way. Pancake Lane is on the left 300 yards past the Leather Bottle Public House. Ground is 300 yards on left. All visitors are requested to park inside the ground.

LONDON COLNEY - Cotlandswick Playing Fields, London Colney, Herts AL2 1DW Tel: 01727 822132.
From M25 J22, follow the A1081 signposted to St Albans. At London Colney roundabout take A414, signposted Hemel Hempstead/Watford. There is a hidden turn into the ground after approximately 500 metres (just after lay-by) signposted Sports Ground and London Colney FC. Follow the ground around between the Rugby and Irish clubs to ground entrance.

LONDON LIONS - Midweek: Hemel Hempstead Town FC. Saturdays: Rowley Lane Sports Ground, Rowley Lane, Arkley, Barnet, Herts EN5 3HW Tel 020 84441 6051
From M25, exit at junction 23 (South Mimms) and take the A1 South. Come off at Borehamwood exit with the Elstree Moat House Holiday Inn visible on the right, and go past the A1 Driving Range (on the left) and turn first left into Rowley Lane. Go through the width restriction and the ground is 200 yards on the right.
From Apex Corner, take the A1 North to Borehamwood and exit at the A5136, doubling back over the A1 towards Barnet and turn first right into Rowley Lane, Then proceed as above.

SPARTAN SOUTH MIDLANDS LEAGUE - STEP 5/6/7

LONDON TIGERS - Avenue Park, Western Avenue, Perivale, Greenford, Middlesex UB6 8GA Tel 020 7289 3395 (10am-6pm) – out of hours please call 07949 189191

Exit junction 16 of the M25 onto the A40 (M) towards London. After you pass the Target roundabout there will be a sharp left turn at the 200yard marker for the Greenford slip road from the A40 into Avenue Park, just past the overhead footbridge. If coming from Central London or Hangar Lane, drive up to the Target roundabout and do a U-turn onto the eastbound carriageway and turn left into Avenue Park after the footbridge. The nearest Tube station is Greenford on the Central Line, which is a 10-minute walk.

NEW BRADWELL ST PETER - Recreation Ground, Bradwell Road, Bradville, Milton Keynes MK13 7AD Tel: 01908 313835.

From M1 J14 go towards Newport Pagnell, turn left at first roundabout into H3 (A422 Monks Way). Go six roundabouts then turn right into V6 (Grafton Street). At first roundabout drive all the way around and then take the first left. At first mini-roundabout, turn left. Go 1/2 mile and straight across next mini-roundabout. Ground is then immediately on the left.

From Bushey Station, take Pinner Road (A4008) and continue along Oxhey Lane (towards Harrow). At the traffic lights turn right into Little Oxhey Lane. Altham Way is on left just after crossing Railway Bridge. Clubhouse is located next to swimming pool. Please park in the Pool/Jets overflow car park to avoid either blocking in cars, or being blocked in yourself.

OXHEY JETS - Boundary Stadium, Altham Way (off Little Oxhey Lane), South Oxhey, Watford WD19 6FW Tel: 020 8421 6277

From Bushey + Oxhey Station, take Pinner Road (A4008) and continue along Oxhey Lane towards Harrow. At the traffic lights turn right into Little Oxhey Lane. Altham Way is on left just after crossing a narrow railway bridge. Please park in the large swimming pool car park marked "Jets overflow parking" to avoid either blocking in cars, or being blocked in.

SOUTHALL - Hanwell Town FC, Perivale Lane, Perivale, Greenford, Middlesex UB6 8TL Tel 020 8998 1701

See Hanwell Town for directions.

ST. MARGARETSBURY - Station Road, St. Margarets, Herts SG12 8EH Tel: 01920 870473

A10 to Cambridge. Exit at A414 Harlow & Chelmsford. Proceed 400 yards to Amwell roundabout and take 3rd exit (B181) to Stanstead Abbotts. Ground is 1/2 mile on the right-hand side.

STONY STRATFORD TOWN - Ostlers Lane, Stony Stratford, Milton Keynes MK11 1AR Tel: 07914 012709

From Dunstable on the A5 heading north: On approaching Bletchley continue on the main A5 trunk road signposted to Towcester & Hinckley. Continue to the very end of dual carriageway, where you will meet a main roundabout. This is where the main A5 intersects with the A508 to Northampton. At this roundabout take first exit, this is the old (single carriageway) A5. Follow the main road, straight through the traffic lights, over the river bridge and take the second turning right into Ostlers Lane. The ground is approx 200yds on the right.

From Buckingham on the A422: Continue on the A422, straight on at the first roundabout (pedestrian footbridge overhead). Continue on until you meet the next roundabout and take the last exit (the old single carriageway A5). Then proceed as above.

STOTFOLD - Roker Park, The Green, Stotfold, Hitchin, Herts SG5 4AN Tel 01462 730765

At A1 junction 10, take the A507 to Stotfold and right into town. Proceed along High Street and at traffic lights turn right (from Hitchin – straight over traffic lights) towards Astwick Turn right at the Crown pub into The Green. The ground is set back from The Green on the left.

SUN POSTAL SPORTS - Sun Postal Sports Club, Mountwood Avenue, Watford, Herts WD17 3BM Tel: 01923 227453

From Watford town centre take the A411 (Hempstead Road) away from the Town Hall towards Hemel Hempstead. At 2nd set of traffic lights turn left into Langley Way. At the next roundabout, where there is a parade of shops on the left and the "Essex Arms" on the right, take the third exit into Cassiobury Drive. Then take the first turn left into Bellmountwood Avenue then at the left hand bend turn right into the Club entrance.

TRING ATHLETIC - The Grass Roots Stadium, Pendley Sports Centre, Cow Lane, Tring, Herts HP23 5NT. Tel: 01442 891144

From M25 take A41 to Aylesbury. At roundabout at junction take last exit sign-posted Berkhamsted. Turn next left into Cow Lane. Stadium is on the right at end of Cow Lane.

WELWYN GARDEN CITY - Herns Way, Welwyn Garden City, Herts AL7 1TA Tel: 01707 329358

Best Route to the Ground: From A1 (M) follow Welwyn Garden City signpost A1000. Take second exit off one-way system, sign-posted Panshanger. Ground is 400 yards on left.

WINSLOW UNITED - The Recreation Ground, Elmfields Gate, Winslow, Bucks MK18 3JG Tel 01296 713057

Best Route to the Ground: A413 from Aylesbury to Winslow, turn right from High Street into Elmfields Gate. Ground is100 yards on left. A421 Milton Keynes to Buckingham, turn left through Great Horwood to Winslow. Turn left from High Street into Elmfields Gate. PLEASE PARK IN PUBLIC CAR PARK OPPOSITE GROUND IF POSSIBLE.

WODSON PARK - Ware FC, Wadesmill Road, Herts SG12 0UQ Tel 01920 463247

From the South: leave the M25 at junction 25 and take the A10 north past Cheshunt and Hoddesdon. After crossing the Lea Valley with Ware below and to your right, leave the A10 at the junction for the A1170 (signposted for Wadesmill and Thundridge). The slip road comes off the A10 onto a roundabout. Turn left (first exit) onto Wadesmill Road (A1170) and come back over the A10 to a second roundabout. Go straight over and take the first turn on the left into Wodson Park Sports Centre. The football ground is on the far left of the car park. From the North: Leave the A10 at the Ware North turn off (A1170). The slip road takes you to a roundabout. Turn right (3rd exit) into Wadesmill Road and take the first left into Wodson Park Sports Centre.

SUSSEX COUNTY LEAGUE

Sponsored by: No sponsor

Founded: 1920

Recent Champions:
2007: Eastbourne Town. 2008: Crowborough Athletic. 2009: Eastbourne United Association.
2010: Whitehawk. 2011: Crawley Down

scfl.org.uk

DIVISION ONE	P	W	D	L	F	A	Pts
1 (P) Three Bridges	38	28	5	5	75	37	89
2 Lancing	38	26	8	4	88	37	86
3 Rye United	38	26	6	6	99	44	84
4 Hassocks	38	22	6	10	89	58	72
5 Peacehaven & Telscombe	38	21	8	9	83	51	71
6 Pagham	38	21	8	9	83	54	71
7 Lingfield (-3)	38	20	8	10	90	56	65
8 AFC Uckfield	38	16	7	15	71	72	55
9 East Grinstead Town	38	17	4	17	71	77	55
10 Redhill	38	16	6	16	85	68	54
11 Sidley United	38	15	5	18	45	60	50
12 Selsey	38	13	5	20	62	75	44
13 Crowborough Athletic	38	12	7	19	69	82	43
14 Worthing United	38	10	12	16	63	91	42
15 Ringmer	38	11	7	20	50	62	40
16 Horsham YMCA	38	12	3	23	53	79	39
17 Arundel	38	10	8	20	59	88	38
18 Shoreham	38	9	9	20	65	93	36
19 St Francis Rangers	38	2	13	23	40	87	19
20 Chichester City	38	4	3	31	36	105	15

DIVISION TWO	P	W	D	L	F	A	Pts
1 (P) East Preston	34	29	3	2	124	34	90
2 (P) Hailsham Town	34	24	6	4	86	34	78
3 (P) Dorking Wanderers	34	21	6	7	80	48	69
4 Littlehampton Town	34	15	12	7	67	39	57
5 Lowood	34	17	4	13	65	68	55
6 Eastbourne Utd Association	34	15	8	11	54	49	53
7 Bexhill United	34	16	5	13	60	64	53
8 Southwick	34	12	12	10	44	40	48
9 Storrington	34	11	8	15	62	59	41
10 Mile Oak	34	12	4	18	55	65	40
11 Rustington	34	10	10	14	52	68	40
12 Westfield	34	9	10	15	58	73	37
13 Steyning Town	34	9	8	17	54	74	35
14 Wick	34	9	6	19	40	70	33
15 Midhurst & Easebourne (-1)	34	10	4	20	62	102	33
16 Little Common	34	8	8	18	53	69	32
17 Seafod Town	34	9	4	21	47	64	31
18 Oakwood	34	5	12	17	44	87	27

DIVISION ONE	1	2	3	4	5	6	7	8	9	10	11	12	13	14	15	16	17	18	19	20
1 AFC Uckfield		2-3	4-1	4-1	3-3	2-0	3-1	0-6	0-3	1-6	0-4	3-0	0-2	3-3	2-0	4-2	1-2	4-1	1-3	4-2
2 Arundel	1-2		2-1	3-2	1-3	2-6	4-3	1-2	1-1	2-4	2-0	1-3	0-1	1-2	1-3	0-5	1-4	2-5	0-2	1-1
3 Chichester City	0-3	1-0		1-2	1-4	1-5	1-4	0-3	1-6	1-2	0-2	1-6	1-1	0-3	2-3	1-3	2-0	4-0	1-2	2-3
4 Crowborough Athletic	1-3	2-2	4-0		4-0	1-2	6-2	0-2	2-2	0-1	2-3	1-7	2-1	3-5	3-1	3-2	0-2	5-0	1-2	4-0
5 East Grinstead Town	1-0	5-2	4-1	2-0		3-0	5-1	0-3	0-4	0-3	0-7	1-3	3-2	1-2	0-3	2-2	2-0	2-1	1-2	4-1
6 Hassocks	4-1	3-3	3-1	2-1	1-2		1-0	0-0	0-1	3-1	1-2	4-2	2-3	2-1	3-1	1-0	1-0	0-0	2-2	4-4
7 Horsham YMCA	0-1	0-2	HW	5-1	4-2	3-1		0-4	0-6	3-3	1-2	0-5	0-1	0-2	0-2	0-1	1-1	1-1	0-1	1-3
8 Lancing	3-0	5-1	2-1	4-2	5-0	2-2	2-1		2-1	5-2	3-3	3-1	2-1	2-3	3-2	1-0	2-0	1-0	2-1	1-2
9 Lingfield	2-1	2-2	5-1	2-4	2-1	1-4	2-1	1-1		3-4	2-4	5-1	1-1	0-5	2-0	2-0	4-1	3-0	1-1	3-0
10 Pagham	3-1	0-3	1-1	1-1	1-1	1-2	1-0	0-1	2-1		2-3	2-1	2-1	3-0	1-1	3-2	3-0	2-0	3-0	4-1
11 Peacehaven & Telscombe	1-3	1-3	2-1	1-1	1-1	0-3	1-2	2-2	3-0	3-0		2-2	1-0	1-3	2-1	1-2	1-0	4-0	1-2	5-1
12 Redhill	1-1	1-1	4-2	1-1	1-1	0-7	7-3	1-2	3-0	0-1	2-1		6-1	1-2	1-0	3-3	5-1	2-2	1-2	2-5
13 Ringmer	1-1	0-1	2-0	1-2	1-0	1-2	2-1	0-2	1-3	3-0	1-2	3-0		1-2	2-3	2-2	0-1	0-0	0-3	2-1
14 Rye United	2-2	5-2	5-0	7-1	3-2	2-3	1-0	1-1	2-2	1-2	1-0	2-0	2-1		8-1	4-0	0-0	5-2	3-0	3-1
15 Selsey	2-1	4-2	0-1	2-0	1-2	2-5	0-2	0-1	4-3	2-2	1-3	0-2	2-2	1-3		6-2	1-1	1-1	0-1	2-0
16 Shoreham	2-5	1-1	2-0	0-0	2-1	0-5	2-4	0-3	1-3	1-1	2-2	0-1	3-5	2-1	0-4		3-4	4-0	1-3	2-2
17 Sidley United	3-1	2-0	HW	5-2	1-3	0-5	0-2	0-3	1-3	0-3	1-3	2-1	1-0	0-2	4-0	4-0		1-1	0-2	0-0
18 St Francis Rangers	1-1	1-1	2-2	0-3	2-3	1-3	4-5	2-1	2-4	2-4	3-2	0-0	0-1	2-5	3-4	0-1		0-1	0-1	
19 Three Bridges	1-3	1-0	5-1	3-0	3-1	2-0	3-0	2-0	3-1	2-2	2-2	2-1	4-2	1-0	3-1	3-2	0-1	2-0		1-0
20 Worthing United	0-0	2-4	6-1	1-1	3-6	2-1	1-3	2-2	0-5	0-7	0-0	1-4	4-2	2-2	2-0	5-5	2-1	0-0	2-2	

SUSSEX COUNTY LEAGUE - STEP 5/6/7

DIVISION THREE	P	W	D	L	F	A	Pts
1 (P) Newhaven	30	22	4	4	94	32	70
2 (P) Saltdean United	30	21	7	2	88	26	70
3 Pease Pottage Village	30	22	1	7	94	44	67
4 Barnham	30	19	3	8	91	44	60
5 (P) Broadbridge Heath	30	17	5	8	67	43	56
6 Forest	30	15	6	9	63	50	51
7 Ferring	30	14	4	12	51	56	46
8 Rottingdean Village	30	14	3	13	53	71	45
9 Uckfield Town	30	10	10	10	60	61	40
10 Ifield Edwards	30	10	5	15	50	60	35
11 Bosham	30	9	6	15	45	58	33
12 Hurstpierpoint	30	9	6	15	45	61	33
13 TD Shipley	30	10	1	19	49	70	31
14 Clymping	30	5	3	22	31	96	18
15 Haywards Heath Town	30	3	7	20	29	69	16
16 Roffey	30	2	5	23	33	102	11

RESERVE DIVISION PREMIER	P	W	D	L	F	A	Pts
1 Eastbourne Town Reserves	22	16	2	4	48	26	50
2 Hassocks Reserves	22	14	5	3	82	38	47
3 Pagham Reserves	22	13	4	5	54	25	43
4 Eastbourne Utd Ass Reserves	22	13	1	8	46	40	40
5 East Preston Reserves	22	11	3	8	56	47	36
6 Rye United Reserves	22	10	5	7	46	41	35
7 Lancing Reserves (-1)	22	8	3	11	51	66	26
8 Mile Oak Reserves	22	7	2	13	49	60	23
9 St Francis Rangers Reserves	22	7	2	13	35	65	23
10 Hailsham Town Reserves (-1)	22	5	5	12	32	43	19
11 Sidley United Reserves	22	4	5	13	43	73	17
12 P'haven & Telscom. Reserves	22	4	3	15	32	52	15

RESERVE DIVISION EAST	P	W	D	L	F	A	Pts
1 Ringmer Reserves	22	14	5	3	69	29	47
2 Saltdean United Reserves	22	13	5	4	56	35	44
3 Shoreham Reserves	22	12	3	7	55	39	39
4 Bexhill United Reserves	22	12	2	8	43	44	38
5 AFC Uckfield Reserves	22	10	4	8	49	43	34
6 Newhaven Reserves	22	9	7	6	49	43	34
7 Little Common Reserves	22	8	6	8	45	40	30
8 Southwick Reserves	22	9	1	12	39	44	28
9 Haywards Heath Town Res.	22	7	3	12	33	44	24
10 Westfield Reserves	22	7	3	12	38	64	24
11 Steyning Town Reserves	22	6	3	13	30	44	21
12 Seaford Town Reserves	22	3	2	17	21	58	11

RESERVE DIVISION WEST	P	W	D	L	F	A	Pts
1 Littlehampton Town Reserves	20	18	1	1	85	19	55
2 Dorking Wanderers Reserves	20	13	3	4	67	25	42
3 Selsey Reserves (-3)	20	13	2	5	62	31	38
4 Storrington Reserves	20	12	2	6	59	28	38
5 Rustington Reserves	20	9	3	8	53	43	30
6 Pease Pottage Village Res.	20	9	2	9	31	53	29
7 Loxwood Reserves	20	7	3	10	42	54	24
8 Ferring Reserves	20	4	5	11	36	71	17
9 Bosham Reserves	20	5	1	14	30	59	16
10 Broadbridge Heath Reserves	20	3	3	14	44	64	12
11 Midhurst & Easebourne Res.	20	3	3	14	22	84	12

DIVISION TWO	1	2	3	4	5	6	7	8	9	10	11	12	13	14	15	16	17	18
1 Bexhill United		2-0	1-3	1-1	1-4	2-1	2-1	4-0	4-2	3-2	6-3	2-0	0-0	1-0	3-2	1-3	0-1	0-0
2 Dorking Wanderers	4-2		4-2	0-4	1-3	1-0	4-1	5-1	2-2	2-1	3-3	1-2	3-2	3-1	2-1	3-2	2-2	3-1
3 East Preston	5-3	2-1		2-2	5-1	4-0	3-1	7-0	12-0	7-1	3-0	4-1	3-2	2-1	3-3	1-2	4-1	5-0
4 Eastbourne United Association	3-0	0-4	1-2		1-0	1-3	1-0	0-2	1-1	1-0	1-0	3-1	4-0	1-0	0-2	3-3	4-1	0-2
5 Hailsham Town	4-0	3-1	2-3	0-1		3-2	1-1	5-0	2-1	4-3	5-0	2-2	1-0	2-2	3-2	1-0	7-0	W-L
6 Little Common	1-1	1-2	0-4	2-3	0-1		1-5	5-2	0-2	2-6	5-0	1-3	2-0	1-0	2-2	0-0	1-1	3-0
7 Littlehampton Town	6-0	0-0	1-1	2-2	2-2	1-1		1-3	2-1	3-1	4-0	3-0	2-1	2-2	0-1	3-1	1-1	6-1
8 Loxwood	4-3	1-3	1-3	1-1	0-4	2-2	1-4		5-0	1-0	1-2	2-1	4-1	2-0	1-1	2-1	0-1	W-L
9 Midhurst & Easebourne	1-2	0-3	0-7	3-2	0-2	3-2	1-2	2-4		2-4	3-3	5-2	2-1	0-3	4-3	1-4	2-2	2-5
10 Mile Oak	2-0	1-1	0-1	0-2	1-4	1-2	1-2	0-3	3-0		1-2	0-2	3-1	2-2	1-4	2-1	1-3	2-1
11 Oakwood	2-2	2-5	2-7	3-1	2-2	1-1	0-2	4-3	2-5	0-3		3-3	0-2	0-1	0-2	0-4	4-4	2-4
12 Rustington	2-1	2-2	0-3	2-2	0-3	1-4	1-5	0-0	0-0		2-1		0-0	0-0	2-2	4-0	6-0	
13 Seaford Town	0-2	1-3	0-2	4-1	1-5	4-2	2-2	0-1	3-0	4-0	0-0	2-3		0-2	5-1	1-2	1-3	2-0
14 Southwick	3-1	0-3	0-2	3-2	1-2	2-1	0-0	1-1	2-1	1-2	0-0	4-1	3-1		0-0	1-1	1-0	2-1
15 Steyning Town	1-2	3-2	1-2	0-1	0-3	4-3	1-2	1-3	1-5	0-4	1-3	3-2	3-0	1-1		1-1	6-3	0-2
16 Storrington	2-3	0-4	1-3	4-1	0-0	0-2	2-2	1-4	3-2	2-3	2-2	2-2	0-1	0-1	5-0		3-4	1-2
17 Westfield	1-3	0-2	1-2	0-2	1-2	2-2	0-0	3-2	6-0	1-3	1-1	1-2	2-3	2-2	2-2	2-4		4-0
18 Wick	0-2	0-1	0-5	1-1	0-3	4-1	1-0	1-4	2-4	1-1	0-0	3-1	1-1	2-2	4-1	1-3	0-2	

DIVISION THREE	1	2	3	4	5	6	7	8	9	10	11	12	13	14	15	16
1 Barnham		2-0	4-2	6-0	0-0	1-3	2-1	4-1	2-4	2-2	1-4	7-0	9-0	3-0	2-3	8-1
2 Bosham	2-4		0-4	2-3	1-3	1-1	1-1	0-2	1-1	1-4	2-3	2-1	0-2	0-1	2-1	1-1
3 Broadbridge Heath	3-1	3-1		4-0	0-2	1-2	5-1	1-3	2-1	2-1	2-5	3-0	0-0	2-3	3-0	3-2
4 Clymping	0-2	2-4	1-7		0-1	1-2	2-0	2-1	1-2	1-3	2-0	1-4	2-3	0-1	1-1	2-2
5 Ferring	0-3	2-1	3-0	6-0		1-1	2-0	0-3	2-1	0-2	4-3	3-0	4-0	1-3	0-1	2-2
6 Forest	1-2	2-1	2-2	0-1	3-2		3-1	2-0	5-1	0-2	0-3	2-2	1-2	1-1	4-0	3-1
7 Haywards Heath Town	0-0	1-5	1-2	6-1	3-0	1-3		1-1	1-1	1-5	1-3	1-1	2-0	2-2	1-3	0-0
8 Hurstpierpoint	3-6	2-2	0-2	3-0	1-1	2-5	3-1		2-1	0-4	2-6	3-0	0-1	1-1	4-3	1-0
9 Ifield Edwards	1-4	0-2	1-3	4-1	1-3	2-3	1-0	1-1		0-2	1-4	3-2	1-2	1-4	3-1	1-1
10 Newhaven	5-2	1-0	0-0	6-0	9-0	3-2	4-0	4-1	1-1		3-1	4-1	3-1	2-2	4-2	1-2
11 Pease Pottage Village	3-1	1-3	2-1	5-1	2-1	4-1	5-0	1-0	2-3	3-5		4-1	9-1	0-2	3-0	3-1
12 Roffey	0-1	1-5	2-3	1-3	0-3	2-2	2-0	0-1	0-3	2-7	1-5		0-3	0-8	1-2	3-3
13 Rottingdean Village	0-3	7-1	0-1	3-1	4-1	1-3	4-1	0-0	1-5	0-2	2-1	6-2		0-4	2-0	2-2
14 Saltdean United	3-4	1-1	2-2	8-0	6-1	2-0	2-0	5-0	3-1	2-1	2-0	4-1	8-0		1-0	4-1
15 TD Shipley	0-4	2-1	1-2	6-2	2-3	4-6	2-0	5-3	1-2	0-2	0-2	8-1	1-3	0-2		3-1
16 Uckfield Town	2-1	0-1	2-2	1-0	4-0	3-0	4-1	2-1	3-4	2-3	2-5	2-2	4-3	1-1	5-0	

A.F.C. UCKFIELD
Founded: 1988   Nickname:

Secretary: Anthony Harvey   **(T)** 07976 935 787   **(E)** anthony@aharvey.fsnet.co.uk
Chairman: Dave Shearing   **Manager:**   **Prog Ed:** Anthony Harvey
Ground: The Oaks, Old Eastbourne Road, Uckfield TN22 5QL   **(T)** 07847 662 337
Capacity: **Seats:**   **Covered:**   **Midweek Matchday:**   **Clubhouse:** Yes   **Shop:**

Colours(change): All light blue (All orange)
Previous Names: Wealden 1988-2010.
Previous Leagues:
Records:
Senior Honours: Sussex County League Division 2 League Cup 2004-05, Division Two 2010-11.

10 YEAR RECORD

02-03		03-04		04-05		05-06		06-07		07-08		08-09		09-10		10-11		11-12	
SxC2	7	SxC2	14	SxC2	5	SxC2	6	SxC2	4	SxC2	9	SxC2	15	SxC2	8	SxC2	1	SxC1	8

ARUNDEL
Founded: 1889   Nickname: Mulletts

Secretary: Kathy Wilson   **(T)** 07778 783 294   **(E)** kathymwilson@btinternet.com
Chairman: Bob Marchant   **Manager:**   **Prog Ed:** Kathy Wilson
Ground: Mill Road, Arundel, W. Sussex BN18 9QQ   **(T)** 01903 882 548
Capacity: 2,200   **Seats:** 100   **Covered:** 200   **Midweek Matchday:** Tuesday   **Clubhouse:** Yes   **Shop:** No

Colours(change): Red/white/red (All Blue)
Previous Names:
Previous Leagues: West Sussex
Records: **Att:** 2,200 v Chichester (League) 1967-68   **Goalscorer:** Paul J Bennett   **App:** 537 Paul Bennett (Goalkeeper)
Senior Honours: Sussex County Champions 1957-58, 58-59, 86-87.

10 YEAR RECORD

02-03		03-04		04-05		05-06		06-07		07-08		08-09		09-10		10-11		11-12	
SxC1	17	SxC1	6	SxC1	9	SxC1	7	SxC1	3	SxC1	3	SxC1	2	SxC1	12	SxC1	9	SxC1	17

CHICHESTER CITY
Founded: 2000   Nickname: Chi

Secretary: Michael Maiden   **(T)** 07971 818 761   **(E)** michael.maiden@virgin.net
Chairman: Sean Forry   **Manager:**   **Prog Ed:**
Ground: Oaklands Way, Chichester, W Sussex PO19 6AR   **(T)** 01243 533 368
Capacity: 2,000   **Seats:** none   **Covered:** 200   **Midweek Matchday:** Tuesday   **Clubhouse:** Yes   **Shop:** Yes

Colours(change): White/green/green (Orange/black/orange)
Previous Names: Chichester FC (pre 1948), Chichester City 1948-2000. Merged with Portfield in 2000, Chicester City Utd 2000-08
Previous Leagues:
Records:
Senior Honours: Sussex County Division One 2003-04.

10 YEAR RECORD

02-03		03-04		04-05		05-06		06-07		07-08		08-09		09-10		10-11		11-12	
SxC1	4	SxC1	1	SxC1	16	SxC1	8	SxC1	11	SxC1	16	SxC1	7	SxC1	3	SxC1	14	SxC1	20

CROWBOROUGH ATHLETIC
Founded: 1894   Nickname: The Crows

Secretary: Eric Gillett   **(T)** 07879 434 467   **(E)** emgillett@hotmail.com
Chairman: Malcolm Boyes   **Manager:**   **Prog Ed:**
Ground: Crowborough Co. Stadium, Alderbrook Rec, Fermor Rd, TN6 3DJ   **(T)** 01892 661 893
Capacity: 2,000   **Seats:**   **Covered:** 150   **Midweek Matchday:**   **Clubhouse:**   **Shop:**

Colours(change): Sky blue & navy blue/navy/navy (All red).
Previous Names:
Previous Leagues: Sussex County 1974-2008. Isthmian 2008-09
Records:
Senior Honours: Sussex County Division One 2007-08. League Cup 2006-07.

10 YEAR RECORD

02-03		03-04		04-05		05-06		06-07		07-08		08-09		09-10		10-11		11-12	
SxC3	3	SxC3	1	SxC2	1	SxC1	6	SxC1	4	SxC1	1	Isth1S	22	SxC1	18	SxC1	12	SxC1	13

Chichester City. Photo: Roger Turner.

Lingfield. Photo: Roger Turner.

DORKING WANDERERS

Founded: Nickname:

Secretary: Rob Cavallini   **(T)** 07806 590 019   **(E)** rob_cavallini@hotmail.com
Chairman: Marc White   **Manager:** Marc White   **Prog Ed:** Rob Cavallini
Ground: West Humble Playing Fields, London Road, Dorking, Surrey   **(T)** 07841 671 825
Capacity: **Seats:**   **Covered:**   **Midweek Matchday:**   **Clubhouse:**   **Shop:**

Colours(change):   Blue & black stripes/black/black (All yellow).
Previous Names:
Previous Leagues:
Records:
Senior Honours: Sussex County League Division Three 2010-11.

10 YEAR RECORD

02-03	03-04	04-05	05-06	06-07	07-08	08-09	09-10	10-11	11-12
								SxC3 1	SxC2 3

EAST GRINSTEAD TOWN

Founded: 1890   Nickname: The Wasps

Secretary: Brian McCorquodale   **(T)** 07802 528 513   **(E)** brian.mcc@egtfc.co.uk
Chairman: Richard Tramontin   **Manager:**   **Prog Ed:**
Ground: The GAC Stadium, East Court, College Lane, East Grinstead RH19 3LS   **(T)** 01342 325 885
Capacity: 3,000 **Seats:** none **Covered:** 400 **Midweek Matchday:**   **Clubhouse:** Yes **Shop:** No

Colours(change):   Yellow & black/black & black (Blue & yellow/blue & yellow/royal blue)
Previous Names: East Grinstead > 1997.
Previous Leagues: Mid Sussex, Sussex County, Souhern Amateur
Records: **Att:** 2,006 v Lancing F A Am Cup **App:** Guy Hill
Senior Honours: Sussex County League Division Two 2007-08.

10 YEAR RECORD

02-03	03-04	04-05	05-06	06-07	07-08	08-09	09-10	10-11	11-12
SxC2 3	SxC1 9	SxC1 18	SxC2 7	SxC2 11	SxC2 1	SxC1 17	SxC1 15	SxC1 7	SxC1 9

EAST PRESTON

Founded: 1966   Nickname:

Secretary: Keith Freeman   **(T)** 07986 596913   **(E)** keweia@btinternet.com
Chairman: Andrew Kinchin   **Manager:**   **Prog Ed:**
Ground: Roundstone Recreation Ground, Lashmar Road, East Preston BN16 1ES   **(T)** 01903 776 026
Capacity: **Seats:**   **Covered:**   **Midweek Matchday:**   **Clubhouse:**   **Shop:**

Colours(change):   All white (All blue)
Previous Names:
Previous Leagues:
Records:
Senior Honours: Sussex County League Division Three 1983-84, Division Two 1997-98, 2011-12.

10 YEAR RECORD

02-03	03-04	04-05	05-06	06-07	07-08	08-09	09-10	10-11	11-12
SxC1 10	SxC1 3	SxC1 11	SxC1 16	SxC1 10	SxC1 4	SxC1 18	SxC2 14	SxC2 14	SxC2 1

HAILSHAM TOWN

Founded: 1885   Nickname: The Stringers

Secretary: Lorraine Mans   **(T)** 07748 926 070   **(E)** lozzamaris@aol.com
Chairman: Mervyn Walker   **Manager:**   **Prog Ed:**
Ground: The Beaconsfield, Western Road, Hailsham BN27 3JF   **(T)** 01323 840 446
Capacity: 2,000 **Seats:** none **Covered:** 100 **Midweek Matchday:** Tuesday   **Clubhouse:** Yes **Shop:**

Colours(change):   Yellow/green/green (All light blue)
Previous Names: Hailsham.
Previous Leagues: East Sussex, Southern Combination
Records: **Att:** 1350 v Hungerford T. FA Vase Feb 89 **Goalscorer:** Howard Stephens 51 **App:** Phil Comber 713
Senior Honours:

10 YEAR RECORD

02-03	03-04	04-05	05-06	06-07	07-08	08-09	09-10	10-11	11-12
SxC1 15	SxC1 12	SxC1 12	SxC1 10	SxC1 6	SxC1 13	SxC1 15	SxC1 19	SxC1 16	SxC2 2

Peacehaven & Telscombe. Photo: Roger Turner.

Redhill. Photo: Alan Coomes.

HASSOCKS
Founded: 1902 **Nickname:** The Robins

Secretary: Dave Knight **(T)** 01273 842 023 **(E)** dw.knight45@googlemail.com
Chairman: Dave John **Manager:** **Prog Ed:**
Ground: The Beacon, Brighton Road, Hassocks BN6 9NA **(T)** 01273 846 040
Capacity: 1,800 **Seats:** 270 **Covered:** 100 **Midweek Matchday:** Tuesday **Clubhouse:** Yes **Shop:** No

Colours(change): All Red. (Yellow/black/yellow)
Previous Names:
Previous Leagues: Mid Sussex, Brighton & Hove & Dist and Southern Counties Comb
Records: Att: 610 v Burgess Hill Town **Goalscorer:** Pat Harding 43
Senior Honours:

10 YEAR RECORD

02-03		03-04		04-05		05-06		06-07		07-08		08-09		09-10		10-11		11-12	
SxC1	8	SxC1	7	SxC1	8	SxC1	9	SxC1	5	SxC1	7	SxC1	16	SxC1	14	SxC1	6	SxC1	4

HORSHAM YMCA
Founded: 1898 **Nickname:** YM's

Secretary: Andy Flack **(T)** 0777 585 7392 **(E)** andy.flack@horsham.gov.uk
Chairman: Mick Browning **Manager:** **Prog Ed:**
Ground: Gorings Mead, Horsham, West Sussex RH13 5BP **(T)** 01403 252 689
Capacity: 1,575 **Seats:** 150 **Covered:** 200 **Midweek Matchday:** **Clubhouse:** Yes **Shop:** No

Colours(change): White/black/red (Navy & sky blue/navy/navy)
Previous Names:
Previous Leagues: Horsham & District, Brighton & Hove, Mid Sussex, Sussex County > 2006, Isthmian 2006-11.
Records: 950 v Chelmsford City - FA Cup 2000
Senior Honours: Sussex League 2004-05, 05-06.
John O'Hara Cup 2001-02.

10 YEAR RECORD

02-03		03-04		04-05		05-06		06-07		07-08		08-09		09-10		10-11		11-12	
SxC1	3	SxC1	13	SxC1	1	SxC1	1	Isth1S	9	Isth1S	21	SxC1	3	Isth1S	11	Isth1S	22	SxC1	16

LANCING
Founded: 1941 **Nickname:**

Secretary: John Rea **(T)** 07598 301 296 **(E)** john.rea62@yahoo.com
Chairman: Barry Leigh **Manager:** **Prog Ed:**
Ground: Culver Road, Lancing, West Sussex BN15 9AX **(T)** 01903 767 285
Capacity: **Seats:** **Covered:** **Midweek Matchday:** **Clubhouse:** Yes **Shop:**

Colours(change): Yellow/blue/yellow (All light blue)
Previous Names: Lancing Athletic
Previous Leagues: Brighton & Hove & District.
Records:
Senior Honours: Brighton League 1946-47, 47-48.

10 YEAR RECORD

02-03		03-04		04-05		05-06		06-07		07-08		08-09		09-10		10-11		11-12	
SxC2	9	SxC2	17	SxC2	13	SxC2	12	SxC2	14	SxC2	12	SxC2	9	SxC2	11	SxC2	2	SxC1	2

LINGFIELD
Founded: 1893 **Nickname:**

Secretary: Pamela Tomsett **(T)** 07903 428 228 **(E)** pamtomsettlfc@hotmail.co.uk
Chairman: Bill Blenkin **Manager:** **Prog Ed:**
Ground: Sports Pavillion, Godstone Road, Lingfield, Surrey RH7 6BT **(T)** 01342 834 269
Capacity: 1,000+ **Seats:** Yes **Covered:** Yes **Midweek Matchday:** Tuesday **Clubhouse:** Yes **Shop:** No

Colours(change): Red & Yellow/black/yellow.(Blue & white/blue/blue)
Previous Names: None.
Previous Leagues: Redhill. Surrey Intermediate. Combined Counties. Mid Sussex.
Records:
Senior Honours:

10 YEAR RECORD

02-03		03-04		04-05		05-06		06-07		07-08		08-09		09-10		10-11		11-12	
SxC3	9	SxC3	8	SxC3	3	SxC3	2	SxC2	10	SxC2	2	SxC1	8	SxC1	10	SxC1	11	SxC1	7

PAGHAM

Founded: 1903   Nickname: The Lions

Secretary: Peter Craddock   **(T)** 07760 771 099   **(E)** paghamfootballclub@btconnect.com
Chairman: Brent Williams   **Manager:**   **Prog Ed:**
Ground: Nyetimber Lane, Pagham, W Sussex PO21 3JY   **(T)** 01243 266 112
Capacity: 2,000 **Seats:** 200   **Covered:** 200   **Midweek Matchday:**   **Clubhouse:** Yes   **Shop:** No

Colours(change): White & black/black/black (Green/white/green & white)
Previous Names: None
Previous Leagues: Chichester 1903-50, West Sussex 50-69
Records: **Att:** 1,200 v Bognor 1971 **Goalscorer:** Dick De Luca **App:** Graham Peach
Senior Honours: Sussex County Division Two 1978-79, 86-87, 2006-07. Division One 80-81, 87-88, 88-89.

10 YEAR RECORD

02-03	03-04	04-05	05-06	06-07	07-08	08-09	09-10	10-11	11-12
SxC1 9	SxC1 17	SxC1 19	SxC2 13	SxC2 1	SxC1 9	SxC1 11	SxC1 17	SxC1 4	SxC1 6

PEACEHAVEN & TELSCOMBE

Founded: 1923   Nickname:

Secretary: Derek Earley   **(T)** 07717 178 483   **(E)** derek@peacehavenfc.com
Chairman: Jim Edwards   **Manager:**   **Prog Ed:**
Ground: The Sports Park, Piddinghoe Ave, Peacehaven, BN10 8RH   **(T)** 01273 582 471
Capacity: **Seats:**   **Covered:**   **Midweek Matchday:**   **Clubhouse:**   **Shop:**

Colours(change): All black & white (All white)
Previous Names: Formed when Peacehaven Rangers and Telscombe Tye merged.
Previous Leagues:
Records:
Senior Honours: Sussex County Division Three 2005-06. Division Two 2008-09.

10 YEAR RECORD

02-03	03-04	04-05	05-06	06-07	07-08	08-09	09-10	10-11	11-12
SxC1 18	SxC2 12	SxC2 17	SxC3 1	SxC2 5	SxC2 4	SxC2 1	SxC1 2	SxC1 3	SxC1 5

REDHILL

Founded: 1894   Nickname: Reds/Lobsters

Secretary: Phil Whatling   **(T)** 07929 742 081   **(E)** phil.whatling@ntlworld.com
Chairman: John Park   **Manager:**   **Prog Ed:**
Ground: Kiln Brow, Three Arch Road, Redhill, Surrey RH1 5AE   **(T)** 01737 762 129
Capacity: 2,000 **Seats:** 150   **Covered:** 150   **Midweek Matchday:** Tuesday   **Clubhouse:** Yes   **Shop:** Yes

Colours(change): Red & white/red/red. (Yellow/blue/blue).
Previous Names:
Previous Leagues: E & W Surrey. Spartan. Southern Sub. London. Athenian.
Records: **Att:** 8,000 v Hastings U FA Cup 1956 **Goalscorer:** Steve Turner 119 **App:** Brian Medlicott 766
Senior Honours: Athenian League (2) Surrey Senior cup 28-29, 65-66.

10 YEAR RECORD

02-03	03-04	04-05	05-06	06-07	07-08	08-09	09-10	10-11	11-12
SxC1 12	SxC1 11	SxC1 13	SxC1 18	SxC1 15	SxC1 8	SxC1 7	SxC1 5	SxC1 8	SxC1 10

RINGMER

Founded: 1906   Nickname: Blues

Secretary: Sally Crouch   **(T)** 07510 109 509   **(E)** sallycrouch@ringmerfc.co.uk
Chairman: Bob Munnery   **Manager:** Bob Munnery   **Prog Ed:**
Ground: Caburn Ground, Anchor Field, Ringmer BN8 5QN   **(T)** 01273 812 738
Capacity: 1,000 **Seats:** 100   **Covered:** Yes   **Midweek Matchday:** Tuesday   **Clubhouse:** Yes   **Shop:** Yes

Colours(change): Navy & light blue/navy/navy. (All white).
Previous Names: None.
Previous Leagues: Brighton.
Records: 1,350 v Southwick, Sussex County League, 1970-71.
Senior Honours: Sussex County Division Two 1968-69. Division One 1970-71. Sussex Senior Cup 1972-73.

10 YEAR RECORD

02-03	03-04	04-05	05-06	06-07	07-08	08-09	09-10	10-11	11-12
SxC1 7	SxC1 10	SxC1 6	SxC1 2	SxC1 9	SxC1 10	SxC1 9	SxC1 13	SxC1 10	SxC1 15

RYE UNITED
Founded: Nickname: United

Secretary: Roger Bond **(T)** 07738 154 685 **(E)** e.r.bond@btinternet.com
Chairman: Clive Taylor **Manager:** **Prog Ed:** Roger Bond
Ground: Rye Football & Cricket Salts, Fish Market Rd, Rye TN31 7LU **(T)** 01797 223 855
Capacity: 1,500 **Seats:** **Covered:** 100 **Midweek Matchday:** Tuesday **Clubhouse:** Yes **Shop:** No

Colours(change): Red & black/black/black (All blue).
Previous Names:
Previous Leagues: Sussex County & Kent County until 2000
Records: **Att:** 120 **App:** Scott Price
Senior Honours: Sussex County League Division Three 2000-01, Division Two 1955-56, 2001-02, 02-03, 09-10.

10 YEAR RECORD

02-03		03-04		04-05		05-06		06-07		07-08		08-09		09-10		10-11		11-12	
SxC2	1	SxC1	2	SxC1	2	SxC1	19	SxC1	19	SxC1	19	SxC2	6	SxC2	1	SxC1	2	SxC1	3

SELSEY
Founded: 1903 Nickname: Blues

Secretary: Gordon Weller **(T)** 07852 954 042 **(E)** g.weller1@btinternet.com
Chairman: David Lee **Manager:** **Prog Ed:** Gordon Weller
Ground: High Street Ground, Selsey, Chichester, PO20 0QG **(T)** 01243 603 420
Capacity: 1,000 **Seats:** 25 **Covered:** 98 **Midweek Matchday:** Tuesday **Clubhouse:** Yes **Shop:** No

Colours(change): All blue (All yellow).
Previous Names:
Previous Leagues: Chichester & District, West Sussex.
Records: **Att:** 750-800 v Chichester or Portfield 1950's
Senior Honours: Sussex County Division Two 1963-64, 75-76.

10 YEAR RECORD

02-03		03-04		04-05		05-06		06-07		07-08		08-09		09-10		10-11		11-12	
SxC1	11	SxC1	18	SxC2	14	SxC2	2	SxC1	8	SxC1	15	SxC1	10	SxC1	11	SxC1	17	SxC1	12

SHOREHAM
Founded: 1892 Nickname: Musselmen

Secretary: Gary Millis **(T)** 07801 477 979 **(E)** g.millis@sky.com
Chairman: Matthew Major **Manager:** **Prog Ed:** Gary Millis
Ground: Middle Road, Shoreham-by-Sea, W Sussex, BN43 6LT **(T)** 01273 454 261
Capacity: 1,500 **Seats:** 150 **Covered:** 700 **Midweek Matchday:** **Clubhouse:** Yes **Shop:** No

Colours(change): All blue (All orange).
Previous Names: None.
Previous Leagues: West Sussex.
Records: **Att:** 1,342 v Wimbledon
Senior Honours: Sussex County Division One 1951-52, 52-53, 77-78. Division Two 61-62, 76-77, 93-94. John O'Hara League Cup 2007-08.

10 YEAR RECORD

02-03		03-04		04-05		05-06		06-07		07-08		08-09		09-10		10-11		11-12	
SxC1	16	SxC1	19	SxC2	3	SxC1	13	SxC1	13	SxC1	12	SxC1	6	SxC1	9	SxC1	18	SxC1	18

SIDLEY UNITED
Founded: 1906 Nickname: Blues

Secretary: Dane Martin **(T)** 07815 425 682 **(E)** dane.martin88@yahoo.co.uk
Chairman: Dicky Day **Manager:** **Prog Ed:** Dane Martin
Ground: Gullivers Sports Ground, Glovers Lane, Sidley Bexhill on Sea TN39 5BL **(T)** 01424 217 078
Capacity: 1,500 **Seats:** none **Covered:** 150 **Midweek Matchday:** **Clubhouse:** Yes **Shop:**

Colours(change): Navy blue & sky blue/navy/navy blue & sky blue (Yellow & black/black/yellow).
Previous Names:
Previous Leagues: East Sussex & Hastings & Dist
Records: **Att:** 1,300 in 1959 **App:** Jimmy Watson
Senior Honours: Sussex Division Two 1958-59, 64-65, 98-99, Division One 2000-01, Sussex Int Cup 1947-48, Sussex Jnr Cup 1924-25

10 YEAR RECORD

02-03		03-04		04-05		05-06		06-07		07-08		08-09		09-10		10-11		11-12	
SxC1	13	SxC1	16	SxC1	15	SxC1	11	SxC1	14	SxC1	20	SxC2	8	SxC2	3	SxC1	13	SxC1	11

ST. FRANCIS RANGERS

Founded: 2002   Nickname: Saints/Rangers

Secretary: John Goss   **(T)** 07748 785 240   **(E)** j.goss462@btinternet.com

Chairman: John Goss   **Manager:**   **Prog Ed:** John Goss

Ground: Princess Royal Hospital, Lewes Rd, Haywards Hth RH16 4EX   **(T)** 01444 474 021

Capacity: 1,000   **Seats:** None   **Covered:** 100   **Midweek Matchday:** Tuesday   **Clubhouse:** Yes   **Shop:** No

Colours(change): Black & white/black/black (Yellow/black/yellow)
Previous Names: Formed when Ansty Rangers & St Francis merged 2002.
Previous Leagues: None
Records:
Senior Honours:

10 YEAR RECORD

02-03		03-04		04-05		05-06		06-07		07-08		08-09		09-10		10-11		11-12	
SxC3	6	SxC3	2	SxC2	4	SxC2	3	SxC2	2	SxC1	14	SxC1	12	SxC1	16	SxC1	19	SxC1	19

WORTHING UNITED

Founded: 1952   Nickname:

Secretary: Malcolm Gamlen   **(T)** 07743 322 571   **(E)** helsnmark@aol.com

Chairman: Glen Houchen   **Manager:** Jim Baker & Martyn Rea   **Prog Ed:** helsnmark@aol.com

Ground: The Robert Albon Memorial Ground, Lyons Way BN14 9JF   **(T)** 01903 234 466

Capacity: **Seats:**   **Covered:**   **Midweek Matchday:**   **Clubhouse:**   **Shop:**

Colours(change): Sky blue & whites/blue/white (Red & white/red/red)
Previous Names: Wigmore Athletic 1952-88. Amalgamated with Southdown to form Worthing United in 1988.
Previous Leagues:
Records:
Senior Honours: Sussex County Division 2 1973-74, Division 3 1989-90.

10 YEAR RECORD

02-03		03-04		04-05		05-06		06-07		07-08		08-09		09-10		10-11		11-12	
SxC2	14	SxC2	2	SxC1	14	SxC1	16	SxC1	18	SxC1	17	SxC1	20	SxC2	2	SxC2	3	SxC1	14

Selsey. Photo: Alan Coomes.

DIVISION TWO

BEXHILL UNITED

Founded: Nickname:

Secretary: Mrs Tracy Aston   **(T)** 07791 368 049   **(E)** tracyaston21@aol.com
Chairman: Robin Powell   **Manager:**   **Prog Ed:** Mrs Tracy Aston
Ground: The Polegrove, Brockley Road, Bexhill on Sea TN39 3EX   **(T)** 07791 368 049   **Capacity:**
Colours(change): White & black/black/black (Light blue & yellow/blue/blue)

ADDITIONAL INFORMATION:

BROADBRIDGE HEATH

Founded: Nickname:

Secretary: Andrew Crisp   **(T)** 07501 057 654   **(E)** crispandy@hotmail.com
Chairman: Keith Soane   **Manager:**   **Prog Ed:**
Ground: Broadbridge Leisure Centre, Wickhurst Lane Broadbridge Heath Horsham RH12 3YS   **(T)** 01403 211 311   **Capacity:**
Colours(change): All blue (Red & black/red/red)

ADDITIONAL INFORMATION:

EASTBOURNE UNITED ASSOCIATION

Founded: 1894   Nickname: The U's

Secretary: Brian Dowling   **(T)** 07507 225 450   **(E)** brian.dowling@btinternet.com
Chairman: Les Aisbitt   **Manager:**   **Prog Ed:** Brian Dowling
Ground: The Oval, Channel View Road, Eastbourne, BN22 7LN   **(T)** 01323 726 989   **Capacity:** 3,000
Colours(change): White/black/white (Claret & blue/claret/claret).

ADDITIONAL INFORMATION: Att: 11,000 at Lynchmore

LITTLE COMMON

Founded: 1966   Nickname:

Secretary: Mrs Margaret Cherry   **(T)** 01424 217 191   **(E)** danieleldridge11@btinternet.com
Chairman: Ken Cherry   **Manager:**   **Prog Ed:**
Ground: Little Common Recreation Ground, Green Lane, Bexhill on Sea TN39 4PH   **(T)** 01424 845 861   **Capacity:**
Colours(change): Claret & blue/claret/claret (Yellow/blue/blue)

ADDITIONAL INFORMATION:
Previous Name: Albion United > 1986. **Previous League:** East Sussex 1994-2005.
Honours: East Sussex League 1975-76, 76-77, 2004-05.

LITTLEHAMPTON TOWN

Founded: 1896   Nickname: Golds

Secretary: Paul Cox   **(T)** 07771 623 224   **(E)** cox121@yahoo.com
Chairman: Neil Taylor   **Manager:**   **Prog Ed:**
Ground: Sportsfield, St Flora's Road, Littlehampton BN17 6BD   **(T)** 01903 716 390   **Capacity:**
Colours(change): Yellow/black/black (All white)

ADDITIONAL INFORMATION:
Lost in the F.A. Cup Preliminary Round v Tunbridge Wells 15-16 on penalties after 40 kicks had been taken - At the time a European record and only one short of the World record.

LOXWOOD

Founded: Nickname:

Secretary: George Read   **(T)** 07791 766 857   **(E)** thomasread00@btinternet.com
Chairman: Derek Waterman   **Manager:**   **Prog Ed:** George Read
Ground: Loxwood Sports Ass., Plaistow Road, Loxwood RH14 0RQ   **(T)** 07791 766 857   **Capacity:**
Colours(change): Black & white/white/white (All red)

ADDITIONAL INFORMATION:
Previous League: West Sussex.
Honours: Sussex County League Division 3 2007-08.

MIDHURST & EASEBOURNE

Founded: Nickname:

Secretary: Ted Dummer MBE   **(T)** 01730 813 887   **(E)** acs@harrisonrenwick.com
Chairman: Darren Chiverton   **Manager:**   **Prog Ed:** Ted Dummer MBE
Ground: Rotherfield, Dodsley Lane, Easebourne, Midhurst GU29 9BE   **(T)** 01730 816 557   **Capacity:**
Colours(change): Blue/black/blue (Orange/blue/orange)

ADDITIONAL INFORMATION:
Previous League: West Sussex 1999-2002.
Honours: Sussex County League Division 2 Cup 1988-89, Division 3 Cup 2002-03.

MILE OAK
Founded: 1960   Nickname: The Oak

Secretary: Chris Tew   **(T)** 07733 323 453   **(E)** chris_tew@lineone.net
Chairman: Leslie Hamilton   **Manager:**   **Prog Ed:**
Ground: Mile Oak Recreation Ground, Chalky Road, Portslade BN41 2YU   **(T)** 01273 423 854   **Capacity:**
Colours(change): Orange & black/black/orange (All green)

ADDITIONAL INFORMATION:
Previous League: Brighton & Hove District.
Honours: Brighton & Hove District 1980-81. Sussex County League Division 2.

NEWHAVEN
Founded: Nickname:

Secretary: John Carpenter   **(T)** 07733 370 398   **(E)** jgcarpenter@cicestra.co.uk
Chairman: Andrew Lloyd   **Manager:**   **Prog Ed:**
Ground: Fort Road Newhaven East Sussex BN9 9DA   **(T)** 01273 513 940   **Capacity:**
Colours(change): All red & white (All yellow & blue)

ADDITIONAL INFORMATION:
Honours: Sussex County League Division Three 2011-12.

OAKWOOD
Founded: 1962   Nickname:

Secretary: Kelly Whittaker   **(T)** 07973 752 761   **(E)** beccakel@hotmail.com
Chairman: Stuart Lovegrove   **Manager:**   **Prog Ed:** Kelly Whittaker
Ground: Tinsley Lane, Three Bridges, Crawley RH10 8AJ   **(T)** 01293 515 742   **Capacity:**
Colours(change): Red & black/black/black (Blue & white/white/white)

ADDITIONAL INFORMATION:
Previous League: Southern Counties Combination 1980-84.
Honours: Sussex County Division 2 Cup 1989-90.

RUSTINGTON
Founded: Nickname:

Secretary: John Virgoe   **(T)** 07966 217 603   **(E)** johnvirgoe@hotmail.com
Chairman: Frank Sumner   **Manager:**   **Prog Ed:**
Ground: Recreation Ground, Jubilee Avenue, Rustington BN16 3NB   **(T)** 01903 770 495   **Capacity:**
Colours(change): All blue (Red & black/black/red)

ADDITIONAL INFORMATION:
Honours: Sussex County League Division 3 2006-07.

SALTDEAN UNITED
Founded: 1966   Nickname:

Secretary: Iain Feilding   **(T)** 07880 870 886   **(E)** fieldings@thec.fsnet.co.uk
Chairman: Robert Thomas   **Manager:**   **Prog Ed:**
Ground: Hill Park, Coombe Vale Saltdean Brighton East Sussex BN2 8HJ   **(T)** 01273 309 898   **Capacity:**
Colours(change): Red & black/black/black (Green & black/green/green)

ADDITIONAL INFORMATION:
Previous Leagues: Brighton > 1984.

SEAFORD TOWN
Founded: Nickname:

Secretary: John Smith   **(T)** 07940 511 504   **(E)** johnsmithn@btinternet.com
Chairman: Bob Thomsett   **Manager:**   **Prog Ed:**
Ground: The Crouch, Bramber Road, Seaford BN25 1AG   **(T)** 01323 892 221   **Capacity:**
Colours(change): All red (White/black/black)

ADDITIONAL INFORMATION:
Honours: Sussex County League Division Two 2005-06.

SOUTHWICK
Founded: 1882   Nickname:

Secretary: Paul Symes   **(T)** 07908 289 758   **(E)** p.p.symes@btinternet.com
Chairman: Alan Petken   **Manager:**   **Prog Ed:** Paul Symes
Ground: Old Barn Way, Southwick BN42 4NT   **(T)** 01273 701 010   **Capacity:**
Colours(change): Red & black/black/red (Yellow & black/yellow/black)

ADDITIONAL INFORMATION:
Previous League: Isthmian 1985-92.
Honours: Sussex County League Division 1 x6. Sussex Senior Cup x10.

STEYNING TOWN

Founded: Nickname:

Secretary: David Kennett **(T)** 07585 601 213
Chairman: Carol Swain **Manager:**
Ground: The Shooting Field, Steyning, West Sussex BN44 3RQ
Colours(change): All red (All yellow)

(E) diddy.kennett1@btinternet.com
Prog Ed: David Kennett
(T) 01903 814 601 **Capacity:**

ADDITIONAL INFORMATION:
Honours: Sussex County League Division 2 1977-78, Division 1 1984-85, 85-86, League Cup 1978-79, 83-84, 85-86.

STORRINGTON

Founded: 1920   Nickname:

Secretary: Keith Dalmon **(T)** 07889 367 956
Chairman: Stan Rhodie **Manager:**
Ground: Recreation Ground, Pulborough Road, Storrington RH20 4HJ
Colours(change): All blue (White/black/white)

(E) keithdalmon@btinternet.com
Prog Ed:
(T) 01903 745 860 **Capacity:**

ADDITIONAL INFORMATION:
Honours: Sussex County League Division 2 Cup 1979, Division 3 Cup 1998, Division 3 2005.
Vernon Wentworth Cup 1998, 2003.

WESTFIELD

Founded: 1927   Nickname:

Secretary: Gill Attewell **(T)** 07928 176 658
Chairman: Graham Drinkwater **Manager:**
Ground: The Parish Field, Main Road, Westfield TN35 4SB
Colours(change): Yellow/green/green (White/blue/blue)

(E) gilljordan@rocketmail.com
Prog Ed: Gill Attewell
(T) 01424 751 011 **Capacity:**

ADDITIONAL INFORMATION:
Previous League: East Sussex 1971-97.
Honours: East Sussex 1977-78, League Cup 77-78. Hastings Senior Cup 2007-08.

WICK

Founded: 1892   Nickname: Wickers

Secretary: Steven Cox **(T)** 07880 608 090
Chairman: Keith Croft **Manager:**
Ground: Crabtree Park, Coomes Way, Wick, Littlehampton, W Sussex BN17 7LS
Colours(change): Red & black/black & white/red (White/black/black).

(E) coxsteven1@aol.com
Prog Ed:
(T) 01903 713 535 **Capacity:** 1,000

ADDITIONAL INFORMATION: Att: 900
Sussex Senior Cup 92-93.

SUSSEX COUNTY DIVISION THREE CONSTITUTION 2012-13

BARNHAM..Mill Road, Slindon, Nr Arundel, West Sussex BN18 0LZ 07738 625 795

BILLINGHURST ....Jubilee Field, Three Bridges Road Three Bridges Sussex RH10 1LQ...........................01293 442000

CLYMPING .... Clymping Village Hall, Clymping, Littlehampton BN17 5GW...................................07762 498 840

FERRING ....The Glebelands, Ferring, West Sussex BN12 5JL 01903 243 618

HAYWARDS HEATH TOWN ....Hanbury Park Stadium, Haywards Heath RH16 4GL..01444 412 837

HURSTPIERPOINT....................Fairfield Recreation Ground, Cuckfield Road, Hurstpierpoint BN6 9SD.........................07985 126 432

IFIELD ....Edwards Sports & Social Club, Ifield Green, Rusper Road, Crawley...........................01293 536 569

ROFFEY... Bartholomew Way, Horsham RH12 5JL ....

ROTTINGDEAN VILLAGE ....Rottingdean Sports Centre, Falmer Road, Rottingdean BN2 7DA...........................01273 306 436

SIDLESHAM.............................. Recreation Ground, Selsey Road Sidlesham Nr Chichester PO20 7RD 01243 641538

T D SHIPLEY ....The Pavilion, Dragons Lane, Shipley RH13 8GB 07804 325 228

UCKFIELD TOWN.. Victoria Pleasure Ground, Uckfield TN22 5DJ ....

Hailsham Town. Photo: Roger Turner.

GROUND DIRECTIONS

AFC UCKFIELD - The Oaks, Old Eastbourne Road, Uckfield, East Sussex TN22 5QL - 07847 662 337
Next to Rajdutt Restaurant on Old Eastbourne Road, south of Uckfield town centre.

ARUNDEL - Mill Road, Arundel, West Sussex BN18 9QQ - 01903 882 548
A27 from Worthing to Arundel over Railway Bridge to roundabout . Second exit into Queen Street to town centre and turn right over bridge. Car park leading to ground 100 yards on right.

CHICHESTER CITY - Oaklands Park, Oaklands Way, Chichester PO19 6AR - 07845 105 822
Half a mile north of the city centre, adjacent to festival theatre. Turn into Northgate car park and entrance to the ground is next to the Chichester Rackets Club.

CROWBOROUGH ATHLETIC - Crowborough Community Stadium, Alderbrook Recreation Ground, Fermor Road, TN6 3DJ
Entering Crowborough from the south on the A26, about half a mile past the Crow and Gate Pub, take the next right into Sheep Plain - This is also signposted for the Railway Station, which meanders into Hurtis Hill. At the mini-roundabout go straight into Fermor Road, take the second turning on the right and turn right immediately into Alderbrook Recreation Ground. The Stadium and parking is ahead of you.

DORKING WANDERERS - West Humble Playing Fields, London Road, Dorking.
Take A24 to Dorking at roundabout stay on A24 to Leatherhead. Go past Denbies Vineyard on left. At end of vineyard take 2nd turning on the left straight into the playing field.

EAST GRINSTEAD TOWN - East Court, East Grinstead RH19 3LS - 01342 325885
A264 Tunbridge Wells road (Moat Road) until mini roundabout at bottom of Blackwell Hollow ,turn immediately right by club sign then 1st left, ground 200 yards down lane past rifle club on right.

HAILSHAM TOWN - The Beaconsfield, Western Road, Hailsham, East Sussex BN27 3DN - 01323 840446
A22 to Arlington Road, turn east, then left into South Road- left into Diplocks Way until Daltons. Four miles from Polegate BR (Brighton-Eastbourne line).

HASSOCKS - The Beacon, Brighton Rd., Hassocks BN6 9NA - 01273 846040
Off A273 Pyecombe Road to Burgess Hill. Ground is 300 yards south of Stonepound crossroads (B2116) to Hurstpeirpoint or Hassocks.

HORSHAM YMCA - Gorings Mead, Horsham, West Sussex RH13 5BP - 01403 252 689
From the east, take A281 (Brighton Road) and the ground is on the left and sign posted opposite Gorings Mead.

LANCING - Culver Road, Lancing, West Sussex BN15 9AX. - 01903 767 285.
From A27 turn south at Lancing Manor roundabout into Grinstead Lane, 3rd turning on right North Farm Rd. Turn left then immedlately. right into Culver Rd. From railway station take 3rd turning on left heading north.

LINGFIELD - Sports Pavilion, Godstone Road, Lingfield, Surrey RH7 6BT - 01342 834269
A22, 4 miles north of East Grinstead, to Mormon Temple roundabout, take exit Lingfield (B2028) Newchapel Road for 1 1/2 miles. Left at T junction into Godstone Road (B2029) and ground is 1/2 mile on left.

PAGHAM - Nyetimber Lane, Pagham, West Sussex PO21 3JY - 01243 266 112
Turn off A27 Chichester by-pass (signposted A259 Pagham). Ground in village of Nyetimber. Three miles from Bognor (BR). Buses 260 & 240

PEACEHAVEN & TELSCOMBE - The Sports Park, Piddinghoe Avenue, Peacehaven, E. Sussex BN10 8RJ - 01273 582471
From Brighton on A259, over roundabout & Piddinghoe Ave. is next left after 2nd set of lights - ground at end. From Newhaven, Piddinghoe Ave. is 1st right after 1st set of lights. 3 miles from Newhaven(BR). Peacehaven is served by Brighton to Newhaven & Eastbourne buses

REDHILL - Kiln Brow, Three Arch Road, Redhill, Surrey - 01737 762 129
On left hand side of A23 two and a half miles south of Redhill.

RINGMER - Caburn Ground, Anchor Field, Ringmer - 01273 812 738
From Lewes road turn right into Springett Avenue, opposite Ringmer village

RYE UNITED - Sydney Allnut Pavilion, Rye Football & Cricket Salts, Fishmarket Road, Rye TN31 7NU - 01797 223 855
Outskirts of Rye on the A268 joins A259 opposite Skinners Rover garage.

SELSEY - High Street Ground, Selsey, Chichester, West Sussex - 01243 603420
Through Selsey High Street to fire station. Take turning into car park alongside the station. Entrance is in the far corner. Regular buses from Chichester.

SHOREHAM - Middle Road, Shoreham-by-Sea, West Sussex BN43 6LT - 01273 454 261
From Shoreham (BR) go east over level crossing, up Dolphin Road. Ground is 150 yards on right.

SIDLEY UNITED - Gullivers Sports Ground, Glovers Lane, Sidley, Bexhill on Sea TN39 5BL - 01424 217 078
From Brighton: On A259 turn left at Little Common roundabout into Pear Tree Lane. Turn right into Turkey Road. Turn right onto A269 from Ninfield. Turn left at Glovers Lane and first left into North Road.

ST FRANCIS RANGERS - The Princess Royal Hospital, Lewes Road, Haywards Heath, RH16 4EX Tel No: 01444 474 021 and social club 01444 441 881
Enter through the main hospital entrance on the Lewes Road and follow signs to Sports Complex.

WORTHING UNITED - The Robert Albion Memorial Ground, Lyons Way, Worthing BN14 9JF. 01903 234 466.
From the West past Hill Barn roundabout to second set of traffic lights, turn left into Lyons Way. From East first set of traffic lights at end of Sompting bypass, turn right into Lyons Way.

DIVISION TWO

BEXHILL UNITED - The Polegrove, Brockley Road, Bexhill-on-Sea, East Sussex TN39 3EX - 07815 425 682.
A27 to Little Common then fourth exit off roundabout to Cooden Beach. Left and follow to end, turn right into Brockby Road. Ground at bottom of hill on the right.

BROADBRIDGE HEATH - Wickhurst Lane, Broadbridge Heath, Horsham RH12 3YS - 01403 211 311
Alongside A24, Horsham north/south bypass. From the A24 Horsham Bypass, at the large roundabout/underpass take the Broadbridge Heath Bypass towards Guildford and then at the first roundabout turn left into Wickhurst Lane.

EASTBOURNE UNITED AFC - The Oval, Channel View Ropad, Eastbourne, East Sussex BN22 7LN - 011323 726989
From A22 follow signs to Eastbourne East seafront. Turn left onto seafront and left again into Channel View Road at Princess Park & ground is first right.

LITTLE COMMON - Little Common Spts Pavilion, Little Common Rec., Green Lane, Bexhill-on-Sea, TN39 4PH - 01424 845 861.
From the west take the A259, at Little Common roundabout take second exit into Peartree Lane and then left into Little Common Recreation Ground car park.

LITTLEHAMPTON TOWN - The Sportsfield, St Flora's Road, Littlehampton BN17 6BD - 01903 716 390
Leave A259 at Waterford Business Park and turn into Horsham Road. After Shell Garage turn left into St. Floras Road. Ground is at the end of road on the left.

LOXWOOD - Loxwood Sports Association, Plaistow Road, Loxwood RH14 0SX - 01404 753 185
Leave A272 between Billinghurst and Wisborough Green and join the B2133 for 3.4 miles. On entering Loxwood Village take 1st left into Plaistow Road, ground situated 100 yards on the left.

MIDHURST & EASEBOURNE - Rotherfield, Dodsley Lane, Easebourne, Midhurst, W. Sussex GU29 9BE - 01730 816 557.
Ground one mile out of Midhurst on London Road (A286) opposite Texaco Garage. Ample car parking.

MILE OAK - Mile Oak Recreation Ground, Chalky Road, Portslade - 01273 423 854.
From A27 (Brighton Bypass) leave at A293 exit. Right at first roundabout. Ground 1 mile on right. Parking in the Sports Centre opposite the ground (park) entrance.

NEWHAVEN - Fort Road Recreation Ground, Newhaven, East Sussex BN9 9EE. - 01273 513 940.
A259, follow one-way system around town, left at Police Station into South Road, which becomes Fort Road.

SUSSEX COUNTY LEAGUE - STEP 5/6/7

OAKWOOD - Tinsley Lane, Three Bridges, Crawley RH10 8AJ - 01293 515 742.
From the South on M23, take junction 10 exit left onto A2011, next roundabout take fourth exit right, next roundabout second exit, take first right into Tinsley Lane. Ground entrance 100 metres on left.

RUSTINGTON - Recreation Ground, Jubilee Avenue, Rustington, West Sussex BN16 3NB - 01903 770 495.
From the East follow A259 past Sainsburys. Left at next roundabout on to B2187 over Windmill Bridge. Straight on at roundabout, first right, then first left into Woodlands Avenue. Car park is 80 yards on your right, next to the Village hall. From the West proceed to Watersmead roundabout with Bodyshop on your left. Take B2187 half a mile, past BP garage, take third right into Albert Road, then first right into Woodlands Avenue.

SALTDEAN UNITED - Hill Park, Coombe Vale, Saltdean, Brighton BN2 8HJ - 01273 309 898.
A259 coast road east from Brighton to Saltdean Lido, left into Arundel Drive West, and Saltdean Vale to bridle path at beginning of Combe Vale. Club 200yds along track.

SEAFORD TOWN - The Crouch, Bramber Road, Seaford BN25 1AG - 01323 892 221.
A259 to Seaford. At mini roundabout by station, turn left (coming from Newhaven) or RIGHT (from Eastbourne). At end of Church Street, across junction, then left at end. After 500m turn left up Ashurst Road Bramber Road is at the top.

SOUTHWICK - Old Barn Way, off Manor Hall Way, Southwick, Brighton BN42 4NT - 01273 701 010
A27 from Brighton take first left after Southwick sign to Leisure Centre. Ground adjacent. Five minutes walk from Fishergate or Southwick stations.

STEYNING TOWN - The Shooting Field, Steyning, W. Sussex BN44 3RP. - 01903 812 228.
Entering Steyning from the west. Take 1st left in the High St (Tanyard Lane) Follow into Shooting Field estate, ground is 4th turn on the left. Entering Steyning from the east. From the High St., turn right into Church St.. Turn left by Church into Shooting Field estate. NB Coaches MUST park in Church Street Car Park.

STORRINGTON - Recreation Ground, Pulborough Road, Storrington RH20 4HJ - 01903 745 860.
A24 right at roundabout at Washington. Four miles to Storrington through village. Third exit at roundabout and second right into Spearbridge Road.

WESTFIELD - The Parish Field, Main Road, Westfield TN35 4SB - 01483 751 011.
From Hastings take the A21, turning right onto the A28 towards Ashford. Travel through Westfield, and the ground is located off Westfield Lane on the left.

WICK - Crabtree Park, Coomes Way, Wick, Littlehampton, West Sussex BN17 7LS Tel No: 01903 713 535
A27 to Crossbush.A284 towards Littlehampton. After one mile over level crossing left into Coomes Way next to Locomotive pub. Ground at end.

DIVISION THREE

BARNHAM - Mill Road, Slindon, Nr Arundel, West Sussex BN18 0LZ - 07738 625 795
On the A27 at Fontwell take the A29 to Slindon and at the Slindon crossroads the ground is on the right.

BILLINGHURST - Jubilee Field, Three Bridges Road Three Bridges Sussex RH10 1LQ - 01293 442 000
Heading towards Crawley past Three Bridges railway station on the left, take the 2nd right into Three Bridges Road, and then 1st left 75 yards down. The ground is down Jubilee Walk (80 yards)opposite the Plough Inn.

CLYMPING - Clymping Village Hall, Clymping, Littlehampton BN17 5GW - 07951 196 784.
Follow A259 west of Littlehampton. Just over the Bridge, on the right hand side before the small roundabout.

FERRING - The Glebelands, Ferring, West Sussex BN12 5JL
To Ferring main shops, turn right into Greystoke Road.

HAYWARDS HEATH TOWN - Hanbury Park Stadium, Haywards Heath RH16 3PX - 01444 412 837.
A272 to Haywards Heath town centre. At Sussex roundabout, north on B2708 (Hazelgrove Road) take first right into New England Road, then the 4th right (Allen Road) leads to ground.

HURSTPIERPOINT - Fairfield Rec. Ground, Cuckfield Road, BN6 9SD - 01273 834 783.
At Hurstpierpoint crossroads, go north into Cuckfield Road (B2117) for 1km. Ground entrance between houses nos.158 & 160.

IFIELD - Edwards Sports & Social Club, Ifield Green, Rusper Road, Crawley. - 01293 420 598.
From A23 Crawley by-pass going north, left at roundabout signed Charlwood. Third left into Ifield Green, first right past Royal Oak (PH) into Rusper Road.

ROFFEY - Bartholomew Way, Horsham RH12 5JL.
A24 heading South, turn left at Rusper roundabout. Take first left into Lemmington Way. Take left at T junction into Bartholomew Way.

ROTTINGDEAN VILLAGE - Rottingdean Sports Centre, Falmer Road, Rottingdean BN2 7DA. - 01273 306 436
After leaving the Rottingdean Village one way system go past Bazehill Road and the entrance to the ground is next on the right.

TD SHIPLEY - The Pavilion, Dragons Lane, Shipley RH13 8GB - 07804 325 228.
Exit the A24 onto the A272 at the Buckbarn crossroads signposted Billinghurst. The ground is 1.5 miles on the right.

UCKFIELD TOWN - Victoria Pleasure Ground, Uckfield TN22 5DJ - 01825 769 400.
Take Eastbourne road (old A22) south of Uckfield town centre. Entrance to ground is 1/2 mile on the right (just after the Police station).

UNITED COUNTIES LEAGUE

Sponsored by: ChromaSport & Trophies
Founded: 1895
Recent Champions:
2007: Deeping Rangers
2008: Stotfold
2009: Stewarts & Lloyds Corby
2010: Daventry Town
2011: St Neots Town
nwcfl.co.uk

LEAGUE CUP

PRELIMINARY ROUND
Daventry United 1-6 Holbeach United
Yaxley 1-2 Long Buckby AFC
Bourne Town 0-4 Eynesbury Rovers
Thrapston Town 1-0 Blackstones FC
Kings Lynn Town 3-0 AFC Kempston Rovers
Peterborough Northern Star 6-4 Huntingdon Town
ROUND 1
Spalding United 0-2 Holbeach United
Boston Town 0-1 Wootton Blue Cross
Long Buckby AFC 3-0 Olney Town
Eynesbury Rovers 1-4 Deeping Rangers
Wellingborough Town 3-2 Rothwell Town
Northampton ON Chenecks 0-6 St Ives Town
Desborough Town 1-5 Bugbrooke St Michaels
Thrapston Town 2-0 Northampton Sileby Ranger
Kings Lynn Town 2-1 Raunds Town
Northampton Spencer 3-3 4-2p Burton Park Wanderers
Newport Pagnell Town 2-1 Rothwell Corinthians
Sleaford Town 0-1 Cogenhoe United
Buckingham Town 0-3 Peterborough Northern Star
Potton United 3-0 Irchester United
Wellingborough Whitworth 1-3 Rushden and Higham United
Stewarts & Lloyds Corby 4-3 Harborough Town
ROUND 2
olbeach United 1-0 Wootton Blue Cross
Long Buckby AFC 2-3 Deeping Rangers
Wellingborough Town 1-4 St Ives Town
Bugbrooke St Michaels 2-1 Thrapston Town
Kings Lynn Town 2-1 Northampton Spencer
Newport Pagnell Town AW Cogenhoe United
Peterborough Northern Sta 3-0 Potton United
Rushden and Higham United 0-4 Stewarts & Lloyds Corby
QUARTER FINALS
Holbeach United 2-1 Deeping Rangers
St Ives Town 5-1 Bugbrooke St Michaels
Kings Lynn Town 5-3 Cogenhoe United
Peterborough Northern Sta 4-1 Stewarts & Lloyds Corby 1
SEMI-FINALS
Holbeach United 0-4 St Ives Town
Kings Lynn Town 7-0 Peterborough Northern Star
FINAL
St Ives Town 4-1 Kings Lynn Town

PREMIER DIVISION

		P	W	D	L	F	A	Pts
1	Long Buckby	40	35	3	2	130	26	108
2	(P) Kings Lynn Town	40	34	4	2	122	32	106
3	St Ives Town	40	28	4	8	107	51	88
4	Deeping Rangers	40	24	8	8	102	59	80
5	Newport Pagnell Town (-3)	40	24	4	12	99	51	73
6	Holbeach United	40	23	4	13	89	52	73
7	Peterborough Northern Star	40	21	4	15	87	59	67
8	Wellingborough Town 2004	40	17	8	15	79	72	59
9	Stewart & Lloyds Corby	40	17	6	17	78	64	57
10	AFC Kempston Rovers	40	16	9	15	72	72	57
11	Blackstones	40	16	7	17	60	72	55
12	Cogenhoe United	40	15	6	19	58	79	51
13	Spalding United	40	13	11	16	69	79	50
14	Boston Town	40	13	9	18	55	66	45
15	Daventry United	40	11	10	19	64	87	43
16	Desborough Town	40	8	10	22	50	95	34
17	(R) Northampton Spencer (-3)	40	9	9	22	48	97	33
18	Yaxley	40	8	5	27	41	85	29
19	Sleaford Town	40	7	7	26	45	103	28
20	Irchester United (-1)	40	6	7	27	42	115	24
21	(R) Thrapston Town	40	4	7	29	37	118	19

PREMIER DIVISION	1	2	3	4	5	6	7	8	9	10	11	12	13	14	15	16	17	18	19	20	21
1 AFC Kempston Rovers		3-4	0-1	2-0	1-1	0-2	6-0	1-0	4-0	0-1	0-3	1-1	3-1	1-5	2-1	4-2	0-3	0-2	4-3	2-1	1-1
2 Blackstones	1-1		1-0	0-1	3-1	1-1	2-1	1-2	3-0	0-2	1-11	1-2	1-2	0-3	2-1	2-0	0-5	2-1	2-0	2-2	5-2
3 Boston Town	1-1	0-0		1-0	3-0	0-3	2-1	1-2	4-1	1-1	1-7	0-0	0-0	1-2	0-1	2-2	1-3	3-3	2-1	1-2	1-3
4 Cogenhoe United	1-4	1-3	4-1		2-2	0-7	3-2	2-1	0-2	1-3	1-1	0-2	1-0	3-1	4-1	4-0	0-2	1-1	4-1	0-3	2-1
5 Daventry United	2-6	1-3	3-2	2-0		3-3	2-2	1-1	2-2	0-1	0-3	1-2	1-1	3-1	5-0	1-4	1-6	0-1	0-0	2-1	2-1
6 Deeping Rangers	6-1	2-0	2-1	3-1	4-3		2-0	3-0	3-0	1-5	2-3	1-1	5-0	2-2	3-1	4-2	1-1	1-1	1-0	4-4	2-0
7 Desborough Town	2-1	1-1	1-2	1-1	0-4	4-1		0-0	4-1	0-5	0-4	1-7	1-3	1-1	3-0	3-3	1-1	2-1	2-0	2-4	1-0
8 Holbeach United	1-2	4-2	1-4	2-0	4-0	3-3			2-0	2-2	3-3	2-0	10-1	1-2	4-1	3-2	2-0	3-0	5-0	0-3	3-2
9 Irchester United	1-2	1-3	0-2	1-3	4-5	1-7	2-1	1-4		0-5	0-6	0-1	2-0	1-1	2-2	1-1	1-1	0-2	6-2	1-1	4-3
10 Kings Lynn Town	2-0	3-1	2-0	5-1	3-0	2-1	1-1	1-0	6-1		0-1	2-1	6-0	2-1	3-3	3-2	5-1	5-0	5-1	4-3	3-2
11 Long Buckby	3-1	2-1	3-0	2-0	2-2	2-1	4-1	3-0	6-1	2-1		1-3	4-0	5-0	4-0	2-1	2-0	3-2	4-0	3-0	0-1
12 Newport Pagnell Town	1-2	2-1	0-3	1-2	6-1	3-4	3-2	2-1	3-0	0-2	1-2		6-2	1-0	5-0	5-1	6-0	3-5	6-0	0-2	2-1
13 Northampton Spencer	3-3	1-3	0-3	1-1	1-0	1-3	2-0	2-4	1-0	1-2	0-2	0-2		2-4	6-3	1-1	0-2	1-1	3-3	3-2	0-1
14 Peterborough Northern Star	4-1	3-0	1-0	1-1	3-2	5-0	2-1	6-0	2-1	0-1	1-4	3-0		6-2	6-0	1-2	5-1	2-0	2-4	2-1	
15 Sleaford Town	1-1	1-2	1-3	0-3	3-0	2-3	1-0	0-5	1-0	2-3	0-2	1-2	1-1	0-2		0-0	2-4	1-3	1-0	3-3	1-0
16 Spalding United	2-3	1-1	1-1	3-0	2-2	1-1	5-0	2-0	7-0	0-4	0-4	2-1	5-0	4-1	3-3		1-2	1-0	2-1	2-1	2-1
17 St Ives Town	1-0	3-1	5-1	4-0	4-2	6-0	4-1	2-1	7-1	0-1	0-4	4-3	1-2	2-1	2-1	5-0		2-1	4-0	1-4	5-0
18 Stewart & Lloyds Corby	3-2	0-1	1-1	3-4	4-1	0-1	4-1	1-2	1-0	1-2	1-3	1-2	5-1	0-2	2-0	3-1	0-0		7-1	1-2	2-1
19 Thrapston Town	2-2	2-2	2-3	1-1	0-4	0-3	1-2	0-3	1-1	0-4	1-7	0-5	0-4	1-0	3-1	4-0	0-4	0-4		1-3	2-1
20 Wellingborough Town 2004	2-2	2-1	2-1	2-1	2-0	0-2	1-1	0-1	1-3	0-5	0-3	0-2	1-1	3-1	6-0	0-1	2-3	2-6	3-2		3-0
21 Yaxley	1-2	1-0	1-3	4-1	0-2	0-5	2-1	1-2	1-0	1-8	0-1	1-1	1-0	0-1	1-2	0-0	1-5	0-3	1-1	2-2	

UNITED COUNTIES LEAGUE - STEP 5/6

DIVISION ONE

		P	W	D	L	F	A	Pts
1	(P) Huntingdon Town	32	24	2	6	101	27	74
2	(P) Harborough Town	32	22	6	4	78	31	72
3	Bugbrooke St Michaels	32	20	4	8	82	37	64
4	Wellingborough Whitworth	32	19	6	7	77	49	63
5	Rushden & Higham United	32	16	5	11	61	56	53
6	Eynesbury Rovers	32	16	4	12	71	53	52
7	Olney Town	32	15	7	10	70	54	52
8	Rothwell Corinthians	32	15	6	11	54	55	51
9	Burton Park Wanderers	32	12	9	11	64	58	45
10	Wootton Blue Cross	32	11	9	12	41	57	42
11	Buckingham Town	32	10	10	12	57	64	40
12	Northampton ON Chenecks	32	11	5	16	44	66	38
13	Raunds Town	32	8	7	17	38	62	31
14	Bourne Town	32	6	9	17	38	66	27
15	Potton United (-3)	32	8	5	19	46	71	26
16	Northampton Sileby Rangers	32	5	3	24	45	76	18
17	(R) Rothwell Town (-10)	32	4	3	25	26	111	5

RESERVE DIVISION ONE

		P	W	D	L	F	A	Pts
1	Kings Lynn Town Reserves	26	21	3	2	77	34	66
2	Cogenhoe United Reserves	26	19	4	3	81	24	61
3	Stewart & Lloyds Corby Res.	26	17	0	9	67	37	51
4	Blackstones Reserves	26	13	5	8	69	46	44
5	Wellingborough Whitworth Res.	26	12	8	6	64	48	44
6	Peterborough Northern Star R.	26	12	2	12	64	55	38
7	Huntingdon Town Reserves	26	9	5	12	53	54	31
8	AFC Kempston Rovers Res.(-1)	26	9	4	13	47	56	31
9	Desborough Town Reserves	26	8	5	13	49	57	29
10	Northampton Spencer Res. (-3)	26	9	3	14	49	60	29
11	Wellingborough Town 2004 R. (-3)	26	8	5	13	40	66	26
12	Thrapston Town Reserves	26	7	3	16	44	79	24
13	Woodford United Reserves (-1)	26	6	5	15	38	74	22
14	North'ton ON Chenecks Res.	26	4	4	18	31	83	16

RESERVE DIVISION TWO

		P	W	D	L	F	A	Pts
1	Bugbrooke St Michaels Res.	22	19	1	2	80	15	58
2	Harborough Town Reserves	22	12	5	5	49	24	41
3	Eynesbury Rovers Reserves	22	11	3	8	46	47	36
4	Olney Town Reserves	22	10	3	9	45	41	33
5	Rothwell Corinthians Reserves	22	10	2	10	33	35	32
6	Long Buckby Reserves (-3)	22	10	4	8	52	39	31
7	Irchester United Reserves	22	9	4	9	40	51	31
8	Rushden & Higham Utd Res.	22	9	1	12	36	46	28
9	Boston Town Reserves	22	8	3	11	40	62	27
10	Bourne Town Reserves	22	7	2	13	42	52	23
11	Burton Park Wanderers Res.	22	6	3	13	30	50	21
12	Raunds Town Reserves	22	5	1	16	30	61	16

DIVISION ONE

	DIVISION ONE	1	2	3	4	5	6	7	8	9	10	11	12	13	14	15	16	17
1	Bourne Town		0-0	1-4	0-2	0-0	2-1	0-3	1-1	0-3	1-1	1-2	4-0	0-4	4-1	2-3	2-3	2-0
2	Buckingham Town	5-1		1-3	1-1	1-1	2-3	1-5	0-0	3-2	2-2	4-1	2-2	0-2	1-1	1-4	1-3	2-0
3	Bugbrooke St Michaels	5-0	3-4		3-1	4-1	1-1	1-0	3-1	0-1	5-1	3-2	0-0	3-1	7-0	1-1	3-2	1-1
4	Burton Park Wanderers	2-2	3-2	3-2		3-1	3-3	0-4	0-2	5-0	1-1	2-2	0-1	4-0	6-1	1-3	1-2	4-1
5	Eynesbury Rovers	3-1	1-2	3-0	2-3		1-2	2-2	6-0	3-1	1-2	2-0	4-1	0-2	4-0	4-3	2-1	2-2
6	Harborough Town	0-0	2-2	2-1	4-2	4-2		3-1	1-1	4-0	4-0	2-0	0-0	2-1	5-0	1-0	3-1	7-0
7	Huntingdon Town	1-0	7-2	2-1	4-0	2-1	0-1		7-0	4-0	3-2	8-0	1-0	4-2	3-0	7-1	4-1	1-2
8	Northampton ON Chenecks	1-2	0-2	1-2	3-1	1-0	0-5	0-5		3-2	2-3	2-2	2-0	0-1	1-0	1-4	2-3	4-0
9	Northampton Sileby Rangers	4-1	3-4	1-2	1-2	0-1	1-2	0-3	1-2		0-3	4-4	2-5	0-1	0-2	2-3	1-1	2-3
10	Olney Town	1-1	3-2	3-4	3-3	2-5	3-0	0-1	1-2	3-2		0-3	2-0	2-0	6-1	1-1	4-1	4-0
11	Potton United	1-1	0-1	0-3	0-2	3-4	1-2	0-4	2-4	2-1	3-1		0-3	1-2	1-2	2-3	0-1	1-1
12	Raunds Town	3-1	3-4	0-3	2-2	4-1	1-5	0-2	3-1	2-0	0-3	0-2		0-2	2-0	1-3	1-1	0-1
13	Rothwell Corinthians	1-0	1-1	0-5	3-2	0-1	2-1	1-1	3-1	2-5	2-5	2-1	2-2		2-0	3-3	0-2	1-2
14	Rothwell Town	3-4	1-0	0-6	0-1	1-7	0-4	0-7	0-3	0-5	0-2	3-6	3-0	1-3		1-4	0-0	2-2
15	Rushden & Higham United	3-1	2-1	2-1	2-1	0-1	0-1	2-1	2-1	2-0	1-5	1-2	1-1	3-3	2-0		1-3	0-1
16	Wellingborough Whitworth	3-3	3-2	1-0	2-2	5-1	2-1	4-0	3-1	3-0	3-1	2-1	6-0	3-3	7-2	3-0		1-2
17	Wootton Blue Cross	2-0	1-1	0-2	1-1	1-4	1-2	0-4	1-1	1-1	0-0	0-1	2-1	0-2	6-1	2-1	5-1	

PREMIER DIVISION

AFC KEMPSTON ROVERS

Founded: 1884   Nickname: Walnut Boys

Secretary: Kevin Howlett   **(T)** 07721 849 671   **(E)** howlett.home@btinternet.com

Chairman: Russell Shreeves   **Manager:**   **Prog Ed:** Mark Kennett

Ground: Hillgrounds Leisure, Hillgrounds Road, Kempston, Bedford MK42 8SZ   **(T)** 01234 852 346

Capacity: 2,000 **Seats:** 100 **Covered:** 250 **Midweek Matchday:** Tuesday **Clubhouse:** Yes **Shop:**

Colours(change): Red & white stripes/black/black (Blue & black stripes/blue/blue or yellow & black)
Previous Names: Kempston Rovers > 2004.
Previous Leagues: South Midlands 1927-53
Records:
Senior Honours: U.C.L. Prem. 1973-74, Div 1 1957-58, 85-86, Div 2 1955-56, KO Cup 1955-56, 57-58, 59-60, 74-75, 76-77. UCL Division One 2010-11. Beds Senior Cup 1908-09, 37-38, 76-77, 91-92. Hinchingbrooke Cup 2010-11.

10 YEAR RECORD

02-03	03-04	04-05	05-06	06-07	07-08	08-09	09-10	10-11	11-12
UCL P 21	UCL 1 16	UCL 1 16	UCL 1 4	UCL 1 3	UCL P 12	UCL 1 5	UCL 1 5	UCL 1 1	UCL P 10

BLACKSTONES

Founded: 1920   Nickname: Stones

Secretary: Ian MacGillivray   **(T)** 07749 620 825   **(E)** imacgilli@aol.com

Chairman: Kevin Boor   **Manager:**   **Prog Ed:** Kevin Boor

Ground: Lincoln Road, Stamford, Lincs PE9 1SH   **(T)** 01780 757 835

Capacity: 1,000 **Seats:** 100 **Covered:** yes **Midweek Matchday:** Wednesday **Clubhouse:** Yes **Shop:** No

Colours(change): Green/black/green. (Orange/black/orange)
Previous Names: Rutland Ironworks & Blackstone (until 1975)
Previous Leagues: Peterborough Works, Peterborough, Stamford & District
Records: **Att:** 700 v Glinton
Senior Honours: Lincolnshire Senior Cup A 1992-93, 2003-04. Lincolnshire Senior Trophy 2010-11.

10 YEAR RECORD

02-03	03-04	04-05	05-06	06-07	07-08	08-09	09-10	10-11	11-12
UCL P 16	UCL P 11	UCL P 15	UCL P 10	UCL P 8	UCL P 4	UCL P 13	UCL P 13	UCL P 9	UCL P 11

BOSTON TOWN

Founded: 1964   Nickname: Poachers

Secretary: Edward Graves   **(T)** 07963 418 434   **(E)** btfcsec@hotmail.co.uk

Chairman: Mick Vines   **Manager:** Ian Dunn & Matt Hocking   **Prog Ed:** Pat Megginson

Ground: Tattershall Road, Boston, Lincs PE21 9LR   **(T)** 01205 365 470

Capacity: 6,000 **Seats:** 450 **Covered:** 950 **Midweek Matchday:** Tuesday **Clubhouse:** Yes **Shop:**

Colours(change): Sky blue/navy blue/sky blue (Yellow/black/black or white with red flash/red/red)
Previous Names: Boston > 1994
Previous Leagues: Lincs, Central Alliance, Eastern co, Midland N. Co. E, C. Mids
Records: **Att:** 2,700 v Boston United FA Cup 1970. **Goalscorer:** Gary Bull 57 during 2006-07 season.
Senior Honours: Midland League 1974-75, 78-79, 80-81. Central Midlands 88-89. United Counties League 1994-95, 2000-01.

10 YEAR RECORD

02-03	03-04	04-05	05-06	06-07	07-08	08-09	09-10	10-11	11-12
UCL P 8	UCL P 5	UCL P 11	UCL P 6	UCL P 2	UCL P 6	UCL P 5	UCL P 5	UCL P 7	UCL P 14

COGENHOE UNITED

Founded: 1958   Nickname: Cooks

Secretary: Phil Wright   **(T)** 07540 380 357   **(E)** secretary@cogenhoeunited.co.uk

Chairman: Derek Wright   **Manager:**   **Prog Ed:** Phil Wright

Ground: Compton Park, Brafield Road, Cogenhoe NN7 1ND   **(T)** 01604 890 521

Capacity: 5,000 **Seats:** 100 **Covered:** 200 **Midweek Matchday:** Tuesday **Clubhouse:** Yes **Shop:** No

Colours(change): All Blue (White with black trim/black/black or Red/black/red)
Previous Names:
Previous Leagues: Central Northants Comb, prem 67-84
Records: **Att:** 1,000 Charity game 90 **Goalscorer & Appearances:** Tony Smith
Senior Honours: United Counties League 2004-05. Buckingham Charity Cup 2010-11.

10 YEAR RECORD

02-03	03-04	04-05	05-06	06-07	07-08	08-09	09-10	10-11	11-12
UCL P 9	UCL P 6	UCL P 1	UCL P 5	UCL P 5	UCL P 9	UCL P 9	UCL P 8	UCL P 15	UCL P 12

DEEPING RANGERS
Founded: 1964   Nickname: Rangers

Secretary: Haydon Whitham   **(T)** 07736 548 500   **(E)** roegroup@btconnect.com

Chairman: Kevin Davenport   **Manager:** Tuncay Korkmaz   **Prog Ed:** Robin Crowson

Ground: Deeping Sports Club, Outgang Road, Market Deeping, PE6 8LQ   **(T)** 01778 344 701

Capacity: 1,000   **Seats:** 180   **Covered:** 250   **Midweek Matchday:** Tuesday   **Clubhouse:** Yes   **Shop:**

Colours(change): All claret & blue. (White/sky blue/sky blue or Sky blue/claret/claret)
Previous Names: None
Previous Leagues: Peterborough & District 1966 - 1999.
Records:
Senior Honours: Lincs Sen Cup, B Cup, Peterborough FA Cup (3). UCL Premier Champions 2006-07

10 YEAR RECORD

02-03		03-04		04-05		05-06		06-07		07-08		08-09		09-10		10-11		11-12	
UCL P	5	UCL P	17	UCL P	12	UCL P	20	UCL P	1	UCL P	7	UCL P	4	UCL P	4	UCL P	14	UCL P	4

DESBOROUGH TOWN
Founded: 1896   Nickname: Ar Tam

Secretary: John Lee   **(T)** 01536 760 002   **(E)** johnlee@froggerycottage85.fsnet.co.uk

Chairman: Ernie Parsons   **Manager:** Steve Walker   **Prog Ed:** John Lee

Ground: Waterworks Field, Braybrooke Rd, Desborough NN14 2LJ   **(T)** 01536 761 350

Capacity: 8,000   **Seats:** 250   **Covered:** 500   **Midweek Matchday:** Tuesday   **Clubhouse:** Yes   **Shop:**

Colours(change): All Blue (Yellow/yellow/black)
Previous Names: None
Previous Leagues: None
Records: **Att:** 8,000 v Kettering Town
Senior Honours: N'hants/Utd Co. Champs 1900-01, 01-02, 06-07, 20-21, 23-24, 24-25, 27-28, 48-49, 66-67. Lge C 77-78, 00-01, 07-08.
N'hants Sen C 1910-11, 13-14, 28-29, 51-52. Northants Senior Cup 1910-11, 13-14, 28-29, 51-52.

10 YEAR RECORD

02-03		03-04		04-05		05-06		06-07		07-08		08-09		09-10		10-11		11-12	
UCL P	18	UCL P	16	UCL P	10	UCL P	18	UCL P	14	UCL P	3	UCL P	11	UCL P	18	UCL P	19	UCL P	16

HARBOROUGH TOWN
Founded: Forme   Nickname:

Secretary: Pauline Winston   **(T)** 07446 415 329   **(E)** p.winston2402@btinternet.com

Chairman: Andrew Winston   **Manager:**   **Prog Ed:** Tony Sansome

Ground: Bowden's Park, Northampton Road, Market Harborough, Leics. LE16 9HF   **(T)** 01858 467 339

Capacity: **Seats:**   **Covered:**   **Midweek Matchday:**   **Clubhouse:**   **Shop:**

Colours(change): Yellow/black/black (All green)
Previous Names:
Previous Leagues: Northants Combination
Records:
Senior Honours: Northants Combination 2009-10.

10 YEAR RECORD

02-03	03-04	04-05	05-06	06-07	07-08	08-09	09-10		10-11		11-12	
							NhCo	1	UCL 1	17	UCL 1	2

HOLBEACH UNITED
Founded: 1929   Nickname: Tigers

Secretary: Karl Fawcett   **(T)** 07955 947 606   **(E)** holbeachunitedfc@yahoo.co.uk

Chairman: Dave Dougill   **Manager:** John Chand   **Prog Ed:** Jamie Hiller

Ground: Carters Park, Park Road, Holbeach, Lincs PE12 7EE   **(T)** 01406 424 761

Capacity: 4,000   **Seats:** 200   **Covered:** 450   **Midweek Matchday:** Tuesday   **Clubhouse:** Yes   **Shop:** No

Colours(change): Gold & black/black/gold & black.(Blue & white/blue/blue & white or All white)
Previous Names:
Previous Leagues: Peterborough U Co L 46-55, Eastern 55-62, Midland Co 62-63
Records: **Att:** 4,094 v Wisbech 1954
Senior Honours: United Counties League 1989-90, 02-03. Lincs Sen A Cup (4), Senior Cup B 57-58
Lincolnshire Senior Trophy 2011-12.

10 YEAR RECORD

02-03		03-04		04-05		05-06		06-07		07-08		08-09		09-10		10-11		11-12	
UCL P	1	UCL P	7	UCL P	3	UCL P	17	UCL P	11	UCL P	11	UCL P	16	UCL P	16	UCL P	17	UCL P	6

HUNTINGDON TOWN

Founded: 1995   Nickname:

Secretary: Russell Yezek   **(T)** 07974 664818   **(E)** russell.yezek@ntlworld.com

Chairman: Paul Hunt   **Manager:** Ricky Marheineke   **Prog Ed:** Gemma Redgate

Ground: Jubilee Park, Kings Ripton Road,, Huntingdon, Cambridgeshire PE28 2NR   **(T)** 07929 651 226

Capacity: **Seats:**   **Covered:**   **Midweek Matchday:**   **Clubhouse:**   **Shop:**

Colours(change): Red & black/red/red & black (Yellow & black/black/black or White/red/red)
Previous Names:
Previous Leagues: Cambridgeshire.
Records:
Senior Honours: Cambridgeshire Div.1B 1999-2000. Hunts. Junior Cup 1999-00, 2000-01, 01-02. Hunts Scott Gatty Cup 2001-02. United Counties League Division One 2011-12.

10 YEAR RECORD

02-03	03-04	04-05	05-06	06-07	07-08	08-09	09-10	10-11	11-12
	UCL 1 17	UCL 1 14	UCL 1 12	UCL 1 14	UCL 1 4	UCL 1 14	UCL 1 8	UCL 1 5	UCL 1 1

IRCHESTER UNITED

Founded: 1883   Nickname:

Secretary: Glynn Cotter   **(T)** 07802 728 736   **(E)** glynn.cotter@btinternet.com

Chairman: Geoff Cotter   **Manager:** Colin Ridgway   **Prog Ed:** Geoff Cotter

Ground: Alfred Street, Irchester NN29 7DR   **(T)** 01933 312877

Capacity: 1,000 **Seats:** none **Covered:** yes   **Midweek Matchday:**   **Clubhouse:** Yes   **Shop:**

Colours(change): All blue (All red or Red & black stripes/black/black)
Previous Names: Irchester Eastfield 1980-90
Previous Leagues: Northamptonshire/United Counties 1896-97, 30-36, Rushden & District 1936-69
Records:
Senior Honours: Northants Lge Div 2 1930-31, 31-32, Rushden & District Lge (9), Northants Jnr Cup 1929-30, 33-34, 48-49, 75-76. United Counties League Division 1 2009-10.

10 YEAR RECORD

02-03	03-04	04-05	05-06	06-07	07-08	08-09	09-10	10-11	11-12
UCL 1 3	UCL 1 14	UCL 1 9	UCL 1 15	UCL 1 16	UCL 1 16	UCL 1 16	UCL 1 1	UCL P 10	UCL P 20

LONG BUCKBY AFC

Founded: 1937   Nickname: Bucks

Secretary: Dave Austin   **(T)** 07701 723 477   **(E)** lbafc.dja@gmail.com

Chairman: Dave Austin   **Manager:** Scott Goodwin   **Prog Ed:** Dave Austin

Ground: Station Road, Long Buckby NN6 7QA   **(T)** 01327 842 682

Capacity: 1,000 **Seats:** 200 **Covered:** 200 **Midweek Matchday:** Tuesday   **Clubhouse:** Yes   **Shop:** No

Colours(change): Claret & white/claret & white/claret (White/black/black or All orange).
Previous Names: Long Buckby Nomads
Previous Leagues: Rugby & District Central, Northants Combination pre 68
Records: Att: 750 v Kettering Town
Senior Honours: United Counties League Div.2 1970-71, 71-72, Premier Division 2011-12. Northants Senior Cup 2008-09. Munsell Cup 2009.

10 YEAR RECORD

02-03	03-04	04-05	05-06	06-07	07-08	08-09	09-10	10-11	11-12
UCL P 20	UCL P 21	UCL P 8	UCL P 21	UCL P 12	UCL P 2	UCL P 8	UCL P 3	UCL P 4	UCL P 1

NEWPORT PAGNELL TOWN

Founded: 1963   Nickname: Swans

Secretary: Stephen Handley   **(T)** 07867 528 475   **(E)** julieandsteveh1@sky.com

Chairman: Geoff Cardno   **Manager:**   **Prog Ed:** Wayne Harmes

Ground: Willen Road, Newport Pagnell MK16 0DF   **(T)** 01908 611 993

Capacity: 2,000 **Seats:** 100 **Covered:** 100 **Midweek Matchday:** Tuesday   **Clubhouse:** Yes   **Shop:** No

Colours(change): White & green hoops/white/green & black (All sky Blue)
Previous Names: Newport Pagnell Wanderers > 1972.
Previous Leagues: North Bucks 1963-71. South Midlands 1971-73.
Records:
Senior Honours: United Counties Div.1 1981-82, 2001-02. Bucks & Berks Intermediate Cup 2001-02. Berks & Bucks Senior Trophy 2009-10, 10-11.

10 YEAR RECORD

02-03	03-04	04-05	05-06	06-07	07-08	08-09	09-10	10-11	11-12
UCL P 2	UCL P 13	UCL P 18	UCL P 15	UCL P 7	UCL P 15	UCL P 3	UCL P 6	UCL P 3	UCL P 5

PETERBOROUGH NORTHERN STAR
Founded: 1900   Nickname:

Secretary: Glen Harper   **(T)** 07884 288 756   **(E)** ghdjfc@hotmail.com

Chairman: TBC   **Manager:** Jamie Watson   **Prog Ed:** Rodney Payne

Ground: Chestnut Ave, Dogsthorpe, Eye, Peterborough, Cambs PE1 4PE   **(T)** 01733 552 416

Capacity: 1,500   **Seats:** none   **Covered:** yes   **Midweek Matchday:** Wednesday   **Clubhouse:**   **Shop:**

Colours(change): Black & white stripes/black/black (Yellow/navy blue/yellow)
Previous Names: Eye Utd >2005
Previous Leagues: Peterborough Lge >2003
Records:
Senior Honours: Peterborough League 2002-03. Hinchingbrooke Cup 2009-10. United Counties League Division 1 2008-09.
UCL Knock-out Cup 2010-11.

10 YEAR RECORD

02-03	03-04	04-05	05-06	06-07	07-08	08-09	09-10	10-11	11-12
	UCL 1 3	UCL 1 4	UCL 1 9	UCL 1 5	UCL 1 2	UCL 1 1	UCL 1 2	UCL P 6	UCL P 7

QUORN
Founded: 1924   Nickname: Reds

Secretary: Reg Molloy   **(T)** 07729 173 333   **(E)** k.molloy@ntlworld.com

Chairman: Stuart Turner   **Manager:** Tommy Brookbanks   **Prog Ed:** Malcolm Unwin

Ground: Farley Way Stadium, Farley Way, Quorn, Leicestershire LE12 8RB   **(T)** 01509 620 232

Capacity: 1,550   **Seats:** 350   **Covered:** 250   **Midweek Matchday:**   **Clubhouse:** Yes   **Shop:** Nk

Colours(change): All red (Yellow/blue/blue)
Previous Names: Quorn Methodists
Previous Leagues: Leicestershire Senior, Midland Alliance > 2007. NPL 2007-2012.
Records: Not known
Senior Honours: Leicestershire Senior Cup 1940, 1952, 1954.
Leicestershire Senior League 2000-01

10 YEAR RECORD

02-03	03-04	04-05	05-06	06-07	07-08	08-09	09-10	10-11	11-12
MidAl 5	MidAl 4	MidAl 4	MidAl 7	MidAl 3	NP 1 12	NP1S 12	NP1S 20	NP1S 15	NP1S 21

SHEPSHED DYNAMO
Founded: 1994   Nickname: Dynamo

Secretary: Danny Pole   **(T)** 07866 500 187   **(E)** dannypole@aol.com

Chairman: Peter Bull   **Manager:** Chris White   **Prog Ed:** Ben Reed

Ground: The Dovecote, Butt Hole Lane, Shepshed, Leicestershire LE12 9BN   **(T)** 01509 650 992

Capacity: 2,050   **Seats:** 570   **Covered:** 400   **Midweek Matchday:**   **Clubhouse:** Yes   **Shop:** Yes

Colours(change): Black and white stripes/black/black (All claret with sky blue trim)
Previous Names: Shepshed Albion/Charterhouse > 1994
Previous Leagues: Leics Sen 1907-16, 19-27, 46-50, 51-81, Mid Co 81-82, N.C.E. 82-83, Sth 83-88, 96-2004, N.P.L.88-93 2004-12, Mid Com 93-94, Mid All 94-95.
Records: 2,500 v Leicester City - Friendly 1996-97
Senior Honours: Midland Counties League 1981-82, League Cup 81-82. Northern Counties East 1982-83, League Cup 82-83.
Midland Alliance 1995-96. Leicestershire Senior Cup x7

10 YEAR RECORD

02-03	03-04	04-05	05-06	06-07	07-08	08-09	09-10	10-11	11-12
SthW 17	SthW 21	NP 1 15	NP 1 10	NP 1 20	NP 1 15	NP1S 8	NP1S 17	NP1S 21	NP1S 22

SLEAFORD TOWN
Founded: 1968   Nickname: Town

Secretary: Jamie Shaw   **(T)** 07870 271 751   **(E)** gotimhesgone@hotmail.com

Chairman: Ian Clawson   **Manager:** Glen Maddison   **Prog Ed:** Steve Thomas

Ground: Eslaforde Park, Boston Road, Sleaford, Lincs NG34 7HG   **(T)** 01529 415 951

Capacity: **Seats:** 88   **Covered:** 88   **Midweek Matchday:**   **Clubhouse:** Yes   **Shop:**

Colours(change): Green/black/green (All red).
Previous Names:
Previous Leagues: Lincolnshire
Records:
Senior Honours: United Counties League Division One 2005-06.

10 YEAR RECORD

02-03	03-04	04-05	05-06	06-07	07-08	08-09	09-10	10-11	11-12
Lincs 2	Lincs 1	UCL 1 6	UCL 1 1	UCL 1 2	UCL P 14	UCL P 15	UCL P 9	UCL P 18	UCL P 19

SPALDING UNITED
Founded: 1921   Nickname: Tulips

Secretary: Audrey Fletcher   **(T)** 07778 411 916   **(E)** tulips@uk2.net

Chairman: Chris Toynton   **Manager:** Pat Raymond   **Prog Ed:** Andrew Clucas

Ground: Sir Halley Stewart Playing Fields, Winfrey Avenue, Spalding PE11 1DA   **(T)** 01775 713 328

Capacity: 2,700 **Seats:** 300   **Covered:** 500   **Midweek Matchday:**   **Clubhouse:** Yes   **Shop:** Yes

Colours(change): All royal blue (Yellow/black/black or Orange/blue/blue)
Previous Names: Not known
Previous Leagues: Peterborough, Utd Co.31-55,68-78,86-88,91-99,03-04, Ea. Co.55-60, Cen. All. 60-61, Midland Co.61-68, N.C.E.82-86, Sth.88-91, 99-03. NPL03-11.
Records: 6,972 v Peterborough - FA Cup 1982
Senior Honours: United Counties League 1954-55, 75-75, 87-88, 98-99, 2003-04. Northern Counties East 1983-84.
Lincolnshire Senior Cup 1952-53.

10 YEAR RECORD

02-03		03-04		04-05		05-06		06-07		07-08		08-09		09-10		10-11		11-12	
SthE	21	UCL P	1	NP 1	18	NP 1	20	SthM	19	NP 1	18	NP1S	17	NP1S	21	NP1S	22	UCL P	13

ST. IVES TOWN
Founded: 1887   Nickname: Saints

Secretary: Simon Clark   **(T)** 07884 398 770   **(E)** simon.clark@stivestownfc.co.uk

Chairman: Paul Reason   **Manager:**   **Prog Ed:** Simon Clark

Ground: Westwood Road, St. Ives PE27 6WU   **(T)** 01480 463 207

Capacity: **Seats:** Yes   **Covered:** Yes   **Midweek Matchday:** Tuesday   **Clubhouse:** Yes   **Shop:** No

Colours(change): White & black/black/black & white. (All red)
Previous Names: None
Previous Leagues: Cambs, Central Amateur, Hunts, Peterborough & District
Records:
Senior Honours: Hunts Senior Cup 2011-12, Hunts Premier Cup, Hinchingbrooke Cup 2006-07. UCL Knockout Cup 2009-10.

10 YEAR RECORD

02-03		03-04		04-05		05-06		06-07		07-08		08-09		09-10		10-11		11-12	
UCL 1	9	UCL 1	10	UCL 1	3	UCL P	9	UCL P	10	UCL P	5	UCL P	6	UCL P	10	UCL P	11	UCL P	3

STEWARTS & LLOYDS CORBY
Founded: 1935   Nickname: The Foundrymen

Secretary: Kevin O'Brien   **(T)** 07768 974 101   **(E)** kvnob@aol.com

Chairman: John Davies   **Manager:** Lee Duffy   **Prog Ed:** Kevin O'Brien

Ground: Recreation Ground, Occupation Road, Corby NN17 1EH   **(T)** 01536 401 497

Capacity: 1,500 **Seats:** 100   **Covered:** 200   **Midweek Matchday:** Tuesday   **Clubhouse:** Yes   **Shop:** No

Colours(change): White & grey/grey/grey (All navy blue or Maroon & red/maroon/maroon)
Previous Names: Hamlet S & L 1989-92.
Previous Leagues: Kettering Amateur
Records: **Goalscorer:** Joey Martin 46
Senior Honours: United Counties League Division One 1973-74, 74-75, Premier 85-86, 08-09.

10 YEAR RECORD

02-03		03-04		04-05		05-06		06-07		07-08		08-09		09-10		10-11		11-12	
UCL P	6	UCL P	19	UCL P	21	UCL P	16	UCL P	16	UCL P	12	UCL P	1	UCL P	12	UCL P	8	UCL P	9

WELLINGBOROUGH TOWN 2004
Founded: 2004   Nickname: Doughboys

Secretary: Mick Walden   **(T)** 07817 841 752   **(E)** mwalden@dsl.pipex.com

Chairman: Martin Potton   **Manager:**   **Prog Ed:** Ian Parry

Ground: The Dog & Duck, London Road, Wellingborough NN8 2DP   **(T)** 01933 441 388

Capacity: **Seats:** Yes   **Covered:** Yes   **Midweek Matchday:** Tuesday   **Clubhouse:** Yes   **Shop:**

Colours(change): Yellow/royal blue/royal blue. (All white)
Previous Names: Original team (Formed 1867) folded in 2002 reforming in 2004
Previous Leagues: Metropolitan. Southern.
Records:
Senior Honours: United Counties League 1964-65.

10 YEAR RECORD

02-03		03-04		04-05		05-06		06-07		07-08		08-09		09-10		10-11		11-12	
						UCL 1	2	UCL P	3	UCL P	10	UCL P	18	UCL P	11	UCL P	5	UCL P	8

YAXLEY

Founded: 1900   **Nickname: The Cuckoos**

Secretary: Mrs Sandra Cole   **(T)** 07847 123 898   **(E)** sandracole22@ntlworld.com

Chairman: Alan Andrews   **Manager:** Brett Whaley   **Prog Ed:** Jeff Lenton

Ground: Leading Drove, Holme Road, Yaxley, Peterborough PE7 3NA   **(T)** 01733 244 928

Capacity: 1,000   **Seats:** 150   **Covered:** yes   **Midweek Matchday:** Tuesday   **Clubhouse:** Yes   **Shop:** Yes

Colours(change): All blue (All red).
Previous Names: Yaxley Rovers.
Previous Leagues: Peterborough & Dist., Hunts & West Anglia
Records: **Goalscorer:** Ricky Hailstone 16
Senior Honours: United Counties League Division One 1996-97. Hunts Senior Cup (7), UCL Cup 2005-2006

10 YEAR RECORD

02-03	03-04	04-05	05-06	06-07	07-08	08-09	09-10	10-11	11-12
UCL P 7	UCL P 8	UCL P 4	UCL P 7	UCL P 15	UCL P 16	UCL P 14	UCL P 19	UCL P 16	UCL P 18

Huntingdon Town celebrate winning the United Counties Division One title. Photo: Gordon Whittington.

St. Ives Town. Photo: Roger Turner.

DIVISION ONE

AFC RUSHDEN & DIAMONDS

Founded: 2012   Nickname:

Secretary: David Albon   **(T)** 07905 451 535   **(E)** secretary@afcdiamonds.com
Chairman: Ralph Burditt   **Manager:** Mark Starmer   **Prog Ed:** Miss Stephanie Webb
Ground: The Dog and Duck, London Road, Wellingborough, Northants NN8 2DP   **(T)** 01933 441 388   **Capacity:**
Colours(change): White/royal blue/white (Yellow/black/yellow)

ADDITIONAL INFORMATION:

BOURNE TOWN

Founded: 1883   Nickname: Wakes

Secretary: Rob Lambert   **(T)** 07514 804 404   **(E)** roblambert@btinternet.com
Chairman: Nicky Hawkins   **Manager:**   **Prog Ed:** Rob Lambert
Ground: Abbey Lawn, Abbey Road, Bourne, Lincs PE10 9EN   **(T)** 07949 533 521 (MD only) **Capacity:**
Colours(change): Claret & sky blue stripes/claret/claret (All sky blue).

ADDITIONAL INFORMATION:
Record Att: FA Trophy 1970 **Goalscorer:** David Scotney.
U.C.L. Champions 1968-69, 69-70, 71-72, 90-91. Lincolnshire Senior A Cup 1971-72, 2005-06.

BUCKINGHAM TOWN

Founded: 1883   Nickname: Robins

Secretary: Darren Seaton   **(T)** 07808 792 486   **(E)**
Chairman: Vince Hyde   **Manager:** Steve Orchard   **Prog Ed:** Ms Odette Crocombe
Ground: Irish Centre, Manor Fields, Bletchley, Milton Keynes MK2 2HS   **(T)** 01908 375 978   **Capacity:**
Colours(change): All red (Yellow/blue/blue or white/black/black)

ADDITIONAL INFORMATION:
Paid: £7,000 to Wealdstone for Steve Jenkins 1992 Received: £1,000 from Kettering Town for Terry Shrieves.
Honours: Southern League Southern Division 1990-91. U.C.L. 1983-84, 85-86. Berks & Bucks Senior Cup 1983-84.

BUGBROOKE ST MICHAELS

Founded: 1929   Nickname: Badgers

Secretary: Debbie Preston   **(T)** 07940 453 883   **(E)** billdebbiepreston@hotmail.com
Chairman: William Marriott   **Manager:** Paul Field   **Prog Ed:** Debbie Preston
Ground: Birds Close, Gayton Road, Bugbrooke NN7 3PH   **(T)** 01604 830 707   **Capacity:**
Colours(change): Yellow & blue/royal blue/royal blue (Black & white/black/black)

ADDITIONAL INFORMATION:
Record Att: 1,156. **Golascorer:** Vince Thomas. **Apps:** Jimmy Nord.
Honours: Northants Junior Cup 1989-90, 2011-12, Central Northants Comb. x6. U.C.L. Division 1 Champions 1998-99.

BURTON PARK WANDERERS

Founded: 1961   Nickname: The Wanderers

Secretary: Mrs Sam Gordon   **(T)** 07980 013 506   **(E)** samgordon30@gmail.com
Chairman: Stewart Glendenning   **Manager:**   **Prog Ed:** Sam Gordon
Ground: Latimer Park, Polwell Lane, Burton Latimer, Northants NN15 5PS   **(T)** 07980 013506   **Capacity:**
Colours(change): Azure/black/black (Green/white/green & white or Red/black/red)

ADDITIONAL INFORMATION:
Record Att: 253 v Rothwell, May 1989.

EYNESBURY ROVERS

Founded: 1897   Nickname: Rovers

Secretary: Deryck Irons   **(T)** 01234 268111   **(E)** deryckirons@aol.com
Chairman: Brian Abraham   **Manager:** Matt Plumb & Martin Field   **Prog Ed:** Graham Mills
Ground: Alfred Hall Memorial Ground, Hall Road, Eynesbury, St Neots PE19 2SF   **(T)** 01480 477 449   **Capacity:**
Colours(change): Royal & white stripes/royal/royal (All yellow)

ADDITIONAL INFORMATION:
Record Att: 5,000 v Fulham 1953 (Stanley Matthews guested for Eynesbury). **Honours:** U.C.L. Division 1 1976-77.
Huntingdonshire Senior Cup x11. Huntingdonshire Premier Cup 1950-51, 90-91, 95-96.

HARROWBY UNITED

Founded: 2012   Nickname:

Secretary: Miss Corenza Powell   **(T)** 07729 062 511   **(E)** corenza@btinternet.com
Chairman: Mick Dwane   **Manager:** Mark Fardell & Jason Harrison   **Prog Ed:** Ian Weatherstone
Ground: Harrowby Lane Playing Fields, Harrowby Lane, Grantham, Lincs NG31 9QY   **(T)**   **Capacity:**
Colours(change): Red & black/black/black (Blue & black/black/black or Red & white/black/red)

ADDITIONAL INFORMATION:
Lincolnshire Junior Cup 2011-12.

NORTHAMPTON O.N. CHENECKS
Founded: 1946   Nickname:

Secretary: Trevor Cadden **(T)** 07894 425 823 **(E)** trevorcadden@btinternet.com
Chairman: Eddie Slinn **Manager:** Graham Cottle **Prog Ed:** Bryan Lewin
Ground: Old Northamptonians Sports Ground,Billing Road,Northampton NN1 5RX **(T)** 01604 634 045 **Capacity:**
Colours(change): White/navy/white (All red or Yellow & blue/blue/yellow)

ADDITIONAL INFORMATION:
Honours: U.C.L. Div 1 1977-78, 79-80. Northants Junior Cup 2009-10.

NORTHAMPTON SILEBY RANGERS
Founded: 1968   Nickname: Sileby

Secretary: Dave Battams **(T)** 07913 909 068 **(E)** david@djbattams.f2s.com
Chairman: Robert Clarke **Manager:** Glenn Botterill **Prog Ed:** Dave Battams
Ground: Fernie Fields Sports Ground, Moulton, Northampton NN3 7BD **(T)** 01604 670366 **Capacity:**
Colours(change): All red (Blue/white/blue)

ADDITIONAL INFORMATION:
Record Att: 78.
Honours: Northampton Town Lg 1988-89 89-90. UCL Div 1 1993-94, 2002-03. Northants Jnr Cup 93-94, 96-97, 97-98, 2002-03

NORTHAMPTON SPENCER
Founded: 1936   Nickname: Millers

Secretary: Nick Hillery **(T)** 07894 150 853 **(E)**
Chairman: Graham Wrighting **Manager:** Ben Stone **Prog Ed:** Andy Goldsmith
Ground: Kingsthorpe Mill, Studand Road, Northampton NN2 6NE **(T)** 01604 718 898 **Capacity:** 2,000
Colours(change): Green & yellow/green/green (All royal blue).

ADDITIONAL INFORMATION: Att: 800 v Nttm Forest 1993 **App;** P. Jelley 622 1984-2002
United Counties League Division One 1984-85. Premier 1991-92. Northants Senior Cup Winners 2005-06.

OADBY TOWN
Founded: 1937   Nickname: The Poachers

Secretary: Kev Zupp **(T)** 01162 796 483 **(E)** zuppy101@hotmail.co.uk
Chairman: Brian Fletcher-Warington **Manager:** Clem Dublin & Lee Harriman **Prog Ed:** Kev Zupp
Ground: Green King Park, Wigston Road, Oadby LE2 5QG **(T)** 01162 715 728 **Capacity:** 5,000
Colours(change): White & red/red/red

ADDITIONAL INFORMATION:
Leicestershire Senior Div.2 1951-52. Prem 63-64, 67-68, 68-69, 72-73, 94-95, 96-97, 97-98, 98-99. Midland Alliance 99-00.

OLNEY TOWN
Founded: 1903   Nickname:

Secretary: Andrew Baldwin **(T)** 07932 141 623 **(E)** andew@abaldwin.go-plus.net
Chairman: Paul Tough **Manager:** **Prog Ed:** Paul Tough
Ground: Recreation Ground, East Street, Olney, Bucks MK46 4DW **(T)** 01234 712 227 **Capacity:**
Colours(change): Green & white/green/green & white (Yellow & green/green/yellow)

ADDITIONAL INFORMATION:
Previous League: Rushden & District.
Honours: U.C.L. Div 1 1972-73. Berks & Bucks Intermediate Cup 1992-93.

POTTON UNITED
Founded: 1943   Nickname: Royals

Secretary: Mrs Bev Strong **(T)** 07703 442 565 **(E)** bev.strong@tiscali.co.uk
Chairman: Alan Riley **Manager:** Darren Staniforth **Prog Ed:** Mrs Bev Strong
Ground: The Hollow, Bigglewade Road, Potton, Beds SG19 2LU **(T)** 01767 261 100 **Capacity:**
Colours(change): All blue (Red/black/black)

ADDITIONAL INFORMATION:
Record Att: 470 v Hastings Town, FA Vase 1989.
Honours: U.C.L. 1986-87, 88-89, Div.1 2003-04. Beds Senior Cup x5. Huntingdonshire Premier Cup x4. E.Anglian Cup 1996-97

RAUNDS TOWN
Founded: 1946   Nickname: Shopmates

Secretary: Dave Jones **(T)** 07763 492 184 **(E)** david.jones180@ntlworld.com
Chairman: Pete Scanlon **Manager:** Lee Howard & Russ Baxter **Prog Ed:** Dave Jones
Ground: Kiln Park, London Rd, Raunds, Northants NN9 6EQ **(T)** 01933 623 351 **Capacity:** 3,000
Colours(change): Red & black/black/black (White & blue/blue/blue or White/red/black).

ADDITIONAL INFORMATION: Att: 1500 v Crystal Palace 1991 **Goalscorer:** Shaun Keeble. **App:** Martin Lewis - 355
Northants Senior Cup 1990-91.

ROTHWELL CORINTHIANS
Founded: 1934   Nickname: Corinthians

Secretary: Mark Budworth   **(T)** 07730 416 960   **(E)** mbudworth@budworthhardcastle.com
Chairman: Mark Budworth   **Manager:** Matt Clarke   **Prog Ed:** Mark Budworth
Ground: Sergeants Lawn, Desborough Road, Rothwell, NN14 6JQ   **(T)** 01536 418 688   **Capacity:**
Colours(change): Red/black/red. (blue/black/blue).

ADDITIONAL INFORMATION:

RUSHDEN & HIGHAM UNITED
Founded: Formed: 2007 Nickname:

Secretary: Chris Ruff   **(T)** 01933 358 862   **(E)** chrisruff@talktalk.net
Chairman: Bill Perry   **Manager:**   **Prog Ed:** Chris Ruff
Ground: Hayden Road, Rushden, Northants NN10 0HX   **(T)** 01933 410 036   **Capacity:**
Colours(change): Orange/black/black (Light blue & white stripes/light blue/light blue & white)

ADDITIONAL INFORMATION:
Club was formed after the merger of Rushden Rangers and Higham Town.

THRAPSTON TOWN
Founded: 1960   Nickname: Venturas

Secretary: Mrs Cathy Stevens   **(T)** 07972 355 880   **(E)** cathy.stevens@uwclub.net
Chairman: TBC   **Manager:** Ian Walker   **Prog Ed:** Mrs Cathy Stevens
Ground: Chancery Lane, Thrapston, Northants NN14 4JL   **(T)** 01832 732 470   **Capacity:** 1,000
Colours(change): All royal blue (Red/black/red or All white)

ADDITIONAL INFORMATION:
Kettering Amateur League 1970-71, 72-73, 73-74, 77-78. Northants Junior Cup 1987-88, 98-99, 03-04.

WELLINGBOROUGH WHITWORTH
Founded: Formed: 1973 Nickname: Flourmen

Secretary: Julian Souster   **(T)** 07825 632 545   **(E)** julian.souster@yahoo.co.uk
Chairman: Brian Higgins   **Manager:** Matt Freeman & Steve Sargent   **Prog Ed:** Julian Souster
Ground: London Road, Wellingborough, Northants NN8 2DP   **(T)**   **Capacity:**
Colours(change): Red & black/black/red (Blue & white/black/red or Maroon & blue/blue/blue)

ADDITIONAL INFORMATION:
Previous Name: Whitworths. **Previous League:** East Midlands Alliance > 1985.
Honours: Rushden & District League 1976-77. Northants Junior Cup 1996. U.C.L. Division One 2006-07.

WOOTTON BLUE CROSS
Founded: Nickname:

Secretary: Kieran Day   **(T)** 07903 826 225   **(E)** kieran.day87@gmail.com
Chairman: Eric Day   **Manager:** Charlie Standish   **Prog Ed:** Kieran Day
Ground: Weston Park, Bedford Rd., Wootton MK43 9JT   **(T)** 01234 767 662   **Capacity:**
Colours(change): Blue & white/blue/blue (Red & black stripes/black/red & black or Blue & white/blue/blue)

ADDITIONAL INFORMATION:
Previous Grounds: Recreation Ground, Fishers Field, Rose & Crown, Cockfield.
Record Att: 838 v Luton Beds Prem.Cup 1988. **Honours:** Beds Senior Cup 1970-71, 2001-02.

GROUND DIRECTIONS

AFC KEMPSTON ROVERS
Take A421 Bedford by pass turning as indicated to Kempston onto A5140 Woburn Road. At roundabout turn left into St John's Street then right into Bedford Road. After the shops and park on the left turn immediately left into Hillgrounds Road. Ground is past the swimming pool on right hand side.

AFC RUSHDEN & DIAMONDS
Leave A.45 at Wellingborough turn-off, pass Tesco's Store on left-hand side, up to roundabout. Take first exit to town centre. Ground is 300 yards on right-hand side. Entry just past the Dog & Duck public house adjacent to entry to Whitworths ground.

BLACKSTONES FC
From Stamford Centre take A6121 towards Bourne. Turn left into Lincoln Road. Ground on the right hand side.
Go into town on A16 from Spalding. Turn left at roundabout into Liquor Pond Street becoming Queen Street over railway crossing along Sleaford Road. Turn right into Carlton Road then right at crossroads into Fydell Street. Over railway crossing and river take 2nd left (sharp turn) into Tattershall Road. Continue over railway crossing, ground on left.

UNITED COUNTIES LEAGUE - STEP 5/6

BOSTON TOWN
Go into town on A16 from Spalding. Turn left at roundabout into Liquor Pond Street becoming Queen Street over railway crossing along Sleaford Road. Turn right into Carlton Road then right at crossroads into Fydell Street. Over railway crossing and river take 2nd left (sharp turn) into Tattershall Road. Continue over railway crossing, ground on left.

BOURNE TOWN
From Town Centre turn east on A151 towards Spalding into Abbey Road. Ground approximately half a mile on right.

BUCKINGHAM TOWN
Take A413 out of Buckingham and continue on that road until entering Winslow. As you enter Winslow there is a garage on the right hand side. Take the 1st turn right past the garage (Avenue Road) and then the 1st turn right again into Park Road. Entrance at end of road through the blue gates. Bear left into the car park..

BUGBROOKE ST MICHAELS
At M1 Junction 16 take A45 to Northampton. At first roundabout follow signs to Bugbrooke. Go straight through village, ground entrance immediately past last house on the left.

BURTON PARK WANDERERS
From A14 take J10 towards Burton Latimer, at Alpro roundabout turn right, then straight over roundabout next to Versalift then right at Morrisions. Follow the round around the top of Morrisions continue until you are past the small Alumasc building on the left. Entrance to ground is next left.

COGENHOE UNITED
From A45 Northampton Ring Road turn as indicated to Billing/Cogenhoe. Go over River Nene and up hill ignoring first turning on left to Cogenhoe. Take next left and ground is on right hand side.

DEEPING RANGERS
From Town Centre head north on B1524 towards Bourne. Turn right onto Towngate East at Towngate Tavern Pub. Go straight over mini roundabout onto Outgang Road. Ground 1/4 mile on left. From A16 by pass at roundabout with the A15 Bourne Road turn towards Deeping then left into Northfields Road, then left into Towngate/Outgang Road. Ground 1/4 mile on left.

DESBOROUGH TOWN
Take exit 3 marked Desborough off the A14 and follow bypass for 2 miles. At roundabout turn right and ground is 200 yards on the left hand side.

EYNESBURY ROVERS
From the A1 take the A428 towards Cambridge. Turn left at the Tesco roundabout and continue on Barford Road for half a mile going straight on at 4 roundabouts. Turn left into Hardwick Road and left into Hall Road. Ground at end of road

HARBOROUGH TOWN
Half a mile south of Market Harborough on the A508. 4 miles north of the A14 junction 2 towards Market Harborough turn left towards Leisure Centre, but keep left passed inflatable dome on the right, then through large car park, club house straight in front, with parking area.

HARROWBY UNITED
From A1 take B6403, go past roundabout, past Ancaster turn and take road for Harrowby. Follow the road into Grantham, ground on right opposite Cherry Tree public house.

HOLBEACH UNITED
Approaching Town Centre traffic lights from Spalding Direction take Second Left, or from Kings Lynn direction take sharp right, into Park Road. Ground is 300 yards on the left.

HUNTINGDON TOWN
At the A1 Brampton Hut roundabout, follow signs for A14 East until reaching the Spittals Interchange roundabout, Follow the A141 towards St Ives/March and go over 3 roundabouts. Take next left turn at traffic lights towards Kings Ripton and the ground is on the left.

IRCHESTER UNITED
From A509 Wellingborough/Newport Pagnell Road turn into Gidsy Lane to Irchester. Turn left into Wollaston Road B659. Alfred Street is on left hand side with the ground at the end.

LONG BUCKBY AFC
From the Village Centre turn into Station Road. Ground on left hand side. Parking is available in South Close adjacent to the Rugby Club (do NOT park "half on half off" the pavement outside the ground)

NEWPORT PAGNELL TOWN
From the A422 Newport Pagnell by pass turn into Marsh End Road, then first right into Willen Road.

NORTHAMPTON ON CHENECKS
Leave A45 at exit marked Bedford A428 and Town Centre. Take exit into Rushmere Road marked Abington, Kingsthorpe and County Cricket. At first set of lights turn left into Billing Road, sports ground 250 yards on the right.

NORTHAMPTON SILEBY RANGERS
Approach from A43 (Kettering): From large roundabout with traffic lights, take the A5076 Talavera Way exit, signposted to Market Harborough, Moulton Park and Kingsthorpe. The entrance to the ground is about a quarter of a mile on the left. Approach from A45: Take exit to A43 Ring Road / Kettering / Corby. Go straight over 1 roundabout to large roundabout with traffic lights. Then follow directions above.

NORTHAMPTON SPENCER
The ground is in Kingsthorpe area of Northampton on A508, Market Harborough road out of Town. Look for W Grose's garage (Vauxhall) and turn left at traffic lights into Thornton Rd, then first right into Studlands Rd. Follow to bottom of hill and onto track between allotments. Ground is after a right turn at end of track.

OADBY TOWN
Greene King Park, Wigston Road, Oadby, Leicestershire LE2 5QG - 01162 715728

OLNEY TOWN
From the North enter via A509 Warrington Road then turn left into Midland Road and immediately right into East Street. Ground on left hand side after Fire Station. From Milton Keynes: Follow the A509 into Olney, over river bridge, 200 metres past the Swan Bistro and public house and take the first turning right onto the market square immediately before the traffic lights), follow road to the right onto a one way system into East Street. Follow East Street for 500 metres, the ootball Club is on the right hand side, car park entrance being the immediately following right turn.

PETERBOROUGH NORTHERN STAR
From A1 turn on to A1139 Fletton Parkway. Follow signs for A47 Wisbech. Exit at Junction 7 (near Perkins Engines Site). At top of slip road turn left into Eastfield Road. At Traffic lights turn right into Newark Avenue and then first right in to Eastern Avenue. Take 2nd left in to Chestnut Avenue and the club is on the right behind steel Palisade Fencing

POTTON UNITED
From Sandy, take B1042 into Potton. Head towards Potton Town Centre and take right turn towards Biggleswade (B1040). The ground is on left hand side at foot of hill

QUORN
Follow A6 through Leicester towards Loughborough. At roundabout 2 miles from Loughborough take first exit, then first left. Ground on left.

RAUNDS TOWN
From North, East or West, take A14 J13 and follow A45 signs to Raunds. Turn left at roundabout by BP garage. From South follow A45 towards Thrapston. Turn right at roundabout by BP garage. Ground on left.

ROTHWELL CORINTHIANS
A14 to Rothwell. Take B669 towards Desborough. Ground on right at rear of cricket field opposite last houses on the left. Parking on verge or in adjacent field if gate open. Access to ground via footpath.

RUSHDEN AND HIGHAM UNITED
From A6/A45 Junction take Higham/Rushden bypass. At third roundabout turn right, then turn right immediately after the school. From Bedford (A6) take bypass and turn left at first roundabout then turn right immediately after the school

SHEPSHED DYNAMO
The Dovecote Stadium Butt Hole Lane Shepshed Leicestershire LE12 9BN - 01509 650992

SLEAFORD TOWN
A15 Sleaford By-pass, roundabout to A17 Holdingham Roundabout third exit towards Boston on A17 Take second exit of A17 towards Sleaford ground is 1 mile on right hand side before you enter Sleaford

SPALDING UNITED
Follow signs to Spalding Town Centre. From the north drive south down Pinchbeck Road towards Spalding. At traffic lights turn right into Kings Road. At the next set of lights turn left into Winfrey Avenue. The Ground is on the left. From the south follow signs to The Railway station and Bus Stations. The Ground is opposite the Bus Station on Winfrey Avenue. There is parking outside the ground in a pay and display car park.

ST IVES TOWN
From A1123 Houghton Road rurn right at traffic lights into Ramsey Road. After Fire Station turn right into Westwood Road. Ground at end of road on right hand side immediately before St Ivo Recreation Centre Car Park

STEWARTS & LLOYDS CORBY
From the Oundle/Weldon Road turn at roundabout into A6086 Lloyds Road and continue to roundabout. Take second exit going over railway line along Rockingham Road. Continue over speed bumps then turn left into Occupation Road and first right into Cannock Road. Ground is beyond the British Steel Club and Rugby pitch.

THRAPSTON TOWN
Exit A14 at A605 roundabout, travel towards Peterborough till 1st roundabout (approx 700 metres).Take first exit into Thrapston. AT traffic lights turn into Oundle Road adjacent to Masons Arms Pub. Turn left into Devere Road and ground at bottom of hill

WELLINGBOROUGH TOWN 2004
Leave A.45 at Wellingborough turn-off, pass Tesco's Store on left-hand side, up to roundabout. Take first exit to town centre. Ground is 300 yards on right-hand side. Entry just past the Dog & Duck public house adjacent to entry to Whitworths ground

WELLINGBOROUGH WHITWORTH
Leave A45 by pass and go past Tescos etc. Turn left at roundabout then turn right immediately after Dog and Duck pub and go through 2nd gate down to the ground .

WOODFORD UNITED
A361 Daventry to Banbury Road. Turn left in Byfield. Follow road to Woodford Halse. Ground on left just past industrial estate.

WOOTTON BLUE CROSS
From A421 turn into Wootton as sign posted. Passing a garage on left hand side, turn right. Ground set back on right hand side behind post office and fish and chip shop.

YAXLEY
Leave A1 at Norman Cross and travel towards Peterborough. Turn off A15 at traffic lights. Bear immediately right and go past cemetery. At bottom of hill turn right into Main Street then left into Holme Road. After short distance go over small bridge and turn left between a bungalow and house into Leading Drove. Ground on left hand side.

WESSEX LEAGUE

Sponsored by: Sydenhams

Founded: 1986

Recent Champions:
2007: Gosport Borough. 2008: AFC Totton.   2009: Poole Town
2010: Poole Town. 2011: Poole Town

ncel.org.uk

PREMIER DIVISION	P	W	D	L	F	A	Pts
1 (P) Winchester City	42	33	5	4	138	39	104
2 Bemerton Heath Harlequins	42	28	6	8	104	39	90
3 Christchurch	42	26	7	9	78	45	85
4 Moneyfields	42	26	6	10	105	62	84
5 GE Hamble	42	27	3	12	90	53	84
6 Downton	42	24	4	14	80	65	76
7 Hamworthy United	42	21	8	13	69	62	71
8 Romsey Town	42	21	4	17	77	66	67
9 Bournemouth	42	18	10	14	61	54	64
10 Alton Town	42	19	4	19	74	83	61
11 Totton & Eling	42	17	8	17	80	77	59
12 Fareham Town	42	14	14	14	77	68	56
13 Newport (IOW)	42	17	5	20	59	80	56
14 Lymington Town	42	16	5	21	63	78	53
15 Alresford Town	42	14	8	20	62	80	50
16 Blackfield & Langley	42	12	7	23	63	79	43
17 Horndean	42	10	8	24	47	68	38
18 Hayling United	42	10	8	24	59	104	38
19 Fawley	42	10	7	25	56	81	37
20 New Milton Town	42	10	6	26	64	108	36
21 (R) Brading Town	42	10	6	26	54	102	36
22 (R) Laverstock & Ford	42	7	5	30	59	126	26

DIVISION ONE	P	W	D	L	F	A	Pts
1 (P) Verwood Town	34	25	5	4	91	38	80
2 (P) AFC Portchester	34	24	4	6	114	52	76
3 Team Solent	34	19	7	8	75	52	64
4 East Cowes Victoria Athletic	34	19	6	9	82	46	63
5 Brockenhurst	34	18	9	7	72	41	63
6 Cowes Sports	34	15	5	14	62	45	50
7 Fleet Spurs	34	14	7	13	45	46	49
8 Whitchurch United	34	13	8	13	50	45	47
9 Ringwood Town	34	13	7	14	62	59	46
10 Andover New Street (-3)	34	13	10	11	53	56	46
11 Pewsey Vale	34	12	8	14	51	61	44
12 Petersfield Town	34	12	3	19	67	74	39
13 United Services Portsmouth	34	11	6	17	59	69	39
14 Amesbury Town	34	9	7	18	55	93	34
15 Stockbridge	34	7	12	15	34	63	33
16 Warminster Town	34	8	8	18	56	83	32
17 Tadley Calleva	34	8	4	22	39	82	28
18 Hythe & Dibden	34	6	4	24	47	109	22

PREMIER DIVISION	1	2	3	4	5	6	7	8	9	10	11	12	13	14	15	16	17	18	19	20	21	22
1 Alresford Town		2-2	0-3	2-1	2-0	1-0	1-1	4-2	3-2	2-0	2-5	2-2	1-2	1-2	3-0	1-2	0-4	2-2	2-0	1-2	1-1	0-4
2 Alton Town	4-1		1-1	2-0	0-0	2-0	0-5	3-1	2-0	2-2	0-2	4-0	1-3	0-3	1-3	2-0	3-2	5-0	2-0	1-2	0-3	1-0
3 Bemerton Heath Harlequins	5-1	6-1		2-1	6-0	1-0	1-3	2-1	2-3	3-0	1-0	1-1	6-0	1-0	5-1	3-1	1-2	5-1	3-0	3-0	1-2	3-1
4 Blackfield & Langley	0-0	0-2	2-1		0-0	1-0	0-1	5-1	1-2	2-3	1-3	0-1	2-5	0-5	3-2	2-3	1-1	3-0	6-1	5-4	1-3	0-1
5 Bournemouth	3-1	0-2	0-3	1-2		5-0	0-0	0-1	3-1	3-0	1-1	0-0	3-0	2-0	3-0	1-2	1-1	0-2	3-1	3-1	1-0	1-3
6 Brading Town	2-2	3-2	2-5	3-1	1-1		2-4	1-2	1-3	1-2	3-2	2-3	4-0	2-1	1-1	2-3	3-4	1-3	0-4	0-3	2-3	0-8
7 Christchurch	2-0	2-1	0-0	2-1	0-2	1-0		3-1	3-1	1-0	0-2	4-1	2-1	3-0	3-2	2-1	3-0	2-2	2-1	2-1	3-2	1-1
8 Downton	3-2	2-1	2-2	2-1	2-1	6-1	1-1		0-2	2-1	1-2	2-1	3-0	1-0	3-1	3-1	2-0	1-1	3-1	3-1	5-4	0-2
9 Fareham Town	2-1	1-3	1-2	0-0	4-1	2-2	0-2	1-2		1-0	2-2	1-1	1-1	0-0	2-2	5-4	0-1	4-1	1-1	3-1	2-0	3-2
10 Fawley	2-0	3-2	2-3	0-3	1-2	0-1	1-1		1-1		1-1	2-3	3-1	2-1	0-1	0-1	1-2	1-2	1-3		0-1	
11 GE Hamble	3-0	1-4	2-1	3-1	1-2	4-0	0-2	2-1	5-2	4-2		0-1	3-1	4-1	2-3	1-0	2-1	3-0	3-1	2-0	2-1	2-3
12 Hamworthy United	0-3	4-1	0-3	2-0	1-1	2-0	2-0	3-1	0-7	2-1	1-2		2-0	3-0	4-0	3-2	2-2	4-1	4-0	1-1	2-1	0-2
13 Hayling United	2-1	3-4	2-2	2-5	1-2	2-0	1-3	2-1	2-2	1-1	3-5	2-1		2-1	2-2	0-3	1-2	3-3	1-3	1-2	4-1	0-9
14 Horndean	0-2	2-4	0-3	3-1	3-1	0-1	3-0	1-1	0-0	3-0	0-1	1-4	0-3		1-1	1-1	1-0	0-1	0-1	0-2	2-2	0-1
15 Laverstock & Ford	3-5	2-3	0-5	1-4	2-2	1-2	1-4	0-2	4-2	1-6	0-1	1-2	3-2	2-5		1-4	0-8	7-3	1-4	1-0	0-3	1-4
16 Lymington Town	1-0	1-2	0-3	0-0	1-2	2-2	0-1	0-1	2-1	1-3	3-2	1-2	0-0	0-0	4-1		0-3	1-5	2-1	3-2	4-1	2-3
17 Moneyfields	1-1	3-1	1-2	4-2	1-2	2-4	3-2	3-1	3-3	5-2	1-0	4-0	3-0	4-0	2-0	5-1		4-3	5-0	6-5	2-1	1-2
18 New Milton Town	1-2	5-1	0-2	2-3	1-2	0-4	0-3	0-4	1-1	1-3	0-4	1-2	2-1	3-1	2-4	0-1	1-2		5-2	2-3	2-3	0-6
19 Newport IOW	4-1	1-0	0-1	1-0	0-4	1-0	2-1	3-4	0-0	2-1	2-0	1-0	4-0	2-0	2-1	2-1	0-0	1-3		1-0	3-3	0-3
20 Romsey Town	0-1	6-2	1-0	1-1	1-0	3-0	1-0	0-1	2-1	3-4	0-3	2-1	5-0	4-1	3-1	0-1	3-0	1-0	1-3		0-3	2-3
21 Totton & Eling	3-1	4-0	2-0	1-1	1-1	1-1	2-1	4-2	2-6	2-2	2-3	2-0	1-1	1-3	1-0	3-1	1-3	2-4	5-2	0-1		0-2
22 Winchester City	2-4	4-0	2-2	6-0	5-1	8-0	4-2	2-0	2-1	3-0	2-0	1-1	2-1	0-0	6-1	6-2	5-2	5-1	5-1	3-3	4-0	

LEAGUE CUP

ROUND 1
Brading Town 4-1 Hayling United
Ringwood Town 1-4 Bemerton Heath Harlequins
Brockenhurst 2-2 4-1p Team Solent
Fleet Spurs 1-2 Petersfield Town
Warminster Town 3-2 Fawley
Romsey Town 1-0 AFC Portchester
Whitchurch United 2-0 Winchester City
Downton 1-0 Hythe & Dibden

ROUND 2
Bournemouth 7-0 Stockbridge
Lymington Town 2-1 Brading Town
Totton & Eling 2-3 Cowes Sports
Bemerton Heath Harlequins 3-0 Hamworthy United
Brockenhurst 5-1 Andover New Street
Laverstock & Ford 2-1 Pewsey Vale
Alton Town 6-0 United Services Portsmout
Alresford Town 2-7 Moneyfields
Petersfield Town 1-2 Tadley Calleva
Christchurch 1-0 Warminster Town
Amesbury Town 0-5 Romsey Town
Verwood Town 1-2 New Milton Town
Newport (IOW) 2-0 Horndean
East Cowes Victoria 2-0 Fareham Town
Winchester City 0-0 3-4p GE Hamble
Downton 2-1 Blackfield & Langley

ROUND 3
Bournemouth 5-0 Lymington Town
Cowes Sports 0-0 4-5p Bemerton Heath Harlequins
Brockenhurst 4-1 Laverstock & Ford
Alton Town HW Moneyfields
Tadley Calleva 0-3 Christchurch
Romsey Town 1-0 New Milton Town
Newport (IOW) 1-0 East Cowes Victoria
GE Hamble 1-2 Downton

QUARTER FINALS
Bournemouth 4-0 Bemerton Heath Harlequins
Brockenhurst 2-2 4-2p Alton Town
Christchurch 3-1 Romsey Town
Newport (IOW) 2-4 Downton

SEMI-FINALS
Bournemouth 0-1 Brockenhurst
Christchurch 2-1 Downton

FINAL
Brockenhurst 1-3 Christchurch

DIVISION ONE	1	2	3	4	5	6	7	8	9	10	11	12	13	14	15	16	17	18
1 AFC Portchester		4-1	HW	2-0	2-1	0-2	2-0	4-1	2-1	5-2	2-2	6-0	4-0	4-5	5-0	3-2	3-1	5-0
2 Amesbury Town	2-8		0-1	2-2	2-1	2-5	2-1	5-2	0-3	2-1	2-2	2-2	3-2	1-2	1-4	3-6	3-2	4-1
3 Andover New Street	2-4	3-2		1-2	2-1	1-2	1-2	3-3	2-2	3-1	1-2	1-0	2-1	3-3	0-0	0-2	3-3	1-1
4 Brockenhurst	4-2	0-0	5-0		3-1	1-1	1-1	0-1	3-1	1-1	3-2	2-0	7-0	0-1	3-1	3-3	4-0	1-0
5 Cowes Sports	3-2	2-0	1-2	1-1		1-0	0-1	6-0	5-1	0-3	3-2	2-3	1-0	1-1	2-0	0-1	7-2	2-1
6 East Cowes Victoria Athletic	1-5	1-4	2-3	1-1	2-0		3-0	4-0	5-2	0-1	2-0	0-0	1-1	4-1	3-2	0-6	0-2	2-1
7 Fleet Spurs	0-5	4-0	1-1	1-1	2-1	0-0		5-2	1-0	1-1	2-1	2-0	1-0	2-0	2-0	1-3	1-3	0-2
8 Hythe & Dibden	0-3	0-1	0-0	2-6	0-3	0-4	4-1		1-4	1-1	5-2	1-2	0-0	0-2	2-6	1-5	4-0	0-4
9 Petersfield Town	2-4	2-1	5-1	3-4	2-3	0-3	1-0	2-1		0-2	2-1	4-2	2-3	4-0	2-3	2-4	1-2	1-1
10 Pewsey Vale	2-7	3-2	1-1	2-0	0-2	2-1	1-1	4-0	3-2		1-2	4-3	0-2	0-0	2-1	1-1	2-2	0-3
11 Ringwood Town	4-2	6-0	0-2	0-3	2-2	2-2	0-1	5-1	2-0	3-0		4-3	3-1	3-3	1-0	1-3	1-2	3-0
12 Stockbridge	2-0	1-1	0-0	1-3	0-0	0-5	1-4	2-1	0-3	2-1	3-1		2-1	1-3	0-0	0-5	1-1	0-0
13 Tadley Calleva	2-4	3-2	3-4	1-2	1-0	0-8	2-3	1-4	0-2	2-3	0-0	1-1		0-5	2-1	2-1	1-7	1-0
14 Team Solent	1-4	1-1	2-1	4-2	1-0	3-4	2-1	8-3	3-1	3-2	3-0	2-0	1-0		1-2	2-2	3-0	1-2
15 United Services Portsmouth	3-3	3-0	0-3	0-1	1-3	1-4	2-1	2-3	3-3	0-2	2-2	1-1	3-2	1-5		0-2	6-0	4-2
16 Verwood Town	2-4	8-0	3-1	2-1	2-2	1-5	1-0	5-0	1-0	3-0	3-0	1-0	2-1	3-1	2-1		1-0	1-0
17 Warminster Town	3-3	3-3	1-2	1-2	0-3	1-5	2-2	5-2	2-4	1-0	0-2	1-1	2-3	0-2	3-4	2-3		1-0
18 Whitchurch United	1-1	4-1	1-2	2-0	3-2	2-0	1-0	4-2	6-3	4-2	0-1	0-0	1-0	0-0	1-2	1-1	1-1	

AFC PORTCHESTER

Founded: Nickname:

Secretary: Jason Brooker   **(T)** 07972 165 077   **(E)** jason.brooker@afcportchester.co.uk

Chairman: Paul Kelly   **Manager:**   **Prog Ed:** Peter Stiles

Ground: Wicor Recreation Ground Cranleigh Road Portchester Hampshire PO16 9DP   **(T)** 07831 532 208

Capacity: **Seats:**   **Covered:**   **Midweek Matchday:** Tuesday   **Clubhouse:**   **Shop:**

Colours(change): Tangerine/tangerine & black/tangerine & black (Black & white stripes/white/white)
Previous Names:
Previous Leagues:
Records:
Senior Honours:

10 YEAR RECORD

02-03		03-04		04-05		05-06		06-07		07-08		08-09		09-10		10-11		11-12	
Hant1	10	Hant1	13	Wex3	14	Wex3	11	Wex2	4	Wex1	14	Wex1	19	Wex1	6	Wex1	3	Wex1	2

ALRESFORD TOWN

Founded: 1898   Nickname:

Secretary: Keith Curtis   **(T)** 07703 346672   **(E)** secretary.alresfordtownfc@gmail.com

Chairman: Trevor Ingram   **Manager:**   **Prog Ed:** Gregory Boughton

Ground: Alresbury Park, The Avenue, Alresford, Hants SO24 9EP   **(T)** 01962 735 100

Capacity: **Seats:** Yes   **Covered:** Yes   **Midweek Matchday:** Tuesday   **Clubhouse:** Yes   **Shop:**

Colours(change): Black & white stripes/black/black & white. (All yellow)
Previous Names:
Previous Leagues: Winchester League, North Hants league, Hampshire League
Records:
Senior Honours: Winchester League Division Two & One

10 YEAR RECORD

02-03		03-04		04-05		05-06		06-07		07-08		08-09		09-10		10-11		11-12	
Hant1	11	Hant1	8	Wex2	10	Wex2	20	Wex1	2	WexP	21	WexP	18	WexP	17	WexP	15	WexP	15

ALTON TOWN

Founded: 1919   Nickname:

Secretary: Jim McKell   **(T)** 07740 099 374   **(E)** secretary@altontownfc.com

Chairman: Jim McKell   **Manager:**   **Prog Ed:** Imageprint

Ground: Alton (Bass) Sports Ground, Anstey Road, Alton, Hants GU34 2RL   **(T)**

Capacity: 2,000 **Seats:** 200 **Covered:** 250 **Midweek Matchday:** Tuesday   **Clubhouse:** Yes **Shop:** No

Colours(change): White/black/black   (Yellow/green/yellow)
Previous Names: Present club formed in 1990 when Alton Town and Bass Alton merged.
Previous Leagues: Hampshire League >2002
Records:
Senior Honours: Hants Senior Cup 1958, 1969, 1972 & 1978. Hampshire Champions 2001-02.

10 YEAR RECORD

02-03		03-04		04-05		05-06		06-07		07-08		08-09		09-10		10-11		11-12	
Wex1	17	Wex1	18	Wex1	19	Wex1	20	WexP	17	WexP	14	WexP	19	WexP	18	WexP	13	WexP	10

BEMERTON HEATH HARLEQUINS

Founded: 1989   Nickname: Quins

Secretary: Andy Hardwick   **(T)** 07561 164 068   **(E)** secretarybhhfc@hotmail.com

Chairman: Steve Slade   **Manager:**   **Prog Ed:** Steve Brooks

Ground: The Clubhouse, Western Way, Bemerton Heath Salisbury SP2 9DT   **(T)** 01722 331925 (Club) 331218 (Office)

Capacity: 2,100 **Seats:** 250 **Covered:** 350 **Midweek Matchday:** Monday   **Clubhouse:** Yes **Shop:** No

Colours(change): Black & white quarters/black/black & white (Amber/white/white)
Previous Names: Bemerton Athletic, Moon FC & Bemerton Boys merged in 1989
Previous Leagues: Salisbury & Wilts Comb, Salisbury & Andover Sunday
Records: **Att:**1,118 v Aldershot Town   **App:** Keith Richardson
Senior Honours: Wiltshire Senior Cup 1992-93. Wessex League Cup 2009-10.

10 YEAR RECORD

02-03		03-04		04-05		05-06		06-07		07-08		08-09		09-10		10-11		11-12	
Wex	18	Wex	12	Wex1	14	Wex1	14	WexP	11	WexP	13	WexP	12	WexP	3	WexP	2	WexP	2

BLACKFIELD & LANGLEY

Founded: 1935   Nickname:

Secretary: Lisa Bray   **(T)** 07870 813 501   **(E)** lee775@btinternet.com

Chairman: Owen Lightfoot   **Manager:**   **Prog Ed:** Andrew Hartman

Ground: Gang Warily Rec., Newlands Rd, Southampton, SO45 1GA   **(T)** 02380 893 603

Capacity: 2,500   **Seats:** 180   **Covered:** nil   **Midweek Matchday:** Tuesday   **Clubhouse:** Yes   **Shop:**

Colours(change): White/green/white (Yellow/yellow/yellow).
Previous Names:
Previous Leagues: Southampton Senior. Hampshire.
Records: **Att:** 240
Senior Honours: Hampshire League 1987-88, Division Two 1984-85, Southampton Senior Cup (4).

10 YEAR RECORD

02-03		03-04		04-05		05-06		06-07		07-08		08-09		09-10		10-11		11-12	
Wex	21	Wex	21	Wex2	7	Wex2	14	Wex1	16	Wex1	10	Wex1	2	WexP	8	WexP	14	WexP	16

BOURNEMOUTH

Founded: 1875   Nickname: Poppies

Secretary: Mike Robins   **(T)** 07947 687 808   **(E)** poppies1875@hotmail.co.uk

Chairman: Bob Corbin   **Manager:** Ken Vaughan   **Prog Ed:** Mike Robins

Ground: Victoria Park, Namu Road, Winton, Bournemouth, BH9 2RA   **(T)** 01202 515 123

Capacity: 3,000   **Seats:** 205   **Covered:** 205   **Midweek Matchday:** Tuesday   **Clubhouse:** Yes   **Shop:** Yes

Colours(change): All Red (All blue)
Previous Names: Bournemouth Rovers, Bournemouth Wanderers, Bournemouth Dean Park
Previous Leagues: Hampshire
Records: Goalscorer (since 1990) DARREN McBRIDE 95 (111+26 games) Apps (since 1990) MARK DANCER 358 (318+40 games)
Senior Honours: Wessex League Cup Winners: 2011.

10 YEAR RECORD

02-03		03-04		04-05		05-06		06-07		07-08		08-09		09-10		10-11		11-12	
Wex	14	Wex	20	Wex1	11	Wex1	7	WexP	5	WexP	5	WexP	15	WexP	4	WexP	5	WexP	9

CHRISTCHURCH

Founded: 1885   Nickname: Priory

Secretary: Ian Harley   **(T)** 07900 133 954   **(E)** secretary@christchurchfc.co.uk

Chairman: Mark Duffy   **Manager:**   **Prog Ed:** Fiona Kegg

Ground: Hurn Bridge S.C, Avon Causeway, Christchurch BH23 6DY   **(T)** 01202 473 792

Capacity: 1,200   **Seats:** 215   **Covered:** 265   **Midweek Matchday:** Tuesday   **Clubhouse:** Yes   **Shop:**

Colours(change): All Blue (All red)
Previous Names:
Previous Leagues: Hampshire
Records: **App:** John Haynes
Senior Honours: Hants Jnr Cup (3), Hants Intermediate Cup 86-87, Bournemouth Senior Cup (5)

10 YEAR RECORD

02-03		03-04		04-05		05-06		06-07		07-08		08-09		09-10		10-11		11-12	
Wex	13	Wex	11	Wex1	17	Wex1	10	WexP	14	WexP	16	WexP	7	WexP	5	WexP	6	WexP	3

DOWNTON

Founded: 1905   Nickname: The Robins

Secretary: Mike Turner   **(T)** 07903 376 231   **(E)** mike.turner@sport4salisbury.com

Chairman: Mark Smith   **Manager:**   **Prog Ed:** Mark Smith

Ground: Brian Whitehead Sports Ground Wick Lane Downton Wiltshire SP5 3NF   **(T)** 01725 512162

Capacity: **Seats:**   **Covered:**   **Midweek Matchday:** Tuesday   **Clubhouse:**   **Shop:**

Colours(change): Red/white/red (Yellow/blue/yellow)
Previous Names:
Previous Leagues: Hampshire > 1993.
Records: **Att:** 55 v AFC Bournemouth - Friendly.
Senior Honours: Wiltshire Senior Cup 1979-80, 80-81. Wiltshire Junior Cup 1949-50. Wessex League Cup 1995-96.
Wessex League Division One 2010-11.

10 YEAR RECORD

02-03		03-04		04-05		05-06		06-07		07-08		08-09		09-10		10-11		11-12	
Wex	19	Wex	19	Wex1	22	Wex2	4	WexP	18	WexP	23	Wex1	17	Wex1	4	Wex1	1	WexP	6

FAREHAM TOWN

Founded: 1946   Nickname: The Robins

Secretary: Paul Procter   **(T)** 07445 805 122   **(E)** splodge68@gmail.com

Chairman: Nick Ralls   **Manager:** Paul Tanner   **Prog Ed:** Paul Proctor

Ground: Cams Alders, Palmerston Drive, Fareham, Hants PO14 1BJ   **(T)** 07930 853 235

Capacity: 2,000   **Seats:** 450   **Covered:** 500   **Midweek Matchday:** Wednesday   **Clubhouse:** Yes   **Shop:** Yes

Colours(change): Red/black/red (White/black/black)
Previous Names:
Previous Leagues: Portsmouth, Hampshire & Southern
Records: **Att:** 2,015 v Spurs (friendly 1985)
Senior Honours: Hampshire Senior Cup 1957, 1963, 1968, 1993. Hampshire League Champions.

10 YEAR RECORD

02-03	03-04	04-05	05-06	06-07	07-08	08-09	09-10	10-11	11-12
Wex 5	Wex 7	Wex1 16	Wex1 9	WexP 8	WexP 8	WexP 10	WexP 6	WexP 8	WexP 12

FAWLEY

Founded: 1923   Nickname:

Secretary: Richard Coxall   **(T)** 07774 716 663   **(E)** fawleysecretary@hotmail.co.uk

Chairman: Kevin Mitchell   **Manager:**   **Prog Ed:** Jeff Moore

Ground: Waterside Spts & Soc. club, 179 Long Lane, Holbury, Soto, SO45 2QD   **(T)** 02380 893750 (Club) 896621 (Office)

Capacity: **Seats:**   **Covered:**   **Midweek Matchday:** Wednesday   **Clubhouse:**   **Shop:**

Colours(change): All Blue (All yellow)
Previous Names: Esso Fawley > 2002
Previous Leagues: Hampshire Premier > 2004.
Records:
Senior Honours:

10 YEAR RECORD

02-03	03-04	04-05	05-06	06-07	07-08	08-09	09-10	10-11	11-12
HantP 18	HantP 16	Wex2 21	Wex2 7	Wex1 5	Wex1 6	Wex1 9	Wex1 2	WexP 20	WexP 19

GE HAMBLE

Founded: 1938   Nickname:

Secretary: Matthew Newbold   **(T)** 07917 451 823   **(E)** hamble.assc@hotmail.co.uk

Chairman: Gilly Bowers   **Manager:**   **Prog Ed:** Matthew Newbold

Ground: Folland Park, Kings Ave, Hamble, Southampton SO31 4NF   **(T)** 02380 452 173

Capacity: 1,000   **Seats:** 150   **Covered:** 150   **Midweek Matchday:** Tuesday   **Clubhouse:** Yes   **Shop:** No

Colours(change): Sky blue/sky blue/maroon (White/red/red)
Previous Names: Folland Sports (pre 1990), Aerostructures SSC 1990-97, Hamble ASSC 1997-2011.
Previous Leagues:
Records:
Senior Honours: Southampton Senior Cup 1984-85, 86-87, 91-92. Wessex League Division 1 2009-10.

10 YEAR RECORD

02-03	03-04	04-05	05-06	06-07	07-08	08-09	09-10	10-11	11-12
Wex 16	Wex 13	Wex1 21	Wex1 15	WexP 20	WexP 17	WexP 21	Wex1 1	WexP 12	WexP 5

HAMWORTHY UNITED

Founded: 1926   Nickname:

Secretary: Peter Gallop   **(T)** 07897 959270   **(E)** ham-utd-fc-secretary@hotmail.co.uk

Chairman: TBA   **Manager:**   **Prog Ed:** Stuart Tanner

Ground: The County Ground, Blandford Close, Hamworthy, Poole, BH15 4PR   **(T)** 01202 674 974

Capacity: 2,000   **Seats:**   **Covered:**   **Midweek Matchday:** Tuesday   **Clubhouse:** Yes   **Shop:** No

Colours(change): Maroon & sky blue/sky blue/sky blue (Yellow & black stripes/black/black)
Previous Names: Hamworthy St. Michael merged with Trinidad Old Boys 1926
Previous Leagues: Dorset Premier
Records:
Senior Honours: Dorset Premier League 2002-03, 03-04.

10 YEAR RECORD

02-03	03-04	04-05	05-06	06-07	07-08	08-09	09-10	10-11	11-12
Dor P 1	Dor P 1	Wex1 15	Wex1 6	WexP 15	WexP 10	WexP 8	WexP 16	WexP 9	WexP 7

HAYLING UNITED
Founded: 1884 Nickname:

Secretary: Shirley Westfield **(T)** 07724 540 916 **(E)** shirley.westfield@ntlworld.com

Chairman: Argyll McLetchie **Manager:** Lee Paul **Prog Ed:** Mark Griffiths

Ground: Hayling College, Church Road, Hayling Island, Hampshire PO11 0NU **(T)** 07724 540 916

Capacity: **Seats:** **Covered:** **Midweek Matchday:** Tuesday **Clubhouse:** Yes **Shop:** No

Colours(change): Black & white/black/white (Yellow/yellow/white).
Previous Names:
Previous Leagues: Waterlooville & District > 1952 , Portsmouth 1952-91, Hampshire 1991-2004
Records:
Senior Honours: Hampshire League Division One 2002-03. Wessex Division One 2006-07.

10 YEAR RECORD

02-03		03-04		04-05		05-06		06-07		07-08		08-09		09-10		10-11		11-12	
Hant1	1	Hant1	5	Wex3	2	Wex2	2	Wex1	1	WexP	12	WexP	16	WexP	15	WexP	21	WexP	18

HORNDEAN
Founded: 1887 Nickname:

Secretary: Michael Austin **(T)** 07983 969644 **(E)** horndeanfc1887@yahoo.co.uk

Chairman: David Sagar **Manager:** **Prog Ed:** Joe Albertella

Ground: Five Heads Park Five Heads Road Horndean Hampshire PO8 9NZ **(T)** 02392 591 363

Capacity: **Seats:** **Covered:** **Midweek Matchday:** Tuesday **Clubhouse:** **Shop:**

Colours(change): All red (All blue)
Previous Names:
Previous Leagues: Hampshire 1972-86, 1995-2004. Wessex 1986-95
Records: **Att:** 1,560 v Waterlooville, Victory Cup, April 1971. **Goalscorer:** Frank Bryson 348 (including 83 during the 1931-32 season)
Senior Honours:

10 YEAR RECORD

02-03		03-04		04-05		05-06		06-07		07-08		08-09		09-10		10-11		11-12	
HantP	5	HantP	5	Wex2	9	Wex2	6	WexP	16	WexP	11	WexP	22	Wex1	12	Wex1	2	WexP	17

LYMINGTON TOWN
Founded: 1876 Nickname:

Secretary: Barry Torah **(T)** 07849 645 234 **(E)** barry.torah@sky.com

Chairman: George Shaw **Manager:** **Prog Ed:** Derek Webb

Ground: The Sports Ground, Southampton Road, Lymington SO41 9ZG **(T)** 01590 671 305

Capacity: 3,000 **Seats:** 200 **Covered:** 300 **Midweek Matchday:** Tuesday **Clubhouse:** **Shop:**

Colours(change): Red/white/black (Yellow/blue/yellow)
Previous Names:
Previous Leagues: Hampshire.
Records:
Senior Honours: Wessex League Cup 2006-07.

10 YEAR RECORD

02-03		03-04		04-05		05-06		06-07		07-08		08-09		09-10		10-11		11-12	
HantP	15	HantP	7	Wex2	1	Wex1	17	WexP	12	WexP	20	WexP	18	WexP	20	WexP	11	WexP	14

MONEYFIELDS
Founded: 1987 Nickname: Moneys

Secretary: Wayne Dalton **(T)** 07766 411 346 **(E)** wayne.dalton@ntlworld.com

Chairman: Paul Gregory **Manager:** Miles Rutherford & Graeme Gee **Prog Ed:** David Hayter

Ground: Moneyfields Sports Ground, Moneyfield Ave, Copnor, P'mouth PO3 6LA **(T)** 02392 665 260

Capacity: 1,500 **Seats:** 150 **Covered:** 150 **Midweek Matchday:** Tuesday **Clubhouse:** Yes **Shop:** Yes

Colours(change): Yellow & navy blue/navy/yellow (White & blue/blue/white).
Previous Names: Portsmouth Civil Service
Previous Leagues: Portsmouth. Hampshire.
Records: **Att:** 250 v Fareham, WexD1 05-06 **Goalscorer:** Lee Mould 86 **App:** Matt Lafferty - 229 **Win:** 9-0v Blackfield & Langley 01-02.
Senior Honours: Portsmouth Premier Champions 1990-91, 91-92. Senior Cup 1990-91.
Hampshire Division Three 1991-92, Division Two 1992-93, Division One 1996-97.

10 YEAR RECORD

02-03		03-04		04-05		05-06		06-07		07-08		08-09		09-10		10-11		11-12	
Wex	10	Wex	17	Wex1	10	Wex1	11	WexP	7	WexP	7	WexP	3	WexP	12	WexP	7	WexP	4

NEW MILTON TOWN
Founded: 2007　　Nickname: The Linnets

Secretary: Richard Phippard　　**(T)** 07515 775 442　　**(E)** secretary.newmilton@yahoo.co.uk

Chairman: John Breaker　　**Manager:**　　**Prog Ed:** Richard Phippard

Ground: Fawcett Fields, Christchurch Road, New Milton, BH25 6QB　　**(T)** 01425 628 191

Capacity: 3,000　**Seats:** 262　**Covered:** 262　**Midweek Matchday:** Tuesday　　**Clubhouse:**　**Shop:**

Colours(change): Maroon & sky blue/white/sky blue (Yellow & green/green/green)
Previous Names: Lymington Town > 1988, AFC Lymington 1988-98, Lymington & New Milton 1998-07.
Previous Leagues: Isthmian. Southern.
Records:
Senior Honours: Wessex League 1998-99, 04-05.

10 YEAR RECORD

02-03		03-04		04-05		05-06		06-07		07-08		08-09		09-10		10-11		11-12	
Wex	6	Wex	4	Wex1	1	Isth1	16	SthS	17	WexP	19	WexP	9	WexP	19	WexP	19	WexP	20

NEWPORT I.O.W.
Founded: 1888　　Nickname: The Port

Secretary: John Simpkins　　**(T)** 07771 964 704　　**(E)** simmo123@my-inbox.net

Chairman: Paul Phelps　　**Manager:**　　**Prog Ed:** Sam Turner

Ground: St George's Park, St George's Way, Newport PO30 2QH　　**(T)** 01983 525 027

Capacity: 5,000　**Seats:** 300　**Covered:** 1,000　**Midweek Matchday:** Wednesday　　**Clubhouse:** Yes　**Shop:** Yes

Colours(change): Yellow/blue/yellow. (All green)
Previous Names:
Previous Leagues: I.O.W. 1896-28. Hants 28-86. Wessex 86-90.
Records: **Att:** 2,270 v Portsmouth (friendly) 07.07.2001. **Goalscorer:** Roy Grilfillan - 220 1951-57. **Apps:** Jeff Austin - 540 1969-87.
Senior Honours: Southern League Eastern Division 2000-01. Hants Senior Cup (x8). I.O.W. Cup (34)

10 YEAR RECORD

02-03		03-04		04-05		05-06		06-07		07-08		08-09		09-10		10-11		11-12	
SthE	16	SthE	19	Isth1	18	Isth1	22	SthS	20	SthS	22	WexP	6	WexP	9	WexP	10	WexP	13

ROMSEY TOWN
Founded: 1886　　Nickname:

Secretary: David White　　**(T)** 07876 743 651　　**(E)** romseytownfc@hotmail.co.uk

Chairman: Ken Jacobs　　**Manager:**　　**Prog Ed:** Cameron Melling

Ground: The Bypass Ground, South Front, Romsey, SO51 8GJ　　**(T)** 07876 743 651

Capacity:　**Seats:**　**Covered:**　**Midweek Matchday:** Tuesday　　**Clubhouse:** Yes　**Shop:**

Colours(change): White/black/black. (All blue).
Previous Names: None
Previous Leagues: Hampshire.
Records:
Senior Honours: Wessex League Champions 1989-90.

10 YEAR RECORD

02-03		03-04		04-05		05-06		06-07		07-08		08-09		09-10		10-11		11-12	
Hant2	13	Hant2	2	Wex2	4	Wex2	13	Wex1	3	WexP	18	WexP	11	WexP	10	WexP	16	WexP	8

TOTTON & ELING
Founded: 1925　　Nickname:

Secretary: Mike Clarke　　**(T)** 07825 576 359　　**(E)** michael@clarke96.orangehome.co.uk

Chairman: Edmond Holmes　　**Manager:**　　**Prog Ed:** Margaret Fiander

Ground: Little Testwood Farm, Southampton SO40 3ND　　**(T)** 02380 862 143

Capacity:　**Seats:** Yes　**Covered:** Yes　**Midweek Matchday:** Tuesday　　**Clubhouse:**　**Shop:**

Colours(change): Red/black/red (All yellow)
Previous Names: BAT Sports > 2007
Previous Leagues: Hampshire.
Records: 2,763 v AFC Wimbledon, FA Vase (game switched to AFC Wimbedon).
Senior Honours: Hampshire Champions 1987-88, 88-89. Wessex Division 1 2008-09.

10 YEAR RECORD

02-03		03-04		04-05		05-06		06-07		07-08		08-09		09-10		10-11		11-12	
Wex	11	Wex	15	Wex1	9	Wex1	18	Wex2	5	Wex1	5	Wex1	1	WexP	7	WexP	18	WexP	11

VERWOOD TOWN

Founded: 1920s   Nickname:

Secretary: Roy Mortimer   **(T)** 07801 713 462   **(E)** secretary@vtfc.co.uk
Chairman: Michael Fry   **Manager:**   **Prog Ed:** Dan Scott
Ground: Potterne Park Potterne Way Verwood Dorset BH21 6RS   **(T)** 01202 814 007
Capacity: **Seats:**   **Covered:**   **Midweek Matchday:** Wednesday   **Clubhouse:**   **Shop:**

Colours(change): Red & white/black/black (Blue & white stripes/blue/yellow)
Previous Names:
Previous Leagues: Hampshire
Records:
Senior Honours: Wessex League Division One 2011-12.

10 YEAR RECORD									
02-03	03-04	04-05	05-06	06-07	07-08	08-09	09-10	10-11	11-12
Hant1 2	Hant1 12	Wex3 16	Wex3 3	Wex1 6	Wex1 4	Wex1 13	Wex1 7	Wex1 9	Wex1 1

DIVISION ONE

AMESBURY TOWN

Founded: 1904   Nickname:

Secretary: Arthur Mundy   **(T)** 07528 438103   **(E)** a.mundy094@virginmedia.com
Chairman: Jason Cameron   **Manager:**   **Prog Ed:** Mark Hilton
Ground: Bonnymead Park Recreation Road Amesbury SP4 7BB   **(T)** 01980 623489   **Capacity:**
Colours(change): All blue (All yellow)

ADDITIONAL INFORMATION:
Previous Name: Amesbury FC. **Previous League:** Hampshire.
Record Att: 625 - 1997.

ANDOVER NEW STREET

Founded: 1895   Nickname:

Secretary: Mick Bugg   **(T)** 07584 562 948   **(E)** andovernewstreetfc@hotmail.co.uk
Chairman: Martin Tobin   **Manager:**   **Prog Ed:** Jimmy Wilson
Ground: Foxcotte Park Charlton Andover Hampshire SP11 0HS   **(T)** 01264 358358   **Capacity:**
Colours(change): Green & black/black/black (White/blue/white)

ADDITIONAL INFORMATION:
Record Att: 240.
Honours: Trophyman Cup 2003-04.

BROCKENHURST

Founded: 1898   Nickname: The Badgers

Secretary: Mike Prince   **(T)** 07891 851 857   **(E)** mikeprince@live.com
Chairman: Pete Lynes   **Manager:**   **Prog Ed:** Pete Lynes
Ground: Grigg Lane, Brockenhurst, Hants SO42 7RE   **(T)** 01590 623 544   **Capacity:** 2,000
Colours(change): Blue & white/blue/blue. (All green).

ADDITIONAL INFORMATION: Att: 1,104 v St Albans City
Hampshire League 1975-76.

COWES SPORTS

Founded: 1881   Nickname: Yachtsmen

Secretary: Glynn M Skinner   **(T)** 07854 889 446   **(E)** csfcsecretary@yahoo.com
Chairman: Ian Lee   **Manager:**   **Prog Ed:** Peter Jeffery
Ground: Westwood Park Reynolds Close off Park Rd Cowes Isle of Wight PO31 7NT   **(T)** 01983 293 793   **Capacity:**
Colours(change): Blue & White stripes/black/blue (Red/white/white)

ADDITIONAL INFORMATION:
Previous League: Hampshire > 1994.
Honours: Hampshire League 1993-94.

EAST COWES VICTORIA ATHLETIC

Founded: Nickname:

Secretary: Darren Dyer   **(T)** 07725 128701   **(E)** ecvics@live.co.uk
Chairman: Kenny Adams   **Manager:**   **Prog Ed:** Darren Dyer
Ground: Beatrice Avenue Whippingham East Cowes Isle of Wight PO32 6PA   **(T)** 01983 297 165   **Capacity:**
Colours(change): Red & white stripes/black/black (All green)

ADDITIONAL INFORMATION:

FLEET SPURS

Founded: **Nickname:**

Secretary: Paul Hampshire **(T)** 07850 810 133 **(E)** secretary@fleetspursfc.co.uk
Chairman: Bryan Sheppard **Manager:** **Prog Ed:** Paul Hampshire
Ground: Kennels Lane Southwood Farnborough Hampshire, GU14 0ST **(T)** **Capacity:**
Colours(change): Blue with red trim/blue/blue (Yellow/black/yellow)

ADDITIONAL INFORMATION:

HYTHE & DIBDEN

Founded: **Nickname:**

Secretary: Nikki Oakley **(T)** 07769 951982 **(E)** hythedibdenfc@aol.com
Chairman: Robert J Parsons **Manager:** **Prog Ed:** Dee Harvey
Ground: Ewart Recreation Ground Jones Lane Hythe Southampton SO45 6AA **(T)** 02380 845264 (MD) **Capacity:**
Colours(change): Green/white/white (All blue)

ADDITIONAL INFORMATION:

LAVERSTOCK & FORD

Founded: 1956 **Nickname:**

Secretary: Brian Ford **(T)** 07743 538 984 **(E)** sec.laverstockandfordfc@gmail.com
Chairman: Gino Nardiello **Manager:** Nev Beal **Prog Ed:** Michael Eyers
Ground: The Dell, Church Road, Laverstock, Salisbury, Wilts SP1 1QX **(T)** 01722 327 401 **Capacity:**
Colours(change): Green & white hoops/green/green (Yellow/blue/white)

ADDITIONAL INFORMATION:

PETERSFIELD TOWN

Founded: **Nickname:**

Secretary: Mark Nicoll **(T)** 07949 328240 **(E)** m.nicoll1@ntlworld.com
Chairman: Graeme Moir **Manager:** Matt Short **Prog Ed:** Graeme Moir
Ground: Love Lane Petersfield Hampshire GU31 4BW **(T)** 01730 233416 **Capacity:**
Colours(change): Red & black stripes/black/black (All blue)

ADDITIONAL INFORMATION:
Previous Name: Petersfield United.
Previous League: Isthmian.

PEWSEY VALE

Founded: 1948 **Nickname:**

Secretary: Julie Wootton **(T)** 07789 168 303 **(E)** pewseyvalefc@hotmail.co.uk
Chairman: Alan Ritchie **Manager:** **Prog Ed:** Julie Wootton
Ground: Recreation Ground Kings Corner Ball Road Pewsey **(T)** 07789 168 303 **Capacity:**
Colours(change): White/navy/navy (All yellow)

ADDITIONAL INFORMATION:
Previous League: Wiltshire.

RINGWOOD TOWN

Founded: 1879 **Nickname:**

Secretary: Aubrey Hodder **(T)** 07754 460 501 **(E)** ringwoodtownfc@live.co.uk
Chairman: Steve Simpson **Manager:** **Prog Ed:** Ian Claxton
Ground: The Canotec Stadium Long Lane Ringwood Hampshire BH24 3BX **(T)** 07706 903 959 **Capacity:**
Colours(change): All red (All blue)

ADDITIONAL INFORMATION:

STOCKBRIDGE

Founded: 1894 **Nickname:**

Secretary: Robin Smith **(T)** 01980 629 781 **(E)** stockbridgefc@hotmail.co.uk
Chairman: Paul Barker **Manager:** **Prog Ed:** Mavis Savage
Ground: Stockbridge Recreation Ground High Street Stockbridge SP20 6EU **(T)** 07963 453 162 **Capacity:**
Colours(change): All red (Blue & yellow/blue/blue & yellow)

ADDITIONAL INFORMATION:
Previous League: Hampshire.

TADLEY CALLEVA

Secretary: Steve Blackburn   **(T)** 07787 501 028
Chairman: Sandy Russell   **Manager:**
Ground: Barlows Park Silchester Road Tadley Hampshire RG26 3PX
Colours(change): Yellow & black/black/yellow (Burgundy & blue/burgundy/blue)

Founded: Nickname:
(E) tadleycallevafc@sky.com
Prog Ed: Steve Blackburn
(T) 07787 501 028   **Capacity:**

ADDITIONAL INFORMATION:

TEAM SOLENT

Secretary: Claire Taylor   **(T)** 07786 970 340
Chairman: Phil Green   **Manager:**
Ground: Test Park, Lower Broomhill Road, Southampton SO16 9QZ
Colours(change): Red & white/red/red (White & black/black/black).

Founded: Nickname:
(E) claire.taylor@solent.ac.uk
Prog Ed: Sport Solent
(T)   **Capacity:**

ADDITIONAL INFORMATION:
Previous Lge: Hampshire > 2011.

UNITED SERVICES PORTSMOUTH

Secretary: Bob Brady   **(T)** 07887 541 782
Chairman: Richard Stephenson Lt. RN   **Manager:** Bob Brady
Ground: Victory Stadium HMS Temeraire Burnaby Road Portsmouth PO1 2HB
Colours(change): All royal blue (Red & white/red/red)

Founded: Nickname:
(E) usportsmouthfc@hotmail.co.uk
Prog Ed: Charlie Read
(T) 02392 724 235 (Club)   **Capacity:**

ADDITIONAL INFORMATION:
Previous Name: Portsmouth Royal Navy.

WHITCHURCH UNITED

Secretary: Phil Cooper   **(T)** 07825 112 677
Chairman: Gary Shaughnessy   **Manager:**
Ground: Longmeadow Winchester Road Whitchurch Hampshire RG28 7RB
Colours(change): All red (All blue)

Founded: 1903   Nickname:
(E) secretary.wufc@gmail.com
Prog Ed: John Rutledge
(T) 01256 892 493   **Capacity:**

ADDITIONAL INFORMATION:

GROUND DIRECTIONS

AFC PORTCHESTER - Wicor Recreation Ground Cranleigh Road Portchester Hampshire PO16 9DP 07798 734678 (M)

Leave the M27 at Junction 11 and follow the signs to Portchester into Portchester Road. Carry on for approx 1 mile at the large roundabout, take the 3rd exit into Cornaway Lane and at the 'T' junction turn right in Cranleigh Road and follow the road to the end. Postcode for Satellite Navigation systems PO16 9DP

ALRESFORD TOWN FC - Arlebury Park The Avenue Alresford Hampshire SO24 9EP 01962 735 100

Alresford is situated on the A31 between Winchester and Alton. Arlebury Park is on the main avenue into Alresford opposite Perins School.
Postcode for Satellite Navigation systems SO24 9EP

ALTON TOWN FC - Alton (Bass) Sports Ground Anstey Road Alton Hampshire GU34 2RL

Leave the A31 at the B3004 signposted to Alton. Follow the road round to the left passing Anstey Park on the right, the ground is then immediately on the left – opposite the turning into Anstey Lane. Postcode for Satellite Navigation systems GU34 2RL

AMESBURY TOWN FC - Bonnymead Park Recreation Road Amesbury SP4 7BB 01980 623489

From Salisbury take A345 to Amesbury, turn left just past the bus station and proceed through the one way system, when road splits with Friar Tuck Café and Lloyds Bank on left turn left and follow road over the river bridge and when road bears sharp right turn left into Recreation Road.
From A303 at Countess Roundabout go into Amesbury, straight over traffic lights, at mini-roundabout turn right into one way system and follow directions as above.
Postcode for Satellite Navigation systems SP4 7BB

ANDOVER NEW STREET FC - Foxcotte Park Charlton Andover Hampshire SP11 0HS 01264 358358 Weekends from Midday, Evenings from 1900 hrs

From Basingstoke follow the A303 to Weyhill roundabout. At roundabout turn right and 2nd roundabout turn left on to A342. Approx 1/2 mile turn right into Short Lane, continue into Harroway Lane to the 'T' junction at the top. Turn right into Foxcotte Lane and continue for about 3/4 mile then turn left, this still Foxcotte Lane, to the top some 3/4 mile to the roundabout straight across into Foxcotte Park. Postcode for Satellite Navigation systems SP11 0TA.

BEMERTON HEATH HARLEQUINS FC - The Clubhouse Western Way Bemerton Heath Salisbury Wiltshire SP2 9DT 01722 331925 (Club) 331218 (Office)

Turn off the A36 Salisbury to Bristol road at Skew Bridge (right turn if coming out of Salisbury), 1st left into Pembroke Road for 1/2 mile, 2nd left along Western Way – Ground is 1/4 mile at the end of the road. 40 minutes walk fro Salisbury railway station. Bus service 51 or 52 from the city centre.
Postcode for Satellite Navigation systems SP2 9DP

BLACKFIELD & LANGLEY FC - Gang Warily Community and Recreation Centre Newlands Road Fawley Southampton SO45 1GA   02380 893 603

Leave M27 at Junction 2 signposted A326 to Fawley. Head South along A326 through several roundabouts. Pass the Holbury P/H on your right at roundabout take the right fork signposted Lepe and Fawley.At the 1st set of traffic lights turn left then turn left into the ground, approx 200 yards. There is a sign at the traffic lights indicating Blackfield & Langley FC. Postcode for Satellite Navigation systems SO45 1GA

BOURNEMOUTH FC - Victoria Park Namu Road Winton Bournemouth Dorset BH9 2RA 01202 515 123

From the North and East – A338 from Ringwood. Take the 3rd exit signed A3060 Wimborne, going under the road you've just left. Stay on this road passing Castlepoint Shopping Centre (on your right), then the Broadway Hotel on your right, keep straight ahead passing the Horse & Jockey on your left, keep to the nearside lane. At roundabout take the 1st exit marked A347, pass Redhill Common on your right and the fire station on your left: continue on the A347 turning left at the filter with the pub – The Ensbury Park Hotel – immediately in front of you. 1st left into Victoria Avenue, and then third right into Namu Road, turning right at the end into the lane for the ground entrance.

From the West – A35 from Poole. Take the A3049 Dorset Way passing Tower Park (which is hidden from view) on your right, at the next roundabout take the second exit, and then the first exit at the next roundabout, taking up a position in the outside lane. At the next roundabout (with a pub called the Miller and Carter Steakhouse on your right) take the third exit, Wallisdown Road A3049. Go through the shopping area of Wallisdown across two roundabouts and at the third one take the first exit, you will see the ground on your right as you approach the pelican crossing. Turn right into Victoria Avenue, then third right into Namu Road, turning right at the end into the lane for the ground entrance. Postcode for Satellite Navigation systems BH9 2RA

BROCKENHURST FC - Grigg Lane Brockenhurst Hampshire SO42 7RE 01590 623544

Leave the M27 at Junction 1 and take the A337 to Lyndhurst. From Lyndhurst take the A337 signposted Brockenhurst, turn right at Careys Manor Hotel into Grigg Lane. Ground situated 200 yards on the right. Postcode for Satellite Navigation systems SO42 7RE

CHRISTCHURCH FC - Hurn Bridge Sports Club Avon Causeway Hurn Christchurc Dorset BH23 6DY 01202 473 792

A338 from Ringwood turn off at sign for Bournemouth International Airport (Hurn) on left. At T junction turn right, continue through traffic lights, at the small roundabout in Hurn turn right away from the Airport, exit signed Sopley and 100 yards on the right is Hurn Bridge Sports Ground. Postcode for Sat. Nav. systems BH23 6DY

COWES SPORTS FC - Westwood Park Reynolds Close off Park Road Cowes Isle of Wight PO31 7NT 01983 293 793

Turn left out of the Cowes pontoon, 1st right up Park Road approx 1/2 mile take the 4th right into Reynolds Close. Postcode for Sat. Nav. systems PO31 7NT

DOWNTON FC - Brian Whitehead Sports Ground Wick Lane Downton Wiltshire SP5 3NF 01725 512 162

The ground is situated 6 miles south of Salisbury on the A338 to Bournemouth. In the village – sign to the Leisure Centre (to west) – this is Wick Lane – football pitch and Club approx 1/4 mile on the left. Postcode for Satellite Navigation systems SP5 3NF

EAST COWES VICTORIA FC - Beatrice Avenue Whippingham East Cowes Isle of Wight PO32 6PA 01983 297 165

From East Cowes ferry terminal follow Well Road into York Avenue until reaching Prince of Wells PH, turn at the next right into Crossways Road then turn left into Beatrice Avenue, from Fishbourne follow signs to East Cowes and Whippingham Church, ground is 200 yards from the church on Beatrice Avenue. Postcode for Satellite Navigation systems PO32 6PA

FAREHAM TOWN FC - Cams Alders Football Stadium Cams Alders Palmerston Drive Fareham Hampshire PO14 1BJ 07930 853 235 (Club)

Leave the M27 at Junction 11. Follow signs A32 Fareham – Gosport. Pass under the viaduct with Fareham Creek on your left, straight over at the roundabout then fork right – B3385 sign posted Lee-on-Solent. Over the railway bridge, Newgate Lane and turn immediately first right into Palmerston Business Park, follow the road to the ground. Postcode for Satellite Navigation systems PO14 1BJ

FAWLEY AFC - Waterside Sports and Social Club 179-182 Long Lane Holbury Southampton Hampshire SO45 2PA 02380 893750 (Club) 896621 (Office)

Leave the M27 at Junction 2 and follow the A326 to Fawley/Beaulieu. Head south for approx 7 miles. The Club is situated on the right hand side 2/3 mile after crossing the Hardley roundabout. The Club is positioned directly behind the service road on the right hand side. Postcode for Satellite Navigation systems SO45 2PA

FLEET SPURS FC - Kennels Lane Southwood Farnborough Hampshire, GU14 0ST

From the M3 Junction 4A take the A327 towards Farnborough/Cove. Left at the roundabout, over the railway line, left at the next roundabout Kennels Lane is on the right opposite the Nokia building, entrance is 100 yards on the left. Postcode for Satellite Navigation systems GU14 0ST

GE HAMBLE - Folland Park Kings Avenue Hamble-Le-Rice Southampton Hampshire SO31 4NF 02380 452 173

Leave the M27 at Junction 8 and take the turning for Southampton East At the Windhover roundabout take the exit for Hamble (B3397) Hamble Lane, proceed for 3 miles. Upon entering Hamble the ground is on the right via Kings Avenue, opposite the Harrier P/H. Postcode for Satellite Navigation systems SO31 4NF

HAMWORTHY UNITED FC - The County Ground Blandford Close Hamworthy Poole Dorset BH15 4BF 01202 674 974

From M27 to Cadnam – follow A31 to Ringwood – A347/A348 Ferndown - Bearcross – follow on this road until you pass the Mountbatten Arms on your left – turn right at next roundabout onto the A3049 and follow the signs to Dorchester and Poole. Continue on this dual carriageway over the flyover to the next roundabout – straight across and take the 2nd exit left off the dual carriageway to Upton / Hamworthy – go straight across 2 mini roundabouts and continue to Hamworthy passing the Co-op store on your left – then turn left at the 2nd set of traffic lights into Blandford Close.   Postcode for Satellite Navigation systems BH15 4BF

HAYLING UNITED FC - College Ground The Hayling College Church Road Hayling Island,Hampshire PO11 0NU

From A27 take the Hayling Island exit, after crossing the Langstone Bridge continue past the Yew Tree P/H. After a mile turn left at the small roundabout into Church Road and after 1/2 mile turn left into Hayling College grounds.

NB All parking must be in front car park. Coaches to be parked in the lay-by outside the college. Postcode for Satellite Navigation systems PO11 0NU

HORNDEAN FC - Five Heads Park Five Heads Road Horndean Hampshire PO8 9NZ 02392 591 363

Leave A3(M) at Junction 2 and follow signs to Cowplain. Take the slip road passing Morrisons store on the right crossing over the mini roundabout then continue to the set of traffic lights ensuring you are in the right hand lane signed Horndean. Turn right at these traffic lights and continue on for approximately 400 yards until you reach the Colonial Bar on your left, next junction on your left after the Colonial Bar is Five Heads Road, turn left into Five Heads Road and the ground is approx 1/4 mile along this road. Postcode for Satellite Navigation systems PO8 9NZ

HYTHE & DIBDEN FC - Ewart Recreation Ground Jones Lane Hythe Southampton SO45 6AA 02380 845264 (Match days only) 07769 951982 (B)

Travel along the A326 then at the Dibden roundabout take the first left into Southampton Road. Continue for approx. 1 mile and then turn left into Jones Lane just before the Shell Filling Station and the ground is 200 yards on your left. Car parking is available in the Dibden Parish Hall car park at the bottom end of the ground. Postcode for Satellite Navigation systems SO45 6AA

LAVERSTOCK & FORD FC - The Dell Church Road Laverstock Salisbury Wiltshire SP1 1QX 01722 327 401

From Southampton – At the end of the carriageway from Southampton (A36) turn right at traffic lights for the Park & Ride by the Tesco store. Turn left at the traffic lights over the narrow bridge then take the next turning into Manor Farm Road. Take the next turning right into Laverstock Road, (do not turn left under the railway bridge). Keep left into Laverstock village, past the Church and the Club is situated on the left hand side directly opposite the Chinese takeaway and shop.

From Bournemouth – Follow the A36 to Southampton past Salisbury College and straight across the Tesco roundabout take left at traffic lights into the Park & Ride (take the corner slowly, the road goes back on itself) then follow directions as above. Postcode for Satellite Navigation systems SP1 1QX

LYMINGTON TOWN FC - The Sports Ground Southampton Road Lymington Hampshire SO41 9ZG 01590 671 305 (Club)

From the North & East – Leave the M27 at Junction 1 (Cadnam/New Forest) and proceed via Lyndhurst then Brockenhurst on the A337. On the outskirts of Lymington proceed through main set of traffic lights with Royal Quarter Housing Development and the Police Station on your right hand side. Continue for just another 250 metres and turn left immediately into St Thomas's Park with he ground in front of you.

Alternatively, turn left at the traffic lights into Avenue Road then first right, Oberland Court, with the Lymington Bowling Club facing you.

If travelling from the direction of Christchurch & New Milton using the A337 pass the White Hart P/H on the outskirts of Pennington and proceed down and up Stanford Hill. Passing the Waitrose Supermarket on your left hand side, the ground is situated immediately on your right hand side sign posted St Thomas Park. Postcode for Satellite Navigation systems SO41 9ZG

MONEYFIELDS FC - Moneyfields Sports Ground Moneyfield Avenue Copnor Portsmouth Hampshire PO3 6LA 02392 665 260 (Club) 07766 250 812 (M)

Leave the A27 from the West and East at the Southsea turn off (A2030). Head down the Eastern Road and turn right into Tangiers Road at the fourth set of traffic lights – continue along this road until you pass the school and shops on your left and take the next right into Folkestone Road carrying on through to Martins Road and the Moneyfields Sports & Social Club is directly in front of you. Postcode for Satellite Navigation systems PO3 6LA

NEW MILTON TOWN FC - Fawcett Fields Christchurch Road New Milton Hampshire BH25 6QB 01425 628 191

Leave the M27 at Junction 2 and follow the signs to Lyndhurst. Carry on this road over four roundabouts and take the next slip road.At the traffic lights turn right to Lyndhurst. Go around the one way system and follow the signs to Christchurch (A35). After 10 miles at the Cat and Fiddle Public House turn left and continue towards the Chewton Glen Hotel. First exit at roundabout A337 to New Milton.The ground is one mile on the left. Postcode for Sat. Nav. systems BH25 6QB

NEWPORT (IOW) FC LTD. - St Georges Park St Georges Way Newport Isle of Wight PO30 2QH 01983 525 027 (Club)

From the Fishbourne Car Ferry Terminal take the A3054 towards Newport. At the large roundabout in the town centre take the A3020 towards Sandown, under the footbridge then 1st exit off the next roundabout. The ground is 200 yards on the left. Postcode for Satellite Navigation systems PO30 2QH

PETERSFIELD TOWN FC - Love Lane Petersfield Hampshire GU31 4BW 01730 233 416

Off circulatory one-way system in the town centre. Approx 10 minutes walk from Petersfield train station. Postcode for Satellite Navigation systems GU31 4BW

PEWSEY VALE FC - Recreation Ground Kings Corner Ball Road Pewsey 01672 562 900

From Pewsey's King Alfred statue, take the B3087 Burbage Road for 100 yards and then turn right into the Co-op car park, park in top right hand corner next to the bowls and tennis club and then walk through to the ground. Postcode for Satellite Navigation systems SN9 5BS

RINGWOOD TOWN FC - The Canotec Stadium Long Lane Ringwood Hampshire BH24 3BX 01425 473 448

Travel to Ringwood via the A31 (M27). From Ringwood town centre travel 1 mile on the B3347 towards Christchurch. At the Texaco petrol station turn into Moortown Lane and after 200 yards turn right into Long Lane. The ground is situated 250 yards on your left. Postcode for Satellite Navigation systems BH24 3BX

ROMSEY TOWN FC - The Bypass Ground South Front Romsey Hampshire SO51 8GJ

The ground is situated on the south of the town on the A27/A3090 roundabout (Romsey by pass), adjacent to the Romsey Rapids and Broadlands Estate. Postcode for Satellite Navigation systems SO51 8GJ

STOCKBRIDGE FC - Stockbridge Recreation Ground High Street Stockbridge SP20 6EU 07963 453 162 (M)

From Stockbridge High Street turn right at BT Substation into ground. Postcode for Satellite Navigation systems SP20 6EU

TADLEY CALLEVA FC - Barlows Park Silchester Road Tadley Hampshire RG26 3PX

From M3 Basingstoke Junction 6 take the A340 to Tadley, travel through Tadley and at the main traffic lights turn right into Silchester Road, proceed for 0.5 mile then turn left into the car park. Postcode for Satellite Navigation systems RG26 3PX

TEAM SOLENT - Test Park, Lower Broomhill Road, Southampton SO16 9QZ

Leave the M27 at junction 3 for M271. Take the first slip road off the M271 and then first exit off the roundabout on to Lower Broomhill Road. Carry on to the next roundabout and take the last exit, (coming back on yourself) into Redbridge lane and the entrance to Test Park is approx. 500m on right.

From City centre take the Millbrook road to the M271, first slip road off on to roundabout, 3rd exit on to Lower Broomhill Way and then as above. Postcode for Satellite Navigation systems SO16 9QZ

TOTTON & ELING FC - Little Testwood Farm, Southampton SO40 3ND 02380 862 143

Foreword on to the M27, Signposted Southampton. Exit the M27 at Junction2, at the roundabout take the 3rd exit onto the A326. Signposted Fawley, Totton. Branch left and then turn Left on to the A36 signposted Totton Town Centre. At the Roundabout take the 2nd exit onto the A36. Follow this road until the entrance to Little Testwood Farm appears on your left hand side.

UNITED SERVICES PORTSMOUTH FC - Victory Stadium HMS Temeraire Burnaby Road Portsmouth Hampshire PO1 2HB 02392 724235 (Clubhouse) 02392 725315 (Office)

Leave the M27 at Junction 12 and join the M275 to Portsmouth. Follow the signs to Gunwharf, turn right at the traffic lights into Park Road then left at the next set of lights into Burnaby Road and the entrance is at the end of this road on the right.via HMS Temeraire.

NB Car parking in HMS Temeraire is for Senior Club and Match Officials only on the production of a current Sydenhams League (Wessex) pass. Free car parking for players and supporters is at the Portsmouth University Nuffield car park opposite the Registry Public House – follow Anglesea Road and signs for Southsea/Ferry Terminals, go under railway bridge past lights, keeping US Rugby Stadium on your right into Hampshire Terrace and keeping right, LOOP back into Anglesey Road, go through pedestrian lights and then immediately left into the car park. From car park turn right past pedestrian lights into Cambridge Road, then right into Burnaby Road. Postcode for Satellite Navigation systems PO1 2HB

VERWOOD TOWN FC - POTTERNE PARK POTTERNE WAY VERWOOD DORSET BH21 6RS 01202 814 007

Turn off the A31 at Verwood/Matchams junctions just West of Ringwood Town centre exit (immediately after garage if coming from the East) to join the B3081. Follow the B3081 through the forest for approximately 4 miles coming into Verwood itself. At the second set of traffic lights turn left into Black Hill. At the roundabout take the 1st exit left into Newtown Road. At the end of Newtown Road turn left and then 1st left into Potterne Way. Note: Along Black Hill on the left you will pass Bradfords Building Merchants and the entrance to the Verwood Sports & Social Club where post match refreshments are made available. Postcode for Satellite Navigation systems BH21 6RS

WHITCHURCH UNITED FC - Longmeadow Winchester Road Whitchurch Hampshire RG28 7RB 01256 892 493

From the South – take the A34 (North), 2 miles north of Bullington Cross take the Whitchurch exit. Head for Whitchurch Town Centre. The ground is 500 yards on your right. Postcode for Satellite Navigation systems RG28 7RB

A click away from memory lane!

Over 35 years of publishing the Non-League Club Directory has filled a room full of information and photographs covering the game we know and love.

What we intend, over time, is to create a website that shares with you everything we have accumulated, which we hope will bring back some fond memories of season's gone by.

Log on to **www.non-leagueclubdirectory.co.uk** today and see how many faces from teams gone by you recognise

WEST MIDLANDS (REGIONAL) LEAGUE

Sponsored by: No sponsor
Founded: 1889
Recent Champions:
2007: Shifnal Town
2008: Bridgnorth Town
2009: AFC Wulfrunians
2010: Ellesmere Rangers
2011: Tividale

LEAGUE CUP WINNERS

2000	PREMIER	TIPTON TOWN
	FIRST	WELLINGTON
2002	PREMIER	WESTFIELDS
	FIRST	GREAT WYRLEY
2003	PREMIER	KINGTON TOWN
	FIRST (SOUTH)	WYRE FOREST BRINTONS
2004	PREMIER	BRIERLEY & HAGLEY
	FIRST	BILSTON TOWN
2005	PREMIER	TIPTON TOWN
	ONE	HINTON
	TWO	ELLESMERE RANGERS
2006	PREMIER	WYRLEY RANGERS
	ONE	STAFFORD TOWN
	TWO	AFC WULFRUNIANS
2007	PREMIER	SHIFNAL TOWN
	ONE	DARLASTON TOWN
	TWO	WEDNESBURY TOWN
2008	PREMIER	DUDLEY SPORTS
	ONE	W'TON DEVELOPMENT
	TWO	BENTLEY YOUTH
2009	PREMIER	NOT COMPLETED
	ONE	AFC WOMBOURNE UNITED
	TWO	BLACK COUNTRY RANGERS
2010	PREMIER	BUSTLEHOLME
	ONE	BLACKHEATH TOWN
	TWO	BLACK COUNTRY RANGERS
2011	PREMIER	TIVIDALE
	ONE	WELLINGTON AMATEURS
	TWO	AFC SMETHWICK
2012	PREMIER	AFC WULFRUNIANS
	ONE	WELLINGTON AMATEURS
	TWO	MAHAL

PREMIER DIVISION

		P	W	D	L	F	A	Pts
1	(P) Gornal Athletic	42	33	6	3	149	47	105
2	Black Country Rangers	42	32	6	4	158	62	102
3	Wolverhampton Casuals	42	25	10	7	100	47	85
4	Bewdley Town	42	26	6	10	88	53	84
5	AFC Wulfrunians	42	24	7	11	95	66	79
6	Wednesfield	42	23	8	11	91	64	77
7	Dudley Town	42	20	9	13	93	71	69
8	Cradley Town	42	19	8	15	98	74	65
9	Goodrich	42	17	11	14	73	68	62
10	Shawbury United	42	17	7	18	66	69	58
11	Wellington	42	17	7	18	79	83	58
12	Dudley Sports	42	17	7	18	60	82	58
13	Malvern Town	42	15	10	17	75	81	55
14	Sporting Khalsa	42	16	3	23	69	106	51
15	Lye Town	42	13	11	18	60	80	50
16	Shifnal Town	42	13	9	20	82	88	48
17	Pegasus Juniors	42	14	6	22	50	68	48
18	Stafford Town	42	12	10	20	80	101	46
19	Wolverhampton Sporting Comm	42	10	12	20	43	63	42
20	Bustleholme	42	6	5	31	49	102	23
21	Bromyard Town	42	5	8	29	35	111	23
22	Darlaston Town	42	4	2	36	41	148	14.

PREMIER DIVISION

		1	2	3	4	5	6	7	8	9	10	11	12	13	14	15	16	17	18	19	20	21	22
1	AFC Wulfrunians		1-2	1-2	0-1	4-0	3-1	2-1	1-1	1-1	1-1	1-3	1-0	2-1	2-0	4-2	1-1	1-0	5-2	4-1	3-0	3-3	2-2
2	Bewdley Town	0-5		1-1	5-2	3-1	2-4	1-0	2-3	2-1	5-1	1-2	3-1	4-0	2-1	1-3	1-0	3-1	3-0	1-1	5-0	1-3	1-0
3	Black Country Rangers	6-1	3-1		3-2	3-1	3-0	4-2	3-2	4-3	6-3	5-2	2-0	6-1	5-3	3-2	5-1	8-0	8-2	2-3	6-3	2-2	3-0
4	Bromyard Town	1-3	1-1	0-8		2-0	0-4	1-4	2-2	2-6	1-1	1-2	0-1	2-1	0-3	0-2	0-1	0-3	1-0	1-5	1-3	1-4	0-2
5	Bustleholme	2-2	2-4	2-8	0-0		0-2	4-1	0-2	1-2	0-4	1-3	1-2	0-1	0-3	1-2	4-0	2-4	1-1	1-3	0-2	2-0	0-0
6	Cradley Town	6-2	0-2	4-4	4-0	7-1		6-0	1-2	1-4	1-2	1-1	0-0	2-1	3-2	2-1	2-0	4-4	2-1	1-1	1-4	2-1	0-1
7	Darlaston Town	0-5	0-2	1-6	1-3	0-4	0-8		2-2	1-4	1-5	1-8	2-3	1-2	3-0	0-6	0-4	2-5	3-6	0-6	1-3	0-3	0-2
8	Dudley Sports	1-2	1-1	1-2	4-2	3-0	1-2	1-0		1-0	0-3	0-7	2-0	1-4	3-1	1-0	0-0	2-1	4-3	1-3	1-3	2-4	1-2
9	Dudley Town	2-0	0-2	2-3	6-0	2-1	1-2	5-1	3-0		0-2	0-1	2-2	2-0	4-2	3-3	2-3	1-1	2-2	4-1	2-2	3-2	3-1
10	Goodrich	0-3	4-3	0-0	3-0	3-1	2-2	0-1	3-0	0-0		0-3	0-0	4-4	2-1	3-2	1-2	1-2	3-1	2-2	1-3	1-4	2-3
11	Gornal Athletic	3-1	3-0	3-1	7-1	4-2	5-1	4-0	4-0	3-3	1-1		3-0	6-2	1-0	1-0	4-1	8-2	4-0	7-1	1-1	1-2	1-1
12	Lye Town	1-3	1-2	1-4	3-2	2-2	2-1	4-2	2-2	0-2	3-3	0-5		0-5	0-0	3-0	4-2	0-1	1-1	2-1	1-2	1-5	2-1
13	Malvern Town	2-4	2-4	1-6	1-1	2-1	3-1	4-1	1-1	3-3	1-2	1-2	0-0		3-0	2-0	2-2	1-1	5-0	0-3	1-3	0-1	2-0
14	Pegasus Juniors	1-2	0-1	1-1	2-1	2-1	4-3	3-1	2-0	0-1	2-1	1-5	0-4	2-1		0-2	1-0	3-0	1-0	1-3	1-3	0-1	0-0
15	Shawbury United	1-2	0-4	1-6	1-1	1-0	1-2	2-0	1-3	2-3	0-1	1-4	2-1	1-1		2-2	0-1	1-0	1-1	0-0	2-1	3-2
16	Shifnal Town	1-2	0-0	0-3	2-0	4-2	1-2	5-1	2-3	8-0	0-3	4-5	4-1	4-2	1-1	2-3		1-3	3-2	1-2	2-0	1-5	2-3
17	Sporting Khalsa	1-3	1-2	0-3	3-0	3-2	0-6	3-0	1-2	1-4	2-0	1-6	1-1	3-4	6-2	2-1	0-5		2-7	1-2	0-6	1-3	2-1
18	Stafford Town	0-5	0-2	1-1	2-2	3-0	3-2	0-1	5-1	4-1	4-3	1-5	1-4	1-2	0-0	0-2	3-3	2-5		3-2	0-3	1-1	3-1
19	Wednesfield	1-0	0-3	1-3	3-0	2-0	5-2	4-1	2-0	1-2	0-0	3-2	2-2	0-2	1-0	2-3	4-2	6-1	0-0		3-2	1-1	2-0
20	Wellington	5-6	2-0	3-1	2-0	0-4	1-2	3-2	1-2	1-1	0-1	3-3	3-2	2-2	0-4	2-4	5-0	0-4	2-3	1-3		0-3	1-1
21	Wolverhampton Casuals	5-1	1-1	3-1	0-0	5-0	2-1	3-1	4-0	2-0	4-0	1-3	4-1	1-1	2-0	0-2	2-2	1-0	2-4	2-3	3-1		1-1
22	Wolverhampton Sporting Comm	2-0	1-4	1-4	3-0	1-2	0-0	2-2	0-1	2-1	0-1	0-3	1-2	0-1	1-0	0-0	2-2	2-0	0-5	1-1	0-1	0-0	

WEST MIDLANDS LEAGUE - STEP 6/7

DIVISION ONE	P	W	D	L	F	A	Pts
1 (P) Wellington Amateurs	30	20	5	5	96	42	65
2 Hanwood United	30	18	8	4	72	35	62
3 AFC Wombourne United	30	18	7	5	74	40	61
4 AFC Smethwick	30	18	6	6	73	47	60
5 Stone Old Alleynians	30	16	9	5	72	36	57
6 Wyrley Juniors	30	14	4	12	48	54	46
7 Bridgnorth Town Res.	30	12	6	12	57	55	42
8 Warstones Wanderers	30	12	4	14	60	59	40
9 Bilston Town	30	12	4	14	58	58	40
10 Trysull	30	11	5	14	50	51	38
11 Leominster Town	30	11	5	14	68	88	38
12 Wem Town	30	10	7	13	68	74	37
13 Shenstone Pathfinder	30	10	4	16	39	59	34
14 Penn Croft	30	8	7	15	49	59	31
15 Blackheath Town	30	5	4	21	41	82	19
16 (R) Wolverhampton United	30	2	1	27	33	119	7

DIVISION TWO	P	W	D	L	F	A	Pts
1 (P) Haughmond	26	22	4	0	103	27	70
2 Hereford Lads Club	26	16	5	5	64	29	53
3 (P) Mahal	26	14	6	6	63	40	48
4 Penkridge Town	26	14	5	7	70	54	47
5 (P) St Martins	26	13	5	8	75	53	44
6 Sikh Hunters	26	11	5	10	55	49	38
7 Team Dudley	26	11	3	12	55	58	36
8 Wrens Nest United	26	11	1	14	54	55	34
9 Ettingshall Park Farm	26	10	4	12	45	50	34
10 Riverway	26	9	5	12	65	71	32
11 Tenbury United	26	9	4	13	57	69	31
12 Red Star Alma	26	6	2	18	29	62	20
13 Malvern Town Res.	26	5	1	20	33	91	16
14 W'pton Sporting Comm Res.	26	4	4	18	28	88	16

DIVISION ONE	1	2	3	4	5	6	7	8	9	10	11	12	13	14	15	16
1 AFC Smethwick		2-1	0-1	2-2	1-0	3-1	7-2	2-1	2-0	1-1	3-0	3-0	1-2	4-2	2-0	5-0
2 AFC Wombourne United	2-2		2-0	2-3	5-3	3-3	8-1	2-1	1-0	1-1	3-2	2-0	3-3	1-1	2-1	6-0
3 Bilston Town	3-1	2-3		2-1	4-1	1-2	2-2	3-1	3-1	2-2	1-1	2-4	1-3	4-1	7-1	1-2
4 Blackheath Town	4-2	0-3	1-3		0-3	1-1	1-4	1-2	4-1	2-2	1-2	1-4	1-6	3-3	4-0	0-3
5 Bridgnorth Town Reserves	0-2	1-1	2-1	4-1		1-1	3-2	2-3	2-3	1-2	3-1	3-1	1-3	3-0	6-1	3-1
6 Hanwood United	5-2	1-3	3-0	2-1	2-2		6-1	2-0	1-0	0-2	2-1	4-0	2-1	4-2	7-0	2-0
7 Leominster Town	1-2	1-2	3-2	3-0	2-2	2-6		2-1	2-2	2-5	0-1	2-1	1-1	2-4	5-1	5-2
8 Penn Croft	2-2	0-3	0-1	6-2	2-3	0-1	2-2		0-2	3-2	2-2	1-1	4-6	5-2	3-1	0-2
9 Shenstone Pathfinder	1-4	1-4	7-1	2-1	0-0	1-1	2-1	0-1		1-2	3-1	2-1	1-4	1-0	3-1	1-2
10 Stone Old Alleynians	2-3	1-2	2-1	2-0	2-2	1-1	4-3	4-0	5-0		2-0	6-0	2-2	1-0	6-0	1-1
11 Trysull	1-4	1-2	0-2	5-0	3-0	1-1	1-2	0-0	3-0	2-3		2-1	1-3	4-0	5-4	0-0
12 Warstones Wanderers	1-1	1-0	2-2	4-2	3-0	3-0	2-3	1-1	1-2	1-0	2-3		1-5	2-0	10-1	4-0
13 Wellington Amateurs	1-3	2-1	4-2	3-1	1-2	2-2	10-0	2-1	6-0	0-1	2-1	6-2		2-2	4-0	3-0
14 Wem Town	7-2	2-2	4-2	2-1	4-1	1-2	3-7	2-2	2-0	2-2	0-4	3-2	0-4		5-4	1-1
15 Wolverhampton United	2-3	3-2	0-2	1-2	2-3	0-4	0-4	1-4	1-1	2-6	1-2	1-2	1-4	0-8		3-1
16 Wyrley Juniors	2-2	1-2	2-0	3-0	1-0	0-3	5-1	3-1	2-1	1-0	4-0	1-3	4-1	2-5	2-0	

DIVISION TWO	1	2	3	4	5	6	7	8	9	10	11	12	13	14
1 Ettingshall Park Farm		1-6	1-3	1-0	8-0	1-1	2-0	4-3	0-2	2-1	0-1	3-1	4-1	1-3
2 Haughmond	1-1		2-1	5-3	3-0	4-0	3-1	4-2	3-2	5-1	7-1	11-0	2-0	5-1
3 Hereford Lads Club	2-0	1-2		0-0	4-0	3-0	5-1	2-4	3-2	3-2	1-0	0-0	2-0	7-0
4 Mahal	2-0	0-0	1-1		3-2	0-6	6-0	3-3	0-3	2-1	1-0	4-1	3-2	0-0
5 Malvern Town Reserves	2-1	0-8	1-8	1-5		2-4	1-2	4-2	1-1	1-2	1-4	1-0	1-3	2-3
6 Penkridge Town	3-5	0-4	0-0	3-2	5-1		2-0	6-1	3-1	4-5	3-1	4-2	5-2	2-1
7 Red Star Alma	5-1	1-2	0-2	0-3	0-4	0-1		3-1	4-0	2-2	1-3	0-3	1-5	3-0
8 Riverway	1-1	3-6	2-4	0-7	5-1	3-7	4-0		2-2	1-0	2-3	6-3	1-0	6-1
9 Sikh Hunters	1-1	1-1	2-3	1-5	2-0	3-1	4-0	1-4		1-2	4-1	3-4	4-2	4-0
10 St Martins	2-0	1-5	3-4	3-3	4-2	5-1	1-1	3-1	1-1		3-1	4-4	2-1	4-0
11 Team Dudley	4-1	1-5	2-1	1-2	5-1	2-2	4-1	1-1	5-2	1-7		0-3	2-3	6-1
12 Tenbury United	5-0	1-2	1-1	1-2	1-2	2-2	2-1	2-5	2-4	3-7	1-3		2-1	1-0
13 Wrens Nest United	0-4	3-3	2-1	2-4	4-0	2-3	1-0	1-0	0-2	3-1	3-2	2-5		2-1
14 W'pton Sporting Comm Reserves	0-2	1-4	1-2	3-2	4-2	2-2	0-2	2-2	1-2	1-8	1-1	1-7	0-9	

A.F.C. WULFRUNIANS

Founded: 2005   Nickname:

Secretary: Simon Cater   **(T)** 07870 164631   **(E)** simoncater@compton-hospice.org.uk
Chairman: Ian Round   **Manager:**   **Prog Ed:**
Ground: Castlecroft Stadium, Castlecroft Road, Wolverhampton WV3 8NA   **(T)** 01902 761410   **Capacity:**
Colours(change): Red & white/black/red

ADDITIONAL INFORMATION:
Honours: West Midlands (Regional) League Premier Division 2008-09.

BARTLEY GREEN

Founded: 1949   Nickname:

Secretary: Richard Earl   **(T)** 07534 644 161   **(E)** richardearl2007@hotmail.co.uk
Chairman: David Shepherd   **Manager:**   **Prog Ed:**
Ground: Illey Lane, Halesowen, Birmingham, West Midlands B62 0HF   **(T)**   **Capacity:**
Colours(change): Amber & black/black/black

ADDITIONAL INFORMATION:
Previous Leagues: Midland Combination > 2012.
Honours: Midland Combination Division 2 2005-06, Division 1 2006-07.

BEWDLEY TOWN

Founded: 1978   Nickname:

Secretary: Steve Godfrey   **(T)** 07739 626 169   **(E)** steve_g09@fsmail.net
Chairman: Geoff Edwards   **Manager:**   **Prog Ed:**
Ground: Ribbesford Meadows, Ribbesford, Bewdley, Worcs DY12 2TJ   **(T)** 07739 626 169   **Capacity:**
Colours(change): Royal blue with yellow trim/royal blue/royal blue

ADDITIONAL INFORMATION:

BLACK COUNTRY RANGERS

Founded: 1996   Nickname:

Secretary: Jamie Hurdman   **(T)** 07525 795 332   **(E)** blackcountryrangers@hotmail.co.uk
Chairman: Paul Garner   **Manager:**   **Prog Ed:**
Ground: Tividale FC, The Beeches, Packwood Road, Tividale B69 1UL   **(T)** 01384 211 743   **Capacity:**
Colours(change): All red.

ADDITIONAL INFORMATION:
Honours: West Midlands (Regional) Division One 2010-11.

BROMYARD TOWN

Founded: 1893   Nickname:

Secretary: Richard Haverfield   **(T)** 07885 849 948   **(E)** tony.haverfield@virgin.net
Chairman: Richard Greenhall   **Manager:**   **Prog Ed:**
Ground: Delahay Meadow, Stourport Road, Bromyard HR7 4NT   **(T)** 01885 483 974   **Capacity:**
Colours(change): All blue

ADDITIONAL INFORMATION:

BUSTLEHOLME

Founded: 1975   Nickname:

Secretary: Geoff Bowden   **(T)** 07805 829 354   **(E)** geoff.benbow@hotmail.co.uk
Chairman: Geoff Benbow   **Manager:**   **Prog Ed:**
Ground: Tipton Town F C, Wednesbury Oak Road, Tipton, West Mid. DY4 0BS   **(T)** 0121 502 5534   **Capacity:**
Colours(change): Yellow/green/green

ADDITIONAL INFORMATION:

CRADLEY TOWN

Founded: 1948   Nickname:

Secretary: David Attwood   **(T)** 07708 659 636   **(E)** d.attwood@sky.com
Chairman: Trevor Thomas   **Manager:**   **Prog Ed:**
Ground: The Beeches, Beeches View Avenue, Cradley, Halesowen B63 2HB   **(T)** 07746 231 195   **Capacity:**
Colours(change): All red

ADDITIONAL INFORMATION:

DARLASTON TOWN

Founded: 1874   Nickname:

Secretary: Steven Poole   **(T)** 07988 189 378   **(E)** steven.poole@sandwell.ac.uk
Chairman: Paul Tonks   **Manager:**   **Prog Ed:**
Ground: City Ground, Waverley Road, Darlaston, West Mids WS10 8ED   **(T)**   **Capacity:**
Colours(change): Blue & white/blue/blue

ADDITIONAL INFORMATION:

DUDLEY SPORTS

Founded: 1978   Nickname:

Secretary: John Lewis   **(T)** 07737 099 385   **(E)** kath-john.lewis@blueyonder.co.uk
Chairman: Ashley Forrest   **Manager:**   **Prog Ed:**
Ground: Hillcrest Avenue, Brierley Hill, West Mids DY5 3QH   **(T)** 01384 826 420   **Capacity:**
Colours(change): Green & black/green/green

ADDITIONAL INFORMATION:

DUDLEY TOWN

Founded: 1893   Nickname:

Secretary: Pater Evans   **(T)** 07758 460 191   **(E)** peterevans22@hotmail.co.uk
Chairman: Stephen Austin   **Manager:**   **Prog Ed:**
Ground: The Dell Stadium, Bryce Road, Brierley Hill, West Mids DY5 4NE   **(T)** 01384 812 943   **Capacity:**
Colours(change): Red/black/red & black

ADDITIONAL INFORMATION:

LYE TOWN

Founded: 1930   Nickname:

Secretary: Yvonne Bignell   **(T)** 07921 662 837   **(E)**
Chairman: Brian Blakemore   **Manager:**   **Prog Ed:**
Ground: Sports Ground, Stourbridge Road, Lye, Stourbridge, West Mids DY9 7DH   **(T)** 01384 422 672   **Capacity:**
Colours(change): All blue

ADDITIONAL INFORMATION:

MALVERN TOWN

Founded: 1947   Nickname:

Secretary: Margaret Scott   **(T)** 07944 110 402   **(E)** margscott55@hotmail.com
Chairman: TBC   **Manager:**   **Prog Ed:**
Ground: Langland Stadium, Lamgland Avenue, Malvern WR14 2QE   **(T)** 01684 574 068   **Capacity:** 2,500
Colours(change): Claret/sky blue/claret

ADDITIONAL INFORMATION: Att: 1,221 v Worcester City FA Cup. **Goals:** Graham Buffery. **Apps:** Nick Clayton.
Honours: Worcestershire Senior Urn (x7). Midland Combination Division One 1955-56.

PEGASUS JUNIORS

Founded: 1955   Nickname: The Redmen

Secretary: Chris Wells   **(T)** 07980 465 995   **(E)** cwells@freenetname.co.uk
Chairman: Roger Hesten   **Manager:**   **Prog Ed:**
Ground: Old School Lane, Hereford HR1 1EX   **(T)** 07980 465 995   **Capacity:** 1,000
Colours(change): Red/white/red

ADDITIONAL INFORMATION: Att: 1,400 v Newport AFC, 1989-90.
Honours: Worcestershire Senior Urn 85-86. Hellenic Div.1 Champions 84-85, 98-99.
Previous Lge: Hellenic > 2011.

SHAWBURY UNITED

Founded: 1992   Nickname:

Secretary: Tracie Howells   **(T)** 07950 740 089   **(E)** traciehowells72@yahoo.co.uk
Chairman: David Kirkup   **Manager:**   **Prog Ed:**
Ground: Butler Sports Ground, Bowensfield, Wem, Shrewsbury SY4 5AP   **(T)** 01939 233 287   **Capacity:**
Colours(change): All blue

ADDITIONAL INFORMATION:

SHIFNAL TOWN
Founded: 1964   Nickname:

Secretary: Derek Groucott   **(T)** 07910 120 512   **(E)** carolderek2@blueyonder.co.uk
Chairman: Glyn Davies   **Manager:**   **Prog Ed:**
Ground: Phoenix Park, Coppice Green Lane, Shifnal, Shrops TF11 8PB   **(T)** 01952 463 257   **Capacity:**
Colours(change): Red & white stripes/black/black with red trim

ADDITIONAL INFORMATION:
Honours: West Midlands (Regional) League Premier Division 2006-07.

SPORTING KHALSA
Founded: 1991   Nickname:

Secretary: Parmjit Singh Gill   **(T)** 07976 606 132   **(E)** parm@sportingkhlsa.com
Chairman: Rajinder Singh Gill   **Manager:**   **Prog Ed:**
Ground: Aspray Arena, Noose Lane, Willenhall WV13 3BB   **(T)** 01902 219 208   **Capacity:**
Colours(change): Yellow/blue/yellow.

ADDITIONAL INFORMATION:

WEDNESFIELD
Founded: 1961   Nickname:

Secretary: Ronald Brown   **(T)** 07528 589 508   **(E)** rbwedfc@gmail.com
Chairman: David Saville   **Manager:**   **Prog Ed:**
Ground: Cottage Ground, Amos Lane, Wednesfield WV11 1ND   **(T)**   **Capacity:**
Colours(change): Red & white stripes/black/black

ADDITIONAL INFORMATION:

WELLINGTON
Founded: 1968   Nickname:

Secretary: Michael Perkins   **(T)** 07842 186 643   **(E)** perkins@haworth13.freeserve.co.uk
Chairman: Phillip Smith   **Manager:**   **Prog Ed:**
Ground: Wellington Playing Field, Wellington, Hereford HR4 8AZ   **(T)**   **Capacity:**
Colours(change): Orange/orange/orange & white

ADDITIONAL INFORMATION:

WELLINGTON AMATEURS
Founded: 1950   Nickname:

Secretary: Graeme McDermott   **(T)** 07837 355 380   **(E)** graeme.mcdermott@wellingtonamateurs.co.uk
Chairman: Dave Gregory   **Manager:**   **Prog Ed:**
Ground: Wickes Stadium, School grove, Oakengates, telford, Shrops TF2 6BQ   **(T)**   **Capacity:**
Colours(change): Red/black/black

ADDITIONAL INFORMATION:

WILLENHALL TOWN
Founded: 1953   Nickname: The Lockmen

Secretary: Simon Hall   **(T)** 07901 560 691   **(E)** sdhwin@aol.com
Chairman: Sean Coliglan   **Manager:**   **Prog Ed:**
Ground: Aspray Arena, Noose Lane, Willenhall, West Midlands WV13 3BB   **(T)** 01902 219 208   **Capacity:** 5,000
Colours(change): All red

ADDITIONAL INFORMATION:
Previous Leagues: Staffs Co, West Mids 1975-78, 1991-94, Southern 1982-91, 2005-08, Midland All. 1994-2004, 2010-12, N.P.L 2004-05, 2008-10.
Honours: Staffs County Premier 1974-75. West Mids Division 1 1975-76, Premier 77-78. Southern League Midland Division 1983-84.

WOLVERHAMPTON CASUALS
Founded: 1899   Nickname:

Secretary: Barry Austin   **(T)** 01902 831 519   **(E)** judy_barry@blueyonder.co.uk
Chairman: Garth Deacon   **Manager:**   **Prog Ed:**
Ground: Brinsford Stadium, Brinsford Lane, Wolverhampton WS10 7PR   **(T)** 01902 783 214   **Capacity:**
Colours(change): Green & white/white/green

ADDITIONAL INFORMATION:

WOLVERHAMPTON SPORTING COMMUNITY Founded: 2001   Nickname:

Secretary: Mark Hopson   **(T)** 07966 505 425   **(E)** hopsonma@tiscali.co.uk
Chairman: John Quarry   **Manager:**   **Prog Ed:**
Ground: Wednesfield F C, Cottage Ground, Amos Lane, Wednesfield. WV11 1ND   **(T)** 01902 735 506   **Capacity:**
Colours(change): Orange & black/black/orange

ADDITIONAL INFORMATION:
Previous Name: Heath Town Rangers 2001-10.

WEST MIDLANDS (REGIONAL) LEAGUE DIVISION ONE CONSTITUTION 2012-13

A F C SMETHWICK ....York Road Social and Sports Club, York Road, Oldbury, West Mids. B65 0RR...................0121-559-5563

A F C WOMBOURNE UNITED ....AFC Wulfrunians, Castlecroft Road, Wolverhampton. WV3 3NA...............................01902-761410

BILSTON TOWN (2007)...Queen Street, Bilston WV14 7EX ....No number

BLACKHEATH TOWN..............Halesowen Town FC, The Grove, Old Hawne Lane, Halesowen. B63 3TB......................0121-661-9392

BRIDGNORTH TOWN RESERVES.........Crown Meadow, Innage Lane, Bridgnorth WV16 4HS 01746-763001

HANWOOD UNITED....................................Hanwood Recreation Ground, Hanwood SY5 8JN ....No number

HAUGHMOND............................. Shrewsbury Sports Village, Sundorne Road, Shrewsbury. SY1 4RG...........................01743-256260

LEOMINSTER TOWN .... The Briarwood Stadium, Bridge Street Park, Bridge Street, Leominster HR6 8EA 01568-611172

MAHAL ....Hadley Stadium, Wilson Road, Smethwick B68 9JW 0121-434-4848

PENNCROFT ....Aldersley Leisure Village, Aldersley Road, Wolverhampton WV6 9NW 01902-556200

SHENSTONE PATHFINDER...... Shenston PF Pavilion Club, Birmingham Road, Shenstone WS14 0LR..........................01543-481658

ST MARTINS................................. The Venue, Burma Road, Parkhall, Oswestry, Shrops. SY11 8AS...............................01691-684840

STONE OLD ALLEYNIANS.....................Springbank Park, Yarnfield Lane, Yarnfield ST15 0NF 01785-761891

TRYSULL.....................Wolverhampton Casuals FC, Brinsford Road, Coven Heath, Wolverhampton WV10 7PR 01902-783214

WARSTONES WANDERERS ......Long Lane Park, Long Lane, Essington, Wolverhampton. WV11 2AA.............................01922 406604

WEM TOWN...Butler Sports Centre, Bowens Field, Wem SY4 5AP 01939-233287

WOLVERHAMPTON UNITED...................... Prestwood Road West, Wednesfield WV11 1HL.......................................01902-730881

WYRLEY JUNIORS.....................Long Lane Park, Long Lane, Essington, Wolverhampton. WV11 2AA..........................01922-406604

WEST MIDLANDS (REGIONAL) LEAGUE DIVISION TWO CONSTITUTION 2012-13

BARTESTREE..Bartestree Playing Fields, Bartestree, Hereford .... 07980 305118 (Matchdays only)

ETTINGSHALL PARK FARM .... Pendeford Lane, off Wobaston Road, Wolverhampton. WV9 5HQ...............................01902 396666

GORNAL ATHLETIC RESERVES.... Garden Walk Stadium, Garden Walk, Lower Gornal, Dudley. DY3 2NR 01384 358398

HEREFORD LADS CLUB .... Hereford Leisure Centre, Holmer Road, Hereford. HR4 9UD.................................01432 278178

LEDBURY TOWN...Ledbury Town FC., New Street, Ledbury. HR8 2ED 01531 631463

MAHAL RESERVES..................................Hadley Stadium, Wilson Road, Smethwick B68 9JW 0121 434 4848

MALVERN RANGERS............... Dyson Perrins Sports Academy, Yates Hay Road, Malvern. WR14 1WD 01684 572945

MALVERN TOWN RESERVES........... Langland Stadium, Langland Avenue, Malvern. WR14 2QE....................................01684 574068

NEWPORT TOWN .... Harper Adams University College, Edgmond, Newport, Shrops. TF10 8NB.......................01952 820280

PENKRIDGE TOWN ....Monkton Recreation Centre, Pinfold Lane, Penkridge ST19 5QP ....No number

RED STAR ALMA.............................Bentley Youth FC, Bentley Road South, Darlaston. WV10 8LN...................................No number

RIVERWAY...Rowley Park Stadium, Averill, Stafford. ST17 9XX 01785 251060

SIKH HUNTERS.................... York Road Sports & Social Club, York Road, Oldbury, West Mids. B65 0RR.......07887 505491 (MD only)

TEAM DUDLEY.......................................The Dell Stadium, Bryce Road, Brierley Hill DY5 4NE 01384 812943

TENBURY UNITED ....Palmers Meadow, Burford, Tenbury Wells WR15 8AP 07817 200234

WOLVERHAMPTON SPORTING COM. RES Pendeford Lane, Wolverhampton WV9 5HQ..No number

WRENS NEST.......................................Handrahan Sports Stadium, Mile Flat, Wallheath DY6 0AX ....No number

GROUND DIRECTIONS - PREMIER DIVISION

AFC WULFRUNIANS - Castlecroft Stadium, Castlecroft Road, Wolverhampton WV3 8NA. Tel: 01902-761410

From Wolverhampton, depart on Darlington Street. At the roundabout, take the second exit onto Chapel Ash A41. Bear left onto Merridale Road. Turn right onto Merridale Lane. Turn left onto Compton Road A454. Bear right onto Bridgnorth Road A454. At the roundabout, take the first exit onto Bridgnorth Road A454 Turn left onto Windmill Lane. Turn right onto Castlecroft Avenue. Turn right onto Castlecroft Road.

Ground is on left hand side.

BARTLEY GREEN - Bartley Green FC, Illey Lane, Illey, Halesowen, West Mids. B62 0HF

From Junction 3 M5 follow the A456 for Halesowen/Kidderminster for approximately 1.5 miles to Grange Island. Turn 1st left along the B4551 Bromsgrove Road for approximately 400 yards and take the 1st turning left into Illey lane.

Ground is approximately 1 mile on left hand side.

BEWDLEY TOWN - Ribbesford Meadows, Ribbesford, Bewdley, Worcs. DY12 2TJ Tel: 07739-626169

From Kidderminster follow signs to Bewdley on A456 past West Midlands Safari Park and follow signs to Town Centre at next Island. Go over River Bridge into Town and turn left at side of Church (High Street). Stay on this road for 1 ½ miles. Entrance to ground is on left.

BLACK COUNTRY RANGERS - Tividale F C, The Beeches, Packwood Road, Tividale, West Mids. B69 1UL Tel: 01384-211743

Leave M5 at Junction 2. Follow signs to Dudley A4123. Approximately 1 mile past school and playing fields on right, go under Pedestrian walkway to traffic lights. Turn left into Regent Road. Turn left into Elm Terrace. First left into Birch Crescent, second left into Packwood Road. Ground is at the end of the Cul-de-sac.

BROMYARD TOWN - Delahay Meadow, Stourport Road, Bromyard. HR7 4NT Tel: 01885-483974

From M5, leave motorway at Junction 7 for Worcester (South) and follow A4440 Southern Link through to last roundabout, and then take A44 signposted Bromyard. Pass through Broadwas and over Bringsty Common to Bromyard. After passing narrow stone bridge on the perimeter of town, turn first right into Sherwood Street and follow signs for Stourport and Kidderminster (B4203).

Keep straight on into Church Street, passing Post Office on your right and St Peters Church on your left. Ground is approximately ½ mile on right hand sided through a wide entrance and steel gates, immediately before cottages, next to The Holly Tree Inn.

From Stourport, follow B4203 from Great Witley, up and over Downs, and ground is at bottom of hill, on left, 100 yards after passing the Holly Tree Inn. From Leominster, keep on A44 down by-pass and turn first left after "Ford" garage into Sherwood Street, then as above.

BUSTLEHOLME - Tipton Town F C, Wednesbury Oak Road, Tipton, West Mids. DY4 0BS Tel: 0121-502-5534

From M6 Junction 9, take A461 through Wednesbury Town Centre to Ocker Hill island. Follow signpost here taking a full right turn towards Bilston A4098 for half mile, turning left at traffic lights A4037. Ground is 50 yards on left. From M5 junction 2, take A4123 for about three miles until you reach Burnt Tree island. Take 2nd Exit towards Wolverhampton and continue to next set of traffic lights. Turn right onto A4037 and follow this road for about three miles. After passing Asda on your right, ground is down hill, 200 yards on right.

CRADLEY TOWN - The Beeches, Beeches View Avenue, Cradley, Halesowen, West Mids. B63 2HB Tel: 07799-363467

From M5 junction 3 take A456 Manor Way (signposted to Kidderminster) Turn right at second island into Hagley Road pass Foxhunt Inn on left and turn third left into Rosemary Road. Straight on into Landsdowne Road/Dunstall Road and turn left at T Junction into Huntingtree Road/Lutley Mill Road. Left again at next T junction into Stourbridge Road and immediately left again into Beecher Road East, first left into Abbey Road straight up to the end and turn right into Beeches View Avenue. The entrance to ground is 20 yards on the left between houses 50 and 48.

DARLASTON TOWN - City Ground, Waverley Road, Darlaston, West Mids. WS10 8ED

Leave M6 at Junction 10. Take the A454 towards Willenhall. Turn left at the traffic lights, outside the Lane Arms Public House into Bentley Road North. Follow this road down the hill, over the railway and canal bridges to the traffic lights. Cross over the lights into Richards Street and along into Victoria Road. Take the first right into Slater Street and the ground is on the left. Entrance next left in Waverley Road.

DUDLEY SPORTS - Hillcrest Avenue, Brierley Hill, West Mids. DY5 3QH Tel: 01384-826420

The Ground is situated in Brierley Hill, just off A461. It can be approached from Stourbridge off the Ring Road to Amblecote, turning right at third set of traffic lights or from Dudley passing through Brierley Hill Town centre. A – Z ref, 4H, page 67.

DUDLEY TOWN - The Dell Stadium, Bryce Road, Brierley Hill, West Mids. DY5 4NE Tel: 01384-812943

From M5 Junction 4 follow signs for Stourbridge.

From the Ring Road, take A491 sign posted Wolverhampton.

At the second set of lights, turn right onto Brettle Lane A461. After approx 6 miles you will approach Brierley Hill High Street. Turn left at lights onto bank Street. You will see Civic hall and Police Station. Carry on over small bridge and at next set of traffic lights you will see Bryce Road and Stadium is on your left. A-Z Birmingham 5F 93 A-Z West Midlands 5B 88

LYE TOWN - Sports Ground, Stourbridge Road, Lye, Stourbridge, West Mids. DY9 7DH Tel: 01384-422672

Situated on A458 Birmingham to Stourbridge Road.

From M5 Junction 3, take road marked Kidderminster, as far as lights at the bottom of Hagley Hill. Turn right, then take the third turning off the first island. Carry straight on at the next island. Turn left at Lights/Crossroads, onto the A458. Ground approximately 400 yards on the left hand side.

MALVERN TOWN - Langland Stadium, Langland Avenue, Malvern. WR14 2QE Tel: 01684-574068

Leave M5 at Junction 7 and turn towards Worcester. Turn left at next roundabout onto A4440 towards Malvern. Straight over next two roundabouts and take left slip road onto A449 at next roundabout. When approaching Malvern, turn left onto B4208 signposted Welland. Straight over three roundabouts and then take the third left into Orford Way. Take the third left into Langland Avenue. Ground is 300 yards on left.

PEGASUS JUNIORS - Old School Lane, Hereford. HR1 1EX Tel: 07980-465995

Approach City on A4103 from Worcester. At roundabout on outskirts take 2nd exit (A4103) over railway bridge, traffic light controlled. Take 2nd turning on left into Old School Lane. Ground entrance 150 metres on left.

Approach City on A49 from Leominster. On City outskirts take 1st exit at roundabout – Roman Road. First turning on right is Old School Lane. Ground entrance 150 metres on left.

SHAWBURY UNITED - Butler Sports Ground, Bowensfield, Wem, Shrewsbury. SY4 5AP Tel: 01939-233287

From the A5 Shrewsbury by-pass, take the A49 heading towards Whitchurch. Go through the villages of Hadnall & Preston Brockhurst and then take a left turn at crossroads onto the B5063 sign posted Wem. At next junction turn right under Railway Bridge on to the B5476 into Mill Street. At next Junction by Church turn right into High Street, take the next left after pedestrian crossing into New Street and then next left by the Public House into Pyms Road. Take the 2nd left into Bowens Field and ground is 100 yards straight ahead.

SHIFNAL TOWN - Phoenix Park, Coppice Green Lane, Shifnal, Shrops. TF11 8PB Tel: 01952-463257

From M54 junction 3, take A41 towards Newport and Whitchurch. Take first left signposted Shifnal. As you enter Shifnal, take first turning on right signposted football stadium. The ground is approximately 500 yards on left past Idsall School.

If travelling along A464 Wolverhampton Road to Shifnal. On entering Shifnal, just under the railway bridge and before the traffic lights turn right and sharp right again along Aston Street. Continue along this street until sharp right hand bend. Take left turn and then sharp right along Coppice Green Lane. Ground is approximately 500 yards on left past Idsall School.

SPORTING KHALSA - Aspray Arena, Noose Lane, Willenhall. WV13 3BB Tel: 09102-219208

From M6 junction 10, take 2nd exit onto A454 to Wolverhampton/Dudley A463. Take the A454 exit towards Wolverhampton. At Keyway junction take 2nd exit onto the Keyway A454 and continue on A454 going through one roundabout. At next traffic lights make a u turn at Nechells Lane. Turn left into Noose Lane and over roundabout. Ground is located on your left.

WEDNESFIELD - Cottage Ground, Amos Lane, Wednesfield. WV11 1ND

Going south, leave M6 at Junction 11 onto A460 towards Wolverhampton. After approx. 3 miles turn left at the Millhouse Public House into Pear Tree Lane. Continue on across mini-island into Knowle Lane. At Red Lion Public House continue across mini-island into Long Knowle Lane. Continue across mini-island into Amos Lane. Ground is about ½ mile along on left hand side.

Going north, leave M6 at Junction 10A onto M54. Leave M54 at Junction 1 onto A460 towards Wolverhampton. Turn left at Millhouse Public House and continue as above.

WELLINGTON - Wellington Playing Field, Wellington, Hereford. HR4 8AZ

The Ground is situated in Wellington, behind School and opposite the Church. Wellington is 8 miles South of Leominster or 6 miles North of Hereford on the A49. At the Hereford end of the dual carriageway take the turn for Wellington.

WELLINGTON AMATEURS - Wickes Stadium, School Grove, Oakengates, Telford, Shrops. TF2 6BQ

From M54 take Junction 5. At roundabout take first left onto Rampart Way. At traffic lights take the first left onto A442 (Eastern Primary). Leave A442 at next junction. At roundabout (Greyhound Interchange), take the second exit onto B5061 (Holyhead Road). Just after red brick Church on right, turn right onto Vicar Street. Take the next left into School Grove. Continue to the end of the street and proceed up the slope onto the Car Park.

WILLENHALL TOWN - Aspray Arena, Noose Lane, Willenhall. WV13 3BB - Tel: 01902-219208

From M6 junction 10, take 2nd exit onto A454 to Wolverhampton/Dudley A463. Take the A454 exit towards Wolverhampton. At Keyway junction take 2nd exit onto the Keyway A454 and continue on A454 going through one roundabout. At next traffic lights make a u turn at Nechells Lane. Turn left into Noose Lane and over roundabout. Ground is located on your left.

WOLVERHAMPTON CASUALS - Brinsford Stadium, Brinsford Lane, Wolverhampton. WV10 7PR Tel: 01902-783214

Turn onto M54 off M6 Northbound. Take Junction 2 and turn right onto A449 to Stafford. Go to next island and come back on yourself towards M54. Brinsford Lane is approximately ½ mile from island on left.

Ground is 200 yards on left in Brinsford Lane.

WOLVERHAMPTON SPORTING C. - Wednesfield F C, Cottage Ground, Amos Lane, Wednesfield. WV11 1ND Tel: 01902-735506

Going south, leave M6 at Junction 11 onto A460 towards Wolverhampton. After approx. 3 miles turn left at the Millhouse Public House into Pear Tree Lane. Continue on across mini-island into Knowle Lane. At Red Lion Public House continue across mini-island into Long Knowle Lane. Continue across mini-island into Amos Lane. Ground is about ½ mile along on left hand side.

Going north, leave M6 at Junction 10A onto M54. Leave M54 at Junction 1 onto A460 towards Wolverhampton. Turn left at Millhouse Public House and continue as above.

WESTERN LEAGUE

Sponsored by: Toolstation
Founded: 1892
Recent Champions:
2007: Corsham Town
2008: Truro City
2009: Bitton
2010: Bideford
2011: Larkhall Athletic
toolstationleague.com

LES PHILLIPS CUP

PRELIMINARY ROUND
Brislington 2-3 Bitton
Chard Town 1-0 Oldland Abbotonians
Hallen 0-2 Calne Town
Shrewton United 2-3 Street
Wells City 3-0 Almondsbury UWE
ROUND 1
Barnstaple Town 3-0 Corsham Town
Bitton 7-0 Portishead Town
Bridport 0-1 Odd Down
Bristol Manor Farm 4-0 Sherborne Town
Calne Town 3-0 Cadbury Heath
Chard Town 0-4 Radstock Town
Elmore 3-2 Bishop Sutton
Gillingham Town 2-0 Wellington
Melksham Town 2-0 Hengrove Athletic
Merthyr Town 3-0 Wells City
Roman Glass St George 1-4 Larkhall Athletic
Shepton Mallet 1-0 Keynsham Town
Street 1-4 Bradford Town
(Bradford Town removed from the competition)
Welton Rovers 2-1 Longwell Green Sports
Westbury United 0-4 Ilfracombe Town
Willand Rovers 2-0 Devizes Town
ROUND 2
Barnstaple Town 2-1 Gillingham Town
Bitton 3-0 Welton Rovers
Bristol Manor Farm 1-5 Odd Down
(Odd Down removed from the competition)
Ilfracombe Town 2-0 Melksham Town
Merthyr Town 1-0 Elmore
Radstock Town 6-7 Calne Town
Street 1-0 Shepton Mallet
Willand Rovers 4-2 Larkhall Athletic
QUARTER FINALS
Barnstaple Town 0-1 Calne Town
Ilfracombe Town 0-2 Bristol Manor Farm
Merthyr Town 4-0 Street
Willand Rovers 1-0 Bitton
SEMI-FINALS
Calne Town 2-3 Willand Rovers
Merthyr Town 1-2 Bristol Manor Farm
FINAL
Bristol Manor Farm 2-1 Willand Rovers

PREMIER DIVISION	P	W	D	L	F	A	Pts
1 (P) Merthyr Town	34	22	9	3	96	32	75
2 Bitton	34	23	4	7	74	35	73
3 Larkhall Athletic	34	21	4	9	67	29	67
4 Hallen	34	19	8	7	59	41	65
5 Willand Rovers	34	18	7	9	62	37	61
6 Bishop Sutton	34	16	10	8	60	37	58
7 Brislington	34	14	11	9	49	34	53
8 Bristol Manor Farm	34	13	8	13	63	57	47
9 Odd Down (Bath) (-1)	34	13	9	12	54	48	47
10 Street	34	14	4	16	56	58	46
11 Ilfracombe Town	34	12	8	14	52	52	44
12 Wells City	34	13	5	16	54	66	44
13 Longwell Green Sports	34	10	8	16	30	47	38
14 Bridport	34	10	4	20	42	81	34
15 Barnstaple Town	34	9	5	20	45	66	32
16 Radstock Town	34	8	3	23	33	74	27
17 (R) Sherborne Town	34	8	3	23	36	91	27
18 (R) Corsham Town	34	6	4	24	21	68	22

PREMIER DIVISION	1	2	3	4	5	6	7	8	9	10	11	12	13	14	15	16	17	18
1 Barnstaple Town		0-5	1-3	3-0	1-2	4-1	4-0	0-1	0-0	0-0	0-1	2-4	2-0	3-1	4-1	1-2	0-1	1-2
2 Bishop Sutton	5-0		1-0	4-0	0-0	1-1	1-0	1-2	2-2	2-0	1-1	1-1	0-5	3-2	1-1	1-2	0-4	0-2
3 Bitton	2-0	1-0		6-1	1-2	2-3	4-0	1-1	2-0	0-2	5-0	0-2	3-0	1-0	3-0	1-4	4-0	1-1
4 Bridport	0-1	1-2	1-3		3-2	1-3	1-0	0-3	2-0	0-2	1-0	1-2	0-4	3-1	2-1	4-4	2-4	0-2
5 Brislington	2-1	1-1	2-3	2-2		0-0	2-0	1-0	1-1	1-0	1-0	0-1	0-0	1-1	6-0	2-2	5-0	0-1
6 Bristol Manor Farm	2-0	3-1	3-3	0-1	1-2		3-0	2-2	5-2	2-2	2-1	3-5	1-1	0-1	4-0	4-1	2-1	1-1
7 Corsham Town	2-3	0-2	1-3	2-0	2-0	1-0		1-1	1-3	2-1	1-0	0-0	0-6	0-1	2-1	1-2	1-4	0-3
8 Hallen	3-1	0-0	0-2	4-0	1-1	1-3	4-2		2-2	3-2	2-0	1-1	2-1	3-0	3-1	3-2	1-0	1-1
9 Ilfracombe Town	4-2	0-1	1-2	2-2	2-0	5-3	0-0	0-1		0-3	0-2	0-5	3-3	1-0	2-0	0-1	7-0	1-0
10 Larkhall Athletic	2-1	0-2	1-3	3-0	4-0	1-1	3-0	1-1	5-1		1-0	1-0	2-1	5-1	4-0	4-0	2-0	0-2
11 Longwell Green Sports	0-0	0-4	0-2	2-1	0-2	2-0	1-1	2-1	0-2	0-3		2-1	0-2	2-0	3-0	1-4	1-3	1-1
12 Merthyr Town	7-2	1-1	2-0	3-3	2-1	4-1	4-0	4-1	1-0	1-3	0-0		7-1	8-0	3-0	5-1	4-1	6-1
13 Odd Down	3-0	2-3	1-2	0-1	2-2	3-2	1-0	0-1	0-3	0-1	1-1	2-2		3-2	3-2	2-1	0-0	1-1
14 Radstock Town	2-3	1-4	0-2	4-5	0-0	2-0	1-0	0-1	1-3	0-3	1-1	0-3	0-1		3-2	0-2	2-1	1-3
15 Sherborne Town	1-1	1-6	1-3	2-0	1-0	0-3	1-0	3-1	1-1	2-1	1-3	1-4	0-1	2-4		0-5	3-4	2-1
16 Street	4-2	1-3	1-2	0-2	0-2	3-0	4-0	0-1	0-1	0-2	2-1	1-1	1-2	1-0	1-3		1-1	0-3
17 Wells City	2-1	1-0	0-1	6-2	0-4	1-4	3-1	2-5	1-3	1-2	1-1	1-1	0-0	2-0	1-2	1-2		4-0
18 Willand Rovers	1-1	1-1	3-3	4-0	1-2	2-0	1-0	3-0	2-1	2-1	0-1	0-1	3-2	3-0	8-0	2-1	1-2	

WESTERN LEAGUE - STEP 5/6

	DIVISION ONE	P	W	D	L	F	A	Pts
1	(P) Cadbury Heath	36	25	9	2	88	32	84
2	(P) Melksham Town	36	24	6	6	77	42	78
3	(P) Gillingham Town	36	22	6	8	94	52	72
4	Calne Town	36	21	7	8	60	34	70
5	Bradford Town	36	16	10	10	72	44	58
6	Chard Town	36	15	7	14	62	54	52
7	Welton Rovers (-1)	36	14	8	14	61	57	49
8	Roman Glass St George	36	13	10	13	48	51	49
9	Almondsbury UWE	36	14	6	16	70	67	48
10	Hengrove Athletic	36	12	10	14	53	59	46
11	Oldland Abbotonians	36	11	11	14	52	53	44
12	Portishead Town	36	12	8	16	48	61	44
13	Keynsham Town (-3)	36	11	13	12	52	59	43
14	Elmore	36	12	6	18	51	64	42
15	Shrewton United	36	10	9	17	63	88	39
16	Shepton Mallet	36	9	10	17	59	84	37
17	Westbury United	36	10	5	21	48	65	35
18	Wellington	36	9	5	22	40	84	32
19	Devizes Town	36	5	8	23	34	82	23

DIVISION ONE	1	2	3	4	5	6	7	8	9	10	11	12	13	14	15	16	17	18	19
1 Almondsbury UWE		1-1	0-1	2-0	1-0	9-0	2-0	1-3	1-1	3-1	1-4	1-1	0-2	1-0	5-2	4-3	3-1	3-1	3-1
2 Bradford Town	4-0		0-1	1-3	2-2	4-1	7-0	4-1	1-1	4-2	1-2	2-1	0-1	3-3	1-2	1-1	3-1	4-1	2-0
3 Cadbury Heath	5-3	0-1		3-0	2-0	7-1	2-0	3-3	1-1	1-1	2-2	3-0	2-0	1-1	7-1	3-3	3-0	2-1	4-1
4 Calne Town	3-1	2-0	2-3		0-2	1-2	2-1	3-0	1-0	0-0	1-0	1-2	0-0	2-0	2-2	1-0	4-0	2-0	1-0
5 Chard Town	2-1	0-0	1-1	0-0		4-0	5-1	1-2	3-1	3-2	2-3	2-2	2-1	2-0	1-3	3-1	2-0	2-1	3-3
6 Devizes Town	1-0	1-4	1-2	1-2	0-2		0-3	0-2	0-2	2-2	0-1	0-2	1-2	0-0	0-2	1-2	1-2	0-2	1-3
7 Elmore	2-3	0-2	0-1	1-2	2-4	3-0		1-2	2-1	1-0	2-2	0-2	1-0	1-4	2-2	1-0	4-1	0-3	2-0
8 Gillingham Town	3-2	3-3	1-7	2-3	6-0	1-0	1-2		2-0	7-0	1-2	4-0	6-0	2-2	2-2	11-1	3-0	2-1	3-2
9 Hengrove Athletic	2-1	3-1	0-1	1-1	2-1	2-2	1-0	2-3		3-0	2-6	1-0	3-3	3-1	2-2	0-2	0-4	0-2	1-1
10 Keynsham Town	2-2	2-1	0-2	2-0	4-3	1-3	3-3	2-2	0-1		0-2	0-0	1-2	2-0	3-1	2-0	4-0	2-2	1-1
11 Melksham Town	5-1	1-3	1-0	1-4	1-0	1-1	4-0	3-1	1-0	3-0		2-1	1-0	1-3	2-1	3-2	2-2	1-3	2-1
12 Oldland Abbotonians	1-1	0-0	0-1	1-2	2-0	3-1	0-4	2-3	4-0	0-0	1-1		0-1	1-3	4-4	7-1	3-0	1-0	0-2
13 Portishead Town	0-1	2-0	2-2	0-3	1-5	1-3	1-5	1-2	2-3	1-1	2-0	1-1		1-2	2-1	3-1	0-1	2-2	2-0
14 Roman Glass St George	5-2	2-1	1-3	1-1	1-0	2-2	0-2	0-0	1-1	0-1	0-1	3-1	0-3		1-1	2-1	1-0	2-1	1-0
15 Shepton Mallet	3-2	1-4	0-1	4-2	1-0	2-2	1-1	0-1	1-7	1-3	1-3	3-1	2-2	0-2		3-1	1-3	0-1	1-2
16 Shrewton United	5-2	0-3	0-4	0-0	3-2	2-2	1-1	1-6	2-2	2-4	2-2	2-2	2-0	0-0	5-1		5-1	4-2	2-3
17 Wellington	0-7	0-0	1-3	0-4	0-0	2-1	1-0	0-1	1-2	1-1	0-3	1-2	4-4	3-1	3-4	1-2		3-1	1-4
18 Welton Rovers	0-0	3-3	2-2	0-3	4-1	1-1	1-1	1-0	3-1	1-2	1-5	1-1	2-0	3-2	2-1	3-1	5-1		4-1
19 Westbury United	2-0	0-1	1-2	1-2	0-2	1-2	3-2	0-2	2-1	1-1	0-3	2-3	1-3	4-1	2-2	2-3	0-1	1-0	

BARNSTAPLE TOWN
Founded: 1906 Nickname: Barum

Secretary: David Cooke **(T)** 07939 217 084 **(E)** dcooke81@yahoo.com
Chairman: David Cooke **Manager:** Peter Buckingham **Prog Ed:**
Ground: Mill Road, Barnstaple, North Devon EX31 1JQ **(T)** 01271 343 469
Capacity: 5,000 **Seats:** 250 **Covered:** 1,000 **Midweek Matchday:** Tuesday **Clubhouse:** Yes **Shop:** Yes

Colours(change): All red. (All blue)
Previous Names: Pilton Yeo Vale
Previous Leagues: North Devon, Devon & Exeter, South Western
Records: **Att:** 6,200 v Bournemouth FA Cup 1st Round 51-52 **App:** Ian Pope
Senior Honours: Western Champions 1952-53, 79-80, Devon Pro Cup (12), Devon Senior Cup 1992-93.
Western League Division One 1993-94.

10 YEAR RECORD

02-03	03-04	04-05	05-06	06-07	07-08	08-09	09-10	10-11	11-12
WestP 15	WestP 10	WestP 12	WestP 13	WestP 7	WestP 12	WestP 18	WestP 15	WestP 11	WestP 15

BISHOP SUTTON
Founded: 1977 Nickname: Bishops

Secretary: Malcolm Hunt **(T)** 07799 623 901 **(E)** bishopsuttonafcsecretary@hotmail.co.uk
Chairman: George Williams **Manager:** Lee Lashenko **Prog Ed:**
Ground: Lakeview, Wick Road, Bishops Sutton, Bristol BS39 5XN. **(T)** 01275 333 097
Capacity: 1,500 **Seats:** 100 **Covered:** 200 **Midweek Matchday:** Tuesday **Clubhouse:** Yes **Shop:** No

Colours(change): All blue (All yellow)
Previous Names:
Previous Leagues: Weston & District (youth), Bristol & Avon, Somerset Senior >1991
Records: **Att:** 400 v Bristol City
Senior Honours: Somerset Junior Cup 1980-81. Western League Division One 1997-98.

10 YEAR RECORD

02-03	03-04	04-05	05-06	06-07	07-08	08-09	09-10	10-11	11-12
WestP 12	WestP 16	WestP 18	WestP 16	WestP 21	WestP 19	WestP 15	WestP 4	WestP 5	WestP 6

BITTON
Founded: 1922 Nickname: The Ton

Secretary: Mrs Becky Jones **(T)** 07909 446 291 **(E)** rebeccalangdon@btconnect.com
Chairman: John Langdon **Manager:** John Lester **Prog Ed:**
Ground: Rapid Solicitors Ground, Bath Road, Bitton, Bristol BS30 6HX. **(T)** 01179 323 222
Capacity: 1,000 **Seats:** 48 **Covered:** 200 **Midweek Matchday:** Wednesday **Clubhouse:** Yes **Shop:** No

Colours(change): Red & white/black/black (Yellow/green/yellow)
Previous Names:
Previous Leagues: Avon Premier Combination, Gloucestershire County
Records: **Goalscorer:** A. Cole
Senior Honours: Somerset Senior Cup 1992-93. Les Phillips Cup 2007-08. Western League Premier Division 2008-09.

10 YEAR RECORD

02-03	03-04	04-05	05-06	06-07	07-08	08-09	09-10	10-11	11-12
West1 8	West1 2	WestP 8	WestP 8	WestP 8	WestP 7	WestP 1	WestP 8	WestP 2	WestP 2

BRIDPORT
Founded: 1885 Nickname: Bees

Secretary: Chris Tozer **(T)** 07500 064 317 **(E)** bridportfc@btconnect.com
Chairman: Adrian Scadding **Manager:** Trevor Senior **Prog Ed:**
Ground: St Mary's Field, Bridport, Dorset DT6 5LN **(T)** 01308 423 834
Capacity: **Seats:** **Covered:** **Midweek Matchday:** Tuesday **Clubhouse:** **Shop:**

Colours(change): Red & black/black/black (All blue)
Previous Names:
Previous Leagues: Dorset Combination 1984-89.
Records: **Att:** 1,150 v Exeter City 1981.
Senior Honours: Dorset Senior Cup x8. Dorset Senior Amateur Cup x6.

10 YEAR RECORD

02-03	03-04	04-05	05-06	06-07	07-08	08-09	09-10	10-11	11-12
WestP 14	WestP 12	WestP 19	West1 6	West1 11	West1 18	West1 13	West1 10	West1 3	WestP 14

BRISLINGTON

Founded: 1956   Nickname: Bris

Secretary: Kevin Jacobs   **(T)** 07976 724 202   **(E)** kevinjacobs919@btinternet.com

Chairman: Fred Hardwell   **Manager:** Jeff Meacham   **Prog Ed:**

Ground: Ironmould Lane, Brislington, Bristol BS4 4TZ   **(T)** 01179 774 030

Capacity: 2,000 **Seats:** 144   **Covered:** 1,500   **Midweek Matchday:** Tuesday   **Clubhouse:** Yes   **Shop:** No

Colours(change): Red & black/black/red. (All yellow)
Previous Names:
Previous Leagues: Somerset Senior until 1991
Records:
Senior Honours: Somerset Senior League 1988-89. Somerset Premier Cup 1992-93. Western League Division One 1994-95.

10 YEAR RECORD

02-03		03-04		04-05		05-06		06-07		07-08		08-09		09-10		10-11		11-12	
WestP	2	WestP	7	WestP	10	WestP	10	WestP	17	WestP	13	WestP	10	WestP	9	WestP	15	WestP	7

BRISTOL MANOR FARM

Founded: 1964   Nickname: The Farm

Secretary: Andy Radford   **(T)** 07747 038 423   **(E)** andy@bristolmanorfarm.com

Chairman: Geoff Sellek   **Manager:** John Black   **Prog Ed:**

Ground: The Creek, Portway, Sea Mills, Bristol BS9 2HS   **(T)** 0117 968 3571

Capacity: 2,000 **Seats:** 98   **Covered:** 350   **Midweek Matchday:** Tuesday   **Clubhouse:** Yes   **Shop:** No

Colours(change): Claret & blue/blue/blue (All yellow)
Previous Names:
Previous Leagues: Bristol Suburban 64-69, Somerset Senior 69-77
Records: **Att;** 500 v Portway **App:** M. Baird
Senior Honours: Glos Trophy 1987-88, Glos Am. Cup 1989-90. Western League Division One 1982-83.

10 YEAR RECORD

02-03		03-04		04-05		05-06		06-07		07-08		08-09		09-10		10-11		11-12	
WestP	11	WestP	3	WestP	7	WestP	3	WestP	12	WestP	16	WestP	5	WestP	7	WestP	7	WestP	8

BUCKLAND ATHLETIC

Founded: 1977   Nickname: The Bucks

Secretary: Christine Holmes   **(T)** 07856 525 730   **(E)** phardingham@virginmedia.com

Chairman: Roy Holmes   **Manager:** Anthony Lynch   **Prog Ed:**

Ground: Homers Heath, South Quarry, Kingskerswell Road, Newton Abbot TQ12 5JU   **(T)** 01626 361 020

Capacity: **Seats:** Yes   **Covered:** Yes   **Midweek Matchday:** Tuesday   **Clubhouse:** Yes   **Shop:**

Colours(change): All yellow (All blue)
Previous Names:
Previous Leagues: Devon County League 2000-07. South West Pininsula.
Records:
Senior Honours: South West Peninsula League Premier Division 2009-10, 10-11. Throgmorton Cup 2009-10.

10 YEAR RECORD

02-03		03-04		04-05		05-06		06-07		07-08		08-09		09-10		10-11		11-12	
Devon	6	Devon	3	Devon	8	Devon	7	Devon	13	SWPP	14	SWPP	3	SWPP	1	SWPP	1	SWPP	2

CADBURY HEATH

Founded: Nickname:

Secretary: Martin Painter   **(T)** 07971 399 268   **(E)** martinbristol1955@hotmail.com

Chairman: Steve Plenty   **Manager:** Andy Black   **Prog Ed:**

Ground: Springfield, Cadbury Heath Road, Bristol BS30 8BX   **(T)** 07971 399 268

Capacity: **Seats:**   **Covered:**   **Midweek Matchday:** Tuesday   **Clubhouse:**   **Shop:**

Colours(change): Red & white/red/red (Yellow/blue/blue)
Previous Names:
Previous Leagues: Gloucestershire County 1968-75, 80-2000. Midland Combination 1975-77.
Records:
Senior Honours: Gloucestershire County League 1998-99. Western League Division One 2011-12.

10 YEAR RECORD

02-03		03-04		04-05		05-06		06-07		07-08		08-09		09-10		10-11		11-12	
West1	14	West1	15	West1	13	West1	14	West1	9	West1	5	West1	4	West1	11	West1	4	West1	1

GILLINGHAM TOWN

Founded: **Nickname:**

Secretary: Terry Lucas   **(T)** 07873 587 455   **(E)** terrylucas@sky.com

Chairman: Dave Graham   **Manager:** Adrian Foster   **Prog Ed:**

Ground: Hardings Lane, Gillingham, Dorset SP8 4HX   **(T)** 01747 823 673

Capacity: **Seats:**   **Covered:**   **Midweek Matchday:** Tuesday   **Clubhouse:** Yes   **Shop:**

Colours(change): All tangerine (Navy & sky/navy/sky)
Previous Names:
Previous Leagues: Dorset Premier 1970-2008.
Records:
Senior Honours:

10 YEAR RECORD

02-03	03-04	04-05	05-06	06-07	07-08	08-09	09-10	10-11	11-12
Dor P 2	Dor P 4	Dor P 5	Dor P 4	Dor P 9	Dor P 2	Dor P 12	Dor P 3	Dor P 7	West1 3

HALLEN

Founded: 1949   **Nickname:**

Secretary: Richard Stokes   **(T)** 07791 492 640   **(E)** sinbad88@hotmail.co.uk

Chairman: Barrie Phillips   **Manager:** Paul Owen   **Prog Ed:**

Ground: Hallen Centre, Moorhouse Lane, Hallen Bristol BS10 7RU   **(T)** 01179 505 559

Capacity: 2,000 **Seats:** 200 **Covered:** 200 **Midweek Matchday:** Wednesday **Clubhouse:** Yes **Shop:**

Colours(change): Blue & black/black/blue (white/green/green)
Previous Names: Lawrence Weston Ath, Lawrence Weston Hallen
Previous Leagues: Gloucestershire County, Hellenic
Records: **Att:** 803 v Bristol Rovers 1997
Senior Honours: Gloucestershire Co. Lge 1988-89, 92-93. Western Division One 2003-04.

10 YEAR RECORD

02-03	03-04	04-05	05-06	06-07	07-08	08-09	09-10	10-11	11-12
West1 4	West1 1	WestP 4	WestP 9	WestP 9	WestP 15	WestP 9	WestP 12	WestP 16	WestP 4

ILFRACOMBE TOWN

Founded: 1902   **Nickname:** Bluebirds

Secretary: Tony Alcock   **(T)** 07973 469 673   **(E)** afalcock@aol.com

Chairman: M. Hayne & K. Robertson   **Manager:** Ross Middleton   **Prog Ed:**

Ground: Marlborough Park, Ilfracombe, Devon EX34 8PD   **(T)** 01271 865 939

Capacity: 2,000 **Seats:** 60 **Covered:** 450 **Midweek Matchday:** Tuesday **Clubhouse:** Yes **Shop:**

Colours(change): All blue (Yellow/red/red)
Previous Names:
Previous Leagues: North Devon, East Devon Premier, Exeter & District, Western,
Records: **Att:** 3,000 v Bristol City **Goalscorer:** Kevin Squire **App:** Bob Hancock 459
Senior Honours: East Devon Premier League, North Devon Senior League, North Devon Premier League.

10 YEAR RECORD

02-03	03-04	04-05	05-06	06-07	07-08	08-09	09-10	10-11	11-12
West1 18	West1 16	West1 8	West1 4	West1 3	WestP 8	WestP 14	WestP 3	WestP 3	WestP 11

LARKHALL ATHLETIC

Founded: 1914   **Nickname:** Larks

Secretary: Garry Davy   **(T)** 07942 445 498   **(E)** garrydvy@aol.com

Chairman: Paul Rankin   **Manager:** Wayne Thorne   **Prog Ed:**

Ground: Plain Ham, Charlcombe Lane, Larkhall, Bath BA1 8DJ   **(T)** 01225 334 952

Capacity: 1,000 **Seats:** Yes **Covered:** 50 **Midweek Matchday:** Wednesday **Clubhouse:** Yes **Shop:**

Colours(change): All royal blue (All yellow)
Previous Names: None
Previous Leagues: Somerset Senior
Records:
Senior Honours: Somerset Senior Cup 1975-76, Somerset Senior Champions. Western Division One 1988-89, 93-94, 94-95, 08-09. Western Premier Division 2010-11.

10 YEAR RECORD

02-03	03-04	04-05	05-06	06-07	07-08	08-09	09-10	10-11	11-12
West1 13	West1 8	West1 5	West1 7	West1 5	West1 3	West1 1	WestP 14	WestP 1	WestP 3

LONGWELL GREEN SPORTS

Founded: 1966   Nickname: The Green

Secretary: David Heal   **(T)** 07917 778 463   **(E)** dave@monaghannorthern.co.uk

Chairman: Chris Wyrill   **Manager:** Spencer Thomas   **Prog Ed:**

Ground: Longwell Green Com. Centre, Shellards Road BS30 9AD   **(T)** 01179 323 722

Capacity: 1,000 **Seats:** Yes **Covered:** 100 **Midweek Matchday:** Tuesday   **Clubhouse:** Yes **Shop:** Yes

Colours(change): Blue & white/black/black (All green)
Previous Names: None
Previous Leagues: Gloucestershire County.
Records: **Att:** 500 v Mangotsfield 2005
Senior Honours:

10 YEAR RECORD

02-03	03-04	04-05	05-06	06-07	07-08	08-09	09-10	10-11	11-12
		GlCo 2	West1 12	West1 8	West1 8	West1 2	WestP 11	WestP 17	WestP 13

MELKSHAM TOWN

Founded: 1876   Nickname:

Secretary: Mark Jeffery   **(T)** 07739 905 575   **(E)** markmtfc@virginmedia.com

Chairman: Dave Wiltshire   **Manager:** Dave Clayton   **Prog Ed:**

Ground: The Conigre, Market Place, Melksham, Wiltshire SN12 6ES   **(T)** 01225 702 843

Capacity: **Seats:** **Covered:** **Midweek Matchday:** Monday   **Clubhouse:** **Shop:**

Colours(change): Yellow/black/yellow (All red)
Previous Names: Melksham > 1951.
Previous Leagues:
Records: **Att:** 2,821 v Trowbridge Town, FA Cup 1957-58.
Senior Honours: Western League Division 1 1979-80, 96-97. Wiltshire Shield x6. Wiltshire Senior Cup x4.

10 YEAR RECORD

02-03	03-04	04-05	05-06	06-07	07-08	08-09	09-10	10-11	11-12
WestP 8	WestP 14	WestP 14	WestP 14	WestP 5	WestP 11	WestP 11	WestP 19	WestP 8	West1 2

ODD DOWN (BATH)

Founded: 1901   Nickname: The Down

Secretary: Lorraine Brown   **(T)** 07734 924 435   **(E)** lorainebrown@btinternet.com

Chairman: Dave Loxton   **Manager:** Lee Burns   **Prog Ed:**

Ground: Lew Hill Memorial Ground, Combe Hay Lane, Odd Down BA2 8PA   **(T)** 01225 832 491

Capacity: 1,000 **Seats:** 160 **Covered:** 250 **Midweek Matchday:** Tuesday   **Clubhouse:** Yes **Shop:** No

Colours(change): Royal blue/black/black (Yellow & green/green/yellow)
Previous Names:
Previous Leagues: Wilts Premier, Bath & District & Somerset Senior
Records: **App:** Steve Fuller 475 **Goalscorer:** Joe Matano 104
Senior Honours:

10 YEAR RECORD

02-03	03-04	04-05	05-06	06-07	07-08	08-09	09-10	10-11	11-12
WestP 9	WestP 9	WestP 13	WestP 15	WestP 11	WestP 21	West1 19	West1 2	WestP 8	WestP 9

RADSTOCK TOWN

Founded: 1895   Nickname:

Secretary: Simon Wilkinson   **(T)** 07557 276 619   **(E)** rtfc@hotmail.co.uk

Chairman: Jason Holt   **Manager:** Ben Newby   **Prog Ed:**

Ground: Southfields Recreation Ground, Southfields, Radstock BA3 2NZ   **(T)** 01761 435 004

Capacity: 1,500 **Seats:** 80 **Covered:** yes **Midweek Matchday:** Tuesday   **Clubhouse:** Yes **Shop:** No

Colours(change): Red & black/red/red (All sky blue)
Previous Names: Radstock.
Previous Leagues: Somerset Senior League.
Records:
Senior Honours:

10 YEAR RECORD

02-03	03-04	04-05	05-06	06-07	07-08	08-09	09-10	10-11	11-12
SomP 10	SomP 3	West1 3	WestP 12	WestP 16	WestP 17	WestP 17	WestP 16	WestP 12	WestP 16

STREET

Founded: 1880   Nickname: The Cobblers

Secretary: Dave Green   **(T)** 07920 742 086   **(E)** daveg55@hotmail.co.uk

Chairman: Phil Norton-Ashley   **Manager:** Daniel Badman   **Prog Ed:** Phil Norton-Ashley

Ground: The Tannery Ground, Middlebrooks, Street BA16 0TA   **(T)** 01458 445 987

Capacity: 2,000 **Seats:** 120 **Covered:** 25 **Midweek Matchday:** Tuesday   **Clubhouse:** Yes   **Shop:**

Colours(change): White/green/white (Red/red/yellow)
Previous Names: None
Previous Leagues: Somerset Senior.
Records: **Att;** 4,300 v Yeovil Town FA Cup 47
Senior Honours: Somerset Senior League 1996-97.

10 YEAR RECORD

02-03		03-04		04-05		05-06		06-07		07-08		08-09		09-10		10-11		11-12	
West1	15	West1	12	West1	7	West1	3	WLaP	19	WestP	18	WestP	13	WestP	6	WestP	13	WestP	10

WELLS CITY

Founded: 1890   Nickname:

Secretary: Mark Grant   **(T)** 07974 726 607   **(E)** mlgrant62@hotmail.co.uk

Chairman: Steve Loxton   **Manager:** Ray Johnston   **Prog Ed:**

Ground: Athletic Ground, Rowdens Road, Wells, Somerset BA5 1TU   **(T)** 01749 679 971

Capacity: **Seats:** **Covered:** **Midweek Matchday:** Tuesday   **Clubhouse:**   **Shop:**

Colours(change): Blue/blue/white (All yellow)
Previous Names:
Previous Leagues: Somerset County.
Records:
Senior Honours: Western League Division One 2009-10.

10 YEAR RECORD

02-03		03-04		04-05		05-06		06-07		07-08		08-09		09-10		10-11		11-12	
SomP	15	SomP	14	SomP	9	SomP	5	SomP	5	SomP	2	West1	10	West1	1	WestP	9	WestP	12

WILLAND ROVERS

Founded: 1946   Nickname: Rovers

Secretary: Tony Baker   **(T)** 07887 587 811   **(E)** tonybakerwillandrovers@gmail.com

Chairman: Mike Mitchell   **Manager:** Clive Jones   **Prog Ed:**

Ground: Silver Street, Willand, Collumpton, Devon EX15 2RG   **(T)** 01884 33885

Capacity: 2,000 **Seats:** 75 **Covered:** 150 **Midweek Matchday:** Tuesday   **Clubhouse:** Yes   **Shop:**

Colours(change): All White (Yellow/blue/yellow)
Previous Names: None.
Previous Leagues: Devon County.
Records: **Att:** 650 v Newton Abbot 1992-3 **Goalscorer:** Paul Foreman
Senior Honours: Devon County League 1998-99, 00-01, Western League Division One 2004-05, Les Phillips Cup 2006-07.

10 YEAR RECORD

02-03		03-04		04-05		05-06		06-07		07-08		08-09		09-10		10-11		11-12	
West1	7	West1	6	West1	1	WestP	6	WestP	6	WestP	3	WestP	3	WestP	2	WestP	4	WestP	5

WINTERBOURNE UNITED

Founded: 1911   Nickname: The Bourne

Secretary: Geoff Endicott   **(T)** 07778 678 823   **(E)** g.endicott@btopenworld.com

Chairman: Robyn Maggs   **Manager:** David Wilson   **Prog Ed:** Robyn Maggs

Ground: Oakland Park, Alomondsbury, Bristol BS32 4AG   **(T)** 07976 255 666

Capacity: **Seats:** **Covered:** **Midweek Matchday:** Wednesday   **Clubhouse:**   **Shop:**

Colours(change): Red & black/red/red (Yellow/blue/yellow)
Previous Names:
Previous Leagues:
Records: **Att:** 229 v Malmesbury Victoria, 29/08/2004.
Senior Honours: Gloucestershire County League 2000-01. Hellenic League Division 1 West 2005-06, 07-08.

10 YEAR RECORD

02-03		03-04		04-05		05-06		06-07		07-08		08-09		09-10		10-11		11-12	
Hel1W	4	Hel1W	9	Hel1W	9	Hel1W	1	Hel1W	10	Hel1W	1	Hel1W	7	Hel1W	13	Hel1W	10	Hel1W	3

ALMONDSBURY U.W.E.

Founded: Nickname:

Secretary: Douglas Coles **(T)** 07748 655 399 **(E)** doug2004.coles@blueyonder.co.uk
Chairman: Mike Blessing **Manager:** David Hillier **Prog Ed:**
Ground: The Field, Almondsbury, Bristol BS32 4AA **(T)** 01454 612 240 **Capacity:**
Colours(change): White & green/green/green (All yellow)

ADDITIONAL INFORMATION:

BRADFORD TOWN

Founded: 1992 Nickname:

Secretary: Nikki Akers **(T)** 07866 693 167 **(E)** bradfordtownfc@gmail.com
Chairman: Les Stevens **Manager:** Paul Shanley **Prog Ed:**
Ground: Bradford Sports & Social Club, Trowbridge Rd, Bradford on Avon BA15 1EE **(T)** 07801 499 168 **Capacity:**
Colours(change): Navy & white/navy/navy (Yellow/black/yellow)

ADDITIONAL INFORMATION:
Previous League: Wiltshire Senior.

CALNE TOWN

Founded: 1886 Nickname: Lilywhites

Secretary: Shaun Smith **(T)** 07817 476 898 **(E)** s_k_smith@hotmail.com
Chairman: Terry Roberts **Manager:** Jeff Roberts **Prog Ed:**
Ground: Bremhill View, Calne, Wiltshire SN11 9EE **(T)** 07920 864 879 **Capacity:**
Colours(change): All white (All blue)

ADDITIONAL INFORMATION:
Record Att: 1,100 v Swindon, friendly 1987. **Goalscorer:** Robbie Lardner. **Apps:** Gary Swallow - 259.
Honours: Wiltshire Senior Cup x3.

CHARD TOWN

Founded: Nickname: The Robins

Secretary: Michael Hawes **(T)** 07906 904 138 **(E)** michael.hawes2@virgin.net
Chairman: Willie Whitelaw **Manager:** Adam Fricker (Caretaker) **Prog Ed:**
Ground: Denning Sports Field, Zembard Lane, Chard, Somerset TA20 1JL **(T)** 01460 61402 **Capacity:**
Colours(change): Red & black/black/black (All yellow)

ADDITIONAL INFORMATION:
Honours: Somerset Senior League 1949-50, 53-54, 59-60, 67-68, 69-70. Somerset Senior Cup 1952-53, 66-67.
South West Counties Cup 1988-89.

CHEDDAR

Founded: 1892 Nickname: The Cheesemen

Secretary: Bruce Harvey **(T)** 07500 908 538 **(E)** bruce.harvey@aventria.co.uk
Chairman: Steve Bayliss **Manager:** Tim Richens **Prog Ed:**
Ground: Bowdens Park, Draycott Road, Cheddar BS27 3RL **(T)** 01934 707 271 **Capacity:**
Colours(change): Yellow/black/yellow (White/black/white)

ADDITIONAL INFORMATION:
Previous Leagues: Cheddar Valley. Weston Super Mare & District. Somerset Senior > 2012.
Honours: Cheddar Valley League 1910-11. Somerset Senior League Premier Division 2011-12.

CORSHAM TOWN

Founded: 1884 Nickname:

Secretary: Richard Taylor **(T)** 07944 183 973 **(E)** richtaylor_ctfc@hotmail.com
Chairman: Ken Baldwin **Manager:** Trevor Rawlings **Prog Ed:**
Ground: Southbank Ground, Lacock Road, Corsham SN13 9HS **(T)** 07963 030 652 **Capacity:** 1,500
Colours(change): Red & white/red/red (Yellow/blue/blue)

ADDITIONAL INFORMATION: Att: 550 v Newport Co. FA Cup **App:** Craig Chaplin
Wiltshire Senior Cup 1975-76, 96-97, 04-05. Western Premier Division 2006-07.

CRIBBS FRIENDS LIFE

Founded: 1958 Nickname:

Secretary: Simon Hartley **(T)** 07970 744 063 **(E)** welshwizard1973@aol.com
Chairman: Dave Nelson **Manager:** Gavin Tufton **Prog Ed:**
Ground: Friends Life Sports Ground, Station Road, Henbury, Bristol BS10 7TB **(T)** 0117 950 2302 **Capacity:**
Colours(change): Blue/blue/red (Red/red/white)

ADDITIONAL INFORMATION:
Previous Leagues: Gloucestershire County > 2012.
Honours: Gloucester County League 2011-12.

DEVIZES TOWN
Founded: 1885   Nickname:

Secretary: Neil Fautley   **(T)** 07891 341 344   **(E)** neil@hallmarkflooring.co.uk
Chairman: Shaun Moffat   **Manager:** Mark Love   **Prog Ed:**
Ground: Nursteed Road, Devizes, Wiltshire SN10 3DX   **(T)** 01380 722 817   **Capacity:**
Colours(change): Red & white/black/red (All blue)

ADDITIONAL INFORMATION:
Honours: Western League Division One 1999-2000. Wiltshire Senior Cup x14.

ELMORE
Founded: 1947   Nickname: Eagles

Secretary: Keith Humphreys   **(T)** 07855 122 683   **(E)** keith_humphreys@sky.com
Chairman: Julian (Jed) Hewitt   **Manager:** Ryan German   **Prog Ed:**
Ground: Horsdon Park, Heathcoat Way, Tiverton, Devon EX16 4DB   **(T)** 01884 252 341   **Capacity:**
Colours(change): All green (Red & white/red/white)

ADDITIONAL INFORMATION:
Record Att: 1,713 v Tiverton Town Friday April 14th 1995. **Apps:** P Webber. **Win:** 17-0. **Defeat:** 2-7.
Honours: East Devon Senior Cup 1972-73, 75-76. Devon Senior Cup 1987-88.

HENGROVE ATHLETIC
Founded: 1948   Nickname:

Secretary: Graham Whitaker   **(T)** 07970 848 285   **(E)** graham.whitaker@btinternet.com
Chairman: Nigel Gray   **Manager:** Jamie Hillman   **Prog Ed:**
Ground: Norton Lane, Whitchurch, Bristol BS14 0BT   **(T)** 01275 832 894   **Capacity:**
Colours(change): All green (Sky blue/navy blue/sky blue)

ADDITIONAL INFORMATION:
Previous League: Somerset County 1974-2006.
Honours: Somerset County League Premier Division 2005-06. Somerset Senior Cup 1979-80.

KEYNSHAM TOWN
Founded: 1895   Nickname: K's

Secretary: John Peake   **(T)** 07704 340 170   **(E)** helejohn@btinternet.com
Chairman: Malcolm Trainer   **Manager:** Steve Cains   **Prog Ed:**
Ground: Crown Field, Bristol Road, Keynsham BS31 2BE   **(T)** 01179 865 876   **Capacity:**
Colours(change): Gold/black/gold (All white)

ADDITIONAL INFORMATION:
Previous League: Somerset Senior.
Honours: Somerset Senior Cup 1951-52, 57-58, 2002-03.

OLDLAND ABBOTONIANS
Founded: 1910   Nickname: The O's

Secretary: Derek Jones   **(T)** 07836 648 327   **(E)** avontruckandvan@btconnect.com
Chairman: Robert Clarke   **Manager:** Paul Britton   **Prog Ed:**
Ground: Aitchison Playing Field, Castle Road, Oldland Common, Bristol BS30 9PP   **(T)** 01179 328 263   **Capacity:**
Colours(change): Blue & white/blue/blue (All yellow)

ADDITIONAL INFORMATION:
Previous League: Somerset County.
Honours: Les Phillips Cup 2008-09.

PORTISHEAD TOWN
Founded: 1910   Nickname: Posset

Secretary: Brian Hobbs   **(T)** 07791 412 724   **(E)** hobbs.posset@hotmail.co.uk
Chairman: Adrian Green   **Manager:** Dave Pettitt   **Prog Ed:**
Ground: Bristol Road, Portishead, Bristol BS20 6QG   **(T)** 01275 817 600   **Capacity:**
Colours(change): White/black/black (All blue)

ADDITIONAL INFORMATION:
Previous League: Somerset County.
Honours: Somerset County League 2004-05.

ROMAN GLASS ST GEORGE
Founded: Nickname:

Secretary: Emily Baldwin   **(T)** 07708 277 592   **(E)** emilyjaynebaldwin@blueyonder.co.uk
Chairman: Roger Hudd   **Manager:** Bob Johnson   **Prog Ed:**
Ground: Oaklands Park, Gloucester Road, Alomndsbury BS32 4AG   **(T)** 01454 250 566   **Capacity:**
Colours(change): White/black/white (All red)

ADDITIONAL INFORMATION:
Previous League: Gloucestershire County.
Honours: Gloucestershire County League 2006-07.

SHEPTON MALLET

Founded: 1986   Nickname:

Secretary: Gary Banfield   **(T)** 07762 880 705   **(E)** gkrkb@tiscali.co.uk

Chairman: John Hugill   **Manager:** Andrew Jones   **Prog Ed:**

Ground: Playing Fields, Old Wells Road, West Shepton, Shepton Mallet BA4 5XN   **(T)** 01749 344 609   **Capacity:**

Colours(change): Black & white/black/black (Claret/white/yellow)

ADDITIONAL INFORMATION:
Record Att: 274 v Chippenham Town FA Cup 2000-01.
Honours: Somerset Senior League 2000-01.

SHERBORNE TOWN

Founded: 1894   Nickname:

Secretary: Colin Goodland   **(T)** 07929 090 612   **(E)** goody@cgoodland.freeserve.co.uk

Chairman: Steve Paradise   **Manager:** Jamie Manley   **Prog Ed:** Gavin Dodge

Ground: Raleigh Grove, Terrace Playing Field, Sherborne DT9 5NS   **(T)** 01935 816 110   **Capacity:**

Colours(change): Black & white/black/black (Yellow/white/white).

ADDITIONAL INFORMATION: Att: 1,000 v Eastleigh, Andy Shephard Memorial match 27.07.03.
Dorset Premier League 1981-82, Dorset Senior Cup 2003-04.

SHREWTON UNITED

Founded: Nickname:

Secretary: Paul Robinson   **(T)** 07786 802 688   **(E)** paul@shrewtonunitedfc.net

Chairman: Gemma Foot   **Manager:** Steve Chalk   **Prog Ed:**

Ground: Recreation Ground, Mill Lane, Shrewton, Wilts SP3 4JY   **(T)** 07786 802 688   **Capacity:**

Colours(change): Marron & sky blue/sky blue/maroon (Yellow/royal blue/royal blue)

ADDITIONAL INFORMATION:
Previous League: Wiltshire > 2003.
Honours: Wiltshire League Premier Division 2001-02, 02-03, Senior Cup 2001-02, 02-03.

WARMINSTER TOWN

Founded: 1878   Nickname:

Secretary: Jan Loftus   **(T)** 07730 135 920   **(E)** warminstertownfc@hotmail.com

Chairman: Pete Russell   **Manager:** Adam Collington   **Prog Ed:**

Ground: Weymouth Street, Warminster BA12 9NS   **(T)** 01985 217 828   **Capacity:**

Colours(change): Red & black/black/red (Dark blue & light blue/dark blue/dark blue)

ADDITIONAL INFORMATION:
Previous Leagues: Wiltshire County > 1930, 1945-83, 2002-06. Western League 1930-39, 83-2002. Wessex 2006-12.

WELLINGTON

Founded: 1892   Nickname: Wellie

Secretary: David Derrick   **(T)** 07516 482 923   **(E)** david230275@googlemail.com

Chairman: Mike Hall   **Manager:** Colin Merrick   **Prog Ed:**

Ground: Wellington Playing Field, North St, Wellington TA21 8NE   **(T)** 01823 664 810   **Capacity:** 3,000

Colours(change): All tangerine (Claret/blue/claret)

ADDITIONAL INFORMATION: Goalscorer: Ken Jones

WELTON ROVERS

Founded: 1887   Nickname: Rovers

Secretary: Malcolm Price   **(T)** 07970 791 644   **(E)** malcolm@weltonr.plus.com

Chairman: Maurice Down   **Manager:** Stuart Minall   **Prog Ed:**

Ground: West Clewes, North Road, Midsomer Norton, Bath BA3 2QD   **(T)** 01761 412 097   **Capacity:** 2,400

Colours(change): Green & white/white/green (Yellow/blue/yellow).

ADDITIONAL INFORMATION: Att: 2,000 v Bromley FA Am Cup 1963   **Goalscorer:** Ian Henderson 51
Somerset Senior Cup (10). Somerset Premier Cup 2009-10.

WESTBURY UNITED

Founded: 1921   Nickname: White Horsemen

Secretary: Roger Arnold   **(T)** 07584 318 302   **(E)** rogerarnold33@hotmail.com

Chairman: Philip Alford   **Manager:** Sam Gooding   **Prog Ed:**

Ground: Meadow Lane, Westbury, Wiltshire BA13 3AF   **(T)** 01373 823 409   **Capacity:**

Colours(change): Green & white/green/green (Blue & red/blue/blue)

ADDITIONAL INFORMATION:
Record Att: 4,000 v Llanelli FA Cup 1st Round 1937 & v Walthamstow Avenue FA Cup 1937.
Honours: Wiltshire League 1934-35, 37-38, 38-39, 49-50, 50-51, 55-56. Western League Div.1 1991-92. Wilts Senior Cup x4.

GROUND DIRECTIONS

BARNSTAPLE TOWN - Mill Road, Barnstaple, North Devon EX31 1JQ 01271 343469
From M5 South, exit junction 27, take A361 to Barnstaple, in town take A361 for Ilfracombe, then first left over bridge is Mill Road.

BISHOP SUTTON - Lakeview, Wick Road, Bishop Sutton BS39 5XN 01275 333097
On main A368 Bath to Weston-Super-Mare road at rear of Butchers Arms Public House.

BITTON - Recreation Ground, Bath Road, Bitton, Bristol BS30 6HX 0117 932 3222
From M4 leave at Junction 18. Take A46 towards Bath, at first roundabout take A420 for Wick / Bridgeyate. On approach to Bridgeyate turn left at mini-roundabout onto A4175 and follow for 2.2 miles, then turn left for Bath on A431. The ground is 100 yards on the right.
From Bath take A431, go through Kelston and Bitton village. Ground is on the left.
From Chippenham take A420 to Bristol and turn left at mini-roundabout onto A4175 and follow as above.

BRIDPORT - St Marys Field, Bridport, Dorset DT6 5LN 01308 423 834
Follow Bridport by-pass in any direction to the Crown Inn roundabout. Take exit to town centre, at first set of traffic lights (Morrisons) turn left. Ground is 200 yards on the right.

BRISLINGTON - Ironmould Lane, Brislington, Bristol BS4 4TZ 0117 977 4030
On A4 Bristol to Bath road, about 500 yards on Bath side of Park & Ride. Opposite the Wyevale Garden Centre.

BRISTOL MANOR FARM - The Creek, Portway, Sea Mills, Bristol BS9 2HS 0117 968 3571
Leaving M5 at Junction 18, take A4 marked Bristol. U-turn on dual carriageway by Bristol and West Sports Ground and then ground is half-mile on left hand side

BUCKLAND ATHLETIC - Homers Heath, Kingskerwell Road, Newton Abbot TQ12 5JU - 01626 361020
From Plymouth : Take the exit off the A38 marked Newton Abbot. Travel for approx 5 miles until you come to a roundabout. Turn left and head downhill towards another Roundabout. Turn right & drive for approx 800 yards. Go straight across the B&Q R/bout. Travel along the avenue, and at the top end of this road, turn left and head towards the train Station. Go past the station, go over the railway and get into the right hand lane. At the 2nd set of traffic lights turn right. Go under the railway and follow this road to the next mini roundabout. Go straight across. Go up the hill and down the other side. The ground is situated on the right hand side, opposite Combined linen services.
From Exeter: Take the A380 signposted Torquay and travel along this road until you reach Penn Inn roundabout. Take the right hand lane and follow the road around which takes you into the left lane and towards the town centre. Take the 1st left and you are now on the main road towards Decoy. The same directions then apply as above. Coaches will not be able to go through the tunnel at Decoy. Please phone for these directions.

CADBURY HEATH - Springfield, Cadbury Heath Road, Bristol BS30 8BX 0117 967 5731 (social club)
M5-M4-M32 Exit 1 follow signs for ring road, exit roundabout for Cadbury Heath left, 100m mini roundabout straight across, 400m mini roundabout turn right into Tower Road North, 150m turn right into Cadbury Heath Road, ground 50m on right via Cadbury Heath Social Club car park.

GILLINGHAM TOWN - Hardings Lane, Gillingham, Dorset SP8 4HX 01747 823 673
Proceed to middle of town to the High Street. Hardings Lane is a turning off of the High Street, at the Shaftesbury or Southern end of the High Street.

HALLEN - Hallen Centre, Moorhouse Lane, Hallen, Bristol BS10 7RU 0117 950 5559
From Junction 17 M5 follow A4018 towards Bristol. At third roundabout turn right into Crow Lane. Proceed to T junction - turn right and right again at mini roundabout by Henbury Lodge Hotel. At next mini roundabout turn left into Avonmouth Way. Continue for 1.5 miles into Hallen village. At crossroads turn left into Moorhouse Lane

ILFRACOMBE TOWN - Marlborough Park, Ilfracombe, Devon EX34 8PD 01271 865 939
Take A361 for Ilfracombe and in town take first right after traffic lights. Follow Marlborough Road to top and ground is on the left.

LARKHALL ATHLETIC - Plain Ham, Charlcombe Lane, Larkhall, Bath BA1 8DJ 01225 334 952
Take A4 east from Bath city centre. After approximately 1 mile fork left into St Saviours Road. In Larkhall Square take left exit and turn right at T Junction. Road bears left into Charlcombe Lane where ground is on right as road narrows.

LONGWELL GREEN SPORTS - Longwell Green Community Centre, Shellards Road, Longwell Green BS30 9DW 0117 932 3722
Leave Junction 1 M32 follow signs for Ring Road (A4174). At Kingsfield roundabout turn into Marsham Way. At first set of traffic lights turn left into Woodward Drive. Continue to min roundabout and turn right into Parkway Road and continue to Shellards Road. Ground is situated to the rear of the Community Centre.

MELKSHAM TOWN - The Conigre, Market Place, Melksham, Wiltshire SN12 6ES 01225 702 843
Turn into Market Place car park and then left into grounds of Cooper Avon Tyres Sports & Social Club (Melksham House) Ground situated at end of drive.

ODD DOWN - Lew Hill, Memorial Ground, Combe Hay Lane, Odd Down, Bath BA2 8AP 01225 832 491
Situated behind Odd Down Park & Ride on main A367 Bath to Exeter road.

RADSTOCK TOWN - Southfields Recreation Ground, Southfields, Radstock BA3 2NZ 01761 435 004
The town of Radstock is situated 15 miles south east of Bristol and 8 miles southwest of Bath on the A367. At the double roundabout in Radstock town centre take the A362 towards Frome. The ground is on the right hand bend, third turning. Turn right into Southfield, ground is 200 yards ahead.

STREET - The Tannery Field, Middlebrooks, Street, Somerset BA16 0TA 01458 445 987
Ground is signposted from both ends of A39 and B3151.

WELLS CITY - Athletic Ground, Rowdens Road, Wells, Somerset BA5 1TU 01749 679 971
From North & Southwest - Follow A39 to Strawberry Way to roundabout, follow A371 East Somerset Way and take right turn into Rowdens Road. Ground is on left. From East - Follow A371 from Shepton Mallet. After approximately 5 miles on East Somerset Way take left turn into Rowdens Road. Ground is on left.

WILLAND ROVERS - Silver Street, Willand, Cullompton, Devon EX15 2RG 01884 33885
Leave M5 Junction 27 and take first left at roundabout. Follow signs to Willand. After passing Halfway House pub on right, go straight over mini-roundabout (signposted to Cullompton) ground is 400 metres on left hand side.

WINTERBOURNE UNITED - Oaklands Park, Almondsbury, Bristol BS32 4AG - 01454 612220
From M4 (West) leave at junction 20 to M5 (Sth West). Leave immediately at junction 16 (A38 Thornbury), turn right onto A38, then first left 100 yards from junction, in front of Motorway Police HQ, Ground next door. Signposted from A38 'Gloucestershire FA HQ'.

WESTERN LEAGUE - STEP 5/6

DIVISION ONE

ALMONDSBURY UWE - The Field, Almondsbury, Bristol BS34 4AA 01454 612 240
Exit M5 at Junction 16. Arriving from the south take the left exit lane. Turn left at lights and ground is 150m on right hand side. Arriving from east take right hand lane on slip road. Take 3rd exit and ground is 150m on right hand side.

BRADFORD TOWN - Bradford Sports & Social Club, Trowbridge Road, Bradford on Avon, Wiltshire BA15 1EW 01225 866 649
From Bath or Melksham on entering Bradford on Avon follow the signs for A363 to Trowbridge. The ground is after a mini roundabout and behind a stone wall on the right hand side. From Trowbridge, follow A363 to Bradford-on-Avon. The ground is just past shop on right, behind stone wall on left.

CALNE TOWN - Bremhill View, Calne, Wiltshire SN11 9EE
Take A4 to Calne from Chippenham, on approaching Calne turn left at the first roundabout on to A3102 Calne bypass. At the next roundabout turn right, next left and then right and right again.

CHARD TOWN - Dening Sports Field, Zembard Lane, Chard, Somerset TA20 1JL 01460 61402
From A30 High Street, follow Swimming Pool/Sports Centre signs via Helliers road. Turn right into Crimchard, turn left into Zembard Lane. Ground is on right hand side.

CHEDDAR - Bowdens Park, Draycott Road, Cheddar BS27 3RL - 01934 707 271
FROM WELLS: Take the A371 (Weston Super Mare) through Draycott and Bowdens Park is on your left about half a mile past Cheddar Garden Centre (if you get to the church you've gone too far).
FROM WESTON: Head towards Wells on the A371 and go through the village of Cheddar. The church is on your right as you come out of the village and Bowdens Park is 200 yards past the church on your right hand side.

CORSHAM TOWN - Southbank, Lacock Road, Corsham, Wiltshire SN13 9HS 01249 715609
A4 into Corsham, at Hare and Hounds Roundabout take the Melksham Road B3353 until the War Memorial, then Lacock Road. Ground a half a mile on the right side.

CRIBBS FRIENDS LIFE - Friends Life Sports Ground, Station Road, Henbury, Bristol BS10 7TB - 0117 950 2303
From M5 J17 follow signs to Bristol West & Clifton on the A4018 dual carriageway cross two roundabouts, at 3rd roundabout take fourth exit and follow signs to M5, take 1st turning left after car dealers, ground straight ahead.

DEVIZES TOWN - Nursteed Road, Devizes, Wiltshire SN10 3DX 01380 722 817
Leave Devizes on A342 for Andover. Ground is on the right hand side opposite Eastleigh Road.

ELMORE - Horsdon Park, Heathcoat Way, Tiverton, Devon EX16 4DB 01884 252 341
Leave M5 at Junction 27. Follow A373 towards Tiverton, dual-carriageway, for approximately 7 miles. Follow signpost Tiverton and Industrial Estate, ground is 320 metres on right.

HENGROVE ATHLETIC - Norton Lane, Whitchurch, Bristol BS14 0BT 01275 832 894
Take A37 from Bristol through Whitchurch village past Maes Knoll pub, over hump bridge taking next turning on right, which is Norton Lane. Ground is immediately after Garden Centre.

KEYNSHAM TOWN - Crown Field, Bristol Road, Keynsham BS31 2DZ 0117 986 5876
On A4175 off the Bristol to Bath A4. On left immediately after 30mph sign.

OLDLAND ABBOTONIANS - Aitchison Playing Field, Castle Road, Oldland Common, Bristol BS30 9PP 0117 932 8263
Exit M4 at Jct19 to M32. Exit M32 at Jct 1after 400 yds and take 1st exit from roundabout for A4174. Straight over traffic lights to next roundabout continuing on A4174. Go over five roundabouts for approximately 4.8 miles. At next roundabout take 1st exit to Deanery Road (A420) and continue for 0.9 miles to Griffin Public house and turn right into Bath Road (A4175) . Continue for 1.3 miles to Oldland Common High Street and look for Dolphin Public House. Turning for Castle Street is next left between Chinese Chip Shop and Post Office. Ground is at the end of Castle Road.

PORTISHEAD - Bristol Road, Portishead, Bristol BS20 6QG 01275 817 600
Leave M5 at Junction 19 and take road to Portishead. At outskirts of town take 1st exit from small roundabout signposted Clevedon and Police H.Q. Ground is 150 yds along road on left by bus stop.

ROMAN GLASS ST GEORGE - Oaklands Park, Gloucester Road, Almondsbury BS32 4AG 07708 277592
Exit M5 at Junction 16. Arriving from the south take the left exit lane. Turn left at lights and ground is 100m on left hand side. Arriving from east take right hand lane on slip road. Take 3rd exit nd ground is 100m on left hand side.

SHEPTON MALLET - Playing Fields, Old Wells Road, West Shepton, Shepton Mallet BA4 5XN - 01749 344 609
From the town take B3136 (Glastonbury Road) for approximately 1/2 mile. Turn right at junction of Old Wells Road near King William Public House. Approximately 300 yards up the Old Wells Road turn left into the playing fields.

SHERBORNE TOWN - Raleigh Grove, The Terrace Playing Field, Sherborne, Dorset DT9 5NS 01935 816 110
From Yeovil take A30 - marked Sherborne. On entering town turn right at traffic lights, over next traffic lights and at the next junction turn right. Go over bridge, take second left marked 'Terrace Pling Fields'. Turn into car park, football club car park is situated in the far right-hand corner.

SHREWTON UNITED - Recreation Ground, Mill Lane, Shrewton, Wilts SP3 4JY 07786 802 688
At the mini roundabout in the village turn into High Street and then turn left at the George Inn. Follow signs to the football club, approximately 200 metres on right hand side.

WARMINSTER TOWN - Weymouth Street, Warminster, BA12 9NS - 01454 612220
A36 from Salisbury, head for town centre, turn left at traffic lights in the town centre signposted A350 Shaftesbury. Club is situated approx. 400 yards at top of Weymouth Street.

WELLINGTON - The Playing Field, North Street, Wellington, Somerset TA21 8NA 01749 679 971
Leave the M5 motorway at Junction 26 and follow directions to Wellington. At town centre traffic lights take turning into North Street. Take the next left adjacent to the Fire Station and signposted 'Car Park'. The ground is in the corner of the car park.

WELTON ROVERS - West Clewes, Nth Road, Midsomer Norton BA3 2QD 01761 412 097
The ground is on the main A362 in Midsomer Norton.

WESTBURY UNITED - Meadow Lane, Westbury, Wiltshire BA13 3AF 01373 823 409
From town centre proceed along Station Road towards rail station. At double mini roundabout turn right. Ground is 300 metres on left hand side opposite Fire Station.

ANGLIAN COMBINATION LEAGUE

Sponsored by: Gleave & Associates
Founded: 1964
Recent Champions:
2007: Blofield United
2008: Wroxham Reserves
2009: Kirby Muxloe SC
2010: Blofield United
2011: Cromer Town
angliancombination.org.uk

PREMIER DIVISION	P	W	D	L	F	A	Pts
1 Cromer Town	30	22	6	2	79	28	72
2 Acle United	30	21	7	2	84	26	70
3 Blofield United	30	19	5	6	85	45	62
4 Spixworth	30	15	8	7	55	38	53
5 Norwich St Johns	30	15	6	9	79	56	51
6 Kirkley & Pakefield Reserves	30	15	3	12	59	45	48
7 Mattishall	30	13	6	11	60	44	45
8 Loddon United	30	13	5	12	45	46	44
9 Beccles Town	30	12	7	11	50	53	43
10 Wroxham Reserves	30	13	3	14	53	54	42
11 Sheringham	30	9	7	14	40	58	34
12 St Andrews	30	8	2	20	51	76	26
13 North Walsham Town	30	7	4	19	39	81	25
14 Wymondham Town	30	5	9	16	39	58	24
15 Hempnall	30	6	5	19	41	85	23
16 Wells Town	30	5	1	24	34	100	16

DON FROST CUP

(Premier Division champions v Mummery Cup holders)

Cromer Town 1-0 Spixworth

MUMMERY CUP
(Premier and Division One Clubs)

ROUND 1
Reepham Town 3-1 Wymondham Town
Hellesdon 1-3 St Andrews
Dersingham Rovers 1-2 Beccles Town
Norwich CEYMS 1-0 Bradenham Wanderers
Sprowston Athletic 0-2 Stalham Town
Hindringham 1-1 4-5p Wells Town
Watton United 4-1 Poringland Wanderers
Blofield United 5-0 Kirkley & Pakefield Reserves
Loddon United 0-2 Mattishall
Long Stratton 2-8 Spixworth
Norwich St Johns 3-1 North Walsham Town
Horsford United 1-2 Cromer Town
Brandon Town 2-3 Acle United
Corton 2-0 Hempnall
Holt United 5-3 (aet) Wroxham Reserves
Sheringham 0-1 Caister

ROUND 2
Reepham Town 3-1 St Andrews
Beccles Town 4-0 Norwich CEYMS
Stalham Town 0-2 Wells Town
Watton United 1-2 Blofield United
Mattishall HW Spixworth
Norwich St Johns 3-1 Cromer Town
Acle United 3-2 Corton
Holt United 6-0 Caister

QUARTER FINALS
Reepham Town 5-2 Beccles Town
Wells Town 0-1 Blofield United
Mattishall 3-4 Norwich St Johns
Acle United 3-0 Holt United

SEMI-FINALS
Reepham Town 0-0 1-3p Blofield United
Norwich St Johns 1-0 Acle United

FINAL
Blofield United 3-6 Norwich St Johns

PREMIER DIVISION	1	2	3	4	5	6	7	8	9	10	11	12	13	14	15	16
1 Acle United		5-1	4-1	2-2	3-1	1-0	2-1	5-0	4-3	4-0	5-1	1-1	2-0	8-1	5-1	3-1
2 Beccles Town	0-5		1-2	0-0	1-4	2-0	2-0	1-0	0-1	4-4	1-1	1-1	7-5	4-0	1-2	2-1
3 Blofield United	1-1	5-2		3-1	11-0	3-2	5-1	1-2	3-1	4-1	4-1	1-1	5-2	3-1	1-3	1-1
4 Cromer Town	1-0	2-0	3-0		5-3	3-0	3-0	1-0	6-2	0-1	3-0	3-3	3-3	2-0	5-1	6-1
5 Hempnall	0-4	4-0	0-7	1-4		0-3	1-2	1-3	0-1	1-4	0-3	2-2	4-1	3-2	1-4	1-1
6 Kirkley & Pakefield Reserves	2-0	2-0	1-2	0-1	3-0		3-3	2-5	5-0	3-2	0-1	2-2	3-1	3-4	1-0	1-0
7 Loddon United	0-2	1-2	1-1	2-3	0-0	1-3		1-0	3-1	3-1	0-1	1-0	3-1	4-0	3-2	0-0
8 Mattishall	2-2	2-2	0-2	0-0	2-3	3-0	5-0		3-2	1-1	6-0	0-0	1-2	3-0	2-1	2-0
9 North Walsham Town	0-3	0-2	0-3	0-3	5-1	1-1	0-4	2-2		2-3	1-1	3-2	4-3	1-2	0-4	1-0
10 Norwich St Johns	0-0	0-2	6-1	0-2	2-1	2-5	1-0	4-1	7-1		1-1	2-4	4-3	5-0	3-2	2-2
11 Sheringham	0-1	2-1	1-1	1-2	4-3	1-4	1-2	2-1	1-2	3-3		0-2	1-1	1-0	2-0	3-1
12 Spixworth	2-2	0-1	1-2	0-2	2-1	3-1	2-3	2-1	2-0	3-2	3-1		1-0	3-0	0-2	2-0
13 St Andrews	0-1	1-2	3-2	2-4	0-1	0-1	1-3	1-4	4-3	0-4	1-0	1-4		4-1	1-2	4-1
14 Wells Town	1-5	0-5	2-5	1-3	3-3	1-3	0-1	2-4	1-0	1-8	3-1	2-3	3-1		2-3	0-3
15 Wroxham Reserves	2-2	2-2	1-3	0-4	1-1	3-1	2-1	1-3	6-0	0-2	3-2	1-2	1-2	2-0		W-L
16 Wymondham Town	1-2	1-1	1-2	2-2	2-0	0-4	1-1	3-2	2-2	2-4	3-3	0-2	1-3	6-1	2-1	

ANGLIAN COMBINATION PREMIER DIVISION CONSTITUTION 2012-13

ACLE UNITED	Bridewell Lane, Acle, Norwich NR13 3RA	01493 752989
BECCLES TOWN	College Meadow, Common Lane, Beccles NR34 7FA	07729 782817
BLOFIELD UNITED	Old Yarmouth Road, Blofield, Norwich NR13 4LE	07748 863203
CROMER TOWN	Cabbell Park, Mill Road, Cromer NR27 0AD	07940 092131
DERSINGHAM ROVERS	Behind Feathers Hotel, Manor Road, Dersingham, King's Lynn PE31 6LN	01485 542707
HEMPNALL	Bungay Road, Hempnall, Norwich NR15 2NG	01508 498086
KIRKLEY & PAKEFIELD RESERVES	Kirkley & Pakefield Comm Cnte, Walmer Road, Lowestoft NR33 7LE	01502 513549
LODDON UNITED	George Lane Playing Field, Loddon, Norwich NR14 6NB	01508 528497
MATTISHALL	Mattishall Playing Fields, South Green, Mattishall, Norwich NR20 3JY	01362 850246
NORTH WALSHAM TOWN	Sports Centre, Greens Road, North Walsham NR28 0HW	01692 406888
SHERINGHAM	Recreation Ground, Weybourne Road, Sheringham NR26 8WD	01263 824804
SPIXWORTH	Spixworth Village Hall, Crostick Lane, Spixworth, Norwich NR10 3NQ	01603 898092
ST ANDREWS	Thorpe Recreation Ground, Laundry Lane, Thorpe St Andrew, Norwich NR7 0XQ	01603 300316
WROXHAM RESERVES	Trafford Park, Skinners Lane, Wroxham NR12 8SJ	01603 783538
WYMONDHAM TOWN	Kings Head Meadow, Back Lane, Wymondham NR18 0LB	01953 607326

DIVISION ONE

		P	W	D	L	F	A	Pts
1	Dersingham Rovers	30	18	5	7	63	45	59
2	Reepham Town	30	18	3	9	60	38	57
3	Stalham Town	30	17	5	8	71	46	56
4	Long Stratton	30	17	4	9	80	46	55
5	Poringland Wanderers	30	14	6	10	59	46	48
6	Horsford United	30	15	3	12	61	62	48
7	Caister	30	12	5	13	73	67	41
8	Hellesdon	30	11	7	12	55	64	40
9	Hindringham	30	11	5	14	62	74	38
10	Norwich CEYMS	30	10	6	14	59	52	36
11	Bradenham Wanderers	30	10	6	14	52	57	36
12	Brandon Town	30	11	3	16	51	74	36
13	Corton	30	9	7	14	40	55	34
14	Holt United	30	9	6	15	58	74	33
15	Watton United	30	9	5	16	61	80	32
16 (R)	Sprowston Athletic	30	9	4	17	39	64	31

DIVISION TWO

		P	W	D	L	F	A	Pts
1	Harleston Town	28	21	0	7	103	39	63
2	Aylsham	28	18	4	6	46	29	58
3	Thetford Rovers	28	16	5	7	69	36	53
4	Mundford	28	16	4	8	70	40	52
5	Bungay Town	28	14	6	8	48	41	48
6	East Harling	28	15	3	10	60	59	48
7	Acle United Reserves	28	12	9	7	51	39	45
8	Attleborough Town	28	13	4	11	60	44	43
9	Scole United	28	13	3	12	75	52	42
10	Foulsham	28	12	6	10	65	55	42
11	Downham Town Reserves	28	7	4	17	27	60	25
12	Sprowston Wanderers	28	7	3	18	46	86	24
13	Beccles Caxton	28	7	0	21	50	91	21
14	Hempnall Reserves	28	4	7	17	24	69	19
15	Thorpe Village	28	5	2	21	21	75	17

CYRIL BALLYN TROPHY
(Division Two, Three, Four, Five and Six first teams and external league reserve sides)

ROUND 1
Redgrave Rangers 6-2 Martham
Hemsby 3-1 (aet) Waveney
Saham Toney 1-0 Downham Town Reserves
Southwold Town 6-1 Fakenham Town Reserves
Freethorpe 0-1 Hingham Athletic

ROUND 2
UEA 9-2 Foulsham
Buxton 2-5 East Harling
Mulbarton Wanderers 5-1 Attleborough Town
Aylsham 1-0 Acle United Reserves
Redgrave Rangers 4-0 Hempnall Reserves
Newton Flotman 0-3 Bungay Town
CNSOBU 7-1 Hemsby
Hoveton Wherrymen 5-6 (aet) Thorpe Village
South Walsham 4-3 Swaffham Town Reserves
Yelverton 0-7 Harleston Town
Sprowston Wanderers 1-3 Beccles Caxton
Mundford 4-2 Saham Toney
Marlingford 1-1 4-5p Southwold Town 1
Easton 1-4 Scole United
Thetford Rovers 6-0 Hingham Athletic
Thorpe Rovers 0-4 Costessey Sports

ROUND 3
UEA 1-0 East Harling
Mulbarton Wanderers 1-0 Aylsham
Redgrave Rangers 3-1 Bungay Town
CNSOBU 5-1 Thorpe Village
South Walsham 1-5 Harleston Town
Beccles Caxton 2-4 (aet) Mundford
Southwold Town 0-5 Scole United
Thetford Rovers 4-2 Costessey Sports

QUARTER FINALS
UEA 4-3 (aet) Mulbarton Wanderers
Redgrave Rangers 2-1 CNSOBU
Harleston Town 1-2 Mundford
Scole United 4-2 (aet) Thetford Rovers

SEMI-FINALS
UEA 3-2 Redgrave Rangers
Mundford 3-1 (aet) Scole United

Final
UEA 1-0 Mundford 0

DIVISION ONE	1	2	3	4	5	6	7	8	9	10	11	12	13	14	15	16
1 Bradenham Wanderers		2-1	6-0	1-1	1-5	1-1	0-2	3-1	1-2	2-3	3-0	3-2	1-1	3-2	2-4	2-3
2 Brandon Town	0-1		0-5	4-1	0-1	0-1	4-2	6-4	3-2	3-2	2-2	2-0	4-0	3-1	1-2	0-7
3 Caister	6-3	1-1		0-2	3-4	6-2	3-4	3-1	1-1	1-4	3-2	2-1	3-5	5-2	4-0	5-5
4 Corton	0-4	2-4	1-1		3-2	1-4	4-1	0-0	0-1	2-1	1-1	0-1	2-1	0-0	2-1	2-3
5 Dersingham Rovers	2-0	2-4	3-1	2-3		1-1	2-1	1-0	4-1	3-2	4-2	1-1	1-0	2-0	0-5	2-1
6 Hellesdon	4-2	1-1	2-0	3-0	3-5		2-3	1-1	2-3	0-5	1-4	0-5	2-5	1-0	3-3	4-2
7 Hindringham	1-1	6-2	0-2	1-2	1-4	3-0		1-3	2-4	1-1	3-1	3-2	1-2	1-2	3-1	6-4
8 Holt United	2-1	2-3	2-6	1-1	0-0	0-3	1-2		10-4	5-4	2-4	4-1	1-3	1-0	1-5	1-2
9 Horsford United	0-1	5-1	1-0	2-1	1-3	2-0	6-1	1-5		2-1	2-1	2-1	0-2	1-0	2-4	6-3
10 Long Stratton	2-0	2-0	5-3	4-1	2-2	2-0	8-2	5-1	1-1		2-1	2-3	3-0	3-3	4-0	2-1
11 Norwich CEYMS	2-2	2-0	2-2	2-1	0-2	1-3	1-1	4-1	1-2	0-1		1-2	4-0	5-1	1-4	5-1
12 Poringland Wanderers	0-0	6-1	3-0	2-0	3-2	0-0	2-2	1-3	3-3	3-1	2-6		0-2	4-1	2-0	0-0
13 Reepham Town	4-0	4-0	2-1	1-1	4-0	2-2	1-2	5-0	1-0	1-0	1-0	1-2		1-0	4-2	2-1
14 Sprowston Athletic	2-1	3-0	1-3	2-1	0-2	2-5	3-2	2-2	4-1	0-2	1-0	0-3	1-3		2-1	2-1
15 Stalham Town	2-1	3-0	0-3	5-0	0-0	3-1	4-2	0-0	3-2	3-1	1-1	3-1	1-0	5-0		1-1
16 Watton United	2-4	2-1	2-0	0-5	2-1	1-3	2-2	2-3	2-1	2-5	1-3	1-3	3-2	2-2	2-5	

ANGLIAN COMBINATION DIVISION ONE CONSTITUTION 2012-13

AYLSHAM	Sir Williams Lane, Aylsham, Norwich NR11 6AN	07777 661117
BRADENHAM WANDERERS	Hale Road, Bradenham, Thetford IP25 7RA	01603 880109
BRANDON TOWN	Remembrance Playing Field, Church Road, Brandon IP27 0JB	01842 813177
CAISTER	Caister Playing Fields, off Allendale Road, Caister-on-Sea NR30 5ES	07852 212210
CORTON	The Street, Corton, Lowestoft NR32 5HE	None
HARLESTON TOWN	Rec & Memorial Leisure Centre, Wilderness Lane, Harleston IP20 9DD	01379 854519
HELLESDON	Hellesdon Community Centre, Wood View Road, Hellesdon, Norwich NR6 5QB	01603 427675
HINDRINGHAM	Sports & Social Club, Wells Rd, Hindringham, Fakenham NR21 0PN	01328 878608
HOLT UNITED	Sports Centre, Kelling Road, Holt NR25 7DU	01263 711217
HORSFORD UNITED	Village Hall, Holt Road, Horsford NR10 3DN	01603 893317
LONG STRATTON	Manor Road Playing Fields, Long Stratton, Norwich NR15 2XR	07806 792840
NORWICH CEYMS	Hilltops Sports Centre, Main Road, Swardeston, Norwich NR14 8DU	01508 578826
PORINGLAND WANDERERS	Poringland Memorial Field, The Footpath, Poringland, Norwich NR14 7RF	01508 495198
STALHAM TOWN	Rivers Park, Stepping Stone Lane, Stalham, Norwich NR12 9EP	07818 418677
WATTON UNITED	Watton Playing Field, Dereham Road, Watton, Thetford IP25 6EZ	01953 881281
WELLS TOWN	Beach Road, Wells-next-the-Sea NR23 1DR	01328 710907

DIVISION TWO	1	2	3	4	5	6	7	8	9	10	11	12	13	14	15
1 Acle United Reserves		1-3	0-2	1-0	1-4	2-0	2-1	2-2	2-4	1-1	1-2	5-3	1-1	0-2	0-0
2 Attleborough Town	0-1		1-0	8-1	3-0	5-0	1-3	0-1	0-2	1-0	2-2	2-3	3-2	2-2	4-0
3 Aylsham	2-2	2-0		4-1	0-0	2-0	1-0	2-1	2-1	5-0	0-3	1-1	1-0	2-1	3-0
4 Beccles Caxton	1-8	0-5	1-2		1-3	4-2	1-4	3-5	2-7	6-0	1-0	4-1	1-2	0-2	0-4
5 Bungay Town	1-5	2-2	0-1	2-0		1-1	1-0	3-2	2-1	4-0	2-1	1-0	4-0	2-2	2-0
6 Downham Town Reserves	0-0	0-2	0-1	1-6	1-0		0-1	2-1	1-5	0-0	0-2	2-2	3-2	0-3	1-0
7 East Harling	1-1	4-1	4-2	0-4	4-1	2-0		3-3	1-5	2-1	2-1	4-3	5-2	2-1	3-1
8 Foulsham	0-3	0-4	2-2	4-2	1-4	0-1	6-2		3-1	7-1	1-2	4-3	1-1	3-1	2-0
9 Harleston Town	4-1	5-2	1-2	5-2	4-0	6-1	4-1	5-2		6-0	8-2	3-2	5-1	3-2	4-0
10 Hempnall Reserves	0-0	1-1	1-2	3-0	1-1	0-4	2-1	1-1	2-1		1-2	0-3	0-1	1-1	1-2
11 Mundford	2-4	3-0	3-0	8-0	3-0	2-0	1-2	3-3	3-2	2-1		2-1	5-0	0-1	7-0
12 Scole United	0-1	3-2	4-1	3-0	1-1	3-2	5-1	1-2	1-2	7-2	1-3		7-0	2-0	6-2
13 Sprowston Wanderers	1-3	6-1	1-3	1-7	0-2	3-2	3-4	1-2	1-4	2-1	3-3	1-5		2-4	5-0
14 Thetford Rovers	2-2	0-2	1-0	5-2	3-4	5-1	4-1	1-0	1-0	6-0	2-2	3-0	8-2		3-1
15 Thorpe Village	0-1	0-3	0-1	1-0	3-1	0-2	2-2	1-6	0-5	0-3	2-1	1-4	1-2	0-3	

ANGLIAN COMBINATION DIVISION TWO CONSTITUTION 2012-13

ACLE UNITED RESERVES	Bridewell Lane, Acle, Norwich NR13 3RA	01493 752989
ATTLEBOROUGH TOWN	Recreation Ground, Station Road, Attleborough NR17 2AS	01953 455365
BECCLES CAXTON	Caxton Meadow, Adj. Beccles Station, Beccles NR34 9QH	01502 712829
BUNGAY TOWN	Maltings Meadow, Ditchingham, Bungay NR35 2RU	01986 894028
DOWNHAM TOWN RESERVES	Memorial Playing Field, Lynn Road, Downham Market PE38 9QE	01366 388424
EAST HARLING	Memorial Fields, Church Street, East Harling NR16 2NA	01953 718251
FOULSHAM	Playing Field, Guist Road, Foulsham, Dereham NR20 5RZ	07981 341810
HEMPNALL RESERVES	Bungay Road, Hempnall, Norwich NR15 2NG	01508 498086
HEMSBY	Walters Lane, Hemsby NR29 4LE	01493 733543
MARTHAM	Coronation Recreation Ground, Rollesby Road, Martham, Great Yarmouth NR29 4SP	01493 740252
MUNDFORD	The Glebe, Mundford, Thetford IP26 5EJ	01842 878339
SCOLE UNITED	Ransome Avenue Playing Field, Scole, Diss IP21 4EA	01379 741204
SPROWSTON ATHLETIC	Sprowston Sports & Social Club, Blue Boar Lane, Sprowston, Norwich NR7 8RJ	01603 427688
SPROWSTON WANDERERS	Sprowston Cricket Club, Barkers Lane, Sprowston, Norwich NR7 8QZ	01603 404042
THETFORD ROVERS	Euston Park, Euston, Thetford IP24 2QP	None

DIVISION THREE

		P	W	D	L	F	A	Pts
1	Martham	28	19	6	3	73	36	63
2	Hemsby	28	18	3	7	60	35	57
3	UEA	28	18	2	8	102	39	56
4	Cromer Town Reserves	28	18	2	8	74	50	56
5	Easton	28	13	8	7	68	53	47
6	Marlingford (-1)	28	15	2	11	58	53	46
7	Freethorpe	28	13	6	9	74	45	45
8	Loddon United Reserves	28	12	8	8	52	55	44
9	Swaffham Town Reserves	28	13	3	12	59	48	42
10	Southwold Town	28	10	6	12	51	55	36
11	Costessey Sports	28	7	7	14	57	79	28
12	Blofield United Reserves	28	8	3	17	50	88	27
13	North Walsham Town Reserves	28	7	3	18	40	73	24
14	Wymondham Town Reserves	28	4	3	21	35	80	15
15	(R) Sprowston Athletic Reserves	28	4	0	24	33	97	12

DIVISION FOUR

		P	W	D	L	F	A	Pts
1	Mulbarton Wanderers	28	22	5	1	98	28	71
2	Hoveton Wherrymen	28	22	2	4	83	30	68
3	Sheringham Reserves	28	20	5	3	90	31	65
4	Caister Reserves	28	16	4	8	63	36	52
5	Waveney	28	16	3	9	74	54	51
6	South Walsham (-1)	28	16	2	10	86	48	49
7	Redgrave Rangers	28	14	3	11	58	41	45
8	St Andrews Reserves	28	13	3	12	49	61	42
9	Fakenham Town Reserves (-3)	28	10	4	14	64	55	31
10	Mattishall Reserves	28	8	2	18	52	93	26
11	Newton Flotman	28	7	5	16	34	83	26
12	Bungay Town Reserves	28	6	5	17	35	85	23
13	Long Stratton Reserves	28	5	6	17	35	66	21
14	Beccles Town Reserves	28	6	2	20	31	73	20
15	Thorpe Rovers	28	3	1	24	29	97	10

DIVISION FIVE

		P	W	D	L	F	A	Pts
1	Saham Toney	26	23	2	1	76	24	71
2	Norwich CEYMS Res. (-1)	26	18	2	6	65	28	55
3	Corton Reserves	26	16	4	6	69	38	52
4	Bradenham Wanderers Res.	26	16	3	7	55	32	51
5	Watton United Reserves	26	14	4	8	69	41	46
6	Attleborough Town Reserves	26	12	2	12	57	54	38
7	Holt United Reserves	26	10	5	11	58	53	35
8	Buxton	26	10	2	14	54	64	32
9	Aylsham Reserves (-1)	26	9	5	12	53	53	31
10	Hindringham Reserves	26	9	3	14	60	90	30
11	Poringland Wanderers Reserves	26	7	5	14	51	67	26
12	Mundford Reserves	26	7	3	16	30	65	24
13	Wells Town Reserves (-2)	26	6	2	18	36	79	18
14	Reepham Town Reserves (-1)	26	3	2	21	33	78	10

DIVISION SIX

		P	W	D	L	F	A	Pts
1	Yelverton	26	20	2	4	96	36	62
2	Stalham Town Reserves	26	20	1	5	87	40	61
3	Horsford United Reserves	26	18	3	5	76	44	57
4	Easton Reserves	26	17	2	7	95	47	53
5	Scole United Reserves	26	15	4	7	71	47	49
6	CNSOBU (-1)	26	15	2	9	80	44	46
7	Hingham Athletic	26	12	5	9	84	49	41
8	Brandon Town Reserves	26	10	3	13	64	100	33
9	Foulsham Reserves (-1)	26	10	1	15	76	83	30
10	Thorpe Village Reserves (-1)	26	9	4	13	44	61	30
11	East Harling Reserves	26	8	3	15	48	64	27
12	Martham Reserves	26	4	4	18	29	110	16
13	Freethorpe Reserves	26	3	2	21	39	96	11
14	Hemsby Reserves	26	2	2	22	38	106	8

CS MORLEY CUP
(Anglian Combination reserve teams)

Final
Stalham Town Reserves 1-2 North Walsham Town Reserves

DIVISION THREE	1	2	3	4	5	6	7	8	9	10	11	12	13	14	15
1 Blofield United Reserves		2-1	1-5	0-4	2-2	4-2	2-4	1-2	0-4	2-2	4-1	2-1	1-6	0-6	3-4
2 Costessey Sports	1-1		2-2	2-2	0-5	1-4	3-1	1-3	3-4	3-1	2-3	6-1	3-1	3-2	7-4
3 Cromer Town Reserves	3-1	3-2		4-0	5-1	3-4	2-4	2-1	L-W	5-3	2-1	1-3	3-0	0-6	2-4
4 Easton	1-0	1-0	1-1		2-1	0-1	2-2	9-2	2-4	7-0	4-4	3-2	3-3	3-9	1-0
5 Freethorpe	6-1	9-3	3-2	4-1		0-2	2-2	2-3	1-1	2-1	3-2	12-0	3-2	1-1	2-0
6 Hemsby	4-0	1-1	0-2	2-2	0-0		1-2	0-2	1-3	4-1	2-1	1-0	3-2	1-0	4-0
7 Loddon United Reserves	2-4	3-3	0-5	2-0	1-0	0-1		0-0	1-2	2-2	2-1	2-0	2-1	1-8	1-3
8 Marlingford	1-0	2-0	2-5	1-5	2-0	1-4	1-2		3-2	5-4	0-3	4-0	3-2	1-2	6-0
9 Martham	4-2	4-0	1-3	3-3	1-1	3-1	2-2	2-2		3-0	2-0	5-3	2-1	3-2	2-0
10 North Walsham Town Reserves	5-0	2-2	2-3	1-2	1-2	1-2	0-6	3-1	0-2		1-3	2-0	2-3	0-4	1-0
11 Southwold Town	5-1	3-2	0-1	1-1	2-1	1-2	1-1	1-2	2-2	3-0		2-1	1-1	2-7	4-0
12 Sprowston Athletic Reserves	3-7	2-5	2-3	0-2	1-6	0-5	1-4	0-3	1-5	1-2	3-0		0-1	0-2	4-1
13 Swaffham Town Reserves	2-3	7-0	2-1	1-0	3-2	2-1	0-1	0-4	1-0	0-1	1-1	6-0		5-1	3-1
14 UEA	6-1	6-1	3-4	2-3	2-0	1-3	6-0	W-L	1-2	5-0	7-0	4-1	5-1		2-2
15 Wymondham Town Reserves	1-5	0-0	1-2	1-4	2-3	2-4	2-2	3-1	0-5	1-2	0-3	1-3	1-2	1-2	

ANGLIAN COMBINATION DIVISION THREE CONSTITUTION 2012-13

BLOFIELD UNITED RESERVES	Old Yarmouth Road, Blofield, Norwich NR13 4LE	07748 863203
COTESSEY SPORTS		
CROMER TOWN RESERVES	Cabbell Park, Mill Road, Cromer NR27 0AD	07940 092131
EASTON	Easton College, Bawburgh Road, Norwich NR9 5DX	01603 731208
FREETHORPE	School Road, Freethorpe, Norwich NR13 3NZ	01493 701533
HOVETON WHERRYMEN	Playing Field, Stalham Road, Hoveton, Wroxham NR12 8DG	07826 544378
LODDON UNITED RESERVES	George Lane Playing Field, Loddon, Norwich NR14 6NB	01508 528497
MARLINGFORD	Bayer Social Club, Marlpit Lane, Norwich NR5 8YT	01603 787661
MULBARTON WANDERERS	Mulberry Park, Mulbarton NR14 8AE	07979 728821
NORTH WALSHAM TOWN RESERVES	Sports Centre, Greens Road, North Walsham NR28 0HW	01692 406888
SOUTHWOLD TOWN	York Road, Southwold, Suffolk IP18 6A	07917 631969
SWAFFHAM TOWN RESERVES	Shoemakers Lane, off Cley Road, Swaffham PE37 7NT	01760 722700
THORPE VILLAGE	Thorpe Recreation Ground, Laundry Lane, Thorpe St Andrew, Norwich NR7 0XQ	01603 300316
UEA	UEA Sports Ground, Colney Lane, Norwich NR4 7RG	None
WYMONDHAM TOWN RESERVES	Kings Head Meadow, Back Lane, Wymondham NR18 0LB	01953 607326

DIVISION FOUR	1	2	3	4	5	6	7	8	9	10	11	12	13	14	15
1 Beccles Town reserves		2-2	0-1	0-6	0-3	1-0	0-1	1-5	1-0	0-1	2-6	1-5	1-3	2-3	3-0
2 Bungay Town Reserves	0-3		0-2	0-6	0-4	3-2	4-5	3-5	4-2	2-5	0-2	W-L	0-1	4-2	1-4
3 Caister Reserves	0-1	0-0		3-3	1-3	3-1	5-0	0-1	7-0	1-1	2-2	2-0	2-0	3-2	4-0
4 Fakenham Town Reserves	4-1	2-2	0-6		L-W	2-0	1-3	2-4	1-1	0-1	1-4	L-W	5-0	5-2	3-0
5 Hoveton Wherrymen	3-2	5-1	1-2	5-2		1-0	6-1	2-2	5-0	2-1	4-1	4-2	8-2	5-0	3-1
6 Long Stratton Reserves	1-1	3-1	0-1	3-3	2-4		6-0	2-7	1-2	0-3	2-0	1-1	2-2	1-0	0-3
7 Mattishall Reserves	0-5	1-3	6-1	1-2	1-3	1-1		0-6	6-0	1-7	1-2	2-3	4-3	8-0	0-6
8 Mulbarton Wanderers	3-0	1-1	2-1	4-1	3-0	2-0	5-1		1-1	2-0	1-1	6-1	5-1	6-0	4-4
9 Newton Flotman	2-1	2-0	2-5	W-L	0-1	4-0	1-0	0-4		1-1	1-1	1-6	2-2	1-3	2-5
10 Redgrave Rangers	2-0	0-3	3-1	3-2	0-1	4-0	6-0	0-3	5-0		3-3	0-2	1-2	2-1	2-3
11 Sheringham Reserves	11-2	7-0	2-1	2-1	0-0	5-2	7-1	3-1	5-0	3-1		3-2	4-0	3-1	0-1
12 South Walsham	4-0	7-0	0-1	5-2	4-3	6-0	6-2	2-3	7-1	1-2	0-4		1-2	5-3	5-1
13 St Andrews Reserves	3-1	4-1	0-1	5-2	2-1	0-0	3-1	0-3	5-1	2-1	0-3	1-4		4-0	2-1
14 Thorpe Rovers	1-0	0-0	3-6	1-3	0-1	1-2	0-4	0-4	2-6	1-2	1-4	0-4	1-4		1-5
15 Waveney	3-0	8-0	3-1	3-2	0-5	5-3	1-1	1-5	4-1	4-1	0-2	3-3	2-0	3-0	

ANGLIAN COMBINATION DIVISION FOUR CONSTITUTION 2012-13

BECCLES TOWN RESERVES	College Meadow, Common Lane, Beccles NR34 7FA	07729 782817
BUNGAY TOWN RESERVES	Maltings Meadow, Ditchingham, Bungay NR35 2RU	01986 894028
CAISTER RESERVES	Caister Playing Fields, off Allendale Road, Caister-on-Sea NR30 5ES	None
FAKENHAM TOWN RESERVES	Clipbush Park, Clipbush Lane, Fakenham NR21 8SW	01328 855445 Club:01328 855859
LONG STRATTON RESERVES	Manor Road Playing Fields, Long Stratton, Norwich NR15 2XR	None
MATTISHALL RESERVES	Mattishall Playing Fields, South Green, Mattishall, Norwich NR20 3JY	01362 850246
NEWTON FLOTMAN	Newton Flotman Village Centre, Grove Way, Newton Flotman, Norwich NR15 1PU	None
NORWICH CEYMS RESERVES	Hilltops Sports Centre, Main Road, Swardeston, Norwich NR14 8DU	01508 578826
REDGRAVE RANGERS	Redgrave Sports Field, Church Way, Redgrave, Diss IP22 1RL	None
SAHAM TONEY	Pages Lane, Saham Toney, Thetford IP25 7H	07590 335600
SHERINGHAM RESERVES	Recreation Ground, Weybourne Road, Sheringham NR26 8WD	01263 824804
SOUTH WALSHAM	The Playing Field, South Walsham	None
SPROWSTON ATHLETIC RESERVES	Sprowston Sports & Social Club, Blue Boar Lane, Sprowston, Norwich NR7 8RJ	01603 427688
ST ANDREWS RESERVES	Thorpe Recreation Ground, Laundry Lane, Thorpe St Andrew, Norwich NR7 0XQ	01603 300316
WAVENEY	Denes Community Centre, Yarmouth Road, Lowestoft NR32 4AH	None

BEDFORDSHIRE COUNTY LEAGUE

Sponsored by: No sponsor
Founded: 1904
Recent Champions:
2007: Westoning Recreation Club
2008: Campton
2009: Caldecote
2010: Blunham
2011: Blunham
bedfordshirefootballleague.co.uk

BRITANNIA CUP

ROUND 1
Oakley Sports M&DH 6-2 Sharnbrook
Blunham 1-5 Bedford Hatters
AFC Kempston Town & Bedfo 4-2 Dunton
Wilshamstead 0-2 Caldecote
Shefford Town & Campton 9-1 Arlesey Town Reserves
Potton Wanderers AW Woburn Athletic

QUARTER FINALS
Oakley Sports M&DH 4-1 Bedford Hatters
AFC Kempston Town & Bedfo 2-2 5-4p Renhold United
Caldecote 4-5 Shefford Town & Campton
Woburn Athletic 4-3 (aet) Flitwick Town

SEMI-FINALS
Oakley Sports M&DH 3-0 AFC Kempston Town & Bedfo
Shefford Town & Campton 7-2 Woburn Athletic

FINAL
Oakley Sports M&DH 1-0 Shefford Town & Campton

PREMIER DIVISION	P	W	D	L	F	A	Pts
1 Shefford Town & Campton	24	21	1	2	89	24	64
2 Caldecote	23	18	2	3	78	31	56
3 Bedford Hatters	24	16	3	5	60	40	51
4 Renhold United	24	12	3	9	58	39	39
5 Oakley Sports M&DH	24	10	7	7	57	39	37
6 Wilshamstead	24	10	6	8	53	51	36
7 Arlesey Town Reserves	24	9	3	12	38	44	30
8 Blunham	24	9	3	12	45	54	30
9 Sharnbrook	24	8	4	12	32	61	28
10 AFC Kempston Town & Bedford Col.	24	6	5	13	43	64	23
11 Flitwick Town	24	6	4	14	35	55	22
12 Dunton	24	4	3	17	29	64	15
13 Woburn Athletic	23	3	2	18	32	83	11

DIVISION ONE	P	W	D	L	F	A	Pts
1 Ickwell & Old Warden	26	21	4	1	94	27	67
2 Bedford SA	26	19	4	3	86	39	61
3 Marston Shelton Rovers	26	15	7	4	57	30	52
4 Lidlington United Sports	26	14	7	5	66	37	49
5 FC Meppershall	26	14	5	7	72	43	47
6 Sandy	26	13	5	8	80	56	44
7 Caldecote Reserves	26	11	3	12	62	65	36
8 Lea Sports PSG	26	7	12	7	48	40	33
9 Henlow	26	9	5	12	49	61	32
10 Luton Boys	26	8	5	13	70	80	29
11 AFC Kempston Tn & Bedf Coll Res	26	7	3	16	36	68	24
12 Kings	26	4	5	17	49	96	17
13 Meltis Albion	26	3	3	20	22	103	12
14 Westoning	26	2	2	22	32	78	8

DIVISION TWO	P	W	D	L	F	A	Pts
1 Elstow Abbey	26	21	4	1	95	20	67
2 AFC Turvey	26	19	3	4	84	33	60
3 Pavenham	26	16	3	7	73	35	51
4 Shefford Town & Campton Res.	26	14	4	8	59	52	46
5 Sundon Park Rangers (Saturday)	26	13	6	7	81	53	45
6 Bromham United	26	13	3	10	58	46	42
7 Co-op Sports	26	12	3	11	67	55	39
8 Potton United Reserves	26	11	3	12	55	59	36
9 Queens Park Crescents	26	9	7	10	55	63	34
10 Marabese Ceramics	26	8	4	14	43	62	28
11 Stopsley Park	26	8	4	14	57	77	28
12 M & DH Oakley	26	7	0	19	35	70	21
13 Clifton	26	5	3	18	31	71	18
14 Great Barford	26	2	1	23	16	113	7

PREMIER DIVISION	1	2	3	4	5	6	7	8	9	10	11	12	13
1 AFC Kempston Town & Bedford College		1-4	3-3	3-2	1-2	4-0	2-3	0-6	1-5	1-2	1-3	2-4	3-0
2 Arlesey Town Reserves	2-1		1-2	HW	1-2	4-1	2-1	1-1	2-4	0-0	0-2	2-3	1-2
3 Bedford Hatters	2-2	3-0		7-2	1-5	1-0	3-0	3-1	0-3	3-1	4-3	AW	2-0
4 Blunham	1-4	6-2	2-3		0-4	1-0	4-2	4-0	2-1	3-1	1-3	4-1	3-1
5 Caldecote	7-0	2-0	3-0	4-0		4-1	4-1	4-2	1-0	6-2	1-4	5-3	5-2
6 Dunton	4-1	1-3	0-2	3-4	2-0		0-0	2-4	1-6	2-1	1-6	0-0	1-3
7 Flitwick Town	0-1	HW	1-4	1-0	3-7	3-2		2-2	1-2	1-2	1-4	2-3	4-1
8 Oakley Sports M&DH	1-1	0-1	2-4	4-1	2-2	6-0	2-2		0-1	2-1	2-1	0-0	HW
9 Renhold United	3-3	2-1	1-2	0-0	4-2	2-1	1-1	0-4		6-0	2-3	2-4	5-1
10 Sharnbrook	2-1	1-2	3-3	HW	0-5	1-1	1-0	3-7	0-5		AW	2-2	3-2
11 Shefford Town & Campton	4-1	5-3	5-1	7-2	1-1	3-0	3-0	3-1	1-0	6-0		2-1	8-0
12 Wilshamstead	2-2	1-3	0-2	2-2	1-2	3-2	5-2	2-2	4-1	1-3	0-7		6-1
13 Woburn Athletic	2-4	3-3	2-5	1-1		2-4	0-4	1-6	4-2	2-3	1-5	1-5	

BEDFORDSHIRE COUNTY PREMIER DIVISION CONSTITUTION 2012-13

AFC BIGGLESWADE	Biggleswade Town FC Biggleswade, Bedfordshire SG18 9JT	Tel: 07811197191
AFC KEMPSTON & BEDFORD COLL.	Hillgrounds Road, Kempston, Bedford MK42 8SZ	01234 852346
ARLESEY TOWN RESERVES	Hitchin Road, Arlesey SG15 6RS	01462 734504
		Boardroom: 01462 734512
BEDFORD HATTERS	Meltis Sports & Social Club, 12 Miller Road, Bedford MK42 9NY	01234 352872
BEDFORD SA	Grane Lane, Cople, Bedfordshire MK44 3T	07919 898106
BLUNHAM	The Playing Fields, Blunham Road, Moggerhanger, Sandy MK44 3RG	07813 305238
CALDECOTE	Harvey Close, Upper Caldecote, Biggleswade SG18 9BQ	01767 600236
FLITWICK TOWN	Flitwick Leisure Centre, Flitwick, Bedford MK45 1TH	01462 611575
ICKWELL & OLD WARDEN	Ickwell Green, Ickwell, Bedfordshire SG18 9E	01767 627747
LEIGHTON UNITED SPORTS	Stanbridge Road, Tilsworth LU7 9PL	01525 211792
MARSTON SHELTON ROVERS	Bedford Road, Marston Moretaine, Bedford MK43 0L	01234 765579
OAKLEY SPORTS M&DH	Oakley Village Sports Centre, Oakley, Bedford MK43 7RG	07872 532890
RENHOLD UNITED	Renhold Playing Fields, Renhold, Bedford MK41 0LR	01234 871178
SHARNBROOK	Playing Fields, Lodge Road, Sharnbrook MK44 1JP	07774 612293
SHEFFORD TOWN & CAMPTON	STMA Digswell, Hitchin Road, Shefford SG17 5JA	01462 813377
WILSHAMSTEAD	Jubilee Playing Fields, Bedford Road, Wilshamstead MK45 3HN	01234 740165

DIVISION ONE

		1	2	3	4	5	6	7	8	9	10	11	12	13	14
1	AFC Kempston Town & BC Reserves		0-2	2-2	0-1	1-0	0-1	W-L	1-5	2-2	3-2	2-3	0-2	1-3	2-1
2	Bedford SA	8-2		5-1	3-2	3-1	0-3	5-1	2-1	3-4	4-1	2-0	5-1	1-2	1-0
3	Caldecote Reserves	5-1	1-4		W-L	1-0	0-2	6-3	1-1	3-0	8-1	2-5	3-4	0-2	5-3
4	FC Meppershall	1-3	1-4	5-1		0-1	4-4	3-1	1-1	2-0	4-2	1-1	11-0	7-5	4-1
5	Henlow	1-0	1-5	4-2	1-5		1-3	5-5	3-3	0-3	4-3	1-2	2-2	1-2	5-1
6	Ickwell & Old Warden	3-2	3-3	2-0	2-1	6-1		6-1	1-1	6-0	7-1	1-0	7-0	4-1	5-0
7	Kings	2-4	3-10	2-5	0-3	0-2	0-5		2-2	0-2	5-5	2-4	3-0	1-4	2-1
8	Lea Sports PSG	3-3	2-4	2-2	2-4	0-2	0-3	2-2		1-2	2-2	1-1	4-0	1-1	2-0
9	Lidlington United Sports	3-0	1-1	3-0	0-1	3-1	2-2	7-2	1-1		3-1	0-0	7-0	6-3	4-1
10	Luton Boys	5-0	1-2	6-1	4-4	2-2	4-3	7-2	0-3	1-5		0-4	2-2	3-4	2-0
11	Marston Shelton Rovers	7-1	1-1	1-2	2-2	2-2	1-2	6-1	W-L	2-0	4-3		3-1	2-1	W-L
12	Meltis Albion	0-5	1-1	0-4	0-1	0-3	0-7	0-3	0-4	1-5	L-W	1-4		1-7	0-2
13	Sandy	2-0	4-5	4-2	4-1	4-1	2-3	1-1	1-2	2-2	4-6	1-1	9-0		4-4
14	Westoning	4-1	1-2	3-5	1-3	3-4	2-3	1-5	1-2	1-1	0-6	0-1	1-6	0-3	

DIVISION THREE

		P	W	D	L	F	A	Pts
1	Cranfield United Reserves	25	19	1	5	68	30	58
2	Eastcotts AFC	26	18	1	7	65	43	55
3	Goldington	26	16	4	6	79	44	52
4	Renhold Village	26	17	1	8	70	44	52
5	Stevington	26	16	1	9	66	45	49
6	Sundon Park Rangers Colts	26	15	2	9	89	36	47
7	Riseley Sports	26	14	4	8	57	48	46
8	Wilshamstead Reserves	26	11	3	12	43	46	36
9	Potton Town	26	9	4	13	48	61	31
10	Westoning Reserves	26	9	2	15	54	66	29
11	Kempston Hammers Sports	26	8	3	15	49	73	27
12	Royal Oak Kempston	26	8	1	17	38	67	25
13	Flitwick Town Reserves	26	4	1	21	40	89	13
14	Dunton Reserves	25	2	2	21	27	101	8

DIVISION FOUR

		P	W	D	L	F	A	Pts
1	Bedford Park Rangers	27	23	1	3	115	43	70
2	Marsh Leys	28	19	5	4	90	42	62
3	Thurleigh	28	19	3	6	100	48	60
4	Clifton Reserves	28	16	6	6	98	58	54
5	Ickwell & Old Warden Reserves	28	14	5	9	63	50	47
6	Stewartby Village	28	11	7	10	66	61	40
7	Caldecote A	27	11	6	10	77	62	39
8	Sandy Reserves	28	11	4	13	71	85	37
9	Wootton Village	28	11	3	14	55	64	36
10	Shefford Town & Campton A	28	10	5	13	68	76	35
11	Kempston Athletic	28	9	5	14	69	89	32
12	Bedford Panthers	28	8	5	15	44	68	29
13	Dinamo Flitwick [former Reserves]	28	7	6	15	71	83	27
14	Goldington Hammers	28	5	3	20	52	115	18
15	Dunton A	28	2	2	24	31	126	8

CENTENARY CUP

Final
Sandy 0-2 Ickwell & Old Warden

JUBILEE CUP

Final
AFC Turvey 2-1 Elstow Abbey

WATSON SHIELD

Final
Goldington 4-2 Bedford Park Rangers

CAMBRIDGESHIRE COUNTY LEAGUE

Sponsored by: Kershaw and BIS
Founded: 1891
Recent Champions:
2007: Great Shelford
2008: Waterbeach
2009: Fulbourn Institute
2010: Fulbourn Institute
2011: Lakenheath

PREMIER DIVISION	P	W	D	L	F	A	Pts
1 Linton Granta	32	25	4	3	110	31	79
2 Lakenheath	32	21	6	5	99	42	69
3 Great Shelford	32	22	3	7	74	30	69
4 Over Sports	32	16	8	8	65	49	56
5 Fulbourn Institute (-3)	32	17	6	9	84	49	54
6 West Wratting	32	14	8	10	69	64	50
7 Foxton	32	13	5	14	69	54	44
8 Hardwick	32	14	1	17	62	61	43
9 Cottenham United	32	11	8	13	56	60	41
10 Brampton	32	11	8	13	68	75	41
11 Waterbeach	32	9	9	14	64	71	36
12 Littleport Town	32	8	12	12	46	57	36
13 Chatteris Town	32	8	9	15	56	77	33
14 Eaton Socon	32	10	3	19	40	80	33
15 Somersham Town (-3)	32	10	4	18	45	83	31
16 Ely City Reserves (-3)	32	6	4	22	40	96	19
17 Newmarket Town Reserves (-6)	32	5	6	21	43	111	15

PREMIER DIVISION CUP

ROUND 1
Over Sports 0-2 Somersham Town
ROUND 2
Ely City Res 3-4 Lakenheath
Waterbeach 5-6 (aet) West Wratting
Foxton 1-4 Newmarket Town Reserves
Chatteris Town 1-4 Great Shelford
Eaton Socon 2-0 Somersham Town
Littleport Town 4-1 Brampton
Fulbourn Institute 1-1 4-2p Hardwick
Cottenham United 2-3 Linton Granta
QUARTER FINALS
Lakenheath 2-1 West Wratting
Newmarket Town Res 1-3 Great Shelford
Eaton Socon 1-3 Littleport Town
Fulbourn Institute 1-1 4-2p Linton Granta
SEMI-FINALS
Lakenheath 2-1 Great Shelford
Littleport Town 1-2 Fulbourn Institute 2
FINAL
Lakenheath 1-0 Fulbourn Institute 0

PREMIER DIVISION	1	2	3	4	5	6	7	8	9	10	11	12	13	14	15	16	17
1 Brampton		1-1	2-1	2-0	2-4	2-4	1-3	2-1	3-2	1-3	2-2	1-2	3-1	1-3	1-2	2-2	4-4
2 Chatteris Town	3-3		3-3	2-0	1-3	3-2	2-1	0-4	2-1	0-4	1-1	4-4	2-2	0-2	4-1	3-2	3-4
3 Cottenham United	2-3	3-0		1-2	3-1	1-5	1-1	2-1	1-3	1-1	0-3	3-1	5-0	2-1	2-4	1-0	2-2
4 Eaton Socon	0-5	4-0	1-0		1-0	0-4	0-4	1-1	0-2	1-1	0-2	5-0	4-1	4-1	4-2	1-2	3-4
5 Ely City Reserves	4-4	3-4	1-0	1-1		0-2	1-7	0-3	0-1	0-1	0-6	0-4	0-1	2-2	2-0	1-3	1-4
6 Foxton	1-1	1-3	2-2	2-3	8-0		1-1	2-1	1-2	1-3	1-3	0-1	7-0	4-1	0-1	3-3	3-1
7 Fulbourn Institute	8-3	1-0	5-2	2-2	6-0	6-0		1-4	1-2	1-2	1-2	4-2	3-3	1-3	4-1	4-1	4-2
8 Great Shelford	3-2	3-2	2-1	4-0	1-0	1-0	1-2		2-0	3-0	2-1	1-1	4-0	2-0	1-2	2-1	1-3
9 Hardwick	2-1	5-1	0-2	6-1	6-3	3-2	2-2	0-4		2-1	2-5	3-2	9-1	2-1	0-2	1-4	0-1
10 Lakenheath	4-1	4-3	1-1	6-1	6-0	4-0	3-0	1-3	2-1		2-1	3-3	4-2	2-2	4-0	7-1	4-0
11 Linton Granta	6-1	4-1	7-0	6-0	4-0	1-0	0-2	3-2	2-0	2-2		1-0	7-1	6-2	5-1	3-2	1-1
12 Littleport Town	2-1	0-0	1-1	0-1	2-0	1-3	0-2	0-0	2-0	2-3	1-5		2-5	1-1	2-0	2-2	2-1
13 Newmarket Town Reserves	0-2	2-6	0-5	4-0	1-7	2-6	1-2	0-4	3-2	1-6	1-4	1-1		0-1	2-3	0-4	1-1
14 Over Sports	1-2	1-1	1-1	4-0	1-0	4-0	3-1	0-0	2-1	4-1	1-5	3-3	4-2		6-0	1-0	2-1
15 Somersham Town	2-2	2-2	1-0	1-0	7-0	0-1	0-1	0-4	1-0	0-8	1-7	0-0	0-2	2-4		3-6	2-4
16 Waterbeach	1-4	1-0	1-3	6-0	2-3	0-0	2-2	1-4	3-2	1-4	1-2	1-1	2-2	1-1	4-3		1-3
17 West Wratting	1-3	5-3	4-1	2-0	3-3	0-3	2-1	2-3	3-0	3-2	0-3	2-1	1-1	1-2	1-1	3-3	

CAMBRIDGESHIRE COUNTY PREMIER DIVISION CONSTITUTION 2012-13

BRAMPTON	Thrapston Road Playing Fields, Brampton, Huntingdon PE28 4TB	07718 303074
CHATTERIS TOWN	West Street, Chatteris PE16 6HW	01354 692139
COTTENHAM UNITED	King George V Playing Field, Lamb Lane, Cottenham, Cambridge CB4 8TB	01954 250873
EATON SOCON	River Road, Eaton Ford, St Neots PE19 3AU	01480 474337
ELY CITY RESERVES	The Unwin Ground, Downham Road, Ely CB6 2SH	01353 662035
FOXTON	Hardman Road, off High Street, Foxton CB22 6RP	07711 012841
FULBOURN INSTITUTE	Fulbourn Recreation, Home End, Fulbourn CB1 5BS	07703 328575
GREAT SHELFORD	Recreation Ground, Woollards Lane, Great Shelford CB2 5LZ	01223 842590
HARDWICK	Egremont Road, Hardwick, Cambridge CB3 7XR	07813 587652
LAKENHEATH	The Nest, Wings Road, Lakenheath IP27 9HW	07810 225223
LINTON GRANTA	Recreation Ground, Meadow Lane, Linton, Cambridge CB21 6HX	07739 962564
LITTLEPORT TOWN	Sports Centre, Camel Road, Littleport, Ely CB6 1PU	01353 860600
OVER SPORTS	Over Recreation Ground, The Doles, Over, Cambridge CB4 5NW	07779 595862
SAWSTON UNITED	Spicers Sports Ground, New Road, Sawston CB22 4BW	07731 749593
SOHAM TOWN RANGERS RESERVES	Julius Martin Lane, Soham, Ely CB7 5EQ	01353 720732/722139
	Fax: 01353 722139 Club: 01353 722139	
WATERBEACH	Waterbeach Reacreation Ground, Cambridge Road, Waterbeach CB5 9NJ	01223 861206
WEST WRATTING	Recreation Ground, Bull Lane, West Wratting CB21 5NJ	07771 925686
WISBECH ST MARY	Station Road, Wisbech St Mary, Wisbech PE13 4RT	07711 221475

SENIOR DIVISION A

		P	W	D	L	F	A	Pts
1	Sawston United	30	24	3	3	112	34	75
2	Soham Town Rangers Reserves	30	17	7	6	79	53	58
3	Wisbech St Mary	30	18	3	9	82	39	57
4	Cambridge City Reserves	30	15	8	7	89	48	53
5	Great Paxton	30	14	6	10	62	55	48
6	Hemingfords United	30	12	9	9	79	59	45
7	Castle Camps	30	13	5	12	67	73	44
8	Cherry Hinton	30	12	4	14	52	56	40
9	Debden	30	11	7	12	63	68	40
10	Soham United	30	12	4	14	57	69	40
11	Milton	30	7	11	12	53	65	32
12	Wisbech Town Reserves (-3)	30	8	8	14	52	71	29
13	Hundon	30	7	8	15	52	74	29
14	Wimblington	30	7	8	15	40	80	29
15	Girton United	30	7	6	17	52	92	27
16	Needingworth United	30	5	5	20	32	87	20

WILLIAM COCKELL CUP

ROUND 1

Cherry Hinton 3-4 Soham Town Rangers Reserves
Soham United 0-3 Cambridge City Reserves
Hemingfords United 2-2 6-5p Great Paxton
Needingworth United 1-6 Sawston United
Wisbech Town Res 2-4 Castle Camps
Debden FC 4-1 Hundon
Wimblington 3-4 Girton United
Wisbech St Mary 4-0 Milton

QUARTER FINALS

Soham Town Rangers Res 2-6 Cambridge City Reserves
Hemingfords United 2-3 Sawston United
Castle Camps 1-4 Debden FC
Girton United 1-7 Wisbech St Mary

SEMI-FINALS

Cambridge City Res 2-4 Sawston United
Debden FC 3-1 Wisbech St Mary

FINAL

Sawston United 4-0 Debden FC

SENIOR 'A' DIVISION

		1	2	3	4	5	6	7	8	9	10	11	12	13	14	15	16
1	Cambridge City Reserves		10-1	6-1	10-0	5-0	2-3	1-1	4-1	3-0	2-2	2-2	2-3	3-0	2-0	2-1	3-3
2	Castle Camps	4-4		4-1	3-1	4-3	3-1	1-3	2-2	4-2	2-0	2-7	4-4	2-4	5-1	1-0	1-1
3	Cherry Hinton	0-1	2-0		0-1	4-0	1-0	2-1	1-0	2-2	3-0	1-2	0-2	3-0	2-0	1-5	5-0
4	Debden	2-4	0-3	4-2		5-1	0-3	2-2	0-1	2-2	1-2	1-2	3-1	0-0	2-2	3-0	4-4
5	Girton United	0-1	5-1	2-5	0-6		1-1	3-5	1-1	1-2	2-1	2-7	2-3	0-1	1-3	4-3	2-2
6	Great Paxton	0-3	1-0	0-0	0-2	4-5		3-2	2-3	3-1	4-0	1-2	4-1	4-1	3-3	1-1	3-2
7	Hemingfords United	1-1	0-2	5-3	2-3	2-2	5-1		5-3	2-2	3-0	3-4	3-3	0-3	7-0	2-3	3-0
8	Hundon	5-1	0-5	1-0	1-4	5-5	1-3	2-1		2-2	2-3	2-3	1-1	2-1	2-3	3-4	3-3
9	Milton	4-3	2-2	0-3	5-2	1-4	5-3	1-1	1-0		1-2	0-4	1-2	1-3	0-0	2-3	1-3
10	Needingworth United	0-3	4-3	1-4	3-3	0-1	3-4	1-4	1-1	1-1		0-2	0-1	0-5	6-1	0-2	0-2
11	Sawston United	3-1	6-0	4-0	5-1	5-0	2-2	5-0	5-2	0-2	7-1		4-2	3-0	9-0	3-0	5-0
12	Soham Town Rangers Reserves	2-2	3-1	2-2	2-1	3-0	2-1	4-4	1-2	3-3	3-0	3-1		6-1	2-1	0-2	6-0
13	Soham United	1-6	2-1	3-3	5-1	2-3	2-2	2-4	3-1	1-1	4-1	0-4	0-5		3-1	4-3	2-1
14	Wimblington	3-1	1-4	2-0	2-2	0-0	1-2	0-5	4-0	4-4	0-0	2-3	0-6	2-1		0-3	2-2
15	Wisbech St Mary	4-0	3-1	6-1	1-2	5-0	0-1	0-1	2-2	2-0	11-0	2-2	7-1	1-0	3-0		2-1
16	Wisbech Town 'A'	1-1	0-1	2-0	0-5	5-2	1-2	2-2	3-1	0-4	5-0	2-1	1-2	5-3	0-2	1-3	

CAMBRIDGESHIRE COUNTY SENIOR 'A' DIVISION CONSTITUTION 2012-13

CAMBRIDGE CITY RESERVES	The City Ground , Milton Road , Cambridge CB4 1UY 01223 357973 Fax: 01223 351582
CAMBRIDGE UNIVERSITY PRESS RES.	CUP Sports Ground , Shaftesbury Road , Cambridge CB2 2BS
CASTLE CAMPS	Recreation Ground, Bumpstead Road, Castle Camps, Cambridge CB1 6SN
CHERRY HINTON	Recreation Ground, High Street, Cherry Hinton, Cambridge CB1 9HX
FENSTANTON	Hall Green Lane, Fenstanton, Huntingdon PE28 9JH
FULBOURN INSTITUTE RESERVES	Fulbourn Recreation, Home End, Fulbourn CB1 5BS
GIRTON UNITED	Girton Recreation Ground, Cambridge Road, Girton CB3 0FH
GREAT PAXTON	Recreation Ground, High Street, Great Paxton, St Neots PE19 6RG
HEMINGFORDS UNITED	Peace Memorial Playing Fields, Manor Road, Hemingford Grey, Huntingdon PE28 9BX
HUNDON	Upper North Street, Hundon CO10 8EE
MILTON	Milton Recreation Ground, The Sycamores, Milton, Cambridge CB4 6ZN
NEEDINGWORTH UNITED	Mill Field, Holywell Road, Needingworth PE27 8TE
SOHAM UNITED	Qua Fen Common, Soham, Ely CB7 5DQ
WIMBLINGTON	Parkfield Sports & Social Club, Chapel Lane, Wimblington, March PE15 0QX 01354 741555
WISBECH TOWN RESERVES	Tom Woods Beer Fenland Stadium, Lynn Road, Wisbech PE14 7AL

CAMBRIDGESHIRE COUNTY LEAGUE - STEP 7

SENIOR DIVISION B

		P	W	D	L	F	A	Pts
1	Fenstanton	24	21	2	1	83	20	65
2	Cambridge Univ Press Res.	24	14	7	3	77	26	49
3	Fulbourn Institute Reserves	24	15	3	6	79	47	48
4	West Row Gunners	24	14	4	6	62	33	46
5	Comberton United	24	13	4	7	61	43	43
6	West Wratting Reserves	24	8	5	11	36	47	29
7	Longstanton	24	6	9	9	53	58	27
8	St Ives Rangers	24	7	5	12	37	49	26
9	Duxford United	24	6	6	12	36	54	24
10	Swavesey Institute	24	7	3	14	34	67	24
11	Outwell Swifts	24	6	1	17	37	89	19
12	Saffron Crocus	24	5	3	16	28	75	18
13	Lakenheath Reserves (-6)	24	7	2	15	54	69	17

Mildenhall Town Reserves - record expunged

PERCY OLDHAM CUP

ROUND 1
Outwell Swifts 0-3 Ely City "A"
Fulbourn Institute Res 2-1 West Row Gunners
Comberton United 1-3 (aet) Duxford United
Cambridge University Pres 1-3 Longstanton
Fenstanton 2-2 9-8p St Ives Rangers
West Wratting Res 1-1 4-3p Saffron Crocus
Lakenheath Res 5-2 Swavesey Institute
QUARTER FINALS
Ely City "A" AW Fulbourn Institute Res W
Duxford United 5-2 Longstanton
Mildenhall Town Res 0-4 Fenstanton
West Wratting Res 5-3 (aet) Lakenheath Reserves 3
SEMI-FINALS
Fulbourn Institute Res 3-0 Duxford United
Fenstanton 6-3 West Wratting Reserves
FINAL (@ Histon, 4/5/11))
Fulbourn Institute Res 0-2 Fenstanton

CREAKE CHARITY SHIELD FINAL
Hemingfords United Res 1-1 5-4p Royston Town A
JOHN ABLETT CUP FINAL
Balsham 0-4 Bar Hill Sports & Social
REG HAIGH & ARTHUR PECK CUP FINAL
Melbourn 1-0 Therfield & Kelshall

	SENIOR 'B' DIVISION	1	2	3	4	5	6	7	8	9	10	11	12	13
1	Cambridge Universtiy Press Reserves		10-0	2-2	1-2	2-2	4-1	2-2	6-0	5-0	1-0	3-0	3-1	1-1
2	Comberton United	1-0		6-0	0-2	3-5	4-1	2-1	2-1	4-2	6-0	6-1	3-0	3-0
3	Duxford United	0-5	1-2		1-1	1-2	2-0	3-3	4-2	2-0	1-1	0-2	2-4	4-0
4	Fenstanton	2-1	5-0	4-0		3-1	2-0	6-0	4-0	9-0	2-1	2-1	8-3	3-2
5	Fulbourn Institute Reserves	3-4	2-1	2-0	1-1		5-4	5-3	19-0	5-1	0-1	3-0	4-1	3-2
6	Lakenheath Reserves	2-2	1-8	4-0	0-8	2-4		2-0	1-3	0-2	7-1	7-1	3-2	1-3
7	Longstanton	1-3	1-1	3-3	1-4	1-1	3-3		3-6	2-2	1-1	1-2	2-3	5-2
8	Outwell Swifts	0-4	1-4	2-0	2-5	1-3	4-3	1-2		4-0	2-3	2-2	0-3	1-4
9	Saffron Crocus	1-5	4-1	1-3	0-1	4-3	2-1	2-5	1-2		2-1	1-4	0-2	0-0
10	St Ives Rangers	2-4	2-2	2-2	1-3	5-1	3-2	0-1	5-1	2-1		2-1	1-2	1-3
11	Swavesey Institute	0-6	2-2	0-4	2-4	1-3	0-3	2-8	4-1	5-0	1-0		0-6	1-1
12	West Row Gunners	0-0	0-0	4-1	1-2	6-0	4-0	2-2	4-0	7-0	1-1	1-0		3-1
13	West Wratting Reserves	3-3	1-0	2-0	1-0	0-2	2-6	0-2	3-1	2-2	2-1	1-2	0-2	

CAMBRIDGESHIRE COUNTY SENIOR 'B' DIVISION CONSTITUTION 2012-13

BLUNTISHAM RANGERS	Bluntisham Recreation Ground	
COMBERTON UNITED	Recreation Ground, Hines Lane, Comberton CB3 7BZ	
DUXFORD UNITED	Duxford Recreation Ground, Hunts Road, Duxford, Cambridge CB22 4RE	
GAMLINGAY UNITED	Gamlingay Eco Hub, Stocks Lane, Gamlingay, Sandy, Bedfordshire SG19 3JR	
HARDWICK RESERVES	Egremont Road, Hardwick, Cambridge CB23 7X	07813 587652
HEMINGFORDS UNITED RESERVES	Peace Memorial Playing Fields, Manor Road, Hemingford Grey, Huntingdon PE28 9BX	
LAKENHEATH RESERVES	The Nest, Wings Road, Lakenheath IP27 9HW	
LITTLEPORT TOWN RESERVES	Sports Centre, Camel Road, Littleport, Ely CB6 1PU	01353 860600
LONGSTANTON	Longstanton Recreation Ground, Over Road, Longstanton CB24 5DW	
OUTWELL SWIFTS	The Nest, Wisbech Road, Outwell, Wisbech PE14 8PA	
ROYSTON TOWN A	Garden Walk, Royston SG8 7H	07772 086709
SAFFRON CROCUS	Ickleton Recreation Ground, Frogge Street, Ickleton CB10 1NS	
ST IVES RANGERS	California Road, St Ives, Huntingdon PE27 6SJ	
SWAVESEY INSTITUTE	The Green, High Street, Swavesey CB24 4QU	
WEST ROW GUNNERS	Beeches Road, West Row, Bury St Edmunds IP28 8NY	
WEST WRATTING RESERVES	Recreation Ground, Bull Lane, West Wratting CB1 5NJ	

DIVISION ONE A

		P	W	D	L	F	A	Pts
1	Hardwick Reserves	22	16	2	4	55	16	50
2	Royston Town "A"	22	13	6	3	63	27	45
3	Gamlingay United	22	13	5	4	43	27	44
4	RHS United	22	12	2	8	58	38	38
5	Whittlesford United	22	11	4	7	48	34	37
6	Sawston Rovers	22	11	3	8	58	40	36
7	Eaton Socon Reserves	22	10	3	9	45	40	33
8	Bottisham Sports	22	7	6	9	33	43	27
9	Fowlmere	22	7	2	13	39	56	23
10	Clare Town	22	6	3	13	37	73	21
11	Barrington	22	3	4	15	23	61	13
12	Steeple Bumpstead	22	2	2	18	21	68	8

DIVISION ONE B

		P	W	D	L	F	A	Pts
1	Bluntisham Rangers	22	17	1	4	49	17	52
2	Littleport Town Reserves	22	16	3	3	64	14	51
3	Hemingfords United Reserves	22	15	5	2	73	28	50
4	Somersham Town Reserves	22	11	4	7	33	32	37
5	Earith United	22	11	2	9	40	45	35
6	Burwell Swifts	22	9	4	9	47	40	31
7	Huntingdon United RGE	22	9	3	10	44	41	30
8	March Town United Reserves	22	7	1	14	36	49	22
9	Buckden	22	6	4	12	36	62	22
10	Chatteris Town Reserves	22	7	1	14	35	61	22
11	Waterbeach Reserves	22	5	4	13	37	58	19
12	Cottenham United Reserves	22	2	2	18	23	70	8

DIVISION ONE PLAY-OFF
Hardwick Reserves 2-2 2-4p Bluntisham Rangers

DIVISION TWO A

		P	W	D	L	F	A	Pts
1	Howden Sports	26	21	2	3	64	24	65
2	Great Chishill	26	16	6	4	79	47	54
3	Glemsford & Cavendish United	26	16	6	4	59	30	54
4	Sawston United Reserves	26	16	4	6	87	30	52
5	Bassingbourn	26	15	4	7	57	33	49
6	Ashdon Villa	26	10	6	10	52	47	36
7	Cambridge University Press A	26	11	2	13	55	60	35
8	Papworth	26	10	5	11	49	55	35
9	Great Chesterford	26	11	2	13	54	67	35
10	Girton United Reserves	26	9	2	15	48	60	29
11	Thaxted Rangers	26	7	2	17	48	81	23
12	City Life	26	7	2	17	35	76	23
13	Cambourne Rovers	26	5	3	18	41	78	18
14	Great Shelford Reserves	26	3	4	19	48	88	13

DIVISION TWO B

		P	W	D	L	F	A	Pts
1	Witchford 96	24	19	1	4	80	32	58
2	Manea United	24	18	2	4	71	32	56
3	Doddington United	24	17	4	3	62	27	55
4	Godmanchester Rovers Res	24	16	3	5	74	31	51
5	Isleham United	24	11	5	8	49	42	38
6	Over Sports Reserves	24	11	2	11	62	41	35
7	Sutton United	24	9	6	9	54	48	33
8	St Ives Town Reserves	24	9	5	10	43	44	32
9	Wisbech St Mary Reserves	24	9	4	11	51	62	31
10	Milton Reserves	24	6	4	14	50	68	22
11	March Rangers	24	5	2	17	34	57	17
12	Bluntisham Rangers Reserves	24	3	5	16	25	78	14
13	Tydd United (-6)	24	1	1	22	25	118	-2

DIVISION TWO PLAY-OFF
Howden Sports 3-1 Witchford 96

DIVISION THREE A

		P	W	D	L	F	A	Pts
1	Linton Granta Reserves	22	20	1	1	111	15	61
2	Balsham	22	16	2	4	56	31	50
3	Orwell	22	14	4	4	71	35	46
4	Abington United	22	12	2	8	78	50	38
5	Steeple Morden	22	12	2	8	48	37	38
6	"Fulbourn Institute 'A'"	22	10	0	12	52	65	30
7	Hardwick A	22	9	2	11	53	30	29
8	Hundon Reserves	22	7	2	13	39	73	23
9	Eaton Socon A	22	7	1	14	33	48	22
10	Lode	22	7	1	14	29	77	22
11	Wilbraham	22	5	2	15	26	83	17
12	Comberton United Reserves	22	3	1	18	30	82	10

DIVISION THREE B

		P	W	D	L	F	A	Pts
1	Bar Hill Sports & Social	24	22	2	0	91	16	68
2	Brampton Reserves	24	14	6	4	46	29	48
3	Mepal Sports	24	14	4	6	53	32	46
4	Wisbech St Mary A	24	12	4	8	46	33	40
5	Fordham	24	11	4	9	56	47	37
6	Stretham Hotspurs	24	9	8	7	72	61	35
7	Exning Athletic	24	7	10	7	36	43	31
8	West Row Gunners Reserves	24	9	4	11	37	46	31
9	Little Downham Swifts	24	8	5	11	50	62	29
10	Hemingfords United A	24	7	6	11	51	58	27
11	Estover Park	24	7	4	13	51	66	25
12	Barton Mills	24	2	5	17	17	54	11
13	Wimblington Reserves	24	1	4	19	19	78	7

DIVISION THREE PLAY-OFF
Linton Granta Reserves 3-1 Bar Hill Sports & Social

DIVISION FOUR A

		P	W	D	L	F	A	Pts
1	Fowlmere Reserves	24	18	4	2	68	24	58
2	Saffron Rangers	24	15	2	7	82	48	47
3	Meldreth	24	14	2	8	71	51	44
4	Gransden	24	12	5	7	58	48	41
5	Great Paxton Reserves	24	12	3	9	56	50	39
6	Litlington Athletic	24	10	8	6	62	54	38
7	Haverhill Athletic	24	10	5	9	45	48	35
8	Cherry Hinton Reserves	24	9	3	12	58	58	30
9	Debden	24	9	3	12	56	66	30
10	Cambridge Ambassadors	24	7	4	13	43	65	25
11	West Wratting A	24	6	2	16	38	57	20
12	Duxford United Reserves	24	5	5	14	35	55	20
13	Foxton Reserves	24	5	2	17	33	81	17

DIVISION FOUR B

		P	W	D	L	F	A	Pts
1	Longstanton Reserves	24	21	2	1	94	26	65
2	Elsworth Sports	24	18	5	1	105	30	59
3	Fenstanton Reserves	24	14	2	8	77	35	44
4	Benwick Athletic	24	13	4	7	63	44	43
5	Soham United Reserves	24	11	5	8	65	58	38
6	Willingham Wolves	24	10	6	8	61	51	36
7	Burwell Swifts Reserves	24	9	6	9	44	55	33
8	Chatteris Town A	24	8	8	8	49	47	32
9	Wicken Amateurs	24	7	3	14	53	81	24
10	Haddenham Rovers	24	5	6	13	58	97	21
11	Wisbech St Mary B	24	5	2	17	32	80	17
12	Milton A	24	4	3	17	31	72	15
13	Cottenham United A	24	2	6	16	30	86	12

DIVISION FOUR PLAY-OFF (@ Bar Hill Sports & Social, 12/5/11)
Fowlmere Reserves 2-0 Longstanton Reserves

DIVISION FIVE A

		P	W	D	L	F	A	Pts
1	Glemsford & Cavendish Utd Res	20	17	2	1	61	14	53
2	Thurlow Royal Exchange (-3)	20	16	2	2	70	27	47
3	Studlands Park	20	12	3	5	72	44	39
4	Castle Camps Reserves	20	10	2	8	51	38	32
5	Sawston Rovers Reserves	20	8	4	8	53	49	28
6	City Life Reserves	20	8	2	10	43	51	26
7	"Sawston United A"	20	7	1	12	47	59	22
8	Saffron Crocus Reserves	20	5	5	10	37	47	20
9	Newport	20	6	2	12	46	60	20
10	Saffron Dynamos	20	5	3	12	34	53	18
11	Linton Granta A	20	3	0	17	26	98	9

DIVISION FIVE B

		P	W	D	L	F	A	Pts
1	Royston United	22	18	3	1	75	26	57
2	Therfield & Kelshall	22	16	2	4	81	36	50
3	Bar Hill Sports & Social Res.	22	15	2	5	76	28	47
4	Buckden Reserves	22	14	4	4	73	37	46
5	Melbourn	22	12	2	8	40	35	38
6	Mott MacDonald	22	9	3	10	37	50	30
7	Great Chishill Reserves	22	8	2	12	49	62	26
8	Papworth Reserves (-3)	22	8	3	11	44	38	24
9	Barrington Reserves	22	6	6	10	26	41	24
10	Haslingfield	22	5	3	14	41	76	18
11	Cambourne Rovers Reserves	22	2	2	18	31	75	8
12	Steeple Morden Reserves	22	2	2	18	20	89	8

DIVISION FIVE C

		P	W	D	L	F	A	Pts
1	Red Lodge	22	18	1	3	88	21	55
2	Waterbeach A	22	13	4	5	65	26	43
3	Earith United Reserves	22	13	2	7	45	30	41
4	Witchford 96 Reserves	22	12	4	6	56	47	40
5	St Ives Rangers Reserves	22	12	3	7	82	45	39
6	Isleham United Reserves	22	10	5	7	29	25	35
7	Isleham Warriors	22	8	5	9	37	51	29
8	The Eagle	22	8	4	10	45	42	28
9	Bottisham/Lode Reserves	22	7	2	13	25	76	23
10	Burwell Swifts A	22	5	5	12	38	50	20
11	Prickwillow	22	4	3	15	36	93	15
12	Swavesey Institute Reserves	22	0	6	16	25	65	6

DIVISION FIVE D

		P	W	D	L	F	A	Pts
1	Doddington United Reserves	24	18	2	4	71	24	56
2	Mepal Sports Reserves	24	17	4	3	78	26	55
3	Chatteris Fen Tigers	24	15	2	7	91	44	47
4	Coldham United	24	13	4	7	65	30	43
5	March Rangers Reserves	24	13	2	9	61	55	41
6	Estover Park Reserves	24	12	3	9	71	46	39
7	Gorefield Athletic	24	12	3	9	62	60	39
8	Wisbech St Mary C	24	12	1	11	57	47	37
9	Wimblington A	24	10	2	12	57	60	32
10	Manea United Reserves	24	8	2	14	51	63	26
11	Outwell Swifts Reserves	24	6	4	14	42	78	22
12	Upwell Town	24	3	1	20	32	96	10
13	Walsoken United	24	1	2	21	18	127	5

DIVISION FIVE PLAY-OFFS
Semi-Finals
Glemsford & Cavendish United Reserves 2-1 Royston United
Red Lodge 3-2 Doddington United Reserves
Final
Glemsford & Cavendish United Reserves 2-3 Red Lodge

CENTRAL MIDLANDS LEAGUE

Sponsored by: Windsor Foodservice
Founded: 1971
Recent Champions:
2007: Bottesford Town
2008: Askern Welfare
2009: Radcliffe Olympic
2010: Louth Town
2011: Sheffield Parramore

LEAGUE CHALLENGE CUP

PRELIMINARY ROUND
Kiveton Park 1-2 FC 05 Bilsthorpe
Parkhouse 2-1 Basford United
South Normanton 2-1 Kimberley Town
Thorne Colliery 2-1 Bentley Colliery
ROUND 1
Belper United 2-2 Harworth C I
Harworth C I 1-0 Belper United
Real United 3-5 Dronfield Town
Blidworth Welfare 2-3 Clipstone Welfare
Ollerton Town 2-4 Kinsley Boys
AFC Hucknall 1-5 Newark Town
Westella & Willerby 4-1 Thoresby CW
Nottinghamshire Police 0-4 Clifton
Nottingham United 5-1 FC 05 Bilsthorpe
Bilborough Pelican 1-1 Southwell City
Southwell City 1-1 Bilborough Pelican
(Southwell City won on penalties)
Phoenix 2-1 Calverton MW
Glapwell 0-1 Parkhouse
South Normanton 1-0 Sutton Town AFC
Easington United 6-0 DFS Welbeck Welfare
ROUND 2
Kinsley Boys 1-4 Clifton
Harworth C I 1-2 South Normanton
Parkhouse 3-1 Nottingham United
Phoenix 1-1 Westella & Willerby
Westella & Willerby 8-1 Phoenix
Yorkshire Main 0-1 Newark Town
Easington United 2-1 Southwell City
Pinxton 3-4 Clipstone Welfare
Thorne Colliery 2-2 Dronfield Town
Dronfield Town 6-2 Thorne Colliery
QUARTER FINALS
Newark Town 2-2 Clipstone Welfare
(Clipstone Welfare won on penalties)
Clifton 3-2 South Normanton
Westella & Willerby 6-3 Parkhouse
Easington United 0-4 Dronfield Town
SEMI-FINALS
Clipstone Welfare 0-3 Clifton
Dronfield Town 2-1 Westella & Willerby
FINAL
Clifton 2-5 Dronfield Town

NORTH DIVISION

		P	W	D	L	F	A	Pts
1	Westella & Willerby	32	24	3	5	95	36	75
2	Thoresby CW	32	22	7	3	90	24	73
3	Dronfield Town	32	23	3	6	95	34	72
4	Clipstone Welfare	32	22	4	6	108	42	70
5	Yorkshire Main	32	18	3	11	73	39	57
6	Kinsley Boys	32	16	9	7	77	46	57
7	Ollerton Town	32	17	4	11	74	53	55
8	Parkhouse	32	16	3	13	79	71	51
9	Kiveton Park	32	13	4	15	64	49	43
10	Easington United	32	12	7	13	60	64	43
11	Harworth CI	32	11	5	16	53	71	38
12	Phoenix	32	11	5	16	54	74	38
13	Bentley Colliery	32	9	5	18	49	71	32
14	Thorne Colliery	32	8	7	17	57	90	31
15	FC 05 Bilsthorpe	32	7	4	21	52	113	25
16	Glapwell	32	3	6	23	38	92	15
17	DFS Welbeck Welfare	32	0	1	31	21	170	1

SOUTH DIVISION

		P	W	D	L	F	A	Pts
1	Basford United	30	22	6	2	87	26	72
2	Pinxton	30	20	5	5	91	37	65
3	South Normanton	30	19	6	5	94	41	63
4	Clifton	30	18	2	10	80	43	56
5	Newark Town	30	17	3	10	85	43	54
6	Bilborough Pelican	30	17	3	10	87	53	54
7	Sutton Town	30	16	4	10	83	65	52
8	Southwell City	30	14	6	10	61	55	48
9	Belper United	30	12	5	13	59	51	41
10	Nottingham United	30	12	2	16	63	104	38
11	Real United	30	10	6	14	63	71	36
12	Blidworth Welfare	30	9	5	16	49	65	32
13	AFC Hucknall	30	9	3	18	43	81	30
14	Calverton MW	30	7	3	20	49	87	24
15	Nottinghamshire Police	30	3	5	22	30	100	14
16	Kimberley Town	30	1	4	25	28	130	7

NORTH DIVISION

NORTH DIVISION	1	2	3	4	5	6	7	8	9	10	11	12	13	14	15	16	17
1 Bentley Colliery		3-5	5-0	1-2	1-2	2-2	5-2	2-4	2-3	0-4	0-1	3-1	2-0	0-0	0-1	0-2	0-3
2 Clipstone Welfare	3-0		8-0	1-2	2-1	5-2	3-1	6-0	2-2	2-2	3-1	4-2	5-2	2-0	4-1	3-0	1-2
3 DFS Welbeck Welfare	1-2	1-6		0-6	0-3	0-8	0-2	0-6	2-4	1-3	2-3	0-4	2-4	0-6	3-4	0-6	
4 Dronfield Town	0-2	3-2	12-2		1-1	7-0	4-0	2-0	5-1	3-0	2-1	1-2	4-0	4-1	6-2	0-1	3-2
5 Easington United	4-1	1-1	3-0	0-1		3-2	9-1	1-1	0-4	0-6	4-1	1-3	1-0	1-5	5-2	1-4	3-1
6 FC 05 Bilsthorpe	2-2	0-7	9-0	0-3	4-2		4-2	2-1	2-4	2-1	2-6	1-2	0-5	0-9	1-2	0-3	1-2
7 Glapwell	3-3	1-4	5-0	1-4	1-1	2-3		1-3	1-2	0-2	0-6	0-2	1-2	1-4	1-1	0-1	0-1
8 Harworth CI	1-1	0-3	5-1	1-0	1-1	3-1	3-2		0-2	2-1	1-2	3-4	0-0	0-4	3-2	1-4	1-5
9 Kinsley Boys	3-2	2-0	9-1	0-1	1-3	5-0	3-0	4-4		1-2	4-0	5-0	1-2	1-0	2-2	1-1	2-1
10 Kiveton Park	1-2	0-2	4-0	1-3	2-2	4-0	2-3	1-2	1-1		4-0	1-3	6-1	2-2	4-1	0-3	3-0
11 Ollerton Town	3-2	3-1	5-1	2-3	2-0	0-0	2-2	1-0	1-0	6-0		4-3	4-3	0-0	6-0	0-4	0-2
12 Parkhouse	0-3	4-7	7-1	3-3	1-3	6-1	3-2	2-3	2-1	2-1	2-2		0-2	1-3	2-2	2-3	3-0
13 Phoenix	0-1	0-7	2-2	2-1	5-2	7-0	2-2	2-0	1-1	1-2	0-6	1-5		1-1	2-5	2-4	0-2
14 Thoresby CW	3-0	0-0	8-0	1-0	3-2	10-1	2-0	4-1	4-1	1-0	1-0	5-1	1-0		2-1	1-1	1-1
15 Thorne Colliery	3-0	0-6	6-1	3-3	0-2	2-2	0-0	2-1	2-2	1-2	2-1	1-4	1-3	2-6		0-4	2-3
16 Westella & Willerby	7-1	5-0	5-0	0-4	6-0	8-0	4-1	3-1	2-3	2-1	4-3	3-1	4-0	0-1	4-1		0-0
17 Yorkshire Main	5-1	1-3	4-0	1-2	1-0	W-L	5-0	5-1	2-2	2-1	1-2	1-2	1-2	0-1	8-1	5-1	

SOUTH DIVISION	1	2	3	4	5	6	7	8	9	10	11	12	13	14	15	16
1 AFC Hucknall		1-3	0-4	0-2	0-1	2-0	2-4	4-2	2-1	3-4	0-0	2-7	1-2	0-3	0-4	5-2
2 Basford United	1-1		2-1	1-1	2-1	3-0	1-0	7-0	0-1	5-2	4-1	2-2	1-1	1-1	5-0	3-1
3 Belper United	4-1	1-2		0-6	0-0	5-2	2-1	3-3	3-1	2-3	4-1	0-1	6-1	1-2	2-2	1-2
4 Bilborough Pelican	3-1	3-0	3-1		4-2	4-1	1-2	6-2	1-2	9-0	7-0	0-4	2-3	2-1	1-3	6-1
5 Blidworth Welfare	1-3	0-2	2-0	0-2		6-2	1-7	2-2	2-1	2-2	2-2	0-0	0-2	1-4	3-4	2-3
6 Calverton MW	1-2	0-8	1-0	0-1	1-2		1-3	5-2	0-4	3-4	2-1	2-4	2-2	2-3	2-1	1-4
7 Clifton	0-2	1-3	1-1	2-1	1-2	5-1		10-1	2-1	2-4	1-2	1-3	3-0	1-0	2-2	3-0
8 Kimberley Town	0-2	1-3	1-2	0-5	0-3	0-11	1-4		0-2	0-5	1-0	2-3	0-4	1-7	1-2	1-8
9 Newark Town	6-0	1-2	1-2	4-3	1-0	0-0	0-2	2-2		4-1	7-0	5-2	5-1	1-3	1-0	5-1
10 Nottingham United	3-2	0-11	1-4	3-3	3-2	1-2	0-7	5-1	7-4		4-1	0-1	0-3	3-5	0-4	1-5
11 Nottinghamshire Police	2-3	1-3	0-3	0-2	1-6	1-2	1-4	4-1	1-10	2-4		0-5	3-3	1-1	2-1	0-2
12 Pinxton	2-0	1-2	3-0	2-2	3-1	3-1	3-2	12-0	1-3	5-0	1-1		6-2	1-2	3-0	4-0
13 Real United	5-0	1-2	2-4	6-1	2-1	1-1	1-2	4-0	1-5	0-3	5-0	1-5		0-2	1-2	4-4
14 South Normanton	8-0	0-5	1-1	8-1	1-2	8-1	4-1	1-1	2-0	5-0	5-0	4-1	3-2		3-5	2-2
15 Southwell City	4-2	1-2	2-0	2-5	3-1	2-1	2-3	2-1	2-2	5-0	2-0	1-1	1-1	1-1		1-3
16 Sutton Town	2-2	1-1	3-2	2-0	7-1	5-1	0-3	2-1	0-5	2-0	5-2	1-2	6-2	3-4	6-0	

CENTRAL MIDLANDS NORTHERN DIVISION CONSTITUTION 2012-13

AFC MANSFIELD	Clipstone Road, Mansfield Nottinghamshire NG19 0EE	01623 623443
BENTLEY COLLIERY	Bentley Miners Welfare , The Avenue, Bentley , Doncaster DN5 0PN	01302 874420
BRODSWORTH WELFARE AFC	Welfare Road, Woodlands, Doncaster DN6	07967 708430
CLAY CROSS TOWN	Mill Lane, Holmgate, Clay Cross, Chesterfield	07980 354522
DFS WELBECK WELFARE	Elkesley Road, Meden Vale, Mansfield, Nottinghamshire NG20 9P	07791 155891
DRONFIELD TOWN	Stonelow Playing Fields, Stonelow Road, Dronfield S18 2DA	None
EASINGTON UNITED	Low Farm, Beak Street, Easington, Hull HU12 0TT	None
GLAPWELL (2011)	Hall Corner, Glapwell, Chesterfield, Derbyshire S44 5P	07870 195684
HARWORTH COLLIERY INSTITUTE	Recreation Ground, Scrooby Road, Bircotes, Doncaster DN11 8JT	01302 750614
KIVETON PARK	Kiveton Park MW, Hard Lane, Kiveton Park, Sheffield S26 6NB	07763 467979
OLLERTON TOWN	The Lane, Walesby Lane, New Ollerton, Newark NG22 9UX	None
PHOENIX SPORTS & SOCIAL	Phoenix Sports Complex, Bawtry Road, Brinsworth, Rotherham S60 5PA	01709 363864
SHERWOOD COLLIERY	Debdale Lane, Mansfield Woodhouse, Mansfield, Nottinghamshire NG19 7N	07813 718302
THORESBY COLLIERY WELFARE	Thoresby Colliery Spts Ground, Fourth Avenue, Edwinstowe NG21 9NS	07802 417987
THORNE COLLIERY	Moorends Welfare, Grange Road, Moorends, Thorne, Doncaster DN8 4LU	07855 545221
WESTELLA HANSON	Blackburn Leisure Social Club, Prescott Avenue, Brough HU15 1BB	01482 667353
YORKSHIRE MAIN	Edlington Lane, Edlington, Doncaster DN12 2DA	07775 714558

CENTRAL MIDLANDS SOUTHERN DIVISION CONSTITUTION 2012-13

BELPER UNITED	Alton Manor, Nailers Way, Belper DE56 0HT	None
BILBOROUGH PELICAN	Brian Wakefield Sports Ground, Trentside Lane,Old Lenton Lane, Nottingham NG7 2SA	0115 929 4728
BLACKWELL MWFC	Primrose Hill, Blackwell, Alfreton, Derbyshire DE55 5J	07817 019174
BLIDWORTH WELFARE	Blidworth Welfare Miners SC, Mansfield Road, Blidworth, Mansfield NG21 0LR	01623 793361
CALVERTON MINERS WELFARE	Calverton Miners Welfare, Hollinwood Lane, Calverton NG14 6NR	0115 965 4390
CLIFTON	Green Lane, Clifton, Nottingham NG11 9AY	0115 921 5401
HOLBROOK ST MICHAELS	Mackney Road, Holbrook, Belper, Derbyshire DE56 0T	07885 499358
HUCKNALL TOWN AFC	Watnall Road, Hucknall, Nottingham, Nottinghamshire NG15 6E	07535 124295
KIMBERLEY TOWN	The Stag Ground, Nottingham Road, Kimberley NG16 2ND	0115 938 2788
LINBY COLLIERY	Church Lane, Linby, Nottinghamshire NG15 8A	07932 591068
MICKLEOVER ROYALS	Station Road, Micleover, Derby, Derbyshire DE3 9F	01332 736356
NEWARK TOWN	Collingham FC, Station Road, Collingham NG23 7RA	01636 892303
NOTTINGHAM UNITED	Pavillion Road, Kirkby-in-Ashfield, Nottinghamshire NG17 7L	07891 380620
PINXTON	Welfare Ground, Wharf Road, Pinxton NG16 6LG	07989 324249
REAL UNITED	Grove Farm, Lenton Lane, Nottingham NG7 2SA	None
SOUTH NORMANTON ATHLETIC	ExChem Sports Ground, Lees Lane, South Normanton, Alfreton DE55 2AD	01773 581491
SOUTHWELL CITY	War Memorial Recreation Ground, Bishop's Drive, Southwell NG25 0JP	01636 814386
SUTTON TOWN	The Fieldings, Huthwaite Road, Sutton-in-Ashfield NG17 2HB	01623 552376

CHESHIRE LEAGUE

Sponsored by: No sponsor
Founded: 1919
Recent Champions:
2007: Middlewich Town
2008: Styal
2009: Woodley
2010: Club AZ
2011: Greenalls Padgate St Oswalds

DIVISION ONE	P	W	D	L	F	A	Pts
1 Knutsford	30	23	3	4	68	23	72
2 Greenalls Padgate St Oswalds	30	20	3	7	72	41	63
3 Eagle Sports	30	18	5	7	74	32	59
4 Denton Town	30	14	4	12	67	55	46
5 Gamesley	30	14	4	12	67	57	46
6 Linotype Cheadle HN	30	13	7	10	73	70	46
7 Lostock Gralam	30	13	5	12	65	63	44
8 Middlewich Town	30	12	7	11	48	52	43
9 Pilkington	30	12	7	11	55	63	43
10 Styal	30	11	8	11	44	44	41
11 Billinge	30	11	5	14	50	54	38
12 Rylands	30	10	7	13	40	45	37
13 Grappenhall Sports	30	9	6	15	61	84	33
14 Garswood United	30	7	8	15	36	58	29
15 Golborne Sports	30	7	6	17	49	74	27
16 Tarporley Victoria	30	3	1	26	23	77	10

DIVISION TWO	P	W	D	L	F	A	Pts
1 Whaley Bridge	24	17	2	5	71	31	53
2 Crewe	24	15	6	3	65	28	51
3 Rudheath Social	24	15	5	4	62	21	50
4 Poynton	24	14	6	4	70	41	48
5 Sandbach United	24	13	2	9	64	46	41
6 Runcorn Town Reserves	24	11	4	9	55	51	37
7 Whitchurch Alport	24	10	4	10	40	45	34
8 Maine Road Reserves	24	10	1	13	50	64	31
9 Congleton Town Reserves	24	7	6	11	56	80	27
10 Malpas	24	7	5	12	34	56	26
11 Moore United	24	5	3	16	41	64	18
12 Daten	24	5	2	17	37	60	17
13 Barnton	24	2	4	18	25	83	10

DIVISION ONE CUP

ROUND 1
Tarporley Victoria 0-2 Golborne Sports 2
Denton Town 4-4 4-5p Billinge FC
Rylands 2-0 Pilkington 0
Lostock Gralam 2-5 Greenalls Padgate St Oswa
Knutsford 8-1 Garswood United
Eagle Sports 4-2 Styal
Grappenhall Sports 0-2 Middlewich Town
Linotype Cheadle HN 1-0 Gamesley
QUARTER FINALS
Golborne Sports 2-3 Billinge FC
Rylands 2-1 Greenalls Padgate St Oswa
Knutsford 2-3 Eagle Sports
Middlewich Town 2-0 Linotype Cheadle HN
SEMI-FINALS
Billinge FC 2-1 Rylands
Eagle Sports 2-0 Middlewich Town
FINAL
Billinge FC 0-2 Eagle Sports

DIVISION TWO CHALLENGE CUP

ROUND 1
Maine Road Reserves 0-2 Daten
Malpas 2-3 Sandbach United
Barnton 3-9 Congleton Town Reserves
Rudheath Social 0-1 Whitchurch Alport
Poynton 0-5 Whaley Bridge
QUARTER FINALS
Daten 1-4 Runcorn Town Reserves
Sandbach United 7-1 Congleton Town Reserves
Moore United 2-1 Crewe
Whitchurch Alport 1-3 Whaley Bridge
SEMI-FINALS
Runcorn Town Res 2-5 Sandbach United
Moore United 1-3 Whaley Bridge
FINAL
Sandbach United 0-2 Whaley Bridge

RESERVES CHALLENGE CUP

FINAL
Billinge Reserves 1-2 Pilkington Reserves

DIVISION ONE	1	2	3	4	5	6	7	8	9	10	11	12	13	14	15	16
1 Billinge		1-2	1-1	4-1	2-1	1-2	1-1	0-3	0-1	3-0	4-1	0-3	1-4	2-3	2-1	5-0
2 Denton Town	7-1		0-2	5-0	3-0	2-1	3-4	1-3	1-1	0-1	4-2	3-2	1-1	2-0	2-2	3-0
3 Eagle Sports	3-2	3-0		4-2	0-1	1-2	5-0	2-3	1-0	2-1	5-2	2-1	1-2	4-0	3-0	2-0
4 Gamesley	0-3	5-1	1-2		6-0	2-1	3-2	2-3	0-0	3-2	2-2	1-2	2-1	1-1	1-2	6-2
5 Garswood United	1-1	1-2	1-1	2-1		3-2	2-2	1-0	0-3	5-1	1-1	1-1	2-2	1-1	1-2	3-1
6 Golborne Sports	0-1	4-4	1-6	0-3	3-1		2-2	2-4	0-1	2-5	4-1	2-2	2-4	1-1	0-3	2-0
7 Grappenhall Sports	1-1	2-4	1-4	4-3	2-1	1-4		1-2	3-6	2-4	3-5	1-3	1-1	4-0	4-1	2-0
8 Greenalls Padgate St Oswalds	6-3	3-2	1-1	5-1	3-1	2-0	2-2		1-0	5-1	2-1	0-2	0-2	1-0	1-2	3-1
9 Knutsford	0-0	4-1	1-0	2-0	2-0	6-0	4-2	1-0		4-2	3-0	2-0	5-0	3-4	1-0	3-0
10 Linotype Cheadle HN	4-2	2-1	1-9	2-5	3-0	2-2	2-1	4-4	2-3		4-4	3-0	6-1	2-3	2-2	1-1
11 Lostock Gralam	3-1	3-0	2-0	2-4	4-2	1-4	5-2	1-4	0-2	1-1		1-3	6-2	3-1	2-0	2-0
12 Middlewich Town	1-5	0-4	1-1	1-3	1-1	4-1	1-3	3-1	4-3	0-5	1-3		2-0	1-1	1-2	2-0
13 Pilkington	1-0	4-1	3-1	1-3	3-0	3-1	4-5	0-4	1-2	1-3	1-1	2-2		0-3	2-2	2-1
14 Rylands	2-0	1-0	1-2	0-1	1-0	2-2	8-0	1-2	0-1	2-2	0-2	0-2	1-2		0-3	1-0
15 Styal	1-2	1-3	0-0	1-1	2-0	2-0	3-2	2-1	0-1	2-3	2-1	1-1	2-2	1-1		1-2
16 Tarporley Victoria	0-1	1-5	1-6	0-4	2-3	4-2	0-1	1-3	1-3	0-2	1-3	0-1	2-3	0-1	2-1	

CHESHIRE LEAGUE DIVISION ONE CONSTITUTION 2012-13

BILLINGE	Billinge Comm. Spts/Soccer Cte , Carrmill Road , Billinge WN5 7TX	01744 893533
CREWE	Cumberland Arena, Thomas Street, Crewe CW1 2BD	01270 537150
DENTON TOWN	Whittles Park, Heather Lea, Denton M34 6EJ	07951 829551
EAGLE SPORTS	Eagle Sports Club, Thornton Road, Great Sankey, Warrington WA5 2SZ	01925 632926
GAMESLEY	Melandra Park, Melandra Castle Road, Gamesley, Glossop SK13 0JR	07590 204594
GARSWOOD UNITED	The Wooders, Simms Lane End, Garswood Road, Garswood, Ashton-in-Makerfield WN4 0XH	01744 893968
GRAPPENHALL SPORTS	Grappenhall Sports Club, Stockton Lane, Grappenhall, Warrington WA4 3HQ	01925 600899
GREENALLS PADGATE ST OSWALDS	Carlsberg Tetley Social Club, Long Lane, Warrington WA2 8PU	01925 634904
KNUTSFORD	Manchester Road, Knutsford WA16 0GU	07825 843506
LINOTYPE & CHEADLE HN	The Heath, Norbreck Avenue, Cheadle, Stockport SK8 2ET	0161 282 6574
LOSTOCK GRALAM	The Park Stadium, Manchester Road, Lostock Gralam CW9 7PJ	01606 42148
MIDDLEWICH TOWN	Seddon Street, Middlewich CW10 9DT	01606 835842
PILKINGTON	Ruskin Drive, Dentons Green, St Helens WA10 6RP	01744 22893
RYLANDS	Rylands Recreation Club, Gorsey Lane, Warrington WA2 7RZ	01925 625700
STYAL	Altrincham Road, Styal, Wilmslow SK9 4JE	01625 529303
WHALEY BRIDGE	Park Road, Whaley Bridge, High Peak SK23 7DJ	07759 218399

DIVISION TWO

	DIVISION TWO	1	2	3	4	5	6	7	8	9	10	11	12	13
1	Barnton		3-5	0-5	0-1	2-3	2-2	1-5	1-0	1-4	1-4	1-1	0-4	1-4
2	Congleton Town Reserves	5-3		2-3	1-0	5-3	3-0	6-2	1-2	2-2	1-3	0-9	2-5	1-2
3	Crewe	2-0	3-3		3-2	7-0	2-0	0-0	5-1	2-1	6-1	2-1	1-2	2-2
4	Daten	3-4	2-3	3-5		2-1	3-1	2-3	1-3	1-1	1-2	2-3	1-3	1-4
5	Maine Road Reserves	4-1	6-2	1-3	2-2		2-1	5-3	0-3	1-3	0-2	2-1	1-0	1-0
6	Malpas	4-0	2-2	2-2	0-2	3-1		2-0	0-4	1-1	2-7	3-1	1-5	0-2
7	Moore United	4-0	3-3	1-3	4-3	2-4	1-2		2-4	0-2	3-1	0-3	0-5	1-3
8	Poynton	3-0	3-3	3-2	4-1	4-2	9-2	1-1		2-2	2-2	2-2	1-2	4-1
9	Rudheath Social	7-0	10-0	0-1	3-0	3-1	0-1	1-0	3-3		3-1	2-0	4-1	2-0
10	Runcorn Town Reserves	1-1	2-2	2-1	2-1	3-4	2-3	3-0	0-3	1-3		5-3	2-1	3-3
11	Sandbach United	8-0	5-1	1-5	4-1	5-3	2-1	3-1	1-4	0-4	1-0		1-3	2-0
12	Whaley Bridge	2-2	5-2	0-0	4-0	4-2	3-1	4-3	5-0	2-0	4-1	2-3		1-2
13	Whitchurch Alport	2-1	2-1	0-0	0-2	3-1	0-0	3-2	2-5	0-1	2-5	2-4	1-4	

CHESHIRE LEAGUE DIVISION TWO CONSTITUTION 2012-13

BARNTON	Townfield, Townfield Lane, Barnton, Northwich CW8 4LH	07597 143886
CHEERY BROOK	Montrose Avenue, Wigan, Lancashire WN5 9X	07867 553901
CONGLETON VALE	Congleton High School, Box Lane, Congleton, Cheshire CW12 4NS	07854 232978
DATEN	Culcheth Sports Club, Charnock Road, Culcheth, Warrington WA3 5SH	01925 763096
EGERTON	Mereheath Lane, Knutsford, Cheshire WA16 6S	07970 963992
GOLBORNE SPORTS	Simpson Playing Fields, Stone Cross Road, Lowton WA3 2SL	01942 510161
MAINE ROAD RESERVES	Manchester Co. FA Ground, Branthingham Rd, Chorlton-cum-Hardy M21 0TT	0161 604 7620
MALPAS	Malpas & District Sports Club, Oxheys, Wrexham Road, Malpas SY14 7EJ	01948 860662
MOORE UNITED	Carlsberg Tetley Club, Long Lane, Warrington WA2 8PU	01925 634904
PENLAKE	Sutton Road, St Helens, Merseyside WA9 3D	07990 765532
POYNTON	London Road North (A523), Poynton, Stockport SK12 1AG	01625 875765
RUDHEATH SOCIAL	Moss Farm Leisure Complex, Winnington, Northwich CW8 4BG	01606 783835
RUNCORN TOWN RESERVES	Pavilions Club, Sandy Lane, Weston Point, Runcorn WA7 4EX	01928 590508
SANDBACH UNITED	Winsford United FC, The Barton Stadium, Wharton Road, Winsford CW7 3AE	01606 558447
TARPORLEY VICTORIA	Tattenhall Recreation Club, Field Lane, Tattenhall CH3 9QF	01829 770710

RESERVE DIVISION		P	W	D	L	F	A	Pts
1	Billinge Reserves	30	19	5	6	82	38	62
2	Pilkington Reserves	30	18	4	8	92	64	58
3	Eagl Sports Reserves	30	17	3	10	66	58	54
4	Denton Town Reserves	30	17	2	11	81	74	53
5	Linotype Cheadle HN Reserves	30	16	4	10	82	61	52
6	Poynton Reserves	30	13	7	10	64	52	46
7	Greenalls Padgate St O Res.	30	13	7	10	55	50	46
8	Rylands Reserves	30	13	7	10	46	42	46
9	Grappenhall Sports Reserves	30	14	1	15	63	70	43
10	Gamesley Reserves	30	12	5	13	55	69	41
11	Golborne Sports Reserves	30	12	4	14	64	69	40
12	Styal Reserves	30	12	2	16	69	72	38
13	Middlewich Town Reserves	30	9	5	16	47	59	32
14	Lostock Gralam Reserves	30	7	7	16	75	84	28
15	Garswood United Reserves	30	7	6	17	53	83	27
16	Daten Reserves	30	4	5	21	42	91	17

DORSET PREMIER LEAGUE

Sponsored by: Magna
Founded: 1957
Recent Champions:
2007: Westland Sports
2008: Portland United
2009: Portland United
2010: Hamworthy Recreation
2011: Hamworthy Recreation

LEAGUE CUP

PRELIMINARY ROUND
Hamworthy Recreation 8-1 Cranborne
Bridport Reserves 8-5 Holt United
Sturminster Marshall 2-3 Westland Sports
ROUND 1
Parley Sports 3-1 Wincanton Town
Hamworthy Recreation 9-1 Sherborne Town Reserves
Shaftesbury Town 3-1 Weymouth Reserves
Hamworthy United Reserves 0-3 Blandford United
Poole Borough 2-5 Portland United
Swanage Town & Herston F. 7-1 Tintinhull
Chickerell United 3-0 Merley Cobham Sports
Bridport Reserves 0-2 Westland Sports
ROUND 2
Parley Sports 0-2 Hamworthy Recreation
Shaftesbury Town 0-4 Blandford United
Portland United 1-2 (aet) Swanage Town & Herston
Chickerell United 0-3 Westland Sports
SEMI FINALS
Hamworthy Recreation 4-1 Blandford United
Swanage Town & Herston 2-3 Westland Sports
FINAL
Hamworthy Recreation 2-2 2-4p Westland Sports

	P	W	D	L	F	A	Pts
1 Westland Sports	36	30	4	2	139	30	94
2 Hamworthy Recreation	36	29	2	5	115	31	89
3 Portland United	36	27	5	4	102	28	86
4 Wincanton Town (-3)	36	26	7	3	101	32	82
5 Holt United	36	21	6	9	92	49	69
6 Chickerell United	36	19	5	12	71	55	62
7 Bridport Reserves	36	16	6	14	70	65	54
8 Parley Sports	36	15	6	15	63	58	51
9 Sturminster Marshall	36	14	6	16	70	64	48
10 Swanage Town & Herston	36	14	5	17	65	94	47
11 Blandford United	36	13	5	18	77	87	44
12 Weymouth Reserves (-6)	36	12	6	18	57	71	36
13 Tintinhull (-3)	36	10	6	20	47	80	33
14 Hamworthy United Reserves	36	9	6	21	61	117	33
15 Merley Cobham Sports	36	8	8	20	56	81	32
16 Poole Borough	36	9	5	22	76	116	32
17 Cranborne	36	8	3	25	50	100	27
18 Shaftesbury	36	7	4	25	51	114	25
19 Sherborne Town Reserves	36	6	3	27	29	120	21

	1	2	3	4	5	6	7	8	9	10	11	12	13	14	15	16	17	18	19
1 Blandford United		3-1	4-2	3-4	0-3	6-1	2-1	0-1	2-5	6-3	1-6	5-2	5-1	1-3	4-1	2-1	3-3	3-2	0-1
2 Bridport Reserves	5-1		1-3	2-0	1-5	5-0	1-1	1-1	3-1	3-3	2-2	7-2	3-1	2-2	1-0	2-0	1-5	3-1	0-2
3 Chickerell United	1-0	2-1		0-1	0-1	3-0	1-0	1-1	3-2	2-3	0-1	5-1	2-1	3-1	2-4	1-0	1-1	0-0	0-6
4 Cranborne	2-2	0-4	0-2		0-8	2-0	4-5	2-2	1-2	1-2	1-1	4-1	7-0	0-3	2-0	2-3	1-2	4-3	0-5
5 Hamworthy Recreation	2-0	4-0	5-0	5-1		8-1	2-1	1-0	1-0	5-2	2-1	4-2	1-0	4-3	7-0	4-0	1-1	2-1	3-0
6 Hamworthy United Reserves	5-2	2-0	1-4	2-1	0-3		2-7	2-2	1-2	0-4	1-6	2-1	4-1	1-3	3-4	2-3	0-3	5-1	3-3
7 Holt United	3-1	3-1	4-2	1-0	3-0	3-3		1-0	1-1	2-0	0-4	4-2	4-0	0-0	2-0	5-0	0-1	4-0	0-2
8 Merley Cobham Sports	1-5	0-2	1-1	3-1	1-0	3-5			3-1	0-0	2-2	9-0	0-2	2-4	4-4	1-4	1-3		3-5
9 Parley Sports	2-0	2-1	0-3	3-0	1-2	7-2	0-1	1-3		5-0	1-3	1-1	4-0	1-1	0-0	3-1	0-3	4-1	1-0
10 Poole Borough	2-4	2-3	3-5	1-2	0-3	1-1	2-2	0-3	1-2		1-3	6-1	7-0	1-5	4-3	6-5	1-6	3-3	3-3
11 Portland United	3-1	4-0	1-2	4-0	1-0	3-0	0-0	6-0	5-1	3-1		4-1	1-0	2-0	4-0	5-1	2-1	1-2	
12 Shaftesbury	2-1	0-1	0-3	5-4	0-7	3-4	0-6	2-3	2-2	4-1	1-2		3-0	2-0	2-1	1-2	2-3	1-3	0-6
13 Sherborne Town Reserves	1-3	0-0	0-7	2-0	1-4	1-6	0-6	2-1	0-1	6-1	0-8	2-1		1-4	2-3	1-0	0-6	2-0	0-4
14 Sturminster Marshall	7-0	1-5	1-5	3-2	0-3	1-1	1-2	4-1	1-0	5-4	0-1	1-1	5-1		0-1	3-0	2-3	3-3	1-2
15 Swanage Town & Herston	2-1	1-3	1-0	3-1	2-2	6-2	0-7	2-2	3-3	8-0	0-4	5-0	1-0	3-2		0-1	1-0	0-1	1-4
16 Tintinhull	1-1	6-2	2-3	1-0	1-4	1-1	4-1	2-1	0-1	1-2	0-5	1-2	1-1	1-0	4-2		0-5	1-3	0-3
17 Westland Sports	3-1	2-1	3-1	8-0	2-1	11-0	3-1	4-0	3-2	3-1	5-1	8-0	2-1	6-1	18-1	3-0		4-0	0-2
18 Weymouth Reserves	2-2	1-2	1-1	3-0	0-2	2-1	5-3	1-2	2-0	3-2	1-2	1-0	5-0	0-1	3-2	0-0	0-2		1-2
19 Wincanton Town	2-2	2-0	3-0	6-0	3-2	4-1	2-1	3-1	8-0	6-2	3-1	2-1	1-1	1-0	2-2	0-0	1-2	5-0	

DORSET PREMIER LEAGUE CONSTITUTION 2012-13

BLANDFORD UNITED	Recreation Ground, Park Road, Blandford Forum DT11 7BX	07932 414524
BRIDPORT RESERVES	St Marys Field, Skilling Hill Road, Bridport DT6 5LN	01308 423834
CHICKERELL UNITED	Weymouth College, Cranford Avenue, Weymouth DT4 7LQ	01305 208892
CRANBORNE	Recreation Ground, Penny's Lane, Cranborne, Wimborne BH21 5QE	01725 517440
HAMWORTHY RECREATION	Hamworthy Rec. Club, Magna Road, Canford Magna, Wimborne BH21 3AP	01202 881922
HAMWORTHY UNITED RESERVES	The County Ground, Blandford Close, Hamworthy, Poole BH15 4BF	01202 674974
HOLT UNITED	Gaunts Common, Holt, Wimborne BH21 4JR	01258 840379
MERLEY COBHAM SPORTS	Cobham Sports & Social Club, Merley House Lane, Wimborne BH21 3AA	01202 885773
PARLEY SPORTS	Parley Sports Club, Christchurch Road, West Parley BH22 8SQ	01202 573345
POOLE BOROUGH	Turlin Moor Recreation Ground, Blandford Moor, Hamworthy, Poole BH21 5XX	
		Club Office: 01202 674973
PORTLAND UNITED	New Grove Corner, Grove Road, Portland DT5 1DP	01305 861489
SHAFTESBURY TOWN	Cockrams, Coppice Street, Shaftesbury SP7 8PF	01747 853990
SHERBORNE TOWN RESERVES	Raleigh Grove, The Terrace Playing Fields, Sherborne DT9 5NS	01935 816110
SWANAGE TOWN & HERSTON	Day's Park, off De Moulham Road, Swanage BH19 2JW	01929 424673
TINTINHULL	Montacute Road, Tintinhull, Yeovil BA22 8QD	07876 520800
WAREHAM RANGERS	Worgret Road, Wareham, Dorset BH20 4P	07854 380615
WEYMOUTH RESERVES	Wessex Stadium, Radipole Lane, Weymouth DT4 9XJ 01305 785558 Fax: 01305 766658	
WINCANTON TOWN	Wincanton Sports Ground, Moor Lane, Wincanton BA9 9EJ	01963 31815

ESSEX & SUFFOLK BORDER LEAGUE

Sponsored by: Kent Blaxill
Founded: 1911
Recent Champions:
2007: Gas Recreation
2008: Gas Recreation
2009: West Bergholt
2010: Gas Recreation
2011: Brightlingsea Regent

LEAGUE CUP

QUARTER-FINALS

Harwich & Parkeston 1-0 West Bergholt

Coggeshall Town 2-1 Mersea Island

Gas Recreation 6-1 Clacton United

Newbury Forest 3-2 Holland FC

SEMI-FINALS

Harwich & Parkeston 4-0 Newbury Forest

Coggeshall Town 1-0 Gas Recreation

FINAL

Coggeshall Town 0-1 Harwich & Parkeston

PREMIER DIVISION

		P	W	D	L	F	A	Pts
1	West Bergholt	30	22	4	4	77	27	70
2	Harwich & Parkeston	30	21	6	3	78	28	69
3	Newbury Forest	30	20	2	8	78	36	62
4	Gas Recreation	30	19	4	7	92	47	61
5	Lawford Lads (-3)	30	17	6	7	67	48	54
6	Little Oakley	30	17	3	10	63	47	54
7	Alresford Colne Rangers	30	10	9	11	54	42	39
8	Hatfield Peverel	30	8	10	12	48	58	34
9	Hedinghams United	30	10	4	16	39	59	34
10	Rowhedge	30	9	5	16	57	73	32
11	Dedham Old Boys	30	9	5	16	56	76	32
12	Holland	30	8	8	14	39	59	32
13	University of Essex	30	10	2	18	35	65	32
14	Great Bentley	30	8	5	17	50	79	29
15	Wormingford Wanderers (+3)	30	5	7	18	43	78	25
16	White Notley	30	5	4	21	35	89	19

PREMIER DIVISION

		1	2	3	4	5	6	7	8	9	10	11	12	13	14	15	16
1	Alresford Colne Rangers		3-0	0-1	3-3	2-4	2-5	2-0	2-2	4-0	0-1	3-4	5-1	4-0	0-1	0-0	1-1
2	Dedham Old Boys	2-3		0-7	0-0	1-1	3-1	4-3	5-1	5-0	1-3	1-4	2-4	2-2	2-3	3-2	2-5
3	Gas Recreation	1-1	9-2		3-1	2-1	6-2	4-0	1-1	1-3	5-1	2-0	5-4	1-0	4-2	5-1	6-3
4	Great Bentley	3-3	1-3	1-3		0-5	0-1	1-2	3-0	0-2	2-3	3-7	3-4	1-0	1-4	3-1	2-2
5	Harwich & Parkeston	1-0	2-0	1-1	6-0		0-0	1-0	2-0	4-1	4-3	1-1	1-0	2-0	0-2	5-0	2-1
6	Hatfield Peverel	2-0	4-2	2-3	2-3	2-2		1-0	1-1	2-5	1-0	1-3	0-0	0-3	0-4	3-1	1-1
7	Hedinghams United	1-5	0-3	2-0	2-4	3-5	3-3		2-1	2-0	1-3	1-0	1-0	1-2	1-3	2-0	6-2
8	Holland	2-1	3-1	0-4	5-0	1-1	1-1	1-1		2-2	L-W	0-3	4-2	1-2	1-1	2-1	2-0
9	Lawford Lads	0-1	3-1	4-2	3-1	2-1	1-1	2-2	2-1		2-2	0-2	5-1	1-0	3-1	4-0	4-1
10	Little Oakley	0-0	2-1	2-1	2-4	0-3	2-1	3-0	6-0	2-1		2-3	5-0	5-0	0-3	6-1	2-1
11	Newbury Forest	3-1	1-1	2-3	3-1	1-2	5-1	5-0	6-0	3-4	4-1		W-L	3-0	1-2	2-1	2-0
12	Rowhedge	1-5	3-2	1-7	0-2	0-3	0-0	3-0	1-3	1-1	2-0	2-3		6-0	0-3	2-2	1-1
13	University of Essex	1-3	1-2	6-3	1-2	1-4	1-1	1-0	1-0	0-3	0-2	0-3	1-3		2-3	4-1	3-2
14	West Bergholt	0-0	3-1	1-0	1-1	1-2	2-0	0-0	3-0	1-2	4-0	2-1	4-1	5-0		4-3	5-0
15	White Notley	2-0	1-3	2-2	4-2	1-7	1-7	0-1	3-2	2-2	0-3	1-0	1-6	1-2	0-5		0-1
16	Wormingford Wanderers	0-0	1-1	1-0	4-2	2-5	3-2	0-2	1-2	2-5	2-2	0-3	4-8	0-1	1-4	1-2	

ESSEX & SUFFOLK BORDER LEAGUE PREMIER DIVISION CONSTITUTION 2012-13

ALRESFORD COLNE RANGERS	Ford Lane, Alresford, Colchester CO7 8AU	07796 036467
DEDHAM OLD BOYS	Old Grammar School Ground, The Drift, Dedham, Colchester CO7 6AH	None
EARLS COLNE	Green Farm Meadow, Halstead Road, Earls Colne, Colchester CO6 2NG	01787 223584
GAS RECREATION	Bromley Road, Colchester CO4 3JE	01206 860383
GREAT BENTLEY	The Green, Heckfords Road, Great Bentley, Colchester CO7 8LY	01206 251532
HARWICH & PARKESTON	The Royal Oak, Main Road, Dovercourt, Harwich CO12 4AA	01255 503643
HATFIELD PEVEREL	Strutt Memorial Field, Maldon Road, Hatfield Peverel CM3 2HT	None
HAVERHILL SPORTS ASSOCIATION	The New Croft, Chalkerstone Way, Haverhill CB9 0LD	01440 702137
HEDINGHAMS UNITED	Lawn Meadow, Yeldham Road, Sible Hedingham, Halstead CO9 3QH	None
HOLLAND	Eastcliff Sports Ground, Dulwich Road, Holland-on-Sea CO15 5HP	01255 814874
LAWFORD LADS	School Lane, Lawford, Manningtree CO11 2JA	01206 397211
LITTLE OAKLEY	War Memorial Club Ground, Harwich Road, Little Oakley, Harwich CO12 5ED	01255 880370
MALDON ST MARYS	Tiptree Sports Centre, Maypole Road, Tiptree, Colchester CO5 0EJ	01621 817499
UNIVERSITY OF ESSEX	University Essex Sports Centre, Wivenhoe Park, Colchester CO4 3SQ	01206 873250
WEST BERGHOLT	Lorkin Daniel Field, Lexden Road, West Bergholt, Colchester CO6 3BW	01206 241525
WHITE NOTLEY	Oak Farm, Faulkbourne, Witham CM8 1SF	01376 519864

ESSEX & SUFFOLK BORDER LEAGUE - STEP 7

DIVISION ONE

		P	W	D	L	F	A	Pts
1	Haverhill Sports Association	30	24	3	3	119	32	75
2	Maldon St Marys (-2)	30	20	4	6	88	35	62
3	Earls Colne	30	18	2	10	78	50	56
4	Tiptree Jobserve	30	17	5	8	62	51	56
5	Coggeshall Town (+3)	30	15	5	10	68	39	53
6	Colne Engaine & Bell United	30	16	3	11	64	36	51
7	Boxted Lodgers	30	15	2	13	48	51	47
8	Clacton United (+2)	30	12	8	10	66	66	46
9	Foxash Social (-2)	30	12	5	13	55	63	39
10	Barnston	30	10	6	14	49	64	36
11	St Osyth	30	10	6	14	48	78	36
12	Kirby Athletic	30	9	7	14	45	51	34
13	Mersea Island (+4)	30	6	9	15	44	59	31
14	Rayne	30	8	4	18	44	98	28
15	Bradfield Rovers	30	5	3	22	37	81	18
16	Gosfield United (-2)	30	3	8	19	28	89	15

TOMMY THOMPSON KNOCK-OUT CUP

FINAL

Great Bentley Reserves 0-2 Harwich & Parkeston Reserves

AV LEE MEMORIAL TROPHY

(League winners v League Cup holders)

Brightlingsea Regent 5-0 West Bergholt

RESERVE KNOCKOUT CUP

FINAL

Great Bentley Reserves 2-3 Little Oakley Reserves

DIVISION ONE

	DIVISION ONE	1	2	3	4	5	6	7	8	9	10	11	12	13	14	15	16
1	Barnston		0-2	1-0	2-3	1-5	1-3	2-3	2-6	2-2	L-W	1-2	1-1	2-0	3-1	3-2	2-3
2	Boxted Lodgers	0-1		2-1	1-1	1-2	2-1	1-3	1-2	0-0	0-4	3-2	1-0	1-0	1-4	2-3	2-0
3	Bradfield Rovers	0-0	1-6		1-2	1-2	0-1	0-3	2-5	2-1	1-4	0-2	0-4	2-2	1-2	1-2	2-3
4	Clacton United	4-2	0-1	3-4		2-2	2-1	3-2	2-2	W-L	1-2	1-0	4-2	2-2	5-2	2-2	2-3
5	Coggeshall Town	0-0	0-1	3-1	6-2		2-3	1-2	5-0	1-2	2-4	4-0	0-1	2-0	2-0	4-1	1-0
6	Colne Engaine & Bell United	3-1	3-0	0-1	4-1	1-1		1-2	1-2	1-1	1-2	2-1	1-2	4-3	2-3	6-0	1-1
7	Earls Colne	3-2	3-0	1-2	0-2	2-3	2-0		7-3	0-0	0-4	1-0	1-4	3-0	2-2	1-2	4-0
8	Foxash Social	1-2	0-4	3-3	3-2	1-5	1-4	1-4		5-0	0-4	1-0	2-3	4-1	0-0	W-L	0-0
9	Gosfield United	2-3	0-3	3-2	1-3	0-5	0-4	0-6	0-4		0-4	1-1	3-3	2-2	1-2	3-0	1-4
10	Haverhill Sports Association	10-0	2-1	7-2	6-6	3-3	1-2	5-1	2-0	7-0		3-1	6-0	3-1	9-1	5-1	9-1
11	Kirby Athletic	1-3	3-1	2-0	2-2	2-0	0-2	4-2	0-2	2-0	2-2		1-2	1-1	4-0	1-1	2-3
12	Maldon St Marys	2-0	9-1	1-0	6-2	3-0	1-0	4-1	2-0	6-1	0-1	2-1		0-0	5-1	12-0	1-1
13	Mersea Island	2-2	1-3	4-0	1-1	2-2	1-2	1-3	2-0	3-0	3-1	0-0	1-6		2-0	1-2	2-1
14	Rayne	1-5	0-3	4-2	1-5	2-1	1-8	0-7	1-1	3-3	0-4	4-6	3-2	4-3		1-3	0-1
15	St Osyth	2-2	4-1	2-5	3-1	0-4	0-2	1-5	0-3	6-0	0-5	2-2	0-3	2-0	4-0		1-1
16	Tiptree Jobserve	0-3	1-3	6-0	2-0	1-0	1-0	2-4	4-3	5-1	2-0	5-0	2-1	4-3	3-1	2-2	

ESSEX & SUFFOLK BORDER LEAGUE DIVISION ONE CONSTITUTION 2012-13

BARNSTON	High Easter Road , Barnston , Dunmow CM6 1LZ	07712 129459
BOXTED LODGERS	The Playing Field, Cage Lane, Boxted, Colchester CO4 5RE	01206 271969
BRADFIELD ROVERS	The Playing Field, The Street, Bradfield, Manningtree CO11 2UU	None
CLACTON UNITED	Vista Road Recreation Ground, Vista Road, Clacton-on-Sea CO15 6DB	01255 429647
COGGESHALL TOWN	The Crops, West Street, Coggeshall CO6 1NS	01376 562843
COLNE ENGAINE & BELL UNITED	Kynaston Road, Panfield, Braintree CM7 1WX	None
FOXASH SOCIAL	Foxash Playing Field, Harwich Road, Lawford, Manningtree CO11 2LP	01206 231309
GOSFIELD UNITED	The Playing Field, Church Lane, Gosfield, Halstead CO9 1UB	None
KIRBY ATHLETIC	Kirby Playing Field, Halstead Road, Kirby Cross CO13 0LS	None
MERSEA ISLAND	The Glebe, Colchester Road, West Mersea CO5 8RS	01206 385216
RAYNE	Rayne Village Hall, Oak Meadow, Gore Road, Rayne, Braintree CM77 6TX	01376 349408
TIPTREE JOBSERVE	Warriors Rest, Maypole Road, Tiptree CO5 0EN	None
TOLLESBURY	Elysian Gardens, Tollesbury, Maldon CM9 8Q	07746 631670
WORMINGFORD WANDERERS	Wormingford Playing Field, Main Road, Wormingford, Colchester CO6 3AF	None

ESSEX OLYMPIAN LEAGUE

Sponsored by: ProKit UK
Founded: 1966
Recent Champions:
2007: White Ensign
2008: White Ensign
2009: Harold Wood Athletic
2010: Harold Wood Athletic
2011: Kelvedon Hatch

SENIOR CUP

ROUND 1

Sandon Royals 2-1 (aet) Herongate Athletic
Sungate 3-0 Thurrock Reserves
Basildon Town 1-2 Frenford Senior
Toby 1-4 (aet) Harold Wood Athletic
Ryan F.C. 3-2 Canning Town
Upminster 2-4 Benfleet
Kelvedon Hatch 3-1 (aet) Leigh Ramblers
Leytonstone United 3-2 Ramsden Scotia
Stambridge United 6-1 Chingford Athletic
Rayleigh Town 5-5 6-5p Westhamians
Broomfield 3-1 Lakeside
M & B Club 1-2 Forest Glade
Southminster St. Leonards 5-0 Galleywood
Springfield 1-2 White Ensign
Runwell Hospital 2-4 Old Southendian
Old Chelmsfordians 5-0 Burnham Ramblers Reserves
Harold Hill 3-2 Ongar Town
Epping 3-7 Hutton

PREMIER DIVISION	P	W	D	L	F	A	Pts
1 Frenford Senior	26	17	6	3	49	25	57
2 Kelvedon Hatch	26	15	6	5	62	29	51
3 Hannakins Farm	26	14	3	9	56	46	45
4 Rayleigh Town	26	13	5	8	69	45	44
5 Buckhurst Hill	26	14	2	10	48	41	44
6 Westhamians	25	13	3	9	62	46	42
7 Hutton	26	11	4	11	66	59	37
8 White Ensign (+3)	25	10	3	12	49	50	36
9 Harold Wood Athletic	26	11	2	13	50	41	35
10 Manford Way	26	11	2	13	42	63	35
11 M & B Club (-6)	26	7	9	10	37	43	24
12 Galleywood (+3)	26	6	3	17	24	82	24
13 Harold Hill (-3)	26	7	4	15	37	42	22
14 Canning Town (-3)	26	2	8	16	34	73	11

PREMIER DIVISION	1	2	3	4	5	6	7	8	9	10	11	12	13	14
1 Buckhurst Hill		3-1	1-2	5-1	1-2	1-1	2-1	3-5	0-4	3-0	1-2	2-1	1-2	4-1
2 Canning Town	0-1		1-1	3-1	2-3	2-2	1-3	2-5	1-4	0-0	1-4	1-6	1-3	1-6
3 Frenford Senior	0-1	2-2		0-0	3-0	1-0	0-1	1-3	3-1	2-1	2-1	3-1	1-0	5-0
4 Galleywood	0-3	0-4	1-1		1-3	2-1	1-6	3-1	2-1	3-1	2-2	0-3	0-5	0-6
5 Hannakins Farm	2-1	3-1	1-2	3-2		3-0	3-7	2-3	1-3	2-2	2-3	3-0	3-3	3-0
6 Harold Hill	0-2	6-0	0-1	1-3	4-0		1-0	3-0	2-1	0-2	0-1	4-4	1-3	1-2
7 Harold Wood Athletic	0-2	2-1	1-3	4-0	0-1	2-1		4-2	0-1	0-2	4-1	4-4	1-3	3-1
8 Hutton	6-0	2-2	1-2	7-1	3-1	0-1	1-1		1-3	1-1	4-1	1-4	2-4	5-3
9 Kelvedon Hatch	1-1	1-1	1-1	6-0	1-3	3-0	2-1	6-1		2-0	6-0	3-1	2-1	2-2
10 M & B Club	2-4	0-0	3-4	2-0	0-0	1-4	3-2	1-1	2-2		3-1	1-1	1-1	1-2
11 Manford Way	1-2	4-1	0-3	1-0	0-5	2-0	1-0	1-0	1-1	3-2		2-5	2-4	2-1
12 Rayleigh Town	3-0	5-0	3-3	0-1	1-0	2-1	2-1	3-4	1-2	3-4	5-2		1-1	4-1
13 Westhamians	2-4	4-3	0-1	7-0	2-4	3-2	1-0	3-6	1-2	2-0	6-2	0-4		V
14 White Ensign	1-0	2-2	1-2	6-0	1-3	1-1	1-2	3-1	2-1	0-2	3-2	1-2	2-1	

V - Westhamians v White Ensign was declared void and left unplayed

ESSEX OLYMPIAN LEAGUE PREMIER DIVISION CONSTITUTION 2012-13

ALDBOROUGH ATHLETIC	Fairlop Oak Playing Fields, Forest Road, Hainault IG6 3HJ	020 8500 3777
BUCKHURST HILL	Roding Lane, Buckhurst Hill IG9 6BJ	020 8504 1189
FRENFORD SENIOR	Oakfields Sports Ground, Forest Road, Barkingside IG6 2JL	020 8500 1998
HANNAKINS FARM	Hannakins Farm Community Centre, Rosebay Avenue, Billericay CM12 0SY	01277 630851
HAROLD HILL	Brentwood Town FC, The Arena, The Brentwood Centre, Doddinghurst Road, Brentwood CM15 9NN	07776 232071
HAROLD WOOD ATHLETIC	Harold Wood Recreation Park, Harold View, Harold Wood RM3 0LX	01708 375698
HUTTON	Hall Green Lane, Hutton, Brentwood CM13 2Q	07850 766819
KELVEDON HATCH	New Hall, School Road, Kelvedon Hatch, Brentwood CM15 0DH	07774 129867
M & B CLUB	Sanofi-Aventis Spts/Soc. Club, Dagenham Road, Dagenham RM7 0QX	020 8919 2156
MANFORD WAY	London Marathon Sports Ground, Forest Road, Hainault IG6 3HJ	020 8500 3486
RAYLEIGH TOWN	Rayleigh Town Sports/Soc. Club, London Road, Rayleigh SS6 9DT	01268 784001
SOUTHMINSTER ST LEONARDS	King George V Playing Fields, Station Road, Southminster CM0 7EW	07718 869883
WESTHAMIANS	Fairlop Oak Playing Field, Forest Road, Hainault IG6 3HJ	07968 770896
WHITE ENSIGN	Borough Football Comb. HQ, Eastwoodbury Lane, Southend-on-Sea SS2 6XG	01702 520482

ESSEX OLYMPIAN LEAGUE - STEP 7

SENIOR CHALLENGE CUP
(Premier Champions v Senior Cup Holders)

Kelvedon Hatch 5-2 Rayleigh Town

DIVISION ONE	P	W	D	L	F	A	Pts
1 Southminster St Leonards	24	17	5	2	66	34	56
2 Ongar Town	24	14	3	7	83	48	45
3 Aldborough Athletic	24	13	3	8	57	43	42
4 Wadham Lodge (+2)	24	11	4	9	54	51	39
5 Sandon Royals (-3)	24	13	2	9	53	35	38
6 Bish Stort. Swifts (-3)	24	12	3	9	44	37	36
7 Runwell Hospital	23	10	5	8	38	38	35
8 Thurrock Reserves	23	10	4	9	43	44	34
9 Herongate Ath (+1)	24	11	1	12	45	49	33
10 Old Chelmsfordians	24	10	0	14	50	57	30
11 Benfleet (-3)	24	8	5	11	42	52	26
12 Epping	24	4	3	17	31	74	15
13 Lakeside	24	2	2	20	34	78	8

SENIOR CUP continued...

ROUND 2
Hannakins Farm 2-1 Sandon Royals
Sungate 1-3 Frenford Senior
Harold Wood Athletic 2-1 Ryan F.C.
Benfleet 1-3 Kelvedon Hatch
Leytonstone United 3-6 (aet) Stambridge United
Rayleigh Town 5-0 Catholic United
Broomfield 1-3 Debden Sports
Roydon 2-3 Forest Glade
Aldborough Athletic 4-3 Southminster St. Leonards
White Ensign 3-1 Manford Way
Old Southendian 4-1 Old Chelmsfordians
Buckhurst Hill 0-1 (aet) Harold Hill
Hutton 3-2 Wadham Lodge
Castle United 7-1 Bishops Stortford Swifts
Newham United 2-1 Writtle
Old Barkabbeyans 1-0 Shenfield A.F.C.

ROUND 3
Hannakins Farm 2-1 Frenford Senior
Harold Wood Athletic 0-1 Kelvedon Hatch
Stambridge United 1-4 Rayleigh Town
Debden Sports 4-2 Forest Glade
Aldborough Athletic 4-3 (aet) White Ensign
Old Southendian 0-1 Harold Hill
Hutton 1-4 Castle United
Newham United 1-5 Old Barkabbeyans

DIVISION ONE	1	2	3	4	5	6	7	8	9	10	11	12	13
1 Aldborough Athletic		1-2	3-0	7-3	1-0	2-1	2-1	4-0	0-1	3-1	3-1	1-1	3-3
2 Benfleet	2-3		2-3	3-4	2-1	2-2	1-0	3-5	2-0	1-1	2-2	1-1	2-5
3 Bishops Stortford Swifts	1-1	2-1		4-1	5-3	2-2	3-1	5-2	3-0	0-2	1-2	3-0	1-0
4 Epping	0-2	1-6	1-0		1-2	0-2	1-3	1-4	0-0	2-6	1-2	0-3	0-1
5 Herongate Athletic	4-1	2-0	0-2	2-1		3-1	5-2	0-3	1-0	1-6	0-1	4-0	4-4
6 Lakeside	1-4	0-1	1-2	2-3	2-4		2-3	2-10	0-3	1-2	1-4	3-2	3-4
7 Old Chelmsfordians	2-4	0-1	1-0	5-2	4-3	4-3		1-9	2-3	2-0	3-4	4-0	1-2
8 Ongar Town	2-5	4-2	1-1	8-1	0-2	4-3	3-2		0-1	5-0	3-3	0-1	4-1
9 Runwell Hospital	5-1	1-1	2-1	2-2	3-0	4-0	3-2	1-1		1-7	3-3	1-4	1-4
10 Sandon Royals	3-2	4-0	0-1	1-2	3-0	4-0	3-0	2-6	2-1		0-2	2-1	0-1
11 Southminster St Leonard's	4-1	4-0	2-0	5-1	4-1	4-1	3-1	2-4	1-0	W-L		0-0	7-3
12 Thurrock Reserves	3-2	4-0	6-4	3-2	2-1	3-0	0-3	3-2	V	2-2	2-3		1-2
13 Wadham Lodge	2-1	2-5	3-0	1-1	1-2	4-1	0-3	2-3	1-2	1-2	3-3	4-1	

V - Thurrock reserves v Runwell Hospital was declared void and left unplayed

ESSEX OLYMPIAN LEAGUE DIVISION ONE CONSTITUTION 2012-13

BENFLEET	The Club House, Woodside Extension, Manor Rd, Benfleet, Rayleigh SS7 4BG	01268 743957
BISHOP'S STORTFORD SWIFTS	Silver Leys, Hadham Road (A1250), Bishop's Stortford CM23 2QE	01279 658941
CANNING TOWN	Terence McMillan Stadium, Newham Leisure Centre, 281 Prince Regents Lane, London E13 8SD	020 7511 4477
GALLEYWOOD	Clarkes Field, Slades Lane, Galleywood, Chelmsford CM2 8RW	01245 352975
HERONGATE ATHLETIC	Adjacent to 77 Billericay Road, Herongate, Brentwood CM13 3PU	01277 810717
NEWBURY FOREST	Forest Road, Hainault, Ilford IG6 3H	07711 073344
OLD CHELMSFORDIANS	Lawford Lane, Roxwell Road, Chelmsford CM1 2NS	01245 420442
OLD SOUTHENDIAN	Warner's Bridge Park, Chandlers Way, Southend-on-Sea SS2 5RR	01702 549000
ONGAR TOWN	Sports Ground, Love Lane, High Street, Ongar CM5 9BL	01277 363838
RUNWELL HOSPITAL	Runwell Hospital, Runwell Chase, Wickford SS11 7QA	07764 560614
SPRINGFIELD	Springfield Hall Park, Arun Close, Springfield, Chelmsford CM1 7QE	01245 492441
WADHAM LODGE	Wadham Lodge Sports Ground, Kitcheher Road, Walthamstow E17 4JP	020 8527 2444

DIVISION TWO	P	W	D	L	F	A	Pts
1 Springfield	22	16	2	4	56	34	50
2 Old Southendian	22	16	1	5	49	30	49
3 Castle United	22	15	2	5	61	34	47
4 Roydon	22	11	3	8	48	38	36
5 Broomfield	22	11	2	9	53	44	35
6 Ryan (+3)	22	9	2	11	39	40	32
7 Burnham Ramblers "A"	22	10	1	11	49	48	31
8 Leigh Ramblers	22	8	5	9	52	44	29
9 Upminster	22	9	2	11	38	43	29
10 Leytonstone United	22	7	1	14	39	55	22
11 Sungate (-3)	22	2	2	18	26	74	5
12 Forest Glade (-15)	22	6	1	15	35	61	4

SENIOR CUP continued...

QUARTER-FINALS
Hannakins Farm 5-3 (aet) Kelvedon Hatch
Rayleigh Town 7-0 Debden Sports
Aldborough Athletic 1-1 5-4p Harold Hill
Castle United 1-0 Old Barkabbeyans

SEMI-FINALS
Hannakins Farm 0-1 Rayleigh Town
Aldborough Athletic 3-0 Castle United

FINAL
Rayleigh Town 3-4 Aldborough Athletic

DENNY KING MEMORIAL CUP
(Senior Cup first and second round losers)

ROUND 1
Chingford Athletic 4-1 Galleywood
Runwell Hospital 4-3 Springfield
ROUND 2
M & B Club 5-0 Broomfield
Ramsden Scotia 2-3 Sungate
Westhamians HW Sandon Royals
Catholic United 3-0 Ongar Town
Basildon Town 1-2 Ryan F.C.
Wadham Lodge 3-4 Canning Town
Chingford Athletic 6-4 (aet) Sheffield A.F.C.
Southminster St. Leonards 0-2 Buckhurst Hill
Burnham Ramblers Res 0-2 Toby
Leytonstone United 3-2 Writtle
Bishops Stortford Swifts 4-0 Roydon
Thurrock Res. 1-2 Upminster

DIVISION TWO	1	2	3	4	5	6	7	8	9	10	11	12
1 Broomfield		0-0	2-4	6-2	5-1	2-1	0-4	1-2	5-2	1-2	2-0	2-0
2 Burnham Ramblers 'A'	1-4		1-6	3-0	0-2	6-2	2-3	2-3	4-2	4-2	5-0	2-1
3 Castle United	4-4	2-0		W-L	3-2	4-0	2-3	3-1	1-2	1-2	1-1	4-2
4 Forest Glade	1-3	2-4	1-3		5-2	2-0	1-2	1-4	1-3	3-3	4-0	3-2
5 Leigh Ramblers	3-1	2-0	1-4	8-1		6-1	2-3	1-1	3-0	2-2	9-1	0-2
6 Leytonstone United	3-1	3-4	1-2	W-L	3-3		2-3	1-5	5-1	2-3	4-3	0-1
7 Old Southendian	1-4	2-1	4-0	4-2	3-0	2-1		2-1	1-1	3-1	2-1	3-0
8 Roydon	3-2	1-2	1-6	5-0	0-0	1-2	2-0		4-2	2-3	2-1	1-1
9 Ryan	0-1	2-3	1-2	1-2	4-0	1-0	2-0	2-3		0-3	6-0	3-0
10 Springfield	3-1	3-2	3-0	4-1	0-1	2-1	3-2	2-1	1-2		2-0	5-2
11 Sungate	2-4	2-1	1-7	1-3	2-2	3-4	0-1	2-4	0-1	2-5		2-0
12 Upminster	5-2	4-2	1-2	3-0	3-2	0-3	2-1	2-1	1-1	1-2	5-2	

ESSEX OLYMPIAN LEAGUE DIVISION TWO CONSTITUTION 2012-13

BROOMFIELD	The Angel Meadow, Main Road, Broomfield, Chelmsford CM1 7AH	01245 443819
BURNHAM RAMBLERS RESERVES	Leslie Field, Springfield Road, Burnham-on-Crouch CM0 8TE	01621 784383
CASTLE UNITED	Town Mead Leisure Centre, Brooker Road, Waltham Abbey EN9 1JH	01992 714949
EPPING	Stonards Hill Rec Ground, Tidy's Lane, Epping CM16 6SP	07817 357378
LAKESIDE	Lakeside Pitches, Lakeside Retail Park, Thurrock RM20 2ZL	01375 379352
LEIGH RAMBLERS	Belfairs Park, Eastwood Road North, Leigh-on-Sea SS9 4LR	01702 421077
LEYTONSTONE UNITED	Ilford Wanderers RFC, Forest Road, Hainault IG6 3HJ	020 8500 4622
NEWHAM UNITED	Cave Road, Plaistow E13 9DX	07939 788048
OLD BARKABBEYANS	Barking Abbey Comprehensive, South Park Drive, Ilford IG11 8UF	07773 880961
ROYDON	Roydon Playing Fields, Harlow Road, Roydon, Harlow CM19 5HE	01992 465056
RYAN F.C.	Town Mead Leisure Park, Brooker Road, Waltham Abbey EN9 1JH	01992 714949
UPMINSTER	Hall Lane Playing Fields, Hall Lane, Upminster, Romford RM14 1AU	01708 220320

DIVISION THREE

		P	W	D	L	F	A	Pts
1	Newham United	20	13	2	5	54	26	41
2	Old Barkabbeyans (+2)	20	11	4	5	43	25	39
3	Catholic United (-1)	20	11	4	5	47	30	36
4	Debden Sports	20	10	5	5	49	27	35
5	Stambridge United	20	10	4	6	54	35	34
6	Shenfield	20	9	3	8	44	46	30
7	Basildon Town	20	8	5	7	43	42	29
8	Toby	20	6	7	7	32	37	25
9	Chingford Athletic	20	6	4	10	42	56	22
10	Ramsden	20	4	1	15	34	65	13
11	Writtle	20	2	1	17	20	73	7

DENNING CUP continued...

Manford Way 7-0 Leigh Ramblers
Lakeside 1-0 (aet) Old Chelmsfordians
Benfleet 3-2 Epping
Herongate Athletic 3-4 (aet) Runwell Hospital
ROUND 3
M & B Club 4-1 Sungate
Westhamians 1-0 Catholic United
Ryan F.C. 2-1 Canning Town
Chingford Athletic HW Buckhurst Hill
Toby 3-2 Leytonstone United
Bishops Stortford Swifts 3-1 Upminster
Manford Way 4-2 (aet) Lakeside
Benfleet 0-2 Runwell Hospital
QUARTER-FINALS
M & B Club 2-0 Westhamians
Ryan F.C. 5-4 (aet) Chingford Athletic
Toby 4-5 (aet) Bishops Stortford Swifts
Manford Way 0-1 Runwell Hospital
SEMI-FINALS
M & B Club 4-1 Ryan F.C.
Bishops Stortford Swifts 0-1 Runwell Hospital
FINAL
M & B Club 1-0 Runwell Hospital

RESERVE DIVISION LEAGUE CUP

FINAL
Harold Wood Athletic Reserves 5-2 Kelvedon Hatch Reserves

DIVISION THREE	1	2	3	4	5	6	7	8	9	10	11
1 Basildon Town		2-1	1-3	3-3	0-1	2-2	2-1	1-2	2-1	1-1	3-0
2 Catholic United	5-3		4-1	0-0	2-0	1-2	4-0	2-1	0-3	0-4	3-1
3 Chingford Athletic	0-4	1-1		2-4	1-2	0-7	4-1	4-2	2-4	4-2	3-3
4 Debden Sports	1-2	0-3	4-0		0-0	3-0	3-0	5-4	4-1	1-1	5-0
5 Newham United	4-0	0-2	4-1	4-2		2-1	5-2	6-3	0-2	1-1	5-1
6 Old Barkabbeyans	4-1	1-1	3-1	2-1	1-0		3-3	1-3	1-2	1-1	2-1
7 Ramsden	4-2	2-6	3-4	1-2	1-6	0-2		1-3	1-3	1-3	3-1
8 Shenfield	2-2	3-1	2-2	2-1	2-5	1-5	2-1		1-0	1-1	3-0
9 Stambridge United	3-5	3-3	2-2	1-1	1-4	2-0	6-1	6-3		1-1	10-0
10 Toby	4-4	1-3	0-5	0-4	3-1	0-1	2-5	2-0	2-0		1-0
11 Writtle	0-3	2-5	3-2	1-5	0-4	0-4	2-3	0-4	2-3	3-2	

ESSEX OLYMPIAN LEAGUE DIVISION THREE CONSTITUTION 2012-13

BASILDON TOWN	Selex Sports Ground , Gardiners Lane South , Gardiners Way, Basildon SS14 3AP	01268 883128
CATHOLIC UNITED	SE Essex College Spts Ground, Wellstead Gardens, Westcliff-on-Sea SS0 0AY	01702 348786
CHINGFORD ATHLETIC	Wadham Lodge Sports Ground, Kitchener Road, Walthamstow E17 4JP	020 8527 2444
DEBDEN SPORTS	Chigwell Lane, Loughton, Ilford IG10 3TP	020 8508 9392
FOREST GLADE	Barleylands Road, Billericay SS15 4B	07805 955937
FOREST UNITED	Harrow Road, Leytonstone E11 3Q	07904 194841
LOASS	Town Mead Leisure Park, Brooker Road, Waltham Abbey EN9 1JH	01992 714949
RAMSDEN SCOTIA	Nursery Sports Ground, Downham Road, Ramsden Heath, Billericay CM11 1PU	01268 711502
SHENFIELD ASSOCIATION	The Drive, Warley, Brentwood CM13 3BH	01277 226816
STAMBRIDGE UNITED	Stambridge Recreation Ground, Rochford Road, Gt Stambridge, Rochford SS4 2AX	01702 258988
SUNGATE	Ford Sports & Social Club, Aldborough Rd South, Newbury Pk, Ilford IG3 8HG	020 8590 3797
TOBY	Fairlop Oak Playing Field, Forest Road, Hainault IG6 3HJ	None
WRITTLE	Paradise Road Playing Fields, Writtle, Chelmsford CM1 3HW	01245 420332

GLOUCESTERSHIRE COUNTY LEAGUE

Sponsored by: Surridge
Founded: 1968
Recent Champions:
2007: Roman Glass St George
2008: Hardwicke
2009: Slimbridge
2010: Thornbury Town
2011: Brimscombe and Thrupp

		P	W	D	L	F	A	Pts
1	Cribbs Friends Life	34	24	5	5	90	34	77
2	Henbury	34	20	7	7	61	45	67
3	Tuffley Rovers	34	21	2	11	72	44	65
4	Patchway Town	34	18	5	11	55	34	59
5	Ellwood	34	16	8	10	64	62	56
6	DRG Stapleton	34	15	8	11	60	46	53
7	Bristol Academy	34	13	9	12	61	52	48
8	Kings Stanley	34	14	6	14	70	71	48
9	Longlevens (-3)	34	14	6	14	57	52	45
10	Hanham Athletic	34	12	7	15	49	56	43
11	Kingswood	34	12	6	16	50	61	42
12	Yate Town Reserves (-3)	34	14	3	17	55	74	42
13	Taverners	34	11	8	15	39	49	41
14	Bishops Cleeve Reserves	34	9	13	12	51	58	40
15	Berkeley Town	34	10	8	16	40	57	38
16	Thornbury Town	34	11	3	20	46	59	36
17	Rockleaze Rangers	34	10	5	19	53	70	35
18	Chipping Sodbury Town	34	6	3	25	40	89	21

LES JAMES LEAGUE CUP

PRELIMINARY ROUND
D.R.G. Stapleton 5-2 Patchway Town
Henbury 4-1 Yate Town Res

ROUND 1
Bishops Cleeve Res 1-2 Kings Stanley
Bristol Academy 2-2 4-3p Rockleaze Rangers
D.R.G. Stapleton 6-1 Henbury
Ellwood 2-3 Berkeley Town
Hanham Athletic 0-0 4-5p Longlevens
Taverners 1-1 4-3p Kingswood
Thornbury Town 1-2 Chipping Sodbury Town
Tuffley Rovers 1-2 Cribbs Friends Life

QUARTER FINALS
Berkeley Town 2-2 3-2p Kings Stanley
Cribbs Friends Life 1-1 3-0p G. R. G. Stapleton
Longlevens 3-0 Chipping Sodbury Town
Taverners 0-1 Bristol Academy

SEMI-FINALS
Berkeley Town 0-2 Cribbs Fiends Life
:Longlevens 3-0 Bristol Academy

FINAL
Cribbs Friends Life 5-0 Longlevens

	1	2	3	4	5	6	7	8	9	10	11	12	13	14	15	16	17	18
1 Berkeley Town		2-1	1-1	3-1	0-1	3-1	1-1	2-0	1-2	1-8	0-2	1-1	0-1	2-0	1-2	2-2	2-0	0-3
2 Bishops Cleeve Reserves	4-0		3-2	2-0	1-1	2-1	2-2	1-0	0-0	2-5	2-3	1-3	0-0	1-2	1-3	0-3	0-0	1-0
3 Bristol Academy	2-2	1-1		3-1	2-2	0-1	0-0	4-1	3-3	2-1	4-1	4-0	4-3	1-4	4-2	2-1	2-0	1-0
4 Chipping Sodbury Town	2-2	2-0	3-2		1-1	3-2	1-2	0-3	2-3	2-4	0-1	0-5	1-3	1-0	2-3	1-4	5-1	
5 Cribbs Friends Life	2-0	2-2	1-0	4-0		2-2	2-3	2-0	4-0	4-0	2-1	4-2	3-2	3-0	3-1	3-2	0-3	5-0
6 DRG Stapleton	0-2	0-0	2-2	2-0	3-1		1-2	3-0	0-0	4-0	6-1	2-6	0-3	1-0	2-0	0-1	2-1	1-1
7 Ellwood	2-1	1-2	2-2	3-0	3-5	0-5		0-1	1-2	5-3	4-2	1-1	1-0	3-1	0-1	1-0	2-1	7-1
8 Hanham Athletic	2-1	1-1	2-1	3-2	0-3	1-1	1-1		1-2	1-3	2-2	3-1	1-1	4-1	1-1	2-1	1-2	3-1
9 Henbury	2-0	3-2	0-2	3-0	2-1	2-2	2-1	2-0		3-1	1-0	1-0	0-1	3-2	1-0	4-0	0-3	3-4
10 Kings Stanley	2-2	1-1	0-2	3-3	0-6	0-1	2-2	5-2	1-1		2-1	2-3	3-0	1-3	2-0	2-3	1-4	1-2
11 Kingswood	0-1	3-3	2-1	3-1	2-3	1-0	2-1	1-0	3-3	1-2		0-1	0-0	2-2	1-1	2-0	1-3	4-2
12 Longlevens	2-0	1-3	2-0	4-0	0-2	1-1	1-2	2-1	1-2	1-2	3-1		1-0	1-4	1-1	1-5	0-1	5-0
13 Patchway Town	3-0	3-0	2-0	4-0	1-0	0-1	4-2	1-3	2-0	1-2	2-0	0-0		4-0	1-0	4-2	0-3	1-0
14 Rockleaze Rangers	2-3	2-2	1-2	3-0	1-3	2-4	1-1	3-3	1-2	1-3	2-4	3-2	0-3		2-1	3-0	2-1	4-1
15 Taverners	1-0	2-1	1-1	3-2	0-4	0-3	1-3	1-0	1-1	1-1	2-1	1-2	1-1	3-0		2-1	1-2	1-1
16 Thornbury Town	0-0	3-5	2-1	5-0	0-2	1-2	1-2	1-3	0-2	1-2	3-1	0-0	0-2	1-0	1-0		0-1	1-2
17 Tuffley Rovers	3-4	5-3	3-2	4-1	0-3	6-3	0-2	1-0	4-2	5-1	2-0	4-0	2-0	0-0	1-3	1-2		1-3
18 Yate Town Reserves	1-0	1-1	2-1	1-0	0-2	2-1	12-1	2-1	1-4	0-4	0-1	0-3	4-2	2-1	2-1	3-0	0-1	

GLOUCESTERSHIRE COUNTY LEAGUE CONSTITUTION 2012-13

BERKELEY TOWN	Station Road, Berkeley GL13 9AJ	07831 232100
BISHOPS CLEEVE RESERVES	Kayte Lane, Southam, Cheltenham GL52 3PD	01242 676166
BRISTOL ACADEMY	Filton College WISE Campus, New Road, Stoke Gifford, Bristol BS34 8LP	0117 919 2601
CHIPPING SODBURY TOWN	The Ridings, Wickwar Road, Chipping Sodbury, Bristol BS37 6BQ	07787 522100
DRG STAPLETON	Frenchay Park Road, Frenchay, Bristol BS16 1LG	07954 132819
ELLWOOD	Bromley Road, Ellwood, Coleford GL16 7LY	01594 832967
FRAMPTON UNITED	The Bell Field, Bridge Road, Frampton on Severn, Gloucestershire GL2 7HA	07971 233861
HANHAM ATHLETIC	The Playing Fields Pavilion, 16 Vicarage Road, Hanham, Bristol BS15 3AH	07840 660527
HENBURY	Arnell Drive Playing Field, Lorain Walk, Henbury, Bristol BS10 7AS	0117 959 0475
KINGS STANLEY	Marling Close, Broad Street, Kings Stanley, Stonehouse GL10 3PN	01453 828975
KINGSWOOD	Kingswood PF, Wickwar Road, Kingswood, Wotton-under-Edge GL12 8RF	07971 682091
LONGLEVENS	The Pavilion, Longlevens PF, Longford Lane, Longlevens, Gloucester GL2 9EU	01452 530388
PATCHWAY TOWN	Scott Park, Coniston Road, Patchway, Bristol BS34 5JR	0117 949 3952
ROCKLEAZE RANGERS	Coombe Dingle Sport Complex, Coombe Dingle, Bristol BS9 2BJ	0117 962 6718
SOUTHMEAD CS ATHLETIC	Pen Park Sports Pavillion, Jarratts Road, Bristol BS10 6WF	07414 956559
TAVERNERS	Nailsworth Primary School, Forest Green, Nailsworth, Stroud GL6 0ET	07826 8419700
THORNBURY TOWN	Mundy Playing Fields, Kington Lane, Thornbury BS35 1NA	01454 413645
TUFFLEY ROVERS	Glevum Park, Lower Tuffley Lane, Gloucester GL2 6DT	01452 423402
YATE TOWN RESERVES	Lodge Road, Yate, Bristol BS37 7LE	Club: 01454 228103

CRIBBS FRIENDS LIFE CELEBRATE WINNING THE LEAGUE TITLE
Lef to right: Dominic Graffagnino, Tony Beecham, Tim O'Loughlin, Tom Burns, Nathan Lumber, Chris Kite, Andy Forward, Matt Shaughnessy, Danny Thorpe, Nick Lloyd, Justin Cattle, Scott Burnell, Matt Turner, Ryan McKillop, Simon Bone & Dave Truan.

CRIBBS FRIENDS LIFE LEAGUE CUP WINNERS
From back to front, left to right: Tim O'Loughlin, Chris Kite, Justin Cattle, Simon Hartley, Gavin Tufton, Jack Kinnerly, Tom Burns, Scott Burnell, Simon Bone, Danny Thorpe, Nathan Lumber, Dominic Graffagnino, Tony Beecham, Matt Shaughnessy, Dave Truan, Nick Lloyd, Ryan McKillop & Matt Turner.

HAMPSHIRE PREMIER LEAGUE

Sponsored by: Puma Engineering
Founded: 2007
Recent Champions:
2008: AFC Stoneham
2009: Colden Common
2010: Colden Common
2011: Liphook United

SENIOR DIVISION	P	W	D	L	F	A	Pts
1 Liphook United	34	28	4	2	105	25	88
2 QK Southampton	34	23	4	7	89	48	73
3 Locks Heath	34	21	5	8	97	40	68
4 AFC Stoneham	34	21	3	10	94	57	66
5 University of Portsmouth	34	21	1	12	90	35	64
6 Bournemouth Sports	34	17	4	13	78	48	55
7 Hedge End Rangers	34	14	9	11	61	62	51
8 Fleetlands (-1)	34	15	5	14	64	62	49
9 AFC Aldermaston	34	14	6	14	61	65	48
10 Clanfield	34	12	10	12	59	64	46
11 Paulsgrove	34	13	6	15	59	64	45
12 Winchester Castle	34	12	9	13	54	60	45
13 Colden Common	34	11	6	17	78	77	39
14 Sporting BW	34	11	6	17	68	72	39
15 Hamble Club	34	8	6	20	48	104	30
16 Otterbourne	34	6	6	22	55	100	24
17 Overton United	34	6	4	24	34	132	22
18 Liss Athletic	34	3	6	25	46	125	15

SENIOR CUP

ROUND 1
Liss Athletic 1-1 3-4p University of Portsmouth
Hedge End Rangers 1-1 7-6p Hamble Club
ROUND 2
Fleetlands 0-1 (aet) Liphook United
AFC Stoneham 2-1 (aet) Clanfield
Winchester Castle 1-6 University of Portsmouth
Colden Common 4-1 Bournemouth Sports
Otterbourne 0-1 Hedge End Rangers
QK Southampton 1-2 Locks Heath
Overton United 2-3 Paulsgrove
AFC Aldermaston 0-1 Sporting BW
QUARTER FINALS
Liphook United 2-0 AFC Stoneham
University of Portsmouth 2-1 Colden Common
Hedge End Rangers 3-2 Locks Heath
Paulsgrove 2-1 Sporting BW
SEMI-FINALS
Liphook United 1-0 University of Portsmouth
Hedge End Rangers 0-1 (aet) Paulsgrove
FINAL
Liphook United 2-1 Paulsgrove

COMBINATION CUP

FINAL
Fleetlands Reserves 0-2 AFC Stoneham Reserves

SENIOR DIVISION	1	2	3	4	5	6	7	8	9	10	11	12	13	14	15	16	17	18
1 AFC Aldermaston		6-2	1-3	2-1	1-5	2-3	4-2	3-1	0-5	3-3	0-3	3-2	3-0	0-1	1-3	4-1	2-0	1-1
2 AFC Stoneham	3-0		4-0	3-2	1-0	1-3	6-0	2-2	1-5	6-2	1-2	6-0	4-0	3-1	2-0	2-0	2-1	5-1
3 Bournemouth Sports	3-0	0-1		2-1	4-3	1-2	0-0	2-2	1-2	4-0	0-2	5-2	7-1	5-1	3-2	1-2	1-0	0-1
4 Clanfield	2-2	1-4	3-0		3-0	1-1	1-1	2-3	0-4	3-2	1-0	2-2	1-2	2-1	1-1	1-0	0-0	1-2
5 Colden Common	1-1	4-1	0-3	2-2		1-1	1-5	4-0	1-3	3-1	1-5	3-1	2-2	5-5	0-2	3-1	0-1	1-2
6 Fleetlands	0-2	1-4	4-3	4-3	1-5		5-1	1-2	1-2	1-3	2-0	2-3	4-0	3-2	0-2	2-1	1-0	3-1
7 Hamble Club	1-4	1-1	0-5	3-5	0-6	1-6		0-2	1-4	2-2	0-5	5-2	4-1	1-3	1-3	1-6	0-2	1-1
8 Hedge End Rangers	2-2	3-2	1-1	7-2	3-3	2-1	4-0		0-4	2-0	1-6	1-0	3-1	2-0	1-1	2-2	1-0	0-2
9 Liphook United	3-2	2-0	1-0	4-1	4-0	1-0	8-0	3-1		5-1	2-0	1-1	4-0	1-0	0-0	3-3	2-0	6-1
10 Liss Athletic	1-2	2-2	0-0	3-4	0-5	2-4	1-3	1-5	0-8		1-5	2-2	1-3	2-5	2-5	2-7	1-0	1-5
11 Locks Heath	0-1	0-2	1-3	2-2	3-0	0-0	0-2	2-2	2-1	10-0		9-1	6-0	3-1	4-2	3-1	0-2	1-1
12 Otterbourne	2-0	2-4	2-4	1-1	2-6	0-0	4-5	2-3	1-3	2-3	2-5		1-4	0-2	2-1	1-1	1-3	1-6
13 Overton United	0-2	0-9	0-6	0-3	0-4	0-3	2-1	1-4	1-1	2-3	1-4		3-1	0-2	2-2	1-15	3-3	
14 Paulsgrove	2-2	5-0	2-1	0-1	2-1	0-0	5-0	1-1	1-0	4-2	0-4	0-2	7-1		0-2	1-1	1-0	1-1
15 QK Southampton	1-0	5-3	5-4	1-2	6-2	5-1	2-0	2-0	3-5	4-1	3-3	3-2	1-0	6-0		3-2	0-1	5-1
16 Sporting BW	4-2	1-4	0-4	1-3	3-2	6-1	1-3	2-0	1-2	4-0	0-1	2-1	4-1	1-2	2-4		2-3	3-1
17 University of Portsmouth	4-0	5-2	1-2	4-1	4-0	3-1	3-0	4-0	1-2	2-1	2-3	3-2	9-1	4-1	1-2	7-1		4-1
18 Winchester Castle	0-3	0-1	1-0	0-0	4-1	2-1	1-1	2-1	1-1	4-2	1-4	1-2	1-2	4-1	1-2	0-0	0-1	

HAMPSHIRE PREMIER LEAGUE SENIOR DIVISION CONSTITUTION 2012-13

AFC ALDERMASTON	AWE Recreational Society, Aldermaston, Reading RG7 4PR	0118 982 7614/4544
AFC STONEHAM	Pirelli Sports Ground, Chestnut Avenue, Eastleigh, Southampton SO50 9PF	07765 046429
BOURNEMOUTH SPORTS	Bournemouth Sports Club, Chapel Gate, East Parley, Christchurch BH23 6BD	01202 581933
CLANFIELD	Peel Park, Chalton Lane, Clanfield, Waterlooville PO8 0PR	07765 238231
COLDEN COMMON	Colden Common Rec., Main Road, Colden Common, Winchester SO21 1RP	01962 712365
FLEETLANDS	DARA Fleetlands, Lederle Lane, Gosport PO13 0AA	023 9223 9723
HAMBLE CLUB	Shell Mex Ground, Hamble Lane, Hamble-le-Rice, Southampton SO31 4TS	07818 204400
HEDGE END RANGERS	Norman Rodaway Rec Ground, Heathouse Lane, Hedge End, Southampton SO30 0LE	07771 927886
LIPHOOK UNITED	Recreation Ground, London Road, Liphook GU30 7AN	07974 983114
LISS ATHLETIC	Newman Collard Ground, Hill Brow Road, Liss GU33 7LH	07980 424834
LOCKS HEATH	Locksheath Rec, 419 Warsash Rd, Titchfield Common, Fareham PO14 4JX	01489 600932
OTTERBOURNE	Oakwood Park, Oakwood Avenue, Otterbourne SO21 2ED	01962 714681
OVERTON UNITED	Overton Recreation Centre, Bridge Street, Overton RG25 3LZ	01256 770561
PAULSGROVE	Paulsgrove Social Club, Marsden Road, Paulsgrove, Portsmouth PO6 4JB	02392 324102
QK SOUTHAMPTON	Lordshill Recreation Centre, Redbridge Lane, Lordshill, Southampton SO16 0XN	07801 550337
SPORTING BISHOPS WALTHAM	Priory Park, Elizabeth Way, Bishop Waltham, Southampton SO32 1SQ	07740 506777
UNIVERSITY OF PORTSMOUTH	Langston Campus, Furze Lane, Milton, Portsmouth PO4 8LW	023 9284 4526
WINCHESTER CASTLE	Hants Co. Council Spts Ground, Petersfield Rd (A31),Chilcombe, Winchester SO23 8ZB	01962 866989

HERTS SENIOR COUNTY LEAGUE

Sponsored by: No sponsor **Founded:** 1898 **Recent Champions:** 2007: Whitewebbs 2008: Hatfield Town 2009: Metropolitan Police Bushey 2010: London Lions 2011: Hinton	**AUBERY CUP** **ROUND 1** Belstone 4-2 AFC Hertford **ROUND 2** Belstone 4-3 Panshanger Bovingdon 11-0 Wodson Park Seniors 1st XI Old Parmiterians 3-4 (aet) Wormley Rovers Buntingford Town 3-2 Sarratt Sandridge Rovers 2-0 Knebworth Bushey Rangers 0-3 AFC Hatfield Croxley Guild 0-7 Letchworth Garden City Eagles FC Evergreen HW Ware United London Colney Blues 1-3 Lemsford Hertford Heath 2-1 Chipperfield Corinthians Codicote 2-3 Hinton Baldock Town 2-0 Mill End Sports St Peters 1-4 Metropolitan Police Bushey Bedmond S & S Club 8-4 Standon & Puckeridge Goff's Oak 5-1 Whitwell Kimpton Rovers 2-5 Cuffley

PREMIER DIVISION	P	W	D	L	F	A	Pts
1 Baldock Town	30	25	2	3	96	38	77
2 Metropolitan Police Bushey	30	19	7	4	106	44	64
3 Codicote	30	18	4	8	73	34	58
4 Letchworth Garden City Eagles	30	17	6	7	76	43	57
5 Goff's Oak	30	14	8	8	59	45	50
6 Standon & Puckeridge	30	13	8	9	70	61	47
7 Sarratt	30	13	8	9	49	45	47
8 Wormley Rovers	30	12	3	15	56	64	39
9 Bovingdon	30	11	6	13	51	66	39
10 Sandridge Rovers	30	11	5	14	61	65	38
11 Chipperfield Corinthians	30	11	5	14	71	86	38
12 Cuffley	30	11	3	16	62	66	36
13 Hinton (-3)	30	10	4	16	45	55	31
14 Mill End Sports	30	6	4	20	40	81	22
15 St Peters	30	5	6	19	37	92	21
16 Buntingford Town	30	3	3	24	45	112	12

PREMIER DIVISION	1	2	3	4	5	6	7	8	9	10	11	12	13	14	15	16
1 Baldock Town		4-0	4-1	11-1	0-0	5-3	1-6	4-2	2-4	2-0	HW	0-2	1-0	7-1	5-1	3-0
2 Bovingdon	0-10		3-2	3-2	1-1	6-1	2-0	4-1	0-2	1-1	0-0	3-3	0-2	1-0	2-4	5-1
3 Buntingford Town	AW	4-2		2-6	5-2	1-3	2-2	0-1	1-8	1-4	1-1	0-3	0-2	4-3	0-1	1-4
4 Chipperfield Corinthians	3-4	1-3	4-2		1-4	1-5	2-3	0-1	2-1	0-3	1-1	2-2	3-2	4-2	5-6	7-3
5 Codicote	0-1	0-1	8-1	1-2		2-0	2-0	4-0	2-1	3-0	3-2	2-0	0-1	6-0	3-2	3-0
6 Cuffley	1-2	4-3	5-2	6-1	1-3		0-1	0-1	1-3	1-2	4-0	4-4	2-3	6-1	2-1	3-0
7 Goff's Oak	0-1	1-1	5-4	1-3	2-0	1-1		1-1	1-5	4-1	2-0	3-1	2-2	2-0	2-1	1-2
8 Hinton	0-2	1-1	2-1	2-2	3-1	6-0	1-1		AW	1-3	0-1	3-5	1-5	4-0	1-4	1-2
9 Letchworth Garden City Eagles	1-5	3-1	5-1	1-1	5-1	5-0	0-1	1-3		2-2	3-0	0-3	0-0	3-2	2-2	2-1
10 Metropolitan Police Bushey	3-4	4-1	7-0	4-2	2-2	4-0	1-1	3-0	4-2		8-0	7-2	3-1	10-0	5-5	5-2
11 Mill End Sports	0-2	0-4	2-1	3-5	1-2	1-0	2-5	2-3	3-3	0-5		4-2	0-3	4-1	2-3	1-2
12 Sandridge Rovers	0-3	3-0	5-2	1-2	0-4	0-3	1-2	0-2	2-3	2-5	4-2		1-2	3-0	2-0	4-1
13 Sarratt	1-1	0-2	4-1	2-2	1-7	2-2	1-0	1-0	0-3	0-2	3-1	1-3		3-1	1-2	2-1
14 St Peters	4-6	0-0	4-4	1-0	0-2	0-4	2-2	1-0	1-6	3-3	0-1	2-0	2-2		2-2	2-1
15 Standon & Puckeridge	2-3	6-1	2-0	3-5	1-1	3-0	4-2	2-1	1-1	1-1	5-3	2-2	2-2	1-0		1-3
16 Wormley Rovers	2-3	2-0	8-1	3-1	0-4	2-0	1-5	4-1	0-1	1-1	6-3	1-1	0-0	1-2	2-0	

HERTS SENIOR COUNTY PREMIER DIVISION CONSTITUTION 2012-13

BALDOCK TOWN	North Herts Arena, Norton Road, Baldock SG6 2EN	01462 892288
BELSTONE	The Medburn Ground, Watling Street, Radlett WD6 3AB	020 8207 2395
BOVINGDON	Green Lane, Bovingdon, Hemel Hempstead HP3 0LA	01442 832628
BUSH HILL RANGERS	Goldsdown Road, Brimsdown, Enfield, Middlesex EN3 7R	07956 470127
CHIPPERFIELD CORINTHIANS	Queens Street, Chipperfield, Kings Langley WD4 9BT	07958 744441
CUFFLEY	King George's Playing Fields, Northaw Road East, Cuffley EN6 4LU	07815 174434
HINTON	Holtwhites Sports & Social, Kirkland Drive, Enfield EN2 0RU	020 8363 4449
KNEBWORTH	The Recreation Ground, Watton Road, Knebworth, Stevenage SG3 6AH	07967 140219
LETCHWORTH GARDEN CITY EAGLES	Pixmore Playing Fields, Ledgers Lane, Baldock Road, Letchworth SG6 2EN	07855 337175
METROPOLITAN POLICE BUSHEY	Aldenham Road, Bushey, Watford WD2 3TR	01923 243947 Fax:01923 245963
MILL END SPORTS	King George V Playing Fields, Penn Road, Mill End, Rickmansworth WD3 8QX	01923 776392
SANDRIDGE ROVERS	Spencer Recreation Ground, Sandridge, St Albans AL4 9DD	01727 835506
SARRATT	King George V Playing Fields, George V Way, Sarratt WD3 6AU	None
STANDON & PUCKERIDGE	Station Road, Standon, Ware SG11 1QT	01920 823460
WHITWELL VILLAGE	King George V Recreation Grnd, Bradway, Whitwell SG4 8BE	07796 111970
WORMLEY ROVERS	Wormley Sports Club, Church Lane, Wormley EN10 7QF	01992 460650

DIVISION ONE

		P	W	D	L	F	A	Pts
1	Whitwell	26	25	0	1	86	19	75
2	Belstone	26	20	2	4	78	22	62
3	Knebworth	26	16	5	5	62	45	53
4	Hertford Heath	26	13	4	9	76	44	43
5	AFC Hatfield Town (-3)	26	12	6	8	53	47	39
6	Evergreen	26	10	7	9	39	30	37
7	AFC Hertford	26	10	6	10	58	47	36
8	Panshanger	26	10	2	14	63	67	32
9	Bedmond S & S Club	26	9	3	14	40	67	30
10	Kimpton Rovers	26	7	5	14	43	69	26
11	Old Parmiterians	26	6	5	15	34	65	23
12	Lemsford	26	6	5	15	32	63	23
13	London Colney Blues	26	4	6	16	37	65	18
14	Croxley Guild	26	3	6	17	30	81	15

Bushey Rangers - record expunged
Wodson Park Seniors - record expunged

RESERVE DIVISION ONE

		P	W	D	L	F	A	Pts
1	Baldock Town Reserves	22	14	5	3	66	31	47
2	Cuffley Reserves	22	14	3	5	56	30	45
3	Chi'field Corinthians Reserves	22	12	2	8	53	35	38
4	L'worth G C Eagles Reserves	22	12	2	8	43	46	38
5	Met Police Bushey Reserves	22	10	4	8	53	39	34
6	Sarratt Reserves	22	10	4	8	43	39	34
7	Sandridge Rovers Reserves	22	7	5	10	37	51	26
8	Bovingdon Reserves	21	7	4	10	41	51	25
9	Hinton Reserves	21	7	2	12	46	40	23
10	Codicote Reserves	22	7	2	13	43	60	23
11	Buntingford Town Reserves	22	6	3	13	37	53	21
12	Wormley Rovers Reserves	22	5	4	13	33	76	19

RESERVE DIVISION TWO

		P	W	D	L	F	A	Pts
1	Goff's Oak Reserves	21	19	1	1	90	23	58
2	Standon & Puc'ridge Reserves	21	14	1	6	62	38	43
3	Knebworth Reserves	21	12	1	8	65	49	37
4	Lemsford Reserves	21	11	1	9	57	51	34
5	Evergreen Reserves	21	7	3	11	66	75	24
6	Old Parmiterians Reserves	21	8	0	13	41	56	24
7	Bedmond S & S Club Reserves	21	6	0	15	34	75	18
8	London Colney Blues Reserves	21	3	1	17	37	85	10

Bushey Park Rangers Reserves - record expunged
Wodson Park Seniors Reserves - record expunged

AUBERY CUP continued...

ROUND 3

Belstone 4-1 Bovingdon

Wormley Rovers 3-1 Buntingford Town

Sandridge Rovers 1-1 4-5p AFC Hatfield

Letchworth Garden City Eagles FC 2-1 Evergreen

Lemsford 0-4 Hertford Heath

Hinton 2-2 2-4p Baldock Town

Metropolitan Police Bushey 7-1 Bedmond S & S Club

Goff's Oak 2-0 Cuffley

QUARTER FINALS

Belstone 0-1 Wormley Rovers

AFC Hatfield 1-5 Letchworth Garden City Eagles FC

Hertford Heath 1-7 Baldock Town

Metropolitan Police Bushey 2-1 (aet) Goff's Oak

SEMI-FINALS

Wormley Rovers 1-2 Letchworth Garden City Eagles FC

Baldock Town 1-2 Metropolitan Police Bushey

FINAL

Letchworth Garden City Eagles FC 0-0 6-5p Met. Police Bushey

RESERVES CUP

FINAL)

Chipperfield Corinthians Reserves 2-1 Hinton Reserves

DIVISION ONE

		1	2	3	4	5	6	7	8	9	10	11	12	13	14
1	AFC Hatfield Town		1-2	3-0	0-4	1-2	0-0	2-10	1-1	2-4	3-1	3-2	1-0	5-0	1-4
2	AFC Hertford	1-1		2-2	0-4	3-2	2-0	1-1	0-1	1-2	2-2	1-2	5-3	0-2	1-2
3	Bedmond S & S Club	1-1	1-3		0-1	W-L	1-2	1-0	3-5	0-2	2-1	2-1	2-0	4-2	1-5
4	Belstone (Saturday)	2-3	3-0	4-2		7-0	0-1	4-3	2-1	2-1	8-1	5-0	4-0	3-2	1-2
5	Croxley Guild	0-4	1-13	1-5	0-6		0-1	0-5	2-2	1-1	1-1	1-1	3-3	5-3	1-3
6	Evergreen	1-2	1-1	1-1	0-2	6-0		3-0	1-2	0-0	1-1	1-1	4-0	3-1	0-2
7	Hertford Heath	1-1	5-1	10-4	0-1	W-L	1-4		4-2	1-2	1-1	4-2	4-1	2-2	1-2
8	Kimpton Rovers	1-3	2-3	4-0	0-4	2-4	1-1	0-7		1-2	2-1	4-1	1-2	3-3	1-3
9	Knebworth	1-3	1-0	3-1	3-3	4-3	3-2	1-4	2-2		4-2	2-1	4-1	5-4	1-4
10	Lemsford	0-5	1-2	0-1	0-3	2-0	1-0	3-1	5-0	1-3		3-1	1-2	3-1	0-8
11	London Colney Blues	1-5	3-3	2-4	0-0	2-1	0-2	0-1	1-2	3-3	3-0		0-1	5-0	0-8
12	Old Parmiterians	1-1	0-5	2-1	0-2	0-0	0-2	1-4	8-0	0-6	1-1	2-2		1-3	1-4
13	Panshanger	2-1	1-5	8-0	0-2	5-2	4-1	2-4	4-2	0-2	4-0	4-3	5-2		0-2
14	Whitwell	5-0	3-1	4-1	3-1	1-0	4-1	3-2	2-1	3-0	4-0	3-0	0-2	2-1	

HERTS ENIOR COUNTY DIVISION ONE CONSTITUTION 2012-13

AFC HATFIELD TOWN	Birchwood Leisure Centre, Birchwood, Longmead, Hatfield AL10 0AN	01707 270772
AFC HERTFORD	Hertingfordbury Park, West Street, Hertford SG13 8EZ	01992 583716
ASLAN	Randolph Avenue, Maida Vale, London W9 1B	07504 895135
BEDMOND SPORTS & SOCIAL	Toms Lane Recreation Ground, Toms Lane, Bedmond, Abbots Langley WD5 0RB	01923 267991
BUNTINGFORD TOWN	Sainsburys Distribution Centre, London Road, Buntingford SG9 9JR	01763 271522
BUSHEY RANGERS	Moatfield, Bournehall Lane, Bushey WD23 3JU	020 8386 1875
CROXLEY GUILD	Croxley Guild of Sport, The Green, Croxley Green, Watford WD3 3JX	01923 770534
EVERGREEN	South Way, Abbotts Langley WD4 8PN	01923 267812
HARVESTERS 2012	Oaklands Lane, Smallford, St Albans, Hertfordshire AL4 0H	07855 075739
HATFIELD RBL	Briars Lane, Hatfield	07757 961884
HATFIELD TOWN BLUES	Lemsford Village Hall, Brocket Road, Lemsford AL8 7TT	01707 333548
HERTFORD HEATH	The Playing Field, Trinity Road, Hertford Heath SG13 7QS	07960 338324
KIMPTON ROVERS	Kimpton Recreation Ground, High Street, Kimpton, Hitchin SG4 8RA	078905 47613
LEMSFORD	Welwyn Playing Fields, Ottway Walk, Welwyn AL6 9AT	07970 025962
OLD PARMITERIANS	Thomas Parmiter Sports Centre, Garston, Watford WD25 0JU	01923 682805
PANSHANGER	Moneyhole Lane Playing Fields, Sylvan Way, Welwyn Garden City AL7 2RT	07963 336630
ST PETERS	Colney Heath FC, Rec Ground, High Street, Colney Heath AL4 0NS	01727 826188

Baldock Town celebrate with the Anagram Records Trophy - they were also Herts Senior County League Premier Division Champions. Photo: Gordon Whittington.

Bedfordshire League Premier Division Champions Shefford Town and Campton. Photo: Gordon Whittington.

HUMBER PREMIER LEAGUE

Sponsored by: No sponsor
Founded: 2000
Recent Champions:
2007: Sculcoates Amateurs
2008: Sculcoates Amateurs
2009: Chalk Lane
2010: Reckitts
2011: Sculcoates Amateurs

PREMIER DIVISION

		P	W	D	L	F	A	Pts
1	Reckitts	30	24	2	4	68	29	74
2	Sculcoates Amateurs	30	22	3	5	83	19	69
3	Chalk Lane	30	18	5	7	86	35	59
4	North Cave	30	16	6	8	66	39	54
5	Hornsea Town	30	15	7	8	69	59	52
6	Beverley Town	30	13	7	10	49	54	46
7	Hessle Rangers	30	13	5	12	48	52	44
8	Crown (-3)	30	13	4	13	66	58	43
9	Hall Road Rangers Reserves	30	13	2	15	92	68	38
10	Pocklington Town	30	11	4	15	46	61	37
11	Westella & Willerby Reserves	30	9	9	12	48	68	36
12	North Ferriby United Reserves	30	10	4	16	62	70	34
13	Bridlington Sports Club	30	8	4	18	52	90	28
14	Hodgsons	30	8	4	18	50	95	28
15	St Andrews	30	6	7	17	39	60	25
16	Hedon Rangers	30	4	1	25	33	100	13

DIVISION ONE

		P	W	D	L	F	A	Pts
1	Scarborough Town	26	21	1	4	118	37	64
2	Bransholme Athletic	26	20	2	4	97	48	62
3	East Riding Rangers	26	15	7	4	74	46	52
4	Hessle Sporting Club	26	15	5	6	69	47	50
5	Brandesburton	26	13	5	8	59	63	44
6	Scarborough Athletic Reserves	26	10	7	9	62	49	37
7	North Ferriby Athletic	26	10	6	10	73	68	36
8	Withernsea AFC	26	10	5	11	69	81	35
9	Malet Lambert YC	26	9	5	12	56	67	32
10	Driffield Evening Institute	26	9	3	14	55	60	30
11	Hessle United (-3)	26	9	4	13	64	64	28
12	Driffield JFC	26	6	4	16	55	88	22
13	Long Riston	26	3	3	20	32	83	12
14	Howden	26	2	3	21	49	131	9

GRAYS CUP

ROUND 1
Malet Lambert YC 2-3 Hessle Sporting Club
Crown FC - BYE
Pocklington Town 1-2 North Cave
Hessle Rangers 2-4 North Ferriby United Reseerves
Hodgsons FC 4-1 Hedon Rangers
North Ferriby Athletic 1-6 Sculcoates Amateurs
Chalk Lane 3-2 St. Andrews
Bridlington Sports Club 2-4 Hall Road Rangers Res.
Hornsea Town 4-0 Brandesburton
Bransholme Athletic 2-2 3-1p Beverley Town
Westella & Willerby 0-3 Reckitts AFC
East Riding Rangers 2-0 Driffield Evening Institute
Hessle United FC 2-1 Scarborough Athletic Res.
Withernsea AFC 3-4 Driffield JFC
Scarborough Town - BYE
Howden AFC 6-2 Long Riston 2

ROUND 2
Hessle Sporting Club 1-3 Crown FC
North Cave 0-2 North Ferriby United Reseerves
Hodgsons FC 3-1 Sculcoates Amateurs
Chalk Lane 5-2 Hall Road Rangers Reserves
Hornsea Town 2-1 Beverley Town
Reckitts AFC 5-2 East Riding Rangers
Hessle United FC 3-2 Driffield JFC
Scarborough Town 9-0 Howden AFC

QUARTER FINALS
Crown FC 2-4 (aet) North Ferriby United Reseerves
Hodgsons FC 2-6 Chalk Lane
Hornsea Town 0-4 Reckitts AFC
Hessle United FC 0-5 Scarborough Town

SEMI-FINALS
North Ferriby United Reserves 2-0 Chalk Lane
Reckitts AFC 1-2 Scarborough Town

FINAL
North Ferriby United Reserves 1-3 Scarborough Town

PREMIER DIVISION

		1	2	3	4	5	6	7	8	9	10	11	12	13	14	15	16
1	Beverley Town		6-2	1-5	3-1	2-1	2-0	4-2	1-3	2-1	0-5	1-2	0-4	0-2	1-4	1-0	3-3
2	Bridlington Sports Club	0-2		1-3	1-3	3-2	3-1	4-2	1-4	0-0	0-0	3-1	3-4	1-3	1-3	3-1	2-3
3	Chalk Lane	2-2	9-1		2-2	7-1	4-1	0-1	2-3	4-1	4-1	2-1	2-3	1-2	0-1	5-0	2-2
4	Crown	1-1	6-1	0-4		3-2	4-3	7-1	7-2	1-6	1-1	2-3	5-0	1-3	1-3	1-0	1-0
5	Hall Road Rangers Reserves	6-2	4-2	1-4	5-4		5-0	0-2	3-1	9-0	5-2	8-0	0-1	1-2	1-2	2-2	3-3
6	Hedon Rangers	1-3	1-0	1-4	0-4	0-3		0-1	2-4	2-5	1-7	2-5	0-3	1-2	0-3	3-0	3-2
7	Hessle Rangers	2-2	1-5	1-1	3-1	4-2	2-1		0-1	4-0	1-1	2-2	2-1	0-2	1-3	1-0	0-1
8	Hodgsons	1-2	2-2	0-4	1-2	2-7	2-3	2-0		2-2	4-3	0-7	1-2	1-2	0-2	3-0	1-6
9	Hornsea Town	0-0	5-1	0-1	2-0	5-3	7-2	4-3	4-0		5-4	1-1	3-2	2-1	0-0	1-2	4-2
10	North Cave	0-1	6-2	2-1	2-1	2-0	5-1	1-0	2-2	3-0		2-1	1-0	0-1	1-1	0-2	4-0
11	North Ferriby United Reserves	2-1	0-2	3-4	4-2	1-2	2-1	3-4	7-1	2-3	1-4		0-3	0-0	0-4	2-2	4-0
12	Pocklington Town	1-1	5-0	0-3	1-3	0-6	4-2	1-1	3-2	1-2	0-0	1-0		0-2	1-2	1-2	1-1
13	Reckitts	3-1	4-3	0-2	2-0	3-2	2-0	0-2	7-0	1-1	1-3	3-1	5-1		1-0	2-1	4-1
14	Sculcoates Amateurs	0-1	5-0	0-2	1-0	5-1	7-0	2-0	4-0	3-0	0-1	5-1	5-1	1-2		2-0	5-0
15	St Andrews	0-3	2-3	2-2	1-1	4-1	4-0	1-2	2-2	1-3	2-3	2-5	3-1	0-3	2-2		1-1
16	Westella & Willerby Reserves	0-0	2-2	1-0	0-1	0-6	1-1	0-3	6-3	2-2	1-0	3-1	3-1	2-3	1-7	1-0	

Charlton Athletic Community F.C. Photo: Alan Coomes.

Fleet Leisure F.C. Photo: Alan Coomes.

KENT COUNTY LEAGUE

Sponsored by: Haart **Founded:** 1922 **Recent Champions:** 2007: Holmesdale 2008: Norton Sports 2009: Hollands & Blair 2010: Stansfield O & B Club 2011: Hollands & Blair	**BILL MANKLOW** **INTER REGIONAL CHALLENGE CUP** **ROUND 1**

BILL MANKLOW INTER REGIONAL CHALLENGE CUP

ROUND 1

Milton & Fulston Utd. 4-0 Staplehurst Monarchs Utd.

Belvedere 4-3 (aet) Eltham Palace

Fleetdown Utd. 3-6 Metrogas

Forest Hill Park 4-2 (aet) Fleet Leisure

Farnborough OB Guild 5-1 Chipstead

AFC Sevenoaks 2-3 Coney Hall

Tonbridge Invicta 0-4 Charlton Athletic Community

Stansfeld O&B Club 3-4 Hildenborough Athletic

Tudor Sports 3-1 Greenways

Saga Sports & Social 0-1 APM Contrast

Sheerness East 4-1 New Romney

Snodland Town 1-4 Bromley Green

University of Kent 2-1 (aet) Otford Utd

ROUND 2

Milton & Fulston Utd. 1-2 Bredhurst Juniors

Belvedere AW Metrogas

Forest Hill Park 4-2 Farnborough OB Guild

Coney Hall 3-2 (aet) Charlton Athletic Community

Hildenborough Athletic 2-1 Tudor Sports

APM Contrast 3-1 Sheerness East

Sheppey United 5-0 Kennington

Bromley Green 2-3 University of Kent

QUARTER FINALS

Bredhurst Juniors 1-2 Metrogas

Forest Hill Park 1-2 Coney Hall

Hildenborough Athletic 1-2 APM Contrast

Sheppey United 2-3 University of Kent

SEMI-FINALS

Metrogas 2-0 Coney Hall

APM Contrast 1-2 University of Kent

FINAL

Metrogas 2-1 University of Kent

PREMIER DIVISION

		P	W	D	L	F	A	Pts
1	Bromley Green	26	22	1	3	69	17	67
2	Stansfeld O&B Club (-3)	26	21	1	4	64	33	61
3	Eltham Palace	26	16	2	8	58	28	50
4	Fleet Leisure	26	15	3	8	57	36	48
5	Tudor Sports	26	13	6	7	53	28	45
6	APM Contrast	26	13	4	9	42	33	43
7	Charlton Ath. Community	26	12	3	11	60	50	39
8	Greenways	26	10	5	11	35	43	35
9	Farnborough OB Guild (-3)	26	9	3	14	45	48	27
10	Sheerness East	26	7	6	13	31	42	27
11	Bredhurst Juniors (-3)	26	8	4	14	29	70	25
12	Staplehurst Monarchs United	26	4	5	17	27	54	17
13	Snodland (-1)	26	5	2	19	28	64	16
14	Tonbridge Invicta	26	3	3	20	32	84	12

DIVISION ONE

		P	W	D	L	F	A	Pts
1	Hildenborough Athletic	28	23	2	3	88	32	71
2	Metrogas	28	22	4	2	97	16	70
3	Saga Sports & Social	28	17	2	9	49	37	53
4	Sheppey United	28	14	8	6	55	31	50
5	Chipstead	27	15	2	10	66	54	47
6	Forest Hill Park	28	13	7	8	54	49	46
7	University of Kent (-4)	28	14	5	9	77	51	43
8	Fleetdown United	28	13	4	11	49	41	43
9	Coney Hall	28	9	5	14	60	56	32
10	Belvedere	28	9	4	15	45	67	31
11	Kennington	28	8	3	17	51	78	27
12	Otford United	28	8	2	18	47	70	26
13	Milton & Fulston United (-1)	27	7	3	17	34	92	23
14	AFC Sevenoaks	28	6	3	19	38	78	21
15	New Romney (-1)	28	3	2	23	21	79	10

PREMIER DIVISION

		1	2	3	4	5	6	7	8	9	10	11	12	13	14
1	APM Contrast		1-1	0-1	0-2	3-1	3-3	2-1	2-0	1-0	4-0	1-0	5-1	2-0	2-4
2	Bredhurst Juniors	2-1		0-3	1-11	1-5	0-5	2-2	0-0	1-0	1-0	1-4	0-6	3-1	2-3
3	Bromley Green	0-1	5-0		2-0	3-2	2-1	3-0	4-2	1-0	7-2	3-0	1-0	2-0	1-1
4	Charlton Athletic Community	1-2	6-0	0-2		0-2	3-1	3-2	0-1	2-1	2-1	2-3	2-1	4-2	3-3
5	Eltham Palace	3-1	3-1	0-2	2-3		4-2	2-2	3-0	4-0	5-1	0-1	4-0	3-0	2-1
6	Farnborough OB Guild	2-1	2-3	0-2	1-3	0-3		3-1	1-2	0-2	2-0	1-2	1-4	2-1	1-0
7	Fleet Leisure	2-0	1-0	3-4	4-2	0-1	1-0		2-1	3-0	3-1	1-0	5-0	9-0	0-2
8	Greenways	0-1	3-0	0-4	3-0	2-0	2-2	0-2		1-4	1-0	4-2	1-1	3-1	1-0
9	Sheerness East	0-2	3-2	0-5	2-2	0-3	2-1	1-1	1-1		3-0	0-1	1-1	1-1	0-1
10	Snodland	2-0	2-3	1-0	0-2	1-2	2-3	2-3	2-1	2-2		0-4	4-0	2-1	0-2
11	Stansfeld O&B Club	3-2	2-1	3-2	3-3	1-0	4-2	5-0	6-1	1-0	2-1		2-1	6-2	1-0
12	Staplehurst Monarchs United	0-1	0-2	0-2	1-0	1-1	0-2	0-3	0-3	1-3	1-1	2-3		2-0	2-4
13	Tonbridge Invicta	2-2	1-2	0-6	6-2	1-3	1-7	2-4	2-2	3-5	3-1	1-2	1-0		0-5
14	Tudor Sports	2-2	0-0	1-2	4-2	1-0	0-0	0-2	3-0	1-0	7-0	2-3	2-2	4-0	

Snodland F.C. Photo: Alan Coomes.

Tudor Sports F.C. (front cover stars!) Photo: Alan Coomes.

KENT COUNTY LEAGUE PREMIER DIVISION CONSTITUTION 2012-13

APM CONTRAST	Cobdown Sports & Social Club, Ditton Corner, Station Road, Aylesford ME20 6AU	01622 717771
BREDHURST JUNIORS	Sheppey Sports Club, Holm Place, Halfway, Sheerness ME12 3DG	01795 668054
BROMLEY GREEN	Waterside, Turner Close, Newton Rd, South Willesborough, Ashford TN24 0BB	01233 645982
CHARLTON ATHLETIC COMMUNITY	Eltham Town FC, Starbuck Close, Eltham SE9 2TD	07932 913817
CHIPSTEAD	Chipstead Rec, Chevening Road, Chipstead, Sevenoaks TN13 2SA	07753 603944
FARNBOROUGH OLD BOYS GUILD	Farnborough (Kent) Sports Club, High Street, Farnborough BR6 7BA	01689 862949
FLEET LEISURE	Fleet Leisure Sports Club, Nelson Road, Northfleet DA11 7EE	01474 359222
GREENWAYS	Fleet Leisure Sports Club, Nelson Road, Northfleet DA11 7EE	01474 359222
HILDENBOROUGH ATHLETIC	Racecourse Sports Ground, The Slade, Tonbridge TN9 1DS	07595 386657
METROGAS	Marathon Playing Fields, Forty Foot Way, Avery Hill Road, New Eltham SE9 2EX	020 8859 1579
SHEERNESS EAST	Sheerness East WMC, 47 Queensborough Road, Halfway, Sheerness ME12 3BZ	01795 662049
SHEPPEY UNITED	Holm Place, Queensborough Road, Sheerness ME12 3DD	07729 290351
SNODLAND	Potyn's Field, Paddlesworth Road, Snodland ME6 5DL	01634 241946
STANSFELD O & B CLUB	Metrogas Sports Grd, Marathon PF, Forty Foot Way, Avery Hill Rd, New Eltham SE9 2EX	020 8859 1579
STAPLEHURST & MONARCHS UNITED	Jubilee Sports Ground, Headcorn Road, Staplehurst TN12 0DS	07703 288622
TUDOR SPORTS	STC Sports Ground, Ivor Grove, New Eltham SE9 2AJ	020 8850 2057

DIVISION ONE

		1	2	3	4	5	6	7	8	9	10	11	12	13	14	15
1	AFC Sevenoaks		0-2	1-3	0-3	2-2	2-3	2-3	1-3	3-2	4-1	1-1	1-0	1-6	1-3	3-1
2	Belvedere	0-1		1-3	0-3	1-2	0-2	2-1	4-2	0-7	3-5	3-1	1-3	0-1	0-0	1-1
3	Chipstead	2-1	3-5		2-3	2-2	5-1	2-3	3-1	0-5		2-0	3-0	0-2	1-2	6-2
4	Coney Hall	3-3	3-2	2-3		0-2	1-4	0-3	4-1	0-0	11-0	4-0	1-1	0-2	3-1	2-2
5	Fleetdown United	4-2	1-1	2-1	2-0		0-1	1-2	1-3	1-2	0-1	4-0	4-1	2-1	0-3	0-1
6	Forest Hill Park	3-0	1-1	1-1	2-1	0-0		0-4	3-2	0-5	7-0	1-2	4-0	1-2	2-2	0-3
7	Hildenborough Athletic	11-0	4-2	3-2	4-1	3-2	4-4		4-2	0-4	11-0	2-0	2-1	2-1	3-1	5-0
8	Kennington	1-2	1-2	1-6	5-1	2-3	3-3	2-1		0-7	0-1	3-0	4-2	0-3	0-2	1-3
9	Metrogas	4-0	5-1	2-0	3-0	3-2	4-1	0-1	6-0		7-0	3-1	4-2	6-0	0-0	3-1
10	Milton & Fulston United	2-1	0-3	0-2	1-1	2-4	0-2	1-3	3-3	0-1		5-1	3-1	1-2	0-6	1-4
11	New Romney	3-0	0-3	2-3	0-6	1-2	0-1	1-2	0-2	1-6	3-5		0-1	0-2	1-1	1-6
12	Otford United	5-4	2-3	3-4	4-3	0-3	2-2	0-2	4-2	1-3	4-0	4-1		2-3	0-3	0-5
13	Saga Sports & Social	1-0	3-2	2-3	3-1	2-0	0-2	0-3	5-2	0-0	3-0	0-1	1-0		1-2	1-5
14	Sheppey United	1-0	6-2	2-4	1-0	3-0	0-1	1-2	1-2	1-1	1-1	2-0	3-2	1-1		2-2
15	University of Kent	5-2	6-0	5-0	5-3	1-3	5-2	0-0	3-3	0-4	4-1	5-0	1-2	0-1	1-4	

One game remained unplayed.

KENT COUNTY LEAGUE DIVISION ONE 2012-13

AFC SEVENOAKS	Waller Park, Wood Lane, Darenth, Dartford DA2 7LR	01322 221006
BELVEDERE	War Memorial Sports Ground, 101a Woolwich Road, Abbey Wood SE2 0DY	01322 436724
BEXLEIANS	Footscray Sports Club, 239 Footscray Road, London SE9 2EL	020 8850 4698
CONEY HALL	Tiepigs Lane, Coney Hall, Bromley BR4 9BT	020 8462 9103
ERITH '147 SPORTS	STC Sports Ground, Ivor Grove, New Eltham SE9 2AJ	020 8858 2057
FLEETDOWN UNITED	Heath Lane Open Space, Heath Lane (Lower), Dartford DA1 2QE	01322 273848
FOREST HILL PARK	Ladywell Arena, Doggett Road, Catford SE6 4QX	020 8314 1986
KENNINGTON	Kennington Cricket Club, Ulley Road, Kennington, Ashford TN24 9HY	07887 995219
MALGO	The Old County Ground, Norman Road, West Malling ME19 6RL	07850 751595
MILTON & FULSTON UNITED	UK Paper Sports Ground, Gore Court Road, Sittingbourne ME10 1QN	01795 477047
NK ACES	Istead Rise Community Centre, Worcester Close, Gravesend DA13 9LB	01474 833903
OTFORD UNITED	Otford Recreation Ground, High Street, Otford, Sevenoaks TN14 5PG	07802 736279
TONBRIDGE INVICTA	Swanmead Sports Ground, Swanwead Way, off Cannon Lane, Tonbridge TN9 1PP	01732 350473
UNIVERSITY OF KENT	The Oast House, Park Wood Road, Giles Lane, University of Kent, Canterbury CT2 7SY	01227 827430

DIVISION TWO EAST	P	W	D	L	F	A	Pts	DIVISION TWO WEST	P	W	D	L	F	A	Pts
1 Malgo	26	20	2	4	108	29	62	1 Bexlians	26	19	1	6	64	34	58
2 NK Aces	25	20	2	3	96	35	62	2 Erith 147 Sports	26	18	3	5	67	43	57
3 Sevenoaks	26	17	4	5	93	38	55	3 AFC Mottingham	26	15	3	8	63	34	48
4 Swale United	25	17	1	7	84	33	52	4 Dulwich Village	26	13	5	8	71	53	44
5 Broadstairs	26	16	4	6	79	47	52	5 Bexley	26	11	5	10	53	51	38
6 Guru Nanak	26	14	5	7	68	38	47	6 Halstead	26	10	6	10	44	40	36
7 Deal Town Rangers	26	14	1	11	65	61	43	7 Blackheath United	26	10	4	12	58	58	34
8 Hadlow Evolution	26	10	5	11	48	55	35	8 Holland Sports	26	9	5	12	51	56	32
9 Larkfield & N Hythe W (-1)	26	10	3	13	51	61	32	9 Halls	26	8	7	11	41	51	31
10 Hawkenbury	26	7	5	14	60	89	26	10 Crofton Albion	26	8	5	13	52	59	29
11 Greenhill (-3)	26	7	2	17	44	83	20	11 Parkwood Rangers (-1)	26	9	3	14	52	76	29
12 Tenterden Town	26	3	3	20	40	122	12	12 Phoenix Academy (-1)	26	8	4	14	40	60	27
13 Borden Village (-1)	26	3	3	20	36	90	11	13 LanesEnd	26	8	3	15	39	62	27
14 Platt United	26	1	4	21	34	125	7	14 Bexley Borough	26	7	4	15	46	64	25

KENT COUNTY LEAGUE - STEP 7

LES LECKIE CUP

ROUND 1
Broadstairs 3-3 7-6p Malgo
Hawkenbury 8-2 Borden Village
Platt Utd 2-1 Greenhill
Swale Utd. 5-2 Deal Town Rangers
Hadlow Evolution 0-3 Guru Nanak
Sevenoaks 4-1 Larkfield & New Hythe Wan

QUARTER FINALS
Broadstairs 5-3 Hawkenbury
Platt Utd 0-5 Swale Utd.
NK Aces 9-1 Guru Nanak
Sevenoaks 6-0 Tenterden Town

SEMI-FINALS
Broadstairs 0-2 Swale Utd.
NK Aces 0-2 Sevenoaks

FINAL
Swale Utd. 1-2 Sevenoaks

BARRY BUNDOCK WEST KENT SHIELD

ROUND 1
Halstead 3-0 Phoenix Academy
Parkwood Rangers 3-2 Lanes End
Crofton Albion 2-0 Dulwich Village
Bexley 3-1 Blackheath Utd
AFC Mottingham 7-2 Bexley Borough

QUARTER FINALS
Bexlians 0-4 Erith 147 Sports
Halls AFC 0-3 Halstead
Parkwood Rangers 4-3 (aet) Crofton Albion
Bexley 0-1 AFC Mottingham

SEMI-FINALS
Erith 147 Sports 2-1 (aet) Halstead
Parkwood Rangers 2-2 5-6p AFC Mottingham

FINAL
Erith 147 Sports 1-2 AFC Mottingham

DIVISION TWO EAST	1	2	3	4	5	6	7	8	9	10	11	12	13	14
1 Borden Village		1-5	4-6	2-0	1-5	2-3	2-2	1-3	2-7	0-3	1-1	0-7	0-3	6-1
2 Broadstairs	7-2		5-1	3-2	2-0	2-1	4-3	1-3	4-3	1-2	8-1	2-4	2-2	7-0
3 Deal Town Rangers	4-2	1-2		3-1	4-2	4-1	3-3	2-1	1-3	2-3	5-1	3-1	1-4	4-2
4 Greenhill	2-2	0-1	3-4		2-4	4-0	1-0	1-5	0-3	1-4	7-0	0-4	2-4	1-1
5 Guru Nanak	3-0	2-3	1-0	1-2		2-0	3-1	0-0	1-0	1-1	8-3	4-2	4-2	6-0
6 Hadlow Evolution	4-1	2-1	5-0	0-1	0-0		5-5	3-1	1-5	1-2	5-1	2-1	0-1	3-2
7 Hawkenbury	3-0	1-5	1-2	3-1	1-4	3-3		5-1	3-5	1-5	3-2	2-2	0-4	8-2
8 Larkfield & New Hythe Wanderers	3-0	3-2	0-1	6-4	1-1	1-2	5-1		1-3	2-6	3-1	2-6	0-3	4-2
9 Malgo	5-0	2-2	5-3	17-0	2-0	3-0	1-0	5-0		3-0	6-0	3-1	1-3	6-0
10 NK Aces	3-2	4-0	6-1	1-2	2-0	3-1	9-1	4-2	2-2		11-0	3-2	A	8-0
11 Platt United	3-1	1-3	1-6	2-5	3-7	1-1	1-4	1-1	1-3	2-4		1-7	2-7	5-5
12 Sevenoaks	2-1	2-2	2-1	7-0	2-2	1-1	8-1	1-0	3-2	5-1	6-0		3-1	4-1
13 Swale United	5-1	0-1	2-0	2-1	3-2	7-0	9-0	4-0	1-2	0-4	6-0	1-3		7-0
14 Tenterden Town	0-2	4-4	0-3	4-1	1-5	1-4	2-5	1-3	0-11	3-5	2-0	2-7	4-3	

NK Aces v Swale United was abandoned and not replayed.

DIVISION TWO WEST	1	2	3	4	5	6	7	8	9	10	11	12	13	14
1 AFC Mottingham		3-2	1-0	6-1	2-1	3-1	0-3	0-1	3-1	1-1	4-0	6-1	1-2	3-1
2 Bexley	1-1		1-2	0-4	4-4	0-4	3-2	1-4	3-0	2-2	1-1	1-1	1-0	7-1
3 Bexley Borough	0-3	4-1		5-2	0-3	2-2	0-2	8-2	2-2	1-2	1-1	3-2	2-1	2-0
4 Bexlians	3-1	2-0	3-1		0-2	1-0	3-4	1-0	4-1	2-1	2-0	5-0	1-1	3-2
5 Blackheath United	1-2	1-4	5-2	1-4		3-3	0-3	2-4	1-1	0-1	2-1	2-3	3-4	4-1
6 Crofton Albion	3-6	3-0	2-2	0-3	0-2		2-3	1-2	6-2	2-1	2-2	2-0	3-0	2-4
7 Dulwich Village	1-1	2-4	4-0	2-3	3-4	3-3		5-2	1-1	1-2	4-3	1-1	3-1	1-2
8 Erith 147 Sports	5-2	1-2	2-0	1-0	3-0	2-0	4-2		2-0	2-2	2-1	4-2	4-1	0-0
9 Halls	0-3	0-3	4-1	2-1	0-3	1-0	2-2	2-5		0-0	3-0	4-0	6-1	1-0
10 Halstead	1-0	3-1	3-1	0-1	1-3	5-1	3-5	2-2	1-2		2-3	1-0	2-2	1-2
11 Holland Sports	2-1	1-2	6-3	2-5	2-3	5-4	1-5	5-1	2-0	0-3		4-1	3-1	1-1
12 Lanes End	1-0	1-2	2-1	1-3	4-3	1-2	3-2	2-3	1-0	4-3	1-1		2-3	0-1
13 Parkwood Rangers	1-8	1-6	6-2	1-6	3-2	1-3	3-4	0-1	4-4	2-1	2-0	2-5		3-2
14 Phoenix Academy	0-2	3-1	2-1	0-1	3-3	5-1	2-3	2-8	2-2	0-1	0-4	3-0	1-6	

KENT COUNTY LEAGUE DIVISION TWO EAST CONSTITUTION 2012-13

BORDEN VILLAGE	Borden Playstool, Wises Lane, Borden, Sittingbourne ME9 8LP	07921 912209
BROADSTAIRS	Jackey Bakers Sports Groud, Highfield Road, Ramsgate CT12 6QX	01843 592166
DEAL TOWN RANGERS	Castle Community College, Mill Road, Deal CT14 9HH	01304 373363
GREENHILL	Bridge Road Recreation Ground, Bridge, Canterbury CT4 5BL	07804 822533
GURU NANAK	Guru Nanak Sports Ground, Khalsa Avenue, Gravesend DA12 1LV	07956 514264
HADLOW EVOLUTION	Hadlow College, Hadlow TN11 0EH	07973 489377
HAWKENBURY	Hawkenbury Recreation Ground, Hawkenbury Road, Tunbridge Wells TN2 5BJ	07899 806170
LARKFIELD & NEW HYTHE WANDERERS	Larkfield & NH Sports Club, New Hythe Lane, Larkfield, Maidstone ME20 6PU	07724 050971
NEW ROMNEY	The Maud Pavilion, Station Road, New Romney TN28 8LQ	07710 077702
PARK REGIS	Armstrong Road, Maidstone, Kent ME15 6A	07926 111762
PLATT UNITED	Stonehouse Field, Longmill Lane, St Marys Platt, Sevenoaks TN15 8ND	07702 634344
SEVENOAKS	Greatness Park, Seal Road (on main A25), Sevenoaks TN14 5BL	01732 741987
SWALE UNITED	UK Paper Sports Ground, Gore Court Road, Sittingbourne ME10 1QN	01795 564213
TENTERDEN TOWN	Recreation Ground Road, High Street, Tenterden TN30 6RB	07720 785001

KENT COUNTY LEAGUE DIVISION TWO WEST CONSTITUTION 2012-13

AFC MOTTINGHAM	Coldharbour Leisure Centre, Chapel Farm Road, New Eltham SE9 3LX	020 8851 8692
BEXLEY	St Marys Recreation Ground, Lesley Close, Bourne Road, Bexley DA5 1LX	07944 552763
BEXLEY BOROUGH	Apex Arena, Danson Yth Centre, Brampton Road, Bexleyheath DA7 4EZ	020 8303 6052
BLACKHEATH UNITED	Segas Sports Ground, Worsley Bridge Road, Beckenham BR3 1RL	07773 716607
CROFTON ALBION	Crofton Albion Sports & Social, Weigall Road, Lee SE12 8HF	020 8856 8385
DULWICH VILLAGE	Dulwich Sports Ground, Tierney Road, Dulwich SE21 7JH	020 7733 7671
HALLS AFC	Stone Recreation Ground, London Road, Greenhithe DA9 9DQ	01322 224246
HALSTEAD	Halstead Recreation Ground, Station Road, Halstead TN14 7DH	07884 428658
HOLLAND SPORTS	Holland Sports & Social Club, The Pavilion, Mill Lane, Hurst Green RH8 9DF	01883 716529
IDE HILL	Quebec Avenue, off Costello Meadow, Westerham, Kent TN16 1B	None
LANES END	Waller Park, Wood Lane, Darenth, Dartford DA2 7LR	01322 221006
LONG LANE	Dursley Road, Kidbrooke, Greater London SE3 8P	07732 250792
OLD BROMLEIANS	Scrubbs Farm, Lower gravel Road, Bromley, Kent BR2 8L	07956 626937
PECKHAM TOWN	Dulwich Common, West Dulwich, London SE21 7E	07572 351184
PHOENIX ACADEMY	Phoenix Sports Club, Mayplace Road East, Barnehurst DA7 6JT	01322 526159

	RESERVE DIVISION EAST	P	W	D	L	F	A	Pts
1	Hollands & Blair	24	16	6	2	56	20	54
2	Canterbury City	24	14	6	4	65	41	48
3	Lydd Town	24	11	6	7	56	58	39
4	Swale United	24	11	4	9	79	48	37
5	Bromley Green	24	11	3	10	65	56	36
6	Kennington (-1)	24	10	6	8	63	50	35
7	Otford United (-1)	24	10	6	8	43	44	35
8	Bearsted	24	10	5	9	40	46	35
9	New Romney	24	8	6	10	37	37	30
10	APM Contrast	24	6	7	11	51	68	25
11	Staplehurst Monarchs United	24	6	4	14	33	63	22
12	Bly Spartans	24	6	3	15	40	60	21
13	Sheerness	24	4	4	16	36	73	16

	RESERVE DIVISION WEST	P	W	D	L	F	A	PTS
1	Sutton Athletic	24	17	5	2	84	31	56
2	Fleetdown United	24	17	4	3	75	35	55
3	Tudor Sports	24	16	1	7	78	39	49
4	Seven Acre & Sidcup	23	13	2	8	59	50	41
5	Bridon Ropes (-4)	24	13	5	6	55	28	40
6	Fleet Leisure (-3)	23	12	2	9	60	61	35
7	Greenways	24	9	4	11	42	55	31
8	Stansfeld O&B Club	24	8	4	12	51	59	28
9	Crockenhill	24	6	5	13	37	53	23
10	Bexlians	24	5	7	12	37	57	22
11	Orpington	24	5	4	15	38	67	19
12	Coney Hall (-4)	24	7	1	16	36	61	18
13	Chipstead (-1)	24	4	2	18	37	93	13

One game remained unplayed.

RESERVES CUP

ROUND 1
Sutton Athletic Reserves 1-0 Fleetdown Utd. Reserves
Bexlians Reserves 0-6 Bridon Ropes Reserves
Fleet Leisure Reserves 3-3 4-2p Belvedere Reserves
Lydd Town Reserves 2-0 Sheerness East Reserves
Seven Acre & Sidcup Reser 3-2 Crockenhill Reserves
Stansfeld O&B Club Reserves 1-2 Tudor Sports Reserves
Coney Hall Reserves AW Orpington Reserves
New Romney Reserves 0-5 Kennington Reserves
Otford Utd Reserves HW Platt Utd Reserves
Staplehurst Mon. Utd. Res 4-4 1-3p Bromley Green Reserves
Bly Spartans Reserves 3-4 Hollands & Blair Reserves
Swale Utd Reserves 1-3 (aet) Bearsted Reserves

ROUND 2
Sutton Athletic Reserves 2-0 Greenways Reserves
Bridon Ropes Reserves 2-1 Fleet Leisure Reserves
Lydd Town Reserves 4-3 APM Contrast Reserves
Seven Acre & Sidcup Reser 3-5 (aet) Tudor Sports Reserves
Chipstead Reserves 1-5 Orpington Reserves

Kennington Reserves 5-1 Otford Utd Reserves
Canterbury City Reserves 3-4 Bromley Green Reserves
Hollands & Blair Reserves 1-2 Bearsted Reserves

QUARTER FINALS
Sutton Athletic Reserves 2-0 (aet) Bridon Ropes Reserves
Lydd Town Reserves 1-2 Tudor Sports Reserves
Orpington Reserves 3-5 Kennington Reserves
Bromley Green Reserves 0-6 Bearsted Reserves

SEMI-FINALS
Sutton Athletic Reserves 0-2 Tudor Sports Reserves
Kennington Reserves 4-2 Bearsted Reserves

FINAL
Tudor Sports Reserves 1-2 Kennington Reserves

haart of kent county league

AFC Mottingham
Barry Bundock West Kent Challenge Shield Winners

Bromley Green FC
Premier Division Champions

Metrogas FC
Bill Manklow Inter-Regional Challenge Cup Winners

University of Kent FC
Fair Play Award Winners

Sevenoaks FC
Les Leckie Cup Winners

Roy Davies - Metrogas FC
Aford awards Manager of the Year

Kennington FC Reserves
Reserve Division Cup Winners

haart of Kent County League
Representative

Danny Hill - Bexlians FC
Secretary of the Year

Referee of the Year

Hildenborough Athletic FC
Division One Champions

Bernard Hust - Bly Spartans - Personality of the Year

LEICESTERSHIRE SENIOR LEAGUE

Sponsored by: Everards Brewery
Founded: 1919
Recent Champions:
2007: Stapenhill
2008: Kirby Muxloe SC
2009: Anstey Nomads
2010: Thurmaston Town
2011: Ashby Ivanhoe

PREMIER DIVISION

		P	W	D	L	F	A	Pts
1	Rothley Imperial	30	23	3	4	87	31	72
2	Lutterworth Athletic	30	21	3	6	87	27	66
3	Aylestone Park	30	21	2	7	75	28	65
4	Thurmaston Town	30	16	9	5	75	37	57
5	Stapenhill	30	16	8	6	65	34	56
6	Birstall United	30	17	3	10	84	53	54
7	Desford	30	14	5	11	60	54	47
8	Ashby Ivanhoe	30	13	7	10	86	57	46
9	Sileby Town	30	13	5	12	45	51	44
10	Highfield Rangers	30	11	3	16	51	86	36
11	Kirby Muxloe Reserves (-3)	30	10	6	14	51	57	33
12	Dunton & Broughton Rangers	30	8	6	16	52	59	30
13	Saffron Dynamo	30	8	1	21	33	92	25
14	FC Dynamo	30	6	3	21	60	88	21
15	Ratby Sports	30	3	5	22	38	120	14
16	Cottesmore Amateurs (-3)	30	4	3	23	25	100	12

DIVISION ONE

		P	W	D	L	F	A	Pts
1	Caterpillar	28	25	1	2	124	22	76
2	Sileby Saints	28	20	2	6	73	39	62
3	Friar Lane & Epworth	28	18	2	8	79	38	56
4	Barlestone St Giles	28	13	4	11	53	41	43
5	Newhall United	28	13	3	12	53	52	42
6	Melton Mowbray	28	12	5	11	59	51	41
7	Castle Donington Town	28	13	2	13	55	51	41
8	Hathern	28	12	5	11	57	58	41
9	Narborough & Littlethorpe	28	12	4	12	57	72	40
10	Earl Shilton Albion	28	11	3	14	52	57	36
11	Belgrave (-3)	28	11	4	13	52	65	34
12	Shepshed Dynamo Reserves	28	7	4	17	34	82	25
13	FC Khalsa (-3)	28	8	3	17	38	70	24
14	Lutterworth Town	28	6	5	17	26	59	23
15	Asfordby Amateurs (-3)	28	4	3	21	26	81	12

BEACON BITTER CUP

ROUND 1
Belgrave 3-3 Castle Donington Town
(Belgrave won on penalties)
Birstall United 4-0 Kirby Muxloe Reserves
Caterpillar 6-0 Asfordby Amateurs
Desford 0-2 Lutterworth Athletic
Dunton & Broughton Rangers 1-1 Rothley Imperial
(Rothley Imperial won on penalties)
Earl Shilton Albion 3-1 Narborough & Littlethorpe
FC Khalsa 0-3 Sileby Saints
Melton Mowbray 4-2 Hathern
Newhall United 7-5 Shepshed Dynamo Reserves
Ratby Sports 1-2 Cottesmore Amateurs
Sileby Town 1-3 Ashby Ivanhoe
Stapenhill HW Saffron Dynamo
Thurmaston Town 1-2 Highfield Rangers
Aylestone Park 7-2 FC Dynamo
Lutterworth Town 1-1 Friar Lane & Epworth
(Lutterworth Town won on penalties)

ROUND 2
Aylestone Park 2-1 Stapenhill
Birstall United 5-1 Cottesmore Amateurs
Caterpillar 3-1 Barlestone St Giles
Highfield Rangers 0-7 Lutterworth Athletic
Lutterworth Town 2-0 Earl Shilton Albion
Melton Mowbray 2-3 Newhall United
Rothley Imperial 4-0 Ashby Ivanhoe
Sileby Saints 3-6 Belgrave

QUARTER FINALS
Belgrave 3-0 Birstall United
Caterpillar 0-0 Aylestone Park
(Aylestone Park won on penalties)
Lutterworth Town 0-6 Lutterworth Athletic
Newhall United 1-3 Rothley Imperial

SEMI-FINALS
Aylestone Park 1-3 Rothley Imperial
Lutterworth Athletic 3-2 Belgrave

FINAL
Lutterworth Athletic 2-2 Rothley Imperial
(Rothley Imperials won on penalties)

PREMIER DIVISION

		1	2	3	4	5	6	7	8	9	10	11	12	13	14	15	16
1	Asfordby Amateurs		0-1	2-4	2-0	4-2	5-2	3-1	12-0	3-2	1-4	8-1	0-3	5-0	1-1	2-2	4-2
2	Ashby Ivanhoe	1-0		3-1	5-0	0-1	3-1	7-3	5-1	3-0	1-0	6-0	4-2	4-0	0-0	1-0	2-3
3	Aylestone Park	5-4	3-0		5-0	3-4	1-2	2-0	8-4	4-2	3-2	5-0	1-3	7-1	2-2	2-2	3-2
4	Birstall United	1-4	0-2	0-8		1-2	1-6	2-5	2-4	2-2	0-5	3-2	1-1	1-5	0-1	0-4	0-1
5	Blaby & Whetstone Athletic	3-3	2-3	2-1	2-1		3-4	3-2	2-2	1-0	1-4	3-1	1-0	4-0	1-2	1-1	2-2
6	Cottesmore Amateurs	1-3	0-1	0-0	4-3	1-1		0-1	0-2	1-0	1-2	2-2	4-5	1-2	5-0	0-2	1-2
7	Highfield Rangers	3-1	1-3	0-1	8-0	1-3	2-2		3-4	3-3	0-3	1-4	1-4	7-0	1-6	0-3	2-5
8	Leicestershire Constabulary	2-1	0-4	2-1	3-0	0-1	1-0	2-1		0-1	2-3	5-1	2-5	3-1	0-3	1-4	0-5
9	Lutterworth Athletic	1-1	0-5	1-0	0-1	3-2	2-1	2-1	5-0		0-1	7-1	2-1	0-1	4-3	1-3	2-2
10	Ratby Sports	1-0	4-1	5-1	6-0	3-1	3-0	5-1	1-1	7-2		6-1	2-0	4-0	0-1	0-0	0-1
11	Rothley Imperial	4-4	1-5	1-2	1-1	0-6	1-5	5-4	1-1	0-3	1-6		1-4	1-1	3-1	0-5	1-7
12	Saffron Dynamo	3-1	2-0	3-0	6-1	4-1	3-1	6-1	3-2	0-0	2-1	7-1		3-0	1-0	2-0	1-0
13	Sileby Town	1-5	1-5	1-3	0-2	1-3	3-1	2-1	4-1	3-2	1-3	3-1	0-6		0-1	0-2	0-7
14	Stapenhill	2-2	1-0	4-1	1-2	1-0	1-2	1-5	2-4	2-1	1-5	2-1	0-2	3-2		2-0	1-1
15	Thurmaston Town	3-4	0-0	1-4	3-0	1-0	2-2	5-0	4-1	3-1	2-0	2-1	3-3	1-0	4-0		2-2
16	Thurnby Nirvana	1-1	1-0	0-3	2-0	5-2	2-2	1-1	3-1	2-2	1-1	5-0	0-2	5-0	1-0	4-1	

LEICESTERSHIRE SENIOR LEAGUE PREMIER DIVISION CONSTITUTION 2012-13

ASHBY IVANHOE	Hood Park, North Street, Ashby-de-la-Zouch LE65 1HU	01530 412181
BIRSTALL UNITED	Meadow Lane, Birstall LE4 4FN	0116 267 1230
CATERPILLAR SPORTS	Peckleton Lane, Desford, Leicester LE9 9JT	07856 179485
COTTESMORE AMATEURS	Rogues Park, Main Street, Cottesmore, Oakham LE15 4DH	01572 813486
DESFORD	Sport in Desford, Peckleton Lane, Desford, Leicester LE9 9JU	01455 828786
DUNTON & BROUGHTON RANGERS	Station Road, Dunton Bassett LE17 5LF	07780 957479
FC DYNAMO	Nanpantan Sports Ground, Nanpantan Road, Loughborough LE11 3YD	01509 237148
HIGHFIELD RANGERS	443 Gleneagles Avenue, Rushey Mead, Leicester LE4 7YJ	0116 266 0009
KIRBY MUXLOE SC RESERVES	Ratby Lane, Kirby Muxloe, Leicester LE9 9AQ	0116 239 3201
ROTHLEY IMPERIAL	Loughborough Road, Mountsorrel, Leicester LE7 7NH	0116 292 0538
SAFFRON DYNAMO	Cambridge Road, Whetstone LE8 3LG	07957 151630
SILEBY SAINTS	Seagrave Road, Sileby LE12 7N	07810 852670
SILEBY TOWN	Memorial Park, Seagrave Road, Sileby, Loughborough LE12 7TP	07708 231563/07860 842056
STAPENHILL	Maple Grove, Stapenhill, Burton-on-Trent DE15 1RW	01283 533133

DIVISION ONE	1	2	3	4	5	6	7	8	9	10	11	12	13	14	15
1 Asfordby Amateurs		0-1	1-1	3-1	0-1	1-1	3-2	0-6	0-2	1-0	1-1	3-7	0-1	2-4	1-4
2 Barlestone St Giles	10-0		2-3	0-1	2-4	3-1	1-2	5-1	4-3	1-1	1-1	0-2	3-0	3-2	1-0
3 Belgrave	5-1	3-0		1-1	0-2	7-0	2-0	0-4	3-1	1-2	1-5	2-2	3-1	1-1	0-2
4 Castle Donington Town	5-0	5-2	2-3		1-5	2-1	5-3	3-2	1-3	2-0	2-0	6-1	2-1	2-2	0-1
5 Caterpillar	6-1	2-1	11-2	1-2		5-0	3-1	5-2	2-0	4-0	8-0	1-2	2-0	10-0	3-0
6 Earl Shilton Albion	2-0	1-1	2-0	2-1	2-5		4-0	3-1	5-0	4-0	3-2	3-4	4-1	0-3	0-3
7 FC Khalsa	1-0	1-2	4-2	0-3	3-3	1-0		0-2	2-4	0-0	0-6	0-1	0-4	3-1	1-0
8 Friar Lane & Epworth	4-0	2-0	5-1	4-0	0-2	6-4	2-0		0-0	3-0	0-1	2-6	3-1	5-0	0-1
9 Hathern	4-1	0-2	4-1	3-2	1-5	2-0	2-3	1-1		3-1	5-5	5-0	3-2	1-0	1-2
10 Lutterworth Town	2-1	2-3	0-3	1-0	0-5	1-0	2-2	2-4	2-1		0-3	2-2	1-1	4-0	0-1
11 Melton Mowbray	2-0	0-1	0-1	3-1	1-3	2-2	6-0	1-6	1-2	4-2		2-1	0-2	4-0	2-3
12 Narborough & Littlethorpe	2-1	2-1	4-3	3-2	0-5	1-3	2-3	0-2	3-2	2-0	1-3		1-1	1-2	1-5
13 Newhall United	0-1	1-0	3-1	3-0	0-9	1-0	3-2	0-3	1-1	4-1	2-0	6-2		5-1	6-2
14 Shepshed Dynamo Reserves	2-1	0-2	0-1	0-1	0-9	0-4	3-2	1-7	2-2	1-0	1-2	3-3	3-1		1-2
15 Sileby Saints	4-3	1-1	5-1	3-2	1-3	4-1	4-2	1-2	7-1	3-0	2-2	4-1	4-2	4-1	

LEICESTERSHIRE SENIOR LEAGUE DIVISION ONE CONSTITUTION 2012-13

ALLEXTON & NEW PARKS	Glenfield Road, Leicester LE3 6D	07413 679783
ASFORDBY AMATEURS	Hoby Road Sports Ground, Hoby Road, Asfordby, Melton Mowbray LE14 3TL	01664 434545
BARLESTONE ST GILES	Barton Road, Barlestone CV13 0EP	01455 291392
CASTLE DONINGTON TOWN	Moira Dale Playing Fields, Castle Donington, Derby DE74 2BJ	07890 886176
EARL SHILTON ALBION	Stoneycroft Park, New Street, Earl Shilton LE9 7FR	01455 844277
FC KHALSA	Judge Meadow Community College, Marydene Drive, Evington, Leicester LE5 6HP	0116 2417580
FRIAR LANE & EPWORTH	Knighton Lane East, Aylestone Park, Leicester LE2 6FT	0116 283 3629
HATHERN	Pasture Lane, Hathern, Loughborough LE12 5LJ	07952 113090
LUTTERWORTH TOWN	Hall Lane, Bitteswell, Lutterworth LE17 4LN	01455 554046
MELTON MOWBRAY	All England Sports Ground, Saxby Road, Melton Mowbray LE13 1BP	07977 266729
NARBOROUGH & LITTLETHORPE	Leicester Road, Narborough LE19 2DG	0116 275 1855
RATBY SPORTS	Desford Lane, Ratby, Leicester LE6 0LE	0116 239 2474
SHEPSHED DYNAMO RESERVES	The Dovecote, Butt Hole Lane, Shepshed, Loughborough LE12 9BN	01509 650992

LIVERPOOL COUNTY PREMIER LEAGUE

Sponsored by: No sponsor
Founded: 2006
Recent Champions:
2007: Waterloo Dock
2008: Waterloo Dock
2009: Waterloo Dock
2010: Waterloo Dock
2011: Waterloo Dock

I ZINGARI CUP

ROUND 1
Red Rum 0-4 Essemmay Old Boys
Old Xaverians 1-1 4-5p Ford Motors
Waterloo Dock 2-3 (aet) Page Celtic
Cheshire Lines 0-1 Croxteth
South Sefton Borough 0-3 Warbreck
ROMA 1-2 REMYCA United
East Villa 1-2 (aet) Aigburth Peoples Hall

QUARTER FINALS
Essemmay Old Boys AW Ford Motors
Sacre Coeur FP 0-1 Page Celtic
Croxteth HW Warbreck
REMYCA United 2-7 Aigburth Peoples Hall

SEMI-FINALS
Ford Motors 2-1 Page Celtic
Croxteth 3-1 Aigburth Peoples Hall

FINAL (@ LCFA, Wavertree, 24/5/11)
Ford Motors 3-2 (aet) Croxteth

PREMIER DIVISION	P	W	D	L	F	A	Pts
1 Aigburth Peoples Hall	28	22	4	2	79	28	70
2 East Villa	28	18	3	7	68	41	57
3 Waterloo Dock	28	18	2	8	69	35	56
4 Old Xaverians	28	17	2	9	64	48	53
5 Croxteth	28	16	4	8	75	47	52
6 Page Celtic	28	14	5	9	55	42	47
7 South Sefton Borough	28	14	4	10	41	39	46
8 ROMA	28	14	3	11	61	65	45
9 Essemmay Old Boys	28	10	6	12	48	52	36
10 Warbreck	28	11	1	16	47	67	34
11 Ford Motors	28	10	3	15	42	49	33
12 Red Rum	28	8	1	19	46	63	25
13 Sacre Coeur	28	5	5	18	38	61	20
14 Cheshire Lines	28	5	2	21	32	79	17
15 REMYCA United	28	5	1	22	39	88	16

PREMIER DIVISION	1	2	3	4	5	6	7	8	9	10	11	12	13	14	15
1 Aigburth Peoples Hall		4-1	1-1	2-1	HW	3-0	2-1	3-1	2-1	7-0	7-1	2-1	3-0	3-2	0-2
2 Cheshire Lines	0-2		1-6	2-4	1-2	0-2	1-5	2-5	0-2	2-3	2-6	0-5	0-1	1-3	0-6
3 Croxteth	AW	4-1		2-3	2-5	4-0	1-3	0-0	1-0	2-0	5-4	2-2	2-1	0-1	2-2
4 East Villa	3-2	2-0	3-2		HW	0-3	3-3	1-2	3-0	2-2	2-3	5-0	0-1	4-2	2-1
5 Essemmay Old Boys	3-3	1-1	AW	0-2		0-3	AW	1-1	4-4	3-0	7-3	2-2	2-0	2-5	A-W
6 Ford Motors	1-4	3-1	1-2	1-0	2-3		0-2	2-3	1-3	3-2	0-3	3-3	0-3	6-1	0-1
7 Old Xaverians	0-5	3-2	2-3	2-7	4-1	0-0		2-3	2-0	3-2	2-1	5-1	2-0	2-0	4-3
8 Page Celtic	1-2	0-1	2-6	1-3	2-1	2-1	3-1		2-0	2-0	5-2	2-0	0-1	3-0	1-2
9 Red Rum	2-5	1-2	3-1	0-1	3-1	1-0	1-2	0-3		5-1	6-2	0-2	1-2	4-3	4-3
10 REMYCA United	3-6	1-3	2-6	2-5	2-3	1-4	3-1	0-2	3-2		1-3	2-1	0-2	2-1	1-2
11 ROMA	1-1	1-4	3-2	1-4	0-0	3-1	1-3	1-0	2-1	6-3		4-1	1-1	2-0	2-0
12 Sacre Coeur FP	AW	2-2	2-3	1-3	1-2	0-1	0-2	2-3	3-0	3-0	2-3		2-1	1-1	0-2
13 South Sefton Borough	1-2	2-0	2-3	2-2	1-2	3-1	1-0	5-5	2-1	2-1	1-0	1-1		2-1	0-4
14 Warbreck	1-5	0-1	1-8	3-0	4-1	2-1	4-3	1-1	3-2	2-1	0-2	3-1	1-2		1-3
15 Waterloo Dock	0-0	3-1	1-4	1-2	1-2	2-0	0-4	2-1	5-1	5-1	4-0	6-0	2-1	5-1	

LIVERPOOL COUNTY PREMIER LEAGUE PREMIER DIVISION CONSTITUTION 2012-13

AIGBURTH PEOPLE'S HALL	Cheshire Lines FC, Southmead Road, Allerton, Liverpool L19 5NB	0151 427 7176
CHESHIRE LINES	Southmead Road, Allerton, Liverpool L19 5NB	0151 427 7176
EAST VILLA	Litherland Sports Park, Boundary Road, Litherland, Liverpool L21 7NW	0151 288 6338
FORD MOTORS	Ford Sports & Social Club, Cronton Lane, Widnes WA8 5AJ	0151 424 7078
LIVERPOOL NORTH	Playfootball.com, Drummond Road, Thornton L20 6DX	0151 2102417
OLD XAVERIANS	St Francis Xaviers College, Beconsfield Road, Liverpool L25 6EG	07799 148866
PAGE CELTIC	Huyton Arts & Sports Centre, Seel Road, Huyton, Liverpool L36 6DG	0151 477 8860
REMYCA UNITED	Litherland Sports Park, Liverpool L21 7L	07504 096330
RED RUM	Croxteth Comm. Comp. School, Parkstile Lane, Liverpool L11 0PB	0151 546 4168
ROMA	Kirkby Sports Centre, Valley Road, Kirkby L20 9PQ	0151 443 4404
SOUTH SEFTON BOROUGH	Boundary Road, Litherland, Sefton Town L21 7L	07979 375574
STONEYCROFT	Maiden Lane Playing Fields, Maiden Lane, Liverpool L13 9AN	07900 915722
WARBRECK	Playfootball.com, Drummond Road, Thornton L20 6DX	07788 776111
WATERLOO DOCK	Edinburgh Park, Townsend Lane, Liverpool L6 0BB	0151 263 5267
WEST EVERTON XAVERIANS	St Francis Xavier College, Beconsfield Road, Liverpool L25 6EQ	0151 288 1000

DIVISION ONE

		P	W	D	L	F	A	Pts
1	West Everton Xaviers	24	19	2	3	65	30	59
2	Stoneycroft	24	18	3	3	71	28	57
3	Liverpool North	24	18	1	5	88	42	55
4	Leyfield	24	12	7	5	60	37	43
5	Edge Hill BCOB	24	14	1	9	62	46	43
6	Pinewoods	24	12	2	10	56	44	38
7	Old Holts	24	9	3	12	40	60	30
8	Collegiate Old Boys	24	8	2	14	45	54	26
9	BRNESC	24	8	2	14	45	60	26
10	Waterloo Grammar Sch OB	24	7	4	13	42	64	25
11	Alumni	24	6	2	16	38	63	20
12	Copperas Hill	24	4	3	17	42	90	15
13	Lucas Sports	24	4	2	18	31	67	14

DIVISION TWO

		P	W	D	L	F	A	Pts
1	Kingsley United	22	17	3	2	74	22	54
2	Allerton	22	17	2	3	91	30	53
3	Park Brow	22	15	3	4	71	42	48
4	Alder	22	12	3	7	60	44	39
5	KCFC	22	11	3	8	73	48	36
6	Warbreck Reserves	22	12	0	10	47	46	36
7	AFC Liverpool Reserves	22	11	2	9	49	28	35
8	Collegiate Old Boys Reserves	22	10	1	11	59	59	31
9	Eli Lilly	22	5	3	14	43	74	18
10	Quarry Bank	22	3	5	14	39	69	14
11	Liobians	22	4	2	16	35	98	14
12	Redgate Rovers	22	0	1	21	19	95	1

CUP COMPETITIONS

ROY WADE DIVISION ONE CUP

Edge Hill Boys Club Old B 1-1 4-5p Liverpool North

LORD WAVERTREE DIVISION TWO CUP

Kingsley United 4-1 Allerton 1

DAVE HUGHES MEMORIAL CUP

Salisbury Athletic 1-4 Holy Cross

JOHN GREGSON MEMORIAL CUP

Collegiate Old Boys 2-1 Leyfield

LIVERPOOL COUNTY PREMIER LEAGUE DIVISION ONE CONSTITUTION 2012-13

ALDER	Alder Road Sports Club, Alder Road, West Derby, Liverpool L12 2BA	07943 094372
ALLERTON	Woolton Road, Liverpool L19 5N	07875 746480
ALUMNI	Jericho Lane , Aigburth , Liverpool L17 5AR	
BRNESC	Melling Road, Aintree, Liverpool L9 0LQ	
COLLEGIATE OLD BOYS	Alder Road Sports Club, Alder Road, West Derby, Liverpool L12 2BA	
COPPERAS HILL	Breckside Park, Liverpool L6 4DJ	
EDGE HILL BCOB	William Collins Mem. Ground, Commercial Road, Liverpool L5 7QY	
KINGSLEY UNITED	Quarry Bank School Playing Fds, Greenhill Road, Allerton, Liverpool L18 6HF	
LEYFIELD	Thomas Lane Playing Fields, Thomas Lane, Liverpool L14 5NR	
LUCAS SPORTS	William Collins Mem. Ground, Commercial Road, Liverpool L5 7QY	
OLD HOLTS	Simpson Ground, Hillfoot Road, Liverpool L25 0ND	0151 486 3166
PINEWOODS	Carr Lane Playing Fields, Carr Lane, Ainsdale, Southport PR8 3EE	
WATERLOO GSOB	Moss Lane, Litherland, Liverpool L21 7NW	

LIVERPOOL COUNTY PREMIER LEAGUE DIVISION TWO CONSTITUTION 2012-13

AINTREE VILLA	Melling Road, Liverpool L9 5A	0151 5269287
ALDER RESERVES	Alder Road Sports Club, Alder Road, West Derby, Liverpool L12 2BA	07943 094372
CARNATIC	Abbottshey Avenue, Liverpool L18 7J	07894 488880
ELI LILLY	Thomas Lane Playing Fields, Thomas Lane, Liverpool L14 5NR	None
HOLLY CROSS	Holy Cross Sisters' School, Bloemhof Street, Bellville	07347 12194
KCFC	Breckside Park, Liverpool L6 4ES	None
LIVER ACADEMY	Lower Breck Road, Liverpool L6 4D	07818 415817
OLD HOLTS RESERVES	Hollies Road, Halewood L26 0T	07886 569103
OLD XAVERIANS RESERVES	St Francis Xaviers College, Beconsfield Road, Liverpool L25 6EG	07799 148866
QUARRY BANK OLD BOYS	Calderstone Playing Field, Greenhill Road, Liverpool L18 6JJ	None
REMYCA UNITED RESERVES	Litherland Sports Park, Liverpool L21 7L	07504 096330
THE FAMOUS GRAPES	Pool Hey, Haswell Drive, Liverpool L28 5RY	07818 509238
WARBRECK RESERVES	Playfootball.com, Drummond Road, Thornton L20 6DX	None
WOODSTREET	Clubmoor, Townsend Lane, Liverpool	07957 100560

MANCHESTER LEAGUE

Sponsored by: Bridgewater Office Supplies
Founded: 1893
Recent Champions:
2007: Prestwich Hays
2008: Wigan Robin Park
2009: Gregorians
2010: AVRO
2011: AVRO

GILGRYST CUP

ROUND 1
Walshaw Sports 3-1 West Didsbury & Chorlton
Stockport Georgians 4-3 Heywood St James
Hindsford 2-3 AFC Bury
Old Alts 0-1 AVRO
Manchester Gregorians 1-4 Springhead
Dukinfield Town 3-2 AFC Monton
East Manchester 1-0 Prestwich Heys
Wythenshawe Amateurs 1-2 Royton Town

QUARTER FINALS
Walshaw Sports 3-4 Stockport Georgians
AFC Bury 1-3 AVRO
Springhead 2-1 (aet) Dukinfield Town
East Manchester 5-1 Royton Town

SEMI-FINALS
Stockport Georgians 7-2 AVRO
Springhead 3-1 (aet) East Manchester

FINAL
Stockport Georgians 2-3 Springhead

PREMIER DIVISION	P	W	D	L	F	A	Pts
1 Hindsford	30	22	5	3	84	40	71
2 East Manchester	30	18	3	9	71	45	57
3 Walshaw Sports	30	15	5	10	76	53	50
4 Springhead	30	13	11	6	63	47	50
5 Stockport Georgians	30	14	7	9	47	44	49
6 AVRO (-3)	30	15	6	9	86	60	48
7 West Didsbury & Chorlton	30	13	6	11	41	52	45
8 Royton Town	30	12	8	10	58	53	44
9 Wythenshawe Ams	30	12	8	10	45	40	44
10 Old Alts	30	12	5	13	47	56	41
11 Manchester Gregorians	30	11	2	17	37	48	35
12 AFC Monton	30	7	8	15	45	60	29
13 Prestwich Heys (-1)	30	8	6	16	45	66	29
14 Heywood St James	30	8	2	20	58	95	26
15 Dukinfield Town (-3)	30	8	4	18	44	63	25
16 AFC Bury	30	5	8	17	35	60	23

PREMIER DIVISION	1	2	3	4	5	6	7	8	9	10	11	12	13	14	15	16
1 AFC Bury		1-1	1-3	1-3	2-1	1-1	2-2	0-1	4-1	1-1	1-1	1-1	1-2	2-0	4-1	0-2
2 AFC Monton	4-2		3-3	1-0	2-4	4-2	0-1	0-2	1-1	3-1	1-2	1-2	0-2	1-3	0-2	1-2
3 AVRO	5-0	3-1		4-3	1-3	4-2	4-3	3-2	3-2	4-1	1-1	0-1	2-4	1-2	1-2	6-0
4 Dukinfield Town	0-0	1-2	1-3		1-5	5-0	0-3	0-1	2-3	0-2	1-1	3-1	0-1	1-2	2-0	0-1
5 East Manchester	3-1	3-2	4-0	3-1		5-4	1-2	1-0	0-1	0-2	2-6	0-1	3-3	3-2	1-2	3-0
6 Heywood St James	3-1	2-1	5-4	2-2	2-4		3-6	3-2	0-5	2-3	1-2	2-4	3-4	2-4	0-1	3-2
7 Hindsford	5-2	3-3	3-6	5-0	2-0	3-1		1-0	4-1	2-0	2-2	4-2	4-1	3-2	2-1	2-1
8 Manchester Gregorians	1-0	0-1	3-2	2-3	0-3	4-0	0-1		1-0	1-5	0-1	0-2	1-2	1-5	1-2	2-1
9 Old Altrinchamians	2-0	2-2	1-5	2-1	0-1	4-2	0-4	1-0		1-3	2-4	3-2	2-0	2-1	1-2	1-1
10 Prestwich Heys	3-3	3-3	2-2	3-2	0-5	1-2	1-6	0-1	1-3		2-1	2-2	3-0	0-3	0-3	2-3
11 Royton Town	1-0	1-3	1-1	3-4	1-3	3-1	0-1	2-3	0-2	2-1		4-4	2-1	5-3	1-1	0-0
12 Springhead	3-1	2-1	1-4	6-0	1-1	6-2	2-0	1-0	4-0	1-1	2-3		1-0	3-3	3-1	0-4
13 Stockport Georgians	3-0	1-1	3-1	2-4	1-0	2-1	2-2	2-1	1-1	2-0	2-1	2-2		3-1	1-1	0-2
14 Walshaw Sports	2-3	4-1	2-0	1-3	1-3	5-1	1-3	3-3	3-1	5-1	3-3	1-1	2-1		5-0	2-1
15 West Didsbury & Chorlton	1-0	1-1	0-5	2-0	2-2	1-3	0-3	2-1	2-1	3-0	1-4	1-1	2-2	0-3		0-1
16 Wythenshawe Amateurs	3-0	4-1	1-1	1-1	2-4	2-3	2-2	1-2	0-0	1-0	1-0	1-1	2-0	0-0	3-4	

MANCHESTER LEAGUE PREMIER DIVISION CONSTITUTION 2012-13

AFC MONTON	Off Worlsey Road, Winton, Salford M30 8J	07836 321193
AVRO	Lancaster Club, Broadway, Failsworth, Oldham M35 0DX	0161 681 3083
BEECHFIELD UNITED	Salford Sports Village, Littleton Road, Salford M7 3NQ	0161 604 7600
EAST MANCHESTER	Wright Robinson Sports College, Abbey Hey Lane, Gorton M18 8RL	0161 370 5121
HEYWOOD ST JAMES	Phoenix Ground, Shepherd Street, Heywood OL10 1JW	07929 915828
HINDSFORD	Squires Lane, Tyldesley M29 8JF	None
LEIGH ATHLETIC	Leigh Sports Village, Madley Park, Charles Street, Leigh WN7 4GX	01942 673500
MANCHESTER GREGORIANS	MCFC, Platt Lane Complex, Yew Tree Road, Fallowfield M14 7UU	07740 585459
OLD ALTRINCHAMIANS	Crossford Bridge Sports Ground, Danefield Road, Sale M33 7WR	0161 767 9233
PRESTWICH HEYS	Sandgate Road, Whitefield M45 6WG	0161 773 8888
ROYTON TOWN	Crompton Cricket Club Complex, Christine Street, Shaw, Oldham OL2 7SF	01706 847421
SPRINGHEAD	Ashfield Crescent PF, St John Street, Lees, Oldham OL4 4DG	0161 627 0260
STOCKPORT GEORGIANS	Cromley Road, Woodsmoor, Stockport SK2 7DT	0161 483 6581
WALSHAW SPORTS CLUB	Walshaw Sports Club, Sycamore Road, Tottington, Bury BL8 3EG	01204 882448
WEST DIDSBURY & CHORLTON	Brookburn Road, Chorlton-cum-Hardy M21 8EH	07891 298441
WYTHENSHAWE AMATEUR	Longley Lane, Northenden, Wythenshawe M22 4LA	0161 998 7268

DIVISION ONE

		P	W	D	L	F	A	Pts
1	Wythenshawe Town	26	19	4	3	88	52	61
2	Beechfield United	26	17	5	4	66	36	56
3	Leigh Athletic	26	16	2	8	96	60	50
4	Rochdale Sacred Heart	26	14	4	8	86	49	46
5	Fives Athletic	26	12	4	10	64	47	40
6	Pennington (-1)	26	11	6	9	62	52	38
7	Breightmet United	26	11	5	10	61	58	38
8	Elton Vale	26	11	4	11	66	64	37
9	Chapel Town	26	10	6	10	42	52	36
10	Atherton Town	26	9	4	13	59	66	31
11	Hollinwood	26	9	3	14	68	89	30
12	Woodley Sports Reserves	26	8	4	14	37	64	28
13	Salford Victoria	26	4	4	18	44	82	16
14	Wilmslow Albion	26	3	1	22	23	91	10

MURRAY SHIELD

ROUND 1

Pennington 7-1 Woodley Sports Reserves

Elton Vale 5-0 Wilmslow Albion

Fives Athletic 5-2 Atherton Town

Salford Victoria 1-4 Wythenshawe Town

Beechfield United 3-1 Leigh Athletic

Hollinwood 3-2 Breightmet United

QUARTER FINAL

Rochdale Sacred Heart 3-2 Pennington

Elton Vale 1-2 Fives Athletic

Wythenshawe Town 2-1 Beechfield United

Chapel Town 3-0 Hollinwood

SEMI-FINALS

Rochdale Sacred Heart 5-2 Fives Athletic

Wythenshawe Town 1-0 Chapel Town

FINAL

Rochdale Sacred Heart 3-1 Wythenshawe Town

DIVISION ONE

		1	2	3	4	5	6	7	8	9	10	11	12	13	14
1	Atherton Town		1-2	0-2	2-2	4-2	1-0	2-1	4-2	1-2	2-3	3-3	4-3	6-1	2-5
2	Beechfield United	1-0		1-4	2-0	3-0	0-2	4-0	1-5	1-1	5-4	3-1	4-0	2-1	2-4
3	Breightmet United	3-3	3-4		3-0	3-2	2-0	4-4	2-4	3-4	2-7	3-3	2-0	1-1	3-3
4	Chapel Town	2-1	0-3	0-4		1-2	5-3	2-1	4-1	1-4	3-3	1-1	3-1	4-1	1-2
5	Elton Vale	0-0	2-2	3-2	7-0		4-1	3-1	6-5	1-3	2-5	2-0	4-0	2-1	4-6
6	Fives Athletic	4-2	2-2	3-2	1-1	4-1		3-4	1-1	3-2	3-3	7-1	4-0	3-2	2-3
7	Hollinwood	3-5	1-4	5-0	2-2	1-1	1-5		3-11	3-4	1-6	7-1	3-1	4-3	5-2
8	Leigh Athletic	3-1	1-5	2-5	3-0	4-0	2-1	7-3		2-2	3-2	5-2	5-0	1-0	4-1
9	Pennington	1-2	1-3	1-2	2-2	4-4	1-0	5-0	2-3		2-1	4-1	4-2	1-2	0-3
10	Rochdale Sacred Heart	3-1	1-1	4-2	0-1	2-1	1-5	3-4	3-2	2-2		4-2	6-0	6-0	7-0
11	Salford Victoria	7-4	1-4	1-0	1-2	4-6	1-3	1-2	3-0	3-3	1-3		0-1	3-0	1-3
12	Wilmslow Albion	2-7	0-2	1-2	0-3	1-3	2-3	2-1	1-7	0-4	0-5	1-0		2-2	2-3
13	Woodley Sports Reserves	2-1	0-4	0-1	1-2	4-3	2-1	0-3	4-10	2-1	2-1	2-0	2-0		1-1
14	Wythenshawe Town	7-0	1-1	2-1	1-0	3-1	1-0	8-5	4-3	5-2	2-1	9-2	8-1	1-1	

MANCHESTER LEAGUE DIVISION ONE CONSTITUTION 2012-13

AFC BURY	Cams Lane, Radcliffe M26 3SW	
ATHERTON TOWN	Eckersley Fold Lane, Leigh Road, Atherton M46 0QQ	01942 884882
BREIGHTMET UNITED	Moss Park, Bury Road, Breightmet, Bolton BL2 6NY	01204 533930
CHADDERTON RESERVES	Andrew Street, Chadderton, Oldham OL9 0J	07846 170895
CHAPEL TOWN	Rowton Park, Willow Drive, Chapel-en-le-Frith, High Peak SK23 0ND	
DUKINFIELD TOWN	Woodhams Park, Birch Lane, Dukinfield SK16 5AP	0161 343 4529
ELTON VALE	Elton Sports Club, Elton Vale Road, Bury BL8 2RZ	0161 762 0666
FIVES ATHLETIC	Harriet Street, Walkden, Worsley M28 3QA	
HOLLINWOOD	Chapel Road Playing Fields, Grammar School Rd, Hollinwood, Oldham OL8 4QY	0161 911 5017
IRLAM STEEL	Liverpool Road, Irlam, Salford M44 6A	07961 080389
PENNINGTON	Jubilee Park, Leigh Road, Atherton M46 0PJ	
ROCHDALE SACRED HEART	Fox Park, Belfield Mill Lane, Rochdale OL16 2UB	
SALFORD VICTORIA	Salford Sports Village, Lower Kersal, Littleton Road, Salford M7 3NQ	0161 604 7600
STOCKPORT SPORTS RESERVES	Lambeth Grove, Woodley, Stockport SK6 1Q	07920 232074
WILMSLOW ALBION	Oakwood Farm, Styal Road, Wilmslow SK9 4HP	01625 535823

MIDDLESEX COUNTY LEAGUE

Sponsored by: Cherry Red Books
Founded: 1984
Recent Champions:
2007: Sport London E Benfica
2008: Indian Gymkhana
2009: Bethnal Green United
2010: Interwood
2011: Willesden Constantine

PREMIER DIVISION	P	W	D	L	F	A	Pts
1 Interwood	30	27	1	2	116	32	82
2 FC Romania	30	23	1	6	94	39	70
3 Southall	30	19	3	8	91	49	60
4 Willesden Constantine	30	16	5	9	82	54	53
5 Singh Sabha Slough	30	15	8	7	64	51	53
6 Indian Gymkhana (SSH)	30	16	5	9	76	65	53
7 Sloane	30	12	6	12	49	53	42
8 Broadfields United	30	10	7	13	67	66	37
9 Hounslow Wanderers	30	11	4	15	63	72	37
10 Sporting Hackney	30	11	3	16	51	60	36
11 West Essex	30	10	5	15	39	60	35
12 FC Deportivo Galicia	30	9	2	19	52	83	29
13 North Kensington	30	8	4	18	49	71	28
14 Hillingdon	30	7	7	16	48	73	28
15 Kodak (Harrow)	30	6	4	20	32	81	22
16 Springfield	30	5	5	20	41	105	20

ALEC SMITH PREMIER DIVISION CUP

ROUND 1
Sporting Hackney 1-4 Hounslow Wanderers
FC Romania 2-3 FC Deportivo Galicia
West Essex 1-3 Indian Gymkhana (S.S.H)
Sloane 1-3 Interwood
Kodak (Harrow) 2-1 North Kensington
Southall 2-1 Singh Sabha Slough
Hillingdon 2-5 Broadfields United
Springfield 1-3 Willesden Constantine
QUARTER FINALS
Southall 2-2 Willesden Constantine
(Southall won on penalties)
FC Deportivo Galicia 2-2 Interwood
(FC Deportivo Galicia won on penalties)
Hounslow Wanderers 3-5 Broadfields United
Kodak (Harrow) 1-3 Indian Gymkhana (S.S.H)
SEMI-FINALS
FC Deportivo Galicia 2-4 Southall
Indian Gymkhana (S.S.H) 2-4 Broadfields United
FINAL
Southall 1-4 Broadfields United

PREMIER DIVISION	1	2	3	4	5	6	7	8	9	10	11	12	13	14	15	16
1 Broadfields United		L-W	1-2	3-1	9-2	2-2	4-7	1-1	2-0	0-1	2-1	1-4	0-1	1-1	1-1	4-4
2 FC Deportivo Galicia	1-2		1-5	2-3	1-0	4-2	1-6	0-3	2-3	2-8	1-3	2-4	1-2	2-2	1-2	3-2
3 FC Romania	7-1	2-1		5-1	4-0	4-2	3-4	3-0	6-1	3-4	3-0	2-0	2-1	3-3	1-0	4-3
4 Hillingdon	1-5	1-2	2-4		4-1	1-3	0-2	1-2	1-4	2-3	0-0	0-3	0-0	3-1	1-1	0-0
5 Hounslow Wanderers	3-1	1-2	2-4	4-1		4-0	2-4	3-1	2-3	1-3	0-3	5-1	1-3	4-2	4-0	3-3
6 Indian Gymkhana	0-6	2-1	3-2	2-2	3-0		1-4	5-0	0-0	5-3	3-5	0-3	4-2	6-1	1-4	2-1
7 Interwood	4-1	5-1	0-1	5-1	5-2	4-0		6-0	5-1	5-1	4-0	1-2	4-0	10-1	2-0	2-1
8 Kodak (Harrow)	1-3	3-4	0-3	2-3	1-1	0-0	2-6		1-3	0-3	0-2	3-2	2-1	0-2	6-2	1-4
9 North Kensington	2-2	2-1	0-3	2-5	1-3	2-3	2-3	0-1		2-3	1-0	2-5	1-3	5-0	4-0	1-3
10 Singh Sabha Slough	3-3	3-6	0-3	0-0	1-1	1-1	0-3	3-0	2-2		1-1	1-1	1-0	W-L	0-0	3-2
11 Sloane	W-L	2-1	3-1	2-2	4-4	2-6	0-1	5-0	4-1	0-3		2-2	2-3	0-0	1-3	3-1
12 Southall	2-1	2-1	2-1	4-1	1-2	2-4	2-3	9-0	4-2	2-1	6-0		3-1	5-1	2-3	3-3
13 Sporting Hackney	5-4	3-3	0-3	4-2	0-1	1-2	1-5	2-0	1-1	2-4	2-1	1-3		7-0	1-0	2-4
14 Springfield	3-5	5-3	0-5	2-4	1-6	3-5	0-0	W-L	3-0	0-3	0-3	0-6	2-1		4-5	1-5
15 West Essex	1-2	1-2	1-3	0-1	3-1	0-6	0-2	1-1	1-0	1-5	2-0	2-4	1-0	2-1		1-2
16 Willesden Constantine	5-0	4-0	3-2	5-4	3-0	1-3	2-4	3-1	2-1	3-0	L-W	3-2	3-1	6-2	1-1	

MIDDLESEX COUNTY LEAGUE PREMIER DIVISION CONSTITUTION 2012-13

BRITISH AIRWAYS	Crane Lodge Road, Cranford TW5 9P	07779 638080
BROADFIELDS UNITED	The Hive, Camrose Avenue, Edgware HA8 6DQ	020 8238 5920
FC ASSYRIA	Cayton Road, Greenford UB6 8B	07946 314344
FC DEPORTIVO GALICIA	Osterley Sports Club, Tentelow Lane, Osterley, Southall UB2 4LW	020 8574 7055
FC ROMANIA	The Stadium, Theobalds Lane, Cheshunt EN8 8R	07931 789838
HILLINGDON	Hillingdon Athletics Stadium, Gatting Way, Park Road, Uxbridge UB8 1ES	0845 130 7324
HOUNSLOW WANDERERS	Rosedale College, Wood End Green Road, Hayes UB3 2SE	020 8573 2097
INDIAN GYMKHANA	Indian Gymkhana Club, Thornbury Avenue, Osterley TW7 4NQ	020 8568 4009
INTERWOOD	Leyton Stadium, 282 Lea Bridge Road, Leyton E10 7LD	020 8988 7642
KILBURN	Forby Avenue, Wembley HA9 9J	07432 606406
KODAK (HARROW)	Zoom Leisure Centre, Kodak Sports Ground, Harrow View, Harrow HA2 6QQ	020 8427 1957
NORTH KENSINGTON	Vale Farm Sports Ground, Sudbury Court, East Lane, Wembley HA0 4UR	020 8904 8169/8908 5461
SINGH SABHA SLOUGH	Eton Wick FC, Haywards Mead, Eton Wick, Windsor SL4 6JN	
SLOANE	King's Sports Ground, Windsor Avenue, New Malden KT3 5HA	
SPORTING HACKNEY	Haggerston Park, Hackney E2 8NH	
WEST ESSEX	Rolls Sports Ground, Hickmans Avenue, Hickmans Park E4 9JG	020 8527 3889

DIVISION ONE CENTRAL & EAST

		P	W	D	L	F	A	Pts
1	Kilburn	20	14	2	4	69	45	44
2	Stonewall	20	12	4	4	51	30	40
3	Chiswick Homefields	20	11	1	8	68	47	34
4	The Wilberforce Wands	20	10	4	6	55	45	34
5	Cricklewood Wanderers	20	11	1	8	59	55	34
6	Horseed	20	10	3	7	66	51	33
7	West End	20	7	5	8	45	36	26
8	St Lawrence	20	7	4	9	47	43	25
9	Vallance	20	8	1	11	38	63	25
10	St Johns DFC	20	6	1	13	60	74	19
11	Elite Youth	20	0	2	18	14	83	2

East Fulham - record expunged

Greens United - record expunged

DIVISION ONE WEST

		P	W	D	L	F	A	Pts
1	FC Assyria	20	14	4	2	66	33	46
2	Sandgate	20	13	2	5	61	38	41
3	West London Saracens	20	12	2	6	65	33	38
4	Kensington Dragons	20	11	4	5	58	23	37
5	LPOSSA	20	11	3	6	53	37	36
6	Pitshanger Dynamo	20	10	4	6	45	26	34
7	Brentham	20	8	4	8	48	40	28
8	Imperial College Old B	20	6	5	9	32	39	23
9	HFC	20	5	4	11	43	55	19
10	CB Hounslow United Social	20	3	0	17	27	90	9
11	Lancaster Town	20	1	0	19	16	100	3

Belmullet Town - record expunged

DIVISION TWO

		P	W	D	L	F	A	Pts
1	Bay	18	13	3	2	51	20	42
2	Glenister	18	13	1	4	65	41	40
3	Hearts of Teddlothian	18	10	4	4	47	32	34
4	AFC Southall	18	10	2	6	51	37	32
5	CB Hounslow United Soc "A"	18	9	2	7	56	42	29
6	AFC Heathrow	18	7	4	7	36	35	25
7	Wembley Park	18	6	3	9	40	50	21
8	Ariana Football Academy	18	5	4	9	31	40	19
9	Centenary Park	18	2	1	15	27	62	7
10	West London Somaliland Com.	18	1	4	13	32	77	7

Lampton Legends - record expunged

Tokyngton Manor reserves - record expunged

SENIOR OPEN CUP

ROUND 1
Kensington Dragons 0-4 Southall
FC Assyria 6-0 Greens Utd
C.B. Hounslow United Social 2-1 Horseed
Chiswick Homefields 1-2 Springfield
Hounslow Wanderers 4-5 Vallance
Pitshanger Dynamo 3-2 The Wilberforce Wanderers
Stonewall 0-3 Brentham
West London Saracens 4-3 H F C

ROUND 2
FC Assyria 0-5 Interwood
West End 0-3 FC Romania
Pitshanger Dynamo 2-1 LPOSSA
Belmullet Town 1-3 Singh Sabha Slough
C.B. Hounslow United Social 1-3 Brentham
Southall 2-0 St Johns DFC
Springfield 0-2 Sandgate
Imperial College Old Boys 2-2 West Essex
(imperial College OB won on penalties)
Cricklewood Wanderers 0-7 Indian Gymkhana (S.S.H)
Lancaster Town 1-3 Sloane
Willesden Constantine 6-2 Vallance
FC Deportivo Galicia v Kilburn
West London Saracens 5-2 Broadfields United
Hillingdon 3-0 Sporting Hackney
Elite Youth 1-2 North Kensington
St Lawrence 2-1 Kodak (Harrow)

ROUND 3
Bye - St Lawrence
Pitshanger Dynamo 4-2 Sloane
Southall 1-0 Singh Sabha Slough
Willesden Constantine 2-1 Indian Gymkhana (S.S.H)
Hillingdon 1-4 Sandgate
West London Saracens 1-1 FC Romania
(FC Romania won on penalties)
North Kensington 1-2 Brentham
Imperial College Old Boys 0-4 Interwood

QUARTER FINALS
Willesden Constantine 1-1 Pitshanger Dynamo
(Pitshanger Dynamo won on penalties)
Southall 2-4 Interwood
Brentham 3-1 St Lawrence
Sandgate 0-3 FC Romania

SEMI-FINALS
Interwood AW Brentham
FC Romania 3-2 Pitshanger Dynamo

FINAL
039 Brentham 1-3 FC Romania

NORTH BERKSHIRE LEAGUE

Sponsored by: No sponsor
Founded: 1909
Recent Champions:
2007: Ardington & Lockinge
2008: Lambourn Sports
2009: Saxton Rovers
2010: Saxton Rovers
2011: Lambourn Sports
nbfl.co.uk

NORTH BERKS CUP

ROUND 1
Harwell Village 1-5 Wootton & Dry Sandford
Blewbury 4-3 Stanford-in-the-Vale
Benson Lions 0-3 Hagbourne United
Childrey United 2-3 Long Wittenham Athletic
Saxton Rovers 8-0 Grove Rangers
Kintbury Rangers 0-1 Hanney United
Sutton Courtenay 2-3 Crowmarsh Gifford
Didcot Casuals 3-4 Ardington & Lockinge
Benson AFC 4-3 (aet) Faringdon Town
Berinsfield 2-0 AFC Wallingford
East Hendred 12-1 Appleton Stars
Coleshill United 2-0 Dorchester
Uffington United 0-5 Marcham
Drayton 3-0 Steventon
Harwell International 4-0 Warborough United
ROUND 2
Wootton & Dry Sandford 8-0 Blewbury
Hagbourne United 1-1 11-10p Long Wittenham Athletic
Saxton Rovers 4-0 Hanney United
Crowmarsh Gifford 3-0 Westminster
Ardington & Lockinge 3-2 (aet) Benson AFC
Berinsfield 5-1 East Hendred
Coleshill United 4-2 Marcham
Drayton 1-0 Harwell International
QUARTER FINALS
Wootton & Dry Sandford 3-0 Hagbourne United
Saxton Rovers 2-3 (aet) Crowmarsh Gifford
Ardington & Lockinge 4-5 (aet) Berinsfield
Coleshill United 2-3 Drayton
SEMI-FINALS
Wootton & Dry Sandford 4-3 Crowmarsh Gifford
Berinsfield 4-0 Drayton
FINAL
Wootton & Dry Sandford 2-1 Berinsfield

DIVISION ONE	P	W	D	L	F	A	Pts
1 Crowmarsh Gifford	26	17	5	4	68	35	56
2 Didcot Casuals	26	17	4	5	76	25	55
3 Wootton & Dry Sandford	26	16	4	6	64	40	52
4 Saxton Rovers	26	15	4	7	59	35	49
5 Harwell International	26	12	9	5	44	33	45
6 Faringdon Town	26	11	8	7	46	47	41
7 Long Wittenham Athletic	26	10	9	7	49	35	39
8 Benson	26	11	4	11	45	51	37
9 Childrey United	26	10	5	11	51	51	35
10 East Hendred	26	6	9	11	41	46	27
11 AFC Wallingford	26	7	3	16	24	55	24
12 Kintbury Rangers	26	4	7	15	28	57	19
13 Drayton	26	5	4	17	39	69	19
14 Harwell Village	26	2	3	21	28	83	9

DIVISION ONE	1	2	3	4	5	6	7	8	9	10	11	12	13	14
1 AFC Wallingford		1-1	2-3	0-2	0-0	2-5	1-4	0-2	0-0	2-0	2-0	1-0	1-3	3-2
2 Benson	4-0		0-1	0-4	0-5	3-1	1-0	3-1	4-4	4-4	1-0	1-3	3-1	1-3
3 Childrey United	4-0	1-2		1-2	2-3	2-2	4-2	2-1	3-1	5-0	3-2	2-2	4-1	1-2
4 Crowmarsh Gifford	4-1	5-1	3-1		2-0	2-0	3-0	1-1	3-0	4-2	2-2	3-4	2-0	6-1
5 Didcot Casuals	7-1	0-3	5-0	4-0		4-0	0-0	5-0	4-1	5-1	3-0	1-1	1-2	2-2
6 Drayton	0-1	2-3	1-0	2-4	1-7		0-3	0-2	0-3	3-1	2-5	3-3	2-1	1-2
7 East Hendred	1-0	1-2	1-1	2-2	2-3	3-3		1-1	0-2	2-0	1-1	2-3	3-5	3-2
8 Faringdon Town	2-0	1-1	2-1	2-2	1-4	2-1	1-4		1-1	4-1	4-1	1-1	3-2	1-1
9 Harwell International	2-0	2-1	2-2	1-4	2-0	3-0	2-2	3-0		0-0	2-1	1-1	3-1	1-1
10 Harwell Village	3-4	1-3	2-1	1-3	0-2	1-6	3-2	2-4	0-3		2-3	0-3	1-2	0-5
11 Kintbury Rangers	HW	1-0	2-3	1-3	1-5	1-1	0-0	1-2	1-1	1-1		2-5	0-1	1-7
12 Long Wittenham Athletic	0-1	1-0	2-2	3-0	2-4	4-0	4-1	2-2	0-1	2-0	0-0		1-1	1-3
13 Saxton Rovers	4-0	4-1	5-1	2-2	1-0	5-2	0-0	7-1	1-2	3-0	2-0	2-1		3-1
14 Wootton & Dry Sandford	2-1	4-2	4-1	3-0	0-2	2-1	2-1	0-4	3-1	7-2	4-1	1-0	0-0	

NORTH BERKSHIRE LEAGUE DIVISION ONE CONSTITUTION 2012-13

AFC WALLINGFORD	Wallingford Sports Park , Hithercroft Road , Wallingford OX10 9RB	01491 835044
BENSON	Benson Recreation Ground, Benson	07787 547346
BERINSFIELD	Lay Avenue, Berinsfield OX10 7N	07983 399992
CHILDREY UNITED	Childrey Playing Field, Sparsholt Road, Childrey, Wantage OX12 9PN	01235 751275
CROWMARSH GIFFORD	Crowmarsh Recreation Ground, Crowmarsh Gifford, Wallingford OX10 8EB	07951 959090
DIDCOT CASUALS	Didcot Town Training Pitch, Ladygrove, Didcot OX11 7GA	07979 521253
EAST HENDRED	Hendred Sports & Social Club, Mill Lane, East Hendred OX12 8JS	01235 821008
FARINGDON TOWN	Tucker Park, Park Road, Faringdon SN7 7DP	01367 241759
HARWELL INTERNATIONAL	Main Gate, Harwell International Bus. Cte, Didcot OX11 0RA	01235 820220
KINTBURY RANGERS	Inkpen Road, Kintbury, Hungerford RG17 9TY	01488 657001
LONG WITTENHAM ATHLETIC	Bodkins Sports Field, East End of Village, Long Wittenham	01865 407202
SAXTON ROVERS	Recreation Ground, Caldecott Road, Abingdon OX14 5HR	07752 390039
SUTTON COURTENAY	Old Wallingford Way, Sutton Courtenay, Abingdon OX14 4A	07776 363488
WOOTTON & DRY SANDFORD	Community Centre, Besseleigh Road, Wootton OX13 6DN	07789 003397

DIVISION TWO

	P	W	D	L	F	A	Pts
1 Berinsfield	16	14	0	2	53	19	42
2 Lambourn Sports Reserves	16	10	0	6	45	26	30
3 Sutton Courtenay	16	10	0	6	48	29	30
4 Ardington & Lockinge	16	9	0	7	54	27	27
5 Marcham	16	8	2	6	35	41	26
6 Steventon	16	7	1	8	28	40	22
7 Benson Reserves	16	5	2	9	15	40	17
8 Benson Lions	16	2	3	11	21	55	9
9 Saxton Rovers Reserves	16	2	2	12	21	43	8

DIVISION THREE

	P	W	D	L	F	A	Pts
1 Dorchester	22	18	2	2	95	30	56
2 Coleshill United	22	16	2	4	48	31	50
3 Wantage Town 'A'	22	13	5	4	62	35	44
4 Hagbourne United	22	12	6	4	52	26	42
5 Kintbury Reserves	22	10	6	6	55	38	36
6 Blewbury	22	10	2	10	52	50	32
7 Stanford-in-the-Vale	22	9	4	9	60	51	31
8 Didcot Casuals Reserves	22	8	2	12	42	52	26
9 Faringdon Town Reserves	22	7	4	11	31	44	25
10 Shrivenham 'A'	22	7	2	13	62	65	23
11 Wootton & DS Reserves	22	3	1	18	46	92	10
12 Drayton Reserves	22	1	0	21	20	111	3

DIVISION FOUR EAST

	P	W	D	L	F	A	Pts
1 Harwell International Reserves	20	20	0	0	73	14	60
2 East Hendred Reserves	20	14	2	4	56	22	44
3 Blewbury Reserves	20	11	2	7	48	47	35
4 Westminster	20	10	3	7	43	32	33
5 Steventon Reserves	20	10	2	8	58	46	32
6 Long Wittenham Ath. Res.	20	8	2	10	36	45	26
7 Radley United	20	7	4	9	41	51	25
8 Hagbourne United Reserves	20	7	0	13	42	70	21
9 Sutton Courtenay Reserves	20	6	0	14	47	54	18
10 Benson Lions Reserves	20	5	1	14	26	42	16
11 Didcot Casuals "A"	20	4	0	16	39	86	12

DIVISION FOUR WEST

	P	W	D	L	F	A	Pts
1 Marcham Reserves	18	14	2	2	77	27	44
2 Childrey United Reserves	18	10	8	0	63	14	38
3 Grove Rangers	18	10	4	4	66	31	34
4 Hanney United	18	9	2	7	36	34	29
5 Stanford-in-the-Vale Reserves	18	8	2	8	53	45	26
6 Ardington & Lock. Reserves	18	8	2	8	56	53	26
7 Coleshill United Reserves	18	8	1	9	44	53	25
8 Faringdon Town "A"	18	6	2	10	36	37	20
9 Uffington United	18	5	1	12	31	50	16
10 Appleton Stars	18	0	0	18	13	131	0

NORTH BERKS CHARITY SHIELD

ROUND 1
Saxton Rovers 4-0 AFC Wallingford
Ardington & Lockinge 5-2 Harwell Village
Long Wittenham Athletic 3-4 Sutton Courtenay
Faringdon Town 1-5 Benson AFC
Benson Lions 6-1 Hanney United
Didcot Casuals 3-1 Coleshill United
Appleton Stars 0-5 Marcham
Wootton & Dry Sandford 6-0 Kintbury Rangers
Steventon 0-2 Crowmarsh Gifford
East Hendred 4-2 (aet) Childrey United
Grove Rangers 1-6 Harwell International
Stanford-in-the-Vale 2-4 Dorchester
Drayton 1-5 Blewbury
Hagbourne United 11-0 Warborough United
Uffington United 0-4 Berinsfield

ROUND 2
Saxton Rovers 3-3 (2-4p) Ardington & Lockinge
Sutton Courtenay 0-3 Benson AFC
Benson Lions 1-4 Didcot Casuals
Marcham 0-2 Wootton & Dry Sandford
Crowmarsh Gifford 5-3 (aet) East Hendred
Harwell International 0-1 Dorchester
Blewbury 1-2 Hagbourne United
Berinsfield 7-1 Westminster

QUARTER FINALS
Ardington & Lockinge 3-2 Benson AFC
Didcot Casuals 2-5 Wootton & Dry Sandford
Crowmarsh Gifford 3-1 Dorchester
Hagbourne United 0-4 Berinsfield

SEMI-FINALS
Ardington & Lockinge 1-1 3-2p Wootton & Dry Sandford
Crowmarsh Gifford 1-1 2-4p Berinsfield

FINAL
Ardington & Lockinge 0-2 Berinsfield

AG KINGHAM CUP

FINAL
Wantage Town 'A' 2-1 Shrivenham 'A'

NAIRNE PAUL TROPHY

FINAL
Marcham Reserves 2-0 Shrivenham 'A'

LEAGUE CUP

FINAL
Didcot Casuals 'A' 3-1 East Hendred Reserves

WAR MEMORIAL TROPHY

FINAL
Berinsfield 5-2 Sutton Courtenay

NORTHAMPTONSHIRE COMBINATION

Sponsored by: MDH Teamwear
Founded: N/K
Recent Champions:
2007: Harpole
2008: Harpole
2009: Harpole
2010: Harborough Town
2011: Brixworth All Saints
northantscombination.co.uk

PREMIER DIVISION CUP

ROUND 1

Harpole 5-0 Medbourne

Heyford Athletic 2-1 Brixworth All Saints

Corby Khalsa 3-2 Kislingbury

Roade 2-2 4-5p Gretton

Weldon United 1-1 7-6p Milton

Welford Victoria 3-1 Ringstead Rangers

QUARTER-FINALS

Harpole 5-0 Heyford Athletic

Corby Pegasus 5-5 1-4p Corby Khalsa

Moulton 2-1 Gretton

Weldon United 2-0 Welford Victoria

SEMI-FINALS

Harpole 3-0 Corby Khalsa

Moulton 2-3 Weldon United

FINAL

Harpole 2-1 Weldon United

PREMIER DIVISION	P	W	D	L	F	A	Pts
1 Harpole	26	20	5	1	76	14	65
2 Welford Victoria	26	18	6	2	75	27	60
3 Brixworth All Saints	26	19	3	4	69	31	60
4 Ringstead Rangers	26	19	2	5	72	39	59
5 Weldon United	26	14	3	9	60	41	45
6 Roade	26	13	1	12	51	40	40
7 Moulton	26	12	3	11	53	47	39
8 Corby Pegasus	26	9	2	15	56	60	29
9 Milton	26	6	6	14	37	53	24
10 Gretton (-12)	26	10	4	12	48	60	22
11 Heyford Athletic	26	5	5	16	27	68	20
12 Corby Khalsa	26	5	3	18	35	93	18
13 Medbourne	26	3	5	18	32	76	14
14 Kislingbury	26	3	4	19	23	65	13

PREMIER DIVISION	1	2	3	4	5	6	7	8	9	10	11	12	13	14
1 Brixworth All Saints		7-0	4-0	4-1	2-2	3-0	2-0	2-0	2-1	5-0	3-2	1-0	3-3	1-1
2 Corby Khalsa	2-4		4-1	0-4	0-4	3-1	3-1	2-3	1-1	0-6	1-3	4-3	0-5	0-7
3 Corby Pegasus	3-1	4-5		D	1-0	3-1	6-0	1-2	1-3	1-3	1-3	1-4	1-2	1-3
4 Gretton	0-3	7-2	4-2	0	-5	2-0	4-1	4-0	2-0	3-1	2-5	3-1	1-2	2-9
5 Harpole	5-1	7-0	1-1	D	3	-0	5-0	5-1	5-2	1-0	0-0	3-0	2-1	2-2
6 Heyford Athletic	2-3	1-0	1-8	3-1	1-3	0	-0	2-1	1-1	1-1	2-5	1-1	0-3	0-5
7 Kislingbury	0-2	4-1	3-2	1-0	0-3	2-2		2-3	1-5	2-3	0-2	0-1	1-2	1-2
8 Medbourne	1-6	3-3	1-3	1-3	0-5	1-4	1-1		2-2	1-1	1-4	2-4	1-2	1-4
9 Milton	1-3	2-0	0-2	1-1	0-5	3-0	1-0	2-2		0-1	2-5	1-2	0-5	0-1
10 Moulton	3-1	2-0	2-4	7-0	0-1	1-3	5-1	3-0	3-0		1-2	0-4	1-5	2-2
11 Ringstead Rangers	3-2	6-0	1-4	4-2	0-3	2-0	3-1	3-1	2-1	2-0		2-0	3-4	2-2
12 Roade	0-1	3-1	4-1	5-1	0-1	3-0	5-0	1-0	4-3	1-3	3-4		0-2	0-3
13 Weldon United	0-1	2-2	4-2	3-1	1-3	3-0	0-0	5-3	0-3	2-3	1-3	1-2		1-2
14 Welford Victoria	1-2	2-1	4-2	D-D	1-2	7-1	2-1	2-0	2-2	5-1	2-1	1-0	3-1	

NORTHANTS COMBINATION PREMIER DIVISION CONSTITUTION 2012-13

BRIXWORTH ALL SAINTS	St Davids Close, off Froxhill Crescent, Brixworth NN6 9EA	01604 880073
CORBY PEGASUS	West Glebe South Pavilion, Cottingham Road, Corby NN17 1EL	01536 402041
CORBY S&L KHALSA	Corby Rugby Club, Rockingham Road, Corby NN17 1AE	01536 204466
GRETTON	Kirby Road, Gretton, Corby NN17 3DB	None
HARPOLE	Playing Field, Larkhall Lane, Harpole NN7 4DP	None
HEYFORD ATHLETIC	Nether Heyford Playing Field, Nether Heyford NN7 3LL	None
JAMES KING BLISWORTH	Blisworth Playing Field, Courteenhall Road, Blisworth	07974 006484
MILTON	Collingtree Road, Milton Malsor, Northampton NN7 3AU	None
MOULTON	Brunting Road, Moulton, Northampton NN3 7QF	01604 492675
RINGSTEAD RANGERS	Gladstone Street, Ringstead NN14 4DE	None
ROADE	Connolly Way, Hyde Road, Roade NN7 2LU	01604 862814
STANION QUANTUM PRINT	Brigstock Road, Stanion, Corby	None
WELDON UNITED	Oundle Road, Weldon NN17 3JT	None
WELFORD VICTORIA	Welford Sports Field, Newlands Road, Welford NN6 6HR	None

NORTHANTS COMBINATION LEAGUE - STEP 7

DIVISION ONE	P	W	D	L	F	A	Pts
1 Corby Quantum Print Vikings	20	17	2	1	77	22	53
2 James King Blisworth	20	13	4	3	50	29	43
3 Kettering Nomads	20	12	4	4	43	25	40
4 Corby Everards	20	11	3	6	41	32	36
5 Stanwick Rovers	20	9	2	9	44	45	29
6 Stanion United	20	9	1	10	46	49	28
7 Earls Barton United	20	8	1	11	38	31	25
8 Burton United	20	5	4	11	33	44	19
9 Finedon Volta	20	5	3	12	29	59	18
10 Wootton St George	20	4	3	13	20	45	15
11 Spratton	20	3	1	16	23	63	10

DIVISION TWO	P	W	D	L	F	A	Pts
1 Corby Locomotives	18	12	1	5	62	31	37
2 Kettering Ise Lodge	18	11	2	5	56	27	35
3 Kettering Orchard Park	18	9	5	4	48	34	32
4 Wollaston Victoria	18	8	5	5	36	26	29
5 Wellborough O Grammarians	18	7	5	6	36	45	26
6 Wellingborough Rising Sun	18	7	4	7	36	41	25
7 Weedon	18	7	1	10	41	42	22
8 Corby Strip Mills	18	7	0	11	35	62	21
9 Clipston	18	5	2	11	32	47	17
10 Great Doddington	18	3	3	12	27	54	12

DIVISION THREE	P	W	D	L	F	A	Pts
1 Corby Redstar	20	15	1	4	95	27	46
2 Daventry Comms	20	13	1	6	73	37	40
3 Corby Eagles	20	12	4	4	70	34	40
4 Wilby	20	13	1	6	61	40	40
5 Dainite Sports	20	13	1	6	52	31	40
6 Northampton Exiles	20	13	0	7	70	41	39
7 Hillmorton (-3)	20	9	2	9	52	66	26
8 Islip United	20	7	3	10	42	57	24
9 West Haddon	20	4	0	16	31	74	12
10 Wilbarston	20	2	2	16	19	96	8
11 Ristee Towers	20	1	1	18	27	89	4

DIVISION FOUR	P	W	D	L	F	A	Pts
1 Daventry Drayton Grange	18	17	1	0	63	19	52
2 FC Higham	18	13	2	3	70	40	41
3 Ferrers	18	12	2	4	73	42	38
4 Walgrave Amber	18	12	1	5	67	33	37
5 Corby Kingswood	18	9	3	6	47	34	30
6 Kettering Park Rovers	18	6	1	11	44	52	19
7 Higham Town	18	6	0	12	40	46	18
8 Corby United	18	4	2	12	34	60	14
9 Corby Hellenic Fisher	18	4	1	13	47	79	13
10 Kettering Weekley Eagles	18	0	1	17	20	100	1

RESERVE PREMIER DIVISION	P	W	D	L	F	A	Pts
1 Weldon United Reserves	22	17	2	3	61	22	53
2 Corby Pegasus Reserves	22	15	5	2	52	28	50
3 Moulton Reserves	22	13	3	6	65	24	42
4 Brixworth All Saints Reserves	22	13	3	6	59	46	42
5 Harpole Reserves	22	11	4	7	54	39	37
6 Kettering Nomads Reserves	22	11	3	8	51	47	36
7 Gretton Reserves	22	10	1	11	45	46	31
8 Roade Reserves	22	8	5	9	39	43	29
9 James King Blisworth Reserves	22	7	5	10	42	43	26
10 Milton Reserves	22	4	3	15	20	66	15
11 ON Chenecks "A"	22	4	2	16	25	59	14
12 Kislingbury Reserves	22	0	2	20	20	70	2

RESERVE DIVISION ONE	P	W	D	L	F	A	Pts
1 Bugbrooke St.Michaels "'A"	24	20	2	2	84	26	62
2 Ringstead Rangers Reserves	24	16	2	6	78	34	50
3 Welford Victoria Reserves	24	13	5	6	57	35	44
4 Weldon United "A"	24	14	2	8	57	42	44
5 Heyford Athletic Reserves	24	10	6	8	46	35	36
6 Stanion United Reserves	24	11	3	10	53	47	36
7 Weedon Reserves	24	10	5	9	50	39	35
8 Corby Everards Reserves	24	9	4	11	47	68	31
9 Earls Barton Utd Reserves	24	9	1	14	57	54	28
10 W'boro Old Gr. Reserves	24	7	5	12	48	70	26
11 Kettering Orch Park Reserves	24	6	4	14	43	70	22
12 Medbourne Reserves	24	5	3	16	32	77	18
13 Finedon Volta Reserves	24	3	4	17	20	75	13

RESERVE DIVISION TWO	P	W	D	L	F	A	Pts
1 Bugbrooke St.Michaels "B"	26	21	0	5	88	38	63
2 Corby Qu. Print Vikings Res.	26	19	2	5	93	42	59
3 Corby Locomotives Reserves	26	19	2	5	88	43	59
4 Islip United Reserves (-3)	26	14	6	6	65	37	45
5 Wollaston Victoria Reserves	26	12	5	9	53	53	41
6 Stanwick Rovers Reserves	26	11	7	8	47	48	40
7 Corby Kingswood Reserves	26	12	4	10	42	49	40
8 West Haddon "A"	26	10	4	12	47	48	34
9 Spratton Reserves	26	8	6	12	52	56	30
10 Harborough Town "A"	26	7	8	11	51	54	29
11 Corby Strip Mills Reserves	26	6	7	13	41	54	25
12 Dainite Sports Reserves	26	6	3	17	38	65	21
13 Wilby Reserves	26	4	4	18	38	87	16
14 Corby United Reserves	26	2	4	20	31	100	10

NORTHERN ALLIANCE

Sponsored by: Pin Point Recruitment
Founded: 1890
Recent Champions:
2007: Harraby Catholic Club
2008: Walker Central
2009: Walker Central
2010: Harraby Catholic Club
2011: Heaton Stannington

CHALLENGE CUP (KICKS LEISURE)

ROUND 1
Ashington Colliers 1-2 Whitley Bay A
Carlisle City 5-3 Seaton Delaval Amateurs
Gateshead Rutherford 0-2 Stocksfield
Heaton Stannington 1-0 Shankhouse
Killingworth Sporting 1-2 Blyth Town
Murton 2-6 Hebburn Reyrolle
Percy Main Amateurs 3-0 Ponteland United
Walker Central 1-2 Harraby Catholic Club

QUARTER FINALS
Hebburn Reyrolle 3-5 Heaton Stannington
Blyth Town 2-3 Carlisle City
Whitley Bay A 3-1 Stocksfield
Harraby Catholic Club 1-0 Percy Main Amateurs

SEMI-FINALS
Heaton Stannington 3-2 Carlisle City
Whitley Bay A 2-1 Harraby Catholic Club

FINAL
Heaton Stannington 2-2 Whitley Bay A
(Whitley Bay A won on penalties)

PREMIER DIVISION

		P	W	D	L	F	A	Pts
1	Heaton Stannington	30	21	3	6	86	35	66
2	Hebburn Reyrolle	30	19	6	5	83	39	63
3	Whitley Bay "A"	30	18	5	7	68	41	59
4	Harraby Catholic Club	30	18	2	10	68	48	56
5	Carlisle City	30	16	4	10	64	37	52
6	Ashington Colliers	30	13	7	10	53	54	46
7	Shankhouse	30	14	3	13	49	54	45
8	Seaton Delaval Amateurs	30	13	5	12	68	59	44
9	Killingworth Sporting	30	12	7	11	47	45	43
10	Percy Main Amateurs	30	11	7	12	47	58	40
11	Blyth Town	30	11	4	15	51	56	37
12	Stocksfield	30	9	5	16	52	74	32
13	Gateshead Ruttherford (-3)	30	9	6	15	49	70	30
14	Walker Central	30	8	3	19	40	62	27
15	Ponteland United	30	6	5	19	45	88	23
16	Murton	30	5	2	23	39	89	17

PREMIER DIVISION	1	2	3	4	5	6	7	8	9	10	11	12	13	14	15	16
1 Ashington Colliers		2-1	4-3	3-2	1-1	0-4	2-0	2-3	4-1	0-1	1-1	3-2	4-0	1-2	2-1	1-0
2 Blyth Town	3-0		1-0	2-1	1-2	0-3	2-2	1-2	3-2	0-3	5-0	3-1	0-0	1-2	2-3	1-1
3 Carlisle City	0-1	2-3		3-0	4-1	1-2	1-3	1-0	7-1	5-2	3-0	0-1	4-0	4-1	1-1	0-0
4 Gateshead Rutherford	2-2	1-4	2-2		3-0	2-5	1-4	1-3	2-1	2-0	4-3	0-3	1-0	1-1	4-2	3-5
5 Harraby Catholic Club	3-1	4-3	1-2	4-0		1-3	2-0	2-0	5-1	3-0	5-2	2-2	1-2	4-0	4-3	0-3
6 Heaton Stannington	1-1	4-0	1-0	2-3	1-4		2-4	5-0	4-2	1-0	6-0	3-0	1-2	4-1	3-1	1-2
7 Hebburn Reyrolle	3-1	3-2	1-1	3-2	4-2	0-0		4-1	3-0	1-2	6-1	3-2	4-0	2-2	6-4	2-1
8 Killingworth Sporting	4-4	0-0	3-1	0-0	2-0	2-6	0-0		4-0	0-0	1-1	2-2	3-1	2-0	2-1	0-1
9 Murton	2-2	2-0	1-2	3-3	0-1	0-3	0-9	1-4		0-2	2-1	5-2	3-1	3-5	1-2	0-4
10 Percy Main Amateurs	1-1	3-1	1-2	1-1	1-0	2-5	2-6	1-4	2-1		3-3	0-2	3-0	0-4	1-1	2-2
11 Ponteland United	2-4	3-1	0-2	1-3	0-2	1-5	1-1	0-4	2-1	2-4		4-2	2-0	1-2	0-1	1-8
12 Seaton Delaval Amateurs	3-1	2-3	2-3	5-1	4-3	1-1	3-0	2-0	1-0	5-1	5-3		2-3	1-0	3-5	1-2
13 Shankhouse	2-0	2-0	2-1	4-1	3-4	2-3	1-0	1-0	5-2	1-2	0-3	1-1		3-1	2-0	3-2
14 Stocksfield	1-2	1-5	1-5	1-3	1-3	2-3	1-3	2-0	3-2	1-5	4-4	2-2	0-2		3-2	3-3
15 Walker Central	1-2	0-1	1-2	1-0	0-2	0-4	0-4	4-0	0-1	1-0	0-1	2-4	1-1	0-4		1-0
16 Whitley Bay 'A'	4-1	4-2	0-2	2-0	1-2	1-0	0-2	1-0	3-1	2-2	3-2	3-2	5-4	3-1	2-1	

NORTHERN ALLIANCE PREMIER DIVISION CONSTITUTION 2012-13

AMBLE UNITED	Running Track Pitch, Coquet High School, Acklington Road , Amble NE65 0NG	01665 710636
ASHINGTON COLLIERS	Ashington FC, Hirst Welfare, Alexandra Road, Ashington NE63 9HF	07517 764653
BLYTH TOWN	South Newsham Playing Fields, Blyth NE24 3PP	None
CARLISLE CITY	Sheepmount Sports Complex, Sheepmount, Carlisle CA3 8XL	01228 625599
GATESHEAD RUTHERFORD	Farnacres, Beggarswood Park, Coach Lane, Lobley Hill, Gateshead NE11 8HJ	None
HARRABY UNITED	British Rail Sports Club, Petteril Bank Road, Carlisle, Cumbria CA1 3A	07736 698156
HEATON STANNINGTON	Grounsell Park, Newton Road, High Heaton, Newcastle-upon-Tyne NE7 7HP	None
HEBBURN REYROLLE	Hebburn Sports Ground, 16 South Drive, Hebburn NE31 1UN	0191 483 5101
KILLINGWORTH SPORTING	Amberley Park, Garth 21, Killingworth, Newcastle-upon-Tyne NE6 4YA	None
PERCY MAIN AMATEURS	Purvis Park, St John's Green, Percy Main, North Shields NE29 6HE	0191 257 4831
SEATON DELAVAL AMATEURS	Wheatridge Park, Seaton Delaval, Whitley Bay NE25 0QH	None
SHANKHOUSE	Northburn Sports Complex, Crawhall Lane, Cramlington NE23 3YP	01670 714154
STOCKSFIELD	Stocksfield Sports Ground, Main Road, Stocksfield NE43 7NN	None
WALKER CENTRAL	Monkchester Green, Walker, Newcastle-upon-Tyne NE6 5LJ	0191 265 7270
WALLSEND TOWN	Langdale School Ground, Mitford Gardens, Wallsend NE28 0HG	None
WHITLEY BAY A	Hillheads Park, Rink Way, off Hillheads Road, Whitley Bay NE25 8HR	0191 291 3637

DIVISION ONE

		P	W	D	L	F	A	Pts
1	Amble United	20	17	2	1	54	13	53
2	Wallsend Town	20	15	2	3	69	36	47
3	Wallington	20	14	2	4	48	26	44
4	Heddon	20	11	2	7	38	36	35
5	Gosforth Bohemians	20	10	3	7	41	29	33
6	Cullercoats	20	8	4	8	43	46	28
7	Cramlington Town	20	5	3	12	29	65	18
8	Newcastle University (-3)	20	5	4	11	42	38	19
9	Newcastle Chemfica (Indep.)	20	3	4	13	26	51	13
10	Forest Hall (-6)	20	5	2	13	29	53	17
11	Morpeth Sporting Club	20	2	2	16	20	46	8

COMBINATION CUP (PIN POINT RECRUITMENT)

PRELIMINARY ROUND
Gosforth Bohemians 2-0 Berwick United Ultras
ROUND 1
Hebburn Reyrolle 3-0 Morpeth Sporting Club
Amble United 4-0 South Shields United
Chopwell Officials Club 0-8 Cullercoats
Forest Hall 3-1 North Shields Athletic
Newcastle East End 0-2 Whitley Bay "A"
Peterlee Town 0-2 Wallington
Newcastle University 2-1 Gosforth Bohemians
Stobswood Welfare 2-5 Heddon
QUARTER FINALS
Amble United 1-2 Hebburn Reyrolle
Newcastle University 3-0 Forest Hall
Heddon 2-1 Cullercoats
Whitley Bay "A" 2-1 Wallington
SEMI-FINALS
Hebburn Reyrolle 2-0 Whitley Bay "A"
Newcastle University 1-0 Heddon
FINAL (@ Percy Main Amateurs, 2/5/11)
Hebburn Reyrolle 2-0 Newcastle University

GEORGE DOBBIN LEAGUE CUP (KICKS LEISURE)

ROUND 1
Alnwick Town Reserves 2-4 Harton & Westoe CW
Alston 3-1 Cramlington United
Ashington Colliers 4-0 Shankhouse
Blyth Town 1-1 Carlisle City
(Blyth Town won on penalties)
Cullercoats 1-1 Bedlington Terriers Reserves
(Cullercoats won on penalties)
Hexham 0-6 Harraby Catholic Club
New Fordley 4-1 Willington Quay Saints
Newcastle University 0-4 Whitley Bay A
Northbank Carlisle 2-2 Hebburn Reyrolle
(Hebburn Reyrolle won on penalties)
Seaton Burn 2-0 Cramlington Town
Seaton Delaval Amateurs 3-1 Forest Hall
Wideopen & District 0-4 Heaton Stannington
Wallsend Town AW Killingworth Sporting

ROUND 2
Harton & Westoe CW 1-6 Murton
Ashington Colliers 6-2 Wallsend Boys Club
Blyth Town 1-4 Hebburn Reyrolle
Cullercoats 2-1 Gateshead Rutherford
Gosforth Bohemians 4-1 Percy Main Amateurs
Harraby Catholic Club 2-4 Heaton Stannington
Heddon 2-1 Whickham Lang Jacks
New Fordley 2-4 Walker Central
Newcastle Chemfica (Independent) 1-2 Wallington
North Shields Athletic 1-5 Amble United
Ponteland United 0-1 Red House Farm
Seaton Burn 1-3 Killingworth Sporting
Stocksfield 4-0 Alston
Swalwell 1-3 Whitley Bay A

DIVISION ONE

DIVISION ONE	1	2	3	4	5	6	7	8	9	10	11
1 Amble United		3-0	2-0	6-1	1-0	0-2	1-0	2-1	4-1	3-0	3-2
2 Cramlington Town	0-0		1-2	1-2	3-0	3-3	1-0	2-3	0-3	1-2	2-3
3 Cullercoats	0-8	9-1		4-2	3-3	4-3	3-0	1-2	2-7	1-3	0-1
4 Forest Hall	0-2	0-4	1-3		1-3	1-1	3-0	4-2	2-1	1-2	0-5
5 Gosforth Bohemians	0-1	1-2	2-0	2-2		3-2	4-1	1-0	3-0	2-2	2-3
6 Heddon	1-5	3-0	0-1	3-1	1-0		1-0	3-2	2-1	2-4	0-4
7 Morpeth Sporting Club	1-4	1-2	1-2	4-2	0-3	0-1		2-2	1-1	1-2	1-3
8 Newcastle Chemfica (Independent)	1-2	3-3	1-1	2-4	0-2	1-4	0-4		3-2	0-2	1-4
9 Newcastle University	0-2	9-0	2-2	1-0	1-2	2-3	4-1	0-0		2-4	3-4
10 Wallington	2-2	10-0	2-1	1-0	4-1	1-2	2-1	2-1	2-1		0-1
11 Wallsend Town	1-3	8-3	4-4	6-2	2-7	3-1	5-1	6-1	1-1	3-1	

NORTHERN ALLIANCE DIVISION ONE CONSTITUTION 2012-13

BEDLINGTON TERRIERS RESERVES	Welfare Park, Park Road, Bedlington NE22 5DA	01670 825485
CRAMLINGTON TOWN	Sporting Club of Cramlington, Highburn, Cramlington NE23 6YB	01670 591970
CULLERCOATS	Links Avenue, Farringdon Road, Cullercoats NE30 3EY	None
FOREST HALL	East Palmersville Sports, Great Lime Road, Forest Hall NE12 9HW	None
GATESHEAD REDHEUGH 1957	Cornmoor Road, Whickham, Newcastle	07788 927746
GOSFORTH BOHEMIANS	Benson Road, Gosforth, Newcastle-upon-Tyne NE3 2EJ	None
HEDDON	Walbottle Campus, Hexham Road, Newcastle-upon-TYne NE15 9TP	0191 229 3307
HEXHAM	Wentworth Leisure Centre, Wentworth Park, Hexham NE46 3PD	01434 607080
MORPETH SPORTING CLUB	Morpeth Town FC, Craik Park, Morpeth Common, Morpeth NE61 2YX	01670 513785
NEWCASTLE CHEMFICA	Heaton Sports Ground, Heaton, Newcastle-upon-Tyne NE6 5NY	None
NEWCASTLE UNIVERSITY	Cochrane Park, Etherstone Avenue, Newcastle-upon-Tyne NE7 7JX	None
NORTHBANK CARLISLE	Sheepmount Sports Complex, Sheepmount, Carlisle CA3 8XL	01228 625599
PONTELAND UNITED	The Leisure Centre Ground, Callerton Lane, Ponteland, Newcastle-upon-Tyne NE20 9EG	01661 825441
RED HOUSE FARM	Kingston Park Road, Newcastle-upon-Tyne NE3 2HY	0191 285 2181
WALLINGTON	Oakford Park, Scots Gap, Morpeth NE61 4EJ	None
WILLINGTON QUAY SAINTS	Wallsend Rising Sun Ground, King's North Road, Wallsend NE28 9JJ	None

NORTHERN ALLIANCE - STEP 7

DIVISION TWO	P	W	D	L	F	A	Pts
1 Hexham	30	19	8	3	78	40	65
2 Red House Farm	30	17	9	4	82	55	60
3 Northbank Carlisle (-3)	30	19	4	7	78	39	58
4 Harton & Westoe CW	30	15	8	7	94	55	53
5 Whickham Lang Jacks	30	15	4	11	95	73	49
6 Bedlington Terriers Reserves	30	15	4	11	65	43	49
7 Willington Quay Saints	30	14	4	12	77	65	46
8 Wallsend Boys Club (-7)	30	14	6	10	77	62	41
9 New Fordley	30	11	7	12	77	65	40
10 Alston	30	11	6	13	62	76	39
11 Wideopen & District	30	10	8	12	53	54	38
12 Alnwick Town Reserves	30	12	1	17	49	69	37
13 North Shields Athletic	30	10	6	14	61	79	36
14 Seaton Burn	30	6	9	15	60	75	27
15 Swalwell	30	6	4	20	43	88	22
16 Cramlington United	30	1	2	27	26	139	5

GEORGE DOBBIN LEAGUE CUP continued...

ROUND 3
Stocksfield 2-1 Walker Central
Hebburn Reyrolle 5-1 Gosforth Bohemians
Morpeth Sporting Club 1-4 Heddon
Killingworth Sporting 1-1 Amble United
(Killingworth Sporting won on penalties)
Ashington Colliers 9-2 Murton
Red House Farm 0-1 Wallington
Whitley Bay A 4-1 Cullercoats
Seaton Delaval Amateurs 2-1 Heaton Stannington
QUARTER FINALS
Ashington Colliers 5-1 Heddon
Seaton Delaval Amateurs 3-2 Hebburn Reyrolle
Stocksfield 1-3 Wallington
Whitley Bay A 2-1 Killingworth Sporting
SEMI-FINALS
Whitley Bay A 0-1 Seaton Delaval Amateurs
Wallington 2-3 Ashington Colliers
FINAL
Ashington Colliers 1-3 Seaton Delaval Amateurs

DIVISION TWO	1	2	3	4	5	6	7	8	9	10	11	12	13	14	15	16
1 Alnwick Town Reserves		3-1	3-0	3-0	1-3	2-6	2-1	1-0	0-1	1-2	4-1	3-0	0-3	0-4	1-1	1-6
2 Alston	3-0		2-4	3-0	6-6	1-1	2-1	1-5	2-2	2-0	1-3	2-2	2-4	1-6	2-4	0-2
3 Bedlington Terriers Reserves	3-0	2-2		3-2	2-0	2-3	0-1	2-2	2-0	1-1	3-0	4-0	4-2	4-0	1-0	9-0
4 Cramlington United	1-5	1-3	0-2		2-2	3-3	1-8	1-2	2-1	1-5	0-6	1-3	3-7	2-5	1-3	0-6
5 Harton & Westoe CW	2-3	1-2	3-2	9-0		0-1	6-0	0-1	2-0	1-1	4-1	9-1	4-2	1-3	4-1	3-1
6 Hexham	3-1	3-2	1-0	2-1	2-2		3-1	2-0	1-2	2-2	0-0	2-0	2-2	4-3	3-1	5-1
7 New Fordley	7-0	2-2	2-0	9-1	2-2	3-2		5-0	5-1	2-4	4-3	1-1	2-3	1-4	1-3	3-5
8 North Shields Athletic	5-1	2-6	2-1	6-2	3-6	1-3	2-2		2-1	2-2	4-2	0-4	4-1	5-5	1-5	2-2
9 Northbank Carlisle	1-0	7-1	1-0	5-0	0-0	4-0	3-0	3-1		3-3	4-3	7-1	4-0	2-1	3-0	2-1
10 Red House Farm	2-1	3-2	3-1	11-0	2-2	1-1	3-1	5-2	2-1		2-2	3-2	2-5	3-5	2-2	2-6
11 Seaton Burn	0-2	0-2	2-2	8-0	3-6	1-1	3-3	1-1	2-4	1-4		6-1	1-3	1-3	0-0	1-0
12 Swalwell	5-2	1-2	3-0	3-0	1-4	1-7	3-4	1-3	0-6	1-2	1-4		0-1	1-1	1-5	0-1
13 Wallsend Boys Club	1-3	4-1	4-2	6-0	4-5	0-3	2-2	2-1	0-0	1-2	2-2	2-3		5-1	1-1	3-5
14 Whickham Lang Jacks	3-2	2-3	1-4	6-0	5-2	0-6	1-3	5-1	2-5	1-3	8-1	2-2	1-3		7-0	3-2
15 Wideopen & District	1-2	5-1	1-2	2-0	1-3	2-4	2-0	2-0	2-4	0-1	2-2	1-0	1-1	2-2		2-3
16 Willington Quay Saints	3-2	0-2	2-3	2-1	2-2	1-2	1-1	5-1	4-1	3-4	4-0	3-1	1-3	4-5	1-1	

NORTHERN ALLIANCE DIVISION TWO CONSTITUTION 2012-13

ALNWICK TOWN RESERVES	St James's Park , Weavers Way , Alnwick NE66 1BG	01665 603162
ALSTON MOOR SC	Tyne Willows Playing Field, Station Road, Alston CA9 3HZ	None
BIRTLEY ST JOSEPHS	Birtley Welfare Park, Ravensworth Road, Birtley, Tyne and Wear DH3 1E	07428 123585
BLYTH ISABELLA	Briardale Road, Cowpen, Blyth, Northumberland	07816 852620
CRAMLINGTON UNITED	Shankhouse FC, Northburn Sports Complex, Crawhall Lane, Cramlington NE23 3YP	01670 714154
GRAINGER PARK B C	Denton Road, Newcastle upon Tyne, Tyne and Wear NE15 7H	07910 046902
HIGH HOWDON S C	Seatonville Road, Whitley Bay, Tyne and Wear	07538 291227
LONGBENTON	Longbenton, Newcastle upon Tyne NE12 8L	07505 004043
NEW FORDLEY	John Willie Sams Centre, Cramlington NE23 7HS	None
NEWCASTLE BENFIELD RESERVES	Benfield Road, Newcastle upon Tyne, Tyne and Wear NE6 4N	07973 699506
NORTH SHIELDS ATHLETIC	John Spence Community School, Preston Road, North Shields NE29 9PU	0191 200 5220
SEATON BURN	Seaton Burn Welfare, Seaton Burn, Newcastle-upon-Tyne NE13 6BW	None
SWALWELL	Spa-Well Road, Derwenthaugh, Blaydon-on-Tyne NE21 6JA	None
WALLSEND BOYS CLUB	Rheydt Avenue, Wallsend NE28 7LQ	None
WIDEOPEN & DISTRICT	Lockey Park, Great North Road, Wideopen, Newcastle-upon-Tyne NE13 6LN	None
WOOLER	The Martins, Wooler, Northumberland	07778 772358

OXFORDSHIRE SENIOR LEAGUE

Sponsored by: No sponsor
Founded: N/K
Recent Champions:
2007: Garsington
2008: Rover Cowley
2009: Garsington
2010: Adderbury Park
2011: Hinksey

PREMIER DIVISION	P	W	D	L	F	A	Pts
1 OUP	26	15	4	7	53	40	49
2 Hinksey	26	14	5	7	73	37	47
3 Adderbury Park	25	13	4	8	42	35	43
4 Oxford Irish	25	12	3	10	62	51	39
5 Stonesfield	26	11	6	9	44	37	39
6 Mansfield Rd	23	12	3	8	49	46	39
7 Garsington	25	11	5	9	57	57	38
8 Slade Farm	26	10	6	10	41	33	36
9 Horspath	26	9	6	11	47	57	33
10 Bletchingdon	26	10	3	13	33	55	33
11 Marston Saints	26	8	8	10	54	54	32
12 Freeland	26	9	5	12	41	51	32
13 Kennington	26	8	6	12	34	47	30
14 Launton Sports	26	2	6	18	25	55	12

PRESIDENTS CUP

ROUND 1
Adderbury Park 0-2 Riverside
Stonesfield 3-1 Bletchingdon
Broughton & NN 4-3 Enstone
Watlington 1-3 Chadlington
Charlton 5-1 Mansfield Rd
Eynsham 5-1 Long Crendon
Freeland 2-1 Horspath
North Oxford 1-4 Garsington
Yarnton 0-6 Hinksey
Slade Farm 1-3 Kennington
Northway 1-4 Kidlington OB
Launton Sports 1-3 Oxford Irish
Marston Saints 2-1 OUP
Middleton Cheney 4-1 Oakley
ROUND 2
Riverside 3-1 Freeland
Kidlington OB 1-0 Kennington
Eynsham 2-6 Oxford Irish
Broughton & NN 0-3 Garsington
Marston Saints 3-1 Middleton Cheney
Charlton 2-3 Stonesfield
QUARTER FINALS
Riverside 5-1 Stonesfield
Kidlington OB 3-1 Oxford Irish
Garsington 2-1 Hinksey
Marston Saints 4-0 Chadlington
SEMI-FINALS
Kidlington OB 0-2 Riverside
Marston Saints 4-0 Garsington
FINAL
Marston Saints 1-2 Riverside

PREMIER DIVISION	1	2	3	4	5	6	7	8	9	10	11	12	13	14
1 Adderbury Park		2-0	3-1	3-0	2-2	3-0	4-1	1-0			1-3	1-0	2-3	1-1	2-0
2 Bletchingdon	0-2		0-1	1-3	0-3	2-2	2-2	2-1	3-0	0-7	0-1	1-3	2-1	4-3
3 Freeland	2-1	0-1		2-2	0-4	2-3	3-2	2-2	1-2	3-2	1-2	4-1	1-1	1-0
4 Garsington	4-0	3-1	3-1		3-7	3-3	4-1	6-1	1-1	2-6	2-4	1-5	0-3	1-0
5 Hinksey	5-0	6-0	0-1	1-4		5-2	6-2	2-0	5-0	4-4	1-4	5-2	2-0	3-3
6 Horspath	2-3	0-1	3-2	3-1	4-2		0-1	1-1	1-2	2-2	1-2	3-1	3-1	2-1
7 Kennington	1-0	0-2	5-1	2-1	1-2	1-1		0-0	1-3	0-0	1-3	1-2	0-0	1-3
8 Launton Sports	1-2	1-2	1-1	1-2	2-2	1-1	1-2		2-3	1-2	0-3	0-3	2-3	1-2
9 Mansfield Road	1-3	5-1	2-3		HW	1-2	2-2	2-1		1-2	3-4		3-5	1-1
10 Marston Saints	1-3	0-2	2-1	3-4	1-1	6-2	0-3	1-2	2-6		2-2	2-1	2-3	1-1
11 OUP	2-2	0-2	2-3	0-0	2-3	4-2	2-0	5-1	1-2	3-2		1-8	0-0	2-0
12 Oxford Irish	3-1	3-1	3-3	6-4	HW	6-1	0-1	2-1	3-4	0-0	0-1		2-5	4-4
13 Slade Farm	0-0	0-0	2-0	1-2	0-2	2-1	2-3	0-1	0-2	5-0	1-2	3-1		2-0
14 Stonesfield	2-0	6-3	2-1	1-1	HW	1-2	3-0	3-0	2-3	1-1	2-1	2-0	1-0	

OXFORDSHIRE SENIOR LEAGUE PREMIER DIVISION CONSTITUTION 2012-13

ADDERBURY PARK	Lucy Plackett Playing Field, Round Close Road, Adderbury, Banbury OX17 3EE	None
BLETCHINGTON	Rover Cowley Sports Ground, Romanway, Cowley, Oxford OX4 6NL	None
CHARLTON UNITED	Charlton PF, Oddington Road, Charlton-on-Otmoor, Kidlington OX5 2TJ	None
FREELAND	The Simon Hole Memorial Ground, Wroslyn Road, Freeland, Witney OX29 8HL	None
GARSINGTON	Garsington Sports Club, Denton Lane, Garsington, Oxford OX44 9EL	01865 361720
HORSPATH	Rover Cowley Sports Ground, Romanway, Cowley, Oxford OX4 6NL	None
KENNINGTON UNITED	Playfield Road, Kennington, Oxford OX1 5RS	None
LAUNTON SPORTS	The Playing Field, Bicester Road, Bicester OX26 5DP	01869 242007
MANSFIELD ROAD	The University Club, Mansfield Road, Oxford OX1 3SZ	01865 271044
MARSTON SAINTS	Boults Lane, Old Marston, Oxford OX3 0PW	01865 203970
OXFORD IRISH	Rover Cowley Sports Ground, Romanway, Cowley, Oxford OX4 6NL	None
OXFORD UNIVERSITY PRESS	Jordan Hill, Banbury Road, Oxford OX2 8EF	None
RIVERSIDE	Quarry Recreation Ground, Margaret Road, Headington, Oxford OX3 8AJ	None
STONESFIELD SPORTS	Stonesfield Playing Field, Field Close, Longmore, Stonesfield OX29 8HA	None

OXFORDSHIRE SENIOR LEAGUE - STEP 7

DIVISION ONE

		P	W	D	L	F	A	Pts
1	Riverside	25	20	2	3	96	26	62
2	Charlton	26	19	2	5	66	35	59
3	Eynsham	26	16	5	5	93	47	53
4	Middleton Cheney	26	16	4	6	79	44	52
5	Northway	26	15	3	8	81	52	48
6	Oakley	26	14	3	9	80	61	45
7	Enstone	26	14	2	10	62	55	44
8	Broughton & NN	24	12	2	10	56	44	38
9	Kidlington OB	25	9	3	13	60	63	30
10	North Oxford	24	8	2	14	36	67	26
11	Chadlington	26	5	6	15	43	66	21
12	Watlington	26	5	3	18	29	74	18
13	Yarnton	26	4	4	18	44	87	16
14	Long Crendon	26	1	1	24	30	134	4

BEN TURNER CUP

ROUND 1
Mansfield Rd 2-0 North Oxford
OUP 1-2 Enstone
Watlington 0-1 Oakley
Slade Farm 4-1 Northway
Bletchingdon 3-0 Yarnton
Launton Sports 0-7 Horspath

QUARTER FINALS
Bletchingdon 0-1 Slade Farm
Horspath 2-2 Enstone
(Horspath won on penalties)
Adderbury Park 0-3 Mansfield Rd
Long Crendon 4-1 Oakley

SEMI-FINALS
Horspath 4-0 Long Crendon
Slade Farm 3-1 Mansfield Rd

FINAL
Horspath 0-2 Slade Farm

DIVISION ONE

		1	2	3	4	5	6	7	8	9	10	11	12	13	14
1	Broughton & North Newington		4-0	0-4	3-1	3-0		7-2	4-3		1-2	1-4	0-6	2-0	3-0
2	Chadlington	2-2		0-2	0-2	1-4	2-4	2-2	1-3	2-2	3-3	5-0	0-2	3-3	5-2
3	Charlton	1-0	5-0		1-3	2-1	1-0	8-0	3-1	6-2	2-1	4-3	1-1	3-0	2-1
4	Enstone	3-7	6-3	1-0		1-1	4-1	4-2	3-2	1-0	2-3	0-4	1-2	4-1	8-0
5	Eynsham	2-1	2-1	2-3	7-1		4-1	4-1	2-2	2-0	1-1	3-3	0-7	6-1	7-2
6	Kidlington OB	0-3	4-1	1-2	2-2	3-3		5-1	2-2	5-0	1-4	1-4	2-3	5-0	3-2
7	Long Crendon	0-4	1-3	2-3	0-4	1-10	1-7		1-6	0-3	1-4	4-10	0-3	1-2	0-3
8	Middleton Cheney	1-3	4-1	1-1	5-1	2-4	5-1	6-0		6-1	3-0	5-0	0-5	3-0	1-0
9	North Oxford	3-1	2-1	0-3	1-3	0-6	4-3	6-0	1-3		2-6	0-0		2-0	1-0
10	Northway	3-0	3-0	4-3	2-4	1-6	3-2	5-1	2-3	1-2		6-2	1-3	7-0	4-4
11	Oakley	0-4	1-3	4-0	1-0	2-4	2-1	7-2	3-5	7-0	0-4		5-2	6-0	2-2
12	Riverside	3-0	HW	6-0	2-0	4-5	10-1	11-1	2-2	3-2	2-1	2-3		4-0	5-0
13	Watlington	1-0	1-1	1-2	1-2	2-1	0-3	2-4	2-3	3-0	2-5	2-3	0-1		3-3
14	Yarnton	3-3	2-3	0-4	4-1	1-6	0-2	5-2	1-2	5-2	2-5	1-4	1-7	0-2	

OXFORDSHIRE SENIOR LEAGUE DIVISION ONE CONSTITUTION 2012-13

BROUGHTON & NORTH NEWINGTON	Shutford Road, North Newington, Banbury OX16 9AT	None
CHALGROVE	Chalgrove, Oxfordshire OX4	07867 972775
ENSTONE SPORTS	Charlbury Road, Enstone OX2 6UT	01608 677823
EYNSHAM ASSOCIATION	Oxford Road, Eynsham, Witney OX29 4DA	None
KIDLINGTON OLD BOYS	Exeter Close, Crown Road, Kidlington OX5 1AP	None
LONG CRENDON	Rec Ground, Chearsley Road, Long Crendon, Aylesbury HP18 9AP	None
MIDDLETON CHENEY	Astrip Road, Middleton Cheney, Banbury OX17 2PG	None
NORTH OXFORD	Rover Cowley Cricket Ground, Romanway, Cowley, Oxford OX4 6NL	None
NORTHWAY	Northway Sports Centre, Maltfield Road, New Marston, Oxford OX3 9RG	01865 742048
OAKLEY UNITED	Playfield Fields, Oxford Road, Oakley, Aylesbury HP18 9RE	None
WATLINGTON TOWN	Shirburn Road, Watlington OX49 5BZ	None
YARNTON	Green Lane, Yarnton OX5 1TE	01865 842037

PETERBOROUGH & DISTRICT LEAGUE

Sponsored by: ChromaSport
Founded: 1902
Recent Champions:
2007: Peterborough Sports
2008: Perkins Sports
2009: Ramsey Town
2010: Rutland Rangers
2011: Ramsey Town

PREMIER DIVISION	P	W	D	L	F	A	Pts
1 Pinchbeck United	32	22	5	5	95	31	73
2 Kings Cliffe United	32	19	7	6	88	45	64
3 Peterborough Sports Parkway	32	19	4	9	92	49	61
4 Moulton Harrox	32	18	7	7	71	37	61
5 Eye Sports	32	17	7	8	80	45	60
6 Netherton United	32	18	5	9	77	50	59
7 Ramsey Town	32	14	12	6	59	34	56
8 Deeping Rangers Reserves	32	14	6	12	54	55	48
9 Coates Athletic	32	13	7	12	53	53	46
10 Crowland Town	32	12	3	17	42	77	41
11 Leverington Sports	32	10	5	17	65	67	38
12 Oakham United	32	11	4	17	54	78	38
13 Parson Drove	32	10	6	16	56	62	30
14 Whittlesey United	32	9	7	16	57	66	30
15 Oundle Town	32	10	6	16	59	88	30
16 Uppingham Town	32	5	6	21	53	84	21
17 Alconbury	32	2	1	29	23	157	4

DIVISION ONE	P	W	D	L	F	A	Pts
1 Riverside Rovers Senior	30	23	5	2	109	36	77
2 Stilton United	30	19	7	4	95	36	64
3 Whittlesey Blue Star	30	18	4	8	76	43	60
4 Moulton Harrox Res	30	18	4	8	81	41	58
5 Langtoft United	30	16	7	7	74	37	55
6 Holbeach Reserves	30	16	8	6	85	51	52
7 Long Sutton Athletic	30	13	6	11	75	70	45
8 Netherton United Reserves	30	12	3	15	65	71	41
9 Ketton	30	12	3	15	58	63	39
10 Powerleague AFC	30	11	7	12	52	67	38
11 Thorney	30	11	4	15	65	71	37
12 Sawtry	30	10	0	20	68	91	30
13 Peterborough FC Internazionale	30	8	4	18	39	68	28
14 Stamford Belvedere	30	8	2	20	35	93	26
15 Hampton Sports	30	5	4	21	53	98	19
16 Warboys Town FC	30	3	6	21	35	129	15

PETERBOROUGH & DISTRICT LEAGUE PREMIER DIVISION CONSTITUTION 2012-13

COATES ATHLETIC	Manor Leisure Centre, Station Road, Whittsey, Peterborough PE17 1UA	01733 202298
CROWLAND TOWN	Snowden Field, Thorney Road, Crowland PE6 0AL	01733 211548
DEEPING RANGERS RESERVES	Outgang Road, Towngate East, Market Deeping PE6 8LQ	01778 344701
KINGS CLIFFE UNITED	Kings Cliffe Sports Centre, Kings Cliffe, Peterborough	None
LEVERINGTON SPORTS	Church Road, Leverington, Wisbech PE12 5ED	01945 465082
MOULTON HARROX	Broad Lane, Moulton, Spalding PE12 6PN	01406 371991
NETHERTON UNITED	The Grange, Mayors Walk, Peterborough PE3 6EU	None
OAKHAM UNITED	Greetham Community Centre, Great Lane, Greetham, Oakham LE15 7NG	01572 813117
PARSON DROVE	Main Road, Parson Drove, Wisbech PE13 4LA	None
PETERBOROUGH ICA SPORTS	Riverside Pavilion, Candy Street, Sugar Way, Woodston, Peterborough PE2 9RE	01733 567797
PETERBOROUGH SPORTS PARKWAY	Peterborough Sports & Leisure, Lincoln Road, Peterborough PE1 3HA	01733 567835
PINCHBECK UNITED	Glebe Playing Fields, Knight Street, Pinchbeck, Spalding PE11 3RB	07966 303275
RAMSEY TOWN	Cricketfield Lane, Ramsey, Huntingdon PE26 1BG	01487 814218
RIVERSIDE ROVERS	Riverside Pavilion, Candy Street, Sugar Way, Woodston, Peterborough PE2 9RE	01733 567797
STILTON UNITED	Yaxley FC, Leading Drove, Holme Road, Yaxley PE7 3NA	01733 244928
UPPINGHAM TOWN	North Street East, Uppingham LE15 9QL	01572 821446
WHITTLESEY BLUE STAR	Candy Street, Sugar Way, Peterborough Cambridgeshire PE2 9R	07850 770315
WHITTLESEY UNITED	Manor Leisure Centre, Station Road, Whittlesey, Peterborough PE7 1UA	01733 202298

DIVISION TWO	P	W	D	L	F	A	Pts
1 Ryhall United	24	17	3	4	70	31	54
2 Castor & Ailsworth	24	16	3	5	78	38	53
3 Sutton Bridge United	24	13	5	6	83	51	48
4 Hartford Sun FC	24	14	2	8	78	55	46
5 Farcet United	24	14	1	9	75	52	43
6 Eye Sports & Social Res	24	14	3	7	87	51	39
7 Pinchbeck Utd Res	24	12	3	9	89	62	39
8 Woodston	24	10	1	13	55	81	31
9 Guyhirn	24	9	5	10	55	56	30
10 Oakham United Reserves	24	8	2	14	45	69	26
11 Peterborough Rovers	24	5	6	13	39	67	23
12 Gedney Hill	24	3	3	18	45	100	12
13 Parkside	24	1	3	20	25	111	2

DIVISION THREE	P	W	D	L	F	A	Pts
1 Langtoft United Res	22	16	4	2	72	23	52
2 Peterborough Spts P. Reserves	22	13	3	6	70	44	42
3 Oundle Town Reserves	22	13	5	4	69	34	40
4 Leverington S Res	22	14	2	6	56	37	38
5 Deeping Rangers A	22	10	4	8	50	43	37
6 Crowland Town Res	22	10	2	10	62	51	32
7 Ramsey Town Reserves	22	9	2	11	44	46	31
8 Long Sutton Athl Res	22	8	5	9	29	40	27
9 Whittlesey United Res	22	7	3	12	38	54	24
10 Peterborough FC Inter Reserves	22	7	2	13	55	79	22
11 Uppingham Town Res	22	2	5	15	20	78	11
12 Alconbury Res	22	2	5	15	36	72	10

READING LEAGUE

Sponsored by: No sponsor
Founded: 1989
Recent Champions:
2007: Ascot United
2008: Westwood United
2009: Woodley Town
2010: Reading YMCA
2011: Highmoor Ibis

SENIOR CUP (BERKSHIRE TROPHY CENTRE)

ROUND 1
R.E.M.E Arborfield 2-2 4-5p Westwood United
Ashridge Park 0-4 Woodcote Stoke Row
Cookham Dean 1-3 Barton Rovers
Taplow United 2-1 S.R.C.C.
Marlow United 4-3 Unity

ROUND 2
Westwood United - Bye
Theale 6-0 Woodley Town Reserves
Frilsham & Yattendon 2-5 Woodcote Stoke Row
Mortimer 0-3 Highmoor Ibis Reserves
Park United 0-4 South Reading
Barton Rovers 3-2 Sandhurst Devels
Woodley Saints 1-2 Reading YMCA
Taplow United 1-3 Marlow United

QUARTER FINALS
Westwood United 1-0 Theale
Woodcote Stoke Row 1-0 Highmoor Ibis Reserves
South Reading 6-5 (aet) Barton Rovers
Reading YMCA 2-2 3-4p Marlow United

SEMI-FINALS
Westwood United 1-2 Woodcote Stoke Row
South Reading 2-0 Marlow United

FINAL
Woodcote Stoke Row 1-5 South Reading

SENIOR DIVISION

		P	W	D	L	F	A	Pts
1	South Reading	26	17	4	5	93	47	55
2	Woodcote Stoke Row	26	16	6	4	70	41	54
3	Westwood United	26	17	3	6	63	34	54
4	Marlow United	26	15	2	9	56	44	47
5	Mortimer	26	14	5	7	53	42	47
6	Cookham Dean	26	13	5	8	53	36	44
7	Reading YMCA	26	12	4	10	56	44	40
8	Unity	26	10	4	12	48	55	34
9	Sandhurst Devels	26	10	3	13	57	62	33
10	Theale	26	6	6	14	43	66	24
11	Highmoor Ibis Reserves	26	6	5	15	37	61	23
12	Taplow United	26	6	3	17	36	69	21
13	Park United	26	5	5	16	28	54	20
14	Frilsham & Yattendon	26	5	5	16	49	87	20

SENIOR DIVISION	1	2	3	4	5	6	7	8	9	10	11	12	13	14
1 Cookham Dean		6-0	3-1	2-0	3-2	2-2	1-1	1-0	3-2	6-2	2-0	4-0	0-2	1-2
2 Frilsham & Yattendon	0-2		2-2	2-2	1-5	1-3	2-1	3-1	1-4	12-4	2-2	2-5	0-3	2-3
3 Highmoor Ibis Reserves	2-2	4-0		0-5	2-3	2-1	0-3	4-1	2-2	2-0	1-0	1-2	0-5	AW
4 Marlow United	2-1	3-2	2-0		3-1	3-0	3-1	2-5	1-2	2-0	5-2	0-2	0-2	4-2
5 Mortimer	1-0	3-4	4-0	1-0		2-2	0-4	2-1	3-3	2-1	3-0	2-1	3-2	1-1
6 Park United	1-1	1-1	1-2	0-1	1-3		2-1	0-1	0-3	0-2	2-2	3-1	2-1	0-6
7 Reading YMCA	3-4	3-1	4-3	2-1	1-2	1-0		4-2	2-4	4-0	3-3	3-2	3-0	1-6
8 Sandhurst Devels	2-3	8-1	5-2	2-2	1-1	4-2	0-5		3-6	2-1	2-3	2-2	3-0	1-4
9 South Reading	3-1	1-1	6-3	6-0	4-1	3-4	1-0	8-0		5-3	7-4	4-0	2-4	1-4
10 Taplow United	0-3	4-0	0-0	0-1	0-2	3-0	2-0	1-2	0-4		2-3	5-4	2-2	2-3
11 Theale	0-0	5-2	3-1	3-5	1-4	1-0	1-3	0-3	2-5	0-1		3-1	1-6	2-3
12 Unity	3-0	2-5	2-0	0-2	1-1	1-0	3-2	3-2	0-4	1-1	1-1		5-0	2-3
13 Westwood United	3-1	6-2	3-1	4-1	3-0	2-0	0-0	2-1	3-1	3-0	1-0	3-1		2-2
14 Woodcote Stoke Row	2-1	4-0	2-2	2-6	2-1	4-1	1-1	0-3	2-2	6-0	1-1	2-3	3-1	

READING LEAGUE SENIOR DIVISION CONSTITUTION 2012-13

BARTON ROVERS	Turnhams Farm, Little Heath Road, Tilehurst, Reading RG31 5TX	None
COOKHAM DEAN	Alfred Major Rec Ground, Hillcrest Avenue, Cookham Rise , Maidenhead SL6 9NB	01628 819423
HIGHMOOR-IBIS RESERVES	Prudential IBIS Sports Club, Scours Lane, Reading RG3 6AY	0118 942 4130
MARLOW UNITED	Gossmore Park, Gossmore Lane, Marlow SL7 1QF	None
MORTIMER	Alfred Palmer Memorial PF, West End Road, Mortimer, Reading RG7 3TW	None
READING YMCA	Reading Town FC, Scours Lane, Tilehurst, Reading RG30 6AY	0118 945 3555
ROTHERFIELD PARK UNITED	Bishopswood Sports Ground, Horsepond Rd, Gallowstree Common RG4 9BT	0118 9722295
SANDHURST DEVELS	Sandhurst Memorial Ground, York Town Road, Sandhurst GU47 9BJ	None
SOUTH READING	Lower Whitley Rec Ground, Basingstoke Road, Reading RG2 0JA	None
TAPLOW UNITED	Stanley Jones Field, Berry Hill, Taplow SL6 0DA	01628 621745
THEALE	Theale Recreation Ground, Englefield Road, Theale, Reading RG7 5AS	None
UNITY	Cintra Park, Cintra Avenue, Reading RG2 7AU	0118 954 7275
WESTWOOD UNITED	Cotswold Sports Centre, Downs Way, Tilehurst, Reading RG31 6LS	0118 941 4690
WOODCOTE & STOKE ROW	Woodcote Recreation Ground, Woodcote, Reading RG8 0QY	None

PREMIER DIVISION

		P	W	D	L	F	A	Pts
1	Barton Rovers	16	12	2	2	32	14	38
2	R.E.M.E Arborfield	16	11	2	3	44	18	35
3	Reading YMCA Rockets	16	8	1	7	29	27	25
4	Ashridge Park	16	7	3	6	34	31	24
5	Woodley Saints	16	6	6	4	24	26	24
6	Woodley Town Reserves	16	5	1	10	28	45	16
7	S.R.C.C. (-1)	16	4	4	8	21	30	15
8	Sandhurst Devels Res (-1)	16	3	4	9	39	37	12
9	Westwood United Reserves	16	2	5	9	24	47	11

DIVISION ONE

		P	W	D	L	F	A	Pts
1	AFC Corinthians	20	17	2	1	62	24	53
2	Goring United	20	12	5	3	43	26	41
3	Cookham Dean Reserves	20	11	3	6	49	35	36
4	Sonning	20	11	2	7	54	43	35
5	Hurst	20	11	2	7	41	32	35
6	Wargrave	20	7	4	9	35	36	25
7	"Highmoor Ibis ""A"""	20	6	5	9	52	58	23
8	Woodley Saints Reserves	20	7	1	12	29	35	22
9	Woodcote Stoke Row Res.	20	5	3	12	34	51	18
10	"Woodley Town ""A"""	20	3	4	13	31	60	13
11	Theale Reserves	20	3	3	14	21	51	12

DIVISION TWO

		P	W	D	L	F	A	Pts
1	Berkshire United	20	14	4	2	80	32	46
2	Winnersh Rangers	20	15	1	4	68	23	46
3	Mortimer Res	20	13	3	4	61	29	42
4	Royal Albion	20	11	4	5	40	28	37
5	Hurst Res	20	10	1	9	47	56	31
6	Turnpike Sports	20	9	1	10	53	43	28
7	Frilsham & Yattendon Res	20	7	3	10	43	71	24
8	Wokingham & Emmbrook ""A""	20	6	2	12	42	65	20
9	Twyford & Ruscombe	20	5	1	14	29	58	16
10	Taplow United Res	20	4	2	14	23	63	14
11	Rotherfield Park United Res.	20	3	4	13	32	50	13

INTERMEDIATE CUP (BERKSHIRE TROPHY CENTRE)

ROUND 1
Woodley Town "A" 2-1 Sandhurst Devels Reserves
Sonning 5-1 Twyford & Ruscombe
Frilsham & Yattendon Res 3-1 Woodley Saints Reserves
Royal Albion 1-2 Berkshire United
AFC Corinthians 7-0 Taplow United Reserves
Theale Reserves 0-0 1-3p Wargrave
Hurst 4-2 Winnersh Rangers
Goring United 4-1 Cookham Dean Reserves

ROUND 2
Woodcote Stoke Row Reserves 0-3 Woodley Town "A"
Sonning 13-2 Frilsham & Yattendon Reserves
Berkshire United 3-4 AFC Corinthians
Park United Res 0-4 Westwood United Reserves
Wargrave 1-3 Hurst
Highmoor Ibis "A" 1-3 Goring United
Reading YMCA Rapids 4-1 Wokingham & Emmbrook "A"
Turnpike Sports 0-1 Mortimer Reserves

QUARTER FINALS
Woodley Town "A" 2-2 4-2p Sonning
AFC Corinthians 2-2 2-3p Westwood United Reserves
Hurst 2-3 Goring United
Reading YMCA Rapids 3-1 Mortimer Reserves

SEMI-FINALS
Woodley Town "A" 1-3 Westwood United Reserves
Goring United 1-0 Reading YMCA Rapids

FINAL
Westwood United Reserves 1-2 Goring United

DIVISION THREE (TOP THREE)

		P	W	D	L	F	A	Pts
1	Pinewood	20	17	2	1	71	13	53
2	Woodley Hammers	20	17	1	2	77	24	52
3	Goring United Reserves	20	13	1	6	53	23	40

DIVISION FOUR (TOP THREE)

		P	W	D	L	F	A	Pts
1	Emmbrook	16	15	0	1	64	14	45
2	Eldon Celtic	16	14	0	2	93	20	42
3	Unity Reserves (-3)	16	11	0	5	47	23	30

PREMIER DIVISION

		1	2	3	4	5	6	7	8	9
1	Ashridge Park		0-3	4-1	4-1	1-1	1-4	4-2	1-0	2-1
2	Barton Rovers	3-2		2-3	5-2	2-1	W-L	W-L	1-1	2-0
3	Reading YMCA Rapids	2-1	2-1		0-1	1-0	5-0	6-0	9-0	2-1
4	REME Arborfield	3-1	L-W	0-1		2-2	2-1	5-1	1-0	5-1
5	Sandhurst Devels Reserves	2-2	L-W	0-4	1-4		2-1	4-5	0-3	2-1
6	SRCC	3-3	1-1	0-1	1-2	1-2		4-1	3-3	4-8
7	Westwood United Reserves	2-5	0-5	4-4	3-0	1-1	3-3		0-0	1-3
8	Woodley Saints	2-1	0-1	3-3	4-0	W-L	3-2	1-1		2-1
9	Woodley Town Reserves	1-2	2-6	1-0	2-1	2-3	0-11	2-0	2-2	

READING LEAGUE PREMIER DIVISION CONSTITUTION 2012-13

AFC CORINTHIANS	James Lane, Burghfield, Reading RG30 3R	07961 159710
ASHRIDGE PARK	Cantley Park , Twyford Road , Wokingham RG40 5QT	None
COOKHAM DEAN RESERVES	Alfred Major Rec Ground, Hillcrest Avenue, Cookham Rise , Maidenhead SL6 9NB	01628 819423
FRILSHAM & YATTENDON	Frilsham Playing Field, Frilsham Common, Frilsham, near Hermitage	01635 201847
GORING UNITED	Upper Red Cross Road, Goring on Thames, Oxford	07799 430276
NEWBURY FC RESERVES	Faraday Road, Newbury RG14 2A	07855 031000
REME ARBORFIELD	Sports Pavilion, Biggs Lane, Hazelbrook Barracks,Arborfield, Reading RG2 9NH	None
READING YMCA RAPIDS	Reading Town FC, Scours Lane, Tilehurst, Reading RG30 6AY	0118 945 3555
SANDHURST DEVELS RESERVES	Sandhurst Memorial Ground, York Town Road, Sandhurst GU47 9BJ	None
WESTWOOD UNITED RESERVES	Cotswold Sports Centre, Downs Way, Tilehurst, Reading RG31 6LS	0118 941 4690
WOODLEY TOWN RESERVES	East Park Farm, Park Lane, Charvil, Reading RG10 9QP	None

SHEFFIELD & HALLAMSHIRE SENIOR LEAGUE

Sponsored by: Windsor Food Services
Founded: N/K
Recent Champions:
2007: Athersley Recreation
2008: Wombwell Main
2009: Athersley Recreation
2010: Sheffield Reserves
2011: Swallownest Miners Welfare

PREMIER DIVISION

		P	W	D	L	F	A	Pts
1	Athersley Recreation	26	20	2	4	67	19	62
2	Stocksbridge Park Steels Res.	26	16	8	2	41	16	56
3	Swallownest Miners Welfare	26	16	4	6	60	29	52
4	Penistone Church	26	14	9	3	66	29	51
5	High Green Villa	26	9	10	7	42	39	37
6	Millmoor Juniors	26	9	8	9	41	47	35
7	Wombwell Main	26	10	4	12	42	44	34
8	Everest	26	8	9	9	33	37	33
9	Handsworth Reserves	26	7	7	12	35	44	28
10	South Kirkby Colliery	26	6	7	13	38	49	25
11	Davy FC	25	6	6	13	35	59	24
12	Ecclesfield Red Rose	26	7	3	16	29	55	24
13	Hallam Reserves	25	4	8	13	43	80	20
14	Sheffield Reserves (-1)	26	5	3	18	32	57	17

DIVISION ONE

		P	W	D	L	F	A	Pts
1	Houghton Main	26	19	6	1	91	20	63
2	Aqua Force Barnsley	25	16	4	5	67	35	52
3	Frecheville CA	26	16	4	6	64	46	52
4	Penistone Church Reserves	26	13	4	9	54	45	43
5	Thorpe Hesley (-1)	26	12	6	8	60	38	41
6	Worksop Parramore	25	12	3	10	49	53	39
7	Swinton Station Athletic	26	10	8	8	66	46	38
8	Oughtibridge WMSC	26	11	4	11	45	48	37
9	Silkstone United	26	9	9	8	50	48	36
10	Worsbrough Bridge Ath. Res.	26	8	5	13	43	67	29
11	Bramley Sunnyside Juniors (-3)	26	9	5	12	51	80	29
12	Wickersley	26	6	4	16	34	51	22
13	Sheffield Athletic	26	4	3	19	54	92	15
14	Caribbean Sports	26	2	3	21	35	94	9

LEAGUE CUP (from 3rd Round)

ROUND 3

Athersley Recreation Reserves 2-0 South Kirkby Colliery

Clowne Villa 1-3 Aqua Force Barnsley

Frecheville CA 7-1 Frecheville CA Reserves

Houghton Main 1-2 Wombwell Main

Millmoor Juniors Reserves 2-4 Thorpe Hesley

Penistone Church 2-0 Athersley Recreation

Bramley Sunnyside Juniors 5-5, 5-4p Caribbean Sports

Wickersley 3-2 Thorncliffe

QUARTER FINALS

Aqua Force Barnsley 2-0 Frecheville CA

Thorpe Hesley 3-1 Bramley Sunnyside Juniors

Wickersley 4-2 Athersley Recreation Reserves

Wombwell Main 2-4 Penistone Church

SEMI-FINALS

Aqua Force Barnsley 1-2 Thorpe Hesley

Penistone church 4-2 Wickersley

FINAL

Thorpe Hesley 0-2 Penistone Church

DIVISION TWO

		P	W	D	L	F	A	Pts
1	Athersley Recreation Reserves	20	17	1	2	53	15	52
2	Gleadless	20	16	1	3	71	21	49
3	Thorncliffe	20	11	2	7	44	33	35
4	Sheffield Bankers	20	9	4	7	42	43	31
5	Millmoor Juniors Reserves	20	8	3	9	37	32	27
6	Clowne Villa	20	8	3	9	40	38	27
7	Boynton Sports	20	7	5	8	40	37	26
8	Frecheville CA Reserves	20	7	2	11	35	52	23
9	De La Salle Old Boys	20	5	3	12	24	47	18
10	New Bohemians	20	5	3	12	25	50	18
11	Sheffield Lane Top	20	2	3	15	20	63	9

PREMIER DIVISION

		1	2	3	4	5	6	7	8	9	10	11	12	13	14
1	Athersley Recreation		5-1	8-1	1-0	5-1	2-0	3-0	6-0	1-2	5-1	2-1	0-1	0-1	2-0
2	Davy	1-2		2-3	1-1	3-3	0-5	2-2	2-4	1-1	3-2	3-1	0-4	2-3	2-1
3	Ecclesfield Red Rose	0-1	2-0		1-1	3-1	1-3	1-3	1-3	1-2	2-1	1-1	0-0	0-2	1-3
4	Everest	0-1	4-1	3-1		2-0	0-0	1-1	0-4	3-2	5-3	3-1	0-1	0-0	0-2
5	Hallam Reserves	1-3	4-1	1-1	1-1		4-4	0-1	3-0	7-0	3-2	0-2	0-4	2-2	
6	Handsworth Reserves	0-4	0-1	1-2	3-1	2-2		2-0	2-2	0-1	0-1	2-1	3-3	4-1	2-2
7	High Green Villa	1-5	2-1	1-0	3-0	1-1	4-0		2-0	1-1	5-1	6-2	0-0	0-2	0-4
8	Millmoor Juniors	0-1	2-2	2-0	3-4	5-1	1-1	4-1		3-2	0-1	1-1	0-2	0-0	1-0
9	Penistone Church	1-0	3-0	5-1	2-2	16-2	3-0	0-0	4-1		3-2	3-1	0-0	2-2	3-2
10	Sheffield Reserves	0-2	0-1	1-4	2-0	3-0	0-1	0-0	1-1	2-2		1-2	0-1	0-2	3-0
11	South Kirkby Colliery	1-1	3-0	2-1	0-1	2-2	2-0	2-2	1-1	0-0	3-2		0-1	2-4	1-3
12	Stocksbridge Park Steels Reserves	1-2	3-3	1-0	0-0	3-2	4-0	1-0	2-2	0-0	1-0	3-2		0-1	4-1
13	Swallownest Miners Welfare	1-2	1-2	4-0	3-1	11-1	3-2	1-1	7-0	1-4	3-2	1-0	0-2		2-1
14	Wombwell Main	3-3	2-1	0-1	0-0	3-1	2-1	1-2	3-0	0-4	4-3	2-4	0-1	1-0	

SOMERSET COUNTY LEAGUE

Sponsored by: Errea
Founded: 1890
Recent Champions:
2007: Burnham United
2008: Nailsea United
2009: Bridgwater Town Reserves
2010: Bridgwater Town Reserves
2011: Shirehampton

ERREA PREMIER/FIRST DIVISION CUP

ROUND 1
Purnell Sports 3-0 Cheddar
Watchet Town HW Congresbury
Glastonbury Town 1-4 Burnham United
Brislington Reserves 1-2 Shepton Mallet Reserves

ROUND 2
Ashton and Backwell United 4-3 St George Easton in Gorda
Street Reserves 2-1 Nailsea Town
Ilminster Town 3-2 Bridgwater Town Reserves
Fry Club 4-1 Winscombe
Yatton Athletic 1-2 Clevedon United
Langford Rovers 2000 2-0 Minehead
Weston St Johns 1-0 Purnell Sports
Cutters Friday 2-3 (aet) Watchet Town
Cleeve West Town 1-3 Burnham United
Clutton 1-0 Stockwood Green
Nailsea United 4-2 Bishops Lydeard
Castle Cary 1-5 Shirehampton
Saltford 0-1 Frome Collegians
Taunton Blackbrook 3-1 Shepton Mallet Reserves
Bishop Sutton Res 5-1 Odd Down Reserves
Berrow 2-0 Larkhall Athletic Reserves

PREMIER DIVISION	P	W	D	L	F	A	Pts
1 Nailsea United	34	26	2	6	125	53	80
2 Cheddar	34	23	4	7	84	43	73
3 Ashton and Backwell United	34	20	9	5	81	37	69
4 Watchet Town	34	21	4	9	73	38	67
5 Langford Rovers 2000	34	20	6	8	86	55	66
6 Cutters Friday	34	19	7	8	84	48	64
7 Berrow	34	16	5	13	82	68	53
8 Shirehampton	34	15	7	12	86	53	52
9 Nailsea Town	34	15	7	12	55	48	52
10 Stockwood Green	34	16	2	16	60	51	50
11 Bishops Lydeard	34	11	10	13	66	68	43
12 Minehead	34	11	10	13	54	67	43
13 Bridgwater Town Res	34	10	5	19	49	86	35
14 Taunton Blackbrook	34	7	9	18	42	94	30
15 Clevedon United	34	6	10	18	50	77	28
16 St George Easton in Gordano	34	6	5	23	49	119	23
17 Odd Down Res (-1)	34	6	5	23	44	94	22
18 Glastonbury Town	34	3	3	28	33	104	12

PREMIER DIVISION	1	2	3	4	5	6	7	8	9	10	11	12	13	14	15	16	17	18
1 Ashton and Backwell United		5-0	4-0	6-0	2-6	2-0	1-3	9-1	3-1	1-1	0-0	3-2	6-3	1-1	1-1	0-1	6-0	2-0
2 Berrow	0-0		2-1	3-0	0-1	1-3	1-2	4-1	2-5	1-1	2-2	5-1	7-0	2-2	4-5	3-2	6-2	0-1
3 Bishops Lydeard	1-2	5-2		3-0	1-1	2-2	1-1	2-0	0-0	5-2	1-2	0-4	3-1	2-5	7-0	4-3	3-1	1-2
4 Bridgwater Town Reserves	1-2	2-4	3-3		2-1	3-1	2-2	2-1	1-4	0-1	1-2	2-3	1-0	0-5	4-0	1-3	1-1	2-1
5 Cheddar	5-3	3-2	4-1	0-3		1-0	0-2	8-0	2-2	2-2	2-0	3-0	3-1	3-1	2-0	1-0	5-1	1-1
6 Clevedon United	0-0	1-2	1-0	6-3	0-4		1-4	1-1	1-3	2-0	1-2	3-5	0-0	1-1	8-1	2-2	0-0	2-4
7 Cutters Friday	1-2	2-1	2-2	7-0	6-2	5-1		4-2	3-1	1-2	1-0	3-2	0-0	2-3	4-1	3-1	3-0	1-2
8 Glastonbury Town	2-3	1-6	1-2	0-2	0-4	5-4	1-2		2-5	1-4	1-1	0-2	1-2	0-3	2-1	0-1	2-0	1-2
9 Langford Rovers 2000	1-2	4-2	4-2	2-2	2-0	4-1	1-2	2-1		4-0	1-3	3-3	4-1	2-1	4-3	2-0	3-3	1-3
10 Minehead	0-2	1-4	1-1	4-1	0-3	2-2	1-1	3-2	0-1		2-0	4-8	1-0	2-2	2-0	0-3	2-1	0-2
11 Nailsea Town	0-2	2-3	1-1	3-2	2-1	0-0	2-2	1-0	1-3	3-2		0-1	3-1	1-1	1-0	1-3	5-0	3-0
12 Nailsea United	0-2	4-0	5-2	4-2	5-2	2-1	5-0	2-0	2-4	2-2	4-2		7-3	4-0	10-1	5-0	10-1	2-1
13 Odd Down Reserves	1-1	3-1	1-2	0-1	1-3	1-0	1-5	0-0	1-1	2-4	1-4	0-7		3-2	2-3	0-1	1-2	2-5
14 Shirehampton	1-2	1-2	5-1	1-1	1-3	6-0	3-1	8-0	0-3	2-1	0-1	2-4	4-3		6-0	2-1	8-0	0-0
15 St George Easton in Gordano	0-4	2-2	1-3	3-1	1-3	2-3	2-7	4-3	2-3	3-3	1-5	0-3	6-1	2-1		1-8	1-1	1-2
16 Stockwood Green	2-0	1-2	2-2	3-0	1-2	5-0	1-0	1-0	1-3	1-2	3-1	0-2	1-3	1-0	5-0		1-0	0-1
17 Taunton Blackbrook	1-1	0-2	1-1	2-3	0-1	2-2	1-0	2-1	3-2	2-2	2-1	1-3	5-4	2-5	1-1	3-1		0-5
18 Watchet Town	1-1	2-4	2-1	5-0	0-2	2-0	2-2	7-0	2-1	2-0	3-0	1-2	0-1	2-3	3-0	5-1	2-1	

SOMERSET COUNTY LEAGUE PREMIER DIVISION CONSTITUTION 2012-13

ASHTON & BACKWELL UNITED	The Playing Fields, West Town Road, Backwell, Bristol BS48 3HG	01275 462612
BERROW	Red Road Playing Fields, Berrow, Burnham-on-Sea TA8 2LY	07714 122050
BISHOPS LYDEARD	Darby Way, Bishops Lydeard TA4 3BE	07771 506613
BRIDGWATER TOWN RESEVES	Fairfax Park, College Way, Bath Road, Bridgwater TA6 4TZ	01278 446899
CLEVEDON UNITED	Coleridge Vale Playing Flds, Southley Road, Clevedon BS21 6PF	01275 871878
CUTTERS FRIDAY	The Cutters Club, Stockwood Lane, Stockwood, Bristol BS14 8SJ	01275 839830
ILMINSTER TOWN	Recreation Ground, Ilminster TA19 0EF	07875 378663
LANGFORD ROVERS 2000	Westland United FC, Winterstoke Road, Weston-super-Mare BS24 9AA	01934 632037
MINEHEAD	Recreation Ground, Irnham Road, Minehead TA24 5DP	01643 704989
NAILSEA TOWN	Fryth Way, Pound Lane, Nailsea BS48 2AS	07763 925811
NAILSEA UNITED	Grove Sports Ground, Old Church, Nailsea BS48 4ND	01275 856892
ODD DOWN RESERVES	Lew Hill Memorial Ground, Combe Hay Lane, Odd Down, Bath BA2 8PH	01225 832491
SHIREHAMPTON	Recreation Ground, Penpole Lane, Shirehampton, Bristol BS11 0EA	0117 923 5461
ST GEORGE EASTON-IN-GORDANO	Court Hay, Easton-in-Gordano, Bristol BS20 0PY	01275 374235
STOCKWOOD GREEN	Hursley Lane, Woolard Lane, Whitchurch, Bristol BS14 0QY	01275 891300
STREET RESERVES	The Tannery Ground, Middlebrooks, Street BA16 0TA	01458 445987
WATCHET TOWN	Memorial Ground, Doniford Road, Watchet TA23 0TG	01984 631041
WESTON ST JOHNS	Coleridge Road, Bournville Estate, Weston-super-Mare BS23 3UP	01934 612862

SOMERSET COUNTY LEAGUE - STEP 7

DIVISION ONE

		P	W	D	L	F	A	Pts
1	Ilminster Town	34	18	7	9	71	46	61
2	Street Reserves (-1)	34	19	5	10	59	41	61
3	Weston St Johns	34	19	3	12	80	59	60
4	Larkhall Athletic Reserves	34	17	6	11	74	57	57
5	Frome Collegians	34	17	5	12	66	56	56
6	Fry Club	34	16	7	11	84	52	55
7	Burnham United	34	16	7	11	78	62	55
8	Brislington Reserves	34	16	7	11	60	54	55
9	Yatton Athletic	34	16	6	12	83	64	54
10	Clutton	34	15	8	11	60	49	53
11	Cleeve West Town	34	15	7	12	55	44	52
12	Shepton Mallet Reserves	34	13	4	17	50	71	43
13	Bishop Sutton Reserves	34	11	9	14	69	74	42
14	Purnells Sports FC	34	10	9	15	58	64	39
15	Castle Cary	34	11	5	18	48	68	38
16	Saltford (-4)	34	9	6	19	48	67	29
17	Winscombe (-4)	34	7	10	17	49	84	27
18	Congresbury (-4)	34	4	3	27	33	113	11

PREMIER/FIRST DIVISION CUP continued...

ROUND 3
Ashton and Backwell Unite 2-2 2-3p Street Reserves
Ilminster Town 2-1 Fry Club
Clevedon United 1-4 Langford Rovers 2000
Weston St Johns 4-4 4-2p Watchet Town
Burnham United 1-4 (aet) Clutton
Nailsea United 2-1 Shirehampton
Frome Collegians 2-0 Taunton Blackbrook
Bishop Sutton Res 1-2 Berrow

QUARTER FINALS
Street Res 0-3 Ilminster Town
Langford Rovers 2000 3-1 Weston St Johns
Clutton 2-3 Nailsea United
Frome Collegians 4-1 (aet) Berrow

SEMI-FINALS
Ilminster Town 0-3 Langford Rovers 2000
Nailsea United 5-1 Frome Collegians

FINAL
Langford Rovers 2000 1-2 Nailsea United

DIVISION ONE

		1	2	3	4	5	6	7	8	9	10	11	12	13	14	15	16	17	18
1	Bishop Sutton Reserves		1-1	5-2	2-1	0-2	3-2	2-0	3-2	4-1	2-2	1-3	2-5	3-1	3-2	1-4	2-4	4-0	5-2
2	Brislington Reserves	2-1		1-3	1-1	2-2	1-1	4-2	1-1	2-1	2-0	2-0	1-1	1-0	2-3	2-1	0-3	6-1	3-2
3	Burnham United	3-2	3-0		3-1	0-2	0-3	7-2	1-3	3-2	1-0	2-2	1-2	5-1	4-2	2-2	5-4	2-2	3-3
4	Castle Cary	3-0	3-1	0-1		2-0	4-0	2-0	2-1	0-5	1-3	2-4	2-0	3-2	2-1	0-1	0-3	2-1	1-5
5	Cleeve West Town	1-1	0-3	2-1	4-2		2-2	2-0	3-1	1-0	0-3	2-1	3-1	5-0	1-1	2-0	4-1	0-2	0-1
6	Clutton	0-2	1-1	1-0	2-2	2-1		6-0	6-1	1-2	5-0	2-1	1-4	1-1	0-0	4-2	4-1	1-6	
7	Congresbury	3-1	2-0	1-7	1-3	2-1	0-2		0-1	0-10	1-2	0-2	1-3	2-1	1-3	0-1	1-4	2-4	3-4
8	Frome Collegians	2-1	0-1	1-3	4-1	0-0	2-0	3-2		2-2	1-2	2-1	5-2	1-2	3-1	2-4	2-1	1-0	0-2
9	Fry Club	2-2	1-3	2-2	3-1	1-2	0-2				1-0	2-2	6-0	2-2	6-1	1-0	5-0	1-2	3-1
10	Ilminster Town	2-2	4-1	3-3	2-0	1-1	3-1	10-0	0-1	2-3		2-1	1-3	3-1	2-2	0-0	3-1	4-2	3-1
11	Larkhall Athletic Reserves	1-1	1-4	3-0	3-2	1-0	2-1	8-0	2-5	3-2	2-3		3-0	1-1	2-1	2-0	1-2	4-0	4-2
12	Purnells Sports	2-2	1-3	0-2	5-0	5-1	0-1	2-2	1-1	4-4	1-2	0-0		5-1	1-2	4-1	0-1	1-1	2-2
13	Saltford	4-0	4-1	0-2	1-0	1-2	2-0	3-0	2-4	1-2	0-3	1-2			1-2	1-2	2-2	2-0	1-1
14	Shepton Mallet Reserves	3-1	3-1	1-0	3-1	2-1	0-1	2-1	0-6	1-1	3-2	1-4	1-2	3-1		0-4	1-0	2-3	0-5
15	Street Reserves	3-2	2-1	2-1	1-1	2-1	2-1	1-1	1-2	1-2	1-0	4-1	2-0	0-1	2-0		2-1	3-0	5-0
16	Weston St Johns	4-3	4-2	2-2	3-1	0-0	1-2	5-1	3-2	1-0	5-1	2-3	2-1	4-0	2-1	4-1		3-0	2-1
17	Winscombe	2-2	0-2	3-1	1-1	1-6	2-2	1-1	2-2	1-4	0-1	2-2	1-1	1-1	2-1	3-4	3-2		3-4
18	Yatton Athletic	3-3	1-2	2-3	1-1	2-1	0-1	3-0	4-0	2-4	0-2	4-2	4-0	2-2	2-0	2-0	3-2	6-2	

SOMERSET COUNTY LEAGUE DIVISION ONE CONSTITUTION 2012-13

BANWELL	Riverside Ground, Riverside, Banwell BS29 6EE	01934 820773
BISHOP SUTTON RESERVES	Lake View, Wick Road, Bishop Sutton, Bristol BS39 5XP	01275 333097
BRISLINGTON RESERVES	Ironmould Lane, Brislington, Bristol BS4 5SA	0117 977 4030
BURNHAM UNITED	Burnham Road Playing Fields, Cassis Close, Burnham-on-Sea TA8 1NN	01278 794615
CASTLE CARY	Donald Pither Memorial PF, Catherines Close, Castle Cary BA7 7HP	01963 351538
CLEEVE WEST TOWN	King George V Playing Fields, Meeting House Lane, Cleeve BS49 4PD	01934 832173
CLUTTON	Warwick Fields, Upper Bristol Road, Clutton, Bristol BS39 5TA	None
FROME COLLEGIANS	Selwood School, Berkley Road, Frome BA11 2EF	None
FRY CLUB	Fry Club, Somerdale, Keynsham, Bristol BS31 2AU	0117 937 6500/6501
GLASTONBURY TOWN	Abbey Moor Stadium, Godney Road, Glastonbury BA6 9AF	01458 831460
KEYNSHAM TOWN RESERVES	Crown Field, Bristol Road, Keynsham, Bristol BS31 2BE	0117 986 5876
LARKHALL ATHLETIC RESERVES	Plain Ham, Charlcombe Lane, Larkhall, Bath BA1 8DJ	01225 334952
PURNELL SPORTS	Paulton Rovers FC, Athletic Ground, Winterfield Road, Paulton BS39 7RF	01761 412907
SALTFORD	Playing Fields, Norman Road, Saltford BS31 0BQ	01225 873725
SHEPTON MALLET RESERVES	West Shepton Playing Fields, Old Wells Road, Shepton Mallet BA4 5XN	01749 344609
WESTFIELD	Fosseway Playing Fields, Charlton Lane, Midsomer Norton BA3 4BD	None
WRINGTON-REDHILL	Recreation Ground, Silver Street, Wrington BS40 5QE	None
YATTON ATHLETIC	Hangstones Playing Fields, Stowey Road, Yatton BS49 4HY	None

DIVISION TWO EAST

		P	W	D	L	F	A	Pts
1	Keynsham Town Reserves	28	19	4	5	63	40	61
2	Westfield FC	28	17	6	5	68	39	57
3	Peasedown Athletic	28	15	9	4	53	29	54
4	Dundry Athletic	28	14	7	7	65	40	49
5	Fry Club Reserves	28	13	5	10	58	37	44
6	Welton Rovers Reserves	28	12	7	9	57	43	43
7	Timsbury Athletic	28	12	6	10	44	49	42
8	Tunley Athletic	28	11	7	10	70	54	40
9	Cutters Friday Reserves	28	9	9	10	41	39	36
10	Radstock Town Reserves	28	9	8	11	45	38	35
11	Hengrove Athletic Reserves	28	9	7	12	49	64	34
12	Imperial FC	28	8	8	12	49	61	32
13	Stockwood Green Reserves	28	6	11	11	28	42	29
14	Farrington Gurney	28	6	1	21	34	76	19
15	Purnells Sports Reserves (-3)	28	1	3	24	19	92	3

DIVISION TWO WEST

		P	W	D	L	F	A	Pts
1	Wrington Redhill	26	15	6	5	69	30	51
2	Banwell	26	16	3	7	58	39	51
3	Combe St Nicholas	26	15	4	7	49	32	49
4	Wells City Reserves	26	15	4	7	48	31	49
5	Portishead Town Res	26	14	4	8	54	34	46
6	Churchill Club 70 (-3)	26	13	9	4	65	37	45
7	Nailsea United Reserves	26	13	4	9	53	48	43
8	Ashton and Backwell Utd Res.	26	10	5	11	34	39	35
9	Cheddar Reserves	26	10	4	12	52	65	34
10	Worle	26	6	6	14	41	60	24
11	Westland United	26	7	3	16	49	72	24
12	Burnham United Reserves	26	6	6	14	42	70	24
13	Creech North Curry	26	5	6	15	39	56	21
14	Long Ashton	26	3	4	19	35	75	13

ERREA DIVISION TWO CUP

ROUND 1
Banwell 4-0 Imperial FC
Farrington Gurney 0-0 5-4p Timsbury Athletic 0
Burnham United Reserves 3-4 Creech North Curry
Worle 1-3 Nailsea United Reserves
Wells City Reserves 2-0 Keynsham Town Reserves
Purnells Sports Reserves 0-3 Welton Rovers Reserves
Combe St Nicholas 1-2 Cutters Friday Reserves
Portishead Town Reserves 2-0 Long Ashton
Dundry Athletic 2-5 Ashton and Backwell United
Westland United 0-3 Churchill Club 70
Westfield FC 2-1 Cheddar Reserves
Stockwood Green Reserves 6-1 Hengrove Athletic Reserves
Tunley Athletic 3-2 Peasedown Athletic

ROUND 2
Banwell 3-0 Farrington Gurney
Radstock Town Res 6-1 Wrington Redhill
Creech North Curry 1-0 Nailsea United Reserves
Wells City Reserves 1-0 (aet) Welton Rovers Reserves
Fry Club Reserves 1-1 4-3p Cutters Friday Reserves
Portishead Town Res 2-1 Dundry Athletic
Churchill Club 70 3-4 Westfield FC
Stockwood Green Reserves 3-1 (aet) Tunley Athletic

QUARTER FINALS
Banwell 3-3 3-1p Radstock Town Reserves
Creech North Curry 3-2 (aet) Wells City Reserves
Fry Club Reserves 2-1 Portishead Town Reserves
Westfield FC 2-1 Stockwood Green Reserves

SEMI-FINALS
Banwell 1-2 Creech North Curry
Fry Club Reserves 3-2 Westfield FC 2

FINAL
Creech North Curry 0-2 Fry Club Reserves

DIVISION TWO EAST

		1	2	3	4	5	6	7	8	9	10	11	12	13	14	15
1	Cutters Friday Reserves		0-2	5-2	1-0	2-1	1-2	1-1	1-2	1-1	0-0	1-2	1-2	5-1	2-2	
2	Dundry Athletic	5-2		3-0	2-1	6-3	4-2	1-2	3-2	0-0	2-4	2-1	5-0	3-3	2-0	2-1
3	Farrington Gurney	1-3	1-8		3-1	1-2	2-4	0-3	0-3	3-1	0-3	1-2	1-2	1-4	1-4	1-5
4	Fry Club Reserves	0-0	2-1	1-2		1-1	4-0	1-4	1-1	4-0	2-1	2-0	2-4	5-0	0-3	4-1
5	Hengrove Athletic Reserves	2-1	2-2	1-2	1-2		5-3	1-4	0-3	1-1	2-1	1-1	3-1	5-0	0-4	1-5
6	Imperial	2-2	5-4	2-1	3-3	3-4		1-2	2-1	1-1	2-1	1-1	1-3	0-1	2-3	1-2
7	Keynsham Town Reserves	2-1	1-0	4-2	1-0	1-5	3-2		2-1	10-1	1-0	1-2	0-2	3-2	1-4	1-1
8	Peasedown Athletic	1-1	1-1	3-0	2-1	3-0	2-2	2-0		3-1	1-1	1-1	0-0	2-2	3-2	0-1
9	Purnells Sports Reserves	1-3	0-2	1-3	0-4	1-3	2-3	1-2	1-3		1-3	2-1	0-2	1-12	0-6	0-1
10	Radstock Town Reserves	1-1	1-1	3-2	1-4	1-2	0-1	2-2	2-3	3-0		1-0	5-1	1-0	0-1	1-1
11	Stockwood Green Reserves	1-0	0-2	2-0	0-0	2-1	1-1	0-2	1-2	2-0	1-1		1-2	1-3	2-2	0-2
12	Timsbury Athletic	2-0	0-0	1-2	1-6	0-0	3-0	2-2	1-2	4-3	0-0			0-3	1-3	2-1
13	Tunley Athletic	0-1	2-0	0-0	2-3	2-2	1-1	1-2	1-4	5-1	0-4	7-0	2-2		3-1	3-4
14	Welton Rovers Reserves	0-1	1-1	2-1	0-3	1-1	0-3	2-3	0-0	4-0	0-0	2-2	5-2	3-3		3-1
15	Westfield	2-2	3-1	3-1	2-1	5-2	4-0	2-2	1-2	2-1	3-1	3-3	2-1	6-1	2-0	

DIVISION TWO WEST

		1	2	3	4	5	6	7	8	9	10	11	12	13	14
1	Ashton and Backwell United Reserves		1-1	5-0	0-1	1-0	0-4	1-0	2-2	0-0	1-1	0-2	2-1	1-0	0-3
2	Banwell	0-1		5-0	1-5	0-0	2-1	4-0	5-0	3-3	1-0	1-2	5-1	2-10	2-1
3	Burnham United Reserves	0-2	0-4		4-2	3-1	1-1	1-3	3-0	3-5	2-5	4-2	3-2	3-0	0-2
4	Cheddar Reserves	4-1	0-3	3-0		1-5	3-2	2-3	3-1	1-3	2-2	2-4	1-3	1-1	1-0
5	Churchill Club 70	4-2	2-1	2-2	5-0		3-1	2-1	2-2	2-0	1-1	5-3	4-2	3-1	
6	Combe St Nicholas	3-2	1-2	3-1	1-0	4-2		2-0	4-2	2-1	2-0	1-0	2-1	4-0	0-2
7	Creech St Michael	1-4	0-2	6-1	1-1	0-0	1-1		1-0	2-5	1-2	0-2	4-0	3-4	1-4
8	Long Ashton	1-2	2-1	2-2	2-5	0-5	2-5	3-2		1-2	1-5	3-5	3-2	1-2	2-2
9	Nailsea United Reserves	2-1	1-2	3-3	4-1	3-1	0-4	3-1	4-1		2-0	1-0	2-3	1-0	2-2
10	Portishead Town Reserves	1-2	2-3	1-0	4-1	2-4	2-0	2-0	1-0	2-2		3-2	5-0	3-0	0-1
11	Wells City Reserves	2-1	3-1	4-0	0-0	2-1	0-1	2-2	5-1	2-0	1-0		2-1	1-0	1-3
12	Westland United	2-1	1-2	3-3	4-6	1-1	0-0	3-2	3-2	4-3	1-2	1-3		1-3	1-6
13	Worle	0-0	1-3	3-2	2-4	3-3	0-1	2-2	2-1	0-4	2-4	0-0	1-6		2-2
14	Wrington Redhill	4-1	1-2	1-1	10-1	3-3	2-2	2-2	2-1	5-0	1-2	3-0	3-1	3-1	

SOMERSET COUNTY LEAGUE DIVISION TWO EAST CONSTITUTION 2012-13

CUTTERS FRIDAY RESERVES	The Cutters Club , Stockwood Lane, Stockwood , Bristol BS14 8SJ	01275 839830
DUNDRY ATHLETIC	Dundry Playing Field, Crabtree Lane, Dundry, Bristol BS41 8LN	0117 964 5536
FARRINGTON GURNEY	Farrington Recreation Ground, Farrington Gurney	
FRY CLUB RESERVES	Fry Club, Somerdale, Keynsham, Bristol BS31 2AU	0117 937 6500/6501
HENGROVE ATHLETIC RESERVES	Norton Lane, Whitchurch, Bristol BS14 0BT	01275 832894
IMPERIAL	Bristol Imperial Sports Club, West Town Lane, Whitchurch, Brislington BS4 5DT	01275 546000
PEASEDOWN ATHLETIC	Miners Welfare Park, Church Road, Peasedown St John, Bath BA2 8AF	01761 437319
PURNELL SPORTS RESERVES	Greyfield Sports & Social Club, Bristol Road, Paulton BS39 7NX	01761 412809
RADSTOCK TOWN RESERVES	Southfield Recreation Ground, Frome Hill, Radstock BA3 3NZ	01761 435004
STOCKWOOD GREEN RESERVES	Hursley Lane, Woolard Lane, Whitchurch, Bristol BS14 0QY	01275 891300
TIMSBURY ATHLETIC	Recreation Ground, North Road, Timsbury, Bath BA2 0JH	01761 472523
TUNLEY ATHLETIC	The Recreation Centre, Bath Road, Tunley BA2 0EB	None
WELTON ROVERS RESERVES	West Clewes, North Road, Midsomer Norton BA3 2QD	01761 412097

SOMERSET COUNTY LEAGUE DIVISION TWO WEST CONSTITUTION 2012-13

ASHTON & BACKWELL UNITED RES.	The Playing Fields , West Town Road, Backwell , Bristol BS48 3HG	01275 462612
BURNHAM UNITED RESERVES	Burnham Road Playing Fields, Cassis Close, Burnham-on-Sea TA8 1NN	01278 794615
CHEDDAR RESERVES	Bowdens Park, Draycott Road, Cheddar BS27 3RL	01934 743736
CHURCHILL CLUB 70	Ladymead Lane, Churchill, Winscombe BS25 5NH	01934 852739
COMBE ST NICHOLAS	Slades Cross, Combe St Nicholas TA20 3HQ	01460 234743
CONGRESBURY	Broadstones Playing Fields, Stonewell Lane, Congresbury BS49 5DL	01934 832150
CREECH NORTH CURRY	White Street, North Curry TA3 6A	07734 078921
MIDDLEZOY ROVERS	Westonzoyland Parish, Westonzoyland, Somerset	07881 504050
NAILSEA TOWN RESERVES	Fryth Way, Pound Lane, Nailsea BS48 2AS	07763 925811
NAILSEA UNITED RESERVES	Grove Sports Ground, Old Church, Nailsea BS48 4ND	01275 856892
PORTISHEAD TOWN RESERVES	Bristol Road Playing Fields, Portishead, Bristol BS20 6QB	01275 847136
WELLS CITY RESERVES	The Athletic Ground, Rowdens Road, Wells BA5 1TU	01749 679971
WESTLAND UNITED	Westland Sports Club, Winterstoke Road, Weston-super-Mare BS24 9AA	01934 632037
WESTON ST JOHNS RESERVES	Coleridge Road, Bournville Estate, Weston-super-Mare BS23 3UP	01934 612862
WINSCOMBE	Recreation Ground, The Lynch, Winscombe BS25 1AP	01934 842720(cricket club)
WORLE	Worle Recreation Ground, Station Road, Worle, Weston-super-Mare BS22 6AU	None

STAFFORDSHIRE COUNTY SENIOR LEAGUE

Sponsored by: No sponsor
Founded: 1957
Recent Champions:
2007: Wolstanton United
2008: Wolstanton United
2009: Foley
2010: Stretton Eagles
2011: Ball Haye Green

CUP WINNERS

CHALLENGE CUP
Wolstanton United

PRESIDENTS TROPHY
Wolstanton United Reserves

DIVISION TWO CUP
AFC Milton

PREMIER DIVISION	P	W	D	L	F	A	Pts
1 Hanley Town	30	23	3	4	80	27	72
2 Redgate Clayton	30	22	5	3	79	27	71
3 Wolstanton United	30	22	5	3	83	32	71
4 Biddulph Town	30	22	1	7	103	48	67
5 Abbey Hulton United	30	15	8	7	81	56	53
6 Audley	30	15	6	9	49	34	51
7 Kidsgrove Athletic Reserves	30	14	2	14	63	57	44
8 Eccleshall AFC	30	10	6	14	66	76	36
9 Newcastle Town Reserves	30	10	5	15	41	54	35
10 Congleton Vale	30	10	4	16	43	58	34
11 Ball Haye Green	30	8	7	15	59	70	31
12 Florence	30	7	8	15	52	76	29
13 Stone Dominoes Reserves	30	8	4	18	37	78	28
14 Stretton	30	7	2	21	36	79	23
15 Norton	30	5	6	19	46	103	21
16 Keele University	30	4	4	22	40	83	16

DIVISION ONE	P	W	D	L	F	A	Pts
1 Hanley Town Reserves	30	22	5	3	96	35	71
2 Cheadle Town	30	22	4	4	87	35	70
3 Wolstanton United Reserves	30	22	1	7	85	30	67
4 MMU	30	18	5	7	87	49	59
5 Congleton Athletic	30	17	3	10	81	46	54
6 Redgate Clayton Reserves	30	17	0	13	75	51	51
7 Rugeley Rangers	30	15	4	11	76	64	49
8 Alsager Town	30	13	8	9	75	45	47
9 Lea Hall FC	30	14	3	13	66	82	45
10 Foley	30	14	2	14	73	65	44
11 Bradeley Town	30	11	3	16	61	74	36
12 Chesterton AFC	30	9	5	16	68	65	32
13 Ashbourne FC	30	7	3	20	66	101	24
14 Sandbach United Reserves	30	6	4	20	49	94	22
15 Abbey Hulton Reserves	30	6	3	21	41	104	21
16 Longton Harriers	30	0	1	29	33	179	1

PREMIER DIVISION	1	2	3	4	5	6	7	8	9	10	11	12	13	14	15	16
1 Abbey Hulton United		2-0	2-2	1-2	1-1	10-0	6-2	1-4	2-1	1-0	4-3	6-1	4-1	2-1	3-1	1-2
2 Audley	1-0		1-0	0-4	4-0	1-0	4-2	3-2	5-2	0-1	1-0	0-0	1-1	2-2	3-0	1-2
3 Ball Haye Green	3-3	0-2		2-3	0-0	4-0	4-2	3-4	3-0	4-2	1-2	7-2	0-0	4-0	2-1	0-4
4 Biddulph Town	3-2	3-1	8-1		5-3	4-2	3-1	3-2	6-0	5-1	6-2	0-3	5-0	3-2	0-1	
5 Congleton Vale	0-1	1-0	2-1	4-3		1-2	3-0	0-2	0-1	4-1	1-4	6-1	0-2	1-2	1-1	0-6
6 Eccleshall AFC	2-2	1-6	7-2	4-7	0-2		6-3	2-2	1-1	1-5	5-0	4-0	1-2	2-0	5-0	2-2
7 Florence	2-2	2-1	0-0	0-7	2-1	3-3		1-2	0-0	2-1	2-2	4-5	3-4	2-2	3-0	1-1
8 Hanley Town	6-1	1-0	1-1	3-0	2-0	1-2	3-2		2-2	2-1	2-0	4-2	2-0	1-0	6-1	1-2
9 Keele University	1-4	1-2	1-3	2-4	0-2	1-2	3-1	0-4		1-4	1-2	9-1	1-4	1-3	0-3	2-6
10 Kidsgrove Athletic Reserves	4-4	0-1	3-2	0-3	5-1	3-2	4-0	0-2	4-0		3-3	2-1	1-4	1-3	4-1	2-3
11 Newcastle Town Reserves	2-2	0-1	5-2	3-1	2-1	2-0	1-3	0-3	0-0	0-1		1-0	0-2	3-1	1-3	2-1
12 Norton	1-1	2-2	2-3	2-2	2-2	0-4	0-5	5-2	2-4	1-0			0-2	2-0	3-2	2-10
13 Redgate Clayton	4-2	1-1	2-0	4-0	4-0	2-1	2-0	2-1	5-2	2-1	5-2	4-0		4-0	7-0	0-1
14 Stone Dominoes Reserves	2-4	2-4	3-2	0-8	1-0	1-3	2-2	0-3	2-1	0-4	0-0	3-2	0-3		3-2	1-3
15 Stretton	3-4	1-0	2-1	0-3	1-2	1-5	1-3	0-3	1-2	1-2	1-0	2-1	1-1	4-3		0-1
16 Wolstanton United	1-3	1-1	6-3	1-1	2-4	2-0	3-0	2-1	5-0	1-0	1-0	4-2	2-2	3-0	4-0	

STAFFS COUNTY SENIOR LEAGUE PREMIER DIVISION CONSTITUTION 2012-13

ABBEY HULTON UNITED	Birches Head Road, Abbey Hulton, Stoke-on-Trent ST2 8DD	01782 544232
ALSAGER TOWN RESERVES	The Town Ground, Woodland Court, Alsager ST7 2DP	01270 882336
AUDLEY & DISTRICT	Town Fields, Old Road, Bignall, Stoke-on-Trent ST7 8QH	01782 723482
BALL HAYE GREEN	Ball Haye Green WMC, Ball Haye Green, Leek ST13 6BH	01538 371926
BIDDULPH TOWN	Knypersley Sports & Social, Tunstall Road, Knypersley, Stoke-on-Trent ST8 7AQ	01782 522737
CHEADLE TOWN OLD BOYS	South Moorlands Leisure Centre, Allen Street, Cheadle ST10 1SA	01538 753883
ECCLESHALL AFC	Pershall Park, Chester Road, Eccleshall ST21 6NE	01785 851351
FLORENCE	Florence Sports & Social, Lightwood Road, Longton, Stoke-on-Trent ST3 4JS	01782 312881
HANLEY TOWN	Abbey Lane, Abbey Hulton, Bucknall, Stoke-on-Trent ST2 8AU	01782 267234
KEELE UNIVERSITY	Sports Centre, Keele University, Keele ST5 5BG	01782 733368
KIDSGROVE ATHLETIC RESERVES	The Seddon Stadium, Hollinwood Road, Kidsgrove, Stoke-on-Trent ST7 1DH	01782 782412
NEWCASTLE TOWN RESERVES	Lyme Valley Parkway Stadium, Buckmaster Avenue, Clayton, Newcastle-under-Lyme ST5 3BF	01782 662351 Club: 01782 622350
NORTON	Norton CC & MW Institute, Community Drive, Smallthorne, Stoke-on-Trent ST6 1QF	01782 838290
REDGATE CLAYTON	Northwood Lane, Clayton, Newcastle-under-Lyme ST5 4BN	01782 717409
STONE DOMINOES RESERVES	Motiva Park, Yarnfield Lane, Yarnfield, Stone ST15 0NF	01782 761891
STRETTON	Shobnall Sports & Social Club, Shobnall Road, Burton-on-Trent DE14 2BB	01283 567991
WOLSTANTON UNITED	Bradwell Community Centre, Riceyman Road, Bradwell, Newcastle-under-Lyme ST5 8LF	01782 660818

STAFFORDSHIRE COUNTY SENIOR LEAGUE - STEP 7

	DIVISION TWO	P	W	D	L	F	A	Pts
1	Audley Reserves	28	20	4	4	94	36	64
2	Vodafone Stoke	28	19	3	6	87	40	60
3	Cheadle SMU	28	18	5	5	94	34	59
4	Hilton Harriers	28	17	6	5	78	29	57
5	AFC Milton	28	19	4	5	112	41	55
6	Bradwell	28	17	3	8	107	56	54
7	Stone Old Alleynians Reserves	28	15	1	12	93	57	46
8	Kidsgrove Athletic Youth	28	14	2	12	101	62	44
9	Hawkins Sports	28	12	8	8	81	54	44
10	Norton Reserves	28	13	1	14	87	84	40
11	Cheadle Town "B"	28	11	3	14	74	78	36
12	Congleton Vale Reserves	28	6	0	22	48	118	18
13	Whittington	28	4	1	23	46	114	13
14	Stone Dominoes Youth	28	4	1	23	40	121	13
15	Tunstall Town	28	0	0	28	10	228	0

STAFFS COUNTY SENIOR LEAGUE DIVISION ONE CONSTITUTION 2012-13

ABBEY HULTON UNITED RESERVES	Birches Head Road, Abbey Hulton, Stoke-on-Trent ST2 8DD	01782 544232
ASHBOURNE	Cockayne Avenue, Ashbourne DE6 1NF	None
BRADELEY TOWN	Bradeley Sports Centre, Chell Heath Road, Bradeley ST6 7LH	None
BRADWELL	Tricketts Lane, Willaston, Nantwich CW5 6PX	None
CHEADLE SOUTH MOORLANDS UtD	South Moorlands Leisure Centre, Thorley Drive, Cheadle ST10 1SA	01538 753883
CHESTERTON	Red Street Community Centre, Talke Road, Chesterton, Newcastle-under-Lyme ST5 7AH	None
CONGLETON ATHLETIC	Back Lane Playing Fields, Back Lane, Congleton CW12 4RB	None
FOLEY	Whitcombe Road, Meir, Stoke-on-Trent ST3 6NU	01782 595274
HANLEY TOWN RESERVES	Abbey Lane, Abbey Hulton, Bucknall, Stoke-on-Trent ST2 8AU	01782 267234
HILTON HARRIERS ATHLETIC	Main Street, Church Broughton DE65 5AS	None
LEEK TOWN	Ball Haye Green Sports & Social., Leek, ST13 6BH	01538 371926
MMU CHESHIRE	Alsager Campus, Hassall Road, Alsager ST7 2HL	None
REDGATE CLAYTON RESERVES	Northwood Lane, Clayton, Newcastle-under-Lyme ST5 4BN	01782 717409
SANDBACH UNITED RESERVES	Bentley FC, Sunny Bank Road, Crewe CW2 8WD	01270 656868
UTTOXETER TOWN	Oldfields Sports Ground, Springfield Road, Uttoxeter, ST14 7JX	01889 564347
VODAFONE STOKE	Milton Youth & Adult Centre, Leek Road, Stoke-on-Trent ST2 7AF	None
WOLSTANTON UNITED RESERVES	Bradwell Community Centre, Riceyman Road, Bradwell, Newcastle-under-Lyme ST5 8LF	01782 660818

STAFFS COUNTY SENIOR LEAGUE DIVISION TWO CONSTITUTION 2012-13

BETLEY FC	South Cheshire College, Danebank Avenue, Crewe, CW2 8AB	01270 654654
BIDDULPH TOWN RESERVES	Knypersley Sports & Social, Tunstall Road,ST8 7AQ	None
CHEADLE TOWN OLD BOYS RES.	South Moorlands Leisure Centre, Allen Street, Cheadle ST10 1SA	01538 753883
CONGLETON VALE ROVERS RES.	Congleton High School, Box Lane, Congleton CW12 4NS	01260 387000
FC VIBROMAC JCB	JCB Lakeside Club, Hollington Lane, Rocester, ST14 5HY	None
FLORENCE RESERVES	Florence Sports & Social, Lightwood Road, Longton	01782 312881
HALL HEATH	HMP Stoke Heath, Warrant Road, Stoke Heath, Market Drayton Shropshire, TF9 2JL	
		01630 636100
HAWKINS SPORTS	Hawkins Sports Club, Coppice Lane, Cheslyn Hay, Walsall WS6 7EY	01922 417286
HILTON HARRIERS RESERVES		
LONGTON	Longton Rugby Club, Stanley Matthews Way, Trentham Lakes Stoke-on-Trent, ST4 8GR	
		01782 594016
NORTON RESERVES	Norton CC & MW Institute, Community Drive, Smallthorne, Stoke-on-Trent ST6 1QF	01782 838290
SILVERDALE ATHLETIC	Silverdale Colliery, Scot Hay Road, Silverdale	None
STAPENHILL	Maple Grove, Stapenhill, Burton-on-Trent, DE15 9NN	None
TUNSTALL TOWN	Sandyford Cricket Club, Shelford Road	01782 839007
WHITTINGTON	Whittington Barracks, Lichfield WS14 9PY	None

SUFFOLK & IPSWICH LEAGUE

Sponsored by: TouchlineSIL
Founded: 1896
Recent Champions:
2007: Grundisburgh
2008: Brantham Athletic
2009: Grundisburgh
2010: Old Newton United
2011: Grundisburgh

TOUCHLINE SPORTS INTERMEDIATE CUP

SEMI-FINAL
Achilles 2-1 East Bergholt United
Haughley United 3-2 Wenhaston United

FINAL
Achilles 1-3 Haughley United

GIPPING PRESS CUP

SEMI-FINAL
Grundisburgh Reserves 2-0 Ransomes Sports
Ipswich Athletic Reserves 4-0 East Bergholt

FINAL
Achilles 1-3 Haughley United

CLUB COLOURS JUNIOR CUP

FINAL
Coplestonians A 3-1 Sporting 87 Reserves

SENIOR DIVISION

		P	W	D	L	F	A	Pts
1	Woodbridge Athletic	30	22	4	4	67	25	70
2	Grundisburgh	30	24	3	3	86	22	69
3	Leiston St Margarets	30	14	10	6	66	54	52
4	Melton St Audrys	30	13	10	7	49	45	49
5	Ipswich Athletic	30	13	8	9	57	48	47
6	Achilles	30	14	5	11	71	64	47
7	Felixstowe United	30	14	4	12	65	63	46
8	East Bergholt United	30	13	5	12	64	54	44
9	Haughley United	30	11	7	12	54	60	40
10	Stanton	30	10	7	13	46	60	37
11	Old Newton United	30	11	5	14	54	61	32
12	Wickham Market	30	9	3	18	44	61	30
13	Crane Sports	30	10	2	18	45	61	29
14	Capel Plough	30	8	5	17	33	57	29
15	Ransomes Sports	30	5	5	20	41	73	20
16	Framlingham Town	30	5	5	20	47	81	20

SENIOR DIVISION

		1	2	3	4	5	6	7	8	9	10	11	12	13	14	15	16
1	Achilles		0-1	0-7	2-2	2-3	5-2	0-3	2-2	3-3	5-3	4-0	3-0	4-3	4-2	2-2	2-5
2	Capel Plough	4-1		0-1	2-0	1-3	0-3	0-2	1-1	2-2	0-5	4-2	0-5	0-1	0-1	2-1	1-2
3	Crane Sports	1-0	2-1		0-4	1-6	4-1	0-5	3-2	1-3	2-4	0-1	2-3	4-2	3-0	0-1	0-2
4	East Bergholt United	1-3	0-0	3-1		3-2	2-0	1-3	2-2	2-1	3-2	6-0	1-3	5-2	3-2	0-2	1-6
5	Felixstowe United	2-2	4-1	2-1	1-5		3-2	1-4	2-3	3-3	0-1	0-1	3-2	1-0	1-2	3-1	1-1
6	Framlingham Town	4-2	4-1	1-1	3-1	0-2		1-1	1-2	1-1	1-2	0-2	0-2	2-4	1-3	1-4	0-5
7	Grundisburgh	0-1	2-0	1-0	0-3	5-1	5-1		5-0	0-1	3-1	2-2	4-2	2-1	4-1	4-0	4-1
8	Haughley United	4-3	2-0	5-0	3-2	0-4	1-1	0-2		0-2	1-4	1-1	3-3	4-3	0-2	4-0	1-0
9	Ipswich Athletic	0-2	3-1	1-0	3-2	1-2	4-2	0-4	2-1		3-4	1-2	0-0	1-0	1-1	4-1	2-4
10	Leiston St Margarets	3-2	2-2	1-0	1-5	3-4	6-5	2-2	3-3	4-2		1-1	0-3	2-0	0-0	1-0	1-1
11	Melton St Audrys	2-4	0-0	1-1	2-2	5-2	5-0	0-3	2-0	1-2	2-2		3-1	1-0	3-0	2-1	0-2
12	Old Newton United	0-2	1-2	3-2	4-2	3-2	2-4	1-4	3-2	0-4	0-3	2-2		2-1	5-2	1-1	2-3
13	Ransomes Sports	1-4	0-5	1-3	1-1	1-2	2-1	1-2	0-2	1-1	1-1	2-2	3-1		1-0	3-3	0-3
14	Stanton	2-3	3-0	4-1	1-0	1-1	3-3	0-3	0-5	3-3	2-2	2-3	0-0	4-3		2-4	0-2
15	Wickham Market	1-4	1-2	0-2	0-1	4-3	3-0	0-6	4-0	0-3	1-2	0-1	2-0	5-2	1-2		0-2
16	Woodbridge Athletic	1-0	3-0	3-2	2-1	4-1	3-2	0-1	3-0	1-0	0-0	0-0	1-0	5-1	0-1	2-1	

SUFFOLK & IPSWICH LEAGUE SENIOR DIVISION CONSTITUTION 2012-13

ACHILLES	Pauls Social Club, Salmet Close, Ipswich IP2 9BA	01473 604874
CAPEL PLOUGH	Friars, Capel St Mary, Ipswich IP9 2XS	None
COPLESTONIANS	Woodbridge Town FC, Notcutts Park, Fynn Road, Woodbridge IP12 4DA	01394 385308
CRANE SPORTS	Gresham Sports & Social Club, Tuddenham Road, Ipswich IP4 3QJ	01473 250816
EAST BERGHOLT UNITED	Gandish Road, East Bergholt, Colchester CO7 6TP	01473 728581
FELIXSTOWE UNITED	Trimley Sports & Social Club, High Road, Trimley St Martin, Felixstowe IP11 0RJ	01394 275240
GRUNDISBURGH	The Playing Field, Ipswich Road, Grundisburgh, Woodbridge IP13 6TJ	07974 047221
HAUGHLEY UNITED	King George V Playing Field, Green Road, Haughley IP14 3RA	01449 673460
IPSWICH ATHLETIC	Bourne Vale Social Ground, Halifax Road, Ipswich IP2 8RE	01473 687685
IPSWICH EXILES	Rushmere Sports Club, The Street, Rushmere St Andrew IP5 1DE	01473 272525
IPSWICH VALLEY RANGERS	Rock Barracks, Sutton Heath, Woodbridge IP12 3LU	None
LEISTON ST MARGARETS	Junction Meadow, Abbey Road, Leiston IP16 4RD	01728 831239
MELTON ST AUDRYS	St Audrys Sports & Social Club, Lodge Farm Lane, Melton, Woodbridge IP12 1LX	None
OLD NEWTON UNITED	Church Road, Old Newton, Stowmarket IP14 4ED	01449 770035
STANTON	Stanton Recreation Ground, Old Bury Road, Stanton, Bury St Edmunds IP31 2BX	None
WICKHAM MARKET	The Playing Field, Wickham Market IP13 0HE	01728 747303

SUFFOLK & IPSWICH LEAGUE - STEP 7

DIVISION ONE

		P	W	D	L	F	A	Pts
1	Coplestonians	26	17	4	5	65	31	55
2	Ipswich Exiles	26	18	1	7	69	45	55
3	Wenhaston United	26	17	3	6	80	29	54
4	Westerfield United	26	16	5	5	73	30	53
5	BT Trimley	26	16	4	6	45	21	52
6	Trimley Red Devils	26	14	3	9	61	42	45
7	Mendlesham	26	10	7	9	46	54	37
8	St Johns	26	10	3	13	45	70	33
9	Henley Athletic	26	9	3	14	34	45	30
10	Bramford United	26	7	4	15	54	74	25
11	Saxmundham Sports	26	7	4	15	34	62	25
12	Cockfield United	26	6	3	17	40	79	21
13	Thurston	26	4	7	15	44	72	19
14	Stonham Aspal	26	3	5	18	33	69	14

INTERMEDIATE DIVISION A

		P	W	D	L	F	A	Pts
1	Crane Sports Reserves	26	21	1	4	82	28	64
2	Grundisburgh Reserves	26	17	5	4	78	39	56
3	Ipswich Athletic Reserves (-1)	26	17	3	6	92	49	53
4	Achilles Res	26	15	4	7	80	73	49
5	Coplestonians Res	26	12	6	8	70	47	42
6	East Bergholt United Res	26	11	6	9	61	48	39
7	Melton St Audrys Res	26	12	2	12	69	48	38
8	Ransomes Sports Res	26	10	4	12	61	60	34
9	Old Newton United Res	26	9	3	14	62	70	30
10	Woodbridge Athletic Res (-2)	26	10	2	14	47	70	30
11	Capel Plough Reserves (-1)	26	8	5	13	53	67	28
12	Westerfield United Res	26	8	4	14	44	64	28
13	Felixstowe United Res (-5)	26	5	4	17	37	85	14
14	Stanton Reserves (-1)	26	2	1	23	22	110	6

INTERMEDIATE DIVISION B

		P	W	D	L	F	A	Pts
1	Henley Athletic Reserves	28	20	6	2	109	35	66
2	Stonham Aspal Reserves	28	16	8	4	63	25	56
3	Haughley United Reserves	28	16	6	6	82	39	54
4	Trimley Red Devils Reserves	28	16	3	9	82	42	51
5	Wenhaston United Reserves	28	16	3	9	74	44	51
6	Wickham Market Res (-10)	28	18	4	6	78	38	48
7	Framlingham Town Res (-7)	28	16	3	9	80	53	44
8	Bramford United Reserves	28	12	4	12	66	64	40
9	Leiston St Margarets Res (-1)	28	10	5	13	56	49	34
10	Mendlesham Reserves	28	10	4	14	52	79	34
11	Ipswich Exiles Reserves (-1)	27	10	2	15	42	62	31
12	Saxmundham Sports Res (-1)	28	7	4	17	40	80	24
13	Thurston Reserves (-2)	27	6	3	18	37	102	19
14	BT Trimley Reserves (-2)	28	3	6	19	31	84	13
15	Cockfield United Res (-3)	28	1	3	24	30	126	3

DIVISION TWO

		P	W	D	L	F	A	Pts
1	AFC Crowley	26	19	4	3	62	27	61
2	Sporting 87	26	19	3	4	82	24	60
3	Bacton United 89	26	16	5	5	72	30	53
4	Claydon	26	15	2	9	71	43	47
5	Sproughton Sports (-3)	26	15	5	6	69	42	47
6	Parkside United	26	12	6	8	71	46	42
7	Bramford Road Old Boys	26	12	3	11	55	52	39
8	Benhall St Mary	26	10	3	13	62	48	33
9	Bildeston Rangers	26	9	4	13	46	80	31
10	Somersham	26	8	6	12	57	58	30
11	Salvation Army	26	7	8	11	45	52	29
12	Stowupland Falcons (-4)	26	7	8	11	38	45	25
13	Great Blakenham (-2)	26	4	1	21	22	98	11
14	Halesworth Town	26	0	0	26	13	120	0

DIVISION THREE

		P	W	D	L	F	A	Pts
1	Waterside	24	21	2	1	116	17	65
2	AFC Hoxne	24	17	6	1	102	31	57
3	Bacton United 89 Reserves	24	14	5	5	72	50	47
4	Coplestonians 'A'	24	13	4	7	59	43	43
5	Tacket Street BBOB	24	12	6	6	57	35	42
6	Walsham Le Willows 'A'	24	11	3	10	45	58	36
7	Willis	24	10	2	12	60	67	32
8	Coddenham	24	10	1	13	58	61	31
9	Elmswell	24	9	1	14	43	60	25
10	John Bull United	24	6	4	14	39	60	21
11	St Clements Hospital	24	5	1	18	30	98	16
12	Claydon Reserves	24	3	5	16	42	69	14
13	Tattingstone United	24	3	4	17	42	116	13

DIVISION FOUR

		P	W	D	L	F	A	Pts
1	Cedars Park	22	20	2	0	87	22	62
2	AFC Crowley Reserves	22	14	3	5	65	44	45
3	Aldeburgh Town	22	13	4	5	70	36	43
4	AFC Hoxne Reserves (-3)	22	15	0	7	78	46	42
5	Sporting 87 Reserves (-1)	21	10	8	3	44	32	37
6	Felixstowe Harpers	22	11	3	8	65	42	36
7	Stradbroke United	22	8	2	12	60	54	26
8	Sizewell Associates (-1)	21	7	0	14	43	68	20
9	Bramford Road O. B. Res (-1)	22	6	2	14	32	63	19
10	Ufford Sports	22	4	4	14	38	66	16
11	Stowupland Falcons Reserves	22	4	1	17	36	90	13
12	Woolverstone United (-3)	22	2	5	15	29	84	8

DIVISION FIVE

		P	W	D	L	F	A	Pts
1	Cedars Park Res	24	21	1	2	74	31	64
2	FC Adhara	24	19	3	2	95	29	60
3	Witnesham Wasps	24	13	2	9	63	40	41
4	Benhall St Mary Reserves (-2)	24	13	2	9	71	50	39
5	East Bergholt United 'A'	24	11	5	8	61	55	38
6	Coddenham Reserves (-1)	24	9	4	11	49	58	30
7	Salvation Army Res	24	8	4	12	56	64	28
8	Sproughton United	24	8	4	12	51	59	27
9	Dennington United (-1)	24	7	5	12	58	65	25
10	Stonham Aspal 'A'	24	6	7	11	34	69	25
11	Sproughton Sports Res (-3)	24	6	5	13	60	80	21
12	Elmswell Reserves (-2)	24	6	4	14	42	80	20
13	Shotley (-1)	24	4	4	16	61	95	15

DIVISION SIX

		P	W	D	L	F	A	Pts
1	Waterside Res	20	15	3	2	98	27	48
2	Aldeburgh Town Res	20	14	2	4	71	29	44
3	Witnesham Wasps Res	20	12	3	5	50	36	39
4	Kesgrave Kestrels	20	12	1	7	53	29	37
5	Somersham Res	20	11	4	5	56	50	37
6	Old Newton United 'A' (-4)	20	9	3	8	50	40	26
7	Willis Reserves (-2)	20	6	5	9	43	52	21
8	AFC Titans (-1)	20	6	2	12	33	62	19
9	Bacton United 89 'A'	20	4	5	11	35	56	17
10	Tattingstone United Res (-1)	20	4	2	14	38	82	13
11	Halesworth Town Res	20	0	4	16	21	85	4

SURREY ELITE INTERMEDIATE LEAGUE

Sponsored by: No Sponsor

Founded: 2008

Recent Champions:

2009: Eversley

2010: Epsom Eagles

2011: Spelthorne Sports

INTERMEDIATE LEAGUE CHALLENGE CUP

ROUND 1
AFC Cubo 1-3 Tooting Bec
Virginia Water 1-2 Farnborough North End
Epsom Athletic 4-3 Oxted & District
Horsley 1-1 Battersea Ironsides
(Horlsey won on penalties)
Abbey Rangers 1-2 Crescent Rovers
Bletchingley 1-2 Weston Green Sports
Reigate Priory 4-2 Ripley Village
Coulsdon Town 1-0 Old Farnboronians

QUARTER FINALS
Epsom Athletic 1-3 Coulsdon Town
Farnborough North End 0-9 Weston Green Sports
Reigate Priory 5-0 Tooting Bec
Horsley 4-1 Crescent Rovers

SEMI-FINALS
Reigate Priory 1-2 Horsley
Coulsdon Town 3-2 Weston Green Sports

FINAL
Horsley 0-1 Coulsdon Town

INTERMEDIATE DIVISION	P	W	D	L	F	A	Pts
1 Epsom Athletic	28	23	3	2	88	26	72
2 Horsley	28	21	2	5	66	33	65
3 Battersea Ironsides	28	16	5	7	46	29	53
4 Coulsdon Town	28	16	2	10	67	40	50
5 AFC Cubo	28	15	5	8	59	40	50
6 Old Farnboronians	28	13	8	7	52	37	47
7 Weston Green Sports	28	14	3	11	51	43	45
8 Reigate Priory	28	14	2	12	51	57	44
9 Ripley Village	28	11	6	11	61	60	39
10 Abbey Rangers	28	9	8	11	56	52	35
11 Oxted & District	28	8	4	16	37	58	28
12 Crescent Rovers	28	9	0	19	71	75	27
13 Tooting Bec	28	7	3	18	43	56	24
14 Virginia Water	28	5	5	18	41	77	20
15 Farnborough North End	28	1	0	27	17	123	3

INTERMEDIATE DIVISION	1	2	3	4	5	6	7	8	9	10	11	12	13	14	15
1 Abbey Rangers		0-0	2-1	0-2	5-4	0-2	7-1	1-2	2-1	1-3	1-4	0-2	2-1	3-3	4-1
2 AFC Cubo	2-2		2-1	2-0	1-3	3-5	6-0	0-2	1-0	3-0	1-2	2-2	1-0	3-2	1-1
3 Battersea Ironsides	3-1	3-1		3-1	2-1	2-1	3-1	0-1	0-0	3-0	4-2	1-1	2-1	1-1	1-0
4 Coulsdon Town	0-1	3-0	1-2		1-3	3-3	5-0	3-1	1-2	2-1	3-1	6-0	5-2	2-1	0-3
5 Crescent Rovers	3-5	2-3	1-2	1-3		1-4	7-2	1-3	1-2	1-2	2-4	4-1	4-0	2-0	3-4
6 Epsom Athletic	2-1	2-0	3-1	4-0	6-2		3-0	1-1	1-2	2-2	1-0	4-0	3-1	3-1	3-0
7 Farnborough North End	0-6	0-5	1-0	1-4	2-8	0-6		0-5	0-1	1-2	1-2	1-2	0-7	0-4	2-5
8 Horsley	3-2	2-0	3-1	0-2	2-1	1-4	3-1		2-0	1-0	2-0	3-1	2-1	0-0	2-3
9 Old Farnboronians	1-1	0-2	1-1	3-2	2-3	1-4	4-1	2-3		1-0	5-0	3-1	1-1	5-2	2-0
10 Oxted & District	2-2	2-5	0-1	0-3	0-5	0-4	5-0	2-4	1-1		0-1	1-1	2-1	4-1	2-5
11 Reigate Priory	2-1	1-2	2-1	2-8	4-2	0-6	7-0	1-3	0-0	2-1		0-2	1-2	2-2	1-4
12 Ripley Village	0-0	3-3	1-3	3-2	3-1	1-4	7-0	3-4	4-4	4-0	1-3		1-4	2-1	3-0
13 Tooting Bec	2-2	1-2	0-2	0-3	3-2	2-3	4-0	0-1	2-2	0-3	0-1	2-5		3-1	0-2
14 Virginia Water	5-4	1-6	0-0	1-2	4-2	0-2	5-2	0-9	0-4	1-2	1-4	1-5	0-1		1-4
15 Weston Green Sports	0-0	0-2	0-2	D-D	5-1	1-2	HW	3-1	1-2	2-0	1-2	3-2	3-2	0-2	

SURREY ELITE INTERMEDIATE LEAGUE INTERMEDIATE DIVISION CONSTITUTION 2012-13

AFC CUBO	Barn Elms Sports Ground, Queen Elizabeth Walk, Barnes SW13 0DG	None
ABBEY RANGERS	Addlestone Moor, Addlestone Moor Road, Addlestone KT15 2QH	01932 442962
BATTERSEA IRONSIDES	Battersea Ironsides S&S Club, Burntwood Lane, Earlsfield SW17 0AW	020 8874 9913
BOOKHAM	Dorking Road, Bookham KT23 4P	07824 884046
CLAYGATE & DITTON	Ewell Road, Long Ditton KT6 5L	07776 191481
COULSDON TOWN	Woodplace Lane, Coulsdon CR5 1NF	01737 557509
CRESCENT ROVERS	Wallington Sports/Social Club, Mollison Drive, Wallington SM6 9BY	020 8647 2558
HORSLEY	Toms Field, Long Reach, West Horsley KT24 6NE	01483 282516
OLD FARNBORONIANS	Cody S&S Club, Armstrong Way, The Fairway, Farnborough GU14 0LP	01252 543009
OXTED & DISTRICT	Master Park, Church Lane, Oxted RH8 9LD	01883 716001
REIGATE PRIORY	Reigate Priory Cricket Club, off Park Lane, Reigate RH2 8JX	01737 240872
RIPLEY VILLAGE	The Green, Ripley, Woking GU23 6AN	01483 225484
TOOTING BEC	Raynes Park Vale FC, Princes Georges PF,Grand Drive, Raynes Park SW20 9DZ	020 8540 8843
VIRGINIA WATER	The Timbers, Crown Road, Virginia Water GU25 4HS	01344 843811
WESTON GREEN SPORTS	Weston Green Sports Ground, Longmead Road, Thames Ditton KT7 0JF	07903 261206
YATELEY GREEN	Chandlers Lane, Yateley, Hampshire GU46 7S	07736 827258

WEARSIDE LEAGUE

Sponsored by: No Sponsor
Founded: 1892
Recent Champions:
2007: Birtley Town
2008: New Marske Sports Club
2009: Newton Aycliffe
2010: Ryhope Colliery Welfare
2011: Ryhope Colliery Welfare

LEAGUE CUP

SEMI-FINALS
Redcar Athletic 1-2 Stockton Town
Ryhope Colliery Welfare 3-0 Sunderland West End
FINAL
Stockton Town 0-2 Ryhope Colliery Welfare

MONKWEARMOUTH CHARITY CUP

SEMI-FINALS
Ashbrooke Bleford House 0-2 Ryhope Colliery Welfare
Boldon CA 6-3 Wolviston
FINAL
Ryhope Colliery Welfare 3-1 Boldon CA

SUNDERLAND SHIPOWNERS CUP

SEMI-FINALS
Redcar Athletic 3-1 Peterlee Town
Ryhope Colliery Welfare 3-2 Annfield Plain
FINAL
Redcar Athletic 0-2 Ryhope Colliery Welfare

		P	W	D	L	F	A	Pts
1	Ryhope Colliery Welfare	36	30	5	1	136	30	95
2	Redcar Athletic	36	29	3	4	104	32	90
3	Stockton Town	36	22	6	8	74	46	72
4	Sunderland West End	36	23	2	11	81	56	71
5	Willington	36	20	5	11	72	63	65
6	Jarrow	36	17	9	10	83	62	60
7	Cleator Moor Celtic	36	17	6	13	76	55	57
8	Darlington Cleveland Bridge	36	15	8	13	65	69	53
9	Boldon CA	36	16	4	16	78	74	52
10	Peterlee Town	36	15	6	15	71	90	51
11	Ashbrooke Belford House	36	13	10	13	61	63	49
12	Hartlepool	36	15	2	19	69	80	47
13	Prudhoe Town	36	13	7	16	78	89	46
14	Wolviston	36	10	10	16	57	61	40
15	Annfield Plain	36	9	7	20	56	80	34
16	Gateshead Leam Rangers	36	8	3	25	46	91	27
17	Kirkbymoorside	36	7	4	25	50	100	25
18	Silksworth Rangers	36	6	4	26	38	98	22
19	Coxhoe Athletic	36	4	5	27	34	90	17

		1	2	3	4	5	6	7	8	9	10	11	12	13	14	15	16	17	18	19
1	Annfield Plain		0-3	2-3	1-5	4-0	0-2	2-1	2-3	2-2	1-1	2-5	0-2	1-1	0-5	5-0	1-3	1-3	1-1	2-2
2	Ashbrooke Belford House	2-0		1-1	2-1	4-2	1-1	0-0	2-4	1-3	2-0	2-2	1-4	0-4	1-2	3-2	2-1	0-1	2-2	2-3
3	Boldon CA	3-0	4-0		2-3	2-0	1-2	5-1	1-3	2-3	4-1	1-1	4-3	2-3	0-10	2-0	2-3	3-4	1-0	1-1
4	Cleator Moor Celtic	3-1	0-2	1-1		3-0	6-0	3-2	7-3	2-3	3-0	0-2	0-1	1-1	1-3	3-2	3-0	1-2	0-2	3-0
5	Coxhoe Athletic	1-1	3-1	0-2	1-2		0-1	0-1	1-4	1-7	2-0	2-4	1-4	0-1	3-3	2-0	0-1	0-1	1-1	2-2
6	Darlington Cleveland Bridge	5-1	1-5	0-5	4-1	2-0		3-1	1-0	1-2	3-3	2-2	4-0	1-2	0-7	2-0	1-2	2-0	5-0	0-6
7	Gateshead Leam Rangers	2-3	3-4	3-1	0-3	1-0	3-1		0-1	2-3	2-4	1-3	1-3	2-4	0-3	0-2	1-2	2-0	2-0	1-2
8	Hartlepool	2-3	1-3	1-5	1-0	4-2	2-1	0-2		3-1	5-1	0-2	1-3	0-4	0-2	2-1	0-2	4-1	2-3	1-1
9	Jarrow	1-1	2-2	3-2	0-0	5-2	3-2	2-2	2-2		1-0	2-0	2-0	2-3	2-5	4-1	0-1	2-3	1-1	0-0
10	Kirkbymoorside	1-3	2-3	0-3	4-4	2-1	1-3	2-0	1-0	1-3		2-1	5-1	1-2	2-3	0-0	2-3	2-0	0-1	
11	Peterlee Town	0-6	2-2	0-1	0-3	4-1	2-0	5-2	3-2	2-6	5-2		4-3	1-5	1-7	5-2	0-1	5-4	1-3	1-0
12	Prudhoe Town	2-0	1-1	3-4	2-3	4-0	2-2	8-3	3-5	6-4	1-0	1-1		0-2	3-4	5-4	0-3	3-3	0-4	1-1
13	Redcar Athletic	3-1	2-0	2-0	2-0	4-2	3-3	3-0	3-0	2-1	6-0	6-0	8-1		0-1	5-1	1-2	3-2	0-1	3-1
14	Ryhope CW	3-2	1-1	8-1	3-2	4-0	2-2	5-0	3-1	1-1	8-0	5-0	5-1	1-3		4-0	3-0	3-0	3-0	3-1
15	Silksworth Rangers	0-2	3-3	1-0	1-1	2-0	1-1	1-4	0-2	2-6	1-8	1-0	1-0	0-3	0-4		1-2	0-1	1-3	0-2
16	Stockton Town	2-3	2-0	4-2	4-4	4-0	0-0	3-1	4-1	3-2	6-2	4-0	1-1	0-2	1-1	3-1		1-2	4-3	2-0
17	Sunderland West End	1-0	1-0	3-5	2-3	0-1	5-1	5-0	3-1	2-0	5-0	6-2	2-0	3-1	0-3	2-1	1-1		2-3	2-1
18	Willington	4-1	1-0	2-1	2-1	3-1	3-2	1-2	5-4	1-0	4-1	1-3	3-3	0-4	0-5	6-1	1-0	0-3		4-3
19	Wolviston	3-1	1-3	2-1	0-2	2-2	0-1	1-1	3-0	1-2	3-0	2-2	2-3	1-3	3-4	1-1	4-2	1-3	0-4	

WEARSIDE LEAGUE CONSTITUTION 2012-13

ANNFIELD PLAIN	Derwent Park , West Road , Annfield Plain DH9 8PZ	07833 366056
ASHBROOKE BELFORD HOUSE	Silksworth Park, Blind Lane, Silksworth, Sunderland SR3 1AX	07505 503873
BOLDON COMMUNITY ASSOCIATION	Boldon Welfare, New Road, Boldon Colliery NE35 9DS	0191 536 4180 (Cricket Club)
CLEATOR MOOR CELTIC	Celtic Club, Birks Road, Cleator Moor CA25 5HR	01946 812476
COXHOE ATHLETIC	Beechfield Park, Coxhoe DH6 4SD	07956 159916
DARLINGTON CLEVELAND BRIDGE	Eastbourne Sports Complex, Bourne Avenue, Darlington DL1 1LJ	01325 243177/243188
EASINGTON COLLIERY AFC	Easington Welfare Park SR8 3JJ	07720 611905
GATESHEAD LEAM RANGERS	Dawdon Welfare Park, Green Drive, Dawdon, Seaham SR7 7XL	07859 0066432
HARTLEPOOL	Grayfields Enclose, Jesmond Gardens, Hartlepool TS24 8QS	01429 299428
HARTON AND WESTOE	Harton Colliery Welfare, Boldon Lane. NE34 ONA	07847 271495
JARROW	Perth Green Community Assoc., Inverness Road, Jarrow NE32 4AQ	0191 489 3743
KIRKBYMOORSIDE	Kirkby Mills, Kirkbymoorside, York YO62 6NS	01751 431752
PETERLEE TOWN	Eden Lane Playing Fields, Peterlee SR8 5DS	0191 586 3004
PRUDHOE TOWN	Kimberley Park, Broomhouse Road, Prudhoe NE42 5EH	01661 835900
REDCAR ATHLETIC	Green Lane, Redcar TS10 3RW	07854 935380
RICHMOND TOWN	Earls Orchard Playing Field. DL10 4RH	07970 789526
SEATON CAREW	Hornby Park, Elizabeth Way, Seaton Carew. TS25 2AZ	07877 077515
SILKSWORTH RANGERS	Silksworth Park, Blind Lane, Silksworth, Sunderland SR3 1AX	07423 014566
STOCKTON TOWN	Bishopton Road West, Stockton-on-Tees TS19 0QD	07832 967008
SUNDERLAND WEST END	Ford Quarry, Keelmans Lane, Pennywell, Sunderland	07812 439248
WILLINGTON	Hall Lane Ground, Hall Lane Estate, Willington DL15 0QF	01388 746221
WOLVISTON	Metcalfe Park, Wynyard Road, Wolviston, Billingham TS22 5NE	07768 321651

WEST CHESHIRE LEAGUE

Sponsored by: Carlsberg
Founded: 1892
Recent Champions:
2007: West Kirby
2008: West Kirby
2009: West Kirby
2010: Cammell Laird Reserves
2011: West Kirby

PYKE CUP

ROUND 1
West Kirby 0-1 Ellesmere Port
ROUND 2
Upton A.A. 2-3 Marshalls
Mossley Hill Athletic 3-4 Ellesmere Port
Willaston 0-1 Chester Nomads
Christleton 1-2 Ashville
Vauxhall Motor Reserves 2-1 Heswall
Newton 1-2 Marine Reserves
Maghull 2-0 Southport Trinity
Cammell Laird Reserves 6-4 Blacon Youth Club
QUARTER FINALS
Marshalls 1-2 Ellesmere Port
Chester Nomads 0-2 Ashville
Vauxhall Motors Reserves 5-4 Marine Reserves
Maghull 2-1 Cammell Laird Reserves
SEMI-FINALS
Ellesmere Port 2-1 Ashville
Vauxhall Motors Reserves 0-3 Maghull
FINAL
Ellesmere 0-3 Maghull

DIVISION ONE

		P	W	D	L	F	A	Pts
1	Ashville (-3)	32	23	4	5	95	30	70
2	Marine Reserves	32	17	6	9	64	45	57
3	Heswall	32	16	4	12	56	44	52
4	Maghull	32	15	6	11	51	32	51
5	Chester Nomads	32	14	9	9	59	44	51
6	West Kirby	32	15	5	12	62	60	50
7	Newton	32	14	5	13	66	56	47
8	Vauxhall Motors Reserves	32	14	4	14	63	63	46
9	Mossley Hill Athletic	32	12	9	11	56	51	45
10	Christleton	32	11	10	11	42	38	43
11	Southport Trinity	32	13	4	15	56	67	43
12	Upton AA	32	10	9	13	46	62	39
13	Ellesmere Port	32	10	8	14	37	70	38
14	Blacon Youth Club	32	10	7	15	46	75	37
15	Cammell Laird Reserves	32	8	11	13	62	64	35
16	Marshalls	32	6	9	17	49	68	27
17	Willaston	32	6	6	20	39	80	24

W H WEIGHT MEMORIAL CUP
(Divisional Champions and Pyke Cup Winners)

FINAL
Runcorn Linnets Reserves 0-2 Ashville

DIVISION ONE		1	2	3	4	5	6	7	8	9	10	11	12	13	14	15	16	17
1	Ashville		5-0	1-0	2-3	3-1	8-0	3-0	1-2	1-3	5-0	2-1	3-2	2-0	6-0	1-2	6-0	4-1
2	Blacon Youth Club	2-5		3-1	1-1	1-1	0-0	1-3	0-5	0-1	2-2	1-1	3-1	5-3	2-2	0-1	2-2	2-1
3	Cammell Laird Reserves	2-2	4-2		0-0	1-0	3-4	1-1	0-1	3-3	2-2	2-2	1-1	1-2	9-1	2-3	1-4	2-2
4	Chester Nomads	3-2	2-3	5-2		1-1	5-0	2-2	2-0	3-1	4-1	0-1	2-1	2-0	2-2	3-1	3-3	0-1
5	Christleton	0-1	0-1	0-0	1-0		2-2	0-1	0-3	1-0	1-1	3-1	4-3	0-1	2-0	2-1	2-1	
6	Ellesmere Port	0-2	2-1	2-1	1-0	1-1		0-3	1-0	1-0	1-1	0-0	0-2	3-1	2-0	0-0	1-2	2-2
7	Heswall	0-2	3-1	1-3	0-1	2-3	4-2		2-0	0-4	2-0	2-0	1-0	1-2	1-0	6-1	3-0	4-1
8	Maghull	0-0	4-0	3-0	2-1	2-2	0-0	0-2		1-1	4-0	2-2	2-3	1-0	1-1	4-2	0-2	3-1
9	Marine Reserves	1-1	4-0	4-3	0-3	3-2	4-1	4-0	0-2		1-4	1-1	2-0	3-2	1-2	4-0	4-0	2-0
10	Marshalls	1-2	1-3	3-4	1-1	1-1	4-2	0-1	1-1		1-0	1-5	3-1	1-2	1-1	3-2	8-0	
11	Mossley Hill Athletic	2-3	0-1	2-2	1-2	2-0	4-1	0-3	2-1	4-0	2-2		4-1	1-2	4-1	0-1	4-3	2-6
12	Newton	1-1	5-1	0-3	1-1	1-4	3-1	1-1	1-0	3-0	4-0	1-3		4-0	3-2	3-0	2-2	3-1
13	Southport Trinity	0-6	2-3	3-1	3-2	0-2	3-1	2-2	1-0	1-1	5-2	3-3	3-2		1-3	2-3	5-1	1-0
14	Upton Athletic Association	1-5	1-2	0-0	1-1	0-0	4-2	2-0	1-5	0-1	2-1	1-3	3-0	1-1		4-0	0-1	0-0
15	Vauxhall Motors Reserves	1-3	3-1	3-4	5-1	2-2	11-2	1-3	2-0	3-0	1-0	0-1	5-2	1-2	3-1		2-4	1-0
16	West Kirby	0-3	6-1	3-2	3-0	1-0	1-2	1-0	1-0	2-3	2-1	5-0	1-3	1-2	3-3	2-1		2-0
17	Willaston	1-4	3-1	1-2	1-3	0-4	1-0	2-1	1-4	1-4	2-2	0-3	2-6	2-0	1-4	3-3	1-1	

WEST CHESHIRE LEAGUE DIVISION ONE CONSTITUTION 2012-13

ASHVILLE	Villa Park, Cross Lane, Wallasey Village, Wallasey CH45 8RH	0151 638 2127
BLACON YOUTH CLUB	Cairns Crescent Playing Fields, Blacon, Chester CH1 5JF	None
CAMMELL LAIRD RESERVES	Kirklands, St Peters Road, Rock Ferry, Birkenhead CH42 1PY	0151 645 3121
CHESTER NOMADS	Garrison Ground, Eaton Road, Chester CH4 7ER	None
CHRISTLETON	Little Heath Road, Christleton, Chester CH3 7AH	01244 336589
ELLESMERE PORT	Whitby Sports & Social Club, Chester Road, Whitby, Ellesmere Port CH66 2NX	0151 200 7080/7050
HALE	Hale Park, The High Street, Hale Village, Liverpool L24 4AF	None
HESWALL	Gayton Park, Brimstage Road, Heswall CH60 1XG	0151 342 8172
MAGHULL	Old Hall Field, Hall Lane, Maghull L31 7BB	0151 526 7320
MARINE RESERVES	Arriva Stadium, College Road, Crosby, Liverpool L23 3AS	0151 924 1743
		Club: 0151 924 4046
MOSSLEY HILL ATHLETIC	Mossley Hill Athletic Club, Mossley Hill Road, Liverpool L18 8DX	0151 724 4377
NEWTON	Millcroft, Frankby Road, Greasby CH47 0NB	0151 677 8282
SOUTHPORT TRINITY	Rookery Sports Ground, Roe Lane, Southport PR9 7HR	01704 225841
UPTON ATHLETIC ASSOCIATION	Cheshire County S & S Club, Plas Newton Lane, Chester CH2 1PR	01244 318167
VAUXHALL MOTORS RESERVES	Vauxhall Sports Ground, Rivacre Road, Hooton, Ellesmere Port CH66 1NJ	0151 328 1114
		Club: 0151 327 2294
WEST KIRBY	Marine Park, Greenbank Road, West Kirby CH48 5HL	None

WEST CHESHIRE LEAGUE - STEP 7

DIVISION TWO

		P	W	D	L	F	A	Pts
1	Hale	27	18	3	6	82	56	57
2	Ashville Reserves	28	18	3	7	68	32	57
3	New Brighton	27	16	5	6	58	42	53
4	Prescot Cables Reserves	28	16	4	8	54	44	52
5	AFC Bebington Athletic	28	15	6	7	56	43	51
6	Manor Athletic	28	13	8	7	55	46	47
7	Capenhurst Villa	27	12	8	7	55	39	44
8	Runcorn Linnets Reserves	27	11	5	11	70	58	38
9	Mallaby	27	11	2	14	51	63	35
10	Maghull Reserves	27	7	7	13	43	54	28
11	Bronze Social (-3)	22	8	3	11	41	51	24
12	Richmond Raith Rovers (-3)	27	6	8	13	52	67	23
13	Heswell Reserves	28	4	6	18	37	66	18
14	West Kirby Reserves (-6)	28	6	4	18	45	71	16
15	Marshalls Reserves (-3)	27	4	4	19	38	73	13

DIVISION THREE

		P	W	D	L	F	A	Pts
1	South Liverpool	30	26	2	2	107	26	80
2	Helsby	30	22	5	3	114	30	71
3	Mossley Hill Athletic Reserves	30	17	7	6	80	49	58
4	Mersey Royal	30	13	7	10	58	45	46
5	New Brighton Reserves	30	12	10	8	69	57	46
6	Chester Nomads Reserves	30	13	6	11	66	57	45
7	Merseyside Police	30	12	5	13	57	65	41
8	Belfry	30	13	2	15	75	85	41
9	Christleton Reserves	30	11	7	12	66	61	40
10	Upton AA Reserves	30	10	7	13	54	73	37
11	AFC Bebington Athletic Res.	30	11	3	16	54	67	36
12	Capenhurst Villa Reserves	30	9	6	15	48	63	33
13	Manor Athletic Reserves	30	6	11	13	47	60	29
14	Ellesmere Port Reserves	30	8	4	18	50	88	28
15	Neston Nomads	30	9	1	20	47	93	28
16	Hale Reserves	30	4	5	21	40	113	17

WEST CHESHIRE LEAGUE DIVISION TWO CONSTITUTION 2012-13

AFC BEBINGTON ATHLETIC	Unilever Sports Ground, , Bromborough CH62 3PU	None
ASHVILLE RESERVES	Villa Park, Cross Lane, Wallasey Village, Wallasey CH45 8RH	0151 638 2127
CAPENHURST VILLA	Capenhurst Sports Ground, Capenhurst Lane, Capenhurst CH1 6ER	None
HELSBY	Helsby Community Sports Club, Chester Road, Helsby WA6 0DL	01928 722267
HESWALL RESERVES	Gayton Park, Brimstage Road, Heswall CH60 1XG	0151 342 8172
MAGHULL RESERVES	Old Hall Field, Hall Lane, Maghull L31 7BB	0151 526 7320
MALLABY	Unilever Sports Ground, Bromborough CH62 3PU	None
MANOR ATHLETIC	OC Sports & Leisure Club, 28 Bridle Road, Bromborough CH62 6AR	0151 356 6159
MARSHALLS	IM Marsh Campus, Barkhill Road, Aigburth, Liverpool L17 6BD	0151 231 5233
MERSEY ROYAL	Unilever Sports Ground, Bromborough CH62 3PU	None
MOSSLEY HILL ATHLETIC RESERVES	Mossley Hill Athletic Club, Mossley Hill Road, Liverpool L18 8DX	0151 724 4377
PRESCOT CABLES RESERVES	St Helens Sports College, Elton Head Road, Lea Green, St Helens WA9 5AU	01744 678859
RICHMOND RAITH ROVERS	Childwall Sports College, Queens Drive, Fiveways L15 6XZ	0151 722 1561
SOUTH LIVERPOOL	Jericho Lane, Aigburth, Liverpool L17 5AR	None
WEST KIRBY RESERVES	Marine Park, Greenbank Road, West Kirby CH48 5HL	None
WILLASTON	Johnston Recreation Ground, Neston Road, Willaston CH64 2TL	None

WEST CHESHIRE LEAGUE DIVISION THREE CONSTITUTION 2012-13

AFC BEBINGTON ATHLETIC RES.	Unilever Sports Ground, , Bromborough CH62 3PU	None
BELFRY	Hillside School, Breeze Hill, Bootle L20 9NU	
CAPENHURST VILLA RESERVES	Capenhurst Sports Ground, Capenhurst Lane, Capenhurst CH1 6ER	None
CHESTER NOMADS RESERVES	Garrison Ground, Eaton Road, Chester CH4 7ER	None
CHRISTLETON RESERVES	Little Heath Road, Christleton, Chester CH3 7AH	01244 336589
ELLESMERE PORT RESERVES	Whitby Sports & Social Club, Chester Road, Whitby, Ellesmere Port CH66 2NX	0151 200 7080/7050
GATEACRE	Gateacre School, Hedgefield Road, Liverpool L25 2RW	None
HALE RESERVES	Hale Park, The High Street, Hale Village, Liverpool L24 4AF	None
MANOR ATHLETIC RESERVES	OC Sports & Leisure Club, 28 Bridle Road, Bromborough CH62 6AR	0151 356 6159
MARSHALLS RESERVES	IM Marsh Campus, Barkhill Road, Aigburth, Liverpool L17 6BD	0151 231 5233
MERSEYSIDE POLICE	Riversdale Road, Aigburth, Liverpool L19 3QN	0151 724 5214
NESTON NOMADS	Neston Recreation Centre, Neston CH64 9NQ	None
SOUTH LIVERPOOL RESERVES	Jericho Lane, Aigburth, Liverpool L17 5AR	None
UPTON ATHLETIC ASSOCIATION RES.	Cheshire County S & S Club, Plas Newton Lane, Chester CH2 1PR	01244 318167
WIDNES TOWN	Stobart Stadium Halton, Lowerhouse Lane,, Widnes, Cheshire WA8 7DZ	0151 495 2250

WEST LANCASHIRE LEAGUE

Sponsored by: Bay Radio

Founded: 1904

Recent Champions:

2007: Kirkham & Wesham

2008: Garstang

2009: Charnock Richard

2010: Blackpool Wren Rovers

2011: Blackpool Wren Rovers

PREMIER DIVISION	P	W	D	L	F	A	Pts
1 Charnock Richard	30	18	8	4	84	34	62
2 Blackpool Wren Rovers	30	17	6	7	61	35	57
3 Euxton Villa	30	17	3	10	67	46	54
4 Eagley	30	16	5	9	67	46	53
5 Burnley United	30	16	3	11	58	40	51
6 Coppull United	30	15	5	10	58	48	50
7 Lostock St. Gerards	30	13	9	8	51	51	48
8 Thornton Cleveleys	30	12	7	11	43	34	43
9 Poulton Town	30	11	10	9	56	50	43
10 Vickerstown	30	12	6	12	47	49	42
11 Fulwood Amateurs	30	11	6	13	46	54	39
12 Slyne With Hest	30	8	6	16	36	60	30
13 Fleetwood Hesketh	30	7	5	18	55	81	26
14 Tempest United	30	5	9	16	60	89	24
15 Stonecleough	30	6	6	18	40	80	24
16 Garstang	30	3	12	15	30	62	21

PREMIER DIVISION	1	2	3	4	5	6	7	8	9	10	11	12	13	14	15	16
1 Blackpool Wren Rovers		2-1	1-1	3-0	0-3	2-1	0-4	1-2	4-0	5-3	2-2	4-0	3-0	2-2	0-0	2-1
2 Burnley United	0-1		1-0	1-0	1-1	0-1	3-1	4-0	0-1	4-0	5-1	1-2	3-4	2-3	0-4	1-0
3 Charnock Richard	3-1	2-3		2-0	3-0	4-2	4-0	2-1	3-1	2-2	2-0	4-1	4-0	11-1	2-2	1-1
4 Coppull United	1-4	1-3	1-5		2-3	0-1	2-0	1-1	3-1	3-2	1-2	3-0	3-2	5-1	0-0	2-0
5 Eagley	0-1	0-1	3-5	2-0		1-6	5-0	0-2	2-2	6-0	1-1	1-0	3-0	2-2	1-2	0-1
6 Euxtton Villa	1-0	3-5	2-1	1-3	0-4		4-2	3-1	1-1	3-4	1-0	1-3	3-0	6-2	5-0	3-0
7 Fleetwood Hesketh	2-3	0-4	0-7	1-2	1-4	3-1		7-2	5-0	0-0	2-3	1-0	5-1	4-5	1-1	1-3
8 Fulwood Amateurs	1-2	2-3	1-1	0-2	0-1	2-1	4-1		0-0	3-3	0-2	2-0	1-0	2-1		2-4
9 Garstang	0-4	2-1	1-1	0-1	1-2	1-4	2-2	1-1		0-1	0-1	3-1	1-1	2-2	0-5	0-1
10 Lostock St Gerards	2-1	0-3	1-3	3-5	2-2	0-0	3-1	2-2	4-1		1-1	0-0	4-2	1-0	2-0	1-0
11 Poulton Town	0-5	1-1	3-1	1-1	4-5	2-3	0-0	4-0	2-2	1-2		2-0	4-0	2-2	0-2	3-1
12 Slyne With Hest	1-0	1-1	2-3	1-5	2-5	0-3	2-4	2-4	2-2	2-1	1-1		2-0	2-2	0-2	1-2
13 Stonecleough	1-4	1-2	0-3	2-2	2-3	2-3	2-2	1-3	4-2	0-0	4-2	0-0		2-1	3-2	0-5
14 Tempest United	2-2	3-1	2-3	1-3	2-3	1-1	6-3	4-2	3-3	4-4	2-4	2-3	3-4		1-3	0-3
15 Thornton Cleveleys	0-1	2-0	0-0	4-5	0-2	2-0	2-1	0-1	1-0	0-1	0-1	2-0	1-1	3-0		1-3
16 Vick	1-1	1-3	1-1	1-1	3-2	0-3	6-1	0-4	0-0	0-4	0-5	1-3	5-1	2-1	1-1	

WEST LANCASHIRE LEAGUE PREMIER DIVISION CONSTITUTION 2012-13

BLACKPOOL WREN ROVERS	Bruce Park, School Road, Marton, Blackpool FY4 5DX	01253 349853
BURNLEY UNITED	Barden Sports Ground, Barden Lane, Burnley BB10 1JQ	01282 437943
CHARNOCK RICHARD	Mossie Park, Charter Lane, Charnock Richard, Chorley PR7 5LZ	01257 794288
COPPULL UNITED	Springfield Road, Coppull PR7 5EJ	01257 795190
CROOKLANDS CASUALS	Longlands Park, Greystone Lane, Dalton-in-Furness LA15 8JF	01229 465010
EAGLEY	Eagley Sports Complex, Dunscar Bridge, Bolton BL7 9PQ	01204 306830
EUXTON VILLA	Jim Fowler Memorial Ground, Runshaw Hall Lane, Euxton, Chorley PR7 6HH	07778 678221
FLEETWOOD HESKETH	Fylde Road, Southport PR9 9XH	01704 227968
FULWOOD AMATEURS	Lightfoot Lane, Fulwood, Preston PR2 3LP	01772 861827
LONGRIDGE TOWN	Inglewhite Road, Longridge, Preston PR3 2NA	01772 782044
LOSTOCK ST GERARDS	Wateringpool Lane, Lostock Hall, Preston PR5 5UA	01772 610636
POULTON TOWN	Cottam Hall Playing Fields, Blackpool Old Road, Poulton-le-Fylde FY6 7RH	01253 896150
SLYNE-WITH-HEST	Bottomdale Road, Slyne, Lancaster LA2 6BG	07770851787
TEMPEST UNITED	Tempest Road, Chew Moor Village, Lostock, Bolton BL6 4HP	01942 811938
THORNTON CLEVELEYS	Bourne Road, Cleveleys, Thornton Cleveleys FY5 4QA	01253 869666
VICKERSTOWN CC	Park Vale, Mill Lane, Walney, Barrow-in-Furness LA14 3NB	07974 007901

WEST LANCASHIRE LEAGUE - STEP 7

DIVISION ONE		P	W	D	L	F	A	Pts
1	Longridge Town	26	18	5	3	91	35	59
2	Crooklands Casuals	26	16	6	4	62	43	54
3	Dalton United	26	16	5	5	76	49	53
4	Norcross & Warbreck	26	15	5	6	59	29	50
5	Hesketh Bank	26	16	1	9	60	52	49
6	Lytham Town	26	12	3	11	68	53	39
7	Bac/Ee/Springfields	26	11	6	9	59	61	39
8	Hawcoat Park	26	7	6	13	43	55	27
9	Wyre Villa	26	8	3	15	53	71	27
10	Furness Rovers	26	7	5	14	35	46	26
11	Haslingden St.Mary`s	26	7	5	14	41	61	26
12	Turton	26	7	4	15	49	64	25
13	Millom	26	7	2	17	51	91	23
14	Mill Hill St. Peters	26	5	4	17	33	70	19

DIVISION ONE		1	2	3	4	5	6	7	8	9	10	11	12	13	14
1	Bac/Ee/Springfields		0-4	4-3	3-3	3-0	2-5	1-3	0-6	3-0	3-1	6-3	2-1	2-2	0-4
2	Crooklands Casuals	0-0		4-4	2-1	2-0	2-2	2-3	4-3	3-1	3-0	2-2	1-1	3-2	3-1
3	Dalton United	3-4	3-2		2-1	3-3	4-0	1-3	3-1	0-2	5-2	4-2	1-0	4-1	6-2
4	Furness Rovers	1-1	0-2	3-3		3-0	0-1	2-0	1-3	0-1	3-0	3-2	2-3	1-0	0-6
5	Haslingden St Mary's	4-2	0-1	1-4	3-2		2-1	0-2	1-3	0-1	4-1	3-4	0-5	2-3	3-3
6	Hawcoat Park	4-5	1-2	2-2	0-0	1-1		1-3	1-4	1-3	3-3	2-0	0-3	3-2	2-0
7	Hesketh Bank	1-3	2-3	1-3	3-2	1-2	2-0		1-4	4-1	3-2	5-3	1-0	1-1	4-2
8	Longridge Town	3-3	3-2	1-4	4-1	3-2	3-1	7-1		0-0	4-1	8-0	2-2	4-0	2-1
9	Lytham Town	0-4	7-1	2-3	2-0	1-3	1-2	0-3	1-1		2-2	10-2	3-5	4-5	5-1
10	Mill Hill St Peters	0-6	0-3	2-5	0-1	1-1	1-0	4-6	1-5	0-3		3-1	0-1	3-2	1-0
11	Millom	2-1	1-2	4-1	0-3	5-5	3-2	3-2	3-5	1-4	2-1		1-2	1-0	2-3
12	Norcross & Warbreck	4-0	2-2	1-1	2-1	4-0	3-2	1-2	0-0	5-1	0-2	1-0		5-0	4-2
13	Turton	3-0	2-3	0-2	0-0	0-1	1-1	3-1	0-9	3-4	2-0	8-3	1-3		7-1
14	Wyre Villa	1-1	2-4	1-2	3-1	2-0	3-5	1-2	1-3	1-9	2-2	5-1	2-1	3-1	

WEST LANCASHIRE LEAGUE DIVISION ONE CONSTITUTION 2012-13

AMBLESIDE UNITED	Hillard Park, Vicarage Road, Ambleside LA22 0EE	None
BAC/EE SPRINGFIELD	BAC Sports Ground, South Meadow Lane, Preston PR1 8JP	01772 464351
BURSCOUGH RICHMOND	Richmond Park, Junction Lane, Burscough L40 5SN	None
DALTON UNITED	Railway Meadow, Beckside Road, Dalton-in-Furness LA15 8DP	None
FURNESS ROVERS	Wilkie Road, Barrow-in-Furness LA14 5UG	None
GARSTANG	The Riverside, High Street, Garstang PR3 1EB	01995 601586
HASLINGDEN ST MARY'S	South Shore Street, Haslingden, Rossendale BB4 5DX	01706 221814
HAWCOAT PARK	Hawcoat Park Sports Ground, Hawcoat Lane, Barrow-in-Furness LA14 4HF	01229 825296
HESKETH BANK	Centenary Sports Ground, Station Road, Hesketh Bank PR4 6SR	None
LYTHAM TOWN	Lytham Academy, Ballam Road, Lytham St Annes FY8 4LE	01253 733873
MILL HILL ST PETERS	Queen Victoria Street, Mill Hill, Blackburn BB2 2RZ	None
MILLOM	Millom RL Club, Devonshire Road, Millom LA18 4PG	01229 772030
NORCROSS & WARBRECK	Anchorsholme Lane, Thornton Cleveleys, Blackpool FY5 3DA	01253 859836
STONECLOUGH	Brook Street, opposite Europa Business Park, Stoneclough, Kearsley, Bolton M26 1HE	None
TURTON	Thomasson Fold, Turton, Edgworth, Bolton BL7 0PD	None
WYRE VILLA	Hallgate Park, Stalmine Village, Poulton-le-Fylde FY6 0LB	01253 701468

DIVISION TWO	P	W	D	L	F	A	Pts
1 Ambleside United	24	16	6	2	104	40	54
2 Burscough Richmond	24	16	5	3	60	20	53
3 Kendal County	24	13	7	4	49	26	46
4 Askam United	24	11	7	6	48	35	40
5 Croston Sports	24	9	8	7	45	38	35
6 Todmorden Borough	24	9	8	7	44	43	35
7 Ladybridge	24	9	6	9	40	45	33
8 Milnthorpe Corinthians	24	8	7	9	44	50	31
9 Bolton County	24	6	7	11	38	54	25
10 Furness Cavaliers	24	6	6	12	29	51	24
11 Gsk Ulverston Rangers	24	7	2	15	43	65	23
12 Whinney Hill	24	5	3	16	31	58	18
13 Walney Island	24	3	4	17	35	85	13

DIVISION TWO	1	2	3	4	5	6	7	8	9	10	11	12	13
1 Ambleside United		4-2	1-1	2-0	2-2	3-1	6-0	4-2	7-1	3-3	2-3	12-4	8-2
2 Askam United	1-6		1-1	0-0	4-1	1-1	2-0	2-1	1-2	2-0	4-1	4-2	3-0
3 Bolton County	3-2	3-2		0-3	1-3	1-2	2-1	1-2	3-0	3-3	5-1	3-3	3-3
4 Burscough Richmond	2-2	2-2	2-0		2-0	2-0	11-1	1-1	1-2	3-2	4-1	3-1	4-0
5 Croston Sports	0-5	1-1	5-1	0-1		2-0	3-1	3-3	3-3	2-0	1-1	3-0	2-2
6 Furness Cavaliers	2-6	2-2	1-1	0-3	1-6		3-2	1-3	1-2	1-3	0-0	3-2	1-1
7 GSK Ulverston Rangers	5-7	2-4	8-2	0-3	1-2	1-4		1-0	1-0	2-2	1-2	5-0	0-1
8 Kendal County	2-2	2-2	2-1	0-3	1-1	2-0	2-0		2-1	3-0	1-1	3-0	3-0
9 Ladybridge	1-4	1-2	1-1	2-0	1-1	3-2	4-1	1-5		1-2	1-1	5-2	1-2
10 Milnthorpe Corinthians	0-6	0-3	1-0	0-2	3-2	0-1	2-2	0-0	1-1		4-3	8-2	1-3
11 Todmorden Borough	1-6	1-0	4-0	1-1	2-0	4-0	0-2	0-3	1-1	4-4		7-0	1-0
12 Walney Island	1-1	1-0	0-1	1-4	2-1	1-1	2-4	0-2	0-3	1-4	2-2		2-3
13 Whinney Hill	1-3	1-3	3-1	2-3	0-1	0-1	1-2	1-4	1-2	0-1	1-2	3-6	

WEST LANCASHIRE LEAGUE DIVISION TWO CONSTITUTION 2012-13

ASKAM UNITED	Duddon Road, James Street, Askam-in-Furness LA16 7AH	01229 464576
BARROW WANDERERS	Lesh Lane, Barrow in Furness LA13 9DY	07709 075577
BOLTON COUNTY	Radcliffe Road, Darcy Lever, Bolton BL3 1AN	None
CMB	CMB Sports Ground, Tempest Road, Lostock, Bolton BL6 4ER	07766 605677
CROSTON SPORTS	Old Emmanuel School, Westhead Road, Croston, Leyland PR26 9RR	01772 600261
FURNESS CAVALIERS	Rampside Road, Barrow-in-Furness LA13 0HN	None
GSK ULVERSTON RANGERS	off North Lonsdale Road, Ulverston LA12 9DZ	01229 582261
HURST GREEN	Hurst Green Memorial Hall, Avenue Road, Hurst Green BB7 9PB	07875 561879
KENDAL COUNTY	Netherfield Cricket Club, Parkside Road, Kendal LA9 7BL	01539 724051
LADYBRIDGE	Tempest Road, Lostock, Bolton BL6 4EP	None
LEYLAND UNITED	Leyland, Lancs PR26 4GU	07974 933820
MILNTHORPE CORINTHIANS	Strands Lane, Milnthorpe LA7 7AE	01539 562135
TODMORDEN BOROUGH	Bellholme, Warland, Rochdale Road, Todmorden OL14 6UH	None
WALNEY ISLAND	Tummerhill Play Flos, Ocean Road, Walney, Barrow-in-Furness LA14 3HN	None
WHINNEY HILL	Burnley Road, Clayton-le-Moors, Accrington BB5 5NF	None

WEST YORKSHIRE LEAGUE

Sponsored by: No sponsor
Founded: 1928
Recent Champions:
2007: Bardsey   2008: Carlton Athletic
2009: Knaresborough Town   2010: Bardsey
2011: Bardsey

PREMIER DIVISION

		P	W	D	L	F	A	Pts
1	Beeston St Anthony's	30	20	4	6	82	44	64
2	Bardsey	30	18	7	5	79	38	61
3	Knaresborough Town (-3)	30	19	5	6	65	38	59
4	Otley Town	30	15	6	9	55	46	51
5	Carlton Athletic	30	15	3	12	67	68	48
6	Field	30	14	5	11	73	63	47
7	Leeds City	30	14	4	12	59	49	46
8	Ripon City	30	12	5	13	47	57	41
9	Boroughbridge	30	12	3	15	51	54	39
10	Oxenhope Recreation	30	10	7	13	54	58	37
11	Wetherby Athletic (-1)	30	11	5	14	49	56	37
12	Whitkirk Wanderers	30	11	3	16	58	70	36
13	Pool	30	9	6	15	48	71	33
14	East End Park	30	8	4	18	39	62	28
15	Sherburn White Rose	30	8	8	16	37	52	26
16	Altofts	30	6	5	19	41	78	23

DIVISION ONE

		P	W	D	L	F	A	Pts
1	Rothwell	30	24	0	6	86	34	72
2	Brighouse Old Boys	30	23	2	5	67	38	71
3	Kippax	30	22	2	6	94	45	68
4	Robin Hood Athletic	30	17	5	8	67	46	56
5	Horbury Town	30	12	7	11	50	48	43
6	Wyke Wanderers	30	11	8	11	54	50	41
7	Ilkley Town	30	10	6	14	56	61	36
8	Swillington Saints	30	10	6	14	55	66	36
9	Old Headingley	30	9	8	13	57	57	35
10	Old Centralians	30	10	4	16	52	65	34
11	Baildon Trinity Athletic	30	10	3	17	48	81	33
12	Rothwell Athletic	30	8	8	14	53	61	32
13	FC RIASA (-9)	30	11	6	13	53	56	30
14	Mount St. Mary's	30	7	8	15	50	70	29
15	Kellingley Welfare	30	7	8	15	61	92	29
16	Aberford Albion	30	5	7	18	43	76	22

DIVISION TWO

		P	W	D	L	F	A	Pts
1	Shelley	30	26	1	3	144	39	79
2	Hunslet Club	30	24	3	3	108	38	75
3	Old Modernians	30	21	5	4	101	31	68
4	Stanley United (-6)	30	19	5	6	87	50	56
5	Rothwell Town	30	16	3	11	63	57	51
6	Glasshoughton Welfare Res.	30	14	7	9	73	63	49
7	Featherstone Colliery	30	13	8	9	101	65	47
8	Woodhouse Hill WMC	30	13	6	11	64	69	45
9	Howden Clough	30	12	4	14	59	99	40
10	Hartshead	30	10	6	14	62	71	36
11	Barwick	30	9	5	16	44	90	32
12	Nostell Miners Welfare Res.	30	8	5	17	55	76	29
13	Garforth Rangers	30	7	2	21	38	89	23
14	Ossett Common Rovers	30	6	3	21	50	78	21
15	Great Preston	30	3	3	24	29	112	12
16	Yorkshire Amateur Res. (-6)	30	4	4	22	29	80	10

LEAGUE CUP

ROUND 1
Stanley United 3-1 Hunslet Club
Ossett Common Rovers 0-2 (aet) Brighouse Old Boys
Howden Clough 3-0 Baildon Trinity Athletic
Robin Hood Athletic 5-2 Rothwell Town
Yorkshire Amateur 2-3 Barwick
Hartshead 2-4 Rothwell
Kellingley Welfare 0-0, 3-4p Old Headingley
Old Centralians 3-1 Garforth Rangers
Old Modernians 2-1 (aet) Horbury Town
Ilkley Town 1-2 Kippax
Rothwell Athletic 3-4 Shelley
Featherstone Colliery 3-0 Mount St. Mary's
Glasshoughton Welfare 2-1 Great Preston
Woodhouse Hill WMC 5-4 Swillington Saints
Wyke Wanderers 4-0 Aberford Albion
Nostell Miners Welfare 0-6 FC RIASA

ROUND 2
Stanley United 3-2 Wetherby Athletic
Brighouse Old Boys 7-2 Howden Clough
Pool 3-1 Ripon City
Robin Hood Athletic 1-4 Beeston St Anthony's
Field 1-0 Otley Town
Carlton Athletic 3-4 Oxenhope Recreation
Leeds City 1-2 Whitkirk Wanderers
Sherburn White Rose 3-0 Barwick
Rothwell 3-2 Old Headingley
Bardsey 4-0 Old Centralians
Old Modernians 2-1 Altofts
Kippax 4-2 Shelley
Featherstone Colliery 1-2 Glasshoughton Welfare
Knaresborough Town 4-0 Woodhouse Hill WMC
Wyke Wanderers 4-1 FC RIASA
Boroughbridge 3-0 East End Park

ROUND 3
Field 4-0 Oxenhope Recreation
Whitkirk Wanderers 0-1 Sherburn White Rose
Rothwell 0-5 Bardsey
Old Modernians 2-1 Kippax
Glasshoughton Welfare 1-2 Knaresborough Town
Wyke Wanderers 3-4 Boroughbridge

QUARTER-FINALS
Stanley United 0-1 (aet) Beeston St Anthony's
Field 4-1 Sherburn White Rose
Bardsey 5-2 Old Modernians
Knaresborough Town 1-2 Boroughbridge

SEMI-FINALS
Beeston St Anthony's 3-3, 9-10p Field
Bardsey 5-1 Boroughbridge

FINAL
Field 1-1, 2-3p Bardsey

LEAGUE TROPHY - FINAL
Bardsey Reserves 0-2 Knaresborough Town Reserves

PREMIER DIVISION

		1	2	3	4	5	6	7	8	9	10	11	12	13	14	15	16
1	Altofts		2-2	0-2	0-3	2-4	3-2	2-1	1-1	1-3	0-2	2-1	4-3	2-2	1-3	5-3	1-2
2	Bardsey	4-0		2-2	3-1	3-1	4-2	3-4	4-0	5-1	2-2	1-0	2-2	4-2	2-2	7-3	1-1
3	Beeston St Anthony's	7-2	2-1		2-3	8-0	2-1	3-2	2-2	4-1	1-0	1-0	6-1	3-1	3-1	0-1	3-3
4	Boroughbridge	2-0	0-3	6-2		1-2	0-2	2-0	1-1	1-1	2-4	4-1	2-3	1-3	1-5	2-0	3-0
5	Carlton Athletic	2-2	2-0	2-0	1-0		5-1	2-6	0-2	5-3	3-5	5-3	4-2	2-3	2-3	1-2	3-1
6	East End Park	2-0	1-8	0-1	2-1	2-3		3-1	4-1	0-1	0-1	2-1	0-1	2-2	3-2	0-0	2-3
7	Fields	4-2	0-0	3-2	2-3	2-5	5-0		2-3	0-5	2-0	2-1	2-3	1-2	5-2	3-0	5-3
8	Knaresborough Town	4-0	0-2	2-2	3-1	2-2	1-0	3-2		1-0	1-2	7-2	1-0	2-0	3-1	2-1	2-5
9	Leeds City	3-1	0-1	0-2	2-1	0-2	2-1	1-2	2-1		1-0	6-1	1-1	3-0	1-1	2-2	3-0
10	Otley Town	4-2	3-0	0-6	3-0	5-2	1-3	2-3	0-2	1-1		1-1	5-0	3-0	1-0	2-1	1-0
11	Oxenhope Recreation	1-1	2-3	2-4	0-1	2-3	4-1	4-1	1-2	3-1	1-1		3-2	1-1	0-0	2-1	1-3
12	Pool	1-0	1-4	0-3	2-1	1-2	1-1	3-3	0-4	5-3	2-2	0-2		2-0	3-2	0-2	2-3
13	Ripon City	3-0	0-3	2-4	1-0	2-1	1-0	2-2	0-4	0-4	0-1	2-3	4-2		3-1	2-0	1-2
14	Sherburn White Rose	2-1	2-0	1-2	0-1	1-1	2-2	1-2	1-2	3-2	1-1	0-0	1-1	0-1		0-1	3-0
15	Wetherby Athletic	5-2	0-1	0-3	3-3	2-0	2-0	1-1	0-3	3-1	4-1	0-1	3-4	1-1	4-1		3-0
16	Whitkirk Wanderers	0-2	0-4	5-0	4-2	2-0	1-2	1-4	0-3	0-2	3-4	2-2	2-0	3-4	2-0	6-1	

LEAGUE TABLES 2011-12

ACCRINGTON COMBINATION
ALDERSHOT & DISTRICT LEAGUE
ALTRINCHAM & DISTRICT LEAGUE
AMATEUR COMBINATION
ANDOVER & DISTRICT LEAGUE
ARMY FOOTBALL ASSOCIATION
ARTHURIAN LEAGUE
AYLESBURY & DISTRICT LEAGUE
BANBURY & LORD JERSEY FA
BASINGSTOKE & DISTRICT LEAGUE
BATH & DISTRICT LEAGUE
BECKETT LEAGUE
BIRMINGHAM AFA
BISHOP'S STORTFORD, STANSTED &
DISTRICT LEAGUE
BLACKBURN & DISTRICT
COMBINATION
BOSTON & DISTRICT LEAGUE
BOURNEMOUTH LEAGUE
BRIGHTON, HOVE & DISTRICT
LEAGUE
BRISTOL & AVON FOOTBALL LEAGUE
BRISTOL & DISTRICT LEAGUE
BRISTOL DOWNS LEAGUE
BRISTOL PREMIER COMBINATION
BRISTOL SUBURBAN LEAGUE
BURTON & DISTRICT FOOTBALL
ASSOCIATION
CAPITAL LEAGUE
CENTRAL & SOUTH NORFOLK
LEAGUE
CHELTENHAM ASSOCIATION LEAGUE
CHESTER & DISTRICT LEAGUE
CHORLEY & DISTRICT ALLIANCE
CIRENCESTER & DISTRICT LEAGUE
COLCHESTER & EAST ESSEX LEAGUE
CORNWALL COMBINATION
CRAVEN & DISTRICT LEAGUE
CREWE & DISTRICT LEAGUE
CROOK & DISTRICT LEAGUE
CUMBERLAND COUNTY LEAGUE
DEVON & EXETER LEAGUE
DONCASTER & DISTRICT SENIOR
LEAGUE
DORSET FOOTBALL LEAGUE
DRIFFIELD & DISTRICT LEAGUE
DUCHY LEAGUE
DURHAM FOOTBALL ALLIANCE
EAST BERKSHIRE LEAGUE
EAST CHESHIRE LEAGUE
EAST CORNWALL LEAGUE
EAST LANCASHIRE LEAGUE
EAST RIDING AMATEUR LEAGUE
EAST RIDING COUNTY LEAGUE
EAST SUSSEX LEAGUE
ENFIELD ALLIANCE
ESKVALE & CLEVELAND LEAGUE
ESSEX BUSINESS HOUSES LEAGUE

FURNESS PREMIER LEAGUE
GAINSBOROUGH & DISTRICT LEAGUE
GLOUCESTERSHIRE NORTHERN
SENIOR LEAGUE
GRANTHAM & DISTRICT LEAGUE
GRAVESEND LEAGUE
GREAT YARMOUTH & DISTRICT
LEAGUE
GRIMSBY & DISTRICT LEAGUE
GUERNSEY LEAGUE
GUILDFORD & WOKING ALLIANCE
HALIFAX & DISTRICT LEAGUE
HALSTEAD & DISTRICT LEAGUE
HAMPSHIRE LEAGUE 2004
HARROGATE & DISTRICT LEAGUE
HEREFORDSHIRE LEAGUE
HOPE VALLEY AMATEUR LEAGUE
HUDDERSFIELD & DISTRICT LEAGUE
HUDDERSFIELD & DISTRICT WORKS &
COMBINATION LEAGUE
I ZINGARI COMBINATION
ILFORD & DISTRICT LEAGUE
INTER LEAGUE COMPETITION
ISLE OF MAN SENIOR LEAGUE
ISLE OF WIGHT LEAGUE
JERSEY FOOTBALL COMBINATION
KIDDERMINSTER & DISTRICT LEAGUE
KINGSTON & DISTRICT LEAGUE
LANCASHIRE & CHESHIRE LEAGUE
LANCASHIRE AMATEUR LEAGUE
LANCASHIRE LEAGUE
LEEDS RED TRIANLE LEAGUE
LEICESTER & DISTRICT LEAGUE
LINCOLN & DISTRICT LEAGUE
LINCOLNSHIRE LEAGUE
LIVERPOOL CMS LEAGUE
LONDON COMMERCIAL LEAGUE
LOWESTOFT & DISTRICT LEAGUE
LUTON DISTRICT & SOUTH BEDS
LEAGUE
MAIDSTONE & DISTRICT LEAGUE
MID-ESSEX LEAGUE
MID-SOMERSET LEAGUE
MID-SUSSEX LEAGUE
MIDLAND REGIONAL ALLIANCE
NORTH & MID-HERTS LEAGUE
NORTH BUCKS & DISTRICT LEAGUE
NORTH DEVON LEAGUE
NORTH EAST NORFOLK LEAGUE
NORTH GLOUSCESTERSHIRE LEAGUE
NORTH LANCS & DISTRICT LEAGUE
NORTH LEICS LEAGUE
NORTH NORTHUMBERLAND LEAGUE
NORWICH & DISTRICT LEAGUE
NOTTS AMATEUR ALLIANCE
NOTTS SENIOR LEAGUE
PERRY STREET & DISTRICT
PLYMOUTH & WEST DEVON
COMBINATION

PORTSMOUTH LEAGUE
PRESTON & DISTRICT LEAGUE
REDDITCH & SOUTH WARWICKSHIRE
COMBINATION
REDHILL & DISTRICT LEAGUE
ROCHDALE ALLIANCE
SALISBURY & DISTRICT LEAGUE
SCUNTHORPE & DISTRICT
SELBY & DISTRICT LEAGUE
SEVENOAKS & DISTRICT LEAGUE
SHROPSHIRE COUNTY LEAGUE
SOUTH DEVON LEAGUE
SOUTH LONDON ALLIANCE
SOUTH WEST GLOUCESTERSHIRE
NORTHERN SENIOR LEAGUE
SOUTH YORKSHIRE AMATEUR
LEAGUE
SOUTHAMPTON FOOTBALL LEAGUE
SOUTHEND & DISTRICT LEAGUE
SOUTHEND BOROUGH COMBINATION
SOUTHERN AMATEUR LEAGUE
SOUTHPORT & DISTRICT LEAGUE
SPEN VALLEY & DISTRICT
STRATFORD ALLIANCE
STROUD & DISTRICT LEAGUE
SUBURBAN LEAGUE
SURREY ELITE INTERMEDIATE
LEAGUE
SURREY INTERMEDIATE (WEST)
SURREY SOUTH EASTERN
COMBINATION
SWINDON & DISTRICT LEAGUE
TAUNTON & DISTRICT LEAGUE
TEESSIDE LEAGUE
THANET & DISTRICT LEAGUE
TONBRIDGE & DISTRICT
TYNESIDE AMATEUR LEAGUE
WAKEFIELD & DISTRICT LEAGUE
WARRINGTON & DISTRICT LEAGUE
WEARSIDE
WEARSIDE COMBINATION
WENSLEYDALE LEAGUE
WEST END LEAGUE
WEST RIDING COUNTY AMATEUR
LEAGUE
WEST SUSSEX LEAGUE
WESTMORLAND
WIGAN & DISTRICT LEAGUE
WILTSHIRE LEAGUE
WIMBLEDON & DISTRICT LEAGUE
WITNEY & DISTRICT LEAGUE
WORCESTER & DISTRICT LEAGUE
WORTHING & DISTRICT LEAGUE
WYCOMBE & DISTRICT LEAGUE
YEOVIL & DISTRICT LEAGUE
YORK LEAGUE
YORKSHIRE AMATEUR LEAGUE

LEAGUE TABLES
ACCRINGTON COMBINATION

Division One

	P	W	D	L	F	A	Pts
Royal Oak	16	13	1	2	68	27	40
Crown Rovers	16	12	3	1	67	20	39
Park	16	10	1	5	57	26	31
Oswaldtwistle St Mary's 'A'	16	10	0	6	39	24	30
Hapton	16	6	2	8	44	57	20
Great Harwood Rovers (-3)	16	5	5	6	27	29	17
Arden Athletic F.C.	16	4	1	11	30	64	13
St Mary's Coll. OB	16	3	1	12	33	62	10
Whinney Hill Res	16	2	0	14	20	76	6

Division Two

	P	W	D	L	F	A	Pts
Victoria	20	14	2	4	73	35	44
Calderstones Utd	20	11	7	2	49	34	40
Coppice (-3)	20	11	4	5	50	31	34
The Commercial F.C.	20	10	3	7	63	44	33
Accrington Town	20	10	3	7	57	45	33
Burnley Road	20	9	5	6	51	42	32
Globe Bullough Park	20	8	3	9	53	60	27
Rishton Rovers	20	6	4	10	32	42	22
Lowmoor	20	5	1	14	36	72	16
AFC Burnley	20	5	0	15	35	66	15
Sydney Street WMC	20	4	2	14	31	59	14

ALDERSHOT & DISTRICT LEAGUE

Senior Division

	P	W	D	L	F	A	Pts
Bagshot (-3)	22	17	2	3	80	20	50
Shalford Social	22	14	5	3	60	34	47
Aldershot Spartans	22	14	4	4	64	44	46
Headley United	22	13	6	3	63	31	45
Hale Rovers	22	13	3	6	60	46	42
Frimley Select	22	11	2	9	55	46	35
Old Farboronians Res	22	8	4	10	58	56	28
Wrecclesham	22	8	3	11	57	55	27
Alton Athletic	22	6	3	13	48	71	21
West Meon & Warnford	22	5	4	13	28	48	19
Fleet Spurs Reserves	22	3	3	16	27	70	12
Hindhead Athletic	22	0	1	21	15	94	1

Division One

	P	W	D	L	F	A	Pts
West End Village	18	14	2	2	67	22	44
Sandhurst Sports (-3)	18	14	0	4	49	31	39
Eversley A	18	11	5	2	41	26	38
Fleet Spurs A	18	7	5	6	41	34	26
Letef Select	18	7	3	8	44	39	24
Wey Valley	18	6	5	7	38	36	23
Hartley Wintney A	18	4	5	9	38	59	17
South Farnborough	18	4	5	9	24	49	17
Farnham United	18	3	3	12	32	55	12
AFC Froyle	18	3	1	14	26	49	10

Division Two

	P	W	D	L	F	A	Pts
Headley Utd Res	18	16	1	1	65	12	49
Courtmoor	18	10	4	4	55	28	34
Alton United	18	10	1	7	46	36	31
Hawley	18	10	1	7	38	29	31
Wrecclesham Res	18	9	3	6	51	44	30
Lindford	18	7	3	8	33	30	24
Four Marks Res	18	7	2	9	39	42	23
Normandy	18	5	2	11	31	57	17
Hindhead Athletic Res	18	4	2	12	25	49	14
Shalford Social Res	18	2	1	15	20	76	7

Division Three

	P	W	D	L	F	A	Pts
BOSC United	14	13	0	1	52	18	39
Rushmoor Community	14	9	4	1	50	18	31
Ropley	14	7	2	5	48	34	23
West End Village Res	14	6	1	7	32	27	19
Fleet Spurs Vet	14	5	4	5	26	23	19
Yateley A	14	5	3	6	30	51	18
South Farnborough Res	14	3	1	10	33	54	10
Normandy Res	14	0	1	13	15	61	1

ALTRINCHAM & DISTRICT LEAGUE

Division One

	Pld	W	D	L	F	A	Pts
AFC Quarry (+2)	24	18	4	2	70	23	60
Atlantic	24	16	4	4	65	33	52
Sale Amatuers	24	13	7	4	52	33	46
Wilmslow Sports	24	14	3	7	67	31	45
Sale Rovers	24	12	4	8	47	36	40
Sale United	24	12	3	9	56	59	39
Sale Town (+2)	24	10	5	9	63	46	37
Knutsford Reserves (+2)	24	9	6	9	50	42	35
Egerton	24	5	6	13	36	57	21
Salford	24	5	4	15	47	79	19
Broadheath Central JFC(-4)	24	5	7	12	34	49	18
Kartel Sports	24	5	3	16	27	71	18
Old Altinchamians (+2)	24	2	4	18	34	89	12

Division Two

	Pld	W	D	L	F	A	Pts
Broadheath Central (+2)	20	15	2	3	74	23	49
Irlam "A"	20	14	4	2	63	25	46
Flixton Juniors	20	15	1	4	64	33	46
Swinton	20	12	4	4	54	32	40
Broadheath Central JFC R.	20	9	2	9	44	46	29
Baroni	20	8	2	10	48	50	26
Northenden Victoria	20	6	3	11	43	67	21
Styal "A"	20	6	2	12	48	69	20
Unicorn Athletic	20	4	3	13	37	73	15
Sale Town Reserves	20	3	2	15	35	62	11
APFC (-1)	20	1	9	10	28	58	11

PFC Academy -record expunged.
Cornishman United - record expunged.

AMATEUR COMBINATION

Premier Division	P	W	D	L	F	A	Pts
Old Minchendenians	18	12	3	3	53	27	39
Honorable Artillery Company	18	11	5	2	51	19	38
Albanian	18	9	4	5	43	33	31
Old Meadonians	18	8	6	4	37	28	30
Old Hamptonians	18	9	2	7	37	36	29
Old Parmiterians	18	8	2	8	30	25	26
Bealonians	18	6	2	10	23	40	20
Parkfield	18	6	1	11	23	36	19
UCL Academicals	18	5	0	13	25	43	15
Old Salvatorians	18	3	1	14	15	50	10

Senior One	P	W	D	L	F	A	Pts
Old Suttonians	20	16	2	2	72	25	50
Old Aloysians	20	15	3	2	55	18	48
Old Ignatians	20	12	3	5	51	30	39
Hale End Athletic	20	10	1	9	43	30	31
Economicals	20	9	1	10	55	61	28
Wood Green Old Boys	20	9	0	11	58	75	27
Old Belgravians	20	8	1	11	39	55	25
Enfield Old Grammarians	20	6	3	11	43	49	21
Southgate County	20	6	2	12	42	60	20
Sinjuns Grammarians	20	5	2	13	34	70	17
Old Uffingtonians	20	3	4	13	42	61	13

Senior Two	P	W	D	L	F	A	Pts
Honorable Artillery Company II	20	17	0	3	61	25	51
Dorkinians	20	15	4	1	53	23	49
Old Thorntonians	20	10	4	6	54	37	34
Old Tenisonians	20	7	7	6	40	45	28
Shene Old Grammarians	20	8	3	9	36	37	27
Latymer Old Boys	20	7	3	10	38	43	24
UCL Academicals II	20	5	8	7	30	32	23
Clapham Old Xaverians	20	7	2	11	37	48	23
Old Hamptonians II	20	5	5	10	29	52	20
Pegasus	20	4	3	13	31	47	15
Old Woodhouseians	20	4	3	13	32	52	15

Senior Three South	P	W	D	L	F	A	Pts
Kings Old Boys	20	14	3	3	59	27	45
Old Suttonians II	20	12	5	3	50	31	41
Old Meadonians II	20	12	2	6	41	30	38
Old Pauline	20	9	6	5	40	35	33
Old St Marys	20	7	5	8	35	45	26
Old Bromleians	20	7	3	10	48	45	24
Old Vaughanians	20	7	3	10	59	57	24
Chertsey Old Salesians	20	7	3	10	39	43	24
Old Isleworthians	20	7	3	10	45	62	24
Hampstead Heathens	20	5	1	14	30	51	16
Fulham Compton Old Boys	20	2	8	10	23	43	14

Senior Three North	P	W	D	L	F	A	PTS
Albanian II	18	12	2	4	50	22	38
Old Parmiterians II	18	9	3	6	43	36	30
Birkbeck College	18	7	6	5	30	26	27
Old Manorians	18	6	6	6	32	28	24
Old Salvatorians II	18	7	3	8	45	44	24
Mayfield Athletic	18	7	3	8	42	46	24
Bealonians II	18	7	3	8	37	43	24
Globe Rangers	18	6	5	7	36	43	23
Old Magdalenians	18	5	5	8	22	34	20
Old Minchendenians II	18	5	2	11	37	52	17

Intermediate South	P	W	D	L	F	A	PTS
Old Wokingians	20	14	5	1	57	12	47
Royal Bank of Scotland	20	12	6	2	71	38	42
John Fisher Old Boys	20	12	3	5	55	35	39
Old Meadonians III	20	10	4	6	47	38	34
Old Tiffinians	20	10	3	7	35	33	33
Wandsworth Borough	20	8	6	6	47	31	30
Economicals II	20	9	3	8	47	46	30
Old Pauline II	20	5	4	11	33	52	19
Old Guildfordians	20	4	5	11	37	46	17
Old Sedcopians	20	3	5	12	44	72	14
Old Hamptonians III (-3)	20	0	2	18	24	94	-1

Intermediate North	P	W	D	L	F	A	PTS
Lea Valley	22	16	2	4	80	33	50
Albanian III	22	15	3	4	63	33	48
Old Ignatians II	22	13	4	5	64	38	43
UCL Academicals III	22	13	4	5	60	36	43
Enfield Old Grammarians II	22	13	2	7	67	42	41
Leyton County Old Boys	22	11	3	8	56	43	36
Old Aloysians II	22	9	2	11	50	45	29
Old Salvatorians III	22	7	4	11	42	55	25
Old Buckwellians	22	8	1	13	38	67	25
Old Tollingtonians	22	5	3	14	34	57	18
Parkfield II	22	4	3	15	32	82	15
Hale End Athletic II	22	1	3	18	32	87	6

Division One South	P	W	D	L	F	A	PTS
Reigatians	20	18	0	2	77	22	54
Old Tenisonians II	20	13	6	1	48	23	45
National Westminster Bank	20	13	2	5	65	36	41
Dorkinians II	20	8	5	7	46	36	29
Mickleham Old Boxhillians	20	9	2	9	58	49	29
Glyn Old Boys	20	9	2	9	40	49	29
Royal Bank of Scotland II	20	8	4	8	44	43	28
Witan	20	8	3	9	45	51	27
Clapham Old Xaverians II	20	5	1	14	30	55	16
Sinjuns Grammarians II	20	4	2	14	29	69	14
Chertsey Old Salesians II	20	1	1	18	20	69	4

LEAGUE TABLES

Division One North

	P	W	D	L	F	A	PTS
Old Parmiterians III	18	11	3	4	48	34	36
Oakhill Tigers	18	9	6	3	39	26	33
Globe Rangers II	18	10	1	7	47	36	31
Hale End Athletic III	18	8	6	4	43	28	30
Bealonians III	18	9	1	8	43	40	28
Old Aloysians III	18	8	1	9	34	42	25
Queen Mary College Old Boys	18	6	4	8	30	30	22
University of Hertfordshire	18	7	1	10	34	47	22
Southgate County II	18	5	1	12	31	48	16
Old Manorians II	18	4	2	12	25	43	14

Division One West

	P	W	D	L	F	A	PTS
Old Danes	18	18	0	0	124	21	54
Fitzwilliam Old Boys	18	10	1	7	43	40	31
Old Vaughanians II	18	10	0	8	55	40	30
Brent	18	6	5	7	50	49	23
Old Salvatorians IV	18	7	2	9	40	52	23
Old Magdalenians II	18	7	1	10	38	44	22
Birkbeck College II	18	5	6	7	44	47	21
Old Isleworthians II	18	6	0	12	40	92	18
Old Challoners	18	5	1	12	27	70	16
Old Meadonians IV (-8)	18	7	2	9	34	40	15

Division Two West

	P	W	D	L	F	A	PTS
Old Danes II	18	16	2	0	88	26	50
Old Pegasonians	18	11	3	4	62	33	36
Cardinal Manning Old Boys	18	11	3	4	56	31	36
Teddington	18	10	1	7	47	36	31
Phoenix Old Boys III	18	8	4	6	44	40	28
London Welsh	18	7	5	6	43	34	26
Old Vaughanians III	18	6	4	8	51	53	22
Brent II	18	4	3	11	21	51	15
Old Challoners II	18	2	3	13	28	68	9
Ealing Association	18	0	2	16	20	88	2

Division Two South

	P	W	D	L	F	A	PTS
Citigroup	18	14	2	2	62	15	44
National Westminster Bank II	18	12	3	3	61	20	39
Economicals III	18	10	4	4	39	26	34
Shene Old Grammarians II	18	9	2	7	34	41	29
Standard Chartered Bank (-3)	18	9	2	7	40	35	26
Old Suttonians III	18	5	4	9	27	42	19
City of London	18	5	3	10	33	38	18
Old Meadonians V	18	3	7	8	22	51	16
Old Bromleians II	18	4	3	11	36	47	15
Old Whitgiftian	18	3	2	13	30	69	11

Division Two North

	P	W	D	L	F	A	PTS
Wood Green Old Boys II	18	15	1	2	69	26	46
Old Edmontonians	18	13	0	5	60	31	39
Old Manorians III	18	9	4	5	40	28	31
Old Kingsburians	18	9	0	9	58	52	27
Albanian IV	18	8	2	8	43	42	26
Latymer Old Boys II	18	8	2	8	33	40	26
Mill Hill County Old Boys	18	7	3	8	47	42	24
Old Parmiterians IV	18	7	1	10	37	52	22
Old Uffingtonians II	18	5	1	12	39	76	16
Egbertian	18	1	2	15	24	61	5

Division Three West

	P	W	D	L	F	A	PTS
Somerville Old Boys	16	12	2	2	82	22	38
Heathrow Seniors	16	11	3	2	53	17	36
Hampstead Heathens II	16	9	2	5	62	36	29
Old Isleworthians III	16	8	2	6	65	69	26
London Welsh II	16	7	1	8	48	36	22
Phoenix Old Boys IV	16	5	2	9	41	42	17
Old Uxonians	16	4	3	9	40	70	15
Old Vaughanians IV	16	4	1	11	40	98	13
Brent III	16	3	2	11	36	77	11

Division Three North

	P	W	D	L	F	A	PTS
Leyton County Old Boys II	20	12	5	3	61	29	41
Enfield Old Grammarians III	20	12	2	6	48	36	38
Phoenix Old Boys	20	11	4	5	65	42	37
Old Aloysians IV	20	12	1	7	45	35	37
Old Woodhouseians II	20	9	4	7	55	45	31
Old Minchendenians III	20	9	2	9	58	49	29
Egbertian II	20	8	4	8	37	43	28
Queen Mary College Old Boys II	20	9	0	11	53	60	27
Old Ignatians III	20	6	6	8	44	47	24
Latymer Old Boys III	20	3	2	15	30	71	11
Parkfield III (-3)	20	3	2	15	41	80	8

Division Three South

	P	W	D	L	F	A	PTS
Economicals IV	20	15	4	1	71	31	49
Old Grantonians	20	14	2	4	81	38	44
Old Thorntonians II	20	13	3	4	66	34	42
Clapham Old Xaverians III	20	11	4	5	55	43	37
Tilburg Regents	20	10	6	4	56	42	36
National Westminster Bank III	20	8	1	11	55	52	25
Glyn Old Boys II	20	6	3	11	50	46	21
Old Crosbeians	20	6	3	11	53	54	21
Old Sedcopians II	20	7	0	13	39	76	21
Royal Sun Alliance	20	4	2	14	26	73	14
Reigatians II	20	2	0	18	27	90	6

Division Four South	P	W	D	L	F	A	PTS
Kings Old Boys II	20	12	5	3	52	25	41
Old St Marys II	20	12	4	4	51	35	40
Wandsworth Borough II	20	12	2	6	59	27	38
Old Wokingians II	20	11	2	7	57	37	35
John Fisher Old Boys II	20	11	1	8	53	50	34
Old Meadonians VI	20	7	5	8	34	46	26
City of London II	20	7	3	10	51	56	24
Glyn Old Boys III	20	7	2	11	39	50	23
Fulham Compton Old Boys II	20	5	4	11	42	52	19
Old Tenisonians III	20	5	4	11	37	70	19
Comets MPSSA	20	4	2	14	23	50	14

Division Four North	P	W	D	L	F	A	PTS
Ravenscroft Old Boys	20	16	2	2	82	42	50
Egbertian III	20	13	6	1	65	25	45
Old Parmiterians V	20	14	2	4	83	30	44
Old Salvatorians V (-3)	20	9	3	8	50	46	27
Albanian V	20	7	4	9	29	33	25
Hale End Athletic IV	20	7	4	9	52	57	25
Bealonians IV	20	7	2	11	43	65	23
UCL Academicals IV	20	6	1	13	40	56	19
Wood Green Old Boys III	20	5	4	11	46	66	19
Old Buckwellians II	20	4	4	12	34	61	16
London Hospital O.B. (-3)	20	5	2	13	30	73	14

Division Five North	P	W	D	L	F	A	PTS
Old Parmiterians VI	16	14	0	2	67	13	42
Old Minchendenians IV	16	13	1	2	62	15	40
Oakhill Tigers II	16	13	0	3	79	24	39
Old Manorians IV	16	9	0	7	58	32	27
Lea Valley II	16	7	1	8	54	59	22
Bealonians V	16	5	1	10	45	48	16
Southgate County III	16	5	1	10	37	72	16
Old Tollingtonians II	16	4	0	12	24	74	12
Egbertian IV	16	0	0	16	16	105	0

Division Five South	P	W	D	L	F	A	PTS
Economicals V	22	20	2	0	73	12	62
Old Suttonians IV	22	16	3	3	93	33	51
Witan II	22	12	6	4	62	44	42
Phoenix Old Boys II	22	11	4	7	62	43	37
Fulham Compton Old Boys III	22	9	4	9	46	58	31
Old Wokingians III	22	8	6	8	52	41	30
Old Bromleians III	22	7	5	10	56	85	26
Clapham Old Xaverians IV	22	7	4	11	51	51	25
Old Meadonians VII	22	6	1	15	44	71	19
Old Thorntonians III	22	5	4	13	39	70	19
Dorkinians III	22	6	1	15	39	73	19
Old Tiffians II	22	3	4	15	34	70	13

Division Six North	P	W	D	L	F	A	PTS
UCL Academicals V	18	16	0	2	80	34	48
Ravenscroft Old Boys II	18	14	0	4	72	34	42
Old Edmontonians II	18	11	1	6	62	39	34
Old Minchendenians V	18	7	4	7	54	53	25
Old Woodhouseians III	18	6	3	9	42	57	21
Old Parmiterians VII	18	5	5	8	37	38	20
Mayfield Athletic II	18	6	2	10	34	46	20
Enfield Old Grammarians IV	18	6	2	10	40	64	20
Old Aloysians V	18	5	3	10	35	53	18
Parkfield IV (-6)	18	3	2	13	33	71	5

Division Six South	P	W	D	L	F	A	PTS
Glyn Old Boys IV	18	11	5	2	53	29	38
Wandgas	18	11	2	5	36	31	35
John Fisher Old Boys III	18	11	1	6	49	29	34
Old Pauline III	18	10	3	5	54	38	33
Old Suttonians V	18	8	4	6	39	31	28
Old Sedcopians III	18	8	2	8	36	36	26
Old Guildfordians II	18	6	3	9	35	45	21
Fulham Compton Old Boys IV	18	5	4	9	26	41	19
Shene Old Grammarians III	18	4	2	12	30	52	14
Reigatians III	18	2	2	14	24	50	8

Division Seven South	P	W	D	L	F	A	PTS
Old Josephians	20	16	0	4	72	31	48
John Fisher Old Boys IV	20	14	3	3	58	31	45
Old Guildfordians III	20	13	4	3	73	30	43
Old Tenisonians IV	20	12	3	5	57	37	39
Glyn Old Boys V	20	11	2	7	55	31	35
Old Wokingians IV	20	10	2	8	54	53	32
Old Suttonians VI	20	8	2	10	53	49	26
Old Tiffinians III	20	6	1	13	21	55	19
Old Sedcopians IV	20	3	5	12	30	58	14
Old Whitgiftian II	20	2	4	14	27	70	10
Reigatians IV	20	1	2	17	18	73	5

Division Seven North	P	W	D	L	F	A	PTS
Albanian VI	16	12	1	3	52	35	37
Old Edmontonians III	16	10	1	5	57	32	31
Queen Mary College O.B. III	16	9	2	5	60	44	29
Bealonians VI	16	8	0	8	44	43	24
UCL Academicals VI	16	7	1	8	45	34	22
Latymer Old Boys IV	16	5	3	8	31	40	18
Old Parmiterians VIII	16	5	2	9	36	53	17
Old Ignatians IV	16	5	1	10	35	62	16
Old Kingsburians II	16	4	3	9	26	43	15

Division Eight South	P	W	D	L	F	A	PTS
Old St Marys III	16	14	1	1	63	16	43
Old Suttonians VII	16	12	1	3	67	29	37
Mickleham Old Boxhillians II	16	11	1	4	46	34	34
Wandsworth Borough III	16	8	1	7	56	33	25
City of London III	16	5	3	8	38	43	18
Dorkinians IV	16	5	2	9	41	54	17
Clapham Old Xaverians V	16	4	3	9	31	38	15
Old Wokingians V	16	4	1	11	28	59	13
Fulham Compton O.B. V (-3)	16	2	1	13	28	92	4

LEAGUE TABLES

Division Eight North	P	W	D	L	F	A	PTS
Oakhill Tigers III	18	14	2	2	71	30	44
Wood Green Old Boys IV	18	13	1	4	60	37	40
Ravenscroft Old Boys III	18	11	1	6	70	37	34
Mill Hill Village	18	10	0	8	46	34	30
Old Salvatorians VI	18	9	3	6	50	40	30
Old Manorians V	18	9	2	7	50	38	29
Bealonians VII	18	6	0	12	28	54	18
Old Woodhouseians IV	18	4	3	11	30	57	15
Southgate County IV	18	3	3	12	37	61	12
Davenant Wanderers O.B. (-3)	18	3	1	14	31	85	7

Division Nine South	P	W	D	L	F	A	PTS
Old Thorntonians IV	20	13	3	4	74	46	42
Shene Old Grammarians IV	20	13	2	5	86	42	41
Old St Marys IV	20	12	2	6	61	44	38
Reigatians V	20	11	1	8	70	52	34
Old Meadonians VIII	20	10	3	7	57	47	33
Wandsworth Borough IV	20	8	5	7	57	43	29
Old Suttonians VIII	20	9	2	9	48	52	29
Old Grantonians II	20	5	5	10	49	46	20
Old Sedcopians V	20	5	3	12	41	60	18
Old Wokingians VI	20	5	2	13	27	82	17
Dorkinians V	20	4	2	14	43	99	14

Division Nine North	P	W	D	L	F	A	PTS
Mill Hill Village II	18	14	3	1	88	38	45
Old Edmontonians IV	18	13	3	2	60	31	42
Old Uffingtonians III (-3)	18	12	0	6	67	37	33
Old Minchendenians VI	18	10	0	8	56	79	30
Old Parmiterians IX	18	8	2	8	65	38	26
Enfield Old Grammarians V	18	8	2	8	56	44	26
Latymer Old Boys V	18	7	1	10	61	70	22
Old Kingsburians III	18	5	3	10	44	61	18
Leyton County Old Boys III	18	3	4	11	37	66	13
Old Ignatians V (-3)	18	0	2	16	19	89	-1

Division Ten South	P	W	D	L	F	A	PTS
Sinjuns Grammarians III	20	13	4	3	73	27	43
Old Pauline IV	20	12	2	6	65	46	38
Tilburg Regents II	20	11	4	5	44	35	37
Reigatians VI	20	11	3	6	69	54	36
Old Guildfordians IV	20	9	4	7	53	49	31
John Fisher Old Boys V	20	9	2	9	66	59	29
Old Sedcopians VI	20	8	3	9	51	48	27
Old Meadonians IX	20	8	2	10	57	60	26
Old Suttonians IX	20	6	3	11	36	42	21
Old Wokingians VII	20	6	3	11	34	66	21
Dorkinians VI	20	1	2	17	31	93	5

Division Ten North	P	W	D	L	F	A	PTS
Albanian VII	18	15	1	2	88	29	46
Mayfield Athletic III	18	11	4	3	58	35	37
Old Kingsburians IV	18	9	5	4	53	36	32
Mill Hill Village III	18	9	3	6	67	42	30
Old Salvatorians VII	18	8	3	7	52	48	27
Old Woodhouseians V	18	6	2	10	40	60	20
Goffs Old Boys II (-3)	18	7	1	10	37	61	19
Old Parmiterians X	18	5	3	10	27	57	18
Wood Green Old Boys V	18	4	4	10	36	49	16
Bealonians VIII	18	2	2	14	30	71	8

ANDOVER & DISTRICT LEAGUE

	P	W	D	L	F	A	Pts
Andover New St Swifts	22	19	2	1	81	15	59
Whitchurch United "A"	22	16	2	4	74	34	50
Sutton Scotney	22	15	1	6	83	31	46
Ludgershall Sports Res.	22	12	2	8	41	33	38
ABC United (-3)	22	13	1	8	94	39	37
Kings Somborne	22	11	3	8	54	37	36
Wolversdene 213	22	11	2	9	64	38	35
Sparten	22	8	4	10	49	43	28
Broughton Reserves	22	7	2	13	49	54	23
Wolversdene	22	6	3	13	41	63	21
Wykeham Warriors (+3)	22	2	0	20	11	120	9
Wykeham Gerri's	22	1	0	21	19	153	3

ARTHURIAN LEAGUE

Premier Division	P	W	D	L	F	A	Pts
Old Carthusians	18	14	2	2	54	20	44
Old Harrovians	18	12	2	4	38	28	38
Lancing Old Boys	18	11	4	3	48	24	37
Old Brentwoods (-3)	18	8	3	7	42	26	24
Old Foresters	18	7	2	9	24	38	23
Old Etonians	18	6	4	8	28	45	22
Old Chigwellians	18	4	8	6	20	26	20
Old Cholmeleians	18	4	4	10	30	39	16
Old Haileyburians (-3)	18	3	4	11	31	53	10
Old Wykehamists (-3)	18	2	5	11	28	44	8

Division One	P	W	D	L	F	A	Pts
Old King's (Wimbledon)	16	12	2	2	57	27	38
Old Tonbridgians	16	12	2	2	38	21	38
Old Salopians	16	9	3	4	48	22	30
Old Westminsters	16	8	1	7	38	45	25
Old Radleians	16	6	1	9	32	42	19
Old Aldenhamians	16	5	2	9	23	42	17
Old Bradfieldians	16	4	3	9	28	37	15
Old King's Scholars	16	3	4	9	23	42	13
Old Malvernians	16	3	2	11	25	34	11

Division Two	Pld	W	D	L	F	A	Pts
Old Carthusians III	14	11	1	2	33	20	34
Old Carthusians II	14	8	2	4	30	18	26
Old Chigwellians II	14	7	1	6	31	25	22
Lancing Old Boys II	14	7	1	6	24	24	22
Old Haberdashers	14	5	1	8	27	31	16
Old Reptonians	14	5	1	8	25	31	16
Old Wellingtonians	14	5	1	8	20	26	16
Old Foresters II	14	4	0	10	23	38	12

Division Three	P	W	D	L	F	A	Pts
Old Cholmeleians II	16	11	3	2	53	27	36
Old Salopians II	16	9	2	5	38	28	29
Old King's (Wimbledon) II	16	8	4	4	50	33	28
Old Etonians II	16	8	1	7	47	35	25
Old Aldenhamians II	16	7	0	9	49	47	21
Old Brentwoods II	16	6	2	8	34	42	20
Old Harrovians II	16	6	2	8	39	48	20
Old Westminsters II (-3)	16	6	1	9	36	53	16
Old Amplefordians	16	3	1	12	25	58	10

Division Four

	P	W	D	L	F	A	Pts
Old Marlburians	14	10	0	4	58	16	30
Old Wykehamists II	14	8	4	2	42	26	28
Old Chigwellians III	14	8	1	5	34	32	25
Old Epsomians	14	7	3	4	31	23	24
Old Cholmeleians III	14	6	4	4	30	35	22
Old Eastbournians	14	5	3	6	29	39	18
Old Brentwoods III	14	3	1	10	22	41	10
Old Foresters III	14	0	2	12	16	50	2

Division Five

	P	W	D	L	F	A	Pts
Old Berkhamstedians	14	11	1	2	42	11	34
Old Harrovians III	14	10	0	4	28	12	30
Old Foresters IV	14	9	0	5	25	22	27
Old Citizens	14	7	3	4	43	22	24
Old Malvernians II	14	6	1	7	27	32	19
Old Brentwoods IV	14	6	1	7	28	37	19
Old Chigwellians IV	14	1	2	11	12	39	5

ARMY FOOTBALL ASSOCIATION

Massey Trophy Div. One

	P	W	D	L	F	A	Pts
Royal Electrical & M. E.	12	8	1	3	30	18	25
Royal Engineers	12	8	1	3	32	24	25
Royal Logistic Corps	12	6	2	4	25	21	20
Royal Signals	12	6	0	6	30	24	18
Royal Army Physical T.C.	12	5	1	6	28	37	16
Royal Artillery	12	3	4	5	31	27	13
Adjutants General's Corps	12	0	3	9	16	41	3

Massey Trophy Div. Two

	P	W	D	L	F	A	Pts
Infantry	8	8	0	0	29	1	24
Army Medical Services	8	3	2	3	18	12	11
Intelligence Corps	7	3	2	2	7	11	11
Army Air Corps	8	2	1	5	8	15	7
Royal Armoured Corps	7	0	1	6	6	29	1

AYLESBURY & DISTRICT LEAGUE

Premier Division

	P	W	D	L	F	A	Pts
Bucks CC	20	16	1	1	75	26	49
Walton Court Wanderers	20	14	2	3	76	30	44
Aston Park	20	12	3	5	59	28	39
Downley Albion	20	11	4	5	50	31	37
Berkhamsted Sports	20	10	3	6	47	35	33
Aylesbury Dynamos	20	10	1	9	48	54	31
Bierton	20	9	2	9	44	39	29
P & IC United	20	5	2	13	35	64	17
Bedgrove United	20	4	4	11	28	51	16
Elmhurst	20	2	1	16	15	65	7
St Johns Magnets	20	2	1	17	11	65	7

Division One

	P	W	D	L	F	A	Pts
Bedgrove Dynamos	16	10	2	4	41	22	32
FC Spandits	16	10	2	4	53	44	32
Long Marston	16	10	2	4	42	36	32
Britannia	16	9	1	6	61	45	28
Haddenham United	16	8	2	6	37	33	26
Aston Clinton	16	8	1	7	35	30	25
Wingrave	16	5	2	9	36	51	17
Wendover	16	2	3	11	17	49	9
FC Bedgrove	16	2	1	13	31	43	7

Division Two

	P	W	D	L	F	A	Pts
AFC Victoria	18	14	2	2	76	22	44
FC Mandeville	18	14	2	2	58	25	44
Cheddington	18	14	1	3	51	20	43
Haydon United	18	11	3	4	58	28	36
Aston Clinton Reserves	18	8	1	9	41	41	25
Quarrendon Royals	18	5	5	8	36	47	20
Bucks CC Reserves	18	3	3	12	34	50	12
Ludgershall	18	2	6	10	24	42	12
P & IC United Reserves	18	2	6	10	24	65	12
Long Marston Reserves	18	1	3	14	22	84	6

Division Three

	P	W	D	L	F	A	Pts
Oving	20	17	1	2	82	26	52
Great Milton	20	15	1	4	71	29	46
St Johns Magnets Res.	20	12	3	5	72	34	39
Downley Albion Reserves	20	10	1	9	55	49	31
Haddenham United Res.	20	9	1	10	50	48	28
Wendover Reserves	20	8	2	10	35	45	26
Quainton	20	6	7	7	36	47	25
Aylesbury Park Rangers	20	5	6	9	43	47	21
Haydon United Reserves	20	5	5	10	24	38	20
Bedgrove Dynamos Res.	20	5	4	11	21	78	19
Brill United	20	2	1	17	21	69	7

Division Four

	P	W	D	L	F	A	Pts
Northchurch	20	15	3	2	72	25	48
Tring Bell Titans	20	13	3	4	76	33	42
Aylesbury Wanderers	20	12	3	5	80	65	39
Cuddington	20	11	3	6	64	49	36
Tetsworth	20	9	3	8	50	49	30
Wingrave Reserves	20	9	2	9	57	57	29
Bedgrove United Reserves	20	8	3	9	53	44	27
Ludgershall Reserves	20	7	4	9	55	51	25
FC Spandits Reserves	20	4	4	12	34	58	16
Aylesbury Park Rangers R.	20	4	3	13	29	59	15
AC Meadowcroft	20	1	3	16	34	114	6

LEAGUE TABLES

BANBURY & LORD JERSEY FA

Premier Division	P	W	D	L	F	A	Pts
Bodicote Sports	20	15	3	2	70	17	48
Woodford United	20	12	1	7	69	43	37
Sinclair United	20	11	4	5	41	31	37
Heyford Athletic	20	11	3	6	44	31	36
Deddington Town	20	10	4	6	49	39	34
Highfield O.B.	20	8	5	7	46	55	29
Cropredy	20	8	3	9	45	46	27
Bardwell	20	5	6	9	32	50	21
Sporting Hethe	20	5	2	13	30	52	17
Steeple Aston	20	4	5	11	30	53	17
K.E.A.	20	2	2	16	32	71	8

Division One	P	W	D	L	F	A	Pts
Abba Athletic	20	19	1	0	84	13	58
F.C. Naranja	20	13	5	2	55	25	44
Bloxham	20	13	1	6	48	25	40
Bishops Itchington	20	12	1	7	61	49	37
Fenny Compton	20	9	5	6	46	32	32
Heyford United	20	7	1	12	40	48	22
Kings Sutton	20	5	5	10	31	60	20
Hornton	20	6	1	13	46	60	19
Sinclair United Reserves	20	4	7	9	29	68	19
The Swan	20	4	2	14	34	63	14
Middleton Cheney	20	3	1	16	27	58	10

Division Two	P	W	D	L	F	A	Pts
Highfield O.B. Reserves	20	14	3	3	72	29	45
Deddington Town Reserves	20	14	2	4	57	28	44
Chesterton	20	12	2	6	65	34	38
F.C. Langford	20	11	3	6	63	52	36
Hardwick O.B.	20	9	4	7	56	40	31
Sams United	20	9	4	7	53	40	31
Brackley Sports	20	7	7	6	34	37	28
Banbury Town	20	7	2	11	43	49	23
Kings Sutton Reserves	20	5	2	13	19	49	17
Bodicote Sports Reserves	20	5	1	14	34	65	16
Wroxton Sports	20	1	2	17	34	107	5

Division Three	P	W	D	L	F	A	Pts
Finmere	22	18	0	4	89	33	54
Souldern	22	14	3	5	60	35	45
Bloxham Reserves	22	14	2	6	64	34	44
K.E.A. Reserves	22	11	2	9	63	58	35
Merton	22	10	4	8	67	49	34
Swis F.C.	22	10	4	8	48	43	34
Heyford Athletic Reserves	22	10	2	10	54	45	32
Steeple Aston Reserves	22	10	2	10	44	53	32
Banbury Galaxy	22	8	5	9	40	39	29
Paragon United	22	7	3	12	52	66	24
Wroxton Sports Reserves	22	4	0	18	46	100	12
Woodford United Reserves	22	2	1	19	29	101	7

BASINGSTOKE & DISTRICT LEAGUE

Premier Division	P	W	D	L	F	A	Pts
FC Censo	18	15	3	0	53	13	48
Basingstoke Royals FC	18	10	2	6	60	27	32
Hook FC	18	9	2	7	64	50	29
Welly Old Boys FC	18	8	5	5	35	36	29
Basingstoke Rangers FC	18	9	1	8	37	33	28
Kingsclere FC	18	7	4	7	41	50	25
New Inn Sports FC	18	5	6	7	30	31	21
Bramley United FC	18	6	3	9	40	46	21
Sherborne St John	18	5	3	10	32	55	18
Tadley Calleva FC (A)	18	1	1	16	30	81	4

Division One	P	W	D	L	F	A	Pts
Tron FC	18	12	4	2	57	23	40
Heathpark FC	18	13	0	5	67	35	39
Chineham Albion FC	18	12	2	4	53	30	38
Bounty Utd FC	18	10	1	7	63	34	31
Herriard Sports FC	18	10	1	7	61	46	31
Welly Old Boys FC Res. (+3)	18	7	4	7	34	35	28
Sherfield FC	18	8	2	8	45	42	26
FC Burghclere	18	4	2	12	35	82	14
Baughurst AFC	18	3	2	13	46	85	11
Pure Lounge Bar FC (-3)	18	2	0	16	21	70	3

Division Two	P	W	D	L	F	A	Pts
MFC Popley FC	20	16	1	3	76	26	49
Kingsclere FC Reserves	20	15	2	3	84	34	47
Tron FC Reserves	20	14	0	6	51	34	42
Hook FC Reserves	20	10	3	7	55	37	33
AFC Aldermaston A	20	10	1	9	60	45	31
Chineham Albion FC Res.	20	8	3	9	49	50	27
AFC Berg	20	7	2	11	40	59	23
King of Wessex FC	20	7	1	12	43	73	22
Sherborne St John FC Res.	20	6	3	11	37	50	21
Overton Utd FC (A)	20	4	2	14	32	98	14
Basingstoke Labour Club FC	20	4	0	16	38	59	12

BATH & DISTRICT LEAGUE

Division One	P	W	D	L	F	A	Pts
AFC Durbin United	14	11	3	0	59	13	36
Odd Down "A"	14	11	3	0	56	19	36
Trowbridge House	14	8	2	4	35	28	26
University of Bath	14	7	1	6	44	32	22
Old Crown Weston	14	5	1	8	24	34	16
Rising Sun	14	4	0	10	21	41	12
Saltford Reserves	14	3	1	10	13	51	10

Bath Spa University - record expunged.

Division Two	P	W	D	L	F	A	Pts
University of Bath Res	20	18	1	1	104	20	55
Full Moon	20	15	2	3	82	26	47
Stothert & Pitt	20	12	2	6	68	31	38
Newbridge	20	11	2	7	61	37	35
Civil Service Larkhall	20	10	2	8	58	52	32
Saltford "A"	20	9	2	9	37	42	29
Frys Club Old Boys Res	20	7	2	11	36	63	23
Aces Reserves	20	7	1	12	42	61	22
Chew Magna Reserves	20	5	3	12	24	52	18
Fairfield Park Rangers	20	4	2	14	38	82	14
Westfield "A"	20	2	1	17	20	104	7

BECKETT LEAGUE

Division One	P	W	D	L	F	A	Pts
Kirkbymoorside Reserves	18	15	2	1	73	14	47
Sinnington	18	13	2	3	63	23	41
Thornton Dale	18	11	3	4	43	24	36
Union Rovers	18	10	5	3	47	28	35
Rosedale	18	10	1	7	34	33	31
Heslerton	18	9	0	9	34	33	27
Gillamoor	18	7	0	11	42	48	21
Bagby & Balk	18	5	3	10	29	49	18
Kirkdale United	18	1	0	17	17	70	3
Norton United	18	1	0	17	22	82	3

BIRMINGHAM AFA

Premier	P	W	D	L	F	A	Pts
SUTTON UNITED '	26	17	5	4	73	35	56
VILLAGE 'A' F.C	26	14	6	6	55	29	48
BOLDMERE SPORTS	26	13	6	7	58	39	45
ST FRANCIS F.C	26	12	7	7	54	34	43
AFC SOMERS F.C	26	11	7	8	62	52	40
ST GEORGES WARR	26	13	1	12	49	49	40
CRESCONIANS 'A'	26	11	6	9	61	60	39
SHIRLEY ATHLETI	26	10	4	12	55	63	34
OLD WULFRUNIANS	26	8	8	10	44	49	32
SILHILL 'A' F.C	26	10	2	14	50	68	32
HANDSWORTH GSOB	26	9	4	13	60	69	31
INTER VAUGHANS	26	10	1	15	37	57	31
WAKE GREEN AMS	26	8	5	13	31	47	29
HARBORNE TOWN F	26	3	4	19	30	68	13

Division One	P	W	D	L	F	A	Pts
ATHLETIC SPARKH	26	16	7	3	79	37	55
KINGSTANDING WA	26	16	5	5	69	36	53
VILLAGE 'B' F.	26	14	4	8	54	38	46
SUTTON UNITED '	26	14	3	9	70	46	45
CRUSADERS F.C	26	13	5	8	55	36	44
WALSALL PHOENIX	26	11	8	7	44	42	41
PARKFIELD AMATE	26	10	5	11	41	54	35
SHIRLEY ATHLETI	26	8	8	10	43	46	32
FLAMENGO F.C	26	9	4	13	43	50	31
SHERE PUNJAB F.	26	9	4	13	59	75	31
CPA F.C	26	7	6	13	41	50	27
HANDSWORTH G.S.	26	6	7	13	43	66	25
ST PAULS F.C	26	6	5	15	35	66	23
DESI 'A' F.C	26	6	3	17	47	81	21

Division Two	P	W	D	L	F	A	Pts
SMITHSWOOD FIRS	22	18	1	3	76	30	55
FAIRFAX SPORTS	22	15	4	3	76	34	49
OLD HILL F.C	22	15	1	6	62	30	46
WEST HAGLEY F.C	22	11	2	9	54	42	35
SILHILL 'B' F.C	22	10	3	9	43	55	33
SUTTON UNITED '	22	9	3	10	55	52	30
WAKE GREEN AMAT	22	8	3	11	28	35	27
MALREMO RANGERS	22	7	2	13	43	49	23
BEARWOOD ATHLET	22	7	2	13	37	62	23
BRITANNIA OB's (-3)	22	8	1	13	56	83	22
VILLAGE 'C' F.C	22	6	2	14	36	68	20
OLD WULFRUNIANS	22	5	2	15	45	71	17

Division Three	P	W	D	L	F	A	Pts
HANDSWORTH UNIT	20	15	4	1	57	21	49
CASTLE VALE UNI	20	14	1	5	97	36	43
ASTON 'A' F.C	20	12	6	2	62	24	42
BENTLEY HEATH U (-3)	20	14	2	4	63	36	41
EASY REDS F.C	20	9	3	8	60	43	30
WALSALL PHOENIX	20	8	3	9	43	47	27
WAKE GREEN AMAT	20	5	2	13	34	64	17
GREAT BARR F.C	20	4	5	11	23	60	17
CRESCONIANS 'B'	20	4	3	13	48	67	15
WEDNESBURY ATHL (-6)	20	5	4	11	35	70	13
SILHILL 'C' F.C	20	1	5	14	28	79	8

Division Four	P	W	D	L	F	A	Pts
ROSSI & ROSSI '	22	16	4	2	80	25	52
SHIRLEY ATHLETI	22	12	3	7	60	56	39
WHITE HART CCC'	22	10	8	4	76	40	38
ASTON 'B' F.C	22	12	2	8	61	43	38
ST. GEORGES WAR	22	10	7	5	51	35	37
PATHFINDER F.C	22	9	4	9	41	46	31
BT F.C	22	9	1	12	49	57	28
MERIDEN ATHLETI	22	8	3	11	42	57	27
OLD WULFRUNIANS	22	8	3	11	31	46	27
SPORTSCO F.C	22	7	5	10	48	53	26
A.G WYTHALL F.C	22	6	1	15	47	82	19
VILLAGE 'D F.C	22	4	1	17	28	74	13

Division Five	P	W	D	L	F	A	Pts
BOURNVILLE COLT	18	16	0	2	49	25	48
PREMIER F.C 200	18	15	1	2	90	16	46
COLDLANDS F.C	18	14	3	1	71	28	45
PARKFIELD AFC B	18	7	3	8	37	35	24
BOLDMERE SPORTS	18	7	1	10	36	33	22
SUTTON UNITED '	18	7	0	11	41	49	21
REAL RIVERSIDE	18	6	1	11	30	43	19
CRUSADERS 'B' F (-3)	18	7	1	10	27	41	19
SILHILL 'D' F.C (-3)	18	4	0	14	25	74	9
WOOD WANDERERS	18	2	0	16	23	85	6

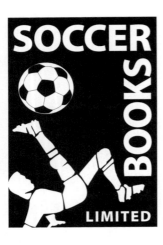

SOCCER BOOKS LIMITED
72 ST. PETERS AVENUE (Dept. NLD)
CLEETHORPES
N.E. LINCOLNSHIRE
DN35 8HU
ENGLAND

Tel. **01472 696226**   Fax **01472 698546**

Web site   www.soccer-books.co.uk
e-mail   info@soccer-books.co.uk

Established in 1982, Soccer Books Limited has one of the largest ranges of English-Language soccer books available. We continue to expand our stocks even further to include many more titles including German, French, Spanish and Italian-language books.

With well over 200,000 satisfied customers over the past 30 years, we supply books to virtually every country in the world but have maintained the friendliness and accessibility associated with a small family-run business. The range of titles we sell includes:

YEARBOOKS – All major yearbooks including many editions of the Sky Sports Football Yearbook (previously Rothmans), Supporters' Guides, Playfair Annuals, South and North & Central American Yearbooks, Non-League Club Directories, Almanack of World Football.

CLUB HISTORIES – Complete Statistical Records, Official Histories, Definitive Histories plus many more including photographic books.

WORLD FOOTBALL – World Cup books, European Championships History, Statistical histories for the World Cup, European Championships, South American and European Club Cup competitions and foreign-language Season Preview Magazines for dozens of countries.

BIOGRAPHIES & WHO'S WHOS – of Managers and Players plus Who's Whos etc.

ENCYCLOPEDIAS & GENERAL TITLES – Books on Stadia, Hooligan and Sociological studies, Histories and hundreds of others, including the weird and wonderful!

DVDs – Season reviews for British clubs, histories, European Cup competition finals, World Cup matches and series reviews, player profiles and a selection of almost 60 F.A. Cup Finals with many more titles becoming available all the time.

For a printed listing showing a selection of our titles, contact us using the information at the top of this page. Alternatively, our web site offers a secure ordering system for credit and debit card holders and Paypal users and lists our full range of 2,000 new books and 400 DVDs.

Division Six

	P	W	D	L	F	A	Pts
MAYPOLE A.F.C	22	20	1	1	120	36	61
ANCHOR ROVERS F	22	16	3	3	82	29	51
BIRMINGHAM IRIS	22	15	1	6	79	32	46
ST. GEORGES WAR (-3)	22	15	3	4	89	43	45
BIRMINGHAM CITA	22	13	2	7	76	40	41
AMANAH F.C	22	12	2	8	67	55	38
VILLAGE 'E' F.C	22	7	3	12	43	74	24
WAKE GREEN AMAT	22	6	3	13	50	81	21
DESI 'B' F.C (-3)	22	7	1	14	53	76	19
COTON GREEN F.C	22	3	3	16	45	95	12
SUTTON UNITED '	22	3	2	17	20	99	11
WALSALL PHOENIX	22	2	2	18	24	88	8

Division Seven

	P	W	D	L	F	A	Pts
TRIUMPH MERIDEN	20	18	0	2	75	15	54
BIRMINGHAM MEDI	20	17	0	3	87	32	51
PREMIER F.C 200	20	12	2	6	40	22	38
OLYMPIA 808 SC	20	11	4	5	58	38	37
GARDEN HOUSE RA	20	8	4	8	38	39	28
DOSTHILL BOYS C	20	7	5	8	28	47	26
BOLDMERE SPORTS	20	6	3	11	46	51	21
HANDSWORTH G.S. (-3)	20	7	3	10	43	49	21
COLDFIELD RANGE	20	4	3	13	20	54	15
MANCHESTER WAND	20	4	2	14	34	76	14
SELLY OAK LEGEN (-6)	20	3	0	17	29	75	3

Division Eight

	P	W	D	L	F	A	Pts
RED STAR GALAXY	26	19	4	3	103	48	61
ROSSI & ROSSI '	26	16	7	3	84	25	55
FAIRFAX SPORTS	26	16	4	6	67	40	52
CRUSADERS 'C' F	26	12	4	10	58	49	40
REAL BIRMINGHAM (-3)	26	12	5	9	59	53	38
PARKFIELD AMATE	26	11	5	10	53	50	38
RAILWAY HOCKLEY	26	10	8	8	48	45	38
HANDSWORTH G.S.	26	9	6	11	53	55	33
EDGBASTON UNITE	26	8	8	10	53	64	32
STEELHOUSE LANE	26	8	6	12	46	56	30
VILLAGE 'F' F.C	26	6	8	12	32	57	26
REAL RIVERSIDE	26	6	5	15	46	64	23
WAKE GREEN AMAT	26	6	3	17	40	93	21
SMETHWICK RAIDE (-3)	26	5	3	18	44	87	15

BISHOP'S STORTFORD, STANSTED & DISTRICT LEAGUE

Premier Division

	P	W	D	L	F	A	Pts
North Weald	16	15	1	0	53	13	46
Heath Rovers Reserves	16	9	0	7	36	22	27
Sheering	16	8	3	5	38	26	27
Frontiers	16	6	6	4	37	38	24
Hertfordshire Rangers	16	7	2	7	46	34	23
Langley Rangers	16	6	3	7	24	35	21
Avondale Rangers	16	4	4	8	30	41	16
Albury	16	5	1	10	28	39	16
Birchanger	16	1	2	13	10	54	5

Division One

	P	W	D	L	F	A	Pts
Northolt	20	14	2	4	53	28	44
Harbridge Athletic	20	14	1	5	64	40	43
Sheering Reserves	20	12	5	3	72	42	41
Avondale Rangers Reserves	20	11	3	6	76	50	36
Hatfield Heath	20	11	2	7	65	54	35
North Weald Reserves	20	8	4	8	51	53	28
Badgers	20	8	1	11	50	74	25
Dunmow Rhodes	20	6	4	10	38	40	22
Potter Street	20	6	3	11	35	53	21
Lower Street	20	4	2	14	41	69	14
Frontiers Reserves	20	2	1	17	39	81	7

BLACKBURN & DISTRICT COMBINATION

Premier Division

	P	W	D	L	F	A	Pts
The Ivy Hotel	18	18	0	0	121	21	54
Knuzden	18	10	1	7	62	42	31
The Manxman	18	9	1	8	57	61	28
Feildens Arms	18	8	1	9	38	56	25
Blackburn United	18	7	3	7	36	40	24
Islington	18	6	0	11	45	51	18
Blue Star	18	1	0	17	19	107	0

Second Division

	P	W	D	L	F	A	Pts
Rishton UNited	21	12	6	3	59	34	42
Blackburn Olympic	21	10	1	10	44	46	31
Hindle Arms (Darwen)	21	9	4	8	42	52	31
Blackburn United Reserves	21	9	3	9	53	46	30
Greenfield	21	8	5	8	49	32	29
Clifton	21	8	5	8	50	52	29
Feniscowles & Pleasington Res	21	8	4	9	52	62	28
The Lion	21	3	6	12	44	69	12

Division Three

	P	W	D	L	F	A	Pts
Ossy Social	21	16	2	3	99	36	50
Hole Ith Wall	21	15	1	5	78	43	46
Manxman Amateurs	21	13	0	8	68	53	39
Whalley Range	21	10	4	7	60	53	34
Rishton United Reserves	21	9	2	10	62	65	29
Worth Avenue	21	5	3	13	41	72	18
Vauxhall Inn	21	5	3	13	44	80	18
Mill Hill	21	3	1	17	36	86	10

BOSTON & DISTRICT LEAGUE

Premier Division

	P	W	D	L	F	A	Pts
Tavern Colts	22	18	3	1	99	28	57
Old Leake	22	16	3	3	55	27	51
Billinghay Athletic (-1)	22	13	4	5	63	43	42
Kirton Town	22	12	2	8	62	43	38
Swineshead Institute	22	12	2	8	55	40	38
Pointon	22	9	6	7	54	41	33
Spilsby Town (-3)	22	9	6	7	43	41	30
Skegness Town Reserves	22	8	2	12	37	62	26
Old Doningtonians	22	6	3	13	50	62	21
Wyberton	22	5	3	14	34	56	18
Freiston	22	2	5	15	33	89	11
Woodhall Spa United	22	1	3	18	34	87	6

LEAGUE TABLES

Division One	P	W	D	L	F	A	PTS
Benington	22	17	3	2	84	24	54
Fishtoft	22	15	3	3	80	28	48
Billinghay Athletic Reserves	22	14	3	4	57	33	45
Spalding Harriers	22	13	3	6	63	32	42
Wainfleet United	22	13	1	8	67	42	40
Coningsby	22	10	3	9	43	35	33
Mareham United	22	9	4	9	55	56	31
Boston United Community	22	9	0	13	39	51	27
Wyberton Reserves	22	7	3	12	50	58	24
Spalding Town	22	5	3	14	42	55	18
Holbeach Bank	22	4	1	17	57	72	13
Sutterton	22	1	1	20	17	168	4

Division Two	P	W	D	L	F	A	PTS
Wrangle United	26	22	3	1	90	23	69
Freiston Reserves	26	17	6	3	103	44	57
Pointon Reserves	26	18	3	5	77	34	57
Fosdyke (-3)	26	16	5	5	80	34	50
Tavern Colts Reserves (-1)	26	14	7	5	81	39	48
Westside Rangers	26	15	1	10	60	50	46
Tydd St.Mary	26	11	4	11	70	68	37
Park United	26	9	4	13	60	69	31
Coningsby Reserves	26	7	2	17	47	72	23
Fishtoft Reserves (-3)	26	7	4	15	62	76	22
Nelson	26	5	7	14	49	77	22
Mareham United Reserves	26	3	7	16	33	111	16
Spalding Town Reserves	26	3	6	17	36	85	15
F.C. Kirton	26	4	3	19	39	105	12

Division Three	P	W	D	L	F	A	PTS
Queens Rangers (-4)	24	18	1	5	87	32	51
Old Doningtonians Res (+2)	24	13	8	3	64	36	49
Kirton Town Reserves (-1)	24	14	4	6	76	34	45
Swineshead Institute Res.	24	13	5	6	56	46	44
Spilsby Town Reserves	24	14	0	10	59	45	42
Fosdyke Reserves	24	12	0	12	57	56	36
Wainfleet United Res. (-1)	24	9	6	9	42	40	32
Friskney	24	10	2	12	41	44	32
Spalding Harriers Reserves	24	8	4	12	43	50	28
Pointon "A"	24	7	2	15	50	102	23
F.C. Hammers (+2)	24	5	4	15	30	54	21
Woodhall Spa United Res.	24	6	3	15	47	87	21
Holbeach Bank Reserves	24	5	5	14	43	69	20

BOURNEMOUTH LEAGUE

Premier Division	P	W	D	L	F	A	Pts
Bournemouth Manor	22	18	2	2	51	20	56
Portcastrian	22	17	3	2	53	25	54
Bournemouth Electric	22	12	4	6	53	34	40
Westover Bournemouth	22	12	4	6	53	41	40
Bosuns Chair	22	8	8	6	36	31	32
Sway	22	9	4	9	45	47	31
Hamworthy Recreation	22	8	6	8	43	44	30
Parley Sports	22	8	2	12	43	46	26
Allendale	22	6	6	10	44	52	24
Redlynch and Woodfalls	22	4	2	16	30	49	14
Old Oakmeadians	22	2	7	13	32	49	13
Trinidad	22	3	2	17	27	72	11

Division One	P	W	D	L	F	A	Pts
Mudeford Mens Club	18	13	1	4	53	27	40
FC Bournemouth	18	11	3	4	68	34	36
Harrington Utd	18	9	4	5	49	29	31
Bournemouth Electric Res.	18	8	5	5	38	39	29
Ferndown Sports	18	7	5	6	36	37	26
Alderholt	18	7	4	7	29	36	25
Sturminster Marshall	18	6	3	9	32	42	21
Ferndown Town	18	6	3	9	32	43	21
Holt	18	3	4	11	29	60	13
Twynham Rangers	18	3	2	13	42	61	11

Division Two	P	W	D	L	F	A	Pts
Richmond Park Con Club	22	19	0	3	97	24	57
Queens Park Athletic	22	14	3	5	75	40	45
New Milton Linnets	22	14	3	5	60	41	45
Sway Reserves	22	12	2	8	61	38	38
South Coast Demolition	22	11	2	9	61	43	35
Westover Bournemouth R.	22	10	5	7	39	57	35
Galleon	22	11	0	11	47	45	33
Bournemouth Manor Res.	22	9	0	13	38	68	27
Mploy	22	7	4	11	55	76	25
St Marys	22	6	2	14	48	63	20
Fordingbridge Turks	22	5	3	14	36	68	18
Seyward Windows	22	2	0	20	28	82	6

Division Three	P	W	D	L	F	A	Pts
Bournemouth Electric A	22	16	3	3	86	30	51
Parley Sports A	22	14	2	6	66	40	44
Bisterne Rangers	22	11	4	7	56	46	37
Winton Borough	22	10	3	9	57	63	33
Redlynch and Woodfalls R.	22	9	5	8	49	47	32
Downton Sports	22	9	4	9	58	58	31
Redhill Rangers	22	10	1	11	57	71	31
Mudeford Mens Club Res.	22	8	6	8	65	60	30
AFC Burton	22	7	6	9	53	60	27
FC Athletico	22	7	5	10	45	50	26
Seabournes	22	6	0	16	41	73	18
Old Oakmeadians Res.	22	5	1	16	32	67	16

Division Four	P	W	D	L	F	A	Pts
BU Staff	20	15	3	2	73	23	48
AFC Pennington	20	14	2	4	60	24	44
Ferndown Sports Reserves	20	12	2	6	51	34	38
New Milton Eagles	20	9	3	8	62	48	30
Queens Park Athletic Res.	20	9	3	8	41	37	30
Burley	20	8	3	9	45	43	27
AFC Bransgore	20	7	5	8	49	36	26
Fifa Standards	20	7	2	11	33	41	23
Napoleons	20	6	5	9	41	59	23
Magpies	20	6	3	11	39	45	21
Milford	20	1	1	18	18	122	4

Division Five

	P	W	D	L	F	A	Pts
Richmond Park Con Club R	18	15	2	1	58	13	47
Allendale Reserves	18	12	1	5	48	24	37
Screw It Carpentry	18	10	1	7	62	42	31
FC Boscelona	18	9	3	6	47	35	30
Bournemouth Manor A	18	9	0	9	60	62	27
Witchampton Reserves	18	9	0	9	45	55	27
Bournemouth Poppies A	18	6	3	9	34	55	21
Bransgore United (-3)	18	6	2	10	49	50	17
Shamrock	18	3	4	11	36	68	13
Boldre Royals	18	2	2	14	30	65	8

Division Six

	P	W	D	L	F	A	Pts
Portcastrian Reserves	20	15	3	2	89	30	48
A & T Athletic (-3)	20	16	2	2	93	22	47
West Howe	20	12	3	5	82	47	39
Ferndown Tn Greenfields R	20	12	3	5	68	53	39
Lower Parkstone CFC	20	12	2	6	80	48	38
AFC Burton Reserves	20	6	4	10	40	42	22
Ringwood Athletic	20	6	4	10	43	57	22
Everton & Lymington Argyle	20	6	4	10	35	64	22
Bransgore Utd Reserves	20	5	1	14	36	75	16
Alderholt Reserves	20	4	3	13	34	49	15
Redhill Rangers Reserves	20	1	1	18	26	139	4

BRIGHTON, HOVE & DISTRICT LEAGUE

Premier

	P	W	D	L	F	A	Pts
Hair Razors	14	11	0	3	31	15	33
O & G United	14	10	1	3	28	16	31
Brighton Electricity	14	8	1	5	36	34	25
CCK	14	7	1	6	29	30	22
Portslade Athletic	14	5	2	7	17	29	17
Montpelier Villa	14	5	1	8	25	19	16
AFC Stanley	14	3	1	10	18	29	10
AFC Falmer Falcons	14	3	1	10	23	35	10

Division One

	Pld	W	D	L	F	A	Pts
BSM08	18	15	3	0	73	20	48
Ovingdean	18	15	2	1	64	24	47
Terrace Barbers	18	11	4	3	44	23	37
AFC Brighton & Hove S	18	9	2	7	63	37	29
Midway	18	8	2	8	40	46	26
Montpelier Villa Reserves	18	7	1	10	41	40	22
Vista	18	6	3	9	33	76	21
Montpelier View	18	3	4	11	31	52	13
Constant Service	18	2	2	14	21	48	8
Millhouse (Saturday)	18	1	3	14	16	60	6

Division Two

	Pld	W	D	L	F	A	Pts
Royal Hove	14	12	1	1	54	15	37
Boys Brigade Old Boys	14	11	1	2	63	15	34
ATS Southern	14	7	2	5	35	33	23
Rottingdean Village	14	7	2	5	34	36	23
TMG	14	4	3	7	28	36	15
Southwick Rangers	14	4	1	9	34	60	13
White Crow	14	4	0	10	22	44	12
Olympic Saltdean Oval	14	2	0	12	20	51	6

Division Three

	Pld	W	D	L	F	A	Pts
Hobgoblin	18	15	1	2	89	24	46
Deans Dynamos	18	13	0	5	59	46	39
Montpelier Villa "A"	18	11	2	5	44	23	35
Boys Brigade Old B Res.	18	7	5	6	36	38	26
Southwick Rangers Res.	18	7	5	6	39	44	26
Midway Reserves	18	7	4	7	43	48	25
Portslade Athletic Res.	18	4	5	9	29	37	17
CCK Reserves	18	4	5	9	38	52	17
FCShepherds	18	3	6	9	27	42	15
Hove Park Tavern	18	2	1	15	24	74	7

BRISTOL & AVON FOOTBALL LEAGUE

Premier Division

	P	W	D	L	F	A	Pts
AFC Hartcliffe (+3)	22	19	1	2	123	20	61
Amana SYF	22	16	1	5	63	34	49
Carmel United	22	16	0	6	104	32	48
Bailey Sports (-3)	22	15	2	5	92	25	44
Cutters Friday 'A'	22	13	2	7	47	27	41
De-Veys Reserves	22	12	0	10	48	46	36
Imperial Reserves	22	10	1	11	56	58	31
Real St George	22	8	2	12	59	79	26
Iron Acton 'B'	22	6	2	14	43	92	20
Greyfriars Athletic 'B'	22	6	0	16	33	70	18
Golden Hill Sports 'A'	22	3	2	17	15	95	11
Wanderers Reserves	22	1	1	20	22	127	4

Division One

	P	W	D	L	F	A	Pts
Broadwalk Reserves	21	19	1	1	127	25	58
Broad Plain 'A'	21	13	3	5	53	38	42
Sea Mills 'A'	21	10	6	5	67	50	36
Long Ashton 'A'	21	9	4	8	61	61	31
AFC Hartcliffe Reserves	21	8	3	10	60	54	27
Bradley Stoke Town 'B'	21	7	4	10	55	76	25
Iron Acton 'C'	21	3	2	16	36	86	11
Wessex Wanderers 'A'	21	3	1	17	31	100	10

BRISTOL & DISTRICT LEAGUE

Senior Dlivision

	P	W	D	L	F	A	Pts
Brislington Cricketers	26	20	3	3	100	31	63
Eden Grove	26	20	1	5	115	41	61
Cribbs Friends Life Res.	26	19	3	4	89	31	60
Hanham Athletic Reserves	26	14	5	6	65	40	47
Chipping Sodbury Town R.	26	15	2	9	57	53	47
Shirehampton Reserves	26	12	3	11	64	70	39
Sea Mills Park	26	11	5	10	63	42	38
Wick Reserves	26	10	6	10	50	46	36
Bristol Barcelona	26	9	4	13	70	67	31
Roman Glass St George 'A'	26	9	4	13	45	56	31
Nicholas Wanderers Res	26	6	5	15	28	52	23
Longwell Green Sports 'A'	26	7	2	16	47	83	23
Hallen 'A' (-3)	26	5	5	16	47	95	17
Lloyd Coalpit Heath	26	0	0	26	18	151	0

LEAGUE TABLES

Division One

	P	W	D	L	F	A	Pts
Warmley Saints	26	21	2	3	126	37	65
Crosscourt United	26	18	5	3	75	33	59
Iron Acton	26	18	3	5	91	39	57
Stockwood Wanderers	26	18	1	7	92	48	55
Mendip United Reserves	26	15	1	10	62	56	46
AEK Boco Reserves	26	14	3	9	65	33	45
Rangeworthy	26	13	1	12	67	57	40
St Pancras (-3)	25	12	2	12	62	47	35
Hambrook	26	9	5	12	66	54	32
Talbot Knowle United	26	10	2	14	62	72	32
Miners	26	5	3	17	32	87	18
Seymour United Reserves	26	6	0	20	39	105	18
DRG Frenchay Reserves	26	5	1	20	25	122	16
Bitton 'A'	26	2	1	21	27	101	7

Division Two

	P	W	D	L	F	A	Pts
Portville Warriors	24	20	1	3	80	28	61
De Veys	24	19	0	5	80	28	57
Stanton Drew	24	16	1	7	77	54	49
Bradley Stoke Town	24	14	3	7	72	47	45
Pucklechurch Sports	24	13	3	8	51	38	42
Hanham Athletic 'A'	24	12	4	8	51	47	40
Bendix	24	8	4	12	62	58	28
Wnterbourne United 'A'	24	9	1	14	52	57	28
Frys Club 'A'	24	8	2	14	42	71	26
Nicholas Wanderers 'A'	24	6	3	15	31	73	21
South Bristol Central	24	5	4	15	36	61	19
Iron Acton Res	24	5	3	16	32	68	18
Chipping Sodbury Town 'A'	24	5	3	16	29	65	18

Division Three

	P	W	D	L	F	A	Pts
Lebeq FC.Res	24	22	1	1	98	26	67
Hartcliffe	24	17	4	3	92	33	55
Totterdown United Reserves	24	16	4	4	59	34	52
Soundwell Victoria	24	15	5	4	57	38	50
Roman Glass St George 'B'	24	9	4	10	49	54	31
Horfield United	24	9	3	12	63	53	30
Greyfriars Athletic Reserves	24	9	3	12	55	58	30
Bristol Barcelona	24	8	3	13	44	52	27
Henbury F C 'A'	24	8	3	13	37	50	27
Olveston United Reserves	24	6	5	13	35	64	23
Yate Athletic	24	5	6	13	38	66	21
Lawrence Rovers Res	24	5	2	17	39	81	17
Hambrook Reserves	24	3	3	18	35	92	12

Division Four

	P	W	D	L	F	A	Pts
Real Thornbury	26	23	1	2	106	30	70
Patchway North End	26	21	2	3	77	34	65
Frampton Athletic Reserves	26	16	3	7	64	34	51
Cribbs Friends Life 'A'	26	15	1	10	80	64	46
AEK Boco 'A'	26	14	2	10	73	54	44
Shirehampton 'A'	26	10	3	13	71	88	33
Wick 'A' (-3)	26	9	7	10	52	59	31
Pucklechurch Sports Res.	26	8	6	12	47	53	30
Hallen 'B'	26	8	4	14	64	71	28
Hillfields Old Boys (-3)	26	10	1	15	63	73	28
Shaftesbury Crusade Res.	26	8	3	15	54	72	27
Talbot Knowle United	26	8	1	17	49	80	25
Brislington Cricketers Res.	26	7	3	16	59	103	24
Made for Ever Reserves	26	6	1	19	45	89	19

Division Five

	P	W	D	L	F	A	Pts
Sea Mills Park Res	26	20	3	3	103	54	63
Bishopsworth United	26	19	2	5	93	37	59
Soundwell Victoria Res	26	16	2	8	81	55	50
Bradley Stoke Town Res.	26	14	4	8	65	49	46
Crosscourt United Reserves	26	14	2	9	57	51	44
Warmley Saints Res	26	11	6	9	59	44	39
Fishponds Athletic	26	13	0	13	76	66	39
Roman Glass St George C.	26	11	4	11	56	48	**37**
Highridge United 'A'	26	9	7	9	54	54	34
Bendix Reserves	26	9	0	17	50	110	27
Oldland Abbotonians 'A'	26	7	5	14	56	66	26
Seymour United 'A'	26	6	2	18	43	77	20
Iron Acton 'A'	26	5	4	17	39	81	19
Brimsham Green Reserves	26	2	9	15	37	77	15

Division Six

	P	W	D	L	F	A	Pts
Broadlands F.C	24	20	0	4	114	31	60
South Bristol Central Res.	24	18	3	3	113	44	57
Old Sodbury Res	24	17	2	5	97	45	53
Greyfriars Athletic 'A'	24	16	1	7	94	53	49
Westerleigh Sports	24	14	4	6	87	54	46
Frys Club 'B'	24	11	6	6	66	47	39
Rangeworthy Reserves	24	8	4	12	60	78	28
Yate Athletic	24	7	2	14	45	112	23
Cribbs Friends Life 'B'	24	6	4	14	61	92	22
Nicholas Wanderers 'B'	24	6	4	14	45	77	22
Winford PH 'A'	24	6	3	15	57	101	21
Bradley Stoke Town 'A'	24	4	3	17	47	91	15
Stanton Drew Res	24	3	2	19	42	103	11

BRISTOL DOWNS LEAGUE

Division One

	P	W	D	L	F	A	Pts
Torpedo	26	22	2	2	102	27	68
Sneyd Park	26	16	7	3	90	40	55
Lawes Juniors	26	17	4	5	86	41	55
Sporting Greyhound	26	15	4	7	67	43	49
Ashley	26	13	4	9	65	59	43
Saints Old Boys	26	13	4	9	60	60	43
Cotswool	26	12	1	13	51	62	37
Retainers	26	11	1	14	42	55	34
Clifton Rockets	26	9	4	13	43	67	31
AFC Bohemia	26	7	4	15	54	65	25
Clifton St Vincents	26	5	9	12	42	56	24
Jamaica Bell	26	6	3	17	32	65	21
Portland Old Boys	26	5	3	18	36	72	18
Evergreen	26	5	2	19	41	102	17

Division Two

	P	W	D	L	F	A	Pts
DAC Beachcroft	22	14	5	3	68	31	47
Torpedo Res	22	13	6	3	54	29	45
Easton Cowboys	22	13	6	3	48	26	45
Hare on the Hill	22	12	6	4	52	27	42
Sneyd Park Res	22	9	6	7	43	39	33
Ashley Res	22	8	7	7	53	48	31
Sporting Greyhound Res	22	8	3	11	43	47	27
Jersey Rangers	22	7	5	10	52	49	26
Tebby AFC	22	5	7	10	32	49	22
Clifton St Vincents Res	22	5	5	12	29	43	20
Lion FC	22	4	7	11	43	56	19
Cotswool Res	22	1	3	18	20	93	6

Division Three

	P	W	D	L	F	A	Pts
Saints Old Boys Res	26	19	0	7	71	42	57
St Andrews	26	17	5	4	77	39	56
Greens Park Rangers	26	16	5	5	65	29	53
Torpedo A	26	12	3	11	46	36	39
Portland Old Boys Res	26	10	5	11	49	58	35
Corinthians	26	8	9	9	45	40	33
Clifton Rockets Res (-3)	26	11	3	12	54	60	33
Clifton St Vincents A	26	9	6	11	60	71	33
Sneyd Park A	26	9	5	12	53	51	32
Retainers Res (-3)	26	10	5	11	51	51	32
Easton Cowboys Res	26	9	5	12	52	57	32
Wellington Wanderers (-3)	26	9	5	12	59	74	29
Bengal Tigers	26	9	2	15	48	71	29
Durdham Down Adult School	26	4	2	20	34	85	14

Division Four

	P	W	D	L	F	A	Pts
Helios FC	26	20	3	3	89	43	63
Cotham Old Boys	26	20	2	4	97	35	62
Old Cliftonians	26	16	7	3	80	48	55
Clifton St Vincents B	26	17	1	8	88	53	52
West Town United	26	15	2	9	73	59	47
Torpedo B	26	10	6	10	61	64	36
Retainers A	26	10	5	11	47	59	35
NCSF United	26	9	7	10	65	67	34
Sneyd Park B	26	10	3	13	79	65	33
Tebby AFC Res	26	8	3	15	55	79	27
Lion FC Res	26	6	4	16	41	62	22
Jersey Rangers Res	26	5	4	17	31	79	19
Conham Rangers (-3)	26	5	6	15	41	80	18
Luccombe Garage	26	1	7	18	40	94	10

BRISTOL PREMIER COMBINATION

Premier Division

	P	W	D	L	F	A	Pts
Mendip United	22	17	3	2	72	22	54
Longwell Green Reserves	22	16	3	3	59	23	51
Lebeq (Saturday) FC	22	15	2	5	67	34	47
Hallen Reserves	22	12	3	7	53	41	39
Wick	22	11	4	7	67	41	37
Winterbourne United Res.	22	9	5	8	60	57	32
Bitton Reserves	22	9	1	12	54	52	28
Nicholas Wanderers	22	6	6	10	39	61	24
Totterdown United	22	6	5	11	46	60	23
Roman Glass/St George R.	22	6	3	13	36	63	21
Hartcliffe	22	3	5	14	34	77	14
Lawrence Rovers	22	0	4	18	30	86	4

Premier One

	P	W	D	L	F	A	Pts
Shaftesbury Crusade	26	22	0	4	70	26	66
A.E.K. Boco	26	17	3	3	84	25	63
Old Sodbury	26	14	5	7	70	37	47
Bristol Manor Farm Res.	26	13	6	7	70	44	45
Highridge United	26	14	3	9	68	43	45
Frampton Athletic	26	12	6	8	58	54	42
Patchway Town Reserves	26	10	3	13	40	48	33
Seymour United	26	8	6	12	42	60	30
Olveston United	26	8	5	13	51	55	29
Greyfriars Athletic	26	7	8	11	39	52	29
Henbury AFC Reserves	26	7	8	11	47	62	29
Brimsham Green	26	3	7	16	33	65	16
Made for Ever (-6)	26	5	5	16	46	117	14
Oldland Abbotonians R. (-3)	26	2	9	15	36	66	12

BRISTOL SUBURBAN LEAGUE

Premier Division One

	P	W	D	L	F	A	Pts
Southmead CS Athletic	24	18	3	3	95	40	57
Broad Plain House	24	17	6	1	73	24	57
Bristol Telephones	24	18	1	5	75	37	55
Little Stoke	24	15	3	6	80	46	48
Lawrence Weston	24	14	4	6	51	29	46
Ashton United	24	11	3	10	53	50	36
St Aldhelms	24	9	2	13	60	76	29
Winford PH	24	7	5	12	48	55	26
Avonmouth	24	7	5	12	46	61	26
Fishponds Old Boys	24	7	5	12	50	68	26
Cadbury Heath Reserves	24	4	4	16	25	66	16
Old Georgians	24	4	3	17	35	81	15
Almondsbury Town	24	1	4	19	25	83	7

Premier Division Two

	P	W	D	L	F	A	Pts
Stoke Gifford United	24	20	3	1	105	27	63
Severn Beach	24	15	6	3	60	30	51
Easton Cowboys Suburbia	24	15	3	6	75	24	47
Southmead CS Athletic Res	24	14	3	7	67	44	45
Brislington A	24	13	3	8	63	51	42
Tytherington Rocks Res	24	12	4	8	49	45	40
Bristol Athletic	24	10	7	7	42	45	37
Ridings High	24	9	5	10	49	40	32
Glenside 5 Old Boys	24	8	3	13	47	65	27
Almondsbury UWE Res	24	7	5	12	33	43	26
Whitchurch	24	4	2	18	37	77	14
Avonmouth Res	24	2	6	16	25	72	12
St Aldhelms Res	24	0	4	20	23	112	4

Division One

	P	W	D	L	F	A	Pts
Ridings High Res	24	18	5	1	95	39	59
Rockleaze Rangers Res	24	18	1	5	70	29	55
Totterdown POB	24	14	3	7	72	52	45
Ingleside	23	12	6	5	62	39	40
Wessex Wanderers	23	11	6	6	47	35	39
Golden Hill Sports	24	10	4	10	49	49	34
Broad Plain House Res	24	7	9	8	56	53	30
Parson Street Old Boys	24	8	6	10	45	52	30
Ashton Backwell Colts	24	9	1	14	52	61	28
Filton Athletic	24	7	4	13	33	49	25
Tyndalls Park Rangers	24	7	4	13	37	56	25
Fishponds Old Boys Res	24	4	4	16	27	81	16
Old Cothamians	24	2	3	19	18	68	9

Ingleside v Wessex Wanderers not played, points awarded to Wessex Wanderers.

LEAGUE TABLES

Division Two

	P	W	D	L	F	A	Pts
Lebeq United	26	19	4	3	87	46	61
CAB Olympic SC	26	19	2	5	105	30	59
Downend Foresters	26	16	1	9	82	51	49
AFC Mangotsfield	26	14	5	7	51	43	47
Cleeve Colts	26	14	1	11	76	57	43
Little Stoke Res	26	12	2	12	64	65	38
Lawrence Weston Res	26	11	3	12	66	59	36
Hengrove Athletic	26	10	3	13	49	51	33
Oldbury FC	26	9	5	12	46	63	32
Stoke Gifford United Res	26	8	5	13	53	72	29
Almondsbury UWE A	26	8	5	13	48	85	29
Wanderers	26	7	6	13	47	58	27
Corinthian Sports	26	8	0	18	54	96	24
Bristol Telephones Res	26	3	6	17	27	79	15

Division Three

	P	W	D	L	F	A	Pts
Poker County UK	24	21	1	2	110	31	64
Stoke Rangers	24	18	2	4	90	35	56
Whitchurch Res	24	16	1	7	82	56	49
Fry's Club OB	24	14	3	7	56	42	45
Hydez Futebol Clube	24	14	3	7	51	39	45
Keynsham Town A	24	11	2	11	69	63	35
Filton Athletic Res	24	9	4	11	40	61	31
Ashton United Res	24	9	2	13	41	56	29
Hanham Athletic Colts	24	7	5	12	43	56	26
Old Cothamians Res	24	8	2	14	44	63	26
Emersons Green	24	6	6	12	53	60	24
Fishponds Old Boys A	24	2	4	18	25	82	10
Old Georgians Res	24	2	3	19	47	107	9

Division Four

	P	W	D	L	F	A	Pts
St Annes Town	24	17	3	4	76	30	54
Glenside 5 Old Boys Res	24	15	4	5	66	39	49
Long Ashton Reserves	24	13	7	4	54	33	46
AEK Boco Colts	24	12	7	5	63	45	43
Severn Beach Res	24	11	7	6	47	31	40
Rockleaze Rangers 'A'	24	11	6	7	50	41	39
Bristol Sports Utd	24	11	4	9	63	49	37
Coupland Insulation	24	9	7	8	56	59	34
AFC Keynsham	24	8	6	10	34	45	30
Winford PH Res	24	5	5	14	52	64	20
Rhubarb Athletic	24	5	5	14	48	74	20
Wessex Wanderers Res	24	6	1	17	37	79	19
Brandon Sports	24	2	0	22	27	84	6

Division Five

	P	W	D	L	F	A	Pts
Downend Foresters Res	28	21	2	5	113	45	65
Broadwalk	28	21	1	6	119	39	64
Rockleaze Rangers B	28	18	3	7	94	42	57
Southern Athletic	28	18	3	7	84	69	57
Ridings High 'A'	28	17	2	9	115	64	53
Parson Street Old Boys Res	28	17	2	9	90	68	53
Cadbury Heath 'A'	28	13	3	12	74	83	42
Totterdown POB Res	28	12	2	14	65	96	38
Lawrence Weston A	28	10	2	16	59	86	32
Severnside	28	9	2	17	63	95	29
Oldbury FC Res	28	8	4	16	52	75	28
Knowle Rangers	28	8	3	17	65	89	27
Stoke Gifford United A	28	8	3	17	47	99	27
Rolls Royce	28	7	2	19	65	112	23
Golden Hill Sports Res	28	5	2	21	50	93	17

BURTON & DISTRICT FOOTBALL ASSOCIATION

Premier Division

	P	W	D	L	F	A	Pts
Lonny FC	18	15	1	2	69	23	46
Uxbridge FC	18	13	4	1	54	25	43
Stretton Spartans	18	10	4	4	58	35	34
Real Medina F C	18	10	3	5	42	31	33
Gresley	18	7	4	7	43	37	25
Barton United	18	6	5	7	40	36	23
Ashbourne F C Reserves	18	6	3	9	44	44	21
The Dart	18	5	1	12	43	58	16
The Sump	18	3	2	13	24	58	11
Blacksmiths Arms	18	0	3	15	21	91	3

Championship

	P	W	D	L	F	A	Pts
Midway B	20	15	3	2	114	22	48
Overseal Saint Matthews	20	14	2	4	82	21	44
Willington	20	12	5	3	67	27	41
T L Darby	20	7	2	11	39	46	23
Midway A	20	5	0	15	32	102	15
Whittington	20	1	0	19	21	137	3

CAPITAL LEAGUE

Western Division

	P	W	D	L	F	A	Pts
Wealdstone	18	14	1	3	64	31	43
Wingate & Finchley	18	12	1	5	50	28	37
Harrow Borough	18	12	1	5	43	26	37
Staines Town	18	11	3	4	61	24	36
Ashford Town (Mdx)	18	7	4	7	53	44	25
Bedfont Town	18	8	0	10	41	50	24
Chertsey Town	18	7	1	10	36	70	22
Aylesbury	18	6	2	10	47	44	20
Burnham	18	3	5	10	23	39	14
Kentish Town	18	1	0	17	24	86	3

Eastern Division

	P	W	D	L	F	A	Pts
Billericay Town (-3)	20	15	2	3	54	27	44
Braintree Town	20	14	2	4	52	28	44
Ebbsfleet United	20	13	3	4	62	22	42
Chelmsford City	20	10	4	6	46	25	34
Cheshunt	20	7	5	8	32	34	26
Enfield Town	20	6	4	10	39	51	22
Harlow Town	20	6	4	10	25	41	22
Enfield 1893	20	4	7	9	31	54	19
Potters Bar Town	20	4	6	10	28	49	18
AFC Hornchurch	20	4	5	11	20	41	17
Brentwood Town	20	3	6	11	21	38	15

CENTRAL & SOUTH NORFOLK LEAGUE

Division One

	P	W	D	L	F	A	Pts
Feltwell Utd	24	17	3	4	85	38	54
Morley Village	24	14	5	5	70	43	47
Dereham Town A	24	14	3	7	65	39	45
Tacolneston	24	13	6	5	59	47	45
Northwold S&SC	24	12	4	8	64	50	40
Shipdham	24	10	6	8	55	43	36
Bridgham Utd.	24	9	4	11	56	64	31
Gressenhall	24	6	11	7	51	45	29
Thetford Rovers Res	24	7	8	9	48	46	29
Swaffham Town A	24	8	4	12	59	75	28
Shropham Utd.	24	8	3	13	41	53	27
Rockland Utd.	24	4	5	15	32	82	17
Narborough	24	1	4	19	20	80	7

Division Two

	P	W	D	L	F	A	Pts
Castle Acre Swifts	24	23	1	0	106	31	70
Yaxham	24	19	3	2	121	41	60
North Elmham	24	19	2	3	113	46	59
Sporle	24	12	5	7	94	69	41
Nostro (-3)	24	14	2	8	61	47	41
Thurton & Ashby	24	10	1	13	86	65	31
Methwold Rovers	24	8	3	13	49	86	27
Necton	24	8	2	14	69	62	26
Breckland Wanderers	24	7	2	15	65	108	23
West End	24	5	4	15	46	76	19
Saham Toney Res.	24	5	4	15	47	91	19
Hethersett Athletic	24	5	3	16	41	86	18
Cockers	24	4	2	18	48	138	14

Division Three

	P	W	D	L	F	A	Pts
Tugas Utd	28	22	5	1	89	29	71
Scarning	28	21	3	4	103	39	66
Mulbarton Wanderers Res	28	20	5	3	102	28	65
Bawdeswell	28	19	8	1	89	30	65
Rampant Horse	28	14	3	11	76	57	45
Marham Wanderers	28	12	9	7	69	56	45
Mattishall A	28	13	2	13	57	58	41
Wendling	28	12	5	11	69	76	41
Colkirk	28	9	6	13	58	58	33
Stoke Ferry	28	9	1	18	56	79	28
Splitz Utd	28	7	3	18	44	77	24
Hingham Athletic Res.	28	6	5	17	47	73	23
Rockland Utd. Res.	28	6	4	18	36	74	22
Great Cressingham	28	5	5	18	40	91	20
Narborough Res	28	2	2	24	27	137	8

Division Four

	P	W	D	L	F	A	Pts
Litcham	28	24	2	2	117	27	74
Watton Utd A	28	23	2	3	84	25	71
North Elmham Res	28	18	3	7	101	39	57
Shropham Utd. Res.	28	17	5	6	84	54	56
Methwold Rovers Res	28	15	5	8	72	44	50
Nostro Res	28	15	3	10	71	55	48
Yaxham Res	28	14	5	9	66	53	47
Weasenham Wanderers	28	12	3	13	68	63	39
Walsingham	28	9	9	10	68	65	36
Beetley Utd	28	9	6	13	55	77	33
Tacolneston Res	28	8	4	16	63	68	28
Castle Acre Swifts Res	28	6	3	19	33	78	21
Dereham Cockers Utd	28	5	2	21	38	112	17
Shipdham Res	28	4	4	20	36	96	16
Methwold Utd	28	2	2	24	19	119	8

CHELTENHAM ASSOCIATION LEAGUE

Division One

	P	W	D	L	F	A	Pts
Real Whaddon	22	16	4	2	94	32	52
Charlton Rovers	22	13	4	5	59	28	43
Falcons	22	13	4	5	48	32	43
Kings AFC	22	12	5	5	53	30	41
AC Olympia	22	12	4	6	48	33	40
Whaddon United	22	10	4	8	54	45	34
Finlay Rovers (-1)	22	9	7	6	38	29	33
Gloucester Elmleaze (-3)	22	7	6	9	27	35	24
Star FC Res	22	4	4	14	39	63	16
Apperley & Tewkesbury D.	22	4	4	14	30	56	16
Bishops Cleeve III	22	4	1	17	26	78	13
Newton FC	22	3	3	16	28	83	12

Division Two

	P	W	D	L	F	A	Pts
Bibury	20	18	0	2	87	17	54
Butlers FC	20	14	2	4	57	32	44
Tewkesbury Town	20	9	5	6	44	47	32
Northway	20	10	1	9	41	43	31
Bredon Res	20	8	5	7	36	31	29
Gala Wilton Reserves	20	8	3	9	48	46	27
Winchcombe Town Res.20	8	3	9	36	44	27	
Brockworth Albion Res	20	7	2	11	43	60	23
Northleach Town	20	5	5	10	29	56	20
FC Barometrics Res	20	3	5	12	14	34	14
Prestbury Rovers	20	4	1	15	25	50	13

Division Three

	P	W	D	L	F	A	Pts
Hanley Swan	24	18	2	4	100	42	56
Shurdington Rovers	24	15	5	4	77	35	50
Southside	24	15	3	6	75	41	48
R.S.G.	24	14	4	6	90	41	46
Moreton Rangers Res	24	14	3	7	57	32	45
Upton Town	24	13	4	7	52	30	43
Churchdown Panthers	24	12	5	7	69	49	41
Chelt Civil Service Res.	24	8	2	14	47	66	26
Chelt Saracens III	24	7	4	13	69	82	25
Andoversford	24	6	2	16	49	110	20
Tivoli Rovers	24	5	2	17	46	94	17
Belmore (-7)	24	5	5	14	41	82	13
Charlton Rovers Res (-3)	24	3	1	20	28	96	7

LEAGUE TABLES

Division Four	P	W	D	L	F	A	Pts
FC Lakeside	26	23	1	2	146	28	70
Whaddon United Reserves	26	20	2	4	115	46	62
Villagereal	26	20	2	4	91	31	62
Naunton Park Rovers	26	16	3	7	85	53	51
W.M.K.	26	14	2	10	88	58	44
Falcons Res	26	13	0	13	77	75	39
Kings AFC Reserves	26	11	4	11	49	62	37
Hatherley Rangers (-3)	26	10	4	12	69	61	31
Elmbridge OB	26	8	3	15	72	103	27
Chelt Civil Service III	26	8	2	16	61	98	26
Bredon III	26	5	6	15	50	89	21
Bourton Rovers Res (-3)	26	6	4	16	46	87	19
Chelt Saracens IV (-3)	26	6	0	20	43	148	15
Star FC III (-3)	26	3	5	18	36	89	11

Division Five	P	W	D	L	F	A	Pts
Welland FC (-3)	26	20	4	2	85	33	61
Priors	26	18	1	7	100	50	55
Cheltonians FC	26	16	4	6	101	53	52
Fintan (-3)	26	17	4	5	75	38	52
Montpellier (-3)	26	14	3	9	78	46	42
AC Olympia Res	26	12	6	8	78	48	42
Tewkesbury Town Res	26	13	3	10	58	72	42
Gala Wilton III	26	11	3	12	58	50	36
Leckhampton Rovers	26	10	3	13	57	49	33
Sherborne Harriers	26	8	2	16	48	71	26
Apperley & Tewkesbury D.R	26	6	5	15	51	89	23
Smiths Athletic Res (-3)	26	7	3	16	38	61	21
FC Barometrics III (-3)	26	5	4	17	25	97	16
Andoversford Reserves	26	2	1	23	25	120	7

Division Six	P	W	D	L	F	A	Pts
Newlands Athletic (-2)	24	22	1	1	132	17	65
Dowty Dynamos	24	18	2	4	94	43	56
Hesters Way United (-7)	24	20	1	3	109	36	54
Pittville United	24	13	3	8	69	48	42
Southside Reserves	24	13	2	9	63	47	41
Charlton Rovers III	24	11	3	10	60	64	36
Shurdington Rovers Res	24	9	1	14	36	48	28
Winchcombe Town III	24	9	1	14	45	74	28
Fintan Reserves (-7)	24	8	2	14	46	78	19
Chelt Civil Service IV (-5)	24	7	1	16	48	81	19
Northleach Town Reserves	24	6	1	17	33	86	19
Apperley & Tewkesbury D.III	24	5	2	17	34	101	17
Hatherley FC	24	4	2	18	25	71	14

Division One	P	W	D	L	F	A	Pts
Peacock 09 FC	22	18	2	2	61	18	56
Shaftsbury Youth FC	22	16	1	5	102	35	49
Raby Villa FC	22	14	4	4	71	49	46
Halfwayhouse Celtic FC	22	14	2	6	62	38	44
Uberlube FC	22	11	4	7	49	43	37
Orange Athletic Chester FC	22	9	6	7	52	47	33
Chester Nomads III FC	22	10	3	9	45	48	33
Chester Celtic FC	22	7	3	12	37	58	24
Ashton FC	22	5	4	13	43	70	19
Cestrian Alex FC	22	4	4	14	43	66	16
Duddon Utd FC	22	3	4	15	28	60	13
Hoole Rangers Res FC	22	2	1	19	15	76	7

Division Two	P	W	D	L	F	A	Pts
Lache FC	20	18	1	1	123	21	55
FC Village	20	16	2	2	82	27	50
Woodlands Santos FC	20	14	2	4	80	38	44
Pensby Athletic FC	20	13	2	5	64	39	41
Neston Nomads FC	20	10	3	7	54	54	33
Lodge Bar FC	20	7	4	9	47	55	25
Boughton Athletic FC	20	5	3	12	45	92	18
Peacock 09 FC	20	5	1	14	32	62	16
Rangers Breaks FC	20	4	2	14	29	67	14
Crossway Res FC	20	3	2	15	32	82	11
Orange Ath. Chester II FC	20	3	2	15	37	88	11

Division Three	P	W	D	L	F	A	Pts
Birkenhead Town FC	18	14	1	3	90	24	43
Elton Rigger FC	18	13	4	1	87	27	43
Seven Stiles FC	18	13	0	5	73	25	39
Ellesmere Port Town FC	18	11	4	3	61	22	37
Little Sutton Villa FC	18	8	5	5	42	41	29
Ridgewood Rangers FC	18	7	1	10	44	62	22
Central Park FC	18	6	2	10	45	71	20
Bronze Social FC	18	4	2	12	23	64	14
Oldershaw FC	18	3	1	14	25	87	10
Chester Athletic FC	18	1	0	17	20	87	3

CHESTER & DISTRICT LEAGUE

Premier Division	P	W	D	L	F	A	Pts
Kelsall FC	20	15	3	2	72	34	48
Waggon & Horses FC	20	13	3	4	72	42	42
Kelma FC	20	12	3	5	47	32	39
Hoole Rangers FC	20	10	5	5	51	46	35
Tarvin 2000 Athletic FC	20	9	2	9	47	54	29
Cross Foxes FC	20	8	4	8	59	47	28
BYC Highfield FC	20	7	4	9	44	53	25
Ellesmere Port III FC	20	5	4	11	45	60	19
Groves Sports & Social FC	20	5	3	12	40	73	18
Levers Athletic FC	20	4	3	13	41	58	15
Crossway FC	20	4	2	14	52	71	14

CHORLEY & DISTRICT ALLIANCE

	P	W	D	L	F	A	Pts
Eagle	21	17	1	3	119	41	52
Whittle	21	15	0	6	92	42	45
Gillibrand Saints	21	11	2	8	76	60	35
Hop Pocket	21	10	3	8	67	44	33
Croston Sports Club	21	9	4	8	64	55	31
Eagle Reserves	21	6	3	12	73	69	21
International Allstars	21	7	0	14	58	79	21
Chorley Crusaders	21	2	1	18	29	164	7

Swan- record expunged.

CIRENCESTER & DISTRICT LEAGUE

Division One	P	W	D	L	F	A	Pts
Down Ampney	18	13	4	1	61	37	43
Real Fairford	18	11	3	4	65	34	36
Poulton	18	9	4	5	61	37	31
South Cerney	18	9	3	6	35	36	30
CHQ United (-6)	18	10	4	4	55	33	28
The Beeches	18	6	4	8	41	43	22
Oaksey	18	5	2	11	35	60	17
Stratton United	18	4	2	12	29	66	14
Ashton Keynes Res. (-7)	18	4	2	12	35	46	7
Lechlade FC 87 (-7)	18	4	2	12	33	58	7

Division Two	P	W	D	L	F	A	Pts
Bibury Reserves	18	15	3	0	80	19	48
CHQ United Reserves	18	11	3	4	56	34	36
Corinium Sports (-3)	18	11	3	4	69	34	33
Oaksey Reserves (-3)	18	9	2	7	41	46	26
The Beeches Reserves	18	8	0	10	54	50	24
Sherston	18	7	1	10	45	51	22
Kingshill Sports Reserves	18	7	1	10	33	51	22
South Cerney Reserves	18	6	1	11	48	73	19
Down Ampney Reserves (-2)	18	5	2	11	42	67	15
Poulton Reserves	18	3	0	15	22	65	9

COLCHESTER & EAST ESSEX LEAGUE

Premier Division	Pld	W	D	L	F	A	Pts
Tollesbury	22	16	5	1	77	19	53
Stoke-by-Nayland	22	14	3	5	72	36	45
Boxford Rovers	22	14	1	7	68	46	43
Colchester Athletic	22	12	4	6	49	46	40
Cinque Port	22	11	4	7	54	48	37
Univ'y of Essex "A"	22	9	5	8	42	40	32
Oyster	22	7	6	9	53	49	27
Horkesley	22	7	5	10	45	48	26
Castle	22	7	4	11	43	52	25
Clacton United Reserves	22	6	5	11	45	55	23
Brantham Athletic "A"	22	4	3	15	34	65	15
Wimpole 2000	22	1	3	18	22	100	6

CORNWALL COMBINATION

	Pld	W	D	L	F	A	Pts
Falmouth Town Reserves	36	25	8	3	111	37	83
Penryn Athletic Reserves	36	23	8	5	94	47	77
St Ives Town	36	23	3	10	72	51	72
Illogan RBL	36	22	5	9	97	43	71
St Agnes	36	20	8	8	79	49	68
St Just (-3)	36	19	5	12	86	59	59
RNAS Culdrose (-1)	36	15	6	15	81	82	50
Falmouth Athletic DC	36	18	4	14	107	80	58
Newquay Reserves	36	15	9	12	76	68	54
Perranwell	36	15	8	13	87	65	53
Wendron United	36	15	7	14	71	72	52
Pendeen Rovers	36	14	6	16	60	67	48
St Day (-4)	36	14	8	14	62	77	46
Troon	36	13	6	17	65	71	45
Hayle Reserves	36	9	8	19	45	78	**35**
Porthleven Reserves	36	7	3	26	54	110	24
Mullion	36	6	4	26	62	101	22
Holman Sports Club (-3)	36	6	6	24	42	105	21
Penzance Reserves	36	5	4	27	35	130	19

CRAVEN & DISTRICT LEAGUE

Premier Division	Pld	W	D	L	F	A	Pts
Skipton LMS	20	13	5	2	70	34	44
Cowling	20	14	2	4	47	24	44
Rolls	20	12	2	6	62	34	38
Carleton	20	8	6	6	55	47	30
Grassington United	20	8	4	8	36	39	28
WFC Clitheroe	20	8	3	9	40	47	27
Grindleton	20	7	3	10	45	51	24
Ighton Leigh	20	7	1	12	44	66	22
Embsay	20	6	3	11	33	44	21
Pendle Athletic	20	4	5	11	31	51	17
Settle United	20	5	2	13	33	59	17

Division One	Pld	W	D	L	F	A	Pts
Cross Hills	20	16	1	3	53	33	49
Trawden Celtic	20	15	2	3	57	30	47
Cononley Sports	20	11	3	6	48	41	36
Wilsden Athletic	20	10	3	7	59	30	33
Chatburn	20	9	3	8	48	50	30
Earby Town	20	8	5	7	36	38	29
Gargrave	20	7	2	11	34	39	23
Silsden Whitestar	20	6	4	10	37	44	22
Oakworth	20	5	3	12	27	44	18
Skipton LMS Reserves	20	5	0	15	35	56	15
Bingley Town	20	3	4	13	28	57	13

Division Two	Pld	W	D	L	F	A	Pts
Gargrave Reserves	20	15	2	3	67	36	47
Hellifield Sports	20	12	2	6	60	35	38
Pendle	20	12	2	6	49	36	38
Rolls Reserves	20	9	5	6	58	52	32
Skipton Town	20	9	2	9	61	52	29
Pendle Renegades	20	8	3	9	50	48	27
Ingrow and Worh Valley	20	8	3	9	49	60	27
Barnoldswick Barons	20	5	7	8	48	56	22
Embsay Reserves	20	6	3	11	35	51	21
Bradley	20	4	6	10	31	51	18
Grassington United Res.	20	4	1	15	33	64	13

Division Three	Pld	W	D	L	F	A	Pts
Earby Town Reserves	18	11	2	5	55	28	35
AFC Colne	18	10	4	4	56	36	34
Silsden Whitestar Res.	18	8	4	6	57	62	28
Oakworth Reserves	18	8	2	8	48	35	26
Grindleton Reserves	18	8	2	8	58	57	26
Settle United Reserves	18	8	1	9	36	38	25
Oxenhope Recreat'n "A"	18	7	3	8	34	42	24
Cononley Sports Reserves	18	7	1	10	42	68	22
Cowling Reserves	18	6	3	9	26	37	21
Barnoldswick Barons Res	18	5	2	11	42	51	17
Bingley Town Reserves - record expunged							

LEAGUE TABLES

Division Four	Pld	W	D	L	F	A	Pts
Cross Hills Reserves	18	14	2	2	56	17	44
Ingrow&Worh Valley Res	18	11	4	3	68	27	37
Carleton Reserves	18	10	3	5	34	22	33
Pendle Renegades Ress	18	9	3	6	53	29	30
Horton	18	8	4	6	57	40	28
Skipton Town Reserves	18	8	2	8	45	55	26
Sutton	18	7	4	7	49	50	25
Bradley Reserves	18	6	1	11	43	53	19
Addingham	18	3	1	14	32	74	10
Barn'wick Barons "A"	18	1	2	15	21	91	5

CREWE & DISTRICT LEAGUE

	P	W	D	L	F	A	Pts
Cuddington	24	21	3	0	109	26	66
Sandbach Town	24	17	3	4	99	36	54
Curshaws	24	16	2	6	68	46	50
Winnington Avenue	24	15	4	5	82	35	49
MMU Cheshire	24	15	2	7	80	44	47
Barnton Wanderers	24	13	4	7	69	64	43
Rudheath Social Reserves	24	10	4	10	58	51	34
Malpas Reserves	24	10	3	11	69	58	33
Tarporley Victoria Reserves	24	8	5	11	52	47	29
Bentley (-3)	24	6	3	15	68	88	18
Barnton Reserves	24	3	2	19	40	86	11
Barnton Wanderers Res.	24	1	3	20	31	147	6
Winnington Reserves	24	1	2	21	18	115	5

CROOK & DISTRICT LEAGUE

Division One	Pld	W	D	L	F	A	Pts
Bowes	18	15	0	3	83	32	45
Witton Park (-3)	18	14	1	3	69	32	40
Heighington	18	10	3	5	47	34	33
Middlestone Moor MA	18	8	2	8	38	48	26
Shildon Elm Rd WMC (-3)	18	8	3	7	45	47	24
Evenwood White Swan	18	7	3	8	42	44	24
Willington WCC	18	5	4	9	43	51	19
DSRM Social Club	18	5	2	11	50	52	17
Framwellgate Moor Salutation	18	4	4	10	34	63	16
Howden-le-W Aust. (-3)	18	2	2	14	35	83	5

CUMBERLAND COUNTY LEAGUE

Premier Division	P	W	D	L	F	A	Pts
Netherhall	18	15	1	2	59	18	46
Aspatria	18	13	1	4	63	37	40
Carlisle City Reserves	18	8	6	4	39	24	30
Wigton Harriers	18	8	4	6	41	35	28
Workington Red House	18	8	4	6	44	41	28
Longtown	18	8	3	7	36	35	27
Borough	18	7	2	9	42	52	23
Mirehouse	18	5	3	10	41	49	18
Cockermouth	18	3	2	13	39	65	11
Frizington Whitestar	18	0	4	14	17	65	1

DEVON & EXETER LEAGUE

Premier Division	P	W	D	L	F	A	Pts
St Martins	30	24	3	3	87	37	75
Seaton Town	30	23	3	4	107	46	72
Topsham Town	30	20	4	6	105	58	64
Newtown	30	16	4	10	79	51	52
Heavitree Social United	30	13	8	9	68	49	47
Hatherleigh Town	30	13	8	9	68	57	47
Willand Rovers Reserves	30	14	4	12	51	47	46
Thorverton	30	13	5	12	49	53	44
Morchard Bishop	30	12	6	12	62	65	42
Barnstaple Ton Reserves	30	11	8	11	53	50	41
Beer Albion	30	12	4	14	49	53	40
Budleigh Salterton Reserves	30	8	4	18	35	78	28
University of Exeter Reserves	30	8	3	19	40	73	27
Clyst Valley	30	7	2	21	40	71	23
East Budleigh (-4)	30	7	2	21	35	72	19
Alphington Reserves	30	4	2	24	25	93	14

Division One	P	W	D	L	F	A	Pts
Exmouth Amateurs	28	22	3	3	47	16	69
Bow AAC	28	19	5	4	60	17	62
Feniton (-4)	28	20	2	6	91	35	58
Phoenix Club (-4)	28	17	6	5	61	37	53
Tipton St John	28	13	6	9	55	42	45
Wellington Reserves	28	14	3	11	56	48	45
Cullompton Rangers Res.	28	11	5	12	39	42	38
Witheridge Reserves (-4)	28	9	6	13	56	63	31
University of Exeter "A"	28	8	6	14	38	48	30
Culm United	28	9	3	16	56	68	30
Heavitree Social United Res	28	7	7	14	46	63	28
Sidbury United	28	7	7	14	35	65	28
Exeter Civil Service Reserves	28	9	1	18	52	89	28
Beacon Knights	28	7	1	20	43	70	22
Chagford	28	4	7	17	40	72	19

Division Two	P	W	D	L	F	A	Pts
Tiverton Town Reserves	28	24	2	2	100	28	74
Chard Town Reserves	28	17	7	4	63	30	58
Colyton	28	16	4	8	77	51	52
Topsham Town Reserves	28	15	3	10	69	41	48
Sidmouth Town Reserves	28	14	4	10	55	48	46
Westexe Rovers	28	11	7	10	55	56	40
Elmore Reserves	28	12	3	13	51	59	39
Honiton Town	28	11	5	12	55	64	38
Halwill	28	11	4	13	59	64	37
Uplowman Athletic	28	10	4	14	58	63	34
Clyst Valley Reserves	28	8	6	14	52	70	30
Pinhoe	28	8	5	15	50	71	29
University of Exeter "B"	28	8	3	17	49	89	27
Broadclyst	28	6	6	16	46	71	24
Newtown Reserves	28	6	3	19	46	80	21

Division Three

	P	W	D	L	F	A	Pts
Bickleigh Reserves	22	16	4	2	70	22	52
Dawlish United	22	15	4	3	63	28	49
Colaton Raleigh	22	14	4	4	67	34	46
South Zeal United (-1)	22	13	3	6	55	35	41
Upottery	22	12	2	8	59	37	38
Sandford	22	10	3	9	43	52	33
Lympstone	22	10	2	10	61	52	32
Offwell Rangers	22	8	2	12	35	47	26
Tedbury St Mary	22	6	3	13	49	55	21
Winkleigh	22	5	2	15	40	62	17
North Tawton	22	5	2	15	37	81	17
Axminster Town Reserves	22	2	1	19	28	102	5

Crescent - record expunged.

Division Four

	P	W	D	L	F	A	Pts
Dolphin	26	18	3	5	112	39	57
Thorverton Reserves	26	17	2	7	62	42	53
Newton St Cyres	26	14	7	5	67	46	49
Hemyock	26	15	2	9	55	44	47
Crediton United Reserves	26	14	2	10	54	36	44
Okehampton Argyle Res.	26	12	4	10	59	52	40
Exmouth Amateurs Res (-1)	26	11	5	10	39	47	37
Whipton & Pinhoe	26	10	5	11	69	63	35
University of Exeter "C"	26	10	5	11	61	73	35
Kentisbeare	26	10	2	14	50	85	32
Seaton Town Reserves	26	7	4	15	48	68	25
Bampton	26	6	3	17	34	61	21
Countess Wear Dynamoes (-8)	26	7	5	14	48	63	18
Lapford	26	3	7	16	37	76	16

Sidbury United Reserves - record expunged.

Division Five

	P	W	D	L	F	A	Pts
Newtown "A"	24	19	1	4	80	31	58
Exmouth Town Reserves	24	18	3	3	103	38	57
Lords XI	24	15	3	6	75	39	48
Woodbury	24	13	4	7	65	46	43
Heavitree United "A"	24	11	4	9	64	58	37
Axmouth United	24	10	4	10	56	56	34
Culm United Reserves	24	9	4	11	57	61	31
Hatherleigh Town Reserves	24	7	7	10	46	58	28
Beer Albion Reserves	24	8	3	13	31	45	27
Cullompton Rangers "A"	24	8	3	13	51	86	27
Sampford Peverell	24	7	1	16	57	76	22
St Martins Reserves (-1)	24	5	4	15	42	68	18
Dunkeswell Rovers	24	3	5	16	39	104	14

Division Six

	P	W	D	L	F	A	Pts
Chulmleigh	26	25	1	0	129	28	76
Bow AAC Reserves	26	19	2	5	71	34	59
UAU Exeter	26	16	1	9	83	60	49
Cheriton Fitzpaine	26	15	1	10	77	55	46
Topsham Town "A"	26	14	3	9	71	58	45
Awliscombe United	26	13	3	10	57	49	42
Clyst Valley "A" (-1)	26	11	4	11	57	54	36
Uplowman Athletic Reserves	26	10	4	12	52	79	34
Westexe Rovers Reserves	26	10	3	13	52	60	33
Feniton Reserves	26	8	5	13	56	62	29
Priory	26	8	4	14	46	64	28
Chagford Reserves	26	8	3	15	56	80	27
East Budleigh Reserves (-3)	26	4	3	19	38	89	12
Honiton Town Reserves	26	2	1	23	27	100	7

Division Seven

	P	W	D	L	F	A	Pts
Morchard Bishop Reserves	28	23	3	2	105	25	72
Amory Park Rangers	28	21	2	5	106	48	65
Dawlish United Reserves	28	19	3	6	80	30	60
Silverton	28	16	2	10	78	71	50
Amory Argyle	28	15	4	9	82	74	49
Langdon (-2)	28	17	4	7	92	47	47
North Tawton Reserves	28	11	4	13	55	96	37
Exwick Village	28	10	5	13	68	73	35
Stoke Hill	28	9	5	14	55	77	32
Topsham Town "B"	28	9	4	15	54	101	31
Newton St Cyres Reserves	28	8	5	15	53	67	29
Halwill Reserves (-1)	28	8	1	19	54	84	24
Hemyock Reserves (-2)	28	7	5	16	50	84	24
Bampton Reserves (-1)	28	5	3	20	48	83	17
Sandford Reserves (-2)	28	6	2	20	53	94	16

Division Eight

	P	W	D	L	F	A	Pts
Tipton St John Reserves	28	21	3	4	83	35	66
Lympstone Reserves	28	20	4	4	99	45	64
Otterton	28	18	5	5	89	41	59
Met Office	28	17	2	9	82	40	53
Colaton Raleigh Reserves	28	14	2	12	71	52	44
Cheriton Fitzpaine Res (-1)	28	12	6	10	67	60	41
Tedburn St Mary Reserves	28	13	2	13	61	59	41
Offwell Rangers Reserves	28	12	4	12	70	64	40
Langdon Reserves (-1)	28	12	4	12	71	56	39
Woodbury Reserves	28	9	6	13	48	67	33
Folly Gate	28	10	1	17	60	114	31
Colyton Reserves	28	9	2	17	50	80	29
Lapford Reserves	28	9	2	17	48	85	29
Newtown "B" (-1)	28	7	1	20	50	107	21
Winkleigh Reserves (-2)	28	3	4	21	37	81	11

DONCASTER & DISTRICT SENIOR LEAGUE

Premier Division

	P	W	D	L	F	A	Pts
Sutton Rovers	26	20	3	3	72	32	63
Rossington MW	26	18	2	6	87	35	56
Bramley Sunnyside	26	16	2	8	77	48	50
Hatfield Main	26	15	2	9	67	53	47
South Elmsall Utd Services	26	13	4	9	67	37	43
Mexborough Town	26	13	2	11	64	58	41
Brodsworth Welfare AFC	26	11	6	9	39	47	39
Hemsworth Town	26	9	7	10	57	54	34
Kinsley Boys	26	10	3	13	65	59	33
Bawtry Town	26	9	5	12	75	76	32
Edlington Town	26	10	2	14	59	83	32
Carcroft Village	26	7	5	14	52	82	26
Swinton Athletic	26	5	1	20	41	95	16
South Kirkby Colliery	26	2	4	20	23	86	10

LEAGUE TABLES

Division One

	P	W	D	L	F	A	Pts
Denaby United	24	22	1	1	118	31	67
Shafton Villa	24	19	3	2	71	30	60
Scawthorpe & Bentley Rh.	24	15	3	6	61	31	48
Ackworth United	24	15	2	7	66	43	47
South Kirkby Town	23	12	2	9	72	57	38
Hemsworth MW	24	10	7	7	57	49	37
Dunscroft United	23	9	4	10	52	67	31
Rovers Foundation	24	8	3	13	57	67	27
Bawtry Town Reserves	24	6	7	11	47	73	25
ISG Doncaster	24	5	4	15	45	54	19
Newton Arms	24	4	7	13	41	72	19
Woodlands Rhinos	24	5	2	17	35	68	17
Askern Athletic	24	2	1	21	33	113	7

DORSET FOOTBALL LEAGUE

Senior League

	P	W	D	L	F	A	Pts
Portland United Reserves	26	14	10	2	72	31	52
Wareham Rangers	26	15	6	5	70	43	51
Upwey and Broadwey	26	16	2	8	60	47	50
Kingston Lacy	26	14	5	7	57	36	47
Witchampton United	26	13	2	11	56	54	41
Okeford United	26	11	7	8	66	39	40
Sturminster Newton United	26	11	5	10	42	34	38
Stourpaine	26	11	4	11	57	52	37
Weymouth Sports	26	9	8	9	45	48	35
Bishops Caundle	26	7	8	11	41	56	29
Piddletrenthide United	26	8	4	14	37	50	28
Gillingham Town Reserves	26	6	4	16	42	76	22
Blandford United Reserves	26	5	5	16	27	62	20
Chickerell United Reserves	26	4	6	16	21	65	18

Division One

	P	W	D	L	F	A	Pts
Mere Town	26	22	3	1	126	29	69
Westland Sports Reserves	26	22	2	2	96	23	68
Granby Rovers	26	17	4	5	65	33	55
Poundbury Rovers	26	14	6	6	56	36	48
Bere Regis	26	14	3	9	81	51	45
Poole Borough Reserves	26	12	3	11	73	63	39
Dorchester Town A (-1)	26	11	3	12	58	65	35
Wincanton Town Reserves	26	10	3	13	59	67	33
Merley Cobham Reserves	26	10	2	14	45	71	32
Kangaroos	26	9	3	14	57	72	30
Swanage Tn & Herston R.	26	9	1	16	53	92	28
Dorchester Borough	26	6	3	17	40	66	21
Ship Inn, Wool	26	5	3	18	40	72	18
Shaftesbury Reserves	26	1	1	24	24	133	4

Division Two

	P	W	D	L	F	A	Pts
11 Signal Regiment FC	26	21	0	5	120	45	63
Corfe Mullen United	26	20	2	4	94	34	62
Bridport A	26	19	3	4	89	32	60
Milborne Sports	26	18	2	6	99	38	56
Dorchester Sports	26	15	5	6	69	41	50
Gillingham Town A	26	13	8	5	72	41	47
Weymouth Spartans	26	13	4	9	62	48	43
The Balti House	26	12	1	13	65	66	37
Wareham Rangers Res.	26	8	4	14	61	86	28
Wyke Regis Social Club	26	7	4	15	42	93	25
Crossways	26	6	0	20	49	94	18
Sturminster Newton Res.	26	4	2	20	31	88	14
Corfe Castle	26	4	2	20	33	97	14
Lytchett Red Triangle	26	3	1	22	27	110	10

Division Three

	P	W	D	L	F	A	Pts
AFC Cobham	18	14	1	3	63	31	43
Donhead Utd	18	14	1	3	65	36	43
Galaxy FC	18	10	1	7	45	34	31
Portesham United	18	10	1	7	41	39	31
Piddlehinton United	18	9	3	6	53	34	30
Bere Regis Reserves	18	7	2	9	45	39	23
Stickland United	18	7	2	9	46	74	23
Maiden Newton & Cattistock	18	5	1	12	40	49	16
Okeford Utd Reserves	18	4	3	11	35	60	15
Cranborne Reserves	18	2	1	15	18	61	7

Division Four

	P	W	D	L	F	A	Pts
Handley Sports	18	11	4	3	76	34	37
Stalbridge	18	10	3	5	32	26	33
Owermoigne	18	7	6	5	24	28	27
Weymouth Spartans Reserves	18	8	2	8	39	42	26
Galaxy FC Reserves	18	6	7	5	41	39	25
Poundbury Rovers Res.	18	7	4	7	33	39	25
Littlemoor	18	6	6	6	37	43	24
Bishops Caundle Reserves	18	7	1	10	39	48	22
Puddletown	18	6	1	11	30	39	19
Swanage Tn & Herston A (-1)	18	3	4	11	28	41	12

Division Five

	P	W	D	L	F	A	Pts
Mere Town Reserves	20	18	1	1	99	23	55
AFC Blandford	20	16	1	3	84	32	49
Broadstone	20	14	1	5	82	38	43
Donhead Utd Reserves	20	13	4	3	68	27	43
Pimperne Sports	20	9	4	7	79	48	31
Marnhull	20	7	3	10	48	63	24
Dorchester Community Church	20	7	0	13	43	65	21
Maiden Newton & Cattistock Res.	20	5	1	14	44	86	16
Milborne Sports Reserves	20	4	3	13	32	57	15
Handley Sports Reserves	20	4	3	13	37	88	15
Poundbury Rovers A	20	1	3	16	19	108	6

DRIFFIELD & DISTRICT LEAGUE

Premier Division

	P	W	D	L	F	A	Pts
Bridlington Snooker Centre	13	10	1	2	60	17	31
Driffield E.I	13	8	1	4	34	34	25
Bay Horse kilham	14	7	2	5	40	32	23
Middleton Rovers	12	6	2	4	36	22	20
Bridlington Excelsior	13	6	1	6	39	31	19
Langtoft	13	4	3	6	39	36	15
Foresters Athletic	13	2	3	8	18	52	9
Bridlington Seabirds	11	1	1	9	12	54	4

Division One

	P	W	D	L	F	A	Pts
Flamborough	18	12	1	5	65	40	37
Bridlington Tigers	18	11	2	5	49	31	35
Bridlington Rovers	18	9	6	3	58	41	33
northcote fc	18	9	5	4	60	42	32
Bridlington Snooker Club 2nd	18	9	4	5	47	42	31
Spiders Fc	18	7	1	10	42	60	22
Driffield FC 3rds	18	5	4	9	45	52	19
Hutton Cranswick	18	5	4	9	39	53	19
Little Driffield	18	3	4	11	33	51	13
Foresters Athletic 2nd	18	3	3	12	38	64	12

Division Two

Division Two	P	W	D	L	F	A	Pts
Stirling Wanderers FC	18	12	5	1	76	26	41
Driffield Red Lion	18	10	2	6	68	36	32
Driffield Star	18	10	1	7	62	45	31
Flamborough 2nd	18	10	1	7	59	43	31
Driffield Town	18	8	3	7	48	52	27
Mermaid United Old Boys	18	8	2	8	42	28	26
Pocklington 4th	18	7	3	8	55	55	24
Bridlington Sports Club 3rd	18	6	2	10	49	70	20
Driffield FC 3rd	18	5	3	10	39	57	18
North Frodingham	18	2	2	14	18	104	8.

DUCHY LEAGUE

Premier	P	W	D	L	F	A	Pts
Fowey United	24	17	3	4	83	47	54
Saltash United "A"	24	13	5	6	62	40	44
Mevagissey	24	11	7	6	52	50	40
Bodmin Saints	24	12	3	9	83	65	39
St Cleer	24	11	4	9	50	59	37
Lamerton	24	11	2	11	56	59	35
Torpoint Athletic "A"	24	11	1	12	46	45	34
Calstock	24	9	6	9	45	44	33
St Mawgan	24	9	4	11	54	58	31
St Newlyn East	24	8	6	10	59	54	30
Probus Reserves	24	8	1	15	48	68	25
Altarnun	24	6	6	12	32	50	24
Gunnislake	24	4	4	16	36	67	16

Division One	P	W	D	L	F	A	Pts
AFC St Austell Reserves	24	18	3	3	76	33	57
St Columb Major	24	17	3	4	65	35	54
Pelynt	24	13	5	6	68	57	44
St Dominick Reserves	24	12	5	7	64	51	41
Grampound	24	12	4	8	51	47	40
Bere Alston Utd Reserves	24	10	6	8	61	53	36
Polperro	24	9	4	11	62	54	31
Week St Mary	24	9	3	12	48	52	30
Looe Town	24	7	6	11	45	58	27
Godolphin Atlan. Reserves	24	7	4	13	50	60	25
St Dennis Reserves	24	6	4	14	39	62	22
Foxhole Stars Reserves	24	6	3	15	37	63	21
Boscastle	24	4	2	18	41	82	14

Division Two	P	W	D	L	F	A	Pts
Biscovey Reserves	24	20	3	1	81	25	63
Pensilva	24	19	2	3	72	27	59
Maker with Rame	24	16	4	4	74	48	52
Sticker Reserves	24	13	4	7	60	39	43
Premier Sixes	24	11	5	8	86	56	38
Lostwithiel	24	11	3	10	60	49	36
Lanreath Reserves	24	9	3	12	42	45	30
Queens Rangers	24	8	3	13	35	56	27
St Breward	24	8	3	13	39	62	27
Lewdown Rovers	24	8	1	15	43	60	25
Gerrans & St Mawes U.	24	7	2	15	45	69	23
Holywell and Cubert	24	5	7	12	51	62	22
St Stephen Reserves	24	0	2	22	24	114	2

DURHAM FOOTBALL ALLIANCE

	P	W	D	L	F	A	Pts
Brandon British Legion	30	27	2	1	140	30	83
Hartlepool Town	30	25	2	3	116	41	77
Coundon & Leeholm	30	20	4	6	98	38	64
Whitehill	30	19	6	5	92	61	63
Birtley St Josephs	30	15	6	9	83	66	51
Sunderland Hylton CW(-3)	30	16	3	11	74	69	48
Durham Garden House	30	13	5	12	77	65	44
Gateshead Leam Rangers	30	12	4	14	66	74	37
Shildon Railway	30	10	5	15	69	97	35
Wheatley Hill WMC	30	11	0	19	68	94	33
Ebchester Consett Reserves	30	10	2	18	63	87	32
Hartlepool Stranton SFC	30	9	4	17	71	93	31
Washington Town (-3)	30	10	4	16	64	86	31
Coxhoe United	30	7	3	20	53	100	24
Swalwell Amateurs	30	5	6	19	52	103	21
Brandon United Reserves	30	3	0	27	35	117	9

EAST BERKSHIRE LEAGUE

Premier	P	W	D	L	F	A	Pts
Orchard Park Rangers	16	10	4	2	45	19	34
Alpha Arms Academicals	16	10	2	4	43	29	32
Eton Wick	16	7	6	3	49	31	27
Slough Heating	16	7	3	6	31	30	24
Slough Laurencians	16	7	3	6	32	40	24
Farnham WMC	16	6	3	7	34	41	21
Stoke Green Rovers	16	5	2	9	37	37	17
Chalvey (WMC) Sports	16	5	0	11	30	43	15
FC Beaconsfield	16	3	1	12	29	60	10
Bracknell Forest	0	0	0	0	0	0	0
Burnham Beeches	0	0	0	0	0	0	0

Division One	P	W	D	L	F	A	Pts
Iver (-1)	18	15	3	0	59	18	47
Slough Irish Society	18	11	1	6	48	38	34
Thorney Mill (-3)	18	11	3	4	57	38	33
Delaford	18	8	3	7	44	41	27
Old Windsor	18	8	3	7	44	44	27
Admiral Cunningham (+3)	18	6	1	11	46	62	22
Richings Park	18	7	1	10	37	53	22
New Hanford	18	5	4	9	45	48	19
KS Gryf (+2)	18	4	4	10	31	40	18
Falcons	18	2	3	13	35	64	9
North Hillingdon	0	0	0	0	0	0	0

Division Two	P	W	D	L	F	A	Pts
Slough Heating Res	18	12	4	2	68	31	40
Slough Laurencians Res	18	13	1	4	68	37	40
Windsor Great Park (-1)	18	11	1	6	54	33	33
Stoke Green Rovers Res	18	8	4	6	34	29	28
Maidenhead Town	18	8	4	6	49	47	28
Cippenham Sports	18	9	1	8	46	44	28
Upton Lea	18	6	6	6	48	42	24
Red Lion Burnham (-2)	18	5	4	9	37	46	17
Orchard Park Rers Res (-1)	18	3	5	10	30	52	13
Stoke Road Legion	18	0	0	18	18	91	0

LEAGUE TABLES

Division Three

	P	W	D	L	F	A	Pts
Britwell	20	18	0	2	92	31	54
Swinley Forest	20	13	1	6	60	47	40
Bracknell Rovers	20	10	4	6	53	40	34
Langley FC	20	10	2	8	48	54	32
AFC Ascot	20	9	3	8	52	53	30
Frontline	20	8	3	9	39	45	27
Maidenhead Magpies	20	8	1	11	35	49	25
Stanwell	20	7	1	12	35	47	22
Braybrooke	20	6	1	13	45	54	19
Iver Heath Rovers	20	5	4	11	39	63	19
The Black Horse	20	5	2	13	37	52	17

Division Four

	P	W	D	L	F	A	Pts
Old Windsor Res	18	15	0	3	63	19	45
Windsor Great Park Res	18	11	4	3	40	26	37
Hurley	18	10	4	4	37	25	34
Robertswood FC (+2)	18	8	2	8	38	36	28
Willow Wanderers (-3)	18	9	3	6	41	37	27
Upton Park Rangers	18	7	4	7	41	39	25
Beaconsfield Town (-1)	18	5	5	8	36	47	19
Red Lion Burnham Res	18	5	2	11	33	47	17
Wexham Park Rangers	18	4	3	11	38	51	15
FC Beaconsfield Res (+3)	18	1	3	14	16	56	9

Division Five

	P	W	D	L	F	A	Pts
Langley FC Res (-1)	21	18	2	1	90	18	55
Real Saracens FC (-3)	22	17	2	3	65	28	50
Britwell Res (3)	21	12	4	5	66	42	43
The Wolfpack	22	12	0	10	50	55	36
Chalvey (WMC) Sports Res	22	10	4	8	52	54	34
St Peters Iver	21	10	4	7	43	51	34
Falcons Res	21	9	1	11	45	38	28
New Park United	22	7	3	12	44	45	24
Wexham Park Rangers Res	22	7	0	15	43	78	21
Frontline Res	22	6	2	14	50	73	20
Mercian United (-1)	22	5	1	16	38	71	15
Langley Hornets	22	4	3	15	33	66	15

EAST CHESHIRE LEAGUE

	P	W	D	L	F	A	Pts
FC Flyers	18	16	2	0	98	31	50
Club AZ	18	14	1	3	89	34	43
Cheadle Hulme (-1)	18	13	1	4	66	33	39
Poynton Kings	18	10	5	3	57	33	35
Poynton Nomads	18	9	1	8	61	40	28
High Lane (-6)	18	9	1	8	56	34	22
Mary Dendy	18	6	1	11	42	81	19
Old Alts "B"	18	4	1	13	43	85	13
Old Alts East	18	1	1	16	28	82	4
Poynton Village (-3)	18	1	0	17	16	103	0

EAST CORNWALL LEAGUE

Premier Division

	Pld	W	D	L	F	A	Pts
Torpoint Athletic Reserves	30	25	5	0	110	27	80
Sticker	30	21	3	6	102	37	66
Launceston Reserves	30	18	5	7	94	47	59
Bude Town	30	18	5	7	76	46	59
Plymouth Parkway Reserves	30	17	7	6	98	56	58
Tavistock Reserves	30	17	4	9	85	47	55
Elburton Villa Reserves	30	16	5	9	68	52	53
Saltash United Reserves	30	13	4	13	63	58	43
Morwenstow	30	13	3	14	66	78	42
Bere Alston United	30	13	0	17	79	70	39
St Dominick	30	10	7	13	62	76	37
Probus	30	9	6	15	69	68	33
Lanreath	30	6	6	18	34	89	24
Wadebridge Town Reserves	30	4	7	19	40	83	19
Bodmin Town Reserves	30	4	2	24	45	144	14
St Stephens Borough	30	0	3	27	30	143	3

Division One

	Pld	W	D	L	F	A	Pts
Liskeard Athletic Reserves	28	21	5	2	107	33	68
Millbrook	28	21	4	3	104	35	67
Polperro	28	19	5	4	98	37	62
St Teath	28	17	4	7	69	43	55
Plymstock United Reserves	28	15	5	8	73	45	50
Kilkhampton	28	14	4	10	49	47	46
Edgcumbe	28	14	3	11	79	54	45
St Blazey Reserves	28	10	3	15	63	71	33
St Stephen	28	9	5	14	53	78	32
Camelford Reserves	28	9	5	14	44	77	32
Callington Town Reserves	28	9	4	15	65	68	31
Roche	28	8	3	17	33	72	27
Holsworthy Reserves	28	8	3	17	40	83	27
Biscovey	28	5	1	22	36	99	16
Nanpean Rovers	28	3	2	23	24	95	11

EAST LANCASHIRE LEAGUE

Division One

	P	W	D	L	F	A	Pts
Rimington (+3)	26	19	3	3	85	40	63
Langho	26	17	6	3	88	35	57
Enfield (-3)	26	16	4	6	74	51	49
Pendle Forest	26	13	6	6	56	34	45
Mill Hill	26	13	4	9	68	41	43
Worsthorne	26	12	4	10	62	45	40
Hurst Green (+5)	26	9	5	12	42	50	37
Oswaldtwistle St Marys (-1)	26	10	5	11	42	48	34
Feniscowles & Pleasington	26	10	4	12	43	60	34
Edenfield	26	9	4	12	57	61	31
Read United	26	6	5	15	40	64	23
Burnley GSOB (-1)	26	6	5	15	39	79	22
Colne United	26	4	7	15	29	73	19
Stacksteads St Josephs	26	4	4	18	48	92	16

Division Two

	P	W	D	L	F	A	Pts
Rock Rovers	22	18	3	1	69	20	57
Calder Vale	22	15	2	5	55	31	47
Borrowdale United	22	14	3	5	78	45	45
Padiham "A" (+3)	22	11	3	8	69	55	39
Churchtown (-3)	22	12	5	5	70	46	38
Barrowford Celtic	22	10	5	7	49	41	35
Burnley Bel'dere (-3)	22	9	5	8	58	40	29
Waddington	22	6	8	8	45	40	26
Bacup CC (+1)	22	3	8	11	41	64	18
Clitheroe RBL	22	4	3	15	27	76	15
Daneshouse	22	4	1	17	49	85	13
Peel Park (-1)	22	1	4	17	25	92	6

Sacred Heart Celtic - record expunged.

EAST RIDING AMATEUR LEAGUE

Premier

	P	W	D	L	F	A	Pts
Pinefleet Wolfreton	22	17	3	2	77	35	54
Quaddy Rangers	22	16	2	4	71	35	50
Queens County	22	13	4	5	86	47	43
Rapid Solicitors	22	13	3	6	106	42	42
Inter Charter	22	12	2	8	55	44	38
AFC Preston	22	11	4	7	54	44	37
AFC Hull	22	9	5	8	76	56	32
Bev Road Rangers	22	8	4	10	52	50	28
Kingburn Athletic	22	7	3	12	49	75	24
AFC Salthouse Tavern	22	6	1	15	37	70	19
Swiss Cottage	22	2	1	19	29	97	7
Orchard Park United	22	1	2	19	28	125	5

EAST RIDING COUNTY LEAGUE

Premier Division

	P	W	D	L	F	A	Pts
Little Weighton	22	15	4	3	52	20	49
South Cave Sporting Club	22	13	5	4	47	29	44
AFC Woodlands	22	12	5	5	51	36	41
Holme Rovers	22	9	5	8	41	45	32
AFC Rovers	22	8	7	7	47	48	31
Sculcoates Amateurs Res.	22	8	6	8	40	43	30
Park Athletic	22	6	10	6	42	44	28
Wawne United	22	7	6	9	55	50	27
Reckitts Reserves	22	8	3	11	44	50	27
Viking Raiders	22	6	3	13	38	52	21
Beverley Town Reserves	22	3	8	11	29	41	17
Easington United Reserves	22	4	4	14	32	60	16

Division One

	P	W	D	L	F	A	Pts
Bridlington Town Academy	24	18	3	3	90	36	57
Driffield Rangers	24	16	4	4	70	34	52
Greyhound FC	24	14	4	6	79	52	46
St George's FC	24	13	6	5	75	46	45
Wawne United Reserves	24	11	7	6	65	57	40
Gilberdyke Phoenix	24	12	4	8	61	53	40
Hodgsons Reserves	24	10	3	11	54	63	33
Walkington	24	8	5	11	46	44	29
Molescroft Rangers	24	6	3	15	30	52	21
Hedon Rangers Reserves	24	6	3	15	54	89	21
Haltemprice	24	5	5	14	49	66	20
Beverley Town Beavers	24	4	6	14	28	54	18
Lord Nelson	24	5	3	16	33	88	18

Division Two

	P	W	D	L	F	A	Pts
Haltemprice Rangers	20	14	2	4	73	35	44
Hornsea Town Reserves	20	14	1	5	51	30	43
Skirlaugh	20	11	4	5	56	29	37
Leven Members Club	20	11	1	8	50	45	34
Shiptonthorpe United	20	10	3	7	46	50	33
Aldbrough United	20	9	3	8	44	37	30
West Hull Amateurs	20	9	3	8	51	47	30
Eastella Rangers	20	8	2	10	36	40	26
Skidby Millers	20	6	2	12	36	56	20
Long Riston Reserves	20	4	1	15	31	64	13
Withernsea Reserves	20	2	2	16	36	77	8

Division Three

	P	W	D	L	F	A	Pts
Viking Raiders Reserves	26	18	3	5	73	44	57
Malet Lambert Youth Club R	26	19	0	7	93	67	57
Full Measure	26	15	4	7	74	57	49
Eastern Raiders	26	15	3	8	81	57	48
South Cave Sporting Club Res.	26	13	4	9	78	61	43
Old Zoological	26	12	3	11	84	73	39
Roos	26	12	2	12	71	72	38
Priory Athletic	26	10	6	10	72	63	36
Market Weighton United	26	11	2	13	69	78	35
Brandesburton Reserves	26	10	2	14	67	69	32
Mill Lane United	26	9	3	14	52	64	30
Eastrington Village	26	9	2	15	59	79	29
Kings Head Hedon	26	9	1	16	52	70	28
FC Ridings	26	2	1	23	17	88	7

Division Four

	P	W	D	L	F	A	Pts
Skirlaugh Reserves	24	18	5	1	104	40	59
Nafferton Old Boys	24	17	4	3	92	37	55
AFC Woodlands Reserves	24	17	1	6	92	43	52
Gilberdyke Phoenix Reserves	24	17	1	6	92	54	52
Newland Young Boys	24	15	1	8	78	36	46
Long Riston 3rd Team	24	14	2	8	82	48	44
Leven Members Club Res.	24	10	1	13	53	74	31
Holme Rovers Reserves	24	7	4	13	46	79	25
Hornsea Town 3rd Team	24	7	3	14	39	71	24
Cottingham Forest	24	7	2	15	51	77	23
Molescroft Rangers Reserves	24	4	4	16	29	82	16
Market Weighton Utd Res.	24	3	3	18	29	77	12
East Riding Rangers Reserves	24	2	5	17	34	103	11

Division Five

	P	W	D	L	F	A	Pts
Easington United Casuals	18	17	1	0	72	25	52
Newbald United	18	12	2	4	56	33	38
Shiptonthorpe United Reserves	18	12	1	5	66	29	37
Hedon Rangers Juniors	18	10	3	5	41	34	33
Haltemprice Reserves	18	9	2	7	51	39	29
Brandesburton Academy	18	8	1	9	59	59	25
Withernsea 3rd Team	18	4	3	11	34	56	15
Howden 3rd Team	18	4	2	12	34	56	14
Bilton Athletic FC	18	4	2	12	34	69	14
Eastrington Village Reserves	18	0	3	15	31	78	9

LEAGUE TABLES
EAST SUSSEX LEAGUE

Premier Division	P	W	D	L	F	A	Pts
Hollington United	20	20	0	0	73	15	60
Sedlescombe Rangers	20	13	3	4	72	28	42
St Leonards Social	20	10	5	5	42	32	35
Robertsbridge United	20	10	4	6	43	34	34
Peche Hill Select	20	8	3	9	38	41	27
Rock A Nore	20	7	5	8	48	42	26
Old Town Athletic	20	7	3	10	42	38	24
Wadhurst United	20	6	3	11	42	50	21
Iden	20	5	5	10	36	53	20
White Knight	20	6	2	12	34	56	20
Punnetts Town	20	1	1	18	16	97	4

Division One	P	W	D	L	F	A	Pts
Ninfield United	18	13	2	3	47	23	41
Hollington United Reserves	18	13	1	4	48	23	40
Ticehurst	18	12	1	5	41	35	37
Spartan 04	18	11	2	5	62	26	35
Hooe Sports	18	10	2	6	53	28	32
Eastbourne Amateurs	18	9	3	6	40	30	30
Bexhill AAC	18	4	3	11	18	37	15
Catsfield	18	3	2	13	23	53	11
Mountfield United	18	3	1	14	24	55	10
Sandhurst	18	3	1	14	19	65	10

Division Two	P	W	D	L	F	A	Pts
Ore Athletic	18	15	1	2	72	31	46
Langney	18	12	0	6	52	30	36
Crowhurst	18	11	1	6	59	40	34
Eastbourne Albert (-1)	18	10	4	4	43	30	33
Eastbourne Dynamos (+2)	18	6	4	8	33	36	24
Icklesham Casuals	18	7	1	10	40	49	22
Hastings Rangers	18	5	4	9	39	57	19
Cinque Ports	18	6	1	11	35	61	19
Battle Baptists	18	5	3	10	33	48	18
St Helens	18	3	1	14	34	58	10

Division Three	P	W	D	L	F	A	Pts
Orington (-3)	18	14	2	2	89	29	41
Hawkhurst United	18	12	4	2	63	24	40
Hurst	18	9	6	3	32	14	33
Northiam 75 (+3)	18	6	7	5	58	43	28
Herstmonceux	18	6	8	4	43	41	26
Battle Rangers	18	8	0	10	50	50	24
Wittersham	18	6	5	7	44	44	23
Cranbrook Town	18	6	4	8	49	40	22
Peche Hill Select Reserves	18	4	2	12	31	63	14
Magham Down	18	0	0	18	9	120	0

Division Four	P	W	D	L	F	A	Pts
Sedlescombe Rangers Res	18	16	0	2	84	17	48
Rock A Nore Reserves	18	11	3	4	54	28	36
The JC Tackleway	18	11	2	5	58	28	35
Pebsham Sibex	18	11	2	5	47	26	35
Travaux	18	10	3	5	46	41	33
Iden Reserves	18	6	3	9	32	60	21
Burwash	18	6	0	12	22	57	18
Mayfield	18	5	2	11	16	38	17
FCBexhill	18	4	3	11	27	39	15
Bo-Peep Marina	18	1	0	17	20	72	3

Division Five	P	W	D	L	F	A	Pts
AFC Sidley (-3)	18	15	3	0	75	19	45
E'bourne Fishermen (-3)	18	12	4	2	60	23	37
Ninfield United Reserves	18	10	3	5	40	31	33
Hastings Elite (+3)	18	9	2	7	53	46	32
Wadhurst United Reserves	18	9	1	8	43	46	28
Guestling	18	8	3	7	43	43	27
Eastbourne Athletic	18	6	3	9	39	43	21
Grasshoppers Old B (+3)	18	3	3	12	27	50	15
Victoria Baptists	18	3	4	11	34	68	13
Icklesham Casuals Res.	18	1	2	15	28	73	5

Division Six	P	W	D	L	F	A	Pts
Eastbourne Rangers	18	13	3	2	47	18	42
West Hill United	18	10	2	6	46	35	32
Westfield "A" (+3)	18	7	4	7	40	42	28
Bexhill AAC Reserves	18	7	6	5	47	31	27
Eastbourne Royals (-3)	18	9	1	8	48	34	25
Guestling Reserves	18	6	5	7	32	38	23
Herstmonceux Reserves	18	7	2	9	35	42	23
Parkfield	18	6	4	8	27	35	22
Robertsbridge United Res.	18	6	4	8	33	49	22
The JC Tackleway Reserves	18	2	3	13	17	48	9

Division Seven	P	W	D	L	F	A	Pts
Battle Baptists Reserves	18	14	2	2	73	18	44
Wittersham Reserves	18	12	2	4	62	33	38
Orington Reserves	18	11	3	4	53	32	36
Hampden Park United	18	10	2	6	46	29	32
Hawkhurst United Reserves	18	9	4	5	37	31	31
Bexhill Rovers	18	7	3	8	41	44	24
Herstmonceux "A"	18	4	4	10	23	52	16
Northiam 75 Reserves	18	4	2	12	24	69	14
Sandhurst Reserves	18	3	4	11	17	39	13
West Hill United Reserves	18	3	0	15	31	67	9

ENFIELD ALLIANCE

	P	W	D	L	F	A	Pts
Broadwater United	15	9	3	3	36	19	30
Origin	15	9	2	4	39	31	29
Brimsdown Rovers	15	7	4	4	38	34	25
Persian	15	7	3	5	47	30	24
Crescent Rangers	15	3	1	11	25	49	10
FF London	15	2	3	10	24	46	9
Renegades - record expunged.							

ESKVALE & CLEVELAND LEAGUE

	P	W	D	L	F	A	Pts
Lingdale	26	23	1	2	123	35	70
Boosbeck United	26	21	2	3	100	44	65
Lingdale United	26	17	4	5	111	48	55
Lealholm	26	17	2	7	68	41	53
Loftus Athletic	26	15	4	7	90	55	49
Staithes Athletic	26	14	6	6	69	45	48
Stokesley SC Reserves	26	12	2	12	75	63	38
Hollybush United	26	10	3	13	61	77	33
Great Ayton United Res.	26	7	2	17	53	104	23
Goldsborough United	26	6	2	18	55	91	20
Hinderwell	26	5	4	17	48	102	19
North Skelton Bulls Head	26	6	1	19	44	117	19
Carlin How WMC	26	5	3	18	45	78	18
Brotton Railway Arms	26	5	2	19	44	86	**17**

ESSEX BUSINESS HOUSES LEAGUE

Premier	P	W	D	L	F	A	Pts
Telstar	18	13	2	2	42	28	41
Tower Hamlets	18	13	1	3	58	29	40
Flanders	18	11	2	4	31	19	35
Snaresbrook	18	9	0	8	37	33	27
Brampton Park	18	7	3	8	39	43	24
Essex United	18	6	3	8	40	36	21
Ulysees	18	4	5	9	33	40	17
R.W.M.C.	18	5	1	12	21	23	16
Bancroft	18	5	1	11	32	50	16
West Green	18	5	0	13	28	60	15

Division One	P	W	D	L	F	A	Pts
Tower Hamlets Reserves	16	12	2	2	56	15	38
Switch Bar FC	16	11	3	2	57	32	36
Blue Marlin	16	9	2	5	36	26	29
Singh Sabha Barking	16	8	3	5	35	28	27
The Pier FC	16	7	2	6	25	32	23
London APSA Reserves	16	7	0	8	29	35	21
Forest Glade Olympic	16	3	3	10	13	42	12
Barking Borough	16	3	2	11	17	33	11
West Essex Reserves	16	1	3	12	17	42	6

FURNESS PREMIER LEAGUE

Premier Division	P	W	D	L	F	A	Pts
Barrow Wanderers	22	17	2	3	76	21	53
Bootle (-6)	22	14	1	7	67	43	37
Crooklands Casuals Res.	22	10	6	6	55	48	36
Vickerstown Reserves	22	9	5	8	48	42	32
Haverigg United	22	9	5	8	54	52	32
Hawcoat Park Res. (-3)	22	9	5	8	52	46	29
Holker Old Boys Reserves	22	8	4	10	47	52	28
Kirkby United	22	7	7	8	47	57	28
Millom Reserves	22	8	1	13	39	56	25
Furness Rovers Reserves	22	6	6	10	39	48	24
Dalton United Reserves	22	6	2	14	37	60	20
Barrow Celtic	22	6	2	14	45	81	20

Division One	P	W	D	L	F	A	Pts
Britannia	18	14	2	2	72	17	44
Barrow Wanderers Reserves	18	11	3	4	62	39	36
Barrow Island	18	11	2	5	66	46	35
Askam United Reserves	18	9	0	9	46	33	27
Holker Old Boys "A"	18	7	3	8	37	50	24
Walney Island Reserves	18	6	5	7	39	39	23
Vickerstown "A"	18	7	2	9	29	45	23
Furness Cavaliers Reserves	18	6	3	9	34	38	21
Millom "A"	18	5	3	10	40	64	18
Dalton United "A"	18	2	1	15	23	77	7

Division Two	P	W	D	L	F	A	Pts
GSK Ulverston Rang Res.	16	12	2	2	76	24	38
Swarthmoor Social Res.	16	11	2	3	56	24	35
Haverigg United Reserves	16	8	6	2	42	25	30
Hawcoat Park "A"	16	7	3	6	51	42	24
Walney Island "A"	16	5	3	8	33	45	18
Barrow Celtic Reserves	16	4	3	9	31	52	15
Furness Rovers "A"	16	4	3	9	32	54	15
Askam United "A" (-3)	16	5	2	9	30	50	14
Kirkby United Reserves	16	4	0	12	35	70	**12**

GAINSBOROUGH & DISTRICT LEAGUE

	P	W	D	L	F	A	Pts
Mattersey	16	13	3	0	43	7	42
BFC Birches	16	9	2	5	44	27	29
Harworth Colliery	16	9	0	7	38	28	27
East Drayton	16	8	2	6	36	37	26
Bridon	16	7	2	7	40	38	23
Retford Town	16	6	2	8	24	24	20
Gainsborough Tn Canute Res.	16	6	1	9	29	41	19
Fox & Hounds Willingham	16	3	2	11	17	43	11
Haxey	16	3	2	11	17	43	11

GLOUCESTERSHIRE NORTHERN SENIOR LEAGUE

Division One	Pld	W	D	L	F	A	Pts
Shortwood United Reserves	30	19	8	3	63	31	65
Frampton United	30	18	8	4	78	38	62
Gala Wilton	30	18	7	5	75	31	61
Broadwell Amateurs	30	18	7	5	61	33	61
Star	30	15	7	8	52	44	52
Brockworth Albion	30	16	3	11	53	40	51
Sharpness	30	13	5	12	57	52	44
Winchcombe Town	30	11	10	9	51	41	43
Leonard Stanley	30	9	9	12	34	52	36
Stonehouse Town	30	9	7	14	38	47	34
Harrow Hill	30	9	7	14	47	58	34
Smiths Athletic	30	8	7	15	34	57	31
Lydbrook Athletic	30	8	6	16	41	52	30
Dursley Town	30	7	7	16	38	57	28
Ramblers	30	5	9	16	43	67	24
Stroud (-3)	30	2	3	25	23	89	6

LEAGUE TABLES

Division Two	Pld	W	D	L	F	A	Pts
Cheltenham Civil Service	30	23	3	4	92	35	72
Cam Bulldogs	30	19	3	8	66	36	60
Bredon	30	19	3	8	70	49	60
Hardwicke	30	18	2	10	74	50	56
Minsterworth	30	17	4	9	74	52	55
Abbeymead Rovers	30	15	4	11	59	59	49
Moreton Rangers	30	14	6	10	79	51	48
Longford	30	15	3	12	57	48	48
Viney St Swithins	30	13	6	11	72	69	45
Bourton Rovers	30	11	3	16	54	65	36
FCBarometrics	30	11	3	16	38	60	36
Barnwood United	30	10	5	15	43	76	35
Wotton Rovers	30	9	6	15	46	56	33
Chalford	30	6	8	16	46	62	26
Soudley	30	6	4	20	45	82	22
Tetbury Town	30	1	3	26	27	92	6

GRANTHAM & DISTRICT LEAGUE

Premier	P	W	D	L	F	A	Pts
Beehive United	16	15	0	1	69	17	45
Barrowby	16	13	1	2	48	20	40
Buckminster United	16	9	3	4	41	26	30
Bottesford	16	8	3	5	37	41	27
Greyhounders	16	7	2	7	38	23	23
Ruskington Rovers	16	6	1	9	21	38	19
Ancaster Rovers	16	3	1	12	23	49	10
Grantham Squash Club	16	3	1	12	25	57	10
Cranmer Arms	16	2	0	14	17	48	6

GRAVESEND LEAGUE

Division One	P	W	D	L	F	A	Pts
NK Aces Reserves	14	12	2	0	64	18	38
Pavilion Athletic	14	10	2	2	65	26	32
Gravesend Angels	14	9	2	3	72	40	29
Ash Green	14	5	4	5	48	40	19
Culverstone United	14	4	3	7	38	25	15
Oakfield	14	4	3	7	50	49	15
Earl Grey	14	3	1	10	21	65	10
Kent Celts Old Boys	14	0	1	13	20	115	1

Viewpoint reserves - record expunged.

Division Two	Pld	W	D	L	F	A	Pts
Fleetway Printers	16	11	1	4	51	31	34
Oakfield Reserves	16	9	2	5	53	39	29
Horton Kirby	16	9	2	5	35	31	29
AFC Millers	16	9	0	7	61	39	27
Joydens Wood	16	8	0	8	37	54	24
NK Aces "A"	16	7	1	8	34	34	22
Borough Athletic	16	6	2	8	39	47	20
Wellcome	16	4	2	10	33	43	14
Riverview United	16	3	2	11	34	59	11

GREAT YARMOUTH & DISTRICT LEAGUE

Division One	P	W	D	L	F	A	Pts
Catfield	16	15	1	0	71	10	46
Belton	16	12	1	3	58	23	37
Albion (Gorleston)	16	9	0	7	48	30	27
MK United	16	7	1	8	39	42	22
Caister Community Cent.	16	7	1	8	40	50	22
Great Yarmouth United	16	7	1	8	33	53	22
Great Yarmouth International	16	6	3	7	40	24	21
Bohemians	16	2	2	12	23	71	8
Great Yarmouth Peelers	16	2	0	14	23	72	6

Norfolk And Chance - record expunged.

Division Two	P	W	D	L	F	A	Pts
Haven Bridge United	16	13	2	1	117	19	41
Caister Roma	16	12	2	2	96	29	38
MK United Reserves	16	11	1	4	75	35	34
South Yarmouth	16	10	1	5	88	38	31
Prostar Windows	16	8	1	7	54	43	25
Feathers	16	5	3	8	46	61	18
Caister United "A"	16	4	2	10	48	69	14
Filby and Runham	16	2	2	12	32	86	8
Martham"A"	16	0	0	16	11	187	0

GRIMSBY & DISTRICT LEAGUE

Division One	P	W	D	L	F	A	Pts
Immingham Bluestone	8	6	1	1	34	16	19
Number One Pub	8	4	3	1	21	9	15
Everyone Active	8	4	1	3	23	13	13
Caistor Tennyson	8	3	1	4	17	26	10
Immingham Blossom W	8	0	0	8	7	38	0

Division Two	P	W	D	L	F	A	Pts
GY Plates	12	10	0	2	61	19	30
Car Services	12	9	1	2	40	20	28
FC Broadburn	12	7	1	4	39	23	22
Mitchells	12	7	0	5	26	31	21
Fabrique	12	5	0	7	27	30	15
NELC	12	2	0	10	22	36	6
FCSentiments	12	1	0	11	7	63	3

GUERNSEY LEAGUE

Division One	P	W	D	L	F	A	Pts
Northerners	18	15	2	1	63	17	47
St Martins	18	10	3	5	49	36	33
Sylvans	18	10	2	6	34	35	32
Belgrave Wanderers	18	10	1	7	57	29	31
Vale Recreation	18	6	2	10	25	38	20
Rovers	18	4	2	12	27	55	14
Rangers	18	2	0	16	27	72	6

Division Two	P	W	D	L	F	A	Pts
Northerners Reserves	16	13	1	2	55	27	40
Belgrave Wanderers Res.	16	12	3	1	63	22	39
Vale Recreation Reserves	16	9	0	7	43	32	27
Rangers Reserves	16	8	2	6	40	50	26
St Martins Reserves	16	6	4	6	29	30	22
Bavaria Nomads	16	5	1	10	33	38	16
Sylvans Reserves	16	4	4	8	33	48	16
Centrals	16	4	3	9	40	57	15
Rovers Reserves	16	2	0	14	21	53	6

GUILDFORD & WOKING ALLIANCE

Premier	P	W	D	L	F	A	Pts
Millmead	18	15	3	0	65	14	48
Lyne	18	11	4	3	53	39	37
Holmbury St Mary	18	12	0	6	56	37	36
Hambledon	18	9	2	7	41	36	29
Burpham	18	7	6	5	31	32	27
Pirbright Sports	18	5	6	7	21	30	21
Windlesham	18	5	4	9	29	44	19
New Haw Wanderers	18	4	3	11	31	50	15
AFC Bisley	18	3	3	12	20	34	12
Puttenham United	18	2	3	13	20	51	9

Division One	P	W	D	L	F	A	Pts
Staines Lammas 'A'	19	17	1	1	98	18	52
West Byfleet Albion	20	12	3	5	57	39	39
Ockham	20	11	3	6	41	32	36
N.L.U.FC	20	11	1	8	35	21	34
Keens Park Rangers	20	11	1	8	45	40	34
FC Shepperton	20	9	3	8	45	47	30
Guildford United	20	7	5	8	38	45	26
Guildford City Weysiders	19	7	2	10	38	39	23
University of Surrey 'A'	20	5	1	14	29	56	16
Pirbright Sports Reserves	20	4	2	14	34	62	14
Oatlands	20	4	0	16	23	84	12

Division Two	P	W	D	L	F	A	Pts
Guildford Rangers	22	19	1	2	73	20	58
Dunsfold	22	18	1	3	92	21	55
Elstead	22	12	4	6	67	29	40
Holmbury St Mary Reserves	22	11	4	7	47	40	37
AFC Bedfont Green	22	10	4	8	51	38	34
Hersham	22	9	5	8	38	35	32
Merrow 'A'	22	8	5	9	53	43	29
Blackwater Royals	22	8	2	12	44	56	26
Knaphill Athletic 'A'	22	6	3	13	47	67	21
AFC Crown & Anchor	22	6	1	15	25	67	19
Guildford United Reserves	22	5	0	17	22	81	15
Windlesham Reserves	22	3	4	15	27	89	13

Division Three	P	W	D	L	F	A	Pts
Guildford Park	22	20	0	2	106	18	60
Staines Lammas 'B'	22	16	3	3	68	36	51
Freedom Spartans Athletic	22	13	3	6	76	36	42
Worplesdon Phoenix 'A'	22	13	2	7	77	51	41
Ripley Village 'A'	22	13	0	9	72	48	39
AFC Gomshall	22	10	5	7	60	38	35
AFC Bedfont Green Res.	22	10	4	8	60	67	34
Burpham Reserves	22	6	4	12	39	58	22
Hambledon Reserves	22	5	3	14	36	80	18
Shalford 'A'	22	5	2	15	39	112	17
Chobham Burymead 'A'	22	5	1	16	35	86	16
Milford & Witley 'A'	22	2	1	19	35	73	7

Division Four North	P	W	D	L	F	A	Pts
AFC Bedfont Green 'A'	22	19	2	1	121	35	59
Allianz	22	14	3	5	65	44	45
AFC Brooklands Seniors	22	12	4	6	65	46	40
Woking Tigers	22	12	3	7	69	52	39
Christian Club Woking	22	12	1	9	68	50	37
University of Surrey 'B'	21	11	3	7	58	37	36
Lyne 'A'	22	10	1	11	56	68	31
Surrey Athletic	22	7	1	14	49	76	22
Knaphill Athletic 'B'	22	6	3	13	42	72	21
Guildford City Weysiders Res.	22	6	3	13	31	69	21
Byfleet	22	5	1	16	37	61	16
Ockham Reserves	21	3	3	15	29	80	12

Division Four South	P	W	D	L	F	A	Pts
Shalford 'B'	22	19	2	1	79	25	59
Astolat Athletic	22	16	1	5	90	37	49
Millmead Reserves	21	14	0	7	80	45	42
Surrey Athletic Reserves	22	13	2	7	68	64	41
Cranleigh 'A'	22	12	2	8	63	46	38
Dunsfold Reserves	22	9	2	11	55	70	29
Lyne Reserves	22	7	6	9	44	53	27
Worplesdon Phoenix 'B'	22	8	2	12	45	58	26
Elstead Reserves	22	7	4	11	48	59	25
Shottermill & Haslemere 'A'	22	4	4	14	38	71	16
Guildford United 'A'	22	4	2	16	29	76	14
Guildford Park Reserves	21	3	3	15	37	72	12

HALIFAX & DISTRICT LEAGUE

Premier Division	P	W	D	L	F	A	Pts
Elland United	22	17	2	3	73	36	53
Warley Rangers	22	15	2	5	72	40	47
Ryburn United	22	15	2	5	52	39	47
Stump Cross	22	11	3	8	44	30	36
Greetland AFC	22	10	3	9	35	38	33
Calder 76	22	9	2	11	56	50	29
Shelf United	22	8	4	10	55	62	28
AFC Crossleys	22	6	5	11	74	75	23
Sowerby United	22	6	5	11	35	39	23
Holmfield	22	7	2	13	37	56	23
Hebden Royd RS	22	5	6	11	33	50	21
Stainland United	22	4	2	16	36	87	14

N●N LEAGUE DAY

What is Non-League D

- A celebration of the
semi-professional and amateu
game.

- A chance for fans of bigger cl
to experience football at a leve
may be otherwise unfamiliar v

- A chance to shine a light on t
hundreds of clubs in this coun
who are almost exclusively
volunteer run, and do so muc
good for the local community

- And much, much more.

So on the 13th of October 20
why not give **your** local club
support it needs, and deserve

SAT 13TH OCTOBE

For more information:

w w w . n o n l e a g u e d a y . c o . u k

LEAGUE TABLES

Division One

	P	W	D	L	F	A	Pts
Midgley United	22	18	4	0	96	24	58
Copley United	22	16	3	3	110	35	51
Sowerby Bridge	22	14	4	4	89	48	46
Volunteer Arms	22	14	2	6	64	37	44
Salem	22	12	2	8	57	54	38
Northowram	22	10	2	10	75	65	32
Halifax Irish Centre	22	9	1	12	64	62	28
Denholme United	22	7	5	10	53	68	26
Ryburn United Res	22	7	5	10	54	70	26
Mixenden United	22	4	4	14	50	95	16
Brighouse OB	22	2	2	18	32	94	8
Hebden Royd RS Res	22	2	0	20	26	118	6

Division Two

	P	W	D	L	F	A	Pts
Wadsworth United	18	14	2	2	61	22	44
Elland Allstars	18	12	2	4	51	44	38
Sowerby Bridge Res	18	11	2	5	67	39	35
Halifax Athletic	18	7	5	6	50	36	26
Warley Rangers Res	18	6	7	5	32	32	25
Elland United Res	18	6	3	9	29	39	21
Greetland AFC Res (-3)	18	7	2	9	45	52	20
Shelf United Res	18	6	2	10	45	56	20
Halifax Irish Centre Res	18	5	1	12	34	51	16
Sowerby United Res	18	1	4	13	21	64	7

Division Three

	P	W	D	L	F	A	Pts
AFC Crossleys Res	16	13	0	3	88	32	39
Midgley United Res	16	10	3	3	50	37	33
Calder 76 Res	16	10	1	5	35	31	31
Spring Hall Celtic	16	9	2	5	54	40	29
Denholme United Res	16	9	1	6	34	29	28
Junction Inn	16	7	3	6	41	26	24
Elland Allstars Res	16	3	3	10	28	52	12
Volunteer Arms Res	16	4	0	12	32	59	12
Salem Res	16	0	1	15	18	74	1

HALSTEAD & DISTRICT LEAGUE

Premier

	P	W	D	L	F	A	Pts
Belchamps	24	17	3	4	79	30	54
Halstead Wanderers	24	16	3	5	81	36	51
Pebmarsh	22	17	0	5	80	36	51
Punch 68	24	16	3	5	58	29	51
Helions Bumpstead	24	13	4	7	62	31	43
Acton Crown	24	11	4	9	47	41	37
Kedington	23	10	3	10	60	56	33
Sporting 77	24	9	5	10	51	52	32
Bures Res	24	9	2	13	46	61	29
Rayne Res	24	6	2	16	30	70	20
Clare Reserves	24	5	2	17	50	75	17
Glemsford Gladiators	23	4	4	15	35	79	16
Finchingfield	24	3	1	20	30	113	10

HAMPSHIRE LEAGUE 2004

	Pld	W	D	L	F	A	Pts
Durley	22	18	1	3	62	15	55
Infinity	22	15	5	2	60	28	50
Crusaders	22	15	3	4	54	28	48
Andover Lions	22	14	1	7	60	40	43
Upham	22	10	3	9	41	45	33
Horndean United	22	9	5	9	49	38	32
Broughton	22	7	7	8	52	53	28
Four Marks (-6)	22	8	4	12	37	70	22
Mottisfont	22	5	3	14	34	60	18
Fair Oak	22	5	2	16	41	50	17
Michelmersh & Timsbury	22	4	4	14	36	66	16
Portsmouth Royal Navy	22	4	2	16	29	62	14

Botley Village - record expunged.

HARROGATE & DISTRICT LEAGUE

Premier Division

	P	W	D	L	F	A	Pts
Thirsk Falcons	18	14	3	1	72	21	45
Bedale Town	18	14	0	4	62	30	42
Kirk Deighton Rangers	18	11	4	3	47	25	37
Beckwithshaw Saints	18	10	4	4	38	35	34
Harlow Hill	18	8	5	5	45	35	29
Otley Rovers	18	6	1	11	33	43	19
Wigton Moor	18	4	5	9	27	49	17
Otley Town Res	18	4	4	10	29	43	16
Kirkby Malzeard	18	2	3	13	27	57	9
Pateley Bridge	18	2	1	15	29	71	7

Division One

	P	W	D	L	F	A	Pts
Killinghall Nomads	24	17	3	4	121	50	54
Pannal Sports	24	17	3	4	80	35	54
Clifford	24	15	4	5	69	45	49
Ripon Red Arrows	24	13	5	6	77	47	44
Knaresborough Celtic	24	12	3	9	53	38	39
Kirk Deighton Rangers Res.	24	11	1	12	64	57	34
Westbrook YMCA Res	24	10	3	11	62	58	33
Harlow Hill Reserves	24	8	5	11	46	57	29
Thirsk Falcons Reserves	24	8	4	12	71	72	28
Pool Reserves	24	8	3	13	57	68	27
Bedale Reserves	24	7	4	13	45	61	25
Kirkby Malzeard Reserves	24	7	2	15	45	72	23
Boston Spartans	24	2	2	20	25	155	8

Division Two

	P	W	D	L	F	A	Pts
Burley Trojans	22	13	4	5	58	25	43
Hillside	22	12	4	6	61	35	40
Wetherby Athletic A	22	12	3	7	50	48	39
Beckwithshaw Saints Res.	22	10	6	6	48	35	36
Pannal Sports Reserves	22	10	6	6	47	40	36
Hampsthwaite United	22	11	3	8	55	65	36
Boroughbridge A	22	9	4	9	48	43	31
Dalton Athletic	22	7	6	9	37	48	27
Bramham	22	7	3	12	35	57	24
Bramhope	22	7	1	14	42	56	22
Pateley Bridge Reserves	22	6	2	14	39	60	20
Wigton Moor Reserves	22	5	4	13	51	59	19

LEAGUE TABLES

Division Three

	P	W	D	L	F	A	Pts
Leyburn United	22	19	1	2	121	30	58
Wetheby Athletic `B`	22	15	3	4	73	50	48
Ripon Red Arrows Reserves	22	13	2	7	61	45	41
Hampsthwaite HC	22	12	2	8	64	43	38
Ilkley Town 'A'	22	11	0	11	54	50	33
Addingham	22	10	2	10	64	56	32
Pool A	22	7	5	10	47	62	26
Pannal Sports A	22	8	1	13	47	82	25
Helperby United	22	7	3	12	58	67	24
Thirsk Falcons A	22	7	3	12	50	73	24
Catterick Village	22	4	5	13	36	71	17
Hillside Reserves	22	5	1	16	28	74	16

HEREFORDSHIRE LEAGUE

	P	W	D	L	F	A	Pts
Ledbury Town	22	16	2	4	100	35	50
Bartestree	22	16	2	4	88	33	50
Westfields Reserves	22	14	5	3	70	28	47
Ewyas Harold	22	14	4	4	59	21	46
Mercia Athletic	22	14	3	5	74	33	45
Hinton	22	14	0	8	49	42	42
Kington Town	22	8	4	10	36	63	28
Wellington Reserves	22	7	4	11	43	37	25
Pegasus Juniors Reserves	22	6	1	15	42	65	19
Holme Lacy	22	3	4	15	29	81	13
Fownhope	22	3	1	18	26	81	10
Hereford Lads Club Res.	22	2	0	20	19	116	6

HOPE VALLEY AMATEUR LEAGUE

Premier

	P	W	D	L	F	A	Pts
Dove Holes	26	23	2	1	81	20	71
Buxton Town	26	23	0	3	100	16	69
Holmesfield	26	16	2	8	80	42	50
Tintwistle Villa	26	15	5	6	76	61	50
Brampton	26	15	2	9	68	50	47
Bradwell	26	13	4	9	52	41	43
Hathersage (-3)	26	10	7	9	50	41	34
Furness Vale	26	10	4	12	56	66	34
AFC Dronfield Woodhouse	26	8	6	12	44	52	30
Dronfield Town "A" (-3)	26	9	3	14	57	64	27
Hunters Bar	26	6	6	14	38	56	24
Bakewell Town	26	4	5	17	51	79	17
Grindleford	26	3	4	19	33	91	13
Totley Sports	26	1	2	23	33	140	5

A Division

	P	W	D	L	F	A	Pts
Dronfield Woodhouse	24	20	1	3	107	30	61
Tideswell United	24	19	2	3	97	23	59
Whaley Bridge Reserves	24	19	1	4	91	42	58
Youlgrave United	24	12	5	7	64	55	41
Peak Dale	24	12	2	10	60	45	38
Buxworth	24	9	4	11	62	66	31
Blazing Rag	24	8	4	12	75	63	28
Dove Holes Reserves (-3)	24	10	5	9	55	53	32
FCUtd of T'well (-3)	24	9	3	12	50	70	27
Buxton Christians	24	6	5	13	49	60	23
Red Lion	24	5	2	17	41	106	17
Calver (-3)	24	4	4	16	36	94	13
Dronfield Town "B"	24	3	2	19	43	123	11

B Division

	P	W	D	L	F	A	Pts
Chinley	26	21	5	0	107	37	68
Bamford	26	15	4	7	71	47	49
Cote Heath	26	15	4	7	74	51	49
Baslow (-3)	26	14	9	3	90	59	48
Tideswell Blue Star	26	13	7	6	60	38	46
Bradwell Reserves	26	12	2	12	63	62	38
Bakewell Town Reserves	26	10	2	14	60	76	32
Edale	26	8	6	12	64	68	30
Furness Vale Reserves	26	7	9	10	59	71	30
Buxworth Reserves	26	8	5	13	59	90	29
Stoney Middleton	26	7	6	13	47	60	27
Railway	26	7	2	17	55	71	23
Winster Wasps	26	6	3	17	46	88	21
Eyam	26	3	8	15	47	84	17

HUDDERSFIELD & DISTRICT LEAGUE

Division One

	P	W	D	L	F	A	Pts
Hepworth Utd	22	16	5	1	60	26	53
Netherton	22	13	5	4	68	36	44
Uppermill	22	13	4	5	64	40	43
Berry Brow	22	12	1	9	49	41	37
Newsome	22	11	2	9	50	46	35
Moldgreen	22	9	4	9	48	52	31
Diggle	22	8	6	8	45	46	30
Shepley	22	8	5	9	44	40	29
Lepton Highlanders	22	8	1	13	45	58	25
Holmbridge	22	5	3	14	30	59	18
Slaithwaite Utd	22	4	4	14	30	51	16
Britannia Sports	22	3	4	15	48	86	13

Division Two

	P	W	D	L	F	A	Pts
Scholes	22	15	4	3	42	25	49
Royal Dolphins	22	14	5	3	55	34	47
Kirkheaton Rovers	22	13	4	5	52	30	43
Heyside FC	22	13	2	7	75	43	41
Meltham Athletic	22	11	4	7	40	33	37
Cumberworth	22	9	7	6	55	42	34
Shelley	22	8	3	11	45	46	27
Heywood Irish Centre FC	22	7	4	11	43	53	25
Skelmanthorpe	22	7	3	12	48	53	24
Westend	22	6	4	12	42	70	22
Scissett	22	4	3	15	34	57	15
Honley	22	1	5	16	39	84	8

Division Three

	P	W	D	L	F	A	Pts
Dalton Crusaders	20	17	0	3	71	27	51
Holmfirth Town	20	14	3	3	67	24	45
Upperthong SC	20	13	1	6	48	30	40
AFC Waterloo	20	13	1	6	43	32	40
Linthwaite Athletic	20	9	1	10	59	40	28
KKS Sun Inn	20	8	4	8	44	40	28
Grange Moor	20	8	4	8	52	54	28
Wooldale Wanderers	20	8	3	9	31	54	27
H.V.Academicals	20	4	2	14	28	50	14
Brook Motors	20	4	1	15	28	64	13
Paddock Rangers	20	2	0	18	22	78	6

Division Four

	P	W	D	L	F	A	Pts
Moldgreen Con	24	21	2	1	101	32	65
Dewsbury Town OB	24	19	2	3	90	33	59
Flockton FC	24	17	3	4	71	40	54
Hade Edge	24	15	2	7	63	41	47
Waggon & Horses	24	14	5	5	73	54	47
Moorside	24	9	2	13	72	74	29
3D Dynamos	24	9	2	13	52	62	29
Mount	24	7	6	11	53	73	27
AFC Lindley	24	6	5	13	44	83	23
Crowchester United	24	5	6	13	42	54	21
Cartworth Moor	24	5	4	15	45	71	19
Lokomotiv Cowcliffe	24	4	2	18	48	83	14
Yorkshire Lions	24	3	3	18	29	83	12

HUDDERSFIELD & DISTRICT WORKS & COMBINATION LEAGUE

Division One

	P	W	D	L	F	A	Pts
Aimbry F.C.	16	12	3	1	45	16	39
Hepworth Utd.	16	9	2	5	41	29	29
Lindley Saddle	16	9	2	5	40	36	29
Coach & Horses	16	7	3	6	37	33	24
Sovereign Sports	16	7	3	6	28	34	24
Moldgreen F.C	16	5	2	9	42	41	17
Golcar United	16	5	2	9	32	45	17
Ireti Athletic	16	4	3	9	44	61	15
Kirkheaton Rovers	16	3	2	11	17	31	11

Division Two

	P	W	D	L	F	A	Pts
Uppermill "A"	16	14	2	0	77	17	44
Lepton Highlanders	16	12	3	1	81	24	39
Mac Athletic	16	12	3	1	82	27	39
Grange Moor	16	6	1	9	28	47	19
Phoenix Knights	16	5	2	9	34	64	17
Scissett	16	5	1	10	30	63	16
Lindley Saddle Reserves	16	4	2	10	41	66	14
Force United	16	3	3	10	34	70	12
F C Lockwood	16	2	1	13	32	61	7

Bay Athletic - record expunged.

I ZINGARI COMBINATION

Division One

	P	W	D	L	F	A	Pts
Liver Academy	22	19	3	0	74	19	60
Leyfield Reserves	22	15	5	2	58	34	50
Manweb	22	14	4	4	63	35	46
Old Xaverians Reserves	22	13	2	7	70	31	41
Essemmay OB	22	9	6	7	53	46	33
AFC Tuebrook	22	9	3	10	62	45	30
Liverpool Cavaliers	22	8	5	9	37	36	29
Aintree Villa	22	8	1	13	50	57	25
Sacre Coeur FP Reserves	22	7	0	15	31	59	21
Alder	22	6	3	13	30	59	21
BRNESC Reserves	22	3	3	16	29	83	12
Liobians Reserves	22	1	5	16	28	81	8

Division Two

	P	W	D	L	F	A	Pts
South Liverpool Reserves	24	22	1	1	105	21	67
Walton CTC	24	16	5	3	92	42	53
Real Stadium	24	15	5	4	76	44	50
Jaymc	24	14	3	7	54	35	45
FC Martyrs	24	13	4	7	86	55	43
Barrluca	24	12	3	9	57	46	39
Woodstreet	24	10	4	10	46	63	34
The Famous Grapes	24	8	2	14	45	55	26
Childwall Celtic	24	6	3	15	42	71	21
St Lukes	24	6	3	15	48	80	21
Mexoc	24	5	5	14	41	85	20
Mags	24	4	2	18	39	72	14
Rockville (Wallasey) (-1)	24	4	2	18	29	91	13

Liverpool 8 - record expunged.

ILFORD & DISTRICT LEAGUE

Premier Division

	P	W	D	L	F	A	Pts
LOASS	18	16	2	0	85	21	50
Forest United	18	15	3	0	60	21	48
Supreme Athletic	18	13	0	5	53	31	39
Phobians	18	7	2	9	35	42	23
William Fitt	18	6	4	8	38	48	22
Melbourne Sports	18	6	3	9	44	43	21
London & Essex	18	6	1	11	25	48	19
FC Golazo	18	5	2	11	44	48	17
FC Barolle	18	3	4	11	30	62	13
Glendale	18	2	1	15	25	75	7

Division One

	P	W	D	L	F	A	Pts
Ryan Res	18	14	3	1	74	22	45
St Francis	18	13	4	1	61	21	43
East Londoners	18	12	4	2	52	26	40
AAH Romford	18	8	4	6	49	41	28
LOASS Res	18	8	4	6	47	43	28
Chingford Harriers	18	6	4	8	44	50	22
Singh Sabha Barking Re	18	5	3	10	31	37	18
Lansbury	18	3	3	12	23	64	12
Chingford Athletic A	18	3	2	13	31	71	11
Esprit Midland	18	1	3	14	15	52	6

INTER LEAGUE COMPETITION

Inter League Comp	P	W	D	L	F	A	Pts
Sussex County League Div 3	4	3	0	1	14	3	9
Brighton, Hove & District Lge	4	2	2	0	8	5	8
Mid Sussex League	4	1	2	1	7	11	5
West Sussex League	4	0	2	2	7	8	2
Worthing & District League	4	0	2	2	4	13	2

LEAGUE TABLES

Division Two

	P	W	D	L	F	A	Pts
DM United	15	13	0	2	72	27	39
Trelawny	15	10	1	4	47	38	31
AFC Kings	15	9	1	5	57	24	28
Ryan A	15	6	0	9	29	53	18
Lituanica	15	4	0	11	31	57	9
St Francis Res	15	2	0	13	23	60	6

Division Three

	P	W	D	L	F	A	Pts
DM United Res	20	20	0	0	95	24	57
Hainault Wanderers	20	16	1	3	76	36	46
Forest United Res	20	12	1	7	62	50	37
Ascot United	20	12	0	8	43	43	36
Leyton United	20	8	4	8	42	24	28
Lucky Strikes	20	9	0	11	46	47	27
Dynamo Athletic	20	7	2	11	43	70	23
Melbourne Sports Res	20	6	1	13	39	49	19
Custom House	20	5	1	14	44	68	16
Newham Royals	20	5	1	14	36	69	16
Leyton Green	20	3	3	14	34	80	12

ISLE OF MAN SENIOR LEAGUE

Premier League

	P	W	D	L	F	A	Pts
St Georges	24	23	1	0	130	16	70
St Marys	24	19	1	4	88	38	58
Laxey	24	19	0	5	90	38	57
DHSOB	24	14	4	6	78	36	46
Rushen United	24	12	5	7	92	48	41
Peel	24	11	5	8	73	50	38
St Johns	24	10	6	8	62	56	36
Corinthians	24	10	2	12	53	65	32
Ramsey	24	6	6	12	55	55	24
Castletown	24	6	1	17	48	96	19
Gymnasium	24	5	1	18	39	120	16
RYCOB	24	3	2	19	29	93	11
Ayre United	24	1	0	23	25	151	3

Division Two

	P	W	D	L	F	A	Pts
Union Mills First	24	21	0	3	112	23	63
Marown	24	20	1	3	102	24	61
Onchan	24	16	2	6	63	49	50
Foxdale	24	14	2	8	76	42	44
Michael United	24	14	1	9	59	41	43
Douglas Royal	24	12	5	7	55	42	41
Colby	24	8	7	9	51	57	31
Pulrose United	24	9	3	12	45	61	30
Braddan	24	8	2	14	46	76	26
Police	24	6	4	14	51	72	22
Douglas & District	24	6	2	16	42	86	20
Malew	24	3	3	18	34	95	12
Ronaldsway	24	2	2	20	27	95	8

Combination One

	P	W	D	L	F	A	Pts
DHSOB Reserves	24	19	4	1	97	27	61
Peel Reserves (-3)	24	16	3	5	110	38	48
Corinthians Reserves	24	14	4	6	88	49	46
St Marys Reserves	24	14	4	6	79	47	46
Rushen Reserves	24	14	3	7	78	43	45
Laxey Reserves	24	13	3	8	97	70	42
Ramsey Reserves	24	13	2	9	75	58	41
St Georges Reserves	24	12	0	12	68	58	36
St Johns Reserves	24	10	3	11	76	78	33
RYCOB	24	7	3	14	44	102	24
Gymnasium Reserves	24	3	2	19	42	106	11
Castletown Reserves	24	3	0	21	45	157	9
Ayre United	24	2	1	21	35	101	7

Combination Two

	P	W	D	L	F	A	Pts
Marown Reserves	24	20	2	2	89	31	62
Union Mills Reserves	24	16	3	5	82	33	51
Michael United	24	16	3	5	83	43	51
Foxdale	24	16	2	6	87	49	50
Colby	24	14	4	6	75	47	46
Police Reserves	24	11	3	10	62	66	36
Pulrose United	24	10	4	10	63	66	34
Braddan	24	8	3	13	63	76	27
Onchan	24	8	2	14	68	74	26
Douglas Royal (-6)	24	10	2	12	60	74	26
Douglas & District	24	4	4	16	39	84	16
Malew	24	4	2	18	44	99	14
Ronaldsway	24	2	0	22	30	103	6

ISLE OF WIGHT LEAGUE

Division One

	P	W	D	L	F	A	Pts
West Wight	22	19	1	2	69	17	58
Brading Town Reserves	22	17	1	4	58	28	52
Northwood St Johns	22	16	1	5	62	31	49
Cowes Sports Reserves	22	13	5	4	49	27	44
Oakfield	22	11	3	8	73	34	36
Ventnor	22	11	2	9	50	37	35
Shanklin	22	10	1	11	59	42	31
Ryde Saints	22	6	5	11	42	50	23
GKN	22	5	4	13	35	69	19
Niton	22	5	2	15	34	50	17
Binstead & COB	22	4	1	17	29	83	13
Newchurch	22	0	4	18	6	98	4

Division Two

	P	W	D	L	F	A	Pts
Osborne Coburg	20	15	1	4	79	23	46
Pan Sports	20	14	3	3	81	30	45
Sandown	20	14	3	3	67	26	45
St Helens Blue Star	20	11	4	5	72	30	37
Shanklin VYCC	20	9	2	9	39	39	29
Brighstone	20	8	2	10	36	50	26
W'croft & Barton Sports	20	7	4	9	41	38	25
Seaview	20	7	3	10	50	66	24
Carisbrooke United	20	7	2	11	44	63	23
Newport IOW "A"	20	4	2	14	56	64	14
E Cowes Vict Athl "A"	20	1	0	19	11	147	3

Division Three

	P	W	D	L	F	A	Pts
Vectis Nomads	16	14	1	1	67	10	43
Yarmouth & Calbourne	16	12	1	3	71	23	37
Holmwood Athletic	16	11	2	3	65	26	35
Kyngs Towne	16	9	0	7	43	45	27
Wroxall	16	6	1	9	39	41	19
Shanklin "A"	16	5	1	10	32	61	16
Ryde Saints "A"	16	4	2	10	28	56	14
Wakes	16	4	1	11	30	60	13
Rookley	16	2	1	13	20	73	7

JERSEY FOOTBALL COMBINATION

Premiership

	P	W	D	L	F	A	Pts
Jersey Scottish	16	13	2	1	44	18	41
St Paul's	16	8	3	5	44	30	27
Jersey Wanderers	16	8	3	5	36	28	27
Grouville	16	6	6	4	29	26	24
St Peter	16	7	3	6	33	35	24
St Ouen	16	5	3	8	26	28	18
Rozel Rovers	16	4	6	6	25	33	18
Trinity	16	4	3	9	24	30	15
First Tower Utd	16	1	3	12	17	50	6

Championship

	P	W	D	L	F	A	Pts
St Brelade	18	14	2	2	53	17	44
St Lawrence	18	11	2	5	38	26	35
Jersey Portuguese	18	10	2	6	42	23	32
Beeches OB	18	10	2	6	51	42	32
St Martin/SCF	18	9	3	6	49	34	30
St Clement	18	9	3	6	44	30	30
Jersey Nomads	18	7	3	8	41	25	24
St John	18	4	2	12	18	49	14
Magpies	18	4	0	14	21	49	12
Sporting Academics	18	2	1	15	29	91	7

Division One

	P	W	D	L	F	A	Pts
Jersey Scottish Res	16	10	2	4	45	27	32
Jersey Wanderers Res	16	9	2	5	48	33	29
Grouville Res	16	7	4	5	39	32	25
First Tower Utd Res	16	7	3	6	29	33	24
St Ouen Res	16	6	5	5	33	28	23
Rozel Rovers Res	16	7	2	7	47	44	23
St Peter Res (-1)	16	7	3	6	32	34	23 *
St Clement Res	16	3	3	10	18	46	12
St Paul's Res	16	3	2	11	35	49	11

Division Two

	P	W	D	L	F	A	Pts
St Martin/SCF Res (-3)	16	11	3	2	44	20	33
St Brelade Res	16	10	3	3	48	33	33
Trinity Res	16	9	4	3	55	29	31
Magpies Res	16	7	4	5	43	30	25
Jersey Nomads Res (-3)	16	8	3	5	55	40	24
St John Res	16	4	2	10	31	51	14
Sporting Academics Res	16	3	2	11	32	72	11
St Lawrence Res (-3)	16	2	7	7	25	35	10
Beeches OB Res	16	2	4	10	24	47	10

KIDDERMINSTER & DISTRICT LEAGUE

Premier Division

	P	W	D	L	F	A	Pts
Netherton Athletic	30	26	1	3	105	27	79
Kings Heath Old Boys	30	20	3	6	95	42	63
Two Gates	30	19	4	7	90	47	61
Dudley Villa	30	16	6	8	70	50	54
Wyre Forest	30	16	4	10	73	53	52
Dudley Wood Athletic	30	16	3	11	81	66	51
Burlish Olympic	30	15	4	10	83	58	49
Birch Coppice	30	13	5	12	78	55	44
Areley Kings	30	11	8	11	69	58	41
Lodgefield Park	30	11	7	12	59	63	40
Kinver	30	11	6	13	67	80	39
Claverley	30	11	3	16	68	85	36
Orton Vale	30	7	4	19	46	101	25
Oldswinford Harriers (-1)	30	7	2	21	38	89	22
Claverley Colts	30	5	2	23	39	112	17
Castlecroft Rangers	30	4	0	26	35	110	12

KINGSTON & DISTRICT LEAGUE

Premier Division

Premier Division	P	W	D	L	F	A	PTS
Chessington K.C.	14	10	3	1	45	15	33
Summerstown	14	9	2	3	41	19	29
AFC Watermans	14	8	2	4	50	27	26
Parkside	14	6	3	5	30	26	21
A.C.Malden	14	6	1	7	27	39	19
Darkside	14	4	4	6	23	26	16
SHFC London	14	2	3	9	13	53	9
AFC Westend	14	0	4	10	16	40	4
Robin Hood Withdrawn							

Division One

	P	W	D	L	F	A	Pts
Wandle	16	11	3	2	42	26	36
Sunbury Galaxy	16	10	1	5	33	22	31
Kingston Albion	16	8	2	6	30	34	26
Old Roehamptonians	16	7	4	5	29	23	25
Richmond & Kingston O.B.	16	6	4	6	36	34	22
Esher United	16	6	3	7	30	29	21
L.M.United	16	5	5	6	38	37	20
N.P.L.	16	4	4	8	40	37	16
Repton	16	2	0	14	18	54	6

Division Two

	P	W	D	L	F	A	Pts
Kingsbrook	18	12	3	2	35	16	39
Hanworth Sports	18	11	4	23	44	19	37
Chessington K.C.Res	18	9	3	6	49	32	30
Esher	18	9	2	7	33	29	29
Maori Park	18	6	7	5	35	31	25
Thornton Heath	18	6	4	8	31	50	22
St Martins	18	6	3	9	32	35	21
Oxshott Royals	18	4	5	8	28	37	17
Lower Green	18	4	3	11	34	51	15
Surbiton Eagles	18	2	6	10	18	39	12

LEAGUE TABLES

Division Three

	P	W	D	L	F	A	Pts
Monkey Tennis	16	16	0	0	67	10	48
AFC Molesey	16	11	1	4	50	25	34
Surrey Fire	16	9	2	5	44	28	29
Barnslake	16	9	2	5	40	33	29
N.P.L.Res	16	9	0	7	48	39	27
Twickenham Athletic	16	5	0	11	36	54	15
Claygate & Ditton	16	4	1	11	22	59	13
Epsom Casuals	16	2	2	12	14	36	8
Dynamo Kingston	16	2	2	12	15	52	8

Division Four

	P	W	D	L	F	A	Pts
Lennox	18	15	1	2	71	27	46
FC Carlisle	18	10	4	4	45	30	34
AFC Watermans Res	18	10	2	6	42	24	32
Darkside Res	18	8	2	8	47	38	26
Parkside Res	18	7	5	6	43	38	26
AFC Kingston	18	8	1	9	31	31	25
Merton Social	18	7	4	7	36	40	25
Hook Venturers	18	6	4	8	38	46	22
AFC Hampton	18	5	3	10	29	38	18
Westside	18	0	2	16	18	88	2

Division Five

	P	W	D	L	F	A	Pts
Kingston Tigers	16	13	1	2	69	23	40
Chessington K.C. 111	16	10	2	4	48	21	32
AFC Kingston Res	16	10	2	4	37	30	32
St Martins Res	16	8	3	5	43	23	27
Ewell Saxons Seniors	16	8	1	7	42	30	25
Merton Social Res	16	7	1	8	23	43	22
North Leatherhead	16	4	1	11	12	34	13
Lennox Res	16	3	1	12	19	59	10
Lower Green Res	16	3	0	13	15	45	9

Division One

	P	W	D	L	F	A	Pts
Irlam Steel	24	21	3	0	86	27	66
Newton 1st	24	16	6	2	75	34	54
Fletcher Moss 1st	24	14	5	5	68	43	47
Parrswood Celtic	24	11	4	9	57	47	37
Newton Heath	24	9	5	10	58	69	32
Burnage Metro	24	9	4	11	46	55	31
Alkrington Dynamos FC	24	8	5	11	66	70	29
Stoconians 1st	24	7	6	11	46	67	27
Abacus Media	24	6	8	10	59	50	26
Govan Athletic	24	6	5	13	35	52	23
Santos FC	24	5	7	12	54	77	22
Milton FC	24	5	6	13	44	69	21
Heaton Mersey	24	5	4	15	47	81	19

Division Two

	P	W	D	L	F	A	Pts
Ardwick FC 1st	22	17	4	1	82	36	55
Gorse Hill	22	16	2	4	82	29	50
Hollingworth O.B.	22	15	2	5	69	32	47
Castleton FC First	22	12	6	4	84	52	42
Moston Brook	22	12	3	7	52	47	39
Tintwistle Athletic FC	22	10	4	8	62	40	34
Bedians Res	22	7	4	11	41	63	25
Rochdalians Res	22	6	2	14	36	51	20
Eagle	22	5	4	13	39	93	19
Moorside Rangers FC	22	5	3	14	43	63	18
Mellor Res	22	5	2	15	38	67	17
Aldermere	22	4	0	18	27	82	12

Division Three

	P	W	D	L	F	A	Pts
Boothstown FC 1st	18	14	1	3	64	28	43
Whalley Range Res	18	13	3	2	60	28	42
Chorltonians Res	18	10	2	6	50	35	32
Trafford United 1st	18	9	4	5	49	34	31
Bury Amateur AFC 1st	18	7	2	9	39	35	23
Burnage Metro Res	18	6	3	9	34	42	21
Urmston Town 1st	18	6	2	10	42	43	20
Whitworth Park 1st	18	5	5	8	41	52	20
Signol Athletic FC First	18	5	3	10	25	58	18
Oldham Victoria	18	2	1	15	22	71	7

LANCASHIRE & CHESHIRE LEAGUE

Premier Division

	P	W	D	L	F	A	Pts
Whalley Range	26	20	4	2	82	38	64
Cheadle Hulme Villa	26	18	2	6	69	36	56
Spurley Hey	26	15	4	7	72	38	49
AFC Oldham 2005	26	13	2	11	65	47	41
Rochdalians	26	13	2	11	52	46	41
Mellor	26	12	4	10	63	64	40
Bedians	26	12	3	11	66	65	39
Old Ashtonians	26	11	5	10	49	50	38
South Manchester	26	10	2	14	57	70	32
Old Trafford	26	8	5	13	69	72	29
Old Stretfordians	26	8	4	14	50	55	28
Hooley Bridge Celtic	26	9	0	17	48	79	27
Hazel Grove	26	6	3	17	37	86	21
Chorltonians	26	4	6	16	29	62	18

LANCASHIRE AMATEUR LEAGUE

Premier Division

	P	W	D	L	F	A	Pts
Castle Hill	26	19	6	1	74	30	63
Rossendale Amateurs	26	15	7	4	78	34	52
Bury GSOB	26	15	6	5	53	36	51
Failsworth Dynamos	26	13	3	10	60	50	42
Old Boltonians	26	11	8	7	52	42	41
Old Mancunians	26	11	7	8	52	43	40
Rochdale St Clements	26	12	4	10	51	50	40
Prestwich	26	12	3	11	63	47	39
Little Lever SC	26	10	4	12	53	67	34
Horwich Victoria	26	9	4	13	59	47	31
Howe Bridge Mills	26	8	2	16	38	75	26
Chaddertonians	26	7	4	15	41	59	25
CMB	26	7	3	16	29	69	24
Hesketh Casuals	26	2	1	23	35	89	7

Division One

	P	W	D	L	F	A	Pts
Hindley Juniors	26	18	1	7	93	43	55
Old Blackburnians	26	15	5	6	74	44	50
Bolton Wyresdale	26	14	7	5	47	23	49
Mostonians	26	14	7	5	60	45	49
Roach Dynamos	26	13	6	7	56	52	45
Rochdale St Clements Res.	26	14	2	10	57	48	44
Tyldesley United	26	14	0	12	60	43	42
Radcliffe Town	26	12	4	10	68	58	40
Horwich RMI	26	9	6	11	45	57	33
Broughton Amateurs (-4)	26	11	3	12	59	63	32
Rossendale Amateurs Res.	26	7	5	14	45	62	26
Thornleigh	26	6	7	13	46	59	25
Prairie United	26	4	0	22	47	103	12
Ainsworth (-4)	26	3	3	20	50	107	8

Division Two

	P	W	D	L	F	A	Pts
North Walkden	26	19	1	6	104	50	58
Old Boltonians Reserves	26	18	3	5	76	41	57
Accrington Amateurs	26	16	2	8	77	64	50
Oldham Hulmeians	26	16	2	8	67	58	50
Stand AFC	26	13	7	6	67	42	46
Cadley	26	12	5	9	70	64	41
Old Blackburnians Reserves	26	12	1	13	74	71	37
Ashtonians	26	8	7	11	56	66	31
Bury GSOB Reserves	26	8	5	13	50	64	29
Old Mancunians Reserves	26	9	2	15	47	65	29
Little Lever SC Reserves	26	6	7	13	48	67	25
Chadderton	26	6	5	15	49	65	23
Chaddertonians Reserves	26	6	4	16	53	81	22
Radcliffe Boys	26	5	5	16	50	90	20

Division Three

	P	W	D	L	F	A	Pts
Tottington United	24	18	3	3	90	33	57
Blackrod Town	24	17	3	4	80	33	54
Failsworth Dynamos Res.	24	15	3	6	60	31	48
Westhoughton Town	24	13	8	3	85	37	47
Rossendale Amateurs A	24	13	5	6	68	41	44
Old Boltonians A	24	11	2	11	79	53	35
Radcliffe Town Reserves	24	9	5	10	55	67	32
Castle Hill Reserves	24	9	4	11	61	54	31
Bacup United	24	9	3	12	69	67	30
Hesketh Casuals Reserves	24	8	5	11	50	65	29
Bolton Lads Club	24	6	3	15	44	83	21
Lymm	24	3	1	20	24	112	10
Chaddertonians A	24	0	5	19	32	121	5

Division Four

	P	W	D	L	F	A	Pts
Prestwich Reserves	26	23	2	1	93	22	71
Oldham Hulmeians Res.	26	18	3	5	92	51	57
Horwich Victoria Reserves	26	13	7	6	75	42	46
Accrington Amateurs Res.	26	13	3	10	75	70	42
Rochdale St Clements A	26	13	2	11	56	51	41
Old Blackburnians A	26	12	5	9	74	70	41
Broughton Am. Res. (-4)	26	11	6	9	57	47	35
Astley Bridge	26	9	5	12	73	85	32
Mostonians Reserves (-4)	26	9	5	12	60	73	28
Rossendale Amateurs B	26	7	6	13	60	80	27
Horwich RMI Reserves	26	6	8	12	51	78	26
Dobbies (-4)	26	7	5	14	69	91	22
Bolton Wyresdale Reserves	26	6	1	19	43	97	19
Old Standians Reserves	26	4	4	18	49	70	16

Division Five

	P	W	D	L	F	A	Pts
Rossendale Amateurs C	26	18	4	4	75	44	58
Roach Dynamos Reserves	26	18	3	5	86	56	57
Thornleigh Reserves	26	17	2	7	100	45	53
Prestwich A	26	14	4	8	72	53	46
Radcliffe Town A	26	14	2	10	75	60	44
Howe Bridge Mills Reserves	26	13	3	10	74	61	42
Ainsworth Reserves	26	11	3	12	61	64	36
Old Mancunians A	26	11	2	13	57	67	35
Ashtonians Reserves (-4)	26	10	4	12	62	81	30
Bury GSOB A	26	7	6	13	49	66	27
Rochdale St Clements B	26	7	4	15	46	64	25
Hesketh Casuals A	26	7	4	15	57	87	25
Lymm Reserves	26	8	1	17	49	83	25
Radcliffe Boys Reserves	26	5	2	19	47	79	17

Division Six

	P	W	D	L	F	A	Pts
Thornleigh A	22	16	4	2	72	21	52
Old Boltonians B	22	16	3	3	69	34	51
Broughton Amateurs A	22	13	4	5	52	27	43
Bolton Wyresdale A	22	13	2	7	66	52	41
Lymm A	22	13	0	9	65	58	39
Mostonians A	22	12	2	8	56	44	38
Tottington United Reserves	22	10	1	11	52	43	31
Oldham Hulmeians A	22	6	5	11	54	77	23
Old Blackburnians B	22	6	3	13	39	50	21
Old Mancunians B	22	5	4	13	33	52	19
Tyldesley United Reserves	22	4	1	17	31	73	13
Radcliffe Town B	22	2	3	17	27	85	9

Division Seven

	P	W	D	L	F	A	Pts
Horwich Victoria A	20	18	0	2	70	25	54
Old Blackburnians C	20	17	1	2	87	27	52
Hesketh Casuals B	20	12	0	8	73	50	36
Little Lever SC A	20	10	5	5	60	37	35
Thornleigh B	20	8	3	9	52	59	27
Howe Bridge Mills A	20	7	2	11	43	57	23
Horwich RMI A	20	5	5	10	29	40	20
Broughton Amateurs B	20	5	5	10	31	52	20
Bury GSOB B (-4)	20	7	1	12	47	70	18
Oldham Hulmeians B	20	5	2	13	40	65	17
Bolton Wyresdale B	20	3	2	15	32	82	11

LANCASHIRE LEAGUE

East

	P	W	D	L	F	A	Pts
Thackley Reserves	21	13	2	6	62	37	41
Ossett Albion Reserves	21	12	1	8	46	30	37
Harrogate Railway Ath. Res.	21	10	3	8	53	49	33
Tadcaster Albion	21	9	6	6	51	50	33
Farsley Reserves	21	9	3	9	43	42	30
Eccleshill United Reserves	21	8	2	11	42	59	26
Stalybridge Celtic Reserves	21	6	3	12	50	53	21
New Mills "A"	21	6	2	13	39	66	20

LEAGUE TABLES

West	P	W	D	L	F	A	Pts
Lancaster City Reserves	20	14	4	2	61	24	46
AFC Fylde Reserves	20	12	4	4	53	22	40
Bamber Bridge Reserves	20	12	4	4	51	33	40
Fleetwood Town Reseerves	20	10	4	6	61	41	34
Colne Reserves	20	9	3	8	35	44	30
Mossley Reserves	20	8	4	8	46	37	28
Curzon Ashton Reserves	20	8	3	9	46	33	27
Workington Reserves	20	7	5	8	37	41	26
Formby Reserves	20	5	3	12	33	60	18
Kendal Town Reserves	20	2	5	13	31	70	11
Witton Albion Reserves	20	2	3	15	20	69	9

LEEDS RED TRIANLE LEAGUE

Premier Division	P	W	D	L	F	A	Pts
Seacroft WMC	12	10	0	2	41	9	30
Halton Moor	12	9	2	1	38	14	29
Kirkstall Crusaers	12	7	0	5	41	28	21
Morley Town	12	6	1	5	39	40	19
Crossgates	12	5	2	5	26	33	17
Old Headingley "A"	12	1	1	10	18	61	4
Churwell	12	1	0	11	17	35	3

Division One	P	W	D	L	F	A	Pts
Parkfield	10	7	2	1	28	13	23
Wykebeck Arms	10	6	2	2	27	22	20
Drighlington Adwalton	10	3	3	4	12	10	12
Drighlin'ton Malt Shovel	10	3	3	4	21	20	12
Altofts Reserves	10	2	2	6	17	31	8
South Leeds Independent	10	1	1	5	16	25	7

Division Two	P	W	D	L	F	A	Pts
Harehills Liberal Club	14	8	6	0	38	15	30
Belle Isle WMC	14	9	2	3	47	25	29
Kirkstall Crusaders Res	14	8	3	3	45	24	27
Churwell Lions	14	7	4	3	42	30	25
Smiling Mule	14	6	4	4	37	27	22
Swarcliffe WMC	14	2	2	10	24	57	8
Shears Inn	14	1	4	9	25	52	7
Seacroft Colts Old Boys	14	2	1	11	22	50	7

Leeds Deaf - record expunged

LEICESTER & DISTRICT LEAGUE

Premier Division	P	W	D	L	F	A	Pts
Thurnby United	22	19	2	1	114	38	59
Allexton and New Parks	22	16	3	3	79	25	51
Houghton Rangers	22	15	3	4	74	28	48
Glenfield Town	22	12	4	6	58	56	40
Birstall RBL	22	11	4	7	81	58	37
Cosby United	22	11	2	9	72	69	35
Magna 73	22	9	2	11	63	56	29
Mountsorrel Amateurs	22	7	3	12	49	59	24
County Hall	22	6	3	13	42	51	21
Kibworth Town	22	5	3	14	37	74	18
Blaby United	22	5	2	15	42	83	17
Guru Nanak Gurdwara (GNG)	22	0	1	21	21	135	1

Division One	P	W	D	L	F	A	Pts
Braders	24	20	1	3	114	23	61
Huncote	24	15	5	4	54	26	50
Glen Villa	24	13	8	3	83	45	47
Kingsway Celtic	24	12	4	8	73	57	40
North Kilworth	24	12	3	9	65	52	39
Fleckney Athletic	24	11	4	9	76	47	37
Queniborough	24	9	6	9	72	61	33
Ashby Road	24	9	5	10	69	56	32
Saffron Lounge (-3)	24	11	2	11	65	67	32
Burbage Old Boys	24	7	5	12	47	49	26
St Patricks	24	6	7	11	47	80	25
Thurlaston Magpies	24	6	0	18	46	91	18
Earl of Stamford	24	0	0	24	23	180	0

Division Two	P	W	D	L	F	A	Pts
Northfield Emerald	24	19	2	3	99	28	59
Braunstone Trinity	24	16	2	6	87	34	50
Topps Wine Bar	24	15	5	4	99	53	50
NKF Burbage	24	14	3	7	68	46	45
Shoemakers Ath	24	13	2	9	65	57	41
Oadby Boys Club '93	24	11	3	10	69	66	36
Kirkland (-3)	24	11	3	10	70	51	33
Broughton Astley	24	9	4	11	48	55	31
Belgrave A	24	8	1	15	63	91	25
The New Joiners	24	7	3	14	43	94	24
Sporting Sapcote	24	7	1	16	45	88	22
Aylestone Union	24	5	5	14	46	73	20
Park End 74	24	3	2	19	28	94	11

Reserves Premier Division	P	W	D	L	F	A	Pts
Allexton and New Parks Res	18	14	3	1	84	31	45
Birstall RBL Reserves	18	13	2	3	61	30	41
Cosby United Reserves	18	8	4	6	46	42	28
Magna 73 Reserves	18	7	6	5	58	42	27
Houghton Rangers Reserves	18	8	3	7	40	37	27
Glenfield Town Reserves	18	8	2	8	50	41	26
North Kilworth Reserves	18	6	3	9	38	52	21
County Hall Reserves	18	5	1	12	39	68	16
Mountsorrel Amateurs Res.	18	3	3	12	23	54	12
Blaby United Reserves	18	3	3	12	32	74	12

Reserve Division One	P	W	D	L	F	A	Pts
Aylestone Lounge Res	18	15	1	2	69	24	46
Thurnby United Reserves	18	13	2	3	69	27	41
Guru Nanak Gurdwar (GNG) Res.	18	12	1	5	49	27	37
Kibworth Town Reserves	18	10	2	6	59	37	32
Huncote Reserves	18	8	3	7	50	47	27
Queniborough Reserves	18	7	4	7	41	41	25
Glen Villa Reserves	18	7	1	10	41	36	22
Cosby United 'A'	18	4	2	12	31	70	14
Thurlaston Magpies Reserves	18	3	3	12	36	66	12
NKF Burbage Reserves	18	1	1	16	24	94	4

LINCOLN & DISTRICT LEAGUE

	P	W	D	L	F	A	Pts
Gainsbough Town Canute	22	19	2	1	87	15	59
Waddington United	22	16	3	3	68	26	51
Washingborough	22	14	1	7	70	34	43
R.M.Imp	22	11	2	9	63	48	35
Fulbeck United	22	8	5	9	55	50	29
Nettleham	22	9	2	11	48	49	29
Ivy Tavern CSA	22	8	4	10	46	45	28
Clayton Sports (-3)	22	9	4	9	45	52	28
Metheringham	22	7	6	9	44	46	27
Horncastle Town	22	5	3	14	39	76	18
Middle Rasen	22	4	2	16	41	98	14
AFC Ruston Sports	22	4	2	16	34	101	14

LINCOLNSHIRE LEAGUE

	P	W	D	L	F	A	Pts
Cleethorpes Town	32	28	3	1	130	18	87
Skegness United	32	26	3	3	111	46	81
Boston United Reserves	32	23	2	7	99	36	71
Grimsby Borough Reserves	32	19	4	9	61	47	61
Hykeham Town	32	17	9	6	66	46	60
Nettleham	32	17	4	11	87	53	55
Heckington United	32	17	3	12	78	65	54
Louth Town Reserves	32	16	4	12	72	73	52
Horncastle Town	32	12	5	15	62	68	41
CGB Humbertherm	32	12	4	16	56	62	40
Lincoln United Reserves(+2)	32	10	5	17	40	62	37
Skegness Town	32	10	4	18	55	82	34
Swineshead Institute	32	9	6	17	47	66	33
Market Rasen Town	32	7	4	21	43	87	25
Ruston Sports	32	5	7	20	42	90	22
Lincoln Moorlands Railway Res	32	5	5	22	44	88	20
Sleaford Town Reserves (-1)	32	1	4	27	29	133	6

LIVERPOOL CMS LEAGUE

Premier Division

	P	W	D	L	F	A	Pts
Railway	22	18	2	2	86	27	56
Lord Warden	22	16	1	5	84	33	49
Dunnies RCU	22	15	0	7	70	54	45
Western Speke	22	12	2	8	68	61	38
Mersey Harps	22	11	3	8	43	43	36
Polonia Camps	22	9	4	9	44	59	31
Fountains Abbey	22	8	4	10	52	79	28
Mosslane	22	7	5	10	52	80	26
Vale Madrid	22	8	1	13	56	21	25
Dunnings Bridge	22	7	1	14	50	85	22
AFC Kirkby	22	6	4	12	50	89	22
Parkway	22	1	1	20	5	29	4

Division One

	P	W	D	L	F	A	Pts
Brown Cow	24	19	2	3	76	26	59
Elmoore	24	16	3	5	67	37	51
The First Dock	24	15	5	4	75	31	50
The Clock	24	14	7	3	77	33	49
Rose & Crown	24	14	3	7	78	44	45
St Michaels	24	12	1	11	66	65	37
Pipes	24	12	1	11	45	50	37
Monkswell Abbey	24	10	4	10	54	41	34
The Good Shepard	24	9	1	14	42	69	28
Western Speke Reserves	24	8	1	15	49	62	25
Glenbuck 96	24	5	3	16	42	75	18
The Claremont	24	3	1	20	18	78	10
The Botanic	24	3	0	21	25	103	9

LONDON COMMERCIAL LEAGUE

Division One

	P	W	D	L	F	A	Pts
British Airways	18	14	2	2	60	23	44
North Greenford United III	18	9	6	3	36	26	33
Marsh Rangers	18	8	6	4	64	43	30
Fulham Dynamo Sports	18	6	3	9	40	60	21
Northwood III	18	6	3	9	34	61	21
Roxeth	18	4	3	11	30	33	15
Amateur Football Com. Fulham	18	3	3	12	36	54	12

Division Two

	P	W	D	L	F	A	Pts
Paddington Vale	22	15	3	4	63	31	48
Abbey National S & S Club	22	13	3	6	61	46	42
British Airways II	22	11	7	4	53	37	40
Ealing Old Boys	22	11	6	5	69	50	39
Sudbury Court	22	10	7	5	44	32	37
Old Alpertonian	22	11	0	11	56	54	33
Southall Rangers	22	8	3	11	38	27	27
Brentford Athletic	22	8	3	11	58	76	27
Hounslow Wanderers II	22	7	4	11	31	50	25
Charing Cross Association	22	6	5	11	51	59	23
Travaux Saints	22	4	5	13	42	68	17
Hillingdon III	22	4	2	16	39	75	14

Division Three

	P	W	D	L	F	A	Pts
British Airways III	24	19	3	2	107	27	60
Sandgate Old Boys	24	16	6	2	93	32	54
British Airways IV	24	15	4	5	77	50	49
Barnet Municipal Officers	24	13	4	7	71	61	43
New Hanford	24	12	4	8	67	58	40
Lampton Park	24	11	4	9	80	60	37
Old Alpertonians II	24	9	5	10	58	66	32
Chiswick Homefields II	24	8	5	11	47	65	29
West London Hoops	24	8	4	11	55	62	28
LPOSSA II	24	7	3	14	43	59	24
Lampton Lions	24	7	1	16	36	82	22
Hanworth United	24	2	5	16	29	76	11
Harrow Lyons	24	3	2	19	52	117	11

LOWESTOFT & DISTRICT LEAGUE

Division One

	P	W	D	L	F	A	Pts
Hearts of Oak	26	19	5	2	96	43	62
Gt Yarmouth Town Hall	26	19	4	3	68	41	61
DK Consultants	26	14	6	6	90	44	48
Waveney Reserves	26	16	0	10	77	63	48
Barsham	26	12	8	6	65	47	44
Blundeston Magpies	26	12	2	12	70	55	38
Oxford Arms	26	11	3	12	60	59	36
Norton Athletic	26	10	6	10	71	75	36
Hopton	26	9	2	15	57	85	29
Spexhall	26	7	6	13	49	66	27
Kirkley & Pakefield A	26	7	4	15	48	80	25
Pot Black	26	7	3	16	48	99	24
Mutford & Wrentham	26	6	4	16	52	81	22
Pakefield Re-United	26	4	5	17	70	83	17

LEAGUE TABLES

Division Two

	P	W	D	L	F	A	Pts
Earsham	26	20	4	2	80	29	64
Corton Seltic	26	17	3	6	91	51	54
Spexhall Reserves	26	15	3	8	62	38	48
Waveney Gunners	26	14	3	9	70	44	45
Crusaders	26	14	2	10	85	71	44
Norton Athletic Reserves	26	11	9	6	59	48	42
FC Eastport	26	13	1	12	104	81	40
Mutford & Wrentham Res.	26	12	4	10	59	45	40
Beccles Caxton Reserves	26	11	5	10	65	69	38
Waveney A	26	9	4	13	52	66	31
Kirkley & Pakefield B	26	9	4	13	59	75	31
Harleston Town Reserves	26	6	4	16	41	66	22
Bungay Town A	26	5	3	18	57	93	18
Royal Falcon	26	1	1	24	35	143	4

Division Three

	P	W	D	L	F	A	Pts
Oxford Arms Reserves	24	18	3	3	108	37	57
Carlton Rangers	24	18	3	3	91	32	57
Factory Arms	24	17	2	5	103	47	53
Telecom Rovers	24	17	1	6	90	38	52
Corton Seltic Reserves	24	12	5	7	66	44	41
Earsham Reserves	24	11	4	9	67	53	37
Blundeston Magpies Res.	24	11	3	10	65	61	36
Ellingham	24	12	0	12	58	70	36
Southwold Town Reserves	24	8	3	13	52	67	27
Lord Nelson (-3)	24	9	1	14	81	84	25
Westhall	24	6	2	16	43	74	20
Lowestoft Albion	24	1	3	20	25	98	6
Gunton United	24	1	0	23	14	158	3

LUTON DISTRICT & SOUTH BEDS LEAGUE

Premier

	P	W	D	L	F	A	Pts
Farley Boys	16	12	3	1	49	19	39
Real F'n'E	16	11	2	3	50	30	35
St Josephs	16	10	1	5	52	30	31
Offley Social	16	10	1	5	53	42	31
Dunstable Town Reserves	16	7	1	8	47	33	22
Lewsey Park	16	7	1	8	33	47	22
FC Wisla Luton	16	6	0	10	41	49	18
Four Model	16	2	1	13	14	61	7
Christians in Sport	16	2	0	14	29	57	6

Division One

	P	W	D	L	F	A	Pts
St Josephs Reserves	20	16	3	1	87	20	51
CO OP Sports Reserves	20	14	1	5	55	24	43
Caddington Reserves	20	13	2	5	60	25	41
61FC 3rd X1	20	13	0	7	65	29	39
Christians in Sport Reserves	20	12	2	6	87	34	38
Blue Line Aces	20	9	3	8	55	38	30
Square Rangers	20	9	1	10	48	33	28
Luton Leagrave	20	7	2	11	42	71	23
Multi Channel FC	20	5	1	14	31	94	16
Four Model Reserves	20	4	1	15	17	56	13
North Sundon Wanderers	20	0	0	20	9	132	0

MAIDSTONE & DISTRICT LEAGUE

Premier

	P	W	D	L	F	A	Pts
Leeds SV	14	13	1	0	46	11	40
Castle Colts	14	10	1	3	29	14	31
Trisports	14	8	3	3	37	24	27
Eccles	14	5	4	5	30	28	19
Lenham Wanderers	14	5	1	8	25	45	16
Headcorn	14	4	2	8	27	36	14
Hunton	14	2	3	9	21	33	9
East Malling	14	1	1	12	13	37	4

Division One

	P	W	D	L	F	A	Pts
Aylesford	18	13	3	2	74	22	42
West Farleigh	18	12	2	4	51	32	38
Wateringbury Colts	18	11	1	6	39	30	34
Three Suttons	18	10	1	7	60	37	31
Saxon Chief	18	9	4	5	47	38	31
Malgo Res	18	9	1	8	40	42	28
Addington	18	5	2	11	33	46	17
AFC Biddenden	18	4	3	11	42	66	15
Hollingbourne	18	4	2	12	42	74	14
RKP United	18	3	1	14	23	64	10

Division Two

	P	W	D	L	F	A	Pts
Headcorn Res	16	13	3	0	58	22	42
Marden Minors	16	12	2	2	69	29	38
Leybourne Athletic	16	10	5	1	48	20	35
Aylesford Reserves	16	8	2	6	60	37	26
Hunton Res	16	5	4	7	33	45	19
Eccles Res	16	5	2	9	27	37	17
Walnut Tree (Loose)	16	2	4	10	22	51	10
Parkwood Jupitors	16	3	1	12	26	66	10
Maidstone Athletic	16	2	1	13	23	59	7

Division Three

	P	W	D	L	F	A	Pts
Kingshill Spitfires	18	15	1	2	73	13	46
Sutton Saints (+2)	18	13	2	3	68	36	43
Blue Eagles (-1)	18	13	3	2	87	20	41
Lenham Wanderers Res	18	11	3	4	55	34	36
West Farleigh Res	18	8	1	9	46	51	25
Staplehurst Mon A	18	7	0	11	42	59	21
RKP Utd Reserves	18	6	0	12	30	66	18
Trisports Reserves	18	5	0	13	32	66	15
Wheatsheaf Celtic	18	4	1	13	25	68	13
Phoenix Utd	18	2	1	15	24	69	7

MID-ESSEX LEAGUE

Premier

	P	W	D	L	F	A	Pts
Great Baddow FC	21	16	3	2	78	26	51
Braintree & Bocking Utd FC	22	17	0	5	63	27	51
Benfleet Rangers FC	22	11	3	8	59	53	39
St. Clere's FC	22	12	4	6	50	30	37
Utd Chelmsford Churches FC	22	10	6	6	49	33	36
Little Waltham FC	22	11	3	8	47	49	36
Scotia Billericay FC	22	10	3	9	45	40	33
SFC Billericay FC	21	10	2	9	45	54	29
Silver End United FC	22	6	3	13	41	67	21
Harold Wood Athletic FC	22	5	4	13	32	50	19
Beacon Hill Rovers FC	22	3	1	18	30	67	10
Rhodesia United FC	22	2	4	16	28	71	10

Fixture between Great Baddow and SFC Billericay not played.

Division One	P	W	D	L	F	A	Pts
AFC Cranham	16	11	3	2	51	19	36
Writtle Manor FC	16	12	2	2	40	18	35
Swan Mead FC	16	9	2	5	38	23	26
Stifford Town FC	16	9	4	3	30	19	25
Sparta Basildon FC	16	7	1	8	22	33	19
Ferrers Athletic FC	16	4	5	7	28	35	17
Hutton FC	16	6	1	9	26	32	16
Frenford Senior FC	16	4	1	11	27	45	13
Focus Ferrers FC	16	0	1	15	7	45	0

MID-SOMERSET LEAGUE

Premier Division	P	W	D	L	F	A	Pts
Meadow Rangers	20	16	2	2	90	32	50
Chew Magna	20	13	1	6	60	24	40
Mells & Vobster United	20	12	2	6	71	44	38
Welton Arsenal	20	9	6	5	65	47	33
Westfield Reserves	20	9	5	6	65	38	32
Coleford Athletic	20	8	6	6	47	37	30
Belrose	20	8	3	9	49	42	27
Chilcompton Sports	20	7	3	10	42	43	24
Oakhill	20	7	3	10	40	66	24
Pilton United	20	3	3	14	34	95	12
Timsbury Athletic Res	20	1	0	19	17	112	3

Division One	P	W	D	L	F	A	Pts
Frome Town Sports	20	15	1	4	82	22	46
Wells City A	20	13	4	3	50	23	43
Evercreech Rovers	20	13	3	4	53	31	42
Stoke Rovers	20	10	5	5	33	27	35
Interhound	20	10	2	8	52	53	32
Shepton Mallet Town A	20	9	3	8	47	38	30
Frome Collegians Reserves	20	7	3	10	52	57	24
Temple Cloud	20	6	4	10	43	45	22
FC Sun Sports (-1)	20	5	2	13	37	57	16
Glastonbury Town Res. (-1)	20	4	2	14	35	79	13
Meadow Rangers Reserve	20	3	1	16	31	83	10

Division Two	P	W	D	L	F	A	Pts
Pensford FC	24	18	5	1	94	28	59
Purnells Sports A	24	19	2	3	77	33	59
Coleford Athletic Res. (-1)	24	15	4	5	75	37	48
Clutton Reserves	24	14	3	7	62	37	45
Westfield A (-3)	24	14	3	7	75	58	42
Farrington Gurney Reserves	24	10	2	12	69	70	32
High Littleton FC	24	8	6	10	42	54	30
Camerton Athletic	24	7	8	9	67	62	29
Mells & Vobster Utd Res. (-1)	24	7	4	13	65	56	24
Radstock Town A	24	6	5	13	48	78	23
Chilcompton Sports Res. (-4)	24	6	3	15	52	90	17
Tunley Athletic Reserve (-14)	24	8	1	15	42	70	11
Chilcompton United (-6)	24	1	0	23	30	125	-3

Division Three	P	W	D	L	F	A	Pts
Frome Town Sports Reserves	20	16	2	2	56	30	50
Peasedown Athletic Reserves	20	14	2	4	75	33	44
Westhill Sports FC	20	10	3	7	47	28	33
Wells City B (-3)	20	10	4	6	71	46	31
Tor Leisure	20	9	4	7	61	39	31
Belrose Reserves	20	8	4	8	60	48	28
Evercreech Rovers Res. (-3)	20	8	4	8	53	54	25
Purnells Sports B (-4)	20	8	0	12	49	63	20
Tor Sports (-6)	20	7	1	12	47	56	16
Temple Cloud Reserves (-6)	20	5	1	14	26	78	12
Stoke Rovers Reserves	20	2	1	17	29	99	7

MID-SUSSEX LEAGUE

Premier Division	P	W	D	L	F	A	Pts
Dormansland Rockets	22	15	2	5	62	31	47
Crawley Down 3rds	22	14	3	5	46	30	45
Phoenix United (-1)	22	13	3	6	54	36	41
Willingdon Athletic	22	11	4	7	35	30	37
Old Varndeanians	22	10	4	8	44	38	34
East Grinstead United	22	10	4	8	38	35	34
Lindfield	22	8	7	7	47	43	31
Hassocks 3rds (+4)	22	6	7	9	42	51	29
Balcombe (-1)	22	8	2	12	44	50	25
Jarvis Brook	22	7	4	11	28	38	25
Cuckfield Town	22	6	3	13	44	60	21
Maresfield Village	22	1	3	18	23	65	6

Championship	P	W	D	L	F	A	Pts
Rotherfield	20	13	4	3	49	24	43
Furnace Green Galaxy	20	12	1	7	52	43	37
Cuckfield Rangers	20	12	1	7	36	29	37
AFC Grinstead	20	11	2	7	54	38	35
Burgess Hill Albion	20	11	2	7	51	39	35
Polegate Town	20	9	4	7	52	39	31
Buxted	20	8	5	7	36	33	29
Old Varndeanians Res.	20	7	2	11	34	55	23
Turners Hill	20	6	3	11	31	43	21
AFC Ringmer	20	5	2	13	33	57	17
Forest Row	20	1	4	15	24	52	7

Division One	P	W	D	L	F	A	Pts
Peacehaven United	20	14	3	3	49	23	45
Uckfield Town Reserves	20	12	4	4	49	31	40
Three Bridges 3rds	20	11	6	3	67	29	39
St Francis Rangers 3rds	20	11	3	6	37	28	36
Framfield & Blackboys Utd	19	10	4	5	35	24	34
Keymer & Hassocks	19	9	3	7	49	29	30
Lindfield Reserves	20	9	2	9	39	35	29
Ifield Reserves	20	5	2	13	27	56	17
Ardingly	20	5	0	15	30	70	15
Felbridge	20	3	4	13	34	60	13
Sporting Crawley	20	3	3	14	30	61	12

LEAGUE TABLES

Division Two

	P	W	D	L	F	A	Pts
Ditchling	22	16	5	1	62	24	53
Copthorne	22	15	5	2	63	26	50
Village of Ditchling	22	13	1	8	47	34	40
Furnace Green Rovers	22	10	3	9	59	48	33
East Grinstead Tn 3rds (-4)	22	10	5	7	40	33	31
Newick	22	7	7	8	36	37	28
Hartfield (+2)	22	6	8	8	33	40	28
Ashurst Wood	22	6	6	10	43	45	24
East Court (+3)	22	6	3	13	26	37	24
Hurstpierpoint Reserves (+3)	22	5	6	11	36	69	24
Barcombe (-3)	22	6	7	9	43	55	22
West Hoathly	22	2	4	16	22	62	10

Division Three

	P	W	D	L	F	A	Pts
Cuckfield Town Reserves	22	17	2	3	80	39	53
Real Hydraquip	22	15	5	2	73	24	50
Plumpton Athletic	22	15	2	5	78	40	47
Sporting Lindfield	22	13	3	6	60	41	42
Wingspan	22	12	4	6	64	35	40
Ansty Sports & Social	22	11	5	6	59	39	38
Willingdon Athletic Reserves	22	7	4	11	49	58	25
Roffey Reserves	22	5	5	12	42	66	20
Scaynes Hill	22	5	3	14	45	63	18
Maresfield Village Reserves	22	4	4	14	31	71	16
Wisdom Sports Reserves	22	3	4	15	28	76	13
Turners Hill Reserves	22	4	1	17	28	85	13

Division Four

	P	W	D	L	F	A	Pts
Wivelsfield Green	20	14	2	4	83	26	44
Balcombe Reserves	20	13	3	4	56	27	42
Fairwarp	20	11	3	6	59	43	36
Dormansland Rockets Res.	20	11	3	6	56	44	36
Fletching	20	9	8	3	55	40	35
Phoenix United Reserves	20	6	6	8	60	62	24
Copthorne Reserves	20	7	3	10	32	56	24
Old Varndeanians Reserves	20	5	8	7	53	47	23
Burgess Hill Albion Reserves	20	5	7	8	39	46	22
East Grinstead United Res	20	5	5	10	43	41	20
Uckfield Town Reserves	20	0	0	20	15	119	0

Division Five

	P	W	D	L	F	A	Pts
Furnace Green Galaxy Res	18	11	4	3	47	26	37
Halsford Lions	18	11	2	5	54	44	35
Horsted Keynes	18	10	2	6	43	30	32
Buxted Reserves	18	9	4	5	31	25	31
Polegate Town Reserves	18	8	3	7	39	37	27
Handcross Village	18	5	8	5	38	30	23
Cuckfield Rangers Reserves	18	5	5	8	26	30	20
Pease Pottage Village Res	18	4	7	7	41	42	19
Jarvis Brook Reserves	18	3	4	11	23	44	13
Danehill	18	2	5	11	28	62	11

Division Six

	P	W	D	L	F	A	Pts
United Services	22	15	3	4	89	35	48
Ardingly Reserves	22	15	3	4	79	38	48
East Grinstead Mavericks	22	15	3	4	72	36	48
Copthorne Reserves	22	12	4	6	61	34	40
Sporting Crawley Reserves	22	12	3	7	59	44	39
Lindfield Reserves	22	11	4	7	45	35	37
Horley Wanderers	22	9	3	10	57	61	30
Rotherfield Reserves	22	7	2	13	35	52	23
Rottingdean Village Veterans	22	7	2	13	47	65	23
Ditchling Reserves	22	5	3	14	32	63	18
Forest Row Reserves	22	5	1	16	32	90	16
Newick Reserves	22	3	1	18	32	87	10

Division Seven

	P	W	D	L	F	A	Pts
Nutley	20	16	1	3	82	34	49
Felbridge Reserves	20	13	2	5	54	25	41
Peacehaven United Res	20	12	2	6	59	37	38
Fairwarp Reserves	20	9	5	6	59	43	32
Crawley Athletic (-3)	20	10	3	7	60	59	30
Cuckfield Town Reserves	20	8	5	7	41	38	29
Real Hydraquip Reserves	20	8	2	10	34	51	26
Bolney Rovers	20	8	1	11	61	57	25
Ashurst Wood Reserves (+3)	20	7	0	13	36	68	24
Pilgrims	20	5	0	15	34	63	15
Maresfield Village Reserves	20	3	1	16	27	72	10

Division Eight

	P	W	D	L	F	A	Pts
Copthorne 4ths	20	18	1	1	90	19	55
Cherry Lane	20	17	2	1	97	19	53
East Grinstead Town 4ths	20	10	3	7	40	28	33
Plumpton Athletic Reserves	20	10	2	8	51	33	32
Hartfield Reserves	20	9	3	8	41	43	30
Willingdon Athletic Reserves	20	8	3	9	47	30	27
Ansty Sports & Social Res	20	7	6	7	42	48	27
Fairfield	20	5	6	9	33	62	21
Fletching Reserves (-1)	20	5	4	11	27	63	18
West Hoathly Reserves	20	2	3	15	24	64	9
Brighton & H. A. Disability (+2)	20	2	1	17	27	110	9

Division Nine

	P	W	D	L	F	A	Pts
Wivelsfield Green Res. (-1)	16	12	3	1	47	15	38
Framfield & Blackboys Utd Res.	16	11	2	3	41	20	35
Keymer & Hassocks Res.	16	10	3	3	50	22	33
Lindfield 4ths (+2)	16	7	4	5	32	31	27
Stones	16	5	4	7	34	43	19
Ardingly Reserves	16	5	2	9	29	40	17
Cuckfield Rangers Reserves	16	5	2	9	20	44	17
Handcross Village Reserves	16	5	1	10	27	37	16
Barcombe Reserves	16	0	3	13	16	44	3

Division Ten

	P	W	D	L	F	A	Pts
Heath Rangers	20	15	2	3	50	23	47
Wingspan Reserves	20	15	1	4	85	21	46
Sporting Devils	20	12	3	5	56	28	39
Cherry Lane Reserves (-3)	20	13	2	5	63	28	38
Burgess Hill Albion Reserves	20	11	2	7	31	30	35
Lindfield 5ths	20	8	3	9	32	41	27
Copthorne 5ths	20	5	3	12	36	62	18
Roffey Reserves (+3)	20	4	3	13	23	57	18
Scaynes Hill Reserves	20	5	1	14	50	77	16
Buxted Reserves	20	5	1	14	43	71	16
Real Hydraquip Reserves	20	3	7	10	24	55	16

Division Eleven

	P	W	D	L	F	A	Pts
AFC Haywards	21	20	1	0	138	17	61
Ridgewood	21	14	3	4	74	34	45
Burgess Hill Wanderers	21	13	1	7	80	41	40
Pease Pottage Village 4ths	21	10	2	9	50	41	32
Rotherfield Reserves	21	9	1	11	51	62	28
Stones Reserves	21	6	2	13	45	60	20
Ashurst Wood Reserves	21	4	2	15	22	109	14
Scaynes Hill Reserves	21	2	0	19	16	112	6

MIDLAND REGIONAL ALLIANCE

Premier Division

	P	W	D	L	F	A	Pts
Allenton United	30	23	4	3	110	27	73
Melbourne Dynamo	30	19	7	4	93	41	64
Rowsley 86	30	20	2	8	87	52	62
Cromford	30	18	4	8	77	51	58
Derby Royals	30	15	10	5	70	30	55
Mickleover Royal British Legion	30	15	4	11	72	42	49
Derby Rolls Royce Leisure	30	15	4	11	64	58	49
Newmount	30	14	4	12	68	61	46
Wirksworth Town	30	14	3	13	66	58	45
Chellaston	30	12	6	12	67	70	42
Swanwick Pentrich Road	30	13	1	16	66	69	40
Willington	30	10	5	15	52	71	35
Matlock Sports	30	7	3	20	54	102	24
Holbrook St. Michaels	30	7	2	21	30	76	23
Ashover	30	2	5	23	29	104	11
Sandiacre Town	30	2	4	24	28	121	10

Division One

	P	W	D	L	F	A	Pts
Allestree	30	21	2	7	102	48	65
Punjab United (-3)	30	18	8	4	87	51	59
Derby Rolls Royce Leisure Res (-4)	30	19	2	9	81	47	55
Woolley Moor United	30	15	5	10	83	61	50
Derby Singh Brothers	30	15	5	10	73	54	50
Tibshelf	30	13	7	10	65	51	46
Little Eaton	30	11	10	9	64	48	43
Rowsley 86 Reserves	30	13	4	13	67	59	43
Ripley Town	30	12	6	12	72	65	42
Holbrook St. Michaels Res.	30	11	5	14	55	69	38
Swanwick Pentrich Rd Res (-3)	30	11	5	14	58	71	35
Bargate Rovers	30	8	8	14	58	80	32
Pastures	30	8	6	16	64	92	30
Mickleover Royal British Legion Res.	30	8	3	19	52	84	27
Findern	30	7	4	19	37	85	25
Derbyshire Amateurs (-3)	30	7	6	17	47	100	24

Division Two

	P	W	D	L	F	A	Pts
Allenton United Reserves	28	22	2	4	113	24	68
Mackworth St. Francis	28	22	1	5	103	32	67
Wirksworth Ivanhoe	28	19	3	6	81	33	60
Melbourne Dynamo Res.	28	17	6	5	83	41	57
Ambergate (-3)	28	18	3	7	76	37	54
Newton	28	16	5	7	80	48	53
Little Eaton Reserves	28	15	3	10	63	65	48
Wirksworth Town Reserves	28	11	4	13	54	52	37
Chellaston Reserves	28	8	6	14	59	70	30
Derby Royals Reserves	28	8	3	17	54	83	27
Pastures Reserves	28	7	4	17	51	106	25
Bargate Rovers Reserves	28	6	6	16	49	78	24
Hilton Harriers (-1)	28	5	8	15	39	88	22
Punjab Utd Reserves (-4)	28	4	5	19	36	107	13
Roe Farm	28	0	5	23	26	103	5

NORTH & MID-HERTS LEAGUE

	P	W	D	L	F	A	Pts
Potters Bar Crusaders	20	19	0	1	77	11	57
Warriors X1	20	14	2	4	60	33	44
St Ippolyts	20	13	2	5	57	19	41
City Hearts	20	12	2	6	61	35	38
St Albans Wanderers	20	10	1	9	52	46	31
FC Letchworth	20	9	2	9	39	31	29
Tansley FC	20	9	2	9	46	59	29
RBL	20	8	2	10	20	33	26
Asia	20	7	0	13	33	37	21
Global	20	2	0	18	18	57	6
Barmond United	20	0	1	19	15	117	1

NORTH BUCKS & DISTRICT LEAGUE

Senior Division

	P	W	D	L	F	A	Pts
MK Wanderers Res.	28	20	2	6	89	42	62
Thornborough Athletic	28	18	5	5	71	53	59
Loughton Manor	28	16	5	7	83	50	53
Brackley Sports	27	16	2	9	73	43	50
Potterspury	28	15	4	9	77	50	49
Grendon Rangers	28	15	2	11	60	52	47
Great Linford	28	13	6	9	65	52	45
Southcott Village R.A.	28	13	6	9	57	47	45
Wolverton Town	28	11	5	12	61	65	38
Silverstone	28	12	2	14	56	72	38
Stewkley	27	11	3	13	60	56	36
Yardley Gobion	28	9	6	13	60	70	33
MK Titans	26	3	7	16	44	84	16
Deanshanger Athletic	28	4	1	23	30	88	13
Buckingham Town Res.	28	3	2	23	30	92	11

LEAGUE TABLES

Intermediate Division

	P	W	D	L	F	A	Pts
Great Horwood	24	19	5	0	88	26	62
City Colts	24	15	7	2	69	42	52
Brackley Sports Res.	24	16	3	5	65	40	51
Stoke Hammond	24	15	4	5	90	48	49
Celtic MK	24	12	3	9	55	45	39
Bow Brickhill	24	12	2	10	84	60	38
Wicken Sports	24	11	3	10	63	62	36
Syresham	24	9	3	12	61	55	30
Denbigh Sports & Social	23	9	2	12	43	68	29
Hanslope	23	7	3	13	52	80	24
Steeple Claydon	24	6	3	15	50	62	21
AFC Santander	24	2	4	18	29	95	10
Olney	24	0	2	22	28	94	2

Division One

	P	W	D	L	F	A	Pts
Potterspury Res.	26	19	2	5	88	40	59
Stoke Hammond Res.	26	17	3	6	70	43	54
Grendon Rangers Res.	26	16	5	5	81	50	53
Bow Brickhill Res.	26	14	5	7	79	64	47
Marsh Gibbon	26	13	3	10	68	49	42
Charlton & District	26	13	3	10	68	53	42
Southcott Village R.A. Res.	26	12	6	8	62	54	42
Stewkley Res.	26	8	7	11	55	61	31
Woughton	26	9	4	13	56	85	31
Syresham Res.	26	8	6	12	53	62	30
Bletchley Bridge	26	9	1	16	63	74	28
Deanshanger Athletic Res.	26	7	5	14	51	82	26
Twyford United	26	5	2	19	45	85	17
Westbury	26	4	4	18	36	73	16

Division Two

	P	W	D	L	F	A	Pts
City Colts Res.	26	20	3	3	102	28	63
Great Linford Res.	26	18	4	4	78	40	58
University of Buckingham	26	17	2	7	87	40	53
Wicken Sports Res.	26	14	7	5	67	47	49
Real Padbury	26	14	3	9	52	44	45
MK Wanderers 'A'	26	11	4	11	63	58	37
Wing Village Res.	26	11	2	13	72	67	35
Hanslope Res.	26	10	4	12	57	59	34
Marsh Gibbon Res.	26	9	1	16	40	87	28
Steeple Claydon Res.	26	7	5	14	52	76	26
Yardley Gobion Res.	26	7	4	15	46	73	25
Great Horwood Res.	26	7	4	15	49	81	25
Wolverton Town Res.	26	6	4	16	59	86	22
Silverstone Res.	26	5	5	16	35	73	20

NORTH DEVON LEAGUE

Premier Division

	P	W	D	L	F	A	PTS
Boca Seniors	30	24	4	2	146	39	76
Braunton	30	24	3	3	103	34	75
North Molton Sports Club	30	21	2	7	101	40	65
Ilfracombe Town Reserves	30	20	5	5	86	31	65
Torridgeside	30	17	4	9	83	49	55
Bradworthy	30	15	6	9	58	47	51
Shamwickshire Rovers	30	15	3	12	89	74	48
Appledore Reserves	30	15	1	14	58	61	46
Putford	30	12	4	14	57	60	40
Bratton Fleming	30	11	3	16	57	81	36
Dolton	30	10	3	17	54	70	33
Georgeham & Croyde	30	10	1	19	43	84	31
Barnstaple AAC	30	9	1	20	45	99	28
Shebbear United	30	7	3	20	53	90	24
Torrington	30	5	4	21	54	112	19
Combe Martin	30	1	1	28	25	141	4

Senior Division

	P	W	D	L	F	A	PTS
Bideford Reserves	28	26	2	0	131	31	80
Chittlehampton	28	18	3	7	113	62	57
Braunton Reserves	28	16	5	7	81	42	53
Park United	28	15	5	8	122	67	50
Wrey Arms	28	14	6	8	78	54	48
Lynton & Lynmouth	28	15	3	10	78	69	48
Pilton Academicals (-3)	28	14	3	11	88	60	42
Woolsery	28	12	5	11	76	62	41
Bude Town	28	12	3	13	57	64	39
Shamwickshire Rovers Res.	28	10	2	16	66	72	32
South Molton	28	9	3	16	47	96	30
North Molton Sports Club Res.	28	9	2	17	57	90	29
Northam Lions	28	7	6	15	60	92	27
Barnstaple AAC Reserves	28	3	3	22	27	120	12
Torrington Reserves	28	3	3	22	42	142	12

NORTH EAST NORFOLK LEAGUE

Division One

	P	W	D	L	F	A	Pts
Gimingham	22	19	1	2	100	25	58
Coltishall	22	18	2	2	112	30	56
Runton	22	13	4	5	72	38	43
East Ruston	22	11	1	10	46	57	34
Ludham	22	10	3	9	44	56	33
North Walsham A	22	8	6	8	58	57	30
Haisboro Atheltic	22	9	2	11	57	67	29
Horning	22	8	4	10	50	64	28
Corpusty	22	7	4	11	49	63	25
Lyng	22	5	3	14	44	69	18
Worstead	22	4	3	15	35	74	15
Aldborough Lions	22	2	3	17	34	101	9

Division One

	P	W	D	L	F	A	Pts
Mundesley	22	18	3	1	83	14	57
Aylsham 'A'	22	15	1	6	77	35	46
Holt 'A'	22	14	4	4	60	38	46
Cawston	22	12	3	7	63	46	39
Erpingham	22	12	3	7	71	56	39
Cromer Y O B	22	10	4	8	58	45	34
Hickling	22	10	1	11	69	54	31
Blakeney	22	8	5	9	53	45	29
Corpusty Reserves	22	8	5	9	46	62	29
Gimingham Reserves	22	5	1	16	40	89	16
Buxton Res	22	2	2	18	20	87	8
Aldborough Lions Reserves	22	2	0	20	30	99	6

Division Two

	P	W	D	L	F	A	Pts
Plumstead Rangers	18	16	0	2	83	21	48
Glaven Valley fc	18	15	1	2	85	25	46
Worstead Reserves	18	10	1	7	57	51	31
Holt Colts	18	8	1	9	46	51	25
Felmingham	18	7	3	8	54	38	24
Mundesley Reserves	18	6	1	11	33	47	19
East Ruston Reserves	18	6	1	11	46	72	19
Trunch	18	5	3	10	31	55	18
Coltishall Reserves	18	6	0	12	47	73	18
Erpingham Reserves	18	5	1	12	26	75	16

NORTH GLOUSCESTERSHIRE LEAGUE

Premier Division

	P	W	D	L	F	A	Pts
Ruardean Hill Rangers	26	19	6	1	96	24	63
Milkwall	26	20	2	4	70	25	62
Newent Town	26	18	6	2	90	29	60
Woolaston	26	13	6	7	67	38	45
Mitcheldean	26	12	4	10	79	54	40
Broadwell Reserves	26	11	6	9	49	41	39
Lydney Town Reserves	26	10	5	11	75	62	35
English Bicknor	26	10	5	11	54	56	35
Sedbury United	26	10	5	11	51	63	35
Staunton & Corse	26	10	3	13	54	64	33
Whitecroft	26	8	6	12	41	46	30
Westbury United	26	8	3	15	46	68	27
Newnham United	26	3	0	23	27	121	9
Mushet & Coalway United	26	1	1	24	11	119	4

Division One

	P	W	D	L	F	A	Pts
Huntley	24	21	3	0	95	15	66
Redbrook Rovers	24	17	1	6	61	20	52
St Briavels (-1)	24	13	4	7	61	45	42
Bream Amts	24	13	3	8	57	43	42
Yorkley (-1)	24	11	7	6	45	37	39
Newent Town Reserves	24	11	4	9	56	44	37
Coleford Utd	24	10	4	10	59	63	34
Mitcheldean Reserves	24	7	9	8	42	54	30
Ruardean Hill Rangers Res	24	7	3	14	29	47	24
Puma FC	24	6	5	13	34	54	23
Lydbrook Athletic Reserves	24	6	2	16	36	57	20
Ellwood Reserves	24	5	3	16	24	76	18
Howle Hill	24	4	2	18	29	73	14

Division Two

	P	W	D	L	F	A	Pts
Lydney Town A	26	18	3	5	82	30	57
Weston Athletic	26	18	3	5	84	44	57
Whitecroft Reserves	26	16	4	6	74	49	52
Worrall Hill	26	15	4	7	58	36	49
Staunton & Corse Reserves	26	14	4	8	78	41	46
White Horse	26	14	1	11	58	62	43
Blakeney	26	11	7	8	71	53	40
Woolaston Reserves	26	11	6	9	82	35	39
Soudley Reserves	26	11	2	13	59	68	35
Westbury Utd Reserves	26	8	2	16	64	90	26
Lydbrook Athletic A	26	7	4	15	44	81	25
Rank Outsiders	26	6	5	15	37	65	23
Redmarley	26	4	4	18	42	117	16
Harrow Hill Reserves	26	3	3	20	39	101	12

Division Three

	P	W	D	L	F	A	Pts
Viney St Swithins Reserves	26	23	1	2	111	22	70
Milkwall Reserves	26	21	2	3	97	40	65
Utd Longhope	26	19	1	6	93	43	58
English Bicknor Reserves	26	15	2	9	51	32	47
Puma FC Reserves	26	12	8	6	67	51	44
Sling United	26	11	8	7	60	44	41
Bream Amts Reserves	26	12	2	12	59	58	38
Tidenham Reserves	26	10	6	10	41	42	36
Blakeney Reserves	26	9	4	13	50	77	31
Ruardean United	26	9	3	14	37	63	30
Minsterworth Reserves	26	8	1	17	42	80	25
Mushet & Coalway Utd Res	26	4	4	18	24	68	16
Redbrook Rovers Reserves	26	3	5	18	33	77	14
Rank Outsiders Reserves	26	1	3	22	22	90	6

Division Four

	P	W	D	L	F	A	Pts
Sedbury United Reserves	26	21	3	2	119	31	66
Mitcheldean A	26	21	0	5	115	36	63
Ruspidge United	26	18	4	4	101	34	58
Redside	26	18	3	5	86	28	57
Newent Town A	26	16	1	9	103	49	49
Whitecroft A	26	14	3	9	72	71	45
Ruardean Hill Rangers A	26	11	2	13	65	58	35
St Briavels Reserves	26	10	3	13	49	72	33
Littledean	26	9	2	15	53	77	29
Harrow Hill A	26	8	5	13	55	82	29
Yorkley Reserves	26	8	3	15	61	82	27
Sling United Reserves	26	6	2	18	44	109	20
Coleford United Reserves	26	4	0	22	31	119	12
Puma FC A	26	1	3	22	36	142	6

LEAGUE TABLES
NORTH LANCS & DISTRICT LEAGUE

Premier Division	P	W	D	L	F	A	Pts
Highgrove	26	19	4	3	82	27	61
Carnforth Rangers	26	17	6	3	56	30	57
Highgrove	26	16	5	5	76	25	53
Cartmel & District	26	15	4	7	49	28	49
Marsh United	26	13	6	7	42	22	45
Galgate	26	13	6	7	61	48	45
Bentham	26	11	8	7	49	34	41
Bowerham Furness Utd (-6)	26	12	6	8	53	37	36
Morecambe Royals	26	7	6	13	40	46	27
Storeys	26	7	6	13	43	59	27
Caton United	26	6	8	12	49	69	26
Arnside	26	7	4	15	44	70	25
Ingleton	26	5	9	12	40	62	24
Slyne with Hest (-13)	26	7	8	11	44	61	16
Swarthmoor Social Club	26	1	8	17	21	76	11

Division One	P	W	D	L	F	A	Pts
TIC Dynamos of Overton and M.	24	18	4	2	76	22	58
College AFC	24	16	4	4	56	26	52
Kirkby Lonsdale	24	16	3	5	65	24	51
Freehold	24	12	5	7	65	47	41
Trimpell	24	11	5	8	77	51	38
Marsh United Reserves	24	11	3	10	37	47	36
Bolton Le Sands	24	8	4	12	54	64	28
Heysham	24	8	4	12	56	71	28
Boys Club	24	8	3	13	41	66	27
Millhead	24	8	3	13	48	74	27
Cartmel & District Reserves	24	6	6	12	43	53	24
Grange	24	7	3	14	44	60	24
Morecambe Royals Res. (-3)	24	2	3	19	24	81	6

Division Two	P	W	D	L	F	A	Pts
Carnforth Rangers Reserves	22	18	2	2	69	22	56
TIC Dynamos of Overton & M. R.	22	14	6	2	59	30	48
Westgate Wanderers	22	10	6	6	78	50	36
Slyne with Hest Res. (-3)	22	12	3	7	53	38	36
Boys Club Reserves	22	10	6	6	48	35	36
Highgrove Reserves	22	9	4	9	49	38	31
Ingleton Reserves	22	7	7	8	34	50	28
Galgate Reserves	22	8	1	13	43	74	25
Morecambe Gold	22	7	3	12	33	55	24
Storeys Reserves	22	4	4	14	33	57	16
Bentham Reserves (-3)	22	5	3	14	45	57	15
Torrisholme	22	3	5	14	36	74	14

Division Three	P	W	D	L	F	A	Pts
Moor Lane FC	20	15	3	2	55	18	48
Lancaster Rovers	20	14	2	4	59	26	44
Trimpell Reserves	20	10	3	7	70	50	33
Preesall & Pilling (-4)	20	9	5	6	49	45	28
Moghuls	20	8	4	8	43	52	28
Burton Thistle	20	7	6	7	56	42	27
Caton United Reserves (-3)	20	9	3	8	56	46	27
AFC Moorlands	20	6	3	11	45	69	21
Kirkby Lonsdale Reserves	20	5	1	14	32	61	16
Villa Royale (-3)	20	5	2	13	40	61	14
Gregson FC (-3)	20	5	2	13	22	57	14

Division Four	P	W	D	L	F	A	Pts
Millhead Reserves	24	17	4	3	72	25	55
Whittle Wanderers Reserves	24	16	5	3	114	42	53
College AFC Reserves	24	13	6	5	76	47	45
AFC Heaton	24	13	3	8	68	45	42
Freehold F.C. Reserves	24	9	9	6	63	44	36
TIC Dynamos of Overton & M. A	24	11	3	10	49	62	36
Lancaster Rovers Res. (-6)	24	11	6	7	74	51	33
Westgate Wanderers	24	10	1	13	58	82	31
Carnforth Rangers A (-1)	24	8	6	10	46	56	29
Arnside Reserves	24	6	6	12	39	69	24
Bolton Le Sands Res. (-6)	24	7	4	13	52	68	19
Heysham Reserves	24	5	2	17	40	82	17
Gregson (-10)	24	2	1	21	29	107	-3

NORTH LEICS LEAGUE

Premier Division	P	W	D	L	F	A	Pts
Falcons FC	24	19	2	3	80	39	59
Kegworth Imperial	24	17	3	4	81	30	54
Anstey Town	24	16	4	4	69	30	52
Genesis FC	24	15	6	3	72	21	51
East Leake Athletic	24	12	3	9	51	36	39
Loughborough Town	24	10	5	9	47	42	35
Ingles FC	24	8	8	8	42	37	32
Whitwick FC	24	8	4	12	34	46	28
Birstall Old Boys	24	7	5	12	52	73	26
Sileby Victoria	24	6	3	15	33	62	21
Anstey Crown	24	5	3	16	34	91	18
Markfield FC	24	5	2	17	30	67	17
Shepshed Amateurs	24	3	2	19	26	77	11

Division One	P	W	D	L	F	A	Pts
Greenhill YC	20	17	1	2	97	30	52
Butler Court FC (-1)	20	13	4	3	79	22	42
Loughborough FC	20	13	3	4	56	25	42
Cento FC	20	12	2	6	66	50	38
Whitwick United	20	8	3	9	36	43	27
Ravenstone United	20	8	2	10	42	53	26
Sutton Bonington Academicals	20	6	4	10	30	50	22
Sutton Bonington	20	6	1	13	24	60	19
Ingles Reserves FC (-4)	20	6	3	11	33	62	17
Loughborough Athletic	20	5	0	15	24	60	15
Woodhouse Imperial	20	4	1	15	27	59	13

Division Two	P	W	D	L	F	A	Pts
ATI Garryson	18	14	3	1	68	29	45
Ravenstone United Reserves	18	12	3	3	65	32	39
Thringstone MW	18	12	2	4	67	34	38
Markfield FC Reserves (-1)	18	9	4	5	53	34	30
Sileby Saints Reserves (-1)	18	6	5	7	44	48	22
Belton Villa	18	6	4	8	23	33	22
East Leake Athletic Reserves	18	6	2	10	35	41	20
Loughborough FC Reserves	18	6	1	11	28	44	19
Thurmaston Rangers	18	4	3	11	33	63	15
Castle Donington	18	0	3	15	21	79	3

Division Three

	P	W	D	L	F	A	Pts
Ferrari FC	18	13	4	1	68	24	43
Victoria FC	18	12	3	3	56	26	39
Loughborough United	18	11	4	3	69	23	37
Loughborough Emmanuel	18	9	3	6	46	40	30
Measham Imperial	18	8	4	6	45	39	28
Genesis FC Reserves	18	9	0	9	47	38	27
Sileby Victoria Reserves	18	8	3	7	43	49	27
Loughborough Galaxy	18	5	2	11	39	67	17
Woodhouse Imperial Reserves	18	2	0	16	28	84	6
Shepshed Amateurs Res. (-3)	18	1	1	16	28	79	1

Division Four

	P	W	D	L	F	A	Pts
Anstey Crown Reserves	18	15	0	3	65	34	45
Greenhill YC Reserves	18	14	2	2	70	24	44
Kegworth Imperial Reserves	18	13	1	4	71	25	40
Shelthorpe FC	18	12	2	4	50	39	38
ATI Garryson Reserves	18	9	2	7	53	40	29
Birstall Old Boys Reserves	18	7	3	8	43	62	24
Sutton Bonington Reserves	18	5	0	13	26	50	15
Loughborough Ath. Res. (-1)	18	4	0	14	41	67	11 *
Loughborough United Res.	18	3	1	14	36	65	10
Mountsorrel FC	18	2	1	15	20	69	7

NORTH NORTHUMBERLAND LEAGUE

Division One

	P	W	D	L	F	A	Pts
Wooler	14	12	0	2	59	25	36
Berwick United	14	9	1	4	54	31	28
Rothbury	14	7	2	5	46	45	23
Belford	14	7	1	6	28	25	22
Shilbottle C.W.	14	5	2	7	28	33	17
Tweedmouth Harrow	14	4	2	8	24	53	14
Embleton WR	14	4	1	9	30	36	13
Longhoughton Rangers	14	3	1	10	31	52	10

Springhill - record expunged

Stobswood United - record expunged.

Division Two

	P	W	D	L	F	A	Pts
Red Row Welfare	20	18	1	1	143	16	55
AFC Newbiggin	20	15	3	2	138	23	48
North Sunderland	20	13	2	5	88	35	41
Tweedmouth Rangers	20	12	3	5	94	52	39
Alnwick Town U21s	20	12	0	8	80	47	36
Bamburgh Castle	20	11	2	7	81	45	35
Craster Rovers	20	10	3	7	52	44	33
Shilbottle CW Reserves	20	6	0	14	36	106	18
Alnmouth United	20	4	0	16	42	87	12
Hedgeley Rovers	20	2	0	18	25	125	6
Amble St Cuthberts	20	0	0	20	11	210	0

NORTH WEST NORFOLK LEAGUE

Division One

	P	W	D	L	F	A	Pts
Lynn North End	18	16	1	1	102	24	49
Reffley Royals	18	15	2	1	100	15	47
Great Massingham	18	12	1	5	44	34	37
Gayton United	18	9	3	6	48	33	30
Terrington	18	8	3	7	38	39	27
West Winch	18	5	2	11	21	39	17
Heacham	18	5	2	11	25	52	17
Redgate Rangers	18	4	3	11	48	56	15
Ingoldisthorpe	18	3	2	13	19	83	11
Lynn Napier	18	2	3	13	15	85	9

Division Two

	P	W	D	L	F	A	Pts
Sedgeford	18	14	1	3	69	25	43
South Creake	18	13	2	3	54	26	41
Watlington Sports & Social Club	18	11	1	6	51	33	34
William Burt	18	9	2	7	56	44	29
Hunstanton	18	8	5	5	45	40	29
Discovery Royals	18	8	2	8	44	45	26
Dersingham Rovers Reserves	18	5	3	10	27	41	18
Denver (-3)	18	5	5	8	29	41	17
Ingoldisthorpe Reserves	18	5	0	13	37	57	15
Terrington Reserves (-3)	18	1	1	16	18	78	1

Division Three

	P	W	D	L	F	A	Pts
Castle Rising	20	13	4	3	66	29	43
Riverside	20	13	2	5	55	21	41
Flitcham & Hillington	20	10	3	7	42	36	33
Smithdon Hunstanton	20	9	3	8	54	49	30
Gayton United Reserves	20	9	2	9	35	37	29
Gaywood	20	7	4	9	42	55	25
Birchwood	20	6	6	8	61	56	24
Wiggenhall (-3)	20	7	4	9	36	53	22
West Winch Reserves (-3)	20	7	3	10	31	45	21
Greyfriars	20	6	3	11	34	57	21
Heacham Reserves	20	4	4	12	30	48	16

Division Four

	P	W	D	L	F	A	Pts
Lynn Retreat	20	17	1	2	90	25	52
Lynn Williams	20	13	2	5	62	30	41
The Woottons	20	12	4	4	48	25	40
West Lynn Sports & Social Club	20	12	0	8	38	35	36
Redgate Rangers Reserves	20	10	4	6	58	41	34
Docking	20	8	4	8	46	61	28
South Creake Reserves	20	8	3	9	57	55	27
Dersingham Rovers A (-3)	20	4	4	12	34	73	13
Pentney	20	3	3	14	35	79	12
Watlington S & S C Res. (-9)	20	5	3	12	37	64	9
Lynn Napier Reserves (-3)	20	2	4	14	37	54	7

LEAGUE TABLES
NORWICH & DISTRICT LEAGUE

Division One

	P	W	D	L	F	A	Pts
Marlborough OB	16	12	1	3	56	20	37
Jubilee Rangers	16	11	3	2	55	21	36
UEA Reserves (-5)	16	12	2	2	64	23	33
Drayton	16	8	2	6	48	43	26
Marlpitt FC	16	7	2	7	45	54	23
Norwich Medics	16	6	4	6	47	38	22
Eaton Beehive	16	4	2	10	30	46	14
Mousehold Athletic	16	3	2	11	28	42	11
Blofield United A	16	0	0	16	10	96	0

Division Two

	P	W	D	L	F	A	Pts
Circle Anglia	22	15	5	2	65	19	50
Jarrolds	22	15	1	6	72	35	46
Horsford A (-2)	22	14	3	5	57	39	43
Hockering FC	22	11	6	5	61	38	39
Homecare United	22	12	2	8	63	39	38
Loddon United A (-2)	22	10	4	8	37	44	32
UEA A (-5)	22	10	2	10	63	48	27
Newton Flotman Reserves	22	8	2	12	44	61	26
Dyers Arms	22	7	3	12	34	62	24
Wensum Albion	22	6	1	15	31	60	19
Yelverton Reserves (-2)	22	5	3	14	21	71	16
South Walsham Reserves (-2)	22	2	2	18	21	53	6

Division Three

	P	W	D	L	F	A	Pts
Drayton Reserves	20	18	1	1	86	16	55
Hellesdon Rangers	20	16	1	3	84	27	49
Taverham	20	14	2	4	92	37	44
Old Catton Rovers	20	11	2	7	60	35	35
Mousehold Athletic Reserves	20	8	6	6	55	47	30
Hockering reserves	20	8	4	8	48	56	28
Ketts Tavern Toucans	20	7	2	11	39	57	23
CNSOB Reserves (-5)	20	8	1	11	47	66	20
Plumstead Rangers Reserves	20	4	3	13	35	104	15
Hempnall A	20	3	3	14	30	70	12
Anglian Knights	20	0	1	19	23	84	1

NOTTS SENIOR LEAGUE

	P	W	D	L	F	A	Pts
Bulwell	30	26	2	2	106	30	80
FC Cavaliers	30	20	5	5	87	39	65
Awsworth Villa	30	18	5	7	90	48	59
Linby Colliery Welfare	30	18	5	7	74	43	59
Wollaton	30	15	5	10	99	64	50
Hucknall Rolls Leisure	30	11	11	8	57	52	44
Ruddington Village	30	14	2	14	63	68	44
Magdala Amateurs	30	12	5	13	59	62	41
Attenborough	30	11	6	13	71	68	39
Gedling Southbank	30	11	6	13	57	66	39
Selston	30	11	2	17	59	88	35
Keyworth United	30	8	10	12	56	52	34
Kimberley Miners Welfare	30	9	6	15	44	48	33
Cotgrave Welfare	30	8	6	16	57	66	30
Sandhurst	30	6	5	19	50	98	23
Vernon Villa	30	1	1	28	25	162	4

Division One

	P	W	D	L	F	A	Pts
Carlton Town Academy	28	22	3	3	73	32	69
Clifton	28	18	6	4	76	41	60
Southwell St Marys	28	18	4	6	85	44	58
Bilborough Town	28	17	4	7	104	50	55
Arnold Town Reserves	28	14	7	7	65	49	49
Hucknall Rolls Leisure Res	28	13	8	7	81	56	47
Wollaton Reserves	28	13	5	10	67	60	44
Cotgrave Reserves	28	13	3	12	66	75	42
Boots Athletic	28	11	5	12	66	51	38
Nottinghamshire	28	10	4	14	79	78	34
Underwood Villa	28	9	3	16	57	71	30
Keyworth United Reserves	28	8	2	18	55	73	26
Radcliffe Olympic Reserves	28	7	2	19	43	74	23
Gedling Southbank Reserves	28	4	3	21	41	114	15
Netherfield Albion	28	2	3	23	41	131	9

	P	W	D	L	F	A	Pts
Burton Joyce	26	21	1	4	115	38	64
West Bridgford	26	19	3	4	80	33	60
Calverton M. W. AFC	26	19	2	5	70	30	59
Ruddington Village Reserves	26	15	1	10	80	59	46
Beeston AFC	26	14	2	10	75	52	44
Awsworth Villa Reserves	26	13	4	9	77	69	43
Magdala Amateurs Reserves	26	12	5	9	62	53	41
Kimberley Miners Welfare Res	26	12	3	11	63	66	39
Linby Colliery Welfare Reserves	26	11	3	12	45	64	36
Bingham Town	26	9	3	14	61	76	30
Hucknall Town Reserves	26	8	3	15	49	62	27
Nottinghamshire Reserves	26	7	3	16	57	83	24
Selston Reserves	26	4	2	20	30	77	14
Sandhurst Reserves	26	0	1	25	27	129	1

NOTTS AMATEUR ALLIANCE

Premier Division

	P	W	D	L	F	A	Pts
FC Samba	22	16	1	5	58	25	49
Ashland Rovers	22	14	4	4	59	22	46
Kirton Brickworks	22	13	5	4	55	31	44
Santos	22	14	2	6	61	39	44
Bilborough United	22	12	2	8	53	38	38
Nottingham Sikh Lions	22	12	2	8	48	47	38
Gedling Sthbank "A"	22	10	5	7	54	51	35
Kashmir	22	10	2	10	57	49	32
Fox & Crown (-3)	22	6	3	13	46	53	18
Durham Ox	22	4	2	16	37	74	14
Nuthall	22	4	2	16	26	63	14
Real United Reserves	22	1	2	19	20	82	5

Headstocks - record expunged.

Division One

	P	W	D	L	F	A	Pts
AFC Bridgford	24	17	4	3	83	36	55
FCGunthorpe	24	17	2	5	88	49	53
Strelley Rose	24	15	4	5	92	57	49
FCDynamo	24	14	2	8	72	50	44
Kimb'y MW "A" (-3)	24	12	3	9	82	65	36
Bold Forester	24	11	2	11	65	60	35
Vernon Villa Reserve	24	10	4	10	59	52	34
Netherfield Alb Reserves	24	8	7	9	63	76	31
Clifton Wanderers	24	8	3	13	65	68	27
Calverton	24	8	3	13	55	78	27
Nottingham United "A"	24	7	2	15	54	80	23
Ashfield Athletic	24	6	2	16	37	76	20
Heath Hill	24	4	0	20	39	107	12

Division Two

	P	W	D	L	F	A	Pts
Beeston Rovers	24	17	3	4	83	36	54
Kimberley MW Acad	24	16	3	5	74	43	51
AFC Bridgford Reserves	24	15	3	6	68	31	48
Red Heart	24	15	2	7	54	40	47
Crown Inn Selston	24	11	5	8	60	60	38
Clifton Academy	24	10	6	8	62	51	36
Ali Islam	24	11	2	11	63	62	35
Sherwood	24	10	4	10	74	67	34
Boots Athletic "A"	24	8	4	12	51	69	28
Arnold Celtic	24	7	6	11	37	55	27
Skegby United	24	5	6	13	34	45	21
Robin Hood Colts	24	2	5	17	35	69	11
Premium Reserves	24	2	5	17	44	111	11

Division Three

	P	W	D	L	F	A	Pts
Netherfield Town	26	22	2	2	111	38	68
FCGeordie	26	21	1	4	88	28	64
Vernon Villa Academy	26	20	2	4	118	50	62
Bestwood	26	19	0	7	130	62	57
Beeston Rylands	26	17	1	8	94	44	52
Bilborough United Reserves	26	15	1	10	92	68	46
Netherfield Seniors	26	14	2	10	83	56	44
West 8	26	12	5	9	72	63	41
Clifton Wanderers Reserves	26	5	5	16	42	79	20
FCSamba Reserves	26	5	4	17	38	82	19
Gedling Southbank Colts	26	4	5	17	63	106	17
Globo Gym	26	4	2	20	36	98	14
Bingham Town Reserves	26	4	2	20	34	104	14
Ali Islam Reserves	26	3	2	21	29	152	11

PERRY STREET & DISTRICT

Premier Division

	P	W	D	L	F	A	Pts
Lyme Regis	20	18	1	1	87	21	55
Beaminster	20	13	5	2	51	20	44
Winsham	20	12	3	5	58	32	39
Crewkerne Town	20	8	4	8	53	39	28
South Petherton	20	8	4	8	43	46	28
Ilminster Reserves	20	8	2	10	36	41	26
Farway United	20	8	2	10	51	58	26
Combe Reserves	20	7	5	8	38	48	26
Perry Street	20	5	2	13	43	63	17
West & Middle Chinnock	20	3	3	14	31	69	12
Merriott Rovers (-1)	20	3	3	14	19	73	11

Division One

	P	W	D	L	F	A	Pts
Millwey Rise	20	16	2	2	83	20	50
Shepton Beauchamp	20	15	4	1	47	17	49
Misterton	20	13	4	3	51	27	43
Forton Rangers	20	12	2	6	53	42	38
Netherbury	20	10	3	7	50	38	33
Lyme Regis Reserves	20	7	4	9	32	52	25
Perry Street Reserves	20	7	2	11	32	58	23
Barrington	20	5	3	12	38	48	18
Beaminster Reserves	20	5	2	13	39	47	17
Ilminster Colts	20	2	4	14	24	55	10
Norton Athletic	20	2	2	16	22	67	8

Division Two

	P	W	D	L	F	A	Pts
Crewkerne Reserves	20	16	2	2	82	26	50
South Petherton Res (-1)	20	14	3	3	71	36	44
Thorncombe	20	12	2	6	62	44	38
Pymore	20	11	2	7	74	39	35
Uplyme	20	9	5	6	69	34	32
Dowlish & Donyatt	20	9	5	6	67	46	32
Chard Rangers	20	6	5	9	36	55	23
Charmouth (-1)	20	5	5	10	31	54	19
Crewkerne Rangers	20	5	2	13	48	70	17
Misterton Reserves (-1)	20	5	3	12	38	88	17
Hinton St George (-1)	20	1	0	19	16	102	2

Division Three

	P	W	D	L	F	A	Pts
Chard Utd.	20	13	4	3	53	29	43
Waytown Hounds	20	13	2	5	53	36	41
Millwey Rise Reserves	20	10	4	6	64	45	34
Combe A	20	10	4	6	54	45	34
West & M Chinnock Res (-3)	20	11	2	7	76	64	32
Luso-Chard	20	10	2	8	59	48	32
Hawkchurch	20	6	5	9	52	56	23
Winsham Reserves	20	5	4	11	47	60	19
Drimpton	20	5	4	11	54	73	19
Forton Rangers Reserves (-6)	20	6	3	11	52	77	15
Shepton Reserves	20	3	2	15	25	56	11

Division Four

	P	W	D	L	F	A	Pts
Ilminster Town A	20	17	1	2	95	24	52
Chard Utd. Reserves	20	13	3	4	57	41	42
Lyme Bantams	20	13	1	6	79	42	40
Thorncombe Reserves	20	11	4	5	67	31	37
Barrington Reserves	20	8	5	7	58	48	29
Combe B	20	9	2	9	48	47	29
Farway Reserves (-1)	20	8	4	8	43	43	27
Uplyme Reserves	20	6	1	13	39	93	19
Crewkerne Rangers Res. (-3)	20	6	1	13	51	70	16
Chard Rangers Reserves	20	4	1	15	37	77	13
Hawkchurch Reserves	20	3	1	16	36	94	10

PLYMOUTH & WEST DEVON COMBINATION

Division One

	P	W	D	L	F	A	Pts
Roborough Fc	20	14	2	4	72	27	44
Wessex Rangers	20	13	1	6	72	41	40
Bluebird United	20	12	3	5	43	37	39
FC Manadon	20	14	2	4	47	19	38
Mount Gould Athletic	20	11	1	8	41	49	34
Plymouth Marjon	20	8	3	9	41	41	30
Chaddlewood Miners OB's	20	8	2	10	44	45	26
Tavistock Community	20	7	3	10	45	45	24
Chard United	20	6	2	12	41	64	17
Ivybridge Town	20	3	3	14	48	71	15
Horrabridge Rangers SA	20	2	2	16	37	92	8

A click away from memory lane!

Over 35 years of publishing the Non-League Club Directory has filled a room full of information and photographs covering the game we know and love.

What we intend, over time, is to create a website that shares with you everything we have accumulated, which we hope will bring back some fond memories of season's gone by.

Log on to **www.non-leagueclubdirectory.co.uk** today and see how many faces from teams gone by you recognise

Division Two

	P	W	D	L	F	A	Pts
Lee Moor A	18	18	0	0	92	8	54
University of Plymouth A	18	15	1	2	70	18	46
Vospers Oak Villa	18	13	2	3	63	18	41
Shakespeare	18	10	1	7	48	33	31
Windsor Car Sales	18	9	1	8	52	51	28
Plympton RBL	18	8	1	9	46	38	25
Yelverton	18	4	2	12	27	69	14
Wembury Rovers	18	3	3	12	22	63	12
Staddiscombe Colts	18	2	1	15	19	94	7
Cofely	18	1	2	15	17	64	5

PORTSMOUTH LEAGUE

Premier Division

	P	W	D	L	F	A	Pts
Baffins Milton Rovers	14	11	2	1	66	24	35
Waterlooville Social Club	14	10	2	2	52	24	32
St Helena Bobs	14	8	1	5	50	40	25
Wymering	14	7	2	5	30	35	23
Shearer Arms	14	5	2	7	46	40	17
Meon United	14	5	0	9	34	51	15
NAP Construction	14	3	2	9	26	61	11
Portsmouth Kurdish Utd	14	0	3	11	19	48	3

Division One

	P	W	D	L	F	A	Pts
BSS Portsmouth	16	13	0	3	83	18	39
East Lodge (-3)	16	13	2	1	42	25	38
AFC Hereford	16	10	0	6	40	40	30
Swan FC	16	9	2	5	49	43	29
AFC Ventora	16	7	2	7	38	37	23
Newcome Arms	16	7	0	9	51	45	21
Horndean Utd Reserves	16	4	2	10	30	59	14
Rovers United	16	2	3	11	18	65	9
Mead End	16	1	1	14	11	33	4

Division Two

	P	W	D	L	F	A	Pts
Horndean Hawks	18	15	2	1	60	20	47
Carberry	18	12	2	4	75	26	38
Compass Rose	18	8	5	5	51	41	29
Portchester	18	7	4	7	41	36	25
AFC Stella	18	7	2	9	41	48	23
Segensworth FC	18	3	3	12	38	64	12
Cosham Dynamos	18	2	0	16	26	97	6

Division Three

	P	W	D	L	F	A	Pts
Valley FC	14	11	0	3	55	17	33
Cosham Park Rangers	14	10	0	4	40	25	30
Lee Rangers	14	9	0	5	45	31	27
Budd AFC	14	8	0	6	37	29	24
Uplands Utd	14	7	1	6	45	25	22
Fareport Town	14	6	0	8	35	42	18
DCP Utd	14	2	1	11	27	60	7
Tempest Crusaders	14	2	0	12	16	71	6

PRESTON & DISTRICT LEAGUE

To be Renamed The Mid Lancashire Football League from 2012-13

Premier Division

	P	W	D	L	F	A	Pts
Leyland United	24	20	1	3	104	35	61
Preston Wanderers	24	19	2	3	86	29	59
Southport Amateurs	24	16	4	4	84	30	52
Blessed Sacrament	24	14	5	5	94	45	47
Preston GSA	24	11	4	9	57	46	37
Hoole United	24	10	6	8	68	47	36
Eccleston & Heskin	24	10	3	11	52	61	33
Town Green	24	6	11	7	40	44	29
Penwortham Town	24	9	2	13	59	69	29
Appley Bridge	24	6	4	14	35	76	22
Charnock Richard	24	5	3	16	45	74	18
Baxters	24	4	1	19	36	119	13
New Longton Rovers	24	1	4	19	34	119	7

Division One

	P	W	D	L	F	A	Pts
Leyland United	18	13	1	4	63	34	40
Deepdale	18	10	5	3	42	28	35
Walton Le Dale	18	11	1	6	56	33	34
Highcross	18	10	2	6	40	37	32
Penwortham St. Teresas	18	9	1	8	55	39	28
Mawdesley	18	5	4	9	34	49	19
Eccleston & Heskin	18	5	2	11	37	49	17
Southport Amateurs Res	18	6	2	10	39	57	17
Southport Trinity	18	4	4	10	38	48	16
Tarleton Corinthians	18	4	4	10	24	54	16

Division Two

	P	W	D	L	F	A	Pts
Adelphi	18	14	0	4	78	49	42
Walmer Bridge	18	13	2	3	59	16	41
Bolton United	18	13	1	4	67	32	40
Skelmersdale Athletic	18	11	2	5	67	39	35
Leyland Athletic	18	11	0	7	56	54	33
Newman College	18	5	4	9	26	44	19
Burscough Bridge	18	6	2	10	35	55	17
Ribbleton Rovers	18	5	1	12	47	79	16
Chipping	18	3	1	14	41	78	10
Springfields	18	2	1	15	35	65	7

Division Three

	P	W	D	L	F	A	Pts
Preston Academicals	18	15	1	2	63	21	46
Wilbraham	18	12	5	1	88	29	41
Goosnargh	18	10	5	3	51	20	35
Leyland Utd 'A'	18	10	2	6	51	56	32
Fulwood Garrison	18	7	3	8	42	34	24
Ribchester	18	7	1	10	38	51	22
Walmer Bridge Res	18	6	3	9	33	40	21
Hoole United Res	18	3	4	11	29	49	13
Farington Villa	18	1	7	10	22	55	10
New Longton Rovers Res	18	3	1	14	20	82	10

LEAGUE TABLES

Division Four	P	W	D	L	F	A	Pts
Ribble Wanderers	18	14	3	1	63	22	45
Lostock St. Gerards	18	11	3	4	67	39	36
Greenlands	18	11	2	5	49	32	35
Walton Athletic	18	7	5	6	47	44	26
A Preston	18	7	1	10	39	48	22
Scarisbrick	18	6	3	9	40	44	21
Eccleston & Heskin A	18	6	3	9	44	58	21
Southport Trinity	18	6	5	7	47	54	20
Preston Sector	18	6	1	11	39	59	19
Clayton Brook	18	2	2	14	27	62	8

Division Three	P	W	D	L	F	A	Pts
Woodland	18	18	0	0	122	16	54
Merchants FC	18	13	2	3	75	30	41
Rocklands	18	11	1	6	47	24	34
Woodrow	18	10	2	6	43	48	32
Dagnell End Rovers	18	8	3	7	49	34	27
Washford Lions	18	7	2	9	33	38	23
Kingfisher Angling (-1)	18	6	3	9	34	49	20
Hizza United Reserves (+3)	18	3	1	14	21	72	13
Winyates Wanderers (-1)	18	3	2	13	35	81	10
Wythall Wanderers	18	3	0	15	26	93	9

REDDITCH & SOUTH WARWICKSHIRE COMBINATION

Premier Division	P	W	D	L	F	A	Pts
Black Horse	22	18	0	4	69	22	54
Church Hill	22	16	1	5	74	31	49
Bartley Green Sunday(-3)	22	14	5	3	61	27	44
Austin Ex Apprentices	22	14	1	7	51	38	43
Wychbold RBL	22	10	2	10	53	39	32
Arrow Athletic (-3)	22	11	2	9	40	44	32
Alcester Town (-3)	22	9	2	11	40	44	26
Hizza United	22	7	5	10	40	53	26
Athletico	22	7	3	12	50	56	24
Studley Sporting	22	5	3	14	34	63	18
Bromsgrove General La Coruna (-3)	22	3	3	16	32	68	15
South Redditch (-3)	22	3	3	16	24	83	15

Division One	P	W	D	L	F	A	Pts
Webheath (-3)	20	17	3	0	85	25	51
Thomas Brothers	20	14	3	3	36	18	45
Corks (+2)	20	8	5	7	67	50	31
CBH Fasteners	20	9	4	7	62	49	31
Translift Bendi (-3)	20	10	3	7	46	39	30
FC Club (+1)	20	7	5	8	32	42	27
Dog & Pheasant	20	7	5	8	58	60	26
Studley Leisure	20	6	3	11	39	52	21
Greyhound Casuals (-1)	20	4	6	10	43	61	17
Alvechurch Lions (+3)	20	3	4	13	35	82	16
Lodge Park (+3)	20	2	5	13	36	61	14

Division Two	P	W	D	L	F	A	Pts
Redditch Cricket Club (-1)	20	16	2	2	66	19	49
Holloway Park	20	13	4	3	51	25	43
JMC United	20	13	2	5	60	39	41
Fleece	20	13	1	6	63	24	40
Millfield Rovers	20	9	4	7	58	40	31
Beoley Village	20	8	3	9	39	43	27
Kingswood Town	20	7	3	10	56	60	24
Royal Oak Studley	20	6	4	10	44	48	22
Mayfly (+2)	20	4	3	13	30	50	17
Kingfisher	20	3	3	14	26	98	12
Sporting Club Redditch	20	2	3	15	29	76	9

REDHILL & DISTRICT LEAGUE

Premier Division	P	W	D	L	F	A	Pts
Smallfield	20	17	2	1	75	16	53
Limpsfield Blues	20	15	2	3	68	28	47
AFC Reigate	20	11	1	8	56	46	34
Chipstead "A"	20	10	2	8	48	50	32
Merstham Newton	20	10	0	10	54	48	30
Racing Epsom	20	9	2	9	54	46	29
Walton Heath	20	9	2	9	47	41	29
South Park "A"	20	6	3	11	23	52	21
Charlwood	20	6	1	13	28	57	19
South Godstone	20	3	4	13	23	53	13
Frenches Athletic	20	3	3	14	22	61	12

Division One	P	W	D	L	F	A	Pts
Caterham Old Boys	18	13	3	2	56	17	42
Warlingham "A"	18	13	2	3	60	32	41
Woodmansterne Hyde	18	9	4	5	36	33	31
Real Holmesdale Res	18	7	5	6	34	46	26
Heath Old Boys	18	7	2	9	27	25	23
Westcott 35	18	7	1	10	44	54	22
Merstham "A"	18	6	3	9	22	42	21
Nutfield	18	6	2	10	31	40	20
Horley Town "A"	18	5	1	12	19	20	16
Reigate Sala	18	3	5	10	20	40	14

Division Two	P	W	D	L	F	A	Pts
Godstone	18	16	0	2	57	18	48
RH123 Athletic Reserves	18	15	0	3	62	18	45
Frenches Sports	18	11	2	5	51	31	35
Warlingham 'B'	18	8	5	5	32	28	29
Reed	18	8	3	7	37	42	27
Smallfield Reserves	18	7	3	8	38	36	24
Merstham Newton Res	18	5	4	9	43	67	19
Charlwood Reserves	18	3	4	11	22	44	13
AFC Reigate Reserves	18	2	3	13	25	45	9
South Godstone Reserves	18	2	2	14	24	62	8

Division Three

	P	W	D	L	F	A	Pts
Woodm'sterne Hyde Res	18	16	0	2	65	11	48
Kingswood Falcons	18	13	2	3	56	29	41
Horley AFC	18	10	3	5	43	29	33
Tatsfield Rovers	18	10	1	7	35	26	31
Stanley Park Athletic	18	5	5	8	43	58	20
Wallington	18	5	4	9	51	40	19
Overton Athletic	18	5	3	10	27	47	18
Reigate Priory "A"	18	4	4	10	26	45	16
RH123 Athletic "A"	18	4	4	10	27	54	16
Limpsfield Blues Res	18	3	4	11	27	61	13

Division Four

	P	W	D	L	F	A	Pts
Old Tenisonians	18	13	2	3	62	22	41
Brockham Reserves	18	12	1	5	54	36	37
AFC Redhill	18	11	3	4	59	39	36
South Park "B"	18	11	0	7	64	38	33
RH123 Athletic "B"	18	8	3	7	49	46	27
Walton Heath Reserves	18	7	0	11	47	51	21
The Plough Ifield	18	6	3	9	45	59	21
Westcott 35 Reserves	18	6	3	9	39	56	21
Oxted & District "A"	18	6	0	12	41	68	18
Monotype Senior	18	2	1	15	27	72	7

Division Five

	P	W	D	L	F	A	Pts
Warlingham "C"	18	12	4	2	64	30	40
Real Holmesdale "A"	18	10	5	3	48	29	35
Kingswood Falcons Res	18	10	4	4	69	29	34
Horley AFC Reserves	18	11	1	6	60	47	34
RH123 Athletic "C"	18	10	3	5	51	38	33
Nutfield Reserves	18	8	3	7	44	44	27
Merstham "B"	18	8	0	10	54	52	24
Walton Heath "A"	18	5	0	13	38	73	15
Frenches Athletic Res	18	3	2	13	34	75	11
Reigate Priory "B"	18	1	2	15	20	65	5

ROCHDALE ALLIANCE

Premier Division

	P	W	D	L	F	A	Pts
Wardle (+4)	18	8	7	3	49	35	35
Weavers Arms (-2)	18	10	5	3	45	25	33
Whitworth Valley	18	7	4	7	54	39	25
Fothergill & Whittles	18	7	3	8	38	42	24
Asia (+2)	18	5	5	8	54	60	22
Jacks House (-2)	18	6	4	8	51	60	20
FC Bury Town (+2)	18	5	2	11	37	67	19

SALISBURY & DISTRICT LEAGUE

The Wanderers	20	16	2	2	85	19	50
Durrington Dynamoes	20	14	4	2	59	17	46
Alderbury	20	13	5	2	59	38	44
Stockton & Codford	20	11	6	3	55	23	39
Porton Sports	20	9	2	9	55	33	29
South Newton & Wishford	20	7	5	8	41	46	26
Deacon Alms FC	20	8	2	10	41	48	26
Tisbury United	20	7	1	12	45	59	22
West Harnham	20	4	3	13	37	76	15
Nomansland & Landford	20	3	2	15	25	79	11
Durrington WMC	20	2	0	18	17	81	6

Division One

	P	W	D	L	F	A	Pts
Halfway House	14	11	1	2	57	15	34
Figheldean Rangers	14	11	1	2	57	18	34
Whiteparish	14	7	2	5	37	25	23
Deacon Alms FC Res	14	7	1	6	20	36	22
Devizes Inn	14	6	2	6	34	41	20
Tisbury United Res	14	2	4	8	33	45	10
GSB Amesbury Athletic	14	3	1	10	16	47	10
Winterslow	14	2	2	10	19	46	8

Division Two

	P	W	D	L	F	A	Pts
Burgess Trees	18	14	2	2	99	21	44
Chalke Valley	18	12	3	3	58	37	39
Wilton Club	18	12	2	4	56	32	38
Boscombe Down Rec Club	18	12	0	6	69	34	36
Alderbury Res	18	8	3	7	49	46	27
Huntsman Tavern	18	8	2	8	64	41	26
Halfway House Res	18	7	2	9	48	47	23
Value Cars	18	6	1	11	35	59	19
West Harnham Res	18	3	1	14	33	87	10
KJ Carpets	18	0	0	18	14	121	0

LEAGUE TABLES
SCUNTHORPE & DISTRICT

	P	W	D	L	F	A	Pts
College Wanderers	18	14	2	2	58	22	44
Epworth Town	18	14	1	3	71	23	43
Scotter United	18	10	2	6	50	34	32
Swinefleet Juniors	18	10	1	7	48	41	31
Limestone Rangers	18	7	3	8	40	48	24
BBM	18	8	0	10	42	55	24
Scunthonians	18	6	2	10	36	43	20
AFC Brumby	18	5	2	11	45	51	17
Crowle Town Colts	18	4	4	10	30	38	16
Crosby Colts	18	3	1	14	23	88	10

SELBY & DISTRICT LEAGUE

Divison One

	P	W	D	L	F	A	Pts
Pontefract SSC	16	16	0	0	76	15	48
Chequerfield United	16	10	4	2	58	39	32
Garforth Rangers	16	10	4	2	47	31	32
Moorends Comrades (-3)	16	9	4	3	59	27	27
Kellingley Welfare Res (+3)	16	6	9	1	34	56	22
Pontefract Town	16	6	8	2	41	47	20
Fairburn United	16	5	10	1	33	57	16
Garforth Crusaders	16	4	12	0	34	73	12
Kippax Athletic	16	0	15	1	30	67	1

Divison Two

	P	W	D	L	F	A	Pts
South Milford	20	15	4	1	80	31	46
Cas Celtics	20	15	4	1	74	57	46
Carleton South	20	13	4	3	84	46	42
Eggborough Eagles	20	13	5	2	73	50	41
Drax SSC	20	11	6	3	69	45	36
Pollington	20	10	6	4	69	59	34
Kellington	20	6	11	2	72	83	20
Swillington Saints Reserves	20	5	11	4	40	61	19
Sherburn White Rose	20	4	12	4	39	56	16
Hensall Athletic	20	3	13	4	45	71	13
Great Preston	20	0	18	2	12	111	2

SEVENOAKS & DISTRICT LEAGUE

Premier Division

	P	W	D	L	F	A	Pts
Nomads	21	14	2	5	69	42	44
Ide Hill	21	13	3	5	47	32	42
Ightham	21	11	2	8	70	45	35
Potters	21	10	2	9	43	54	32
Eynsford	21	8	4	9	50	47	28
Borough Green United	21	7	3	11	48	52	24
St Lawrence	21	6	1	14	42	67	19
Kemsing United	21	6	1	14	37	67	19

Division One

	P	W	D	L	F	A	Pts
Kingsdown Racers	20	15	4	1	66	27	49
Wilderpark	20	12	1	7	53	33	37
Fleetdown United "A"	20	9	6	5	40	43	33
Eynsford Reserves	20	8	5	7	49	43	29
Borough Green Utd Res	20	8	5	7	42	41	29
Hildenborough Ath Res	20	7	6	7	51	41	27
Halstead United Reserves	20	8	1	11	47	44	25
Seal	20	7	3	10	53	51	24
Sevenoaks Weald	20	6	6	8	32	38	24
Halls Reserves	20	5	3	12	40	69	18
Westerham	20	2	6	12	27	70	12

Division Two

	P	W	D	L	F	A	Pts
Real Mayo	20	19	0	1	78	18	57
Dunton Green	20	15	0	5	85	39	45
Nomads "A"	20	13	4	3	71	31	43
Swanley Oaks	20	10	2	8	56	44	32
Hildenborough Ath "A"	20	9	4	7	38	43	31
Kingsdown Racers Res	20	7	5	8	42	47	26
Kemsing United Reserves	20	7	3	10	54	59	24
Otford United "A"	20	6	3	11	29	57	21
Seal Reserves	20	4	3	13	31	69	15
Westerham Reserves	20	4	2	14	28	57	14
St Lawrence Reserves	20	3	0	17	26	74	9

Division Three

	P	W	D	L	F	A	Pts
Ide Hill Reserves	18	15	2	1	70	26	47
Chipstead "B"	18	12	2	4	66	24	38
Sevenoaks Weald Res	18	12	1	5	52	42	37
Ightham Reserves	18	10	1	7	42	33	31
Tonbridge Baptist Ch Res	18	9	4	5	43	37	31
Borough Green	18	9	3	6	42	30	30
AW London	18	7	2	9	36	39	23
Seal "A"	18	4	1	13	18	51	13
Nomads Reserves	18	3	0	15	25	60	9
Wilderpark Reserves	18	1	0	17	15	67	3

SHROPSHIRE COUNTY LEAGUE

Premier Division

	P	W	D	L	F	A	Pts
Newport Town	26	17	4	5	48	26	55
Ketley Bank United	26	15	6	5	58	31	51
Morda United	26	13	6	7	51	26	45
Wellington Amateurs Res.	26	12	8	6	66	38	44
Telford Juniors	26	12	7	7	52	40	43
Ludlow Town	26	12	6	8	63	34	42
FC Hodnet	26	11	8	7	48	32	41
Ellesmere Rangers Res.	26	10	6	10	69	46	36
Shifnal United	26	9	9	8	47	34	36
Church Stretton Town	26	10	6	10	46	46	36
Dawley Villa	26	8	6	12	49	62	30
Broseley Juniors	26	6	4	16	27	57	22
Whitchurch Alport Res.	26	4	6	16	35	53	18
Impact United	26	1	2	23	16	150	5

Division One

	P	W	D	L	F	A	Pts
Allscott	30	23	5	2	106	50	71
Weston Rhyn	30	20	3	7	57	41	63
Oakengates Athletic	30	20	1	9	89	50	61
Hanwood United Res.	30	18	3	9	80	54	57
Wroxeter Rovers	30	17	2	11	92	60	53
Rock Rovers	30	16	5	9	79	51	53
Prees	30	15	6	9	68	50	51
Oswestry Town Lions	30	16	5	9	73	46	50
Bishops Castle Town	30	12	5	13	66	57	41
Brown Clee	30	11	3	16	61	92	36
Shawbury United Res.	30	10	5	15	48	70	35
Meole Brace	30	9	4	17	63	89	31
Wrockwardine Wood	30	9	1	20	46	71	28
Hopesgate United	30	7	2	21	41	88	23
Ludlow Town Res.	30	5	3	22	49	89	18
Clee Hill United	30	4	3	23	31	91	15

Division Two

	P	W	D	L	F	A	Pts
Watcombe Wanderers	26	21	3	2	117	39	66
Langdon FC	26	20	1	5	87	36	61
Newton Abbot '66	26	16	6	4	81	42	57
Buckland Athletic 3rds (-6)	26	19	2	5	106	34	53
Broadhempston United	26	15	6	5	81	47	51
Newton United	26	10	4	12	64	71	34
Harbertonford (-4)	26	11	2	13	61	73	31
Beesands Rovers	26	8	3	15	51	66	29
Hookhills United (-9)	26	11	3	12	61	62	27
Brixham United Res	26	7	3	16	38	73	27
Paignton Saints	26	6	6	14	56	67	24
Hele Rovers Res	26	6	5	15	36	80	23
Upton Athletic Res (-9)	26	7	4	15	53	103	16
Teign Village	26	1	0	25	30	129	3

SOUTH DEVON LEAGUE

Premier Division

	P	W	D	L	F	A	Pts
Kingskerswell & Chelston	26	21	3	2	91	20	66
Buckland Ath Res (+2)	26	16	8	2	80	25	58
Brixham Villa	26	15	4	7	69	45	49
Upton Athletic	26	15	2	9	86	60	47
Watts Blake Bearne	26	12	5	9	61	52	41
Stoke Gabriel Res	26	11	7	8	48	45	40
Loddiswell Athletic	26	9	7	10	64	55	34
Galmpton United Res (-4)	26	10	4	12	44	60	30
Ipplepen Athletic	26	9	3	14	40	65	30
Abbotskerswell	26	8	5	13	55	67	29
Staverton & Landscove	26	8	4	14	53	67	28
Brixham United	26	8	4	14	57	86	28
East Allington United	26	7	4	15	47	71	25
Totnes & Dartington SC Res (-3)	26	1	4	21	19	96	4

Division Three

	P	W	D	L	F	A	Pts
Bovey Tracey Res	24	22	2	0	111	16	68
Brixham Town	24	19	2	3	116	42	59
Kingsteignton Athletic Res	24	17	3	4	76	26	54
Dartmouth AFC 3rds	24	14	3	7	44	50	45
Staverton & Landscove Res (-3)	24	12	2	10	62	47	35
Liverton United Res	24	9	5	10	69	44	32
South Brent	24	8	6	10	54	47	30
Newton Abbot Spurs 3rds (-3)	24	9	5	10	44	47	29
Watts Blake Bearne Res (-3)	24	7	6	11	52	53	24
Waldon Athletic Res	24	6	5	13	38	66	23
East Allington United Res	24	5	3	16	32	59	18
Meadowbrook Athletic	24	4	3	17	33	100	15
Moretonhampstead (-6)	24	1	1	22	14	148	-2

Division One

	P	W	D	L	F	A	Pts
Teignmouth Res	26	19	4	3	81	35	61
Newton Abbot Spurs Res	26	14	7	5	61	40	49
Kingsteignton Athletic (-6)	26	17	3	6	81	45	48
Stoke Fleming	26	12	7	7	61	49	43
Kingskerswell & Chelston Res	26	12	5	9	59	53	41
Riviera Spurs	26	9	8	9	54	49	35
Hele Rovers	26	8	8	10	51	54	35
Waldon Athletic	26	8	8	10	53	66	32
Chudleigh Athletic	26	9	4	13	55	51	31
Brixham Villa Res	26	8	5	13	50	65	29
Buckfastleigh Rangers	26	8	6	12	60	69	27
Dartmouth AFC Res	26	6	7	13	33	60	25
Paignton Villa	26	6	5	15	49	86	23
Ashburton AFC	26	5	5	16	32	58	20

Division Four

	P	W	D	L	F	A	Pts
Babbacombe Corinthians	24	16	4	4	95	29	52
Stoke Gabriel 3rds	24	16	4	4	83	23	52
Ipplepen Athletic Res	24	15	5	4	74	38	50
Foxhole United	24	16	2	6	69	50	50
Ilsington Villa	24	15	3	6	99	53	48
Bishopsteignton United	24	13	5	6	75	46	44
Kingskerswell & Chelston 3rds	24	11	4	9	53	48	37
Marldon FC	24	10	1	13	71	73	31
Totnes & Dartington SC 3rds	24	7	4	13	51	53	25
Loddiswell Athletic Res	24	6	3	15	47	89	21
Torbay Christians	24	6	1	17	41	79	19
Brixham Villa 3rds	24	3	4	17	35	87	13
Denbury Athletic (-3)	24	2	0	22	25	150	3

LEAGUE TABLES

Division Five

	P	W	D	L	F	A	Pts
Chudleigh Athletic Res	26	19	1	6	88	34	58
Paignton Saints Res	26	18	3	5	94	48	57
South Brent Res	26	16	3	7	102	64	54
Buckland & Milber	26	16	4	6	96	50	52
Paignton Villa Res	26	13	3	10	79	70	42
Dittisham United (-6)	26	13	3	10	85	58	36
Harbertonford Res (-12)	26	14	4	8	82	47	34
Newton Abbot '66 Res	26	8	7	11	58	76	31
Babbacombe Corinthians Res	26	8	5	13	60	78	29
Newton United Res	26	8	4	14	53	78	28
Ashburton AFC Res (-3)	26	8	3	15	32	76	24
Malborough United	26	6	5	15	53	73	23
Buckfastleigh Rangers Res	26	6	4	16	52	97	22
Stoke Fleming Res (-3)	26	3	3	20	38	123	9

Division Six

	P	W	D	L	F	A	Pts
Roselands FC	20	17	2	1	78	26	53
Bovey Tracey 3rds	20	12	3	5	62	39	39
Salcombe Town	20	11	3	6	76	42	38
Watcombe Wanderers Res	20	12	1	7	57	33	37
Newton Rovers	20	9	4	7	50	38	31
Broadhempston United Res (-4)	20	11	1	8	58	56	30
Riviera Spurs Res	20	7	8	5	43	33	29
Riviera United	20	7	3	10	41	60	24
Kingsbridge & Kellaton United	20	5	2	13	26	51	17
Ipplepen Athletic 3rds	20	3	4	13	33	47	13
Teign Village Res (-3)	20	0	1	19	15	114	-2

SOUTH LONDON ALLIANCE

Premier Division

	P	W	D	L	F	A	Pts
Long Lane 'A'	22	15	3	4	73	36	48
Wickham Park	22	13	3	6	51	35	42
Southwark Borough	22	13	2	7	43	40	41
Old Roan	22	12	3	7	51	44	39
Johnson & Phillips	22	11	4	7	52	34	37
Parkhurst Rangers	22	9	5	8	40	46	32
Drummond Athletic	22	8	6	8	40	32	30
Metrogas Reserves	22	9	2	11	44	44	29
Catford Wanderers	22	7	7	8	51	55	28
New Park	22	5	7	10	41	57	22
Tudor Sports 'A'	22	5	4	13	28	61	19
Wickham Wanderers	22	1	2	19	14	44	5

Division One

	P	W	D	L	F	A	Pts
Long Lane	18	11	6	1	68	27	39
Chislehurst Dynamoes	18	11	3	4	41	23	36
Old Roan Reserves	18	10	1	7	46	42	31
Beaverwood	18	10	0	8	49	41	30
Red Velvet	18	9	2	7	48	50	29
Farnborough O.B. Guild Res.	18	7	4	7	43	31	25
Blackheath Wanderers	18	7	2	9	42	47	23
Thames Borough	18	5	5	8	32	43	20
Chislehurst Sports	18	5	5	8	36	49	20
Forest Hill Park Reserves	18	0	2	16	18	70	2

Division Two

	P	W	D	L	F	A	Pts
Lewisham Athletic	20	16	3	1	74	29	51
Long Lane Blue	20	12	1	7	51	25	37
Longlands Athletic	20	11	1	8	53	52	34
Thames Borough Reserves	20	10	3	7	57	42	33
West Bromley Albion	20	11	0	9	43	51	33
Old Roan 'A'	20	10	2	8	69	59	32
Seven Acre Sports	20	9	2	9	45	49	29
Knights Old Boys	20	8	1	11	35	48	25
Avery Hill College	20	6	1	13	39	66	19
Johnson & Phillips Reserves	20	5	2	13	34	52	17
Crofton Albion Reserves	20	2	4	14	28	55	10

Division Three

	P	W	D	L	F	A	Pts
New Park Reserves	20	17	1	2	76	14	52
Heathfield	20	15	0	5	49	33	45
Fleetdown United 'A'	20	13	2	5	41	25	41
Oldsmiths	20	8	5	7	39	35	29
Southmere	20	7	7	6	51	37	28
Elite	20	8	2	10	37	56	26
Bexley Reserves	20	5	9	6	36	39	24
Crown Alexandra	20	6	5	9	36	39	23
Iron Tugboat City	20	4	4	12	20	51	16
Old Colfeians	20	4	2	14	31	47	14
Downham Town	20	3	3	14	20	55	12

Division Four

	P	W	D	L	F	A	Pts
Old Colfeians Reserves	16	12	2	2	60	22	38
Crayford Arrows	16	11	3	2	69	27	36
State Street	16	8	4	4	44	29	28
Junior Reds	16	8	2	6	25	37	26
Our Lady Seniors	16	8	1	7	41	34	25
Farnborough Old Boys Guild 'A'	16	6	4	6	47	43	22
Lewisham Athletic Reserves	16	5	0	11	26	53	15
Seven Acre Sports Reserves	16	3	1	12	28	64	10
Crayford Athletic	16	1	3	12	12	43	6

SOUTH WEST GLOUCESTERSHIRE NORTHERN SENIOR LEAGUE

Division One

	P	W	D	L	F	A	Pts
Shortwood United Res.	30	19	8	3	63	31	65
Frampton United	30	18	8	4	78	38	62
Gala Wilton	30	18	7	5	75	31	61
Broadwell Amateurs	30	18	7	5	61	33	61
Star	30	15	7	8	52	44	52
Brockworth Albion	30	16	3	11	53	40	51
Sharpness	30	13	5	12	57	52	44
Winchcombe Town	30	11	10	9	51	41	43
Leonard Stanley	30	9	9	12	34	52	36
Stonehouse Town	30	9	7	14	38	47	34
Harrow Hill	30	9	7	14	48	58	33
Smiths Athletic	30	8	7	15	34	57	31
Lydbrook Athletic	30	8	6	16	41	52	30
Dursley Town	30	7	7	16	38	57	28
Ramblers	30	5	9	16	43	67	24
Stroud	30	2	3	25	23	89	6

Division Two	P	W	D	L	F	A	Pts
Cheltenham Civil Service	30	23	3	4	92	35	72
Cam Bulldogs	30	19	3	8	66	36	60
Bredon	30	19	3	8	70	49	60
Hardwicke	30	18	2	10	74	50	56
Minsterworth	30	17	4	9	74	52	55
Abbeymead Rovers	30	15	4	11	59	59	49
Moreton Rangers	30	14	6	10	79	51	48
Longford	30	15	3	12	57	48	48
Viney St Swithins	30	13	6	11	72	69	45
Bourton Rovers	30	11	3	16	54	65	36
FC Barometrics	30	11	3	16	38	60	36
Barnwood United	30	10	5	15	43	76	35
Wotton Rovers	30	9	6	15	46	56	33
Chalford	30	6	8	16	46	62	26
Soudley	30	6	4	20	45	82	22
Tetbury Town	30	1	3	26	27	92	6

SOUTH YORKSHIRE AMATEUR LEAGUE

Premier Division	P	W	D	L	F	A	Pts
Jubilee Sports	18	15	3	0	74	14	48
Manor Castle	18	12	2	4	68	26	38
Swallownest MW	18	9	3	6	44	40	30
Noah's Ark	18	9	0	9	44	40	27
Royston	18	8	2	8	43	55	26
Sheffield Medics	18	7	3	8	51	45	24
Byron House	18	7	2	9	47	66	23
Dale Dynamos	18	6	0	12	47	85	18
Sheffield Bankers	18	5	1	12	32	66	16
Sheffield West End	18	3	2	13	40	53	11

Division One	P	W	D	L	F	A	Pts
North Gawber Colliery	18	16	2	0	118	10	50
Shaw Lane Aquaforce Res	18	13	1	4	97	23	40
Renishaw Social Club	18	13	1	4	84	25	40
Beighton Albion	18	9	2	7	46	66	29
Millmoor Juniors	18	9	1	8	52	42	28
Queens Head	18	7	2	9	37	44	23
Tusaale	18	4	2	12	31	84	14
Horse & Groom	18	4	1	13	37	93	13
Thurgoland Welfare	18	2	6	10	27	80	12
New Bohemians	18	3	2	13	29	91	11

SOUTHAMPTON FOOTBALL LEAGUE

Premier Division	P	W	D	L	F	A	Pts
Bush Hill	18	17	0	1	69	21	51
Comrades	18	12	2	4	45	31	38
Forest Town	18	11	1	6	50	33	34
Nursling	18	10	3	5	37	27	33
Southampton University	18	10	2	6	38	21	32
AFC Hiltingbury	18	8	2	8	49	45	26
Cutbush Athletic	18	5	3	10	33	67	18
London Airways	18	4	1	13	26	49	13
Bishopstoke WMC	18	3	3	12	31	46	12
BTC Southampton	18	1	1	16	16	54	4

Senior One	P	W	D	L	F	A	Pts
Netley Central Sports	22	19	3	0	85	11	60
Cadnam United	22	16	3	3	92	25	51
Thornhill	22	14	3	5	80	38	45
Lyndhurst (-3)	22	15	2	5	66	31	44
White Horse	22	12	1	9	67	46	37
Hythe Aztecs	22	11	2	9	65	61	35
Hedge End Town	22	8	3	11	55	69	27
Durley Reserves	22	7	1	14	45	90	22
Burridge AFC	22	6	3	13	47	53	21
Comrades Reserves	22	5	4	13	38	66	19
BTC Southampton Res	22	4	2	16	23	75	14
Michelmersh & Timsbury Res	22	1	1	20	21	119	4

Division Two	P	W	D	L	F	A	Pts
Malvern	22	19	2	1	62	20	59
Academicals	22	18	2	2	98	25	56
Spartans	22	16	3	3	71	32	51
Northend United	22	14	2	6	67	47	44
AFC Hop	22	12	0	10	37	38	36
Bishopstoke WMC	22	10	5	7	55	35	35
Mottisfont Res.	22	7	1	14	35	60	22
M & T Awbridge Res.	22	6	3	13	32	54	21
Compton	22	6	0	16	36	57	18
Braishfield	22	5	2	15	37	80	17
Bacardi	22	4	1	17	32	84	13
BTC Southampton Res.	22	3	3	16	24	54	12

SOUTHEND BOROUGH COMBINATION

Premier Division	P	W	D	L	F	A	Pts
Rochford Town 1st	18	16	2	0	61	18	34
Railway Academicals 1st	18	14	2	2	53	23	30
Shoebury Town 1st	18	8	3	7	48	35	19
Leigh Town 1st	18	7	5	6	45	40	19
Ensign	18	9	1	8	43	46	19
H.D.C. F.C.	18	5	5	8	32	41	15
Castle Point Gas	18	6	2	10	42	37	14
Corinthians 1st	18	6	2	10	27	38	14
Borough Rovers 1st	18	5	2	11	35	64	12
Weir Sports 1st	18	1	2	15	34	78	4

Division One	P	W	D	L	F	A	Pts
F.C. Toro	18	13	4	1	58	17	30
Zebra Sports	18	11	3	4	59	37	25
Heathfield	18	10	3	5	36	29	23
Sceptre Elite FC	18	9	2	7	79	47	20
Leigh Town 2nd	18	9	2	7	48	37	20
Earls Hall United 1st	18	7	4	7	43	30	18
Cupids Country Club 1st	18	7	3	8	39	45	17
Weir Sports 2nd	18	6	2	10	34	48	14
Stambridge United 3rd	18	6	1	11	37	48	13
Southend Collegians 1st	18	0	0	18	14	109	0

LEAGUE TABLES

Division Two

	P	W	D	L	F	A	Pts
Ashingdon 1st	16	11	1	4	59	19	23
Thorpe Athletic	16	11	1	4	55	40	23
Thundersley United 1st	16	10	2	4	38	30	22
Elmwood	16	9	1	6	52	32	19
B.K.S. Sports	16	7	3	6	39	46	17
Little Theatre Club 1st	16	7	2	7	33	33	16
Old Southendian 3rd	16	4	2	10	31	50	10
Corinthians 2nd	16	2	5	9	24	39	9
Leigh Ramblers 3rd	16	1	3	12	13	55	5

Division Three

	P	W	D	L	F	A	Pts
Rayleigh & Rawreth Sports	18	13	3	2	42	23	29
Barnsford Hurricanes	18	11	3	4	38	25	25
Ashingdon 2nd	18	10	4	4	65	31	24
Rochford Town 2nd	18	8	5	5	29	27	21
Torch	18	9	1	8	52	31	19
Sporting Hadleigh	18	6	4	8	37	40	16
Earls Hall United 2nd	18	5	3	10	29	40	13
Southend Collegians 2nd	18	3	6	9	28	44	12
Sceptre Elite FC 2nd	18	5	2	11	24	44	12
Railway Academicals 2nd	18	4	1	13	22	61	9

Division Four

	P	W	D	L	F	A	Pts
Railway Academicals 3rd	18	14	1	3	64	28	29
Westcliff United 1st	18	13	2	3	71	38	28
Little Theatre Club 2nd	18	11	0	7	51	41	22
Shoebury Town 2nd	18	7	4	7	49	50	18
Sceptre Elite FC 3rd	18	5	6	7	44	42	16
Catholic United 3rd	18	6	4	8	49	48	16
Cupids Country Club 2nd	18	7	1	10	29	41	15
Old Southendian 4th	18	5	4	9	28	42	14
Southend Collegians 3rd	18	3	5	10	40	64	11
Leigh Town 3rd	18	4	3	11	33	64	11

Division Five

	P	W	D	L	F	A	Pts
Christchurch	18	17	0	1	141	25	34
Corinthians 3rd	18	15	0	3	94	30	30
Rayford Athletic 1st	18	15	0	3	96	33	30
Landwick	18	11	1	6	67	47	23
Southend Rangers	18	7	3	8	66	62	17
Ashingdon 3rd	18	7	2	9	56	53	16
Westcliff United 2nd	18	5	2	11	41	78	12
Hamlet Court	18	4	1	13	49	98	9
Southend Collegians 4th	18	3	0	15	22	120	6
Old Southendian 5th	18	1	1	16	22	108	3

SOUTHEND & DISTRICT LEAGUE

	P	W	D	L	F	A	Pts
AFC Horndon	18	15	3	0	66	17	48
CT 66	18	14	1	3	87	36	43
Club Sirrus	18	12	3	3	72	36	39
Thundersley Rovers	18	7	2	9	43	43	23
Playfootball Elite	18	6	0	12	53	83	18
Wickford Rangers	18	2	2	14	22	71	8
Sparco	18	1	1	16	21	78	4

SOUTHERN AMATEUR LEAGUE

Senior Divison One

	P	W	D	L	F	A	Pts
Old Salesians	20	14	1	5	38	23	43
Old Wilsonians	20	11	5	4	40	21	38
Nottsborough	20	11	5	4	42	30	38
West Wickham	20	11	4	5	43	20	37
Old Owens	20	9	3	8	33	35	30
Old Parkonians	20	8	5	7	38	37	29
Broomfield	20	9	1	10	44	47	28
Winchmore Hill	20	8	2	10	33	28	26
East Barnet Old Grammarians	20	6	3	11	33	60	21
Norsemen	20	5	2	13	29	44	17
Polytechnic	20	2	1	17	22	50	7

Senior Division Two

	P	W	D	L	F	A	Pts
Civil Service	20	16	3	1	55	17	51
Alleyn Old Boys	20	15	3	2	51	15	48
BB Eagles	20	13	2	5	47	25	41
Old Finchleians	20	11	4	5	39	24	37
Crouch End Vampires	20	8	4	8	39	38	28
Carshalton	20	8	2	10	26	38	26
Old Esthameians	20	6	4	10	20	33	22
Old Actonians Association	20	6	2	12	28	38	20
Merton	20	4	5	11	20	36	17
Weirside Rangers (-3)	20	5	4	11	35	52	16
Old Westminster Citizens	20	0	3	17	26	70	3

Senior Division Three

	P	W	D	L	F	A	Pts
Alexandra Park	20	14	6	0	56	15	48
HSBC	20	13	3	4	56	25	42
Bank of England	20	10	6	4	31	26	36
South Bank Cuaco	20	10	3	7	46	31	33
Ibis	20	8	2	10	39	39	26
Lloyds TSB Bank	20	7	5	8	36	38	26
Old Lyonians	20	8	2	10	40	48	26
Old Stationers	20	7	2	11	40	52	23
Old Latymerians	20	5	2	13	37	53	17
Kew Association	20	4	5	11	32	63	17
Southgate Olympic (-3)	20	4	4	12	35	58	13

SOUTHPORT & DISTRICT LEAGUE

	P	W	D	L	F	A	Pts
Formby Athletic	18	14	1	3	77	26	43
St Pauls	18	13	1	4	70	34	40
Trojan Security	18	12	2	4	61	29	38
Devonshire	18	9	1	8	39	52	28
FC De Corona	18	7	4	7	47	40	25
Sandy Lane	18	7	4	7	47	48	25
Pinewoods	18	7	4	7	40	42	25
Formby Dons	18	3	6	9	28	44	15
Banks Saturday	18	3	2	13	41	83	11
Poulton Wanderers	18	2	1	15	28	80	7
Christ The King - record expunged							
Dales - record expunged							

SPEN VALLEY & DISTRICT

Premier Division

	P	W	D	L	F	A	Pts
Bradford	20	14	3	3	59	34	45
BD3 United	20	13	4	3	73	34	43
Jardy Boys	20	13	3	4	62	32	42
T.V.R United	20	12	5	3	72	38	41
West Bradford Spartans	20	11	2	7	69	52	35
Girlington	20	8	4	8	47	44	28
Fairbank United	19	7	2	10	43	55	23
Ravensthorpe Rangers	20	6	3	11	35	46	21
Thornhill United Seniors	19	4	1	14	35	62	13
Mount Athletic	20	4	1	15	53	89	13
Quarry	20	1	4	15	29	91	7

Division One

	P	W	D	L	F	A	Pts
Vision	21	18	2	1	102	17	56
Marsh	22	16	1	5	67	34	49
Oakwell	22	15	3	4	86	39	48
A.L.C	22	14	2	6	62	37	44
BD3 United Reserves	21	12	3	6	74	40	39
Howden Clough (-1)	22	10	3	9	60	62	32
Bradford All Stars (-2)	21	9	5	7	56	47	30
Norfolk	22	7	4	11	42	67	25
Savile United	21	6	2	13	44	59	20
Inter Batley	22	3	1	18	29	80	10
Thornhill United Seniors B	22	3	1	18	19	77	10
Ravenswharfe Hotel	22	3	1	18	22	104	10

STRATFORD ALLIANCE

Division One

	P	W	D	L	F	A	Pts
Alcester Town	20	16	2	2	72	20	50
Alveston	20	14	1	5	72	50	43
Shipston Excelsior	20	13	2	5	55	32	41
Badsey Rangers	20	10	5	5	55	44	35
Kenilworth Town	20	11	1	8	54	30	34
Quinton (-3)	20	10	3	7	44	40	30
South Redditch Athletic	20	7	2	11	48	38	23
Cubbington Albion	20	6	1	13	34	55	19
FISSC	20	5	4	11	36	59	19
Studley Swan	20	3	1	16	33	86	10
Stoneleigh (-3)	20	3	2	15	25	74	8

Division Two

	P	W	D	L	F	A	Pts
Washford Lions	20	16	1	3	86	26	49
Coventry Spires	20	14	2	4	70	43	44
Welford on Avon	20	13	4	3	60	40	43
Hayes Harriers	20	13	1	6	78	46	40
RS Sports	20	10	2	8	56	50	32
Henley Forest Reserves	20	10	0	10	37	42	30
Snitterfield Snipers	20	6	5	9	47	48	23
Coventry Amateurs (-3)	20	5	2	13	47	77	14
Tysoe United (-3)	20	5	2	13	38	74	14
Alcester Town Res (-3)	20	5	0	15	33	72	12
The Badgers	20	3	1	16	21	55	10

Division Three

	P	W	D	L	F	A	Pts
Badsey United	22	16	2	4	69	33	50
Shipston Excelsior Res	22	15	1	6	59	38	46
Blockley Sports	22	12	2	8	78	61	38
Bretforton Old Boys	22	11	4	7	75	48	37
Kenilworth Town Reserves	22	11	2	9	66	56	35
Claverdon	22	9	5	8	56	55	32
Henley Forest "A"	22	9	2	11	59	73	29
International Football Cl	22	8	4	10	53	56	28
Moreton Rangers	22	7	4	11	57	62	25
Inkberrow	22	6	4	12	54	67	22
Astwood Bank	22	4	6	12	51	84	18
Quinton Reserves	22	5	2	15	33	77	17

Division Four

	P	W	D	L	F	A	Pts
Bidford Boys Club	16	12	3	1	71	19	39
Redditch United Reserves	16	12	1	3	89	27	37
RS Sports Reserves	16	8	2	6	42	48	26
Red Alert	16	7	4	5	37	35	25
FISSC Reserves	16	5	5	6	30	38	20
Hayes Harriers Res (-3)	16	6	4	6	31	40	19
Shipston Excelsior Colts	16	2	3	11	20	55	9
Inkberrow Reserves (-6)	16	4	1	11	20	49	7
Coventry Spires Res (-6)	16	2	5	9	28	57	5

STROUD & DISTRICT LEAGUE

Division One

	P	W	D	L	F	A	Pts
Tuffley Rovers Reserves	24	16	6	2	62	26	54
Slimbridge Reserves	24	16	4	4	74	26	52
Randwick	24	15	6	3	70	30	51
Whitminster	24	13	5	6	59	32	44
Old Richians	24	13	5	6	53	32	44
Kings Stanley Reserves	24	10	5	9	47	39	35
Quedgeley Wanderers	24	10	2	12	46	45	32
Dursley Town Reserves	24	9	3	12	42	53	30
Matson	24	8	4	12	50	52	28
Stonehouse Town Reserves	24	6	7	11	41	66	25
Horsley United	24	7	3	14	34	54	24
Longlevens Reserves	24	6	2	16	31	65	20
Tetbury Town Reserves	24	1	0	23	21	110	3

Division Two

	P	W	D	L	F	A	Pts
Upton St Leonards	24	17	6	1	51	18	57
Cashes Green	24	14	6	4	48	25	48
Frampton United Reserves	24	13	7	4	63	28	46
Kingswood Reserves	24	14	3	7	61	36	45
Uley	24	12	5	7	50	27	41
Taverners Reserves	24	10	6	8	35	36	36
AC Royals	24	11	1	12	45	45	34
Ramblers Reserves	24	9	4	11	39	38	31
Minchinhampton/RDS	24	5	9	10	35	57	24
Charfield	24	6	5	13	36	58	23
Tibberton United	24	7	2	15	25	62	23
Thornbury Town Res (-1)	24	6	4	14	31	48	21
Eastcombe	24	2	2	20	19	62	8

LEAGUE TABLES

Division Three

	P	W	D	L	F	A	Pts
Avonvale United	24	18	2	4	90	20	56
Didmarton	24	14	6	4	70	37	48
Sharpness Res	24	15	2	7	72	44	47
Cam Bulldogs Res	24	13	7	4	46	27	46
Abbeymead Rovers Res	24	12	3	9	51	36	39
Quedgeley Wanderers Res	24	11	6	7	51	40	39
AFC Phoenix	24	12	2	10	51	45	38
Chalford Reserves (-3)	24	10	3	11	43	42	30
Berkeley Town Res	24	8	5	11	50	61	29
Wotton Rovers Res	24	7	3	14	49	63	24
Coaley Rovers	24	6	1	17	36	70	19
Barnwood United Res (-3)	24	5	3	16	34	76	15
Matchplay	24	2	3	19	34	120	9

Division Four

	P	W	D	L	F	A	Pts
Wickwar Wanderers	24	19	2	3	76	27	59
Tredworth Tigers	24	17	3	4	90	36	54
Stroud Imperial	24	12	4	8	65	39	40
Leonard Stanley Res	24	11	6	7	60	48	39
Arlingham	24	10	5	9	54	62	35
Nympsfield (-3)	24	9	8	7	64	56	32
Glevum United	24	9	5	10	52	69	32
Longlevens 3rds	24	7	6	11	54	61	27
Randwick Res	24	8	3	13	45	61	27
Ramblers 3rds (-3)	24	9	3	12	45	65	27
Whitminster Res	24	7	4	13	57	66	25
Minchinhampton/RDS Res	24	5	5	14	47	76	20
Stonehouse Town 3rds	24	5	2	17	43	89	17

Division Five

	P	W	D	L	F	A	Pts
Stroud Harriers	24	19	0	5	98	39	57
Bush FC	24	17	3	4	93	39	54
Avonvale United Res	24	15	3	6	80	36	48
Hardwicke Res	24	15	3	6	84	41	48
Tuffley Rovers 3rds	24	14	4	6	71	31	46
Dursley Town 3rds	24	11	3	10	60	67	36
Sherston	24	11	2	11	59	61	35
Old Richians Res	24	9	6	9	39	40	33
Longford Res	24	10	2	12	40	60	32
Whitminster 3rds	24	8	5	11	52	74	29
Alkerton Rangers	24	5	0	19	41	77	15
Charfield Res (-3)	24	3	2	19	21	92	8
Tetbury Town 3rds	24	2	1	21	35	117	7

Division Six

	P	W	D	L	F	A	Pts
Upton St Leonards Res	22	16	3	3	102	27	51
McCadam	22	15	4	3	87	23	49
Brockworth Albion 3rds	22	13	6	3	70	31	45
Eastcombe Res	22	12	1	9	58	44	37
Quedgeley Wanderers 3rds	22	10	5	7	54	45	35
Cashes Green Res	22	8	5	9	49	50	29
Berkeley Town 3rds	22	7	5	10	45	56	26
Coaley Rovers Res	22	7	3	12	40	61	24
Wotton Rovers 3rds (-3)	22	6	7	9	42	57	22
Uley Res	22	5	4	13	36	74	19
Horsley United Res	22	5	3	14	38	98	18
North Nibley	22	2	6	14	17	73	12

Division Seven

	P	W	D	L	F	A	Pts
Cotswold Rangers	24	19	2	3	129	38	59
St Nicholas Old Boys	24	17	4	3	110	26	55
Hardwicke 3rds	24	17	1	6	104	61	52
Golden Heart (-3)	24	16	5	3	108	40	50
Wickwar Wanderers Res	24	14	4	6	94	40	46
Coney Hill (-3)	24	15	1	8	78	62	43
Cam Bulldogs 3rds	24	7	3	14	52	88	24
Linden Snakes (-3)	24	8	2	14	48	68	23
Sharpness 3rds (-3)	24	8	2	14	51	75	23
Avonvale United 3rds	24	7	2	15	57	91	23
Woodchester (-3)	24	6	1	17	61	141	16
Uley 3rds	24	3	4	17	44	128	13
Longlevens 4ths	24	3	1	20	36	114	10

Division Eight

	P	W	D	L	F	A	Pts
Trident	22	16	3	3	66	28	51
Hawkesbury Stallions	22	16	2	4	94	32	50
Stratford Wanderers	22	16	1	5	100	35	49
The Village FC	22	14	3	5	64	25	45
Chalford 3rds	22	13	2	7	53	36	41
Stroud Imperial Res	22	12	1	9	59	46	37
Randwick 3rds	22	9	4	9	41	39	31
Rodborough Old Boys	22	9	1	12	49	83	28
Stonehouse Town 4ths	22	6	2	14	44	77	20
Cotswold Rangers Res	22	5	2	15	64	71	17
Old Richians 3rds	22	3	3	16	30	72	12
Alkerton Rangers Res (-3)	22	0	2	20	21	141	-1

SUBURBAN LEAGUE

Premier

	P	W	D	L	F	A	Pts
Woking Res	22	14	3	5	47	38	45
AFC Wimbledon Res	22	13	4	5	53	24	43
Eastleigh Res	22	11	4	7	45	34	37
Sutton United Res	22	11	4	7	41	31	37
Eastbourne Borough Res	22	10	6	6	52	35	36
Hampton & Richmond Res	22	10	6	6	49	42	36
Boreham Wood Res	22	8	6	8	36	29	30
Tonbridge Angels Res	22	8	5	9	39	42	29
Hemel Hempstead Town Res	22	7	4	11	46	57	25
Carshalton Athletic Res	22	7	4	11	38	49	25
Tooting & Mitcham Utd Res	22	4	3	15	26	67	15
Farnborough Res	22	3	3	16	34	58	12

Northern Division

	P	W	D	L	F	A	Pts
Hanworth Villa Res	24	17	4	3	72	38	55
Chalfont St Peter Res	24	16	6	2	73	41	54
Barton Rovers Res	24	14	4	6	54	39	46
Leighton Town Res	24	12	1	11	44	37	37
Beaconsfield SYCOB Res	24	11	3	10	50	43	36
Berkhamsted Res	24	10	5	9	56	52	35
Tring Athletic Res	24	11	2	11	46	43	35
Leverstock Green Res	24	10	3	11	56	52	33
Newport Pagnell Town Res	24	7	6	11	39	47	27
Harefield United Res	24	6	7	11	38	51	25
AFC Hayes Res	24	6	4	14	46	58	22
Hartley Wintney Res	24	6	3	15	37	68	21
Ash United Res	24	5	2	17	35	77	17

Southern Division

Southern Division	P	W	D	L	F	A	Pts
Walton & Hersham Res.	26	22	1	3	67	22	67
Thamesmead Town Res.	26	17	4	5	89	48	55
South Park Res.	26	16	2	8	86	55	50
Epsom & Ewell Res.	26	13	6	7	60	42	45
Crowborough Athletic Res.	26	13	6	7	70	56	45
Corinthian Res.	26	13	4	9	64	53	43
Lingfield Res.	26	11	4	11	70	74	37
Molesey Res.	26	9	8	9	46	49	35
Cobham Res.	26	9	3	14	54	72	30
Oakwood Res.	26	7	5	14	43	76	26
Mole Valley SCR Res.	26	7	3	16	42	68	24
Chessington & Hook Utd Res.	26	4	9	13	40	53	21
Redhill Res.	26	5	4	17	48	83	19
Horley Town Res.	26	3	7	16	34	62	16

SURREY INTERMEDIATE (WEST)

Division One	P	W	D	L	F	A	Pts
Yateley Green	24	17	5	2	65	28	56
Abbey	24	14	8	2	52	24	50
Worplesdon Phoenix	24	14	5	5	80	44	47
Shottermill & Haslemere	24	14	3	7	58	30	45
Merrow	24	11	6	7	44	30	39
Milford & Witley	24	11	3	10	42	41	36
Yateley	24	10	3	11	44	49	33
University of Surrey	24	9	3	12	53	56	30
Chiddingfold	24	8	5	11	42	53	29
Cranleigh	24	8	4	12	39	49	28
Royal Holloway Old Boys	24	5	3	16	40	76	18
Unis Old Boys	24	5	2	17	37	76	17
Tongham	24	3	4	17	35	75	13

Division Two	P	W	D	L	F	A	Pts
AFC Spelthorne Sports	22	15	4	3	69	25	49
Godalming & Farncombe Ath	22	14	5	3	50	23	47
Lightwater United	22	13	2	7	53	38	41
Chobham Burymead	22	12	4	6	60	42	40
Knaphill Athletic	22	11	3	8	41	36	36
Pyrford	22	11	2	9	56	43	35
Woking & Horsell	22	11	3	8	58	44	30
Elm Grove Seniors	22	10	0	12	45	51	30
Shalford	22	8	3	11	35	47	27
AFC Leatherhead	22	7	1	14	33	41	22
Old Salesians	22	4	1	17	29	62	13
Ewhurst	22	1	2	19	16	93	5

SURREY SOUTH EASTERN COMBINATION

	P	W	D	L	F	A	Pts
Claygate & Ditton	16	10	4	2	38	19	34
Battersea	16	9	2	5	43	24	29
Real Holmesdale	16	7	6	3	39	25	27
Puretown	16	8	2	6	42	23	26
NPL	16	8	2	6	48	36	26
Westminster Casuals	16	6	5	5	28	30	23
Cheam Village Warriors	16	6	2	8	25	37	20
Old Rutlishians	16	3	1	12	20	50	10
Old Plymouthians	16	3	0	13	21	60	9

SURREY ELITE INTERMEDIATE LEAGUE

Intermediate Division	P	W	D	L	F	A	Pts
Epsom Athletic	28	23	3	2	88	26	72
Horsley	28	21	2	5	66	33	65
Battersea Ironsides	28	16	5	7	46	29	53
Coulsdon Town	28	16	2	10	67	40	50
AFC Cubo	28	15	5	8	59	40	50
Old Farnboronians	28	13	8	7	52	37	47
Weston Green Sports	28	14	3	11	51	43	45
Reigate Priory	28	14	2	12	51	57	44
Ripley Village	28	11	6	11	61	60	39
Abbey Rangers	28	9	8	11	56	52	35
Oxted & District	28	8	4	16	37	58	28
Crescent Rovers	28	9	0	19	71	75	27
Tooting Bec	28	7	3	18	43	56	24
Virginia Water	28	5	5	18	41	77	20
Farnborough North End	28	1	0	27	17	123	3

SWINDON & DISTRICT LEAGUE

Premier Division	P	W	D	L	F	A	Pts
Fratellos	30	28	1	1	183	33	85
Village Inn	30	24	2	4	136	35	74
DJC Marlborough	30	21	3	6	110	48	66
Queensfield United	30	20	3	7	116	36	63
Swiss Chalet Rangers	30	19	3	8	126	49	60
Spectrum	30	18	2	10	97	60	56
Auto Engine Tune	30	17	3	10	102	71	54
Highworth Town	30	14	4	12	74	59	46
Pembroke	30	11	7	12	71	79	40
Chiseldon	30	10	1	19	82	104	31
Lower Stratton	30	9	4	17	71	117	31
Ramsbury	30	9	2	19	48	102	29
Marshall FC	30	7	3	20	62	86	24
Old Town United	30	7	2	21	50	111	23
Fox and Hound	30	2	4	24	39	136	10
Swidon Spitfires	30	2	0	28	15	256	6

LEAGUE TABLES

TAUNTON & DISTRICT LEAGUE

Division One	P	W	D	L	F	A	Pts
Middlezoy Rovers Reserves	18	14	3	1	55	17	45
Predators	18	10	4	4	58	35	34
Highbridge Town	18	9	5	4	40	26	32
Bishops Lydeard Reserves	18	8	4	6	36	29	28
Staplegrove	18	8	3	7	43	35	27
Bridgwater Sports	18	8	3	7	40	34	27
Locomotives	18	7	3	8	39	43	24
Alcombe Rovers	18	5	4	9	36	48	19
North Petherton (-3)	18	5	1	12	32	48	13
Porlock	18	1	0	17	13	77	3

Division Two	P	W	D	L	F	A	Pts
Sampford Blues	20	14	2	4	53	27	44
SRL Allsaints	20	14	1	5	62	35	43
Dulverton Town	20	12	2	6	52	28	38
Wembdon Saints	20	9	3	8	43	44	30
Watchet Town Reserves	20	9	3	8	36	39	30
Staplegrove Reserves	20	7	2	11	54	47	23
Westonzoyland (-3)	20	8	2	10	34	39	23
Nether Stowey	20	7	2	11	41	54	23
Wyvern Rangers	20	6	4	10	27	47	22
Bridgwater Sports Reserves	20	4	4	12	33	61	16

Division Three	P	W	D	L	F	A	Pts
Appletree	22	18	2	2	76	27	56
Hamilton Hawks	22	17	4	1	91	23	55
Bishops Lydeard Colts	22	12	6	4	70	36	42
Bishops Hull	22	12	2	8	78	45	38
Wembdon	22	11	3	8	58	41	36
Redgate	22	8	5	9	43	51	29
Minehead Reserves	22	9	2	11	40	66	29
Sydenham Rangers	22	7	1	14	43	63	22
Stogursey	22	7	1	14	41	65	22
Highbridge Town Reserves	22	5	4	13	32	60	19
Williton	22	4	3	15	36	78	15
Norton Fitzwarren	22	4	3	15	25	78	15

Division Four	P	W	D	L	F	A	Pts
Blagdon Hill	18	15	2	1	108	15	47
The Merry Monk	18	14	1	3	97	34	43
Milverton Rangers	18	13	1	4	66	36	40
The Gallery	18	9	4	5	54	39	31
Bridgwater Sports Colts	18	8	4	6	42	50	28
Alcombe Rovers Reserves	18	7	1	10	36	56	22
Rhode Lane Wanderers	18	6	0	12	36	61	18
Porlock Reserves	18	3	5	10	37	49	14
Dulverton Town Reserves	18	2	4	12	28	101	10
Staplegrove Colts (-3)	18	1	2	15	28	91	2

Division Five	P	W	D	L	F	A	Pts
North Petherton Reserves	22	19	2	1	89	25	59
Morganians	22	15	1	6	72	36	46
Galmington Dragons	22	14	2	6	58	40	44
Exmoor Rangers	22	13	2	7	84	42	41
Sampford Blues Reserves	22	7	6	9	64	47	27
Wembdon Saints Reserves	22	7	4	11	54	63	25
Creech Coogars	22	7	4	11	43	66	25
Nether Stowey Reserves	22	7	3	12	28	54	24
Tone Youth (-3)	22	9	0	13	47	78	24
East Bower	22	6	3	13	56	74	21
Bridgwater Grasshoppers	22	3	1	18	27	99	10

THANET & DISTRICT LEAGUE

	P	W	D	L	F	A	Pts
Soc. Team U Dolphin	24	21	2	1	102	20	65
St Lukes	24	15	7	2	112	46	52
AFC Margate	24	14	5	5	62	37	47
The Rodney Reapers	24	14	3	7	54	37	45
Orb City	24	10	4	10	51	49	34
SI United	24	10	4	10	40	39	34
SLT United	24	10	3	11	67	75	33
Broadstairs Reserves	24	9	1	14	55	73	28
South Eastern Tavern	24	9	3	12	55	57	27
Westcliff United	24	7	6	11	48	50	27
Minster	24	7	3	14	44	73	24
Flying Horse	24	7	3	14	56	59	21
Weston Athletic	24	1	0	23	7	138	3

TEESSIDE LEAGUE

Premier Division	P	W	D	L	F	A	Pts
Carlin How WMC	28	20	3	5	66	28	63
Hartlepool	28	19	3	6	76	52	57
BEADS	28	17	4	7	84	57	55
Nunthorpe Athletic	28	15	4	9	67	51	49
Thornaby Youth Club	28	14	5	9	59	38	47
Fishburn Park	28	13	7	8	58	39	46
Billingham Wanderers	28	13	5	10	56	53	44
Grangetown Boys Club	28	13	4	11	59	44	43
Dormans	28	11	6	11	56	61	39
Richmond Mavericks	28	10	6	12	52	61	36
Richmond Town	28	9	5	14	62	69	32
Thornaby Athletic	28	9	4	15	50	66	28
Thornaby Res.	28	6	7	15	53	75	25
Bedale Athletic	28	6	4	18	42	79	19
Stokesley SC	28	1	1	26	21	88	4

Division One	P	W	D	L	F	A	Pts
Richmond Town	26	20	3	3	82	28	63
Whinney Banks YCC	26	18	3	5	114	49	57
Thornaby Dubliners	26	16	5	5	83	44	53
Cargo Fleet	26	16	3	7	76	46	51
BEADS	26	14	7	5	66	40	49
Grangetown Boys Club	26	14	5	7	66	40	47
Dormans Athletic	26	13	2	11	71	57	38
North Ormesby Sports	26	11	5	10	71	59	38
Richmond Mavericks	26	9	4	13	65	67	31
Great Ayton United	26	8	5	13	65	74	29
Hemlington	26	7	3	16	57	86	24
Fishburn Park	26	5	3	18	30	57	18
Nunthorpe Athletic	26	3	2	21	32	117	11
Darlington Grammar School RA	26	1	4	21	20	134	7

Division Two	P	W	D	L	F	A	Pts
Darlington Rugby Club	24	20	0	4	94	38	60
Guisborough Town Res.	24	16	3	5	81	22	51
Redcar Athletic Res.	24	16	3	5	58	29	51
Northallerton Town Res.	24	14	5	5	65	43	47
Grangetown YCC	24	13	1	10	68	52	37
Stockton West End	24	11	4	9	72	62	37
St Mary's College	24	10	5	9	60	57	35
New Marske	24	8	6	10	54	65	27
Yarm	24	7	5	12	42	66	26
Redcar Newmarket	24	8	1	15	53	67	25
Billingham Synthonia Res.	24	6	3	15	65	77	21
Billingham Town Inter.	24	6	3	15	43	84	21
Mill Hill	24	1	1	22	30	123	1

TONBRIDGE & DISTRICT

Premier Division	P	W	D	L	F	A	Pts
Southborough	20	17	1	2	81	15	52
Blackham & Ashurst	20	17	1	2	68	11	52
Penshurst Park	20	9	6	5	57	46	33
Pembury	20	8	6	6	38	34	30
Tonbridge Invicta Reserves	20	8	5	7	38	41	29
Woodlands	20	8	4	8	47	49	28
East Peckham Juniors (-3)	20	8	2	10	40	45	23
High Brooms Casuals	20	5	6	9	35	37	21
Swan (Edenbridge)	20	5	2	13	29	63	17
Hadlow Harrow	20	4	2	14	28	81	14
AFC Valour	20	1	5	14	24	63	8

Division One	P	W	D	L	F	A	Pts
High Brooms Casuals Res.	20	15	2	3	74	34	47
Rusthall Reserves	20	14	3	3	67	30	45
Castle Rangers	20	12	0	8	54	53	36
Southborough Reserves (-3)	20	10	3	7	39	31	30
Paddock Wood	20	9	3	8	41	35	30
Dowgate (-3)	20	8	4	8	30	36	25
Capel Sports & Social	20	6	3	11	34	60	21
Pembury Reserves	20	5	4	11	46	53	19
Hawkenbury Reserves	20	5	4	11	36	53	19
AFC Valour Reserves (-3)	20	6	2	12	44	51	17
Roselands	20	5	2	13	42	71	17

Division Two	P	W	D	L	F	A	Pts
Swan (Edenbridge) Reserves	22	17	3	2	69	34	54
Frant	22	16	2	4	79	35	50
Leigh	22	15	0	7	71	33	45
Rusthall III (-3)	22	14	4	4	98	52	43
Woodlands Reserves (-3)	22	13	1	8	79	36	37
Ashton Prime	22	11	2	9	63	42	35
F.C. Revolution	22	9	4	9	85	66	31
Brenchley Wanderers (-3)	22	9	1	12	50	69	25
East Peckham Juniors Res (-3)	22	7	5	10	38	39	23
Hawkenbury III	22	5	1	16	45	81	16
Paddock Wood Reserves (-3)	22	2	1	19	22	127	4
Roselands Reserves (-3)	22	1	2	19	25	110	2

TYNESIDE AMATEUR LEAGUE

Division One	P	W	D	L	F	A	Pts
West Jesmond	20	15	1	4	68	28	46
Walker Central Reserves	20	14	3	3	82	41	45
New York (-3)	20	12	4	4	73	46	37
(FOWS) Diggers Utd (-3)	20	10	6	4	56	39	33
Blyth Isabella	20	9	4	7	73	50	31
High Howdon Social Club	20	7	5	8	53	66	26
Blyth Town Reserves (-3)	20	7	4	9	51	50	22
Gosforth Bohemians Res (-3)	20	6	1	13	41	66	16
Cullercoats Reserves (-6)	20	5	5	10	47	61	14
Grainger Park Boys Club	20	4	2	14	35	91	14
Newcastle Medicals	20	2	3	15	34	75	9

Division Two	P	W	D	L	F	A	Pts
Winlaton The Queens Head	18	15	1	2	77	39	46
Cramlington Town "A" (-3)	18	14	0	4	69	28	39
Longbenton	18	11	1	6	49	32	34
Heaton Rifles	18	9	2	7	54	53	29
Lindisfarne Athletic	18	8	3	7	49	45	27
Wardley	18	5	4	9	38	52	19
Newc Chemfica Indpt Res (-3)	18	6	3	9	31	44	18
Gosforth Bohemians "A"	18	5	2	11	34	55	17
Ponteland United Reserves	18	4	4	10	38	48	16
North Shields Town	18	2	2	14	28	71	8

WAKEFIELD & DISTRICT LEAGUE

Premier Division	P	W	D	L	F	A	Pts
Crofton Sports FC	16	13	2	1	69	19	41
Gate FC	16	13	1	2	90	29	40
Woodman FC	16	8	0	8	53	57	24
Walton FC	16	7	1	8	57	53	22
Garforth WMC FC (-3)	16	7	2	7	40	41	20
Rose & Crown (Darton) FC (-3)	16	7	2	7	43	45	20
Thornhill FC	16	6	2	8	45	55	20
Dewsbury Rangers OB	16	3	1	12	27	93	10
Battyeford FC Wasps	16	2	1	13	27	59	7

Division One	P	W	D	L	F	A	Pts
Fieldhead Hospital	22	17	2	3	80	30	53
Thornes FC	22	15	4	3	62	24	49
Wortley FC	22	14	4	4	59	33	46
Eastmoor FC	22	14	2	6	72	34	44
Innter Crown FC	22	12	2	8	54	46	38
Ardsley Athletic	22	10	1	11	50	42	31
Weavers Arms FC	22	7	3	12	40	59	24
Woodhouse Hill WMC (-6)	22	9	2	11	47	49	23
Morley Town AFC	22	6	4	12	38	61	22
Prince of Wales (OCR) FC	22	5	5	12	43	59	20
Ossett Two Brewers FC (-6)	22	6	2	14	36	66	14
Snydale Athletic	22	0	3	19	13	91	3

LEAGUE TABLES

Division Two	P	W	D	L	F	A	Pts
Plough FC (-3)	20	17	1	2	63	24	49
Wortley FC Res	20	11	4	5	55	31	37
Inns of Court FC	20	12	0	8	51	36	36
Old Bank WMC (-3)	20	11	5	4	50	27	35
College FC (-3)	20	10	6	4	58	43	33
White Hart FC	20	8	4	8	55	40	28
Wagon FC (-3)	20	8	4	8	37	41	25
Horbury Town (-3)	20	8	3	9	39	39	24
Nostell Miners Welfare	20	5	4	11	28	39	19
Railway FC	20	2	1	17	30	82	7
Wrenthorpe FC	20	1	2	17	34	98	5

Division Three	P	W	D	L	F	A	Pts
Crown Alverthorpe FC	22	15	1	6	69	36	46
Featherstone Colliery FC	22	14	2	6	66	42	44
Durkar FC	22	13	4	5	51	25	43
Waterloo FC	22	11	5	6	72	29	38
Prostar FC (-6)	22	14	2	6	84	51	38
Horbury Athletic	22	11	2	9	58	57	35
Garforth WMC FC Res	22	10	2	10	52	53	32
Crofton Sports FC Res	22	8	3	11	44	57	27
Brookhouse WMC (-3)	22	8	4	10	47	47	25
Dewsbury Rangers OB Res	22	7	1	14	38	75	22
Inns of Court FC Res	22	3	3	16	39	92	12
Snydale Athletic Res	22	1	5	16	38	94	8

WARRINGTON & DISTRICT LEAGUE

Premier Division	P	W	D	L	F	A	Pts
Runcorn Albion	24	18	3	3	82	24	57
Rainhill Town	24	18	2	4	74	34	56
St.Michaels DH	24	16	1	7	72	40	49
Knauff	24	13	3	8	63	61	42
Haydock	24	11	2	11	56	58	35
Blackbrook	24	11	1	12	61	58	34
Orford	24	10	4	10	57	69	34
Sidac Social	24	10	3	11	70	66	33
Windle Labour Club	24	8	4	12	52	64	28
Halton Borough	24	8	4	12	42	55	28
Cronton Villa	24	8	0	16	35	62	24
Beeches	24	4	5	15	50	68	17
Grange SC	24	4	2	18	31	86	14

Division One	P	W	D	L	F	A	Pts
Fife Rangers	20	15	3	2	55	35	48
Halebank	20	15	1	4	60	36	46
Rainhill Town Reserves	20	13	2	5	62	30	41
Ford Motors Reserves	19	10	3	6	46	34	33
Burtonwood Albion	20	9	2	9	52	45	29
Lomax	20	8	2	10	45	50	26
Croft	20	7	3	10	51	50	24
Avon Athletic	20	6	3	11	54	68	21
Moorfield	20	6	2	12	35	48	20
Penlake	19	5	4	10	39	58	19
Runcorn Albion Reserves	20	2	1	17	26	71	7

WEARSIDE

	P	W	D	L	F	A	Pts
Ryhope Colliery Welfare	36	30	5	1	136	30	95
Redcar Athletic	36	29	3	4	104	32	90
Stockton Town	36	22	6	8	74	46	72
Sunderland West End	36	23	2	11	81	56	71
Willington	36	20	5	11	72	63	65
Jarrow	36	17	9	10	83	62	60
Cleator Moor Celtic	36	17	6	13	76	55	57
Darlington Cleveland Bridge	36	15	8	13	65	69	53
Boldon Community Ass.	36	16	4	16	78	74	52
Peterlee Town	36	15	6	15	71	90	51
Ashbrooke Belford House	36	13	10	13	61	63	49
Hartlepool	36	15	2	19	69	80	47
Prudhoe Town	36	13	7	16	78	89	46
Wolviston	36	10	10	16	57	61	40
Annfield Plain	36	9	7	20	56	80	34
Gateshead Leam Rangers	36	8	3	25	46	91	27
Kirkbymoorside	36	7	4	25	50	100	25
Silksworth Rangers	36	6	4	26	38	98	22
Coxhoe Athletic	36	4	5	27	34	90	17

WEARSIDE COMBINATION

Premier Division	P	W	D	L	F	A	Pts
Sunderland Farringdon Dolphin	22	20	0	2	91	31	60
Sunderland Hylton Colliery	22	15	4	3	62	25	49
Sunderland Hendon	22	14	2	6	92	43	44
Hetton New Inn	22	13	2	7	48	38	41
Sunderland Oddfellows Arms	22	12	2	8	41	36	38
Sunderland Hendon Grange	22	10	3	9	74	36	33
Sunderland Hall Farm	22	10	2	10	53	63	32
Sunderland Three Horse Shoes	22	9	3	10	63	58	30
Sunderland Aquatic Sports	22	8	3	11	40	68	27
Silksworth Golden Fleece	22	5	1	16	39	97	16
Sunderland FC Chesters	22	2	4	16	48	82	10
Sunderland West End Potters	22	0	2	20	27	101	2

Division One	P	W	D	L	F	A	Pts
Wearside Wildcats	26	21	3	2	109	39	66
Seaham Marlborough	26	19	3	4	111	39	60
University of Sunderland	26	19	1	6	110	68	58
Sunderland Thorney Close Inn	26	16	4	6	106	58	52
Shiney Row Wheatsheaf	26	15	2	9	98	67	47
Sunderland Hollycarrside	26	13	3	10	108	68	42
Wearside Athletic FC	26	13	1	12	95	78	40
FC Whitburn	26	13	0	13	68	84	39
Sunderland Blue Stone Construction	26	10	5	11	74	64	35
Sunderland Blue House	26	7	4	15	73	95	25
Sunderland Times Inn	26	7	0	19	51	118	21
East Durham Spartans	26	6	2	18	50	106	20
University of Sunderland B	26	4	2	20	46	140	14
Sunderland Park View	26	3	2	21	47	122	11

WENSLEYDALE LEAGUE

	P	W	D	L	F	A	Pts
Richmond Academy	24	20	3	1	117	28	63
Spennithorne & Harmby	24	17	4	3	79	36	55
Unicorn	24	16	2	6	74	35	50
Hawes United	24	15	5	4	67	35	50
Colburn Town	24	13	3	8	87	48	42
Richmond Mavericks	24	13	2	9	89	44	41
Buck Inn Old Boys	24	11	3	10	88	54	36
Carperby Rovers	24	10	2	12	73	68	32
Reeth & District Ath Club	24	8	3	13	57	56	27
Redmire United	24	7	2	15	59	79	23
Catterick Garrison F'ball Centre	24	6	2	16	36	70	20
Askrigg United	24	3	3	18	39	87	12
Hawes United Reserves	24	0	0	24	15	240	0

WEST END LEAGUE

Premier Division

	P	W	D	L	F	A	Pts
Yalova (Reserves)	16	12	2	2	50	13	38
North Acton 'A'	16	10	2	4	43	36	32
Arian	16	9	4	3	46	28	31
Clissold Park Rangers	16	9	1	6	28	20	28
Bishops Park	16	8	1	7	32	40	25
Primrose Hill	16	4	7	5	36	35	19
Racing Chiswick	16	5	3	8	26	31	18
Earlsberg Eagles	16	2	1	13	17	54	7
Mavericks	16	1	3	12	17	38	6

Division One

	P	W	D	L	F	A	Pts
IB Albion	16	11	3	2	54	24	36
Cambridge Heath	16	11	2	3	60	27	35
Sevenths	16	9	3	4	36	29	30
Olympic Waterloo	16	6	2	8	36	25	20
Atholl 1965	16	6	2	8	38	48	20
BUOB	16	6	1	9	23	28	19
Real	16	5	2	9	26	43	17
Hub Athletic	16	5	1	10	27	46	16
Iranian Association FC	16	4	2	10	22	52	14

Division Two

	P	W	D	L	F	A	Pts
Primrose Hill 'A'	14	11	0	3	47	19	33
Racing Chiswick Legends	14	10	1	3	36	27	31
Viva Capri	14	9	2	3	40	18	29
Milton Rovers	14	8	3	3	41	21	27
City High	14	4	3	7	53	35	15
Clissold Park Rangers 'A'	14	3	2	9	15	56	11
Park Stars	14	2	4	8	18	40	10
Pitshanger Park Rangers	14	1	1	12	11	45	4

WEST RIDING COUNTY AMATEUR LEAGUE

Premier Division

	P	W	D	L	F	A	Pts
Ovenden West Riding	26	20	3	3	84	36	63
Kirkburton	26	15	6	5	65	38	54
Tyersal	26	15	5	6	62	40	52
Bay Athletic	26	16	4	6	66	49	52
Storthes Hall	26	13	4	9	63	50	43
Golcar United	26	13	6	7	59	45	42
Steeton	26	12	3	11	62	52	39
Hall Green United	26	12	0	14	52	52	36
Campion	26	10	5	11	54	60	35
Marsden	26	9	5	12	44	75	32
Littletown	26	7	2	17	55	65	23
Brighouse Town Res.	26	5	3	18	63	80	21
Lower Hopton	26	6	2	18	40	71	20
Wibsey	26	5	0	21	42	98	15

Division One

	P	W	D	L	F	A	Pts
Lepton Highlanders	26	23	3	0	110	32	72
Salts	26	18	3	5	64	39	57
Overthorpe Sports	26	16	5	5	79	54	53
Hunsworth	26	16	4	6	55	33	52
Bay Athletic Res.	26	13	3	10	69	52	42
Ventus & Yeadon Celtic	26	13	2	11	62	57	41
AFC Emley Res.	26	11	4	11	38	41	37
Tingley Athletic	26	9	7	10	53	57	34
Wakefield City	26	9	4	13	55	66	31
Westbrook YMCA	26	9	4	13	42	54	31
Bronte Wanderers	26	6	5	15	58	66	23
Storthes Hall Res.	26	6	0	20	34	85	18
Dudley Hill Rangers	26	4	4	18	36	70	16
Halifax Irish Club	26	4	2	20	46	95	14

Division Two

	P	W	D	L	F	A	Pts
Campion Res.	18	13	1	4	43	19	40
Albion Sports Res.	18	12	1	5	47	26	37
Tyersal Res.	18	8	4	6	97	-8	28
Huddersfield YMCA	18	8	4	6	35	28	28
Rawdon Old Boys	18	9	1	8	26	25	28
Ovenden West Riding Res.	18	7	2	9	45	46	23
Kirkburton Res.	18	7	2	9	32	39	23
Steeton Res.	18	6	3	9	48	47	21
West Horton	18	5	3	10	28	43	18
Golcar United Res.	18	2	5	11	23	49	11

LEAGUE TABLES
WEST SUSSEX LEAGUE

Premier Division

	P	W	D	L	F	A	Pts
Billingshurst	20	15	2	3	50	22	47
Sidlesham	20	13	4	3	59	22	43
Hunston CC	20	10	6	4	42	30	36
Upper Beeding	20	9	5	6	38	28	32
Newtown Villa	20	10	1	9	30	38	31
West Chiltington	20	8	4	8	45	36	28
Cowfold	20	8	4	8	36	29	28
Uni of Chichester	20	5	5	10	44	42	20
Watersfield	20	6	3	11	34	53	20
Lancing Utd	20	6	1	13	21	43	19
Clymping Res	20	2	1	17	17	73	7

Division One

	P	W	D	L	F	A	Pts
Lavant	22	18	4	0	63	17	58
Holbrook FC	22	12	5	5	44	16	41
Barnham Res	22	12	3	7	50	34	39
Faygate Utd	22	10	7	5	58	35	37
Cowfold Res	22	10	3	9	44	37	33
Barns Green	22	9	2	11	35	35	29
Yapton	22	8	4	10	46	39	28
Southwater	22	8	3	11	33	47	27
East Dean	22	7	4	11	36	48	25
Petworth	22	8	3	11	38	46	24
Hunston C.C Res	22	4	4	14	30	71	16
Newtown Villa Res	22	5	0	17	24	76	15

Division Two North

	P	W	D	L	F	A	Pts
Henfield	22	19	0	3	81	24	57
Pulborough	22	12	3	7	58	40	39
Holbrook FC Res	22	11	3	8	58	39	36
Rudgwick	22	9	7	6	48	44	34
Alfold	22	9	6	7	49	48	33
Partridge Green	22	9	2	11	43	59	29
Capel	22	8	4	10	48	49	28
Newdigate	22	8	4	10	47	59	28
Billingshurst Res	22	8	3	11	44	46	27
Upper Beeding Res	22	6	6	10	35	57	24
Ashington Rovers	22	6	3	13	35	59	21
Wisborough Green	22	5	3	14	34	56	18

Division Two South

	P	W	D	L	F	A	Pts
Wittering Utd	18	16	0	2	54	25	48
Selsey FC 'A'	18	11	3	4	51	40	36
Predators	18	10	3	5	48	29	33
Fernhurst	18	9	4	5	55	37	31
Lodsworth	18	9	4	5	48	39	31
Fittleworth	18	8	2	8	47	44	26
Barnham 3rd	18	4	4	10	30	42	16
Boxgrove	18	4	2	12	30	58	14
Lavant Res	18	4	1	13	34	66	13
Stedham Utd	18	2	3	13	34	51	9

Division Three North

	P	W	D	L	F	A	Pts
Ockley	18	16	0	2	68	16	48
Horsham Trinity	18	10	4	4	57	34	34
Faygate Utd Res	18	9	3	6	48	36	30
Rusper	18	9	3	6	45	44	30
Cowfold 3rd	18	9	2	7	39	28	29
T D Shipley Res	18	9	1	8	42	37	28
Henfield Res	18	6	2	10	44	55	20
Southwater Res	18	6	0	12	24	58	18
Pulborough Res	18	3	4	11	22	48	13
Horsham Olympic	18	2	3	13	16	49	6

Division Three South

	P	W	D	L	F	A	Pts
Graffham	18	13	2	3	53	34	41
Tangmere	18	11	2	5	69	45	35
Athletico Arundel	18	11	2	5	39	30	35
Rogate 08	18	10	3	5	59	40	33
Harting	18	8	2	8	37	47	26
The Vardar VIP	18	5	6	7	44	44	21
Whyke Utd	18	6	2	10	30	42	20
Rustington Park Sen	18	5	3	10	22	36	18
Hammer Utd	18	4	3	11	39	47	15
Lancing Utd Res	18	3	3	12	21	48	12

Division Four North

	P	W	D	L	F	A	Pts
Forest Res	18	16	1	1	85	14	49
Horsham Crusaders	18	11	2	5	54	36	35
Slinfold	18	11	2	5	59	44	35
Alfold Res	18	10	1	7	40	39	31
Border Wanderers	18	9	3	6	50	37	30
Henfield 3rd	18	8	3	7	51	51	27
Horsham Trinity Res	18	5	2	11	31	52	17
Rudgwick Res	18	5	1	12	28	66	16
Holbrook F.C III	18	1	6	11	29	52	9
Ockley Res	18	2	3	13	26	62	9

Division Four South

Division Four South	P	W	D	L	F	A	Pts
Wittering Utd Res	18	13	2	3	52	14	41
Yapton Res	18	12	2	4	58	27	38
Ambassadors	18	12	1	5	38	25	37
Sportsman	18	9	4	5	45	28	31
Whyke Utd Res	18	9	3	6	44	36	30
Regis Vets	18	9	2	7	39	33	29
Predators Res	18	9	1	8	59	30	28
Watersfield Res	18	5	1	12	49	61	16
Coal Exchange	18	2	4	12	26	64	10
Chapel	18	0	0	18	6	98	0

Division Five North

Division Five North	P	W	D	L	F	A	Pts
Rowfant Village	18	13	2	3	59	26	41
Capel Res	18	13	2	3	60	30	41
Holbrook FC 4th	18	13	2	3	55	33	41
Newdigate Res	18	8	4	6	39	39	28
Horsham Trinity III	18	7	5	6	38	35	26
Horsham Sparrows	18	5	5	8	30	40	17
Faygate Utd III	18	4	4	10	32	45	16
Barns Green Res	18	5	0	13	28	58	15
Horsham Olympic Res	18	4	2	12	29	49	14
Horsham Bap & Ambass Res	18	3	4	11	34	49	13

Division Five South

Division Five South	P	W	D	L	F	A	Pts
Felpham Colts F.C.	18	15	3	0	76	17	48
Bracklesham	18	13	2	3	71	27	41
Hammer Utd Res	18	9	3	6	53	47	30
Stedham Utd Res	18	9	2	7	38	60	29
Vapours FC	18	8	4	6	45	37	28
Milland	18	5	10	3	28	31	25
Tangmere Res	18	4	4	10	31	41	16
Wheatsheaf BR F.C	18	3	7	8	26	48	16
Petworth Res	18	3	2	13	15	38	11
Lodsworth Res	18	2	1	15	14	51	7

Division Five Central

Division Five Central	P	W	D	L	F	A	Pts
Billingshurst 3rd	20	15	4	1	62	24	49
Horsham Bap & Ambass	20	13	5	2	65	24	44
West Chiltington Res	20	13	2	5	88	35	41
Plaistow	20	11	3	6	63	48	36
Billingshurst Athletic	20	9	0	11	43	43	27
Partridge Green Res	20	7	4	9	47	59	25
Slinfold Res	20	7	3	10	30	52	24
Fittleworth Res	20	6	5	9	34	47	23
Wisborough Green Res	20	5	4	11	42	56	19
Cowfold 4th	20	6	1	13	40	64	19
Southwater 3rd	20	2	1	17	25	87	7

WESTMORLAND

	P	W	D	L	F	A	Pts
Keswick	22	18	2	2	85	19	56
Kirkoswald	22	16	2	4	74	30	50
Wetheriggs United	22	15	2	5	70	29	47
Penrith Rangers	22	14	2	6	47	34	44
Kendal United	22	8	4	10	40	42	28
Appleby	22	8	3	11	38	41	27
Staveley United	22	8	3	11	37	42	27
Kendal Celtic	22	8	2	12	40	55	26
Lunesdale United	22	7	3	12	44	56	24
Sedbergh Wanderers	22	8	0	14	44	60	24
Endmoor KGR	22	6	4	12	30	66	22
Carvetii United	22	1	3	18	26	101	3

WIGAN & DISTRICT LEAGUE

Premier Division

Premier Division	P	W	D	L	F	A	Pts
Winstanley St.Aidans	26	20	2	4	67	32	62
Leigh Rangers	26	17	5	4	73	32	56
Hindley Town	26	14	6	6	61	50	48
Newburgh Harrock United	26	14	3	9	63	35	45
Digmoor	26	11	8	7	51	57	41
Ince Central	26	12	3	11	48	58	39
Standish St.Wilfrid's	26	10	3	13	49	48	33
Shevington	26	9	6	11	42	57	33
AFC Scholes	26	9	3	14	47	53	30
Pemberton	26	9	1	16	55	72	28
Gidlow Athletic	26	7	6	13	46	56	27
Bickerstaffe	26	7	5	14	40	62	26
Ince FC	26	7	4	15	43	59	25
Downall Green United	26	7	3	16	41	55	24

Division One

Division One	P	W	D	L	F	A	Pts
Orrell (-1)	24	19	4	1	82	26	58
Farnworth Town	24	17	1	6	67	26	52
Leigh Phoenix	24	15	4	5	65	40	49
Atherton Royal	24	13	3	8	64	54	42
Standish St.Wilfrid's Res	24	12	5	7	59	51	41
Foundry (-3)	24	13	4	7	58	37	40
Winstanley St.Aidans Res	24	12	1	11	66	58	37
St.Judes	24	11	1	12	42	49	34
AFC Tyldesley	24	6	5	13	43	49	23
Ormskirk (-3)	24	7	1	16	50	95	19
Goose Green United	24	4	5	15	48	82	17
Wigan Rovers	24	4	4	16	32	59	16
Shevington Res	24	3	2	19	32	82	11

LEAGUE TABLES

Division Two

	P	W	D	L	F	A	Pts
Bel Air	24	16	5	3	62	37	53
Aspull	24	14	6	4	70	44	48
Leigh Legion	24	15	3	6	76	51	48
Cherrybrook	24	13	2	9	89	55	41
Boars Head	24	11	4	9	60	42	37
Bickerstaffe Res	24	10	7	7	42	43	37
Leigh Rangers Res	24	11	3	10	57	68	36
UpHolland	24	11	2	11	56	58	35
Farnworth Town Res	24	8	6	10	39	45	30
Hindley Town Res	24	7	4	13	58	67	25
Atherton Hag Fold (-3)	24	8	4	12	55	65	25
Springfield	24	5	4	15	44	65	19
Wigan Rovers Res	24	1	2	21	23	91	5

Division Three

	P	W	D	L	F	A	Pts
Foundry Res	24	18	2	4	75	32	56
A H Leisure	24	18	1	5	74	38	55
Lowton Rams	24	17	2	5	84	33	53
Cart and Horses	24	17	0	7	85	45	51
Wigan Celtic	24	16	2	6	73	43	50
Atherton George	24	11	2	11	66	57	35
Gidlow Athletic Res	24	11	2	11	55	60	35
Ince Central Res	24	8	2	14	64	72	26
Black Bull (-3)	24	8	2	14	62	94	23
Winstanley Warriors (-3)	24	8	1	15	52	87	22
Ashton Villa	24	7	1	16	48	83	22
Billinge Community	24	4	3	17	41	77	15
Sporting Leigh	24	2	2	20	31	89	8

WILTSHIRE LEAGUE

Premier Division

	P	W	D	L	F	A	Pts
FC Sanford	30	24	2	4	103	42	74
AFC Bradford Town	30	20	5	5	102	45	65
FC Chippenham Youth	30	19	5	6	63	36	62
RGV Shrewton	30	15	4	11	61	61	49
Wilts Calne Town	30	14	6	10	64	53	48
Devizes Town Res.	30	12	8	10	48	45	43
Purton Res.	30	12	5	13	61	52	41
SKS Blyskawica	30	12	5	13	57	65	41
Ludgershall Sports	30	12	3	15	51	62	38
Moredon Cheney	30	9	7	14	73	83	34
Vale of Pewsey	30	10	4	16	47	74	34
Marlborough Town	30	8	8	14	30	54	32
Wroughton	30	8	11	11	56	56	28
Corsham Town Res.	30	8	4	18	45	68	27
AFC Amesbury Town	30	7	9	14	48	77	26
Southbrook	30	5	4	21	34	70	19

Division One

	P	W	D	L	F	A	Pts
Box Rovers	26	26	0	0	126	22	78
Old Town Wanderers	26	20	3	3	112	42	63
Madames	26	17	5	4	104	46	56
Malmesbury Victoria Res.	26	15	3	8	74	54	48
Ashton Keynes	26	13	6	7	71	54	45
Marshfield	26	15	0	11	66	52	45
Intel	26	11	8	7	65	55	41
AFC Wroughton	26	13	2	11	65	62	41
FC Sanford Res.	26	8	3	15	42	70	27
FC Chippenham Youth Res.	26	7	5	14	54	81	24
Lower Stratton	26	7	2	17	46	91	22
Ramsbury	26	4	4	18	37	73	14
Wilton Town	26	3	1	22	28	95	10
Marlborough Town Res.	26	0	4	22	26	119	1

WIMBLEDON & DISTRICT LEAGUE

Premier Division

	P	W	D	L	F	A	Pts
P.W.C.A. (Wimbledon)	20	14	2	4	54	26	44
Peckham United	20	14	2	4	38	15	44
UCC Diaspora 1st XI	20	13	2	5	35	23	41
AFC Battersea	20	11	3	6	49	27	36
Brentnal	18	10	1	7	36	26	31
Partizan Wandsworth	20	7	4	9	37	45	25
Claremont	20	6	3	11	21	49	21
AFC Cubo 2nd XI	17	5	4	8	27	33	19
Union	20	5	3	12	32	45	18
Goldfingers	19	4	2	13	26	40	14
Croydon Red Star	20	4	2	14	19	45	14

WITNEY & DISTRICT LEAGUE

Premier Division

	P	W	D	L	F	A	Pts
Hailey,	20	15	1	4	58	23	46
Hanborough,	20	13	1	6	41	22	40
Northleigh A,	20	11	5	4	48	34	38
Ducklington,	20	10	4	6	48	29	34
Witney Royals,	20	10	4	6	47	29	34
Spartan Rangers,	20	7	7	6	36	38	28
Charlbury Town,	20	7	4	9	38	40	25
Carterton FC A,	20	7	3	10	42	37	24
Combe,	20	5	3	12	20	45	18
FC Chequers,	20	3	5	12	20	47	14
Kingham All Blacks,	20	1	5	14	15	69	8

Division One

	P	W	D	L	F	A	Pts
West Witney,	22	20	1	1	104	26	61
Chipping Norton Town	22	14	5	3	73	33	47
Brize Norton,	22	13	3	6	55	29	42
Minster Lovell,	22	11	6	5	46	41	39
Aston FC,	22	8	6	8	40	46	30
Stanton Harcourt,	22	7	5	10	40	51	26
AC Finstock,	22	6	6	10	46	61	24
FC Nomads,	22	6	5	11	30	48	23
Hanborough Reserves,	22	5	7	10	31	48	22
FC Mills,	22	4	9	9	32	49	21
Ducklington Reserves,	22	4	5	13	20	50	17
Witney Royals Reserves,	22	2	6	14	38	73	12

Division Two

	P	W	D	L	F	A	Pts
Freeland FC A	20	15	0	5	70	30	45
Ducklington A	20	14	2	4	67	40	44
Hailey Reserves	20	12	2	6	48	33	38
FC Chequers Reserves	20	10	5	5	67	31	35
Milton	20	10	0	10	35	43	30
Middle Barton	20	8	4	8	51	41	28
Bampton Town	20	7	5	8	46	44	26
Witney Wanderers	20	7	3	10	41	43	24
Charlbury Town Reserves	20	6	2	12	39	77	20
Brize Norton Reserves	20	5	3	12	39	72	18
Wootton Sports	20	2	2	16	16	65	8

Division Three

	P	W	D	L	F	A	Pts
Carterton Pumas	24	20	2	2	82	19	62
Eynsham Sports and SC	24	17	3	4	90	33	54
North Leigh B	24	16	2	6	64	29	50
West Witney Reserves	24	14	5	5	64	39	47
AFC Marlborough	24	12	5	7	67	40	41
Spartan Rangers Reserves	24	10	6	8	58	55	36
FC Hollybush	24	11	2	11	44	51	35
Chipping Norton Town Reserves	24	10	3	11	57	57	33
Minster Lovell Reserves	24	4	9	11	39	64	21
Aston FC Reserves	24	6	2	16	24	78	20
Tackley	24	5	4	15	26	53	19
Kingham All Blacks Reserves	24	2	7	15	34	81	13
Witney Royals A	24	2	4	18	23	73	10

Division Four

	P	W	D	L	F	A	Pts
Carterton Rangers	20	16	4	0	101	26	52
Carterton FC B	20	15	4	1	72	18	49
Freeland FC B	20	14	2	4	80	35	44
Corinthians	20	12	3	5	70	40	39
FC Mills Reserves (-3)	20	11	1	8	62	58	31
Ducklington B	20	9	1	10	52	64	28
Graystones	20	8	3	9	51	58	27
Wychwood Foresters FC	20	6	2	12	37	54	20
Spartan Rangers A	20	3	3	14	32	64	12
Combe Reserves	20	2	2	16	24	52	8
Eynsham Sports & SC Res	20	1	1	18	20	132	4

WORCESTER & DISTRICT LEAGUE

Division One

	P	W	D	L	F	A	Pts
Powick FC	21	17	1	3	80	25	52
VBL Sports	21	16	3	2	67	23	51
Newtown Sports	21	13	1	7	59	46	40
Hallow	21	10	2	9	46	46	32
University of Worcester (-6)	21	9	2	10	51	44	23
Worcester Raiders	21	7	1	13	60	67	22
Nunnery Wood	21	3	2	16	32	94	11
Malvern Town Res	21	2	2	17	28	78	8

Division Two

	P	W	D	L	F	A	Pts
The Railway Train	21	17	2	2	87	29	53
Worcester Rangers	21	13	5	3	82	27	44
Northway	21	9	5	7	70	44	32
Perrywood AFC	21	9	3	9	46	42	30
Worcester Anchors	21	8	5	8	68	63	29
West Malvern TC FC	21	8	2	11	39	53	26
Powick Res	21	6	2	13	56	73	20
Tenbury Colts	21	1	2	18	18	135	5

WORTHING & DISTRICT LEAGUE

Premier Division

	P	W	D	L	F	A	Pts
Sompting	20	18	1	1	78	18	55
Worthing BCOB	20	16	1	3	60	29	49
Worthing Leisure	20	15	2	3	65	27	47
L&S Athletic	20	13	3	4	107	41	42
GSK Sports	20	10	1	9	52	43	31
FC Sporting	20	9	3	8	39	52	30
Goring St Theresa's	20	6	2	12	31	62	20
Shoreham RBL	20	5	2	13	44	76	17
Northbrook	20	4	0	16	31	72	12
Highdown Rovers 1st	20	4	0	16	35	80	12
Durrington RAFA	20	2	1	17	19	61	7

Division One

	P	W	D	L	F	A	Pts
L&S Athletic Reserves (+3)	20	15	1	4	85	33	49
Worthing Dynamos	20	15	1	4	76	27	46
GSK Sports Reserves	20	15	1	4	69	35	46
Real Rustington	20	12	4	4	53	32	40
Goring Cricket Club (-4)	20	10	3	7	48	33	29
Worthing Albion	20	7	3	10	30	43	24
Del United	20	6	3	11	38	67	21
Worthing BCOB Res (+2)	20	4	5	11	30	52	19
Adur Athletic	20	5	2	13	43	75	17
Sompting Reserves	20	3	4	13	33	70	13
Ferring "B"	20	3	3	14	30	68	12

LEAGUE TABLES

Division Two

	P	W	D	L	F	A	Pts
AFC Boundstone (+3)	20	17	0	3	83	34	54
West Worthing Wanderers	20	17	2	1	85	23	53
GSK Sports "B"	20	10	4	6	45	49	34
Worthing Town (+2)	20	9	4	7	48	31	33
Goring Cricket Club Reserves	20	7	5	8	56	51	26
Highdown Rovers Reserves	20	6	6	8	47	60	24
Queens Park Henrys	20	5	8	7	33	44	23
Northbrook Reserves	20	6	2	12	29	51	20
St Marys	20	5	2	13	25	53	17
Goring St Theresa's Res	20	4	4	12	25	57	16
West Tarring WMC (-4)	20	3	5	12	36	59	10

WYCOMBE & DISTRICT LEAGUE

Senior Division

	P	W	D	L	F	A	Pts
Hambleden	18	12	3	3	45	23	39
Prestwood	18	11	3	4	40	28	36
Walters Leisure	18	11	2	5	61	33	35
Wycombe Community United	18	10	0	8	59	33	30
Hazlemere Sports	18	9	3	6	35	37	30
AFC Spartans	18	9	2	7	58	61	29
Stokenchurch	18	8	1	9	75	67	25
Great Missenden	18	7	1	10	32	42	22
HFC Athletic	18	3	0	15	22	69	9
Penn & Tylers Green 'A'	18	2	1	15	34	68	7

Premier Division

	P	W	D	L	F	A	Pts
Lane End	18	18	0	0	81	17	54
Wycombe Athletic	18	14	0	4	45	22	42
Wizards	18	9	1	8	31	37	28
Chinnor 'A'	18	8	3	7	39	39	27
Winchmore Hill	18	8	1	9	28	26	25
Hazlemere Sports Reserves	18	7	2	9	33	35	23
FC Titans	18	7	0	11	36	38	21
AFC Amersham	18	4	4	10	18	39	16
Kings Church(Amersham)	18	4	3	11	22	38	15
Walters Leisure Reserves	18	3	2	13	19	61	11

Division One

	P	W	D	L	F	A	Pts
Hazlemere Sports 'A'	20	17	1	2	82	31	52
Winchmore Hill Reserves	20	15	3	2	76	26	48
Hambleden Reserves	20	9	2	9	57	56	29
Lane End Reserves	20	9	2	9	41	45	29
Holmer Green 'A'	20	8	3	9	40	53	27
West Wycombe	20	8	2	10	52	49	26
APMG Oakridge	20	6	6	8	33	38	24
Chinnor 'B'	20	6	5	9	39	51	23
Prestwood Reserves	20	6	3	11	55	74	21
FC Leisure	20	5	5	10	34	55	20
Stokenchurch Reserves	20	3	4	13	31	62	13

YEOVIL & DISTRICT LEAGUE

Premier Division

	P	W	D	L	F	A	Pts
Henstridge	18	14	0	4	62	25	42
Mermaid United	18	12	0	6	55	41	36
Ilchester	18	10	1	7	42	34	31
Barwick & Stoford	18	8	3	7	40	47	27
Templecombe Rovers	18	7	3	8	39	49	24
Victoria Sports	18	7	2	9	28	39	23
Normalair	18	7	1	10	45	39	22
Baltonsborough	18	6	2	10	46	59	20
Keinton Mandeville (-3)	18	6	2	10	39	45	17
Milborne Port	18	5	2	11	35	53	17

Division One

	P	W	D	L	F	A	Pts
Aller Park Rangers	22	17	2	3	68	33	53
Somerton Town	22	15	5	2	52	18	50
Tor FC (-1)	22	11	3	8	43	37	35
Odcombe	22	10	5	7	58	53	35
Butleigh Dynamos	22	10	2	10	44	48	32
Stoke	22	9	4	9	49	35	31
Normalair Reserves	22	7	7	8	47	50	28
Castle Cary (-1)	22	8	4	10	54	45	27
Abbey Moor	22	7	4	11	51	65	25
Martock United	22	6	2	14	38	55	20
AFC Wessex	22	4	4	14	38	70	16
Clifton Sports (-3)	22	5	4	13	29	62	16

Division Two

	P	W	D	L	F	A	
Brhoden	24	20	4	0	104	21	64
Pen Mill	24	17	3	4	70	40	54
AFC Huish	24	16	1	7	95	52	49
Ilchester Reserves (-3)	24	17	1	6	88	46	49
Bradford Abbas	24	14	4	6	79	50	46
Somerton Town Reserves	24	13	1	10	59	55	40
Wincanton Town	24	11	1	12	69	73	34
Barwick & Stoford Reserves	24	8	3	13	61	62	27
Milborne Port Reserves	24	7	3	14	51	73	24
FC Barton Leverkusen	24	6	4	14	42	76	22
Waggy Athletic (-1)	24	5	3	16	48	60	17
Bruton United	24	4	3	17	43	76	15
Aller Park Rangers Res (-3)	24	1	3	20	16	141	3

Division Three

	P	W	D	L	F	A	
Montacute	24	19	3	2	103	31	60
Mudford	24	19	3	2	62	19	60
Ilchester Colts (-1)	24	16	1	7	71	36	48
Zeal Development	24	12	6	6	65	54	42
Pen Mill Reserves	24	10	1	13	62	59	31
Baltonsborough Res (-1)	24	10	2	12	62	69	31
Templecombe Rovers Res (-5)	24	10	5	9	39	40	30
Stoke Reserves	24	8	6	10	52	65	30
Victoria Sports Reserves	24	6	7	11	49	56	25
Milborne Port A (-1)	24	7	5	12	36	49	25
Martock United Reserves (-3)	24	6	6	12	42	77	21
Odcombe Reserves	24	4	2	18	33	82	14
East Coker (-4)	24	4	3	17	40	79	11

YORK LEAGUE

Premier Division	P	W	D	L	F	A	Pts
Old Malton St Marys	28	21	7	0	97	28	70
Huntington Rovers	28	20	3	5	103	42	63
Dunnington	28	19	5	4	90	31	62
Copmanthorpe	28	17	2	9	77	49	53
Wigginton Grasshoppers	28	14	4	10	72	51	46
Dringhouses	28	14	3	11	75	50	45
York Railway Institute	28	15	0	13	90	69	45
Rowntrees FC (-3)	28	10	6	12	54	73	33
Hamilton Panthers	28	9	3	16	70	82	30
Poppleton United	28	8	5	15	75	89	29
Keystones FC (-3)	28	10	2	16	57	85	29
Easingwold Town	28	8	4	16	51	77	28
Riccall United	28	8	3	17	42	88	27
Wilberfoss	28	7	5	16	33	72	26
Haxby United	28	4	0	24	52	152	12

Division One	P	W	D	L	F	A	Pts
Terrington Glory	20	13	3	4	62	35	42
Selby RSSC (-3)	20	11	2	7	54	38	32
Amotherby & Swinton	20	10	1	9	54	38	31
Malton & Norton	20	8	6	6	36	32	30
Tockwith	20	7	6	7	42	42	27
Pocklington Town	20	7	6	7	33	36	27
St Clements (-3)	20	8	4	8	47	47	25
Hemingbrough United	20	7	2	11	43	53	23
Post Office	20	6	4	10	45	57	22
Bishopthorpe United	20	6	4	10	26	46	22
Heworth (-3)	20	5	6	9	35	53	18

Division Two	P	W	D	L	F	A	Pts
Church Fenton White Horse	20	15	3	2	54	13	48
Aviva	20	13	4	3	69	25	43
Cliffe	20	10	6	4	55	37	36
Stamford Bridge	20	8	5	7	47	42	29
Heslington	20	9	2	9	42	47	29
Thorpe United (-3)	20	9	3	8	41	36	27
Strensall	20	8	2	10	38	45	26
Rawcliffe	20	5	4	11	31	54	19
Osbaldwick	20	5	4	11	22	55	19
Crayke	20	4	5	11	34	48	17
Huby United	20	4	2	14	34	65	14

Division Three	P	W	D	L	F	A	Pts
Tadcaster Magnets	18	17	1	0	71	5	52
Fulford FC United	18	12	2	4	44	15	38
F1 Racing	18	11	2	5	53	27	35
Rufforth United	18	8	3	7	40	45	27
Ouseburn United	18	7	5	6	36	35	26
Barmby Moor	18	7	2	9	26	37	23
Selby Olympia	18	5	7	6	42	42	22
Elvington Harriers	18	5	5	8	42	40	20
Civil Service	18	2	4	12	29	66	10
Wheldrake	18	0	1	17	13	84	1

Division Four	P	W	D	L	F	A	Pts
Sporting Knavesmire	14	13	0	1	65	17	39
Bishop Wilton (-3)	14	11	2	1	41	21	32
Moor Lane	14	7	2	5	35	31	23
Fox	14	6	1	7	32	35	19
Selby Town Reserves	14	5	0	9	26	38	15
LNER Builders	14	4	1	9	34	46	13
KS Polonia/St Clements	14	3	1	10	24	39	10
Melbourne	14	3	1	10	21	51	10

YORKSHIRE AMATEUR LEAGUE

Senior A	P	W	D	L	F	A	Pts
Stanningley OB	22	16	4	2	73	26	52
Huddersfield Amateur	22	16	4	2	68	26	52
Alwoodley FC	22	16	4	2	67	32	52
Leeds Medics & Dentists	22	12	5	5	46	37	41
Ealandians	22	9	2	11	41	50	29
Bainbridge (-1)	22	8	4	10	57	57	27
Trinity & All Saints COB	22	7	3	12	43	52	24
Gildersome Spurs OB	22	6	5	11	55	58	23
FC Headingley	22	6	4	12	45	61	22
Bramley Juniors OB	22	5	5	12	32	56	20
Shire Academics	22	5	2	15	28	63	17
Thornesians	22	4	2	16	29	66	14

Senior B	P	W	D	L	F	A	Pts
North East Leeds	22	17	3	2	88	29	54
Grangefield OB (-1)	22	16	5	1	117	25	52
Beeston OB	22	14	3	5	78	41	45
Leeds Medics & Dentists Res	22	11	6	5	57	39	39
St. Bedes AFC	22	10	3	9	64	68	33
Old Modernians	22	9	5	8	61	53	32
Sandal Athletic	22	10	2	10	46	56	32
Calverley United	22	8	0	14	42	65	24
Old Batelians	22	7	0	15	41	84	21
Collingham Juniors OB	22	6	2	14	30	74	20
Gildersome Spurs OB Res	22	5	0	17	39	82	15
St. Nicholas (-1)	22	3	3	16	39	86	11

LEAGUE TABLES

Division One

	P	W	D	L	F	A	Pts
Stanningley OB Res	20	15	4	1	67	25	49
Beeston St. Anthony's	20	15	3	2	49	24	48
Alwoodley FC Res	20	12	3	5	56	33	39
Huddersfield Amateur Res	20	11	4	5	46	40	37
Farsley Celtic Juniors	20	11	1	8	52	39	34
Leeds Medics & Dentists III	20	8	2	10	36	42	26
East Leeds Trinity OB (-1)	20	7	5	8	39	42	25
Old Centralians	20	5	4	11	43	57	19
Bramley Juniors OB Res	20	5	0	15	21	34	15
Old Collegians	20	3	5	12	36	68	14
East Ardsley Wanderers	20	1	3	16	30	71	6

Division Two

	P	W	D	L	F	A	Pts
Farnley Sports	22	17	4	1	67	29	55
Bramley Juniors OB III	22	12	3	7	48	41	39
Woodhouse Moor Methodists	22	12	2	8	49	46	38
Leeds Independent	22	11	3	8	53	33	36
Leeds Medics & Dentists IV	22	9	9	4	42	34	36
Sandal Wanderers	22	10	4	8	64	58	34
Bainbridge Res (-10)	22	12	4	6	59	46	30
St. Bedes AFC Res	22	7	7	8	45	49	28
Colton Institute	22	5	5	12	46	58	20
Gildersome Spurs OB III (-1)	22	5	4	13	48	56	18
FC Headingley Res (-4)	22	6	4	12	39	49	18
Shire Academics Res (-2)	22	1	1	20	21	82	2

Division Three

	P	W	D	L	F	A	Pts
Old Modernians Res	20	15	4	1	69	19	49
Almondburians Huddersfield	20	15	3	2	79	26	48
Colton Institute Res	20	13	5	2	58	36	44
Ealandians Res	20	9	1	10	48	40	28
Grangefield OB Res (-1)	20	8	4	8	56	44	27
Heckmondwike GSOB	20	8	2	10	42	43	26
Middleton Park	20	8	2	10	46	61	26
Old Batelians Res	20	6	1	13	48	72	19
Leeds City OB	20	5	3	12	42	71	18
Calverley United Res	20	3	6	11	25	61	15
Old Centralians Res	20	4	1	15	27	67	13

Division Four

	P	W	D	L	F	A	Pts
Beeston OB Res	22	19	1	2	136	30	58
Norristhorpe	22	18	1	3	84	33	55
Old Modernians III	22	14	2	6	80	45	44
Leeds City OB III	22	13	1	8	78	58	40
Huddersfield Amateur III	22	13	0	9	86	53	39
Thornesians Res	22	11	3	8	61	41	36
North Leeds	22	9	4	9	84	60	31
Old Collegians Res	22	7	1	14	48	87	22
Sandal Athletic Res	22	5	4	13	36	85	19
Leeds City OB Res	22	5	4	13	45	98	19
Old Centralians III	22	3	4	15	36	84	13
Old Batelians III (-2)	22	2	1	19	24	124	5

Division Five

	P	W	D	L	F	A	Pts
Wheelwright OB	20	18	2	0	92	23	56
Alwoodley FC III	20	13	2	5	51	37	41
Ealandians III	20	12	3	5	75	39	39
East Ardsley Wanderers Res	20	10	4	6	48	38	34
Huddersfield Amateur IV	20	8	2	10	43	52	26
Thornesians IV	20	6	4	10	36	51	22
St. Bedes AFC III	20	5	6	9	56	57	21
Thornesians III	20	6	3	11	36	48	21
Middleton Park Res	20	6	2	12	37	71	20
North Leeds Res	20	5	2	13	30	55	17
Old Modernians IV	20	4	4	12	33	66	16

WELSH TABLES 2011-12

WELSH PREMIER

	P	W	D	L	F	A	Pts
The New Saints	32	23	5	4	75	31	74
Bangor City	32	22	3	7	72	46	69
Neath	32	18	8	6	60	36	62
Llanelli	32	18	5	9	63	36	59
Bala Town	32	14	7	11	48	41	49
Prestatyn Town	32	8	4	20	41	63	28
Airbus UK Broughton	32	10	9	13	48	50	39
Aberystwyth Town (-1)	32	8	10	14	44	50	33
Port Talbot Town	32	8	9	15	39	51	33
Afan Lido	32	7	11	14	40	55	32
Carmarthen Town	32	10	2	20	33	67	32
Newtown (-3)	32	7	5	20	44	82	23

The table splits after each team has played each other twice. Each team then meet twice more, top six to determine the Champions, bottom six the relegation.

CYMRU ALLIANCE

	P	W	D	L	F	A	Pts
Gap Connah's Quay	30	21	5	4	89	23	68
Rhyl	30	19	5	6	80	22	62
Buckley Town	30	19	4	7	67	43	61
Porthmadog	30	19	5	6	68	41	62
Penrhyncoch	30	17	4	9	56	44	55
Cefn Druids	30	17	3	10	58	42	54
Caersws	30	17	4	9	68	49	55
Llandudno Town	30	14	7	9	55	40	49
Flint Town United	30	13	7	10	59	47	46
Conwy United	30	10	7	13	59	65	37
Guilsfield	30	10	4	16	41	58	34
Ruthin Town	30	6	7	17	28	60	25
Penycae	30	7	4	19	30	76	25
Llanrhaeadr YM	30	3	9	18	40	77	18
Llangefni Town	30	4	2	24	32	96	14
Rhos Aelwyd	30	2	7	21	29	76	13

WELSH LEAGUE

Division One

	P	W	D	L	F	A	Pts
Cambrian & Clydach Vale BGC	30	16	10	4	78	25	58
Taffs Well	30	16	4	10	60	42	52
Haverfordwest County	30	15	7	8	58	43	52
Bryntirion Athletic	30	16	3	11	52	43	51
AFC Porth	30	13	9	8	54	36	48
Barry Town	30	12	10	8	48	37	46
Goytre United	30	12	8	10	71	55	44
Bridgend Town	30	13	5	12	50	41	44
Ton Pentre	30	9	16	5	48	40	43
Pontardawe Town	30	11	9	10	48	53	42
West End	30	11	5	14	53	62	38
Cwmbran Celtic	30	12	2	16	32	54	38
Aberaman Athletic	30	8	9	13	46	55	33
Cwmaman Institute	30	7	8	15	36	59	29
Cardiff Corinthians	30	6	10	14	50	67	28
Caerau Ely	30	4	3	23	37	109	15

Division Two

	P	W	D	L	F	A	Pts
Monmouth Town	30	22	4	4	102	33	70
Tata Steel	30	23	1	6	80	36	70
Caerleon	30	18	8	4	68	25	62
Newport YMCA	30	18	3	9	60	38	57
Dinas Powys	30	17	5	8	54	35	56
Penrhiwceiber Rangers	30	13	5	12	50	47	44
Croesyceiliog	30	12	6	12	55	54	42
Garden Village	30	11	8	11	57	50	41
Caldicot Town	30	12	3	15	42	63	39
Caerau United	30	11	5	14	44	58	35
Ely Rangers	30	9	7	14	51	62	34
Ammanford	30	9	6	15	44	67	33
Aberbargoed Buds	30	9	5	16	47	59	32
Bettws	30	7	4	19	31	65	25
Newcastle Emlyn	30	6	3	21	35	66	21
Treharris Athletic Western	30	4	5	21	30	92	17

Division Three

	P	W	D	L	F	A	Pts
Undy Athletic	28	20	3	5	70	32	63
Goytre	28	19	3	6	65	39	60
Briton Ferry Llansawel	28	17	7	4	72	39	58
Bridgend Street	28	16	7	5	72	42	55
Pontypridd Town	28	16	4	8	68	37	52
UWIC	28	13	5	10	49	51	44
Abertillery Bluebirds	28	13	4	11	45	43	43
Risca United	28	12	5	11	58	49	41
Cardiff Grange Harlequins	28	11	3	14	53	58	36
Llanwern	28	7	9	12	43	57	30
Newport Civil Service	28	7	7	14	46	67	28
Tredegar Town	28	5	8	15	31	53	23
Treowen Stars	28	6	5	17	29	70	23
AFC Llwydcoed	28	6	3	19	40	67	21
Pontyclun	28	2	7	19	32	69	13

WELSH ALLIANCE

Division One

	P	W	D	L	F	A	Pts
Holyhead Hotspur	30	25	1	4	87	28	73
Holywell Town	30	23	3	4	77	29	72
Pwllheli	30	19	6	5	58	33	63
Caernarfon Town	30	19	3	8	67	36	60
Bethesda Athletic	30	16	6	8	70	52	54
Llanrug United	30	14	5	11	74	54	47
Denbigh Town	30	14	4	12	58	48	46
Barmouth & Dyffryn United	30	11	3	16	59	83	36
Gwalchmai	30	10	5	15	54	65	35
Llandudno Junction	30	9	7	14	60	71	34
Bodedern Athletic	30	8	10	12	45	53	31
Glan Conwy	30	9	3	18	47	68	30
Nefyn United	30	7	4	19	35	71	25
Llanrwst United	30	4	11	15	45	69	23
Llanfairpwll	30	6	5	19	47	78	23
Caernarfon Wanderers	30	6	4	20	46	91	22

WELSH LEAGUES
WELSH ALLIANCE

Division Two

	P	W	D	L	F	A	Pts
Glantraeth	22	19	1	2	91	25	58
Llanberis	22	17	1	4	53	28	52
Kinmel Bay Sports	22	17	3	2	73	25	51
Llandyrnog United	22	16	2	4	56	18	50
Greenfield	22	10	2	10	51	56	32
Penmaenmawr Phoenix	22	8	4	10	36	39	28
Blaenau Ffestiniog Amateurs	22	7	2	13	49	73	23
Connah's Quay Town	22	6	3	13	27	48	21
Nantlle Vale	22	7	0	15	38	61	21
Amlwch Town	22	3	9	10	33	63	18
Gaerwen	22	5	2	15	34	61	17
Halkyn United	22	2	1	19	29	73	7

CLYWD LEAGUE

Premier Division

	P	W	D	L	F	A	Pts
Rhuddlan Town	18	15	1	2	84	22	46
Meliden	18	14	2	2	66	24	44
St Asaph	18	11	3	4	60	31	36
Prestatyn Rovers	18	8	5	5	48	33	29
Abergele Dragons	18	8	3	7	44	45	27
Rhos United	18	6	4	8	35	55	22
Rhyl Athletic	18	4	3	11	32	70	15
Mochdre Sports	18	4	2	12	37	48	14
Llansannan	18	3	4	11	30	62	13
Y Glannau	18	3	1	14	31	77	10

Division One

	P	W	D	L	F	A	Pts
Betws-Yn-Rhos	12	8	1	3	35	19	25
Llannefydd	12	7	3	2	36	15	24
Cerrigydrudion	12	5	2	5	33	30	17
West Shore (-3)	12	5	3	4	31	34	15
Bro Cernyw	12	4	2	6	33	29	14
Rhyl Hearts	12	2	1	9	15	48	7

GWENT COUNTY LEAGUE

Division One

	P	W	D	L	F	A	Pts
Chepstow Town	30	26	3	1	109	38	81
Fleur-de-Lys Welfare	30	18	5	7	85	55	59
Cwmbran Town	30	17	5	8	73	54	56
Abercarn United	30	16	0	14	75	75	48
Abertillery Excelsior	30	13	7	10	68	55	46
Govilon	30	13	4	13	79	67	43
Albion Rovers	30	11	8	11	76	66	41
Lliswerry	30	12	5	13	65	62	41
PILCS	30	12	4	14	58	69	40
AC Pontymister	30	11	6	13	60	72	39
Clydach Wasps	30	10	8	12	49	55	38
Fairfield United	30	11	4	15	71	78	37
Coed Eva Athletic	30	11	4	15	62	75	37
Pentwynmawr Athletic	30	10	6	14	53	78	36
Blaenavon Blues	30	7	5	18	64	95	26
Spencer Youth & Boys	30	5	0	25	47	100	15

Division Two

	P	W	D	L	F	A	Pts
Pill	30	25	5	0	130	33	80
Panteg	30	22	7	1	119	37	73
Trethomas Bluebirds	30	20	4	6	99	52	64
RTB Ebbw Vale	30	18	2	10	74	57	56
Cwmffrwdoer Sports	30	16	6	8	93	63	54
Cromwell Youth	30	15	7	8	98	76	52
Malpas United	30	13	6	11	65	66	45
Cefn Fforest	30	12	4	14	87	87	40
Sudbrook Cricket Club	30	11	5	14	68	86	38
Newport Corinthians	30	10	3	17	62	82	33
Llanhilleth Athletic	30	7	7	16	69	91	28
Lucas Cwmbran	30	8	4	18	61	85	28
Mardy	30	8	4	18	57	89	28
Rockfield Rovers	30	8	4	18	52	86	28
Rogerstone Welfare	30	9	1	20	59	102	28
Tranch	30	2	3	25	42	143	9

Division Three

	P	W	D	L	F	A	Pts
Tredegar Athletic	24	18	4	2	81	24	58
Blackrock Rovers	24	17	4	3	70	36	55
Marshfield	24	15	4	5	72	45	49
Whiteheads	24	14	3	7	85	61	45
Abergavenny Thursdays	24	11	4	9	53	43	37
Caldicot Castle	24	10	5	9	48	52	35
Trinant	24	10	4	10	85	79	34
Rhymney	24	5	11	8	65	65	26
Sebastopol	24	6	7	11	39	51	25
Pontypool Town	24	7	5	12	40	63	23
New Inn	24	3	6	15	39	70	15
Race	24	4	3	17	36	89	15
Underwood Social Club	24	4	4	16	45	80	12

GWENT CENTRAL LEAGUE

Premier Division

	P	W	D	L	F	A	Pts
Usk Town	26	19	3	4	118	56	60
Pandy	24	18	4	2	89	38	58
Govilon Res.	24	15	4	5	84	58	49
Llanarth (-3)	25	13	7	5	107	68	43
Panteg Res.	19	13	2	4	88	36	41
P.I.L.C.S. Res.	23	10	5	8	64	59	35
Fairfield United Res.	24	10	4	10	71	62	34
Clydach Wasps Res.	21	10	2	9	49	46	32
Llanfoist	24	7	7	10	61	63	28
Crickhowell	26	6	2	18	55	87	20
Blaenavon Blues Res.	23	5	3	15	52	85	18
Gilwern & District (-3)	25	5	6	14	45	88	18
Tranch Res.	21	4	3	14	56	105	15
Mardy Res.	25	4	0	21	51	139	12

GWYNEDD LEAGUE

	P	W	D	L	F	A	Pts
Penrhyndeudraeth	24	20	3	1	104	33	63
Trearddur Bay Utd	24	18	3	3	97	47	57
CPD Bro Goronwy	24	16	2	6	83	53	50
Llanllyfni	24	14	4	6	72	44	46
Holyhead Town	24	14	3	7	62	47	45
Llanystumdwy	24	13	2	9	82	63	41
Holyhead Hotspur	24	10	0	14	58	65	30
Beaumaris Town	24	8	4	12	66	74	28
CPD Bontnewydd	24	9	1	14	51	73	28
Llanfairfechan Town (-3)	24	9	2	13	69	79	26
Bangor City	24	6	1	17	52	77	19
Bangor University	24	4	2	18	47	84	14
CPD Bethel	24	1	1	22	18	122	4

MID WALES LEAGUE

Division One	P	W	D	L	F	A	Pts
Rhayader	28	21	3	4	84	31	66
Montgomery	28	21	2	5	97	28	65
Newbridge	28	18	6	4	61	37	60
Llanidloes Town	28	17	7	4	96	32	58
Carno	28	16	4	8	54	33	52
Builth Wells	28	15	4	9	64	53	49
Berriew	28	11	7	10	54	51	40
Tywyn Bryncrug	28	10	5	13	63	52	35
Waterloo	28	11	2	15	59	63	35
Llansantffraid Village	28	9	7	12	47	59	34
Bow Street	28	10	4	14	50	71	34
Dolgellau	28	7	3	18	45	80	24
Aberystwyth Uni	28	5	6	17	25	56	21
Dyffryn Banw	28	3	6	19	33	91	15
Welshpool	28	2	2	24	24	119	8

Division Two	P	W	D	L	F	A	Pts
Aberaeron	30	24	3	3	97	31	75
FourCrosses	30	22	2	6	104	47	68
LlanfairUnited	30	21	4	5	88	28	67
LlandrindodWells	30	20	5	5	95	24	65
Rhosgoch	30	14	5	11	78	53	47
Knighton	30	14	5	11	68	59	47
LlanfyllinTown	30	13	7	10	73	69	46
Machynlleth	30	14	4	12	72	80	46
Talgarth	30	14	3	13	78	79	45
Kerry	30	8	9	13	41	65	33
Aberdyfi	30	8	6	16	81	90	30
Abermule	30	8	5	17	57	91	29
Bont	30	7	5	18	53	100	26
Tregaron	30	5	9	16	60	78	24
Presteigne	30	5	5	20	53	102	20
Meifod (-6)	30	2	5	23	31	133	5

SOUTH WALES AMATEUR LEAGUE

Division One	P	W	D	L	F	A	Pts
Llantwit Major	28	23	4	1	91	29	73
Treforest	28	15	8	5	67	41	53
Ton & Gelli Boys Club	28	14	6	8	61	43	48
Trefelin BGC	28	14	4	10	62	45	46
Rhoose	28	14	4	10	69	54	46
Caerau Boys Club	28	13	3	12	54	62	42
STM Sports	28	12	4	12	65	56	40
Llantwit Fardre	28	12	4	12	49	56	40
Aber Valley YMCA	28	12	2	14	59	56	38
Splott Albion	28	12	2	14	52	61	38
Cardiff Draconians	28	10	3	15	73	63	33
Kenfig Hill	28	8	4	16	56	82	28
Blaenrhondda	28	7	6	15	48	75	27
Carnetown BGC	28	7	6	15	34	64	27
Graig (-3)	28	4	6	18	42	95	15

Division Two	P	W	D	L	F	A	Pts
Perthcelyn United	30	24	2	4	104	44	74
Trelewis Welfare	30	22	3	5	96	36	69
Baglan Dragons	30	20	4	6	92	35	64
Llangynwyd Rangers	30	19	7	4	94	39	64
Merthyr Saints	30	19	4	7	95	52	61
Hirwaun Welfare Mackworth	30	15	4	11	79	78	49
Pencoed Athletic	30	12	8	10	81	64	44
Cardiff Hibernian	30	12	7	11	76	62	43
Penygraig	30	12	7	11	66	69	43
Llanharry	30	10	10	10	75	86	40
AFC Bargoed Redz	30	9	6	15	70	84	33
Brynna	30	7	2	21	39	82	23
Rhydyfelin	30	5	6	19	46	86	21
Ynysddu Crusaders	30	6	3	21	40	108	21
Ferndale Boys Club	30	5	5	20	41	81	20
FC Abercwmboi	30	2	4	24	31	119	10

SOUTH WALES SENIOR LEAGUE

Division One	P	W	D	L	F	A	Pts
Sully Sports	30	24	3	3	115	36	75
Cogan Coronation	30	17	5	8	61	35	56
Tonypandy Albion	30	16	7	7	85	55	55
Grange Albion	30	17	3	10	75	55	54
Porthcawl Town Athletic	30	16	5	9	75	55	53
Penydarren Boys Club	30	14	9	7	56	45	51
Cwmbach Royal Stars	30	13	11	6	92	61	50
Brecon Corinthians	30	14	5	11	58	56	47
AFC Butetown	30	10	11	9	57	50	41
Lewistown (-2gls)	30	12	5	13	55	56	41
Cwm Welfare	30	11	7	12	60	60	40
Pentwyn Dynamos	30	9	9	12	52	80	36
Llanrumney United	30	9	5	16	58	95	32
Tonyrefail BGC	30	4	5	21	39	77	17
Lisvane/Llanishen	30	3	5	22	43	98	14
Penrhiwceiber Cons Ath.	30	1	5	24	33	102	8

WELSH LEAGUES

SOUTH WALES SENIOR

Division Two	P	W	D	L	F	A	Pts
Fochriw	30	25	3	2	99	36	78
Ynyshir Albion	30	22	6	2	106	35	72
St Josephs (+2)	30	16	9	5	77	38	59
Fairwater (-6 & 11gls)	30	19	4	7	93	50	55
Cadoxton Barry	30	16	3	11	85	66	51
AFC Caerphilly	30	15	3	12	74	74	48
Tongwynlais (+3)	30	13	5	12	60	56	47
Penrhiwfer	30	12	5	13	69	66	41
Stanleytown	30	10	3	17	59	76	33
Llwynypia BGC (-2 & 1gl)	30	10	5	15	61	100	33
AFC Whitchurch	30	7	10	13	60	98	31
St Albans	30	8	6	16	47	75	30
Garw SBGC (-1gl)	30	9	3	18	61	91	30
Max United	30	8	5	17	65	88	29
Brackla (-3)	30	8	5	17	65	80	26
Nelson Cavaliers (+3)	30	2	5	23	43	107	14

CEREDIGION LEAGUE

Division One	P	W	D	L	F	A	Pts
New Quay	22	16	4	2	78	18	52
Maesglas	22	16	1	5	57	28	49
Lampeter	22	12	3	7	77	40	39
St Dogmaels	22	11	5	6	87	49	38
Llanboidy	22	11	5	6	58	47	38
Crannog	22	10	5	7	52	49	35
Pencader (-3)	22	9	3	10	58	81	27
Llanybydder	22	6	5	11	43	51	23
Felinfach	22	7	2	13	35	77	23
Aberaeron Res	22	7	1	14	48	74	22
Cardigan	22	6	3	13	31	49	21
Aberporth	22	2	1	19	23	84	7

Division Two	P	W	D	L	F	A	Pts
NCE Reserves	22	18	3	1	99	23	57
Llanybydder Reserves	22	14	4	4	80	43	46
Bargod Rangers	22	13	6	3	80	36	45
Llandysul	22	12	4	6	74	44	40
Saron	22	11	2	9	52	41	35
Dewi Stars	22	11	2	9	38	45	35
Ffostrasol	22	8	4	10	33	47	28
St Dogmaels Reserves (-3)	22	6	8	8	52	63	26
New Quay Reserves	22	7	4	11	47	55	25
SDUC	22	5	3	14	50	68	18
Lampeter Reserves	22	5	0	17	41	98	15
Cardigan Reserves (-3)	22	1	2	19	23	106	2

MID WALES (SOUTH) LEAGUE

	P	W	D	L	F	A	Pts
Newcastle	28	25	0	3	93	22	75
Hay St Marys	28	20	4	4	111	42	64
Builth Wells Reserves	28	19	3	6	87	42	60
Penybont	28	17	3	8	82	49	54
Rhayader Town Reserves	28	16	4	8	71	52	52
Bronllys	28	14	3	11	72	67	45
Knighton Town Reserves	28	13	4	11	63	72	43
Llandrindod Wells Reserves	28	13	3	12	60	57	42
Radnor Valley	28	11	4	13	69	74	37
Bucknell	28	8	7	13	55	85	31
Brecon Town	28	7	4	17	55	78	25
Presteigne Reserves	28	6	7	15	61	89	25
St Harmon	28	6	2	20	38	83	20
Newbridge Reserves (-3)	28	5	3	20	39	100	15
Talgarth Town Reserves	28	2	5	21	28	72	11

MID WALES LEAGUE

Division One	P	W	D	L	F	A	Pts
Rhayader Town	28	21	3	4	84	31	66
Montgomery Town	28	21	2	5	97	28	65
Newbridge-on-Wye	28	18	6	4	61	37	60
Llanidloes Town	28	17	7	4	96	32	58
Carno	28	16	4	8	54	33	52
Builth Wells	28	15	4	9	64	53	49
Berriew	28	11	7	10	54	51	40
Tywyn & Bryncrug	28	10	5	13	63	52	35
Waterloo Rovers	28	11	2	15	59	63	35
Llansantffraid Village	28	9	7	12	47	59	34
Bow Street	28	10	4	14	50	71	34
Dolgellau AA	28	7	3	18	45	80	24
Aberystwyth University	28	5	6	17	25	56	21
Dyffryn Banw	28	3	6	19	33	91	15
Welshpool	28	2	2	24	24	119	8

Division Two	P	W	D	L	F	A	Pts
Aberaeron	30	24	3	3	97	31	75
Four Crosses	30	22	2	6	104	47	68
Llanfair United	30	21	4	5	88	28	67
Llandrindod Wells	30	20	5	5	95	24	65
Rhosgoch Rangers	30	14	5	11	78	53	47
Knighton Town	30	14	5	11	68	59	47
Llanfyllin Town	30	13	7	10	73	69	46
Machynlleth	30	14	4	12	72	80	46
Talgarth Town	30	14	3	13	78	79	45
Kerry	30	8	9	13	41	65	33
Aberdyfi	30	8	6	16	81	90	30
Abermule	30	8	5	17	57	91	29
Bont	30	7	5	18	53	100	26
Tregaron Turfs	30	5	9	16	60	78	24
Presteigne St Andrews	30	5	5	20	53	102	20
Meifod	30	2	5	23	31	133	8

NEATH & DISTRICT LEAGUE

Premier Division	P	W	D	L	F	A	Pts
Ystradgynlais AFC(A)	19	16	1	2	60	16	49
Park Travellers (A)	19	14	2	3	61	31	44
Cwmamman Utd(A)	19	13	3	3	60	34	42
Giants Grave (A)	19	12	3	4	50	33	39
Seven Sisters FC (A)	19	10	2	7	55	40	32
Bryn Rovers (A)	19	7	5	7	48	43	26
St Ives FC	20	6	0	14	30	57	18
Sunnybank WMC (A)	19	5	1	13	25	46	16
Ynysymeudwy Ath (A)	19	4	3	12	29	48	15
AFC Pontardawe (A)	19	4	1	14	30	70	13
Cwm Wanderers (A)	19	2	3	14	22	52	9

Division One	P	W	D	L	F	A	Pts
FC Clydach (A)	17	11	5	1	52	25	38
Resolven (A)	17	12	1	4	55	33	37
Pontardawe Town	17	10	4	3	54	24	34
Cilfrew Rovers (A)	17	8	3	6	52	36	27
Coelbren Ath	17	8	2	7	51	47	26
Glynneath Town (A)	17	7	3	7	52	58	24
AFC Caewern (A)	17	8	0	9	33	31	21
Ynysygerwen (A)	17	6	1	10	37	54	19
Harp Rovers (A)	17	4	2	11	29	53	14
I.N.C.O Vale FC(A)	17	0	1	16	25	79	1

Division Two	P	W	D	L	F	A	Pts
Briton Ferry (A)	22	20	2	0	118	14	62
Cambrian (A)	22	19	2	1	94	19	59
Rhos (A)	22	14	1	7	75	38	43
Longford (A)	22	11	6	5	56	42	37
Clydach Sports (A)	22	10	4	8	35	43	34
FCNedd	22	9	3	10	57	66	30
FCCimla	22	9	2	11	39	61	29
Bear (A)	22	8	3	11	42	64	27
Godregraig Athletic (A)	22	6	3	13	38	76	21
Tonna (A)	22	6	2	14	45	67	20
Borough (A)	22	4	1	17	27	78	13
Bryncoch (A)	22	1	1	20	16	74	4

NEWPORT & DISTRICT LEAGUE

Premier X Division	P	W	D	L	F	A	Pts
Ponthir AFC	18	14	2	2	69	31	44
Pontnewydd United	18	13	3	2	55	24	42
Villa Dino Christchurch	18	13	2	3	71	36	41
K-2AFC	18	12	0	6	54	26	36
Graig-y-Rhacca	18	6	5	7	47	36	23
Cwmcarn Athletic	18	6	2	10	37	42	20
Docks Cons	18	5	5	8	50	57	20
Oakfield	18	4	5	9	45	63	17
Athletico Cwmbran	18	3	2	13	51	84	11
Caerleon Town	18	1	0	17	22	102	3

Pill Hibernians, M.S.Dynamo, Oasis AFC, Henllys Rangers all withdrawn

Premier Y Division	P	W	D	L	F	A	Pts
Pill AFC	26	21	4	1	113	26	67
Albion Rovers	26	22	1	3	116	39	67
AC Pontymister	26	17	3	6	89	41	54
Lliswerry AFC	26	14	3	9	75	68	45
Coed Eva Athletic	26	12	4	10	116	72	40
Cromwell Youth	26	12	4	10	75	59	40
Malpas United	26	11	1	14	64	73	34
Lucas Cwmbran	26	10	4	12	58	71	34
Cwmbran Celtic	26	9	2	15	56	102	29
Newport Corinthians	26	8	4	14	62	74	28
Spencer Y & B Club	26	7	5	14	54	69	26
Trethomas Bluebirds	26	7	3	6	52	90	24

Marshfield AFC withdrawn

Division One	P	W	D	L	F	A	Pts
Bettws Socialdad	22	20	0	2	137	22	60
Albion Rovers	22	17	2	3	84	38	53
Newport Eagles	22	14	3	5	89	42	45
Crosskeys AFC	22	11	6	5	70	60	39
AC Pontymister	22	8	6	8	52	51	30
Gaer Park Rangers	22	9	2	11	61	78	29
K-2 AFC	22	7	5	10	61	65	26
Villa Dino Christchurch	22	6	8	8	50	57	26
Lliswerry AFC	22	6	3	13	48	74	21
Shaftesbury Youth	22	5	2	15	39	77	17
Pontnewydd United	22	4	3	15	37	108	15
Machen AFC	22	4	2	16	31	94	14

Sporting Baneswell Social and Newport Corinthians both withdrawn

Division Two	P	W	D	L	F	A	Pts
FC Boilermakers	20	17	3	0	98	23	54
Machen AFC	20	17	1	2	80	25	52
Llanyrafon AFC	20	14	1	5	93	48	43
Ponthir AFC	20	11	3	6	72	49	36
Cromwell Youth	20	9	3	8	69	50	30
FC Pockets	20	7	6	7	60	58	27
Cwmcarn Athletic	20	8	3	9	56	63	27
Racing Club Npt	20	6	2	12	56	75	20
Docks Cons AFC	20	5	2	13	57	83	17
Lucas Cwmbran	20	2	1	17	37	87	7
Caerleon Town	20	1	1	18	32	149	4

Pill Hibernians and Cwmbran Celtic both withdrawn

Division Three	P	W	D	L	F	A	Pts
Pill AFC	24	22	0	2	130	33	66
Infusion Sports Bar	24	19	0	5	90	42	57
Racing Club Npt	24	18	1	5	127	54	55
Bettws Socialdad	24	13	3	8	102	78	42
CCYP AFC	24	12	2	10	82	65	38
Albion Rovers	24	10	5	9	81	85	35
AC Pontymister	24	9	4	11	61	87	31
Ponthir AFC	24	9	3	12	52	63	30
Risca Athletic	24	6	9	9	56	57	27
Llanyrafon AFC	24	6	3	15	66	99	21
Coed Eva Athletic	24	5	3	16	47	84	18
Newport Eagles	24	4	2	18	50	118	14
Rogerstone AFC	24	3	5	16	51	130	14

Crosskeys AFC withdrawn

WELSH LEAGUES
PEMBROKESHIRE LEAGUE

Division One

	P	W	D	L	F	A	Pts
Merlins Bridge	26	22	2	2	74	30	68
Hakin United (-1)	26	19	4	3	118	40	60
Monkton Swifts	26	16	2	8	80	58	50
Goodwick United	26	14	6	6	56	35	48
Pennar Robins	26	14	2	10	61	42	44
Neyland	26	12	3	11	62	62	39
Narberth	26	11	5	10	55	47	38
Tenby	26	9	6	11	66	57	33
Johnston	26	9	6	11	72	66	33
Haverfordwest County	26	9	4	13	39	55	28
Hundleton	26	7	5	14	51	62	26
Solva	26	6	2	18	37	96	23
Clarbeston Road	26	6	3	17	62	128	21
Milford United	26	2	2	22	29	84	8

Division Two

	P	W	D	L	F	A	Pts
St Ishmaels (-1)	26	20	2	4	103	22	61
Saundersfoot Sports	26	16	4	6	74	47	52
West Dragons	26	15	4	7	85	47	49
Milford Athletic	26	14	6	6	66	45	48
Prendergast Villa	26	11	8	7	50	35	41
Lamphey (-1)	26	12	5	9	62	64	40
Carew	26	11	6	9	53	47	39
Herbrandston	26	12	3	11	61	57	39
Letterston (-1)	26	10	2	14	49	60	31
Kilgetty	26	9	2	15	63	79	29
Angle	26	9	2	15	54	90	29
Goodwick United II	26	8	4	14	44	60	28
Hakin United II	26	7	4	15	51	83	25
Camrose	26	2	0	24	21	100	6

Division Three

	P	W	D	L	F	A	Pts
St Clears	26	19	4	3	112	37	61
Pennar Robins II	26	18	4	4	94	42	58
Tenby II	26	15	2	9	87	74	47
Narberth II	26	15	2	9	72	66	47
Johnston II	26	14	4	8	83	63	46
Manorbier United	26	14	1	11	82	66	43
Lawrenny	26	12	4	10	83	60	40
Haverfordwest Cricket Club	26	10	7	9	69	56	37
Broad Haven	26	11	3	12	73	71	36
Hubberston	26	9	3	14	71	75	30
Merlins Bridge II (-3)	26	8	3	15	61	96	24
Pembroke Boro	26	5	6	15	56	87	21
Clarbeston Road II	26	5	2	19	52	118	17
Pendine (-5)	26	2	5	19	44	128	6

Division Four

	P	W	D	L	F	A	Pts
Cosheston Cougars	26	17	5	4	100	47	56
Fishguard Sports	26	20	2	4	80	38	53
Pennar Robins III (-1)	26	16	5	5	87	29	52
St Ishmaels II	26	15	6	5	70	41	51
Saundersfoot Sports II	26	12	6	8	78	58	42
Prendergast Villa II	26	12	3	11	60	58	42
Milford Athletic II (-3)	26	10	4	12	60	71	37
St Florence (-1)	26	11	3	12	67	70	35
Milford United II	26	10	4	12	52	58	31
Carew II	26	8	5	13	56	69	29
Monkton Swifts II (-3)	26	8	2	16	47	78	23
Herbrandston II	26	6	4	16	42	89	22
Solva II	26	5	6	15	45	90	21
Camrose II	26	2	5	19	32	80	14

Division Five

	P	W	D	L	F	A	Pts
Neyland II	26	20	3	3	108	32	63
Hundleton II	26	21	3	2	102	36	63
West Dragons II (-3)	26	16	2	8	97	73	47
Cosheston Cougars II	26	15	2	9	72	64	47
St Clears II	26	13	5	8	67	60	44
Hook AFC	26	12	5	9	99	58	41
Letterston II	26	12	4	10	82	65	40
Kilgetty II	26	12	0	14	101	102	39
Haverfordwest Cricket Club II	26	11	3	12	72	78	36
Fishguard Sports II	26	9	5	12	81	76	32
Lawrenny II	26	7	2	17	57	69	23
Pembroke Boro II	26	6	1	19	58	112	19
Lamphey II	26	6	0	20	52	142	18
Manorbier United II (-3)	26	3	3	20	42	123	9

WELSH NATIONAL LEAGUE
(WREXHAM) AREA)

Premier

	P	W	D	L	F	A	Pts
FC Cefn	30	23	3	4	100	45	72
Rhydymwyn	30	23	0	7	100	42	69
Chirk AAA	30	21	2	7	94	45	65
Mold Alex	30	17	8	5	65	34	59
Venture	30	18	4	8	86	49	58
Hawarden Rangers	30	14	9	7	55	40	51
Gresford Athletic	30	15	4	11	63	46	49
Brymbo	30	13	5	12	62	57	44
Llangollen Town	30	12	7	11	70	58	43
Penyffordd	30	13	4	13	66	62	43
Coedpoeth Utd	30	11	3	16	65	74	36
Corwen	30	10	5	15	46	59	35
Overton	30	6	6	18	36	58	24
Brickfield Rangers	30	4	4	22	31	100	16
Llay Welfare	30	3	4	23	42	99	13
Johnstown Youth	30	1	4	25	23	136	7

Division One

	P	W	D	L	F	A	Pts
Saltney Town	24	19	3	2	129	28	60
Borras Park Albion (-3)	24	20	2	2	127	34	59
Argoed United	24	18	4	2	54	19	58
Castell AC	24	14	3	7	79	59	45
Mold Juniors	24	11	3	10	51	66	36
Acrefair Youth (-3)	24	11	5	8	66	52	35
New Brighton	24	9	8	7	54	46	35
Penley	24	8	6	10	67	69	30
Lex X1 (-3)	24	8	4	12	44	46	25
Glyn Ceiriog	24	6	0	18	29	109	18
Garden Village	24	3	6	15	21	65	15
Llanuwchllyn	23	3	3	17	37	84	12
Hawkesbury Villa (-3)	23	1	1	21	19	100	1

WELSH CUP

FIRST QUALIFYING ROUND

Aber Valley YMCA 8-3 Garw
Abercarn United 8-3 Llanharry
AFC Abercynon scr-w/o Perthcelyn
AFC Llwydcoed 3-1 Croesyceiliog
Bettws 0-4 Trefelin
Brecon Corries 1-6 Undy Athletic
Bridgend Street 2-0 Treforest
Briton Ferry Llansawel 3-1 Treharris Athletic Western
Cadoxton Barry 0-1 UWIC
Cardiff Hibernian 0-2 Caerau
Cornelly United 0-6 Ely Rangers
Cwmbran Town 2-1 Hirwaun Welfare/Mackworth
Dinas Powys 6-1 Blaenrhondda
Ferndale scr-w/o Goytre FC
Graig 4-5 STM Sports
Kenfig Hill 1-1 Caerleon
(Caerleon won 4-2 on penalties)
Llangeinor 2-4 Merthyr Saints
Llantwit Fardre 2-1 Baglan Dragons
Llanwern 1-2 Fleur de Lys Welfare
Newport Civil Service 3-2 Cwmamman United
Penrhiwceiber Constitutional 1-3 Aberbargoed Buds
Penrhiwceiber Rangers 2-5 Aberaeron
Pentwynmawr Athletic 0-5 Abertillery Bluebirds
Pontyclun 2-0 Penygraig
Talgarth Town 2-3 Nelson Cavaliers
Tata Steel 3-2 Carnetown
Tonyrefail 3-2 RTB Ebbw Vale
Tredegar Athletic 0-3 Risca United
Tredegar Town 3-2 Cardiff Grange Harlequins
Treowen Stars 4-3 Pontypridd Town
Trethomas Bluebirds 0-1 Splott Albion

WELSH LEAGUES

Acrefair Youth 0-4 Coedpoeth United
Amlwch Town 0-5 Rhydymwyn
Barmouth & Dyffryn United 3-1 Aberdyfi
Bethel 1-2 Caernarfon Wanderers
Blaenau Ffestiniog 3-7 Caernarfon Town
Bow Street 1-9 Mold Alex
Brymbo 0-1 Penmaenmawr Phoenix
Builth Wells 3-2 Llanberis
Carno 4-2 Trearddur Bay
Connah's Quay Town 3-1 Kerry
Dyffryn Nantle Vale 1-2 Llanllyfni
FC Nomads of Connah's Quay 3-2 Llay Miners Welfare
Gaerwen 2-1 Llandudno Junction
Glan Conwy 4-1 Overton Recreational
Greenfield 0-4 FC Cefn
Gwalchmai 6-4 Dolgellau Athletic
Johnstown Youth 1-3 Llandrindod Wells
Kinmel Bay Sports 1-1 Chirk AAA
(Chirk AAA won 5-4 on penalties)
Llandyrnog United 1-0 Holywell Town
Llanfyllin 1-5 Brickfield Rangers
Llanrwst United 0-1 Llangollen United
Llanystumdwy 2-6 Bro Goronwy
Montgomery Town 8-0 Machynlleth
Nefyn United 5-0 Presteigne St Andrew's
Penyffordd 2-5 Glantraeth
Pontrhydfendigaid 4-2 Castell Alun Colts
Pwllheli 1-3 Llanrug United
Rhayader Town 3-3 Hawarden Rangers
(Hawarden Rangers won 3-2 on penalties)
Rhosgoch Rangers 2-1 Halkyn United
Tregaron Turfs 0-4 Llanfair United
Tywyn Bryncrug 3-2 Llanfair PG
Venture Community 3-0 Bodedern
Waterloo Rovers 1-3 Berriew

Second Qualifying Round

Aber Valley YMCA 3-6 Abertillery Bluebirds
Aberbargoed Buds 4-0 Abercarn United
Ammanford 1-3 Dinas Powys
Bridgend Street 2-3 UWIC
Briton Ferry Llansawel 0-1 Tata Steel
Caerleon 2-0 Newport YMCA
Cwmbran Town 3-1 Pontyclun
Fleur De Lys Welfare 3-5 Undy Athletic
Garden Village 1-1 Calidcot Town
(Caldicot Town won 4-2 on penalties)
Goytre 1-0 Llantwit Fadre
Merthyr Town 5-1 Caerau
Monmouth Town 6-2 Tredegar Town
Nelson Cavaliers 0-6 Aberaeron

WELSH LEAGUES

Newcastle Emlyn 0-0 Ely Rangers
(Newcastle Emlyn won 4-2 on penalties)
Perthcelyn United 5-6 Merthyr Saints
Risca United 4-0 Tonyrefail
Splott Albion 1-0 AFC Llwydcoed
STM Sports 2-3 Newport Civil Service
Trefelin 1-2 Treowen Stars
Barmouth & Dyffryn United 4-1 Hawarden Rangers
Brickfield Rangers 1-4 Builth Wells
Caernarfon Town 8-0 Penmaenmawr Phoenix
Caernarfon Wanderers 1-5 Bethesda Athletic
Chirk AAA 1-0 Berriew
Coedpoeth United 5-1 Gaerwen
FC Cefn 3-1 FC Nomads of Connah's Quay
Glantraeth 9-0 Pontrhydfendigaid
Gresford Athletic 3-2 Mold Alexandra
Gwalchmai 3-2 Llansantffraid Village
Holyhead Hotspurs 4-3 Llanfair United
Lex XI 1-3 Connah's Quay Town
Llandyrnog United 1-2 Llanrug United
Llangollen Town 1-2 Carno
Llanidloes Town 4-3 Glan Conwy
Llanllyfni 0-3 Venture Community
Montgomery Town 5-0 Bro Goronwy
Nefyn United 2-3 Llandrindod Wells
Rhydymwyn 0-5 Denbigh Town
Rhosgoch Rangers 2-1 Corwen Amateurs
Tywyn Bryncrug 1-3 Newbridge on Wye

FIRST ROUND

Abertillery Bluebirds 0-2 Caerau
A F C Porth 2-0 Aberbargoed Buds
Bridgend Town 2-0 Splott Albion
Bryntirion Athletic 3-1 Cwmbran Town
Caerleon 1-0 Aberaman Athletic
Caldicot Town 2-4 Newport Civil Service
Cambrian & Clydach 5-1 Monmouth Town
Cardiff Corinthians 2-0 Cwmaman Institute
Dinas Powys 0-2 Builth Wells
Goytre 3-1 Aberaeron
Goytre United 1-0 Ton Pentre
Merthyr Town 0-3 Barry Town
Pontardawe Town 3-0 Treowen Stars
Rhosgoch Rangers 2-6 Merthyr Saintss
Risca United 0-4 Newbridge On Wye
Taffs Well 5-4 Undy Athletic
Tata Steel 3-1 Newcastle Emlyn
UWIC 0-2 Haverfordwest County
West End 3-0 Cwmbran Celtic
Barmouth & Dyffryn 4-1 Ruthin Town
Buckley Town 4-0 Penrhyncoch
Caersws 1-1 Conwy United
(Caersws won 4-2 on penalties)
Carno 0-2 Coedpoeth United
Cefn Druids 6-1 Caernarfon Town

Flint Town United 5-1 Chirk A A A
Connah's Quay Nomads 7-2 Gwalchmai
Llandrindod Wells 3-3 Llanrug United
(Llandrindod Wells won 4-1 on penalties)
Llangefni Town 2-3 Denbigh Town
Llanidloes Town 4-3 Glantraeth
Llanrhaedr ym Mochnant 1-6 Holyhead Hotspur
Montgomery Town 4-0 Connah's Quay Town
Penycae 1-2 FC Cefn
Porthmadog 3-1 Bethesda Athletic
Rhos Aelwyd 0-1 Guilsfield
Rhyl 5-0 Gresford Athletic
Venture Community 1-3 Llandudno Town

SECOND ROUND

A F C Porth 3-0 Pontardawe Town
Bridgend Town 5-3 Tata Steel
Bryntirion Athletic 5-2 Goytre
Builth Wells 0-5 Taffs Well
Caerau 1-8 Goytre United
Caerleon 3-4 Merthyr Saints
Cambrian & Clydach 2-0 Llandrindod Wells
Haverfordwest County 1-2 Barry Town
Newport Civil Service 2-0 Newbridge on Wye
West End 2-1 Cardiff Corinthians
Barmouth & Dyffryn 0-3 Caersws
Buckley Town 5-2 Holyhead Hotspurs
Cefn Druids 8-0 Coedpoeth United
Denbigh Town 1-2 Flint Town United
Guilsfield 1-3 Llandudno Town
Llanidloes Town 0-2 Connah's Quay Nomads
Montgomery Town 3-7 F C Cefn
Porthmadog 2-3 Rhyl

THIRD ROUND

Flint Town United 3-0 Newport County
Port Talbot Town 0-1 Afan Lido
The New Saints 6-0 Bryntirion Athletic
A F C Porth 0-0 Cambrian & Clydach
(AFC Porth won 4-3 on penalties)
Wrexham 1-2 Airbus U K Broughton
Carmarthen Town 2-1 Bridgend Town
Caersws 0-1 Llandudno Town
Buckley Town 4-3 Taffs Well
Neath 4-0 West End
F C Cefn 1-6 Aberystwyth Town
Newtown 1-2 Rhyl
Bangor City 2-4 Llanelli
Prestatyn Town 6-2 Goytre United
Newport County 3-2 Barry Town
Connah's Quay Nomads 1-2 Cefn Druids
Merthyr Saints 0-6 Bala Town

FOURTH ROUND

Rhyl 3-3 Llanelli

(Llanelli won 5-4 on penalties)

Afan Lido 2-2 Airbus U K Broughton (Airbus UK Broughton won 5-4 on

penalties)

Buckley Town 2-4 Bala Town

Flint Town United 1-3 Neath

Aberystwyth Town 1-1 Llandudno Town

(Aberystwyth Town won 5-4 on penalties)

The New Saints 4-0 Newport County

Prestatyn Town 0-2 Cefn Druids

Carmarthen Town 3-1 A F C Porth

QUARTER FINALS

Bala Town 1-1 Llanelli (Bala Town won 5-4 on penalties)

Airbus U K Broughton 3-1 Carmarthen Town

Aberystwyth Town 0-1 Cefn Druids

The New Saints 1-0 Neath

SEMI-FINALS

Cefn Druids 4-1 Airbus U K Broughton (@ Rhyl)

The New Saints 4-0 Bala Town (@ Aberystwyth Town)

FINAL (@ Bangor City, 5/5/12)

Cefn Druids 0-2 The New Saints

WELSH TROPHY

QUALIFYING ROUND

Northern Section

Llanllyfni 5-1 Bethel

Meifod 3-5 Beaumaris Town

Meliden 1-1 Trearrdur Bay United

(Trearrdur Bay United won 3-1 on penalties)

Southern Section

Albion Rovers 3-2 Llantwit Fadre

Bonymaen Colts 0-1 Penlan

Cadoxton Barry 2-4 Dafen Welfare

Cardiff Hibernian 2-0 Abertillery Excelsiors

Cwmfelin Press 0-1 Tongwylais

Garw 2-6 Trelewis Welfare

Gors 5-0 VNU

Hakin United 5-1 Aber Valley YMCA

Hirwaun & Mackworth 8-1 New Inn

Margam Youth Centre 3-1 Splott Albion

Pentwynmawr Athletic 6-0 Albany Cardiff Central

PILCS 2-4 Swansea Dockers

SP Construction 0-4 Kenfig Hill

Stanley Town 2-3 Nelson Cavaliers

ROUND 1

NORTHERN SECTION

Acrefair Youth 3-1 Penley

Amlwch Town 2-0 Welshpool Town

Argoed United 0-3 Chirk AAA

Berriew 5-0 FC Nomads of Connah's Quay

Bodedern 4-1 Rhydymwyn

Borras Park Albion 1-4 Gwalchmai

Brickfield Rangers 1-3 Llanberis

Bro Goronwy 1-0 Greenfield

Brymbo 7-1 Beaumaris Town

Caernarfon Town 2-1 Corwen

Carno 7-0 Halkyn United

Castell Alun Colts 3-3 Four Crosses

(Four Crosses won 6-5 on penalties)

Coedpoeth United 3-0 Llanuwchllyn

Deganwy 2-7 Kinmel Bay Sports

Denbigh Town 5-2 Tywyn Bryncrug

FC Cefn 10-3 Llanfyllin Town

Glantraeth 2-4 Trearrdur Bay United

Gresford Athletic 3-1 Johnstown Youth

Holyhead Hotspurs 11-0 Gaerwen

Lex XI 3-6 Dyffryn Nantlle Vale

Llandudno Junction 3-2 Saltney Town

Llandyrnog United 4-3 Llay Miners Welfare

Llanfair United 3-1 Barmouth & Dyffryn United

Llanllyfni 3-2 Connah's Quay Town

Llanrug United 5-0 Llangollen Town

Llanystumdwy 0-3 Llanfairpwll

Mold Alexandra 2-3 Venture Community

Nefyn United 4-1 Overton Recreational

Penmaenmawr Phoenix 5-3 Caernarfon Wanderers

Penrhyndeudraeth 5-4 Penyffordd

Pwllheli 5-0 Machynlleth

Waterloo Rovers 0-5 Llanrwst United

SOUTHERN SECTION

Abercarn United 3-0 Ferndale

AFC Whitchurch 6-0 FC Brunswick

Albion Rovers 1-2 Trelewis Welfare

Baili Glas 0-7 Aberaeron

Bryn Rovers 3-4 Risca United

Caldicot Town 3-4 Llangynwydd Rangers

Carnetown 3-2 Tregaron Turfs

Cathays Tenants 0-4 Newbridge on Wye

Creigiau 0-1 Llanidloes Town

CRC Rangers 4-0 Graig y Rhacca

Cwm Welfare 3-4 Newport YMCA

Ely Valley 0-4 Baglan Dragons

Gors 2-9 Ragged School

Graig 2-3 Clydach Wasps

Hirwaun & Mackworth 8-0 Llwynypia

Kenfig Hill 1-4 Cogan Coronation

Llandrindod Wells 3-1 Fleur de Lys

Margam Youth Centre 2-7 Rhayader Town

WELSH LEAGUES

Nelson Cavaliers 0-4 Tongwylais
Penlan 3-2 Dafen Welfare
Penrhiwceiber Constitutional 1-3 Lucas Cwmbran
Perthcelyn United 1-3 Cwmamman United
Presteigne St Andrew's 6-0 Cornelly United
RTB Ebbw Vale 3-2 Clwb Cymric
STM Sports 1-0 Cardiff Hibernian
Sully Sports 3-1 Cwmbach Royal Stars
Swansea Dockers 3-1 Coed Eva
Ton & Gelli BC 5-1 Pentwynmawr Athletic
Tredegar Athletic 1-2 Llanharry
Treowen Stars 3-2 Hakin United
Holywell Town and Glan Conwy both received byes

ROUND 2
Northern Section
Acrefair Youth 4-3 Llanberis
Amlwch Town 0-5 Gresford United
Bodedern 0-3 Venture Community
Bro Goronwy 0-5 Glan Conwy
Carno 1-0 Llandyrnog United
Denbigh Town 1-0 Caernarfon Town
Dyffryn Nantlle Vale 0-2 Chirk A A A
Four Crosses 2-3 Brymbo
Gwalchmai 3-0 Coedpoeth United
Holywell Town 3-0 Kinmel Bay Sports
Llandudno Junction 0-2 Holyhead Hotspurs
Llanfair United 2-4 Llanrwst United
Llanrug United 5-0 Penrhyndeudraeth
Nefyn United 2-3 Llanfairpwll
Penmaenmawr Phoenix 0-3 Llanfyllni
Pwllheli 3-2 Berriew
Trearddur Bay United 2-2 F C Cefn
(Trearddur Bay United won 5-4 on penalties)

Southern Section
Aberaeron 4-1 Clydach Wasps
Abercarn United 1-1 Cwmamman United
(Abercarn United won 3-1 on penalties)
A F C Whitchurch 2-5 Trelewis Welfare
Baglan Dragons 4-5 Sully Sports
Carnetown 1-0 Cogan Coronation
Hirwaun & Mackworth 2-1 C R C Rangers
Llandrindod Wells 3-1 Presteigne St Andrew's
Llanidloes Town 0-1 Newbridge on Wye
Llangynwyd Rangers 6-1 Llanharry
Lucas Cwmbran 2-2 Swansea Dockers
(Swansea Dockers won 3-1 on penalties)
Rhayader Town 1-0 Ragged School
Risca United 2-0 Tongwynlais
R T B Ebbw Vale 2-4 Penlan
S T M Sports 4-5 Newport Y M C A
Ton & Gelli B C 1-0 Treowen Stars

ROUND 3
Northern Section
Brymbo 2-1 Glan Conwy
Rhayader Town 3-0 Llanllyfni
Venture Community 3-2 Carno
Llanfairpwll 1-3 Pwllheli
Denbigh Town 4-1 Gresford Athletic
Holyhead Hotspurs 3-2 Gwalchmai
Llanrwst United 3-1 Acrefair Youth
Trearddur Bay United 1-2 Holywell Town
Llanrug United 4-2 Chirk A A A

Southern Section
Swansea Dockers 4-2 Llandrindod Wells
Sully Sports 6-0 Carnetown
Ton & Gelli B C 3-0 Aberaeron
Risca United 3-0 Penlan
Trelewis Welfare 1-3 Abercarn United
Newport Y M C A 3-0 Llangynwyd Rangers
Hirwaun & Mackworth 2-1 Newbridge on Wye

ROUND 4
Northern Section
Holywell Town 0-4 Denbigh Town
Llanrug United 2-3 Holyhead Hotspurs
Llanrwst United 5-2 Venture Community
Pwllheli 1-0 Brymbo

Southern Section
Abercarn United 3-1 Rhayader Town
Risca United 6-3 Hirwaun & Mackworth
Sully Sports 2-1 Newport Y M C A
Ton & Gelli BGC 2-0 Swansea Dockers

QUARTER FINALS
Denbigh Town 0-5 Holyhead Hotspurs
Llanrwst United 2-1 Risca United
Pwllheli 4-1 Ton & Gelli BGC
Sully Sports 5-2 Abercarn United

SEMI-FINALS
Pwllheli 2-3 Sully Sports (@ Aberystwyth Town)
Llanrwst United 1-3 Holyhead Hotspurs(@ Bangor City)

FINAL (@ Aberystwyth Town, 14/4/12)
Sully Sports 2-1 Holyhead Hotspurs

SCOTTISH TABLES 2011-12

EAST OF SCOTLAND LEAGUE

Premier Division

	P	W	D	L	F	A	Pts
Stirling University	22	16	3	3	74	32	51
Spartans	22	16	3	3	66	28	51
Whitehill Welfare	22	12	3	7	45	34	39
Edinburgh University	22	10	3	9	38	26	33
Edinburgh City	22	10	3	9	41	39	33
Gretna 2008	22	9	6	7	40	46	33
Civil Service Strollers	22	10	1	11	38	46	31
Vale of Leithen	22	9	1	12	49	47	28
Tynecastle	22	8	3	11	33	52	27
Lothian Thistle H Vale	22	6	3	13	36	50	21
Leith Athletic	22	5	4	13	32	59	19
Selkirk	22	3	3	16	24	57	12

Division One

	P	W	D	L	F	A	Pts
Heriot-Watt University	24	17	4	3	61	25	55
Preston Athletic	24	14	6	4	73	35	48
Gala Fairydean	24	15	3	6	55	31	48
Eyemouth United	24	14	5	5	63	42	47
Craigroyston	24	10	8	6	37	33	38
Duns	24	10	6	8	48	39	36
Coldstream	24	11	3	10	51	53	36
Kelso United	24	8	4	12	43	54	28
Ormiston	24	8	2	14	27	56	26
Berwick Rangers Reserves	24	5	8	11	53	64	23
Peebles	24	3	9	12	28	48	18
Easthouses Lily	24	3	8	13	37	59	17
Hawick Royal Albert	24	3	4	17	24	61	13

HIGHLAND LEAGUE

	P	W	D	L	F	A	Pts
Forres Mechanics	34	24	5	5	85	35	77
Cove Rangers	34	23	7	4	92	33	76
Nairn County	34	19	9	6	92	44	66
Inverurie Loco Works	34	20	5	9	71	35	65
Buckie Thistle	34	18	7	9	79	45	61
Fraserburgh	34	17	8	9	79	63	59
Deveronvale	34	17	4	13	75	49	55
Wick Academy	34	16	7	11	77	55	55
Keith	34	16	6	12	85	57	54
Clachnacuddin	34	14	8	12	79	65	50
Formartine United	34	14	7	13	62	60	49
Lossiemouth	34	15	4	15	51	52	49
Huntly	34	14	4	16	50	67	46
Turriff United	34	13	4	17	61	64	43
Rothes	34	7	5	22	31	80	26
Brora Rangers	34	6	2	26	33	115	20
Strathspey Thistle	34	3	2	29	27	102	11
Fort William	34	1	4	29	14	122	7

NORTH CALEDONIAN LEAGUE

	P	W	D	L	F	A	Pts
Halkirk United	14	10	3	1	49	20	33
Muir of Ord Rovers	14	9	3	2	36	16	30
Golspie Sutherland	14	8	4	2	43	20	28
Alness United	14	6	2	6	26	18	20
Dingwall Thistle	14	6	1	7	31	28	19
Thurso	14	5	1	8	27	27	16
Clachnacuddin Reserves	14	3	1	10	24	52	10
Balintore	14	0	3	11	18	73	3

SJFA EAST REGION

Superleague

	P	W	D	L	F	A	Pts
Bonnyrigg Rose	20	13	4	3	48	23	43
Hill of Beath Hawthorn	20	11	5	4	39	23	38
Linlithgow Rose	20	10	5	5	42	32	35
Boness United	20	7	6	7	25	26	27
Kelty Hearts	20	7	5	8	24	26	26
Camelon Juniors	20	7	4	9	30	29	25
Lochee United	20	7	3	10	32	37	24
Musselburgh Athletic	20	6	4	10	41	45	22
St Andrews United	20	6	4	10	28	40	22
Carnoustie Panmure	20	5	6	9	32	39	21
Bathgate Thistle	20	5	6	9	27	48	21

Premier League

	P	W	D	L	F	A	Pts
Sauchie Juniors	22	13	6	3	43	23	45
Broxburn Athletic	22	13	4	5	43	31	43
Tayport	22	10	7	5	37	18	37
Penicuik Athletic	22	11	4	7	35	24	37
Oakley United	22	10	6	6	43	36	36
Newtongrange Star	22	8	7	7	44	30	31
Ballingry Rovers	22	8	5	9	35	42	29
Glenrothes	22	7	7	8	39	42	28
Broughty Athletic	22	5	7	10	24	43	22
Armadale Thistle	22	4	8	10	25	33	20
Downfield	22	5	5	12	31	46	20
Arniston Rangers	22	2	6	14	21	52	12

Central Division

	P	W	D	L	F	A	Pts
Jeanfield Swifts	24	20	2	2	104	20	62
Dundonald Bluebell	24	18	4	2	67	33	58
Kinnoull	24	17	2	5	63	39	53
Lochgelly Albert	24	15	3	6	68	46	48
Bankfoot	24	9	6	9	47	40	33
Newburgh	24	9	6	9	46	48	33
Kirkcaldy YM	24	9	5	10	55	60	32
Thornton Hibs	24	8	3	13	54	80	27
Crossgates Primrose	24	6	7	11	39	62	25
Rosyth	24	4	9	11	33	51	21
Lochore Welfare	24	5	4	15	45	62	19
Steelend Vics	24	4	5	15	49	83	17
Luncarty	24	3	2	19	51	97	11

SCOTTISH FOOTBALL

North Division

	P	W	D	L	F	A	Pts
Dundee Violet	20	18	1	1	80	15	55
Dundee North End	20	14	4	2	50	22	46
Montrose Roselea	20	13	4	3	50	17	43
Arbroath Vics	20	10	4	6	37	35	34
East Craigie	20	9	6	5	45	35	33
Kirriemuir Thistle	20	10	2	8	47	26	32
Brechin Vics	20	8	0	12	38	63	24
Lochee Harp	20	6	2	12	33	51	20
Blairgowrie	20	4	3	13	30	40	15
Forfar Albion	20	1	6	13	25	51	9
Coupar Angus	20	0	2	18	25	105	2

South Division

	P	W	D	L	F	A	Pts
Dalkeith Thistle	28	20	3	5	76	41	63
Haddington Athletic	28	17	5	6	104	54	56
Falkirk JFC	28	17	4	7	61	43	55
Fauldhouse United	28	16	5	7	75	37	53
Tranent Juniors	28	16	5	7	54	36	53
Blackburn United	28	14	7	7	57	34	49
Livingston United	28	14	7	7	63	45	49
Whitburn Juniors	28	14	7	7	52	47	49
Dunbar United	28	11	5	12	44	51	38
Spartans	28	11	3	14	59	68	36
Stoneyburn Juniors	28	9	2	17	45	80	29
West Calder United	28	8	4	16	46	64	28
Pumpherston Juniors	28	6	3	19	31	63	21
Edinburgh United	28	2	4	22	31	84	10
Harthill Royal	28	2	2	24	38	89	8

SJFA NORTH REGION

Superleague

	P	W	D	L	F	A	Pts
Hermes	26	24	1	1	79	16	73
Stonehaven	26	19	2	5	69	33	59
Dyce Juniors	26	16	5	5	63	43	53
Culter	26	16	4	6	92	43	52
Banks o'Dee	26	14	5	7	55	30	47
FCStoneywood	26	14	1	11	63	47	43
Banchory St Ternan	26	12	2	12	62	64	38
Ellon United	26	12	1	13	45	55	37
Longside	26	11	2	13	50	67	35
Hall Russell United	26	9	5	12	40	46	32
Lewis United	26	6	1	19	40	80	19
Maud	26	5	3	18	41	76	18
Forres Thistle	26	5	1	20	21	70	16
Sunnybank	26	1	3	22	37	87	6

Division One

	P	W	D	L	F	A	Pts
Inverness City	26	19	2	5	92	32	59
Fraserburgh United	26	19	2	5	62	26	59
Deveronside	26	18	2	6	68	37	56
Glentanar	26	16	2	8	73	42	50
East End	26	13	7	6	62	39	46
New Elgin	26	13	2	11	64	47	41
Parkvale	26	11	4	11	55	55	37
Bridge of Don Thistle	26	9	6	11	43	60	33
Islavale	26	9	5	12	53	64	32
Lossiemouth United	26	9	3	14	47	69	30
Buchanhaven Hearts	26	8	3	15	55	70	27
Dufftown	26	6	2	18	40	80	20
Burghead Thistle	26	4	6	16	40	80	18
Buckie Rovers	26	3	4	19	26	79	13

Division Two

	P	W	D	L	F	A	Pts
Portgordon Victoria	24	17	2	5	71	34	53
Nairn St Ninian	24	15	5	4	72	29	50
Newmachar United	24	13	3	8	68	49	42
Colony Park	24	12	3	9	57	35	39
Cruden Bay	24	10	3	11	49	50	33
Whitehills	24	9	3	12	39	55	30
Bishopmill United	24	8	5	11	41	57	29
RAF Lossiemouth	24	6	2	16	31	69	20
Fochabers	24	4	2	18	27	77	14

SJFA WESTERN REGION

Superleague Premier

	P	W	D	L	F	A	Pts
Irvine Meadow XI	22	15	3	4	54	25	48
Petershill	22	12	7	3	47	26	43
Auchinleck Talbot	22	11	6	5	42	21	39
Clydebank	22	12	3	7	45	32	39
Beith Juniors	22	10	5	7	31	30	35
Ashfield	22	9	7	6	46	36	34
Arthurlie	22	9	3	10	41	41	30
Kirkintilloch Rob Roy	22	8	4	10	36	46	28
Cumnock Juniors	22	6	7	9	38	50	25
Pollok	22	7	2	13	34	45	23
Largs Thistle	22	4	5	13	20	44	17
Kilbirnie Ladeside	22	2	2	18	25	63	8

Superleague Division One

	P	W	D	L	F	A	Pts
Glenafton Athletic	26	15	7	4	58	33	52
Shotts Bon Accord	26	16	4	6	60	38	52
Renfrew	26	13	6	7	63	48	45
Kilsyth Rangers	26	13	4	9	58	46	43
Thorniewood United	26	12	5	9	55	51	41
Rutherglen Glencairn	26	11	4	11	45	45	37
Cumbernauld United	26	12	0	14	43	47	36
Ardrossan Winton Rovers	26	10	4	12	53	49	34
Whitletts Victoria	26	9	7	10	45	47	34
Hurlford United	26	10	4	12	44	49	34
East Kilbride Thistle	26	10	4	12	43	61	34
Lanark United	26	10	3	13	35	34	33
Girvan	26	8	9	9	48	54	33
Dalry Thistle	26	2	1	23	31	79	7

Ayrshire District League

	P	W	D	L	F	A	Pts
Maybole Juniors	22	18	1	3	56	19	55
Kello Rovers	22	17	2	3	73	31	53
Troon	22	16	3	3	74	23	51
Kilwinning Rangers	22	15	2	5	73	24	47
Annbank United	22	12	3	7	63	40	39
Irvine Victoria	22	9	3	10	58	46	30
Saltcoats Victoria	22	9	3	10	43	40	30
Muirkirk Juniors	22	7	1	14	34	54	22
Ardeer Thistle	22	5	2	15	26	77	17
Darvel Juniors	22	4	2	16	30	91	14
Craigmark Burntonians	22	3	4	15	27	74	13
Lugar Boswell Thistle	22	3	2	17	31	69	11
Vale of Leven	26	9	3	14	37	48	30
Vale of Clyde	26	4	2	20	30	77	14

Central District Div. One

	P	W	D	L	F	A	Pts
Glasgow Perthshire	26	20	3	3	63	26	63
Yoker Athletic	26	18	1	7	71	41	55
Greenock Juniors	26	17	4	5	60	36	55
Neilston Juniors	26	12	1	13	46	39	37
Benburb	26	11	3	12	42	49	36
Port Glasgow Juniors	26	10	4	12	45	52	34
Dunipace	26	10	3	13	39	41	33
Shettleston	26	9	6	11	42	53	33
Larkhall Thistle	26	9	7	10	53	52	32
Bellshill Athletic	26	9	5	12	32	32	32
St Anthony's	26	8	8	10	36	42	32
Cambuslang Rangers	26	10	2	14	36	44	32

Central District Div. Two

	P	W	D	L	F	A	Pts
Carluke Rovers	20	13	2	5	56	31	41
St Roch's	20	12	3	5	51	21	39
Lesmahagow Juniors	20	11	4	5	54	42	37
Forth Wanderers	20	12	3	5	47	23	36
Maryhill	20	11	1	8	44	34	34
Johnstone Burgh	20	7	7	6	38	33	28
Wishaw Juniors	20	9	1	10	39	45	28
Rossvale	20	7	1	12	30	53	22
Newmains United	20	6	0	14	32	67	18
Blantyre Victoria	20	6	2	12	33	47	17
Royal Albert	20	3	2	15	21	49	11

SOUTH OF SCOTLAND LEAGUE

	P	W	D	L	F	A	Pts
Dalbeattie Star	24	21	3	0	104	80	66
Threave Rovers	24	20	2	2	111	23	62
Heston Rovers	24	17	0	7	68	57	51
St Cuthbert Wanderers	24	16	1	7	89	48	49
5 Newton Stewart	24	12	2	10	72	54	38
Mid Annandale	24	10	2	12	63	72	32
Stranraer "A" (-10)	24	13	2	9	59	53	31
Crichton	24	6	3	15	50	66	21
Fleet Star	24	6	2	16	42	106	20
Wigtown	24	5	4	15	46	56	19
Abbey Vale	24	5	4	15	45	76	19
Nithsdale Wanderers (-10)	24	9	1	14	42	79	18
Creetown	24	2	2	20	36	112	8

SCOTTISH AMATEUR FOOTBALL LEAGUE

Premier Division

	P	W	D	L	F	A	Pts
Postal United	18	16	2	0	58	14	50
Oban Saints	18	12	2	4	51	26	38
Thorn Athletic	18	11	4	3	42	31	37
Rolls Royce (EK)	18	9	3	6	33	28	30
Castlemilk	18	9	2	7	42	37	29
St. Josephs	18	8	2	8	34	38	26
Aikenhead Thistle	18	8	1	9	40	37	25
Inverclyde	18	4	1	13	26	43	13
Kilbowie Union	18	3	1	14	32	60	10
Kings Park Rangers (-3)	18	1	0	17	17	61	0

Premier Division One

	P	W	D	L	F	A	Pts
Finnart	18	15	2	1	51	16	47
Eaglesham	18	11	3	4	40	19	36
Haldane United	18	11	2	5	44	29	35
Busby	18	10	3	5	46	26	33
Cambria	18	9	3	6	47	30	30
Duncanrig FP	18	6	5	7	30	38	23
Shawlands F.P	18	7	1	10	30	37	22
Arkleston	18	6	3	9	44	45	21
Glencastle Sparta	18	2	1	15	18	62	7
Carlton YM	18	1	1	16	19	67	4

Premier Division Two

	P	W	D	L	F	A	Pts
Alba Thistle	18	15	3	0	59	20	48
Auldhouse	18	12	3	3	46	32	39
Gourock Thistle	18	12	1	5	52	26	37
Campbeltown Pupils	18	10	4	4	43	32	34
Rutherglen	18	7	3	8	31	31	24
Centre	18	5	4	9	39	51	19
Dunoon	18	5	2	11	41	52	17
Port Glasgow Old Boys Union	18	4	3	11	26	48	15
Celtic Community Academy	18	3	3	12	20	39	12
Clydebank	18	2	4	12	23	49	10

Division One

	P	W	D	L	F	A	Pts
Paisley	18	12	2	4	49	32	38
Tarbert	18	8	6	4	52	38	30
Aikenhead Thistle Reserves	18	9	3	6	48	43	30
Millbeg	18	8	5	5	50	46	29
Lochgilphead Red Star	18	8	3	7	35	35	27
Cambria Reserves	18	6	6	6	38	40	24
East Kilbride Y.M.C.A	18	7	2	9	37	39	23
Whitehill F.P	18	6	3	9	47	47	21
Port Glasgow Hibs	18	6	3	9	44	46	21
Duncanrig FP Reserves	18	2	3	13	23	57	9

Division Two

	P	W	D	L	F	A	Pts
East Kilbride AFC	20	17	1	2	85	20	52
Rosehill Star	20	14	3	3	75	41	45
Jamestown	20	11	3	6	65	38	36
Strathaven Dynamo	20	9	7	4	60	36	34
Inverkip Thistle	20	8	6	6	38	37	30
Dunoon Reserves	20	7	7	6	64	48	28
Millerston Thistle	20	7	1	12	37	64	22
Kings Park Rangers Ress	20	6	3	11	41	72	21
Carlton YM Reserves	20	4	3	13	34	68	15
Bothwell & Uddingston Albion	20	4	2	14	37	75	14
Shawlands F.P Reserves	20	3	4	13	33	70	13

SCOTTISH FOOTBALL
ABERDEENSHIRE AMATEUR FOOTBALL ASSOCIATION

Premier Division	P	W	D	L	F	A	Pts
Woodside	26	18	5	3	70	23	59
University	26	17	7	2	93	38	58
Sportsmans Club	26	15	4	7	89	42	49
Kincorth	26	15	4	7	85	55	49
Echt	26	14	3	9	69	59	45
Westdyke	26	12	6	8	53	44	42
Blackburn	26	11	3	12	64	69	36
Cove Thistle	26	9	6	11	80	73	33
Cowie Thistle	26	8	8	10	46	59	32
Great Western United	26	10	1	15	62	73	31
Mearns United	26	8	7	11	65	84	31
Bon Accord City	26	7	4	15	50	63	25
Dyce ITC Hydraulics	26	6	2	18	45	96	20
Kintore	26	1	2	23	28	121	5

Division One (North)	P	W	D	L	F	A	Pts
Insch	26	19	2	5	79	44	59
Tarves	26	19	2	5	96	46	59
Stoneywood Amateurs	26	16	4	6	80	43	52
Nicolls Amateurs	26	16	3	7	81	55	51
Kaimhill United	26	11	5	10	69	68	38
Don Athletic	26	10	6	10	60	74	36
Glendale	26	10	4	12	42	46	34
West End	26	9	6	11	67	72	33
Rattrays XI	26	8	8	10	54	63	32
Beacon Rangers (-6)	26	10	6	10	66	72	30
Ellon Amateurs	26	8	2	16	58	72	26
Westhill	26	6	5	15	58	79	23
Burghmuir	26	4	6	16	38	85	18
University Strollers	26	4	5	17	46	75	17

Insch won the Championship play-off 4-0 against Tarves.

Division One (East)	P	W	D	L	F	A	Pts
Luthermuir	26	17	6	3	72	28	57
Portlethen United	26	17	4	5	70	39	55
RGU	26	14	7	5	80	49	49
Rothie Rovers	26	12	6	8	60	60	42
Johnshaven Athletic	26	12	4	10	81	70	40
Halliburton	26	11	4	11	67	69	37
Newtonhill	26	11	3	12	70	73	36
Lads Club Amateurs	26	10	6	10	61	53	36
Old Aberdonians	26	10	5	11	64	64	35
MS United	26	8	6	12	56	69	30
Newmachar United	26	7	6	13	50	65	27
AC Mill Inn	26	7	6	13	54	58	27
Stonehaven Athletic	26	7	5	14	43	77	26
Banchory	26	3	4	19	37	91	13

Newmachar Utd won the Relegation Play-off 1-0 against AC Mill Inn.

Division Two (North)	P	W	D	L	F	A	Pts
Bervie Caledonian	24	15	6	3	58	29	51
Alford	24	14	4	6	72	48	46
Feughside	24	12	8	4	64	38	44
Mintlaw	24	13	4	7	59	47	43
Cammachmore	24	12	6	6	70	51	42
University Colts	24	11	2	11	65	64	35
JS XI	24	10	3	11	70	60	33
Northern United	24	9	6	9	57	49	33
Ellon Thistle	24	8	6	10	50	50	30
Torry United	24	7	3	14	35	66	24
Grammar FPs	24	6	4	14	34	63	22
FC Polska	24	5	5	14	37	68	20
Continental	24	3	5	16	34	72	14

Division Two (East)	P	W	D	L	F	A	Pts
Hazlehead United	26	22	2	2	149	40	68
Kemnay Youth	26	20	1	5	76	34	61
Scotstown Rovers	26	16	4	6	99	59	52
Glendale XI	26	15	3	8	99	53	48
Torphins	26	14	4	8	87	66	46
Trophies International	26	14	1	11	61	70	43
St Laurence	26	12	3	11	77	65	39
Glentanar Reflex (-4)	26	13	3	10	71	61	38
Glendale Youth	26	10	3	13	56	65	33
Theologians	26	8	6	12	70	70	30
McTeagle	26	7	4	15	50	99	25
West End Electrical	26	6	2	18	49	90	20
Mugiemoss Youth	26	6	1	19	51	96	19
Postal ALC	26	0	1	25	24	151	1

Division Three	P	W	D	L	F	A	Pts
Dee Amateurs	28	22	3	3	124	40	69
Great Northern Athletic	28	21	3	4	111	44	66
Ferryhill	28	21	1	6	100	40	64
Highland Hotel	28	20	2	6	91	53	62
Turriff Thistle	28	17	4	7	110	52	55
Newburgh Thistle	28	13	6	9	72	60	45
Monymusk	28	13	2	13	58	58	41
Auchnagatt Barons	28	11	6	11	78	79	39
Byron FC	28	9	7	12	60	74	34
Bankhead	28	7	1	20	46	114	22
Huntly Amateurs	28	6	4	18	55	104	22
Fintray Thistle	28	6	2	20	55	100	20
Broomhill BC	28	6	2	20	43	98	20
ARI Thistle	28	6	2	20	54	116	20
BSFC (-6)	28	6	7	15	64	89	19

BORDER AMATEUR LEAGUE

A League

	P	W	D	L	F	A	Pts
Pencaitland	20	17	2	1	73	25	53
Leithen Rovers	20	13	4	3	60	30	43
Hawick Waverley	20	13	3	4	63	41	42
Gala Rovers	20	12	3	5	72	35	39
Tweeddale Rovers	20	9	2	9	45	33	29
Langholm Leg.	20	7	3	10	35	59	24
West Barns Star (-3)	20	8	2	10	54	50	23
Chirnside Utd	20	6	5	9	52	49	23
Newtown	20	2	7	11	34	61	13
Duns Ams (-3)	20	3	3	14	24	78	9
Hawick Legion	20	1	4	15	19	70	7

B League

	P	W	D	L	F	A	Pts
Greenlaw	22	13	6	3	53	33	45
Hearts of Liddesdale (-3)	22	14	3	5	64	40	42
Ancrum	22	13	3	6	53	38	42
Linton Hotspur	22	11	7	4	44	26	40
Stow	22	9	7	6	46	35	34
Coldstream Ams	22	7	10	5	55	45	31
Tweedm'th Ams	22	6	6	10	46	45	24
Eyemouth Ams	22	6	5	11	53	62	23
Jed Legion	22	5	4	13	32	56	19
Hawick Utd	22	4	6	12	42	75	18
Selkirk Victoria (-18)	22	8	6	8	46	41	12
Chirnside UC (-3)	22	1	7	14	29	67	7

C League

	P	W	D	L	F	A	Pts
Gala Hotspur	20	15	1	4	82	23	46
CFC Bowholm	20	14	3	3	79	31	45
Winton	20	12	4	4	70	40	40
Lauder	20	10	4	6	36	27	34
Kelso Thistle	20	8	8	4	59	46	32
Tweedm'th AC	20	8	4	8	71	43	28
Peebles Ams (-3)	20	7	6	7	45	50	24
Earlston Rhymers	20	5	4	11	44	73	19
St.Boswells	20	4	3	13	37	85	15
Gala Athletic	20	3	3	14	34	83	12
Hawick LR (-12)	20	2	4	14	28	84	-8

SCOTTISH FOOTBALL
CALADONIAN LEAGUE

Premier Division

	P	W	D	L	F	A	Pts
Glasgow Harp	22	16	4	2	73	21	52
Milton	22	16	2	4	54	28	50
Westerlands	22	14	3	5	60	25	45
Giffnock	N	22	13	5	4	56	44
Dalziel HSFP	22	7	9	6	42	34	30
St. Mungo's	22	7	8	7	42	38	29
Cambusbarron	22	8	4	10	46	49	28
Glasgow University	22	7	4	11	39	35	25
Dumbarton AC (-3)	22	6	6	10	33	49	21
Drumchapel FP	22	6	3	13	33	51	21
Strathclyde United	22	4	3	15	26	70	15
MILNGAVIE (-3)	22	2	1	19	23	94	4

Division One

	P	W	D	L	F	A	Pts
Doune Castle	22	15	4	3	81	33	49
Gartcosh	22	14	7	1	51	22	49
East Kilbride YM	22	13	5	4	75	43	44
Bearsden	22	12	3	7	57	33	39
Hamilton FP	22	10	5	7	56	50	35
Stirling University	22	9	5	8	54	34	32
Rhu	22	9	2	11	61	62	29
Rothesay	22	7	5	10	54	56	26
Weirs	22	5	4	13	44	79	19
Viewfield	22	5	3	14	52	90	18
Balmore	22	4	5	13	35	55	17
Symington	22	4	2	16	33	93	14

Newton Mearns - record expunged

Central Scottish Amateur League

Premier Division

	P	W	D	L	F	A	Pts
Colville Park	22	17	3	2	60	23	54
Drumchapel United	22	15	0	7	74	31	45
St Patricks FP	22	14	0	8	54	38	42
Ashvale Victoria	22	11	3	8	45	42	36
Steins Thistle	22	10	3	9	39	46	33
Wishaw HSFP	22	9	3	10	36	33	30
Uddingston Anvil	22	9	2	11	39	44	29
Kilsyth	22	8	4	10	41	44	28
Harestanes	22	8	3	11	43	45	27
Pollok	22	8	3	11	38	59	27
Brightons	22	6	3	13	36	54	21
Arthurlie United	22	3	1	18	31	77	10

Division One A

	P	W	D	L	F	A	Pts
Campsie Minerva	18	14	2	2	62	25	44
Linwood	18	13	3	2	62	29	42
Garrowhill Thistle	18	9	3	6	46	40	30
Scotia Athletic	18	8	5	5	48	45	29
Waterside	18	8	4	6	40	41	28
Stedfast	18	8	2	8	49	56	26
Mearns	18	5	1	12	44	57	16
Redbrae	18	4	4	10	33	55	16
Gourock Athletic	18	3	3	12	39	54	12
East Kilbride	18	3	3	12	42	63	12

SCOTTISH FOOTBALL

Division One B

	P	W	D	L	F	A	Pts
Bannockburn	18	13	4	1	78	23	43
Wellhouse	18	13	2	3	84	28	41
Drumchapel	18	11	6	1	50	21	39
Greenock HSFP	18	10	3	5	67	35	33
Eastfield	18	8	4	6	35	27	28
Cambusnethan Talbot	18	7	4	7	45	32	25
Chryston	18	4	5	9	41	60	17
Grangemouth	18	3	2	13	29	70	11
Stirling City	18	3	2	13	27	73	11
Cumbernauld Clyde	18	1	2	15	19	106	5

DUMFRIES & DISTRICT AMATEUR LEAGUE

	P	W	D	L	F	A	Pts
Lochar Thistle	21	18	3	0	105	35	57
Lochmaben (-6)	21	15	4	2	82	34	43
Upper Annandale	21	10	2	9	57	39	32
Dumfries YMCA	21	9	3	9	50	60	30
Maxwelltown Thistle	21	8	3	10	52	61	27
Morton Thistle	21	4	5	12	32	69	17
Terregles Athletic	21	4	2	15	35	70	14
Dynamo Star	21	3	3	15	32	77	12

SCOTTISH JUNIOR CUP

ROUND 1

Yoker Athletic 6-0 Craigmark Burntonians
Dyce Juniors 2-5 Kirkintilloch Rob Roy
Lochee Harp 2-3 Ardeer Thistle
Port Glasgow Juniors 2-1 Harthill Royal
Cruden Bay 1-3 Armadale Thistle
Dundee North End 1-2 Hall Russell United
Penicuik Athletic 1-1 Glenrothes
Greenock Juniors 5-1 Fochabers
Shettleston 2-3 Dunbar United
Kello Rovers 5-0 Lossiemouth United
Saltcoats Victoria 4-1 East Kilbride Thistle
Largs Thistle 0-0 St Anthony's
Maybole 7-0 Brechin Victoria
Oakley United 1-0 Rutherglen Glencairn
Islavale 1-3 Annbank United
Sauchie Juniors 1-0 Steelend Victoria
Arthurlie 5-0 Tranent
Lochee United 7-0 Luncarty
Rosyth 4-2 Dundonald Bluebell
Kirriemuir Thistle 0-2 Kelty Hearts
Ardrossan Winton Rovers 2-1 Lochgelly Albert
Ellon United 3-0 Forres Thistle
Newtongrange Star 2-1 Longside
Hurlford United 1-2 Broxburn Athletic
Benburb 0-2 Cambuslang Rangers

Edinburgh United 0-8 Auchinleck Talbot
Colony Park 0-7 Neilston Juniors
Petershill 5-2 Maryhill
Bo'ness United 2-1 Linlithgow Rose
Jeanfield Swifts 8-5 Aberdeen East End
Wishaw 0-6 Dunipace Juniors
Forfar Albion 2-2 Nairn St Ninian
Buchanhaven Hearts 1-5 Dalkeith Thistle
Deveronside 0-1 Whitletts Victoria
Banks O'Dee 1-6 Ashfield
Stoneyburn 1-1 Larkhall Thistle

ROUND 1 REPLAYS
Glenrothes 0-3 Penicuik Athletic
St Anthony's 2-4 Largs Thistle
Nairn St Ninian 0-0 Forfar Albion
(Nairn St Ninian won 5-3 on penalties)
Larkhall Thistle 5-2 Stoneyburn

ROUND 2
Oakley United 5-3 Portgordon Victoria
Crossgates Primrose 1-0 Ardeer Thistle
Hermes 4-2 Stonehaven
Maud 0-2 Shotts Bon Accord
Thorniewood United 5-1 Newmachar United
St Roch's 4-0 Bankfoot Athletic
Forth Wanderers 0-2 Camelon Junior
Lesmahagow 5-1 Whitehills
Ardrossan Winton Rovers 1-2 Armadale Thistle
Dunbar United 1-4 Cumnock Juniors
Kelty Hearts 2-0 Culter
Fraserburgh United 3-2 Downfield
Kirkintilloch Rob Roy 0-2 Auchinleck Talbot
Burghead Thistle 1-2 Pollok
New Elgin 2-2 Kilwinning Rangers
Glasgow Perthshire 0-0 Penicuik Athletic
Maybole 3-1 Falkirk Juniors
Broxburn Athletic 6-0 Dalry Thistle
Dunipace Juniors 5-1 Royal Albert
Kirbirnie Ladeside 4-1 Livingston United
Blackburn United 2-2 Carnoustie Panmure
Troon 4-1 Lochore Welfare
St Andrews United 4-0 FC Stoneywood
Kinnoull 4-2 Irvine Victoria
Sunnybank 1-4 Irvine Meadow XI
Petershill 2-2 Ballingry Rovers
Renfrew 1-1 Sacuhie Juniors
Whitburn Juniors 1-1 Newburgh
West Calder United 0-3 Neilston Juniors
Largs Thistle 2-0 Ellon United
Arthurlie 11-2 Bishopmill United

SCOTTISH FOOTBALL
Blantyre Victoria 2-1 Jeanfield Swifts
Newtongrange Star 0-0 Bonnyrigg Rose Atheltic
Carluke Rovers 3-2 Vale Of Clyde
Pumpherston 0-6 Lochee United
Inverness City 0-3 East Craigie
Musselburgh Athletic 2-1 Hill of Beath Hawthorn
Bellshill Athletic 4-1 Thornton Hibernian
Whitletts Victoria 2-1 Dalkeith Thistle
Kello Rovers 0-1 Annbank United
RAF Lossiemouth 2-1 Dufftown
Dundee United 3-0 Hall Russell United
Larkhall Thistle 4-1 Muirkirk
Forfar West End AW Girvan
Buckie Rovers 1-5 Broughty Athletic
Newmains United 0-5 Glenafton Athletic
Spartans 0-0 Glentanar
Cambuslang Rangers 4-2 Yoker Athletic
Kirkcaldy Y M 7-0 Coupar Angus
Saltcoats Victoria 8-0 Darvel
Arniston Rangers 3-0 Banchory St Ternan
Clydebank 9-2 Rossvale
Haddington Athletic 5-0 Johnstone Burgh
Lugar Boswell Thistle 1-2 Stonehouse Violet
Tayport 5-0 Arbroath Victoria
Bathgate Thistle 1-2 Ashfield
Fauldhouse United 6-1 Port Glasgow Juniors
Lanark United 2-0 Vale Of Leven
Greenock Juniors 3-1 Parkvale
Beith Juniors 5-5 Cumbernauld United
Rosyth 2-3 Nairn St Ninian
Bo'ness United 3-0 Lewis United
Kilsyth Rangers 6-0 Bridge Of Don Thistle
Montrose Roselea 2-3 Blairgowrie

ROUND 2 REPLAYS
Kilwinning Rangers 3-1 New Elgin
Penicuik Athletic 4-1 Glasgow Perthshire
Carnoustie Panmure 2-2 Blackburn United
(Carnoustie Panmure won 5-4 on penalties)
Ballingry Rovers 2-2 Petershill
(Ballingry Rovers won 4-2 on penalties)
Sauchie Juniors 0-0 Renfrew
(Sauchie won 5-4 on penalties)
Newburgh 2-5 Whitburn Juniors
Bonnyrigg Rose Athletic 2-1 Newtongrange Star
Glentanar 2-2 Spartans
(Glentanar won 5-4 on penalties)
Cumbernauld United 0-1 Beith Juniors

SCOTTISH FOOTBALL

ROUND 3

Broxburn Athletic 2-2 Girvan

Stonehouse Violet 1-2 Arniston Rangers

Maybole 4-1 Fauldhouse Violet

Cumnock Juniors 6-2 Kirkcaldy YM

Troon 2-2 Haddington Athletic

Lochee United 2-2 Tayport

Bo'ness United 2-0 Saltcoats Victoria

Cambuslang Rangers 2-0 East Craigie

Kilsyth Rangers 1-1 Armadale Thistle

Oakley United 0-2 Arthurlie

Ashfield 1-1 Whitletts Victoria

Thorniewood United 2-5 Larkhall Thistle

Kilwinning Rangers 3-1 Blantyre Victoria

Hermes 1-4 Glenafton Athletic

Dunipace Juniors 0-1 Irvine Meadow XI

St Andrews United 3-1 Carnoustie Panmure

Sauchie Juniors 2-2 Neilston Juniors

Dundee Violet 3-0 Ballingry Rovers

Shotts Bon Accord 2-2 Annbank United

Camelon Juniors 0-0 Kelty Hearts

Whitburn 1-1 Glentanar

Bellshill Athletic 2-1 Greenock Juniors

Largs Thistle 3-0 Lesmahagow

Fraserburgh United 2-4 St Roch's

Nairn St Ninian 0-3 Lanark United

Blairgowrie 2-2 Pollok

Beith Juniors 2-3 Musselburgh Athletic

Kinnoull 1-0 Crossgates Primrose

Auchinleck Talbot 6-0 Penicuik Athletic

Bonnyrigg Rose Athletic 3-2 Clydebank

Carluke Rovers 2-1 Broughty Rovers

Kilbirnie Ladeside AW RAF Lossiemouth

ROUND 3 REPLAYS

Girvan 4-3 Broxburn Athletic

Haddington Athletic 1-1 Troon

(Troon won 4-3 on penalties)

Tayport 0-3 Lochee United

Armadale Thistle 0-2 Kilsyth Rangers

Whitletts Victoria 0-2 Ashfield

Neilston Juniors 0-1 Sauchie Juniors

Pollok 6-0 Blairgowrie

Kelty Hearts 1-0 Camelon Juniors

Annbank United 0-3 Shotts Bon Accord

Glentanar 1-2 Whitburn

ROUND 4

Kelty Hearts 4-2 Whitburn

Kilwinning Rangers 1-0 Glenafton Athletic

Larkhall Athletic 2-1 Bellshill Athletic

Musselburgh Athletic 1-3 Auchinleck Talbot

Pollok 1-1 Lochee United

St Andrews United 1-1 Cumnock Juniors

Carluke Rovers 0-1 Irvine Meadow XI

Dundee Violet 0-1 Ashfield

Largs Thistle 1-1 Arniston Rangers

Kilsyth Rangers 1-3 Arthurlie

Sauchie Juniors 2-3 Bo'ness United

Cambuslang Rangers 1-2 Shotts Bon Accord

Kilbirnie Ladeside 3-1 Troon

Bonnyrigg Rose Athletic 3-2 Maybole

Girvan 2-3 St Roch's

Lanark United 0-4 Kinnoull

ROUND 4 REPLAYS

Lochee United 5-2 Pollok

Cumnock Juniors 2-4 St Andrews United

Arniston Rangers 1-1 Largs Thistle

(Largs Thistle won 4-2 on penalties)

ROUND 5

Arthurlie 1-1 Bo'ness United

Ashfield 2-3 Bonnyrigg Rose Athletic

Auchinleck Talbot 5-0 St Roch's

Kilwinning Rangers 2-2 Larkhall Thistle

St Andrews United 1-1 Kilbirnie Ladeside

Kinnoull 2-2 Shotts Bon Accord

Lochee United 0-3 Irvine Meadow XI

Largs Thistle 2-1 Kelty Hearts

Round 5 Replays

Bo'ness United 2-0 Arthurlie

Larkhall Thistle 1-2 Kilwinning Rangers

Kilbirnie Ladeside 0-2 St Andrews United

Shotts Bon Accord 4-1 Kinnoull (@ Petershill)

QUARTER FINALS

St Andrews United 0-1 Shotts Bon Accord

Irvine Meadow XI 0-2 Bonnyrigg Rose Athletic

Largs Thistle 2-0 Kilwinning Rangers

Auchinleck Talbot 2-0 Bo'ness United

SEMI-FINALS (2 LEGS)

Bonnyrigg Rose Athletic 1-1 Auchinleck Talbot

Auchinleck Talbot 0-0 Bonnyrigg Rose Athletic

(Aggregate 1-1, Auchinleck Talbot won 6-5 on penalties)

Shotts Bon Accord 1-1 Largs Thistle

Largs Thistle 0-0 Shotts Bon Accord

(Aggregate 1-1, Shotts Bon Accord won 4-2 on penalties)

FINAL

Auchinleck Talbot 1-2 Shotts Bon Accord

the
FOOTBALL
ASSOCIATION
COMPETITIONS

NO

Respect
Referee
Game

One match in three is played without a
referee because of abuse from players.

Isn't it time to show some Respect?

TheFA.com/Respect

ENGLAND C

RESULTS   2011-12

No.	Date	Comp	H/A	Opponents	Att:	Result	Goalscorers
1	Nov 15	F	A	Gibraltar	1,850	L 1 - 3	Jennings 80
2	Feb 28	ICT	H	Italy	4,628	D 1 - 1	Watkins 90
3	June 05	ICT	A	Russia		L 0 - 4	

ICT - International Challenge Trophy (Group A). F - Friendly

THE PLAYERS

NAME		CLUB	2011-12 CAPS	11-12 GOALS	TOTAL CAPS	TOTAL GOALS
Ainge	Simon	Guiseley	1	0	1	0
Beeley	Shaun	Fleetwood	1	0	1	0
Blair	Matty	York City	1	0	2	0
Boyes	Adam	Barrow	2	0	3	0
Brogan	Stephen	Stalybridge Celtic	1	0	1	0
Brown	Junior	Fleetwood Town	2	0	2	0
Chambers	Ashley	York City	2	0	2	0
Coulson	Michael	Grimsby Town	2	0	2	0
Davis	Kenny	Braintree Town	3	0	3	0
Edwards	Preston	Ebbsfleet United	1	0	2	0
Forbes	Kieron	Forest Green Rovers	2	0	2	0
Garner	Scott	Grimsby Town	1	0	2	0
Gray	Andre	Luton Town	1	0	1	0
Hedge	Jonathon	Tamworth	3	0	4	0
Jennings	Connor	Stalybridge Celtic	1	1	1	1
Johnson	Marvin	Kidderminster Harriers	1	0	1	0
Killock	Shane	AFC Telford Utd	1	0	1	0
Kissock	John Paul	Luton Town	1	0	1	0
McAuley	Rory	Cambridge United	2	0	2	0
McDonald	Nathan	Braintree Town	1	0	1	0
Meikle	Lindon	Mansfield Town	2	0	2	0
Newton	Shaun	AFC Telford Utd	1	0	6	0
Oshodi	Edward	Forest Green Rovers	1	0	1	0
Owens	Andy	Southport	2	0	2	0
Reason	Jai	Braintree Town	1	0	2	0
Roberts	Kevin	Cambridge United	1	0	1	0
Rose	Danny	Newport County/Fleetwood	2	0	4	0
Spencer	Scott	Hyde	1	0	1	0
Turley	Jamie	Forest Green	2	0	2	0
Vincent	James	Kidderminster Harriers	1	0	1	0
Watkins	Adam	Luton Town	2	1	2	1
West	Michael	Ebbsfleet United	1	0	1	0
Willmott	Robbie	Luton Town	1	0	1	0
Wilson	Josh	Vauxhall Motors	1	0	1	0
CLUBS REPRESENTATIVE TOTALS						
		1. Luton Town	4	1		
		2. Braintree Town	3	0		
		3. Fleetwood	3	0		
		4. Forest Green Rovers	3	0		
		5. AFC Telford Utd	2	0		
		6. Cambridge United	2	0		
		7. Ebbsfleet United	2	0		
		8. Grimsby Town	2	0		
		9. Kidderminster Harriers	2	0		
		10. Stalybridge Celtic	2	1		
		11. York City	2	0		
		12. Barrow	1	0		
		13. Guiseley	1	0		
		14. Hyde	1	0		
		15. Mansfield Town	1	0		
		16. Newport County/Fleetwood	1	0		
		17. Southport	1	0		
		18. Tamworth	1	0		
		19. Vauxhall Motors	1	0		

The England C squad line up before their International Challenge Trophy Group A match against Itlay, played in front of a crwod of 4,628 at Fleetwood Town.

Junior Brown goes all out to beat Italy's Bencivenga to the ball.

Michael Coulson gets himself between Allievi and the ball.

Italy's Lamorte puts in a strong challenge on England's Coulson.

Photos: Keith Clayton.

ENGLAND'S RESULTS 1979 - 2012

BARBADOS
02.06.08	Bridgetown	2 - 0

BELGIUM
11.02.03	KV Ostend	1 - 3
04.11.03	Darlington	2 - 2
15.11.05	FC Racing Jets	2 - 0
19.05.09	Oxford United	0 - 1
09.02.11	Luton Town	1 - 0

BOSNIA & HERZEGOVINA
16.09.08	Grbavia Stadium	2 - 6

ESTONIA
12.10.10		1 - 0

FINLAND UNDER-21
14.04.93	Woking	1 - 3
30.05.94	Aanekoski	0 - 2
01.06.07	FC Hakka	1 - 0
15.11.07	Helsinki	2 - 0

GIBRALTAR
27.04.82	Gibraltar	3 - 2
31.05.95	Gibraltar	3 - 2
21.05.08	Colwyn Bay	1 - 0
15.11.11	Gibraltar	1 - 3

GRENADA
31.05.08	St. George's	1 - 1

HOLLAND
03.06.79	Stafford	1 - 0
07.06.80	Zeist	2 - 1
09.06.81	Lucca	2 - 0
03.06.82	Aberdeen	1 - 0
02.06.83	Scarborough	6 - 0
05.06.84	Palma	3 - 3
13.06.85	Vleuten	3 - 0
20.05.87	Kirkaldy	4 - 0
11.04.95	Aalsmeer	0 - 0
02.04.96	Irthlingborough	3 - 1
18.04.97	Appingedam	0 - 0
03.03.98	Crawley	2 - 1
30.03.99	Genemuiden	1 - 1
21.03.00	Northwich	1 - 0
22.03.01	Wihemina FC	3 - 0
24.04.02	Yeovil Town	1 - 0
25.03.03	BV Sparta 25	0 - 0
16.02.05	Woking	3 - 0
29.11.06	Burton Albion	4 - 1

HUNGARY
15.09.09	Szekesfehervar	1 - 1

IRAQ
27.05.04	Macclesfield	1 - 5

IRISH PREMIER LEAGUE XI
13.02.07	Glenavon FC	1 - 3

ITALY
03.06.80	Zeist	2 - 0
13.06.81	Montecatini	1 - 1
01.06.82	Aberdeen	0 - 0
31.05.83	Scarborough	2 - 0
09.06.84	Reggio Emilia	0 - 1
11.06.85	Houten	2 - 2
18.05.87	Dunfermline	1 - 2
29.01.89	La Spezia	1 - 1
25.02.90	Solerno	0 - 2
05.03.91	Kettering	0 - 0
01.03.99	Hayes	4 - 1
01.03.00	Padova	1 - 1
20.11.02	AC Cremonese	3 - 2
11.02.04	Shrewsbury	1 - 4
10.11.04	US Ivrea FC	1 - 0
15.02.06	Cambridge United	3 - 1
12.11.08	Benevento	2 - 2
28.02.12	Fleetwood Town	1 - 1

MALTA UNDER-21
17.02.09	Malta	4 - 0

NORWAY UNDER-21
01.06.94	Slemmestad	1 - 2

POLAND
17.11.09	Gradiszk Wielpolski	2 - 1

PORTUGAL
19.05.11	Sixfields Stadium	0 - 1

REPUBLIC OF IRELAND
24.05.86	Kidderminster	2 - 1
26.05.86	Nuneaton	2 - 1
25.05.90	Dublin	2 - 1
27.05.90	Cork	3 - 0
27.02.96	Kidderminster	4 - 0
25.02.97	Dublin	0 - 2
16.05.02	Boston	1 - 2
20.05.03	Merthyr Tydfil	4 - 0
18.05.04	Deverondale	2 - 3
24.05.05	Cork	1 - 0
23.05.06	Eastbourne Boro'	2 - 0
22.05.07	Clachnacuddin	5 - 0
26.05.10	Waterford United	2 - 1

RUSSIA
05.06.12	Russia	0 - 4

SCOTLAND
31.05.79	Stafford	5 - 1
05.06.80	Zeist	2 - 4
11.06.81	Empoli	0 - 0
05.06.82	Aberdeen	1 - 1
04.06.83	Scarborough	2 - 1
07.06.84	Modena	2 - 0
15.06.85	Harderwijk	1 - 3
23.05.87	Dunfermline	2 - 1
18.05.02	Kettering	2 - 0
24.05.03	Carmarthen Town	0 - 0
23.05.04	Deverondale	3 - 1
28.05.05	Cork	3 - 2
27.05.06	Eastbourne Boro'	2 - 0
25.05.07	Ross County	3 - 0
22.05.08	Colwyn Bay	1 - 0

USA
20.03.02	Stevenage Boro.	2 - 1
09.06.04	Charleston USA	0 - 0

WALES
27.03.84	Newtown	1 - 2
26.03.85	Telford	1 - 0
18.03.86	Merthyr Tydfil	1 - 3
17.03.87	Gloucester	2 - 2
15.03.88	Rhyl	2 - 0
21.03.89	Kidderminster	2 - 0
06.03.90	Merthyr Tydfil	0 - 0
17.05.91	Stafford	1 - 2
03.03.92	Aberystwyth	1 - 0
02.03.93	Cheltenham	2 - 1
22.02.94	Bangor	2 - 1
28.02.95	Yeovil Town	1 - 0
23.05.99	St Albans	2 - 1
16.05.00	Llanelli	1 - 1
13.02.01	Rushden & Dia.	0 - 0
14.05.02	Boston	1 - 1
22.05.03	Merthyr Tydfil	2 - 0
20.05.04	Keith FC	0 - 2
26.05.05	Cork	1 - 0
25.05.06	Eastbourne Boro'	1 - 1
27.05.07	Clachnacuddin	3 - 0
21.02.08	Exeter City	2 - 1
24.05.08	Rhyl	3 - 0
15.09.10	Newtown FC	2 - 2

RESULTS SUMMARY 1979 - 2012	P	W	D	L	F	A
Barbados	1	1	0	0	2	0
Belgium	5	2	1	2	6	6
Bosnia & Herzegovina	1	0	0	1	2	6
Finland Under-21	4	2	0	2	4	5
Estonia	1	1	0	0	1	0
Grenada	1	0	1	0	1	1
Gibraltar	4	3	0	1	8	7
Holland	19	14	5	0	40	8
Hungary	1	0	1	0	1	1
Iraq	1	0	0	1	1	5
Irish Premier League XI	1	0	0	1	1	3
Italy	18	5	8	4	24	22
Malta	1	1	0	0	4	0
Norway Under-21	1	0	0	1	1	2
Poland	1	1	0	0	2	1
Portugal	1	0	0	1	0	1
Republic of Ireland	13	10	0	3	30	11
Russia	1	0	0	1	0	4
Scotland	15	10	3	2	30	15
USA	2	1	1	0	2	1
Wales	24	13	7	4	34	20
TOTALS	**116**	**64**	**27**	**24**	**194**	**119**

Scott Spencer shapes up to fire a shot in on goal whilst under pressure from D'Orsi.

Edward Oshodi out jumps Italy's 'keeper Brignoli.

Above: England's goalscorer, Adam Watkins, shields the ball from Italy's Meduki.

Right: Coulson takes the ball around Brignoli but sees his shot go wide.

Photos: Keith Clayton.

GOALSCORERS 1979 - 2011

13 GOALS...
Carter, Mark

7 GOALS...
Cole, Mitchell

6 GOALS...
Ashford, Noel

5 GOALS...
Davison, Jon
Williams, Colin

4 GOALS...
Culpin, Paul
D'Sane, Roscoe
Johnson, Jeff
Mackhail-Smith, Craig

3 GOALS...
Adamson, David
Guinan, Steve
Grayson, Neil
Hatch, Liam
Kirk, Jackson
Morison, Steve
Morrison, Michael
Opponents
Watkins, Dale

2 GOALS...
Alford, Carl
Barnes-Homer, Matthew
Barrett, Keith
Bishop, Andrew
Burgess, Andrew
Casey, Kim
Cordice, Neil
Elding, Anthony
Hayles, Barry
Hill, Kenny
Howell, David
Mutrie, Les
Patmore, Warren
Richards, Justin
Seddon, Gareth
Southam, Glen
Watson, John
Weatherstone, Simon
Whitbread, Barry

1 GOAL...
Agana, Tony
Anderson, Dale
Ashton, John
Benson, Paul
Blackburn, Chris
Boardman, Jon
Bolton, Jimmy
Boyd, George
Bradshaw, Mark
Briscoe, Louis
Brown, Paul
Browne, Corey
Carey-Bertram, Daniel
Carr, Michael
Cavell, Paul
Charles, Lee
Charley, Ken
Charnock, Kieran
Constable, James
Crittenden, Nick
Davies, Paul
Day, Matt
Densmore, Shaun
Drummond, Stewart
Fleming, Andrew
Furlong, Paul
Grant, John
Harrad, Shaun
Hine, Mark
Holroyd, Chris
Humphreys, Delwyn
Howells, Jake
Jennings, Connor
Kennedy, John
Kerr, Scott
Kimmins, Ged
King, Simon
Leworthy, David
McDougald, Junior
McFadzean, Kyle
Mayes, Bobby
Moore, Neil
Moore, Luke
Newton, Sean
O'Keefe, Eamon
Oli, Dennis
Penn, Russell
Pitcher, Geoff
Porter, Max
Ricketts, Sam
Robbins, Terry
Robinson, Mark
Roddis, Nick
Rodgers, Luke
Rodman, Alex
Rogers, Paul
Ryan, Tim
Sellars, Neil
Shaw, John
Sheldon, Gareth
Simpson, Josh
Sinclair, Dean
Smith, Ian
Smith, Ossie
Stansfield, Adam
Stephens, Mickey
Stott, Steve
Taylor, Steve
Thurgood, Stuart
Tubbs, Matthew
Venables, David
Watkins, Adam
Way, Darren
Webb, Paul
Wilcox, Russ

MANAGERS 1979 - 2012

		P	W	D	L	F	A	*Win%
1979	Howard Wilkinson	2	2	0	0	6	1	-
1980 - 1984	Keith Wright	17	9	5	3	30	16	53
1985 - 1988	Kevin Verity	12	7	2	3	23	15	58
1989 - 1996	Tony Jennings	19	10	4	5	27	18	53
1997	Ron Reid	2	0	1	1	0	2	-
1998 - 2002	John Owens	14	8	5	1	22	10	57
2002 -	Paul Fairclough	50	28	10	12	86	56	56

*Calculated for those who managed for 10 games or more.

ENGLAND SEMI-PROFESSIONALS, NATIONAL GAME XI AND ENGLAND 'C' CAPS 1979 - 2012

KEY TO COUNTRY CODES:

Ba - Barbados B - Belgium BH - Bosnia & Herzegovina
E - Eire Es - Estonia F - Finland G - Gibraltar Gr - Granada H - Holland Hu - Hungary
I - Italy IP - Irish Premier Lge IQ - Iraq M - Malta N - Norway P - Poland Por - Portugal
R - Russia S - Scotland W - Wales US - U.S.A.

Gary Abbott (Welling) **87** v I(s), S(s), 92 W(s)	3
David Adamson (Boston Utd) **79 v** S, H **80** v I,S, H	5
Les Afful (Forest Green Rovers) **07** v H, IP	2
Tony Agana (Weymouth) **86** v E	1
Junior Agogo (Barnet) **03** v H, i (s), S	3
Danny Alcock (Stafford Rangers) **07** v IP	1
Carl Alford (Kettering T. & Rushden & Ds) **96** v E,H	2
Dale Anderson (Burton Albion) **02** v H **03** v I	2
Mark Angel (Boston United) **02** v W(s), E, S	3
Simon Ainge (Guiseley) **12** v R.	1
Ian Arnold (Kettering Town) **95** v W(s), H	2
Jim Arnold (Stafford Rangers) **79** v S, H	2
Nathan Arnold (Mansfield Town) **09** v BH	1
Steve Arnold (Grays Athletic) **09** v M	1
Nick Ashby (Kettering & Rushden & Diamonds) **94** v F, N, **95** v G **96** v E, H	5
Noel Ashford (Enfield & Redbridge Forest.) **82** v G,H,S. **83 v** I,H,S, **84** W,H,S,I, **85** W,I(s), **86** E,E, **87** W(s), I,H,S. **90** v W,E **91** I(s)	21
John Ashton (Rushden & Diamonds) **07** v E, S, W, F	4
John Askey (Macclesfield) **90** v W	1
Robert Atkinson (Grimsby Town) **11** v B, Por.	2
Ryan Austin (Burton Albion) **06** v I. **07** v H.	2
Danny Bacon (Hucknall Town) **04** v IQ	1
Carl Baker (Southport) **06** v I. **07** v F.	2
Matt Baker (Hereford United) **03** v I, S, **04** E,S,IQ,US	6
Nicky Bailey (Barnet) **05** v H, E, S, W.	4
Stephen Bailey (Grays Athletic) **09** v BH	1
Paul Bancroft (Kidderminster H.) **89** v I,W **90** I,W.E, **91** v W	6
Chris Banks (Cheltenham T.) **98** v H, 99 W	2
Matthew Barnes-Homer (Luton Town) **10** v P, E. **11** v W, Es, B.	5
Keith Barrett (Enfield) **81** v H,S,I **82 v** G,I,H,S **83** v I,H,S **84** v W(s), H, S **85** I,H,S	16
Adam Bartlett (Blyth Spartans) **07** v F. **08** v G,W,Ba. **09** v I,B	6
Laurence Batty (Woking) **93** v F(s), **95** v W,H,G	4
Shaun Beeley (Fleetwood) **12** v G.1	1
Mark Beeney (Maidstone) **89** v I(s)	1
Paul Beesley (Chester C.) **01** v H(s)	1
Dean Bennett (Kidderminster H) **00** v W(s)	1
Paul Benson (Dagenham & Redbridge) **07** v IP.	1
Graham Benstead (Kettering) **94** v W,F,N(s)	3
Kevin Betsy (Woking) **98** v H(s)	1
Marcus Bignot (Kidderminster H) **97** v H	1
Paul Bignot (Newport County) **11** v B.	1
Andy Bishop (York City) **05** v I,H. **06** v B,I.	4
Neil Bishop (York City) **07** v E, W.	2
James Bittner (Exeter City) **04** v B,I	2
Chris Blackburn (Chester C. & Morecambe) **03** v I. **05** v I,H. **06** v I.	4
Shane Blackett (Dagenham & Red). **06** v E,S.	2
Matthew Blair (Kidderminster Harriers) **11** v Por. **12** v I.	2
Greg Blundell (Northwich Victoria) **03** v H	1
Jon Boardman (Woking) **03** v I, S. **04** I,W,US	5
Jimmy Bolton (Kingstonian) **95** v G	1
Steve Book (Cheltenham Town) **99 v** I,H,W	3
Michael Bostwick (Stevenage Borough) **09** v I	1
George Boyd (Stevenage Boro') **06** v B,I,E,W,S. **07** v H.	6
Adam Boyes (York City/Barrow) **09** v M. **12** v G,I.	3
Lee Boylan (Canvey Island) **04** v US	1
Gary Brabin (Runcorn) **94 v** W,F,N	3
Mark Bradshaw (Halifax T.) **98** v H	1
Leon Braithwaite (Margate) **02** v US	1
John Brayford (Burton Albion) **08** v F,W,G,S,W,Gr.Ba.	7
Paul Brayson (Northwich Victoria) **07** v S.	1
Colin Brazier (Kidderminster) **87** v W	1
David Bridges (Cambridge Utd) **06** v I	1
Stewart Brighton (Bromsgrove) **94** v W	1
Louis Briscoe (Mansfield Town) **10** v Hu.	1
Richard Brodie (York City) **09** v BH. **10** v P	2
Stephen Brogan (Staylbridge Celtic) **12** v R.	1
Steve Brooks (Cheltenham) **88** v W(s) **90** v W,E	3
Derek Brown (Woking) **94 v** F(s),N	2
Kevan Brown (Woking) **95** v W,H,G **96** v H **97** v E	5
Junior Brown (Fleetwood) **12** v I,R.	2
Paul Brown (Barrow) **09** v M	1
Seb Brown (AFC Wimbledon) **11** v W, Es, B.	3
Wayne Brown (Chester C.) **01** v W, H(s), **02** v US, H(s),W,S. **03** v H	7
Corey Browne (Dover) **94** v F(s),N(s), **95** v H(s)	3
Liam Brownhill (Witton Albion) **08** v F,W.	2
David Buchanan (Blyth) **86** v E(s),E	2
Nicki Bull (Aldershot Town) **03** v B. **04** v I, H, E.	4
Andrew Burgess (Oxford United/Rushden & Dia.) **07** v E,S,W. **08** v G,S,W,Gr.Ba.	8
Brian Butler (Northwich) **93** v F	1
Steve Butler (Maidstone) **88** v W, **89** v I,W	3
Gary Butterworth (Rushden & Diamonds) **97** v E,H **98** v H **99** v I,H,W,00 v V	7
Chris Byrne (Macclesfield T.) **97** v H	1
Jack Byrne (Kidderminster Harriers) **11** v Por.	1
Joel Byrom (Northwich Victoria) **09** v B	1
Michael Byron (Droylsden) **09** v M	1
Tom Cadmore (Hayes & Yeading United) **10** v H, E	2
DJ Campbell (Yeading) **05** v E, S.	2
Paul Carden (Burton Albion) **07** v E,W.	2

Daniel Carey-Bertram (Hereford Utd) 06 v B	1
Danny Carlton (Morecambe) 04 v IQ	1
Michael Carr (Northwich) 06 v B,I,E,W,S. 07 v H.IP.	7
Mark Carter (Runcorn & Barnet) v **87 v** W,I,H,S **88 v** W, **89 v** I,W, **90 v** I,E, **91 v** I,W(s)	11
Kim Casey (Kidderminster) 86 v W,E,E(s), **87 v** W,I	5
Paul Cavell (Redbridge) 92 v W 93 v F	2
Peter Cavanagh (Accrington) 04 v B,I,E	3
Jon Challinor (Aldershot Town) 04 v B,I	2
Lewis Chalmers (Altrincham/Aldershot) 07 v H,E,S,F. **08** v F,W,G,W,Gr,Ba.	10
Ashley Chambers (York City) 12 v G,I.	2
Darius Charles (Ebbsfleet United) 09 v B. 10 v P	2
Lee Charles (Hayes) 99 v I(s), H(s), W(s)	3
Anthony Charles (Aldershot/Farnborough) 04 v B,I	2
Kevin Charlton (Telford) 85 v W,I	2
Ken Charlery (Boston U) 01 v H(s)	1
Kieran Charnock (Northwich) 05 v E,W. 06 v B,I,E,W,S. **07** v H,IP,E,W.	11
Sean Clancy (Fleetwood Town) 11 v Por.	1
Andrew Clarke (Barnet) 90 v E,E	2
David Clarke (Blyth Spartans) 80 v I,S(s),H, 81 v H,S,I **82** v I,H,S **83** v H,S **84** v H,S,I	14
Gary Clayton (Burton) 86 v E	1
Paul Clayton (Alfreton Town) 09 v M,B	2
Robert Codner (Barnet) 88 v W	1
Mitchell Cole (Stevenage Borough) 07 v E,S,W,F. **08** v W,G,S,W,Gr,Ba. **09** v BH,I.	12
John Coleman (Morecambe) 93 v F(s)	1
Darren Collins (Enfield) 93 v F(s), 94 v W,F,N	4
Matt Collins (Nuneaton Borough) 04 v I	1
Andy Comyn (Hednesford T.) 98 v H(s), 99 v I(s),H(s),W(s)	4
Steve Conner (Dartford, Redbridge & Dagenham & R) **90** v I **91** v I,W **92** v W **93** v F.	5
James Constable (Kidderminster & Oxford Utd) 08 v F. 09 I,B	3
David Constantine (Altrincham) 85 v I,H,S **86 v** W	4
Robbie Cooke (Kettering) 89 v W(s), **90 v** I	2
Scott Cooksey (Hednesford T.) **97** v E, 98 vH(s) **01** v W(s),H	4
Alan Cordice(Wealdstone)83 v I,H,S **84** vW,S(s), I(s),**85** I,H,S	9
Josh Coulson (Cambridge United) 11 v Por.	1
Michael Coulson (Grimsby Town) 12 v I,R.	2
Rob Cousins (Yeovil Town) **00 I** v I(s),H,W	3
Gavin Cowan (Canvey Island) 04 v B,IQ	2
Ken Cramman (Gateshead & Rushden & Diamonds) **96** v E **97** v E,H	3
Ian Craney (Altrincham & Accrington) 03 v B. 04 US. 05 I. **06** v B,I,E,W.	7
Nick Crittendon (Yeovil Town) 02 v US (s)	1
Lance Cronin (Ebbsfleet United) 07 v H,E,W,F. 08 v F,W. 09 vBH	7
Paul Cuddy (Altrincham) 87 v I,H,S	3
Paul Culpin (Nuneaton B) 84 v W, 85 v W(s) ,I,H,S	5
Jonathan D'Laryea (Mansfield Town) 09 v Bh,I.	2
Michael Danzey (Woking) 99 v I,H	2
Paul Davies (Kidderminster H.) **86** v W, **87** v W,I,S, **88** v W **89** v W	6
Kenny Davis (Braintree Town) 12 v G,I,R.	3
John Davison (Altrincham) 79 v S,H 80 v I,S, 81 **v** H,S ,I. **82 v** G,I,H,S **83** I,H,S. **84** W,H,I,S **85** v I,H,S 86 **v** W,E,E.	24
Jamie Day (Rushden & Diamonds) 11 v B.	1
Matt Day (Oxford United) 09 v BH	1
Sam Deering (Oxford United) 10 v E	1

John Denham (Northwich Victoria) 80 v H	1
Peter Densmore (Runcorn) 88 v W 89 v I	2
Shaun Densmore (Altrincham) 09 v M,B. 10 v P,E.	4
Phil Derbyshire (Mossley) 83 v H(s) S(s)	2
Scott Doe (Weymouth) 09 v M.	1
Mick Doherty (Weymouth) 86 v W(s)	1
Neil Doherty (Kidderminster H.) 97 v E	1
Clayton Donaldson (York City) 07 v H,IP.	2
George Donnelly (Fleetwood Town) 11 v Por.	1
Stuart Drummond (Morecambe) 00 v I(s),H ,W 01 v W ,H **02** v US, W,E(s), S **03** v H, I, W, S (s)	13
Roscoe D'Sane (Aldershot Town) 03 v B(s),H(s),E,W,S. 04 B,I	7
Chris Duffy (Canvey Island) 03 v B	1
Neil Durkin (Leigh RMI) 02 v H(s)	1
Preston Edwards (Ebbsfleet United) 11 v Por. 12 v G.	2
Lee Elam (Morecambe) 03 v H,E,W,S)s)	4
Anthony Elding (Stevenage Borough) 04 v B. 05 v I,H,E,W,S.	6
Paul Ellender (Scarborough) 01 v W(s)	1
Lee Endersby (Harrow Bor.) 96 **v** H	1
Mick Farrelly (Altrincham) 87 **v** I,H,S	3
Steve Farrelly (Macclesfield & Kingstonian) **95** v H(s),G(s), 00 v I,H,W(s)	5
Trevor Finnegan (Weymouth) 81 v H,S	2
Murray Fishlock (Yeovil Town) 99 v H(s)	1
Andrew Fleming (Wrexham) 09 v B. 10 v E.	2
Aden Flint (Alfreton Town) 11 v W, Es.	2
Kieron Forbes (Forest Green Rovers) 12 v I,R.	2
Richard Forsyth (Kidderminster) 95 v W,H,G	3
Danny Foster (Dagenham & Redbridge) 07 v E,S,F.	3
Ian Foster (Kidderminster H) 00 v W(s)	1
Luke Foster (Oxford United) 09 v BH.	1
Amos Foyewa (Woking) 04 v E,W,S	3
Barry Fuller (Stevenage Borough) 07 v IP.	1
Paul Furlong (Enfield) 90 **v** I,E,E 91 **v** I,W	5
Connor Franklin (Alfreton Town) 11 v Por.	1
Mark Gardiner (Macclesfield T.) 97 v E	1
Scott Garner (Grimsby Town) 10 v Hu. 12 v R.	2
Michael Gash (York City) 11 v W.	1
Exodus Geohaghon (Kettering Town) 09 v I,B.	1
Jerry Gill (Yeovil T.) 97 v E	1
Matt Glennon (Carlisle Utd) 05 v W,S.	2
Dan Gleeson (Cambridge Utd) 08 v F,W,G,S,Gr,Ba. 09 v I.	7
John Glover (Maidstone Utd) 85 v W,I,H,S	4
Mark Golley (Sutton Utd.) **87** v H(s),S, **88** v W, **89** v I,W, **92** v W	6
Jason Goodliffe (Hayes) 00 v I, H,W, 01 W 02 US, W,E,S.	8
Paul Gothard (Dagenham & Redb.) 97 v E(s), 99 v I(s),W(s)	3
Jeff Goulding (Fisher Athletic) 08 v W.	1
Mark Gower (Barnet) 02 v H, W, E, S(s)	4
Simon Grand (Carlisle) 05 v H.	1
John Grant (Aldershot Town) 07 v E,S,W,F.	4
Andre Gray (Luton Town) 12 v R.	1
Neil Grayson (Cheltenham T.) 98 v H 99 v I,H,W	4
Matt Green 10 v Hu	1
Steven Gregory (AFC Wimbledon) 10 v E. 11 v W, Es, B.	4
Phil Gridelet (Hendon & Barnet) 89 v I,W, 90 v W,E,E	5
Scott Griffiths (Dagenham & Redbridge) 07 v H,IP.	2
Steve Guinan (Hereford) 04 v E,W,S,US	4
Steve Guppy (Wycombe W.) 93 v W	1
Scott Guyett (Southport) 01 v H, 03 v H,I,W,S.	5
Ryan Hall (Bromley) 10 v E	

Tim Hambley (Havant & Waterlooville) **02** v H	1
Steve Hanlon (Macclesfield) **90** v W	1
Ben Harding (Aldershot) **08** v W,G,W.	3
David Harlow (Farnborough T.) **97** v E(s),H	2
Shaun Harrad (Burton Albion) **07** v F. **08** v F,W,G,S,W,Gr,Ba. **09** v BH,I.	8
Stephen Haslam (Halifax) **05** v E,W,S.	3
Liam Hatch (Barnet) **04** v E,W,S,IQ,US. **05** H.	6
Wayne Hatswell (Chester City/Cambridge Utd) **03** v E(s),W(s). **08** v S,W,Gr,Ba.	6
Sam Hatton (AFC Wimbledon) **11** v W, Es, B.	3
Karl Hawley (Carlisle Utd) **05** v I,H.	2
Barry Hayles (Stevenage Bor.) **96** v E,H	2
Greg Heald (Barnet) **02** v H	1
Brian Healy (Morecambe) **98** v H	1
Liam Hearn (Alfreton Town) **09** v B.	1
John Hedge (FC Halifax Town/Tamworth) **10** v P. **12** v G.I.R.	4
Charlie Henry (Newport County) **11** v W, Es.	2
Ronnie Henry (Stevenage Boro) **06** v S. **07** v IP. **08** v F,W.	4
Tony Hemmings (Northwich) **93** v F	1
Andy Hessenthaler (Dartford) **90** v I	1
Kenny Hill (Maidstone Utd) **80** v I,S,H	3
Mark Hine (Gateshead) **95** v W(s),H	2
Simeon Hodson (Kidderminster) **94** v W,F,N	3
Lewis Hogg (Barnet) **04** v B	1
Colin Hogarth (Guiseley) **95 v** W,H	2
Steven Holden (Kettering) **94** v W,F,N(s) **95** v H,G	5
Ricky Holmes (Chelmsford City) **08** v W.	1
Chris Holroyd (Cambridge United) **10** v H, P	2
Mark Hone (Welling United) **90** v I **93** v F, **94** vW(s),F(s),N	5
Gary Hooley (Frickley) **85** v W	1
Dean Hooper (Kingstonian) **98** v H	1
Keith Houghton (Blyth Spartans) **79** v S	1
Barry Howard (Altrincham) **81** v H,S,I **82** v G,I,H,S	7
Neil Howarth (Macclesfield) **95** v H(s) **97** v E	2
David Howell (Enfield) **85** v H(s),S(s) **86** v W,E **87** v W,I,H,S **88** v W, **89** v I,W **90** v I,E,E	14
Jake Howells (Luton Town) **10** v P. **11** v W, Es, B.	4
Lee Howells (Cheltenham T.) **98** v H **99** v W	2
Lee Hughes (Kidderminster Harriers) **96** v E,H **97** v E,H	4
Delwyn Humphreys (Kidderminster H.) **91** v W(s) **92** v W **94** v W,F,N **95** v W,H	7
Steve Humphries (Barnet) **87** v H(s)	1
Nicky Ironton (Enfield) **83** H(s) **84** v W	2
Jimmy Jackson (Gravesend & Northfleet) 03 v H(s)	1
Simon Jackson (Woking) **05** v I.	1
Justin Jackson (Morecambe & Rushden & Diamonds) **00** v W **01** v W	2
Kirk Jackson (Stevenage Borough) **02** v US, E,S,(Yeovil Town) **03** v E,W,S(s)	6
Shwan Jalal (Woking) **05** v H. **06** v I,E,W,S.	5
Mark Janney (Dagenham & Redbridge) **03** v H	1
Rossi Jarvis (Luton Town) **10** v H, P, E	3
Connor Jennings (Stalybridge Celtic) **12** v G.	1
Tony Jennings (Enfield) **79** v S,H **80** v I,S,H **81 v** H,S,I **82** v G,I,H,S	12
Jeff Johnson (Altrincham) **81** v S,I **82** v G,I,H,S **83** v I,H,S **84** v H,S,I **84 v** I,H,S **86** v W(s),E,E	18
Lee Johnson (Yeovil Town) **03** v I, H(s), E, W, S	5
Marvin Johnson (Kidderminster H.) **12** v R.	1
Paul Jones (Exeter City) **06** v I	
Steve Jones (Leigh RMI) **01** v H	1
Tom Jones (Weymouth) **87** v W	1
Tom Jordan (Tamworth) **04** v B	1
Antone Joseph(Telford U. & Kidderm'terH.)**84** v S(s), **85** v W,I, H,S **86** v W(s), **87** W,I(s),H, **88** v W **89** v I,W **90 v** I,E,E	15
John Keeling (Purfleet) **03** v B(s)	1
Marcus Kelly (Rushden & Diamonds) **07** v IP.	1
Darran Kempson (Morecambe) **06** v E,W.	2
John Kennedy (Canvey Island) **03** v I, B, H, E, W, S. **04** v IQ,US	8
Jon Kennedy (Accrington) **04** v I,IQ,US	3
Andy Kerr (Wycombe) **93** v W	1
Scott Kerr (Scarborough) **04** v E,W,S,IQ. **05** v I,H,E,W,S	9
Lance Key (Kingstonian) 03 v B	1
Shane Killock (AFC Telford Utd) **12** v G.	1
Ged Kimmins (Hyde Utd.) **96** v E(s),H(s) **97 v** E(s)	3
Simon King (Barnet) **05** v I,H,S.	3
John Paul Kissock (Luton Town) **12** v G.	1
Natt Knight-Percival **10** v Hu	1
Scott Laird (Stevenage Borough) **09** v B.	1
Mike Lake (Macclesfield) **89** v I	1
Martin Lancaster (Chester City) **03** vI (s)	
Andy Lee (Telford U. & Witton A.) **89** I(s), **91** v I,W	3
Arran Lee-Barrett (Weymouth) **07** v H.	1
Stuart Lewis (Stevenage Borough) **08** v F.	1
David Leworthy (Farnborough & Rushden & Diamonds) **93 v** W, **94** v W **97** v E,H	4
Adam Lockwood (Yeovil Town) **02** v E **03** v I	2
Stacey Long (Gravesend & Northfleet) **07** v IP.	1
Kenny Lowe (Barnet) **91 v** I,W	2
Junior MacDougald (Dagenham & Redbridge) **01** v H(s) **02** W, E(s), S(s)	4
Craig McAllister (Basingstoke Town) **03** v B	1
Rory McAuley (Cambridge Utd) **12** v G.R.	2
Martin McDonald (Macclesfield) **95** v G(s)	1
Nathan McDonald (Braintree Town) **12** v G.	1
Danny McDonnell (Worcester City) **04** v W	1
Kyle McFadzean (Alfreton Town) **10** v H, E. **11** v	3
Mark McGregor (Forest Green Rovers & Nuneaton Borough) **00** v I(s),H(s) **01** v W(s)	3
Kevin McIntyre (Doncaster Rovers) **00 v** H(s)W, **01** v W(s)H	4
John McKenna (Boston Utd) **88 v** W(s), **90** v I,E,E. **91** v I,W, **92** vW	7
Aaron McLean (Aldershot & Grays) **04** v B,I. **06** v E,W,S.	5
Lewis McMahon (Gainsborough Trinity) **09** v M.	1
David McNiven (Leigh RMI) **04** v W,S,IQ,US	4
Chris McPhee (Ebbsfleet Utd) **08** v G,S,W.	3
Craig Mackhail-Smith (Dag. & Red.) **05** v W,S. **06** v I,E,W,S. **07** v H.	7
Tamika Mkandawire (Hereford Utd) **06** v B,I.	2
Andy Mangan (Wrexham) **11** v B, Por.	2
Fiston Manuella (Aylesbury United) **03** v B	1
John Margerrison (Barnet) **87** v W	1
Simon Marples (Doncaster Rovers) **00** v I,H	2
John Martin (Stevenage Borough) **08** v G,S,W.	3
Leroy May (Stafford R.) **95** v G(s)	1
Bobby Mayes (Redbridge) **92** v W	1
Paul Mayman (Northwich Vic) **80** v I,S	2
Lindon Meikie (Mansfield Town) **12** v G.R.	2
Stewart Mell (Burton) **85** v W	1
Neil Merrick (Weymouth) **80** v I(s),S	2
Adam Miller (Aldershot Town) **04** v I	1

Russell Milton (Dover) 94 v F,N	2
Mark Molesley (Aldershot Town) 07 v E,S,W,F.	4
Luke Moore (Ebbsfleet United) 09 v BH.	1
Neil Moore (Telford United) 02 v US (s),H, W, E,S	5
Steve Morison (Stevenage Borough) 07 v H,IP,F.	
08 v G,S,W,Gr,Ba.	8
Amari Morgan-Smith (Ilkeston Town) 10 v E. 11 v B.	2
Trevor Morley (Nuneaton) 84 v W,H,S,I 85 v W,S(s)	6
Michael Morrison (Cambridge Utd) 07 v H.	
08 v F,W,G,S,W,Gr,Ba.	8
Dean Moxey (Exeter City) 05 v H. 08 v W,S.	3
Chris Murphy (Telford United) 04 v B	1
Karl Murrphy (Woking) 04 v B,I	2
Tarkan Mustafa (Rushden & Diamonds) 01 v W,H	2
Les Mutrie (Blyth Spartans) 79 v S,H, 80 v I,S,H	5
Mark Newson (Maidstone U) 84 v W,H,S,I, 85 v W	5
Doug Newton (Burton) 85 v W,H,S	3
Shaun Newton (Droylsden/AFC Telford Utd) 09 v M,B. 10 v P,E.	
11 v Es. 12 v 1.	6
Paul Nicol (Kettering T) 91 v I,W, 92 v W	3
Kevin Nicholson (Forest Green Rovers/Torquay Utd)	
07 v E.S.W. 08 v G,S,W,Gr,Ba.	8
Kyle Nix (Mansfield Town) 10 v Hu. 11 v Es.	2
Richard Norris (Northwich Victoria) 03 v H, S,	2
Steve Norris (Telford) 88 v W(s)	1
John Nutter (Grays) 06 v E,W.S.	3
Curtis Obeng (Wrexham) 10 v E	1
Joe O'Connor (Hednesford T.) 97 v E,H(s)	2
Eamon O'Keefe (Mossley) 79 v S,H	2
Erkan Okay (Histon) 08 v F.	1
Dennis Oli (Grays) 06 v B,E,W.S. 07 v H.	5
Luke Oliver (Woking) 05 v H.	1
Edward Oshodi (Forest Green Rovers) 12 v I.	1
Frank Ovard (Maidstone) 81 v H(s),S(s),I(s)	3
Andy Owens (Southport) 12 v I,R.	2
Andy Pape (Harrow Bor. & Enfield) 85 v W(s,)H,S.	15
86 v W(s),E, 87 v W,I,H,S 88 v W, 89 IW, 90 I,W,E	
Brian Parker (Yeovil Town) 80 v S	1
Warren Patmore (Yeovil Town) 99 v I,H,W, 00 v I,H, 01 W,H	7
Gary Patterson (Kingstonian) 99 v I,H, 00 v H,W, 01 v W,H	7
Steve Payne (Macclesfield T.) 97 v H	1
Trevor Peake (Nuneaton Bor) 79 v S,H	2
David Pearce (Harrow Bor) 84 v I(s)	1
Russell Penn (Kidderminster) 08 v F,W,G,W,Gr,Ba. 09 v I,B.	8
David Perkins (Morecambe) 04 v B,I,E,S,IQ,US. 05 v I.	
06 v B,I.	9
Warren Peyton (Nuneaton Borough) 02 v H(s) 03 v I	2
Brendan Phillips (Nuneaton Bor. & Kettering T.),	4
79 v S,H, 80 v S(s),H.	
Gary Philips (Barnet) 82 v G	1
Owen Pickard (Yeovil T.) 98 v H(s)	1
Geoff Pitcher (Kingstonian) 99 v W, 00 v I,H,W, 01 v W,H	6
Jon-Paul Pitman (Crawley Town) 09 v I.	1
Max Porter (Rushden & Diamonds) 10 v P, E. 11 v W,Es,B,Por.	6
Phil Power (Macclesfield T.) 96 v E(s),H(s)	2
Ryan Price (Stafford R. & Macclesfield) 92 v W(s) 93 v W,F.	6
96 v E,H 97 v H.	
Steve Prindiville 98 v H(s)	1
Andy Proctor (Accrington Stanley) 04 v IQ	1
Marc Pullan (Crawley Town) 03 v B	1
Robert Purdie (Hereford United) 04 v I. 05 v I.	2

Wayne Purser (Barnet) 03 v I	1
Mark Quayle (Telford United) 02 v H	1
Adam Quinn (Halifax Town) 07 v H,IP,E,S,W,F.	6
Simon Read (Farnborough) 92 v W(s)	1
Jai Reason (Cambridge United/Braintree Town) 10 v P. 12 v G.	2
Matt Redmile (Barnet) 04 v E,W,S	3
Andy Reid (Altrincham) 95 v W	1
Sam Rents 10 v Hu	1
Callum Reynolds (Luton Town) 10 v Hu	1
Martin Rice (Exeter City) 07 v IP.	1
Carl Richards (Enfield) 86 v E	1
Justin Richards (Woking) 06 v E,W,S.	3
Derek Richardson (Maidstone U) 83 v I, 84 v W, 86 v E	4
Ian Richardson (Dagenham & Red) 95 v G	1
Kevin Richardson (Bromsgrove) 94 v W,F,N	3
Paul Richardson (Redbridge) 92 v W, 93 v W, F	3
Scott Rickards (Tamworth) 03 v B. 04 B	2
Sam Ricketts (Telford) 04 v B,E,W,S	4
Adriano Rigoglioso (Morecambe) 03 v H(s)	1
Martin Riley (Kidderminster Harriers) 09 v M.	1
Anthony Rivierre (Welling United) 03 v B	1
Terry Robbins (Welling) 92 v W, 93 v W,F, 94 v W,F,N	6
Dale Roberts (Rushden & Diamonds) 09 v M. 10 v H,P,E. 11 v W.	5
Gary Roberts (Accrington) 06 v I,E,W,S.	4
Kevin Roberts (Cambridge United) 12 v I.	1
Anton Robinson (Weymouth) 09 v BH,I.	2
Mark Robinson (Hereford) 05 v E,W,S.	3
Peter Robinson (Blyth S) 83 v I,H,S 84 W,I 85 v W	6
Ryan Robinson (Morecambe) 06 v B.	1
Nick Roddis (Woking) 01 v H 02 US,H,W,E(s),S	6
Luke Rodgers (Shrewsbury) 04 v B,I.	2
Alex Rodman (Oxford United) 10 v E. 11 v W, Es.	3
John Rogers (Altrincham) 81 v H,S,I 82 v I(s),S	5
Paul Rogers (Sutton) 89 v W, 90 v I, E(2), 91 I,W	6
Colin Rose (Witton Alb.) 96 v E(s), H	2
Danny Rose (Newport Co./Fleetwood) 11 v W, Por. 12 v G.I.	4
Kevin Rose (Kidderminster) 94 v F(s),N	2
Michael Rose (Hereford United) 03 v I, H, E, S	4
Brian Ross (Marine) 93 v W(s),F(s), 94 v W(s) 95 v W,H	5
Carl Ruffer (Chester City) 01 v H(s)	1
Tim Ryan (Southport & Doncaster Rovers) 98 v H.	14
99 v I,H,W, 00 v I,H,W 01 v W,H 02 v US,H,W,I,S	
Brian Saah (Cambridge United) 11 v W.	1
Gareth Seddon (Hyde United) 07 v E.W.	2
Jake Sedgemore (Shrewsbury) 04 v E,W,S,IQ,US.	5
Neil Sellars (Scarboro) 81 v H,S,I 82 v G,H(s),S, 83 v I,H,S	9
Mark Shail (Yeovil T.) 93 v W	1
John Shaw (Halifax Town) 08 v G,S,W,Gr,Ba.	5
Jon Shaw (Burton Albion) 06 v I.	1
Simon Shaw (Doncaster Rovers) 99 v I,H	2
Tom Shaw (Tamworth) 09 v M. 10 v P.	2
Peter Shearer (Cheltenham) 89 v I(s)	1
Gareth Sheldon (Exeter) 04 v I,E,W,S,IQ,US.	6
Paul Shirtliff (Frickley A. & Boston U.) 86 vE,E 87 v W,I,H.	15
88 v W 89 v I, W, 90 v I,W,E,E, 92 v W 93 v W,F	
Paul Showler (Altrincham) 91 v I(s),W	2
Tim Sills (Kingstonian) 03 v B	1
Gordon Simmonite (Boston United) 79 v S(s,)H(s), 80 v I,S,H.	5
Gary Simpson (Stafford R.) 86 v E,E, 87 v I,H,S,90 v I,W,E,E.	9
Josh Simpson (Histon) 09 v I. 10 v Hu. 11 v B, Por.	4
Wayne Simpson (Stafford) 94 v F,N(s)	2

Dean Sinclair (Barnet) **05** v I,H,E,W,S.	5
Terry Skiverton (Yeovil Town) **01 v** W **02 v** US **03** v 1,W,	4
Glenn Skivington (Barrow) **90** v I,W,E **91** v I,W	5
Jamie Slabber (Grays) **06** v B.	1
Adrian Smith (Kidderminster H) **00** v I(s),H(s),W	3
Alan Smith (Alvechurch) **82** v G,I,S	3
Ian Smith (Mossley) **80** v I,S,H(s)	3
James Smith (Ebbsfleet Utd) **08** v Gr,Ba. **09** v BH,I.	4
Mark Smith (Stevenage Bor.) **96** v E,H **98** v H **99** v I,H,W. **00** v I,H,W(s).	9
Ossie Smith (Runcorn) **84** v W	1
Phil Smith (Margate) **04** v B	1
Tim Smithers (Nuneaton) **85** v W(s),I **86** v W	3
Guiseppe Sole (Woking) **07** v H,IP,F.	3
Adam Sollitt (Kettering Town) **00** v I(s),H(s),W	3
Leon Solomon (Welling United) **07** v F.	1
Glen Southam (Bishop's Stort' & Dag & R.) **04** v E,W,S,IQ,US.**12** **05** v W,S. **06** v S. **07** v E,S,W,F.	
Scott Spencer (Hyde) **12** v I.	1
Craig Stanley (Hereford & Morecambe) **05** v E,W. **07** v H,IP.	4
Adam Stansfield (Yeovil Town & Hereford) **02** v W (s), I, S **05** v E,S.	5
Simon Stapleton (Wycombe) **93** v W	1
Mickey Stephens (Sutton), **82** v G,S(s) **86 v** W,E,E(s)	5
Jamie Stevens (Crawley Town) **09** v BH.	1
Billy Stewart (Southport) **98** v H	1
Mark Stimson (Canvey Islland) **02** v US	1
Bob Stockley (Nuneaton Borough) **80** v H	1
David Stockdale (York) **05** v I.	1
Darren Stride (Burton Albion) **02** v H	1
Steve Stott (Kettering T., Rushden & Ds & Yeovil T.) **95** v W,H(s),G **96** v E,H **99** v H,W(s)	7
Reece Styche (Forest Green Rovers) **11** v Por.	1
Ryan Sugden (Chester City) 03 v I	1
Ben Surey (Gravesend & Nflt.) **05** v I.	1
Andy Taylor (Exeter City) **05** v E,W,S.	3
Greg Taylor (Kettering Town) **11** v W.	1
James Taylor (Havant & Waterlooville) **02** v H,W, E(s),S(s)	4
Peter Taylor (Maidstone) **84** v HSI	1
Steve Taylor (Bromsgrove R.) **95** v G	1
Shaun Teale (Weymouth) **88** v W	1
Paul Terry (Dagenham & Redbridge) **03** vE (s), W(s), S	3
Stuart Terry (Altrincham) **95** v W	1
Brian Thompson(Yeovil & Maidstone) **79** v S,H **81** v H,S,I. **15** **82** v I,H,S **83** v I,H,S **84** v W,H,S,I	
Neil Thompson (Scarborough) **87** v W,I,H,S	4
Garry Thompson (Morecambe) **03** v I. **04** v E,W,IQ,US	5
Steve Thompson (Wycombe) **93** v W	1
Stuart Thurgood (Grays Ath.) **05** v I,H. **06** v E,W,S.	5
Kevin Todd (Berwick Rangers) **91** v W	1
Lee Tomlin (Rushden & Diamonds) **09** v M,B.	2
Mike Tomlinson (Runcorn F.C.Halton) **03** v B (s)	1
Anthony Tonkin (Yeovil Town) **02** v US	1
Simon Travis (Forest Green R & Hereford) **02 v** US, H. **05** v E. **06** v E,W,S.	6
Carl Tremarco (Wrexham) **09** v I.	1
Andy Tretton (Hereford) **04** v E,W,S,US	4
Matthew Tubbs (Salisbury City) **07** v E. **08** v F.	2
Mark Tucker (Woking) **96** v E	1
Jamie Turley (Forest Green Rovers) **12** v G.I.	2
Tony Turner (Telford) **85 v** W	

Scott Tynan (Rushden & Diamonds) **07** v S,W. **08** v S,Gr.	4
Paul Underwood (Rushden & D) **99** v I,H **00 v** I**01** v W	4
Lee Vaughan (AFC Telford Utd) **10** v Hu. **11** v Por.	1
David Venables(Stevenage B)**94 v** W(s)**95 v** H,G**96 v** E,H(s)	5
Jamie Victory (Cheltenham T.) **98** vH(s)	1
Ashley Vickers (Dagenham & Redbridge) **04** v IQ	1
James Vincent (Kidderminster Harriers) **12** v R.	1
David Waite (Enfield) **82** v G	1
Steve Wales (Yeading) **06** v B.	1
Jason Walker (Barrow) **09** v M.	1
Paul Walker (Blyth) **86 v** W,E,E(s), **87 v** S(s)	4
Steve Walters (Northwich Victoria) **97** v H	1
Mark Ward (Northwich Victoria) **83** v S(s)	1
Steve Ward (Canvey Island) **03** v B	1
Adam Watkins (Luton Town) **12** v G.I.	2
Dale Watkins (Cheltenham T.) **98** v H **99** v I(s), **00** v I,H,W	5
John Watson (Wealdstone, Scarborough & Maidstone) **79** v S(s),H **80** v I,S,H **81** v H,S,I **82** v I,H,S **83** v I,H,S **84** v W(s),H,S,I	18
Steve Watson (Farnborough Town) **02** v US(s), W(s), S	3
Liam Watson (Marine) **95** v W,H(s)	2
Paul Watts (Redbridge Forest) **89** v W **90** v I,E,E **91** v I **92** v W **93** v W,F	8
Darren Way (Yeovil Town) **03** vI (s), E, W	3
Chris Weale (Yeovil Town) **03** v I (s), H (s), E, W.	4
Simon Weatherstone (Boston United) **02** v W(s),E,S(s)	3
Paul Webb (Bromsgrove R & Kidderminster H) **93** v F **94** v W,F,N(s) **95** v W,H,G **96** v E,H **97** v E,H	11
Aaron Webster (Burton Albion) **02 v** H(s),W,S(s) **03** v I	3
Joe Welch **10** v Hu	1
Ishmael Welsh (Grays Athletic) **09** v M,B.	2
Mark West (Wycombe W) **91** v W	1
Michael West (Ebbsfleet United) **12** v G.	1
Steve West (Woking) **01** v W(s)	1
Barry Whitbread (Runcorn & Altrincham) **79 v** S,H **80** v I,S,H, **81 v** I	6
Tristram Whitman (Doncaster Rovers) **03** v W(s), S	2
Russ Wilcox (Frickley) **86** v W,E	2
Adam Wilde (Worcester City) **03** v B	1
Barry Williams (Nuneaton Borough) **99** v H(s),W	2
Colin Williams (Scarborough & Telford Utd.) **81** v H,S. **82** v I,H,S. **84** v I,H,S. **85** v I,H,S.	12
Roger Willis (Barnet) **91** v I(s)	1
Robbie Willmott (Luton Town) **12** v G.	1
Josh Wilson (Vauxhall Motors) **12** v R.	1
Paul Wilson (Frickley Athletic) **86** v W	1
Martyn Woolford (York City) **08** v Gr,Ba.	2
Andy Woods (Scarborough) **02** v US,H(s),W,S.	4
Simon Wormull (Dover Athletic) **99** v I(s),W **02 v** W,E,S.	5
Ben Wright (Kidderminster Harriers) **11** v W.	2
Jake Wright (Tamworth) **09** v I.	1
Mark Wright (Thurrock) **09** v BH.	1
Nick Wright (Tamworth) **10** v H,P, **11** v Es	3
Nicky Wroe (Torquay United) **09** v M,B.	2
Michael Wylde (Tamworth) **11** v Es, B, Por.	3
Adam Yates (Morecambe) **07** v H,S,W.	3
Mark Yates (Cheltenham Town) **99** v I, W	2
Ismail Yakubu (Barnet) **04** v I,US. **05** v I,E,W,S.	6

THE FA CUP

2011-12

Tamworth's Kyle Patterson is surrounded by Everton players during his side's Third Round tie at Goodison.
Photo: Peter Barnes.

EXTRA PRELIMINARY ROUND

Many football clubs throughout the country have yet to start their season as they are faced with an FA Cup tie but a glance down the Extra Preliminary ties shows that over twenty clubs, some who may have re-formed and changed their names have, in their best years, enjoyed a cup final at Wembley in the FA Trophy, FA Vase or FA Amateur Cup.

Supporters of those teams today have probably seen photos in the clubhouse of past cup highlights, but the famous competition also gives every small club a chance of fresh glory every season.

Many players are on holiday in mid August, others may not be match fit, so luck of the draw is important. The following FA Cup victories, decided by very comfortable margins, gave many clubs the encouragement that they could look forward to the season with confidence. The following clubs scored at least six goals at home, with a special game fought out at Bodmin where old rivals Falmouth Town helped to produce nine goals.

Bridgnorth Town	6	Ellesmere Rangers	0
Oadby Town	6	Northampton Spencer	1
Oxhey Jets	6	Wodson Park	0
Erith Town	6	Crowborough	2
Bodmin Town	6	Falmouth Town	3
Sunderland RCA	7	Birtley Town	0
Fisher	6	Chichester City	1

To achieve away victories in the FA Cup is always a bit special so these results certainly impressed last season, and it was a particularly good day for the town of Billingham!

Stokesley SC	1	Newcastle Benfield	6
Newton Aycliffe	2	Billingham Synthonia	7
Crook Town	2	Billingham Town	6
Chadderton	2	Cheadle Town	8
Nuneaton Griff	0	Stratford Town	7
Three Bridges	1	Camberley Town	6
Westfield	3	Peacehaven & Telscombe	6
Corsham Town	1	Cadbury Heath	6
New Milton Town	0	Alton Town	6

This Causeway Utd attack is halted by a well timed challenge from this Malvern Town player. Although held to a 0-0 draw, Causeway won 5-0 in the replay.
Photo: Jonathan Holloway.

Action from the Extra Preliminary Round tie between AFC Slimbridge and Bradford Town, which the hosts won 3-1. Photo: Peter Barnes.

EXTRA PRELIMINARY ROUND

SATURDAY 20 AUGUST 2011 - WINNING CLUBS TO RECEIVE £750

No	Home		Away	Score	Att
1	Bedlington Terriers	v	Whickham	1-0	130
2	Tow Law Town	v	Marske United	1-2	81
3	Stokesley SC	v	Newcastle Benfield	1-6	46
4	Penrith	v	North Shields	1-1	90
	North Shields	v	Penrith (24/8)	0-1	116
5	West Allotment Celtic	v	Northallerton Town	1-1	80
	Northallerton Town	v	West Allotment Celtic (24/8)	2-1aet	118
6	Spennymoor Town	v	Esh Winning	1-0	183
7	Ryton & Crawcrook Albion	v	Ashington	0-1	57
8	Gillford Park	v	Hebburn Town	1-2	36
9	Newton Aycliffe	v	Billingham Synthonia	2-7	330
10	Crook Town	v	Billingham Town	2-6	93
11	Chester-Le-Street Town	v	South Shields	1-1	104
	South Shields	v	Chester-Le-Street Town (23/8)	2-1	128
12	West Auckland Town	v	Dunston UTS	2-2	103
	Dunston UTS	v	West Auckland Town (23/8)	5-1	226
13	Jarrow Roofing Boldon CA	v	Guisborough Town	1-2	41
14	Sunderland RCA	v	Birtley Town (19/8)	7-0	141
15	Shildon	v	Consett	2-1	166
16	Whitehaven	v	Norton & Stockton Ancients	3-0	38
17	Whitley Bay	v	Bishop Auckland	2-1	456
18	Scarborough Athletic	v	Hallam	4-0	452
19	Thackley	v	Askern Villa	2-1	56
20	Maltby Main	v	Glasshoughton Welfare	1-2	45
21	Silsden	v	Rossington Main	1-1	92
	Rossington Main	v	Silsden (23/8)	2-2aet	85
	(Silsden won 4-2 on kicks from the penalty mark)				
22	Pontefract Collieries	v	Yorkshire Amateur	2-0	91
23	Parkgate	v	Grimsby Borough	4-1	40
24	AFC Emley	v	Hall Road Rangers (19/8)	1-4	131
25	Hemsworth MW	v	Tadcaster Albion	1-2	91
26	Nostell MW	v	Armthorpe Welfare	2-3	72
27	Selby Town	v	Liversedge	1-4	107
28	Pickering Town	v	Dinnington Town (21/8)	2-0	157
29	Staveley MW	v	Winterton Rangers	4-0	102
30	Barton Town Old Boys	v	Bridlington Town	2-2	134
	Bridlington Town	v	Barton Town Old Boys (23/8)	2-3	149
31	Squires Gate	v	Colne	1-0	67
32	Formby	v	Alsager Town	3-0	65
33	Winsford United	v	Maine Road	1-1	110
	Maine Road	v	Winsford United (23/8)	1-0	109
	(at Cheadle Town FC)				
34	Runcorn Town	v	Brighouse Town	4-1	110
35	Padiham	v	Ashton Athletic	1-2	127
36	Holker Old Boys	v	Leek CSOB	3-0	62
37	Bacup Borough	v	AFC Blackpool	2-3	62
38	St Helens Town	v	Atherton LR	0-2	46
39	Atherton Collieries	v	Irlam	4-0	60
40	Chadderton	v	Cheadle Town	2-8	79
41	Congleton Town	v	Eccleshill United	3-1	89
42	Barnoldswick Town	v	Ramsbottom United	0-2	177
43	Bootle	v	Wigan Robin Park	2-0	96
44	AFC Liverpool	v	Runcorn Linnets (21/8)	2-2	222
	Runcorn Linnets	v	AFC Liverpool (24/8)	3-1	320
45	Retford United	v	Gresley	0-2	206
46	Holbeach United	v	Lincoln Moorlands Railway	3-1	93
47	Deeping Rangers	v	Spalding United	2-1	149
48	Holbrook Sports	v	Greenwood Meadows	1-1	51
	Greenwood Meadows	v	Holbrook Sports (23/8)	0-2	34
49	Glossop North End	v	Boston Town	2-4	219
50	Dunkirk	v	Arnold Town	0-2	91
51	Radcliffe Olympic	v	Heanor Town	2-3	79
52	Borrowash Victoria	v	Sleaford Town	5-1	74
53	Gedling MW	v	Louth Town	0-0	52
	Louth Town	v	Gedling MW (23/8)	2-1	117
54	Shirebrook Town	v	Blackstones	2-1	82
55	Nuneaton Griff	v	Stratford Town	0-7	105
56	Rocester	v	Wolverhampton Casuals	3-1	94
57	Southam United	v	Tipton Town	0-2	79
58	Coleshill Town	v	Brocton	5-1	50
59	Highgate United	v	Willenhall Town	2-0	68
60	Westfields	v	Norton United	2-4	107
61	Castle Vale	v	Heath Hayes (19/8)	3-1	80
62	Bustleholme	v	Eccleshall	0-1	104
63	Lye Town	v	Coventry Sphinx (19/8)	0-5	134
64	Studley	v	Walsall Wood	2-1	60
65	Boldmere St Michaels	v	Bartley Green	5-2	55
66	Malvern Town	v	Causeway United (21/8)	0-0	131
	Causeway United	v	Malvern Town (24/8)	5-0	45
	(at Boldmere St Michaels FC)				
67	Bridgnorth Town	v	Ellesmere Rangers	6-0	102
68	Atherstone Town	v	Cadbury Athletic	1-0	142
69	Tividale	v	Alvechurch	1-2	104
70	Gornal Athletic	v	Shifnal Town	2-2	52
	Shifnal Town	v	Gornal Athletic (24/8)	3-4aet	78
71	Stone Dominoes	v	Wellington	3-2	42
72	Cradley Town	v	Continental Star	2-2	45
	Continental Star	v	Cradley Town (24/8)	3-2	60
73	Bloxwich United	v	AFC Wulfrunians	2-2	75
	AFC Wulfrunians	v	Bloxwich United (23/8)	3-0	75
74	Pegasus Juniors	v	Bewdley Town	1-1	43
	Bewdley Town	v	Pegasus Juniors (23/8)	2-1aet	51
75	Friar Lane & Epworth	v	Loughborough University		
	(walkover for Loughborough University – Friar Lane & Epworth removed)				
76	Thrapston Town	v	Irchester United (19/8)	3-2	182
77	Oadby Town	v	Northampton Spencer	6-1	101
78	Rushden & Higham United	v	Cogenhoe United	2-3	92
79	Rothwell Corinthians	v	Wellingborough Town	1-0	77
80	Bugbrooke St Michaels	v	Anstey Nomads	2-1	107
81	Long Eaton United	v	Huntingdon Town	0-4	
82	Long Buckby	v	Stewarts & Lloyds Corby	1-0	52
83	Thurnby Nirvana	v	Desborough Town	3-3	57
	Desborough Town	v	Thurnby Nirvana (23/8)	0-5	57
84	Rothwell Town	v	Raunds Town	2-1	74
85	Barrow Town	v	Kirby Muxloe	3-2	112
86	Daventry United	v	Bardon Hill Sports	2-1	36
87	Yaxley	v	Godmanchester Rovers	0-2	90
88	Stanway Rovers	v	Hadleigh United	2-3	129
89	King's Lynn Town	v	Whitton United	6-1	632
90	Woodbridge Town	v	Gorleston	2-2	114
	Gorleston	v	Woodbridge Town (23/8)	2-1	110
91	St Ives Town	v	Debenham LC	3-2	130
92	Wroxham	v	Dereham Town	3-1	181
93	Ipswich Wanderers	v	Newmarket Town	3-1	62
94	Mildenhall Town	v	Brantham Athletic	0-4	108
95	Walsham Le Willows	v	Thetford Town (19/8)	3-1	126
96	March Town United	v	Kirkley & Pakefield	2-1	92
97	Ely City	v	Diss Town	4-0	103
98	Stowmarket Town	v	Haverhill Rovers	1-4	94
99	Felixstowe & Walton United	v	Norwich United	1-0	60
100	Long Melford	v	Saffron Walden Town		
	(walkover for Long Melford – Saffron Walden Town removed)				
101	Wisbech Town	v	Halstead Town	4-0	246
102	Great Yarmouth Town	v	FC Clacton	0-3	116
103	Burnham Ramblers	v	Barking	1-1	71
	Barking	v	Burnham Ramblers (23/8)	0-1	75
104	Hadley	v	Cockfosters	2-2	47
	Cockfosters	v	Hadley (23/8)	0-0aet	84
	(Cockfosters won 5-4 on kicks from the penalty mark)				
105	Haringey Borough	v	AFC Kempston Rovers	2-0	48
106	Witham Town	v	Bedford	4-1	80
107	St Margaretsbury	v	Dunstable Town	0-3	74
108	Enfield 1893	v	London Colney	3-1	71
109	Kings Langley	v	Stotfold	5-2	54
	(tie awarded to Stotfold – Kings Langley removed)				
110	Colney Heath	v	Langford	3-1	44
111	Clapton	v	Stansted	0-1	42
112	Crawley Green	v	Berkhamsted	1-2	62
113	Hullbridge Sports	v	Royston Town	1-3	53
114	Broxbourne Borough V&E	v	Hoddesdon Town	4-0	135
115	Haringey & Waltham Dev.	v	Bowers & Pitsea (19/8)	4-1	73
116	Sawbridgeworth Town	v	Hatfield Town	2-2	43
	Hatfield Town	v	Sawbridgeworth Town (23/8)	2-1	

Thrapston are denied by a goal-line clearance here but went on to win their first ever FA Cup match 3-2 v Irchester United. Photo: Gordon Whittington.

Above: Hailsham Town's Craig Ottley is unable to stop Lingfield's ex Brighton & Hove player, Nicky Forster, from firing a powerful shot in on goal during the Extra Preliminary Round match. Photo: Roger Turner

Fisher's Richie Monan just misses with this header against Chichester during this Extra Preliminary round tie which Fisher went on to win 6-1. Photo: Alan Coomes.

Shortwood United's Numbers 10 and 9 fire in a shot against Bishop's Sutton in their Preliminary Round tie which ended in a 1-1 draw. Photo: Peter Barnes.

EXTRA PRELIMINARY ROUND
SATURDAY 20 AUGUST 2011 - WINNING CLUBS TO RECEIVE £750

117	AFC Dunstable	v	Eton Manor (21/8)	3-1	94
	(at Waltham Abbey FC)				
118	Biggleswade United	v	Leverstock Green	2-1	54
119	Takeley	v	Southend Manor	3-3	69
	Southend Manor	v	Takeley (23/8)	3-2	25
120	London APSA	v	Basildon United (21/8)	1-0	55
121	Oxhey Jets	v	Wodson Park	6-0	31
122	Barkingside	v	Hertford Town (21/8)	1-3	197
123	Bethnal Green United	v	Kentish Town	2-1	38
124	Holmer Green	v	Harefield United	2-4	80
125	Sandhurst Town	v	Thame United	2-3	58
126	Witney Town	v	Newport Pagnell Town	0-4	94
127	Tring Athletic	v	Hanwell Town	1-0	68
128	Wokingham & Emmbrook	v	Holyport	4-1	106
129	Staines Lammas	v	Clanfield 85	3-0	96
130	Bicester Town	v	Bedfont Sports		
	(walkover for Bedfont Sports – Bicester Town removed)				
131	Old Woodstock Town	v	Wantage Town	1-2	38
132	Ascot United	v	Wembley (19/8)	1-2	1149
133	Abingdon Town	v	Milton United	4-0	56
134	Kidlington	v	Hillingdon Borough	4-2	62
135	Hanworth Villa	v	Shrivenham	4-2	101
136	Ardley United	v	Flackwell Heath	3-0	48
137	Aylesbury United	v	Bracknell Town (21/8)	4-0	128
138	Reading Town	v	Binfield	0-0	59
	Binfield	v	Reading Town (22/8)	3-0	118
139	Molesey	v	Egham Town	0-3	132
140	Raynes Park Vale	v	Hassocks	3-1	48
141	Farnham Town	v	Guildford City	1-0	70
142	Wick	v	Redhill	0-3	57
143	VCD Athletic	v	Bookham	1-1	53
	Bookham	v	VCD Athletic (24/8)	0-2	65
144	Erith & Belvedere	v	St Francis Rangers	2-0	57
145	Lancing	v	Horsham YMCA	2-2	92
	Horsham YMCA	v	Lancing (23/8)	2-5	66
146	Chichester City	v	Fisher	2-2	82
	Fisher	v	Chichester City (22/8)	6-1	75
147	Pagham	v	Herne Bay	1-2	75
148	Colliers Wood United	v	Chessington & Hook United	1-1	41
	Chessington & Hook United	v	Colliers Wood United (23/8)	2-1	63
149	Ringmer	v	Deal Town	0-2	64
150	Arundel	v	Sidley United	2-2	65
	Sidley United	v	Arundel (23/8)	1-5aet	59
	(at Arundel FC)				
151	Three Bridges	v	Camberley Town	1-6	52
152	Sevenoaks Town	v	Ash United	4-0	45
153	Shoreham	v	Holmesdale	3-1	50
154	Corinthian	v	Dorking	4-3	48
155	Mole Valley SCR	v	Lordswood	2-3	22
156	Westfield	v	Peacehaven & Telscombe	3-6	90
157	Tunbridge Wells	v	Warlingham	1-0	158
158	South Park	v	AFC Uckfield	1-0	72
159	Greenwich Borough	v	Horley Town	1-2	
160	Banstead Athletic	v	Woodstock Sports	3-0	58
161	Littlehampton Town	v	Beckenham Town	1-3	33
	(at Beckenham Town FC)				
162	Erith Town	v	Crowborough Athletic	6-2	46
163	Selsey	v	Mile Oak	2-2	105
	Mile Oak	v	Selsey (24/8)	1-2	63
164	Epsom & Ewell	v	Croydon (21/8)	3-1	124
165	Cobham	v	Badshot Lea (19/8)	2-2	105
	Badshot Lea	v	Cobham (23/8)	4-1	45
166	Hailsham Town	v	Lingfield	0-4	93
167	Bridport	v	Hayling United	2-2	141
	Hayling United	v	Bridport (23/8)	0-2	48
168	Cowes Sports	v	Newport (IW)	1-4	234
169	Verwood Town	v	Horndean	0-4	73
170	Romsey Town	v	Brading Town	0-1	33
171	Downton	v	Brockenhurst	3-3	65
	Brockenhurst	v	Downton (23/8)	4-2	70
172	Alresford Town	v	Devizes Town	4-0	45
173	Totton & Eling	v	Fareham Town	5-1	54
174	Cove	v	AFC Portchester	0-2	62
175	Petersfield Town	v	Hartley Wintney	1-2	71
176	Hamworthy United	v	Bournemouth	1-2	107
177	Shrewton United	v	Fleet Spurs	1-0	177
178	Winchester City	v	Ringwood Town	5-0	105
179	Whitchurch United	v	Bemerton Heath Harlequins	3-2	86
180	Alton Town	v	New Milton Town	1-1	45
	New Milton Town	v	Alton Town (23/8)	0-6	47
181	Lymington Town	v	Sherborne Town	3-2	85
	(at Brockenhurst FC)				
182	Blackfield & Langley	v	GE Hamble	3-1	54
183	Gillingham Town	v	Newbury	1-2	136
184	Moneyfields	v	Christchurch	2-0	60
185	Welton Rovers	v	Larkhall Athletic	0-5	71
186	Melksham Town	v	Almondsbury UWE	3-2	85
187	Hallen	v	Calne Town	3-0	64
188	Fairford Town	v	Wellington	3-0	53
189	Street	v	Shortwood United	0-2	92
190	Radstock Town	v	Wootton Bassett Town	2-1	75
191	Brislington	v	Lydney Town	4-1	61
192	Pewsey Vale	v	Bishop Sutton	0-2	92
193	Slimbridge	v	Bradford Town	3-1	66
194	Merthyr Town	v	Bitton	2-2	323
	Bitton	v	Merthyr Town (24/8)	1-2	248
195	Bristol Manor Farm	v	Longwell Green Sports	1-1	83
	Longwell Green Sports	v	Bristol Manor Farm (22/8)	3-2	90
196	Hengrove Athletic	v	Wells City	0-3	39
197	Highworth Town	v	Odd Down (21/8)	1-4	76
198	Corsham Town	v	Cadbury Heath	1-6	65
199	Bodmin Town	v	Falmouth Town	6-3	94
200	Dawlish Town	v	Tavistock		
	(walkover for Tavistock – Dawlish Town removed)				
201	St Blazey	v	Saltash United	1-0	80
202	Chard Town	v	Torpoint Athletic	1-2	106
203	Willand Rovers	v	Barnstaple Town	0-1	100
204	Buckland Athletic	v	Ilfracombe Town	4-0	81
	(at Ilfracombe Town FC)				

PRELIMINARY ROUND

Clubs who have already won a preliminary tie may have given their supporters the idea that it could be their turn for a cup run this season. Being drawn at home in this massive round is important, but at this stage a club is unlikely to face unknown opposition and most clubs and their supporters hope that a couple more victories can produce a chance to take on fresh opposition from different leagues.

Billingham Town were on the other end of the goalscoring headlines and suffered a 0-6 defeat at Bedlington Terriers and an interesting tie saw AFC Fylde drawing 1-1 away to AFC Blackpool before winning a thrilling replay 3-2.

Clubs, normally associated in the past with action in the later rounds, faced up to early involvement as Bognor Regis Town beat Camberley Town 5-1 at home and Maidstone United certainly put their lowly neighbours in their place with a 9-0 victory at Corinthian FC. Another club to score nine was Malden & Tiptree who gave their home supporters a special afternoon by beating Ipswich Wanderers who failed to score. But one club scored even more goals as Yate Town celebrated an extraordinary 10-1 result at home to Melksham Town.

Preliminary Round action between Corinthian and Maidstone United - Shaun Welford nets the first of his five goals in the Stones' 9-0 win. Photo: Gordon Whittington.

Action from the First Round Qualifying match between Yate Town and Larkhall Athletic which Yate won 1-0. Photo: Peter Barnes.

THE FA CUP

1	Newcastle Benfield	v	South Shields	1-1	104
	South Shields	v	Newcastle Benfield (13/9)	0-3	104
	(after abandoned tie (6/9) 2-2, 45mins due to floodlight failure)				
2	Dunston UTS	v	Durham City	4-0	262
3	Spennymoor Town	v	Sunderland RCA	1-0	216
4	Guisborough Town	v	Shildon	0-1	182
5	Bedlington Terriers	v	Billingham Town	6-0	150
6	Whitley Bay	v	Marske United	2-0	524
7	Hebburn Town	v	Whitehaven	2-2	67
	Whitehaven	v	Hebburn Town (6/9)	2-4	49
8	Penrith	v	Billingham Synthonia	3-2	135
9	Ashington	v	Northallerton Town	2-1	176
10	Wakefield	v	Thackley (4/9)	1-0	117
11	Liversedge	v	Pickering Town	2-2	130
	Pickering Town	v	Liversedge (6/9)	3-3aet	137
	(Pickering Town won 5-4 on kicks from the penalty mark)				
12	Armthorpe Welfare	v	Brigg Town	2-0	81
13	Silsden	v	Harrogate Railway Athletic	1-1	161
	Harrogate Railway Athletic	v	Silsden (6/9)	2-0	79
14	Pontefract Collieries	v	Tadcaster Albion	2-3	90
15	Garforth Town	v	Sheffield	3-2	162
16	Ossett Town	v	Glasshoughton Welfare	0-0	98
	Glasshoughton Welfare	v	Ossett Town (6/9)	1-3	72
17	Scarborough Athletic	v	Barton Town OBs	2-2	498
	Barton Town OBs	v	Scarborough Athletic (6/9)	0-1	246
18	Goole	v	Staveley MW	1-1	134
	Staveley MW	v	Goole (6/9)	3-1	140
19	Parkgate	v	Hall Road Rangers	2-2	84
	Hall Road Rangers	v	Parkgate (6/9)	2-0	
	(tie awarded to Parkgate – Hall Road Rangers removed)				
20	AFC Blackpool	v	AFC Fylde	1-1	283
	AFC Fylde	v	AFC Blackpool (6/9)	3-2	156
21	Ramsbottom United	v	Salford City (2/9)	2-1	345
22	Trafford	v	Cheadle Town	3-0	167
23	Ossett Albion	v	Witton Albion	0-6	215
24	Cammell Laird	v	Atherton LR	3-1	79
25	Clitheroe	v	Skelmersdale United	4-0	285
26	Prescot Cables	v	Warrington Town	0-2	263
27	Mossley	v	Runcorn Linnets	0-0	228
	Runcorn Linnets	v	Mossley (6/9)	4-0	269
28	Formby	v	Lancaster City	1-4	142
29	Squires Gate	v	Atherton Collieries	1-0	65
30	Curzon Ashton	v	Bamber Bridge	1-1	135
	Bamber Bridge	v	Curzon Ashton (13/9)	3-2	120
31	Woodley Sports	v	Bootle	3-1	76
	(at Glossop North End FC)				
32	Radcliffe Borough	v	Holker Old Boys	3-0	88
33	Maine Road	v	Ashton Athletic	0-0	110
	Ashton Athletic	v	Maine Road (6/9)	2-3	58
34	Congleton Town	v	Runcorn Town	0-6	148
35	Deeping Rangers	v	Belper Town	2-1	124
36	New Mills	v	Rainworth MW	3-2	148
37	Arnold Town	v	Lincoln United	5-1	91
38	Grantham Town	v	Stamford	1-0	240
39	Gresley	v	Shirebrook Town	1-1	303
	Shirebrook Town	v	Gresley (7/9)	2-3aet	166
40	Hucknall Town	v	Holbeach United	0-0	180
	Holbeach United	v	Hucknall Town (7/9)	1-3aet	226
41	Borrowash Victoria	v	Carlton Town	1-3	132
42	Holbrook Sports	v	Louth Town	1-3	42
43	Heanor Town	v	Boston Town	2-1	133
44	Castle Vale	v	AFC Wulfrunians	1-1	54
	AFC Wulfrunians	v	Castle Vale (6/9)	3-3aet	46
	(AFC Wulfrunians won 5-4 on kicks from the penalty mark)				
45	Causeway United	v	Leek Town (4/9)	3-4	150
46	Newcastle Town	v	Studley	6-2	94
47	Stourport Swifts	v	Stone Dominoes	1-1	84
	Stone Dominoes	v	Stourport Swifts (6/9)	2-1	58
48	Alvechurch	v	Eccleshall	1-1	90
	Eccleshall	v	Alvechurch (7/9)	2-3	90
49	Bedworth United	v	Sutton Coldfield Town	2-1	220
50	Rugby Town	v	Gornal Athletic	0-0	311
	Gornal Athletic	v	Rugby Town (6/9)	4-3	100
51	Kidsgrove Athletic	v	Atherstone Town	5-1	196
52	Rocester	v	Halesowen Town	2-1	189
53	Stratford Town	v	Coventry Sphinx	2-1	244
54	Market Drayton Town	v	Bewdley Town	0-2	102
55	Continental Star	v	Bridgnorth Town	1-2	51
56	Romulus	v	Norton United	3-1	70
	(at Chasetown FC)				
57	Tipton Town	v	Highgate United	4-1	95
58	Boldmere St Michaels	v	Coleshill Town (2/9)	2-2	129
	Coleshill Town	v	Boldmere St Michaels (6/9)	0-1	52
59	Shepshed Dynamo	v	Thrapston Town	0-0	107
	Thrapston Town	v	Shepshed Dynamo (6/9)	2-1	86
60	Rothwell Town	v	Barrow Town	2-7	86
61	Thurnby Nirvana	v	St Neots Town	2-0	92
62	Cogenhoe United	v	Loughborough Dynamo	1-2	103
63	Rothwell Corinthians	v	Long Buckby	2-5	76
64	Woodford United	v	Daventry Town	0-0	190
	Daventry Town	v	Woodford United (6/9)	5-0	85
65	Quorn	v	Oadby Town	0-0	155
	Oadby Town	v	Quorn (6/9)	1-3aet	153
66	Loughborough University	v	Godmanchester Rovers	4-1	57
67	Coalville Town	v	Daventry United	3-4	212
68	Bugbrooke St Michaels	v	Huntingdon Town	1-2	95
69	Leiston	v	FC Clacton	5-0	147
70	Needham Market	v	Felixstowe & Walton United	4-1	237
71	Haverhill Rovers	v	Brantham Athletic	3-2	154
72	Ely City	v	Walsham Le Willows	1-1	111
	Walsham Le Willows	v	Ely City (7/9)	1-2	75
73	King's Lynn Town	v	Soham Town Rangers	2-1	853
74	March Town United	v	Wisbech Town	1-1	1109
	Wisbech Town	v	March Town United (6/9)	3-2	830
75	Hadleigh United	v	Heybridge Swifts	1-4	122
76	St Ives Town	v	AFC Sudbury	0-0	223
	AFC Sudbury	v	St Ives Town (6/9)	3-2aet	199
77	Maldon & Tiptree	v	Ipswich Wanderers	9-0	67
78	Wroxham	v	Long Melford	1-0	116
79	Gorleston	v	Harlow Town	2-0	144
80	Burnham Ramblers	v	Hertford Town	3-3	100
	Hertford Town	v	Burnham Ramblers (6/9)	2-2aet	76
	(Hertford Town won 3-2 on kicks from the penalty mark)				
81	AFC Dunstable	v	Grays Athletic (4/9)	2-3	196
82	Dunstable Town	v	Bethnal Green United	1-1	110
	Bethnal Green United	v	Dunstable Town (6/9)	0-3	41
	(at Dunstable Town FC)				
83	Romford	v	Royston Town (4/9)	3-2	191
84	Potters Bar Town	v	Broxbourne Borough V&E	1-3	81
85	Stotfold	v	Enfield Town	2-1	168

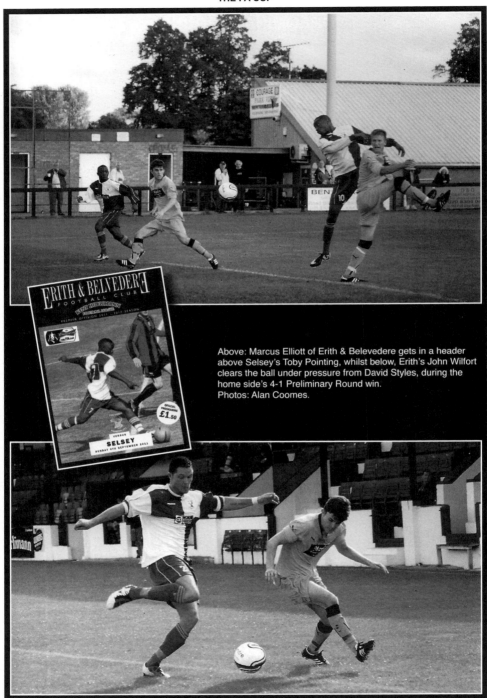

Above: Marcus Elliott of Erith & Beleveдere gets in a header above Selsey's Toby Pointing, whilst below, Erith's John Wilfort clears the ball under pressure from David Styles, during the home side's 4-1 Preliminary Round win.
Photos: Alan Coomes.

PRELIMINARY ROUND
SATURDAY 3 SEPTEMBER 2011 - WINNERS RECEIVE £1,500

86	Tilbury	v Biggleswade United	3-1	89
87	Hatfield Town	v Enfield 1893	1-1	78
	Enfield 1893	v Hatfield Town (6/9)	1-2	65
88	Great Wakering Rovers	v Oxhey Jets	1-1	70
	Oxhey Jets	v Great Wakering Rovers (6/9)	1-0	93
89	Haringey Borough	v Berkhamsted	0-1	77
90	Cheshunt	v Southend Manor	0-0	139
	Southend Manor	v Cheshunt (6/9)	4-2	70
91	Waltham Forest	v Ilford	1-1	55
	Ilford	v Waltham Forest (7/9)	2-3	57
92	Waltham Abbey	v Ware	6-1	108
93	Colney Heath	v Brentwood Town	0-1	74
94	Barton Rovers	v Witham Town	3-0	155
95	Stansted	v London APSA	4-0	90
96	Cockfosters	v Redbridge	1-2	86
97	Biggleswade Town	v Haringey & WD	5-5	107
	Haringey & WD	v Biggleswade Town (7/9)	1-2	60
98	Newport Pagnell Town	v Thame United	1-1	132
	Thame United	v Newport Pagnell Town (6/9)	1-1aet	79
	(Thame United won 4-2 on kicks from the penalty mark)			
99	Wokingham & Emmbrook	v Kidlington	3-0	101
100	Bedfont Sports	v Hanworth Villa	1-1	250
	Hanworth Villa	v Bedfont Sports (6/9)	2-0	193
101	Beaconsfield SYCOB	v Northwood	2-1	122
102	Abingdon Town	v Didcot Town	2-2	100
	Didcot Town	v Abingdon Town (6/9)	3-2aet	106
103	Slough Town	v Binfield (4/9)	3-1	
104	Wantage Town	v Abingdon United	1-2	98
105	Leighton Town	v Uxbridge	2-0	126
106	Aylesbury United	v North Leigh (4/9)	0-0	171
	North Leigh	v Aylesbury United (6/9)	4-2	104
107	Wembley	v Ardley United	1-1	87
	Ardley United	v Wembley (6/9)	1-2	80
108	AFC Hayes	v Tring Athletic	4-2	79
109	Chalfont St Peter	v Aylesbury	4-2	119
110	Burnham	v Ashford Town (Middx)	2-1	103
111	North Greenford United	v Bedfont Town	2-1	45
112	Staines Lammas	v Harefield United	2-2	94
	Harefield United	v Staines Lammas (6/9)	0-2	56
113	Marlow	v Thatcham Town	1-0	132
114	Chatham Town	v Croydon Athletic	1-0	164
115	Badshot Lea	v Chertsey Town	0-1	79
116	Folkestone Invicta	v Whyteleafe	2-2	211
	Whyteleafe	v Folkestone Invicta (6/9)	1-2	90
117	Corinthian	v Maidstone United	0-9	231
118	Walton & Hersham	v Tunbridge Wells	3-1	124
119	Thamesmead Town	v Burgess Hill Town	3-0	47
120	Lingfield	v Fisher (4/9)	4-1	124
	(at Whyteleafe FC)			
121	Crawley Down	v Farnham Town	2-1	55
122	Erith & Belvedere	v Selsey (4/9)	4-1	92
123	Merstham	v Egham Town	1-1	113
	Egham Town	v Merstham (6/9)	2-3	54
124	Dulwich Hamlet	v Eastbourne Town	2-0	288

125	Sittingbourne	v Peacehaven & Telscombe	2-1	117
126	Whitstable Town	v Worthing	1-3	173
127	Epsom & Ewell	v Chipstead (4/9)	1-2	107
128	Banstead Athletic	v Arundel	3-1	65
129	Whitehawk	v Ramsgate	0-0	118
	Ramsgate	v Whitehawk (6/9)	0-1	88
130	Beckenham Town	v Walton Casuals	3-1	108
131	Chessington & Hook United	v Hythe Town	0-1	
132	Lordswood	v VCD Athletic	0-1	84
133	Bognor Regis Town	v Camberley Town	5-1	427
134	Shoreham	v Lancing	1-0	145
135	Herne Bay	v Deal Town	3-0	196
136	Horley Town	v Corinthian Casuals	3-1	73
137	Raynes Park Vale	v Faversham Town	0-1	71
138	Sevenoaks Town	v Redhill	1-3	53
139	Erith Town	v South Park	2-0	40
140	Totton & Eling	v Bournemouth	1-2	42
141	Sholing	v Newbury	9-1	117
142	Shrewton United	v Hungerford Town	0-1	114
143	Fleet Town	v Alton Town	4-3	142
144	Wimborne Town	v Godalming Town	1-2	263
145	Whitchurch United	v Brading Town	2-1	78
146	AFC Portchester	v Newport (IW)	2-2	507
	Newport (IW)	v AFC Portchester (7/9)	2-1	128
147	Moneyfields	v Gosport Borough	2-1	201
148	Winchester City	v Blackfield & Langley	1-3	100
149	Andover	v Poole Town		
	(walkover for Poole Town – Andover removed)			
150	Alresford Town	v Hartley Wintney	1-4	63
151	Lymington Town	v Brockenhurst	1-1	103
	Brockenhurst	v Lymington Town (6/9)	2-1	70
152	Horndean	v Bridport	3-1	100
153	Yate Town	v Melksham Town	10-1	123
154	Merthyr Town	v Longwell Green Sports	1-0	289
155	Slimbridge	v Cadbury Heath	1-2	81
156	Fairford Town	v Cinderford Town	1-3	83
157	Shortwood United	v Bishop Sutton	1-1	99
	Bishop Sutton	v Shortwood United (6/9)	4-1	86
158	Paulton Rovers	v Clevedon Town	1-2	161
159	Mangotsfield United	v Hallen	1-0	187
	(tie awarded to Hallen – Mangotsfield United removed)			
160	Larkhall Athletic	v Odd Down	4-0	192
161	Bishop's Cleeve	v Wells City	0-1	
162	Radstock Town	v Brislington	1-2	50
163	St Blazey	v Tavistock	1-2	105
164	Barnstaple Town	v Bodmin Town	1-2	125
165	Taunton Town	v Buckland Athletic	1-1	219
	Buckland Athletic	v Taunton Town (6/9)	0-2	176
166	Bideford	v Tiverton Town	4-0	289
167	Torpoint Athletic	v Bridgwater Town	2-5	138

FIRST QUALIFYING ROUND

With F.A.Cup ties every two weeks at this stage of the season, a few replays can force some clubs to be involved with more cup ties than league fixtures, but no-one worries if victories keep moving the club on to bigger and better opposition bringing a boost to finances through the gate receipts and the prize money.

Ties in this round are still mainly local pairings so old rivalries are likely to be revived. Grantham Town will have enjoyed their 2-0 victory over Arnold Town while Witton Albion and Beaconsfield supporters will have been thrilled with similar victories over Marine and Wealdstone respectively

An impressive 3-0 result was celebrated at Poole Town who beat Kingstonian and there were outstanding victories at Bradford PA, who thrashed Harrogate Railway Athletic 8-0, and at Banstead Athletic who lost 1-9 to Maidstone United. Ten goals were also scored at the Newcastle Town v Stratford Town tie, with a very different outcome - a 5-5 draw leading to a replay won by Stratford 6-2, which must have left a few defensive problems for all concerned!

Any clubs with two or three cup victories already achieved will be hoping for a home draw and perhaps some glamorous visitors.

Above: Nick Sullivan, Crawley Down, attempts to beat V.C.D. Athletic's captain Gary Cook. Whilst to the left, V.C.D. 'keeper, Jack Bradsure, and defence keep out a Crawley Down attack. Photos: Roger Turner.

FIRST QUALIFYING ROUND
SATURDAY 17 SEPTEMBER 2011 - WINNERS RECEIVE £3,000

1	Spennymoor Town	v	Dunston UTS	3-0	259
2	Bedlington Terriers	v	Newcastle Benfield	4-0	181
3	Kendal Town	v	Whitley Bay	1-0	289
4	Hebburn Town	v	Penrith	2-0	83
5	Shildon	v	Ashington	0-0	157
	Ashington	v	Shilton (20/9)	2-2aet	229
	(Ashington won 5-3 on kicks from the penalty mark)				
6	Armthorpe Welfare	v	Stocksbridge Park Steels	1-1	115
	Stocksbridge Park Steels	v	Armthorpe Welfare (20/9)	3-1	86
7	Garforth Town	v	Frickley Athletic	0-2	170
8	Pickering Town	v	Staveley MW	2-2	118
	Staveley MW	v	Pickering Town (21/11)	4-0	124
9	Parkgate	v	Whitby Town	1-3	116
10	Wakefield	v	Ossett Town	4-0	102
11	North Ferriby United	v	Worksop Town	1-0	168
12	Bradford (Park Avenue)	v	Harrogate RA	8-0	265
13	Tadcaster Albion	v	Scarborough Athletic	3-0	472
14	Ashton United	v	Runcorn Town	5-1	100
15	FC United of Manchester	v	Woodley Sports	1-1	1109
	Woodley Sports	v	FC United or Manchester (20/9)	1-4	328
	(at Glossop North End FC)				
16	Bamber Bridge	v	Warrington Town (20/9)	0-4	159
17	Squires Gate	v	Runcorn Linnets	0-0	179
	Runcorn Linnets	v	Squires Gate (20/9)	1-0	325
18	Ramsbottom United	v	Nantwich Town (20/9)	1-2	217
19	Lancaster City	v	Maine Road	5-1	176
20	AFC Fylde	v	Chorley	1-1	411
	Chorley	v	AFC Fylde (20/9)	0-1	
21	Witton Albion	v	Marine	2-0	246
22	Burscough	v	Clitheroe	2-2	137
	Clitheroe	v	Burscough (20/9)	5-2	184
23	Cammell Laird	v	Radcliffe Borough	1-2	65
24	Trafford	v	Northwich Victoria	0-2	386
25	Deeping Rangers	v	New Mills	5-1	137
26	Louth Town	v	Buxton	0-2	335
27	Grantham Town	v	Arnold Town	2-0	201
28	Mickleover Sports	v	Gresley	4-2	
29	Matlock Town	v	Hucknall Town	2-0	356
30	Carlton Town	v	Heanor Town	1-0	109
31	Romulus	v	Bridgnorth Town (18/9)	1-2	101
	(at Chasetown FC)				
32	Evesham United	v	Rocester	4-0	104
33	Leamington	v	Boldmere St Michaels	5-0	422
34	Leek Town	v	Tipton Town	2-0	281
35	Kidsgrove Athletic	v	Gornal Athletic		3-0
36	Chasetown	v	Alvechurch	6-2	264
37	Rushall Olympic	v	Bedworth United	1-0	168
38	Bewdley Town	v	Stourbridge	1-2	301
39	Redditch United	v	Hednesford Town	0-2	348
40	AFC Wulfrunians	v	Stafford Rangers	2-3	304
41	Newcastle Town	v	Stratford Town	5-5	114
	Stratford Town	v	Newcastle Town (20/9)	6-2	211
42	Barwell	v	Stone Dominoes	3-2	118
43	Thurnby Nirvana	v	Barrow Town	1-1	87
	Barrow Town	v	Thurnby Nirvana (20/9)	3-1	113
44	Long Buckby	v	Thrapston Town	4-1	70
45	Huntingdon Town	v	Daventry Town	1-3	161
46	Quorn	v	Loughborough University	2-1	122
47	Loughborough Dynamo	v	Daventry Town	3-1	103
48	Cambridge City	v	Maldon & Tiptree	2-2	266
	Maldon & Tiptree	v	Cambridge City (20/9)	2-1	98
49	Needham Market	v	Ely City	1-1	224
	Ely City	v	Needham Market (20/9)	3-4aet	163
50	Leiston	v	AFC Sudbury	0-1	283
51	Bury Town	v	Gorleston	3-0	319
52	Heybridge Swifts	v	Lowestoft Town	1-2	198
53	Wisbech Town	v	Wroxham	1-4	441
54	King's Lynn Town	v	Haverhill Rovers	1-0	836
55	Tilbury	v	Arlesey Town	1-2	90
56	Waltham Forest	v	Hitchin Town	2-0	70
57	St Albans City	v	Berkhamsted	0-0	351
	Berkhamsted	v	St Albans City (20/9)	0-3	306
58	Wingate & Finchley	v	Redbridge	0-3	101
59	Barton Rovers	v	Hatfield Town	1-1	110
	Hatfield Town	v	Barton Rovers (20/9)	2-1	144
60	AFC Hornchurch	v	Concord Rangers	1-3	235
61	Canvey Island	v	Stansted	4-1	259
62	Hemel Hempstead Town	v	Brentwood Town	0-0	245
	Brentwood Town	v	Hemel Hempstead Town	0-0	104
	(Hemel Hempstead won 4-2 on kicks from the penalty mark)				
63	Grays Athletic	v	Aveley (18/9)	1-2	257
64	Hertford Town	v	Oxhey Jets	0-1	164
65	East Thurrock United	v	Bedford Town	1-0	
66	Biggleswade Town	v	Waltham Abbey	3-1	140
67	Billericay Town	v	Stotfold	4-0	319
68	Dunstable Town	v	Broxbourne Borough V&E	7-0	49
69	Southend Manor	v	Romford	4-2	139
70	Burnham	v	Chalfont St Peter	1-0	93
71	Leatherhead	v	North Leigh	5-1	175
72	Chesham United	v	Staines Lammas	3-2	237
73	Wokingham & Emmbrook	v	North Greenford United (18/9)	1-2	178
74	Leighton Town	v	Abingdon United	4-1	106
75	Oxford City	v	Didcot Town	1-1	209
	Didcot Town	v	Oxford City (20/9)	0-3	
76	Banbury United	v	Slough Town	1-3	349
77	AFC Hayes	v	Hendon	0-3	93
78	Harrow Borough	v	Marlow	20	113
79	Thame Utd	v	Brackley Town	2-0	217
80	Hanworth Villa	v	Wembley	1-0	106
81	Wealdstone	v	Beaconsfield SYCOB	0-2	266
82	Carshalton Athletic	v	Faversham Town	3-0	211
83	Herne Bay	v	Erith Town	2-3	222
84	Margate	v	Tooting & Mitcham United	3-0	340
85	Chertsey Town	v	Lewes	4-1	212
86	Hastings United	v	Cray Wanderers	0-3	201
87	Bognor Regis Town	v	Sittingbourne	1-0	402
88	Beckenham Town	v	Metropolitan Police	4-2	82
89	Chatham Town	v	Worthing	0-1	234
90	Banstead Athletic	v	Maidstone United	1-9	162
91	Merstham	v	Walton & Hersham	2-1	113
92	Crawley Down	v	VCD Athletic	0-2	75
93	Horley Town	v	Dulwich Hamlet	0-4	115
94	Chipstead	v	Redhill	3-1	106
95	Shoreham	v	Thamesmead Town	0-2	101
96	Hythe Town	v	Erith & Belvedere	5-2	215
97	Folkestone Invicta	v	Whitehawk	0-3	237
98	Horsham	v	Lingfield	2-2	237
	Lingfield	v	Horsham (21/11)	2-4aet	214
	(at Horsham YMCA FC)				
99	Hungerford Town	v	Horndean	3-1	78
100	Whitchurch United	v	Brockenhurst	2-0	200
101	Sholing	v	Blackfield & Langley	2-1	144
102	Poole Town	v	Kingstonian	3-0	507
103	Bournemouth	v	Newport (IW)	2-1	65
104	Hartley Wintney	v	Bashley	1-0	155
105	AFC Totton	v	Fleet Town	2-0	394
106	Godalming Town	v	Moneyfields	1-1	178
	Moneyfields	v	Godalming Town (20/9)	1-3	290
107	Chippenham Town	v	Wells City	3-0	273
	(tie awarded to Wells City – Chippenham Town removed)				
108	Merthyr Town	v	Cinderford Town	1-1	309
	Cinderford Town	v	Merthyr Town (20/9)	2-0aet	157
109	Yate Town	v	Larkhall Athletic	1-0	140
110	Swindon Supermarine	v	Cirencester Town	3-2	183
111	Hallen	v	Frome Town	2-2	
	Frome Town	v	Hallen (21/11)	1-1aet	
	(Frome Town won 4-2 on kicks from the penalty mark)				
112	Clevedon Town	v	Brislington	3-2	127
113	Bishop Sutton	v	Cadbury Heath	0-4	84
114	Bideford	v	Bridgwater Town	2-1	262
115	Weymouth	v	Taunton Town	0-0	367
	Taunton Town	v	Weymouth (19/9)	1-3	270
116	Tavistock	v	Bodmin Town	1-3	94

SECOND QUALIFYING ROUND

The introduction of Blue Square North and South clubs certainly introduced some extra glamour to the draw and Witton Albion supporters will have been thrilled with their clubs' 2-0 victory at Altrincham, a club with a great FA Cup record.

Special results were also celebrated by Daventry Town who beat Leamington 2-1, Godalming Town's 2-1 victory over Worcester City and Barrow Town's 4-1 victory at Mickleover Sports.

Not so long ago, a Slough Town victory over Boreham Wood would have been expected, but not these days, so a 3-2 victory was very welcome for the Buckinghamshire club working hard to regain past standards. Bodmin will also have been very pleased with an away draw at Yate Town and a 4-1 replay victory.

Impressive attendances are expected for FC United matches and 1,147 saw their club lose to Lancaster City by the only goal of the game. Good support was also appreciated by Blyth Spartans, where 835 watched them play Bedlington Terriers, 817 for Boston United 0 Kidsgrove Athletic 0 and 812 for King's Lynn 4 Quorn 2.

A fine penalty save from Heanor Town's 'keeper Mark Frost - unfortunately it was not enough to stop Carlton Town going through to the Second Qualifying Round with a 1-0 victory. Photo: Gordon Whittington.

Above: Action from the Second Qualifying Round tie between Yate Town and Bodmin Town. Photo: Jonathan Holloway.
Left: Carlton Town's Ruben Wiggins-Thomas looks for his options as the Hednesford defender approaches.
Photo: Bill Wheatcroft.

SECOND QUALIFYING ROUND
SATURDAY 1 OCTOBER 2011 - WINNERS RECEIVE £4,500

#	Home		Away	Score	Att
1	Northwich Victoria	v	Nantwich Town	1-2	542
2	Stalybridge Celtic	v	Guiseley	1-2	462
3	Workington	v	Droylsdon	1-2	316
4	FC Halifax Town	v	Tadcaster Albion	2-1	1002
5	Wakefield	v	Kendal Town	1-4	98
	(at Garforth Town FC)				
6	Stocksbridge Park Steels	v	Colwyn Bay	3-1	128
7	Clitheroe	v	Radcliffe Borough	1-3	203
8	Staveley MW	v	Hyde	0-3	320
9	Blyth Spartans	v	Bedlington Terriers	2-1	835
10	Ashton United	v	Spennymoor Town	0-3	324
11	AFC Fylde	v	Gainsborough Trinity	2-2	282
	Gainsborough Trinity	v	AFC Fylde (4/10)	2-1aet	
12	Hebburn Town	v	Runcorn Linnets	1-0	170
13	FC United of Manchester	v	Lancaster City	0-1	1147
14	Bradford (Park Avenue)	v	Warrington Town	3-1	268
15	Whitby Town	v	North Ferriby United	2-1	253
16	Frickley Athletic	v	Harrogate Town	1-1	285
	Harrogate Town	v	Frickley Athletic (4/10)	1-2	274
17	Altrincham	v	Witton Albion	0-2	628
18	Ashington	v	Vauxhall Motors	3-3	444
	Vauxhall Motors	v	Ashington (4/10)	0-1	221
19	Histon	v	Corby Town	1-1	427
	Corby Town	v	Histon (5/10)	3-1aet	642
20	Mickelover Sports	v	Barrow Town	1-4	230
21	Stafford Rangers	v	Stratford Town	2-4	438
22	Deeping Rangers	v	Leek Town	0-2	225
23	Buxton	v	Rushall Olympic	1-2	238
24	Matlock Town	v	Hinckley United	1-3	411
25	Eastwood Town	v	Evesham United	0-3	222
26	Barwell	v	Stourbridge	0-2	236
27	Chasetown	v	Grantham Town	1-2	326
28	Bridgnorth Town	v	Long Buckby	0-2	201
29	Carlton Town	v	Hednesford Town	0-1	201
30	Daventry Town	v	Leamington	2-1	551
31	Needham Market	v	Nuneaton Town	0-3	319
32	Solihull Moors	v	Loughborough Dynamo	2-0	152
33	Boston United	v	Kidsgrove Athletic	0-0	817
	Kidsgrove Athletic	v	Boston United (4/10)	2-0	280
34	King's Lynn Town	v	Quorn	4-2	812
35	Chipstead	v	Billericay Town	0-3	175
36	Oxhey Jets	v	Hendon	1-2	376
37	Hanworth Villa	v	Aveley	1-0	196
38	Cray Wanderers	v	Erith Town (2/10)	5-0	183
39	Arlesey Town	v	Hampton & Richmond Borough	6-2	156
40	Redbridge	v	Bury Town	1-0	120
41	Slough Town	v	Boreham Wood	3-2	277
42	East Thurrock United	v	St Albans City	3-3	181
	St Albans City	v	East Thurrock United (4/10)	1-3	250
43	Southend Manor	v	Chertsey Town	4-2	168
44	Dover Athletic	v	Carshalton Athletic	3-0	639
45	North Greenford United	v	Hythe Town	2-1	107
46	Chelmsford City	v	Tonbridge Angels	3-0	653
47	Sutton United	v	Dulwich Hamlet	5-1	494
48	Wroxham	v	Concord Rangers	2-2	140
	Concord Rangers	v	Wroxham (4/10)	1-2	111
49	Dartford	v	Harrow Borough	5-0	803
50	Margate	v	Thamesmead Town	0-0	267
	Thamesmead Town	v	Margate (4/10)	1-6	141
51	Bromley	v	Welling United	2-1	716
52	Leighton Town	v	Hatfield Town	3-0	213
53	Whitehawk	v	Maldon & Tiptree	0-0	104
	Maldon & Tiptree	v	Whitehawk (4/10)	2-1	92
54	Staines Town	v	Beaconsfield SYCOB	0-0	213
	Beaconsfield SYCOB	v	Staines Town (3/10)	0-2	175
55	Burnham	v	Horsham	2-2	130
	Horsham	v	Burnham (4/10)	2-3	202
56	Dunstable Town	v	Chesham United	2-1	229
57	Biggleswade Town	v	Leatherhead	1-1	242
	Leatherhead	v	Biggleswade Town (4/10)	2-1	240
58	Canvey Island	v	Bishop's Stortford	0-1	316
59	Waltham Forest	v	Eastbourne Borough (2/10)	0-1	175
60	Maidstone United	v	Bognor Regis Town	2-3	386
61	Merstham	v	AFC Sudbury	0-2	123
62	Lowestoft Town	v	Hemel Hempstead Town	3-0	669
63	VCD Athletic	v	Thurrock	2-2	104
	Thurrock	v	VCD Athletic (3/10)	1-0	87
64	Worthing	v	Beckenham Town	0-0	349
	Beckenham Town	v	Worthing (4/10)	1-2	274
65	Havant & Waterlooville	v	Sholing	4-1	370
66	Frome Town	v	Basingstoke Town	0-0	300
	Basingstoke Town	v	Frome Town (4/10)	3-0	262
67	Thame United	v	Oxford City	1-3	462
68	Bournemouth	v	Truro City	0-0	238
	Truro City	v	Bournemouth (4/10)	3-2	182
69	Dorchester Town	v	Weston Super Mare	0-1	329
70	Whitchurch United	v	Gloucester City	0-2	400
71	Wells City	v	Woking	0-7	410
72	Salisbury City	v	Swindon Supermarine	3-0	598
73	Yate Town	v	Bodmin Town	1-1	154
	Bodmin Town	v	Yate Town (5/10)	4-1	
74	Godalming Town	v	Worcester City	2-1	334
75	Poole Town	v	Cadbury Heath	4-0	382
76	Eastleigh	v	Cinderford Town	3-1	225
77	Weymouth	v	Hungerford Town	3-3	404
	Hungerford Town	v	Weymouth (4/10)	1-3	214
78	Hartley Wintney	v	Bideford	2-1	210
79	Maidenhead United	v	Farnborough	1-1	352
	Farnborough	v	Maidenhead United (5/10)	2-3	395
80	Clevedon Town	v	AFC Totton	1-2	140

THIRD QUALIFYING ROUND

Just forty cup ties and only two more victories before the chance of drawing a Football League club and a special pay day.

Barrow Town (East Midland Counties) welcomed Rushall Olympic (Northern Premier League Premier Division) with hope, but lost by three goals. Daventry Town also hoped for better from senior Midland rivals Nuneaton Town but also lost at home and Bodmin Town (South West Peninsular) couldn't take advantage of a home tie against Godalming Town,where they lost in a replay.

However, after achieving a place in the Fourth Qualifying Round draw, there were special celebrations for:
Ashington (Northern League, Division One) who beat Guiseley 1-0.
Hanworth Villa (Combined Counties) who beat Slough Town at home 3-1 watched by 592.
After a 1-1 draw Hebburn Town (Northern League, Division Two) who won 4-2 at Radcliffe Borough.
Kings Lynn (United Counties) who beat Stratford Town.
Southend Manor (Essex Senior) who beat Leighton Town 5-0.

Best Attendances:

Lowestoft Town v Chelmsford City	1,065
Salisbury City v Poole Town	961
King's Lynn v Stratford Town	858
Ashington v Guiseley	731
AFC Totton v Weymouth	712

Just one round to survive and then ?   Perhaps national glory!

FOURTH QUALIFYING ROUND

Five clubs from outside the nation's top nine leagues, those below Step 4, were probably the most excited as they waited for the draw for this last round before The Football League clubs entered the competition. Congratulations to The Northern League who were represented by two member clubs.

Hanworth Villa must have thought there was a chance of success at AFC Totton but after a five goal thriller their cup run was over. Ashington lost heavily at Grimsby while Hebburn Town drew an away trip to Gateshead, and this was probably a disappointment as unknown opposition often seem more exciting than local rivals and sadly for the Northern League club they suffered a 0-3 defeat.

Kings Lynn were also drawn away, but they rose to the challenge of facing a Blue Square Premier club in Tamworth, and only lost by the odd goal in three. This left Southend Manor, and they, like the other three, were drawn away from home and lost, going down 1-3 at Kettering Town.

So where were the heroes and the clubs whose names wouldn't be expected to be in the Fourth Qualifying Round?

Arlesey Town and Redbridge beat Blue Square Premier clubs Forest Green Rovers and Ebbsfleet United with Nantwich Town knocking out Nuneaton Town but the luck of the draw hadn't helped the minnows with five out five being drawn away from home.

The Best Attendances:

Luton Town v Hendon	2,329
Wrexham v York City	2,252
Mansfield Town v Fleetwood Town	1,725
Dartford v Bromley	1,587
Grimsby Town v Ashington	1,540

THIRD QUALIFYING ROUND
SATURDAY 15 OCTOBER 2011 - WINNERS RECEIVE £7,500

1	Nantwich Town	v	Kendal Town	2-1	468
2	Radcliffe Borough	v	Hebburn Town	2-4	215
3	Lancaster City	v	FC Halifax Town	0-3	646
4	Whitby Town	v	Blyth Spartans	1-2	506
5	Gainsborough Trinity	v	Frickley Athletic	2-0	644
6	Hyde	v	Bradford (Park Avenue)	0-1	560
7	Ashington	v	Guiseley	1-0	730
8	Witton Albion	v	Spennymoor Town	3-1	512
9	Droylsden	v	Stocksbridge Park Steels	4-1	230
10	King's Lynn Town	v	Stratford Town	3-2	866
11	Daventry Town	v	Nuneaton Town	1-2	605
12	Hednesford Town	v	Corby Town	2-4	602
13	Kidsgrove Athletic	v	Long Buckby	2-1	343
14	Hinckley United	v	Leek Town	3-3	436
	Leek Town	v	Hinckley United (18/10)	1-2	488
15	Solihull Moors	v	Grantham Town	3-2	308
16	Barrow Town	v	Rushall Olympic	0-3	318
17	Stourbridge	v	Evesham United	5-0	518
18	Billericay Town	v	Leatherhead	0-3	384
19	Worthing	v	Staines Town	0-2	466
20	Redbridge	v	Dunstable Town	3-0	114
21	Eastbourne Borough	v	AFC Sudbury	1-0	529
22	Lowestoft Town	v	Chelmsford City	2-5	1065
23	Cray Wanderers	v	Dartford	1-2	690
24	Maldon & Tiptree	v	Hendon	1-3	159
25	Thurrock	v	Arlesey Town	0-0	73
	Arlesey Town	v	Thurrock (18/10)	4-1	136
26	Burnham	v	Bishop's Stortford	2-5	182
27	Slough Town	v	Hanworth Villa	2-2	525
	Hanworth Villa	v	Slough Town (18/10)	3-1	592
28	East Thurrock United	v	North Greenford United	3-3	123
	North Greenford United	v	East Thurrock United (18/10)	0-3	102
29	Dover Athletic	v	Wroxham	3-1	628
30	Margate	v	Bromley	2-3	515
31	Southend Manor	v	Leighton Town	5-0	309
32	Sutton United	v	Bognor Regis Town	4-0	622
33	Basingstoke Town	v	Hartley Wintney	4-0	577
34	Bodmin Town	v	Godalming Town	1-1	300
	Godalming Town	v	Bodmin Town (18/10)	5-1	360
35	Gloucester City	v	Truro City	7-2	385
36	AFC Totton	v	Weymouth	4-2	712
37	Eastleigh	v	Oxford City	1-3	325
38	Salisbury City	v	Poole Town	6-1	961
39	Weston Super Mare	v	Havant & Waterlooville	3-2	333
40	Maidenhead United	v	Woking	4-1	625

FOURTH QUALIFYING ROUND
SATURDAY 29 OCTOBER 2011 - WINNERS RECEIVE £12,500

1	Tamworth	v	King's Lynn Town	2-1	966
2	Droylsden	v	Blyth Spartans	0-0	393
	Blyth Spartans	v	Droylsden (1/11)	2-1	679
3	Stourbridge	v	Rushall Olympic	5-0	720
4	Kidsgrove Athletic	v	Bradford (Park Avenue)	0-2	1140
5	Gateshead	v	Hebburn Town	3-0	1198
6	Grimsby Town	v	Ashington	5-0	1540
7	Wrexham	v	York City	2-1	2252
8	Mansfield Town	v	Fleetwood Town	1-1	1725
	Fleetwood Town	v	Mansfield Town (1/11)	5-0	1162
9	Nantwich Town	v	Nuneaton Town	1-0	1002
10	Alfreton Town	v	Lincoln City	1-1	1000
	Lincoln City	v	Alfreton Town (1/11)	1-2	1728
11	AFC Telford United	v	Gainsborough Trinity	5-0	1075
12	Southport	v	Stockport County	1-0	1358
13	Solihull Moors	v	FC Halifax Town	0-1	551
14	Kidderminster Harriers	v	Corby Town	0-0	1236
	Corby Town	v	Kidderminster Harriers (2/11)	4-1	1026
15	Darlington	v	Hinckley United	1-1	1175
	Hinckley United	v	Darlington (1/11)	3-0	837
16	Witton Albion	v	Barrow	1-4	860
17	Dover Athletic	v	Bath City	0-1	922
18	Bishop's Stortford	v	Salisbury City	1-2	501
19	Eastbourne Borough	v	East Thurrock United	1-2	603
20	Chelmsford City	v	Gloucester City	1-1	928
	Gloucester City	v	Chelmsford City (1/11)	0-1	490
21	Hayes & Yeading United	v	Cambridge United	2-6	452
22	Godalming Town	v	Maidenhead United	0-5	703
23	Sutton United	v	Leatherhead	3-3	882
	Leatherhead	v	Sutton United (1/11)	2-3aet	940
24	Weston Super Mare	v	Oxford City	2-3	630
25	AFC Totton	v	Hanworth Villa	3-2	764
26	Basingstoke Town	v	Staines Town	2-1	545
27	Arlesey Town	v	Forest Green Rovers	2-1	343
28	Dartford	v	Bromley	1-2	1567
29	Luton Town	v	Hendon	5-1	2329
30	Kettering Town	v	Southend Manor	3-1	987
31	Redbridge	v	Ebbsfleet United	2-0	442
32	Newport County	v	Braintree Town	4-3	1234

Sutton United's Tony Taggart gets in a shot past Bognor's Stuart Axten and Tim Bond in the Third Qualifying Round. Photo: Alan Coomes.

Right: Third Qualifying Round action from Gloucester City's 7-2 win over Truro City. Photo: Peter Barnes.

Gary Elphick, (No.6) Eastbourne Borough, heads the ball over goalkeeper Danny Gay, of AFC Sudbury, for the only goal of this Third Qualifying Round match. Photos: Roger Turner.

Paul terry equalises for Thurrock a minute after Arlesey Town had taken the lead in this Third Qualifying Round tie. Photo: Gordon Whittington.

Alfreton's Jamie Mullen controls the ball under pressure from a Lincoln City player in the Fourth Qualifying Round. Photo: Bill Wheatcroft.

Leon Soloman fires the ball into the roof of the net to complete his hat-trick in a 5-0 win for Maidenhead United over Godalming Town in the Fourth Qualifying Round.
Photo: Gordon Whittington.

Sequence left: Witton's Titchiner breaks through to score against Barrow in the Fourth Qualifying Round. Photos: Keith Clayton.

Carlisle 'keeper Adam Collin, catches the ball before it reaches Alfreton's Anthony Church in the First Round Proper.
Photo: Bill Wheatcroft

Martin, MK Dons, beats Cooke, Nantwich, to the ball during their First Round tie.

Photo: Keith Clayton.

Action from the First Round tie between Bristol Rovers and Corby Town. Photo: Peter Barnes.

FIRST ROUND PROPER

The FA Cup draw for one of the most exciting days of the football year was about to give 32 non-league clubs a big thrill.

Conference Premier: 14 - AFC Telford United, Alfreton Town, Barrow, Bath City, Cambridge United, Fleetwood Town, Gateshead, Grimsby Town, Kettering Town, Luton Town, Newport County, Southport, Tamworth and Wrexham.
Conference South: 6 - Basingstoke Town, Bromley, Chelmsford City, Maidenhead United, Salisbury City and Sutton United.
Conference North: 4 - Blyth Spartans, Corby Town, FC Halifax T & Hinckley United.
Southern Premier: 3 - AFC Totton, Arlesey Town, Oxford City & Stourbridge.
Northern Premier League: 2 - Bradford PA and Nantwich Town.
Isthmian Premier: 1 - East Thurrock United.
Isthmian Div 1 North: 1 - Redbridge.

One of the most staggering results came from one of the smallest clubs in the round, as AFC Totton beat Bradford PA 8-1 in front of 2,315 and plenty of cameras. East Thurrock United's fine high goalscoring cup run came to an end at home to Macclesfield Town who won 3-0 and Nantwich Town were well beaten at MK Dons.

Arlesey Town had no luck at all, being drawn away to Salisbury City where they lost, and Redbridge must have been just as disappointed when drawing at home with Oxford City, but at least they won the replay. They were joined by Gateshead, Chelmsford City, Tamworth, Sutton United and Wrexham who all beat fellow non-leaguers.

The headlines were dominated by Stourbridge who, after a thrilling 3-3 draw at Plymouth beat Argyle 2-0 in the replay and the high flying Fleetwood Town who beat Wycombe Wanderers 2-0.

SECOND ROUND PROPER

When a non-league club reaches the Second Round Proper of the FA Cup it must be frustrating to lose to another non-league team. This is what happened to Gateshead who lost at home to Tamworth and Grimsby Town who went out at Salisbury City in a replay.

AFC Totton found Bristol Rovers far too strong but Chelmsford City took Macclesfield Town to a replay, but the success stories were provided by Wrexham 2-1 winners at Division One Brentford and Fleetwood Town who just forced a replay at home and then outplayed Yeovil in Somerset.

This gave Non-League football four representatives in the hat with The Premier League clubs and a possibly a place in FA Cup history.

THIRD ROUND PROPER

Dreams nearly came true.

Tamworth had the thrill of playing Premier League Everton at Goodison Park and gave a good account of themselves in front of 27,564. A penalty for the home club settling the issue just eleven minutes from time.

Fleetwood Town were given a dream draw against very local rivals Blackpool, but their neighbours, fresh from a season in the Premier League, won 5-1.

Salisbury City, playing well above their league position suggested, battled well, but lost 1-3. to Sheffield United. Wrexham however, stayed in the F.ACup 2011-2012 longer than any other non league team, by taking Brighton to a replay and drawing 1-1 at the Seagulls beautiful new stadium before losing the home replay 4-5 on penalties after another 1-1 draw.

The 2011-2012 FA Challenge Cup campaign was over for clubs outside The Football League. It had brought all types of excitement, thrills and memories to players and supporters of clubs across the country. The most famous club knock out competition in the world is still a competition in which non-league players are very proud to have played.

THE FA CUP

FIRST ROUND PROPER
SATURDAY 12 NOVEMBER 2011 - WINNERS RECEIVE £18,000

No	Home		Away	Score	Att
1	Hereford United	v	Yeovil Town	0-3	2469
2	Bury	v	Crawley Town	0-2	2436
3	Luton Town	v	Northampton Town	1-0	4799
4	Cambridge United	v	Wrexham (11/11)	2-2	2792
	Wrexham	v	Cambridge United (22/11)	2-1	2606
5	Morecambe	v	Sheffield Wednesday (13/11)	1-2	4160
6	Swindon Town	v	Huddersfield Town	4-1	5728
7	Redbridge	v	Oxford City	0-0	465
	Oxford City	v	Redbridge (22/11)	1-2aet	1175
8	Bristol Rovers	v	Corby Town	3-1	3787
9	Oldham Athletic	v	Burton Albion	3-1	3102
10	Preston North End	v	Southend United	0-0	6609
	Southend United	v	Preston North End (22/11)	1-0	4537
11	Dagenham & Redbridge	v	Bath City	1-1	1225
	Bath City	v	Dagenham & Redbridge (23/11)	1-3aet	2089
12	Hartlepool United	v	Stevenage	2-1	2744
13	Blyth Spartans	v	Gateshead	0-2	2763
14	Alfreton Town	v	Carlisle United	0-4	1488
15	Chesterfield	v	Torquay United	1-3	4332
16	Crewe Alexandra	v	Colchester United	1-4	2325
17	Tranmere Rovers	v	Cheltenham Town	0-1	3211
18	Chelmsford City	v	AFC Telford United	4-0	1430
19	Hinckley United	v	Tamworth	2-2	1906
	Tamworth	v	Hinckley United (22/11)	1-0	1583
20	Exeter City	v	Walsall	1-1	3026
	Walsall	v	Exeter City (23/11)	3-2aet	2089
21	Bradford City	v	Rochdale	1-0	3579
22	Notts County	v	Accrington Stanley	4-1	3613
23	Port Vale	v	Grimsby Town	0-0	4450
	Grimsby Town	v	Port Vale (22/11)	1-0	1906
24	Sheffield United	v	Oxford United	3-0	7991
25	FC Halifax Town	v	Charlton Athletic (13/11)	0-4	4601
26	Sutton United	v	Kettering Town	1-0	1532
27	AFC Bournemouth	v	Gillingham	3-3	4282
	Gillingham	v	AFC Bournemouth (22/11)	3-2	4321
28	Milton Keynes Dons	v	Nantwich Town	6-0	4110
29	AFC Totton	v	Bradford (Park Avenue)	8-1	2315
30	Newport County	v	Shrewsbury Town	0-1	2362
31	Leyton Orient	v	Bromley	3-0	4452
32	East Thurrock United	v	Macclesfield Town	0-3	1207
33	AFC Wimbledon	v	Scunthorpe United	0-0	2933
	Scunthorpe United	v	AFC Wimbledon (22/11)	0-1	2036
34	Salisbury City	v	Arlesey Town	3-1	1298
35	Brentford	v	Basingstoke Town	1-0	3553
36	Maidenhead United	v	Aldershot Town	1-1	2281
	Aldershot Town	v	Maidenhead United (22/11)	2-0	2181
37	Fleetwood Town	v	Wycombe Wanderers	2-0	2711
38	Barrow	v	Rotherham United	1-2	3030
39	Southport	v	Barnet	1-2	1939
40	Plymouth Argyle	v	Stourbridge	3-3	6173
	Stourbridge	v	Plymouth Argyle (22/11)	2-0	2519

SECOND ROUND PROPER
SATURDAY 3 DECEMBER 2011 - WINNERS RECEIVE £27,000

No	Home		Away	Score	Att
1	Salisbury City	v	Grimsby Town	0-0	2161
	Grimsby Town	v	Salisbury City (13/12)	2-3aet	1880
2	Stourbridge	v	Stevenage	0-3	3067
3	Sheffield United	v	Torquay United	3-2	10105
4	Colchester United	v	Swindon Town	0-1	3039
5	Chelmsford City	v	Macclesfield Town	1-1	3919
	Macclesfield Town	v	Chelmsford City (14/12)	1-0	1607
6	Leyton Orient	v	Gillingham	0-1	3763
7	Crawley Town	v	Redbridge	5-0	2494
8	Luton Town	v	Cheltenham Town	2-4	4516
9	Fleetwood Town	v	Yeovil Town (2/12)	2-2	3319
	Yeovil Town	v	Fleetwood Town (13/12)	0-2	3276
10	Brentford	v	Wrexham	0-1	3452
11	Bradford City	v	AFC Wimbledon	3-1	3432
12	Shrewsbury Town	v	Rotherham United	2-1	4048
13	Dagenham & Redbridge	v	Walsall	1-1	1237
	Walsall	v	Dagenham & Redbridge (13/12)	0-0aet	1802
	(Dagenham & Redbridge won 3-2 on kicks from the penalty mark)				
14	Barnet	v	Milton Keynes Dons	1-3	2608
15	Gateshead	v	Tamworth	1-2	1163
16	Sheffield Wednesday	v	Aldershot Town	1-0	10162
17	Sutton United	v	Notts County (4/12)	0-2	3704
18	Southend United	v	Oldham Athletic	1-1	4613
	Oldham Athletic	v	Southend United (13/12)	1-0	4207
19	AFC Totton	v	Bristol Rovers (4/12)	1-6	2236
20	Charlton Athletic	v	Carlisle United	2-0	7461

THIRD ROUND PROPER
SATURDAY 7 JANUARY 2012 - WINNERS RECEIVE £67,500

No	Home		Away	Score	Att
1	Middlesbrough	v	Shrewsbury Town	1-0	12631
2	Nottingham Forest	v	Leicester City	0-0	18477
	Leicester City	v	Nottingham Forest (17/1)	4-0	16210
3	Manchester City	v	Manchester United (8/1)	2-3	46808
4	Dagenham & Redbridge	v	Millwall	0-0	3396
	Millwall	v	Dagenham & Redbridge (17/1)	5-0	3751
5	Crawley Town	v	Bristol City	1-0	3779
6	Doncaster Rovers	v	Notts County	0-2	9535
7	Bristol Rovers	v	Aston Villa	1-3	10883
8	Tottenham Hotspur	v	Cheltenham Town	3-0	35672
9	Sheffield Wednesday	v	West Ham United (8/1)	1-0	17916
10	Milton Keynes Dons	v	Queens Park Rangers	1-1	19506
	Queens Park Rangers	v	Milton Keynes Dons (17/1)	1-0	10855
11	Hull City	v	Ipswich Town	3-1	10246
12	Coventry City	v	Southampton	1-2	9000
13	Brighton & Hove Albion	v	Wrexham	1-1	18573
	Wrexham	v	Brighton & Hove Albion (18/1)	1-1aet	8316
	(Brighton & Hove Albion won 5-4 on kicks from the penalty mark)				
14	Fulham	v	Charlton Athletic	4-0	20317
15	Birmingham City	v	Wolverhampton Wanderers	0-0	14594
	Wolverhampton Wanderers	v	Birmingham City (18/1)	0-1	10153
16	Norwich City	v	Burnley	4-1	22898
17	Arsenal	v	Leeds United (9/1)	1-0	59615
18	Derby County	v	Crystal Palace	1-0	10113
19	Fleetwood Town	v	Blackpool	1-5	5092
20	Swindon Town	v	Wigan Athletic	2-1	10488
21	Barnsley	v	Swansea City	2-4	7380
22	Macclesfield Town	v	Bolton Wanderers	2-2	5757
	Bolton Wanderers	v	Macclesfield Town (17/1)	2-0	9466
23	Newcastle United	v	Blackburn Rovers	2-1	30876
24	Everton	v	Tamworth	2-0	27564
25	Sheffield United	v	Salisbury City	3-1	10488
26	LIVERPOOL	v	Oldham Athletic (6/1)	5-1	44558
27	Gillingham	v	Stoke City	1-3	9872
28	CHELSEA	v	Portsmouth (8/1)	4-0	41259
29	Watford	v	Bradford City	4-2	8935
30	Peterborough United	v	Sunderland (8/1)	0-2	8954
31	West Bromwich Albion	v	Cardiff City	4-2	12454
32	Reading	v	Stevenage	0-1	11295

Salisbury City's Anderson and Grimsby Town's Disley contest for the ball during their Second Round match.

Whilst below Salisbury skipper, Giles, gets in a powerful header despite being out numbered by Grimsby defenders. Photos: Keith Clayton.

Action from the Second Round match between AFC Totton and Bristol Rovers. Here we see Totton's Stefan Brown sheidling the ball from Rovers' Danny Woodward.
Photo: Keith Clayton.

Meanwhile in the background is our very own Peter Barnes behind the camera...

...and here's some of the action Peter shot.

FOURTH ROUND PROPER
SATURDAY 28 JANUARY 2012 - WINNERS RECEIVE £90,000

1	Brighton & Hove Albion	v	Newcastle United	1-0	21558	8	Arsenal	v	Aston Villa (29/1)	3-2	60019
2	Sunderland	v	Middlesbrough (291/)	1-1	33275	9	Stevenage	v	Notts County	1-0	4439
	Middlesbrough	v	Sunderland (8/2)	1-2	26707	10	Watford	v	Tottenham Hotspur (27/1)	0-1	15384
3	Millwall	v	Southampton	1-1	8278	11	**LIVERPOOL**	v	Manchester United	2-1	43952
	Southampton	v	Millwall (7/2)	2-3	8493	12	Derby County	v	Stoke City	0-2	22247
4	Hull City	v	Crawley Town	0-1	14473	13	Everton	v	Fulham (27/1)	2-1	25300
5	Queens Park Rangers	v	**CHELSEA**	0-1	15728	14	Bolton Wanderers	v	Swansea City	2-1	11597
6	West Bromwich Albion	v	Norwich City	1-2	17434	15	Sheffield United	v	Birmingham City	0-4	18072
7	Blackpool	v	Sheffield Wednesday	1-1	14042	16	Leicester City	v	Swindon Town	2-0	19942
	Sheffield Wednesday	v	Blackpool (7/2)	0-3	10274						

FIFTH ROUND PROPER
SATURDAY 18 FEBRUARY 2012 - WINNERS RECEIVE £180,000

1	**LIVERPOOL**	v	Brighton & HA (19/2)	6-1	43940	5	Stevenage	v	Tottenham Hotspur (19/2)	0-0	6625
2	Everton	v	Blackpool	2-0	38347		Tottenham Hotspur	v	Stevenage (7/3)	3-1	35757
3	**CHELSEA**	v	Birmingham City	1-1	36870	6	Norwich City	v	Leicester City	1-2	26658
	Birmingham City	v	**CHELSEA** (6/3)	0-2	21822	7	Sunderland	v	Arsenal	2-0	26042
4	Crawley Town	v	Stoke City (19/2)	0-2	4040	8	Millwall	v	Bolton Wanderers	0-2	11320

SIXTH ROUND PROPER
SATURDAY 17 MARCH 2011 - WINNERS RECEIVE £360,000

1	**LIVERPOOL**	v	Stoke City (18/3)	2-1	43962	4	Everton	v	Sunderland (17/3)	1-1	38875
2	**CHELSEA**	v	Leicester City (18/3)	5-2	38276		Sunderland	v	Everton (27/3)	0-2	43140
3	Tottenham Hotspur	v	Bolton Wanderers (27/3)	3-1	30718						

SEMI FINALS
WINNERS RECEIVE £900,000   RUNNERS-UP £450,000

SATURDAY 14 APRIL 2012 - at Wembley Stadium					SUNDAY 15 APRIL 2012 - at Wembley Stadium				
2	**LIVERPOOL**	v	Everton	2-1	87231	1	Tottenham Hotspur	v	**CHELSEA**	1-5	85731

THE FINAL
SATURDAY 5 MAY 2012 - at Wembley Stadium   WINNERS RECEIVE £1.8m   RUNNERS-UP £900,000

CHELSEA	2	1	LIVERPOOL	89102

Alfreton's Jamie Mullen fires in a shot but sees his effort saved by the Lincoln 'keeper during this Fourth Qualifying Round match.
Photo: Bill Wheatcroft.

Action from Tamworth's Third Round tie at Goddison Park against Premiership side Everton.
Photos: Peter Barnes.

Wrexham player/manager, Andy Morrel, runs across the Brighton & Hove Albion defence, whilst above Adrian Cieslewicz fires home Wrexhams goal in this Third Round tie.
Photos: Roger Turner.

THE
FA TROPHY

2011-12

The York City supporters celebrate their sides FA Trophy victory. Photo: Peter Barnes.

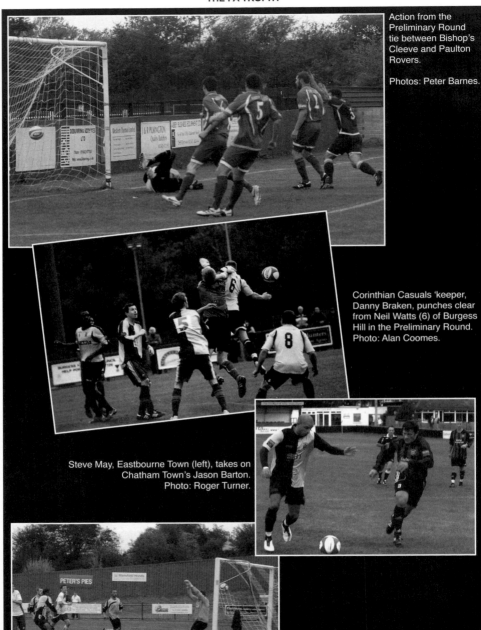

Action from the Preliminary Round tie between Bishop's Cleeve and Paulton Rovers.

Photos: Peter Barnes.

Corinthian Casuals 'keeper, Danny Braken, punches clear from Neil Watts (6) of Burgess Hill in the Preliminary Round. Photo: Alan Coomes.

Steve May, Eastbourne Town (left), takes on Chatham Town's Jason Barton. Photo: Roger Turner.

Adam Somes header goes past Jack Harvey for Rainworth's goal against Hucknall Town. Photo: Bill Wheatcroft.

PRELIMINARY ROUND
SATURDAY 8 OCTOBER 2011 - WINNERS RECEIVE £2,000

#	Home	v	Away	Score	Att
1	Garforth Town	v	Lancaster City	5-1	92
2	Trafford	v	AFC Fylde	1-4	134
3	Prescot Cables	v	Durham City	1-2	132
4	Cammell Laird	v	Bamber Bridge (7/10)	0-3	45
5	Ossett Albion	v	Lincoln United	1-3	82
6	Salford City	v	Clitheroe	2-2	101
	Clitheroe	v	Salford City (11/10)	1-2aet	156
7	Ossett Town	v	Wakefield	2-1	99
8	Brigg Town	v	Mossley	2-1	96
9	Woodley Sports	v	Skelmersdale United	4-3	62
10	New Mills	v	Radcliffe Borough	2-3	151
11	Sheffield	v	Warrington Town	2-2	213
	Warrington Town	v	Sheffield (11/10)	2-3	105
12	Kidsgrove Athletic	v	Loughborough Dynamo	2-1	154
13	Barton Rovers	v	Shepshed Dynamo	2-1	85
14	Rainworth MW	v	Hucknall Town	1-2	124
15	Carlton Town	v	Belper Town	4-5	100
16	Newcastle Town	v	Woodford United	1-0	89
17	Stamford	v	Coalville Town	5-4	279
18	Quorn	v	Biggleswade Town	0-5	132
19	Bedworth United	v	Market Drayton Town	2-1	150
20	Rugby Town	v	Sutton Coldfield Town	1-1	210
	Sutton Coldfield Town	v	Rugby Town (11/10)	4-0	91
21	Halesowen Town	v	Romulus	0-1	277
22	Stourport Swifts	v	Daventry Town	1-1	68
	Daventry Town	v	Stourport Swifts (11/10)	3-1	113
23	Bedfont Town	v	Romford	4-1	82
24	Waltham Abbey	v	Grays Athletic	1-1	171
	Grays Athletic	v	Waltham Abbey (12/10)	4-0	174
25	Ilford	v	Redbridge	2-3	88
26	Ashford Town (Middx)	v	Maidstone United	3-1	102
27	Thamesmead Town	v	Whitstable Town	3-2	53
28	Whyteleafe	v	North Greenford United	4-3	84
29	Ramsgate	v	Needham Market	2-7	160
30	Burgess Hill Town	v	Corinthian Casuals	3-0	142
31	Potters Bar Town	v	Heybridge Swifts	1-0	127
32	Soham Town Rangers	v	Whitehawk	1-7	140
33	Brentwood Town	v	Leiston	1-0	171
34	Ware	v	Chipstead	0-1	85
35	Sittingbourne	v	Northwood	1-1	109
	Northwood	v	Sittingbourne (11/10)	3-4aet	
36	Waltham Forest	v	Tilbury (9/10)	2-1	84
37	AFC Hayes	v	Cheshunt	2-1	51
38	Eastbourne Town	v	Chatham Town	4-3	127
39	Walton Casuals	v	Faversham Town	2-2	72
	Faversham Town	v	Walton Casuals (11/10)	5-3aet	91
40	AFC Sudbury	v	Great Wakering Rovers	6-1	198
41	Walton & Hersham	v	Enfield Town	1-2	135
42	Bideford	v	Beaconsfield SYCOB	2-0	171
43	Bognor Regis Town	v	Mangotsfield United	0-1	344
44	Didcot Town	v	Clevedon Town	3-1	122
45	Yate Town	v	Hungerford Town	2-1	105
46	Worthing	v	Crawley Down	3-3	264
	Crawley Down	v	Worthing (11/10)	0-2aet	
47	Bridgwater Town	v	Tiverton Town	1-3	197
48	Thatcham Town	v	North Leigh	2-0	100
49	Chalfont St Peter	v	Abingdon United	4-3	87
50	Cinderford Town	v	Poole Town	0-3	105
51	Gosport Borough	v	Slough Town	3-0	175
52	Fleet Town	v	Burnham	0-0	89
	Burnham	v	Fleet Town (10/10)	0-1	81
53	Wimborne Town	v	Sholing	0-2	186
54	Bishop's Cleeve	v	Paulton Rovers	0-1	75

PRELIMINARY ROUND

The competition kicked off early in October with a Preliminary Round of 52 ties including 14 clubs who had played in National cup finals. Nine had played in FA Vase Finals, three in FA Amateur Cup Finals and Grays Athletic and Enfield who had reached the FA Trophy Final.

The majority of the best attendance of the day (344) will have gone home disappointed as Bognor Regis were beaten 1-0 at home by Mangotsfield United.

Grays Athletic, who won their F A Trophy Final on penalties in 2005 forced a replay at Waltham Abbey where they won comfortably.

Whitehawk from the Isthmian League Division One South recorded the biggest victory by winning 7-1 at Soham Town (Southern League Division One Central) but impressive victories were also achieved by:

AFC Sudbury	6	Great Wakering	1
Garforth Town	5	Lancaster City	1
Quorn	0	Biggleswade Town	5
Ramsgate	2	Needham Market	7

But for high scoring thrillers, the fans must have enjoyed these cup ties:

Carlton Town	4	Belper Town	5
Chalfont St Peter	4	Abingdon United	3
Eastboune Town	4	Chatham Town	3
Woodley Sports	4	Skelmersdale Utd	3
Whyteleafe	4	North Greenford	3

Top left: Christian Nanetti, Lewes, with the ball is followed by Jack Clark of Cray Wanderers in the First Qualifying Round, whilst above, Lewes' No.9 Michael Malcolm has his shot saved by Cray's Andy Walker. Photo: Roger Turner.

Action from the First Qualifying Round match between Cirencester Town and Leatherhead. Photo: Peter Barnes.

More First Qualifying round action, here we see Evesham United's Marcus Palmer try to cross to the waiting Lewis Poutney whilst under pressure from the Barwell defenders. Photo: Jonathan Holloway.

FIRST QUALIFYING ROUND
SATURDAY 22 OCTOBER 2011 - WINNERS RECEIVE £2,200

#	Home		Away	Score	Att
1	Chester	v	Ashton United	2-1	1624
2	Goole	v	Durham City	2-3	132
3	Bradford (Park Avenue)	v	Worksop Town	1-1	269
	Worksop Town	v	Bradford (Park Avenue) (26/10)	4-1	281
4	Marine	v	Chorley	1-0	279
5	Witton Albion	v	Brigg Town	6-1	209
6	Radcliffe Borough	v	Harrogate Railway Athletic	2-1	112
7	Farsley	v	Curzon Ashton	2-2	217
	Curzon Ashton	v	Farsley (24/10)	2-0	128
8	Buxton	v	Garforth Town	4-2	188
9	Frickley Athletic	v	FC United Of Manchester	0-4	524
10	Northwich Victoria	v	AFC Fylde	4-2	380
11	Sheffield	v	Bamber Bridge	3-0	249
12	Kendal Town	v	Nantwich Town	1-0	192
13	Woodley Sports	v	Whitby Town	3-1	63
14	North Ferriby United	v	Lincoln United	3-1	122
15	Burscough	v	Salford City	0-1	118
16	Stocksbridge Park Steels	v	Ossett Town	2-2	291
	Ossett Town	v	Stocksbridge Park Steels (25/10)	3-2	71
17	St Neots Town	v	Sutton Coldfield Town	3-1	311
18	Chasetown	v	Grantham Town	5-0	241
19	Leek Town	v	Hucknall Town	4-1	223
20	Ilkeston	v	Biggleswade Town	2-0	444
21	Leighton Town	v	Banbury United	0-1	137
22	Rushall Olympic	v	Cambridge City	0-2	153
23	Evesham United	v	Barwell (23/10)	1-1	107
	Barwell	v	Evesham United (25/10)	5-1	104
24	Daventry Town	v	Kidsgrove Athletic	4-3	126
25	Brackley Town	v	Mickleover Sports	1-0	167
26	Romulus	v	Leamington	1-0	154
27	Barton Rovers	v	Belper Town	0-1	106
28	Matlock Town	v	Stamford	3-0	299
29	Bedworth United	v	Hednesford Town	0-1	192
30	Newcastle Town	v	Stafford Rangers	1-1	505
	Stafford Rangers	v	Newcastle Town (25/10)	5-2	374
31	Stourbridge	v	Redditch United	2-1	291
32	Arlesey Town	v	AFC Sudbury	3-1	185
33	Whyteleafe	v	Grays Athletic	0-3	145
34	Brentwood Town	v	Lowestoft Town	2-3	197
35	Potters Bar Town	v	AFC Hayes	1-0	95
36	Lewes	v	Cray Wanderers	2-1	536
37	Dulwich Hamlet	v	Harrow Borough	0-2	294
38	Chipstead	v	Margate	1-3	120
39	Folkestone Invicta	v	Metropolitan Police	1-0	202
40	Aveley	v	Bury Town	0-1	102
41	St Albans City	v	Ashford Town (Middx)	1-3	275
42	Canvey Island	v	Hendon	4-0	262
43	Eastbourne Town	v	Hitchin Town	1-3	181
44	Merstham	v	Maldon & Tiptree	0-4	75
45	Billericay Town	v	Whitehawk	1-0	272
46	Uxbridge	v	Sittingbourne	3-1	99
47	Redbridge	v	Needham Market	3-1	92
48	Concord Rangers	v	Harlow Town	2-3	109
49	Hemel Hempstead Town	v	Croydon Athletic	1-1	214
	Croydon Athletic	v	Hemel Hempstead Town (26/10)	0-2	96
50	Hythe Town	v	Burgess Hill Town	1-0	201
51	Wealdstone	v	Tooting & Mitcham United	3-0	233
52	Bedfont Town	v	Hastings United	1-1	79
	Hastings United	v	Bedfont Town (25/10)	0-2	160
53	East Thurrock United	v	Bedford Town	1-1	141
	Bedford Town	v	East Thurrock United (25/10)	1-2	189
54	Waltham Forest	v	Faversham Town	0-1	36
55	Thamesmead Town	v	Enfield Town	2-0	84
56	Wingate & Finchley	v	AFC Hornchurch	1-2	152
57	Kingstonian	v	Godalming Town (23/10)	0-1	258
58	Marlow	v	Didcot Town	1-1	148
	Didcot Town	v	Marlow (25/10)	4-0	104
59	Andover	v	Swindon Supermarine		
	(walkover for Swindon Supermarine – Andover removed)				
60	Cirencester Town	v	Leatherhead	3-1	116
61	Chertsey Town	v	Chalfont St Peter	2-0	167
62	Gosport Borough	v	Sholing	1-0	174
63	Taunton Town	v	Paulton Rovers	0-3	203
64	Carshalton Athletic	v	Bideford	3-1	200
65	Chesham United	v	Horsham	5-0	303
66	Oxford City	v	Mangotsfield United	0-3	196
67	Fleet Town	v	Yate Town	0-5	88
68	Weymouth	v	AFC Totton	3-2	512
69	Poole Town	v	Chippenham Town	1-1	316
	Chippenham Town	v	Poole Town (25/10)	2-1	244
70	Bashley	v	Worthing	2-2	184
	Worthing	v	Bashley (25/10)	4-2aet	153
71	Aylesbury	v	Tiverton Town	0-0	111
	Tiverton	v	Aylesbury (25/10)	2-1	171
72	Frome Town	v	Thatcham Town	0-1	199

FIRST QUALIFYING ROUND

Some very big names entered the competition in this round but it usually takes three victories before a club and its supporters begin to think it could be their year for a Wembley appearance. Clubs with cup traditions are usually hard to beat, so it wasn't surprising to see Tiverton Town (three FA Vase Finals at Wembley) winning a replay at home against Aylesbury and Billericay Town (also three FA Vase Finals) beating Whitehawk at home, while Northwich Victoria who have experienced three FA Trophy Finals beat AFC Fylde 4-2.

Top individal scorer was Chasetown's Dean Perrow who scored from the penalty spot after 13 minutes and followed up with three more in a fine 5-0 victory over Grantham Town

Hat tricks were also scored by Rob King (Colwyn Bay), Leon Archer (Chesham United) and John Frendo (Hitchin Town).

The best attendances were recorded at:

Chester	v	Ashton United	624
Lewes	v	Cray Wanderers	538
Frickley Athletic	v	FC United	524
Weymouth	v	AFC Totton	512
Newcastle Town	v	Stafford Rangers	505

Some quality clubs will be moving on to the next round with their confidence boosted, and sometimes an early cup run can inspire a successful season.

SECOND QUALIFYING ROUND

The three clubs with special cup pedigree make their points once again as Billericay Town win 2-0 at home to S Neots, Northwich Victoria win 3-0 at home against Buxton and Tiverton Town force a draw away to Chesham United before winning the replay.

What a game at Chertsey Town, who entertained local rivals Ashford Town (Middlesex)and won by the odd goal in eleven with ten different scorers!

Solid victories were also recorded by:

Gosport Borough	4	Godalming Town	0
Marine	5	Chasetown	2
Uxbridge	5	Potters Bar Town	2

Replays:

Kendal Town	0	Stourbridge	6
Weymouth	6	Thatcham Town	1

One of the biggest attendances was attracted at Leek by the clash of two past FA Trophy Wembley finalists.

Chester	v	Stafford Rangers	1,551
FC United	v	Durham City	672
Durham City	v	FC United	533
Ilkeston	v	Woodley Sports	455
Leek Town	v	Witton Albion	443
Northwich Victoria	v	Buxton	421

One more Round before the big names enter and there seem to be one or two clubs who already have the right spirit for a cup run.

An early chance missed for Arlesey Town against Thamesmead Town in the Second Qualifying Round. Photo: Gordon Whittington.

Further action from the Second Qualifying Round, this time between Yate and Swindon Supermarine. Photo: Peter Barnes.

THIRD QUALIFYING ROUND

Some more big names feature in this round but the past cup heroics of Blyth Spartans and Altrincham can't help them through this time, and other fancied clubs to fail include Surrey favourites Sutton United and Woking.

Of the three with cup traditions Billericay Town and Tiverton Town both lost by the only goal of the game against Maidenhead United and Swindon Supermarine respectively.

Northwich Victoria were held to a draw at home by Ilkeston but won the replay away 5-1.

Special victories were produced by:

Guiseley	v	Eastwood Town	7-0
Thurrock	v	AFC Hornchurch	0-5
Sheffield FC	v	Nuneatoon Town	0-4

Chester achieved a fine victory at Stourbridge, who had enjoyed an excellent FA Cup campaign attracting an impressive attendance of 1,481 while Lowestoft Town achieved their third away win in this seasons competition and really deserve a home draw.

The qualifiers in this round will now be in the draw with Non League's best, some of whom could be so wrapped up with promotion and relegation matters that their concentration may not include coping with cup ties.

SECOND QUALIFYING ROUND
SATURDAY 5 NOVEMBER 2011 - WINNERS RECEIVE £3,000

#	Home		Away	Score	Att
1	Chester	v	Stafford Rangers	2-0	1551
2	Northwich Victoria	v	Buxton	3-0	421
3	Hednesford Town	v	Matlock Town	0-0	391
	Matlock Town	v	Hednesford Town (9/11)	2-1	279
4	Stourbridge	v	Kendal Town	3-3	338
	Kendal Town	v	Stourbridge (8/11)	0-6	207
5	Radcliffe Borough	v	Worksop Town	1-1	143
	Worksop Town	v	Radcliffe Borough (9/11)	2-0	261
6	North Ferriby United	v	Salford City	3-0	135
7	Curzon Ashton	v	Belper Town	2-1	137
8	Marine	v	Chasetown	5-2	213
9	Ossett Town	v	Barwell	4-2	71
10	Sheffield	v	Romulus	2-0	231
11	Ilkeston	v	Woodley Sports	2-1	455
12	Durham City	v	FC United Of Manchester	1-1	533
	FC United Of Manchester	v	Durham City (9/11)	3-1aet	672
13	Leek Town	v	Witton Albion	3-3	443
	Witton Albion	v	Leek Town (9/11)	4-1	272
14	Folkestone Invicta	v	Daventry Town	4-2	266
15	Grays Athletic	v	Canvey Island	2-3	344
16	Faversham Town	v	East Thurrock United	2-4	137
17	Margate	v	Wealdstone	1-1	304
	Wealdstone	v	Margate (8/11)	2-1	228
18	Harrow Borough	v	AFC Hornchurch	1-1	123
	AFC Hornchurch	v	Harrow Borough (8/11)	1-0	176
19	Maldon & Tiptree	v	Bedfont Town	3-2	38
20	Harlow Town	v	Lewes	3-2	183
21	Bury Town	v	Hythe Town	3-2	302
22	Uxbridge	v	Potters Bar Town	5-2	124
23	Cambridge City	v	Redbridge	1-2	291
24	Hitchin Town	v	Lowestoft Town	1-3	282
25	Billericay Town	v	St Neots Town	2-0	315
26	Thamesmead Town	v	Arlesey Town	3-2	32
27	Hemel Hempstead Town	v	Brackley Town	2-3	210
28	Banbury United	v	Paulton Rovers	3-1	207
29	Carshalton Athletic	v	Cirencester Town	3-1	225
30	Worthing	v	Didcot Town	0-2	263
31	Chesham United	v	Tiverton Town	2-2	323
	Tiverton Town	v	Chesham United (8/11)	1-0	208
32	Gosport Borough	v	Godalming Town	4-0	170
33	Chippenham Town	v	Mangotsfield United	1-1	361
	Mangotsfield United	v	Chippenham Town (7/11)	0-2	250
34	Chertsey Town	v	Ashford Town (Middx)	6-5	170
35	Thatcham Town	v	Weymouth	1-1	249
	Weymouth	v	Thatcham Town (8/11)	6-1	367
36	Yate Town	v	Swindon Supermarine	0-1	136

THIRD QUALIFYING ROUND
SATURDAY 26 NOVEMBER 2011 - WINNERS RECEIVE £4,000

#	Home		Away	Score	Att
1	Corby Town	v	North Ferriby United	1-1	519
	North Ferriby United	v	Corby Town (29/11)	3-2	170
2	Blyth Spartans	v	Stalybridge Celtic	1-3	324
3	Boston United	v	Workington	1-0	743
4	Sheffield	v	Nuneaton Town	0-4	426
5	Gainsborough Trinity	v	Hinckley United	0-1	320
6	Worcester City	v	Harrogate Town	0-1	676
7	Colwyn Bay	v	FC Halifax Town	0-0	420
	FC Halifax Town	v	Colwyn Bay (29/11)	1-2	717
8	Worksop Town	v	Curzon Ashton	3-2	238
9	Guiseley	v	Eastwood Town	7-0	323
10	Stourbridge	v	Chester	0-2	1481
11	Matlock Town	v	Hyde	0-1	367
12	Solihull Moors	v	Ossett Town	2-2	152
	Ossett Town	v	Solihull Moors (29/11)	0-1	137
13	Droylsden	v	Witton Albion	2-1	304
14	FC United Of Manchester	v	Altrincham (27/11)	2-1	1945
15	Northwich Victoria	v	Ilkeston	1-1	437
	Ilkeston	v	Northwich Victoria (28/11)	1-5	530
16	Vauxhall Motors	v	Marine	3-2	329
17	Farnborough	v	Bury Town	2-2	312
	Bury Town	v	Farnborough (29/11)	0-2	255
18	Maldon & Tiptree	v	Carshalton Athletic	0-1	72
19	Sutton United	v	Basingstoke Town	1-2	460
20	Banbury United	v	Wealdstone	0-0	370
	Wealdstone	v	Banbury United (29/11)	4-0	222
21	Bishop's Stortford	v	Tonbridge Angels	1-1	297
	Tonbridge Angels	v	Bishop's Stortford (29/11)	1-2	274
22	Thamesmead Town	v	Welling United	2-2	273
	Welling United	v	Thamesmead Town (29/11)	3-1	288
23	Chelmsford City	v	Woking	2-0	740
24	Bromley	v	Didcot Town	1-3	277
25	Folkestone Invicta	v	Staines Town	1-3	342
26	Redbridge	v	East Thurrock United	1-2	108
27	Eastbourne Borough	v	Dartford	0-0	508
	Dartford	v	Eastbourne Borough (29/11)	2-1	611
28	Thurrock	v	AFC Hornchurch	0-5	211
29	Uxbridge	v	Histon	2-1	150
30	Harlow Town	v	Lowestoft Town	1-2	343
31	Hampton & Richmond Borough	v	Canvey Island	4-2	289
32	Brackley Town	v	Chertsey Town	2-0	136
33	Maidenhead United	v	Billericay Town	1-0	235
34	Boreham Wood	v	Dover Athletic	1-0	181
35	Tiverton Town	v	Swindon Supermarine	0-1	277
36	Gloucester City	v	Truro City	1-1	300
	Truro City	v	Gloucester City (29/11)	3-2	281
37	Salisbury City	v	Weston Super Mare	2-0	552
38	Dorchester Town	v	Gosport Borough	1-2	381
39	Chippenham Town	v	Eastleigh	1-1	421
	Eastleigh	v	Chippenham Town (29/11)	1-1aet	214
	(Chippenham Town won 8-7 from kicks from the penalty mark)				
40	Weymouth	v	Havant & Waterlooville	0-0	421
	Havant & Waterlooville	v	Weymouth (29/11)	0-2	238

FIRST ROUND PROPER

With all due respect to Fleetwood Town and Wrexham, who were the top two clubs occupying the promotion places for The Football League at the time they were due to play their FA Trophy First Round matches, they would certainly not have been expected to lose to Northwich Victoria or Hinckley United respectively.

Other Blue Square Premier clubs to lose were Mansfield Town at Droylsden, Darlington at Grimsby Town, Hayes & Yeading at Hampton & Richmond, Forest Green Rovers at Newport County, Stockport County in a replay at Stalybridge and Tamworth at Worksop Town

Clubs in mid table of the senior Blue Square division are usually the clubs keenest to achieve a Wembley trip, so it was no surprise to see Alfreton Town, Barrow, Braintree Town, Cambridge United, Gateshead, Grimsby Town, Lincoln City, Newport County and Kidderminster Harriers amongst the First Round winners. However York City and Luton Town, two of the promotion challengers, did reach the Second Round, 'The Hatters' beating Swindon Supermarine at home and York City beating Solihull Moors away in a replay.

Spare a thought for poor Lowestoft Town, drawn away for all four of their Trophy games, and this time they found Salisbury City just too good on the day. Didcot Town, from The Southern League Division One South West and Uxbridge, from Southern League Division One Central, both celebrated an appearance in the competition proper but there were no real 'outsiders' qualifying for the Second Round.

Richard Jolly scored a hat trick for Wealdstone and was proving to be one of non-league footballers leading goalscorers for the season, and three goals were also scored by Ebbsfleet United's Liam Enver-Marum and Dan Flitchett of Salisbury City. A good cup win can also lift sagging spirits and Bath City's fine 3-2 victory at Chelmsford City must have lifted morale during their difficult league campaign.

SECOND ROUND PROPER

There were just two away victories on Second Round Saturday, but they were certainly emphatic as Alfreton Town won 6-0 at Weymouth, and York City's 6-2 away victory over Salisbury City suggested they were taking the competition very seriously.

The result of the Round was surely Wealdstone's 2-1 victory over Barrow with Richard Jolly on the scoresheet again. Bath City once again appreciated a Trophy victory to lift morale, while Carshalton Athletic will also be pleased with their replay victory over Lincoln City. Chester's great run came to an end, but not without a battle, as they went down fighting in a 3-2 defeat to Ebbsfleet United. But Northwich Victoria keep going with a 1-0 win over Staines Town.

Dartford are showing good form, following a 3-0 victory at Brackley Town with a 4-2 home victory over Boston United and Kidderminster Harriers also seemed confident in front of goal. Six goals in two games against Vauxhall Motors being followed by five at home to Droylsden.

THIRD ROUND PROPER

Six Blue Square North clubs featured in this round but the Just one replay in this round which was disturbed by the weather. But there were very few surprises as Gateshead, Grimsby Town, Luton Town and York City all beat fellow Blue Square Premier clubs Alfreton Town, Bath City, Kidderminster Harriers and Ebbsfleet United.

Hampton & Richmond Borough , who were experiencing a difficult season in Blue Square South, did well to reach the Third Round, but lost heavily to Northwich Victoria who were playing in their sixth Trophy tie of the season .

A Third Round tie contested by two clubs outside the Blue Square divisions saw Wealdstone beat Dartford in a replay, but Blue Square clubs proved their seniority with Cambridge United beating Guiseley and Newport County beating Carshalton Athletic.

QUARTER FINALS AND SEMI-FINALS

Three away victories in the Quarter Finals certainly provided thrilling matches with Wealdstone's ace goalscorer Richard Jolly claiming two more to win the match at Cambridge, while York City scored the only goal of the game at Grimsby and Newport County won a thrilling five goal cup tie to defeat brave Northwich Victoria .

The only home winner was Luton Town who beat Gateshead and it was encouraging to see that they and York City were continuing to field strong squads to contest their FA Trophy ties. They were then drawn to play each other in the Semi-Final, and a 1-0 victory booked a place for York City at Wembley on 12th May where they were to meet Newport County, who beat the brave Wealdstone club 3-1 in their semi-final despite another Jolly goal for 'The Stones'.

For the respect shown by the club to The FA Challenge Trophy competition, it was particularly pleasing to see York City win the Trophy and return to Wembley a week later to clinch a Football League place through the Blue Square Premier Play off Final. Good luck to the club in their return to The Football League and a move into their exciting new ground.

FIRST ROUND PROPER
SATURDAY 10 DECEMBER 2011 - WINNERS RECEIVE £5,000

1	Northwich Victoria	v	Fleetwood Town	3-1	484	18	Luton Town	v	Swindon Supermarine	2-0	1298
2	Colwyn Bay	v	Lincoln City	1-3	383	19	Didcot Town	v	Basingstoke Town	0-1	259
3	Vauxhall Motors	v	Kidderminster Harriers	4-4	253	20	Chelmsford City	v	Bath City	2-3	635
	Kidderminster Harriers	v	Vauxhall Motors (13/12)	2-0	746	21	Wealdstone	v	Uxbridge	5-0	373
4	Stockport County	v	Stalybridge Celtic	2-2	1690	22	Truro City	v	Ebbsfleet United	2-5	455
	Stalybridge Celtic	v	Stockport County (13/12)	2-1	1149	23	Hampton & Richmond B.	v	Hayes & Yeading United	2-0	242
5	York City	v	Solihull Moors	2-2	1116	24	Carshalton Athletic	v	Bishop's Stortford	5-0	243
	Solihull Moors	v	York City (13/12)	0-3	275	25	East Thurrock United	v	Welling United	2-1	224
6	Barrow	v	Harrogate Town	3-2	868	26	Staines Town	v	Maidenhead United	0-0	201
7	Nuneaton Town	v	AFC Telford United (11/12)	0-2	945		Maidenhead United	v	Staines Town (13/12)	1-2	154
8	Guiseley	v	FC United of Manchester	2-0	810	27	Weymouth	v	Chippenham Town	2-1	568
9	Wrexham	v	Hinckley United	1-2	1101	28	Boreham Wood	v	Cambridge United	0-1	401
10	Droylsden	v	Mansfield Town	2-1	335	29	Brackley Town	v	Dartford	0-3	291
11	Grimsby Town	v	Darlington	3-0	1527	30	AFC Hornchurch	v	Farnborough	0-0	302
12	Gateshead	v	Kettering Town	3-2	402		Farnborough	v	AFC Hornchurch (14/12)	2-3	204
13	Worksop Town	v	Tamworth	1-0	343	31	Newport County	v	Forest Green Rovers	0-0	724
14	North Ferriby United	v	Chester	1-5	510		Forest Green Rovers	v	Newport County (13/12)	0-2	368
15	Alfreton Town	v	Southport	4-0	394	32	Gosport Borough	v	Braintree Town	0-1	332
16	Boston United	v	Hyde	2-1	710						
17	Salisbury City	v	Lowestoft Town	4-1	494						

SECOND ROUND PROPER
SATURDAY 14 JANUARY 2012 - WINNERS RECEIVE £6,000

1	Ebbsfleet United	v	Chester	3-2	1387	9	East Thurrock United	v	Hampton & Richmond Borough	1-1	231
2	Wealdstone	v	Barrow	2-1	722		Hampton & Richmond B.	v	East Thurrock United (31/1)	4-1	184
3	Weymouth	v	Alfreton Town	0-6	539	10	Grimsby Town	v	AFC Hornchurch	4-0	2415
4	Worksop Town	v	Newport County (24/1)	1-3	538	11	Cambridge United	v	AFC Telford United	4-1	1259
5	Gateshead	v	Braintree Town	2-2	605	12	Northwich Victoria	v	Staines Town	1-0	517
	Braintree Town	v	Gateshead (17/1)	1-1aet	261	13	Hinckley United	v	Luton Town (18/1)	0-0	754
	(Gateshead won 4-3 on kicks from the penalty mark)						Luton Town	v	Hinckley United (23/1)	3-0	1004
6	Lincoln City	v	Carshalton Athletic	0-0	1743	14	Salisbury City	v	York City	2-6	827
	Carshalton Athletic	v	Lincoln City (18/1)	3-1	488	15	Guiseley	v	Stalybridge Celtic	2-0	630
7	Kidderminster Harriers	v	Droylsden	5-1	1104	16	Bath City	v	Basingstoke Town	1-0	633
8	Dartford	v	Boston United	4-2	1166						

THIRD ROUND PROPER
SATURDAY 4 FEBRUARY 2012 - WINNERS RECEIVE £7,000

1	Kidderminster Harriers	v	Luton Town (7/2)	1-2	1186	5	Bath City	v	Grimsby Town (7/2)	1-2	545
2	Northwich Victoria	v	Hampton & RB (14/2)	4-1	237	6	York City	v	Ebbsfleet United (14/2)	1-0	1419
	(at Nantwich Town FC)					7	Gateshead	v	Alfreton Town (14/2)	2-1	347
3	Cambridge United	v	Guiseley (21/2)	1-0	1118	8	Newport County	v	Carshalton Athletic (7/2)	4-0	975
4	Dartford	v	Wealdstone (14/2)	2-2	770						
	Wealdstone	v	Dartford (21/2)	1-0	670						

FOURTH ROUND PROPER
SATURDAY 26 FEBRUARY 2011 - WINNERS RECEIVE £8,000

1	Cambridge United	v	Wealdstone	1-2	2034	3	Grimsby Town	v	York City	0-1	3662
2	Luton Town	v	Gateshead	2-0	2499	4	Northwich Victoria	v	Newport County	2-3	601

SEMI FINALS
WINNERS RECEIVE £16,000

1ST LEG – SATURDAY 10 MARCH 2012						1ST LEG – SUNDAY 10 MARCH 2012				
1	York City	v	Luton Town	1-0	3154	2	Newport County	v	Wealdstone	3-1	2209
2ND LEG – SATURDAY 17 MARCH 2011						2ND LEG – SATURDAY 17 MARCH 2011				
1	Luton Town	v	York City	1-1	5296	2	Wealdstone	v	Newport County	0-0	2093

North Ferriby 'keeper, Steve Wilson, punches clear as Corby Town attack during the Third Qualifying Round.
Photo: Gordon Whittington

Tom Bonner, Dartford (left), clears the ball from Ben Watson of Eastbourne Borough in the Third Qualifying Round.
Photo: Roger Turner.

First Round action between Didcot and Basingstoke. Photo: Peter Barnes.

Action from the First Round between Forest Green Rovers and Newport County. Photos Peter Barnes.

Quarter Final action between Luton and Gateshead. Photos Peter Barnes.

Jonathan North, Wealdstone goalkeeper, collects a high cross during a Newport County attack in their Semi-Final Second Leg match. Photo: Roger Turner.

More Semi-Final Second Leg action this time from the Luton Town versus York City tie. Photo: Peter Barnes.

The Final...

A regular reader, and hopefully there is someone, who scans my viewing of the annual Wembley pilgrimage to observe the final of this competition, will be saying, "He always says there was not much of note on which to comment for it was again a fairly drab affair." Mindful of that accusation I have nevertheless to once more record that this was the case when, out of 266 original entrants for the 2012 competition, the boys from the Monmouthshire valleys came up against the Minstermen from Yorkshire. Either the occasion got to them or both sides were tired, or out of form. Sadly there was such paucity of excitement during the ninety minutes that I was even reflecting on trivia, such as whether Sian Massey's linesmanship was the first for a female in a men's match at Wembley, or if there was any significance in there being 11 prodders of the pitch replacing divots prior to kick off, yet 14 (the team with their 3 subs?) during half time.

The two sets of supporters did their best to raise the tempo but County fans made more of an impact singing their Welsh anthem and, in less acceptable fashion, booing the start of the English anthem until they remembered the manners their mothers had taught them and showed civilised respect, than they did during the ninety minutes of play. True there were slightly more Newport than York supporters although the difference was made to look larger by some unexplained decision to leave vacant a large swathe of seating in the middle of the Newport end. York was the better team on the day and no one can surely argue with that point of view, or that their two goal victory was a fair reflection of the balance of play.

Ten minutes had elapsed before there was any semblance of a chance and then it was a really good opportunity for Newport's Romone Rose who was sent well clear towards the opponents' penalty box. Maybe it would have settled the South Walian nerves and altered the course of the match had he scored. As keeper Michael Ingham advanced from goal he refused to ease Rose's task by committing himself early so that Rose eventually shot tamely whereupon Ingham was able to drop to his right and make a routine grab and pick up. York retaliated, causing panic which Andrew Hughes ended by heading out for a corner, and again when Patrick McLaughlin's shot was deflected wide with keeper Glyn Thompson wrongfooted. A free kick routine between Ashley Chambers, Jason Walker and

McLaughlin resulted in a shot whizzing past Thompson's right hand post before Thompson was able to parry and then knock away a strong effort from Jon Challinor.. At the other end Nat Jarvis flashed a low drive wide, a feat repeated by Lee Evans and Lee Minshull, while Rose shot over from long range. However half time was reached without many nerves having been jangled.

York resumed in much livelier fashion, with their front pair of Chambers and Walker showing promise of a goal. This eventually came from Matty Blair who, put through by Chambers, raced clear, lobbed the ball over the onrushing Thompson, and saw it bounce into the net without any further contact being necessary. Newport's retaliation was minor, Rose shooting over from distance and the powerful Ismail Yakubu heading narrowly over from a corner. They lacked attacking power, Minshull too often a solitary figure up front.

With quarter of an hour to go a northern victory was assured. Chambers, racing down the right, was again instrumental. His accurate low cross found the energetic Lanre Oyebanjo, a Republic of Ireland Under 21 international, who had only to tap in and double the lead. True a Yakubu header hit the post and skipper Gary Warren shot just over as Newport sought a response which no one would have begrudged, although City came closest to a third when substitute Jamal Fyfield raided down the right. Minutes later it was warm handshakes and embraces all round, a fitting display of good sportsmanship before Chris Smith mounted the steps to receive the Trophy.

Having waited so long for a Wembley appearance all associated with York were only too well aware that they would, in eight days time, be returning for an even more significant occasion as they faced Luton Town in the Conference play off for the coveted promotion place to the Football League. Manager Gary Mills, amazingly a schoolboy scorer for England at football and rugby, vowed that the celebrations the following week, should they beat Luton, would be the major ones.

Arthur Evans

NEWPORT COUNTY 0

YORK CITY (Blair 61, Oyebanjo 68) 2

Wembley Stadium
Attendance: 19,844

Lanre Oyebanjo, York City, out jumps Newport County's skipper
Gary Warren. Photo: Roger Turner.

The goalscorers, Matty Balir and Lanre
Oyebanjo, celebrate with the trophy.
Photo: Peter Barnes

York City celebrate after their triumph over Newport County at Wembley. Photo: Eric Marsh.

The FA Carlsberg Trophy
2012 Winners

Newport County: Glyn Thompson, David Pipe, Ismail Yakubu, Gary Warren, Andrew Hughes, Sam Foley, Lee Evans, Nat Jarvis (sub Jake Harris 68th min), Max Porter (sub Darryl Knights 79th min), Romone Rose (sub Elliott Buchanan 68th min), Lee Minshull.
Subs not used – Matthew Swan (g/k), Paul Rodgers.

York City: Michael Ingham, Jon Challinor, Chris Smith, Daniel Parslow, Ben Gibson, Matty Blair, Lanre Oyebanjo, Patrick McLaughlan (sub Jamal Fyfield 82nd min), James Meredith, Ashley Chambers (Adriano Moke 89th min), Jason Walker (Jamie Reed 90th min).
Subs not used – Paul Musselwhite (g/k), Michael Potts.
Man of the match – Lanre Oyebanjo.

Referee Anthony Taylor assisted by Sian Massey and Simon Bennett.
Fourth official – Darren Drysdale

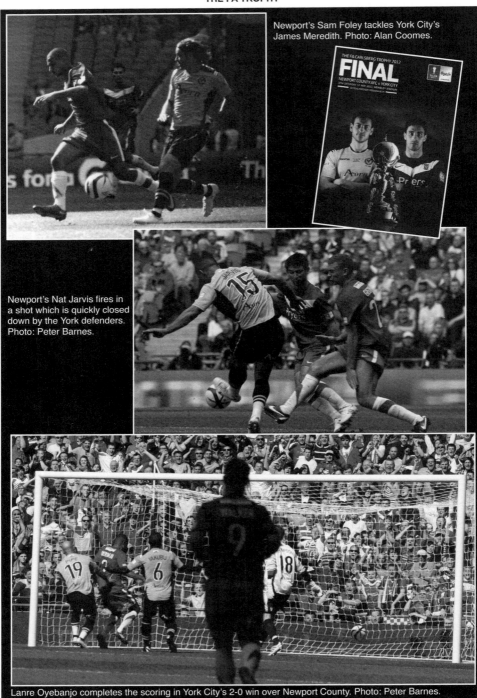

Newport's Sam Foley tackles York City's James Meredith. Photo: Alan Coomes.

Newport's Nat Jarvis fires in a shot which is quickly closed down by the York defenders. Photo: Peter Barnes.

Lanre Oyebanjo completes the scoring in York City's 2-0 win over Newport County. Photo: Peter Barnes.

PAST FINALS

1970 MACCLESFIELD TOWN 2 (Lyons, B Fidler)   **TELFORD UNITED 0**   **Att: 28,000**
Northern Premier League   *Southern League*
Macclesfield: Cooke, Sievwright, Bennett, Beaumont, Collins, Roberts, Lyons, B Fidler,Young, Corfield, D Fidler.
Telford: Irvine, Harris, Croft, Flowers, Coton, Ray,Fudge, Hart, Bentley, Murray, Jagger.   Ref: K Walker

1971 TELFORD UTD 3 (Owen, Bentley, Fudge)   **HILLINGDON BORO. 2 (Reeve, Bishop)**   **Att: 29,500**
Southern League   *Southern League*
Telford: Irvine, Harris, Croft, Ray, Coton, Carr, Fudge, Owen, Bentley, Jagger ,Murray.
Hillingdon B.: Lowe, Batt, Langley, Higginson, Newcombe, Moore, Fairchild,Bishop, Reeve, Carter, Knox.   Ref: D Smith

1972 STAFFORD RANGERS 3 (Williams 2, Cullerton)   **BARNET 0**   **Att: 24,000**
Northern Premier League   *Southern League*
Stafford R.: Aleksic, Chadwick, Clayton, Sargeant, Aston, Machin, Cullerton, Chapman,Williams, Bayley, Jones.
Barnet: McClelland, Lye, Jenkins, Ward, Embrey, King, Powell, Ferry, Flatt, Easton, Plume .   Ref: P Partridge

1973 SCARBOROUGH 2 (Leask, Thompson)   **WIGAN ATHLETIC 1 (Rogers) aet**   **Att:23,000**
Northern Premier League   *Northern Premier League*
Scarborough: Garrow, Appleton, Shoulder, Dunn, Siddle, Fagan, Donoghue, Franks,Leask (Barmby), Thompson, Hewitt.
Wigan: Reeves, Morris, Sutherland, Taylor,Jackson, Gillibrand, Clements, Oats (McCunnell), Rogers, King, Worswick.   Ref: H Hackney

1974 MORECAMBE 2 (Richmond, Sutton)   **DARTFORD 1 (Cunningham)**   **Att: 19,000**
Northern Premier League   *Southern League*
Morecambe: Coates, Pearson, Bennett, Sutton, Street, Baldwin, Done, Webber,Roberts (Galley), Kershaw, Richmond.
Dartford: Morton, Read, Payne, Carr, Burns,Binks, Light, Glozier, Robinson (Hearne), Cunningham, Halleday.   Ref: B Homewood

1975(1) MATLOCK TOWN 4 (Oxley, Dawson, T Fenoughty, N Fenoughty)   **SCARBOROUGH 0**   **Att: 21,000**
Northern Premier League   *Northern Premier League*
Matlock: Fell, McKay, Smith, Stuart, Dawson, Swan, Oxley, N Fenoughy, Scott, T Fenoughty, M Fenoughty.
Scarborough: Williams, Hewitt, Rettitt, Dunn, Marshall, Todd, Houghton, Woodall, Davidson, Barnby, Aveyard.   Ref: K Styles

1976 SCARBOROUGH 3 (Woodall, Abbey, Marshall(p))   **STAFFORD R. 2 (Jones 2) aet**   **Att: 21,000**
Northern Premier League   *Northern Premier League*
Scarborough: Barnard, Jackson, Marshall, H Dunn, Ayre (Donoghue), HA Dunn, Dale,Barmby, Woodall, Abbey, Hilley.
Stafford: Arnold, Ritchie, Richards, Sargeant,Seddon, Morris, Chapman, Lowe, Jones, Hutchinson, Chadwick.   Ref: R Challis

1977 SCARBOROUGH 2 (Dunn(p), Abbey)   **DAGENHAM 1 (Harris)**   **Att: 21,500**
Northern Premier League   *Isthmian League*
Scarborough: Chapman, Smith, Marshall (Barmby), Dunn, Ayre, Deere, Aveyard,Donoghue, Woodall, Abbey, Dunn.
Dagenham: Hutley, Wellman, P Currie, Dunwell,Moore, W Currie, Harkins, Saul, Fox, Harris, Holder.   Ref: G Courtney

1978 ALTRINCHAM 3 (King, Johnson, Rogers)   **LEATHERHEAD 1 (Cook)**   **Att: 20,000**
Northern Premier League   *Isthmian League*
Altrincham: Eales, Allan, Crossley, Bailey, Owens, King, Morris, Heathcote,Johnson, Rogers, Davidson (Flaherty).
Leatherhead: Swannell, Cooper, Eaton, Davies,Reid, Malley, Cook, Salkeld, Baker, Boyle (Bailey).   Ref: A Grey

1979 STAFFORD RANGERS 2 (A Wood 2)   **KETTERING TOWN 0**   **Att: 32,000**
Northern Premier League   *Southern League*
Stafford: Arnold, F Wood, Willis, Sargeant, Seddon, Ritchie, Secker, Chapman, A Wood, Cullerton, Chadwick (Jones).
Kettering: Lane, Ashby, Lee, Eastell, Dixey,Suddards, Flannagan, Kellock, Phipps, Clayton, Evans (Hughes).   Ref: D Richardson

1980(2) DAGENHAM 2 (Duck, Maycock)   **MOSSLEY 1 (Smith)**   **Att: 26,000**
Isthmian League   *Northern Premier League*
Dagenham: Huttley, Wellman, Scales, Dunwell, Moore, Durrell, Maycock, Horan,Duck, Kidd, Jones (Holder).
Mossley: Fitton, Brown, Vaughan, Gorman, Salter, Polliot, Smith, Moore, Skeete, O'Connor, Keelan (Wilson).   Ref: K Baker

1981(3) BISHOP'S STORTFORD 1 (Sullivan)   **SUTTON UNITED 0**   **Att: 22,578**
Isthmian League   *Isthmian League*
Bishop's Stortford: Moore, Blackman, Brame, Smith (Worrell), Bradford, Abery, Sullivan,Knapman, Radford, Simmonds, Mitchell.
Sutton Utd.: Collyer, Rogers, Green, T Rains, Stephens (Sunnucks), Waldon, Pritchard, Cornwell, Parsons, Dennis.   Ref: J Worrall

1982 ENFIELD 1 (Taylor)   **ALTRINCHAM 0**   **Att: 18,678**
Alliance Premier League   *Alliance Premier League*
Enfield: Jacobs, Barrett, Tone, Jennings, Waite, Ironton, Ashford, Taylor,Holmes, Oliver (Flint), King.
Altrincham: Connaughton, Crossley, Davison, Bailey, Cuddy, King (Whitbread), Allan, Heathcote, Johnson, Rogers, Howard.   Ref: B Stevens

Notes:
1   The only occasion three members of the same family played in the same FA Trophy Final team.
2   The first of the Amateurs from the Isthmian League to win the FA Trophy.
3   Goalkeeper Terry Moore had also won an Amateur Cup Winners Medal with Bishop's Stortford in 1974.
     All games played at Wembley (old & new) unless stated.

THE FA TROPHY

1983 TELFORD UTD 2 (Mather 2)   **NORTHWICH VICTORIA 1 (Bennett)**   Att: 22,071
Alliance Premier League   *Alliance Premier League*
Telford: Charlton, Lewis, Turner, Mayman (Joseph), Walker, Easton, Barnett,Williams, Mather, Hogan, Alcock.
Northwich: Ryan, Fretwell, Murphy, Jones, Forshaw, Ward, Anderson, Abel (Bennett), Reid, Chesters, Wilson.   Ref: B Hill

1984 NORTHWICH VICTORIA 1 (Chester)   **BANGOR CITY 1 (Whelan)**   **Att: 14,200**
Replay NORTHWICH VICTORIA 2 (Chesters(p), Anderson) BANGOR CITY 1 (Lunn)   **Att: 5,805 (at Stoke)**
Alliance Premier League   *Alliance Premier League*
Northwich: Ryan, Fretwell, Dean, Jones, Forshaw (Power 65), Bennett, Anderson,Abel, Reid, Chesters, Wilson.   Ref: J Martin
Bangor: Letheren, Cavanagh, Gray, Whelan, Banks,Lunn, Urqhart, Morris, Carter, Howat, Sutcliffe (Westwood 105) . Same in replay.

1985 WEALDSTONE 2 (Graham, Holmes)   **BOSTON UNITED 1 (Cook)**   **Att: 20,775**
Alliance Premier League   *Alliance Premier League*
Wealdstone: Iles, Perkins, Bowgett, Byatt, Davies, Greenaway, Holmes, Wainwright,Donnellan, Graham (N Cordice 89), A Cordice.
Boston: Blackwell, Casey, Ladd,Creane, O'Brien, Thommson, Laverick (Mallender 78), Simpsom, Gilbert, Lee, Cook.   Ref: J Bray

1986 ALTRINCHAM 1 (Farrelly)   **RUNCORN 0**   **Att: 15,700**
Gola League   *Gola League*
Altrincham: Wealands, Gardner, Densmore, Johnson, Farrelly, Conning, Cuddy,Davison, Reid, Ellis, Anderson. Sub: Newton.
Runcorn: McBride, Lee, Roberts,Jones, Fraser, Smith, S Crompton (A Crompton), Imrie, Carter, Mather, Carrodus.   Ref: A Ward

1987 KIDDERMINSTER HARRIERS 0   **BURTON ALBION 0**   **Att: 23,617**
Replay KIDDERMINSTER HARRIERS 2 (Davies 2)   **BURTON ALBION 1 (Groves)**   **Att: 15,685 (at West Brom)**
Conference   *Southern League*
Kidderminster: Arnold, Barton, Boxall, Brazier (sub Hazlewood in rep), Collins (sub Pearson 90 at Wembley), Woodall, McKenzie,
O'Dowd, Tuohy, Casey, Davies. sub:Jones.
Burton: New, Essex, Kamara, Vaughan, Simms, Groves, Bancroft, Land, Dorsett, Redfern, (sub Wood in replay), Gauden.
Sub: Patterson.   Ref: D Shaw

1988 ENFIELD 0   **TELFORD UNITED 0**   **Att: 20,161**
Replay ENFIELD 3 (Furlong 2, Howell)   **TELFORD 2 (Biggins, Norris(p))**   **Att: 6,912 (at W Brom)**
Conference   *Conference*
Enfield: Pape, Cottington, Howell, Keen (sub Edmonds in rep), Sparrow (sub Hayzleden at Wembley), Lewis (sub Edmonds at
Wembley), Harding, Cooper, King,Furlong, Francis.
Telford: Charlton, McGinty, Storton, Nelson, Wiggins, Mayman (sub Cunningham in rep (sub Hancock)), Sankey, Joseph, Stringer (sub
Griffiths at Wembley, Griffiths in replay), Biggins, Norris.   Ref: L Dilkes

1989 TELFORD UNITED 1 (Crawley)   **MACCLESFIELD TOWN 0**   **Att: 18,102**
Conference   *Conference*
Telford: Charlton, Lee, Brindley, Hancock, Wiggins, Mayman, Grainger, Joseph, Nelson, Lloyd, Stringer. Subs: Crawley, Griffiths.
Macclesfield: Zelem, Roberts, Tobin, Edwards, Hardman, Askey, Lake, Hanton, Imrie, Burr, Timmons. Subs: Devonshire, Kendall.

1990 BARROW 3 (Gordon 2, Cowperthwaite)   **LEEK TOWN 0**   **Att: 19,011**
Conference   *Northern Premier League*
Barrow: McDonnell, Higgins, Chilton, Skivington, Gordon, Proctor, Doherty (Burgess), Farrell (Gilmore), Cowperthwaite, Lowe, Ferris.
Leek: Simpson, Elsby (Smith), Pearce, McMullen, Clowes, Coleman (Russell),Mellor, Somerville, Sutton, Millington, Norris   Ref: T Simpson

1991 WYCOMBE W. 2 (Scott, West)   **KIDDERMINSTER HARRIERS 1 (Hadley)**   **Att: 34,842**
Conference   *Conference*
Wycombe: Granville, Crossley, Cash, Kerr, Creaser, Carroll, Ryan, Stapleton,West, Scott, Guppy (Hutchinson).   Ref: J Watson
Kidderminster: Jones, Kurila, McGrath, Weir, Barnett, Forsyth, Joseph (Wilcox), Howell (Whitehouse), Hadley, Lilwall, Humphries

1992 COLCHESTER UTD* 3 (Masters, Smith, McGavin)   **WITTON ALBION 1 (Lutkevitch)**   **Att: 27,806**
Conference   *Conference*
Colchester: Barrett, Donald, Roberts, Knsella, English, Martin, Cook, Masters,McDonough (Bennett 65), McGavin, Smith.   Ref: K P Barratt
Witton: Mason, Halliday, Coathup, McNeilis, Jim Connor, Anderson, Thomas, Rose, Alford, Grimshaw (Joe Connor), Lutkevitch (McCluskie)

1993 WYCOMBE W*. 4 (Cousins, Kerr, Thompson, Carroll)   **RUNCORN 1 (Shaughnessy)**
Att: 32,968
Conference   *Conference*
Wycombe: Hyde, Cousins, Cooper, Kerr, Crossley, Thompson (Hayrettin 65),Carroll, Ryan, Hutchinson, Scott, Guppy. Sub: Casey.
Runcorn: Williams, Bates, Robertson, Hill, Harold (Connor 62), Anderson, Brady (Parker 72), Brown, Shaughnessy, McKenna, Brabin

1994 WOKING 2 (D Brown, Hay)   **RUNCORN 1 (Shaw (pen))**   **Att: 15,818**
Conference   *Conference*
Woking: Batty, Tucker, L Wye, Berry, Brown, Clement, Brown (Rattray 32), Fielder, Steele, Hay (Puckett 46), Walker.   Ref: Paul Durkin
Runcorn: Williams, Bates, Robertson, Shaw, Lee, Anderson, Thomas, Connor, McInerney (Hill 71), McKenna, Brabin. Sub: Parker

1995 WOKING 2 (Steele, Fielder)   **KIDDERMINSTER HARRIERS 1 aet (Davies)**   **Att: 17,815**
Conference   *Conference*
Woking: Batty, Tucker, L Wye, Fielder, Brown, Crumplin (Rattray 42), S Wye, Ellis, Steele, Hay (Newberry 112), Walker. (Sub: Read(gk))
Kidderminster: Rose, Hodson, Bancroft, Webb, Brindley (Cartwright 94), Forsyth, Deakin, Yates, Humphreys (Hughes 105), Davies,
Purdie. Sub: Dearlove (gk)   Ref: D J Gallagher

THE FA TROPHY

1996   MACCLESFIELD TOWN 3 (Payne, OG, Hemmings)   NORTHWICH VICTORIA 1 (Williams)   **Att: 8,672**
Conference   *Conference*
Macclesfield: Price, Edey, Gardiner, Payne, Howarth(C), Sorvel, Lyons, Wood (Hulme 83), Coates, Power, Hemmings (Cavell 88).
Northwich: Greygoose, Ward, Duffy, Burgess (Simpson 87), Abel (Steele), Walters, Williams, Butler (C), Cooke, Humphries, Vicary.
Ref: M Reed

1997   WOKING 1 (Hay 112)   **DAGENHAM & REDBRIDGE 0**   **Att: 24,376**
Conference   *Isthmian League*
Woking: Batty, Brown, Howard, Foster, Taylor, S Wye, Thompson (sub Jones 115), Ellis, Steele (L Wye 108), Walker, Jackson (Hay 77).
Dagenham: Gothard, Culverhouse, Connor, Creaser, Jacques (sub Double 75), Davidson, Pratt (Naylor 81), Parratt, Broom, Rogers,
Stimson (John 65).
                                                                                            Ref: J Winter

1998   CHELTENHAM TOWN 1 (Eaton 74)   **SOUTHPORT 0**   **Att: 26,387**
Conference   *Conference*
Cheltenham: Book, Duff, Freeman, Banks, Victory, Knight (Smith 78), Howells, Bloomer, Walker (sub Milton 78), Eaton, Watkins. Sub:
Wright.
Southport: Stewart, Horner, Futcher, Ryan, Farley, Kielty, Butler, Gamble, Formby (sub Whittaker 80), Thompson (sub Bollard 88),
Ross. Sub: Mitten.
                                                                                            Ref: G S Willard

1999   KINGSTONIAN 1 (Mustafa 49)   **FOREST GREEN ROVERS 0**   **Att: 20,037**
Conference   *Conference*
Kingstonian: Farrelly, Mustafa, Luckett, Crossley, Stewart, Harris, Patterson, Pitcher, Rattray, Leworthy (Francis 87), Akuamoah. Subs
(not used): John, Corbett, Brown, Tranter
Forest Green Rovers: Shuttlewood, Hedges, Forbes, Bailey (Smart 76), Kilgour, Wigg (Cook 58), Honor (Winter 58), Drysdale,
McGregor, Mehew, Sykes. Subs (not used): Perrin, Coupe
                                                                                            Ref: A B Wilkie

2000   KINGSTONIAN 3 (Akuamoah 40, 69, Simba 75)   **KETTERING TOWN 2 (Vowden 55, Norman 64p)**   **Att: 20,034**
Conference   *Conference*
Kingstonian: Farelly, Mustafa, Luckett, Crossley, Stewart (Saunders 77), Harris, Kadi (Leworthy 83), Pitcher, Green (Basford 86),
Smiba, Akuamoah. Subs (not used): Hurst, Allan
Kettering Town: Sollit, McNamara, Adams, Perkins, Vowden, Norman (Duik 76), Fisher, Brown, Shutt, Watkins (Hudson 46), Setchell
(Hopkins 81). Subs (not used): Ridgway, Wilson
                                                                                            Ref: S W Dunn

2001   CANVEY ISLAND 1 (Chenery)   **FOREST GREEN ROVERS 0**   **Att: 10,007**
Isthmian League   *Conference*   **at Villa Park**
Forest Green Rovers: Perrin, Cousins, Lockwood, Foster, Clark, Burns, Daley, Drysdale (Bennett 46), Foster (Hunt 75), Meecham,
Slater. Subs (not used): Hedges, Prince, Ghent
Canvey Island: Harrison, Duffy, Chenery, Bodley, Ward, Tilson, Stimson (Tanner 83), Gregory, Vaughan (Jones 76), Parmenter. Subs
(not used): Bennett, Miller, Thompson.
                                                                                            Ref: A G Wiley

2002   YEOVIL TOWN 2 (Alford, Stansfield)   **STEVENAGE BOROUGH 0**   **Att: 18,809**
Conference   *Conference*   **at Villa Park**
Yeovil Town: Weale, Lockwood, Tonkin, Skiverton, Pluck (White 51), Way, Stansfield, Johnson, Alford (Giles 86), Crittenden (Lindegaard
83), McIndoe. Subs (not used): O'Brien, Sheffield
Stevenage Borough: Wilkerson, Hamsher, Goodliffe, Trott, Fraser, Fisher, Wormull (Stirling 71), Evers (Williams 56), Jackson, Sigere
(Campbell 74), Clarke. Subs (not used): Campbell, Greygoose
                                                                                            Ref: N S Barry

2003   BURSCOUGH 2 (Martindale 25, 55)   **TAMWORTH 1 (Cooper 78)**   **Att: 14,265**
Northern Premier   *Southern Premier*   **at Villa Park**
Burscough: Taylor, Teale, Taylor, Macauley (White 77), Lawless, Bowen, Wright, Norman, Martindale (McHale 80), Byrne (Bluck 84),
Burns. Subs (not used): McGuire (g/k) Molyneux.
Tamworth: Acton, Warner, Follett, Robinson, Walsh, Cooper, Colley, Evans (Turner 64), Rickards (Hatton 88), McGorry,
Sale (Hallam 54). Subs (not used): Grocutt, Barnes (g/k).
                                                                                            Ref: U D Rennie

2004   HEDNESFORD TOWN 3 (Maguire 28, Hines 53, Brindley 87)   CANVEY ISLAND 2 (Boylan 46, Brindley 48 og)   **Att: 6,635**
Southern Premier   *Isthmian Premier Champions*   **at Villa Park**
Hednesford Town: Young, Simkin, Hines, King, Brindley, Ryder (Barrow 59), Palmer, Anthrobus, Danks (Piearce 78), Maguire,
Charie (Evans 55). Subs (not used): Evans (g/k) McGhee.
Canvey Island: Potter, Kennedy, Duffy, Chenery, Cowan, Gooden (Dobinson 89), Minton, Gregory (McDougald 80), Boylan,
Midgley (Berquez 73), Ward. Subs (not used): Theobald, Harrison (g/k).
Ref: M L Dean

2005   GRAYS ATHLETIC 1 (Martin 65) Pens: 6   **HUCKNALL TOWN 1 (Ricketts 75) Pens: 5**   **Att: 8,116**
Conference South   *Conference North*   **at Villa Park**
Grays Athletic: Bayes, Brennan, Nutter, Stuart, Matthews, Thurgood, Oli (Powell 80), Hopper (Carthy 120), Battersby (sub West 61),
Martin, Cole. Subs (not used): Emberson, Bruce..
Hucknall Town: Smith, Asher, Barrick (Plummer 30), Hunter, Timons, Cooke, Smith (Ward 120), Palmer (Heathcote 94), Ricketts,
Bacon, Todd. Subs (not used): Winder, Lindley.
                                                                                            Ref: P Dowd

2006   GRAYS ATHLETIC 2 (Oli, Poole)   **WOKING 0**   **Att: 13,997**
Conference   *Conference*   **at Upton Park**
Grays Athletic: Bayes, Sambrook, Nutter, Stuart, Hanson, Kightly (Williamson 90), Thurgood, Martin, Poole, Oli, McLean.
Subs (not used): Eyre (g/k), Hooper, Olayinka, Mawer.
Woking: Jalal, Jackson, MacDonald, Nethercott (Watson 60), Hutchinson, Murray, Smith (Cockerill 60), Evans (Blackman 85),
Ferguson, McAllister, Justin Richards. Subs (not used): Davis (g/k), El-Salahi.
                                                                                            Ref: Howard Webb (Sheffield)

THE FA TROPHY

2007   KIDDERMINSTER HARRIERS 2 (Constable 2)
Conference

STEVENAGE BOROUGH   3 (Cole, Dobson, Morrison)
Conference

Att: 53,262
(New Trophy record)

Kidderminster Harriers: Bevan, Kenna, Hurren, Creighton, Whitehead, Blackwood, Russell, Penn, Smikle (Reynolds 90),
Christie (White 75) , Constable.
Subs not used: Taylor, Sedgemore, McGrath.
Stevenage Borough: Julian, Fuller, Nutter, Oliver, Gaia, Miller, Cole, Morrison, Guppy (Dobson 63), Henry, Beard.
Subs not used: Potter, Slabber, Nurse, McMahon.   Ref: Chris Foy (Merseyside)

2008   EBBSFLEET UNITED 1 (McPhee)
Blue Square Premier

TORQUAY UNITED 0
Blue Square Premier

Att: 40,186

Ebbsfleet United: Cronin, Hawkins, McCarthy, Smith, Opinel, McPhee, Barrett, Bostwick, Long (MacDonald 84), Moore, Akinde.
Subs not used: Eribenne, Purcell, Ricketts, Mott.
Torquay United: Rice, Mansell, Todd, Woods, Nicholson, D'Sane (Benyon 66), Hargreaves, Adams, Zebroski, Sills (Hill 88),
Phillips (Stevens 46). Subs not used: Hockley and Robertson.   Ref: Martin Atkinson (West Riding)

2009   STEVENAGE BOROUGH 2 (Morison, Boylan)
Blue Square Premier

YORK CITY 0
Blue Square Premier

Att: 27,102

Stevenage Borough: Day, Henry, Bostwick, Roberts, Wilson, Mills, Murphy, Drury, Vincenti (Anaclet 86), Boylan, Morison.
Subs not used: Bayes, Albrighton, Maamria and Willock.
York City:Ingham, Purkiss, McGurk, Parslow, Pejic, Mackin, Greaves(McWilliams 74), Rusk (Russell 80), Brodie, McBreen (Sodje 60),
Boyes. Subs not used – Mimms and Robinson.   Referee: Michael Jones.

2010   BARROW 2 (McEvilly 79, Walker 117)
Blue Square Premier

STEVENAGE BOROUGH 1 (Drury 10)
Blue Square Premier

Att: 21,223

Barrow: Tim Grand, Simon Spender, Paul Jones, Phil Bolland, Paul Edwards, Simon Wiles (sub Carlos Logan 63rd min),
Robin Hulbert, Andy Bond, Paul Rutherford (sub Mark Boyd 109th min), Jason Walker, Gregg Blundell (sub Lee McEvilly 73rd min).
Subs not used – Tim Deasy and Mike Pearson.
Stevenage Borough: Chris Day (sub Ashley Bayes 90th min), Ronnie Henry, Jon Ashton, Mark Roberts, Scott Laird,
Joel Byrom (sub Lawrie Wilson 58th min), David Bridges, Michael Bostwick, Andy Drury, Chris Beardsley (sub Charlie Griffin 64th min),
Yemi Odubade. Subs not used – Stacey Long and Peter Vincenti.
Man of the match – Paul Rutherford.   Referee Lee Probert.

2011   DARLINGTON 1 (Senior 120)
Blue Square Premier

MANSFIELD TOWN 0
Blue Square Premier

Att: 24,668

Darlington: Sam Russell, Paul Arnison, Ian Miller, Liam Hatch, Aaron Brown, Jamie Chandler*, Chris Moore, Marc Bridge-Wilkinson (sub
Paul Terry 100th min), Gary Smith (sub Arman Verma 38th min), John Campbell (sub Chris Senior 75th min), Tommy Wright.
*Subs not used – Danzelle St Louis-Hamilton (gk) and Phil Gray. * - Man of the Match*
Mansfield Town: Alan Marriott, Gary Silk, Stephen Foster, Tom Naylor, Dan Spence, Louis Briscoe, Tyrone Thompson, Kyle Nix, Adam
Smith (sub Ashley Cain 95th min), Adam Murray (sub Danny Mitchley 108th min), Paul Connor
Subs not used – Paul Stonehouse and Neil Collett (gk)   Referee Stuart Atwell

Action from the Third Round tie between Kidderminster Harriers and Luton Town. Photo: Peter Barnes.

THE FA VASE - 2011-12

Many small football clubs playing below national Step 4 level, benefit from time to time from particularly ambitious and hard working chairmen, committees and managers. Consequently outstanding FAVase challengers can spring up in any areas of the country and often take the football world by surprise.

Looking back over the history of the competition, I'm sure not many football followers would have made an early season forecast of a Wembley appearance for the likes of Rainworth Miners Welfare, Kirkham & Wesham or Wroxham.

BEST PLAYERS STAY IN NORTH EAST

On the other hand, the powerful Whitley Bay club proved just too strong and experienced for the average Vase opponent over three consecutive years and it took another Northern League club to prevent a fourth. The best players in the famous North Eastern competition have less senior non league clubs chasing their services, so unless a talented player is lured into the Football League, the best players to stay in the North East as the area's wonderful FA Amateur Cup and FA Vase records have proved over the last fifty years.

It was a shock to realize that 156 small clubs will have lost interest in their special national knock out cup in the first week next September and last year there were some outstanding First Qualifying Round scores. Plymouth Parkway beat Chard in Somerset by 11-0 and Stratford Town supporters must have travelled home happy after their 7-6 success at West Midland club Goodrich FC.

The Second Qualifying Round saw another huge loss of clubs and, those with long memories may have found it difficult to accept that the once powerful Bishop Auckland were knocked out by Sunderland RCA but both clubs now compete in The Northern League with the Wearside club challenging at the top.

Many clubs can look back in history at a great season when their little local club played at Wembley, but form very rarely lasts for more than a couple of seasons and if it does, then the club will probably claw its away up the pyramid and qualify for The FA Trophy.

TEN GOALS FOR ARMTHORPE WELFARE

It is strange to see the Merthyr club featuring in the Vase and they lost a 3-2 thriller at Slimbridge. Armthorpe Welfare scored ten against Kinsley Boys FC and surely when facing opponents with a name like that it creates confidence before a ball is kicked!

Dunston UTS celebrate their FA Vase win. Photo: Eric Marsh.

A look at the First Round Proper results underlines the fact that the North East really do provide the favourites. Who would want to face West Auckland, Newcastle Benfield, or Bedlington Terriers and there were some more still to enter the competition.

Looking at results across the country showed that recent finalists Wroxham and Hillingdon Borough both lost away from home, but could there be a challenge from the deep South West, where Falmouth Town recorded an impressive 5-2 victory over the fast improving Buckland Athletic.

NORTHERN GOAL SPREE

Any one of six clubs could take the FA Vase back to the North East and just to rub in their potency, Dunston UTS scored twelve goals against Blackwell Miners Welfare in the Second Round while Ashington and and Billinghan Synthonia qualified as did Consett scoring four goals and Spennymoor Town with five!

The rest of the country must hope they knock each other out as quickly as possible but the later rounds widen the geographical pairings and it will take good teams to beat them.

With just 32 ties, the FA Vase Third Round now appeared to be remarkably small compared with the hundreds of clubs already eliminated. There was still a strong North South divide so some of the Northern favourites did clash, with Ashington beating Spennymoor away, the holders Whitley Bay showing no respect for BridlingtonTown, who they beat 5-1 and Billingham Synthonia beating Consett at home 4-2. The Northern League leaders West Auckland won a five goal thriller away at Askern Villa a Northern Counties East club

When looking for possible challengers from the South, Enfield 1893 caught the eye and reminds us of Enfield's great years in the Isthmian League and Football Alliance. Willand Rovers beat Falmouth so maybe they will fight for the West's honour and perhaps Reading Town or Wisbech Town can raise their game in the rounds to come.

THREE GAMES AWAY FROM THE SEMI-FINALS

A long mid winter break gives the remaining 32 Vase challengers time to prepare their squads and underline the fact that they are just three games way from a Vase Semi-Final when anything can happen in a battle over two legs.

There are no geographical splits in this round. West Auckland travel down to Bitton and win 3-1 but Herne Bay travel up to beat Newcastle BBP 2-1. Shortwood United ruin another club's ambitions by beating Enfield and ominously Whitley Bay score five at home against Combined Counties club South Park.

Tividale (West Midlands League) gave their supporters hopes for an exciting end to the season with a 7-0 victory at home to Binfield and the eventual line up for the Fifth Round contained these sixteen clubs from ten different leagues:

TEN LEAGUES REPRESENTED

Northern League (5): Ashington, Billingham Synthonia, Dunston UCS,West Auckland,Whitley Bay
Kent League : Herne Bay
Midland Alliance (2): Gresley, Oadby Town
Essex Senior League: Bethnal Green
Hellenic League: Shortwood United
Northern Counties East: Stavely Miners Welfare
Wessex League: Bournemouth,
Western League: Larkhall Athletic
West Midlands(Regional) League: Tividale
United Counties (2) : Peterborough Northern Star & St Ives
who were given Tunbridge Wells place after the Kent club was disqualified
Favourites Meet

Any club that reaches the last sixteen of such a huge competition earns respect and the draw for the Fifth Round did at least give the outsiders a boost when they saw that Whitley Bay had to entertain the Northern League's form club West Auckland. The fixtures in this round were badly affected by the weather which made pre match preparation particularly difficult.

Very few early season bets would have been placed on Peterborough NS, Bournemouth or St Ives but a fine away victory against high scoring Tividale saw the United Counties club through and the Hampshire club's draw at Billingham gave them a chance of a home victory. In very

Action from the Final. Photo: Peter Barnes

strange circumstances, St Ives took advantage of their second chance with a resounding 4-0 victory over Gresley.

All eyes were on just one result and there were great sighs of relief when West Auckland's victory at Whitley Bay seemed to give all the clubs a better chance of a Wembley success- although West Auckland would now be red hot favourites.

The Quarter Final draw spread the ties across the country with the Northern clubs both traveling. Only one home win out of four is surprising and it was Staveley Miners Welfare who pleased their home supporters by finally eliminating St Neots from the competition.

Perhaps the fact that not one of the other three quarter finals attracted a 500 attendance must have been a little disappointing for the home players and the three other visitors duly claimed their semi-final places.

EXCITING SEMI-FINALS

Both first leg matches in the Semi-Finals left all to play for in the second games. Herne Bay and West Auckland played out a storming cup tie with the visitors early two goal lead wiped out by the plucky Kent club with forty minutes still to play.

Supporters of Staveley Miners Welfare would probably have been happy with just a one goal deficit from their visit to the North East, but a week seems a long time to wait for the second leg, with so many conjectures on the vital games ahead for everyone involved with all four clubs.

As it turned out, the original suggestion of an all Northern Final came true,
nut not without two tremendous cup ties. Staveley twice took the lead against Dunston who scored their second vital goal with six minutes of ordinary time remaining, and West Auckland spurred on by a crowd just under 2,000, hit back with two goals before half time after Herne Bay had taken the lead in the twelfth minute.

GREAT DAY FOR THE NORTHERN LEAGUE

There was no doubt that The Northern League deserved their great day at Wembley and over 8,000 fans made the long journey. The remainder of the huge world of leagues providing FA Vase clubs will find it hard to cope with the north eastern determination, tradition and class, but its well worth the challenge. Remember Billericay Town, Halesowen Town and Stamford who all enjoyed their days in the FA Vase headlines. T.W.

Left: Action from Shortwood United's 4-0 win over Wootton Bassett in the First Qualifying Round. Photo: Peter Barnes.

Above: AFC Uckfield 'keeper, Benoit Bekjamon, punches clear a Sidley United attack during their First Qualifying Round match. Photo: Roger Turner.

Sporting Khalsa's Marc Thomas heads the ball toward the Heath Hayes goal during their First Qualifying Round defeat. Photo: Jonathan Holloway.

Further action from the Shortwood United verses Wootton Bassett match. Photo: Peter Barnes.

FIRST QUALIFYING ROUND
SATURDAY 10 SEPTEMBER 2011 - WINNERS RECEIVE £500

#	Home		Away	Score	No.
1	Washington	v	Tow Law Town	1-5	60
2	Newton Aycliffe	v	Shildon	0-0aet	379
	Shildon	v	Newton Aycliffe (14/9)	3-2aet	291
3	Esh Winning	v	Morpeth Town	5-2	47
4	North Shields	v	Northallerton Town	1-3	161
5	Chester-Le-Street Town	v	Bishop Auckland	3-5	119
6	Bedlington Terriers	v	Stokesley SC	9-1	121
7	Whitehaven	v	Horden CW	2-0	37
8	Easington Colliery	v	Prudhoe Town	2-1	37
9	Guisborough Town	v	West Allotment Celtic	2-1	79
10	Whickham	v	Gillford Park (9/9)	1-3	103
11	Hebburn Town	v	Thornaby	5-1	54
12	Crook Town	v	Seaham Red Star	4-2	88
13	WEST AUCKLAND TOWN	v	Cleator Moor Celtic	3-1	75
14	Armthorpe Welfare	v	Appleby Frodingham	3-1	49
15	Maltby Main	v	Kinsley Boys	1-2	63
16	Hallam	v	Rossington Main	2-5	60
	(at Rossington Main FC)				
17	Silsden	v	Askern Villa	2-5	68
18	Brighouse Town	v	Winterton Rangers	1-4	47
19	Atherton LR	v	Ashton Town	3-1	45
20	AFC Blackpool	v	AFC Darwen	3-4	46
21	Congleton Town	v	Runcorn Linnets	1-2	143
22	Holker Old Boys	v	Northwich Villa	4-2	24
23	Bacup Borough	v	Rochdale Town	1-0	81
24	Oldham Boro	v	Daisy Hill	1-0	27
25	Chadderton	v	Alsager Town	3-1	47
26	Barnoldswick Town	v	Irlam	3-1	125
27	Heanor Town	v	Dunkirk	1-2	87
28	Louth Town	v	Borrowash Victoria	1-2	99
29	Retford United	v	Arnold Town	3-3aet	152
	Arnold Town	v	Retford United (13/9)	3-1	125
30	Ollerton Town	v	South Normanton Athletic	3-2	45
31	Shirebrook Town	v	Radcliffe Olympic	3-0aet	152
32	Greenwood Meadows	v	Graham St Prims	1-0	28
33	Blackstones	v	Kimberley Town	5-2	91
34	Gedling MW	v	Boston Town	1-5	48
35	Wolverhampton Casuals	v	Coventry Copsewood	1-3	55
36	Walsall Wood	v	Pershore Town 88	3-2aet	29
37	Warstones Wanderers	v	Norton United (9/9)	2-5	45
38	AFC Wulfrunians	v	Shifnal Town	2-1	63
39	Sporting Khalsa	v	Heath Hayes	0-4	45
40	Lye Town	v	Bartley Green	0-1	65
41	Highgate United	v	Bewdley Town	3-1	62
42	Dudley Sports	v	Pegasus Juniors	2-1aet	29
43	Malvern Town	v	Southam United	0-1	53
44	Castle Vale	v	Cradley Town	3-2aet	30
45	Shawbury United	v	Bridgnorth Town	2-0aet	51
46	Eccleshall	v	Racing Club Warwick	0-5	28
47	Westfields	v	Cadbury Athletic	6-0	103
48	Dudley Town	v	Causeway United	3-2	50
49	Tividale	v	Nuneaton Griff	3-0	71
50	Studley	v	Castle Vale JKS	3-2	53
51	Rocester	v	Ellesmere Rangers	2-3aet	80
52	Willenhall Town	v	Brocton (9/9)	2-3	79
53	Pelsall Villa	v	Coleshill Town	3-2	27
54	Stone Dominoes	v	Alvechurch	0-1	43
55	Goodrich	v	Stafford Town	6-7aet	34
56	Leek CSOB	v	Gornal Athletic	0-1	37
57	Blaby & Whetstone Athletic	v	Yaxley	3-4	45
58	Rothwell Town	v	Bugbrooke St Michaels	0-4	68
59	Stewarts & Lloyds Corby	v	Ibstock United	4-0	31
60	Cogenhoe United	v	Rothwell Corinthians	3-2aet	46
61	Barrow Town	v	Saffron Dynamo	4-0	70
62	Ellistown	v	Friar Lane & Epworth	3-2	38
63	Thrapston Town	v	Wellingborough Whitworths (9/9)	2-1	127
64	Thurnby Nirvana	v	Birstall United	1-3	33
65	Daventry United	v	Wellingborough Town (9/9)	2-0	71
66	Eynesbury Rovers	v	Desborough Town	3-4	70
67	Hadleigh United	v	Stowmarket Town	1-3	101
68	Walsham Le Willows	v	Fakenham Town	4-1	31
69	FC Clacton	v	Ely City	2-1	116
70	Brightlingsea Regent	v	Stanway Rovers	0-2	96
71	Thetford Town	v	Long Melford	2-0	70
72	Kirkley & Pakefield	v	Woodbridge Town	0-3	101
73	Swaffham Town	v	Felixstowe & Walton Utd	3-6aet	61
74	Saffron Walden Town	v	Team Bury		
	(walkover for Team Bury – Saffron Walden Town removed)				
75	Mildenhall Town	v	March Town United	6-1	102
76	Wivenhoe Town	v	Halstead Town	2-6	
77	Basildon United	v	Wootton Blue Cross	1-1aet	43
	Wootton Blue Cross	v	Basildon United (14/9)	1-3	32
78	Barking	v	Crawley Green	2-0	66
79	Takeley	v	Cockfosters	2-0	81
80	London Lions	v	London APSA (11/9)	1-2	30
81	Broxbourne Borough V&E	v	Burnham Ramblers	2-3aet	61
82	Cranfield United	v	Haringey & WD	2-6	73
83	Welwyn Garden City	v	Bedford	1-2aet	30
84	Hullbridge Sports	v	Colney Heath	2-1	21
85	Berkhamsted	v	Stotfold	1-0	113
86	London Colney	v	Codicote	0-2	65
87	St Margaretsbury	v	Langford	1-0	52
88	Sawbridgeworth Town	v	Wodson Park	5-4aet	45
89	Bowers & Pitsea	v	Hertford Town	4-3	73
90	Hoddesdon Town	v	Kentish Town	6-0	62
91	Hatfield Town	v	Sporting Bengal United	2-3aet	28
92	Canning Town	v	Eton Manor (11/9)	1-1aet	80
	(at Aveley FC)				
	Eton Manor	v	Canning Town (14/9)	3-0	36
93	Hanworth Villa	v	Sandhurst Town	8-3	86
94	Thame United	v	Staines Lammas	4-1	71
95	Hook Norton	v	Wokingham & Emmbrook (11/9)	2-2aet	62
	Wokingham & Emmbrook	v	Hook Norton (13/9)	2-0	49
96	Windsor	v	Oxford City Nomads	3-0	127
97	Winslow United	v	Holyport	2-1	73
98	Holmer Green	v	Newbury	4-5aet	42
99	Kidlington	v	Buckingham Athletic	3-1	47
100	Reading Town	v	Harefield United	1-0	55
101	Hillingdon Borough	v	AFC Wallingford	7-0	31
102	Seaford Town	v	Cobham	2-1	35
103	Ashford United	v	Shoreham	2-2aet	124
	Shoreham	v	Ashford United (13/9)	3-2	76
104	Wick	v	Woodstock Sports	0-2	52
105	St Francis Rangers	v	South Park	0-2	
106	Croydon	v	Beckenham Town	1-2	51
107	Lingfield	v	Ringmer	2-3	74
108	Fisher	v	Ash United	4-0	113
109	Chessington & Hook Utd	v	East Preston	1-3	47
110	Lordswood	v	Steyning Town	1-0	55
111	Frimley Green	v	Raynes Park Vale	1-5	27
112	Hailsham Town	v	Epsom & Ewell	1-3	102
113	Holmesdale	v	Erith Town	0-1	49
114	Colliers Wood United	v	Dorking	5-2	30
115	Sidley United	v	AFC Uckfield	4-2aet	84
116	Saltdean United	v	Chichester City	1-2aet	54
117	Selsey	v	Redhill	1-2	115

Dom Fountain hammers home the first of Yaxley's goals in their exciting 4-3 win over Blaby & Whetstone in the First Qualifying Round. Photo: Gordon Whittington.

Below: Farnham Town's Matt Bunyan takes on Gareth Broom of Warlingham during their First Qualifying Round tie. Photo: Alan Coomes.

Merthyr Town full-back, Alun Griffiths is beaten in the air by this Slimbridge player in this Second Qualifying Round match.
Photo: Jonathan Holloway.

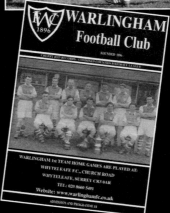

More Second Qualifying Round action - here we see Harry Bass, Chichester City's captain, out jump Sidley United's defence to head City's third goal. Photo: Roger Turner.

FIRST QUALIFYING ROUND
SATURDAY 10 SEPTEMBER 2011 - WINNERS RECEIVE £500

118	Littlehampton Town	v Haywards Heath Town	3-3aet	52
	Haywards Heath Town	v Littlehampton Town (13/9)	0-2	56
119	Erith & Belvedere	v Tunbridge Wells	2-3aet	49
120	Bookham	v Westfield	1-3	
121	Knaphill	v Horley Town	1-4	78
122	Warlingham	v Farnham Town (11/9)	2-3aet	86
123	Arundel	v Crowborough Athletic	5-0	64
124	Swanage Town & Herston	v GE Hamble	0-3	68
125	Alton Town	v Hamworthy United	2-1	56
126	Horndean	v Lymington Town	2-1	70
127	Cove	v Verwood Town	2-1	36
128	Christchurch	v Newport (IW)	4-1	55
129	Totton & Eling	v Cowes Sports	2-3aet	42
130	Fleet Spurs	v Blackfield & Langley	1-6	20
131	East Cowes Victoria Athletic	v Hayling United	0-3	47
	(tie awarded to East Cowes Victoria Athletic – Hayling United removed)			

132	Cheltenham Saracens	v Melksham Town	1-4	32
133	Devizes Town	v Shepton Mallet	5-0	46
134	Street	v Hallen	0-2	
135	Corsham Town	v Pewsey Vale	1-1aet	45
	Pewsey Vale	v Corsham Town (13/9)	2-0	82
136	Slimbridge	v Portishead Town	1-0	49
137	Almondsbury UWE	v Bishop Sutton	2-3	45
138	Merthyr Town	v Brislington	1-0	261
139	Shortwood United	v Wootton Bassett Town	4-0	61
140	Westbury United	v Bradford Town	0-2	105
141	Wells City	v Welton Rovers	2-0	114
142	Longwell Green Sports	v Odd Down	1-1aet	
	Odd Down	v Longwell Green Sports (13/9)	2-1aet	41
143	Radstock Town	v Fairford Town	0-1	53
144	Budleigh Salterton	v Barnstaple Town	1-4	55
145	Cullompton Rangers	v Porthleven	6-3aet	71
146	Chard Town	v Plymouth Parkway	0-11	63

SECOND QUALIFYING ROUND
SATURDAY 24 SEPTEMBER 2011 - WINNERS RECEIVE £700

1	Ryton & Crawcrook Albion	v Crook Town	1-3aet	44
2	Penrith	v Guisborough Town	0-1	95
3	Billingham Town	v Whitehaven	4-2aet	55
4	Sunderland RCA	v Bishop Auckland	5-3	148
5	Jarrow Roofing Boldon CA	v Easington Colliery	2-0	10
6	Hebburn Town	v Brandon United	6-0	56
7	Tow Law Town	v Shildon (23/9)	0-6	135
8	Marske United	v **WEST AUCKLAND TOWN**	2-6	132
9	Esh Winning	v Darlington Railway Athletic	0-1	45
10	Northallerton Town	v Bedlington Terriers	0-1	142
11	Gillford Park	v Willington	1-0	36
12	South Shields	v Birtley Town	2-1	102
13	Liversedge	v AFC Emley	2-3aet	124
14	Dinnington Town	v Grimsby Borough	2-0	38
15	Hemsworth MW	v Barton Town Old Boys	1-3	76
16	Selby Town	v Winterton Rangers	2-1	90
17	Glasshoughton Welfare	v Bottesford Town	6-0	73
18	Scarborough Athletic	v Worsborough Bridge Athletic	5-1	408
19	Armthorpe Welfare	v Kinsley Boys	10-0	52
20	Yorkshire Amateur	v Brodsworth		
	(walkover for Yorkshire Amateur – Brodsworth removed)			
21	Rossington Main	v Eccleshill United	1-2	60
22	Askern Villa	v Hall Road Rangers	1-0	35
23	Pickering Town	v Thackley	1-2	102
24	Pontefract Collieries	v Nostell MW	1-1aet	69
	Nostell MW	v Pontefract Collieries (27/9)	2-3	75
25	Ashville	v West Didsbury & Chorlton	2-0	65
26	Oldham Boro	v Wigan Robin Park (23/9)	3-2	55
27	Atherton LR	v Atherton Collieries	3-2aet	90
28	Bacup Borough	v Ashton Athletic	3-1	56
29	Formby	v Chadderton	4-2	
30	Holker OBs	v Colne (27/9)	0-2	28
31	Squires Gate	v St Helens Town	1-0	51

32	AFC Darwen	v AFC Liverpool	2-2aet	90
	AFC Liverpool	v AFC Darwen (29/9)	1-3aet	117
33	Runcorn Linnets	v Bootle	2-0	254
34	Maine Road	v Cheadle Town	1-2	46
35	Barnoldswick Town	v Abbey Hey	5-2	117
36	Long Eaton United	v Lincoln Moorlands Railway	1-1aet	
	Lincoln Moorlands railway	v Long Eaton United (28/9)	1-4	56
37	Greenwood Meadows	v Sleaford Town	2-0	24
38	Dunkirk	v Pinxton	1-4	51
39	Shirebrook Town	v Glossop North End	1-3	184
40	Holwell Sports	v Blackstones	4-0	
41	Ollerton Town	v Deeping Rangers	0-3	30
42	Holbeach United	v Newark Town	4-0	100
43	Borrowash Victoria	v Blidworth Welfare	1-3	67
44	Arnold Town	v Calverton MW	6-2	110
45	Teversal	v Blackwell MW	1-3	54
46	Boston Town	v Radford	4-2	48
47	Stafford Town	v Pelsall Villa	5-0	47
48	Highgate United	v Dudley Sports	3-2	44
49	Brocton	v Earlswood Town	1-1aet	53
	Earlswood Town	v Brocton (27/9)	0-2	52
50	Alvechurch	v Pilkington XXX	0-1	79
51	Bustleholme	v Bartley Green	0-3	35
52	Coventry Sphinx	v Norton United	0-3	53
53	Studley	v Gornal Athletic	0-2aet	53
54	Wolverhampton Sporting CFC	v Atherstone Town	0-2	60
55	Walsall Wood	v Ellesmere Rangers	0-1	32
56	Coventry Copsewood	v Castle Vale	2-1	26
57	Wellington	v Tividale	0-5	44
58	Racing Club Warwick	v Bromyard Town	2-1aet	40
59	Continental Star	v Shawbury United	3-2	22
60	Westfields	v Dudley Town	3-1	94
61	Stratford Town	v Southam United	2-0	197

Merthyr Town defender, Steve Williams, tracking the Slimbridge player, Alex Higgs. Photo: Jonathan Holloway.

Left: Aiden Pursglove completes his hatrick for VCD against Lordswood in the First Round Proper. Photo: Alan Coomes.

More action from VCD Athletic's First Round win over Lordswood, again we see Aiden Pursglove scoring past 'keeper Matt Byott. Photo: Alan Coomes.

SECOND QUALIFYING ROUND
SATURDAY 24 SEPTEMBER 2011 - WINNERS RECEIVE £700

62	Heath Hayes	v	AFC Wulfrunians	5-1	52	115	Wembley	v	Bedfont Sports	0-0aet	48
63	Oadby Town	v	Huntingdon Town	3-2	111		Bedfont Sports	v	Wembley (27/9)	1-0	70
64	Barrow Town	v	Ellistown	1-2	98	116	Banstead Athletic	v	Erith Town	1-3	50
65	Ashby Ivanhoe	v	St Andrews	2-4	25	117	Hassocks	v	Farnham Town	1-1aet	62
66	Birstall United	v	Yaxley	0-1	50		Farnham Town	v	Hassocks (27/9)	1-1aet	50
67	Lutterworth Athletic	v	Anstey Nomads	3-1	89		(Farnham Town won 8-7 on kicks from the penalty mark)				
68	Godmanchester Rovers	v	Northampton Spencer	6-3aet	82	118	Egham Town	v	Mole Valley SCR	3-2	44
69	Thrapston Town	v	Bardon Hill Sports	1-3	48	119	Erith & Dartford Town	v	Seaford Town	0-2	43
70	Aylestone Park	v	Desborough Town	1-4		120	Deal Town	v	Shoreham	2-1	99
71	Daventry United	v	Harborough Town (23/9)	1-2	72	121	Tunbridge Wells	v	Mile Oak	5-1	51
72	Cogenhoe United	v	Kirby Muxloe	3-2	47	122	Woodstock Sports	v	Westfield	2-1	51
73	Stewarts & Lloyds Corby	v	Irchester United	3-0	30	123	Lordswood	v	Horley Town	2-1aet	51
74	Raunds Town	v	Bugbrooke St Michaels	0-3	42	124	Redhill	v	Colliers Wood United	2-3	75
75	Rushden & Higham United	v	Peterborough Northern Star	1-2	80	125	Corinthian	v	East Preston	1-2	33
76	Framlingham Town	v	Diss Town	0-4	99	126	Three Bridges	v	Sevenoaks Town	3-0	
77	Gorleston	v	Mildenhall Town	2-4aet	155	127	Littlehampton Town	v	Arundel	2-1	144
78	Great Yarmouth Town	v	Felixstowe & Walton United	0-5	96	128	Raynes Park Vale	v	Newhaven	5-3aet	54
79	Ipswich Wanderers	v	Thetford Town	2-5	56	129	South Park	v	Badshot Lea	3-0	61
80	Debenham LC	v	Team Bury	0-1	64	130	Ringmer	v	Epsom & Ewell	2-0	72
81	Cambridge Regional College	v	Brantham Athletic (25/9)	0-2	78	131	Sidley United	v	Chichester City	2-3	77
82	Stowmarket Town	v	Walsham Le Willows	1-2	92	132	Beckenham Town	v	Fisher	5-1	58
83	Whitton United	v	Downham Town	4-1	88	133	Downton	v	Ringwood Town	9-1	51
84	FC Clacton	v	Cornard United	1-0aet	89	134	East Cowes Victoria Athletic	v	Alresford Town	0-4	24
85	Stanway Rovers	v	Woodbridge Town	1-2	74	135	Christchurch	v	Horndean	2-1	47
86	Halstead Town	v	Newmarket Town	2-0		136	Alton Town	v	New Milton Town	2-1	34
87	Haverhill Rovers	v	Norwich United	5-1	101	137	Brockenhurst	v	Cove	2-0	60
88	Clapton	v	Southend Manor	1-3	30	138	Whitchurch United	v	Fareham Town	1-2	96
89	Hullbridge Sports	v	Bowers & Pitsea	2-0	38	139	Romsey Town	v	Fawley	1-3	24
90	Burnham Ramblers	v	Takeley	5-2	55	140	Gillingham Town	v	Moneyfields	3-1	104
91	Barking	v	Potton United	4-0	76	141	Cowes Sports	v	United Services Portsmouth	1-0	75
92	Eton Manor	v	London APSA	2-3	10	142	AFC Portchester	v	Bournemouth	1-3	95
93	Oxhey Jets	v	AFC Dunstable	3-2	38	143	Blackfield & Langley	v	GE Hamble	4-1	57
94	Hadley	v	AFC Kempston Rovers (23/9)	1-0aet	57	144	Andover New Street	v	Bridport	3-6	
95	Codicote	v	Biggleswade United	0-3	34	145	Shrewton United	v	Sherborne Town	3-2aet	40
	(at Biggleswade United FC)					146	Petersfield Town	v	Hartley Wintney	1-5	60
96	Haringey & WD	v	Kings Langley (23/9)	4-3	35	147	Bristol Manor Farm	v	Wells City	1-2	58
97	Sawbridgeworth Town	v	Sporting Bengal United	1-3	48	148	Slimbridge	v	Merthyr Town	3-2	119
98	Bedford	v	Basildon United	1-3	29	149	Bristol Academy	v	Bradford Town	0-2	25
99	Hoddesdon Town	v	Berkhamsted	3-2	67	150	Ashton & Backwell United	v	Fairford Town	0-1aet	53
100	Haringey Borough	v	St Margaretsbury	2-1	38	151	Pewsey Vale	v	Devizes Town	0-0aet	
101	Ampthill Town	v	Ampthill Town	1-1aet	75		Devizes Town	v	Pewsey Vale (27/9)	3-1	125
	Ampthill Town	v	Barkingside (27/9)	1-0	62	152	Keynsham Town	v	Lydney Town	1-2	47
102	Old Woodstock Town	v	Bicester Town			153	Shortwood United	v	Hallen	3-2aet	106
	(walkover for Old Woodstock Town – Bicester Town removed)					154	Hengrove Athletic	v	Winterbourne United	2-4	28
103	Reading Town	v	Aylesbury United	2-1aet	91	155	Melksham Town	v	Odd Down	2-1	97
104	Winslow United	v	Wokingham & Emmbrook	2-1aet	83	156	Calne Town	v	Bishop Sutton	0-2	51
105	Thame United	v	Hanwell Town	2-5	91	157	Barnstaple Town	v	St Blazey	3-0	136
106	Flackwell Heath	v	Windsor	3-1	99	158	Penzance	v	Witheridge	2-3	74
107	Henley Town	v	Milton United	1-0	31	159	Liskeard Athletic	v	Wadebridge Town	4-2	43
108	Carterton	v	Shrivenham	3-1	19	160	Tavistock	v	Crediton United	4-3aet	45
109	Abingdon Town	v	Feltham	2-2aet	22	161	Dawlish Town	v	Saltash United		
	Feltham	v	Abingdon Town (27/9)	2-4aet	52		(walkover for Saltash United – Dawlish Town removed)				
110	Newbury	v	Clanfield 85	3-5	72	162	Wellington	v	Cullompton Rangers	0-3	69
111	Ascot United	v	Buckingham Town	0-1	67		(at Cullompton Rangers FC)				
112	Kidlington	v	Hanworth Villa	2-3	61	163	Buckland Athletic	v	Elmore	5-1	102
113	Bracknell Town	v	Hillingdon Borough	0-1	66	164	Plymouth Parkway	v	Bovey Tracey	1-0	88
114	Witney Town	v	Amersham Town	6-3aet	69	165	Falmouth Town	v	Minehead	7-3	134

FIRST ROUND PROPER
SATURDAY 22 OCTOBER 2011 - WINNERS RECEIVE £900

1	Newcastle Benfield	v	Hebburn Town	2-1	81
2	Shildon	v	**WEST AUCKLAND TOWN**	2-3aet	276
3	Jarrow Roofing Boldon CA	v	Crook Town	2-3aet	27
4	Billingham Town	v	South Shields	5-2	105
5	Guisborough Town	v	Consett	4-4aet	112
	Consett	v	Guisborough Town (26/10)	3-2	82
6	Bedlington Terriers	v	Sunderland RCA	4-1	195
7	Darlington RA	v	Gillford Park	1-4	49
8	Parkgate	v	Scarborough Athletic	2-0	295
9	Armthorpe Welfare	v	Yorkshire Amateur	3-0	55
10	Glasshoughton Welfare	v	AFC Emley	2-0	75
11	Barton Town OBs	v	Pontefract Collieries	1-0	80
12	Dinnington Town	v	Bridlington Town	0-2	52
13	Askern Villa	v	Selby Town	3-1	89
14	Eccleshill United	v	Thackley	1-0	130
15	Ramsbottom United	v	Colne	4-0	194
16	Squires Gate	v	AFC Darwen	3-0	68
17	Formby	v	Ashville	0-1	90
18	Atherton LR	v	Winsford United	1-2	37
19	Oldham Boro	v	Padiham	1-3	43
20	Cheadle Town	v	Bacup Borough	0-2	59
21	Runcorn Linnets	v	Barnoldswick Town	2-3aet	306
22	Blackwell MW	v	Pinxton	1-0	112
23	Deeping Rangers	v	Holbeach United	3-1	176
24	Arnold Town	v	Long Eaton United	0-2	106
25	Boston Town	v	Holwell Sports	3-1	66
26	Glossop Nth End	v	Blidworth Welfare	5-0	250
27	Spalding United	v	Greenwood Meadows	2-1	96
28	Stafford Town	v	Atherstone Town	3-2	86
29	Norton United	v	Heath Hayes	4-0	40
30	Bartley Green	v	Ellesmere Rangers	0-6	25
31	Stratford Town	v	Racing Club Warwick	0-4	226
32	Continental Star	v	Gornal Athletic (23/10)	0-2	40
33	Tipton Town	v	Highgate United	2-1aet	57
34	Tividale	v	Westfields	4-1	91
35	Brocton	v	Coventry Copsewood	3-0	55
36	Pilkington XXX	v	Boldmere St Michaels	2-5	61
37	Loughborough University	v	Godmanchester Rovers (21/10)	1-2	39
38	Bardon Hill Sports	v	Desborough Town	2-0	43
39	Lutterworth Athletic	v	Oadby Town	1-2	148
40	St Andrews	v	Bugbrooke St Michaels	4-2aet	45
41	Ellistown	v	Peterborough North Star	0-2	60
42	Cogenhoe United	v	Yaxley	2-1	57
43	Harborough Town	v	Stewarts & Lloyds Corby	2-2aet	151
	Stewart & Lloyds Corby	v	Harborough Town (25/10)	1-0	82
44	Wisbech Town	v	Walsham Le Willows	3-0aet	239
45	Woodbridge Town	v	Witham Town	1-1aet	98
	Witham Town	v	Woodbridge Town (25/10)	4-1	
46	Felixstowe & Walton United	v	Haverhill Rovers	1-0	89
47	Diss Town	v	Brantham Athletic	1-0	119
48	FC Clacton	v	Whitton United	2-4aet	91
49	Halstead Town	v	Team Bury	0-1	111
50	Dereham Town	v	Thetford Town	0-3	164
51	Mildenhall Town	v	Wroxham	1-0	132
52	Southend Manor	v	Biggleswade United	2-1	70
53	Oxhey Jets	v	Enfield 1893	1-6	74
54	London APSA	v	Haringey & Waltham Dev.	0-3	25
55	Bethnal Green United	v	Hoddesdon Town	3-1	45
56	Haringey Borough	v	Hadley	2-0	49
57	Tring Athletic	v	Hullbridge Sports	3-2	100
58	Basildon United	v	Ampthill Town	0-4	31
59	Burnham Ramblers	v	Sporting Bengal United	1-3	57
60	Barking	v	Royston Town	0-1	105
61	Old Woodstock Town	v	Abingdon Town	4-3	
62	Henley Town	v	Newport Pagnell Town	0-1	44
63	Flackwell Heath	v	Clanfield 85	2-0	49
64	Binfield	v	Hillingdon Borough	3-2aet	110
65	Witney Town	v	Carterton (21/10)	2-1	196
66	Ardley United	v	Reading Town	1-3	51
67	Hanworth Villa	v	Bedfont Sports	3-1	
68	Winslow United	v	Buckingham Town	2-5	180
69	Hanwell Town	v	Wantage Town	1-2	47
70	Camberley Town	v	Littlehampton Town	1-2aet	87
71	South Park	v	Colliers Wood United	1-0aet	
72	Ringmer	v	Woodstock Sports	5-0	66
73	Horsham YMCA	v	Deal Town	1-2	88
74	VCD Athletic	v	Lordswood	5-0	82
75	Three Bridges	v	Beckenham Town	3-0aet	68
76	Erith Town	v	Farnham Town	6-1	42
77	Peacehaven & Telscombe	v	Raynes Park Vale	3-1	91
78	Egham Town	v	Greenwich Borough	3-0	24
79	Seaford Town	v	Tunbridge Wells	1-2	98
80	East Preston	v	Pagham	3-4	69
81	Molesey	v	Chichester City	3-4aet	
82	Shrewton United	v	Fawley	1-2	39
83	Bournemouth	v	Hartley Wintney	2-0	83
84	Christchurch	v	Bridport	2-1	79
85	Downton	v	Fareham Town	3-0	78
86	Cowes Sports	v	Gillingham Town	3-0	115
87	Blackfield & Langley	v	Brockenhurst	2-1	79
88	Brading Town	v	Alton Town	4-5	82
89	Alresford Town	v	Winchester City	1-6	95
90	Bishop Sutton	v	Bradford Town	2-1	53
91	Lydney Town	v	Shortwood United	1-2	87
92	Melksham Town	v	Wells City	2-1aet	110
93	Highworth Town	v	Devizes Town	2-1aet	105
94	Fairford Town	v	Winterbourne United	0-1	48
95	Larkhall Athletic	v	Slimbridge	4-0	111
96	Ilfracombe Town	v	Plymouth Parkway	1-0aet	92
97	Falmouth Town	v	Buckland Athletic	5-2	210
98	Cullompton Rangers	v	Tavistock	2-1	78
99	Saltash United	v	Witheridge	3-2	70
100	Liskeard Athletic	v	Barnstaple Town	1-2	61

SECOND ROUND PROPER
SATURDAY 19 NOVEMBER 2011 - WINNERS RECEIVE £1,200

1	Squires Gate	v	Winsford United	3-1aet	57
2	Glasshoughton Welfare	v	Runcorn Town	0-2	82
3	**DUNSTON UTS**	v	Blackwell MW	12-1	158
4	Bridlington Town	v	Gillford Park	1-0	149
5	Ashville	v	Staveley MW	1-2	120
6	Billingham Town	v	Glossop North End	2-4	
7	Newcastle Benfield	v	Barton Town OB's	2-1	52
8	**WEST AUCKLAND TOWN**	v	Bacup Borough	3-1	152
9	Ashington	v	Norton & Stockton Ancients	1-0	212
10	Billingham Synthonia	v	Crook Town	2-0	107
11	Eccleshill United	v	Armthorpe Welfare	1-3	29
12	Parkgate	v	Bedlington Terriers	4-3	155
13	Whitley Bay	v	Tadcaster Albion	4-1	516
14	Padiham	v	Askern Villa	2-5	116
15	Consett	v	Ramsbottom United	4-2	133
16	Barnoldswick Town	v	Spennymoor Town	0-5	334
17	Norton United	v	Ellesmere Rangers	2-1aet	43
18	Stafford Town	v	Brocton	1-2	231
19	Boston Town	v	Gornal Athletic	0-3	86
20	Godmanchester Rovers	v	Bloxwich United	3-2	273
21	Gresley	v	King's Lynn Town	2-0	419
22	Deeping Rangers	v	Cogenhoe United	5-1	65
23	Tipton Town	v	Bardon Hill Sports	5-1	65
24	Oadby Town	v	St Andrews	1-0	158
25	Long Eaton United	v	St Ives Town	0-3	147
26	Boldmere St Michaels	v	Peterborough Northern Star	0-2	53
27	Stewarts & Lloyds Corby	v	Holbrook Sports	0-2	58
28	Racing Club Warwick	v	Wisbech Town	0-1	130
29	Spalding United	v	Tividale	0-3	102
30	Mildenhall Town	v	Sporting Bengal United	0-2	146
31	Felixstowe & Walton United	v	Bethnal Green United	0-7	129
32	Ampthill Town	v	Haringey & Waltham Dev.	3-2	140
33	Long Buckby	v	Dunstable Town	4-2	77
34	Newport Pagnell Town	v	Stansted	5-0	110
35	Leverstock Green	v	Enfield 1893	0-0aet	100
	Enfield 1893	v	Leverstock Green (22/11)	2-2aet	69
	(Enfield 1893 won 5-4 on kicks from the penalty mark)				
36	Tring Athletic	v	Haringey Borough	2-3	95
37	Diss Town	v	Buckingham Town	1-0	117
38	Witham Town	v	Team Bury	3-1	115
39	Royston Town	v	Thetford Town	3-1	266
40	Southend Manor	v	Whitton United	4-2aet	66
41	Blackfield & Langley	v	VCD Athletic	2-3	60
42	Rye United	v	Three Bridges	1-2	105
43	Alton Town	v	Wantage Town	2-2aet	115
	Wantage Town	v	Alton Town (22/11)	4-1	83
44	Reading Town	v	Erith Town	2-1	66
45	Old Woodstock Town	v	Witney Town (18/11)	4-3	137
46	Egham Town	v	Cowes Sports	0-1	72
47	Tunbridge Wells	v	Chichester City	4-1aet	157
48	Pagham	v	Peacehaven & Telscombe	2-4aet	71
49	Hanworth Villa	v	Deal Town	3-1	141
50	Ringmer	v	Binfield	2-2aet	95
	Binfield	v	Ringmer (21/11)	0-0aet	112
	(Binfield won 5-4 on kicks from the penalty mark)				
51	South Park	v	Fawley	3-0	
52	Herne Bay	v	Winchester City	3-1	302
53	Littlehampton Town	v	Flackwell Heath	0-2	188
54	Lancing	v	Guildford City	2-1	152
55	Ilfracombe Town	v	Winterbourne United	1-0	79
56	Bemerton Heath Harlequins	v	Saltash United	3-1	76
57	Bishop Sutton	v	Shortwood United	2-4	56
58	Willand Rovers	v	Highworth Town	1-1aet	107
	Highworth Town	v	Willand Rovers (22/11)	0-1	113
59	Bodmin Town	v	Larkhall Athletic	1-1aet	124
	Larkhall Athletic	v	Bodmin Town (23/11)	2-1	115
60	Bournemouth	v	Torpoint Athletic	4-0	76
61	Cadbury Heath	v	Falmouth Town	1-2aet	120
62	Bitton	v	Cullompton Rangers	3-2	114
63	Christchurch	v	Melksham Town	3-1	90
64	Barnstaple Town	v	Downton	3-2	125

Callum Reed, of Wisbech, volleying in the winning goal in their Second Round Proper tie versus Racing Club Warwick. Photo: Jonathan Holloway.

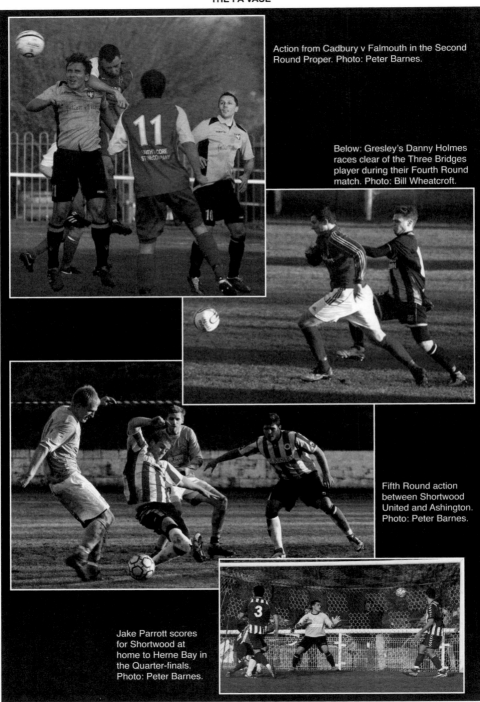

Action from Cadbury v Falmouth in the Second Round Proper. Photo: Peter Barnes.

Below: Gresley's Danny Holmes races clear of the Three Bridges player during their Fourth Round match. Photo: Bill Wheatcroft.

Fifth Round action between Shortwood United and Ashington. Photo: Peter Barnes.

Jake Parrott scores for Shortwood at home to Herne Bay in the Quarter-finals. Photo: Peter Barnes.

THE FA VASE

THIRD ROUND PROPER
SATURDAY 3 DECEMBER 2011 - WINNERS RECEIVE £1,500

1	Tividale	v	Brocton	3-3aet	140
	Brocton	v	Tividale (6/12)	1-2	160
2	Glossop North End	v	Runcorn Town	1-2	322
3	Billingham Synthonia	v	Consett	4-0	104
4	Holbrook Sports	v	Norton United	2-2aet	86
	Norton United	v	Holbrook Sports (6/12)	2-0	81
5	Squires Gate	v	Staveley MW	0-4	70
6	DUNSTON UTS	v	Parkgate	3-1	156
7	Spennymoor Town	v	Ashington	0-2	307
8	Newcastle Benfield	v	Deeping Rangers	3-1	49
9	Askern Villa	v	WEST AUCKLAND TOWN	2-3	142
10	Peterborough Northern Star	v	Armthorpe Welfare	2-0	110
11	Whitley Bay	v	Bridlington Town	5-1	522
12	Gresley	v	Gornal Athletic	4-2	425
13	Oadby Town	v	Tipton Town	1-1aet	168
	Tipton Town	v	Oadby Town (7/12)	1-2	68
14	Hanworth Villa	v	Herne Bay	2-2aet	154
	Herne Bay	v	Hanworth Villa (7/12)	3-1	265
15	Bethnal Green United	v	Sporting Bengal United	5-2	89
16	Newport Pagnell Town	v	Godmanchester Rovers	3-1	177
17	Southend Manor	v	Three Bridges	0-0aet	64
	Three Bridges	v	Southend Manor (6/12)	4-1	66
18	Haringey Borough	v	Royston Town	1-2	100
19	Long Buckby	v	Enfield 1893	1-2	96
20	Binfield	v	Flackwell Heath	3-1	194
21	VCD Athletic	v	Tunbridge Wells	3-3aet	84
	Tunbridge Wells	v	VCD Athletic (6/12)	2-0	139
22	Witham Town	v	Wisbech Town	1-2	132
23	Lancing	v	Ampthill Town	1-3	136
24	South Park	v	Diss Town	2-1	183
25	Peacehaven & Telscombe	v	St Ives Town	1-2	155
26	Willand Rovers	v	Falmouth Town	2-1	160
27	Bemerton Heath Harlequins	v	Shortwood United	0-4	70
28	Bournemouth	v	Barnstaple Town	2-0	90
29	Old Woodstock Town	v	Wantage Town (4/12)	1-0	128
30	Ilfracombe Town	v	Larkhall Athletic	1-1aet	
	Larkhall Athletic	v	Ilfracombe Town (7/12)	1-0	85
31	Bitton	v	Christchurch	3-0	135
32	Reading Town	v	Cowes Sports	1-0	108

FOURTH ROUND PROPER
SATURDAY 21 JANUARY 2012 - WINNERS RECEIVE £2,000

1	Whitley Bay	v	South Park	5-0	761
2	Tunbridge Wells	v	St Ives Town	0-1	404
3	Willand Rovers	v	Staveley MW	1-3	205
4	Shortwood United	v	Enfield 1893	1-0	209
5	Newcastle Benfield	v	Herne Bay	1-2	138
6	Bournemouth	v	Royston Town	2-1	217
7	Old Woodstock Town	v	Bethnal Green United	0-2	70
8	Newport Pagnell Town	v	Ashington	2-3	664
9	Norton United	v	Peterborough Northern Star	1-2	131
10	Wisbech Town	v	DUNSTON UTS	2-2aet	548
	DUNSTON UTS	V	Wisbech Town (28/1)	3-1	381
11	Bitton	v	WEST AUCKLAND TOWN	1-3	246
12	Tividale	v	Binfield	7-1	192
13	Gresley	v	Three Bridges	1-1aet	524
	Three Bridges	v	Gresley (28/1)	2-2aet	308
	(Gresley won 7-6 on kicks from the penalty mark)				
14	Billingham Synthonia	v	Runcorn Town	0-0	184
	Runcorn Town	v	Billingham Synthonia (28/1)	1-2	167
15	Reading Town	v	Larkhall Athletic	2-3	169
16	Oadby Town	v	Ampthill Town	2-1	417

FIFTH ROUND PROPER
SATURDAY 11 FEBRUARY 2012 - WINNERS RECEIVE £2,500

1	Tividale	v	Peterborough N. Star (18/2)	0-2aet	222
2	Shortwood United	v	Ashington (18/2)	3-0	268
3	Staveley MW	v	Oadby Town (15/2)	2-0	340
4	Billingham Synthonia	v	Bournemouth (18/2)	0-0aet	250
	Bournemouth	v	Billingham Synthonia (25/2)	2-1	263
5	DUNSTON UTS	v	Bethnal Green Utd (18/2)	3-0	327
6	Whitley Bay	v	WEST AUCKLAND TOWN (18/2)	1-2	1293
7	St Ives Town	v	Gresley (18/2)	4-0	541
8	Herne Bay	v	Larkhall Athletic (18/2)	1-0	612

SIXTH ROUND PROPER
SATURDAY 3 MARCH 2012 - WINNERS RECEIVE £3,500

1	Shortwood United	v	Herne Bay	1-2	418
2	Staveley MW	v	St Ives Town	3-0	575
3	Peterborough N. Star	v	DUNSTON UTS	3-4 aet	597
4	Bournemouth	v	WEST AUCKLAND TOWN	0-2	414

SEMI FINALS
WINNERS RECEIVE £5,000

1ST LEG – SATURDAY 24 MARCH 2012

| 1 | Herne Bay | v | WEST AUCKLAND TOWN | 2-2 | 1810 |
| 2 | DUNSTON UTS | v | Staveley MW | 1-0 | 975 |

2ND LEG – SATURDAY 31 March 2012

| 1 | WEST AUCKLAND TOWN | v | Herne Bay | 2-1 | 1840 |
| 2 | Staveley MW | v | DUNSTON UTS | 2-2 | 1050 |

The Final...

Further proof that the Northern League has great claims to being the strongest of the Step Five competitions was underlined here with the appearance of two member clubs to contest the final. On top of the previous three finals having been won by fellow Northern Leaguers Whitley Bay, beaten earlier in this year's competition by West Auckland, League chairman Mike Amos has pretty irrefutable evidence now to support the contention. He was there to witness this north eastern derby and in order to stress his neutrality he sported a scarf appropriately half Dunston, half West Auckland colours so he could not lose; neither did the Northern League because both teams showed enterprise, spirit, some skill, determination, sportsmanship and effort to interest and entertain even the uncommitted in the stadium. However the meagre attendance once again raises the question of whether it would not be more practical to play this final at a smaller venue or, my favoured solution, play both Trophy and Vase finals at Wembley, yes, as the unarguably natural Mecca for all footballers, but on the same day.

As another aside, how pleasing it was for we old fashioned mortals to see two teams taking the field numbered from 1 to 11 rather than having to see all manner of digits adorning the shirt rears of the participants. It was an additional bonus that numbers 2 and 3 were also the full backs and number 9 was, in each, case a striker. Already during the season the teams had met three times with one draw and a win each, including an FA Cup extra preliminary qualifying round clash. West Auckland had finished second and Dunston third in the League, so this was anticipated to be a close contest.

Dunston drew first blood, Terry Galbraith's free kick hitting a goalpost, Chris Swailes, he who had originally retired some six years previously after a bad injury when on Oldham's books, netting only to have his celebrations cut short by an offside flag and Andrew Bulford dribbling past three defenders on the right before dragging his shot wide. Slow to start, Auckland retaliated when keeper Liam Connell and Galbraith got in a tangle to let in Michael Rae who unfortunately overran the ball and a defender was able to hoof clear. Captain Mattie Moffatt, wearing a face mask to protect an injury, beat two defenders and got in a low shot which Connell could only stab to safety with his right foot. Next Rae raced through but could not trouble Connell. After a Bulford run had been foiled by John Parker's close attention Dunston took the lead. On yet another sortie Bulford went clear and was able to lob the onrushing Mark Bell, the ball bouncing home to set the Dunston supporters jibing, "You're not singing anymore" at the stunned West Auckland fans. Three times before the break Stuart Banks threatened an equaliser and a Jonny Gibson corner had to be punched away by Connell before half time was reached with Dunston still leading.

Two crosses from Neil Pattinson, an 'offside goal' from Moffat and a good chance over which Mark Hudson hesitated a second too long promised an equaliser early in the second half. A cracking shot against the crossbar from Bulford, a similar bar trembling effort from Goddard and three more close things from Bulford threatened to extend the lead. For a time it was pretty well one way traffic, led by the irrepressible Bulford, so it came as little surprise when, taking advantage of Andrew Green and Parker's hesitancy, Bulford yet again went clear to lob Bell for the second time with ten minutes left on the clock. West Auckland just could not raise their game however beseechingly manager Peter Dixon implored more forward movement but the game ended with Steven Shaw and subs Danny Craggs and Steven Preen interpassing through the Auckland defence before allowing their opponents to thwart a further score.

There could be no argument about whether the victory was deserved as, on the day, Dunston looked decidedly the sharper, particularly up front where Bulford and Goddard always threatened danger. Rae and Moffat in comparison were out of tune and were never able to conjure up much of a test for the Dunston rearguard. Bulford was the outstanding player and was duly, to no one's surprise, declared the man of the match. The victor's manager, Billy Irwin, was particularly pleased with the victory which justified his decision to take the previous week off his work as a self employed decorator. He had felt unable to concentrate on his day job as the Wembley final had taken over his mind. Now perhaps he can relax.

Arthur Evans

DUNSTON UTS (Bulford 32, 79)   2
WEST AUCKLAND TOWN   0

Wembley Stadium   **Attendance: 5,126**

With the game goalless a dramatic save from Dunston UTS 'keeper Liam Connell, moments later his long clearance was flicked on for Andrew Bulford to give his side the lead. Photo: Gordon Whittington.

Right: Dunston's Dixon gets in a good challenge on West Auckland's Nicholls. Photo: Keith Clayton.

Photo: Keith Clayton.

Dunston UTS: Liam Connell, Ben Cattenach, Terry Galbraith, Michael Robson, Chris Swailes, Kane Young, Steven Shaw, Michael Dixon, Stephen Goddard (sub Sreven Preen 84th min), Andrew Bulford (sub Danny Craggs 88th min), Lee McAndrew.
Subs not used – Andrew Clark (g/k), Ian Herron, Jack Burns.

West Auckland Town: Mark Bell, Neil Pattinson, Andrew Green, Jonny Gibson, John Parker, Mark Stephenson (sub Daniel Hindmarsh 76th min), Stuart Banks, Mark Hudson, Mattie Moffatt, Michael Rae, Adam Nicholls (sub Martin Young 60th min).
Subs not used – Daryll Hall, Ross Preston, Matthew Coad.

Referee – Roger East, assisted by Lee Betts and Adrian Holmes. 4th official, Gavin Ward.

Photos (above and right): Peter Barnes.

Dunston's Bulford and Auckland's Green compete for the ball. Photo: Keith Clayton.

Dunston's Stephen Goddard slips the ball away from John Parker (5) of West Auckland. Photo: Alan Coomes.

Michael Rae, West Auckland, and Terry Galbraith in action. Photo: Roger Turner.

Photo: Roger Turner.

PAST FINALS

1975 **HODDESDON TOWN 2** *(South Midlands)*   **EPSOM & EWELL 1** *(Surrey Senior)*   **Att: 9,500**
Sedgwick 2   Wales   Ref: Mr R Toseland
Hoddesdon: Galvin, Green, Hickey, Maybury, Stevenson, Wilson, Bishop, Picking, Sedgwick, Nathan, Schofield
Epsom & Ewell: Page, Bennett, Webb, Wales, Worby, Jones, O'Connell, Walker, Tuite, Eales, Lee

1976 **BILLERICAY TOWN 1** *(Essex Senior)*   **STAMFORD 0 (aet)** *(United Counties)*   **Att: 11,848**
Aslett   Ref: Mr A Robinson
Billericay: Griffiths, Payne, Foreman, Pullin, Bone, Coughlan, Geddes, Aslett, Clayden, Scott, Smith
Stamford: Johnson, Kwiatowski, Marchant, Crawford, Downs, Hird, Barnes, Walpole, Smith, Russell, Broadbent

1977 **BILLERICAY TOWN 1** *(Essex Senior)*   **SHEFFIELD 1 (aet)** *(Yorkshire)*   **Att: 14,000**
Clayden   Coughlan og   Ref: Mr J Worrall
Billericay: Griffiths, Payne, Bone, Coughlan, Pullin, Scott, Wakefield, Aslett, Clayden, Woodhouse, McQueen. Sub: Whettell
Sheffield: Wing, Gilbody, Lodge, Hardisty, Watts, Skelton, Kay, Travis, Pugh, Thornhill, Haynes. Sub: Strutt
Replay BILLERICAY TOWN 2   **SHEFFIELD 1**   **Att: 3,482**
Aslett, Woodhouse   Thornhill   at Nottingham Forest
Billericay: Griffiths, Payne, Pullin, Whettell, Bone, McQueen, Woodhouse, Aslett, Clayden, Scott, Wakefield
Sheffield: Wing, Gilbody, Lodge, Strutt, Watts, Skelton, Kay, Travis, Pugh, Thornhill, Haynes

1978 **NEWCASTLE BLUE STAR 2** *(Wearside)*   **BARTON ROVERS 1** *(South Midlands)*   **Att: 16,858**
Dunn, Crumplin   Smith   Ref: Mr T Morris
Newcastle: Halbert, Feenan, Thompson, Davidson, S Dixon, Beynon, Storey, P Dixon, Crumplin, Callaghan, Dunn. Sub: Diamond
Barton Rovers: Blackwell, Stephens, Crossley, Evans, Harris, Dollimore, Dunn, Harnaman, Fossey, Turner, Smith. Sub: Cox

1979 **BILLERICAY TOWN 4** *(Athenian)*   **ALMONDSBURY GREENWAY 1** *(Glos. Co)*   **Att: 17,500**
Young 3, Clayden   Price   Ref: Mr C Steel
Billericay: Norris, Blackaller, Bingham, Whettell, Bone, Reeves, Pullin, Scott, Clayden, Young, Groom. Sub: Carrigan
Almondsbury: Hamilton, Bowers, Scarrett, Sulllivan, Tudor, Wookey, Bowers, Shehean, Kerr, Butt, Price. Sub: Kilbaine

1980 **STAMFORD 2** *(United Counties)*   **GUISBOROUGH TOWN 0** *(Northern Alliance)*   **Att: 11,500**
Alexander, McGowan   Ref: Neil Midgeley
Stamford: Johnson, Kwiatkowski, Ladd, McGowan, Bliszczak I, Mackin, Broadhurst, Hall, Czarnecki, Potter, Alexander. Sub: Bliszczak S
Guisborough: Cutter, Scott, Thornton, Angus, Maltby, Percy, Skelton, Coleman, McElvaney, Sills, Dilworth. Sub: Harrison

1981 **WHICKHAM 3** *(Wearside)*   **WILLENHALL 2 (aet)** *(West Midlands)*   **Att: 12,000**
Scott, Williamson, Peck og   Smith, Stringer   Ref: Mr R Lewis
Whickham: Thompson, Scott, Knox, Williamson, Cook, Ward, Carroll, Diamond, Cawthra, Robertson, Turnbull. Sub: Alton
Willenhall: Newton, White, Darris, Woodall, Heath, Fox, Peck, Price, Matthews, Smith, Stringer. Sub: Trevor

1982 **FOREST GREEN ROVERS 3** *(Hellenic)*   **RAINWORTH M.W 0** *(Notts Alliance)*   **Att: 12,500**
Leitch 2, Norman   Ref: Mr K Walmsey
Forest Green: Moss, Norman, Day, Turner, Higgins, Jenkins, Guest, Burns, Millard, Leitch, Doughty. Sub: Dangerfield
Rainworth M.W: Watson, Hallam, Hodgson, Slater, Sterland, Oliver, Knowles, Raine, Radzi, Reah, Comerford. Sub: Robinson

1983 **V.S. RUGBY 1** *(West Midlands)*   **HALESOWEN TOWN 0** *(West Midlands)*   **Att: 13,700**
Crawley   Ref: Mr B Daniels
VS Rugby: Burton, McGinty, Harrison, Preston, Knox, Evans, ingram, Setchell, Owen, Beecham, Crawley. Sub: Haskins
Halesowen Town: Coldicott, Penn, Edmonds, Lacey, Randall, Shilvock, Hazelwood, Moss, Woodhouse, P Joinson, L Joinson. Sub: Smith

1984 **STANSTED 3** *(Essex Senior)*   **STAMFORD 2** *(United Counties)*   **Att: 8,125**
Holt, Gillard, Reading   Waddicore, Allen   Ref: Mr T Bune
Stanstead: Coe, Williams, Hilton, Simpson, Cooper, Reading, Callanan, Holt, Reevs, Doyle, Gillard. Sub: Williams
Stamford: Parslow, Smitheringate, Blades, McIlwain, Lyon, Mackin, Genovese, Waddicore, Allen, Robson, Beech. Sub: Chapman

1985 **HALESOWEN TOWN 3** *(West Midlands)*   **FLEETWOOD TOWN 1** *(N W Counties)*   **Att: 16,715**
L Joinson 2, Moss   Moran   Ref: Mr C Downey
Halesowen: Coldicott, Penn, Sherwood, Warner, Randle, Heath, Hazlewood, Moss (Smith), Woodhouse, P Joinson, L Joinson
Fleetwood Town: Dobson, Moran, Hadgraft, Strachan, Robinson, Milligan, Hall, Trainor, Taylor (Whitehouse), Cain, Kennerley

1986 **HALESOWEN TOWN 3** *(West Midlands)*   **SOUTHALL 0** *(Isthmian 2 South)*   **Att: 18,340**
Moss 2, L Joinson   Ref: Mr D Scott
Halesowen: Pemberton, Moore, Lacey, Randle (Rhodes), Sherwood, Heath, Penn, Woodhouse, P Joinson, L Joinson, Moss
Southall: Mackenzie, James, McGovern, Croad, Holland, Powell (Richmond), Pierre, Richardson, Sweales, Ferdinand, Rowe

THE FA VASE

1987 ST. HELENS 3 *(N W Counties)* WARRINGTON TOWN 2 *(N W Counties)*   Att: 4,254
Layhe 2, Rigby   Reid, Cook   Ref: Mr T Mills
St Helens: Johnson, Benson, Lowe, Bendon, Wilson, McComb, Collins (Gledhill), O'Neill, Cummins, Lay, Rigby. Sub: Deakin
Warrington: O'Brien. Copeland, Hunter, Gratton, Whalley, Reid, Brownville (Woodyer), Cook, Kinsey, Looker (Hill), Hughes

1988 COLNE DYNAMOES 1 *(N W Counties)* EMLEY 0 *(Northern Counties East)*   Att: 15,000
Anderson   Ref: Mr A Seville
Colne Dynamoes: Mason, McFafyen, Westwell, Bentley, Dunn, Roscoe, Rodaway, Whitehead (Burke), Diamond, Anderson, Wood (Coates)
Emley: Dennis, Fielding, Mellor, Codd, Hirst (Burrows), Gartland (Cook), Carmody, Green, Bramald, Devine, Francis

1989 TAMWORTH 1 *(West Midlands)*   SUDBURY TOWN 1 (aet) *(Eastern)*   Att: 26,487
Devaney   Hubbick   Ref: Mr C Downey
Tamworth: Bedford, Lockett, Atkins, Cartwright, McCormack, Myers, Finn, Devaney, Moores, Gordon, Stanton. Subs: Rathbone, Heaton
Sudbury Town: Garnham, Henry, G Barker, Boyland, Thorpe, Klug, D Barker, Barton, Oldfield, Smith, Hubbick. Subs: Money, Hunt
Replay TAMWORTH 3   SUDBURY TOWN 0   Att: 11,201
Stanton 2, Moores   at Peterborough
Tamworth: Bedford, Lockett, Atkins, Cartwright, Finn, Myers, George, Devaney, Moores, Gordon, Stanton. Sub: Heaton
Sudbury Town: Garnham, Henry, G Barker, Boyland, Thorpe, Klug, D Barker, Barton, Oldfield, Smith, Hubbick. Subs: Money, Hunt

1990 YEADING 0 *(Isthmian 2 South)*   BRIDLINGTON TOWN 0 (aet) *(N Co East)*   Att: 7,932
                                                                                   Ref: Mr R Groves
Yeading: Mackenzie, Wickens, Turner, Whiskey (McCarthy), Croad, Denton, Matthews, James(Charles), Sweates, Impey, Cordery
Bridlington: Taylor, Pugh, Freeman, McNeill, Warburton, Brentano, Wilkes (Hall), Noteman, Gauden, Whiteman, Brattan (Brown)

Replay YEADING 1   BRIDLINGTON TOWN 0   Att: 5,000
Sweales   at Leeds Utd FC
Yeading: Mackenzie, Wickens, Turner, Whiskey, Croad (McCarthy), Schwartz, Matthews, James, Sweates, Impey (Welsh), Cordery
Bridlington: Taylor, Pugh, Freeman, McNeill, Warburton, Brentano, Wilkes (Brown), Noteman, Gauden (Downing), Whiteman, Brattan

1991 GRESLEY ROVERS 4 *(West Midlands)*   GUISELEY 4 (aet) *(Northern Co East)*   Att: 11,314
Rathbone, Smith 2, Stokes   Tennison 2, Walling, A Roberts   Ref: Mr C Trussell
Gresley: Aston, Barry, Elliott (Adcock), Denby, Land, Astley, Stokes, K Smith, Acklam, Rathbone, Lovell (Weston)
Guiseley: Maxted, Bottomley, Hogarth, Tetley, Morgan, McKenzie, Atkinson (Annan), Tennison, Walling, A Roberts, B Roberts

Replay GUISELEY 3   GRESLEY ROVERS 1   Att: 7,585
Tennison, Walling, Atkinson   Astley   at Bramall Lane
Guiseley: Maxted, Annan, Hogarth, Tetley, Morgan, McKenzie (Bottomley), Atkinson, Tennison (Noteman), Walling, A Roberts, B Roberts
Gresley: Aston, Barry, Elliott, Denby, Land, Astley, Stokes (Weston), K Smith, Acklam, Rathbone, Lovell (Adcock)

1992 WIMBORNE TOWN 5 *(Wessex)*   GUISELEY 3 *(Northern Premier Div 1)*   Att: 10,772
Richardson, Sturgess 2, Killick 2   Noteman 2, Colville   Ref: Mr M J Bodenham
Wimborne: Leonard, Langdown, Wilkins, Beacham, Allan, Taplin, Ames, Richardson, Bridle, Killick, Sturgess (Lovell), Lynn
Guiseley: Maxted, Atkinson, Hogarth, Tetley (Wilson), Morgan, Brockie, A Roberts, Tennison, Noteman (Colville), Annan, W Roberts

1993 BRIDLINGTON TOWN 1 *(NPL Div 1)*   TIVERTON TOWN 0 *(Western)*   Att: 9,061
Radford   Ref: Mr R A Hart
Bridlington: Taylor, Brentano, McKenzie, Harvey, Bottomley, Woodcock, Grocock, A Roberts, Jones, Radford (Tyrell), Parkinson. Sub: Swailes
Tiverton Town: Nott, J Smith, N Saunders, M Saunders, Short (Scott), Steele, Annunziata, K Smith, Everett, Daly, Hynds (Rogers)

1994 DISS TOWN 2 *(Eastern)*   TAUNTON TOWN 1 *(Western)*   Att: 13,450
Gibbs (p), Mendham   Fowler   Ref: Mr K. Morton
Diss Town: Woodcock, Carter, Wolsey (Musgrave), Casey (Bugg), Hartle, Smith, Barth, Mendham, Miles, Warne, Gibbs
Taunton Town: Maloy, Morris, Walsh, Ewens, Graddon, Palfrey, West (Hendry), Fowler, Durham, Perrett (Ward), Jarvis

1995 ARLESEY TOWN 2 *(South Midlands)*   OXFORD CITY 1 *(Ryman 2)*   Att: 13,670
Palma, Gyalog   S Fontaine   Ref: Mr G S Willard
Arlesey: Young, Cardines, Bambrick, Palma (Ward), Hull, Gonsalves, Gyalog, Cox, Kane, O'Keefe, Marshall (Nicholls). Sub: Dodwell
Oxford: Fleet, Brown (Fisher), Hume, Shepherd, Muttock, Hamilton (Kemp), Thomas, Spittle, Sherwood, S Fontaine, C Fontaine. Sub: Torres

1996 BRIGG TOWN 3 *(N Co East)*   CLITHEROE 0 *(N W Counties)*   Att: 7,340
Stead 2, Roach   Ref: Mr S J Lodge
Brigg: Gawthorpe, Thompson, Rogers, Greaves (Clay), Buckley (Mail), Elston, C Stead, McLean, N Stead (McNally), Flounders, Roach
Clitheroe: Nash, Lampkin, Rowbotham (Otley), Baron, Westwell, Rovine, Butcher, Taylor (Smith), Grimshaw, Darbyshire, Hill (Dunn)

1997 WHITBY TOWN 3 *(Northern)*   NORTH FERRIBY UTD. 0 *(N Co East)*   Att: 11,098
Williams, Logan, Toman   Ref: Graham Poll
North Ferriby: Sharp, Deacey, Smith, Brentano, Walmsley, M Smith, Harrison (Horne), Phillips (Milner), France (Newman), Flounders, Tennison
Whitby Town: Campbell, Williams, Logan, Goodchild, Pearson, Cook, Goodrick (Borthwick), Hodgson, Robinson, Toman (Pyle), Pitman (Hall)

1998   TIVERTON TOWN 1 *(Western)*   **TOW LAW TOWN 0** *(Northern Division 1)*   **Att: 13,139**
Varley   **Ref: M A Riley**

Tiverton: Edwards, Felton, Saunders, Tatterton, Smith J, Conning, Nancekivell (Rogers), Smith K (Varley), Everett, Daly, Leonard (Waters)
Tow Law: Dawson, Pickering, Darwent, Bailey, Hague, Moan, Johnson, Nelson, Suddick, Laidler (Bennett), Robinson.

1999   TIVERTON TOWN 1 *(Western)*   **BEDLINGTON TERRIERS 0** *(Northern)*   **Att: 13, 878**
Rogers 88   **Ref: W. C. Burns**

Bedlington Terriers: O'Connor, Bowes, Pike, Boon (Renforth), Melrose, Teasdale, Cross, Middleton (Ludlow), Gibb, Milner, Bond. Subs:
Pearson, Cameron, Gowans
Tiverton Town: Edwards, Fallon, Saunders, Tatterton, Tallon, Conning (Rogers), Nancekivell (Pears), Varley, Everett, Daly, Leonard. Subs:
Tucker, Hynds, Grimshaw

2000   DEAL TOWN 1 *(Kent)*   **CHIPPENHAM TOWN 0** *(Western)*   **Att: 20,000**
Graham 87   **Ref: E. K. Wolstenholme**

Deal Town: Tucker, Kempster, Best, Ash, Martin, Seager, Monteith, Graham, Lovell, Marshall, Ribbens. Subs: Roberts, Warden, Turner
Chippenham Town: Jones, James, Andrews, Murphy, Burns, Woods, Brown, Charity, Tweddle, Collier, Godley. Subs: Tiley, Cutler

2001   TAUNTON TOWN 2 *(Western)*   **BERKHAMPSTED TOWN 1** *(Isthmian 2)*   **(at Villa Park) Att: 8,439**
Fields 41, Laight 45   Lowe 71   **Ref: E. K. Wolstenholme**

Taunton Town: Draper, Down, Chapman, West, Hawkings, Kelly, Fields (Groves), Laight, Cann (Tallon), Bastow, Lynch (Hapgood).
Subs: Ayres, Parker
Berkhampsted Town: O'Connor, Mullins, Lowe, Aldridge, Coleman, Brockett, Yates, Adebowale, Richardson, Smith, Nightingale.
Subs: Ringsell, Hall, Knight, Franklin, Osborne

2002   WHITLEY BAY 1 *(Northern)*   **TIPTREE UNITED 0** *(Eastern)*   **(at Villa Park) Att: 4742**
Chandler 97   **Ref: A Kaye**

Whitley Bay: Caffrey, Sunderland, Walmsley, Dixon (Neil), Anderson, Locker, Middleton, Bowes (Carr), Chandler, Walton, Fenwick (Cuggy).
Subs: Cook, Livermore
Tiptree United: Haygreen, Battell, Wall, Houghton, Fish, Streetley (Gillespie), Wareham (Snow), Daly, Barefield, Aransibia (Parnell), Brady.
Subs: Powell, Ford.

2003   A.F.C SUDBURY 1 *(Eastern Counties)*   **BRIGG TOWN 2** *(Northern Co.East)*   **(at Upton Park) Att: 6,634**
Raynor 30   Housham 2, Carter 68   **Ref: M Fletcher**

AFC Sudbury:- Greygoose, Head (Norfolk 63), Spearing, Tracey, Bishop, Anderson (Owen 73), Rayner,
Gardiner (Banya 79), Bennett, Claydon, Betson. Subs (not used) Taylor, Hyde.
Brigg Town:- Steer, Raspin, Rowland, Thompson, Blanchard, Stones, Stead (Thompson 41), Housham, Borman (Drayton
87), Roach, Carter. Subs (not used) Nevis, Gawthorpe.

2004   A.F.C SUDBURY 0 *(Eastern Counties)*   **WINCHESTER CITY 2** *(Wessex)*   **(at St Andrews) Att: 5,080**
                                              Forbes 19, Smith 73 (pen)   **Ref: P Crossley**

AFC Sudbury:- Greygoose, Head, Wardley, Girling, Tracey, Norfolk, Owen (Banya 62), Hyde (Calver 57), Bennett, Claydon,
Betson (Francis 73n). Subs (not used) - Rayner, Nower.
Winchester City:- Arthur, Dyke (Tate 83), Bicknell, Redwood, Goss, Blake, Webber, Green, Mancey, Forbes (Rogers 70),
Smith (Green 90). Subs (not used) - Lang and Rastall.

2005   A.F.C SUDBURY 2 *(Eastern Counties)*   **DIDCOT TOWN 3** *(Hellenic)*   **(at White Hart Lane) Att: 8,662**
Wardley, Calver (pen)   Beavon (2), Wardley (og)   **Ref: R Beeeby**

AFC Sudbury:- Greygoose, Girling, Wardley, Bennett, Hyde (Hayes 78), Owen (Norfolk 65), Claydon (Banya 59), Head, Calver, Betson,
Terry Rayner. Subs (not used) – Howlett, Nower.
Didcot Town:- Webb, Goodall, Heapy, Campbell, Green, Parrott, Hannigan, Ward, Concannon (Jones 88), Beavon (Bianchini 90), Powell.
Subs (not used) – Cooper, Allen, Spurrett.

2006   HILLINGDON BOROUGH 1 *(Spartan S.Mids P.)*   **NANTWICH TOWN 3** *(NWC 1)*   **(at St Andrews) Att: 3,286**
Nelson   Kinsey (2), Scheuber

Hillingdon Borough:- Brown, Rundell (Fenton 80),Kidson, Phillips, Croft, Lawrence, Duncan (Nelson 46), Tilbury, Hibbs,
Wharton (Lyons 38). Subs (not used): O'Grady, White.
Nantwich Town:- Hackney, A.Taylor, T.Taylor, Smith, Davis, Donnelly, Beasley, Scheuber (Parkinson 69), Kinsey (Marrow 69),
Blake (Scarlett 86) and Griggs. Subs (not used): O'Connor and Read.

2007   AFC TOTTON 1 *(Wessex Division 1)*   **TRURO 3** *(Western Division 1)*   **Att: 27,754 (New Vase record)**
Potter   Wills (2), Broad   **Ref: P Joslin**

AFC Totton: Brunnschweiler, Reacord, Troon (Stevens 60), Potter (Gregory 82), Bottomley, Austen, Roden, Gosney, Hamodu (Goss 89), Osman, Byres.
Subs not used: Zammit, McCormack.
Truro City: Stevenson, Ash, Power, Smith, Martin (Pope 84), Broad, Wills, Gosling, Yetton, Watkins, Walker (Ludlam 90).
Subs not used: Butcher, Routledge, Reski.

THE FA VASE

2008 **KIRKHAM & WESHAM 2** *(North West Co. Div.2)* **LOWESTOFT TOWN 1** *(Eastern Co. Premier)* **Att: 19,537**
  Walwyn (2) Thompson (og) **Ref: A D'Urso**

Kirkham and Wesham: Summerfield, Jackson (Walwyn 79), Keefe (Allen 55), Thompson, Shaw, Eastwood, Clark, Blackwell, Wane,
Paterson (Sheppard 90), Smith. Subs not used: Moffat and Abbott
Lowestoft Town: Reynolds, Poppy, Potter, Woodrow, Saunders, Plaskett (McGee 79), Godbold, Darren Cockrill (Dale Cockrill 46), Stock, Hough,
King (Hunn 55). Subs not used: McKenna and Rix.

2009 **GLOSSOP NORTH END 0** *(North West Co. Prem)* **WHITLEY BAY 2** *(Northern Division One)* **Att: 12,212**
  Kerr, Chow **Ref: K Friend**

Glossop North End: Cooper, Young, Kay, Lugsden, Yates, Gorton, Bailey (Hind 57), Morris, Allen (Balfe 65), Hamilton (Bailey 72), Hodges.
Subs not used: Whelan and Parker.
Whitley Bay: Burke, Taylor, Picton, McFarlane (Fawcett 60), Coulson, Ryan, Moore, Robson, Kerr, Chow (Robinson 73), Johnston (Bell 60).
Subs not used: McLean and Reay.

2010 **WHITLEY BAY 6** *(Northern Division One)* **WROXHAM 1** *(Eastern Counties Premier Division)* **Att: 8,920**
  Chow 21(sec), Easthaugh 16 (og), Kerr, Johnston, Cook 12 **Ref: A Taylor**
  Robinson, Gillies

Whitley Bay: Terry Burke, Craig McFarlane, Callum Anderson, Richard Hodgson, (sub Lee Picton 69th min), Darren Timmons, Leon Ryan,
Adam Johnston (sub Joshua Gillies 77th min), Damon Robson, Lee Kerr, Paul Chow (sub Phillip Bell 61st min), Paul Robinson.
Subs not used – Tom Kindley and Chris Reid.
Wroxham: Scott Howie, Gavin Pauling (sub Ross Durrant 57th min), Shaun Howes, Graham Challen, Martin McNeil (sub Josh Carus 46th min), Andy
Easthaugh (sub Owen Paynter 69th min), Steve Spriggs, Gavin Lemmon, Paul Cook, Danny White, Gary Gilmore.
Subs not used – Danny Self and Gareth Simpson.

2011 **COALVILLE TOWN 2** *(Midland Alliance)* **WHITLEY BAY 3** *(Northern Division One)* **Att: 8,778**
  Moore 58, Goodby 80 Chow 28, 90, Kerr 61 **Ref: S Mathieson**

Coalville Town: Sean Bowles, Ashley Brown (sub Matthew Gardner 88th min), Cameron Stuart, Adam Goodby, Zach Costello, Lee Miveld,
Callum Woodward, Anthony Carney (sub Craig Attwood 90th min), Ryan Robbins (sub Ashley Wells 66th min), Matt Moore, Jerome Murdock.
Subs not used – Richard Williams (gk) and James Dodd.
Whitley Bay: Terry Burke, Craig McFarlane (sub Steve Gibson 90th min), Callum Anderson, Darren Timmons, Gareth Williams (sub David Coulson 68th
min), Damon Robson, Lee Kerr, Paul Chow, Paul Robinson, David Pounder (sub Brian Smith 68th min), Gary Ormston.
Subs not used – Kyle Hayes (gk) and Brian Rowe.

All Finals at Wembley unless otherwise stated.

West Auckland goalkeeper, Mark Bell, and defender are unable to stop Byron Walker scoring Herne Bay's opener
in the first leg of their Semi-Final. Photo: Roger Turner.

PRELIMINARY ROUND

1	Ashington	v	York City		
	(walkover for York City – Ashington withdrawn)				
2	Prudhoe Town	v	Chester-Le-Street Town		
	(walkover for Chester-Le-Street Town – Prudhoe Town withdrawn)				
3	Pickering Town	v	Ryton & Crowcrook Albion (5/9)	6-0	38
4	Congleton Town	v	Stalybridge Celtic (7/9)	2-3aet	69
5	Nantwich Town	v	Altrincham (7/9)	1-5	98
6	Wrexham	v	Stockport County (5/9)	1-4	153
7	Prescot Cables	v	Curzon Ashton (5/9)	3-1	135
8	Woodley Sports	v	AFC Blackpool (8/9)	4-1	45
9	Ashton Athletic	v	Ashton Town (8/9)	5-1	113
10	Salford City	v	Daisy Hill (8/9)	0-2	35
11	Ossett Albion	v	Grimsby Town (8/9)	0-1	62
12	Silsden	v	Pontefract Collieries (5/9)	3-4aet	68
13	New Mills	v	Long Eaton United (6/9)	3-3aet	62
	(New Mills won 5-3 on kicks from the penalty mark)				
14	Boston United	v	Lincoln United (7/9)	3-0	133
15	Bardon Hill Sports	v	Calverton MW (8/9)	2-5	87
16	Glossop North End	v	Blaby & Whetstone Athletic (4/9)	2-4	78
17	Holwell Sports	v	St Andrews (7/9)	2-5	49
18	Arnold Town	v	Carlton Town (5/9)	4-2	47
19	Pegasus Juniors	v	Leek Town (7/9)	7-0	25
20	Coventry Copsewood	v	Walsall Wood (8/9)	2-1	53
21	Chasetown	v	Newcastle Town (7/9)	3-1	85
22	Romulus	v	Rugby Town (9/9)	3-1	67
23	Stourport Swifts	v	Gornal Athletic (7/9)	4-2	
24	Wolverhampton SC	v	Kidsgrove Athletic (8/9)	2-4	15
25	Wolverhampton Casuals	v	Boldmere St Michaels (7/9)	1-0	45
26	Eccleshall	v	Nuneaton Griff		
	(walkover for Nuneaton Griff – Eccleshall withdrawn)				
27	Stone Dominoes	v	Atherstone Town (5/9)	1-0	
28	Malvern Town	v	Coventry Sphinx (6/9)	1-3	45
29	Ellesmere Rangers	v	Nuneaton Town (8/9)	0-3	70
30	Redditch United	v	AFC Telford United (7/9)	0-1	45
31	Bury Town	v	Cornard United (5/9)	5-0	61
32	Kirkley & Pakefield	v	Diss Town (8/9)	9-1	98
33	Brantham Athletic	v	Fakenham Town (7/9)	3-2	46
	(at Fakenham Town FC)				
34	Great Yarmouth Town	v	Swaffham Town (7/9)	2-2aet	50
	(Great Yarmouth Town won 4-3 on kicks from the Penalty Mark)				
35	Leiston	v	Hadleigh United (8/9)	0-1	47
36	Yaxley	v	Dunstable Town		
	(walkover for Yaxley – Dunstable Town withdrawn)				
37	Barton Rovers	v	St Ives Town (9/9)	1-2	65
38	Daventry Town	v	Leighton Town (8/9)	0-1	28
39	Corby Town	v	AFC Kempston Rovers (5/9)	4-0	95
40	Basildon United	v	Ware (6/9)	3-2	53
41	East Thurrock United	v	Barking (5/9)	4-1	87
42	Hullbridge Sports	v	Maldon & Tiptree (8/9)	0-1	32
43	Grays Athletic	v	Thurrock (8/9)	0-3	107
44	Brentwood Town	v	Ilford (8/9)	2-2aet	73
	(Brentwood Town won 3-1 on kicks from the Penalty Mark)				
45	Leverstock Green	v	Stansted (8/9)	1-3	62
46	Romford	v	Cheshunt (7/9)	2-0	90
47	Redbridge	v	Canvey Island (5/9)	8-0	52
48	Hitchin Town	v	FC Clacton (5/9)	0-3	51
49	Boreham Wood	v	Hoddesdon Town (6/9)	8-0	52
50	Hertford Town	v	Witham Town (7/9)	1-3aet	45
51	Halstead Town	v	Tilbury (7/9)	1-7	47
52	Stanway Rovers	v	Sawbridgeworth Town (7/9)	2-0	75
53	Oxhey Jets	v	Hemel Hempstead Town (7/9)	2-4	50
54	Royston Town	v	Bowers & Pitsea (8/9)	4-1	86
55	Bishop's Stortford	v	Berkhamsted (7/9)	5-1	79
56	Enfield Town	v	North Greenford United (8/9)	6-1	
	(at Cheshunt FC)				
57	Uxbridge	v	Kentish Town (7/9)	3-0	61
58	Ashford Town (Middx)	v	Cockfosters (5/9)	2-1aet	73
59	Staines Town	v	Harrow Borough (5/9)	3-2aet	68
60	Whitstable Town	v	Erith & Belvedere (8/9)	3-1	
61	Kingstonian	v	Eastbourne Borough (5/9)	2-0	49
	(at Banstead Athletic FC)				
62	Chipstead	v	Carshalton Athletic (7/9)	3-1	52
63	South Park	v	Horley Town (8/9)	5-1	
64	Eastbourne Town	v	Faversham Town (5/9)	3-1	52
65	Corinthian	v	Dover Athletic (5/9)	4-2	51
66	Ramsgate	v	Ringmer		
	(walkover for Ramsgate – Ringmer withdrawn)				
67	Crowborough Athletic	v	VCD Athletic (8/9)	3-5	56
68	Redhill	v	Welling United (7/9)	0-1	60
69	Chatham Town	v	Tunbridge Wells		
	(walkover for Tunbridge Wells – Chatham Town withdrawn)				
70	Sevenoaks Town	v	Metropolitan Police (6/9)	4-0	46
71	Colliers Wood United	v	Erith Town (8/9)	1-4	48
72	St Francis Rangers	v	Margate (8/9)	3-0	
73	Sutton United	v	Dulwich Hamlet (7/9)	2-3	68
74	Lewes	v	Saltdean United (5/9)	10-0	89
75	Westfield	v	Mile Oak (5/9)	6-0	32
76	Hastings United	v	Tonbridge Angels (8/9)	3-2	87
77	Cray Wanderers	v	Dartford (7/9)	0-3	122
	(at Dartford FC)				
78	Chessington & Hook Utd	v	Whyteleafe (7/9)	0-3	54
79	Woking	v	Dorking (6/9)	4-0	56
80	Horsham	v	Epsom & Ewell (8/9)	1-2	45
	(at Three Bridges FC)				
81	Chichester City	v	Camberley Town (5/9)	0-6	60
82	Chalfont St Peter	v	Binfield	0-8	26
	(at Binfield FC)				
83	Kidlington	v	Banbury United	5-1	47
84	Farnborough	v	AFC Wallingford (5/9)	15-0	60
85	Newport Pagnell Town	v	Ascot United (8/9)	4-0	34
86	Thame United	v	Oxford City	0-2	91
87	Aylesbury	v	Basingstoke Town (8/9)	0-1	58
88	Sandhurst Town	v	Fleet Town (5/9)	3-1	43
89	Witney Town	v	Buckingham Town		
	(walkover for Witney Town – Buckingham Town withdrawn)				
90	Alton Town	v	Marlow (7/9)	5-0	42
91	Burnham	v	Bicester Town		
	(walkover for Burnham – Bicester Town removed)				
92	AFC Porchester	v	Dorchester Town (8/9)	0-3	82
93	Pewsey Vale	v	Salisbury City (12/9)	0-5	74
94	Havant & Waterlooville	v	Petersfield Town (5/9)	4-0	112
95	Yate Town	v	Chard Town (7/9)	2-2aet	40
	(Chard Town won 12-11 on kicks from the Penalty Mark)				
96	Brislington	v	Bishop's Cleeve (7/9)	2-5	39
97	Forest Green Rovers	v	Bath City (8/9)	0-2	110
98	Tiverton Town	v	Paulton Rovers (8/9)	4-1	48
99	Bishop Sutton	v	Newport County (8/9)	0-3	74
100	Almondsbury UWE	v	Mangotsfield United (5/9)	2-3	
101	Gloucester City	v	Merthyr Town (6/9)	3-4	20
	(at Tuffley Rovers FC)				
102	Elmore	v	Weston Super Mare (8/9)	3-5aet	90
103	Wells City	v	Taunton Town	3-0	82

FIRST ROUND QUALIFYING

1	Chester-Le-Street Town	v	Sunderland RCA		
	(walkover for Chester-Le-Street Town – Sunderland RCA withdrawn)				
2	York City	v	Newton Aycliffe (21/9)	5-0	138
3	Pickering Town	v	Scarborough Athletic		
	(walkover for Pickering Town – Scarborough Athletic withdrawn)				
4	Gateshead	v	Darlington (19/9)	0-3	283
5	AFC Fylde	v	Fleetwood Town (19/9)	0-4	68
6	Vauxhall Motors	v	Lancaster City (22/9)	0-1	77
7	Bootle	v	Prescot Cables (21/9)	2-4	81
8	Ashton Athletic	v	Warrington Town (22/9)	2-1aet	60
9	Runcorn Linnets	v	Altrincham (22/9)	5-7	101
10	Northwich Victoria	v	Formby (21/9)	5-0	58
11	Mossley	v	Stalybridge Celtic (20/9)	5-1	25
12	Burscough	v	Marine (21/9)	1-6	37
13	Stockport County	v	Southport (25/9)	12-1	93
	(at Trafford FC)				
14	Woodley Sports	v	Daisy Hill (22/9)	2-0	26
15	Yorkshire Amateur	v	Liversedge (19/9)	5-0	
16	Sheffield	v	FC Halifax Town (21/9)	3-1	65
17	Dinnington Town	v	North Ferriby United (22/9)	0-5	67
18	Grimsby Town	v	Pontefract Collieries (22/9)	4-0	
19	Worksop Town	v	Brighouse Town (22/9)	2-3	66
	(at Shirebrook Town FC)				
20	Staveley MW	v	Hallam (19/9)	4-0	
21	Bottesford Town	v	Stocksbridge Park Steels (21/9)	2-0	45
22	Harrogate Railway Athletic	v	Thackley (21/9)	3-2	48
23	Kirby Muxloe	v	Loughborough Dynamo (21/9)	0-1	30
24	Pinxton	v	Lutterworth Athletic (21/9)	0-0aet	85
	(Pinxton won 3-2 on kicks from the penalty mark)				
25	Deeping Rangers	v	Blaby & Whetstone A. (21/9)	4-1	28
26	Arnold Town	v	Hinckley United (19/9)	1-1aet	58
	(Arnold Town won 5-4 on kicks from the penalty mark)				
27	Mickleover Sports	v	Boston United (22/9)	0-5	57
28	Matlock Town	v	Spalding United (20/9)	5-0	41
29	Teversal	v	New Mills (20/9)	2-0	59
30	Lincoln City	v	Retford United (15/9)	8-0	100
31	Calverton MW	v	Oadby Town (22/9)	2-2aet	
	(Calverton MW won 5-4 on kicks from the penalty mark)				
32	St Andrews	v	Gresley (21/9)	0-1	41
33	AFC Telford United	v	Halesowen Town (19/9)	0-1	53
34	Kidsgrove Ath	v	Racing Club Warwick (22/9)	0-4	71
35	Kidderminster Harriers	v	Nuneaton Griff (21/9)	5-0	45
36	Romulus	v	Bromyard Town (19/9)	1-2	45
37	Hednesford Town	v	Wolverhampton Casuals (21/9)	4-0	63
38	Solihull Moors	v	Highgate United (21/9)	1-3	82
39	Stourbridge	v	Stratford Town (19/9)	0-2	101
40	Coventry Copsewood	v	Tamworth (19/9)	1-2	48
41	Stone Dominoes	v	Bedworth United		
	(walkover for Stone Dominoes – Bedworth United withdrawn)				
42	Stourport Swifts	v	Coventry Sphinx (19/9)	1-0	37
43	Lye Town	v	Pegasus Juniors (19/9)	2-1	72
44	Nuneaton Town	v	Chasetown (22/9)	1-0	
45	Thetford Town	v	Felixstowe & Walton Utd (19/9)	2-1	40
46	Gorleston	v	Ipswich Wanderers (21/9)	2-1aet	41
47	Needham Market	v	Great Yarmouth Town (21/9)	2-0	76
48	Cambridge United	v	Norwich United (21/9)	9-1	50
49	Dereham Town	v	Kirkley & Pakefield (21/9)	5-0	48
50	Soham Town Rangers	v	Stowmarket Town (21/9)	2-1	54
51	Woodbridge Town	v	Bury Town (22/9)	1-0	45
52	Newmarket Town	v	Walsham Le Willows (22/9)	0-1	
53	Brantham Athletic	v	Lowestoft Town (21/9)	2-1aet	78
54	Hadleigh United	v	Histon (21/9)	2-2aet	60
	(Hadleigh won 4-3 on kicks from the penalty mark)				
55	Woodford United	v	Rushden & Higham United (21/9)	2-0aet	42
56	Luton Town	v	Rothwell Corinthians (21/9)	11-1	121
57	Corby Town	v	St Ives Town (19/9)	3-0	69
58	St Neots Town	v	Yaxley (22/9)	3-1	66
59	Cogenhoe United	v	Kettering Town (22/9)	2-3	33
60	Stotfold	v	Biggleswade Town		
	(walkover for Stotfold – Biggleswade Town withdrawn)				
61	Leighton Town	v	Bugbrooke St Michaels (19/9)	4-0	115
62	Thrapston Town	v	Bedford Town (22/9)	0-2	63
63	Tilbury	v	Stanway Rovers (22/9)	5-1	75
64	Stansted	v	AFC Hornchurch (22/9)	1-5	42
65	Clapton	v	Redbridge (21/9)	0-7	50
66	Thurrock	v	St Albans City (21/9)	4-1	30
67	Hemel Hempstead Town	v	Romford (22/9)	3-2	62
68	Billericay Town	v	Royston Town (20/9)	3-0	51
69	Chelmsford City	v	Southend Manor (21/9)	3-0	56
70	East Thurrock United	v	Kings Langley (19/9)	7-3	76
71	FC Clacton	v	Waltham Abbey (19/9)	3-2	74
72	Brentwood Town	v	Boreham Wood (22/9)	0-2	63
73	Bishop's Stortford	v	Basildon United (21/9)	2-1	74
74	Witham Town	v	Maldon & Tiptree (20/9)	0-4	
75	Uxbridge	v	Enfield Town (21/9)	3-2aet	79
76	Staines Town	v	Wealdstone (19/9)	4-2	83
77	Hampton & Richmond B.	v	Wingate & Finchley (21/9)	3-1	48
78	Hayes & Yeading United	v	Northwood (19/9)	5-0	
79	Enfield 1893	v	Hanwell Town (19/9)	1-2	40
80	Ashford Town (Middx)	v	Harefield United (19/9)	3-0	74
81	Molesey	v	Dulwich Hamlet (21/9)	0-4	58
82	Kingstonian	v	South Park (3/10)	6-1	33
	(at Banstead Athletic FC) (19/9 original tie ordered to be replayed, 5-1)				
83	Maidstone United	v	Tooting & Mitcham United (22/9)	4-5	22
	(at Tunbridge Wells FC)				
84	Eastbourne Town	v	Dartford (22/9)	0-4	51
85	Tunbridge Wells	v	Ramsgate (20/9)	2-3aet	46
86	Whitstable Town	v	Chipstead (19/9)	1-8	80
87	Bromley	v	Ebbsfleet United (19/9)	1-2aet	125
88	Three Bridges	v	Croydon Athletic (21/9)	3-1	22
89	Lingfield	v	Welling United (29/9)	0-5	49
90	Westfield	v	Folkestone Invicta (19/9)	2-0	47
91	Erith Town	v	St Francis Rangers (19/9)	4-0	35
92	Corinthian	v	VCD Athletic (20/9)	1-0	72
93	Thamesmead Town	v	Hastings United (22/9)	3-2	55
94	Sevenoaks Town	v	Lewes (22/9)	2-6	56
95	Worthing	v	Shoreham (19/9)	1-0	102
96	Godalming Town	v	Lancing (19/9)	1-2	59
97	Camberley Town	v	Walton & Hersham (19/9)	4-1	55
98	Whyteleafe	v	Woking (22/9)	3-1	55
99	Burgess Hill Town	v	Horsham YMCA (19/9)	7-0	56
100	Leatherhead	v	Cobham (19/9)	3-2	53
101	Epsom & Ewell	v	Arundel		
	(walkover for Epsom & Ewell – Arundel withdrawn)				
102	Pagham	v	Whitehawk (22/9)	1-2	85
103	Chesham United	v	Didcot Town (22/9)	0-1	52
104	Burnham	v	Maidenhead United (21/9)	0-3	89
105	Reading Town	v	Newport Pagnell Town (21/9)	4-2	
106	Basingstoke Town	v	Bracknell Town (21/9)	1-4	130
107	Alton Town	v	Kidlington (19/9)	3-6	41
108	Witney Town	v	Wokingham & Emmbrook (19/9)	3-4	62
109	Fleet Spurs	v	Binfield (19/9)	0-4	61
110	Thatcham Town	v	Cove (21/9)	7-0	47
111	Farnborough	v	Milton United		
	(walkover for Farnborough – Milton United withdrawn)				
112	Oxford City	v	Sandhurst Town (19/9)	10-0	52
113	Chippenham Town	v	Ringwood Town (19/9)	1-3	63
114	Wimborne Town	v	Gosport Borough (21/9)	3-2	66
115	Poole Town	v	Havant & Waterlooville (20/9)	4-1	32
116	Dorchester Town	v	Salisbury City (22/9)	2-5	70
117	Christchurch	v	Eastleigh (22/9)	0-2	63
118	AFC Totton	v	Weymouth (22/9)	7-0	67
119	Gillingham Town	v	Bournemouth (22/9)	8-1	107
120	Moneyfields	v	Sholing (22/9)	2-0	50
121	Radstock Town	v	Larkhall Athletic (19/9)	2-2aet	62
	(Larkhall won 4-2 on kicks from the penalty mark)				
122	Merthyr Town	v	Cirencester Town (21/9)	0-5	51
123	Newport County	v	Bath City (26/9)	6-0	149
124	Chard Town	v	Bishop's Cleeve (20/9)	0-7	
125	Bitton	v	Cheltenham Saracens (19/9)	1-2	40
126	Weston Super Mare	v	Mangotsfield United (19/9)	3-1	170
127	Tiverton Town	v	Wells City (22/9)	4-2	57
128	Lydney Town	v	Portishead Town (19/9)	1-2	61
	(tie awarded to Lydney Town – Portishead Town removed)				

THE FA YOUTH CUP

SECOND ROUND QUALIFYING

1	Chester-Le-Street Town	v	Darlington (6/10)	0-4	108
2	York City	v	Pickering Town (5/10)	2-0	299
3	Altrincham	v	Lancaster City (6/10)	2-2aet	133
	(Altrincham won 4-3 on kicks from the penalty mark)				
4	Fleetwood Town	v	Ashton Athletic (3/10)	0-3	131
5	Northwich Victoria	v	Mossley (6/10)	1-1aet	68
	(Mossley won 4-2 on kicks from the penalty mark)				
6	Stockport County	v	Prescot Cables (9/10)	0-3	96
	(at Trafford FC)				
7	Marine	v	Woodley Sports (5/10)	3-0	99
8	Sheffield	v	Bottesford Town	2-1	74
9	Yorkshire Amateur	v	Staveley MW (3/10)	3-0	36
10	North Ferriby United	v	Harrogate RA (6/10)	4-1	79
11	Brighouse Town	v	Grimsby Town (5/10)	3-2aet	39
12	Boston United	v	Pinxton (5/10)	3-0	138
13	Loughborough Dynamo	v	Arnold Town (6/10)	4-3	
14	Matlock Town	v	Teversal (4/10)	4-3aet	69
15	Calverton MW	v	Deeping Rangers (6/10)	5-0	60
16	Lincoln City	v	Gresley (10/10)	7-0	104
17	Racing Club Warwick	v	Halesowen Town (5/10)	1-2aet	29
18	Bromyard Town	v	Nuneaton Town (4/10)	2-3	34
19	Stratford Town	v	Hednesford Town (6/10)	5-1	81
20	Stourport Swifts	v	Lye Town (5/10)	3-0	59
21	Highgate United	v	Tamworth (5/10)	0-5	54
22	Kidderminster Harriers	v	Stone Dominoes (4/10)	3-2aet	102
23	Dereham Town	v	Gorleston (4/10)	3-1	52
24	Thetford Town	v	Cambridge United (6/10)	0-2	60
25	Soham Town Rangers	v	Woodbridge Town (5/10)	2-1	72
26	Brantham Athletic	v	Needham Market (6/10)	1-2	74
27	Walsham Le Willows	v	Hadleigh United (6/10)	1-2	49
28	Luton Town	v	Leighton Town (5/10)	5-1	149
29	Woodford United	v	Stotfold (5/10)	3-1	31
30	Corby Town	v	Bedford Town (3/10)	8-3	93
31	Kettering Town	v	St Neots Town (3/10)	0-2	
32	AFC Hornchurch	v	Tilbury (6/10)	0-4	91
33	Thurrock	v	Maldon & Tiptree (5/10)	4-1	
34	Chelmsford City	v	Hemel Hempstead Town (5/10)	2-1	68
35	Boreham Wood	v	Bishop's Stortford (5/10)	1-0	51
36	Billericay Town	v	East Thurrock United (5/10)	2-1	71
37	Redbridge	v	FC Clacton (6/10)	7-1	35
38	Ashford Town (Middx)	v	Uxbridge (3/10)	2-3	104
39	Hanwell Town	v	Staines Town (3/10)	0-3	
40	Hayes & Yeading United	v	Hampton & Richmond B. (3/10)	2-0	88
41	Welling United	v	Dulwich Hamlet (12/10)	2-5aet	116
42	Chipstead	v	Kingstonian (12/10)	1-3aet	53
43	Three Bridges	v	Ramsgate (6/10)	1-4	30
44	Corinthian	v	Erith Town (18/10)	4-2	
	(4/10 tie abandoned after 70mins, 5-0)				
45	Dartford	v	Westfield (5/10)	3-2	81
46	Tooting & Mitcham United	v	Ebbsfleet United (5/10)	0-2	93
47	Lewes	v	Thamesmead Town (6/10)	7-1	78
48	Lancing	v	Epsom & Ewell (5/10)	0-9	82
49	Worthing	v	Leatherhead (3/10)	0-1	78
50	Camberley Town	v	Whitehawk (6/10)	3-2aet	
51	Burgess Hill Town	v	Whyteleafe (6/10)	2-2aet	
	(Whyteleafe won 11-10 on kicks from the penalty mark)				
52	Kidlington	v	Maidenhead United (6/10)	0-4	85
53	Didcot Town	v	Bracknell Town (6/10)	2-4	50
54	Wokingham & Emmbrook	v	Binfield (5/10)	3-3aet	75
	(Wokingham & Emmbrook won 12-11 on kicks from the penalty mark)				
55	Farnborough	v	Reading (3/10)	4-3	72
56	Thatcham Town	v	Oxford City (5/10)	0-2	74
57	Wimborne Town	v	Gillingham Town (4/10)	4-2aet	40
58	Mangotsfield Town	v	AFC Totton (5/10)	1-6	92
59	Poole Town	v	Moneyfields (4/10)	3-1	65
60	Eastleigh	v	Salisbury City (3/10)	1-0	102
61	Camberley Town	v	Tiverton Town (3/10)	3-1	49
62	Larkhall Athletic	v	Weston Super Mare (3/10)	1-0	70
63	Newport County	v	Lydney Town (3/10)	9-0	134
64	Cheltenham Saracens	v	Bishop's Cleeve (3/10)	1-5	50

THIRD ROUND QUALIFYING

1	Mossley	v	North Ferriby United (20/10)	0-1	105
2	Sheffield	v	Ashton Athletic (19/10)	1-0	
3	Prescot Cables	v	York City (25/10)	1-3	308
4	Yorkshire Amateur	v	Marine (17/10)	1-2	75
5	Altrincham	v	Darlington (25/10)	0-3	157
6	Nuneaton Town	v	Stratford Town (19/10)	0-5	80
7	Tamworth	v	Lincoln City (19/10)	2-0	115
8	Boston United	v	Stourport Swifts (19/10)	4-3	135
9	Kidderminster Harriers	v	Matlock Town (19/10)	3-0	85
10	Brighouse Town	v	Loughborough Dynamo (19/10)	2-1	38
11	Halesowen Town	v	Calverton MW (19/10)	2-1	81
12	Woodford United	v	Cambridge United (19/10)	0-4	91
13	Boreham Wood	v	Billericay Town (20/10)	2-0	55
14	Dereham Town	v	Luton Town (21/10)	2-1	209
15	Uxbridge	v	Needham Market (19/10)	4-3	99
16	Corby Town	v	Redbridge (17/10)	3-0	82
17	Hadleigh United	v	Thurrock (19/10)	0-5	71
18	Chelmsford City	v	Tilbury (19/10)	2-2aet	91
	(Tilbury won 3-2 on kicks from the penalty mark)				
19	Staines Town	v	Hayes & Yeading United (17/10)	2-4	89
20	Soham Town Rangers	v	St Neots Town (26/10)	2-1	143
	(19/10 – tie abandoned after 35 mins due to serious injury, 1-2)				
21	Leatherhead	v	Camberley Town (17/10)	2-3aet	70
22	Epsom & Ewell	v	Ebbsfleet United (17/10)	2-3	
	(at Raynes Park Vale FC)				
23	Bracknell Town	v	Kingstonian (19/10)	0-2	
24	Oxford City	v	Maidenhead United (17/10)	4-5aet	41
25	Wokingham & Emmbrook	v	Farnborough (8/11)	0-5	
	(at Reading Town FC) (26/10 original tie ordered to be replayed, 2-9)				
26	Dartford	v	Lewes (19/10)	2-5	101
27	Ramsgate	v	Corinthian (27/10)	1-2	93
28	Whyteleafe	v	Dulwich Hamlet (27/10)	1-3	
29	Eastleigh	v	AFC Totton (17/10)	0-2	184
30	Bishop's Cleeve	v	Poole Town (17/10)	7-2	65
31	Larkhall Athletic	v	Cirencester Town (17/10)	0-4	65
32	Wimborne Town	v	Newport County (19/10)	1-7	67

FIRST ROUND PROPER

1	Tranmere Rovers	v	Sheffield United (7/11)	1-2	237
2	North Ferriby United	v	Crewe Alexandra (1/11)	0-4	278
3	York City	v	Macclesfield Town (2/11)	1-3	
4	Hartlepool United	v	Bury (1/11)	1-3	144
5	Rochdale	v	Oldham Athletic (1/11)	2-3	505
6	Rotherham United	v	Accrington Stanley (2/11)	0-1	154
7	Morecambe	v	Preston North End (2/11)	0-3	210
8	Darlington	v	Sheffield (2/11)	7-1	85
9	Scunthorpe United	v	Huddersfield Town (26/10)	1-2	237
10	Carlisle United	v	Sheffield Wednesday (1/11)	4-1	182
11	Bradford City	v	Marine (1/11)	3-2aet	236
12	Burton Albion	v	Boston United (31/10)	1-3	199
13	Hereford United	v	Halesowen Town (3/11)	5-3	130
14	Kidderminster Harriers	v	Brighouse Town (2/11)	4-2	128
15	Chesterfield	v	Tamworth (25/10)	7-0	170
16	Milton Keynes Dons	v	Walsall (26/10)	0-1	556
17	Shrewsbury Town	v	Notts County (1/11)	2-0	197
18	Northampton Town	v	Cambridge United (1/11)	1-2	332
19	Stratford Town	v	Port Vale (7/11)	2-3	260
20	Ebbsfleet United	v	Dulwich Hamlet (2/11)	1-2	133
21	Brentford	v	Lewes (2/11)	3-0	265
22	Crawley Town	v	Wycombe Wanderers (2/11)	5-1	254
23	Tilbury	v	Stevenage (3/11)	0-2aet	299
24	Uxbridge	v	AFC Wimbledon (2/11)	1-3	160
25	Leyton Orient	v	Dereham Town (1/11)	4-3aet	366
26	Corby Town	v	Colchester United (31/10)	2-0	100
27	Gillingham	v	Hayes & Yeading United (1/11)	0-1	380
28	Southend United	v	Corinthian (1/11)	4-0	271
29	Dagenham & Redbridge	v	Barnet (1/11)	3-2	329
30	Thurrock	v	Boreham Wood (2/11)	2-0	
31	Soham Town Rangers	v	Charlton Athletic (7/11)	0-9	509
32	Swindon Town	v	Newport County (1/11)	2-0	304
33	Bishop's Cleeve	v	Torquay United (1/11)	1-3	84
34	Cirencester Town	v	Camberley Town (2/11)	3-1	75
35	Aldershot Town	v	Kingstonian (3/11)	3-2	102
36	Farnborough	v	Yeovil Town (16/11)	1-3	114
37	AFC Bournemouth	v	Plymouth Argyle (1/11)	4-2aet	348

38	Bristol Rovers	v	Maidenhead United (1/11)	4-1	210
39	AFC Totton	v	Exeter City (2/11)	3-2	111
40	Cheltenham Town	v	Oxford United (2/11)	1-3aet	246

SECOND ROUND PROPER

1	Huddersfield Town	v	Crewe Alexandra (23/11)	2-1	248
2	Oldham Athletic	v	Macclesfield Town (23/11)	1-1aet	190
	(Oldham Athletic won 6-5 on kicks from the penalty mark)				
3	Boston United	v	Bradford City (15/11)	2-1	437
4	Sheffield United	v	Port Vale (21/11)	2-2aet	575
	(Sheffield United won 8-7 on kicks from the penalty mark)				
5	Kidderminster Harriers	v	Carlisle United (16/11)	0-1	264
6	Bury	v	Accrington Stanley (15/11)	2-1aet	100
7	Darlington	v	Shrewsbury Town (15/11)	2-0	290
8	Hereford United	v	Chesterfield (15/11)	2-0	160
9	Preston North End	v	Walsall (24/11)	1-1aet	308
	(Preston North End won 5-4 on kicks from the penalty mark)				
10	AFC Bournemouth	v	Swindon Town (15/11)	1-3	385
11	Aldershot Town	v	AFC Totton (24/11)	3-1	79
12	Cambridge United	v	Crawley Town (15/11)	3-1	166
13	AFC Wimbledon	v	Bristol Rovers (15/11)	1-2	214
14	Thurrock	v	Hayes & Yeading United (23/11)	2-0	104
15	Southend United	v	Brentford (15/11)	1-2aet	230
16	Dulwich Hamlet	v	Oxford United (17/11)	0-2	138
17	Stevenage	v	Leyton Orient (16/11)	1-0	306
18	Torquay United	v	Cirencester Town (15/11)	1-1aet	154
	(Torquay United won 3-1 on kicks from the penalty mark)				
19	Charlton Athletic	v	Yeovil Town (23/11)	3-0	230
	(at Welling United FC)				
20	Corby Town	v	Dagenham & Redbridge (14/11)	2-2aet	142
	(Corby Town won 3-2 on kicks from the penalty mark)				

THIRD ROUND PROPER

1	Leicester City	v	Aldershot Town (14/12)	5-0	
2	Stevenage	v	Tottenham Hotspur (21/12)	1-2	865
3	Swindon Town	v	Birmingham City (12/12)	3-2	236
4	Charlton Athletic	v	Cambridge United (7/12)	7-0	211
	(at Welling United FC)				
5	Ipswich Town	v	Leeds United (6/12)	2-0	696
6	**BLACKBURN ROVERS**	v	Thurrock (5/12)	8-0	391
7	Manchester City	v	Corby Town (30/11)	4-1	
	(at Hyde FC)				
8	Southampton	v	Sheffield United (12/12)	7-0	432
9	Oxford United	v	Bolton Wanderers (7/12)	1-2	451
10	Middlesbrough	v	Reading (14/12)	1-2	387
11	Bury	v	Cardiff City (6/12)	2-3	252
12	Sunderland	v	Nottingham Forest (29/11)	1-2	215
	(at Eppleton CW)				
13	**CHELSEA**	v	Doncaster Rovers (14/12)	2-1	482
	(at Staines Town FC)				
14	Hull City	v	Brentford (14/12)	1-2aet	188
	(at North Ferriby United FC)				
15	Portsmouth	v	Bristol City (7/12)	5-1	500
16	Peterborough United	v	Blackpool (7/12)	3-1	608
17	Swansea City	v	Liverpool (6/12)	3-1	819
18	Wolverhampton Wanderers	v	West Ham United (7/12)	2-3	569
19	Manchester United	v	Torquay United (2/12)	4-0	503
	(at Altrincham FC)				
20	Norwich City	v	Oldham Athletic (13/12)	5-0	340
21	Fulham	v	Carlisle United (13/12)	3-1	176
	(at Fulham FC Training Grd, Motspur Pk)				
22	Brighton & Hove Albion	v	Aston Villa (13/12)	1-0	1868
23	Millwall	v	Watford (13/12)	1-2	570
24	Preston North End	v	Stoke City (13/12)	1-2aet	374
25	Crystal Palace	v	Everton (13/12)	1-2aet	1085
26	Bristol Rovers	v	Coventry City (19/12)	2-3	235
27	West Bromwich Albion	v	Barnsley (29/11)	3-0	341
28	Newcastle United	v	Darlington (8/12)	3-0	1137
29	Queens Park Rangers	v	Huddersfield Town (7/12)	2-1	639
30	Boston United	v	Burnley (6/12)	0-7	492
31	Wigan Athletic	v	Hereford United (2/12)	4-0	128
	(at Wigan Robin Park FC)				
32	Arsenal	v	Derby County (14/12)	0-1aet	393
	(at Barnet FC)				

FOURTH ROUND PROPER

1	Bolton Wanderers	v	Southampton (11/1)	1-2	953
2	Charlton Athletic	v	Leicester City (18/1)	2-1aet	346
	(at Welling United FC)				
3	Cardiff City	v	Tottenham Hotspur (11/1)	1-2	1309
4	Queens Park Rangers	v	Everton (12/1)	1-0	
5	Reading	v	West Bromwich Albion (18/1)	1-2	1402
6	Stoke City	v	Brentford (12/1)	2-1aet	2650
7	Burnley	v	Ipswich Town (13/1)	3-1	
8	**BLACKBURN ROVERS**	v	Coventry City (17/1)	2-0	511
9	Swindon Town	v	Manchester City (17/1)	1-4	1601
10	Nottingham Forest	v	Wigan Athletic (19/1)	9-1	676
11	Norwich City	v	**CHELSEA** (11/1)	0-0aet	1099
	(Chelsea won 4-2 on kicks from the penalty mark)				
12	Portsmouth	v	Swansea City (18/1)	1-2	
13	Manchester United	v	Derby County (18/1)	2-1	993
	(at Altrincham FC)				
14	Newcastle United	v	Watford (19/1)	2-1	889
15	West Ham United	v	Brighton & Hove Albion (11/1)	4-1	1603
16	Peterborough United	v	Fulham (12/1)	1-5	1245

FIFTH ROUND PROPER

1	Swansea City	v	Manchester United (2/2)	1-5	4080
2	Manchester City	v	Fulham (15/2)	1-2	490
3	**BLACKBURN ROVERS**	v	Stoke City (6/2)	4-0	474
4	Charlton Athletic	v	Tottenham Hotspur (16/2)	1-0	1371
5	West Bromwich Albion	v	Burnley (8/2)	1-2	434
6	**CHELSEA**	v	West Ham United (15/2)	3-3aet	1588
	(Chelsea won 5-4 on kicks from the penalty mark)				
7	Newcastle United	v	Queens Park Rangers (9/11)	2-1aet	1196
8	Southampton	v	Nottingham Forest (25/1)	1-5	814

SIXTH ROUND PROPER

1	Newcastle United	v	**BLACKBURN ROVERS** 27 Feb 7.00		
2	Manchester United	v	Charlton Athletic (29/2)	3-2	
3	Fulham	v	Burnley (7/3)	1-3	
4	Nottingham Forest	v	**CHELSEA** (22/2)	3-4	4263

SEMI FINALS 1ST LEG

| 1 | **BLCKBURN ROVERS** | v | Burnley | 1-0 | 10000 |
| 2 | Manchester United | v | **CHELSEA** | 1-2 | |

SEMI FINALS 2ND LEG

| 1 | Burnley | v | **BLACKBURN ROVERS** | 1-2 | |
| 2 | **CHELSEA** | v | Manchester United | 1-1 | |

THE FINAL 1ST LEG

| CHELSEA | v | **BLACKBURN ROVERS** | 4-0 |

THE FINAL 2ND LEG

| BLACKBURN ROVERS | v | **CHELSEA** | 1-0 |

PREVIOUS TEN FINALS

Aggregate Score

2011	Manchester Utd	v	Sheffield United	4-1
2010	Chelsea	v	Aston Villa	3-2
2009	Arsenal	v	Liverpool	6-2
2008	Manchester City	v	Chelsea	4-2
2007	Liverpool	v	Manchester Utd	2-2* 4-3p
2006	Liverpool	v	Manchester City	3-2
2005	Ipswich Town	v	Southampton	3-2
2004	Middlesbrough	v	Aston Villa	4-0
2003	Manchester Utd	v	Middlesbrough	3-1
2002	Aston Villa	v	Everton	4-2

FIRST ROUND

1	Lincolnshire	v	Northumberland (8/10)	0-2
2	Westmorland	v	East Riding (10/9)	0-10
3	Lancashire	v	Cheshire (8/10)	0-1
4	Durham	v	Liverpool (8/10)	3-0
5	Manchester	v	Isle of Man (15/10)	3-1
6	Surrey	v	Devon (8/10)	1-3aet
7	Middlesex	v	Dorset (8/10)	3-1
8	Huntingdonshire	v	Suffolk (16/10)	2-1
9	Wiltshire	v	Jersey (15/10)	2-1
10	Sussex	v	London (15/10)	5-1
11	Gloucestershire	v	Berks & Bucks (8/10)	4-8aet
12	Kent	v	Guernsey (15/10)	5-0
13	Herefordshire	v	Cambridgeshire (8/10)	3-2

SECOND ROUND

1	West Riding	v	Manchester (12/11)	1-0
2	Leicestershire & Rutland	v	Durham (29/10)	2-4
3	East Riding	v	Shropshire (29/10)	3-2
4	Sheffield & Hallamshire	v	North Riding (12/11)	3-3aet

(Sheffield & Hallamshire won 3-1 on kicks from the penalty mark)

5	Northumberland	v	Cumberland (12/11)	0-0aet

(Northumberland won 3-2 on kicks from the penalty mark)

6	Nottinghamshire	v	Staffordshire (5/11)	1-0
7	Birmingham	v	Cheshire (19/11)	3-2
8	Devon	v	Somerset (12/11)	2-3aet
9	Hertfordshire	v	Wiltshire (5/11)	1-4
10	Herefordshire	v	Sussex (19/11)	2-3
11	Oxfordshire	v	Kent (6/11)	1-5
12	Essex	v	Bedfordshire (5/11)	5-1
13	Cornwall	v	Huntingdonshire (5/11)	2-0
14	Norfolk	v	Amateur Football Alliance (8/10)	3-2
15	Middlesex	v	Berks & Bucks (12/11)	7-0
16	Northamptonshire	v	Worcestershire (5/11)	2-3

THIRD ROUND

1	Wiltshire	v	Birmingham (10/12)	2-1
2	Middlesex	v	Cornwall (3/12)	1-0
3	West Riding	v	East Riding (10/12)	2-0
4	Somerset	v	Kent (10/12)	1-0
5	Sheffield & Hallamshire	v	Norfolk (11/12)	5-2
6	Durham	v	Nottinghamshire (17/12)	11-0
7	Sussex	v	Worcestershire (10/12)	2-4
8	Northumberland	v	Essex (17/12)	0-2

FOURTH ROUND

1	Middlesex	v	Essex (29/1)	1-2
2	Wiltshire	v	Worcestershire (21/1)	2-1
3	Sheffield & Hallamshire	v	West Riding (18/1)	1-3
4	Durham	v	Somerset (14/1)	0-1

SEMI FINALS

1	West Riding	v	Somerset	
2	Essex	v	Wiltshire (18/2)	4-0

THE FINAL

SATURDAY 22 APRIL 2012

ESSEX	v	WEST RIDING	4-2aet	586

AT COLCHESTER UNITED FC

PREVIOUS TEN FINALS

2011	Norfolk FA	v	Staffordshire FA	4-2
2010	Kent FA	v	Sheffield & Hallamshire	1-0
2009	Birmingham FA	v	Kent FA	2-1
2008	Suffolk FA	v	Cambridgeshire FA	2-1
2007	West Riding FA	v	Suffolk FA	1-1*, 4-3p
2006	Bedfordshire FA	v	Durham FA	3-2
2005	Suffolk FA	v	Hampshire FA	2-1
2004	Durham FA	v	North Riding FA	4-0
2003	Northumberland FA	v	Liverpool FA	1-0
2002	Birmingham FA	v	Durham FA	2-1

FIRST ROUND

1	South Bank (2006)	v	Hartlepool Lion Hillcarter	3-5
2	Kelloe WMC	v	Hartlepool Rovers Quoit	1-0
3	St Bees	v	Stockton Rosegale N&SA	0-6
4	Sunderland RCA Barnes	v	Dawdon Colliery Welfare	2-5
5	Burradon & New Fordley	v	Hetton Lyons Cricket Club	0-1
6	Chapel Town Fforde Grenev		Dengo United	3-1
7	Lobster	v	Alder	6-4aet
8	Eagle Cons	v	Queens Park	1-0

(tie awarded to Queens Park – Eagle Cons removed)

9	Obiter	v	West Bowling	0-4
10	Nicosia	v	Derby Lane Gym	1-4
11	AFC Blackburn Leisure	v	BRNESC	0-2
12	Sandstone	v	Eden Vale	3-5
13	Belt Road	v	Bolton Woods	3-0
14	Hessle Rangers	v	Canada	1-2
15	Poulton Royal	v	Home & Bargain	1-3
16	Mariners	v	St Sebastians	4-3
17	Swanfield	v	Allerton	3-3aet

(Allerton won 5-3 on kicks from the penalty mark)

18	Bighouse	v	Britannia VNC	

(walkover for Britannia VNC – Bighouse withdrawn)

19	JOB	v	Seymour	3-0
20	Salisbury Athletic	v	Thirly	4-1
21	Hundred Acre	v	Advance Couriers	3-4aet
22	Wymeswold	v	Loughborough Falcons	2-1
23	Loughborough Saints	v	Clumber	2-1
24	FC Hoskins	v	Lea Hall Sports & Social	1-4
25	Whitwick Compass 2008	v	Bartley Green Sunday	4-2
26	Magnet Tavern	v	Plough Barfly's	2-1
27	The Dog	v	Hole In The Wall	4-0
28	Kingshurst Punchbowl	v	Birstall Stamford	1-4
29	Travellers	v	R.H.P Sports & Social	3-2
30	Seven Allstars	v	Hamstead YFC	4-4aet

(Seven Allstars won 4-3 on kicks from the penalty mark)

31	St Josephs (Luton)	v	Crawley Green (Sunday)	3-2
32	Rumours	v	FC Houghton Centre	1-5
33	Club Lewsey	v	Duke Of Rutland	4-1
34	AC Cadoza	v	Northampton Duke Of York	0-2
35	AC Sportsman & Ravensborough			v
	Stanbridge & Tilsworth		4-1	
36	Highfield Social Club	v	Houghton Town (Sunday)	7-0
37	St Margarets	v	Celtic SC (Luton)	2-0
38	Co-op Sports	v	Britannia United	2-3
39	Belstone	v	Greengate	0-3
40	Gossoms End	v	Torrun United	0-10
41	Gadeside Rangers	v	FC Nirankari	2-5
42	Bari	v	New Salamis	1-3
43	Sungate	v	Hammer OGB	3-0
44	Royal Falcons	v	Comets Sports Club	1-3
45	Falcons	v	London Maccabi Lions	12-1
46	FC Tripimeni	v	Upshire	4-1
47	Gym United	v	Offley Moat	

(tie awarded to Gym United – Offley Moat failed to fulfil fixture)

48	Elm Farm	v	North London Olympians	7-4
49	CB Hounslow United (Sunday) v		Wrightchoice CSA	0-2
50	Barnes Albion	v	AFC Kumazi Strikers	2-1
51	Bedfont Sunday	v	AFC Rayners Lane	5-2
52	Dee Road Rangers	v	Broadfields United	5-3
53	AFC Donsville	v	Oak Park Rangers	1-1aet

(AFC Donsville won 3-1 on kicks from the penalty mark)

54	Branksome Con	v	Goring Rangers	2-0
55	The Lounge	v	Knighton Arms	3-1
56	Hazelhurst	v	Ajax LA	8-0
57	Nyetimber Pirates	v	Fountain Court	4-2
58	C.K.	v	Kings Tamerton CA	5-2

59	Sporting Bristol	v	Lakeside Athletic	1-2
60	Efford United Bluebird	v	All Saints	1-2
61	The Railway Inn	v	Wonford United	0-2aet
62	Lebeq Tavern Courage	v	Windmill	3-2

SECOND ROUND

1	Home & Bargain	v	JOB	0-4
2	Allerton	v	Dawdon Colliery Welfare	0-3
3	Queens Park	v	Derby Lane Gym	3-0
4	West Bowling	v	Stockton Rosegale N&SA	3-4
5	Eden Vale	v	Kelloe WMC	2-4aet
6	Hetton Lyons Cricket Club	v	Chapel Town Fforde Grene	2-1
7	Oyster Martyrs	v	Belt Road	6-0
8	Paddock	v	Lobster	0-1
9	Britannia VNC	v	Hartlepool Lion Hillcarter	1-0
10	Salisbury Athletic	v	BRNESC	4-0
11	Canada	v	Mariners	3-1
12	Loughborough Saints	v	St Josephs (Luton)	5-0
13	AC Sportsman & Ravensb.v		Northampton Duke Of York	1-6
14	Magnet Tavern	v	Wymeswold	2-0
15	FC Houghton Centre	v	Club Lewsey	2-5
16	The Dog	v	Whitwick Compass 2008	0-6
17	Travellers	v	Seven Allstars	6-3
18	Lea Hall Sports & Social	v	St Margarets	5-0
19	Advance Couriers	v	Birstall Stamford	1-2aet
20	Highfield Social Club	v	Falcons	0-4
21	Greengate	v	Elm Farm	1-2
22	Gym United	v	FC Tripimeni	0-3
23	Comets Sports Club	v	Britannia United	4-0
24	Sungate	v	Torrun United	4-3aet
25	FC Nirankari	v	New Salamis	0-5
26	AFC Donsville	v	Hazelhurst	1-1aet

(Hazelhurst won 5-4 on kicks from the penalty mark)

27	Barnes Albion	v	Nyetimber Pirates	6-1
28	C.K.	v	Dee Road Rangers	3-4aet
29	Wonford United	v	Lebeqs Tavern Courage	1-3
30	Bedfont Sunday	v	Branksome Con	0-1
31	All Saints	v	Lakeside Athletic	0-3
32	Wrightchoice CSA	v	The Lounge	2-0

THIRD ROUND

1	Canada	v	Queens Park	4-1
2	Lobster	v	Whitwick Compass 2008 (8/1)	2-3

(tie reversed - at Bardon Hill Sports FC)

3	Kelloe WMC	v	JOB	5-2
4	Hetton Lyons CC	v	Britannia VNC	4-1
5	Salisbury Athletic	v	Oyster Martyrs (8/1)	0-3

(tie reversed - at Heswall FC)

6	Dawdon Colliery Welfare	v	Stockton Rosegale N&SA	3-5
7	New Salamis	v	Lea Hall Sports & Social	1-3aet
8	FC Tripimeni	v	Falcons	5-2
9	Club Lewsey	v	Magnet Tavern	1-0
10	Loughborough Saints	v	Comets Sports Club	1-3
11	Sungate	v	Northampton Duke Of York	3-0
12	Travellers	v	Birstall Stamford	1-1aet

(Birstall Stamford won 2-1 on kicks from the penalty mark)

13	Barnes Albion	v	Wrightchoice CSA	1-1aet

(Barnes Albion won 5-4 on kicks from the penalty mark)

14	Hazelhurst	v	Dee Road Rangers	0-5
15	Lakeside Athletic	v	Lebeqs Tavern Courage (8/1)	4-2

(tie reversed - at Bristol Manor Farm FC)

16	Elm Farm	v	Branksome Con (8/1)	2-1

(at Aylesbury FC)

(11/12, tie abandoned after 51 mins due to injured player, 2-1)

FOURTH ROUND

1	Canada	v	Stockton Rosegale N&SA	2-0
2	Whitwick Compass 2008	v	Lea Hall Sports & Social	0-1
3	Hetton Lyons CC	v	Kelloe WMC	3-1
4	Birstall Stamford	v	Oyster Martyrs	3-4
5	FC Tripimeni	v	Dee Road Rangers	4-3aet
6	Club Lewsey	v	Lakeside Athletic	2-2aet

(Lakeside Athletic won 4-3 on kicks from the penalty mark)

7	Sungate	v	Comets Sports Club	0-4
8	Elm Farm	v	Barnes Albion	3-1

FIFTH ROUND

1	Lakeside Athletic	v	Comets Sports Club	3-1
2	FC Tripimeni	v	Oyster Martyrs	1-0

(tie awarded to Oyster Martyrs – FC Tripimeni removed)

3	Elm Farm	v	Canada	1-2
4	Lea Hall Sports & Social	v	Hetton Lyons CC	0-5

SEMI FINALS

1	Hetton Lyons Cricket Club	v	Oyster Martyrs	2-1	254

(at Billingham Synthonia FC)

2	Lakeside Athletic	v	Canada	0-1	505

(at Saltash United FC)

THE FINAL

SUNDAY 29 APRIL 2012

HETTON LYONS C.C.	v	CANADA	5-1	1219

AT SUNDERLAND AFC

NATIONAL LEAGUE SYSTEMS CUP

PRELIMINARY ROUND

Gloucestershire County League	v	Mid Sussex League	4-0
Liverpool County FA Premier Lge	v	Teesside League	2-1
Sussex County League (Div 3)	v	Brighton Hove & District League	5-0
Manchester League	v	Wearside League	2-1
Amateur Football Combination	v	Surrey Elite Intermediate League	1 - 2
Northern Football Alliance	v	Lancashire & Cheshire Am Lge	2 - 2

Northern Football Alliance won 3-1 on kicks from the penalty mark

Middlesex County League	v	Herts Senior County League	3-3

Herts Senior County League won 5-4 on kicks from the penalty mark

Reading League	v	Kent County League	1-1

Reading League won 6-5 on kicks from the penalty mark

Lancashire Amateur League	v	Isle of Man League	1-3
Northamptonshire Combination	v	Cambridgeshire County League	1-2
Anglian Combination	v	Nottinghamshire Senior League	

walkover for Anglian Combination - Nottinghamshire Senior League withdrawn

Suffolk & Ipswich League	v	Bedfordshire County League	4-0
Peterborough & District League	v	Lincolnshire League	1-2
Worthing & District League	v	Somerset County League	3-4
Birmingham & District AFA	v	West Riding County Amateur Lge	0-2
Dorset Premier League	v	Hampshire Premier League	2-2

Dorset Premier League won 5-4 on kicks from the penalty mark

FIRST ROUND

SATURDAY 15TH OCTOBER 2011

1	Manchester League	v	Cheshire League	2-3
2	Cumberland County Lge	v	Liverpool County FA Premier League	1-2
3	Northern Football Alliance	v	Yorkshire Amateur League	1-2*
4	West Cheshire League	v	Isle of Man League	0-5
5	Northampton Town Lge	v	Cambridgeshire County League	0-1
6	Lincolnshire League	v	Anglian Combination	3-2
7	West Yorkshire League	v	Humber Premier League	3-0
8	Midland Football Comb (Div 1)	v	Birmingham & District AFA (30/11)	1-0

(29/9 original tie ordered to be replayed, Birmingham & District AFC won 4-2 on pens)

9	Jersey Football Comb.	v	Gloucestershire County League	8-0
10	Somerset County League	v	Hampshire Premier League	5-1
11	Devon & Exeter League	v	Guernsey Senior County League	1-0
12	Sussex County Lge (Div 3)	v	Wiltshire League	WO Sussex Co
13	Spartan South Mid. (Div 2)	v	Southern Amateur League	0-1*
14	Surrey Elite Intermediate	v	Essex & Suffolk Border League	1-2
15	Suffolk & Ipswich League	v	Reading League	3-0

(tie awarded to Reading League – Suffolk & Ipswich League removed)

16	Essex Olympian League	v	Herts Senior County League	1-4

SECOND ROUND

1	Isle of Man League	v	Yorkshire Amateur League	4-3
2	Cheshire League	v	Cambridgeshire County Lge	1-0
3	West Yorkshire League	v	Liverpool County FA Prem Lge	5-4aet

(tie awarded to Liverpool County FA Prem Lge – West Yorkshire Lge removed)

4	Midland Football Comb (Div 1)	v	Lincolnshire League	3-4aet
5	Southern Amateur League	v	Devon & Exeter League	6-1
6	Herts Senior County League	v	Sussex County League (Div 3)	0-2
7	Somerset County League	v	Reading League	2-1
8	Jersey Football Combination	v	Essex & Suffolk Border Lge	1-0

THIRD ROUND

1	Isle of Man League	v	Liverpool County FA Prem Lge	5-3
2	Lincolnshire League	v	Cheshire League	2-4
3	Southern Amateur League	v	Sussex County League	5-2
4	Jersey Combination	v	Somerset County League	4-0

SEMI-FINALS

1	Jersey Football Combination	v	Cheshire League	1-1	376

(Jersey Football Combination won 4-3 on kicks from the penalty mark - at Springfield Stadium, St Helier)

2	Isle of Man League	v	Southern Amateur League	2-1	2012

(at The Bowl, Douglas)

FINAL

Isle of Man	v	Jersey Combination	1-2	3349

(at The Bowl, Douglas)

FIRST QUALIFYING ROUND

1	Lowick United	v	Cramlington Juniors	7-2
2	Lumley	v	Consett	2-1
3	North Shields	v	Norton & Stockton Ancients (9/10)	1-3

(2/10 tie abandoned after 60 minutes, 3-3)

4	Teesside Sport	v	California	0-4
5	Redcar Athletic	v	Percy Main	4-0
6	Abbeytown	v	Forest Hall Women's YPC	3-1
7	St Francis 2000	v	Peterlee Town	6-3
8	Ashington CFC	v	Prudhoe Town	3-2
9	Whitley Bay	v	Kendal Town	8-1
10	Tyneside	v	Whitehaven	

(walkover for Tyneside – Whitehaven withdrawn)

11	Tynedale	v	Birtley Town	3-2
12	Durham Wildcats	v	Penrith	4-0
13	Sheffield United Comm.	v	Hull City	3-0
14	Scunthorpe United	v	Rothwell	2-3
15	Bradford Park Avenue	v	Keighley Oaks	1-6
16	North Ferriby United	v	Appleby Frodingham	4-0
17	Barnsley	v	Ossett Albion	9-0
18	Sheffield Utd Junior Bladesv	v	Steel City Wanderers	1-2
19	Brighouse	v	Padiham	0-2
20	Blackpool	v	Southport Birkdale	13-0
21	Kirklees	v	Crewe Alexandra	0-3
22	Chester City	v	Birkenhead Youth	4-6aet
23	Bolton Wanderers	v	Tranmere Rovers	2-5
24	Lancaster City	v	Warrington Town	2-4
25	Accrington	v	Blackpool Wren Rovers	0-4
26	Morecambe	v	Middleton Athletic	4-2
27	Arnold Town	v	Oadby & Wigston	2-0
28	Retford United	v	Dronfield Town	2-1
29	Mansfield Town	v	Nettleham	7-5
30	Long Eaton United	v	Asfordby Amateurs	8-0
31	Lichfield Diamonds	v	Walsall	2-0
32	Southam United	v	Coventry Sphinx	

(walkover for Coventry Sphinx – Southam United withdrawn)

33	Bilbrook	v	Rugby Town	7-0
34	Crusaders	v	Malvern Town	3-2
35	AFC Telford United	v	Allscott	0-3
36	Stafford Town	v	Wyrley	4-0
37	Hereford Pegasus	v	Stratford Town	1-5
38	Kettering Town	v	Peterborough Hampton	10-0
39	Corby S&L	v	Cogenhoe & Kingsthorpe	

(walkover for Cogenhoe & Kingsthorpe – Corby S&L withdrawn)

40	Moulton	v	Rothwell Town	3-1aet
41	Huntingdon Town	v	AFC Trinity	0-2
42	Peterborough Northern Star v	v	Brackley Sports	2-1
43	Peterborough Sports	v	Daventry Town	5-2
44	Brantham Athletic	v	Bungay Town	5-3
45	Hethersett Athletic	v	Haverhill Rovers	3-1aet
46	Copleston	v	C&K Basildon	0-10
47	Braintree Town	v	Billericay Town	2-3
48	Wymondham Town	v	Chelmsford City	0-8
49	Fakenham Town	v	East Thurrock United	2-1
50	Hannakins	v	Thorpe United	4-2
51	Brandon	v	Woodbridge Town	

(walkover for Woodbridge Town – Brandon withdrawn)

52	Sawbridgeworth Town	v	Arlesey Town	1-6
53	Leyton	v	Haringey Borough	3-1
54	Leighton United Vixens	v	Tring Athletic	2-1aet
55	Kikk United	v	Leverstock Green	7-2
56	MSA	v	Stevenage Borough	2-0
57	Hoddesdon Owls	v	Hemel Hempstead Town	1-5
58	Oxford City	v	Banbury United	4-2
59	Colne Valley	v	Henley Town	

(walkover for Colne Valley – Henley Town withdrawn)

60	Oxford United	v	Maidenhead United	5-2
61	Bracknell Town	v	Beaconsfield SYCOB	7-0
62	Denham United	v	Marlow	3-0
63	Aylesbury United	v	Newbury	1-5
64	Reading Town	v	Brentford	3-4aet
65	Headington	v	Launton	1-3
66	Bexhill United	v	Knaphill	2-1
67	Crawley Wasps	v	Meridian	5-0
68	Abbey Rangers	v	Haywards Heath Town	1-5
69	Eastbourne	v	South Park	1-1aet

(South Park won 5-4 on kicks from the penalty mark)

70	London Corinthians	v	Rottingdean Village	3-2aet
71	Ashford Girls	v	Chichester City	0-4
72	Ramsgate	v	Eastbourne Town	2-9
73	AFC Wimbledon	v	East Preston	3-1
74	Victoire	v	Maidstone Town	1-7
75	Malgo	v	Westfield	1-2
76	Parkwood Rangers	v	Rusthall	3-3aet

(Rustall won 4-2 on kicks from penalty mark)

77	New Forest	v	Boscombe Albion	1-13
78	Salisbury City	v	Weymouth	0-1aet
79	Shanklin	v	Broadstone	12-0
80	Aldershot Town	v	Poole Town	2-0
81	Purbeck	v	Andover New Street	0-4
82	Swindon Spitfires	v	Bridgwater Town	0-1aet
83	Stoke Lane Athletic	v	Frome Town	2-4
84	Swindon Supermarine	v	Forest Of Dean	3-1
85	Bitton	v	AEK-BOCO	4-1
86	Pen Mill	v	St Nicholas	1-2
87	Downend Flyers	v	Bristol Ladies Union	3-5
88	Cheltenham Town	v	Ilminster Town	4-2aet
89	Shepton Mallet	v	Larkhall Athletic	0-8
90	Marine Academy Plymouthv	v	Exeter City	

(walkover for Exeter City – Marine Academy Plymouth withdrawn)

SECOND QUALIFYING ROUND

1	St Francis 2000	v	Lumley	13-2
2	California	v	Tyneside	3-1
3	Tynedale	v	Durham Wildcats	1-6
4	Lowick United	v	Norton & Stockton Ancients	4-2aet
5	Abbeytown	v	Whitley Bay	1-3
6	Ashington CFC	v	Redcar Athletic	4-3
7	Barnsley	v	Keighley Oaks	5-3
8	North Ferriby United	v	Rothwell	0-15
9	Sheffield United Comm.	v	Steel City Wanderers	6-0
10	Warrington Town	v	Crewe Alexandra	0-7
11	Tranmere Rovers	v	Blackpool	3-2
12	Blackpool Wren Rovers	v	Padiham	2-1
13	Birkenhead Youth	v	Morecambe	0-3
14	Sandiacre Town	v	Mansfield Town	1-3
15	Long Eaton United	v	Retford United	8-1
16	Arnold Town	v	West Bridgford	9-0

17	Stratford Town	v FC Reedswood	4-3
18	Stafford Town	v Bilbrook	1-4
19	Crusaders	v Cottage Farm Rangers	2-2aet

(Crusaders won 3-1 on kicks from the penalty mark)

20	Coventry Sphinx	v Kenilworth Town KH	4-1
21	Lichfield Diamonds	v Allscott	6-1
22	Peterborough Northern Star	v Moulton	8-1
23	AFC Trinity	v Cogenhoe & Kingsthorpe	5-3
24	Kettering Town	v Peterborough Sports	0-5
25	Fakenham Town	v C&K Basildon	1-4
26	Chelmsford City	v Hethersett Athletic	0-7
27	Hannakins	v Brantham Athletic	3-1
28	Billericay Town	v Woodbridge Town	

(tie awarded to Billericay Town - Woodbridge Town failed to fulfil fixture)

29	Hemel Hempstead Town	v Leighton United Vixens	3-1
30	MSA	v Leyton	3-1
31	Barking	v Arlesey Town	5-1
32	Kikk United	v Hampstead	0-3
33	Newbury	v Oxford United	0-12
34	Denham United	v Colne Valley	8-1
35	Brentford	v Oxford City	1-2
36	Bracknell Town	v Launton	5-0
37	Eastbourne Town	v Crawley Wasps	2-3
38	South Park	v Westfield	1-4
39	Rusthall	v Panthers	2-2aet

(Rusthall won 4-2 on kicks from the penalty mark)

40	Bexhill United	v Haywards Heath Town	4-2
41	Chichester City	v Maidstone Town	4-1
42	AFC Wimbledon	v London Corinthians	3-4aet
43	Christchurch	v Shanklin	0-6
44	Andover New Street	v Weymouth	0-3
45	Locks Heath	v Boscombe Albion	0-3
46	Aldershot Town	v Southampton	0-2
47	Bristol Ladies Union	v Swindon Supermarine	3-2
48	St Nicholas	v Frome Town	1-3
49	Cheltenham Town	v Bridgwater Town	0-3
50	Bitton	v Larkhall Athletic	0-4
51	Morley Rangers	v Exeter City	0-9
52	Falmouth Town	v Launceston	0-1

THIRD QUALIFYING ROUND

1	Mossley Hill	v Curzon Ashton	6-0
2	Ashington CFC	v California	2-3aet
3	Rothwell	v Newcastle United	0-4
4	Stockport County	v St Francis 2000	8-0
5	South Durham & Cestria	v Wakefield FC Ladies	9-0
6	Tranmere Rovers	v Sheffield Wednesday	0-4
7	Morecambe	v Sheffield United Community	2-3
8	Liverpool Feds	v Salford	1-0aet
9	Blackpool Wren Rovers	v Lowick United	4-2
10	Durham Wildcats	v Barnsley	3-0
11	Whitley Bay	v Middlesbrough	2-3
12	Huddersfield Town	v Bradford City	1-2
13	Arnold Town	v Coventry Sphinx	0-1
14	Lichfield Diamonds	v Stoke City	1-5
15	Leicester City	v Northampton Town	4-0
16	Wolverhampton Wanderersv	v Leafield Athletic	3-2aet
17	Loughborough Students	v Bilbrook	14-0
18	Stratford Town	v Loughborough Foxes	3-6

19	Crewe Alexandra	v Crusaders	2-3
20	Mansfield Town	v Copsewood	3-4
21	AFC Trinity	v Dudley United	

(walkover for AFC Trinity – Dudley United failed to fulfil the tie)

22	Radcliffe Olympic	v Long Eaton United	3-1
23	C&K Basildon	v Hemel Hempstead Town	3-1
24	MSA	v MK Dons	4-3aet
25	Ebbsfleet United	v Barking	3-0
26	Norwich City	v Chesham United	4-3
27	Ipswich Town	v Hannakins	

(walkover for Ipswich Town – Hannakins withdrawn)

28	Hethersett Athletic	v Enfield Town	0-5
29	Old Actonians	v Billericay Town	2-6
30	Peterborough Northern Star	v Brentwood Town	4-3aet
31	Hampstead	v Cambridge Women's	1-2
32	Luton Town Ladies	v Peterborough Sports	0-1
33	London Corinthians	v Oxford United	0-5
34	Bexhill United	v Bracknell Town	1-6
35	Chichester City	v Rusthall	7-0
36	Crystal Palace	v Crawley Wasps	1-2
37	Westfield	v Oxford City	3-0
38	Lewes	v University Of Portsmouth	4-1aet
39	Denham United	v Southampton Saints	1-1aet

(Denham United won 3-2 on kicks from the penalty mark)

40	Yeovil Town	v Shanklin	1-2aet
41	Southampton Women's	v Weymouth	2-3
42	Exeter City	v Keynsham Town Development	4-0
43	Newquay	v Frome Town	3-2
44	Bristol Ladies Union	v Forest Green Rovers	2-6
45	Larkhall Athletic	v Gloucester City	5-2aet
46	Bridgwater Town	v Swindon Town	1-5
47	Boscombe Albion	v Launceston	3-1

Bye – Havant & Waterlooville

FIRST ROUND

1	Sheffield United Comm.	v Middlesbrough (8/1)	0-1

(tie reversed – at Thornaby FC)

2	Stockport County	v South Durham & Cestria	2-3
3	California	v Durham Wildcats (8/1)	0-8

(tie reversed – at Spennymoor Town FC)

4	Bradford City	v Newcastle United	3-2
5	Liverpool Feds	v Sheffield Wednesday (18/12)	1-3
6	Blackpool Wren Rovers	v Mossley Hill (8/1)	3-2

(tie reversed – at Mossley Hill Athletics Club, Liverpool)

7	Crusaders	v Coventry Sphinx	0-3
8	Loughborough Foxes	v Radcliffe Olympic	3-0
9	AFC Trinity	v Leicester City	2-5
10	Loughborough Students	v Wolverhampton Wanderers	5-3aet
11	Copsewood	v Stoke City	3-6aet
12	MSA	v Westfield	2-1
13	Norwich City	v Denham United	0-3
14	C&K Basildon	v Lewes	0-3
15	Ebbsfleet United	v Havant & Waterlooville	1-5
16	Crawley Wasps	v Ipswich Town	

(tie awarded to Crawley Wasps - Ipswich Town failed to fulfil fixture)

17	Cambridge Women's	v Oxford United	2-5
18	Bracknell Town	v Enfield Town	0-5
19	Chichester City	v Peterborough Sports	5-2

20	Billericay Town	v	Peterborough Northern Star	3-6aet
21	Shanklin	v	Boscombe Albion	3-1
22	Newquay	v	Larkhall Athletic	2-2aet
	(Larkhall Athletic won 7-6 on kicks from the penalty mark)			
23	Forest Green Rovers	v	Weymouth	5-1
24	Swindon Town	v	Exeter City	2-1

SECOND ROUND

1	Manchester City	v	Leeds City Vixens	9-1
2	Sheffield Wednesday	v	Durham Wildcats (22/1)	1-4
3	Preston North End	v	Stoke City	7-3
4	Sheffield FC Ladies	v	Middlesbrough (22/1)	10-0
5	South Durham & Cestria	v	Bradford City	0-3
6	Rochdale	v	Blackburn Rovers	1-2
7	Blackpool Wren Rovers	v	Rotherham United (15/1)	3-4
8	Leicester City Ladies	v	Loughborough Students	2-1
9	Derby County	v	Loughborough Foxes	3-1aet
10	Leicester City Women	v	Sporting Club Albion	0-1
11	Coventry Sphinx	v	Peterborough Northern Star	0-1
12	Crawley Wasps	v	MSA	0-0aet
	(MSA won 3-0 on kicks from the penalty mark)			
13	Oxford United	v	Lewes	2-0
14	Enfield Town	v	Queens Park Rangers	1-1aet
	(Enfield Town won 4-3 on kicks from the penalty mark)			
15	Gillingham	v	Colchester United	3-0
16	Brighton & Hove Albion	v	Millwall Lionesses	2-1
17	Tottenham Hotspur	v	Denham United	7-0
18	Chichester City	v	West Ham United	0-3
19	Havant & Waterlooville	v	Plymouth Argyle	3-2
20	Keynsham Town	v	Swindon Town	7-1
21	Larkhall Athletic	v	Shanklin	2-1
22	Portsmouth	v	Forest Green Rovers	4-1

THIRD ROUND

1	Larkhall Athletic	v	Tottenham Hotspur (19/2)	1-1aet
	(Larkhall Athletic won 4-3 on kicks from the penalty mark)			
2	Brighton & Hove Albion	v	Havant & Waterlooville (19/2)	4-2
3	Charlton Athletic	v	Bradford City (19/2)	3-1
4	Enfield Town	v	MSA (19/2)	2-0
5	Portsmouth	v	Sheffield FC Ladies (19/2)	1-3
6	Watford	v	Leeds United Ladies (19/2)	1-6
7	Keynsham Town	v	Gillingham (12/2)	4-1
8	Aston Villa	v	Coventry City (19/2)	0-2
9	Derby County	v	West Ham United (19/2)	4-2aet
10	Leicester City Ladies	v	Cardiff City (12/2)	1-2
11	Sunderland	v	Rotherham United (19/2)	8-0
12	Nottingham Forest	v	Blackburn Rovers (19/2)	0-3
13	Barnet FC Ladies	v	Peterborough Northern Star (19/2)	8-0
14	Manchester City	v	Oxford United (12/2)	4-1
15	Durham Wildcats	v	Preston North End (12/2)	0-2
16	Sporting Club Albion	v	Reading FC Women (19/2)	3-0

FOURTH ROUND

1	Barnet	v	Sporting Club Albion	3-0
2	Brighton & Hove Albion	v	Larkhall Athletic	3-0
3	Charlton Athletic	v	Derby County	2-0
4	Cardiff City	v	Sunderland	0-7
5	Coventry City	v	Leeds United	1-2
6	Preston North End	v	Blackburn Rovers	0-2
7	Enfield Town	v	Manchester City	0-2
8	Keynsham Town	v	Sheffield FC	5-2

FIFTH ROUND

1	Doncaster Rovers Belles	v	Chelsea	0-2	512
1	Bristol Academy	v	Leeds United	3-0	311
2	Barnet	v	Doncaster Rovers Belles	1-2aet	
3	Charlton Athletic	v	Blackburn Rovers	1-5	
4	Lincoln	v	Arsenal	0-1	364
5	Birmingham City	v	Liverpool	3-0	187
6	Manchester City	v	Everton	1-5	
7	Chelsea	v	Brighton & Hove Albion	3-0	282
8	Keynsham Town	v	Sunderland	1-5	150

SIXTH ROUND

1	Doncaster Rovers Belles	v	Chelsea	0-2	512
2	Arsenal	v	Everton	2-1	414
3	Birmingham City	v	Sunderland	4-0	227
4	Bristol Academy	v	Blackburn Rovers	3-0	238

SEMI FINALS

SUNDAY 15 APRIL 2012

| 1 | Birmingham City | v | Bristol Academy | 4-1 | 559 |
| | (at Tamworth FC) | | | | |

THURSDAY 3 MAY 2012

| 2 | Chelsea | v | Arsenal | 2-0 | 358 |
| | (at Brentford FC) | | | | |

THE FINAL

SATURDAY 26 MAY 2012

BIRMINGHAM CITY   v   CHELSEA   2-2aet, 3-2p   8723

AT BRISTOL CITY FC

MEN'S COMPITITION

NORTH	P	W	D	L	F	A	PTS	GD
1 Manchester FC	12	10	1	1	118	27	31	91
2 Middlesbrough FC	12	9	2	1	122	41	29	81
3 Sheffield FC	12	9	1	2	89	36	28	53
4 Tranmere Victoria	12	6	0	6	61	51	18	10
5 Liverpool FC	12	2	0	10	41	103	6	-62
6 Hull City FC	12	2	0	10	43	129	6	-86
7 Crewsadors (-3pts)	12	2	0	10	49	136	3	-87

NORTH DIVISION TWO	P	W	D	L	F	A	PTS	GD
1 Team Northumberland FC	20	18	1	1	90	33	55	57
2 Leeds CYDC	20	10	4	6	62	47	34	15
3 Wakefield FC	20	9	2	9	62	78	29	-16
4 Team Derby FC	20	8	2	10	71	66	26	5
5 Real Club Solihull	20	0	1	19	37	98	1	-61

MIDLANDS	P	W	D	L	F	A	PTS	GD
1 Oxford Lions FC	14	13	0	1	127	48	39	79
2 Team Bath FC	14	12	0	2	94	35	36	59
3 Loughborough University FC	14	9	0	5	96	60	27	36
4 Team United Birmingham FC	14	6	1	7	70	78	19	-8
5 Birmingham Tigers FC	14	5	1	8	43	56	16	-13
6 Hereford FC	14	4	1	9	45	61	13	-16
7 Cardiff City FC	14	2	2	10	53	76	8	-23
8 Team Newbury FC	14	2	1	11	45	159	7	-114

SOUTH	P	W	D	L	F	A	PTS	GD
1 Helvecia FC	14	12	1	1	114	32	37	82
2 Genesis FC	14	11	1	2	114	56	34	58
3 FC Baltic	14	8	1	5	102	40	25	62
4 London United FC	14	6	2	6	71	69	20	2
5 Kickers FC	14	5	3	6	47	60	18	-13
6 West London FC (-2pts)	14	5	1	8	66	111	14	-45
7 Spartans FC	14	3	1	10	67	100	10	-33
8 FC Enfield	14	1	0	13	41	154	3	-113

SOUTH DIVISION TWO	P	W	D	L	F	A	PTS	GD
1 Kaunas FC	20	14	3	3	74	41	45	33
2 Gloucester Futsal Revolution	20	11	4	5	72	47	37	25
3 Reading FC	20	7	2	11	61	77	23	-16
4 Maccabi GB Futsal	20	6	4	10	50	59	22	-9
5 University of Plymouth FC	20	5	1	14	41	74	16	-33

ENGLAND FUTSAL RESULTS 2011-12

Oct 21	World Cup Preliminary Qualifying Round	**ENGLAND**	v	Cyprus	**W**	3-2
Oct 23	World Cup Preliminary Qualifying Round	San Marino	v	**ENGLAND**	**W**	3-5
Jan 24	Friendly	France	v	**ENGLAND**	L	3-1
Jan 25	Friendly	France	v	**ENGLAND**	L	5-3
Mar 9	Friendly	**ENGLAND**	v	Switzerland	**W**	3-1
Mar 10	Friendly	**ENGLAND**	v	Switzerland	**W**	4-1
May 25	Friendly	**ENGLAND**	v	Denmark	L	1-5
May 26	Friendly	**ENGLAND**	v	Denmark	**W**	3-0

Follow us on Twitter or Facebook

For news about the Directory.

Updates from around the Non-League world.

Latest news from all FA Competitions.

Plus have your say on anything Football related.

LOG ON TO: www.non-leagueclubdirectory.co.uk
and join in today!

A click away from memory lane!

Over 35 years of publishing the Non-League Club Directory has filled a room full of information and photographs covering the game we know and love.

What we intend, over time, is to create a website that shares with you everything we have accumulated, which we hope will bring back some fond memories of season's gone by.

Log on to **www.non-leagueclubdirectory.co.uk** today and see how many faces from teams gone by you recognise

COUNTY FOOTBALL ASSOCIATIONS

BEDFORDSHIRE F.A.

Tel: 01582 565 111 Fax: 01582 565 222

Email: info@bedfordshirefa.com

Century House, Skimpot Road,

Dunstable, Bedfordshire LU5 4JU

Chief Executive: Peter D Brown.

BERKS & BUCKS F.A.

Tel: 01367 242 099   Fax: 01367 242 158

Email: info@berks-bucksfa.com

15a London Street, Faringdon,

Oxon SN7 7HD

Chief Executive: Brian Moore

BIRMINGHAM COUNTY F.A.

Tel: 0121 357 4278   Fax: 0121 358 1661

Email: info@birminghamfa.com

Ray Hall Lane, Great Barr, Birmingham

B43 6JF

Chief Executive: Mike Pennick

CAMBRIDGESHIRE F.A.

Tel: 01223 209 025 Fax: 01223 209 030

Email: info@cambridgeshirefa.com

Bridge Road, Impington, Cambridgeshire

CB24 9PH

Chief Executive: Chris Pringle

CHESHIRE F.A.

Tel: 01606 871 166   Fax: 01606 871 292

Email: info@cheshirefa.com

Hartford House, Hartford Moss Rec. Centre,

Winnington, Northwich CW8 4BG

Chief Executive: Ms Maureen Dunford

CORNWALL F.A.

Tel: 01208 269 010   Fax: 01208 892 665

Email: secretary@cornwallfa.com

Kernow House, 15 Callywith Gate

Launceston Road, Bodmin

Cornwall PL31 2RQ

Secretary: Barry Cudmore

CUMBERLAND F.A.

Tel: 01900 872 310 Fax: 01900 616 470

Email: secretary@cumberlandfa.com

17 Oxford Street, Workington, Cumbria,

CA14 2AL

Chief Executive: Geoff Turrell.

DERBYSHIRE F.A.

Tel: 01332 361 422   Fax: 01332 360 130

Email: info@derbyshirefa.com

Units 8-9 Stadium Business Court,

Millennium Way, Pride Park, Derby DE24 8HP

Chief Executive: Dawn Heron.

DEVON F.A.

Tel: 01626 332 077   Fax: 01626 336 814

Email: info@devonfa.com

County Headquarters, Coach Road,

Newton Abbot, Devon TQ12 1EJ

Chief Executive: Paul Morrison.

DORSET F.A.

Tel: 01202 682 375 Fax: 01202 666 577

Email: sue.hough@dorsetfa.com

County Ground, Blandford Close,

Hamworthy, Poole BH15 4BF

Chief Executive: Sue Hough.

DURHAM F.A.

Tel: 01913 872 929

Email: info@durhamfa.com

'Codeslaw', Riverside South,

Chester le Street, Co.Durham DH3 3SJ

Secretary: John Topping.

EAST RIDING F.A.

Tel: 01482 221 158   Fax: 01482 221 169

Email: info@eastridingfa.com

Roy West Centre, 220 Inglemire Lane,

Hull HU6 7TS

Chief Executive: Adam Lowthorpe.

ESSEX F.A.

Tel: 01245 465 271 Fax: 01245 393 089

Email: info@essexfa.com

The County Office, Springfield Lyons Approach,

Springfield, Chelmsford CM2 5LB

Chief Executive: Phil Sammons.

GLOUCESTERSHIRE F.A.

Tel: 01454 615 888   Fax: 01454 618 088

Email: info@gloucestershirefa.com

Oaklands Park, Almondsbury, Bristol

BS32 4AG

Chief Executive: David Neale.

HAMPSHIRE F.A.

Tel: 01256 853 000   Fax: 01256 357 973

Email: info@hampshirefa.com

Winklebury Football Complex,

Winklebury Way, Basingstoke RG23 8BF

Chief Executive: Neil Cassar.

HEREFORDSHIRE F.A.

Tel: 01432 342 179 Fax: 01432 279 265

Email: info@herefordshirefa.com

County Ground Offices,

Widemarsh Common, Hereford HR4 9NA

Chief Executive: Jim Lambert.

HERTFORDSHIRE F.A.

Tel: 01462 677 622   Fax: 01462 677 624

Email: info@hertfordshirefa.com

County Ground, Baldock Road, Letchworth,

Herts SG6 2EN

Chief Executive: Nick Perchard.

HUNTINGDONSHIRE F.A.

Tel: 01480 414 422   Fax: 01480 447 489

Email: info@huntsfa.com

Cromwell Chambers, 8 St Johns Street,

Huntingdon, Cambs PE29 3DD

Secretary: Mark Frost.

KENT F.A.

Tel: 01622 791 850 Fax: 01622 790 658

Email: info@kentfa.com

Invicta House, Cobdown Park,

London Road, Ditton, Nr Aylesford,

Kent ME20 6DQ

Chief Executive: Paul Dolan.

LANCASHIRE F.A.

Tel: 01772 624 000   Fax: 01772 624 700

Email: secretary@lancashirefa.com

The County Ground, Thurston Road, Leyland

PR25 2LF

Chief Executive: David Burgess.

LEICESTERSHIRE & RUTLAND F.A.

Tel: 01162 867 828   Fax: 0116 286 4858

Email: info@leicestershirefa.com

Holmes Park, Dog & Gun Lane, Whetstone

LE8 6FA

Chief Executive: Keith Murdoch.

LINCOLNSHIRE F.A.

Tel: 01522 524 917 Fax: 01522 528 859

Email: secretary@lincolnshirefa.com

Deepdale Enterprise Park, Deepdale Lane,

Nettleham, Lincs LN2 2LL

Secretary: John Griffin.

LIVERPOOL F.A.

Tel: 0151 523 4488   Fax: 0151 523 4477

Email: info@liverpoolfa.com

Liverpool Soccer Centre, Walton Hall Park,

Walton Hall Avenue, Liverpool L4 9XP

Secretary: David Pugh.

LONDON F.A.

Tel: 020 7610 8360   Fax: 020 7610 8370

Email: info@londonfa.com

11 Hurlingham Business Park, Sulivan Road,

Fulham, London SW6 3DU

Chief Executive: David Fowkes.

MANCHESTER F.A.

Tel: 01616 047 620 Fax: 01616 047 622

Email: info@manchesterfa.com

Manchester BT Academy,

Silchester Drive, Manchester, M40 8NT

Chief Executive: Colin Bridgford

MIDDLESEX F.A.

Tel: 020 8515 1919   Fax: 020 8515 1910

Email: info@middlesexfa.com

39 Roxborough Road, Harrow, Middlesex

HA1 1NS

Chief Executive: Peter Clayton.

NORFOLK F.A.

Tel: 01603 704 050   Fax: 01603 704 059

Email: info@norfolkfa.com

11 Meridian Way, Thorpe St Andrew, Norwich

NR7 0TA

Chief Executive: Shaun Turner.

NORTH RIDING F.A.

Tel: 01642 717 770 Fax: 01642 717 776

Email: info@northridingfa.com

Broughton Road, Stokesley, Middlesbrough

TS9 5NY

Chief Executive: Tom Radigan.

NORTHAMPTONSHIRE F.A.

Tel: 01604 670 741   Fax: 01604 670 742

Email: info@northamptonshirefa.com

9 Duncan Close, Red House Square,

Moulton Park, Northampton NN3 6WL

Chief Executive: Kevin Shoemake.

NORTHUMBERLAND F.A.

Tel/Fax: 01912 700 700

Email: rowland.maughan@northumberlandfa.com

Whitley Park, Whitley Road,

Newcastle upon Tyne NE12 9FA

Chief Executive: Rowland E Maughan.

NOTTINGHAMSHIRE F.A.

Tel: 0115 983 7400 Fax: 0115 946 1977

Email: info@nottnghamshirefa.com

Unit 6b, Chetwynd Business Park,

Chilwell, Nottinghamshire NG9 6RZ

Chief Executive: Elaine Oram.

OXFORDSHIRE F.A.

Tel: 01993 894 400   Fax: 01993 772 191

Email: info@oxfordshirefa.com

Unit 3, Witan Park, Avenue 2, Station Lane,

Witney, Oxon OX28 4FH

Secretary: Ian Mason.

SHEFFIELD & HALLAMSHIRE F.A.

Tel: 01142 414 999   Fax: 01142 414 990

Email: info@sheffieldfa.com

Clegg House, 69 Cornish Place, Cornish St.,

Sheffield S6 3AF

Chief Executive: James Hope-Gill.

SHROPSHIRE F.A.

Tel: 01743 362 769 Fax: 01743 270 494

Email: secretary@shropshirefa.com

The New Stadium, Oteley Road,

Shrewsbury, Shropshire SY2 6ST

Chief Executive: David Rowe.

SOMERSET F.A.

Tel: 01458 832 359   Fax: 01458 835 588

Email: info@somersetfa.com

Charles Lewin House,

Unit 10 Landmark House,

Wirral Bus. Park, Glastonbury, Somerset

BA6 9FR

Chief Executive: Jon Pike.

STAFFORDSHIRE F.A.

Tel: 01785 256 994   Fax: 01785 279 837

Email: secretary@staffordshirefa.com

Dyson Court, Staffordshire Technology Park,

Beaconside, Stafford ST18 0LQ

Chief Executive: Brian Adshead.

SUFFOLK F.A.

Tel: 01449 616 606 Fax: 01449 616 607

Email: info@suffolkfa.com

The Buntings, Cedars Park, Stowmarket,

Suffolk IP14 5GZ

Chief Executive: Phil Knight.

SURREY F.A.

Tel: 01372 373 543   Fax: 01372 361 310

Email: info@surreyfa.com

Connaught House, 36 Bridge Street,

Leatherhead, Surrey KT22 8BZ

Secretary: Ray Ward.

SUSSEX F.A.

Tel: 01903 753 547   Fax: 01903 761 608

Email: info@sussexfa.com

Culver Road, Lancing, West Sussex

BN15 9AX

Chief Executive: Ken Benham.

WEST RIDING F.A.

Tel: 01132 821 222 Fax: 01132 821 525

Email: info@wrcfa.com

Fleet Lane, Woodlesford, Leeds

LS26 8NX

Chief Executive: Roy Carter.

WESTMORLAND F.A.

Tel: 01539 730 946   Fax: 01539 740 567

Email: info@westmorlandfa.com

35/37 Appleby Road, Kendal, LA9 6ET

Chief Executive: Peter Ducksbury.

WILTSHIRE F.A.

Tel: 01793 486 047 Fax: 01793 692 699

Email: mike.benson@wiltshirefa.com

Units 2/3 Dorcan Business Village, Dorcan,

Swindon, Wiltshire SN3 5HY

Secretary: Mike Benson.

WORCESTERSHIRE F.A.

Tel: 01905 827 137 Fax: 01905 798 963

Email: info@worcestershirefa.com

Craftsman House, De Salis Drive,

Hampton Lovett Ind.Est., Droitwich WR9 0QE

Secretary: Mervyn Leggett.

ADDITIONAL FOOTBALL ASSOCIATIONS

AMATEUR FOOTBALL ALLIANCE
CEO: Mike Brown
Address: Unit 3, 7 Wenlock Road, London, N1 7SL Tel: 020 8733 2613 Fax: 020 7250 1338
Email: info@amateur-fa.com
ARMY FA
Secretary: Major Billy Thomson
Address: Ministry of Defence (ASCB), Clayton Barracks, Thornhill Road, Aldershot, Hampshire, GU11 2BG
Tel: 01252 348 571/4 Fax: 01252 348 630/b Email: info@armyfa.com
GUERNSEY FA
County Secretary: Geoff Ogier
Address: GFA Headquarters, Corbet Field, Grand Fort Road, St Sampsons, Guernsey, GY2 4FG Tel: 01481 200 443
Fax: 01481 200 451 Email: info@guernseyfa.com
ISLE OF MAN FA
CEO: Frank Stennet
Address: PO Box 53, The Bowl, Douglas, Isle of Man, IM2 1AD Tel: 01624 615 576 Fax: 01624 615 578
Email: ann.garrett@isleofmanfa.com
JERSEY FA
CEO: Paul Creeden
Address: Springfield Stadium, St Helier, Jersey, JE2 4LF Tel: 01534 730 433 Fax: 01534 500 029
Email: paul.creeden@jerseyfa.com
RAF FA
Secretary: Vince Williams
Address: RAF FA, RAF Brize Norton, Carterton, Oxfordshire, OX18 3LX Tel: 01993 895 559 Fax: 01993 897 752
Email: info@royalairforcefa.com
ROYAL NAVY FA
CEO: Lt Cdr Steve Vasey
Address: HMS Temeraire, Burnaby Road, Portsmouth, Hampshire, PO1 2HB Tel: 02392 722 671   Fax: 02932 724 923
Email: secretary@navyfa.com

COUNTY CUPS

A.F.A. Senior Cup

Round 1

Staveley MW	v	Hyde	0-3
Enfield Old Grammarians	v	Kings Old Boys	3 - 3 (4-1p)
Old Brentwoods	v	BB Eagles	2 - 1 (aet)
Chertsey Old Salesians	v	Old Aloysians	0 - 1
Old Manorians	v	South Bank Cuaco	3 - 1 (aet)
Birkbeck College	v	Wandsworth Borough	5 - 2
Old Bromleians	v	Leyton County Old Boys	4 - 1
Southgate Olympic	v	Dorkinians	2 - 1
Old Salvatorians	v	Old Paulines A	2 - 1
HSBC	v	Economicals	3 - 2
Wake Green Amateur	v	Broomfield	5 - 2
Ibis	v	Bank of England	0 - 2
Lloyds TSB Bank	v	Old Suttonians	2 - 1
Old Actonians Association	v	Old Lyonians	3 - 2
Carshalton	v	Old Esthameians	3 - 0
Old Chigwellians	v	Latymer Old Boys	2 - 0
West Wickham	v	Weirside Rangers	2 - 0
Southgate County	v	Crouch End Vampires	2 - 6
Old Owens	v	Old Cholmeleians	8 - 2
Old Westminster	v	Old Haileyburian	1 - 1 (4-2p)
Old Hamptonians	v	Norsemen	1 - 2 (aet)
Old Latymerians	v	Alleyn Old Boys	2 - 5 (aet)
Old Ignatians	v	Old Woodhouseians	4 - 1
Old Guildfordians	v	Old Belgravians	5 - 3

Round 2

Alleyn Old Boys	v	Old Actonians Association	4 - 1
Old Guildfordians	v	Enfield Old Grammarians	1 - 4
Norsemen	v	Carshalton	3 - 1
HSBC	v	Old Aloysians	3 - 3 (4-2p)
Crouch End Vampires	v	Old Brentwoods	0 - 1
Merton	v	Birkbeck College	3 - 1
UCL Academicals	v	Lloyds TSB Bank	3 - 0
Pegasus	v	Old Owens	2 - 4
Lancing Old Boys	v	Wake Green Amateur	6 - 4 (aet)
Old Parkonians	v	Old Westminster	1 - 0
Polytechnic	v	Southgate Olympic	6 - 1
Old Ignatians	v	Parkfield	3 - 1
Old Uffingtonians	v	Bank of England	2 - 3
Old Wilsonians	v	Old Stationers	4 - 1 (aet)
Old Westminster Citizens	v	West Wickham	2 - 3
Old Salvatorians	v	Old Foresters	6 - 4
Old Finchleians	v	Old Bromleians	1 - 0
Nottsborough	v	Globe Rangers	2 - 0
Hale End Athletic	v	Old Isleworthians	3 - 1
Albanian	v	Wood Green Old Boys	3 - 2
East Barnet Old Grammarians	v	Old Manorians	7 - 1
Old Thorntonians	v	Old Chigwellians	2 - 2 (5-3p)
Old Parmiterians	v	Kew Association	6 - 1
Alexandra Park	v	Sinjuns Grammarians	6 - 3

Round 3

Alexandra Park	v	Old Parkonians	0 - 2
Norsemen	v	HSBC	1 - 3
West Wickham	v	Enfield Old Grammarians	3 - 0
Bank of England	v	Old Salvatorians	2 - 3
Old Finchleians	v	Alleyn Old Boys	1 - 4
Old Ignatians	v	Nottsborough	2 - 1
Lancing Old Boys	v	Merton	5 - 0
Old Brentwoods	v	Polytechnic	3 - 2
Old Parmiterians	v	Old Wilsonians	2 - 0
Old Thorntonians	v	Winchmore Hill	0 - 2
Old Owens	v	Old Meadonians	1 - 2
Bealonians	v	Albanian	1 - 3
UCL Academicals	v	Civil Service	2 - 2 (3-4p)
Old Minchendenians	v	East Barnet Old Grammarians	1 - 3
Hale End Athletic	v	Old Salesians	0 - 3
Honourable Artillery Company	v	Old Carthusians	3 - 2
Old Parmiterians	v	Old Meadonians	1 - 0
HSBC	v	Old Salvatorians	3 - 3 (3-4p)
Alleyn Old Boys	v	Winchmore Hill	1 - 2

Old Salesians	v	Albanian	3 - 4
Civil Service	v	East Barnet Old Grammarians	3 - 3 (6-5p)
Honourable Artillery Company	v	Lancing Old Boys	7 - 2
Old Brentwoods	v	Old Parkonians	0 - 3
Old Ignatians	v	West Wickham	0 - 1

Quarter finals

Winchmore Hill	v	Old Salvatorians	5 - 0
Albanian	v	Old Parkonians	1 - 4
West Wickham	v	Honourable Artillery Company	2 - 1
Civil Service	v	Old Parmiterians	2 - 0

Semi-finals

West Wickham	v	Winchmore Hill	1 - 2
Civil Service	v	Old Parkonians	5 - 4

Final

Winchmore Hill	v	Civil Service	1 - 0

Bedfordshire Senior Challenge Cup

Round 1

Stotfold	v	Bedford Town	0 - 3
A. Dunstable	v	Leighton Town	2 - 3
Arlesey Town	v	Barton Rovers	3 - 2

Quarter finals

Biggleswade United	v	Leighton Town	1 - 2
Dunstable Town	v	Arlesey Town	2 - 2 (5-4p)
Biggleswade Town	v	A. Kempston Rovers	3 - 0
Bedford Town	v	Luton Town	0 - 2

Semi-finals

Dunstable Town	v	Leighton Town	3 - 0
Biggleswade Town	v	Luton Town	0 - 1

Final

Luton Town	v	Dunstable Town	5 - 4 (aet)

Bedfordshire Senior trophy

Round 1

Shefford Town & Campton	v	Potton Wanderers	HW
Caldecote	v	Flitwick Town	3 - 2
Bedford	v	Langford	1 - 2
Dunton	v	Ampthill Town	AW
Caddington	v	Oakley Sports M & D.H.	2 - 4 (aet)
Totternhoe	v	Crawley Green	0 - 4
Wootton Blue Cross	v	Wilshamstead	3 - 2 (aet)
Woburn Athletic	v	Leighton United	5 - 1
The 61 (LUTON)	v	Kent Athletic	5 - 1
Bedford Hatters	v	A. Kempston Town & Bedford C.	2 - 2 (3-4p)

Round 2

Oakley Sports M & D.H.	v	Shefford Town & Campton	2 - 4
Ampthill Town	v	Langford	2 - 1
Woburn Athletic	v	Caldecote	2 - 6
Wootton Blue Cross	v	The 61 (LUTON)	1 - 3
Sharnbrook	v	Crawley Green	1 - 9
Renhold United	v	Potton United	2 - 1
Cranfield United	v	Arlesey Town	4 - 1
Blunham	v	A. Kempston Town & Bedford C.	4 - 1

Quarter Finals

Ampthill Town	v	Renhold United	4 - 0
The 61 (LUTON)	v	Blunham	11 - 2
Shefford Town & Campton	v	Caldecote	1 - 2 (aet)
Cranfield United	v	Crawley Green	0 - 4

Semi-Finals

The 61 (LUTON)	v	Crawley Green	1 - 2 (aet)
Caldecote	v	Ampthill Town	2 - 5 (aet)

Final

Crawley Green	v	Ampthill Town	0 - 1

COUNTY CUPS

Berks & Bucks Senior Cup

Round 2

Beaconsfield SYCOB	v	Abingdon United	1-2
Marlow	v	Hungerford Town	1-3
Chalfont St Peter	v	Thatcham Town	2-1
Burnham	v	Aylesbury	2-0
Didcot Town	v	Chesham United	1-2

Quarter Finals

Chesham United	v	Slough Town	3-1
Chalfont St Peter	v	Wycombe Wanderers	2-3
Maidenhead United	v	Abingdon United	4-1
Hungerford Town	v	Burnham	2-0

Semi-Finals

Wycombe Wanderers	v	Hungerford Town	4-0
Chesham United	v	Maidenhead United	3-0

Final

Wycombe Wanderers	v	Chesham United	0-0 (4-2p)

Birmingham Senior Cup

Round 1

Halesowen Town	v	Wolverhampton Wanderers	3-1
Banbury United	v	Rugby Town	3-1
Leamington	v	Highgate United	4-1
Tamworth	v	Boldmere St Michaels	1-0
Alvechurch	v	Birmingham City	0-0 (2-4p)
Stratford Town	v	Redditch United	0-1
Romulus	v	Burton Albion	3-1
Chasetown	v	Bedworth United	1-4
Nuneaton Town	v	Coventry Sphinx	5-2
Rushall Olympic	v	Atherstone Town	3-0
Solihull Moors	v	Causeway United	4-0
Studley	v	West Bromwich Albion	0-5
Tividale	v	Walsall	1-4
Sutton Coldfield Town	v	Coleshill Town	10-0
Tipton Town	v	Stourbridge	1-4
Willenhall Town	v	Hednesford Town	2-6

Round 2

Rushall Olympic	v	Halesowen Town	2-2 (4-2p)
Bedworth United	v	Tamworth	1-2
Stourbridge	v	Birmingham City	3-3 (4-5p)
Sutton Coldfield Town	v	Nuneaton Town	1-2
Hednesford Town	v	Walsall	6-5
Leamington	v	Banbury United	3-0
Redditch United	v	West Bromwich Albion	1-4
Solihull Moors	v	Romulus	3-1

Quarter Finals

Hednesford Town	v	West Bromwich Albion	2-3
Leamington	v	Birmingham City	2-1
Rushall Olympic	v	Solihull Moors	0-1
Nuneaton Town	v	Tamworth	1-0

Semi-Finals

Solihull Moors	v	Nuneaton Town	1-0
Leamington	v	West Bromwich Albion	0-1

Final

West Bromwich Albion	v	Solihull Moors	2-0

Cambridgeshire Professional Cup

Final

Cambridge City	v	Histon	1--1 (3-4p)

Cambridgeshire Invitation Cup

Round 1

Wisbech Town	v	Littleport Town	5-0
Cambridge City	v	Great Shelford	1-0
Soham Town Rangers	v	March Town United	5-1
Ely City	v	Over Sports	3-2
Haverhill Rovers	v	Godmanchester Rovers	2-1
Mildenhall Town	v	C R C	4-3
Royston Town	v	Cambridge University Press	3-1
Histon reserves	v	Lakenheath	1-2

Quarter Finals

Soham Town Rangers	v	Lakenheath	3-2
Mildenhall Town	v	Ely City	1-1 (4-5p)
Royston Town	v	Cambridge City	1-1 (8-7p)
Wisbech Town	v	Haverhill Rovers	1-0

Semi-Finals

Wisbech Town	v	Soham Town Rangers	0-2
Ely City	v	Royston Town	2-1

Final

Ely City	v	Soham Town Rangers	1-1 (5-4p)

Cheshire Senior Cup

Round 1

Stockport Sports	v	Runcorn Town	4 - 1
Runcorn Linnets	v	Warrington Town	0 - 1
Hyde	v	Chester	0 - 2
Cheadle Town	v	Vauxhall Motors	1 - 0
Cammell Laird	v	Congleton Town	0 - 1
Witton Albion	v	Alsager Town	3 - 0
Tranmere Rovers	v	Stockport Sports	1 - 3 (aet)
Winsford United	v	Congleton Town	2 - 0 (aet)
Warrington Town	v	Cheadle Town	5 - 4 (aet)
Stalybridge Celtic	v	Chester	2 - 1
Northwich Villa	v	Nantwich Town	1 - 5
Macclesfield Town	v	Witton Albion	4 - 1
Crewe Alexandra	v	Northwich Victoria	1 - 2
Altrincham	v	Stockport County	3 - 4

Quarter Final

Winsford United	v	Stockport County	4 - 1
Stockport Sports	v	Nantwich Town	2 - 3
Stalybridge Celtic	v	Northwich Victoria	2 - 1
Macclesfield Town	v	Warrington Town	0 - 0 (5-3p)

Semi-Finals

Stalybridge Celtic	v	Winsford United	4 - 0
Macclesfield Town	v	Nantwich Town	0 - 3

Final

Nantwich Town	v	Stalybridge Celtic	1 - 0

Cornwall Senior Cup

Round 1

St Teath	v	St Day	1 - 0 (aet)
Morwenstow	v	Edgcumbe	2 - 2 (2-4p)
Wendron United	v	Polperro	3 - 6
Illogan Rbl	v	Roche	7 - 1
St Just	v	Probus	2 - 1
St Agnes	v	Falmouth Athletic	3 - 1
Troon	v	Sticker	5 - 1
Lanreath	v	Millbrook	0 - 1

Round 2

Launceston	v	Bodmin Town	1 - 3
Penryn Athletic	v	Wadebridge Town	3 - 1
St Blazey	v	Saltash United	0 - 3
Torpoint Athletic	v	Dobwalls	3 - 0
St Teath	v	St Dennis	1 - 3
Troon	v	Camelford	2 - 3
St Just	v	Millbrook	4 - 1
Porthleven	v	St Agnes	9 - 3
Polperro	v	Illogan Rbl	0 - 1
Penzance	v	Godolphin Atlantic	3 - 4 (aet)
Newquay	v	Liskeard Athletic	0 - 0 (4-5p)
Mousehole	v	Truro City	1 - 6
Hayle	v	Callington Town	2 - 3 (aet)
Foxhole Stars	v	Perranporth	4 - 1
Edgcumbe	v	Falmouth Town A Ltd	0 - 10
A St Austell	v	Helston Athletic	1 - 0

Round 3

Porthleven	v	Camelford	2 - 1
Penryn Athletic	v	Illogan Rbl	5 - 1
Torpoint Athletic	v	Truro City	0 - 1
St Dennis	v	A St Austell	0 - 1
St Just	v	Bodmin Town	0 - 2
Godolphin Atlantic	v	Falmouth Town A Ltd	1 - 2 (aet)
Foxhole Stars	v	Liskeard Athletic	0 - 3
Callington Town	v	Saltash United	1 - 5

Quarter Finals

Liskeard Athletic	v	A St Austell	2 - 0
Penryn Athletic	v	Bodmin Town	1 - 6
Truro City	v	Porthleven	3 - 4 (aet)
Saltash United	v	Falmouth Town A Ltd	HW

Semi-final

Porthleven	v	Saltash United	1 - 4
Liskeard Athletic	v	Bodmin Town	0 - 2

Final

Bodmin Town	v	Saltash United	3 - 2

Cumberland Senior Cup

Round 1

Northbank	v	Borough	1-2
Cockermouth	v	Wigton	2-2 (4-2p)
Alston Moor Sports Club	v	Cleator Moor Celtic	2-11
Kirkoswald	v	Windscale	1-4

Round 2

Aspatria	v	Keswick	2-5
Carlisle City	v	Harraby Catholic Club	1-2
Carlisle United	v	Wetheriggs United	9-0
Cockermouth	v	Frizington White Star	3-1

cumberland senior cup Round 2 continued....

Greystoke	v	Penrith	0-7
Mirehouse	v	Whitehaven Miners Social	3-0
Gillford Park	v	Netherhall	2-0
Parton United	v	Penrith Rangers	2-8
Whitehaven	v	Eden Thistle	1-3
Warwick Wanderers	v	Workington	2-0
Bransty Rangers	v	Workington Red House	2-5
Longtown	v	Penrith Saints	12-0
Borough	v	Braithwaite	6-1
Langwathby United	v	St Bees	0-3
Silloth	v	Wigton Athletic	3-1
Windscale	v	Cleator Moor Celtic	0-1

Round 3

Cleator Moor Celtic	v	Penrith	1-3
Eden Thistle	v	Mirehouse	0-7
Warwick Wanderers	v	Keswick	1-0
Cockermouth	v	Penrith Rangers	1-2
St Bees	v	Carlisle United	1-7
Silloth	v	Gillford Park	0-3
Harraby Catholic Club	v	Workington Red House	6-2
Borough	v	Longtown	1-2

Quarter Finals

Gillford Park	v	Warwick Wanderers	3-2
Carlisle United	v	Penrith	6-1
Mirehouse	v	Longtown	5-2
Penrith Rangers	v	Harraby Catholic Club	1-1 (2-3p)

Semi-Finals

Mirehouse	v	Harraby Catholic Club	2-3
Carlisle United	v	Gillford Park	4-0

Final

Carlisle United	v	Harraby Catholic Club	2-1

Devon St Lukes Cup

Round 1

Bovey Tracey	v	Plymouth Parkway	0 - 8
Barnstaple Town	v	Royal Marines Amateur FC	2 - 1
Willand Rovers	v	Ilfracombe Town	3 - 2
Elburton Villa	v	Elmore	4 - 2

Round 2

Ivybridge Town	v	Exeter City	2 - 5
Witheridge	v	Cullompton Rangers	0 - 2
Barnstaple Town	v	Tiverton Town	2 - 2 (4-5p)
Plymouth Parkway	v	Bideford A	1 - 1 (3-4p)
Willand Rovers	v	Torquay United	1 - 1 (6-7p)
Buckland Athletic	v	Tavistock Association	7 - 1
Dartmouth	v	Plymouth Argyle	1 - 2
Dawlish Town	v	Elburton Villa	AW

Quarter finals

Elburton Villa	v	Plymouth Argyle	2 - 3
Cullompton Rangers	v	Exeter City	2 - 2 (7-6p)
Buckland Athletic	v	Torquay United	3 - 0
Bideford A	v	Tiverton Town	1 - 2

Semi-finals

Tiverton Town	v	Plymouth Argyle	1 - 0
Cullompton Rangers	v	Buckland Athletic	2 - 3

Final

Buckland Athletic	v	Tiverton Town	4 - 0

Devon Premier Cup

Semi-finals

| Liverton United | v | Buckland Athletic | 2-1 (aet) |
| Upton Athletic | v | Stoke Gabriel | 1-2 |

Final

| Liverton United | v | Stoke Gabriel | 3-2 |

Devon Senior Cup

Semi-finals

| Lee Moor | v | Uplowman Athletic | 5-0 |
| Bow Amateur Athletic | v | Vospers Oak villa | 2-1 |

Final

| Bow Amateur Athletic | v | Lee Moor | 1-0 |

Dorset Senior Cup

Round 1

Portland United	v	Merley Cobham Sports	4-0
Sturminster Marshall	v	Chickerell United	1-3
Swanage Tn & Herston	v	Tintinhull	2-0
Bridport	v	Shaftesbury	4-0
Hamworthy Recreation	v	Cranborne	4-0
Blandford United	v	Verwood Town	1-2

Round 2

Hamworthy United	v	Gillingham Town	1-4
Poole Town	v	Parley Sports	2-0
Verwood Town	v	Wimborne Town	1-2
Weymouth	v	Dorchester Town	0-1
Chickerell United	v	Hamworthy Recreation	1-3
Portland United	v	Poole Borough	4-0
Bridport	v	Sherborne Town	0-4
Holt United	v	Swanage Town & Herston	4-2

Quarter Finals

Holt United	v	Wimborne Town	0-3
Gillingham Town	v	Hamworthy Recreation	3-4
Sherborne Town	v	Portland United	1-2
Dorchester Town	v	Poole Town	3-2

Semi-Finals

| Dorchester Town | v | Portland United | 2-1 |
| Wimborne Town | v | Hamworthy Recreation 2-1 | |

Final

| Dorchester Town | v | Wimborne Town | 2-0 |

Durham Senior Challenge Cup

Preliminary Round

Consett	v	Hebburn Town	4-1
Jarrow	v	Tow Law Town	4-2
Darlington Railway Ath.	v	Jarrow Roofing B C A	2-0
Annfield Plain	v	Seaham Red Star	1-5
Sunderland Ryhope C Wv	v	Easington Colliery	3-2
Peterlee Town	v	Boldon C A	2-1
Birtley Town	v	Stockton Town	0-1
Coxhoe Athletic	v	Esh Winning	0-6
Shildon	v	Sunderland West End	7-0
South Shields	v	Ryton & Crawcrook Albion	3-2
Darlington	v	Gateshead Leam Rangers	3-0
Washington	v	Sunderland Silksworth R.	3-1
Sunderland Ash. B.H.	v	Darlington Cleveland Bridge	2-3

| Brandon United | v | Horden Colliery Welfare | 1-3 |

Byes : Hartlepool, Willington

Round 1

Spennymoor Town	v	Billingham Synthonia	3-1
Wolviston	v	Hartlepool	1-5
Bishop Auckland	v	West Auckland Town	2-6
Newton Aycliffe	v	Chester-le-Street Town	3-0
Gateshead	v	South Shields	3-0
Shildon	v	Hartlepool United	5-1
Billingham Town	v	Darlington Railway Athletic	4-1
Sunderland Ryhope C Wv	v	Washington	5-2
Dunston U T S	v	Willington	3-0
Whickham	v	Consett	2-2 (3-0p)
Horden Colliery Welfare	v	Crook Town	1-2
Jarrow	v	Norton & Stockton Ancients	1-3
Stockton Town	v	Darlington	0-2
Darlington Cleveland B.	v	Esh Winning	1-2
Durham City	v	Sunderland R C A	3-4
Seaham Red Star	v	Peterlee Town	4-0

Round 1

West Auckland Town	v	Consett	2-3
Newton Aycliffe	v	Shildon	0-1
Seaham Red Star	v	Esh Winning	0-5
Billingham Town	v	Dunston U T S	1-0
Sunderland Ryhope C Wv	v	Crook Town	2-0
Norton & Stockton A.	v	Gateshead	1-3
Sunderland R C A	v	Spennymoor Town	0-2
Darlington	v	Hartlepool (walkover)	

Quarter Finals

Sunderland Ryhope C Wv	v	Spennymoor Town	2-3
Gateshead	v	Shildon U T S	3-1
Billingham Town	v	Consett	4-0
Esh Winning	v	Hartlepool	2-0

Semi-Finals

| Spennymoor Town | v | Esh Winning | 4-1 |
| Gateshead | v | Billingham Town | 4-0 |

Final

| Gateshead | v | Spennymoor Town | 0-3 |

East Riding Senior Cup

Round 1

Dunnington	v	Driffield Evening Institute A	7 - 1
Bridlington Town	v	North Ferriby Athletic	8 - 3
Withernsea A	v	Walkington A	6 - 4
Easington United	v	Riccall United	3 - 1
Gilberdyke Phoenix	v	Driffield Rangers	0 - 2
Greyhound	v	Little Weighton	4 - 1
Beverley Town	v	Hodgsons	2 - 0
Hunmanby United	v	A Rovers	0 - 1
Driffield Junior FC	v	South Cave SC	0 - 0 (4-2p)
Brandesburton A	v	Wilberfoss A	2 - 4
Howden A	v	Lord Nelson A	5 - 3
Park Athletic	v	Haltemprice A	9 - 0
Westella & Willerby A	v	Holme Rovers	AW
Beverley Town	v	Long Riston	5 - 4

Round 2

| Filey Town | v | St George A | 4 - 3 |
| Driffield Rangers | v | Wilberfoss A | 5 - 1 |

East Riding Senior Cup continued...

A Rovers	v	Howden A	HW
Holme Rovers	v	Withernsea A	1 - 2
Park Athletic	v	Driffield Junior Football Club	2 - 4
Dunnington	v	Bridlington Town	5 - 0
Beverley Town	v	Greyhound	1 - 5
Easington United	v	Beverley Town	4 - 1

Quarter Finals

Easington United	v	Driffield Rangers	1 - 5
Withernsea A	v	Driffield Junior Football Club	1 - 0
Dunnington	v	Filey Town	4 - 1
A Rovers	v	Greyhound	4 - 2

Semi-Finals

Dunnington	v	Withernsea A	3 - 0
A Rovers	v	Driffield Rangers	AW

Final

Driffield Rangers	v	Dunnington	0 - 2

Hampshire Senior Cup
Round 1

Tadley Calleva	v	Blackfield & Langley	1 - 5
Horndean	v	GE Hamble	2 - 1 (aet)
Andover New Street	v	Cove	0 - 2
Alresford Town	v	Hayling United	2 - 0
Hythe & Dibden	v	Fleet Spurs	2 - 0
Brockenhurst	v	East Cowes Victoria Athletic	0 - 2
Brading Town	v	Rozel Rovers	1 - 2
Christchurch	v	Eversley & California	3 - 2
Utd Services Portsmouth	v	Stockbridge	2 - 3
A Portchester	v	Newport (IOW)	5 - 3 (aet)
Romsey Town	v	Cowes Sports	7 - 3
Fareham Town	v	Fawley A	4 - 1
Hartley Wintney	v	Team Solent	7 - 2
Moneyfields	v	Totton & Eling	0 - 2
Alton Town	v	New Milton Town	1 - 2

Round 2

Petersfield Town	v	Sholing	1 - 7
A Portchester	v	Lymington Town	2 - 1
Romsey Town	v	Rozel Rovers	2 - 0
Whitchurch United	v	Ringwood Town	1 - 2
Fareham Town	v	Alresford Town	4 - 2 (aet)
Totton & Eling	v	Gosport Borough	1 - 4
Farnborough	v	Fleet Town	AW
Aldershot Town	v	Eastleigh	AW
Hythe & Dibden	v	Christchurch	0 - 2
Stockbridge	v	Winchester City	1 - 4
AFC Totton	v	Cove	7 - 2
Andover	v	Havant & Waterlooville	AW
Bashley	v	Bournemouth (Saturday)	1 - 0
Blackfield & Langley	v	Horndean	3 - 1
New Milton Town	v	East Cowes Victoria Athletic	2 - 1
Basingstoke Town	v	Hartley Wintney	3 - 2

Round 3

Gosport Borough	v	Christchurch	AW
New Milton Town	v	Romsey Town	0 - 5
Eastleigh	v	Fleet Town	4 - 0
Blackfield & Langley	v	Havant & Waterlooville	0 - 2
Winchester City	v	Bashley	2 - 1 (aet)
Sholing	v	Basingstoke Town	2 - 2 (6-5p)

A Portchester	v	Ringwood Town	5 - 1
Fareham Town	v	AFC Totton	1 - 4

Quarter Finals

Christchurch	v	Winchester City	1 - 3
Havant & Waterlooville	v	Sholing	1 - 0
A Totton	v	A Portchester	7 - 2
Eastleigh	v	Romsey Town	3 - 2

Semi-Finals

Winchester City	v	Eastleigh	0 - 1
Havant & Waterlooville	v	AFC Totton	1 - 2

Final

Eastleigh	v	AFC Totton	2 - 0

Herefordshire Challenge Cup
Round 1

Bartestree	v	Mercia Athletic	3 - 0
Holme Lacy	v	Leominster Town	AW
Pegasus Juniors	v	Fownhope	3 - 0
Kington Town	v	Hereford Lads Club	0 - 2
Ledbury Town	v	Hinton	1 - 2
Westfields	v	Wellington	3 - 0

Quarter Finals

Ewyas Harold	v	Hinton	2 - 1
Westfields	v	Hereford Lads Club	3 - 2
Bartestree	v	Leominster Town	8 - 5 (aet)
Bromyard Town	v	Pegasus Juniors	0 - 3

Semi-Finals

Pegasus Juniors	v	Ewyas Harold	1 - 1 (1-4p)
Westfields	v	Bartestree	4 - 0

Final

Westfields	v	Ewyas Harold	3 - 0

Herts Senior Challenge Cup
Round 1

Hertford Town	v	Boreham Wood	1 - 2 (aet)
Potters Bar Town	v	Hatfield Town	1 - 3 (aet)
St Albans City	v	Broxbourne Borough	1 - 2
Cheshunt	v	Ware	4 - 1
Bishop's Stortford	v	Watford	4 - 1
Sawbridgeworth Town	v	Colney Heath	3 - 2
Hitchin Town	v	Tring Athletic	3 - 1

Round 2

Berkhamsted	v	Bishop's Stortford	0 - 4
Hitchin Town	v	Stevenage	0 - 2
Boreham Wood	v	Leverstock Green	0 - 1
Sawbridgeworth Town	v	Broxbourne Borough	2 - 0
Hadley	v	Oxhey Jets	1 - 3
Hemel Hempstead Town	v	Barnet	1 - 2 (aet)
Cheshunt	v	Hatfield Town	6 - 3
Royston Town	v	St Margaretsbury	2 - 1

Quarter Finals

Stevenage	v	Barnet	5 - 0
Sawbridgeworth Town	v	Bishop's Stortford	2 - 5
Oxhey Jets	v	Royston Town	3 - 1
Leverstock Green	v	Cheshunt	3 - 6

Semi-Finals
Oxhey Jets	v	Cheshunt	2 - 2 (4-3p)
Bishop's Stortford	v	Stevenage	3 - 0

Final
Oxhey Jets	v	Bishop's Stortford	2 - 7

Huntingdonshire Senior Cup
Round 1
Brampton	v	Ramsey Town	1 - 2
Eaton Socon	v	Alconbury	3 - 0
Somersham Town	v	Eynesbury Rovers	0 - 1

Quarter Finals
Eaton Socon	v	Ramsey Town	0 - 1
St Neots Town	v	Huntingdon Town	3 - 1
Eynesbury Rovers	v	Godmanchester Rovers	1 - 3
Yaxley	v	St Ives Town	0 - 4

Semi-Finals
St Neots Town	v	St Ives Town	0 - 2
Godmanchester Rovers	v	Ramsey Town	3 - 2

Final
Godmanchester Rovers	v	St Ives Town	1 - 3

Kent Senior Cup
Round 1
Thamesmead Town	v	Tonbridge Angels	0 - 3
Margate	v	Cray Wanderers	2 - 1
Faversham Town	v	Folkestone Invicta	2 - 3 (aet)
Sittingbourne	v	Whitstable Town	5 - 1

Round 2
Hythe Town	v	Erith Town	2 - 1
Welling United	v	Gillingham	2 - 1
Maidstone United	v	Dover Athletic	3 - 6
Tonbridge Angels	v	Sittingbourne	3 - 1
Margate	v	Ramsgate	1 - 0
Folkestone Invicta	v	Dartford	1 - 4
Bromley	v	Charlton Athletic	2 - 3
Ebbsfleet United	v	Chatham Town	6 - 1

Quarter Finals
Dover Athletic	v	Welling United	2 - 0
Ebbsfleet United	v	Hythe Town	1 - 4 (aet)
Tonbridge Angels	v	Dartford	2 - 4 (aet)
Margate	v	Charlton Athletic	3 - 4

Semi-Finals
Hythe Town	v	Dover Athletic	3 - 0
Dartford	v	Charlton Athletic	3 - 1

Final
Dartford	v	Hythe Town	0 - 1

Leicestershire Challenge Cup
Round 1
Uppingham Town	v	Cottesmore Amateurs S & S	1 - 2
Harborough Town	v	Desford	4 - 1
Anstey Nomads	v	Bardon Hill Sports	2 - 1
Barrow Town	v	Oadby Town	1 - 2
Thurnby Nirvana	v	Blaby & Whetstone Athletic	2 - 1
Ratby Sports	v	Saffron Dynamo	4 - 4 (8-7p)
Medbourne	v	Sileby Town	4 - 5
Thurmaston Town	v	Holwell Sports	3 - 1
Ellistown	v	Dunton & Broughton Rgers	2 - 1
Oakham United	v	Ashby Ivanhoe	1 - 2
Highfield Rangers	v	St Andrews	2 - 5
Aylestone Park	v	Birstall United Social	2 - 1

Round 2
Ratby Sports	v	Ellistown	0 - 5
Thurmaston Town	v	Thurnby Nirvana	1 - 3
Anstey Nomads	v	Sileby Town	1 - 2
Oadby Town	v	St Andrews	4 - 1
Guru Nanak Gurdwara	v	Ashby Ivanhoe	2 - 5
Cottesmore Am. S & S	v	Lutterworth Athletic	0 - 7
Harborough Town	v	Rothley Imperial	2 - 1
Ibstock United	v	Aylestone Park	1 - 0

Quarter Finals
Ibstock United	v	Oadby Town	HW
Ellistown	v	Lutterworth Athletic	1 - 5
Ashby Ivanhoe	v	Thurnby Nirvana	3 - 1
Sileby Town	v	Harborough Town	2 - 1

Semi-Finals
Ashby Ivanhoe	v	Sileby Town	1 - 0
Lutterworth Athletic	v	Ibstock United	1 - 3

Final
Ibstock United	v	Ashby Ivanhoe	3 - 1

Lincolnshire Senior Trophy
Round 1
Deeping Rangers	v	Sleaford Town	2 - 0
Cup Committee Decisions - Disqualify Both Teams			
Blackstones	v	Boston Town	4 - 4 (4-5p)
Louth Town	v	Lincoln Moorlands Railway	0 - 4
Grimsby Borough	v	Barton Town Old Boys	2 - 2 (4-5p)
Bottesford Town	v	Winterton Rangers	1 - 2

Quarter Finals
Bourne Town - Bye
Boston Town	v	Holbeach United	0 - 2
Barton Town Old Boys	v	Lincoln Moorlands Railway	5 - 0
Winterton Rangers	v	Appleby Frodingham	1 - 1 (3-5p)

Semi-Finals
Bourne Town	v	Holbeach United	0 - 4
Appleby Frodingham	v	Barton Town Old Boys	1 - 9

Final
Barton Town Old Boys	v	Holbeach United	0 - 2

Lincolnshire Senior Shield

Quarter Finals

Stamford A	v	Brigg Town	4 - 2
Grantham Town	v	Spalding United	4 - 2
Lincoln United	v	Boston United	1 - 3
Gainsborough Trinity - Bye			

Semi-Finals

Grantham Town	v	Stamford A	3 - 2
Gainsborough Trinity	v	Boston United	1 - 2

Final

Grantham Town	v	Boston United	2 - 0

Manchester Challenge Trophy

Round 1

Beechfield United	v	Wythenshawe Town	0 - 5
Chorltonians	v	Irlam	4 - 2
Maine Road	v	Deans Youth & Ladies	HW
Flixton	v	Hollinwood C.C.	AW
Fives Athletic	v	A Oldham 2005	2 - 4
Curzon Ashton	v	Heyside	3 - 0
East Manchester	v	Mossley A	7 - 0

Quarter Finals

Chorltonians	v	Hollinwood C.C.	4 - 1
Avro	v	Curzon Ashton	3 - 2
Wythenshawe Town	v	A Oldham 2005	4 - 2
Maine Road	v	East Manchester	0 - 2

Semi-Finals

Avro	v	Chorltonians	3 - 2
Wythenshawe Town	v	East Manchester	2 - 3

Final

East Manchester	v	Avro	0 - 1

Manchester Premier Cup

Round 1

Oldham Boro	v	Salford City	1 - 3
Hyde	v	Droylsden	1 - 4
Curzon Ashton	v	Chadderton	7 - 1
Ashton United	v	Trafford	2 - 1
Irlam	v	Maine Road	2 - 1
Abbey Hey	v	Radcliffe Borough	3 - 0
Glossop North End	v	New Mills	2 - 3
Mossley A	v	United Of Manchester	2 - 1

Quarter Finals

Salford City	v	Ashton United	1 - 0
Mossley A	v	Abbey Hey	4 - 1
Curzon Ashton	v	Droylsden	0 - 2
Irlam	v	New Mills	2 - 1

Semi-Finals

Salford City	v	Mossley A	1 - 4
Irlam	v	Droylsden	3 - 5

Final

Droylsden FC	v	Mossley AFC	AW
(Droylsden failed to field a side)			

Middlesex Senior Cup

Round 1

Northwood	v	North Greenford United	0 - 2
Ashford Town (Mx)	v	Wealdstone	3 - 4 (aet)
Wembley	v	Harrow Borough	0 - 1
Enfield Town	v	Harefield United	2 - 1

Round 2

North Greenford United	v	Harrow Borough	1 - 0
Enfield Town	v	Wealdstone	0 - 6
Bedfont Town	v	Staines Town	2 - 0
Hampton & Rich. Boro'	v	Hayes & Yeading United	2 - 1
Hanworth Villa	v	Hillingdon Borough	5 - 3 (aet)
Hendon	v	Uxbridge	1 - 1 (4-2p)
Wingate & Finchley	v	Hanwell Town	2 - 0
Enfield 1893	v	A Hayes	1 - 3

Quarter Finals

Hampton & Rich. Boro'	v	Bedfont Town	3 - 2
Wealdstone	v	A Hayes	2 - 0
Wingate & Finchley	v	North Greenford United	3 - 4 (aet)
Hendon	v	Hanworth Villa	1 - 0

Semi-Finals

Hampton & Rich. Boro'	v	Hendon	3 - 2
North Greenford United	v	Wealdstone	0 - 2

Final

Hampton & Rich. Boro'	v	Wealdstone	2 - 0

Norfolk Senior Cup

Round 1

Dersingham Rovers	v	Poringland Wanderers	2 - 0
Caister	v	Holt United	2 - 4
Sprowston Athletic	v	Hellesdon	AW
Long Stratton	v	Reepham Town	0 - 3
Norwich CEYMS	v	Bradenham Wanderers	1 - 3
Watton United	v	Stalham Town	6 - 4
Hindringham	v	Horsford United	3 - 4

Round 2

Bradenham Wanderers	v	Dersingham Rovers	4 - 1
North Walsham Town	v	Holt United	1 - 2
St Andrews	v	Horsford United	1 - 0
Hempnall	v	Watton United	3 - 1
Spixworth	v	Wells Town	5 - 0
Acle United	v	Sheringham	2 - 0
Wymondham Town	v	Reepham Town	1 - 0
Loddon United	v	Hellesdon	2 - 1 (aet)

Round 3

Loddon United	v	Mattishall	2 - 1
Holt United	v	Wymondham Town	3 - 0
Downham Town	v	Blofield United	1 - 3
Hempnall	v	Fakenham Town	2 - 3 (aet)
Swaffham Town	v	Thetford Town	1 - 3
Bradenham Wanderers	v	Spixworth	4 - 0
Cromer Town	v	Norwich St John's	0 - 2
St Andrews	v	Acle United	1 - 2

Round 4

Norwich City	v	Dereham Town	5 - 1
Blofield United	v	Norwich St John's	0 - 5
Fakenham Town	v	Wroxham	0 - 4

Acle United	v	King's Lynn Town	0 - 3
Norwich United	v	Diss Town	0 - 1 (aet)
Bradenham Wanderers	v	Loddon United	4 - 0
Gorleston	v	Great Yarmouth Town	4 - 2 (aet)
Thetford Town	v	Holt United	3 - 2

Quarter Finals

Norwich City	v	King's Lynn Town	1 - 0
Diss Town	v	Gorleston	2 - 2
(R) Gorleston	v	Diss Town	3 - 1
Thetford Town	v	Wroxham	2 - 1
Norwich St John's	v	Bradenham Wanderers	3 - 1

Semi-Finals

Thetford Town	v	Norwich St John's	9 - 0
Norwich City	v	Gorleston	1 - 2 (aet)

Final

Thetford Town	v	Gorleston	0 - 2

North Riding Senior Cup
Round 1

Grangetown Boys Club	v	Kirkbymoorside	4 - 2
Richmond Town	v	Fishburn Park	7 - 1
Scarborough Town	v	Pcikering Town Community	1 - 2
Scarborough Athletic	v	Guisborough Town	1 - 5
North Ormesby	v	Redcar Athletic	1 - 4
Marske United	v	Richmond Town	1 - 0
Northallerton Town	v	Stokesley Sports Club	2 - 2 (2-4p)
Thornaby	v	Grangetown B.C.	2 - 2 (4-5p)

Quarter Finals

Stokesley Sports Club	v	York City	0 - 2
Guisborough Town	v	Redcar Athletic	1 - 0
Marske United	v	Middlesbrough	0 - 4
Grangetown Boys Club	v	Pcikering Town Community	4 - 2

Semi-Finals

Guisborough Town	v	Middlesbrough	1 - 2
York City	v	Grangetown Boys Club	4 - 0

Final

Middlesbrough	v	York City	1 - 0

Northants Hillier Senior Cup
Round 1

Peterborough N'ern Star	v	Irchester United	5-0
Woodford United	v	Cogenhoe United	2-4
Wellingborough Town	v	Thrapston Town	2-1
Corby Stewart & Lloyds	v	Northampton Spencer	2-1
Daventry Town	v	Corby Town	0-4
Daventry United	v	Long Buckby A.F.C. Saturday	0-4
Desborough Town	v	Kettering Town	3-0

Quarter Finals

Long Buckby A.F.C. Sat.	v	Wellingborough Town	3-2
Desborough Town	v	Corby Stewart & Lloyds	2-4
Peterborough N'ern Star	v	Corby Town	1-2
Brackley Town	v	Cogenhoe United	2-1

Semi-Finals

Long Buckby A.F.C. Sat.	v	Corby Town	1-3
Corby Stewart & Lloyds	v	Brackley Town	1-2

Final

Corby Town	v	Brackley Town	0-1

Northumberland Senior Cup
Round 1

West Allotment Celtic	v	Team Northumbria	1 - 4
North Shields	v	Morpeth Town	1 - 2

Quarter Final

Newcastle United Res.	v	Ashington	2 - 0
Morpeth Town	v	Bedlington Terriers C.C.	0 - 2
Whitley Bay	v	Team Northumbria	0 - 5
Blyth Spartans A	v	Newcastle Benfield	1 - 2

Semi-finals

Team Northumbria	v	Newcastle Benfield	2 - 1
Newcastle United Res.	v	Bedlington Terriers C.C.	5 - 1

Final

Newcastle United Res.	v	Team Northumbria	4 - 4 (4-2p)

Nottinghamshire Senior Cup
Round 1

Thoresby Colliery Wel.	v	Ollerton Town	2 - 0
Southwell City	v	Bulwell Town	HW
Kimberley Miners Wel.	v	Clifton	0 - 5
Notts. Police	v	Whatton United	HW
Basford United	v	Radford	2 - 1
Bilborough Pelican	v	Blidworth Welfare	7 - 3
Attenborough	v	Calverton Miners Welfare	2 - 1
Keyworth United	v	Sutton Town A.	2 - 4
Gedling Southbank	v	Teversal	3 - 1
Clipstone Welfare	v	Kimberley Town	5 - 0
Nottingham United	v	Hucknall Rolls Leisure	1 - 2
Radcliffe Olympic	v	Newark Town	0 - 1

Round 2

Bilborough Pelican	v	Hucknall Rolls Leisure	3 - 1
Sutton Town A.	v	Clipstone Welfare	2 - 0
Southwell City	v	Clifton	1 - 5
Notts. Police	v	Newark Town	0 - 5
Basford United	v	Attenborough	1 - 0
Thoresby Colliery Wel.	v	Gedling Southbank	5 - 1

Round 3

Clifton	v	Thoresby Colliery Welfare	3 - 2
Newark Town	v	Bilborough Pelican	4 - 2
Retford United	v	Wollaton	2 - 1
Basford United	v	Rainworth Miners Welfare	2 - 3
Hucknall Town	v	Gedling Miners Welfare	3 - 2
Sutton Town A.	v	Eastwood Town	3 - 5
Greenwood Meadows	v	Dunkirk	3 - 2
Arnold Town	v	Carlton Town	3 - 6

Quarter Finals

Carlton Town	v	Rainworth Miners Welfare	6 - 3
Hucknall Town	v	Eastwood Town	0 - 1
Newark Town	v	Retford United	1 - 0
Greenwood Meadows	v	Clifton	2 - 3

Nottinghamshire Senior Cup continued...

Semi-Finals

Carlton Town	v	Eastwood Town	1 - 2 (aet)
Newark Town	v	Clifton	3 - 4 (aet)

Final

Clifton	v	Eastwood Town	0 - 2

Oxfordshire Senior Cup

Round 1

Adderbury Park	v	Easington Sports	3 - 2 (aet)
Henley Town	v	Clanfield (85)	3 - 1
Marston Saints	v	Hook Norton	2 - 3
Slade Farm United	v	Oxford City Nomads	0 - 2
Bicester Town	v	Bletchingdon	AW
Stonesfield Sports	v	Oxford Irish	3 - 1
Chinnor	v	Garsington	3 - 2
Oxford University Press	v	Woodcote/Stoke Row	1 - 3
Old Woodstock Town	v	Carterton	3 - 0
Mansfield Road	v	A Hinksey	4 - 6
Freeland	v	Launton Sports	0 - 1

Round 2

Henley Town	v	Kidlington	1 - 0
Thame United	v	Old Woodstock Town	3 - 2
A Hinksey	v	Hook Norton	4 - 1
Witney Town	v	Oxford City Nomads	0 - 2
Chinnor	v	Bletchingdon	1 - 2
Headington Amateurs	v	Woodcote/Stoke Row	3 - 2 (aet)
Ardley United	v	Stonesfield Sports	8 - 0
Adderbury Park	v	Launton Sports	3 - 0

Round 3

Oxford City Nomads	v	Thame United	0 - 1
Ardley United	v	A Hinksey	7 - 3
Headington Amateurs	v	Adderbury Park	4 - 2
Bletchingdon	v	Henley Town	1 - 3

Quarter Finals

North Leigh	v	Oxford United	4 - 1
Banbury United	v	Oxford City	AW
Headington Amateurs	v	Ardley United	0 - 2
Thame United	v	Henley Town	2 - 1

Semi-Finals

North Leigh	v	Thame United	2 - 1
Ardley United	v	Oxford City	1 - 2

Final

Oxford City	v	North Leigh	0 - 5

Sheffield & Hallamshire Senior Challenge Cup

Round 1

Hemsworth Miners Wel.	v	Worsbrough Bridge Athletic	1 - 0
Worksop Parramore	v	Handsworth	0 - 2
Staveley Miners Welfare	v	A Sportsman Rovers	HW
South Kirkby Colliery	v	Kiveton Park (Saturday)	3 - 0
Rossington Main	v	Bentley Colliery A.	6 - 0
Penistone Church	v	Phoenix	2 - 1
Parkgate	v	Athersley Recreation	2 - 3
Nostell M.W.	v	Yorkshire Main	2 - 1
Kinsley Boys	v	Maltby Main	2 - 4 (aet)
Harworth Colliery Institute	v	Houghton Main	1 - 2
Dinnington Town	v	Hallam	2 - 0
A Emley	v	Frecheville C.A.	2 - 1

Round 2

Staveley Miners Welfare	v	Maltby Main	2 - 1
Hemsworth Miners Wel.	v	Rossington Main	5 - 0
Handsworth	v	Houghton Main	2 - 1
Nostell M.W.	v	Penistone Church	1 - 2
A Emley	v	Stocksbridge Park Steels	2 - 5
Frickley Athletic	v	Dinnington Town	3 - 1
Worksop Town	v	South Kirkby Colliery	2 - 0
Athersley Recreation	v	Sheffield	1 - 3

Quarter Finals

Sheffield	v	Handsworth	3 - 1 (aet)
Frickley Athletic	v	Stocksbridge Park Steels	2 - 0
Hemsworth Miners Wel.	v	Penistone Church	1 - 2
Worksop Town	v	Staveley Miners Welfare	3 - 0

Semi-Finals

Frickley Athletic	v	Sheffield	1 - 0
Penistone Church	v	Worksop Town	2 - 3

Final

Worksop Town	v	Frickley Athletic	3 - 2

Shropshire Challenge Cup

Round 1

Shifnal United 97	v	St Martins	2 - 1 (aet)
Telford Juniors	v	Morda United	1 - 2
Ludlow Town	v	Hodnet	2 - 0
Newport Town	v	Ketley Bank United	1 - 0
Broseley Juniors	v	Impact United	3 - 0

Round 2

Morda United	v	Ludlow Town	4 - 1
Broseley Juniors	v	Ellesmere Rangers	1 - 4
Wem Town	v	Shawbury United	2 - 3
Newport Town	v	Church Stretton Town	4 - 3
Shifnal Town	v	Hanwood United	0 - 1
Shifnal United 97	v	Wellington Amateurs	2 - 3 (aet)
Haughmond	v	Bridgnorth Town	1 - 3
Whitchurch Alport	v	Dawley Town	3 - 2 (aet)

Quarter Finals

Shawbury United	v	Whitchurch Alport	0 - 2
Ellesmere Rangers	v	Hanwood United	3 - 0
Morda United	v	Newport Town	1 - 0
Wellington Amateurs	v	Bridgnorth Town	2 - 3

Semi-finals

Ellesmere Rangers	v	Morda United	0 - 4
Bridgnorth Town	v	Whitchurch Alport	1 - 0

Final

Morda United	v	Bridgnorth Town	1 - 3

Somerset Senior Cup

Round 1

Weston St Johns	v	Keynsham Town	4 - 3 (aet)

Round 2

Weston St Johns	v	Taunton Blackbrook	6 - 2
Burnham United	v	Worle	6 - 0
Broad Plain House	v	Berrow	4 - 0
Banwell	v	Purnell Sports	2 - 4
St George Easton In Gordanov	v	Combe St Nicholas	1 - 2
Glastonbury Town	v	Portishead Town	2 - 4 (aet)
Clutton	v	Churchill Club 70	3 - 3 (4-1p)
Wrington Redhill	v	Farrington Gurney	4 - 0
Cheddar	v	Fry Club	1 - 0
Hartcliffe	v	Tunley Athletic	5 - 4
Wincanton Town	v	Westfield	4 - 2
Bishops Lydeard	v	Nailsea Town	3 - 1 (aet)
Castle Cary	v	Cleeve West Town	4 - 1
Nailsea United	v	Saltford	3 - 2
Watchet Town	v	Hengrove Athletic	4 - 1
Wellington	v	Winscombe	2 - 4 (aet)
Cutters Friday	v	Minehead	6 - 1
Welton Rovers	v	Imperial	8 - 3
Peasedown Athletic	v	Larkhall Athletic	0 - 0 (4-2p)
Stockwood Green	v	Street	2 - 2 (3-4p)
Bishop Sutton	v	Ilminster Town	2 - 1
Wells City	v	Bridgwater Tn (1984)	0 - 0 (5-4p)
Ashton United	v	Odd Down (BATH)	1 - 3
Langford Rovers 2000	v	Shepton Mallet	3 - 0
Westland United	v	Chard Town	4 - 1
Bristol Manor Farm	v	Clevedon United	4 - 0
Ashton & Backwell Utd	v	Timsbury Athletic	3 - 0
Frome Collegians	v	Creech North Curry	0 - 2
Whitchurch	v	Long Ashton	4 - 5 (aet)
Westland Sports	v	Tintinhull (Yeovil)	3 - 0
Dundry Athletic	v	Congresbury	4 - 2
Radstock Town	v	Brislington	1 - 3

Round 3

Dundry Athletic	v	Westland Sports	0 - 2
Broad Plain House	v	Bristol Manor Farm	2 - 2 (3-4p)
Brislington	v	Winscombe	2 - 3
Odd Down (BATH)	v	Welton Rovers	0 - 2
Cheddar	v	Purnell Sports	4 - 1
Long Ashton	v	Wells City	2 - 5
Hartcliffe	v	Castle Cary	0 - 2
Westland United	v	Weston St Johns	3 - 1
Watchet Town	v	Langford Rovers 2000	1 - 2
Nailsea United	v	Ashton & Backwell United	3 - 2
Burnham United	v	Creech North Curry	5 - 1
Portishead Town	v	Wrington Redhill	1 - 1 (1-4p)
Wincanton Town	v	Bishop Sutton	4 - 1
Bishops Lydeard	v	Clutton	4 - 1
Combe St Nicholas	v	Peasedown Athletic	1 - 3 (aet)
Street	v	Cutters Friday	1 - 4

Round 4

Bishops Lydeard	v	Wincanton Town	1 - 5
Nailsea United	v	Peasedown Athletic	0 - 2
Cheddar	v	Westland Sports	1 - 2 (aet)
Wells City	v	Cutters Friday	0 - 2
Castle Cary	v	Langford Rovers 2000	0 - 1
Westland United	v	Burnham United	2 - 4
Bristol Manor Farm	v	Welton Rovers	1 - 0
Winscombe	v	Wrington Redhill	2 - 2 (9-8p)

Quarter Finals

Langford Rovers 2000	v	Wincanton Town	2 - 3
Burnham United	v	Winscombe	0 - 1
Bristol Manor Farm	v	Cutters Friday	0 - 2
Peasedown Athletic	v	Westland Sports	1 - 2

Semi Finals

Cutters Friday	v	Wincanton Town	1 - 0
Westland Sports	v	Winscombe	8 - 0

Final

Cutters Friday	v	Westland Sports	1 - 3

Suffolk Premier Cup

Round 1

Capel Plough	v	Cornard United	2 - 3
Melton St Audrys	v	Brandon Town	4 - 0
Framlingham Town	v	Ransomes Sports	1 - 1 (4-5p)
East Bergholt United	v	Beccles Town	0 - 1
Team Bury	v	Wickham Market	3 - 0
Achilles	v	Crane Sports	4 - 1
Lakenheath	v	Ipswich Valley Rangers	7 - 1
Old Newton United	v	Felixstowe United	1 - 4
Whitton United	v	Ipswich Wanderers	4 - 1
Debenham LC	v	Ipswich Athletic	0 - 2
Sudbury Athletic	v	Long Melford	1 - 6
Stanton	v	Stowmarket Town	3 - 4

Round 2

Beccles Town	v	Long Melford	1 - 2
Corton	v	Whitton United	1 - 4
Stowmarket Town	v	Haughley United	3 - 1
Lakenheath	v	Melton St Audrys	2 - 1
Ransomes Sports	v	Achilles	2 - 2 (2-4p)
Felixstowe United	v	Team Bury	3 - 1
Cornard United	v	Leiston St Margarets	2 - 3
Ipswich Athletic	v	Grundisburgh	0 - 4

Quarter Finals

Long Melford	v	Achilles	1 - 1 (5-3p)
Leiston St Margarets	v	Felixstowe United	1 - 2 (aet)
Lakenheath	v	Whitton United	0 - 2
Grundisburgh	v	Stowmarket Town	4 - 0

Semi-Finals

Long Melford	v	Felixstowe United	2 - 0
Grundisburgh	v	Whitton United	0 - 1

Final

Long Melford	v	Whitton United	1 - 2

Surrey Saturday Senior Cup

Round 1

Badshot Lea	v	Dorking	1 - 4
Mole Valley SCR	v	Colliers Wood United	3 - 2
Horley Town	v	Camberley Town	4 - 3 (aet)
Redhill	v	Croydon	2 - 1
Guildford City	v	Chertsey Town	4 - 5

Round 2

Horley Town	v	Walton & Hersham	0 - 4
Mole Valley SCR	v	Chipstead	0 - 1
Chertsey Town	v	Walton Casuals	0 - 1
Molesey	v	Corinthian-Casuals	0 - 2
Woking	v	Merstham	2 - 0
Redhill	v	Lingfield	1 - 3
Dorking	v	Leatherhead	2 - 4
South Park	v	Kingstonian	2 - 1
Metropolitan Police	v	Farnham Town	4 - 2
Epsom & Ewell	v	Sutton United	0 - 1
Whyteleafe	v	Chessington & Hook United	4 - 0
Banstead Athletic	v	Godalming Town	1 - 6
Ash United	v	Crystal Palace	4 - 1
Carshalton Athletic	v	Raynes Park Vale	5 - 1
Egham Town	v	Ashford Town (Middx)	0 - 4
Tooting & Mitcham Utd	v	A Wimbledon	1 - 2

Round 3

Corinthian-Casuals	v	A Wimbledon	2 - 1
Walton & Hersham	v	Lingfield	3 - 0
Whyteleafe	v	Carshalton Athletic	0 - 1
Ash United	v	Woking	0 - 3
South Park	v	Leatherhead	1 - 0
Sutton United	v	Godalming Town	6 - 0
Walton Casuals	v	Ashford Town (Middx)	1 - 2
Chipstead	v	Metropolitan Police	0 - 1

Quarter Finals

Woking	v	Ashford Town (Middx)	1 - 0
Walton & Hersham	v	Corinthian-Casuals	1 - 2
Carshalton Athletic	v	Metropolitan Police	4 - 1
South Park	v	Sutton United	1 - 4

Semi-Finals

Corinthian-Casuals	v	Sutton United	1 - 3
Woking	v	Carshalton Athletic	1 - 0

Final

Woking	v	Sutton United	3 - 1

Sussex Senior Challenge Cup

Round 1

Mile Oak	v	A Uckfield	1 - 0
Eastbourne United Ass.	v	Oakwood	4 - 0
Little Common	v	Chichester City	5 - 1
Hailsham Town	v	Ringmer	5 - 5 (3-1p)
Lancing	v	Hassocks	6 - 1
Littlehampton Town	v	Rustington	4 - 1
Bexhill United	v	Worthing United	2 - 3
Steyning Town	v	Westfield	2 - 4
Wick	v	Seaford Town	3 - 1
Southwick	v	Storrington	4 - 3
Crowborough Athletic	v	Selsey	1 - 3
Shoreham	v	East Preston	1 - 5
Midhurst & Easebourne	v	Arundel	1 - 6

Sidley United	v	East Grinstead Town	2 - 3
St Francis Rangers	v	Loxwood	1 - 3

Round 2

Selsey	v	Burgess Hill Town	1 - 6
Whitehawk	v	Hailsham Town	3 - 1
Little Common	v	Southwick	3 - 1
Brighton & Hove Albion	v	Loxwood	3 - 1
Littlehampton Town	v	Worthing United	2 - 1 (aet)
Crawley Down Gatwick	v	Crawley Town	5 - 2
Worthing	v	East Grinstead Town	1 - 3
Pagham	v	Eastbourne Town	3 - 0
Three Bridges	v	East Preston	4 - 3
Horsham	v	Horsham YMCA	3 - 2 (aet)
Westfield	v	Eastbourne United Ass.	2 - 4
Lewes	v	Wick	4 - 0
Rye United	v	Bognor Regis Town	1 - 3
Mile Oak	v	Peacehaven & Telscombe	1 - 2
Eastbourne Borough	v	Arundel	8 - 1
Hastings United	v	Lancing	2 - 1 (aet)

Round 3

Littlehampton Town	v	Horsham	2 - 1
Pagham	v	Three Bridges	0 - 1
Peacehaven & Tels.	v	Brighton & Hove Albion	1 - 3
Bognor Regis Town	v	Burgess Hill Town	3 - 0
East Grinstead Town	v	Lewes	0 - 6
Little Common	v	Eastbourne Borough	1 - 7
Crawley Down Gatwick	v	Hastings United	3 - 1
Whitehawk	v	Eastbourne United Ass.	6 - 1

Quarter Finals

Brighton & Hove Albion	v	Bognor Regis Town	2 - 1
Crawley Down Gatwick	v	Littlehampton Town	1 - 0
Lewes	v	Eastbourne Borough	1 - 2
Three Bridges	v	Whitehawk	0 - 1

Semi-Finals

Eastbourne Borough	v	Crawley Down Gatwick	0 - 1
Whitehawk	v	Brighton & Hove Albion	3 - 2

Final

Crawley Down Gatwick	v	Whitehawk	1 - 2

West Riding County Cup

Round 1

Guiseley A	v	Tadcaster Albion	2 - 0
Thackley	v	Armthorpe Welfare	0 - 1
Brighouse Town	v	Pontefract Collieries	3 - 1
Barnoldswick Town	v	Halifax Town	1 - 2
Goole A	v	Eccleshill Utd Sports Club	1 - 2
Ossett Town	v	Farsley A	2 - 4
Garforth Town	v	Silsden	3 - 2
Yorkshire Amateur	v	Liversedge	0 - 1
Albion Sports	v	Selby Town	6 - 3

Round 2

Halifax Town	v	Brighouse Town	3 - 2
Garforth Town	v	Liversedge	4 - 1
Eccleshill Utd S.C.	v	Farsley A	1 - 2
Albion Sports	v	Ossett Albion	1 - 1 (2-3p)
Harrogate Railway Ath.	v	Guiseley A	3 - 4
Glasshoughton Welfare	v	Bradford (Park Avenue)	1 - 3
Armthorpe Welfare	v	Askern Villa	2 - 1
Wakefield	v	Harrogate Town	AW

Quarter Finals

Ossett Albion	v	Harrogate Town	0 - 1
Guiseley A	v	Halifax Town	1 - 0
Bradford (Park Avenue)	v	Armthorpe Welfare	3 - 1
Garforth Town	v	Farsley A	0 - 1

Semi-Finals

Harrogate Town	v	Bradford (Park Avenue)	1 - 3 (aet)
Guiseley A	v	Farsley A	2 - 1

Final

Bradford (Park Avenue)	v	Guiseley A	0 - 1

Westmorland Senior Cup

Round 1

Kendal County	v	Unisun Athletic	6 - 0
Eden Thistle	v	Kendal Celtic	0 - 1
Penrith Saints	v	Langwathby United	2 - 4
Kirkby Lonsdale	v	Esthwaite Vale United	3 - 1
Kirkoswald	v	Penrith Rangers	2 - 3
Kendal Town	v	Coniston	9 - 2
Corinthians	v	Wetheriggs United	1 - 2
Burneside	v	Shap	HW
Endmoor KGR	v	Ambleside United	0 - 9
Arnside	v	Braithwaite	4 - 2
Staveley United	v	Kendal United	1 - 3
Penrith A	v	Sedbergh Wanderers	4 - 5
Appleby	v	Lunesdale United	5 - 0
Carvetii United	v	Ibis	2 - 1

Round 2

Kendal Town	v	Ambleside United	2 - 9
Penrith Rangers	v	Kendal United	2 - 3
Arnside	v	Appleby	3 - 1
Carvetii United	v	Kendal County	AW
Langwathby United	v	Sedbergh Wanderers	2 - 4
Kendal Celtic	v	Burneside	4 - 3
Keswick	v	Wetheriggs United	3 - 0
Kirkby Lonsdale	v	Burton Thistle	3 - 0

Quarter Finals

Keswick	v	Sedbergh Wanderers	13 - 0
Ambleside United	v	Kendal United	5 - 2
Kirkby Lonsdale	v	Arnside	5 - 5 (0-2p)
Kendal Celtic	v	Kendal County	1 - 2

Semi-Finals

Keswick	v	Ambleside United	1 - 5 (aet)
Arnside	v	Kendal County	1 - 2

Final

Kendal County	v	Ambleside United	1 - 2

Wiltshire Senior Cup

Round 1

Sanford	v	Trowbridge Town (Saturday)	4 - 2
Pewsey Vale	v	Wootton Bassett Town	4 - 2
Warminster Town	v	Purton	4 - 2 (aet)
Calne Town	v	Malmesbury Victoria	3 - 0
Corsham Town	v	Laverstock & Ford	4 - 2
New College Swindon	v	Shrewton United	1 - 4 (aet)
Melksham Town	v	Devizes Town	4 - 0
Fc Chippenham Youth	v	Sks Blyskawica (Saturday)	3 - 1
Southbrook	v	Wroughton	0 - 1

Amesbury Town	v	Westbury United	0 - 0 (4-5p)
Beversbrook	v	Ludgershall Sports	2 - 4
Cricklade Town	v	Marlborough Town	0 - 1

Round 2

Melksham Town	v	Marlborough Town	5 - 3
Downton (Sat)	v	Westbury United	2 - 1
Calne Town	v	Sanford	4 - 0
Fc Chippenham Youth	v	Shrewton United	0 - 8
Bradford Town	v	Bemerton Heath Harlequins	0 - 2
Highworth Town	v	Ludgershall Sports	5 - 0
Warminster Town	v	Wroughton	6 - 1
Corsham Town	v	Pewsey Vale	2 - 1

Quarter Finals

Shrewton United	v	Melksham Town	4 - 3
Highworth Town	v	Warminster Town	4 - 3 (aet)
Bemerton Heath H.	v	Corsham Town	6 - 1
Downton	v	Calne Town	1 - 3

Semi-Finals

Highworth Town	v	Calne Town	2 - 4
Shrewton United	v	Bemerton Heath Harlequins	3 - 5

Final

Bemerton Heath H.	v	Calne Town	1 - 2

Worcestershire Senior Cup

Quarter Finals

Worcester City	v	Redditch United	4-0
Stourport Swifts	v	Evesham United	0-2

Semi-Finals

Stourbridge	v	Worcester City	1-0
Kidderminster Harriers	v	Evesham United	6-2 (aet)

Final

Kidderminster Harriers	v	Stourbridge	0-1

Worcestershire Senior Urn

Quarter Finals

Lye Town	v	Dudley Sports	4-2 (aet)
Pershore Town 88	v	Studley	2-3
Alvechurch	v	Malvern Town	6-0

Semi-Finals

Bewdley Town	v	Studley	2-0
Alvechurch	v	Lye Town	1-0

Final

Alvechurch	v	Bewdley Town	2-3

Arthur Dunn Cup

Round 1

Old Bradfieldians	v	Old Westminsters	3-5
Old Eastbournians	v	Old King's Scholars	4-1
Old Haberdashers	v	Old Cholmeleians	1-5
Old Radleians	v	Old Marlburians	3-1
Old Foresters	v	Old Haileyburians	0-1
Old Harrovians	v	Old Epsomians	8-0
Lancing Old Boys	v	Old Oundelians	HW
Old Salopians	v	Old Brentwoods	4-1
Old Carthusians	v	Old Berkhamstedians	HW
Old Tonbridgians	v	Old Amplefordians	7-1
Old Wellingburians	v	Old Citizens	1-2
Old Wykehamists	v	Old Malvernians	3-2
Old Reptonians	v	Old Etonians	2-2 (3-2p)

Round 2

Old Aldenhamians	v	Old Tonbridgians	2-2 (2-4p)
Old Harrovians	v	Old Cholmeleians	5-1
Old Wykehamists	v	Old Citizens	7-2
Lancing Old Boys	v	Old Carthusians	0-1
Old Radleians	v	Old Westminsters	2-3
Old Aldenhamians	v	Old Chigwellians	2-1
Old Haileyburians	v	Old Wellingtonians	5-3
Old King's (Wimbledon)	v	Old Salopians	1-1 (2-3p)

Quarter Finals

Old Reptonians	v	Old Carthusians	3-2
Old Salopians	v	Old Haileyburians	2-1
Old Tonbridgians	v	Old Harrovians	4-4 (5-4p)
Old Westminsters	v	Old Wykehamists	0-1

Semi-Finals

Old Reptonians	v	Old Wykehamists	1-0
Old Tonbridgians	v	Old Salopians	2-0

Final

Old Reptonians	v	Old Tonbridgians	0-1

ARMY FA CHALLENGE CUP
Final

2 Signal Regt.	v	2 Royal Regiment of Fusilliers	2-0

ARMY FA MINOR UNITS CUP
Final

47 Regt. RA.	v	4 Mech	2-7

ROYAL NAVY FA CUP
Final

40 Cdo Rm (First)	v	HMS Heron (First)	2-3

ROYAL AIR FORCE FA CHALLENGE CUP
Cup Final

RAF Cosford	v	RAF Scampton	3-0

Plate Final

RAF Lossiemouth/Kinloss	v	RAF Odiham	1-3

MARATTI VASE
Round 1

Alderney	v	Guernsey	0-7

Final

Jersey	v	Guernsey	0-2

4 MECH celebrate their convincing Army FA Minor Units Cup win above,
whilst the 'Man-of-the-Match' goes up to receive his trophy. Photos: Eric Marsh.

ENGLISH SCHOOLS' FOOTBALL ASSOCIATION

4, Parker Court, Staffordshire Technology Park, Beaconside, Stafford ST 18 0WP
Tel: 01785 785970; website: www.esfa.co.uk
Chief Executive: John Read (john.read@schoolsfa.com)
Competitions Manager: Darren Alcock (Darren.alcock@schoolsfa.com)
Non-League Directory Contributor: Mike Simmonds (m.simmonds31@btinternet.com)
(0115 9313299)
Photos: RWT Photogrpahy
Website: www.rwt.photography.co.uk

Back Row (L to R): Michael Sweet, Lloyd Harrington, Connor Sidley Adams, Tom Betts, Joe Bunney, Louis Mibbs, Goerge Newton, Oliver Davies

Mieel Row: Dr. Arthur Tabor (Team Doctor), Shaun Hemming (GK Coach), Tom Fouhy, Kyle Downey, James Golby, Peter Glen-Ravenhill, Jack Pounce, Andrew Venning, David Jones, David Burns (Sports Therapist), Andy Buckingham (Asst. Manager).

Front Row: Ashleigh Artwell, Nigel Brown (Chairman of International Committee), John Aplleby (Chairman ESFA), John Read (Chief Executive), Andy Williams (Assistant Team Manager), Tom Axford.

SAFIB UNDER 18 INTERNATIONAL SHIELD 2012

	P	W	D	L	F	A	Pts
England	4	3	0	1	8	2	9
Wales	4	2	1	1	6	5	7
Republic of Ireland	4	1	2	1	5	5	5
Scotland	4	1	1	2	6	5	4
Northern Ireland	4	1	0	3	2	10	3

ENGLAND RESULTS

v. Wales (Haverfordwest AFC)	0-1	
v. Northern Ireland (Windsor Park)	4-0	Mooney, Sweet (2), Glen-Ravenhill
v. Scotland (Newcastle United F.C.)	2-0	Sweet, Glen-Ravenhill
v. Republic of Ireland (Brighton and Hove F.C.)	2-1	Sweet (2)
v. Australia (Friendly)	0-0	
v. Poland (Friendly) (Dagenham and Redbridge F.C.)	0-2	

SAFIB UNDER 15 BOB DOCHERTY SCHOOLS' CUP

England, fielding a girls' squad for only the second season, competed for the first time in the Bob Docherty Cup tournament held at the AUL Complex in Dublin England were disappointed to finish fifth in the final table. Northern Ireland were the winners with Scotland in second place. England drew with Wales but then lost 2-0 to

the Republic of Irelandin their group and 4-0 to Scotland in a play-off match. England also lost 4-0 to Scotland in the Lloyds TSB match between the countries at Glasgow.

Under 15 Squad: Megan Clarkson (Derbyshire), Chelsey Jukes (Cheshire), Sheldon Ashton (South Yorkshire), Courtney Owen (Shropshire), Chloe Chapman (West Midlands), Honor Cantrell (Nottin ghamshire), Rebecca Lloyd (Worcestershire), Rhian O'Callaghan (Derbyshire), Shyla Burgess (Buckinghamshire), Emily Marsh (Lancashire), Sabrina Roach (Hertfordshire)< Molly Wheeler (Hertfordshire), Amber Tullett (Hertfordshire), Amber Tullett (Hertfordshire), Alysha Stojko-Down (Hertfordshire), Asia Harbour Brown (Bedforshire), Holly Jackman (Northumberland), Deyger Zekai (Middlesex), Evie Clarke (Essex).

HIGHLIGHTS OF THE SEASON

After their slump last season the England Schools' Under 18 international squad regained the Centenary Shield despite making a poor start against Wales and having to withstand a second half barrage from the Republic of Ireland in what was the deciding game of the competition. At the start of the game, England were on six points and the Republic on five and two sides produced a memorable match which the Republic dominated for the first 30 minutes but it was the home side which took the lead through Michael Sweet whose five goals during the season were a major contribution to their eventual success. A deflected effort from the same player five minutes before half-time seemed to have ended the Republic's chance of winning the Shield. They fought valiantly after the break with Sean Maguire the outstanding player on the field and it was fitting that he should pull a goal back with 15 minutes remaining. Most of those minutes saw desperate defending from England as the Republic forced four successive corners and hit the bar twice through Lenihan and Doherty but England just held on to win the game and the Shield. It was a fitting end for Manager Andy Williams, goalkeeper coach Shaun Hemmings and physio Dave Burns who all step down from the international scene after giving great service to the English Schools' F.A.

All the Individual Schools' and Inter-Association Finals, apart from the four Primary ones (all of which were either at the excellent facilities of the Chelsea and Watford training grounds) and the two indoor events, were played on the grounds of professional Premier and Football League clubs, a great tribute to the work of the retiring Competitions Manager, Mike Spinks. These provided a great experience for the players who had in some cases, played ten games to reach a final.

Particular highlights were Hampshire's victory in the Under 16 girls' County Championship over Lancashire which required penalties after an exciting 3-3 draw; this continued Hampshire's domination of this particular competition and the longest game the writer can remember when the Under 18 County Championship final between Essex and Merseyside lasted two hours and 25 minutes. Multiple injuries and a penalty competition caused innumerable breaks in play before Essex ended triumphant.

It was also a great year for teams from Oxfordshire and, in particular for a stalwart of schools' football in Des Williams. On May 8th at Nottingham Forest's City Ground, he helped manage the Oxfordshire County Under 16 side who proved far too strong for Durham in the County Championship for that age group, winning 6-2. On the following evening, his Vale of White Horse Under 15 side won the oldest competition in the E.S.F.A' history, the Inter-Association Trophy,at the KC Stadium of Hull City F.C. Their opponents, Newcastle, started very strong favourites but after 80 minutes, the score was 1-1 and the Oxfordshire side won the penalty shoot-out 6-5 to take the trophy for the first time in their history.

UNDER 11 INTER ASSOCIATION 7-A-SIDE TROPHY
Sponsored By Tesco - Saturday 21 April 2012 - Cobham Training Ground, Chelsea FC
Match Officials: Aria Payne, Edward Howford, Glenn LaRoche, Matthew Donnelly
Barking & Dagenham PSFA (Essex CSFA)   2
Plymouth SFA (Devon CSFA)   0
Goal Scorers: Sonny Scott, Jay Bacon (Barking & Dagenham)

UNDER 11 SMALL SCHOOLS SOCCER SEVENS
Sponsored By Tesco - Saturday 19 May 2012 - University College London, Watford FC Training Grd
Match Officials: Daniel Andrews, Ryan Haynes, Ryan McIlravey
St Aidans Catholic Primary School (Huyton SFA)   3
Ditcheat Primary School (Mid Somerset SFA)   1
Goal Scorers: Owen Ravenscroft, Liam Melia, Matthew O'Brien (St Aidans)
    Kai Raghunath (Ditcheat)

UNDER 11 SCHOOLS 7-A-SIDE CUP
Sponsored By Tesco - Saturday 19 May 2012 - University College London, Watford FC Training Grd
Match Officials: Matthew Brough, Daniel Bartlett, Sam Walsh
Victoria College (Jersey PSFA)   0
Gladstone Primary School (Stoke on Trent PSFA)   2
Goal Scorers: Joel Tusevo, Joel Tusevo (Gladstone)

UNDER 11 GIRLS 7-A-SIDE CUP
Sponsored By Tesco - Saturday 19 May 2012 - University College London, Watford FC Training Grd
Match Officials: Mike Kiley, Luke Holmes
Broadstone Middle School (Poole & East Dorset SFA)   3
St Francis Primary School (Maidstone SFA)   0
Goal Scorers: Molly Pike, Ella Wright, Ella Wright (Broadstone)

UNDER 12 BOYS INDOOR 5-A-SIDE CUP FINAL
Sponsored By Munich Trophies - Monday 05 March 2012 - Powerleague, Derby
Match Officials: Gordon Wells, Kevin Gray, Steve Abson, Peter Kenworthy
Malet Lambert School (Kingston Upon Hull SFA)   2
Audenshaw School (Tameside SFA)   3
Goal Scorers: Bradley Wilson, Billy Chadwick (Malet Lambert)
    Jack McKee, Aidan Hopkins, Aidan Hopkins (Audenshaw)

UNDER 12 GIRLS INDOOR 5-A-SIDE CUP FINAL
Sponsored By Munich Trophies - Monday 05 March 2012 - Powerleague, Derby
Match Officials: Ray Brown, Colin Langton, Bill Quirk, Dave Clarke
Houghton Kepier School (Sunderland SFA)   0
Whitechapel Middle School (Spen Valley SFA)   2
Goal Scorers: Rebacca Rayner, Rebecca Rayner (Whitechapel)

UNDER 12 BOYS SCHOOLS CUP FINAL
Sponsored By Danone Nations UK - Friday 18 May 2012 - Stamford Bridge, Chelsea FC
Match Officials: Sean Smith, Mike Barnes, Pauls Watts, John Hayman
Malet Lambert School (Kingston Upon Hull SFA)   1
Forest Hill School (Blackheath SFA)   2
Goal Scorers: Jacob Dale (Malet Lambert)
    Declan Roye-Norgrove, Korrey Henry (Forest Hill)

UNDER 13 BOYS SMALL SCHOOLS CUP FINAL
Friday 18 May 2012 - Portman Road, Ipswich Town FC
Match Officials: Garry Duffy, Jack Morris, Russell White, Robert Claussen
Great Cornard Middle School (West Suffolk SFA)   1
Seaton Burn Community College (North Tyneside SFA)   0
Goal Scorers: Jack Housden (Great Cornard)

UNDER 13 BOYS SCHOOLS CUP FINAL
Monday 21 May 2012 - The Hawthorns, West Bromwich Albion FC
Match Officials: Dan Andrews, Bill Quirk, Ryan Haynes, Roy Burton
Sandwell Academy (West Bromwich SFA)   5
Hove Park School (Brighton & Hove SFA)   2
Goal Scorers: Charlie Gilmour, Alex Beale (Hove Park)
    Yan Dhanda, Jon Leko, Tyler Roberts, Jon Leko, Yan Dhanda (Sandwell)

UNDER 13 GIRLS SCHOOLS CUP FINAL
Monday 21 May 2012 - The B2Net Stadium, Chesterfield FC
Match Officials: Ryan Haynes, Bill Quirk, Roy Burton, Dan Andrews
Warden Park School (Mid Sussex SFA)   1
Stratford Upon Avon High School (Mid & S Warwickshire SFA)   3
Goal Scorers: Chloe Willis (Warden Park)
    Molly Rouse, Lauren Jones, Hana Adler. (Stratford)

UNDER 13 INTER ASSOCIATION TROPHY FINAL
Friday 04 May 2012 - Selhurst Park, Crystal Palace FC
Match Officials: Iain Southgate, Darren Withers, Liam Hobbs, Nick Cornwell

South London SFA (Inner London CSFA)	0
Liverpool SFA (Merseyside CSFA)	3

Goal Scorers: Callum Lucy, Decllan Lewis, Taylor Moss (Liverpool)

UNDER 14 BOYS INTER COUNTY TROPHY FINAL
Monday 21 May 2012 - The B2Net Stadium, Chesterfield FC
Match Officials: Steve Swallow, Mark Grundy, Paul Noble, Calium Birchmore

Merseyside CSFA	3
Essex CSFA	1

Goal Scorers: Jay Bradford, Samuel Llesanmi, Samuel Llesanmi (Merseyside)
Abel Okoghenu (Essex)

UNDER 14 GIRLS INTER COUNTY TROPHY FINAL
Wednesday 16 May 2012 - Carrow Road, Norwich City FC
Match Officials: Andrew Hardy, Sarah Grundy, Jasmine Priddis, Tim Sadler

Lancashire CSFA	1
Essex CSFA	2

Goal Scorers: Gabby Taylor (Lancashire)
Evie Clarke, Zoe Dorrington (Essex)

UNDER 14 BOYS SCHOOLS CUP FINAL
Sponsored By Premier League - Tuesday 08 May 2012
The Stadium of Light, Sunderland AFC
Match Officials: Mark Clattenburg, Daniel Woodward, Lindsey Robinson, Andrew Kitchen, Reece Scott, Adam Burnikell, Cameron Raine

Cardinal Heenan Sports College (Liverpool SFA)	1
Bishop Challoner College (Hackney & Tower Hamlets SFA)	0

Goal Scorers: Lee Jones (Cardinal Heenan)

UNDER 15 INTER ASSOCIATION TROPHY FINAL
Wednesday 09 May 2012 - The KC Stadium, Hull City FC
Match Officials: Geoff Eltringham, Reece Scott, Adam Burnikell, Cameron Raine

Newcastle Upon Tyne SFA (Northumberland CSFA)	1 (5 PENS)
Vale of White Horse SFA (Oxfordshire CSFA)	1 (6 PENS)

Goal Scorers: Wayne Dunn. Jordan Gabriel (P), Reece Richardson (P), John Garrett (P), Wayne Dunn (P), Billy Nicholls (P), Johnathan Archibold (P). (Newcastle)
Luke Thorne. Jack Plosynski (P), Robbie Cundy (P), Eddie Cavanagh (P), Jordan Davies (P), Cameron Taylor (P), Anthony Martin (P), Tom White (P). (Vale of White Horse)

UNDER 15 BOYS SCHOOLS CUP FINAL
Monday 14 May 2012 - Pride Park, Derby County FC
Match Officials: Mark Warren, Matthew Law, Geoff Law, David Clarke

Oasis Academy Shirley Park (Croydon SFA)	3
Ribblesdale High School (Hyndburn & Ribble Valley SFA)	0

Goal Scorers: Hussein Mohammed, Hussein Mohammed, Hussein Mohammed (Oasis)

UNDER 15 GIRLS SCHOOLS CUP FINAL
Monday 14 May 2012 - Pride Park, Derby County FC
Match Officials: Geoff Law, Matthew Law, David Clarke, Mark Warren

Drayton Manor High School (Ealing High SFA)	3 (4 PENS)
Shelfield Community Academy (Walsall SFA)	3 (5 PENS)

Goal Scorers: Grace Ogwel, Demi Beckwith, Grace Ogwel. Buyuk Yiray (P), Grace Ogwel (P), Demi Beckwith (P), Amran Ahmed (P). (Drayton)
Georgia Seedhouse, Natasha Lawrence, Charlie Wellings. Chloe Chapman (P), Natasha Lawrence (P), Charlie Wellings (P), Chelsea Willitts (P), Ellesse Birkett (P). (Shelfield)

UNDER 16 BOYS INTER COUNTY TROPHY FINAL
Tuesday 08 May 2012 - The City Ground, Nottingham Forest FC
Match Officials: David Coote, David Richardson, Declan Bourne, Robin Bourne

Durham CSFA	2
Oxfordshire CSFA	6

Goal Scorers: Connor Halpin, Connor Halpin. (Durham)
Dominic Hyam, Connor Robbins (og), Dominic Hyam, Dominic Hyam, Yassin Elouahabi, Yassin Elouahabi. (Oxfordshire)

UNDER 16 INTER COUNTY GIRLS TROPHY FINAL
Sponsored By bottleit.net - Thursday 03 May 2012
Underhill, Barnet FC
Match Officials: Jamie Richards, Mike Heavey, Shani Minors, Daniel Casey

Lancashire CSFA	3 (4 PENS)
Hampshire CSFA	3 (5 PENS)

Goal Scorers: Helen Seed, Lorrie Doze, Lorrie Doze. Emily Lupton (P), Chloe Adams (P), Eve Kennerley (P). (Lancashire)
Jodie Brett, Atlanta Primus, Millie Farrow. Laura Rafferty (P), Lucy Caunt (P), Jodie Brett (P), Millie Farrow (P) & Atlanta Primus (P). (Hampshire)

UNDER 16 BOYS SCHOOLS CUP FINAL
Monday 26 March 2012 - Pirelli Stadium, Burton Albion FC
Match Officials: Joe Clarke, Andrew Fox, Tessa Ball, Laura Ritchie

St Martin's School (Chelmsford & Mid Essex SFA)	1 (2 PENS)
West Derby School (Liverpool SFA)	1 (4 PENS)

Goal Scorers: Thomas Lapslie. Thomas Lapslie (P), Jason White (P) (St Martin's)
Thomas Roberts. Joss Cummins (P), James Johnson (P), Adam Patterson (P), David Moore (P) (West Derby)

UNDER 16 GIRLS SCHOOLS CUP FINAL
Monday 26 March 2012 - Pirelli Stadium, Burton Albion FC
Match Officials: Tessa Ball, Laura Ritchie, Joe Clarke, Andrew Fox

Maiden Erlegh School (Reading SFA)	4
Countesthorpe Community College (South Leicestershire SFA)	0

Goal Scorers: Nicole Harkness, Rosella Ayene, Rosella Ayene, Rosella Ayene. (Maiden Erlegh)

UNDER 18 BOYS INTER COUNTY TROPHY FINAL
Tuesday 01 May 2012 - The City Ground, Nottingham Forest FC
Match Officials: Richard Harrington, Kris Hames, Lewiss Edwards, Johnathan Bryant

Essex CSFA	1 (5 PENS)
Merseyside CSFA	1 (3 PENS)

Goal Scorers: Daniel Jones. Dan Jones (P), Dan Walshe (P), Jamal Allen (P), Jacob Dingli (P), Calum Ibe (P). (Essex)
John McAuliffe. James Carney (P), Alex Ahmed (P) Tyler Jeffreys (P) (Merseyside)

UNDER 18 GIRLS SCHOOLS TROPHY FINAL
Monday 12 March 2012 - The Don Valley Stadium, Rotherham United FC
Match Officials: Kerry Walker, Josh Bradwell, Ryan Brain, Craig Simpson

St Julie's Catholic High School (Liverpool SFA)	2
Thurstable School (Colchester & North East Essex SFA)	3

Goal Scorers: Inayah Robinson, Inayah Robinson (St Julie's)
Emily Clements, Sophie Blowers, Sian Fagg (Thurstable)

UNDER 18 BOYS SCHOOLS TROPHY FINAL
Wednesday 09 May 2012 - The Molineux, Wolverhampton Wanderers FC
Match Officials: Steve Rushton, Ben Watkiss, Tom Rolls, Scott Liggins

Thomas Telford School (Telford & Wrekin SFA)	2
John Madejski Academy (Reading SFA)	4

Goal Scorers: Wayne Davis, Ryan Bright (Thomas Telford)
Mitchell Parker, Devante Romeo, Devante Romeo, Mitchell Parker (John Madejski)

UNDER 18 BOYS COLLEGES TROPHY FINAL
Wednesday 28 March 2012 - The Moss Rose, Macclesfield Town FC
Match Officials: Paul Wilcox, Nigel Booth, Darren Daly, Derek Nixon

Balby Academy of Sport (Doncaster SFA)	0
Cirencester College (Stroud SFA)	3

Goal Scorers: Joe Shepherd, Danny Hale, Adam Mace. (Cirencester)

UNDER 18 GIRLS COLLEGES TROPHY FINAL
Tuesday 13 March 2012 - Plainmoor, Torquay United FC
Match Officials: Ben Judd, Jon Harris, Josh Hadrill, Ray Brown

Filton College (Bristol & South Gloucestershire SFA)	3
Gateshead College (Gateshead SFA)	2

Goal Scorers: Rhian Cleverly, Allie Leek, Katie Williams. (Filton)
Keira Ramshaw, Dannika Purdham (Gateshead)

Hampshire, winners of the Under 16 Girls' County Championshiop for the seventh time in 12 years.

Below: Sandwell Academy who defeated Hove Park School in the final of the Under 13 ESFA Schools' Final played at the Haswthorns, West Bromwich Albion F.C.

Vale of White Horse, winners of the Under 15 Inter-Association Trophy for the first time.

Winners of the Small Primary Schools' Soccer Sevens.

Oxfordshire County Under 16 squad with the County Championship Trophy after their win against Durahm at Nottingham Forest F.C.

Action from the Samll Schools' Under 13 Cup Final at Portman Road between great Cornard School and Seaton Burn Community College (stripes)

FA PREMIER LEAGUE TABLES 2011-12

NATIONAL DIVISION

		P	W	D	L	F	A	GD	Pts
1	Sunderland WFC	18	13	3	2	49	18	42	31
2	Leeds United LFC	18	13	2	3	36	10	41	26
3	Aston Villa LFC	18	7	6	5	24	21	27	3
4	Barnet FC Ladies	18	7	5	6	30	21	26	9
5	Charlton Athletic WFC	18	7	5	6	24	23	26	1
6	Coventry City LFC	18	7	5	6	19	19	26	0
7	Watford LFC	18	5	2	11	16	39	17	-23
8	Cardiff City LFC	18	4	4	10	11	19	16	-8
9	**Reading FC Women**	18	5	1	12	25	43	16	-18
10	**Nottingham Forest LFC**	18	4	3	11	21	42	15	-21

NORTHERN DIVISION

		P	W	D	L	F	A	GD	Pts
1	**Manchester City LFC**	18	13	1	4	58	19	40	39
2	Sheffield FC Ladies	18	11	2	5	46	28	35	18
3	Leicester City WFC	18	10	4	4	43	21	34	22
4	Blackburn Rovers LFC	18	9	5	4	48	28	32	20
5	Derby County LFC	18	9	5	4	44	30	32	14
6	Sporting Club Albion LFC	18	8	5	5	39	26	29	13
7	Preston North End WFC	18	7	3	8	30	30	24	0
8	**Rochdale AFC Ladies**	18	4	3	11	26	40	15	-14
9	**Rotherham United LFC**	18	3	4	11	26	45	13	-19
10	**Leeds City Vixens LFC**	18	0	0	18	13	106	0	-93

Promoted into the Northern Division for 2012-13 - Newcastle United.

SOUTHERN DIVISION

		P	W	D	L	F	A	GD	Pts
1	**Portsmouth FC Ladies**	18	12	3	3	49	22	39	27
2	Colchester United	18	10	5	3	45	29	35	16
3	West Ham United LFC	18	10	4	4	36	22	34	14
4	Brighton & Hove Albion WFC	18	8	3	7	32	32	27	0
5	Gillingham LFC	18	6	5	7	21	28	23	-7
6	Tottenham Hotspur LFC	18	6	4	8	28	29	22	-1
7	Queens Park Rangers LFC	18	5	5	8	25	34	20	-9
8	Millwall Lionesses	18	4	5	9	25	38	17	-13
9	**Plymouth Argyle LFC**	18	5	2	11	29	48	17	-19
10	**Keynsham Town LFC**	18	3	6	9	28	36	15	-8

Promoted into the Southern Division for 2012-13 - Lewes LFC and Yeovil Town LFC.

FA PREMIER LEAGUE CUP FINAL (@ Northampton Town FC 06/05/2012)
Sunderland WFC 2 - 1 Leeds United LFC

WFAC Quarter Final
Birmingham LFC 4
Sunderland WFC 0

Sunderland forward, Natalie Gutterdge, Tackles Birmingham's, Laura Bassett.

Birmingham's Kerys Harrop, who scored 2 goals in this tie, goes past the Sunderland No.8.

Birmingham full-back, Chelsea Weston, tackles the Sunderland winger, Sophie Williams.

Photos by
Jonathan Holloway

ENGLAND SENIOR TEAM 2011-12

	Date	Opponents	H/A	Comp.	Result	Goalscorers
1	Sept 17	Serbia	A	Euro' Champs. Regional Stage	D 2-2	Yankey 6, Slovic 19 (og)
2	22	Slovenia	H	Euro' Champs. Regional Stage	W 4-0	Yankey 1, White 5, Houghton 56, R.Williams 87
3	Oct 27	Holland	A	Euro' Champs. Regional Stage	D 0-0	
4	Nov 23	Serbia	H	Euro' Champs. Regional Stage	W 2-0	Clarke 41, White 51
5	Feb 28	Finland	A	Cyprus Cup (Friendly)	W 3-1	K.Smith 35, 88 (pens), Carney 50
6	Mar 1	Switzerland	A	Cyprus Cup (Friendly)	W 1-0	F.Williams 75
7	4	France	A	Cyprus Cup (Friendly)	L 0-3	
8	6	Italy	A	Cyprus Cup (Friendly)	L 1-3	Moore 25
9	31	Croatia	A	Euro' Champs. Regional Stage	W 6-0	R.Williams 4, Clarke 15, Unitt 18, White 35, Houghton 45, 68
10	June 17	Holland	H	Euro' Champs. Regional Stage	W 1-0	Yankey 67
11	21	Slovenia	A	Euro' Champs. Regional Stage	W 4-0	J.Scott 29, 43, Carney 54, R.Williams 85

ENGLAND'S SQUAD

(As at 21/06/2012)

	Club	Caps	Goals
GOALKEEPERS			
Karen Bardsley	New Jersey Sky Blue	22	0
Rachel Brown	Everton	78	0
Siobhan Chamberlain	Bristol Academy	23	0
Carly Telford		2	0
DEFENDERS			
Laura Bassett	Birmingham City	25	0
Sophie Bradley	Lincoln Ladies	15	0
Lindsay Johnson		43	1
Claire Rafferty	Chelsea	6	0
Alex Scott	Boston Breakers	90	12
Casey Stoney	Lincoln Ladies	103	4
Dunia Susi	Birmingham City	16	0
Rachel Unitt	Everton	100	8
Fern Whelan	Everton	3	0
Faye White	Arsenal	90	11
MIDFIELDERS			
Anita Asante	New Jersey Sky Blue	55	1
Danielle Buet		8	0
Jess Clarke	Lincoln Ladies	34	9
Steph Houghton	Arsenal	27	4
Jade Moore	Birmingham City	4	1
Jill Scott	Everton	58	10
Sue Smith	Leeds United	93	16
Fara Williams	Everton	105	36
Rachel Yankey	Arsenal	119	18
FORWARDS			
Eniola Aluko	New Jersey Sky Blue	61	11
Karen Carney	Arsenal	75	13
Natasha Dowie	Everton	3	0
Toni Duggan	Everton	0	0
Kelly Smith	Boston Breakers	111	45*
Ellen White	Arsenal	29	9
Rachel Williams	Birmingham City	11	3

*All-time leading goalscorer.

1,000s of results, 100s of matches ONLY ONE Non-League Paper

CLUB INDEX

CLUB INDEX

CLUB INDEX

CLUB INDEX

CLUB INDEX

CLUB INDEX

CLUB INDEX

CLUB INDEX

CLUB INDEX

CLUB INDEX